Plant Finder 2018

Devised by Chris Philip and Realised by Tony Lord

Editor-in-Chief
Janet Cubey

RHS Editors
James Armitage Dawn Edwards Kálmán Könyves
Neil Lancaster Rosalyn Marshall

Compiler
Lindsay Durrant

RHS
Inspiring everyone to grow

Published and compiled by
Royal Horticultural Society
80 Vincent Square
London SW1P 2PE

Reg charity no: 222879/SC038262

First edition 1987
Thirty-second edition 2018

British Library Cataloguing Publication Data
A catalogue record for this book is available from the British Library

ISBN 9781907057830

RHS Publisher – Rae Spencer-Jones

RHS Art Editor – Mark Timothy

RHS Prepress Designer – Anthony Masi

RHS Designer – Sarah Carrington

RHS Head of Editorial – Chris Young

Designer – Peter Cooling

Printed and bound by CPI WILLIAM CLOWES, Copland Way, Ellough, Beccles, Suffolk, NR34 7TL

The compiler and editors of the RHS Plant Finder have taken every care, in the time available, to check all the information supplied to them by the nurseries concerned. Nevertheless, in a work of this kind containing as it does hundreds of thousands of separate computer encodings, errors and omissions will inevitably occur. The RHS, the Publisher and Editors, cannot accept responsibility for any consequences that may arise from such errors.

If you find any mistakes, we hope that you will let us know so that the matter can be corrected in the next edition.

Front cover photograph: *Echinacea purpurea* 'Green Twister' (RHS / Joanna Kossak)

Back cover photographs from top left:
Whitecurrant (RHS / Tim Sandall)
× *Rhodoxis* 'Summer Stars Pink Blush' (Summer Stars Series) (RHS / Joanna Kossak)
The Abbey Nursery, Somerset (RHS / Tim Sandall)
Rosa Winchester Cathedral ('Auscat') (Dorling Kindersley)

The Royal Horticultural Society is the UK's leading gardening charity dedicated to advancing horticulture and promoting good gardening. Its charitable work includes providing expert advice and information, training the next generation of gardeners, creating hands-on opportunities for children to grow plants and conducting research into plants, pests and environmental issues affecting gardeners.

For more information visit www.rhs.org.uk or call 020 3176 5800.

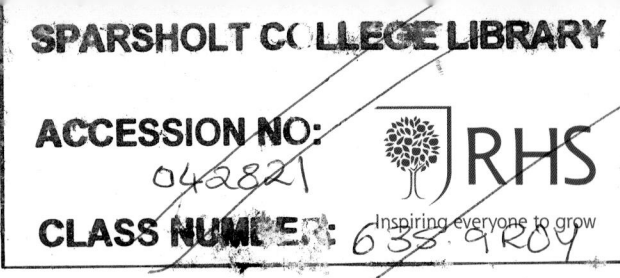

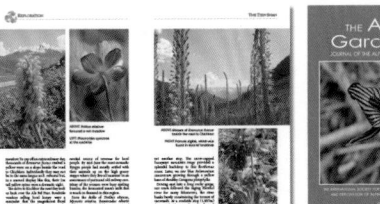

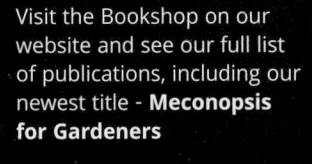

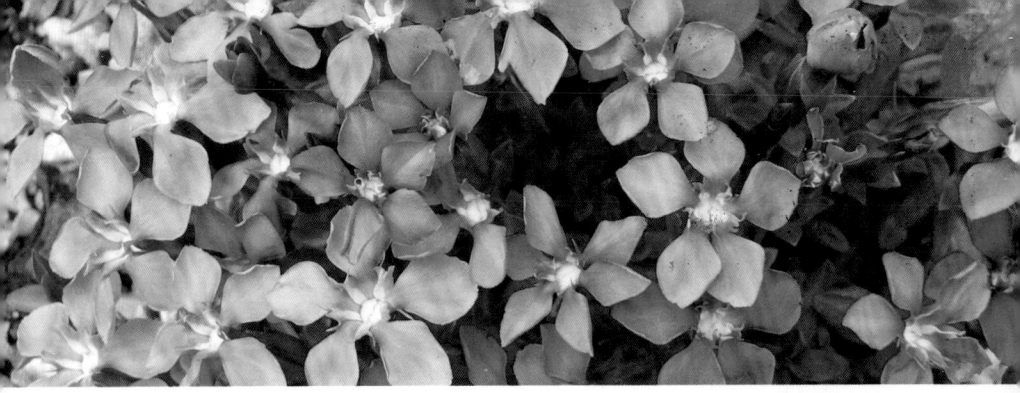

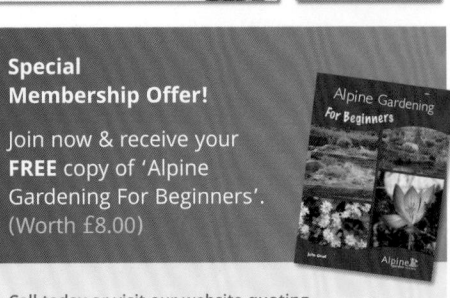

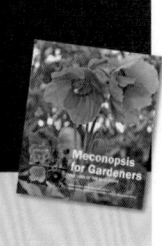

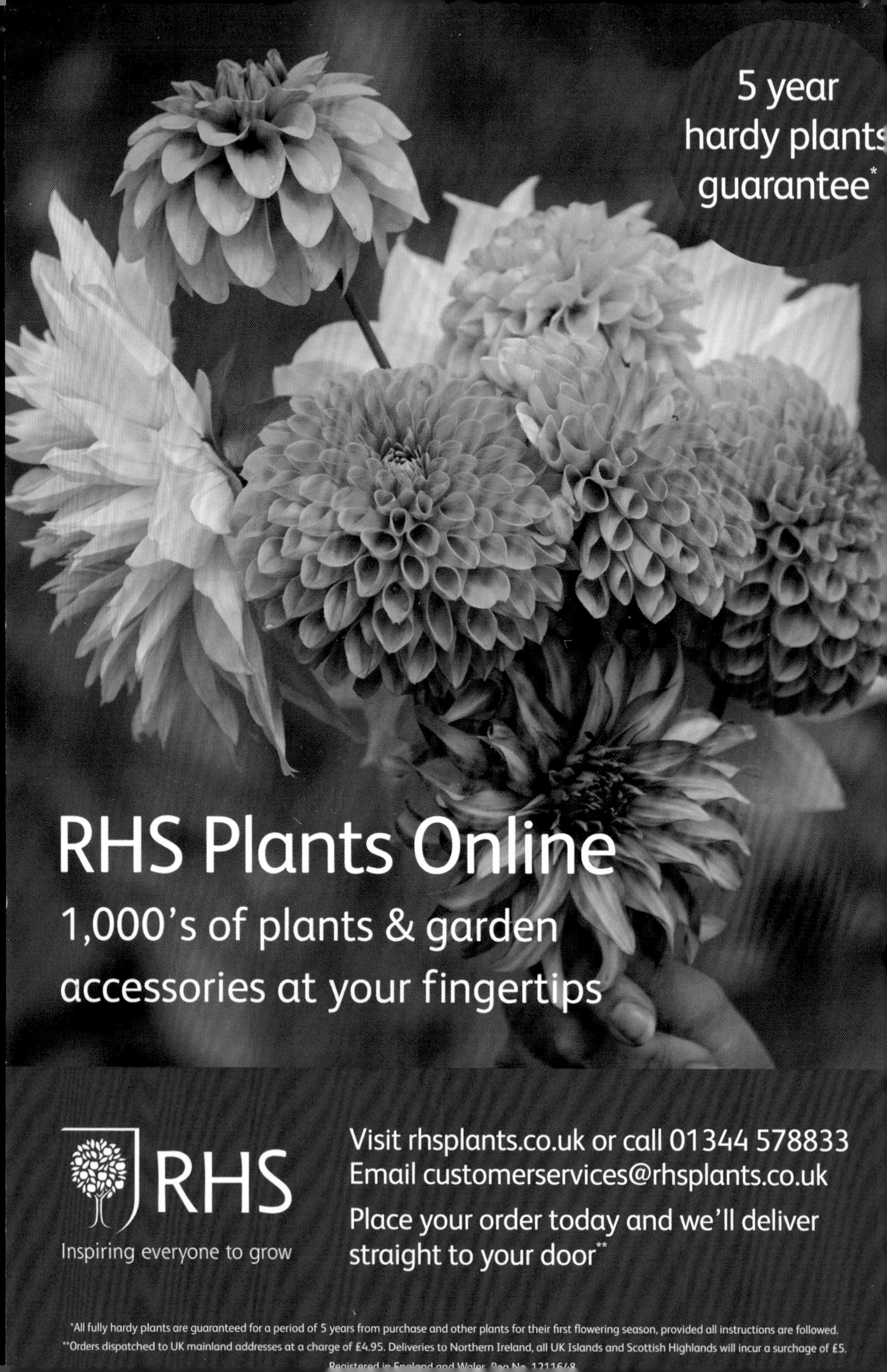

5 year hardy plants guarantee*
RHS Plants Online
1,000's of plants & garden accessories at your fingertips
RHS
Inspiring everyone to grow
Visit rhsplants.co.uk or call 01344 578833
Email customerservices@rhsplants.co.uk
Place your order today and we'll deliver straight to your door**
*All fully hardy plants are guaranteed for a period of 5 years from purchase and other plants for their first flowering season, provided all instructions are followed.
**Orders dispatched to UK mainland addresses at a charge of £4.95. Deliveries to Northern Ireland, all UK Islands and Scottish Highlands will incur a surchage of £5.

CONTENTS

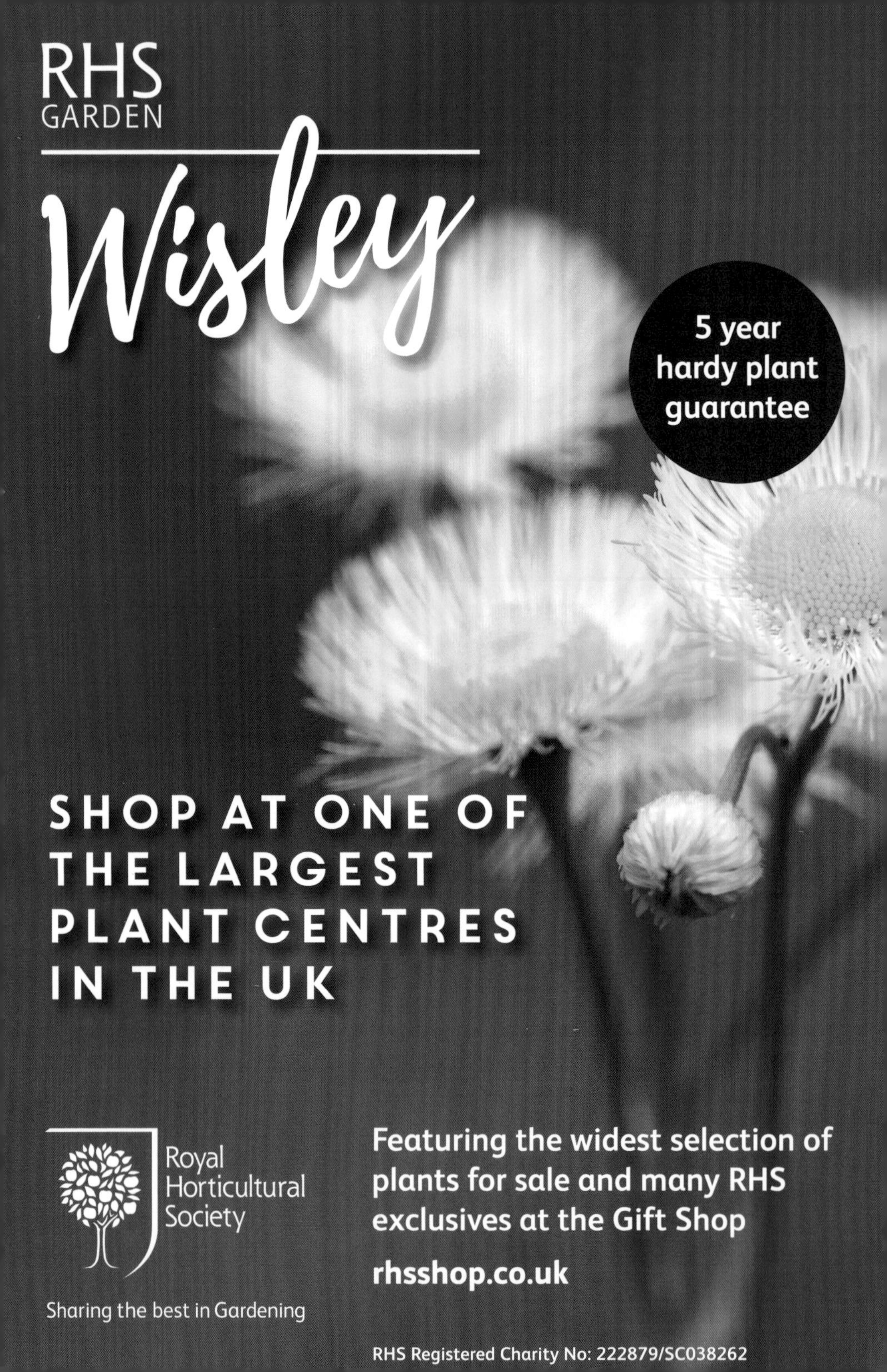
RHS
GARDEN
Wisley
5 year
hardy plant
guarantee
SHOP AT ONE OF THE LARGEST PLANT CENTRES IN THE UK
Royal
Horticultural
Society
Sharing the best in Gardening
Featuring the widest selection of plants for sale and many RHS exclusives at the Gift Shop
rhsshop.co.uk
RHS Registered Charity No: 222879/SC038262

New plant highlights

Each edition of the *RHS Plant Finder* contains more than 3,000 plants that haven't been included before – and the new entries in this 2018 edition show no sign of abating.

Author: **Janet Cubey,** Editor-in-Chief

Much of my work is about celebrating and sharing the joy of plants; that's why I love it!

So recently, while spending long hours proof-reading the Plant Directory of this book, I've been writing lists. There's the list of genera that haven't appeared in the book before (surprisingly long); the smile-raising new cultivar names (such as daylilies 'Silly Wabbit' and 'You had me at Woof'); the shopping list for home (plants of course, not groceries); and this list celebrating just some of the diverse plants that are new to the *RHS Plant Finder* for this, the 2018 edition.

This is my personal choice of 25 of the many gems you'll find in the pages that follow. The only rule for inclusion in this list is that the plant shouldn't have appeared in the book before. As with many good lists, it's in alphabetical order.

CROCUS

1 *Anemone hupehensis* var. *japonica* 'Tiki Sensation'

Bred by Staudegården in Denmark, this hardy perennial is noted for the distinctive multiple layers of ruffled petals. Some people describe the flower as being like a peony; to me it's attractively tousled and rather appeals as a contrast to some of the more formal flowers that some autumn-flowering anemones can have. In spite of being a double flower, it still has the typical green eye with a golden-yellow halo of stamens, so it should still be good for pollinating insects. Flowers start pale pink, turning to their predominant white as they mature, though pink shades can also appear again as winter approaches and temperatures decrease.

2 *Anthriscus sylvestris* 'Golden Fleece'

The white flowers of cow parsley, a UK native, are a floral delight in hedgerows throughout most of the UK in late spring and early summer. In recent years we've also become accustomed to the dark purple, ferny foliage and pink-tinged flowers of *A. sylvestris* 'Ravenswing' as it pops up in many planting schemes and designs. Now, there's a new yellow-leaved cultivar to add to the mix, *A. sylvestris* 'Golden Fleece'. With bright yellow to yellow-green ferny foliage (said not to scorch in full sun) combined with the expected white flower umbels, it's likely to make an impact anywhere. I'm looking forward to seeing how it differs from *A. sylvestris* 'Going for Gold'.

LISA WESLEY @ GROWILD NURSERY

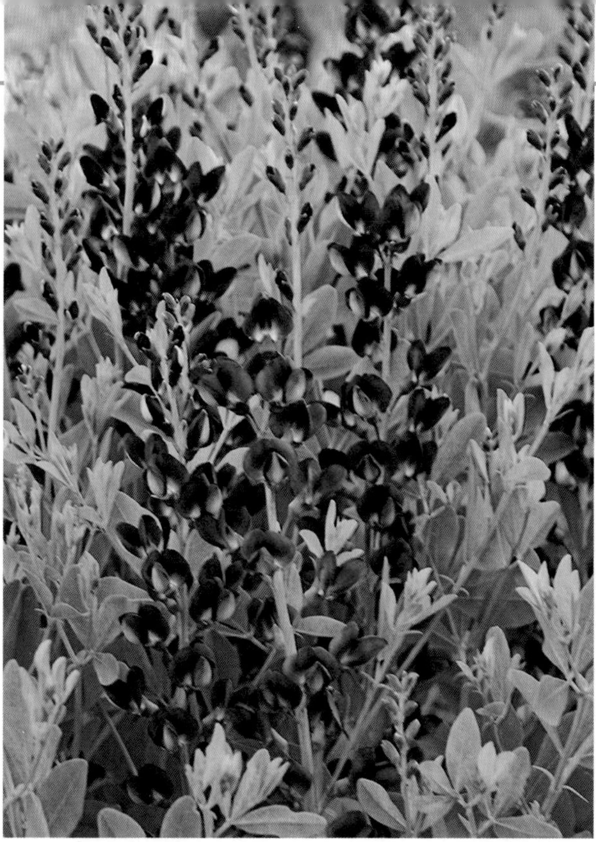

CROCUS

3 *Baptisia* 'Grape Taffy'

One of two new *Baptisia* cultivars appearing in the book this year is 'Grape Taffy'. At less than 90cm tall and wide, it is shorter than most other cultivars. The glaucous, trifoliate, pea-like foliage is attractive in its own right. However, it's the floral spikes, opening from the base upwards, from early summer that is this cultivar's crowning glory. From dark purple buds come rich red-purple, lupin-like flowers with touches of pale creamy-yellow. If you prefer taller cultivars, 'Pink Lemonade' might be the new one for you, with pale yellow flowers that age to dusky pink. Both come from the breeding programme of Hans Hansen at Walters Gardens in the USA. *Baptisia* favour full sun but are surprisingly tolerant of a range of soil types.

4 *Betula* 'Cobhay Cream Spire'

Cultivar names that start with the word 'Cobhay' are from the woody plant breeding programme at Junkers Nursery (CJun). *Betula* 'Cobhay Cream Spire', a selected seedling from a *B. ermanii* × *B. utilis* subsp. *albosinensis* cross, was chosen for its upright, tidy habit (narrower than is usual for *B. ermanii*) and wonderful cream bark with prominent lenticels. A sister seedling, with white bark, has been named 'Cobhay Snow Spire'. It has better resistance to rust than many existing white-barked cultivars as well as lovely yellow autumn tints.

TORSTEN JUNKER

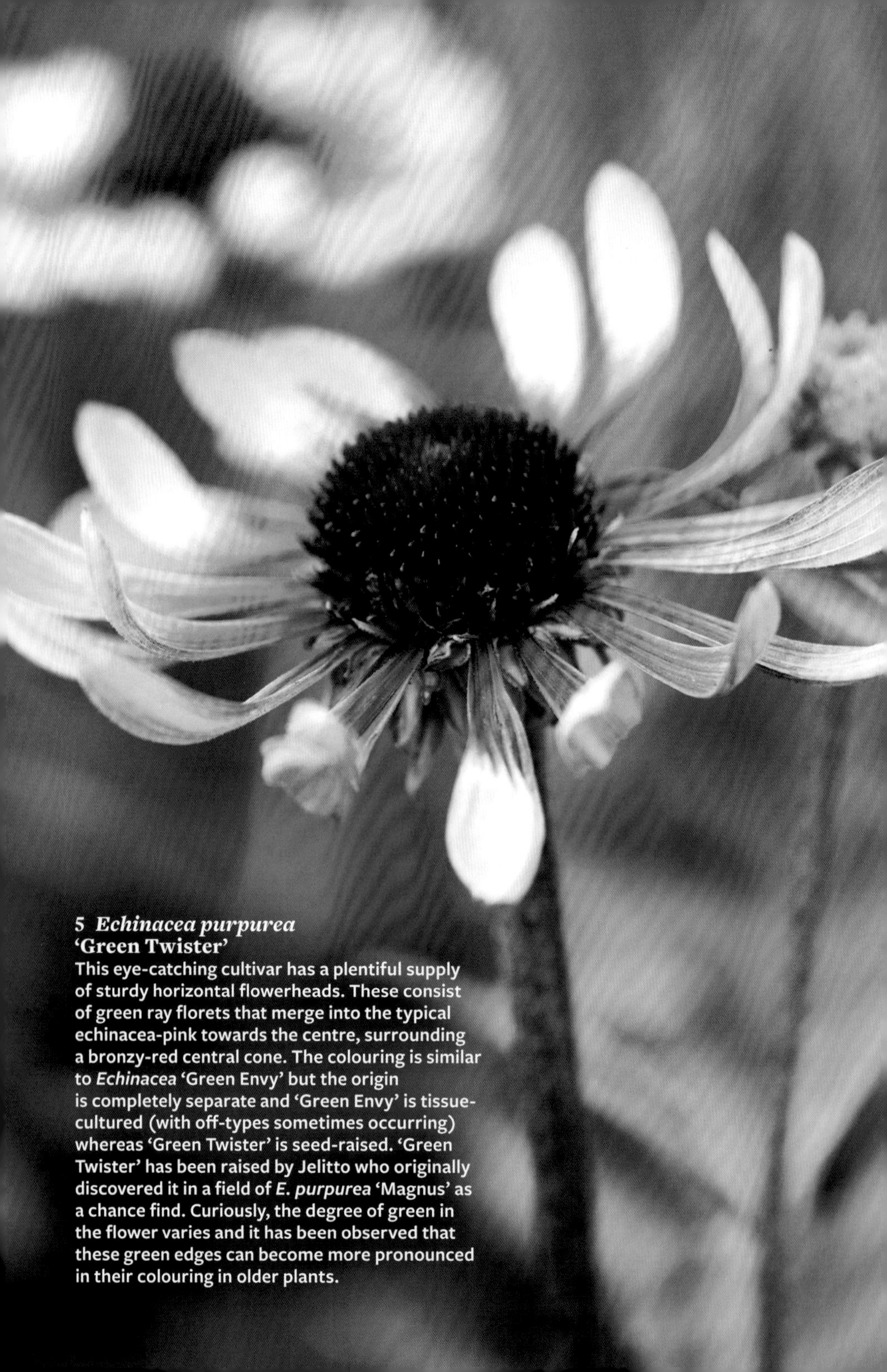

5 *Echinacea purpurea* 'Green Twister'

This eye-catching cultivar has a plentiful supply of sturdy horizontal flowerheads. These consist of green ray florets that merge into the typical echinacea-pink towards the centre, surrounding a bronzy-red central cone. The colouring is similar to *Echinacea* 'Green Envy' but the origin is completely separate and 'Green Envy' is tissue-cultured (with off-types sometimes occurring) whereas 'Green Twister' is seed-raised. 'Green Twister' has been raised by Jelitto who originally discovered it in a field of *E. purpurea* 'Magnus' as a chance find. Curiously, the degree of green in the flower varies and it has been observed that these green edges can become more pronounced in their colouring in older plants.

6 *Enkianthus campanulatus* 'Miyama-beni'

It's exciting when a plant you've been waiting for finally appears in the book. In the June 2011 issue of *The Plantsman* there was an article on *Enkianthus* which included the cultivar 'Miyama-beni'. *Enkianthus campanulatus*, from Japan, is the most widely cultivated species and 'Miyama-beni' is a vigorous cultivar with plentiful deep rose-pink, hanging bell flowers. It was imported into North America from Japan by Heritage Seedlings of Oregon and from there to Europe and the UK. It has a twiggy, vertical growth habit, red-tinged young branches and, because it's deciduous, you get good red autumn colour too. If it didn't require acidic soil, one would be making its way into my garden now.

ESVELD

JUDY'S SNOWDROPS

7 *Galanthus nivalis* 'Llo 'n' Green'

While I wouldn't call myself a galanthophile, I have several named cultivars of snowdrop in my garden and this one does appeal. *Galanthus nivalis* 'Llo 'n' Green' is an early-flowering selection (in December or January), to around 11cm tall, that was discovered in France in the 1990s by nursery owner Joe Sharman and botanist Alan Leslie. The green tips on the outer segments can vary from year to year, typically with five separate, dark green lines in the lower third.

DARWIN PLANTS

8 *Geum* 'Apricot Pearl' (Censation Series)

Geum 'Apricot Pearl' is one of the Censation Series (not just restricted to *Geum*) from CNB New Plants of the Netherlands, along with 'Coral Pearl', 'Pink Fluffy' and 'Two Tone Pearl'. With the exception of 'Pink Fluffy', which has deeply filigreed edges to the petals, they all have semi-double flowers. 'Apricot Pearl' has large, pale apricot-coloured petals, flushed with pink, surrounding a yellow-green central boss of stamens. *Geum* are wonderfully robust plants with a long flowering period in late spring and summer. You might also like to consider some that have been bred in the UK, such as those by *Geum* specialist East of Eden Nursery (NEoE).

9 *Hakonechloa macra* SunFlare ('Habsfl007')

It's always interesting to see which plant enters the book for the first time with the highest number of nurseries supplying it. For 2018, it's *Hakonechloa macra* SunFlare, a sport selected from the well-known cultivar 'All Gold'. SunFlare forms a neat cascading mound of chartreuse-coloured leaves – the brighter the sun the more intensely golden they become – with scattered deep red highlights on the leaf tips. Suitable for containers, as well as the open ground, this might also perform well in living-wall plantings.

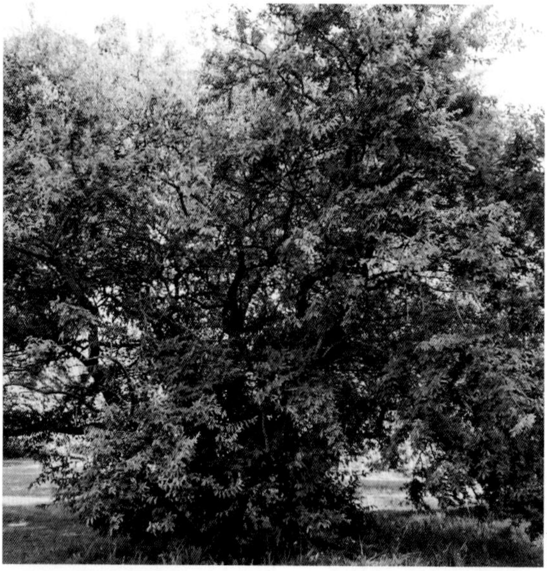

WIKIMEDIA / STEN

CROCUS

10 *Hemiptelea davidii*

Although this species was introduced in 1908 (according to the *Hillier Manual*), it's appearing for the first time this year in the *RHS Plant Finder*. A somewhat different definition of new, this is an example of a species that should be better known. *Hemiptelea*, or thorn-elm, is a monotypic genus that's related to *Zelkova*. *Hemiptelea davidii* forms a small, dense, shrubby tree with spine-tipped branches, winged fruits and toothed, oval leaves. A native of China and the Korean peninsula, it's sometimes seen as a hedging plant in China, where it has multiple uses, such as fibre from the bark and tea from the leaves.

11 *Heuchera* 'Black Pearl'

A *Heuchera villosa* hybrid with sumptuous glossy black leaves, 'Black Pearl' performs in both sun and shade. Its leaves are rich pink-purple on their undersides and, with ruffled margins, this colour can be seen peeking through the black. It is said that the oldest leaves can develop a bit of silvering. The flowers, on tall stems up to 50cm tall, appear in midsummer – they are white with pink calyces.

12 *Ilex crenata*
Luxus Globe ('Annys5')

The quest is on for plants to fill the same niche as *Buxus sempervirens* (common box) in our gardens. Bred by André van Nijnatten, *Ilex crenata* Luxus Globe is being marketed as a challenger in this arena. As expected with this species, it's very hardy and suitable for full sun, partial shade or shade. The leaves are small, dark green, very glossy and slightly crenate towards the tips. It appears to have a naturally rounded shape, up to 60cm tall and wide, and is said to require less pruning than many other hollies. As a male cultivar, no berries will be produced.

13 *Malus toringo* 'Aros'
This beautiful new crab apple won best in show at the Horticultural Trades Association National Plant Show New Plant Awards in June 2017. Bred by Karsten Jensen, *Malus toringo* 'Aros' was exhibited by Frank P Matthews (WMat). A dwarf, pillar-shaped tree, its leaves emerge dark burgundy to black and turn slightly greener as the season progresses. Vibrant dark pink flowers with white stripes down the centre of each petal are followed by small maroon crab apples in autumn that should persist well into the winter months. Flowering and fruiting at a young age, it's ideal for a small garden or patio and is said to require little to no pruning and to be disease resistant. Although tolerant of shade, it grows best in sun.

FRANK P MATTHEWS

STAR ROSE & PLANTS

14 *Metasequoia* Amber Glow ('Wah-08ag')
Arising as a seedling, *Metasequoia* Amber Glow was selected for its smaller stature, compact yellow-green foliage and dense pyramidal habit. With shades of orange on the feathery foliage at different points in the season, the leaves become greyed-orange before leaf fall in autumn. It's reported to have better resistance to leaf scorch (through both temperature and sunlight) than other yellow cultivars, such as Gold Rush.

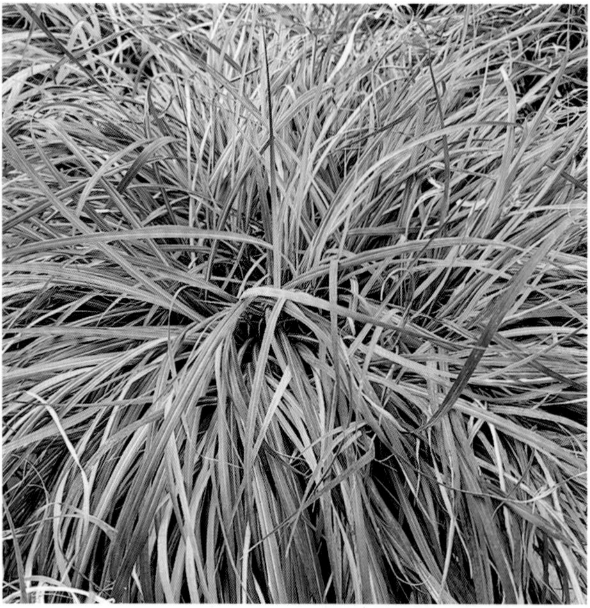

KNOLL GARDENS

15 *Miscanthus sinensis* 'Little Miss'

Of a number of new *Miscanthus sinensis* cultivars to enter the book this year, 'Little Miss' is the only one with more than one supplier, which is often a good sign of the appeal of a new plant. A description of 'Little Miss' as a well-mannered German cultivar (it was bred by Klaus Mendel) made me smile, but as a compact cultivar to less than 1m tall, that is certainly true. With green foliage in spring, the upper portion of the leaf blades mature through pink to reddish-purple and vibrant red as the season progresses.

16 *Nepeta* NEPTUNE ('Bokratune')

Bred by Kees Jan Kraan in the Netherlands, *Nepeta* NEPTUNE is notable for the compactness of its habit combined with the large size of the flowers. Dark green aromatic foliage (which can be used to make tea) is topped by a mass of large, violet-blue flowers. As you'd expect from a catmint, it'll perform well in full sun, flowering from summer to autumn in sandy, loamy or chalky soils. Growing to 30cm tall, it's a very versatile plant for the front of the border or patio container.

PLANTIPP

17 *Pelargonium* 'Rushmoor Amazon' (Rushmoor River Series)

First seen at the RHS Chelsea Flower Show 2017, *Pelargonium* 'Rushmoor Amazon' is classified as a "zonartic" cultivar; a hybrid between a zonale, or zonal cultivar, and *P. articulatum*. These hybrids are the result of three decades of amateur breeding, initially in Australia, but now also in the UK and elsewhere. With a distinctive habit, long flower stems (making them suitable as cut flowers) and more open inflorescences, a wide range of cultivars is now coming into the market, including 'Rushmoor Amazon' with its lovely buttery yellow flowers. You'll find a healthy coverage of these hybrids in the Plant Directory this year: look for cultivar names starting with 'Rushmoor', 'Unicorn', 'Lara' and 'Lovely'.

GENESIS PLANT MARKETING

18 *Penstemon* Pentastic Series

The Pentastic Series of *Penstemon* is the result of a long-term breeding project by Fred Yates, lasting more than two decades. These winter-hardy, naturally compact cultivars (helped by a single pinch when young) are suitable for containers as well as garden beds, flowering to 30cm tall from early summer through until the first frosts. With large, horizontally-held flowers, they are said to re-bloom well, with deadheading helping the best performance. All three cultivars have a prominent white throat that overspills slightly to the base of the petal circle.

Left to right:

PENTASTIC RED ('Yapruby') – deep cherry red

PENTASTIC PINK ('Yapmine') – rosy pink

PENTASTIC ROSE ('Yaprose') – vibrant deep magenta pink

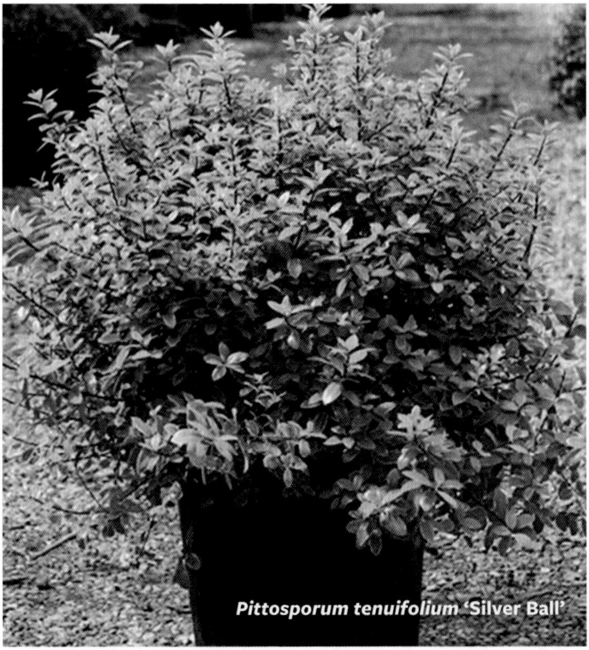

Pittosporum tenuifolium 'Silver Ball'

BIGPLANTNURSERY.CO.UK

Pittosporum tenuifolium 'Golden Ball'

BIGPLANTNURSERY.CO.UK

19 & 20 *Pittosporum tenuifolium* 'Silver Ball' and 'Golden Ball'

Green-leaved *Pittosporum tenuifolium* 'Golf Ball' was introduced a few years ago. It has a neat, rounded, compact habit. Now, also from New Zealand, come the cultivars 'Silver Ball' and 'Golden Ball'. Slow-growing and rarely requiring trimming, 'Silver Ball' has grey-green leaves with an irregular, creamy-white margin, while 'Golden Ball' forms a tidy sphere of shimmering, golden-green foliage. Another option as a box-hedge substitute, perhaps? It looks like we might see more variations on these balls, bouncing their way into the UK in future years.

LUBERA

21 *Prunus* 'Aprisali' (aprium)

So, what's an aprium? It's a hybrid between an apricot and a plum. Aprium 'Aprisali' is a compact tree that crops early in its life. It's also self-fertile, so no pollinating partner is required. Fruit is said to be ready to pick in July and the skin is dark purple with a sweet, plum aroma and it has bright red, juicy flesh. Suitable for partial shade or full sun where the soil is well-drained, 'Aprisali' is also said to be very disease resistant. If you're tempted by hybrid fruit, why not also consider *Prunus* 'Aprimira' – it's a miracot, a hybrid between a mirabelle and an apricot.

22 *Salvia* 'Crystal Blue'

Runner up in the 2017 RHS Chelsea Flower Show Plant of the Year award, 'Crystal Blue' looks set to be seen in our gardens for many years to come. Of the popular herbaceous perennial salvias, it has the distinction of pastel, light sky-blue-coloured flowers. It hails from the USA where it stood out, a chance seedling in a field of darker blue 'Mainacht'. Spotted by Jerry van der Kolk, it was then trialled and introduced by Walters Gardens and has now made its way to the UK. Growing to 45cm high by 60cm wide, this free-flowering cultivar is attractive to insects and ideal for sunny or partly shady borders with any soil type.

CROCUS

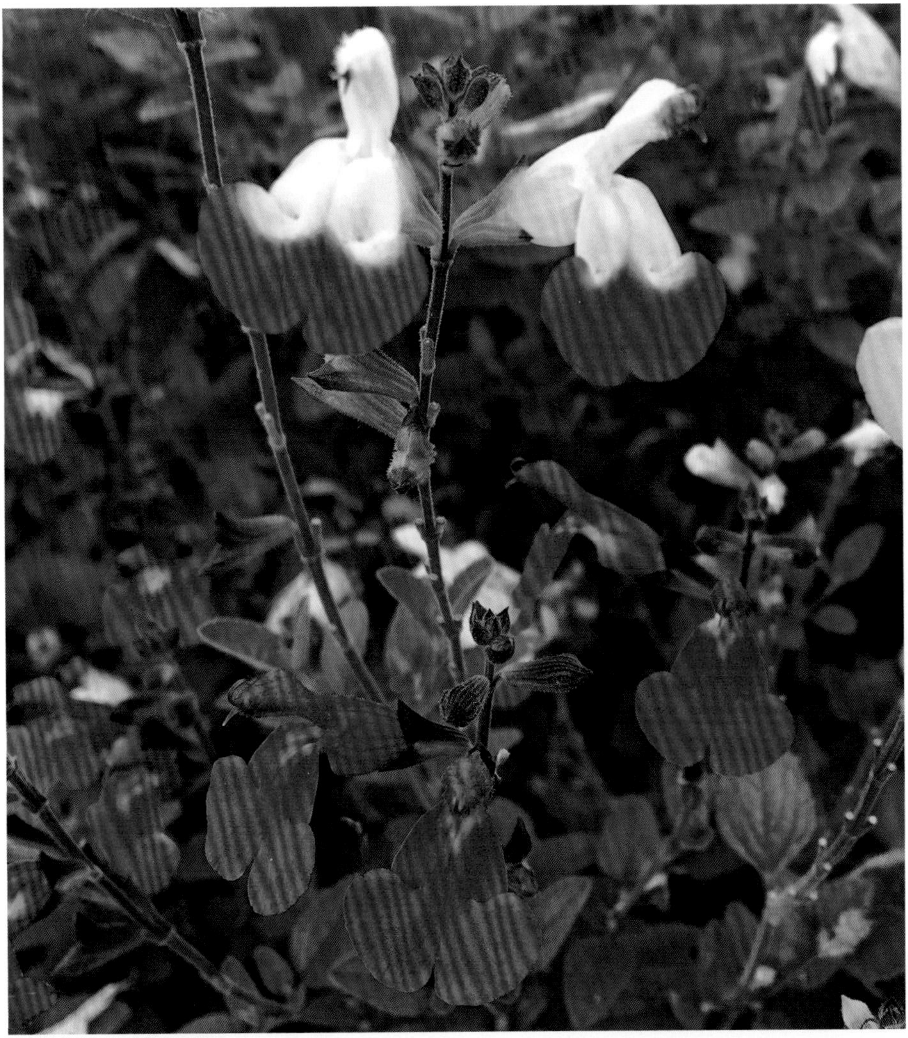

23 **Salvia × jamensis 'Jeremy' (sold as PINK LIPS)**

I couldn't resist including a second *Salvia* in this list, and I bought this one last summer. I'm sure that nearly every gardener in the country is familiar with *Salvia* 'Hot Lips' with its white flowers edged with red (though at various points in the season, with different temperatures, you can also get pure red and pure white flowers). Well, PINK LIPS is just like that but with a deep rich pink edge to the white flowers. It's said that the flowers are 50 percent larger too, although I haven't observed this with mine, but given that 'Hot Lips' is happily established in my garden and PINK LIPS is just a young plant, it isn't really a fair comparison – yet. It was bred by Marc van Lancker, and has a woody base, lovely foliage aroma and flowers from June to October.

BORDER ALPINES

24 *Semiaquilegia* 'Tinkerbell'

Who doesn't love the daintiness of a *Semiaquilegia*? Bred in Devon, at Border Alpines (CBor), 'Tinkerbell' has delicate spurless flowers that are almost pure white with just the merest hint of pink; these hanging bells airily dance up to 25cm tall. Other new treats from Border Alpines include *Helleborus* × *hybridus* 'Chocolate Truffle' – with large, cupped, marbled-chocolate-coloured flowers – and a fine-looking dark form of *Erythronium dens-canis*. This has particularly deep pink, reflexed flowers, very mottled leaves and dark stems – hopefully it might be given a cultivar name one day.

25 *Zamioculcas zamiifolia* RAVEN ('Dowon')

Zamioculcas zamiifolia is a houseplant (or office-plant) that can thrive on a little neglect, capable of going a few weeks without water. It's a stunning architectural plant with structural, thick fleshy stems and glossy, double ranks of leaves. Now, add leaves that emerge green but quickly take on a dark chocolate to near-black colour and you've got even more of an impact; one for the cat-walk perhaps?

CROCUS

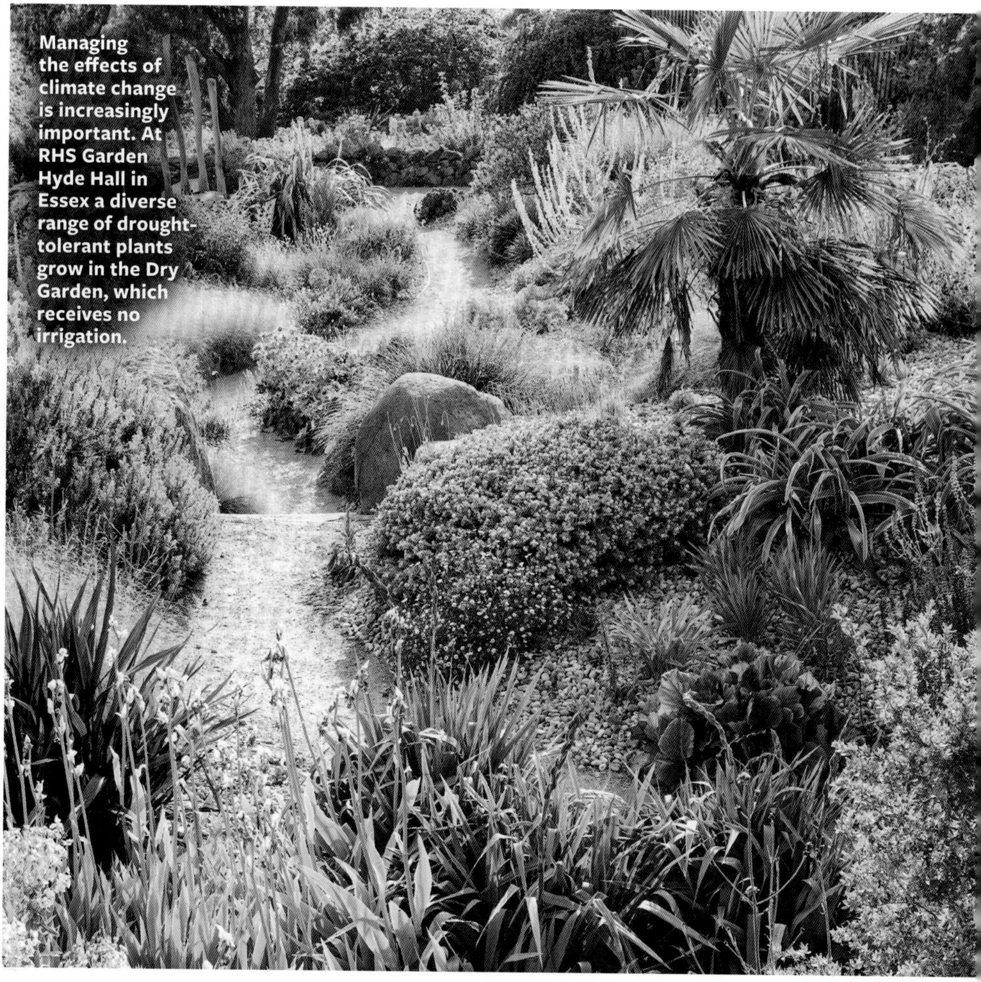

Managing the effects of climate change is increasingly important. At RHS Garden Hyde Hall in Essex a diverse range of drought-tolerant plants grow in the Dry Garden, which receives no irrigation.

Gardening and climate change

Scientific predictions for climate change point to the UK becoming warmer with wetter winters and drier summers. How gardeners respond will be critical for adapting to these changes

Author: **Eleanor Webster,** RHS Climate Scientist

Green roofs (right) bring plants to towns and cities and reduce energy use by insulating buildings while also helping to mitigate the effects of flash flooding. Scientists agree that, because of the air masses affecting Britain (far right) and the weather conditions they bring, the UK will continue to experience variable weather.

Gardens are not isolated entities; they exist as part of the wider landscape and are influenced by the prevailing climate. And in recent years, gardeners have increasingly observed the extension of the growing season, often combined with late frosts and heavy rain.

How is the UK climate changing?
The RHS *Gardening in a Changing Climate* report, published in spring 2017 (see rhs.org.uk/climate), summarises published climate projections and includes a survey of more than 1,000 gardeners. It suggests that the UK in general will have wetter winters and drier summers – but there will be some especially wet years and some especially dry. The report offers advice for coping with weather extremes, particularly when rainfall becomes increasingly concentrated into heavy, intense downpours, followed by prolonged dry periods.

Domestic gardens account for 25 percent of urban space. And with more than half of the UK adult population engaged in gardening, gardens must be managed to maximise opportunities while reducing the risks posed by climate change. (References for these figures appear in the full report.)

In 2002, when the *Gardening in a Global Greenhouse* report was published, models predicted that the UK could look forward to warmer summers similar to those of the Mediterranean. Since then, our greenhouse gas emissions have followed the trajectory of the 'worst-case scenario'. We can now conclude with a high degree of confidence that the world will become hotter, but it will be extreme events – such as heavy rainstorms combined with long periods of

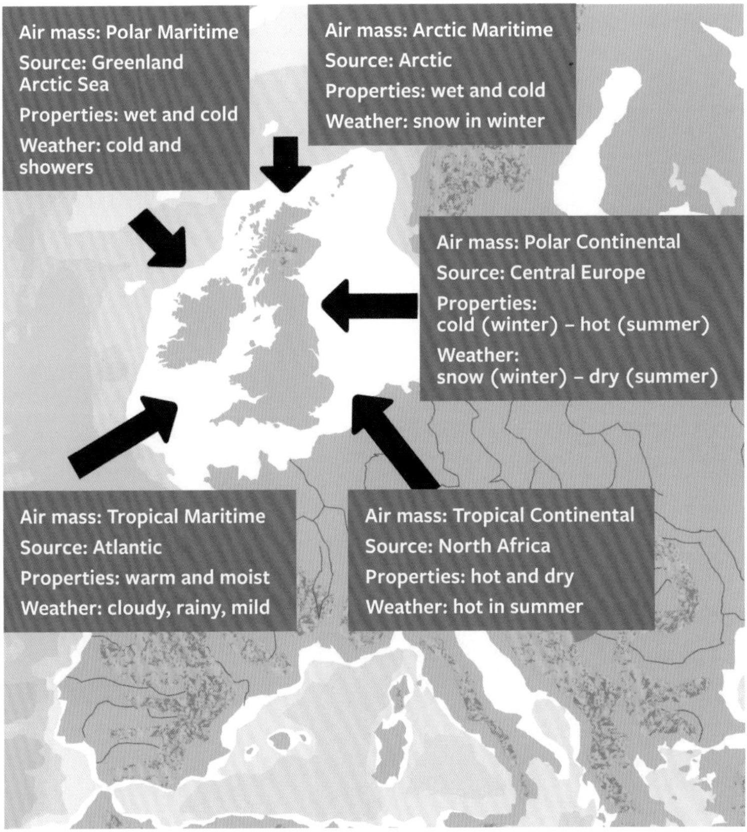

drought – that will present the greatest challenges to society.

Rainfall in the UK will become increasingly variable, with much of Britain expected to be frost-free in some years. There will be noticeable differences in the frequency and intensity of heavy rainfall and prolonged drought between the north and the south of the UK. Significantly wet winter days will increase in number, and this will be most pronounced in northern areas – by the 2050s, winters could be up to 40 percent wetter than 1961–1990 averages. The length of dry spells will increase, especially in summer in southern areas. Summers in the 2050s could be 40 percent drier than 1961–1990. Lower rainfall coupled with higher summer temperatures will lead to significantly drier soils. By the 2050s, eastern, southern and central England could require irrigation needs above anything currently experienced.

Even with big reductions in greenhouse gas emissions, global temperatures may still rise between 1.5 and 2°C (3.6–4.5°F) during the next 100 years. While this might not sound significant, it is the impact on natural systems, such as glacial melt, contributing to the alteration of atmospheric and ocean circulation, that will alter our global climate.

The 'RHS Garden for a Changing Climate' at RHS Chatsworth Flower Show 2017 (left) included plants able to cope with more extreme weather. Created in 2001, the Dry Garden at RHS Garden Hyde Hall (below) contains more than 400 species.

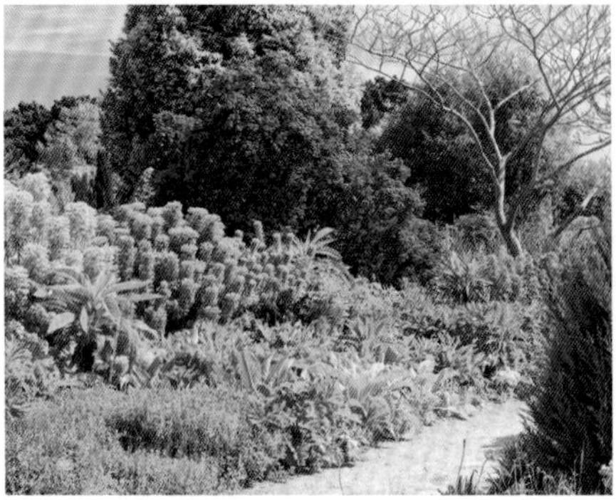

Garden army

The consequences of climate change will be compounded by the rising global human population. Despite an increase in the frequency and intensity of extreme weather events, green space is being replaced by impermeable surfaces as cities grow. Meanwhile, we burn fossil fuels to run the infrastructure on which we all rely. Consequently, the role of gardens in delivering the health and environmental ecosystem services formerly fulfilled by the natural environment is becoming increasingly important.

Gardens will be critical for adapting to climatic changes and mitigating increased harm through further emissions. The way we manage our outdoor spaces can have implications for rainwater flow after a heavy rainfall event, but could also help to reduce carbon emissions. And the prospect of milder winters, longer summers and an extended growing season will present opportunities to all of us who garden.

Gardeners surveyed for *Gardening in a Changing Climate* have shown themselves willing to take up this challenge. Our choices, both of plants and materials, are likely to need to adapt, but our gardens could bring wider benefits to urban society.

Ideal weather-resistant plants

2

1 *Calamagrostis brachytricha* ♀H6
This versatile grass offers green foliage in spring and narrow, purple-tinged, plume-like, fluffy flower sprays in summer and autumn, when leaves also turn a rich golden orange. Bushy and tall in stature, it tolerates most soils, aspects and intermittent wet and dry periods.

1

2 *Primula vialii* ♀H5
With a conical spike of red and violet adding interest to boggy areas in spring, this striking herbaceous perennial thrives in waterlogged, acidic loam soils but can also withstand dry environments for a week or two.

3

CROCUS

3 *Viburnum opulus* 'Roseum' ♀H6
A good option for shady spots, this bushy deciduous shrub suits most soils, aspects and exposures and can tolerate wet soils after a rainstorm. Globular heads of creamy white, sterile flowers in early summer are followed by colourful fruit and red autumn leaves.

4

4 *Stachys byzantina*
Resilient to flooding that lasts for a few days, such as after a heavy downpour, this evergreen perennial is ideal for sunny, southwest-facing borders or cottage gardens. With purple whorls that delight in summer, and silver-coloured, furry leaves, it is a great ground-cover option.

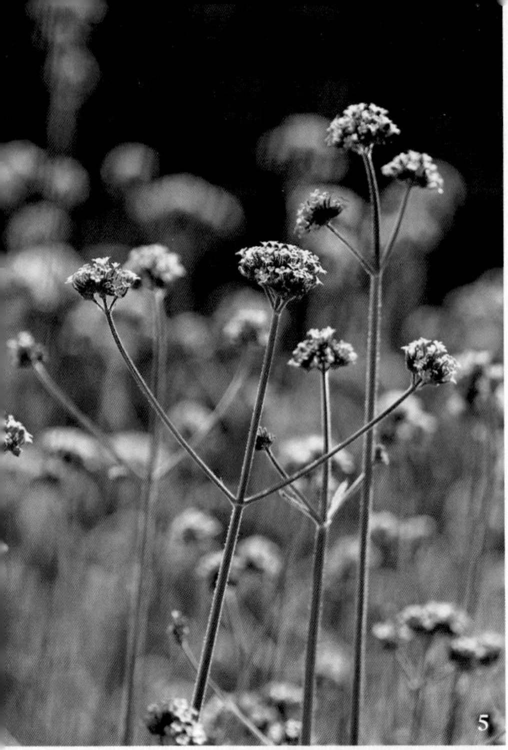

5 *Verbena bonariensis* 🏆^{H4}

Tolerating most soils and happy in wet or dry conditions, even waterlogged soils for a few weeks, this upright-growing perennial boasts purple flowers in summer and autumn in a sunny spot. It reaches 2m but only spreads to 0.5m, making it ideal for smaller spaces.

6 *Sambucus nigra* f. *porphyrophylla*

This deciduous shrub has attractive lacy leaves that intercept rainfall before it reaches ground level, thereby reducing waterlogging. Its rich purple foliage is complemented by tiny pink flowers with an elderflower scent in summer.

CROCUS

7 *Cornus alba* 'Sibirica' 🏆^{H7}

In a sunny spot, this hardy shrub withstands intermittent drying and wetting, and its striking red stems offer winter colour and structure. It is perfect for low-maintenance borders.

8 *Cotinus coggygria* 'Royal Purple' 🏆^{H5}

Reaching 5m in height, this large deciduous shrub with bronze-purple leaves is tolerant of most soil types and aspects. It withstands strong winds and helps regulate soil moisture by transporting water from the soil to the air following heavy rainfall, while using minimal water when the soil starts to dry.

I
GENERAL INFORMATION

INTRODUCTION

The *RHS Plant Finder* exists to put enthusiastic gardeners in touch with suppliers of plants. It is comprehensively updated every year.

The book is divided into two related sections: **PLANTS** and **NURSERIES**.

PLANTS includes an A-Z Directory of around 76,000 plant names, against which are listed a series of nursery codes. These codes point the reader to the full nursery details contained in the **NURSERIES** section towards the back of the book.

It is important to remember when ordering plants that many of the nurseries listed in the book are small, family-run businesses that propagate their own material. They cannot, therefore, guarantee to hold large stocks of the plants they list. Some will, however, propagate to order.

Nurseries appearing in the *RHS Plant Finder* for the first time or re-entering after an absence are printed in bold type in the **Nursery Index by Name** (pp.950-954).

NEW IN THIS EDITION

We'd like to start this edition by highlighting a change in the Compiler. Firstly, many, many thanks to Judith Merrick for her sterling work throughout numerous years in the role. Then, welcome to Lindsay Durrant as the new Compiler. Lindsay worked alongside Judith for the 2017 edition before compiling this 2018 edition.

We've decided to keep the colour section that we started last year for the 30th Anniversary Edition. This year the colour section highlights the work of Dr. Eleanor Webster, RHS Climate Scientist with a piece on Gardening and Climate Change. Alongside this is the first Editor's choice selection of 25 of the plants that are appear in the book for the first time in this edition.

The plant names used in the 2018 edition reflect the decisions made by the RHS Nomenclature and Taxonomy Advisory Group (NATAG). Nomenclatural Notes (p.49) gives a brief overview of these changes made since the compilation of the previous edition of the book.

LISTS OF NURSERIES FOR PLANTS WITH MORE THAN 30 SUPPLIERS

To prevent the book from becoming too big, we do not print nursery codes where more than 30 nurseries offer the same plant. The plant is then listed as being "widely available". See **How to Use the Plant Directory** (p.55).

A full list of all the nurseries held on file as current suppliers can be found by searching the RHS website Find a Plant facility or can be made available in printed form by post from the Compiler at the address below. For the latter, please ensure you include the full name of the plant (as given in the *RHS Plant Finder*) and enclose a stamped addressed envelope.

PLANTS LAST LISTED IN EARLIER EDITIONS

Plants cease to be listed for a variety of reasons. For more information, turn to **How to Use the Plant Directory** (p.55). A listing of more than 60,000 plants listed in earlier editions but for which we have no current suppliers will be made available on the RHS website.

RHS ONLINE

The plant data from the *RHS Plant Finder* is available on the Royal Horticultural Society's website at www.rhs.org.uk/plants under the Find a Plant section.

APPLICATION FOR ENTRY

If you would like your nursery to be considered for inclusion in the next edition of the *RHS Plant Finder*, please contact the Compiler. Entries to the book are free.

Contact details
The Compiler, *RHS Plant Finder*
RHS Garden Wisley
Woking
Surrey
GU23 6QB
Ⓣ (01483) 226577
Ⓔ plantfinder@rhs.org.uk

ACKNOWLEDGEMENTS

This edition was compiled by Lindsay Durrant with Jane Rowlands, assisted by Gill Skilton. Richard Sanford managed the editing of the plant names in the database and Julia Barclay and Rupert Wilson administered the RHS Horticultural Database using the BGBase™ Collection Management Software.

RHS botanists James Armitage, Dawn Edwards, Kálmán Könyves, Neil Lancaster and Rosalyn Marshall undertook the task of editing the new plant names for this edition of the book.

RHS Book Publisher Rae Spencer-Jones collated the colour section and we acknowledge the contribution of Louise Bowering, Louise Tee, Sarah Carrington, Mark Timothy, Marina Jordan-Rugg, John David and Yvette Harvey. We would also like to thank those who have kindly provided plant images.

Special thanks go to RHS Climate Scientist Dr Eleanor Webster for her advice on how best to integrate the Climate Change report into the Climate Change feature. We would also like to thank the Curatorial Team at RHS Garden Wisley for their contribution to the 2017 RHS Plant Finder 30th Anniversary celebrations. We say thank you and farewell to Principal Scientist James Armitage who moves to a new role within the RHS as Editor – Specialist Publications.

As ever, we are grateful for the professional support of Kerry Walter of BG-Base (UK) Ltd and Max Phillips of Strange Software Ltd. Finally, we are greatly indebted to Peter Cooling for his skill in turning our data into a publishable form.

Our colleagues on the RHS Nomenclature and Taxonomy Advisory Group, along with the RHS International Cultivar Registrars, have all provided valuable guidance and information. Many nurseries have supplied useful details on new plants and have suggested corrections to existing entries. Some of these remain to be checked and will be entered in the next edition, although those that contravene the Codes of Nomenclature may have to be rejected. We appreciate your patience while these checks are made. We are also grateful to our regular correspondents and to all those readers who have made helpful comments.

Clematis	D.R. Donald, Int. Cultivar Registrar
Chrysanthemum	J. Barker
Conifers	S. McDonald, Int. Cultivar Registrar
Dahlia	S. McDonald, Int. Cultivar Registrar
Dianthus	Dr A.C. Leslie, Int. Cultivar Registrar
Delphinium	M.R. Underwood, Int. Cultivar Registrar
Ilex	S. Andrews
Lilium	D.R. Donald, Int. Cultivar Registrar
Narcissus	M.R. Underwood, Int. Cultivar Registrar
Nerine	Dr J.C. David
Orchids	J.M.H. Shaw, Int. Cultivar Registrar
Rhododendron	Dr A.C. Leslie, Int. Cultivar Registrar
Sorbus	Dr H. McAllister
Thymus	M. Easter, Int. Cultivar Registrar

Janet Cubey
RHS Editor in Chief
February 2018

Symbols and Abbreviations

Symbols Appearing to the Left of the Name

*	Name not validated. Not listed in the appropriate International Registration Authority checklist nor in works cited in the Bibliography. For fuller discussion see p.37
I	Invalid name. See *International Code of Botanical Nomenclature 2012* and *International Code of Nomenclature for Cultivated Plants 2016*. For fuller discussion see p.37
§	Plant listed elsewhere in the Plant Directory under a synonym
×	Hybrid genus
+	Graft hybrid genus

Symbols Appearing to the Right of the Name

✿	Plant Heritage National Plant Collection® exists for all or part of this genus. Further details can be found by searching the National Plant Collections online or in the Plant Heritage Directory available from www.plantheritage.com or by phone (01483) 447540.
♀H4	The Royal Horticultural Society's Award of Garden Merit, see p.37
(d)	double-flowered
(F)	Fruit
(f)	female
(m)	male
(v)	variegated plant, see p.41
PBR	Plant Breeders' Rights see p.39
new	New plant entry in this edition

For abbreviations relating to individual genera see **Classification of Genera** p.50

For **Collectors' References** see p.45

For symbols used in the **Nurseries** section see p.865

Symbols and Abbreviations used as Part of the Name

×	hybrid species
aff.	affinis (akin to)
agg.	aggregate, a single name used to cover a group of very similar plants, regarded by some as separate species
ambig.	ambiguous, a name used by two authors for different plants and where it is unclear which is being offered
cf.	compare to
cl.	clone
f.	forma (botanical form)
gx	grex
sensu stricto	in the narrow sense
sp.	species
subsp.	subspecies
subvar.	subvarietas (botanical subvariety)
var.	varietas (botanical variety)

It is not within the remit of this book to check that nurseries are applying the right names to the right plants or to ensure nurseries selling plants with Plant Breeders' Rights are licensed to do so.

Please, never use an out of date edition

EXTENDED GLOSSARY

This glossary combines some of the helpful introductory sections from older editions in an alphabetical listing. A fuller, more discursive account of plant names, *Guide to Plant Names,* and a detailed guide to the typography of plant names, *Recommended Style for Printing Plant Names,* are both available as leaflets. To request a copy of either please send an A4 sae to The Compiler at the contact address given on page 34.

ADVISORY COMMITTEE ON NOMENCLATURE AND TAXONOMY

See **Nomenclature and Taxonomy Advisory Group**

AUTHORITIES

In order that plant names can be used with precision throughout the scientific world, the name of the person who coined the name of a plant species (its author, or authority) is added to the plant name. Usually this information is of little consequence to gardeners, except in cases where the same name has been given to two different plants or a name is commonly misapplied. Although only one usage is correct, both may be encountered in books, so indicating the author is the only way to be certain about which plant is being referred to. This can happen equally with cultivars. Authors' names, where it is appropriate to cite them, appear in a smaller typeface after the species or cultivar name to which they refer and are abbreviated following Brummitt and Powell's *Authors of Plant Names.*

♀ AWARD OF GARDEN MERIT

The Award of Garden Merit (AGM) is intended as a practical guide for the gardener and is therefore awarded only after a period of assessment by the RHS Standing and Joint Committees. The AGM is awarded only to plants that are:

- excellent for ordinary use in appropriate conditions
- available
- of good constitution
- essentially stable in form and colour
- reasonably resistant to pests and diseases

The AGM symbol is cited in conjunction with the **hardiness** rating. A full list of AGM plants may be found on the RHS website at www.rhs.org.uk/agmplants.

The AGM list was originally reviewed every ten years, to ensure that every plant still merited the award. The last review took place in 2012; since 2013, the list has been subject to a "rolling review", and AGMs may now be rescinded at any time.

BOTANICAL NAMES

The aim of the botanical naming system is to provide each different plant with a single, unique, universal name. The basic unit of plant classification is the species. Species that share a number of significant characteristics are grouped together to form a genus (plural **genera**). The name of a species is made up of two elements; the name of the genus followed by the specific epithet, for example, *Narcissus romieuxii.*

Variation within a species can be recognised by division into subspecies (usually abbreviated to subsp.), varietas (or variety abbreviated to var.) and forma (or form abbreviated to f.). Whilst it is unusual for a plant to have all of these, it is possible, as in this example, *Narcissus romieuxii* subsp. *albidus* var. *zaianicus* f. *lutescens.*

The botanical elements are always given in italics, with only the genus taking an initial capital letter. The rank indications are never in italics. In instances where the rank is not known it is necessary to form an invalid construction by quoting a second epithet without a rank. This is an unsatisfactory situation, but requires considerable research to resolve.

In some genera, such as *Hosta,* we list the cultivar names alphabetically with the species or **hybrid** to which they are attributed afterwards in parentheses. For example, *Hosta* 'Reversed' (*sieboldiana*). In other situations where the aim is not to create a list alphabetically by cultivar name we would recommend styling this as *Hosta sieboldiana* 'Reversed'.

CLASSIFICATION OF GENERA

Genera that include a large number of species or with many cultivars are often subdivided into informal horticultural classifications or more formal Cultivar Groups, each based on a particular characteristic or combination of characteristics. Colour of flower or fruit and shape of flower are common examples and, with fruit, whether a cultivar is grown for culinary or dessert purposes. How such groups are named differs from genus to genus.

To help users of the *RHS Plant Finder* find the plants they want, the classifications used within cultivated genera are listed using codes and plants are marked with the appropriate code in brackets after its name in the Plant Directory. To find the explanation of each code, simply look it up under the genus concerned in the **Classification of Genera** starting on p.50. The codes relating to edible fruits are also listed here, but these apply across several genera.

Collectors' References

Abbreviations (usually with numbers) following a plant name refer to the collector(s) of the plant. These abbreviations are expanded, with a collector's name or expedition title, in the section **Collectors' References** starting on p.45.

A collector's reference may indicate a new, as yet unnamed range of variation within a species. The inclusion of collectors' references in the *RHS Plant Finder* supports the book's role in sourcing unusual plants.

The Convention on Biological Diversity calls for conservation of biodiversity, its sustainable use and the fair and equitable sharing of any derived benefits. Since its adoption in 1993, collectors are required to have prior informed consent from the country of origin for the acquisition and commercialisation of collected material.

Common Names

In a work such as this, it is necessary to refer to plants by their botanical names for the sake of universal comprehension and clarity. However, at the same time we recognise that with fruit and vegetables most people are more familiar with their common names than their botanical ones. Cross-references are therefore given from common to botanical names for fruit, vegetables and the commoner culinary herbs throughout the Plant Directory.

Cultivar

Literally meaning cultivated variety, cultivar names are given to denote variation within species and that generated by hybridisation, in cultivation. To make them easily distinguishable from botanical names, they are not printed in italics and are enclosed in single quotation marks. Cultivar names coined since 1959 should follow the rules of the International Code of Nomenclature for Cultivated Plants (**ICNCP**).

Descriptive Terms

Terms that appear after the main part of the plant name are shown in a smaller font to distinguish them. These descriptive elements give extra information about the plant and may include the **collector's reference**, **authority**, or what colour it is. For example, *Clematis henryi* B&SWJ 3402, *Penstemon* 'Sour Grapes' M. Fish, *Akebia quinata* cream-flowered.

Families

Genera are grouped into larger groups of related plants called families. Most family names, with the exception of eight familiar names, end with the same group of letters, *-aceae*. While it is still acceptable to use these eight exceptions, the modern trend adopted in the *RHS Plant Finder* is to use alternative names with *–aceae* endings. The families concerned are *Compositae* (*Asteraceae*), *Cruciferae* (*Brassicaceae*), *Gramineae* (*Poaceae*), *Guttiferae* (*Clusiaceae*), *Labiatae* (*Lamiaceae*), *Leguminosae* (split here into *Caesalpiniaceae*, *Mimosaceae* and *Papilionaceae*), *Palmae* (*Arecaceae*) and *Umbelliferae* (*Apiaceae*).

Apart from these exceptions we now follow (from 2010) *Mabberley's Plant-book* (3rd edition).

Genus (plural – genera)

Genera used in the *RHS Plant Finder* were originally based on Brummitt's *Vascular Plant Families and Genera* but are now based on a range of sources. For spellings and genders of generic names, Greuter's *Names in Current Use for Extant Plant Genera* has also been consulted. See **Botanical Names**.

Grex

Within orchids, hybrids of the same parentage, regardless of how alike they are, are given a grex name. Individuals can be selected, given cultivar names and propagated vegetatively. For example, *Pleione* Versailles gx 'Bucklebury', where Versailles is the grex name and 'Bucklebury' is a selected **cultivar**.

Group

This is a collective name for a group of cultivars within a genus with similar characteristics. The word Group is always included and, where cited with a cultivar name, it is enclosed in brackets, for example, *Actaea simplex* (Atropurpurea Group) 'Brunette', where 'Brunette' is a distinct cultivar in a group of purple-leaved cultivars.

Another example of a Group is *Rhododendron polycladum* Scintillans Group. In this case *Rhododendron scintillans* was a species that is now botanically 'sunk' within *R. polycladum*, but it is still recognised horticulturally as a Group.

Group names are also used for swarms of hybrids with the same parentage, for example, *Rhododendron* Polar Bear Group. These were formerly treated as **grex** names, a term now used only for orchids. A single clone from the Group may be given the same cultivar name, for example, *Rhododendron* 'Polar Bear'.

HARDINESS

Hardiness ratings are shown for **Award of Garden Merit** plants. To assist gardeners to determine more clearly which plants are hardy in their local area, the RHS introduced a new, enhanced, hardiness rating scheme in 2013, to coincide with the publication of the new **Award of Garden Merit** plant list. The categories now used are as follows:
Temperature ranges given are intended to be absolute minimum winter temperatures (°C).
H1a = Heated greenhouse – tropical >15
H1b = Heated greenhouse – subtropical 10 to 15
H1c = Heated greenhouse – warm temperate 5 to 10
H2 = Tender – cool or frost-free greenhouse 1 to 5
H3 = Half-hardy – unheated greenhouse/mild winter -5 to 1
H4 = Hardy – average winter -10 to -5
H5 = Hardy – cold winter -15 to -10
H6 = Hardy – very cold winter -20 to -15
H7 = Very hardy <-20

Further definition of these categories can be found on the RHS website, in the Feb 2013 edition of *The Garden* and in the *RHS Plant Finder 2013* essay.

HYBRIDS

Some species, when grown together, in the wild or in cultivation, are found to interbreed and form hybrids. In some instances a hybrid name is coined, for example hybrids between *Primula hirsuta* and *P. minima* are given the name *Primula* × *forsteri*, the multiplication sign indicating hybrid origin. Hybrid formulae that quote the parentage of the hybrid are used where a unique name has not been coined, for example *Eucryphia cordifolia* × *E. lucida*. In hybrid formulae you will find parents in alphabetical order, with the male (m) and female (f) parent indicated where known. Hybrids between different genera are also possible, for example × *Mahoberberis* is the name given to hybrids between *Mahonia* and *Berberis*.

There are also a few special-case hybrids called graft hybrids, where the tissues of two plants are physically rather than genetically mixed. These are indicated by an addition rather than a multiplication sign, so *Laburnum* + *Cytisus* becomes + *Laburnocytisus*.

ICNCP

The ICNCP is the International Code of Nomenclature for Cultivated Plants. First published in 1959, the 9th edition was published in 2016.

Cultivar names that do not conform to this Code, and for which there is no valid alternative, are flagged I (for invalid). This code states that the minimum requirement is for a cultivar name to be given in conjunction with the name of the genus. However, in the *RHS Plant Finder* we choose to give as full a name as possible to give the gardener and botanist more information about the plant, following the Recommendation in the Code.

NOMENCLATURE AND TAXONOMY ADVISORY GROUP

This Group advises the RHS on individual problems of nomenclature regarding plants in cultivation and, in particular, use of names in the *RHS Horticultural Database*, reflected in the annual publication of the *RHS Plant Finder*.

The aim is always to make the plant names in the *RHS Plant Finder* as consistent, reliable and stable as possible and acceptable to gardeners and botanists alike, not only in the British Isles but around the world. Recent proposals to change or correct names are examined with the aim of creating a balance between the stability of well-known names and botanical and taxonomic correctness. In some cases the conflicting views on the names of some groups of plants will not easily be resolved. The Group's policy is then to wait and review the situation once a more obvious consensus is reached, rather than rush to rename plants only to have to change them again when opinions have shifted.

As we start 2018, the Group is chaired by Dr Janet Cubey and includes: Susyn Andrews, Chris Brickell, Dr James Compton, Mike Grant, Dr John Grimshaw, Dr Stephen Jury, Dr Alan Leslie, Dr Tony Lord, Chris Sanders with Björn Aldén, Dr Crinan Alexander, Dr Marco Hoffman, Prof David Mabberley, Svengunnar Ryman and Julian Sutton (corresponding members), James Armitage, Dr John David and Julian Shaw (attending RHS staff) and Dr Dawn Edwards as Secretary.

NOTES ON NOMENCLATURE AND IDENTIFICATION

The **Notes on Nomenclature and Identification**, p.49, give further information for names that are complex or may be confusing. See also **Nomenclature and Taxonomy Advisory Group**.

PLANT BREEDERS' RIGHTS

Plants covered by an *active* grant of Plant Breeders' Rights (PBR) are indicated throughout the Plant Directory. Grants indicated are those awarded by both UK and EU Plant Variety Rights offices. Because grants can both come into force and lapse at any time, this book can only aim to represent the situation at one point in time, but it is hoped that this will act as a useful guide to growers and gardeners. UK and EU grants represent the published position as of the end of December 2017. We do not give any indication where PBR grants may be pending.

To obtain PBR protection, a new plant must be registered and pass tests for distinctness, uniformity and stability under an approved name. This approved name, under the rules of the **ICNCP**, established by a legal process, has to be regarded as the cultivar name. Increasingly however, these approved names are a code or "nonsense" name and are therefore often unpronounceable and meaningless, so the plants are given other names designed to attract sales when they are released. These secondary names are often referred to as selling names but are officially termed **trade designations**. We do our best to link PBR names to their trade descriptions but if you spot any we've missed, do let us know.

For further information on UK PBR contact:
Plant Variety Rights Office,
Animal and Plant Health Agency,
Eastbrook,
Shaftesbury Road,
Cambridge CB2 8DR
Ⓣ **(0208) 026 5993**
Ⓔ **pvs.helpdesk@apha.gsi.gov.uk**
Ⓦ **www.gov.uk/plant-breeders-rights**

For details of plants covered by EU Community Rights contact:
Community Plant Variety Office (CPVO)
3 Boulevard Maréchal Foch, CS 10121
49101 Angers Cedex 2, France
Ⓣ **00 33 (02) 41 25 64 00**
Ⓔ **cpvo@cpvo.europa.eu**
Ⓦ **www.cpvo.europa.eu**

The *RHS Plant Finder* takes no responsibility for ensuring that nurseries selling plants with PBR are licensed to do so.

Reverse Synonyms

It is likely that users of this book will come across names in certain genera that they did not expect to find. This may be because species have been transferred from another genus (or **genera**).

Selling Names

See **Trade Designations**

Series

With seed-raised plants and some popular vegetatively propagated plants, especially bedding plants and pot plants such as *Petunia* or *Glandularia*, Series have become increasingly popular. A Series contains a number of similar cultivars, but differs from a **Group** in that it is a marketing device, with cultivars added to create a range of flower colours in plants of similar habit. Individual colour elements within a Series may be represented by slightly different cultivars over the years.

The word Series is always included and, where cited with a cultivar name it is enclosed in brackets, for example *Aquilegia* 'Robin' (Songbird Series). The Series name usually follows the rest of the plant name, but sometimes in this book we list it before the cultivar name in order to group members of a Series together when they occur next to one another on the page.

Species

See under **Botanical Names**

Subspecies

See under **Botanical Names**

Synonyms

Although the ideal is for each species or cultivar to have only one name, anyone dealing with plants soon comes across a situation where one plant has received two or more names, or two plants have received the same name. In each case, only one name and application, for reasons of precision and stability, can be regarded as correct. Additional names are known as synonyms. Further information on synonyms and why plants change names is available in *Guide to Plant Names*. See the introduction to this glossary for details of how to request a copy.

See also **Reverse Synonyms**.

Trade Designations

A **trade designation** is the name used to market a plant when the cultivar name is considered unsuitable for selling purposes. It is distinguished typographically (see below) from a cultivar name, and is not enclosed in single quotation marks.

In the case of **Plant Breeders' Rights** it is a legal requirement for the cultivar name to appear with the trade designation on a label at the point of sale. Most plants are sold under only one trade designation, but some, especially roses, are sold under a number of names, particularly when cultivars are introduced from other countries. Usually, the correct cultivar name is the only way to ensure that the same plant is not bought unwittingly under two or more different trade designations. The *RHS Plant Finder* follows the recommendations of the **ICNCP** when dealing with trade designations and PBR. These are always to quote the cultivar name and trade designation together and to style the trade designation in small capitals, for example *Choisya* × *dewitteana* GOLDFINGERS ('Limo'[PBR]). Here GOLDFINGERS is the trade designation and 'Limo' is the cultivar name that has been granted **Plant Breeders' Rights**.

TRANSLATIONS

When a cultivar name is translated from the language of first publication, the translation is regarded as a **trade designation** and styled accordingly. We endeavour to recognise the original cultivar name in every case and to give an English translation where it is in general use.

VARIEGATED PLANTS

Following a suggestion from the Variegated Plant Group of the Hardy Plant Society, a (v) is cited after those plants which are "variegated". The dividing line between variegation and less distinct colour marking is necessarily arbitrary and plants with light veins, pale, silver or dark zones, or leaves flushed in paler colours, are not shown as being variegated unless there is an absolutely sharp distinction between paler and darker zones.

For further details of the Variegated Plant Group, please write to:

Brian Dockerill
19 Westfield Road
Glyncoch
Pontypridd
Mid-Glamorgan
CF37 3AG

VARIETY

See under **Botanical Names** and **Cultivar**

HORTAX

The Cultivated Plant Taxonomy Group

If you have an interest in the names of garden plants and wish to learn more or would like to make a comment about the International Code of Nomenclature for Cultivated Plants (ICNCP) visit the HORTAX website:

www.hortax.org.uk

CONSERVATION AND THE ENVIRONMENT

Invasive Plants

As the *RHS Plant Finder* demonstrates, gardens in Britain have been greatly enriched by the diversity of plants introduced to cultivation from abroad. While the vast majority of those introduced have enhanced our gardens, a few have proved to be highly invasive and to threaten native habitats. Once such plants are established it is very difficult, costly and potentially damaging to native ecosystems to eradicate or control the invasive "alien" species. Gardeners can help by choosing not to buy or distribute non-native invasive plants and by taking steps to prevent them escaping into the wild and by disposing of them in a responsible way.

Ten of the most serious invasive non-native species are no longer listed in the *RHS Plant Finder*. Any cultivars or varieties of them that are listed are believed to be less invasive than the species. These 10 plants are:

**Azolla filiculoides* – fairy fern
**Crassula helmsii* – New Zealand pygmy weed
†‡*Elodea nuttallii* – Nuttall's waterweed
Fallopia japonica – Japanese knotweed
†‡*Heracleum mantegazzianum* – giant hogweed
†**Hydrocotyle ranunculoides* – floating pennywort
†‡*Impatiens glandulifera* – Himalayan balsam
†*Lagarosiphon major* – curly waterweed
†**Ludwigia grandiflora* – water primrose
†**Myriophyllum aquaticum* – parrot's feather

From April 2014 the five aquatic species indicated by a * above have been banned from sale in the UK. Anyone trading in these species is liable to a fine of up to £5000 or a six months prison sentence.

The EU Regulation on Invasive Alien Species, which became law early in 2015, has a provision for a list of species of EU-wide (Union) concern. Species that are included in the list attract the strictest measures of control, including a ban on keeping, growing or cultivating, transporting or trading, use or exchange, as well as release into the wider environment. These controls will apply to individuals as well as organisations and businesses that own or hold any of these species. There are now 23 plants on this list, many of which are of marginal importance to gardeners, or are already banned from sale in the UK or excluded from Plant Finder (marked with † in the above list), but four widely grown species, *Eichhornia crassipes*, *Gunnera tinctoria*, *Lysichiton americanus* and *Pennisetum setaceum* are included. The species marked with a ‡ are due to be banned from the beginning of August 2018. Although there are transitionary measures allowing businesses to sell off their stock of these species within one year, to minimise potential for confusion, we have taken the step of not listing the species in the 2018 *RHS Plant Finder*. Those species affected are:

‡*Asclepias syriaca* – milkweed
Baccharis halmifolia – tree groundsel
Cabomba caroliniana – Carolina fanwort
Eichhornia crassipes – water hyacinth
‡*Gunnera tinctoria* – Chilean rhubarb
Ludwigia peploides – water primrose
Lysichiton americanus – American skunk cabbage
‡*Myriophyllum heterophyllum* – broadleaf watermilfoil
Parthenium hysterophorus – Parthenium weed
‡*Pennisetum setaceum* – crimson fountaingrass
Pueraria montana var. *lobata* – Kudzu

Gardeners who already have these species in their gardens are not at risk of prosecution for possession as the Regulation is not retrospective, but will be required to meet the other requirements of the Regulation to ensure that they control the species effectively on their property and do not allow it to spread.

Species control provisions

The UK Government introduced new provisions in the Infrastructure Act (2015) to control invasive non-native species in England and Wales. There are two levels of control: a species control agreement and a species control order. In the former the owner of land where an invasive non-native species is present, when approached by the relevant environmental authority, agrees to take action to limit or remove the species. If the landowner fails to do so, or does not agree, or where it is not known who the landowner is, then the environment authority can take action to enforce the control of the species. This may involve entry of the property by the authority to carry out the control if the owner fails to comply. In the case of an emergency then a species control order may be issued without going through the previous steps. Only those species listed on Schedule 9 of the Wildlife & Countryside Act can be subject to these control measures. For the purposes of the Act, Defra, Natural England, the Environment Agency and the Forestry Commission are defined as Environmental Authorities in England. For Wales it is Natural Resources Wales.

Bringing plants back from abroad

Travelling can be a great source of inspiration for gardeners and often provides an opportunity to encounter new and interesting plants. Anyone wishing to bring plants back into Britain from overseas must realise, however, that this is a complex matter. Various regulations are in force that apply to amateur gardeners as well as to commercial nurseries. The penalties for breaking these can be serious.

Most countries have regulations concerning the collection of plants from the wild, including seed. These regulations are likely to ban collection from certain protected places, such as national parks, ban the collection of rare or endangered species, and require permits to collect where special protection measures are not in place. In addition there is likely to be an additional permit to export any collected plant material. Travellers are frequently reminded of regulations in force at airports and other points of entry to a country. Anyone wishing to collect wild plants, for whatever purpose, will need to contact the country concerned well in advance of travel to seek the relevant permits. Breach of the regulations will result, as a minimum, in the confiscation of plant material if discovered. Any such material brought back to the UK is illegal.

The situation with plants in cultivation in another country is less clear and travellers are advised to check with the authorities in the country, particularly with regard to any Access and Benefit Sharing requirements (see **Nagoya Protocol** below), export permits or phytosanitary certificates that might be needed.

Plant Health regulations are in place to control the spread of pests and diseases. Plants are divided into the categories of prohibited, controlled and unrestricted, but there are also limits that vary according to the part of the world you are travelling from.

Ⓦ www.gov.uk/bringing-food-animals-plants-into-uk/plants

The Convention on International Trade in Endangered Species (CITES) affects the transport of animal and plant material across international boundaries. Its aim is to prevent exploitative trade and thereby to prevent harm and the ultimate extinction of wild populations. A tighter regime on trade in species of wild fauna and flora exists in the EU that requires export permits for any plants listed in Appendices A, B & C and import permits for Appendices A & B. There is a further Appendix D for non-CITES listed species that the EU consider to be endangered. A broad range of plants is covered in these Appendices, including *Cactaceae* and *Orchidaceae* and, although species are mentioned in the convention title, the restrictions cover all cultivars and hybrids of listed species too, except for specific exclusions, where there are annotations in the Appendices.

Ⓦ www.gov.uk/cites-imports-and-exports#cites-species

The Convention on Biological Diversity (CBD or the "Rio Convention") recognises the property rights of individual countries in relation to their own biodiversity. It exists to enable access to that biodiversity, but equally to ensure the sharing of any benefit derived from it. In principle it is possible to collect plant material from other countries that have asserted their rights under the CBD, by ensuring that you have obtained documentary evidence of prior informed consent on the basis of mutually agreed terms for any uses that the material will be put to in the future. In practice the legal requirements for collecting plant material vary from country to country and it is advisable to contact the National Focal Point for further information.

Ⓦ www.cbd.int

The **Nagoya Protocol**, is a supplementary agreement of the CBD which entered into force in 2015, and provides a framework for Access and Benefit Sharing. In the UK this is implemented by the European Union Regulation which is effective from 12 October 2014, and requires anyone utilising genetic resources from another country which is a signatory of the Nagoya Protocol, collected after 12 October 2014, to carry out due diligence to ensure that the material was collected in accordance with the Protocol and the CBD. While the most likely examples of utilisation are the development of new products or medicines from plants, breeding programmes to raise new plants for horticulture would also be covered. Although the burden to prove legitimate use of the genetic resource lies with the person or organisation utilising the genetic resource, anyone providing the source of the genetic resource (such as wild collected plants) will need to be able to provide the relevant paperwork, such as a Material Transfer Agreement and Prior Informed Consent.

Ⓦ http://www.cbd.int/abs/about/

In March 2015 the UK Government put in place the scheme of penalties for failure to comply with the EU Regulation which includes a range of both civil and criminal penalties, with the ultimate sanction of a two-year prison sentence. This legislation also formally appointed Regulatory Delivery (formerly National Measurement and Regulation Office) as the authority to enforce compliance in the UK, effective from June 2015.

Ⓦ https://www.gov.uk/guidance/abs

European Habitats Directive. The full implementation of this Directive into UK law in 2007 extended protection to all of the European Protected Species (EPS) listed in the Appendices of that Directive (these are Appendices II(b) and IV(b) for plants) whether they are native to the UK or not. This requires a licence for material of any of these species collected in the wild after 1994. These are issued by Natural England (for England), Natural Resources Wales (in Wales) and Scottish Natural Heritage (for Scotland).

Ⓦ www.gov.uk/guidance/wild-plants-sell-them-legally

Contact addresses

The UK authorities issue licences for UK plants. For other EU states a collector would need to contact the relevant national authorities.

Department for Environment, Food & Rural Affairs (Defra)
Nobel House
17 Smith Square
London
SW1P 3JR
For biodiversity queries:
Ⓔ biodiversity@defra.gsi.gov.uk

Plant Health is covered by the Plant Health and Seeds Inspectorate (PHSI) which is part of the Animal and Plant Health Agency.

Animal & Plant Health Agency (APHA)
Centre for International Trade – Bristol
1/17 Temple Quay House
2 The Square
Temple Quay
Bristol
BS1 6EB
Ⓣ 0117 372 8774
Ⓕ 0117 372 8206
Ⓔ wildlife.licensing@apha.gsi.gov.uk
Ⓦ www.gov.uk/plant-health-controls

Natural England
Wildlife Management & Licensing
Horizon House
Deanery Road
Bristol
BS1 5AH
Ⓣ 020 8026 1089
Ⓔ wildlife@naturalengland.org.uk

Non-Native Species Secretariat
Animal and Plant Health Agency
Sand Hutton
York
YO41 1LZ
Ⓦ www.nonnativespecies.org

Regulatory Delivery
Stanton Avenue
Teddington
TW110JZ
Ⓣ 020 8943 7272
Ⓔ info@nmro.gov.uk

Supplementary Keys to the Directory

Collectors' References

Abbreviations following a plant name, refer to the collector(s) of the plant. These abbreviations are expanded below, with a collector's name or expedition title. For a fuller explanation, see p.38.

A&JW Watson, A. & J.
A&L Ala, A. & Lancaster, Roy
AB&S Archibald, James; Blanchard, John W. & Salmon, M.
AC Clark, Alan J.
AC&H Apold, J.; Cox, Peter & Hutchison, Peter
AC&W Albury; Cheese, M. & Watson, J.M.
ACE AGS Expedition to China (1994)
ACL Leslie, Alan C.
AER Robinson, Allan
AGS/ES AGS Expedition to Sikkim (1983)
AGSJ AGS Expedition to Japan (1988)
AH Hoog, A.
AIM Avent, Tony Mexico (1994)
Airth Airth, Murray
Akagi Akagi Botanical Garden
AL&JS Sharman, Joseph L. & Leslie, Alan C.
APA Cox, K.; Hootman, S.; Hudson, T.; et al, Expedition to Arunchal Pradesh (2005)
ARG Argent, G.C.G.
ARGS Alaska Rock Garden Society trip to China
ARJA Ruksans, J. & Siesums, A.
B Blanchard, John
B&F MA Brown, Robert & Fisher, Rif & Middle Atlas (2007)
B L. Beer, Len
B&L Brickell, Christopher D. & Leslie, Alan C.
B&M & BM Brickell, Christopher D. & Mathew, Brian
B&S Bird P. & Salmon M.
B&SWJ Wynn-Jones, Bleddyn & Susan
B&V Burras, K. & Vosa, C.G.
BB Bartholomew, B.
BBJMT Boland, Brownless, Jamieson & McNamara
BC Chudziak, W.
BC&W Beckett; Cheese, M. & Watson, J.M.
Beavis Beavis, Derek S.
Berry Berry, P.
Berry & Brako Berry, P. & Brako, Lois
BKBlount Blount, B.K.
BKN Bis, J., Kupčák, P. & Novak, H.
BL&M University of Bangor Expedition to NE Nepal
BM Mathew, Brian F.
BM&W Binns, David L.; Mason, M. & Wright, A.
BOA Boardman, P.
Breedlove Breedlove, D.
BR Rushbrooke, Ben
BS Smith, Basil
BSBE Bowles Scholarship Botanical Expedition (1963)
BSSS Crûg Expedition, Jordan (1991)
Bu Bubert, S.
Burtt Burtt, Brian L.
BWJ Wynn-Jones, Bleddyn
C Cole, Desmond T.
C&C Cox, P.A. & Cox, K.N.E.
C&Cu Cox, K.N.E. & Cubey, J.
C&H Cox, Peter & Hutchison, Peter
C&K Chamberlain & Knott
C&R Christian & Roderick
C&S Clark, Alan & Sinclair, Ian W.J.
C&V K.N.E. Cox & Vergera, S.
C&W Cheese, M. & Watson, J.M.
CC Chadwell, Christopher
CC&H Chamberlain, David F.; Cox, Peter & Hutchison, P.
CC&McK Chadwell, Christopher & McKelvie, A.
CC&MR Chadwell, Christopher & Ramsay
CCH&H Chamberlain, D.F.; Cox, P.; Hutchison, P. & Hootman, S.
CD&R Compton, J.; D'Arcy, J. & Rix, E.M.
CDB Brickell, Christopher D.
CDC Coode, Mark J.E.; Dockrill, Alexander
CDC&C Compton; D'Arcy; Christopher & Coke
CDPR Compton; D'Arcy; Pope & Rix
CE&H Christian, P.J.; Elliott & Hoog
CEE Chengdu Edinburgh Expedition China (1991)

CGG	Glendoick Gardens Expedition to Guizou (2009)
CGV	Vosa, Canio
CGW	Grey-Wilson, Christopher
CH	Christian, P. & Hoog, A.
CH&M	Cox, P.; Hutchison, P. & Maxwell-MacDonald, D.
CHP&W	Kashmir Botanical Expedition
CL	Lovell, Chris
CLD	Chungtien, Lijiang & Dali Exped. China (1990)
CM&W	Cheese M.; Mitchel J. & Watson, J.
CN&W	Clark; Neilson & Wilson
CNDS	Nelson, C. & Sayers D.
COLA	Costin, J.J. & Lancaster, R., Japan (1990)
Cooper	Cooper, R.E.
Cox	Cox, Peter A.
CPC	Cobblewood Plant Collection
CPN	Compton, James
CS	Stapleton, Christopher
CSE	Cyclamen Society Expedition (1990)
CT	Teune, Carla
CW&T	Clark, A., Wilson, H. & Taggart, J., North Vietnam
CWJ	Colley, Finlay; Wynn-Jones, Bleddyn, Taiwan (2007)
Dahl	Dahl, Sally
DBG	Denver Botanic Garden, Colorado
DC	Cheshire, David
DF	Fox, D.
DG	Green, D.
DHTU	Hinkley, D., Turkey (2000)
DJF	Ferguson, Dave
DJH	Hinkley, Dan
DJHC	Hinkley D., China
DJHS	Hinkley, D., Sichuan
DJHV	Hinkley, D., Vietnam
DM	Millais, David
Doleshy	Doleshy, F.L.
DS&T	Drake, Sharman J. & Thompson
DWD	Rose, D.
DZ	Zummell, D.
ECN	Nelson, E. Charles
EDHCH	Hammond, Eric D.
EGM	Millais, T.
EKB	Balls, Edward K.
EM	East Malling Research Station
EMAK	Edinburgh Makalu Expedition (1991)
EMR	Rix, E.Martyn
EN	Needham, Edward F.
ENF	Fuller, E. Nigel
ETE	Edinburgh Taiwan Expedition (1993)
ETOT	Kirkham, T.S.; Flanagan, Mark
F	Forrest, G.
F&M	Fernandez & Mendoza, Mexico
F&W	Watson, J. & Flores, A.
Farrer	Farrer, Reginald
FK	Kinmonth, Fergus W.
FMB	Bailey, F.M.
FO	Otiery, Felix
G	Gardner, Martin F.
G&K	Gardner, Martin F. & Knees, Sabina G.
G&P	Gardner, Martin F. & Page, Christopher N.
GDJ	Dumont, Gerard
GG	Gusman, G.
GS	Sherriff, George
Green	Green, D.
Guitt	Guittoneau, G.G.
Guiz	Guizhou Expedition (1985)
GWJ	Goddard, Sally; Wynne-Jones, Bleddyn & Susan
G-W&P	Grey-Wilson, Christopher & Phillips
H	Huggins, Paul
H&B	Hilliard, Olive M. & Burtt, Brian L.
H&D	Howick, C. & Darby
H&M	Howick, Charles & McNamara, William A.
H&W	Hedge, Ian C. & Wendelbo, Per W.
Harry Smith	Smith, K.A.Harry
Hartside	Hartside Nursery
HCM	Heronswood Expedition to Chile (1998)
HECC	Hutchison; Evans; Cox, P.; Cox, K.
HEHEHE	Zetterlund, H. et al, Gothenburg Botanic Gardens Expedition to northern China
Hird	Hird
HH&K	Hannay, S & S & Kingsbury, N.
HK	Kuenzler, Horst
HLMS	Springate, L.S.
HM&S	Halliwell, B.; Mason, D. & Smallcombe
HOA	Hoog, Anton
HOLUB	Holubec, V.
HRS	Hers, J.
Hummel	Hummel, D.
HW&E	Wendelbo, Per; Hedge, I. & Ekberg, L.
HWEL	Hirst, J.Michael; Webster, D.
HWJ	Crûg Heronswood Joint Expedition
HWJCM	Crûg Heronswood Expedition
HWJK	Crûg Heronswood Expedition, East Nepal (2002)
HZ	Zetterlund, Henrik
ICE	Instituto de Investigaciónes Ecológicas Chiloé & RBGE
IDS	International Dendrological Society
ISI	Int. Succulent Introductions
J&JA	Archibald, James & Jennifer
J. Jurasek	Jurasek, J.
JCA	Archibald, James
JE	Jack Elliott
JJ	Jackson, J.
JJ&JH	Halda, J. & Halda, J.
JJH	Halda, Joseph J.
JL	Lode, Joel
JLS	Sharman, J.L.
JMH	Hoog, J. & M.

JM-MK Mahr, J.; Kammerlander, M.
JMT Mann Taylor, J.
JN Nielson, Jens
JR Russell, J.
JRM Marr, John
JW Watson, J.M.
K Kirkpatrick, George
K&LG Gillanders, Kenneth & Gillanders, L.
K&Mc Kirkpatrick, George & McBeath, Ronald J.D.
K&P Josef Kopec & Milan Prasil
K&T Kurashige, Y. & Tsukie, S.
KC Cox, Kenneth
KEKE Kew/Edinburgh Kanchenjunga Expedition (1989)
KGB Kunming/Gothenburg Botanical Expedition (1993)
KM Marsh, K.
KMR Kupčák, M.
KR Rushforth, K.D.
KRW Wooster, K.R. (distributed after his death by Kath Dryden)
KW Kingdon-Ward, F.
KWJ Crûg-World of Ferns Joint Expedition, Vietnam (2007)
L Lancaster, C. Roy
L&S Ludlow, Francis & Sherriff, George
LA Long Ashton Research Station clonal selection scheme
LB Bercht, L. (*Cactaceae*)
LB Bird P.; Salmon, M.
LEG Lesotho Edinburgh/Gothenburg Expedition (1997)
Lismore Lismore Nursery, Breeder's Number
LM&S Leslie, Mattern & Sharman
LP Palmer, W.J.L.
LS&E Ludlow, Frank; Sherriff, George & Elliott, E. E.
LS&H Ludlow, Frank; Sherriff, George & Hicks, J. H.
LS&T Ludlow, Frank; Sherriff, George & Taylor, George
LZ Lutz, Eberhard
M&PS Mike & Polly Stone
M&T Mathew & Tomlinson
Mac&W McPhail & Watson
McB McBeath, R.J.D.
McLaren McLaren, H.D.
MDM Myers, Michael D.
MECC Scottish Rock Garden Club, Nepal (1997)
MESE Alpine Garden Society Expedition, Greece (1999)
MF Foster, Maurice
MH Heasman, Matthew T.
MK Kammerlander, Michael
MP Pavelka, Mojmir
MPF Frankis, M.P.
MS Salmon, M.
MS&CL Salmon, M. & Lovell, C.
MSF Fillan, M.S.
MUG Uhlig, M.
NAPE Expedition to Naglaland and Arunachal Pradesh (2003)
NICE North India Expedition (1997)
NJM Macer, N.J.
NMWJ Taiwan National Museum of Natural Science; Wynn-Jones, B. & S.
NN Nielsen & Nielsen (2009)
NNS Ratko, Ron
NS Turland, Nick
NVD Expedition to Vietnam
NVFDE Northern Vietnam First Darwin Expedition
Og Ogisu, Mikinori
ORO Oron, Peri
OS Sonderhousen, O.
P. Bon Bonavia, P.
P&C Paterson, David S. & Clarke, Sidney
P&W Polastri & Watson, J. M.
PAB Barney, P.A.
PB Bird, Peter
PBR Bruggeman, P.
PC&H Pattison, G.; Catt, P. & Hickson, M.
PD Davis, Peter H.
PDM Purdom, William
PF Furse, Paul
PG Pichler, G.
PJC Christian, Paul J.
PJC&AH P.J. Christian & A. Hogg
PNMK Nicholls, P.; Kammerlander, M.
Polunin Polunin, Oleg
Pras Prasil, M.
PS&W Polunin, Oleg; Sykes, William & Williams, John
PW Wharton, Peter
R Rock, J.F.C.
RB Brown, R.
RBS Brown, Ray, Sakharin Island
RCB AM Brown, Robert, Expedition to Armenia
RCB/Arg Brown, Robert, Argentina, (2002)
RCB E Brown, Robert, Expedition to Spain (Andalucia)
RCB/Eq Brown, Robert, Ecuador, (1988)
RCB RA Brown, Robert
RCB RL Brown, Robert, Expedition to Lebanon
RCB/TQ Brown, Robert, Turkey (2001)
RE Evans, Ron
RH Hancock, R.
RJN Neilsen, R.
RKMP Ruksans, J.; Krumins, A.; Kitts, M.; Paivel, A.
RM Ruksans, J. & Kitts, M.
RMRP Rocky Mountain Rare Plants, Denver, Colorado
RS Suckow, Reinhart

RSC	Richard Somer Cocks
RV	Richard Valder
RWJ	Crûg Farm-Rickards Ferns Expedition to Taiwan (2003)
S&B	Blanchard, J.W. & Salmon, M.
S&F	Salmon, M. & Fillan, M.
S&L	Sinclair, Ian W.J. & Long, David G.
S&SH	Sheilah & Spencer Hannay
Sandham	Sandham, John
SB	Brack, Steven
SB&L	Salmon, Bird & Lovell
SBEC	Sino-British Expedition to Cangshan
SBEL	Sino-British Lijiang Expedition
SBQE	Sino-British Expedition to Quinghai
Sch	Schilling, Anthony D.
SD	Sashal Dayal
SDR	Rankin, Stella & David
SEH	Hootman, Steve
SEP	Swedish Expedition to Pakistan
SF	Forde, P.
SG	Salmon, M. & Guy, P.
SH	Hannay, Spencer
Sich	Simmons, Erskine, Howick & Mcnamara
SJ	Johansson, Stellan
SLIZE	Swedish-Latvian-Iranian Zagros Expedition to Iran (May 1988)
SOJA	Kew/Quarryhill Expedition to Southern Japan
SS&W	Stainton, J.D. Adam; Sykes, William & Williams, John
SSNY	Sino-Scottish Expedition to NW Yunnan (1992)
T	Taylor, Nigel P.
T&K	Taylor, Nigel P. & Knees, Sabina
TCM	Mitchell, Thomas Carly
TG	Thomas, H-P. & Gilmer, K.
TH	Hudson, T.
TJR	Roberts, Tim
TS&BC	Smythe, T. & Cherry, B.
TSS	Spring Smyth, T.L.M.
TW	Weston, Tony
USDAPI	US Department of Agriculture Plant Index Number
USDAPQ	US Dept. of Agriculture Plant Quarantine Number
USNA	United States National Arboretum
VdL	Van de Laar, Harry
VHH	Vernon H. Heywood
VV	Victor, David
W	Wilson, Ernest H.
W&B	Watkins, D. & Brown, R., Bulgaria (2012)
WJC	Wynn-Jones, B. & S. & Colley, F.
WM	McLewin, William
Woods	Woods, Patrick J.B.
Wr	Wraight, David & Anke
WWJ	Wharton, Peter; Wynn-Jones, Bleddyn & Susan
Yu	Yu, Tse-tsun
ZE&S	Zetterlund, H., Eriksson, A-I. & Strid, A.

NOMENCLATURAL NOTES

The following changes have been made during 2017 to the names used in the *RHS Plant Finder* based on decisions of the RHS Nomenclature and Taxonomy Advisory Group (NATAG). If you have any suggestions for other plant name changes within the *RHS Plant Finder*, then please write, stating your reasons in full to:

The Chairman
Dr Janet Cubey
Nomenclature and Taxonomy Advisory Group
Royal Horticultural Society
RHS Garden Wisley
Woking
Surrey
GU23 6QB

- Inclusion of *Chionodoxa*, and therefore × *Chionoscilla*, within *Scilla*
- Clarification around the earliest name for the purple-leaved *Corylus* as *C. avellana* 'Rotblättrige Zellernuss'
- Changes within *Crocus*, such as inclusion of *C. albiflorus* with *C. vernus*, *C. scepusiensis* within *C. heuffelianus* and corrections of specific attribution of cultivars
- *Eucomis pole-evansii to E. pallidiflorus* subsp. *pole-evansii*, while also recognising that plants in cultivation under this name are actually *E. pallidiflorus* subsp. *pallidiflorus*
- *Lonicera nitida* and *L. pileata* to *Lonicera ligustrina* var. *yunnanensis* and *L. ligustrina* var. *pileata* respectively
- Use of the hybrid genus × *Nananopsis* for hybrids of *Aloinopsis* and *Nananthus*
- Recognition of *Paeonia* × *festiva* for some herbaceous peonies
- Publication of *Papaver* Oriental Group for cultivars previously listed under *P. orientale*
- Adding Zonartic to our horticultural classification of *Pelargonium* (see p.17 for more information)
- Accepting × *Phyllosasa* for the hybrid bamboo, *Hibanobambusa*
- Changes within *Salvia sclarea*

This is not intended to be an exhaustive list of the changes made to the RHS Horticultural Database, reflected in the *RHS Plant Finder*; many more changes are made during the year by the RHS botanical team. This list just highlights some of the NATAG changes.

You'll find some of these have had explanatory articles in *The Plantsman* in the last 12 months. Watch out for articles in the coming year on changes that have already been agreed for the 2019 *RHS Plant Finder* such as, the generic boundaries within *Rosaceae,* similarly within *Gesneriaceae* and changes around *Aloe* and related genera.

Discussions are currently ongoing around the generic boundaries within *Primulaceae* and the start of a review of grasses is on the horizon.

CLASSIFICATION OF GENERA

Genera including a large number of species, or with many cultivars, are often subdivided into informal horticultural classifications, or formal cultivar groups in the case of *Clematis* and *Tulipa*. The breeding of new cultivars is sometimes limited to hybrids between closely related species, thus for *Saxifraga* and *Primula*, the cultivars are allocated to the sections given in the infrageneric treatments cited. Please turn to p.37 for a fuller explanation.

ACER PALMATUM

(A) Amoenum Group
(D) Dissectum Group
(Dw) Dwarf Group
(L) Linearilobum Group
(M) Matsumurae Group
(P) Palmatum Group

ACTINIDIA

(s-p) Self-pollinating

BEGONIA

(C) Cane-like
(R) Rex Cultorum
(S) Semperflorens Cultorum
(T) × *tuberhybrida* (Tuberous)

CHRYSANTHEMUM

(By the National Chrysanthemum Society)
(1) Indoor Large (Exhibition)
(2) Indoor Medium (Exhibition)
(3a) Indoor Incurved: Large-flowered
(3b) Indoor Incurved: Medium-flowered
(3c) Indoor Incurved: Small-flowered
(4a) Indoor Reflexed: Large-flowered
(4b) Indoor Reflexed: Medium-flowered
(4c) Indoor Reflexed: Small-flowered
(5a) Indoor Intermediate: Large-flowered
(5b) Indoor Intermediate: Medium-flowered
(5c) Indoor Intermediate: Small-flowered
(6a) Indoor Anemone: Large-flowered
(6b) Indoor Anemone: Medium-flowered
(6c) Indoor Anemone: Small-flowered
(7a) Indoor Single: Large-flowered
(7b) Indoor Single: Medium-flowered
(7c) Indoor Single: Small-flowered
(8a) Indoor True Pompon
(8b) Indoor Semi-pompon
(9a) Indoor Spray: Anemone
(9b) Indoor Spray: Pompon
(9c) Indoor Spray: Reflexed
(9d) Indoor Spray: Single
(9e) Indoor Spray: Intermediate
(9f) Indoor Spray: Spider, Quill, Spoon or Any Other Type
(10a) Indoor, Spider
(10b) Indoor, Quill
(10c) Indoor, Spoon
(11) Any Other Indoor Type
(12a) Indoor, Charm
(12b) Indoor, Cascade
(13a) October-flowering Incurved: Large-flowered
(13b) October-flowering Incurved: Medium-flowered
(13c) October-flowering Incurved: Small-flowered
(14a) October-flowering Reflexed: Large-flowered
(14b) October-flowering Reflexed: Medium-flowered
(14c) October-flowering Reflexed: Small-flowered
(15a) October-flowering Intermediate: Large-flowered
(15b) October-flowering Intermediate: Medium-flowered
(15c) October-flowered Intermediate: Small-flowered
(16) October-flowering Large
(17a) October-flowering Single: Large-flowered
(17b) October-flowering Single: Medium-flowered
(17c) October-flowering Single: Small-flowered
(18a) October-flowering Pompon: True Pompon
(18b) October-flowering Pompon: Semi-pompon
(19a) October-flowering Spray: Anemone
(19b) October-flowering Spray: Pompon
(19c) October-flowering Spray: Reflexed
(19d) October-flowering Spray: Single
(19e) October-flowering Spray: Intermediate
(19f) October-flowering Spray: Spider, Quill, Spoon or Any Other Type
(20) Any Other October-flowering Type
(21a) Korean: Anemone
(21b) Korean: Pompon
(21c) Korean: Reflexed
(21d) Korean: Single
(21e) Korean: Intermediate
(21f) Korean: Spider, Quill, Spoon, or any other type
(22a) Charm: Anemone

(22b)	Charm: Pompon
(22c)	Charm: Reflexed
(22d)	Charm: Single
(22e)	Charm: Intermediate
(22f)	Charm: Spider, Quill, Spoon or Any Other Type
(23a)	Early-flowering Outdoor Incurved: Large-flowered
(23b)	Early-flowering Outdoor Incurved: Medium-flowered
(23c)	Early-flowering Outdoor Incurved: Small-flowered
(24a)	Early-flowering Outdoor Reflexed: Large-flowered
(24b)	Early-flowering Outdoor Reflexed: Medium-flowered
(24c)	Early-flowering Outdoor Reflexed: Small-flowered
(25a)	Early-flowering Outdoor Intermediate: Large-flowered
(25b)	Early-flowering Outdoor Intermediate: Medium-flowered
(25c)	Early-flowering Outdoor Intermediate: Small-flowered
(26a)	Early-flowering Outdoor Anemone: Large-flowered
(26b)	Early-flowering Outdoor Anemone: Medium-flowered
(27a)	Early-flowering Outdoor Single: Large-flowered
(27b)	Early-flowering Outdoor Single:Medium-flowered
(28a)	Early-flowering Outdoor Pompon: True Pompon
(28b)	Early-flowering Outdoor Pompon: Semi-pompon
(29a)	Early-flowering Outdoor Spray: Anemone
(29b)	Early-flowering Outdoor Spray: Pompon
(29c)	Early-flowering Outdoor Spray: Reflexed
(29d)	Early-flowering Outdoor Spray: Single
(29e)	Early-flowering Outdoor Spray: Intermediate
(29f)	Early-flowering Outdoor Spray: Spider, Quill, Spoon or Any Other Type
(29Rub)	Early-flowering Outdoor Spray: Rubellum
(30)	Any Other Early-flowering Outdoor Type

CLEMATIS

(Cultivar Groups as per Matthews, V. (2002) *The International Clematis Register & Checklist 2002*, RHS, London.)

(A)	Atragene Group
(Ar)	Armandii Group
(C)	Cirrhosa Group
(EL)	Early Large-flowered Group
(F)	Flammula Group
(Fo)	Forsteri Group
(H)	Heracleifolia Group
(I)	Integrifolia Group
(LL)	Late Large-flowered Group
(M)	Montana Group
(T)	Texensis Group
(Ta)	Tangutica Group
(V)	Viorna Group
(Vb)	Vitalba Group
(Vt)	Viticella Group

DAHLIA

(Classification according to The International Dahlia Register (1969), 22nd Supp. (2012) formed through consultation with national dahlia societies.)

(Sin)	1 Single
(Anem)	2 Anemone-flowered
(Col)	3 Collerette
(WL)	4 Waterlily
(D)	5 Decorative
(Ba)	6 Ball
(Pom)	7 Pompon
(C)	8 Cactus
(S-c)	9 Semi-cactus
(Misc)	10 Miscellaneous
(Fim)	11 Fimbriated
(SinO)	12 Single Orchid (Star)
(DblO)	13 Double Orchid
(P)	14 Peony-flowered
(B)	Botanical
(DwB)	Dwarf Bedding
(Lil)	Lilliput

DIANTHUS

(By the RHS)

(b)	Carnation, border
(M)	Carnation, Malmaison
(p)	Pink
(p,a)	Pink, annual
(pf)	Carnation, perpetual-flowering
(pt)	Carnation, pot

FRUIT

(B)	Black (*Vitis*), Blackberry (*Rubus*), Blackcurrant (*Ribes*)
(Ball)	Ballerina (*Malus*)
(C)	Culinary (*Malus, Prunus, Pyrus, Ribes*)
(Cider)	Cider (*Malus*)
(D)	Dessert (*Malus, Prunus, Pyrus, Ribes*)
(F)	Fruit
(G)	Glasshouse (*Vitis*)
(O)	Outdoor (*Vitis*)
(P)	Pinkcurrant (*Ribes*)
(Perry)	Perry (*Pyrus*)

(R)	Red (*Vitis*), Redcurrant (*Ribes*)
(S)	Seedless (*Citrus, Vitis*)
(s-p)	Self-pollinating
(W)	White (*Vitis*), Whitecurrant (*Ribes*)

Fuchsia

(E)	Encliandra
(T)	Variants and hybrids of *F. triphylla*

Gladiolus

(B)	Butterfly
(E)	Exotic
(G)	Giant
(L)	Large
(M)	Medium
(Min)	Miniature
(N)	Nanus
(P)	Primulinus
(S)	Small
(Tub)	Tubergenii

Hepatica nobilis

(Adapted from the International Hepatica Society classification for *Hepatica nobilis*)

(1)	Hyoujun (normal)
(2)	(degenerated anther)
(3)	Otome (degenerated stamen)
(4)	Henka (petal deformity)
(5/d)	Herashibe (semi-double, primitive)
(5A/d)	Choji (semi-double, primitive)
(6/d)	Nidan (semi-double, advanced)
(7/d)	Sandan (double, primitive)
(8/d)	Karako (double, advanced)
(9/d)	Sene-e (double, completed)

Hydrangea macrophylla

(H)	Hortensia
(L)	Lacecap

Impatiens

(NG)	New Guinea Group

Iris

(Adapted from the American Iris Society Classification)

(AB)	Arilbred
(BB)	Border Bearded
(Cal-Sib)	Series *Californicae* × Series *Sibiricae*
(CH)	Californian Hybrid
(DB)	Dwarf Bearded (not assigned)
(Dut)	Dutch (can be assigned to *I.* × *hollandica*)
(IB)	Intermediate Bearded
(J)	Juno (subgenus *Scorpiris*)
(La)	Louisiana Hybrid
(MDB)	Miniature Dwarf Bearded
(MTB)	Miniature Tall Bearded
(Rc)	Regeliocyclus (Section *Regelia* × Section *Oncocyclus*)
(Reticulata)	
(SDB)	Standard Dwarf Bearded
(Sib)	Siberian
(Sino-Sib)	Series *Sibiricae*, chromosome number 2n=40
(SpH)	Species Hybrid
(Spuria)	Spuria
(TB)	Tall Bearded

Lilium

(Classification according to *The International Lily Register* (ed. 4, 2007))

(I)	Asiatic hybrids derived from *L. amabile, L. bulbiferum, L. callosum, L. cernuum, L. concolor, L. dauricum, L. davidii, L.* × *hollandicum, L. lancifolium, L. lankongense, L. leichtlinii, L.* × *maculatum* and *L. pumilum, L.* × *scottiae, L. wardii* and *L. wilsonii.*
(II)	Martagon hybrids derived from *L. dalhansonii, L. hansonii, L. martagon, L. medeoloides and L. tsingtauense*
(III)	Euro-Caucasian hybrids derived from *L. candidum, L. chalcedonicum, L. kesselringianum, L. monadelphum, L. pomponium, L. pyrenaicum* and *L.* × *testaceum.*
(IV)	American hybrids derived from *L. bolanderi, L.* × *burbankii, L. canadense, L. columbianum, L. grayi, L. humboldtii, L. kelleyanum, L. kelloggii, L. maritimum, L. michauxii, L. michiganense, L. occidentale, L.* × *pardaboldtii, L. pardalinum, L. parryi, L. parvum, L. philadelphicum, L. pitkinense, L. superbum, L. vollmeri, L. washingtonianum* and *L. wigginsii.*
(V)	Longiflorum lilies derived from *L. formosanum, L. longiflorum, L. philippinense and L. wallichianum.*
(VI)	Trumpet and Aurelian hybrids derived from *L.* × *aurelianense, L. brownii, L.* × *centigale, L. henryi, L.* × *imperiale, L.* × *kewense, L. leucantheum, L. regale, L. rosthornii, L. sargentiae, L. sulphureum* and *L. sulphurgale* (but excluding hybrids of *L. henryi* with all species listed in Division VII).
(VII)	Oriental hybrids derived from *L. auratum, L. japonicum, L. nobilissimum, L.* × *parkmanii, L rubellum* and *L. speciosum* (but excl. all hybrids of these with *L. henryi*).
(VIII)	Other hybrids not covered by any of the previous divisions (I-VII)
(IX)	Species and cultivars of species
a/	upward-facing flowers
b/	outward-facing flowers
c/	downward-facing flowers

/a	trumpet-shaped flowers
/b	bowl-shaped flowers
/c	flat flowers (or with only tepal tips recurved)
/d	recurved flowers

Malus *see* Fruit

Narcissus

(By the RHS, revised 1998)

(1)	Trumpet
(2)	Large-cupped
(3)	Small-cupped
(4)	Double
(5)	Triandrus
(6)	Cyclamineus
(7)	Jonquilla and Apodanthus
(8)	Tazetta
(9)	Poeticus
(10)	Bulbocodium
(11a)	Split-corona: Collar
(11b)	Split-corona: Papillon
(12)	Miscellaneous
(13)	Species

Nymphaea

(H)	Hardy
(D)	Day-blooming
(N)	Night-blooming
(T)	Tropical

Paeonia

(S)	Shrubby

Pelargonium

(A)	Angel
(C)	Coloured Foliage (in combination)
(Ca)	Cactus (in combination)
(d)	Double (in combination)
(Dec)	Decorative
(Dw)	Dwarf
(DwI)	Dwarf Ivy-leaved
(Fr)	Frutetorum
(I)	Ivy-leaved
(Min)	Miniature
(MinI)	Miniature Ivy-leaved
(R)	Regal
(Sc)	Scented-leaved
(St)	Stellar (in combination)
(T)	Tulip (in combination)
(U)	Unique
(Z)	Zonal
(Za)	Zonartic

Primula

(Classification by Section as per Richards. J. (2002) *Primula* (2nd edition). Batsford, London)

(Ag)	*Auganthus*
(Al)	*Aleuritia*
(Am)	*Amethystinae*
(Ar)	*Armerina*
(Au)	*Auricula*
(A)	Alpine Auricula
(B)	Border Auricula
(S)	Show Auricula
(St)	Striped Auricula
(Bu)	*Bullatae*
(Ca)	*Capitatae*
(Cf)	*Cordifoliae*
(Ch)	*Chartaceae*
(Co)	*Cortusoides*
(Cr)	*Carolinella*
(Cu)	*Cuneifoliae*
(Cy)	*Crystallophlomis*
(Da)	*Davidii*
(De)	*Denticulatae*
(Dr)	*Dryadifoliae*
(F)	*Fedtschenkoanae*
(G)	*Glabrae*
(Ma)	*Malvaceae*
(Mi)	*Minutissimae*
(Mo)	*Monocarpicae*
(Mu)	*Muscarioides*
(Ob)	*Obconicolisteri*
(Or)	*Oreophlomis*
(Pa)	*Parryi*
(Pe)	*Petiolares*
(Pf)	*Proliferae*
(Pi)	*Pinnatae*
(Pr)	*Primula*
(Poly)	Polyanthus (can be assigned to *P.* × *polyantha*)
(Prim)	Primrose
(Pu)	*Pulchellae*
(Py)	*Pycnoloba*
(R)	*Reinii*
(Si)	*Sikkimenses*
(So)	*Soldanelloides*
(Sp)	*Sphondylia*
(Sr)	*Sredinskya*
(Su)	*Suffrutescentes*
(Y)	*Yunnannenses*

Prunus *see* Fruit

Pyrus *see* Fruit

Rhododendron

(A)	Azalea (deciduous, species or unclassified hybrid)
(Ad)	Azaleodendron
(EA)	Evergreen azalea
(G)	Ghent azalea (deciduous)
(K)	Knap Hill or Exbury azalea (deciduous)
(M)	Mollis azalea (deciduous)
(O)	Occidentalis azalea (deciduous)

(R)	Rustica azalea (deciduous)
(V)	Vireya rhododendron
(Vs)	Viscosa azalea (deciduous)

RIBES *SEE* FRUIT

ROSA

(A)	Alba
(Bb)	Bourbon
(Bs)	Boursault
(Ce)	Centifolia
(Ch)	China
(Cl)	Climbing (in combination)
(D)	Damask
(DPo)	Damask Portland
(F)	Floribunda or Cluster-flowered
(G)	Gallica
(Ga)	Garnette
(GC)	Ground Cover
(HM)	Hybrid Musk
(HP)	Hybrid Perpetual
(HT)	Hybrid Tea or Large-flowered
(Min)	Miniature
(Mo)	Moss (in combination)
(N)	Noisette
(Patio)	Patio, Miniature Floribunda or Dwarf Cluster-flowered
(Poly)	Polyantha
(Ra)	Rambler
(RH)	Rubiginosa hybrid (Hybrid Sweet Briar)
(Ru)	Rugosa
(S)	Shrub
(SpH)	Spinosissima Hybrid
(T)	Tea

RUBUS *SEE* FRUIT

SAXIFRAGA

(Classification by Section from Gornall, R.J. (1987). *Botanical Journal of the Linnean Society,* 95(4): 273-292)

(1)	*Ciliatae*
(2)	*Cymbalaria*
(3)	*Merkianae*
(4)	*Micranthes*
(5)	*Irregulares*
(6)	*Heterisia*
(7)	*Porphyrion*
(8)	*Ligulatae*
(9)	*Xanthizoon*
(10)	*Trachyphyllum*
(11)	*Gymnopera*
(12)	*Cotylea*
(13)	*Odontophyllae*
(14)	*Mesogyne*
(15)	*Saxifraga*

TULIPA

(Classification by Cultivar Group from *Classified List and International Register of Tulip Names* by Koninklijke Algemeene Vereniging voor Bloembollencultuur 1996)

(1)	Single Early Group
(2)	Double Early Group
(3)	Triumph Group
(4)	Darwin Hybrid Group
(5)	Single Late Group (including Darwin Group and Cottage Group)
(6)	Lily-flowered Group
(7)	Fringed Group
(8)	Viridiflora Group
(9)	Rembrandt Group
(10)	Parrot Group
(11)	Double Late Group
(12)	Kaufmanniana Group
(13)	Fosteriana Group
(14)	Greigii Group
(15)	Miscellaneous

VIOLA

(C)	Cornuta Hybrid
(dVt)	Double Violet
(ExVa)	Exhibition Viola
(FP)	Fancy Pansy
(P)	Pansy
(PVt)	Parma Violet
(SP)	Show Pansy
(T)	Tricolor
(Va)	Viola
(Vt)	Violet
(Vtta)	Violetta

VITIS *SEE* FRUIT

HOW TO USE THE PLANT DIRECTORY

NURSERY CODES

Look up the plant you require in the alphabetical Plant Directory. Against each plant you will find one or more four or five letter codes, for example WCru, each code represents one nursery offering that plant. The first letter of each code indicates the main area of the country in which the nursery is situated. For this geographical key, refer to the **Nursery Codes and Symbols** on p.864.

Turn to the **Nursery Details by Code** starting on p.868 where, in alphabetical order of codes, you will find details of each nursery which offers the plant in question. For a fuller explanation of how to use the nursery listings please turn to p.865. **Always check that the nursery you select has the plant in stock before you set out.**

PLANTS WITH MORE THAN 30 SUPPLIERS

In some cases, against the plant name you will see the term 'Widely available' instead of a nursery code. If we were to include every plant listed by all nurseries, the *RHS Plant Finder* would become unmanageably bulky. We therefore ask nurseries to restrict their entries to those plants that are not already well represented. As a result, if more than 30 nurseries offer any plant the Directory gives no nursery codes and the plant is listed instead as being 'Widely available'.

You should not have difficulty in locating these in local nurseries or garden centres. If, however, you are unable to find such plants, a list of all the current suppliers we have on file is available by post or online. See the Introduction (p.34).

FINDING FRUIT, VEGETABLES AND HERBS

You will need to search for these by their botanical names. Common names are cross-referenced to their botanical names in the Plant Directory.

IF YOU HAVE DIFFICULTY FINDING YOUR PLANT

If you cannot immediately find the plant you seek, look through the various species of the genus. You may be using an incomplete name. The problem is most likely to arise in very large genera such as *Phlox* where there are a number of possible species, each with a large number of cultivars. A search through the whole genus may well bring success. For space reasons, we are not able to list in the Plant Directory annuals, orchids or cacti (except hardy terrestrial orchids and hardy cacti), or non-ornamental vegetables. For fruit and vegetables with an RHS Award of Garden Merit please see the relevant sections on p.826 and p.838.

CROSS-REFERENCES

It may be that the plant name you seek is a synonym. Our intention is to list nursery codes only against the correct botanical name. Where you find a synonym you will be cross-referred to the correct name.

PLANTS LAST LISTED IN EARLIER EDITIONS

It may be that the plant you are seeking has no known suppliers and is thus not listed.

The loss of a plant name from the Directory may arise for a number of reasons – the supplier may have gone out of business, or may not have responded to our latest questionnaire and has therefore been removed from the book. Such plants may well be available but we have no knowledge of current suppliers. Alternatively, some plants may have been misnamed by nurseries in previous editions and are now appearing under their correct name.

For further information on plants last listed in earlier editions please see the Introduction (p.34).

Please, never use an out of date edition

USING THE PLANT DIRECTORY

The purpose of the Plant Directory is to help the reader correctly identify the plant they seek and find stockists. Each nursery has a unique code which appears to the right of the plant name. **Nursery Details by Code** (p.868) gives details about each nursery. The first letter in each code denotes its geographical region. Turn to the **Nursery Codes and Symbols** (p.864) to find the correct code for an area.

The Plant Directory provides information about plants through symbols and notes. For example: if a plant has an alternative name; is new to the book; or has received the RHS Award of Garden Merit.

Abelia ✿ (*Caprifoliaceae*)

	biflora	see *Zabelia biflora*
	chinensis misapplied	see *A.* × *grandiflora* 'Lake Maggiore'
§	***chinensis*** R. Br.	CBcs CExl CMCN CMac CRos EBee EHyd ELan EPfP LRHS MGil MMuc SEND SPer SRms WGrn WLov
	'Edward Goucher' 🏆H5	CBar CBcs CBod CBrac CDoC CMac CRos EBee ELan EPfP LRHS LSRN MAsh MGil MGos MMuc MRav MSwo SEND SGbt SGol SGsty SPer SPlb SRms SWvt WFar WLov WSHC
	engleriana	CExl CRos EHyd ELan EPfP LRHS MAsh MBlu MGil NLar SLon WLov
	floribunda	see *Vesalea floribunda*
§	× ***grandiflora*** (common clone)	see *A.* × *grandiflora* 'Lake Maggiore'
	- 'Aurea'	see *A.* × *grandiflora* 'Gold Spot'
	- 'Brockhill Allgold'	EMil EPfP LRHS SPoG
	- 'Compacta'	WFar
	- CONFETTI ('Conti'PBR) (v)	CBcs CBod CDoC CMac CRos CSBt EHyd ELan EPfP EWTr LRHS LSRN MGos MRav NLar SEle SGbt SGol SGsty SPer SPoG SWvt WFar
	- dwarf	MSwo
§	- 'Francis Mason' (v)	CBar CBcs CBrac CChe CMac CRos CSBt CTri EBee EHyd ELan EPfP EShb LRHS LSRN MAsh MRav MSwo NQui NRHS SCob SCoo SGol SPoG SRms SWvt WAvo WCFE WFar WLov
§	- 'Gold Spot' (v)	CBod CDoC EPfP NLar SPer
	- 'Gold Strike'	see *A.* × *grandiflora* 'Gold Spot'
	- 'Goldsport'	see *A.* × *grandiflora* 'Gold Spot'
	- 'Hopleys'PBR (v) 🏆H5	CBcs CMac CRos CSBt CTri EHyd ELan EPfP LRHS MAsh MGos NLar SGol SLon SPoG SRms SWvt WGrn WLov
	- 'Kaleidoscope'PBR (v)	CBcs CBod CDoC CMac CRos CWGN EBee ELan EPfP EShb LCro LOPS LRHS LSRN MAsh MGos NLar NRHS SCob SGol SGsty SPer SPoG SRms SWvt WCot WFar
§	- 'Lake Maggiore' 🏆H5	Widely available
	- LUCKY LOTS ('Wevo2') (v)	CBod EBee NLar SCob SGol
	- MAGIC DAYDREAM ('Opstal103') **new**	CBod CWGN LCro LOPS NEoE
	- MYSTIC DAYDREAM ('Opstal40') **new**	EBee
	- 'Panache' (v)	WCot
	- 'Prostrate White'	LRHS NLar SPoG
	- 'Radiance' (v)	EBee NEoE SCob

DESCRIPTIVE TERM
See p.38.

SYMBOLS TO THE LEFT OF THE NAME
Provides information about the name of the plant. See p.36 for the key.

SYMBOLS TO THE RIGHT OF THE NAME
Tells you more about the plant itself, e.g. (v) *indicates that the plant is variegated,* (F) = *fruit. See p.36 for the key.*

ABBREVIATIONS
To save space a dash indicates that the previous heading is repeated. If written out in full the name would be Abelia × grandiflora *'Gold Strike'.*

TRADE DESIGNATION
See p.40.

NEW
Plant new to this edition.

🏆H5
This plant has received the RHS Award of Garden Merit. See p.37.

NURSERY CODE
A unique code identifying each nursery. Turn to p.868 for details of the nurseries.

PBR
Plant Breeders' Rights. See p.39.

CROSS-REFERENCES
Directs you to the correct name of the plant and the nursery codes. See p.55.

WIDELY AVAILABLE
Indicates that more than 30 Plant Finder nurseries supply the plant, and it may be available locally. See p.55.

II
PLANTS

The Plant Directory

A

Abelia ✿ (*Caprifoliaceae*)

	biflora	see *Zabelia biflora*
	chinensis misapplied	see *A.* × *grandiflora* 'Lake Maggiore'
§	***chinensis*** R. Br.	CBcs CExl CMCN CMac CRos EBee EHyd ELan EPfP LRHS MGil MMuc SEND SPer SRms WGrn WLov
	'Edward Goucher' ♀H5	CBar CBcs CBod CBrac CDoC CMac CRos EBee ELan EPfP LRHS LSRN MAsh MGil MGos MMuc MRav MSwo SEND SGbt SGol SGsty SPer SPlb SRms SWvt WFar WLov WSHC
	engleriana	CExl CRos EHyd ELan EPfP LRHS MAsh MBlu MGil NLar SLon WLov
	floribunda	see *Vesalea floribunda*
§	× ***grandiflora*** (common clone)	see *A.* × *grandiflora* 'Lake Maggiore'
	- 'Aurea'	see *A.* × *grandiflora* 'Gold Spot'
	- 'Brockhill Allgold'	EMil EPfP LRHS SPoG
	- 'Compacta'	WFar
	- CONFETTI ('Conti'PBR) (v)	CBcs CBod CDoC CMac CRos CSBt EHyd ELan EPfP EWTr LRHS LSRN MGos MRav NLar SEle SGbt SGol SGsty SPer SPoG SWvt WFar
	- dwarf	MSwo
§	- 'Francis Mason' (v)	CBar CBcs CBrac CChe CMac CRos CSBt CTri EBee EHyd ELan EPfP EShb LRHS LSRN MAsh MRav MSwo NQui NRHS SCob SCoo SGol SPoG SRms SWvt WAvo WCFE WFar WLov
§	- 'Gold Spot' (v)	CBod CDoC EPfP NLar SPer
	- 'Gold Strike'	see *A.* × *grandiflora* 'Gold Spot'
	- 'Goldsport'	see *A.* × *grandiflora* 'Gold Spot'
	- 'Hopleys'PBR (v) ♀H5	CBcs CMac CRos CSBt CTri EHyd ELan EPfP LRHS MAsh MGos NLar SGol SLon SPoG SRms SWvt WGrn WLov
	- 'Kaleidoscope'PBR (v)	CBcs CBod CDoC CMac CRos CWGN EBee ELan EPfP EShb LCro LOPS LRHS LSRN MAsh MGos NLar NRHS SCob SGol SGsty SPer SPoG SRms SWvt WCot WFar
§	- 'Lake Maggiore' ♀H5	Widely available
	- LUCKY LOTS ('Wevo2') (v)	CBod EBee NLar SCob SGol
	- MAGIC DAYDREAM ('Opstal103') **new**	CBod CWGN LCro LOPS NEoE
	- MYSTIC DAYDREAM ('Opstal40') **new**	EBee
	- 'Panache' (v)	WCot
	- 'Prostrate White'	LRHS NLar SPoG
	- 'Radiance' (v)	EBee NEoE SCob
	- 'Semperflorens'	CPla LRHS
	- 'Sherwoodii'	EPfP LRHS MAsh MGil MGos WRHF
	- 'Sparkling Silver' (v)	EMil LRHS SGsty
	- SUNNY CHARMS ('Mindu01'PBR)	CBcs
	- 'Sunrise' (v)	NLar
	- SUNSHINE DAYDREAM ('Abelops'PBR) (v)	CEnd EBee LCro LOPS MMrt NLar SCob SGbt SGol SPad SRms WFar
	- 'Tanya'	WAvo
	- 'Variegata'	see *A.* × *grandiflora* 'Francis Mason'
§	'Lynn'PBR	LRHS MGos SPoG
	mosanensis	CBod CMCN CRos EHyd ELan EPfP LRHS MBlu MGil NQui SLon WCot WGob WLov
	- BRIDAL BOUQUET ('Monia')	CRos LRHS SChF
	parvifolia	CBcs CBod CExl CMCN CMac CSBt CTri EHyd ELan LRHS MGil NLar SLon SPer SPoG SWvt WGrn WLov
	- 'Bumblebee'	CRos LCro LOPS MAsh NLar SPoG SRms
	PASTEL CHARM ('Minduo2')	LRHS
	PETITE GARDEN ('Minedward'PBR)	CBod CDoC LRHS SGol
	PINKY BELLS	see *A.* 'Lynn'
	'Raspberry Profusion'PBR	MPkF
	rupestris misapplied	see *A.* × *grandiflora*
	rupestris Lindl.	see *A. chinensis* R. Br.
	triflora	see *Zabelia triflora*

Abeliophyllum (*Oleaceae*)

distichum	CBcs CEnd CRos CSde EBee ECrN EHyd ELan ELon EPfP IDee LRHS MAsh MBlu MSwo NRHS SGol SPer SWvt WCFE WCot WFar WSHC
- Roseum Group	CBcs CBod CDoC CExl CRos CWld EHyd ELan ELon EPfP EShb EWTr LCro LOPS LRHS MAsh MGil MMuc MRav NQui SGol SLon SMad SPer SPoG WCot

Abelmoschus (*Malvaceae*)

esculentus	SVic

Abies ✿ (*Pinaceae*)

alba	MMuc
- 'Fastigata'	XLot
- 'Green Spiral'	NLar
- 'Münsterland'	CKen
- 'Nana' misapplied	see *Picea glauca* 'Nana'
- 'Pendula'	CKen
- 'Pyramidata'	XLot
- 'Schwarzwald'	CKen SLim
amabilis 'Spreading Star'	SLim XLot
balsamea	MAsh MMuc

- 'Cook's Blue'	CKen
- 'Eugene Gold'	NLar
- Hudsonia Group	CKen LRHS WIce
- - 'Nana'	CKen ELan LRHS MGil XLot
- 'Jamie'	CKen
- 'Le Feber'	CKen
- var. ***phanerolepis*** 'Bear Swamp'	CKen NHol
- 'Piccolo'	CKen LRHS MGil NLar SLim
- 'Renswoude'	CKen NLar
- 'Sky Meadow'	NLar
- 'Tyler Blue'	CKen
- 'Verkade's Prostrate'	CKen
* ***borisii-regis*** 'Pendula'	CKen
- 'Spring Delight'	LRHS
brachyphylla dwarf	see *A. homolepis* 'Prostrata'
cephalonica	CMCN
- 'Greg's Broom'	CKen NLar
§ - 'Meyer's Dwarf'	NLar SLim
- 'Nana'	see *A. cephalonica* 'Meyer's Dwarf'
cephalonica* × *nordmanniana	MHtn
chensiensis	LRHS
cilicica 'Spring Grove'	CKen
concolor	CBcs CTho LMaj LRHS MMuc SCob SEND XLot
- 'Archer's Dwarf'	CKen NLar SLim XLot
§ - 'Argentea' Niemetz, 1903	SAko
- 'Birthday Broom'	CKen
- 'Blue Cloak'	CKen
- 'Blue Sapphire'	CKen
- 'Candicans'	see *A. concolor* 'Argentea' Niemetz, 1903
§ - 'Compacta' ♀H7	CKen LRHS MGos NHol SLim XLot
- 'Fagerhult'	CKen
- 'Gable's Weeping'	CKen
- 'Glauca Compacta'	see *A. concolor* 'Compacta'
- 'Hillier Broom'	see *A. concolor* 'Hillier's Dwarf'
§ - 'Hillier's Dwarf'	CKen
- 'Husky Pup'	CKen
- 'La Veta'	CKen SAko
- (Lowiana Group) 'Creamy'	CKen NLar
- 'Masonic Broom'	CKen
- 'Mike Stearn'	CKen
- 'Mora'	CKen
- 'Piggelmee'	CKen MAsh NLar
- 'Pygmy'	CKen
- 'Scooter'	CKen
- Violacea Group	CKen
- - 'Violacea Prostrate' ♀H7	NHol SAko
- 'Wattez Prostrate'	SLim
- 'Wattezii'	CKen
- 'Wintergold'	CKen LRHS MBlu NHol NLar SLim
- 'Wyoming South'	NLar
delavayi	CMCN EPfP LEdu LRHS SAko WPGP
- var. ***delavayi***	CExl
- - Fabri Group	see *A. fabri*
- 'Major Neishe'	CKen
§ ***fabri***	CKen
fargesii	CKen
forrestii	CKen
fraseri	CBcs CTho EWhm LRHS MMuc WTSh
- 'Blue Bonnet'	CKen
- 'Franklin'	NLar
- 'Kline's Nest'	SLim
- 'Palmeri'	NLar
- 'Raul's Dwarf'	CKen
grandis	CBcs CJun CMCN ELan EPfP MMuc WMou WTSh
- 'Compacta'	CKen
- 'Van Dedem's Dwarf'	CKen SLim
homolepis	CKen
- 'F.R. Newman' **new**	SLim
§ - 'Prostrata'	CKen
koreana ♀H7	CBcs CBrac CCVT CJun CLnd CMCN CMac CTho ELan EPfP GKin LMaj LRHS MBlu MGos MMuc MPri NHol NOra NPoe SCob SGol SLim SWvt WMat WMou WTSh XLot
- 'Alpin Star'	CKen MAsh
- 'Blaue Zwo'	CKen LRHS
- 'Blauer Eskimo' ♀H7	CKen MAsh NLar SLim
- 'Blauer Pfiff'	CKen
- 'Blinsham Gold'	CKen
- 'Blue Emperor'	MBlu NLar
- 'Blue Magic'	CKen NLar
- 'Brilliant'	CKen LRHS
- 'Cis' ♀H7	CKen LRHS NHol NLar SLim
- CRYSTAL GLOBE	see *A. koreana* 'Kristallkugel'
- 'Dark Hill'	NLar
- 'Discus'	NLar
- 'Doni-tajuso'	CKen
- 'Eisregen'	CKen SAko
- 'Festival'	NHol
- 'Frosty'	SLim
- 'Gait'	CKen NLar
- 'Golden Glow'	SLim
- 'Goldener Traum'	CKen NLar
- 'Green Carpet'	CKen LRHS SLim
- 'Grüne Spinne' **new**	MBlu
- 'Horstmann'	CKen
- 'Inge'	NLar
- 'Inverleith'	CKen
- 'Kleiner Prinz'	NLar
- 'Kohout'	CKen
- 'Kohout's Ice Breaker' PBR ♀H7	CKen LRHS MAsh MGos NLar SAko SLim
§ - 'Kristallkugel'	CKen MAsh MBlu NLar
- 'Lippetal'	CKen
- 'Luminetta'	CKen LRHS NHol
- 'Nadelkissen'	CKen NHol
- 'Nisbet'	NHol
- 'Oberon'	CKen MAsh NHol NLar SLim XLot
- 'Piccolo'	CKen
- 'Pinocchio'	CKen MGil NHol
- 'Prostrata'	see *A. koreana* 'Prostrate Beauty'
§ - 'Prostrate Beauty'	CKen
- 'Ry'	MGil
- 'Schneestern'	NLar
- 'Schwedenkönig'	NLar SLim
- 'Sherwood Compact'	CKen
- 'Shorty'	CKen NLar
- 'Silberkugel'	CKen CMen SLim
- 'Silberlocke' ♀H7	CCVT CKen LRHS MAsh MBlu MGos NLar NOra NOrn SCoo SLim SMad WHwl WMat XLot
- 'Silbermavers'	CKen SLim
- 'Silberperl'	CKen CMen LRHS SLim
- 'Silver Show'	LRHS MGil NHol NLar SAko SLim XLot
- 'Silver Star'	NLar
- 'Threave'	CKen NHol
- 'Tundra'	NLar SLim
- 'Wellenseind'	CKen
- 'Winter Goldtip'	SLim
lasiocarpa 'Alpine Beauty'	CKen NLar

§	- var. ***arizonica*** 'Argentea'	XLot
	- - 'Compacta' Hornibr. ♀H7	CCVT CKen LMaj LRHS MAsh MGos NHol SLim SPoG WMat
	- - 'Kenwith Blue'	CKen SLim
	- 'Beano Broom'	CKen NLar
	- 'Chikov'	CKen
	- 'Day Creek'	CKen NLar
	- 'Duflon'	CKen NLar
	- 'Elaine'	CKen
	- 'Glauca'	see *A. lasiocarpa* var. *arizonica* 'Argentea'
	- 'Green Globe'	CKen NLar SLim XLot
	- 'Hurricane Ridge' **new**	CKen
	- 'Joe's Alpine'	CKen
	- 'Kyle's Alpine'	CKen
	- 'Logan Pass'	CKen
	- 'Lopalpun'	CKen
	- 'Mulligan's Dwarf'	CKen
	- 'Prickly Pete'	CKen
	- 'Rhumpa'	SAko
	- 'Stevens Blue'	CKen
	- 'Toenisvorst'	CKen
	- 'Utah'	CKen
	magnifica 'Mount Si'	CKen
I	- 'Nana'	CKen
	- witches' broom	CKen
	nebrodensis	CKen
	- 'Sicilian Gold'	NLar
	nobilis	see *A. procera*
	nordmanniana	CBrac CCVT CJun CMCN CMac CTho ELan EWhm LBuc LMaj MMuc NLar SCob SEND SGsty SLim SPoG SWeb WMou WTSh XLot
	- 'Arne's Dwarf'	CKen
	- 'Barabits' Compact'	LRHS NLar
	- 'Barabits' Spreader'	CKen
	- 'Emmanuel'	NLar
	- subsp. ***equi-trojani*** 'Archer'	CKen
	- - 'Franke'	NLar
	- 'Filip's Gold Heart'	NLar
	- 'Filip's Perfect Column'	NLar
	- 'Golden Spreader' ♀H7	CKen LRHS MAsh MBlu MGos NLar SCoo SLim XLot
	- 'Hasselt'	see *A. nordmanniana* 'Pévé Hasselt'
	- 'Jakobsen'	CKen
	- 'Kbng'	NLar
	- 'Midwinter Gold'	NLar
	- 'Münsterland'	NLar XLot
	- 'Pendula'	LRHS MBlu MGil SMad XLot
§	- 'Pévé Hasselt'	CKen
	- 'Saerling'	NLar
	- 'Silberspitze'	CKen
	numidica	CKen
	- 'Glauca'	CKen
	pinsapo	WMou WThu
	- 'Atlas'	CKen NLar
	- 'Aurea' ♀H6	CCVT CKen ELan LRHS NHol NLar SLim WHwl XLot
I	- 'Aurea Nana'	CKen
	- 'Fastigiata'	SAko SGol
	- 'Fatima'	CKen
	- 'Glauca' ♀H6	CCVT CKen CTho ELan LMaj LRHS MBlu NLar NOrn SEND SLim XLot
	- 'Hamondii'	CKen
I	- 'Horstmann'	CKen NHol NLar SLim
	- 'Marokko'	CKen
	- 'Pendula'	CKen LRHS
	- 'Quicksilver'	CKen
	- 'San Pedro'	CKen
§	***procera***	CBcs CMCN EPfP WMou WTSh
	- 'Aurea'	LRHS
	- 'Bizarro'	NLar XLot
	- 'Blaue Hexe'	CKen LRHS SLim
	- 'Delbar Cascade'	CKen
	- Glauca Group	EPfP GKin LRHS MBlu NHol SLim
	- - 'Glauca' ♀H7	CTho ELan LMaj SAko XLot
	- - 'Glauca Prostrata' ♀H7	CKen LRHS MAsh SLim
	- 'Hupp's Dwarf'	CKen NLar
	- 'Jeddeloh'	CKen
	- 'La Graciosa'	NLar
	- 'Noble's Dwarf'	SLim
	- 'Pospíšil'	CKen
	- 'Prostrata'	NLar
	- 'Rat Tail'	NLar
	- 'Seattle Mount'	CKen
	- 'Sherwoodii'	CKen NLar SLim
	- 'Wiesmoor Nixe' **new**	NLar XLot
	Rosemoor hybrid	CKen
	sachalinensis	CKen
	sibirica	EPfP
	spectabilis	EPfP
	veitchii	WTSh
	- 'Heddergott'	CKen LRHS NHol SLim
	- 'Heine'	CKen
	- 'Kramer'	CKen
	- 'Otovenack'	NLar
I	- 'Pendula'	CKen
	- 'Rumburk'	CKen MAsh SLim
	- 'Secrest'	NLar
	- 'Syców'	CKen
	vejarii	LRHS

Abromeitiella see *Deuterocohnia*

Abutilon ✿ (*Malvaceae*)

'Aphrodite'	SPad
'Ashford Red'	CBcs CCCN ELan GQue LRHS SPalm WKif
'Bartley Schwarz'	MSCN
Bella Series	CDoC
'Canary Bird' ♀H2	CBcs CCCN ELan WKif
'Cannington Carol' (v) ♀H2	CCCN ELan LSRN SEND
'Cannington Peter' (v) ♀H2	CCCN
'Cloth of Gold'	CMac
'Cynthia Pike' (v)	CRos EHyd LRHS NRHS
'Flamenco'	CCCN CWGN
'Hinton Seedling'	CCCN CRHN LSRN SPad
indicum	EBtc
'John Thompson'	CBcs CCCN CWGN
'Kentish Belle' ♀H3	Widely available
'Leila Jackson'	EBee SPad
'Marion' ♀H1b	CCCN CRHN CRos EHyd LRHS LSRN NRHS SPlb
'Master Michael'	CMac
megapotamicum ♀H3	CBcs CBod CCCN CChe CDoC CMac CRHN CTri ELan ELon EPfP LRHS MGos MRav MSCN SCob SDix SEND SEle SLim SPer SPoG SRms WBor WSHC XLum XSen
- 'Big Bell'	CCCN ECre MSCN WFar WGob
- 'Ines'	ELon WPGP
- 'Pink Charm'	ELon SPad
- 'Variegatum' (v) ♀H3	CBcs CCCN CDoC CMac CRos ELon EMil EPfP LRHS MGil SEle SIvy SLim SLon SPer SPoG SWvt WGob

- 'Wisley Red'	CCCN CRHN CTsd ELon LRHS SCob WGob
× ***milleri*** hort. ♀H3	CCCN CMac CRHN ELon WCot WGob
- 'Variegatum' (v)	CCCN CMac EBee LRHS WCot
'Nabob' ♀H2	CBcs CCCN CDow CExl CRHN CSde EBee ELan EPfP EShb SAko SEND SIvy SPalm WBor WCot WFar
'Orange Hot Lava'	CExl EBee WPGP
'Paddy's Nephew'	EBee
'Patrick Synge'	CBcs CCCN CDow SChF SPhx WOld WPGP
pictum 'Thompsonii' (v) ♀H2	CCCN MGil SEND
'Pink Lady'	CCCN
'Red Bells'	SVen
'Red Tiger'	SPad WKif
'Russels Dwarf'	CCCN
'Savitzii' (v) ♀H2	MSCN
'Silver Belle'	CCCN
'Simcox White'	CCCN
'Souvenir de Bonn' (v) ♀H2	CCCN EShb WCot
× ***suntense***	CBcs CCCN CPla CRos CSBt EHyd LRHS MSCN NPer NRHS
- 'Jermyns' ♀H4	CExl LSRN MGos SCob SPoG SWvt
- 'Violetta'	WSpi
'Tango'	CCCN CRos CWGN LRHS MSCN SIvy SPad WCot WGob
'Victory'	CCCN CWGN MSCN
vitifolium	CBcs CCCN CDTJ EBee MGil SPad SPoG WCot WFar WKif WSpi
- 'Album'	CBcs CCCN CExl SPer WSpi
- 'Buckland'	CCCN
- 'Chalk Blues'	SPer
- 'Tennant's White' ♀H4	CCCN CExl CRos EHyd EPfP LRHS NRHS SAko WCot
- 'Veronica Tennant' ♀H4	CExl EBee EPfP LRHS SChF
'Waltz'	CCCN CRos CWGN EBee ELan EShb LRHS MHtn SIvy SPad WBor WCot WGob

Acacia (*Mimosaceae*)

acinacea	SPlb
adunca	SPlb
angustissima	SPlb
armata	see *A. paradoxa*
axillaris	SPlb
baileyana ♀H3	CBcs CCCN CDoC CMac CSBt CTsd EPfP EWTr LRHS LSRN MGos SCoo SPlb SWvt WFar
- var. ***aurea***	SPlb
- 'Purpurea' ♀H3	CBcs CBod CCCN CDoC CEnd CExl CMac CSBt CSpe CTri CTsd EBee ELan EPfP EShb LSRN MGos NOra SCoo SGol SIvy SPer SPlb SPoG SWvt WLov WPGP
- 'Songlines'	CRos LRHS MGos NRHS
boormanii	CAbb CDoC CTsd GBin IDee SPlb WPGP
cultriformis	CTsd ESwi
dealbata ♀H3	Widely available
- 'Gaulois Astier'	CDoC CSBt EMil EPfP LRHS LSRN MGos NRHS SGol SPoG SWeb SWvt WCot
- subsp. ***subalpina***	WPGP
'Exeter Hybrid'	CSBt
glaucoptera	SPlb
gregorii	SPlb
jibberdingensis	SPlb
julibrissin	see *Albizia julibrissin*
karroo	see *Vachellia karroo*
longifolia	CDTJ CMac
macradenia	SPlb
mearnsii	CPla
melanoxylon	CDTJ CMCN CTsd SPlb
nanodealbata	SPad
§ ***paradoxa***	MGil
pataczekii	CSBt WPGP
pendula	SPlb
podalyriifolia	SPlb
pravissima ♀H3	CAbb CBcs CChe CCht CDoC CExl CMac CRos CTri CTsd ELan EMil EPfP GBin IDee ILea LRHS LSRN SArc SPlb SWvt
retinodes	CBcs CCCN CDTJ CTsd ILea MMuc SEND SPad SWvt
- 'Lisette'	MGos
riceana	CTsd SVen
rubida	SPlb
sentis	see *A. victoriae*
spectabilis	SPlb
suaveolens	SPlb
truncata	SPlb
verticillata	CBcs CDTJ CDoC EPfP
- riverine form	CCCN CExl EPfP LRHS SEND
§ ***victoriae***	SPlb

Acaena (*Rosaceae*)

adscendens misapplied	see *A. affinis*, *A. saccaticupula* 'Blue Haze'
adscendens ambig. 'Glauca'	NBir
§ ***affinis***	EBee ECha
anserinifolia misapplied	see *A. novae-zelandiae*
buchananii	EBee EPPr GAbr GBin GKev GWyn MMuc NLar SCob SRms
caerulea hort.	see *A. caesiiglauca*
§ ***caesiiglauca***	CTri EPPr GAbr GMaP GQue
inermis	NWad SPlb
- 'Purpurea'	CSam EBee ECha ECtt ELan EShb GAbr GMaP GQue MMuc NDov NHol NHpl NLar NWad SPlb WCav XLum
magellanica	GAbr GKev
microphylla ♀H5	CBod CSam GQue MBel NLar SCob SPlb SRms
- COPPER CARPET	see *A. microphylla* 'Kupferteppich'
- 'Glauca'	see *A. caesiiglauca*
- 'Grüner Zwerg'	NLar
§ - 'Kupferteppich'	CSam ECtt ELan EPPr GAbr GKev GLog GMaP LEdu MHol MRav NBir NBro NLar SEdd SMHy SRms XLum
minor var. ***antarctica***	GBin
myriophylla	EBee
§ ***novae-zelandiae***	CTri EBee GAbr GKev SDix XLum
ovalifolia	GKev
'Pewter'	see *A. saccaticupula* 'Blue Haze'
poeppigiana	EBee
'Purple Carpet'	see *A. microphylla* 'Kupferteppich'
'Purple Haze'	CSpe
saccaticupula	EBee GKev MMuc
§ - 'Blue Haze'	CRos EBee ECha EDAr EHyd GWyn LRHS MRav NBir NRHS SPlb SRms
tesca	GBin GQue

Acalypha (*Euphorbiaceae*)

§ ***herzogiana***	CCCN EShb
pendula misapplied	see *A. herzogiana*

SCob SHeu SPad SPeP SPer SPoG SRms WBor WCot WHil

Acanthocalyx see *Morina*

Acantholimon (*Plumbaginaceae*)

androsaceum	see *A. ulicinum*
armenum	XSen
§ ***ulicinum***	XEll

Acanthopanax see *Eleutherococcus*

ricinifolius	see *Kalopanax septemlobus*

Acanthus ✿ (*Acanthaceae*)

arboreus	XLum
balcanicus misapplied	see *A. hungaricus*
'Candelabra'	WHil
caroli-alexandri	see *A. spinosus* L.
dioscoridis	IMou WHil
- var. ***perringii***	CDor EBee ECha MNrw NLar WCot WFar WHil XLum
eminens	WCot
greuterianus new	WHil
hirsutus	CDor CFis EPri WCot WHil
- JCA 106.700	WHil
- subsp. ***syriacus***	ECha
'Hollande du Nort'	CRos EBee LRHS NRHS XLum
§ ***hungaricus***	CBod CDoC CDor CMac CRos EBee ELan EMor ILea LCro LOPS LRHS MBel MMuc MRav NLar NRHS SCob SDix WCot WFar WHil XLum
- AL&JS 90097YU	WHil
- MESE 561	WHil
- 'White Lips'	CBod EBee MAvo MNrw NCou NLar WCot WFar WRHF
longifolius Host	see *A. hungaricus*
mollis	Widely available
- from Turkey	WHil
- 'Fielding Gold'	see *A. mollis* 'Hollard's Gold'
- free-flowering	ESwi MAvo SChr WHil XLum
§ - 'Hollard's Gold'	Widely available
- 'Jefalba'	see *A. mollis* (Latifolius Group) 'Rue Ledan'
- Latifolius Group	CDor MRav SRms WHil
§ - - 'Rue Ledan' ♀H6	EBee ECtt ELan EPPr EWTr GBin LRHS MAvo MBel MNrw NGdn NLar NSti SMHy SPhx WCAu WCot WHil XLum
- - 'Sjaak'	MAvo WHil
- 'Long Spike'	WHil
- 'Niger'	EBee
- 'Tasmanian Angel' (v)	CAbb CDor CWGN ECtt ELan ELon EMor ESwi MPri NBPC NHpl SEdd SPoG WCot WFar WSMil XLum
'Morning's Candle'	CBod EBee ECtt ELan EMor MNrw NGdn NLar WFar WHil XLum
sennii	ECha ESwi IMou SMad SPhx WAvo WCot WHil WSHC XLum
spinosus misapplied	see *A. spinosus* Spinosissimus Group
§ ***spinosus*** L.	Widely available
- Ferguson's form	EBee MAvo WCot XLum
- 'Lady Moore' (v)	CDor NBPC NLar WHil XLum
- 'Royal Haughty'	WHil XLum
§ - Spinosissimus Group	CBct CDor EBee ECha ELan EMor EPed GBin LEdu LPot MAvo MGos MRav NChi NLar WCot WFar WHil
'Summer Beauty'	EBee ECtt EWes LRHS MAvo NLar WCot WFar WHil XLum
'Whitewater' (v)	CBct CDor CPla CWGN EBee ECtt ELan EWTr GKin MPri NLar NSti

Acca (*Myrtaceae*)

sellowiana (F)	Widely available
- 'Mammoth' (F)	CBcs CCCN
- 'Triumph' (F)	CBcs CCCN
- 'Variegata' (F/v)	CCCN

Acer ✿ (*Sapindaceae*)

acuminatum	CMCN SReu
albopurpurascens NMWJ 14455	WCru
amoenum B&SWJ 10916	WCru
- B&SWJ 10977	WCru
- 'Firecracker'	see *A. palmatum* 'Firecracker'
'Ample Surprise' PBR	MBlu SMad
'Asian Queen'	CJun
buergerianum	CMen CTho EBee ECrN MMuc MPkF NLar SBrt SGol WHwl WPGP
- B&SWJ 12676 from South Korea	WCru
- var. ***formosanum*** CWJ 12477	WCru
- 'Integrifolium'	see *A. buergerianum* 'Subintegrum'
- 'Naruto'	CMCN MPkF
§ - 'Subintegrum'	CMCN
campbellii	MBlu
- subsp. ***campbellii***	WPGP
- - GWJ 9360	WCru
- - PAB 13.071	LEdu
- 'Exuberance'	CJun
campestre ♀H6	Widely available
- 'Anny's Globe'	MBlu
- 'Carnival' (v) ♀H6	CEnd ELan ELon MAsh MBlu NOrn NPoe SGol SPer SPoG SWvt
- 'Elegant'	see *A. campestre* 'Huiber's Elegant'
- 'Elsrijk'	CCVT CLnd LMaj NOrn SCob SCoo WHwl
- 'Evelyn'	see *A. campestre* 'Queen Elizabeth'
- 'Evenley Red'	EBee ESwi MBlu WMou WPGP
- 'Green Column'	LRHS
§ - 'Huiber's Elegant' new	WHwl
- 'Louisa Red Shine'	CLnd SCob
- 'Nanum'	MBlu
- 'Pendulum'	CEnd
- 'Postelense'	ELan MBlu
§ - 'Queen Elizabeth'	MGos SGol
- 'Red Shine'	EBar MMuc SGol WHwl
- 'Royal Ruby'	MGos
- 'Ruby Glow' ♀H6	CEnd
- 'William Caldwell'	CEnd CTho MBlu
capillipes	CBcs CLnd CMCN CTho EBee ELan GQue LMaj MMuc NOrn SCob SGbt SPlb WMat WTSh
- 'Antoine'	CJun LRHS MBlu
- 'Candy Stripe'	see *A.* × *conspicuum* 'Candy Stripe'
- 'Honey Dew'	CJun SSta
cappadocicum	CCVT CEnd CMCN ECrN LMaj
- 'Aureum' ♀H6	CBcs CEnd CLnd CMCN CTho EBee ELan EPfP GKin IArd MAsh MBlu MRav NLar NOra NOrn SCob SGbt SGol SPer SWvt WFar WMat WMou WTSh
§ - subsp. ***lobelii***	LMaj
- var. ***mono***	see *A. pictum*
- 'Rubrum' ♀H6	CArg CBcs CLnd CMCN EBee ECrN ELan EPfP GKin LMaj MBlu MMuc

		MRav NOra NOrn SEND SGol SPer WFar WHer WMat
	- var. ***tricaudatum***	CExl
	carpinifolium	CMCN EBee EPfP IArd LRHS MBlu MMuc NLar WPGP
	- B&SWJ 10955	WCru
	- B&SWJ 11124	WCru
§	***caudatifolium*** CWJ 12403	WCru
	- NMWJ 14459	WCru
	- RWJ 9843	WCru
§	***caudatum*** GWJ 9279	WCru
	- GWJ 9317	WCru
	- HWJK 2240	WCru
	- HWJK 2338	WCru
	- subsp. ***ukurunduense***	MPkF
	- - B&SWJ 8658	WCru
	- - B&SWJ 12602	WCru
	cinnamomifolium	see *A. coriaceifolium*
	circinatum	CBcs CCVT CJun CMCN ECrN MBlu MMuc NLar SEND SPlb
	- B&SWJ 9565	WCru
	- 'Burgundy Jewel'	CJun LCro LOPS LRHS MPkF WHwl XLot
	- 'Del's Dwarf' **new**	XLot
	- 'Monroe'	CJun CMCN SGol XLot
	- 'Pacific Fire'	CJun NLar XLot
	- 'Sunny Sister'	XLot
	- 'Ven's Dwarf' **new**	XLot
	- 'Victoria' **new**	XLot
	- 'Whitney Broom'	NLar WHwl XLot
	cissifolium	CMCN EPfP NLar
	- B&SWJ 10801	WCru
§	× ***conspicuum*** 'Candy Stripe'	CJun
	- 'Elephant's Ear'	CJun MBlu NLar
	- 'Phoenix'	CEnd CJun CMCN EBee EPfP GKin LRHS MBlu NLar NOra SPoG WLov WPGP
	- 'Silver Ghost'	SWvt
§	- 'Silver Vein'	CEnd CJun CMCN EPfP NLar SSta SWvt
§	***coriaceifolium***	CMCN
	crataegifolium	CMCN SSta
	- B&SWJ 11036	WCru
	- 'Ittai-san-nishiki'	SSta
	- 'Meuri-no-ōfu' (v)	SSta
	- 'Veitchii' (v)	CJun CMCN EBee EPfP LRHS MBlu MPkF SSta
	creticum misapplied	see *A. sempervirens*
	dasycarpum	see *A. saccharinum*
	davidii	CAby CBcs CExl CTsd ECrN LCro LMaj LOPS MBlu MGos MMuc MRav NOrn SCob SGol SSta
§	- 'Canton'	CJun SSta
	- 'Cantonspark'	see *A. davidii* 'Canton'
	- 'Cascade'	MBlu SSta
	- 'George Forrest' ♀H5	CBcs CExl CJun CMCN CMac CTho EBee ECrN ELan EPfP GBin MMuc NLar NOra NOrn SGbt SPoG SSta SWvt WMat
	- 'Hagelunie'	SSta
	- 'Hansu-suru' (v)	SSta
	- 'Karmen'	CJun EPfP SSta
	- 'Purple Bark'	CExl CJun NLar SSta
	- 'Rosalie'	CJun EPfP LRHS MAsh MBlu NLar SSta WHwl
	- 'Sekka'	SSta
	- 'Serpentine'	CBcs CJun CMCN EPfP MAsh MBlu NLar NOrn SSta

	- 'Silver Vein'	see *A.* × *conspicuum* 'Silver Vein'
	- VIPER ('Mindavi')	EBee EPfP LRHS MAsh NOra NOrn SGsty SPer SPoG WHCr WMat
	diabolicum	CMCN
	duplicatoserratum NMWJ 14599	WCru
	elegantulum	CExl CJun GBin SPtp
	erythranthum	WPGP
	- FMWJ 13157	WCru
	fabri	CExl
	- WWJ 11614	WCru
	flabellatum	CJun
	- NJM 11.017	WPGP
	- var. ***yunnanense***	CBcs CMCN MMuc SPtp
	forrestii	CExl CMCN MMuc SPtp
	- BWJ 7515	WCru
	- 'Alice'	CEnd CJun SSta
	- 'Inoense'	SSta
	- 'Sirene'	CJun SSta
	- 'Sparkling'	CJun
	× ***freemanii***	CMCN
	- 'Armstrong'	CCVT LSRN MMuc SGol
	- AUTUMN BLAZE ('Jeffersred') ♀H6	CBcs CCVT CLnd CMCN CTho EPfP IArd LMaj LRHS MBlu MGos MMuc NOra NOrn SCob SCoo SGol SPer SPoG WHwl WMat WMou
	- AUTUMN FANTASY ('Dtr 102')	CTho
	- CELEBRATION ('Celzam')	CArg CCVT CTho EBee MGos
	- 'Indian Summer'	see *A.* × *freemanii* 'Morgan'
§	- 'Morgan'	CJun
	ginnala	see *A. tataricum* subsp. *ginnala*
	glabrum B&SWJ 14119	WCru
	globosum	see *A. platanoides* 'Globosum'
	grandidentatum	see *A. saccharum* subsp. *grandidentatum*
	griseum ♀H5	Widely available
	grosseri	CMCN CTri SGol
	- var. ***hersii***	CBcs CLnd EBee EPfP LSRN MMuc NOra NOrn SSta SWvt WMat
	- 'Leiden'	EPfP LRHS
	heldreichii	CMCN
	henryi	CBcs NLar
	heptaphlebium B&SWJ 11695	WCru
	- B&SWJ 11713	WCru
	- FMWJ 13369	WCru
	japonicum	CMCN SEWo SavN
	- B&SWJ 12847	WCru
	- CWJ 12840	WCru
§	- 'Aconitifolium' ♀H6	Widely available
	- 'Aka-omote' **new**	XLot
	- 'Ao-jutan'	CJun
	- 'Attaryi'	CMen WHwl
	- 'Aureum'	see *A. shirasawanum* 'Aureum'
	- 'Charlotte-Helene' **new**	XLot
	- 'Emmit's Pumpkins'	CJun
	- 'Ezo-no-momiji'	see *A. shirasawanum* 'Ezo-no-momiji'
	- 'Fairy Lights'	WHwl
	- 'Filicifolium'	see *A. japonicum* 'Aconitifolium'
	- 'Green Cascade' ♀H6	CEnd CJun CMCN CMac CMen MGos MPkF NBPC NLar WHwl
	- 'Indian Summer'	XLot
	- 'Itaya-momiji' **new**	XLot
	- 'Kalmthout'	XLot
	- 'King's Copse'	CJun
	- 'Kujaku-bato' **new**	WHwl XLot
	- 'Laciniatum'	see *A. japonicum* 'Aconitifolium'

	- f. ***microphyllum***	see *A. shirasawanum* 'Microphyllum'
§	- 'Mikasa-yama'	XLot
	- 'Ogurayama'	see *A. shirasawanum* 'Ogurayama'
	- 'Ō-isami'	XLot
	- 'Ō-taki'	CJun XLot
	- 'Ruby' **new**	MPkF
	- 'Vitifolium' ♀H6	CDoC CEnd CJun CMCN CMac CTho ELan EPfP GBin LRHS MBlu MGos MPkF NLar SGol SPer SPoG SSta WHwl WLov WTSh XLot
	kawakamii	see *A. caudatifolium*
	laevigatum FMWJ 13378	WCru
	- FMWJ 13439	WCru
	- NJM 10.049	WPGP
§	- var. ***reticulatum*** B&SWJ 11698	WCru
	laurinum FMWJ 13412	WCru
	laxiflorum	SSta
	lobelii Ten.	see *A. cappadocicum* subsp. *lobelii*
	macrophyllum	CMCN EPfP MBlu MMuc
	- B&SWJ 13183	WCru
	mandshuricum	LRHS
	- B&SWJ 12592	WCru
§	***maximowiczianum***	MMuc MPkF SSta
	maximowiczii	MPkF
	micranthum ♀H6	CMCN EPfP LRHS MBlu NLar WPGP
	- CWJ 12843	WCru
	miyabei	MPkF
	mono	see *A. pictum*
	monspessulanum	CMCN LEdu LMaj MMuc SEND XSen
	morifolium B&SWJ 11473	WCru
	morrisonense Hayata	see *A. caudatifolium*
	negundo	CMCN ECrN SCob SWvt
	- B&SWJ 14060	WCru
	- 'Auratum'	CMCN SGol
	- 'Aureomarginatum' (v)	CCVT ECrN SGol
§	- 'Elegans' (v)	CEnd CMCN ELan SCoo
	- 'Elegantissimum'	see *A. negundo* 'Elegans'
	- 'Flamingo' (v)	CBcs CCVT CEnd CMCN CMac ECrN ELan EPfP LRHS MAsh NLar NOra SCob SGol SGsty SPer SPoG SWvt WMat
	- 'Kelly's Gold'	CBcs CCVT ELan NLar SGol SPoG WMat
	- 'Sensation'	NLar
	- 'Variegatum' (v)	ECrN LMaj SCob SGol
	- var. ***violaceum*** ♀H6	CEnd ELan EPfP SVen
	- 'Winter Lightning' ♀H6	NLar
	nikoense misapplied	see *A. maximowiczianum*
	nipponicum	SPtp
	'Norwegian Sunset'	CCVT
	oliverianum	CExl MBlu
	- subsp. ***formosanum*** NMWJ 14460	WCru
	- - NMWJ 14514	WCru
	- - NMWJ 14521	WCru
	opalus	CMCN LMaj SEND WMou
	orientale misapplied	see *A. sempervirens*
	ORIENTALIA ('Minorient')	MMrt NOrn WFar
	orizabense	EBee
	PACIFIC SUNSET ('Warrenred')	LMaj NLar
	palmatum	CAby CBcs CCVT CDoC CMCN CMen CSBt CTri GKin LCro LMaj MBlu MGos NBPC SArc SCob SEWo SGol SGsty SPlb SReu SWvt SavN WFar WLov WTSh
	- (D)	Widely available
	- 'Adrian's Compact' (Dw) **new**	XLot
	- 'Aizumi-nishiki' (P/v) **new**	XLot
	- 'Akane' (P)	CMen MPkF NBPC NLar WHwl XLot
§	- 'Aka-shigitatsu-sawa' (M)	CDoC CJun CMCN CMac CMen ESMi MGos MPkF NLar WHwl XLot
	- 'Akegarasu' (M)	CJun CMCN CMen NLar XLot
	- 'Akishino' (A) **new**	XLot
	- 'Aki-tsuma-gaki' **new**	XLot
	- 'Alloys' (D)	XLot
	- 'Alpenweiss' (P)	CJun XLot
	- 'Alpine Surprise'	SAko
	- 'Amagi-shigure' (M)	CJun LCro LOPS LRHS MPkF NLar WHwl XLot
	- 'Amber Ghost' (M)	CJun NLar WHwl XLot
	- 'Anna's Broom' (Dw) **new**	XLot
	- 'Anne Irene' PBR (P)	LRHS MPkF NLar WHwl XLot
	- 'Annick' **new**	XLot
	- 'Aoba-jo' (Dw)	CJun CMen MPkF NBPC WHwl XLot
	- 'Aoba-nishiki' (A) **new**	XLot
	- 'Ao-kanzashi' (P/v)	MPkF XLot
	- 'Ao-shidare' (D)	CJun
	- 'Ao-shime' (L) **new**	XLot
	- 'Aoshime-no-uchi'	see *A. palmatum* 'Shinobuga-oka'
	- 'Aoyagi' (P)	CEnd CJun CMCN CMen CRos CTho EMac ESMi GKin LRHS MGos MPkF NBPC NLar NRHS SCoo WHwl XLot
	- 'Aoyagi-gawa'	CJun XLot
§	- 'Arakawa' (P)	CEnd CMCN CMen ESMi MPkF NBPC NLar WHwl XLot
	- 'Arakawa-ukon'	CJun
	- 'Arano' **new**	XLot
	- 'Aratama' (Dw)	CJun CMCN CMen EMac LRHS WHwl XLot
	- 'Ariadne' (M/v) ♀H6	CDoC CEnd CJun LRHS MGos MPkF NBPC NLar SCoo SPoG WHwl XLot
	- 'Ariake-nomura' (A)	CMen MPkF
	- 'Asagi-nishiki' (v) **new**	XLot
	- 'Asahi-zuru' (P/v)	CJun CMCN CMen LRHS MGos NBPC NLar NRHS SPer WHwl WMat XLot
	- 'Asuka' (A) **new**	XLot
	- 'Atrolineare' (L)	CMen MPkF NLar WHwl XLot
	- 'Atropurpureum' (A)	Widely available
	- 'Attraction' (P)	CMac CMen XLot
	- 'Aureum' (P)	CMCN CMen CRos CTri ELan EPfP LMil LRHS MAsh MBlu MGos MPkF NLar NRHS SPoG WFar WHwl XLot
	- 'Autumn Fire' (D)	CJun MPkF XLot
	- 'Autumn Glory' (M)	CEnd CJun CMen NBPC XLot
	- 'Autumn Red' (M)	CMen ESMi
*	- 'Autumn Showers'	CEnd CJun XLot
	- 'Azuma-murasaki' (M)	CJun CMen MPkF XLot
	- 'Baby Lace' (Dw)	CWGN SAko
	- 'Baldsmith' (D)	CJun EMac ESMi LRHS MPkF WHwl XLot
	- 'Barrie Bergman' (D)	CJun NLar XLot
	- 'Baton Rouge' (P) **new**	XLot
	- 'Beni-chidori' (P)	CMen ESMi WHwl
	- 'Beni-fushigi' (P)	MPkF XLot
	- 'Beni-gasa' (M)	CJun MPkF WHwl XLot
	- 'Beni-hime' (Dw)	MPkF WHwl
	- 'Beni-hoshi' (Dw)	MPkF WHwl XLot

- 'Beni-kagami' (M) CBcs CEnd CJun CMCN IDee MPkF NLar SGol WHwl XLot
- 'Beni-kawa' (P) CJun CMCN CMen ESMi MPkF NOrn WHwl XLot
- 'Beni-komachi' (P) CBcs CDoC CEnd CMCN CMen EPfP ESMi LRHS MGos MPkF NBPC NOrn SSta WHwl XLot
- 'Beni-kosode' (v) MPkF NLar
- 'Beni-maiko' (P) ♀H6 CDoC CEnd CJun CMCN CMen CRos EPfP ESMi IDee LRHS MGos MPkF NBPC NLar NOrn NRHS SCoo SWeb SWvt WHwl WLov XLot
- 'Beni-musume' MPkF XLot
- 'Beni-otake' (L) CBcs CJun CMen ELan EPfP ESMi LRHS MGos MPkF NLar SAko WHwl
- 'Beni-otome' MPkF WHwl XLot
- 'Beni-sazanami' (M) **new** XLot
- 'Beni-schichi-henge' (P/v) CBcs CDoC CEnd CJun CMCN CMen CRos CWGN ESMi LRHS MAsh MGos MPkF NBPC NHol NLar NOra NOrn NRHS SAko SCoo SGol SSta WHwl WMat
- 'Beni-shidare' (D) WHwl
- 'Beni-shidare Tricolor' see *A. palmatum* 'Toyama-nishiki'
- 'Beni-shidare Variegated' see *A. palmatum* 'Toyama-nishiki'
- 'Beni-shi-en' (P) CJun MPkF
- 'Beni-shigitatsu-sawa' see *A. palmatum* 'Aka-shigitatsu-sawa'
- 'Beni-shirash' (P) **new** XLot
- 'Beni-tsukasa' (P/v) ♀H6 CEnd CJun CMCN CMen ESMi LMaj NBPC SSta WHwl
- 'Beni-tsuru' MPkF XLot
- 'Beni-yubi-gohon' (P) CJun MPkF WHwl XLot
- 'Beni-zashi' (P) **new** XLot
- 'Beni-zuru' (P) XLot
- 'Berrima Bridge' (D) CJun XLot
- 'Berry Broom' MPkF NLar XLot
- 'Berry Dwarf' (Dw) CJun MPkF
- 'Bewley's Red' (D) CJun XLot
- 'Bi Hō' (P) CJun CRos LCro LMil LOPS LRHS MAsh MGos MPkF NLar NRHS SAko SGol WHwl XLot
- 'Black Lace' (M) IArd LRHS MAsh MGos MPkF NLar NRHS WHwl
- 'Bloodgood' (A) ♀H6 Widely available
- 'Bob's Big Green' **new** XLot
- 'Bonfire' misapplied see *A. palmatum* 'Seigai'
- 'Bonfire' ambig. CJun LRHS
- 'Bonnie Bergman' CJun
- 'Boskoop Glory' (A) GKin XLot
- 'Brandt's Dwarf' (Dw) XLot
- 'Briella's Broom' (Dw) **new** XLot
- 'Brocade' (D) CJun MPkF NLar
- 'Bronzewing' (D) CJun
- 'Bujó-ji' (M) **new** XLot
- 'Bultinck' (M) **new** MPkF XLot
- 'Burgundy Lace' (M) ♀H6 CBcs CEnd CJun CMCN CMen CRos ELan EMac EPfP ESMi GKin LMil LRHS LSRN MAsh MGos MPkF NBPC NRHS SCoo SGol SPer SPoG SSta WHwl XLot
- 'Butterfly' (P/v) CEnd CJun CMCN CMac CMen CWGN ELan ELon ESMi LCro LOPS LSRN MAsh MBlu MGos MPkF NBPC NLar NOrn SCoo SGol SPer SWeb SWvt WFar WHwl XLot
- 'Calico' (P) CJun NLar WHwl XLot
- 'Candy Kitchen' see *A. palmatum* 'Kandy Kitchen'
- 'Caperci Dwarf' (Dw) MPkF XLot
- 'Carlis Corner' (Dw) XLot
- 'Carminium' see *A. palmatum* 'Corallinum'
- 'Caroline' (v) NLar XLot
- 'Cascade' **new** NOrn
- 'Cascade Gold' (P) **new** MPkF
- 'Channa Yasmin' **new** XLot
- 'Chantilly Lace' (D) CJun
- 'Chikuma-no' (A) CMen MPkF XLot
- 'Chi-otome' (P) **new** WHwl
- 'Chiri-hime' (M) **new** XLot
- 'Chirimen-nishiki' (P/v) MPkF
- 'Chishio' (P) CMCN CMen ESMi LMil LRHS MPkF NBPC NLar WHwl XLot
- 'Chishio Improved' (P) CDoC CEnd CJun CMCN CMac CMen CTho EPfP LRHS MGos NHol NLar NOrn NRHS SWvt WHwl XLot
- 'Chitose-yama' (M) ♀H6 CEnd CJun CMCN CMen EPfP GKin LMaj LRHS MAsh MGos MPkF NLar NRHS SLim SSta WHwl XLot

§ - 'Chiyo-hime' ESMi LCro LOPS MPri NBPC WFar WHwl XLot
- 'Chūgū-ji' **new** XLot
- 'Cindy' **new** XLot
- 'Coonara Pygmy' (Dw) CJun CMCN CMac CMen EMac ESMi GKin LRHS MPkF SCoo XLot
- 'Coral Magic' **new** XLot
- 'Coral Pink' (Dw) CJun CMen ESMi MPkF SSta

§ - 'Corallinum' (P) ♀H6 CBcs CEnd CJun CMCN CMen EPfP ESMi NBPC NLar SPoG WHwl XLot
- var. ***coreanum*** XLot
- - B&SWJ 8606 WCru
- 'Crimson Carol' (M) CJun NLar WHwl XLot
- 'Crimson Prince' CJun NLar SCoo XLot
- 'Crimson Princess' (D) CBcs CDoC CRos EPfP LMaj LRHS NBPC NOrn NRHS SWeb WMat
- 'Crimson Queen' (D) ♀H6 CBcs CCVT CEnd CJun CMCN CMac CMen CRos CSBt ELan EMac EPfP GKin IArd LRHS MAsh MGos NBPC NLar NOrn NRHS SCob SGol SPer SReu SSta WCFE WFar WMat XLot
- 'Crippsii' (D) CBcs CMac CMen MPkF NBPC SCoo XLot
- 'Cynthia's Crown Jewel' XLot
- 'Dai' (D) **new** XLot
- 'Daiji-sen' **new** XLot
- 'Darwin-nishiki' (v) **new** XLot
- 'Demi-sec' (D) XLot
- 'Deshōjō' (P) CMCN CMen ESMi LMaj MBlu MGos NBPC NLar NPoe SCoo SGol SGsty WHwl WMat XLot
- 'Deshōjō-nishiki' (P) XLot
- 'Dezome-irizome' **new** XLot
- 'Diana' (Dw) CJun CMen SGol XLot
- 'Diana Verkade' (P/v) **new** XLot
- 'Dissectum' (D) CDoC CTho CTri EWTr LBuc LOPS NOra NOrn WCFE WFar WHwl WTSh XLot
- 'Dissectum Atropurpureum' (D) CRos LMil SGsty WHwl
- 'Dissectum Flavescens' (D) CBcs CEnd CJun CMac CMen EMac MBlu MGos MPkF NBPC WHwl WMat XLot

§ - 'Dissectum Nigrum' (D) CJun CMac CMen MAsh MPkF NOrn WHwl XLot

	- 'Dissectum Palmatifidum' (D)	CMen EMac MPkF NOrn SCoo SGol SPer WHwl XLot
	- 'Dissectum Rubrifolium' (D)	MPkF XLot
§	- 'Dissectum Variegatum' (Dw/v)	CJun MPkF WHwl
	- Dissectum Viride Group	CBcs CDoC CJun CMCN CMac CMen CRos CSBt ELan EMac EPfP ESMi LCro LMil LRHS MAsh MBlu MGos MSwo NOra NOrn NRHS SGsty SLim SPer SSta SWvt WCFE WHwl WMat
	- 'Doctor Baker' (D)	XLot
	- 'Doctor Brown' (D) **new**	XLot
	- 'Doctor Tilt' (P)	WHwl
	- 'Dolly Hill' **new**	XLot
	- 'Donzuru-bo'	CJun XLot
	- 'Dora' **new**	XLot
	- 'Dr Seuss' (L)	NLar XLot
	- 'Dragon's Fire'	CJun
	- 'Dwarf Shishi' (Dw)	NLar XLot
	- 'Earthfire'	MPkF XLot
I	- 'Ebbingei'	CMac
	- 'Eddisbury' (P) 🏆H6	CEnd CJun CMen CSBt MBlu NLar SSta WHwl XLot
	- 'Edna Bergman' (M)	CJun XLot
	- 'Effegi'	see *A. palmatum* 'Fireglow'
	- 'Eimini' (Dw)	MPkF NLar XLot
§	- 'Elegans' (M) 🏆H6	CMen CRos EPfP LRHS MPkF NRHS XLot
	- 'Elizabeth' (Dw)	CJun
	- 'Ellen' (D)	CJun MPkF
	- 'Elmwood' (v) **new**	WHwl XLot
	- 'Elmwood Spreader' (D) **new**	XLot
	- 'Emerald Lace' (D) 🏆H6	CJun CRos EBee EMac GKin LBuc LCro LOPS LRHS MGos MPkF NLar NOrn NRHS SPoG SSta WFar WHwl XLot
	- 'Emi' (P/v) **new**	XLot
	- 'Emma' (D)	XLot
§	- 'Emperor 1' (A)	CBcs CJun ELan EMac LMaj MAsh MPkF SPer WMat XLot
	- 'English Lace' (D) **new**	XLot
	- 'Englishtown' (Dw)	MPkF NLar XLot
	- 'Enkan' (L)	CDoC CEnd CJun CMen CWGN IArd LMil LRHS MGos MPkF MPri NLar NOra SPoG WHwl WLov WMat XLot
	- 'Eono-momiji'	CMen
	- 'Ever Red'	see *A. palmatum* 'Dissectum Nigrum'
	- 'Fairy Hair' (L)	CJun
	- 'Fall's Fire' (P)	CJun
	- 'Fascination' (M)	CJun XLot
	- 'Felice' (D)	CJun MPkF WHwl XLot
	- 'Fenna' (L) **new**	XLot
	- 'Festival' **new**	NLar XLot
	- 'Filigree' (Dw/v)	CJun CMCN CMen EPfP LMil MAsh MGos MPkF NBPC NLar SSta WHwl
	- 'Fior d'Arancio' (M)	CJun MPkF NLar WHwl XLot
	- 'Fireball'	CJun XLot
§	- 'Firecracker'[PBR] (D)	CDoC CRos LRHS MAsh MPkF NLar NRHS SWeb WHwl
§	- 'Fireglow' (A)	CBcs CDoC CEnd CJun CMCN CMen CRos CSBt ESMi LMaj LMil LRHS LSRN MGos MPkF NLar NRHS SAko SCoo SGol SGsty SPer SReu SWeb WHwl XLot
	- 'Fireglow' sport **new**	XLot
	- 'First Ghost' (M/v)	CJun XLot
	- 'Flushing'	XLot
	- 'Franny' (A) **new**	XLot
	- 'Frederici Guglielmi'	see *A. palmatum* 'Dissectum Variegatum'
	- 'Fudekage' (M) **new**	XLot
	- 'Fūhjin'	XLot
	- 'Fujinami' **new**	XLot
	- 'Fukaya' (M) **new**	XLot
	- 'Fukui' (M) **new**	XLot
	- 'Furu-kawa' (A) **new**	XLot
	- 'Futai-ji' **new**	XLot
	- 'Gaki-no-sugi' (P/v) **new**	XLot
	- 'Garnet' (D) 🏆H6	Widely available
	- 'Garnet Bond' (D) **new**	XLot
	- 'Garnet Korea' **new**	XLot
	- 'Garnet Tower' (D)	LRHS MPkF NLar
	- 'Garyū' (Dw)	MPkF XLot
	- 'Geisha Gone Wild' (P/v)	CJun NLar XLot
	- 'Gekkō-nishiki'	XLot
	- 'Genji-yama' **new**	XLot
	- 'Genshu-yama-momiji'	XLot
	- 'Gentaku'	CJun XLot
	- 'Germaine's Gyration' (D)	CJun
	- 'Gibbons' (D) **new**	XLot
	- 'Gibbsii'	CMen
I	- 'Globosum' (Dw)	XLot
	- 'Glowing Embers' (P)	CJun MPkF WHwl XLot
	- 'Glowing Embers' sport **new**	XLot
	- 'Going Green'	CRos LCro LOPS LRHS MPkF NLar NRHS WHwl
	- 'Going Red'	LRHS NLar
	- 'Golden Hornet' **new**	NLar
	- 'Golden Pond' (A)	CJun XLot
	- 'Goshiki-kotohime' (Dw/v)	CMCN NLar XLot
	- 'Goshiki-shidare'	see *A. palmatum* 'Toyama-nishiki'
	- 'Goten-nomura'	XLot
	- 'Grandma Ghost' (M)	CJun XLot
	- 'Green Fingers' (D)	NLar XLot
	- 'Green Flag'	CJun
	- 'Green Globe' (D)	CJun WHwl XLot
	- 'Green Hornet' (D)	CJun XLot
	- 'Green Lace' (D)	CMen LMaj MPkF XLot
	- 'Green Mist' (D)	CJun XLot
	- 'Green Trompenburg' (M)	CJun CMen GBin MPkF XLot
	- 'Greenthumb North Carolina Red' (L) **new**	XLot
§	- 'Hagoromo'	CMac CMen ESMi SCoo WHwl XLot
	- 'Hagoromo-nana' **new**	XLot
	- 'Hakodate-yama' **new**	XLot
	- 'Hama-hime-yatsubusa' **new**	XLot
	- 'Hamano-maru'	XLot
	- 'Hamaotome' (A) **new**	WHwl
	- 'Hanabi-no-mai' (M/v) **new**	XLot
	- 'Hana-matoi'[PBR] (v)	CMCN MPkF XLot
	- 'Hanami-nishiki' (Dw)	CMen MPkF XLot
	- 'Hanzel' (D)	NLar XLot
	- 'Happy Corallinum' (A)	CJun
	- 'Haru-iro'	CJun
	- 'Harusame' (P/v)	MPkF NLar XLot
	- 'Harusame' (Shōwa) **new**	XLot
	- 'Hatsukoi' (v)	XLot
	- 'Hatsushigure'	XLot
	- 'Hazeroino' (v)	CMen MPkF XLot
	- 'Heartbeat' (D)	CDoC CJun LRHS MPkF
	- 'Heffner's Red'	CJun

	- 'Heguri' (M) **new**	XLot
	- 'Heissei-nishiki' (A) **new**	XLot
	- 'Helena'	see *A. shirasawanum* 'Helena'
	- 'Hemelrijt' (M) **new**	XLot
	- var. ***heptalobum***	CMCN
	- 'Heptalobum Elegans Purpureum'	see *A. palmatum* 'Hessei'
	- 'Herbstfeuer' (P)	CJun NLar XLot
§	- 'Hessei' (M)	CEnd CMen MPkF XLot
	- 'Hida-hanabi' (M) **new**	XLot
	- 'Higa Broom' **new**	XLot
	- 'Higasa-yama' (P/v)	CEnd CJun CMCN CMen CWGN ESMi LRHS NBPC XLot
	- 'Hime-ha-uchiwa' (Dw) **new**	XLot
	- 'Hime-yatsufusa' (Dw) **new**	XLot
	- 'Hinata-yama' (A) **new**	XLot
	- 'Hino-o' **new**	XLot
	- 'Hino-tori-nishiki'	CMen WHwl XLot
	- 'Hi-no-tsukasa'	XLot
	- 'Hippi-fin-mo' **new**	XLot
	- 'Hiryu' (P)	XLot
	- 'Hiryu' sport **new**	XLot
	- 'Hōgyoku' (A)	CJun CMCN CMen ESMi LRHS MPkF XLot
	- 'Hokuwa' **new**	XLot
	- 'Hondo-ji' (M) **new**	XLot
	- 'Horizontalis' **new**	XLot
	- 'Hoshi-kuzu' (Dw)	MPkF XLot
	- 'Hosoba-koshimino' **new**	XLot
	- 'Hupp's Dwarf' (Dw)	CJun MPkF XLot
	- 'Hupp's Red Willow'	MPkF NLar WMat XLot
	- 'Hyōtei' **new**	XLot
	- 'Ibo-nishiki' (P)	CMen ESMi MPkF XLot
	- 'Ichigyōji' (A)	CEnd CJun CMen MAsh WHwl XLot
	- 'Ichigyōji-nishiki' **new**	XLot
	- 'Ide-no-sato' **new**	XLot
	- 'Ightham Gold'	SSta
	- 'Iijima-sunago' (M)	CMen MPkF XLot
	- 'Ikandi' (P/v) **new**	XLot
	- 'Ikoma' **new**	XLot
	- 'Ilarian' (D/v) **new**	XLot
	- 'Ima-kumano' (A) **new**	XLot
	- 'Inaba-shidare' (D) ♀H6	Widely available
	- 'Inazuma' (M)	CJun CMCN CMen MPkF SCoo SLau WHwl XLot
	- 'Ingolstadt' **new**	XLot
	- 'Irish Lace'	CJun
	- 'Irish Lace' × ***palmatum*** 'Yasemin'	CJun
	- 'Isobel'	NLar XLot
	- 'Iso-chidori' (Dw)	MPkF WHwl XLot
	- 'Issai-nishiki'	CMen MPkF XLot
*	- 'Issai-nishiki-kawazu'	MPkF
	- 'Itami-nishiki'	XLot
	- 'Jane'	CJun MPkF XLot
	- 'Japanese Sunrise' (P)	CBcs CJun MPkF NLar WHwl WMat XLot
	- 'Jeddeloh Orange' (D)	XLot
	- 'Jerre Schwartz' (Dw)	CDoC CRos EPfP IArd LCro LOPS LRHS MGos MPkF NBPC NLar NRHS WHwl XLot
	- 'Jingo-ji' (M) **new**	XLot
	- 'Jirō-shidare' (P)	CJun MPkF NLar
	- 'JJ'	CJun XLot
	- 'Johnnie's Pink' (P) **new**	MPkF
	- 'Julia D.'	CJun XLot
	- 'Junihitoe'	see *A. shirasawanum* 'Jūnihitoe'
	- 'Kaba' (Dw)	CMen MPkF SPoG XLot
	- 'Kaga-kujaku' (M) **new**	XLot
	- 'Kaga-shidare' **new**	XLot
	- 'Kageori-nishiki' (P) **new**	XLot
	- 'Kagero' (A/v)	MPkF XLot
§	- 'Kagiri-nishiki' (P/v)	CJun CMCN CMac CMen CWGN MPkF NBPC SPer WHwl XLot
	- 'Kamagata' (Dw)	CEnd CJun CMCN CMen ESMi LRHS MAsh MGos MPkF NBPC NLar SCoo WHwl XLot
§	- 'Kandy Kitchen' (Dw)	CMen WHwl XLot
	- 'Kansai-akegarasu' (A) **new**	XLot
	- 'Kansai-shichigosan' (A) **new**	XLot
	- 'Kansai-tsukubane' **new**	XLot
	- 'Kanto-hime-yatsufusa' **new**	XLot
	- 'Karaori-nishiki' (P/v)	CMen MPkF NLar XLot
	- 'Karasu-gawa' (P/v)	CJun CMen CWGN MPkF XLot
	- 'Kasagiyama' (M)	CEnd CJun CMen MPkF XLot
	- 'Kasa-nui' **new**	XLot
	- 'Kasen-nishiki' (P)	CMen MPkF XLot
	- 'Kashima' (Dw)	CEnd CJun CMCN CMen ESMi MBlu MPkF NBPC NLar WHwl XLot
	- 'Katja'	CJun CMen MPkF XLot
	- 'Katsura' (P) ♀H6	Widely available
	- 'Katsura-nishiki'	MPkF XLot
	- 'Kawahara Rose'	MPkF NLar XLot
	- 'Kawahara-no-midori' **new**	XLot
I	- 'Kawaii' (D)	CJun
	- 'Kegon' (M) **new**	XLot
	- 'Ken-bu' (A) **new**	XLot
	- 'Kenko-nishiki'	XLot
	- 'Kenzan' (M) **new**	XLot
	- 'Kibune' (M) **new**	XLot
	- 'Ki-hachijō' (M)	CJun CMCN CMen MPkF SWeb XLot
	- 'Killarney' (M)	CJun XLot
	- 'Kim' (D) **new**	XLot
	- 'Kingsville Variegated' (P/v)	XLot
	- 'Kinky Krinkle' (P)	CJun LRHS NLar XLot
	- 'Kinpai' (v) **new**	XLot
	- 'Kinran' (M)	CJun CMen ESMi MPkF WHwl XLot
	- 'Kinshi' (L) ♀H6	CEnd CJun CMCN CMen EPfP GBin MPkF NLar NOra NOrn SAko WHwl WLov WMat XLot
	- 'Kiri-nishiki' (D)	CJun CMen MPkF NLar XLot
	- 'Ki-shuzan' (M)	CJun WHwl XLot
	- 'Kiyohime' (Dw) ♀H6	CMCN CMen ESMi MPkF NBPC WHwl XLot
	- 'Koba-shōjō' (M)	MPkF XLot
	- 'Ko-chidori'	XLot
	- 'Kogane-nishiki' (P)	CMen NLar WHwl XLot
	- 'Kogane-sakae' (A)	CJun MPkF
	- 'Koko' (M)	WHwl XLot
	- 'Kokobunji-nishiki' (v)	MPkF XLot
	- 'Komachi-hime' (Dw)	CJun CMen MPkF NBPC WLov XLot
	- 'Komon-nishiki' (P/v)	CJun CMen ESMi MPkF WHwl XLot
	- 'Komyo-ji' (A) **new**	XLot
	- 'Korean Gem' (M)	CJun CMen MPkF XLot
	- 'Koriba' (P)	CJun MPkF NLar XLot
	- 'Korin' (A) **new**	XLot
	- 'Koshibori-nishiki' (P)	MPkF XLot
§	- 'Koshimino'	XLot
	- 'Kotohime' (Dw)	CJun CMCN CMen MGos MPkF NLar SCoo SPoG WHwl
	- 'Koto-ito-komachi' (Dw/L)	CJun CMen ESMi MPkF NBPC WHwl XLot

- 'Koto-maru' (Dw) NLar XLot
- 'Koto-no-ito' (L) CMCN LMaj LRHS MAsh MBlu MGos MPkF NLar SAko SGol SPoG WHwl XLot
- 'Koyamadani-nishiki' (M) **new** XLot
- 'Koya-san' (Dw) CMen MPkF XLot
- 'Koyō-ao-shidare' XLot
- 'Koyuki' **new** XLot
- 'Kurabu-yama' (M) CMen MPkF XLot
- 'Kurenai-jishi' (Dw) **new** XLot
- 'Kuro-hime' (Dw) MPkF XLot
- 'Kurui-jishi' (Dw) MPkF XLot
- 'Kyogoku-shidare' (M) **new** XLot
- 'Kyōryū' MPkF XLot
- 'Kyra' CMen MPkF XLot
- 'Lace Lady' (D) NOrn
- 'Lemon Lime Lace' (D) XLot
- 'Limelight' (P) CDoC NLar
§ - 'Linearilobum' (L) CBcs CDoC CMen EPfP MGos MPkF NLar NOra SCoo SLau WHwl WMat XLot
- 'Linearilobum Atropurpureum' (L) WHwl
* - 'Lionheart' (D) CBcs CJun CMen CWGN ESMi MGos MPkF NLar SCoo WHwl XLot
- 'Little Princess' see *A. palmatum* 'Chiyo-hime'
- 'Lolli' (Dw) **new** XLot
- 'Long Man' (M) XLot
- 'Lozita' (P) NLar XLot
- 'Lucky Star' (P) **new** XLot
- 'Lutescens' (A) CMen MPkF XLot
- 'Lydia' MPkF XLot
- 'Mahogany' **new** XLot
- 'Maiko' (P) CMen MPkF XLot
- 'Maillot-nishiki' **new** XLot
- 'Mallet' NLar XLot
- 'Malon' **new** XLot
- 'Mama' (P) CMen XLot
- 'Mama-fu' **new** XLot
- 'Manyō-no-sato' (P/v) LCro LRHS MPkF NLar WHwl
- 'Mapi-no-machi-hime' (Dw) CEnd CJun CMCN CMen CRos LRHS MPkF NHol NRHS XLot
- 'Marakumo' (P) MPkF XLot
- 'Marasaki-yama' MPkF
- 'Mardi Gras' CJun
- 'Margaret' MPkF XLot
- 'Margaret Bee' (A) CJun NLar XLot
- 'Marjan' (M) CJun MPkF NLar XLot
- 'Marlo'PBR (D) CRos LRHS MAsh MGos NLar NRHS WHwl
- 'Masamurasaki' CMen MPkF XLot
- 'Masa-yoshi' (P) **new** XLot
- 'Masukagami' (P/v) CEnd CJun MPkF NLar XLot
- 'Matsu-beni-shidare' **new** XLot
- 'Matsu-ga-e' (P/v) CMen MPkF XLot
- 'Matsukaze' CJun CMCN CMen XLot
- 'Matsu-kubo' (A) **new** XLot
- var. ***matsumurae*** B&SWJ 11100 WCru
- - B&SWJ 11195 WCru
- 'Matsumurae-yano' (M) **new** XLot
- 'Matsuyoi' (A) CJun MPkF XLot
- 'Meihō-nishiki' (A/v) CJun
- 'Melanie' CJun XLot
- 'Mendip Fantasy' **new** CMen
- 'Meoto' CJun XLot
- 'Michiko' **new** XLot
- 'Midori-no-teiboku' (Dw) CJun MPkF XLot
- 'Mika' (P) **new** MPkF
- 'Mikasayama' see *A. japonicum* 'Mikasa-yama'
- 'Mikawa-yatsubusa' (Dw) CJun CMCN CMac CMen EMac ESMi MGos MPkF NLar SAko WHwl XLot
- 'Mikazuki' (M/v) CJun LRHS MPkF XLot
- 'Mila' (M) **new** XLot
- 'Mimaye' CJun
- 'Mini Mondo' MPkF
- 'Minobe-gawa' (M) **new** XLot
- 'Mino-gasa' XLot
- 'Minowa' **new** XLot
- 'Mioun' (D) XLot
- 'Mira' **new** XLot
- 'Mirte' (M) CJun CMen MPkF NLar XLot
- 'Mischa' MPkF XLot
- 'Miss Piggy' **new** XLot
- 'Misty Moon' XLot
- 'Mitsuba-yama' XLot
- 'Mitsu-shika' (M) **new** XLot
- 'Miwa' **new** XLot
- 'Miya' **new** XLot
- 'Mizuho-beni' (P) CJun CMen NLar
- 'Mizu-kuguri' (A) CJun MPkF XLot
- 'Momiji-gawa' (A) **new** XLot
- 'Momoiro-koya-san' (Dw) CJun LRHS MPkF NLar SGol WHwl XLot
- 'Mon Papa' (M) CJun CMen MPkF NLar XLot
- 'Mono-zigawa' XLot
- 'Monzukushi' (A) CJun MPkF XLot
- 'Moonfire' (M) CJun CMCN EMac EPfP MAsh MPkF NLar SGol WHwl XLot
- 'Mori-no-miya' **new** XLot
- 'Moss Gold' (D) **new** XLot
- 'Mufuri' XLot
- 'Mugiwara-nishiki' (L/v) **new** XLot
- 'Mukō-buchi' **new** XLot
- 'Mukō-gasa' **new** XLot
- 'Murakumo-shidare' (M) **new** XLot
- 'Murasaki-hime' (Dw) MPkF
- 'Murasaki-iroha' (A) **new** XLot
- 'Murasaki-kiyohime' (Dw) CEnd CJun CMCN CMen ESMi MPkF WHwl XLot
- 'Murasaki-shikibu' XLot
- 'Murasaki-yama' (M) **new** XLot
- 'Mure-hibari' (M) CJun CMen MPkF XLot
- 'Murogawa' (A) CJun CMen XLot
- 'Musashino' (M) CJun XLot
- 'Mutsu-beni-shidare' (D) NLar XLot
- 'Mystic Jewel' (P) **new** MPkF WHwl
- 'Nagisa-hime' (M) **new** XLot
- 'Nakahara-beni' **new** XLot
- var. ***nakai*** XLot
- 'Nakaoku-gawa' (A) **new** XLot
- 'Nakata' NLar
- 'Na-lisa' **new** XLot
- 'Nanase-gawa' (A) MPkF NLar XLot
- 'Nathan' XLot
- 'Natsu-midori-a' (M) **new** XLot
- 'Nicholsonii' (M) CMen MPkF NLar WHwl XLot
- 'Nigrum' (A) CMCN CTri NOra WHwl
- 'Nimura' (A) **new** XLot
- 'Nishiki-gasane' (P/v) CMen MPkF
§ - 'Nishiki-gawa' (P) CEnd CJun CMen ESMi MPkF WHwl XLot
- 'Nishiki-momiji' (P) CMen

- 'Nishiki-no-murasaki' (A) **new**	XLot
- 'Nishiki-yamato'	XLot
- 'Nomura'	CJun CMen XLot
- 'Nomura-kōyō' (M) **new**	XLot
- 'Nomura-nishiki' (Dw/v)	CMen
- 'Nomura-shidare' (M) **new**	XLot
- 'Nomurishidare' misapplied	see *A. palmatum* 'Shōjō-shidare'
- 'Nose-gawa' (P) **new**	XLot
- 'Noto' (A) **new**	XLot
- 'Novum' (A)	SGol XLot
- 'Nuresagi' (M)	CEnd CJun MPkF XLot
- 'Nyaku-oji' (A) **new**	XLot
- 'Obata' (M) **new**	XLot
- 'Octopus' (D)	CJun MPkF NLar XLot
- 'Ōgi-nagashi' (P/v)	MPkF NLar XLot
- 'Ōgi-no-sen'	XLot
- 'Ogi-tsuma-gaki' (A) **new**	XLot
- 'Ōgon-sarasa' (A)	CJun MPkF XLot
- 'Ogon-shidare' (M) **new**	XLot
- 'Oiso-nishiki' (A) **new**	XLot
- 'O-izu' (M) **new**	XLot
- 'Ojishi' (Dw)	CMen MPkF
- 'Ō-kagami' (P)	CBcs CEnd CJun CMac CMen EPfP ESMi LRHS MAsh MGos MPkF NBPC NLar SCoo WHwl XLot
- 'Okken' **new**	XLot
- 'Okukuji-nishiki' (P)	CJun XLot
- 'Okushimo' (P)	CEnd CJun CMCN CMen ESMi MPkF NBPC NLar SSta WHwl XLot
- 'Olga'	XLot
- 'Olsen's Frosted Strawberry' (P) **new**	MPkF XLot
- 'Omato' (A)	CJun MPkF WHwl XLot
- 'Omure-yama' (M)	CBcs CDoC CEnd CJun CMCN CMen EPfP ESMi MGos MPkF NBPC SCoo SGol SSta WHwl XLot
- 'Orange Dream' (P) ♀H6	Widely available
- 'Orangeola' (D) ♀H6	CJun CMen CSBt CTri LRHS MAsh MGos MPkF NBPC NHol NLar NOrn NRHS SCoo SGol SPoG SSta SWeb WHwl WMat XLot
- 'Oranges and Lemons' (M)	CJun SGol XLot
- 'Oregon Sunset' (M)	CJun MPkF WHwl WMat XLot
- 'Oridono-nishiki' (P/v)	CEnd CJun CMCN CMac CMen CWGN ELan ELon EPfP ESMi IArd MBlu MGos MPkF NBPC SLim SPoG SSta SWeb XLot
- 'Oriental Lace' (D) **new**	XLot
- 'Oriental Mystery'	CJun XLot
- 'Ori-zuru'	XLot
- 'Ori-zuru-momohu' (v) **new**	XLot
- 'Ornatum' (D) ♀H6	CMCN CMen EPfP LMaj LSRN MAsh MGos MPkF MPri MRav NBPC NLar NOrn SCoo WCFE XLot
- 'Ōsakazuki' (A) ♀H6	Widely available
- 'Ōshio-beni' (A)	CJun CMen XLot
- 'Ōshū-beni' (M)	CJun XLot
- 'Ōshū-shidare' (M)	CJun CMen ESMi MPkF XLot
- 'Oto-hime' (Dw)	CJun CMen MPkF
- 'Otome-zakura' (P)	CJun CMen MPkF NBPC WHwl XLot
- 'Otto's Dissectum' (D)	CJun
- 'Pam Tramwick' **new**	XLot
- 'Patricia' **new**	WHwl XLot
- 'Patsy' (M) **new**	XLot
- 'Peaches and Cream' (M/v)	CJun CMen ESMi MPkF NBPC NLar SPer WHwl XLot
- 'Pendulum Julian' (D)	CMCN MPkF SPer XLot
- 'Pévé Chameleon'	MPkF NLar XLot
- 'Pévé Dave'	CRos LRHS LSRN MAsh MPkF NLar NRHS WHwl
- 'Pévé Multicolor'	CJun XLot
- 'Pévé Ollie'PBR	MPkF NLar
- 'Pévé Stanley'	MPkF NLar XLot
- 'Pévé Starfish'	NLar
- 'Phoenix' (P)	CBcs CJun LRHS MGos MPkF NBPC NLar WHwl XLot
- 'Pine Bark Maple'	see *A. palmatum* 'Nishiki-gawa'
- 'Pink Ballerina' (Dw/v)	CJun NLar XLot
- 'Pink Filigree' (D)	CJun CMen
- 'Pink Passion' (v)	LSRN
- 'Pixie' (Dw)	CMen CSBt ESMi LBuc LRHS MGos MPkF NOra SAko SWeb WHwl WMat XLot
- 'Princetown Gold'	CCVT
- 'Pung-kil'	LRHS MPkF SAko WHwl XLot
- 'Purple Ghost' (M)	CJun NLar XLot
- 'Rainbow' (M/v) **new**	XLot
- 'Rainbow Sister' (M/v) **new**	XLot
- 'Raraflora' (D)	CJun
- 'Red Autumn Lace' (D)	CJun XLot
- 'Red Autumn Lace' sport **new**	XLot
- 'Red Bamboo' (L) **new**	XLot
- 'Red Baron' (A)	CJun XLot
- 'Red Cloud' (L)	CJun MPkF XLot
- 'Red Crusader'	XLot
- 'Red Dragon' (D)	CJun CMen CWGN LRHS MAsh MPkF NBPC SAko WHwl XLot
- RED EMPEROR	see *A. palmatum* 'Emperor 1'
- 'Red Falcon' (M)	XLot
- 'Red Feather' (D)	CJun MPkF NLar XLot
- 'Red Filigree Lace' (D)	CEnd CJun CMCN CMen CWGN MPkF
- 'Red Flame'	NLar
- 'Red Flash' (A)	CJun CMen MPkF NLar XLot
- 'Red Jonas'	MPkF NLar XLot
- 'Red Lane' (D) **new**	XLot
- 'Red Pygmy' (L) ♀H6	CBcs CEnd CJun CMCN CMac CMen CRos CWGN EPfP GKin LMil LRHS MAsh MBlu MGos MPri NBPC NHol NLar NRHS SAko SCoo SGol SGsty SPer SPoG SReu SSta SWvt WHwl
- 'Red Select' (D)	MPkF XLot
I - 'Red Sentinel' **new**	XLot
- 'Red Spider' (L)	CJun WHwl XLot
- 'Red Spray' (A) **new**	XLot
- 'Red Wood' (P)	CJun SGol SLau XLot
- 'Redwine'PBR (P)	CRos EPfP LRHS MPkF NLar NRHS WHwl
- 'Relish' (M/v) **new**	XLot
- 'Renjaku-maru'	MPkF XLot
- 'Reticulatum'	see *A. palmatum* 'Shigi-tatsu-sawa'
- 'Reticulatum Como' **new**	XLot
- 'Reticulatum Purple' **new**	XLot
- 'Ribesifolium'	see *A. palmatum* 'Shishi-gashira'
- 'Rilas Red' (D)	NLar XLot
- 'Rising Sun'	CJun XLot
- 'Rokugatsu-en-nishiki' (P)	XLot
- 'Roseomarginatum'	see *A. palmatum* 'Kagiri-nishiki'
- 'Rosman' **new**	XLot
- 'Rough Bark Maple'	see *A. palmatum* 'Arakawa'
- 'Royle' (Dw)	XLot
- 'Ruben' (P) **new**	XLot
- 'Rubrum' (A)	CMen XLot

I	– 'Rubrum Kaiser'	CJun
	– 'Ruby' (P) **new**	MPkF
	– 'Ruby Ridge' (M)	CJun
	– 'Ruby Star'	CJun MPkF XLot
	– 'Rufescens' (P)	MPkF
	– 'Ruslyn-in-the-Pink' (Dw)	NLar
	– 'Russel Grace' (P/v) **new**	XLot
	– 'Ryokū-ryū' (P)	CMen MPkF XLot
	– 'Ryusen'	LRHS MBlu MPkF NLar WHwl
	– 'Ryūsho-in' (A) **new**	XLot
	– 'Ryuzu' (Dw)	CJun MPkF NLar XLot
	– 'Sagara-nishiki' (v)	CEnd CMen ESMi MPkF NBPC XLot
	– 'Saho-mokuran' (A) **new**	XLot
	– 'Sai-ho'	MPkF XLot
	– 'Sainan-in-beni' (A) **new**	XLot
	– 'Saint Jean'	MPkF XLot
	– 'Samidare' (A)	CJun MPkF NLar XLot
	– 'Sandra' (Dw)	CMen MPkF XLot
	– 'Sango-kaku' (P) ♀H6	Widely available
	– 'Sango-kaku Vandermaat' **new**	XLot
	– 'Sango-nishiki' **new**	XLot
	– 'Sanguineum' (P) **new**	XLot
	– 'Saoshika' (A)	CJun CMen MPkF NLar
	– 'Sa-otome' (P)	CMen MPkF XLot
	– 'Satsuki-beni' (M)	CJun CMen ESMi MPkF NBPC WHwl XLot
	– 'Sawa-chidori' (M)	MPkF WHwl XLot
	– 'Sazanami' (M)	CEnd CJun CMen MPkF NBPC WHwl
	– 'Scolopendriifolium'	see *A. palmatum* 'Linearilobum'
	– 'Searle's Variegated' (M/v) **new**	XLot
§	– 'Seigai' (M)	CJun
	– 'Seigen' (Dw)	CEnd CJun CMCN CMen ESMi MBlu MPkF
	– 'Sei-hime' (A) **new**	XLot
	– 'Seiren-ji-gawa' (A) **new**	XLot
	– 'Seiryū' (D) ♀H6	Widely available
	– 'Seiun-kaku' (P)	CJun CMen MPkF WHwl XLot
	– 'Sekimori' (D)	CJun NLar XLot
	– 'Sekka-yatsubusa' (P)	CMCN CMen MPkF NLar WHwl XLot
	– 'Semi-no-hane' (M)	CJun WHwl
	– 'Senkaki'	see *A. palmatum* 'Sango-kaku'
	– 'Septemlobum Elegans'	see *A. palmatum* 'Elegans'
	– 'Septemlobum Purpureum'	see *A. palmatum* 'Hessei'
	– 'Seryo' **new**	XLot
	– 'Sessilifolium' dwarf	see *A. palmatum* 'Hagoromo'
	– 'Sessilifolium' tall	see *A. palmatum* 'Koshimino'
	– 'Seuss's Sister' (v) **new**	XLot
	– 'Seuss's Son' **new**	XLot
	– 'Shaina' (P)	CBcs CDoC CEnd CJun CMen CRos CSBt CWGN EBee EPfP LBuc LCro LMaj LOPS LRHS MBlu MGos MPkF NOrn NRHS SCoo SGol SLim SPoG SRms SWeb WHwl WLov XLot
	– 'Sharon'	XLot
	– 'Sharp's Pygmy' (P)	CJun CMen MPkF NBPC XLot
	– 'Sherwood Elfin' (Dw) **new**	XLot
	– 'Sherwood Flame' (M)	CJun CMen LRHS MAsh MBlu MGos MPkF NLar SCoo WHwl XLot
	– 'Shichihenge' (P)	NLar XLot
	– 'Shidava Gold' (Dw)	CJun EMac MPkF XLot
	– 'Shi-en'	XLot
	– 'Shigarami' (P)	CJun CMen MPkF XLot
	– 'Shigi-no-hoshi' (M)	XLot
§	– 'Shigi-tatsu-sawa' (A/v)	CEnd CJun CMCN CMac CMen LRHS MGos MPkF NBPC NLar NRHS SWeb WHwl
	– 'Shigure-bato' (M)	CJun MPkF NLar XLot
	– 'Shigurezome' (M)	MPkF WHwl XLot
	– 'Shikageori-nishiki' (P)	CJun CMen MPkF XLot
	– 'Shime-no-uchi' (L)	CJun CMen XLot
	– 'Shimofuri-nishiki'	XLot
	– 'Shin Nyo' [PBR]	MBlu
	– 'Shin-chishio' (P)	CJun
	– 'Shin-deshōjō' (P) ♀H6	CBcs CEnd CJun CMCN CMac CMen CRos CSBt CWGN EMac EPfP LMil LRHS LSRN MAsh MGos MPkF MPri NBPC NLar NOrn NRHS SCoo SGol SPer SPoG SSta WHwl XLot
	– 'Shin-koba-shōjō' **new**	XLot
	– 'Shin-koto-hime' (M) **new**	XLot
§	– 'Shinobuga-oka' (L)	CJun CMCN CMen LRHS MPkF NLar SLau SWeb XLot
	– 'Shinonome' (M)	CJun CMen MPkF XLot
	– 'Shirazz' (P/v)	CBcs CDoC CRos CWGN EMac ESMi LMil LRHS LSRN MGos MPkF NBPC NLar NOra NRHS SPer SWvt WHwl WMat XLot
	– 'Shiro-fu-nishiki'	XLot
§	– 'Shish geshira' (P) ♀H6	CJun CMCN CMac CMen ESMi LMaj MBlu MGos MPkF NBPC NLar SCoo SWeb WHwl XLot
	– 'Shishio-hime' (Dw)	MPkF XLot
	– 'Shishi-yatsubusa'	CJun MPkF
	– 'Shiyuka' (P) **new**	XLot
	– 'Shōjō' (A)	CJun CMCN WHwl XLot
	– 'Shōjō-no-mai' (P)	CJun
	– 'Shōjō-nomura' (A)	CEnd CMen MPkF SWeb XLot
§	– 'Shōjō-shidare' (D)	CEnd CJun CMen MPkF NOra WHwl WMat XLot
	– 'Shonei-ki-ji' (P) **new**	XLot
	– 'Shōwa-no-mai' (M) **new**	XLot
	– 'Shu-shidare' (D)	CJun
	– 'Shuzen-ji' (A) **new**	XLot
	– 'Silhouette' [PBR]	LCro LOPS LRHS MPkF WLov
	– 'Sister Ghost' (M)	CJun XLot
	– 'Skeeter's Broom' (Dw)	CBcs CJun CMen CRos CSBt EBee ELan EPfP ESMi IArd LMaj LRHS MAsh MGos MPkF NRHS SCoo SPoG WHwl WLov XLot
*	– 'Sode-nishiki' (P)	CJun MPkF
	– 'Soni' (M) **new**	XLot
	– 'Spreading Star'	NOrn XLot
	– 'Spring Delight' (D)	CJun MPkF SAko
	– 'Spring Surprise' (P/v) **new**	XLot
	– 'Stanley's Jewel' (Dw)	MPkF NLar XLot
	– 'Starfish' [PBR]	LBuc LCro LOPS LRHS MPkF
	– 'Stella Rossa' (D)	CEnd CJun LRHS MPkF MPri NBPC NLar XLot
	– 'Suisei' (Dw/v)	MPkF XLot
	– 'Sumi-nagashi' (M)	CBcs CCVT CDoC CJun CMen CRos ESMi LRHS MAsh MGos MPkF NBPC NLar NOra NOrn NRHS SCoo SLau WMat XLot
	– 'Sumi-shidare' (D)	NLar XLot
I	– 'Summer Gold' (P)	CJun CRos LRHS MPkF NLar NRHS SAko SWvt XLot
	– 'Sunset' (D)	CJun MPkF XLot
	– 'Sunshine' (D)	MPkF XLot
	– 'Super Nigrum' (D) **new**	XLot
	– 'Super Ruby' (L)	NLar XLot
	– 'Susan'	MPkF XLot

- 'Syo-ryo' **new**	XLot
- 'Taima' (A) **new**	XLot
- 'Taimin' (A) **new**	XLot
- 'Taiyō-nishiki' (P)	XLot
- 'Takao' (P)	CMen XLot
- 'Takao-beni' (A) **new**	XLot
- 'Takao-nomura' (A) **new**	XLot
- 'Takao-zome' (A) **new**	XLot
- 'Takara-yama' (M) **new**	XLot
- 'Takatori' (A) **new**	XLot
- 'Tama-hime' (Dw)	CJun CMen ESMi MPkF WHwl
- 'Tamukeyama' (D)	CBcs CJun CMCN CMen ELan IDee LBuc LRHS MAsh MGos MPkF NBPC NLar NOra NOrn SAko SCoo SGol SLau WHwl WMat XLot
- 'Tana' (A)	CJun CMCN CMen MPkF XLot
- 'Tanabata' (M) **new**	XLot
- 'Tarō-yama' (Dw)	CJun MPkF XLot
- 'Tatsuta'	CMen MPkF XLot
- 'Tatsuta-gire' (M) **new**	XLot
- 'Taylor'PBR (P/v)	CEnd CRos CWGN EPfP LRHS LSRN MAsh MGos MPkF MPri NLar NRHS SCoo SPoG
- 'Tayo-nishiki' (M) **new**	XLot
- 'Tedori-gawa' (M) **new**	XLot
- 'Tennyo-no-hoshi' (P)	CMen ESMi MPkF NBPC NLar WHwl XLot
- 'Terinha' (M) **new**	XLot
- 'Tess' **new**	XLot
- 'The Bishop' (A)	NLar XLot
- 'Tiger Rose' (M)	CJun XLot
- 'Tiny Leaf' (Dw) **new**	XLot
- 'Tiny Tim'	CJun XLot
- 'Tirza' **new**	XLot
- 'Tobiosho' (P)	CJun
- 'Tōhoku Shichi-henge'	XLot
- 'Toyama' (D) **new**	XLot
§ - 'Toyama-nishiki' (Dw/v)	CJun CMCN CMen CWGN ESMi MPkF NBPC XLot
- 'Trompenburg' (M) 🏆H6	Widely available
- 'Tsuchigumo' (P)	CJun CMen MPkF NLar XLot
- 'Tsukubane' (A)	WHwl
- 'Tsukuma-no'	MPkF XLot
- 'Tsukushigata' (A)	MPkF
- 'Tsuma-gaki' (A)	CJun CMCN CMen LRHS MGos MPkF NLar XLot
- 'Tsuri-nishiki' (M)	CJun CMen MPkF XLot
- 'Tsuru-no-mai' (P) **new**	XLot
- 'Twombly's Red Sentinel'	CJun MBlu MPkF NLar
- 'Ueno-homare' (P)	CMen NBPC XLot
- 'Ueno-yama'	CBcs CJun LRHS SPer
- 'Uki-gumo' (P/v)	CBcs CEnd CJun CMCN CMac CMen ESMi MGos MPkF NBPC NHol SCoo SPer SPoG SSta XLot
- 'Umegae' (A)	CJun
- 'Uncle Ghost' (M)	CJun
- 'Uncle Red' (P) **new**	XLot
- 'Une-bi' (M) **new**	XLot
- 'Ushi-no-tsume' (P) **new**	XLot
- 'Usu-midori'	CJun
- 'Uta-hime' **new**	XLot
- 'Utsu-beni-shidare' **new**	XLot
- 'Utsu-semi' (A)	CJun MPkF WHwl XLot
- 'Van der Akker'	CJun XLot
- 'Van der Maat' (D)	XLot
- 'Vanderhoss Red' (M)	XLot
- 'Vens Red'	XLot
- 'Versicolor' (P/v)	CMCN MPkF XLot
- 'Vic Broom'	XLot
- 'Vic Pink' (D)	CJun XLot
- 'Victoria'	SGol
- 'Villa Taranto' (L) 🏆H6	CEnd CJun CMCN CMen EPfP ESMi MBlu MGos MPkF NBPC NLar NOra SCoo SGol WMat XLot
- 'Volubile' (P)	CMCN CMen ESMi MPkF WHwl XLot
- 'Wabito' (P)	CJun CMen MPkF XLot
- 'Wajima-suo' (A) **new**	XLot
- 'Waka-midori'	CMen WHwl XLot
- 'Waka-momiji' (P/v)	CJun XLot
- 'Waka-tsuki' **new**	XLot
- 'Wakehurst Pink' (M/v)	CMCN NOra NOrn XLot
- 'Waterfall' (D)	CJun CMCN
- 'Watnong' (D)	CJun MPkF XLot
- 'Wendy' (P)	CJun CMen MPkF NLar WHwl XLot
- 'Werner's Pagoda' (P) **new**	XLot
- 'Westonbirt Orange' (A)	NOrn WHwl XLot
- 'Westonbirt Red' (M)	NOrn XLot
- 'Wetumpka Red'	CJun NLar XLot
- 'White Butterfly' (P/v) **new**	XLot
- 'Whitney Red' (A)	CMen XLot
- 'Wild Goose' (P)	MAsh MPkF XLot
- 'Will's Devine'	CJun MPkF XLot
- 'Wilson's Pink Dwarf' (Dw)	CEnd CJun CMen CRos LRHS MAsh MGos MPkF NBPC NLar NRHS SAko SCoo SPoG WFar
- 'Winter Flame' (P)	CJun LRHS MPkF NHol NOrn WHwl XLot
- 'Wou-nishiki'	CMCN CMen MPkF NBPC
- 'Yadawara' (A) **new**	XLot
- 'Yama-kujaku' (M) **new**	XLot
- 'Yama-mura' (A) **new**	XLot
- 'Yamanba' (M) **new**	XLot
- 'Yama-no-ha' **new**	XLot
- 'Yamato-aoyagi' (P) **new**	XLot
- 'Yamato-gire' (M) **new**	XLot
- 'Yamato-koshimino' (M) **new**	XLot
- 'Yamato-koto-no-ito' (A) **new**	XLot
- 'Yamato-shidare' (M) **new**	XLot
- 'Yamato-zoe' **new**	XLot
- 'Yamato-zuta' (A) **new**	XLot
- 'Yana-gawa'	CMen XLot
- 'Yasaka' (A) **new**	XLot
- 'Yasemin' (M)	CBcs CDoC CJun CMen CWGN LRHS MPkF NBPC NLar NOrn XLot
- 'Yashio'	MPkF XLot
- 'Yata-yama' (M) **new**	XLot
- 'Yatsubusa' (Dw)	MPkF XLot
- 'Yellow Bird' (A) **new**	XLot
- 'Yezo-nishiki' (A/v)	CMen MBlu MPkF WHwl XLot
- 'Yoshimizu' (M) **new**	XLot
- 'Yūba-e' (M)	MPkF NOra NOrn XLot
- 'Yūgure' (M)	MPkF XLot
- 'Yuri-hime' (Dw)	MPkF
- 'Yūzen-momiji' (P) **new**	XLot
- 'Yū-fuji'	XLot
- 'Zaaling' (D)	CMen WHwl
- 'Zoë' (Dw)	MPkF NLar XLot
- 'Zokumei' (P) **new**	XLot
papilio	see *A. caudatum*
pauciflorum 'Blaze Away'	CJun
pectinatum	GKev MMuc WPGP
- GWJ 9354	WCru
- 'Mozart'	CBcs CJun MBlu NLar SSta
- subsp. ***pectinatum*** B&SWJ 8270 **new**	EBee

	- - HWJ 569	WCru
	- - HWJ 944	WCru
	pensylvanicum	CBcs CLnd CMCN CTho EBee ECrN EPfP MGos MMuc MRav SCob SPtp SSta
	- 'Erythrocladum'	CBcs CEnd CJun CMCN EPfP MAsh MGos NHol NLar NOrn
	pentaphyllum	CMCN WPGP
§	***pictum***	CMCN
	- B&SWJ 12737	WCru
	- 'Mallet Court'	CMCN
	- subsp. ***okamotoanum***	CMCN
	- - B&SWJ 12623	WCru
	- subsp. ***pictum*** f. ***ambiguum*** B&SWJ 8806	WCru
	- 'Shufu-nishiki'	CMCN
	platanoides	CBcs CBrac CCVT CLnd CMCN CSBt CTri EPfP GQue LMaj MGos MMuc MSwo NOrn SCob SEWo SPer SavN WMat WMou WTSh
	- 'Columnare'	CLnd CMCN LMaj SCob SCoo
	- 'Crimson King' 🏆H7	Widely available
	- 'Crimson Sentry'	CArg CCVT CEnd CLnd CMac CTri EBee ELan LCro LMaj LSRN MAsh MGos MRav NOrn SGol SGsty SPer SWvt
	- 'Deborah'	CLnd CTho EPfP LMaj SCob SPer
	- 'Dissectum'	IArd
	- 'Drummondii' (v)	Widely available
	- 'Emerald Queen'	LMaj SCob
§	- 'Globosum'	CMCN ECrN LMaj NLar SCob SGsty SWvt
	- 'Laciniatum'	CMCN EBtc GBin XLot
	- PRINCETON GOLD ('Prigo'[PBR]) 🏆H7	CBcs CCVT CEnd CLnd CTho EBee ECrN ELan GQue LBuc MAsh MGos NOra NOrn SCob SCoo SEWo SLim SPer SPoG SWvt WMat
	- 'Royal Red'	EPfP LMaj MRav NLar SCoo SEWo
	- 'Schwedleri' 🏆H7	CMCN WTSh
	- SENSATION	see *A. platanoides* 'Ulmers Sensation'
	- subsp. ***turkestanicum***	CMCN SSta
	- 'Ulmers Select'	WMat
§	- 'Ulmers Sensation'[PBR] (v)	SPoG
	pseudoplatanus	CBcs CBrac CCVT CLnd CMCN CTri ECrN ELan MGos SCob SGol SPer SavN WMou WTSh
§	- 'Atropurpureum'	SCob SEND SEWo
	- 'Brilliantissimum' 🏆H7	Widely available
	- f. ***erythrocarpum*** 'Erythrocarpum'	CMac
	- 'Prinz Handjéry'	CEnd CMCN CTri MGos NHol NLar NOra NOrn SGol WMat
	- 'Spaethii' misapplied	see *A. pseudoplatanus* 'Atropurpureum'
	- f. ***variegatum*** 'Esk Sunset' (v)	CLnd EBee ELan LSRN MGos SPer SPoG
	- - 'Leopoldii' ambig. (v)	CCVT CMCN ECrN SEND SWvt
	- - 'Leopoldii' Vervaene (v)	SPer
	- - 'Simon-Louis Frères' (v)	CBcs CCVT CDoC CLnd CMCN ECrN MAsh MGos NLar NOrn SPer SWvt WMat
	- 'Worley'	CMCN CMac MRav SLim SPer
	pseudosieboldianum	CMCN LRHS MBlu MPkF
	- B&SWJ 8468	WCru
	- B&SWJ 8746	WCru
	- B&SWJ 8769	WCru
	- var. ***microsieboldianum*** B&SWJ 8766	WCru
	- subsp. ***takesimense***	MBlu
	- - B&SWJ 8500	WCru
	- - B&SWJ 8540	WCru
	'Red Flamingo' (v)	CBcs CJun CMac CRos EPfP LRHS MAsh MBlu MGos MPkF NLar NOra SGol SGsty SPoG WMat
	'Red Wings' (*A. palmatum* hybrid)	CJun XLot
	reticulatum	see *A. laevigatum* var. *reticulatum*
	rubescens CWJ 12438	WCru
	- NMWJ 14525	WCru
	rubrum	CAgr CBcs CLnd CMCN CSBt CTri EBee ECrN ELan EPfP LCro LMaj LOPS MGos MMuc SCoo SEWo SGol SGsty WCFE WMat WTSh
	- 'Autumn Flame'	CCVT WHCr WMou
	- 'Autumn Spire'	CJun
	- 'Brandywine'	CEnd CJun CMac CTho EPfP LMaj LRHS LSRN MAsh MBlu NLar NOra SCoo SPoG WHwl WMat
	- 'Embers'	CJun
	- FAIRVIEW FLAME	see *A. rubrum* 'Pete's Fairview'
	- 'Firedance'	CJun
	- 'Florida Flame'	CMCN
	- 'Joseph'	NLar
	- 'New World'	SCoo
	- 'October Glory' 🏆H6	Widely available
§	- 'Pete's Fairview'	CJun SPer
	- 'Red King'	CJun
	- 'Red Rocket'	XLot
	- RED SUNSET ('Franksred') 🏆H6	CBcs CEnd CMCN CTho EBee EMil EPfP LMaj NLar SCoo SGol SLim SPer SPoG WHwl
	- 'Scanlon'	CBcs CEnd CJun CMCN CTho EBee EPfP LMaj LRHS NOra SLim SPer WHCr
	- 'Schlesingeri'	CEnd CJun CMac EPfP SPer
I	- 'Sekka'	MBlu
	- 'Somerset'	CJun CTho SCoo WMat
	- SUMMER RED ('Hosr')	EBee EPfP LRHS SCoo SMad WMat
	- 'Sun Valley'	CJun CMac CTho MAsh NOra NOrn WMat
	- 'Tilford'	CJun SSta
§	***rufinerve***	CBcs CLnd CMCN CTho CTri EBee ECrN EPfP EWTr MMuc NLar NOra NOrn SCob SCoo SGol SPtp SSta SWvt WLov WMat WTSh
	- 'Albolimbatum' (v)	CJun CMCN SSta
	- 'Erythrocladum'	CJun MBlu
	- 'Ko-fuji-nishiki'	SSta
I	- 'Sunshine'	SSta
	- 'Winter Gold'	CJun NLar SSta
	- 'Yellow Ribbon'	LRHS
§	***saccharinum***	CBcs CCVT CLnd CMCN CTri EBee ECrN ELan EPfP MGos MMuc NOra SCoo SGol SPer WMat WTSh
	- 'Born's Gracious'	CJun
	- 'Fastigiatum'	see *A. saccharinum* 'Pyramidale'
	- f. ***laciniatum***	EBee MBlu MMuc SGol SPer
	- - 'Laciniatum Wieri'	CMCN NLar SCob SGol
	- 'Lutescens'	CTho
§	- 'Pyramidale'	CLnd LMaj SPer
	saccharum	CAgr CBcs CLnd CMCN CTho EBee ECrN EPfP IArd LMaj LRHS MBlu WTSh
	- 'Fiddlers Creek'	CJun
§	- subsp. ***grandidentatum***	CMCN
§	***sempervirens***	EBee EPfP IArd LEdu SEND
	'Sensu'	CJun MPkF WHwl XLot
	'Serendipity'	SSta

serrulatum	CMCN
- CWJ 12437	WCru
- hybrid NMWJ 14548	WCru
shirasawanum	CMCN LRHS SavN
§ - 'Aureum' ♀H6	Widely available
- 'Autumn Moon'	CBcs CJun CMCN CMen CWGN EMac EPfP IDee MAsh MPkF NBPC NLar NOra SCoo SGol SPer SPoG WHwl WMat XLot
§ - 'Ezo-no-momiji'	CMen MPkF WHwl XLot
- 'Gloria'	CJun MPkF WHwl XLot
- 'Green Snow Flake'	MPkF XLot
§ - 'Helena'	WHwl
- 'Itami-momiji' **new**	XLot
- 'Johin'	MPkF XLot
- 'Jordan'	CBcs CDoC CEnd CMCN CMac CRos CWGN EBee EPfP IArd LBuc LMil LRHS LSRN MAsh MGos MPkF NLar NRHS SPoG SWvt WHwl XLot
§ - 'Jūnihitoe'	XLot
- 'Kakure-gasa'	CJun XLot
- 'Lovett'	CJun
- 'Luna' **new**	XLot
§ - 'Microphyllum'	NLar XLot
- 'Momiji-gasa' **new**	XLot
- MOONRISE ('Munn 001'PBR)	LCro LOPS LRHS MPkF NLar WHwl XLot
- 'Mr Sun'	CJun
- 'Nikkō' **new**	XLot
§ - 'Ogurayama'	CJun CMen WHwl XLot
- 'Ookisa' **new**	XLot
- 'Palmatifolium'	CJun
- 'Red Dawn'	CJun MPkF WHwl XLot
- 'Sonya Marie' (v) **new**	MPkF XLot
- 'Susanne'	CJun CMen NLar
- var. ***tenuifolium***	XLot
- - B&SWJ 11073	WCru
- 'Tsuki-kage-nishiki' (v) **new**	XLot
sieboldianum ♀H6	CMCN CMen CTho CTri ECrN MAsh MBlu MMuc NOra SEND SGol
- B&SWJ 10849	WCru
- B&SWJ 11049	WCru
- B&SWJ 11090	WCru
- 'Ayai-gasa' **new**	XLot
- 'Isis'	XLot
- 'Kinugasayama'	XLot
- 'Miyama-nishiki'	XLot
* - f. ***pilosum*** **new**	XLot
- 'Sode-no-uchi'	CJun CMen
- var. ***tsushimense*** B&SWJ 10962	WCru
sikkimense B&SWJ 11689	WCru
- B&SWJ 11703	WCru
- FMWJ 13166 from northern Vietnam	WCru
- WJC 13674 from Sikkim	WCru
- WWJ 11601	WCru
- WWJ 11613	WCru
- WWJ 11853	WCru
'Silver Cardinal' (v)	CEnd CJun CMCN EPfP MBlu MGos NLar SSta
'Silver Vein'	see *A.* × *conspicuum* 'Silver Vein'
sinense	CMCN
- 'Rogou' **new**	CJun
spicatum	CMCN NLar
§ ***sterculiaceum***	EBee
- PAB 13.135	LEdu
- subsp. ***franchetii***	CMCN
- cf. subsp. ***franchetii***	WPGP
- subsp. ***sterculiaceum*** NJM 13.087	WPGP
tataricum	CMCN SPtp
§ - subsp. ***ginnala***	CArg CBcs CMCN CTri ECrN MBlu MGos NLar SGol SPer
- - 'Flame'	CCVT CJun EBee ECrN EPfP MGos MMuc SGbt SPoG
- subsp. ***semenovii***	SPtp WLov
tegmentosum ♀H5	CJun CMCN EPfP MBlu SMad SSta
- 'Cobhay Ghost'	CJun
- subsp. ***glaucorufinerve***	see *A. rufinerve*
tonkinense subsp. ***liquidambarifolium*** DJHV 06173	WCru
triflorum ♀H7	CBcs CCVT CJun CMCN EBee EPfP LMaj LRHS MBlu NLar NOra WMat WMou
truncatum	MPkF
- 'Akikaze-nishiki' (v)	MPkF
tschonoskii	GKin
- subsp. ***koreanum***	MPkF
- - B&SWJ 12596	WCru
- - B&SWJ 12603	WCru
turkestanicum from Kyrgyzstan	WPGP
velutinum	CMCN
villosum	see *A. sterculiaceum*
wardii	WPGP
'White Tigress'	CBcs CJun EBee EPfP NLar SSta WMat
× ***zoeschense***	CMCN MPkF
- 'Annae'	MMuc

Aceriphyllum see *Mukdenia*

Achillea (*Asteraceae*)

ageratifolia ♀H5	ELan GWyn NGdn SRms WSpi XLum
§ ***ageratum***	CBod CCBP CLau ENfk EWhm GPoy GQue LEdu MHer MNHC SEdi SRms WFar WGwG WJek WTre XLum
'Alabaster'	EBee LRHS NRHS WSpi
ANTHEA ('Anblo')	CDoC EBee ECtt LRHS LSRN MBriF MCot MRav NRHS SHar SRms SWvt WFar
§ 'Apfelblüte' (Galaxy Series)	CAby CBod EBee ECha ECtt ECul ELan EPed EPfP LRHS LSRN MMuc MRav NGdn NHol NQui NRHS NSti SEND SPer SRms WCAu WFar XSen
APPLEBLOSSOM	see *A.* 'Apfelblüte'
'Apricot Beauty'	ECul WSpi
'Apricot Delight' (Tutti Frutti Series)	CRos EMor LRHS NRHS WTor
'Apricot Seduction' (Seduction Series)	ECul WFar
argentea misapplied	see *A. clavennae*, *A. umbellata*
argentea Lamarck	see *Tanacetum argenteum*
argentea ambig.	ELan
'Bahama'	EPPr GQue
'Belle Epoque'	WSpi XSen
biebersteinii	XLum
'Breckland Cream'	EPed
'Breckland Ruby'	EWes
'Carmina Burana'	CMea
chrysocoma 'Grandiflora'	ECha MBel MMuc NGdn WBrk WFar

§	***clavennae***	GKev NBir SPlb SRms WAbe
	clypeolata Sibth. & Sm.	EHyd SPhx SPlb SRms XLum
	coarctata	NBir XSen
	Colorado Group	CBod EHyd LRHS NRHS
	'Coronation Gold' ℽH7	CBod CRos EBee ECtt ECul ELan EPed EPfP LRHS MAsh MHol MRav MWat NChi NDov NRHS SCob SGbt SPer SRms SWvt WCAu WCot WSpi XLum XSen
	'Credo' ℽH7	Widely available
	crithmifolia	XLum XSen
	decolorans	see *A. ageratum*
	(Desert Eve Series) DESERT EVE CREAM ('Deseve')	ECul
	- DESERT EVE DEEP ROSE ('Desderos')	EBee ECul
	- DESERT EVE LIGHT YELLOW	ECul SRms
	- DESERT EVE RED ('Desred'PBR)	EBee ECul
	- DESERT EVE YELLOW ('Desyel'PBR)	EBee
	falcata	GKev
§	'Fanal'	CAby CBod CCBP CRos CWCL EBee ECha ECtt ECul ELan EMor EPed EPfP GWyn LRHS MAsh MRav MTis NBPC NBir NHol NRHS SGbt SPer SWvt WCAu
	'Faust'	CDor ELon
	'Feuerland'	EBee ECha ECtt ELon EPfP LRHS MRav NBir NDov NGdn NRHS SAko SPer SPoG WFar WSpi XSen
	filipendulina 'Cloth of Gold' ℽH7	Widely available
	- 'Gold Plate' ℽH7	Widely available
	- 'Hymne'	EBee
	- 'Parker's Variety' ℽH7	CBod EBee NBre XLum XSen
	'Fleur van Zonneveld'	NDov WGoo
	FLOWERS OF SULPHUR	see *A.* 'Schwefelblüte'
	(Forncett Series) 'Forncett Beauty'	SWvt
	- 'Forncett Bride'	EBee
	- 'Forncett Citrus'	ECtt WFar
	- 'Forncett Fletton'	CWld ECtt EPed EPfP MBel MCot MRav NDov NGdn NHol WFar
	- 'Forncett Ivory'	MAvo
	'Gloria Jean'	SHar
	'Golden Fleece'	GWyn
	grandifolia misapplied	see *Tanacetum macrophyllum* (Waldst. & Kit.) Sch.Bip.
§	***grandifolia*** Friv.	CBod CSam EMor MArl MHol NBro WFar WOld
	'Great Expectations'	see *A.* 'Hoffnung'
	'Heidi' ℽH7	MRav XSen
	'Heinrich Vogeler'	LPla MHol NLar
	'Hella Glashoff' ℽH7	CMea CRos EBee LRHS NLar NRHS SPhx WGoo
§	'Hoffnung'	CWCL NLar NRHS
	× ***huteri***	EDAr MMuc NGdn NHpl NRya SEND SRms SWvt WCav WFar
	'Inca Gold'	CBcs CSam ECha ECtt EPed LRHS MCot MRav MSpe NDov NHol NRHS NSti SPer SPhx SRms SWvt WFar WGwG WHoo WSpi
	× ***kellereri***	XLum XSen
	'King Alfred'	CMea NCou NHpl SRms
	× ***kolbiana***	EWes SRms WFar XSen
§	'Lachsschönheit' (Galaxy Series) ℽH7	CAby CDor CRos CWCL EBee ECha ECtt ELan EPed EPfP GMaP LRHS MBNS MCot MRav NBir NDov NHol NLar NRHS NSti SCob SPer SRms WCAu WFar
	× ***lewisii*** 'King Edward' ℽH5	EBou EDAr NBir SRms WAbe WFar WIce
	'Lucky Break' ℽH7	EBee ECha ECtt EWes LEdu MAvo MHol NBPC WBrk WCot
	macrophylla	MBNS
	'Marie Ann'	CWCL LSRN
	'Marmalade'	CDor MRav NDov
	'Martina' ℽH7	CAby CSam ECtt LRHS MBNS MBel MCot MRav NDov NGdn NHol NRHS WBrk WCot WGwG WHoo
	'McVities'	CWCL
	millefolium	CCBP CHab ENfk GPoy GQue LCro LOPS MBow MNHC NAts NGrd NMir SRms SVic WHer WJek WOut WSFF WSpi WWild XLum
	- 'Bloodstone'	ECtt EWes MRav
	- 'Carla Hussey'	WFar
	- 'Cassis'	CBod CSam CSpe ECul EHyd EPfP LRHS MCot NChi NGBl NLar NRHS WBor WFar
§	- 'Cerise Queen'	Widely available
	- 'Chamois'	MNrw
	- 'Cherry King'	NBir
	- 'Circus'	XLum
	- 'Dark Lilac Beauty'	CWCL
	- KIRSCHKÖNIGIN	see *A. millefolium* 'Cerise Queen'
	- 'Lansdorferglut' ℽH7	CRos EBee LRHS NDov NRHS SPhx
	- 'Laura'	CWGN ECtt EPfP MNrw NBPC WFar
	- 'Lavender Beauty'	see *A. millefolium* 'Lilac Beauty'
§	- 'Lilac Beauty'	CBod ECha ELon EPfP EWTr GBin GMaP GWyn LCro LOPS LRHS LSRN MMuc MRav NBPC NBir NHol NLar SBut SCob SEND SRms WCAu WCav WFar WSpi XLum
*	- 'Lilac Queen'	MArl
	- 'Little Suzie'	CWGN ECtt WFar
	- (New Vintage Series) NEW VINTAGE LILAC	see *A. millefolium* NEW VINTAGE VIOLET
	- - NEW VINTAGE RED ('Balvinred')	CBod LRHS MHol SCob WHil
	- - NEW VINTAGE ROSE ('Balvinrose')	CBod LRHS SCob
§	- - NEW VINTAGE VIOLET ('Balvinviolet')	LRHS MHol SCob
	- - NEW VINTAGE WHITE ('Balvinwite')	CBod SCob
	- 'Old Brocade'	EShb NDov
	- Pastel Shades	WFar
	- 'Peggy Sue'	CWGN ECtt EWes IPot WFar
	- 'Pomegranate' (Tutti Frutti Series)	CRos CWGN ECul IPot LCro LOPS LRHS LSou MNrw NLar NRHS SHar WCot WHil WTor XLum
	- 'Pretty Woman'	CWGN EBee
	- 'Rainbow Tricolor' (Rainbow Series) **new**	LSou
	- 'Raspberry Ripple'	ECul GBin GWyn
	- 'Red Beauty'	CWCL EBee EPfP MBNS MBel SRms XLum
	- 'Red Velvet' ℽH7	Widely available
	- 'Rose Madder'	CBod CWCL ECtt EPfP EWTr GMaP LRHS MCot MHol MMuc MNrw MPie NBPC NBir NChi NGdn NHol NLar NRHS NSti SEND SPer SPoG SWvt WCot WFar WHoo WSpi XLum
	- 'Ruby Port'	WFar
	- 'Salmon Queen'	NHol WFar

	- 'Sammetriese'	EBee ELon MNrw
	- 'Schneetaler'	MAvo MNrw
	- 'Sue's Pink'	CSam
	- (Summer Fruits Series) 'Summer Fruits Carmine'	EBee ELan LRHS
	- - 'Summer Fruits Lemon'	EBee ELan EMor LRHS NRHS WFar WSpi
	- - 'Summer Fruits Salmon'	EBee ELan LRHS WFar
	- 'Summertime'	WFar
	- 'White Beauty'	ECul WCAu
	- 'Wonderful Wampee'	EBee EHyd EWes LRHS MNrw NRHS SCob SPoG
	'Mondpagode' Υ^{H7}	ECtt EPfP LRHS MBNS MCot MRav NGdn SWvt
*	'Moonbeam'	SEND
	'Moonshine' Υ^{H7}	Widely available
	'Moonwalker'	CBod EPfP WCot XLum
	nobilis	XSen
	- subsp. ***neilreichii***	CBod ECha MBNS MMuc NSti SEND SWvt WFar WGwG
*	***odilis***	EWTr
	'Paprika' (Galaxy Series)	Widely available
	'Petra'	EBee MMrt MNrw NLar XLum
	pindicola subsp. ***integrifolia***	EWes
	'Pink Grapefruit' (Tutti Frutti Series)	CRos EMor GWyn IPot LRHS MAvo NLar NRHS WCAu
	'Pretty Belinda'	CDor CRos EBee ECtt EHyd EPfP EWhm GWyn LRHS LSRN MBel MSpe NBPC NLar NRHS NSti SAko SCob SPoG SRms WCAu WFar
	'Prospero'	WCot
	ptarmica	CBod EMor MHer NAts NMir SRms XLum
*	- 'Ballerina'	NDov
	- 'Nana Compacta'	EHyd LRHS NBir SPlb SPoG WFar
	- 'Noblessa'	MHol
	- 'Perry's White' (d)	CBre ECha MNrw WCot
	- The Pearl Group seed-raised (d)	CTri ECul ELan GWyn MMuc SBut SGbt SPlb WFar
	- - 'Boule de Neige' (clonal) (d)	ELan MRav NPer SHar SPer WFar WSpi XLum
	- - 'The Pearl' (clonal) (d)	CBod CMac CRos CSBt EBee ECha EHyd EPfP GQue LCro LPot LRHS LSRN MBel MRav MWat NBid NBir NBro NLar NRHS SCob SRms WBor WBrk WCAu WCot WFar WHil
	pyrenaica	XLum
	'Rougham Salmon'	CDor
	'Ruby Wine'	SHar WFar
	'Safran'	EBee LRHS XLum
	salicifolia 'Silver Spray'	NLar SDix
	'Sally'	EPPr
	SALMON BEAUTY	see *A.* 'Lachsschönheit'
	'Sandra Wagg'	ECtt
	'Sandstone'	see *A.* 'Wesersandstein'
	'Saucy Seduction' (Seduction Series)	CWCL ELan EMor MHol MTis NBid NLar SCob
	'Saucy Sensation' **new**	ECul SCob
§	'Schwefelblüte'	MRav NBir
	'Schwellenburg'	NBre WCot WFar
	sibirica subsp. ***camschatica*** 'Love Parade'	CBod EBee EWTr MHol MNrw NLar SBut SGbt SPer WFar XLum
	'Stephanie'	EWes LSRN
	SUMMER BERRIES (mixed)	CRos ECul EHyd LPot LRHS NGrd NRHS WFar WHil
	Summer Pastels Group	CBod EHyd EPfP GKev LRHS NGrd NLar NRHS SRms WFar XLum
	- 'Peachy Seduction'^{PBR} (Seduction Series)	MCot NLar WCAu
	- 'Strawberry Seduction' (Seduction Series)	ECtt NLar
	'Summerwine' Υ^{H7}	Widely available
	'Sunbeam'	SHar
	'Sunny Seduction' (Seduction Series)	ECtt ELon MTis NLar
I	'Taygetea'	ELan GWyn LCro LOPS MBNS SPer SPoG SRkn WCAu WCot WFar WHil WSpi XLum
	'Terracotta'	Widely available
	'The Beacon'	see *A.* 'Fanal'
	'Tissington Old Rose'	MNrw
	tomentosa Υ^{H5}	CTri EBou ECha GPSL LCro LOPS WFar
§	- 'Aurea'	NBro XLum
	- 'Goldie'	SWvt WFar
	- 'Maynard's Gold'	see *A. tomentosa* 'Aurea'
	'Tri-colour'	MBNS MBel NGdn
§	***umbellata***	LCro LOPS NSla XSen
	'W.B. Childs'	ELan MNrw MRav NDov SHar
	'Walther Funcke'	Widely available
§	'Wesersandstein'	CWCL GMaP IPot MNrw NBir NLar SGbt
	'Wilczekii'	SRms
	'Yellowstone'	EWes

× *Achimenantha* (*Gesneriaceae*)

'Aries'	WDib
'Cool Inferno'	WDib
'Golden Jubilee'	WDib
'Himalayan Sunrise'	WDib
'Inferno' Υ^{H1b}	WDib
'Pisces'	WDib
'Texas Blue Bayou'	WDib

Achimenes (*Gesneriaceae*)

'Addano'	WDib
admirabilis	WDib
'Ambroise Verschaffelt' Υ^{H1c}	EShb SDir WDib
'Ami Van Houtte'	WDib
'Apricot Glow'	WDib
'Aquamarine'	WDib
'Aurora Charm'	WDib
'Ballerina'	WDib
'Beautiful Fire'	WDib
'Big Weiss'	WDib
'Blue Sparks'	SDeJ
'Caligula'	WDib
'Cameo Rose'	WDib
'Candy Shop'	WDib
(Cascade Series) 'Cascade Fairy Pink'	WDib
- 'Cascade Fashionable Pink'	WDib
- 'Cascade Rose Red'	WDib
- 'Cascade Violet Night'	WDib
'Cattleya'	SDir
cettoana	WDib
'Charity'	WDib
'Charm'	SDeJ WDib
'Claret'	WDib
'Crackerjack'	WDib
'Crummock Water'	WDib
'Double Picotee Rose' (d)	WDib
'Double Pink Rose' (d)	WDib
erecta	WDib
'Erlkönig'	WDib

'Extravaganza'	WDib
'Firefly'	WDib
'Flamenco'	WDib
'Glory'	WDib
'Golden Butterfly'	WDib
'Harry Williams'	EShb SDir WDib
'Hilda Michelssen' ♀H1c	WDib
'Himalayan Mandarin' (Himalayan Series)	SDir
'Hugues Aufray'	WDib
'Ice Tea'	WDib
'India'	EShb
(Jay Dee Series) 'Jay Dee Coral'	WDib
- 'Jay Dee Large White'	WDib
- 'Jay Dee Pink'	WDib
- 'Jay Dee Purple'	WDib
'Jennifer Goode'	WDib
'Johanna Michelssen'	WDib
'Just Divine'	WDib
'Kim Blue'	WDib
'Lady in Black'	WDib
'Light Lilac'	WDib
'Little Beauty'	WDib
longiflora var. ***alba*** 'Snow Queen' new	SDir
- 'Major'	WDib
'Melon Ice Cream'	WDib
'Menuett'	WDib
mexicana	SDeJ
misera	WDib
'Opal'	WDib
'Orange Delight'	WDib
'Pally'	WDib
'Patens Major'	WDib
'Peach Blossom'	EShb SDeJ WDib
'Peach Glow'	WDib
pedunculata	WDib
'Petite Fadette'	WDib
'Poil de Carotte'	WDib
'Primadonna'	SDeJ WDib
'Pulcherrima'	SDeJ
'Purple King'	WDib
'Purple Queen'	WDib
'Purple Triumph'	WDib
'Queen of Queens'	WDib
'Rai'	WDib
'Rainbow'	WDib
'Rainbow Warrior'	WDib
'Red Hilda Michelssen'	WDib
'Rozi Roza'	WDib
'Santa Claus'	WDib
'Schneewittchen'	WDib
'Serge Saliba'	WDib
'Serge's Fantasy'	WDib
'Show-off'	WDib
'Shy Sun'	WDib
skinneri	WDib
'Snow Princess'	EShb SDeJ
'Stan's Delight' (d) ♀H1c	WDib
'Sterntaler'	WDib
'Sugarland'	WDib
'Sun Wind'	WDib
'Sweet and Sour'	WDib
'Tango'	WDib
'Tarantella'	WDib
'Tetra Himalayan Purple' (Tetra Series)	WDib
'Tiger Eye'	WDib
'Valse Bleu'	WDib
'Violacea Semiplena' (d)	WDib
'Vivid'	WDib
'Weinrot Elfe'	WDib
'Wetterlow's Triumph'	WDib
'Yellow Beauty'	WDib

Achimenes × *Smithiantha*

see × *Achimenantha*

Achlys (*Berberidaceae*)

japonica	WCru
triphylla	SPhx WCru
- B&SWJ 13541	WCru

Achnatherum see *Stipa*

Achyranthes (*Amaranthaceae*)

bidentata var. ***longifolia*** PAB 8037	LEdu

Acidanthera see *Gladiolus*

Aciphylla (*Apiaceae*)

aurea	GKev SPlb
glaucescens	SPlb
montana	CMen
scott-thomsonii	GKev
squarrosa	GKev

Acis (*Amaryllidaceae*)

§	***autumnalis*** ♀H5	CAvo CBor CBro CTri EAJP ECha EDAr EHyd ELan EPot EWes GKev LRHS NBir NHpl NRHS SBrt SMHy SPhx SRms WAbe WFar WHoo WSHC WShi
	- var. ***oporantha***	CMiW CWCL EPri GKev
	- - f. ***dispathacea***	GEdr GKev
	- var. ***pulchella***	CElw
	- 'September Snow'	ELan EPri GKev
	ionica	GKev
I	- subsp. ***vlorensis***	GKev
	nicaeensis	EHyd EPot GKev LRHS NRHS NWad SMHy WAbe WCot WThu
§	***rosea***	WAbe
§	***tingitana***	CBro
§	***trichophylla***	GKev
	- pink-flowered	EPri
	- f. ***purpurascens***	WCot
§	***valentina***	WCot

Acmella (*Asteraceae*)

§	***oleracea***	CLau

Acnistus (*Solanaceae*)

australis	see *Iochroma australe*

Aconitum (*Ranunculaceae*)

	ACE	EPPr
	'Album'	MPri WSpi
	altissimum	see *A. lycoctonum* subsp. *vulparia*
	anglicum	see *A. napellus* subsp. *napellus* Anglicum Group
§	***anthora***	EBee EPfP GKev MHol SPeP WCot
	arcuatum	see *A. fischeri* var. *arcuatum*
	austroyunnanense	WSHC
	- BWJ 7902	WCru
	autumnale misapplied	see *A. carmichaelii* Wilsonii Group
	autumnale Rchb.	see *A. fischeri* Rchb.
	× ***bicolor***	see *A.* × *cammarum* 'Bicolor'

	'Blue Lagoon'PBR	CWGN EBee MNHC MSCN NLar SCob WHil
	'Blue Opal'	EBee EWes MAvo
	'Blue Sceptre'	NLar SRms
	'Blue Sparrow' **new**	LSou
	'Bressingham Spire' ♀H7	ECtt EHyd ELan EPfP GKin GMaP LRHS MCot MHol NDov NGdn NPer NRHS SRms SSut WFar WSpi
	bulbilliferum HWJK 2120	WSHC
	× *cammarum*	NChi
§	- 'Bicolor' ♀H7	Widely available
	- 'Eleanora'	CBod ECtt EPfP EWld MHol NLar SRms
	- 'Grandiflorum Album'	EMor LPla MNrw WGoo
	- 'Pink Sensation'PBR	NLar
§	***carmichaelii***	CBod CSam EHyd ELan EPfP GAbr GKev GKin LRHS MMuc MNrw MPri NBro NChi NGdn NRHS SEND SRms WCot WFar WHoo WSpi
	- B&SWJ 8809 **new**	ESwi
	- Arendsii Group	CAby EBee ECtt GKev LEdu MWat WCAu WCFE
	- - 'Arendsii' ♀H7	Widely available
	- - 'Cloudy'PBR	CWGN EBee ECtt ELon EMor ITim LEdu LPla MAvo MBel MBriF MHol NGdn NLar NRHS SEdd WCot WHil WSpi
	- 'Moody Blues'	EBee
	- 'Redleaf'	see *A. carmichaelii* 'Royal Flush'
	- 'River Finn'	WCot
	- 'River Lugg'	WCot
	- 'River Medway'	CDor WCot
	- 'River Nene'	WCot
	- 'River Ouse'	WCot
	- 'River Spey'	WCot
	- 'River Teifi'	WCot
	- 'River Trent'	WCot
	- 'River Welland'	WCot
§	- 'Royal Flush'PBR	CDor CWGN EBee ECtt LSun MBNS MCot MHol MNrw NLar SPoG WCot
	- var. ***truppelianum***	WCot
	- - HWJ 732	WCot
§	- Wilsonii Group	CMac EBee LEdu MCot MRav MWat NDov WHoo XLum
	- - 'Autumn Amethyst' **new**	SMHy
	- - 'Barker's Variety'	CKno EBee ELon LRHS NGdn NLar NSti SRms WCot WSpi
	- - 'Kelmscott' ♀H7	ELon MCot MRav SDix SMHy WCot WFar WSpi
	- - 'Spätlese'	CDor CSam CWGN EBee ECtt ELon LEdu LRHS MCot MHol NBir NGdn NLar SPer SPoG WCAu WCot
§	***chasmanthum***	CRos EBee LRHS NRHS
	- GWJ 9393	WCru
	chiisanense B&SWJ 4446	WCru
	cilicicum	see *Eranthis hyemalis* Cilicica Group
	compactum	see *A. napellus* subsp. *vulgare*
	confertiflorum	see *A. anthora*
	delphinifolium	CExl
	elwesii	LEdu
	episcopale	EWld WCot WCru
	excelsum	see *A. lycoctonum* subsp. *lycoctonum*
	ferox	EBee
	- GWJ 9333 from Sikkim	WCru
	- GWJ 9403	WCru
	fischeri misapplied	see *A. carmichaelii*
§	***fischeri*** Rchb.	LRHS NBid NLar WCot
	- B&SWJ 8809	WCru
§	- var. ***arcuatum*** B&SWJ 774	WCru
	formosanum B&SWJ 3057	WCru
	fukutomei B&SWJ 337	MRav WCru
	gammiei GWJ 9418	WCru
	gmelinii	see *A. lycoctonum* subsp. *lycoctonum*
	grossedentatum	LPla NLar
	- subsp. ***paniculatum***	see *A. variegatum* subsp. *paniculatum*
§	***hemsleyanum***	CAby CExl CRHN CWGN ECtt EWld GKev GLog MBel NBid WCru
	- dark blue-flowered	WSpi
	- 'Red Wine'	CBod EWld MBNS MHol NSti
	- var. ***unguiculatum***	GKev
	hyemale	see *Eranthis hyemalis*
	'Ivorine'	CRos CSam EBee ECha EHyd ELan EMor EPfP GMaP ILea LEdu LRHS MCot MHol NGdn NLar NRHS NSti SPer WFar WPnP
	jaluense B&SWJ 8741	WCru
	japonicum	EBee GQue NLar WCot
	- var. ***hakonense***	CExl
	- var. ***montanum*** B&SWJ 5507	WCru
§	- subsp. ***napiforme***	EWes
	- - B&SWJ 943	EBee ELon WCru
§	- subsp. ***subcuneatum*** B&SWJ 6228	WCru
	kitadakense B&SWJ 11173	WCru
	laciniatum GWJ 9254	WCru
	- GWJ 9324	WCru
	lamarckii	see *A. lycoctonum* subsp. *neapolitanum*
	lasianthum	see *A. lycoctonum* subsp. *vulparia*
	leucostomum	EBee
	loczyanum	GKev WCot
	- B&SWJ 11529	WCru WSHC
	lycoctonum	CBod NGrd NLar NSti WSpi
	- 'Darkeyes'	WCot
§	- subsp. ***lycoctonum***	SRms
§	- subsp. ***moldavicum***	WCot
§	- subsp. ***neapolitanum***	CDor EBee GMaP IMou MMuc NLar SEND WBor WHil WSpi
	- 'Russian Yellow'	ESwi EWld
§	- subsp. ***vulparia***	GPoy ILea LEdu MRav NGdn SRms
	mairei	see *A. vilmorinianum*
	moldavicum	see *A. lycoctonum* subsp. *moldavicum*
	nagarum	LEdu WCot
	- KR 7589	EBee
	napellus	CBod ECtt EPfP GAbr GPoy ILea LRHS MBel MCot MHol MMuc MNHC MWat NAts NGrd SEND SPoG SRms WCav WCot WFar WHoo WPnP WShi XLum
	- 'Bergfürst'	EBee
	- 'Blue Valley'	EBee EPfP EWes
	- 'Gletschereis'	EBee LRHS
§	- subsp. ***napellus*** Anglicum Group	MCot MHol MMuc SEND WCot
	- - - 'Spring Yellow'	WCot
	- 'Rubellum'	IMou LRHS MBel NBro NLar WFar
	- 'Schneewittchen'	CSpe EWes MBel SAko SCob
§	- subsp. ***vulgare***	GKev
	- - 'Albidum'	CBod CRos ELon EPfP EWTr GMaP LEdu LRHS MHol NBid NHol NLar NRHS SPer SPoG
	- - 'Carneum'	EBee EPfP NGrd WHer

	- 'William Turner'	NGrd
	napiforme	see *A. japonicum* subsp. *napiforme*
	nasutum	WCot
	- white-flowered	WCot
	neapolitanum	see *A. lycoctonum* subsp. *neapolitanum*
	'Newry Blue'	CBod CRos EBee ECtt ELan EMor IMou LRHS MArl MAvo MBNS MRav NBir NRHS NWad SRms WSpi
	orientale misapplied	see *A. lycoctonum* subsp. *vulparia*
	paniculatum misapplied	see *A. variegatum* subsp. *paniculatum*
	piepunense	EBee GKev
	proliferum	WCot
	- B&SWJ 4107	WCru
	pseudohuiliense	CExl
	pseudolaeve var. ***erectum*** B&SWJ 8466	WCru
	pyramidale	see *A. napellus* subsp. *vulgare*
	pyrenaicum misapplied	see *A. lycoctonum* subsp. *neapolitanum*
	ranunculifolium	see *A. lycoctonum* subsp. *neapolitanum*
	sachalinense	WCot
	- subsp. ***yezoense***	EBee LPla NLar WCot
	senanense var. ***incisum*** B&SWJ 11032	SMad WCru
	- subsp. ***paludicola*** B&SWJ 10866	WCru
	seoulense	EBee
	- B&SWJ 694	WCru
	- B&SWJ 864	WCru
	- BWJ 4107	IMou
	septentrionale	see *A. lycoctonum* subsp. *lycoctonum*
	'Spark's Variety' ♀H7	Widely available
	spicatum GWJ 9394	WCru
	'Stainless Steel' ♀H7	CBcs CBod CExl ECtt EMor EPfP EWTr GMaP LEdu LRHS MBel MHol NBro NDov NGdn NLar SAko SCob SPer SPhx SPoG WCAu WCot WFar WHil WPnP WSHC WSpi
	subcuneatum	see *A. japonicum* subsp. *subcuneatum*
	'Surprise'	WCot
	× ***tubergenii***	see *Eranthis hyemalis* Tubergenii Group
	uchiyamae B&SWJ 1005	WCru
	- B&SWJ 1216	ECha WCru
	- B&SWJ 4446	NLar
	variegatum	EBee
§	- subsp. ***paniculatum***	LPla WCot
	- - 'Roseum'	WFar
§	***vilmorinianum*** BWJ 8055	WCru
	violaceum var. ***robustum***	see *A. chasmanthum*
	volubile misapplied	see *A. hemsleyanum*
	vulparia	see *A. lycoctonum* subsp. *vulparia*
	yamazakii	WCru
	zigzag var. ***ryohakuense*** B&SWJ 8906	WCru

Aconogonon see *Persicaria*

Acorus ✿ (*Acoraceae*)

	calamus	CBen CKno CLau CWat EMor GPoy MNHC NPer WMAq
	- subsp. ***angustatus***	GPoy
	- 'Argenteostriatus' (v)	CWat ECha MMuc SEND SRms WMAq XCre
*	***christophii***	ELon EPPr
	gramineus	GPoy NPer
	- 'Golden Delight'	CBod SRms
	- 'Golden Edge' (v)	ELon NRHS NWad
	- 'Hakuro-nishiki' (v)	GWyn NWad SRms SWvt WFar XLum
	- 'Licorice'	MSCN WBrk WGrn
	- 'Masamune' (v)	EWes
	- 'Minimus Aureus'	CBre
	- 'Oborozuki' misapplied	see *A. gramineus* 'Ōgon'
§	- 'Ōgon' (v)	Widely available
	- var. ***pusillus***	NBro
	- 'Variegatus' (v)	CBcs CBen CBod CChe CExl CRos CWat ELan EMor GMaP LPot LRHS LSun MGos MMuc MRav NBid NBro NRHS SArc SEND SLim SPoG SRms SWvt XLum
	'Intermedius'	NPer

Acradenia (*Rutaceae*)

	frankliniae	CBcs CCCN CMac CTsd EBee EPfP IArd IDee LRHS MBlu MHtn SEND SPlb WPGP

Actaea (*Ranunculaceae*)

	alba misapplied	see *A. pachypoda*, *A. rubra* f. *neglecta*
	arizonica	CRos EBee LPla LRHS NLar NRHS WCru
	asiatica B&SWJ 616	WCru
	- B&SWJ 6351 from Japan	WCru
	- B&SWJ 8694 from Korea	WCru
	- BWJ 8174 from China	WCru
	biternata B&SWJ 8917	NLar WCru
	- B&SWJ 11190	WCru
	'Chocoholic'	CWGN EBee ECtt ELan ELon EMor GEdr ILea IPot LPla LRHS LSou MAvo MHol MMrt MNHC MNrw MPri NRHS SPVi WHil
§	***cimicifuga***	ECha GPoy
	aff. ***cimicifuga*** WJC 13720	WCru
§	***cordifolia***	EBee GBin GMaP LPla LRHS NLar SWvt
	- 'Blickfang'	SPVi
	dahurica	GBin LPla
	- B&SWJ 8426	WCru
	- B&SWJ 8573	WCru
	- tall	NBid
	elata	CPla IMou
	erythrocarpa	see *A. rubra*
	frigida B&SWJ 2966	WCru
§	***japonica***	NLar
	- B&SWJ 5828	WCru
	- B&SWJ 11136	WCru
	- B&SWJ 11526	WCru
	- from Jejudo, South Korea	EBee IMou MNrw NDov
	- var. ***acutiloba*** B&SWJ 6257	WCru
	- 'Cheju-Do'	IPot LPla MBel MMrt NLar SPVi
	- compact B&SWJ 8758A	WCot WCru
	- 'Silver Dance' **new**	CBod NLar
	mairei	IMou LRHS
	- BWJ 7635	WCru
	- BWJ 7939	WCru
§	***matsumurae***	CExl NLar
	- B&SWJ 11187	WCru
	- B&SWJ 11528	WCru
	- 'Elstead Variety' ♀H7	CExl MRav
	- 'White Pearl' ♀H7	Widely available

§ ***pachypoda***	CBod CBro CExl EBee EPfP EWTr GLog GPoy MBel NBid NLar NSti WCru
- MISTY BLUE ('Lk05'[PBR])	CAby CBcs CBod CBro CSpe CWGN EBee ECha ECtt ESwi GEdr LPla MHol MNrw SEdd SMad SPeP SPoG WCot WNPC
- 'Silver Leaf'	CSpe
§ ***podocarpa***	EBee LPla NLar SPlb SRms WCru
'Queen of Sheba'[PBR]	CWGN EBee IPot LPla MBel NDov NLar SPVi
racemosa 🏆[H7]	CBod CMac EBee ELan EPfP GBin GPoy LSun NBid NGdn NLar NSti SEdd SPer SWvt WFar XLum
§ ***rubra***	CBod CSpe EBee ECha ELan LEdu LRHS MBel MMrt NBid NLar NWad SMad SPoG WBor WCru
- B&SWJ 9555	WCru
- ***alba***	see *A. pachypoda*, *A. rubra* f. *neglecta*
§ - f. ***neglecta***	GLog WCot WCru
simplex	CPla EBee GLog WCot
- B&SWJ 8653	WCru
- B&SWJ 8664	WCru
- B&SWJ 10957	WCru
- B&SWJ 11133	WCru
§ - Atropurpurea Group	CBod EBee ECha ELan ELon EMor EPfP GMaP ILea LCro LOPS LRHS MGos MRav NBir NChi NGdn NLar NSti SPeP SPer SRms SWvt WCAu WFar WHil WPGP WPnP
- - 'Black Negligee'	Widely available
- - 'Brunette' 🏆[H7]	Widely available
- - 'Carbonella'	CWGN EBee ECtt ELan MHol MNrw NLar SPVi WFar WHil
- - 'Hillside Black Beauty' 🏆[H7]	CBct CDor EBee ECtt EMor GKin GMaP LRHS MTis NBir NLar
- - 'James Compton' 🏆[H7]	CDor CExl CPar CRos EBee ECha EPfP GKin GMaP GWyn ILea IPot LRHS MAvo MCot NBir NDov NGBl NGdn NLar NRHS SWvt WCAu WCot WFar
- - 'Mountain Wave'	ECtt NDov SPVi
- 'Cally Dappled' (v)	MBriF
- 'Pink Spike'	Widely available
§ - 'Prichard's Giant'	ELon LRHS MNrw MRav NLar WFar
- ***ramosa***	see *A. simplex* 'Prichard's Giant'
- variegated (v)	WCot
spicata	CBod CSpe GBin GPoy LEdu WCru
- PAB 8131	LEdu
- from England	WCru
taiwanensis B&SWJ 3413	WCru
- RWJ 9996	WCru
yesoensis	LPla NLar
- B&SWJ 6355	WCru
- B&SWJ 10860	WCru

Actinella see *Tetraneuris*

Actinidia (*Actinidiaceae*)

sp.	CCCN
BWJ 8161 from China	WCru
arguta	CRHN EBee MGil
- (f/F)	CAgr
- B&SWJ 4455 from Jejudo, South Korea	WCru
- B&SWJ 4823 from Japan	WCru
- B&SWJ 8529 from Ulleungdo, South Korea	WCru
- 'Ambrosia Grande'	NLar
- 'Ananasnaya' (f/F)	CAgr WPGP
- 'Bayern' (f/F)	CAgr CCCN
- 'Geneva 2' (f/F)	CAgr
- 'Honigbeere' (m)	NLar
- 'Issai' (s-p/F)	CAgr CBcs CCCN CMac EPom LBuc LEdu LRHS SVic WKor WPGP
- 'Jumbo' (f/F)	CAgr LEdu SVic
- 'Ken's Red' (f/F)	CAgr CCCN LEdu SVic SWeb
- 'Kokuwa' (s-p/F)	CAgr
- 'Meader' (m)	CAgr
- 'Purpurna Sadowa' (f/F)	NLar
- SCARLET SEPTEMBER KIWI ('Mirzan') (f/F)	CAgr
- 'Shoko' (f/F)	WCru
- 'Unchae' (m)	WCru
- 'Weiki' (m)	CAgr CCCN LEdu SVic
chinensis misapplied	see *A. deliciosa*
chinensis Planch. var. ***setosa*** B&SWJ 3563	WCru
coriacea WWJ 11895	WCru
§ ***deliciosa***	CCCN MRav
- 'Atlas' (m)	NLar
- 'Golden Delight' (f/F)	CBcs
- 'Hayward' (f/F)	CBcs CCCN EPfP LRHS LSRN SCob SWvt WFar
- 'Jenny' (s-p/F)	CAgr CBod CEnd CMac CRos CTri ELan EPfP EPom LBuc LRHS MBros MGos SPoG SPre SSFr SVic WFar
- 'Oriental Delight' (s-p/F)	CRHN
- SOLISSIMO ('Renact'[PBR]) (s-p/F)	CRos EHyd LRHS MAsh MCoo NRHS
- 'Solo' (s-p/F)	CBar CCCN CMac CRHN CRos ECrN EPfP LRHS LSRN NLar SLim SPer SWvt
- 'Tomuri' (m)	CBcs CCCN EBee EPfP LRHS LSRN SWvt
hypoleuca B&SWJ 5942	WCru
'Kiwai Bee'	CCCN
kolomikta 🏆[H5]	Widely available
- B&SWJ 4243	LSRN WCru
- (m)	CDoC MBlu NOra
- 'Adam' (m)	ETho
- 'Doctor Szymanowski' (s-p/F)	CAgr WPGP
- 'Sentyabraskaya' (f/F)	NLar
- 'Tomoko' (f/F)	WCru
- 'Yazuaki' (m)	WCru
melanandra	SPlb
petelotii FMWJ 13137	WCru
- HWJ 628	WCru
pilosula misapplied	see *A. tetramera* var. *maloides*
pilosula (Finet & Gagnep.) Stapf ex Hand.-Mazz.	CAby EHyd ELan IArd IDee IMou LRHS NRHS SPoG SRms WKif
polygama	CMen
- B&SWJ 5444	WCru
- B&SWJ 8525 from Korea	WCru
- B&SWJ 8923 from Japan	WCru
- B&SWJ 12564 from Korea	WCru
rufa B&SWJ 3525	WCru
strigosa WJC 13662	WCru
- WJC 13807	WCru
aff. ***strigosa*** HWJK 2367	WCru
§ ***tetramera*** var. ***maloides*** 🏆[H5]	CBcs CExl CWGN EBee EPfP EWTr MGil NLar NOra SBrt SCoo WBor WCru WLov WPGP WSHC

Adansonia (*Malvaceae*)

grandidieri	SPlb
madagascariensis	SPlb

rubrostipa	SPlb
za	SPlb

Adelocaryum see *Lindelofia*

Adenanthos (*Proteaceae*)

sericeus	SPlb

Adenium (*Apocynaceae*)

obesum ♀H1a	CCCN CDoC
- 'Olivia' **new**	LCro LOPS

Adenocarpus (*Papilionaceae*)

decorticans	SPlb

Adenophora (*Campanulaceae*)

sp.	MHol
'Afterglow'	see *Campanula rapunculoides* 'Afterglow'
asiatica	see *Hanabusaya asiatica*
aurita	SBrt
bulleyana	CBod CRos ELan LRHS NBid NLar SPlb WCot WFar WRHF
* ***campanulata***	WCav
capillaris subsp. ***leptosepala***	NLar
- - BWJ 7986	WCru
coelestis	CExl NBid
- B&SWJ 7998	WCru
confusa	WSHC
divaricata B&SWJ 11018	WCru
'Gaudi Violet'	CBod EMor MAvo MBriF MHol SPad SPoG WCot
grandiflora B&SWJ 8555	WCru
khasiana	CExl EBee GKev NLar XLum
lamarkii B&SWJ 8738	WCru
latifolia misapplied	see *A. pereskiifolia*
liliifolia	CMea EBee EPfP GKev NLar NPer SBut WFar
maximowicziana B&SWJ 11008	WCru
morrisonensis RWJ 10008	MHol WCru
- subsp. ***uehatae***	GEdr
- - B&SWJ 126	WCru
§ ***nikoensis***	EBee GEdr NBid WCot
- B&SWJ 11201	WCru
- f. ***linearifolia*** **new**	EWld
§ ***pereskiifolia***	EWes SBut SHar SPlb WCot
- 'Alba'	SRms
- 'White Blaze'	LCro LOPS
polyantha	NLar SRms
polymorpha	see *A. nikoensis*
potaninii	EBee MMuc SEND WFar WHal
- pale-flowered	MAvo WHal
remotiflora	EBee
- B&SWJ 8714	WCru
- B&SWJ 11016	WCru
stricta subsp. ***sessilifolia***	EBee
takedae	EBee SBrt
- B&SWJ 11424	WCru
taquetii	GEdr
taquetii × ***waldensteinia***	EPot
tashiroi	EBee GKev XLum
triphylla	EBee GKev
- B&SWJ 10916	WCru
- var. ***japonica*** B&SWJ 10933	WCru

Adenostyles (*Asteraceae*)

alpina	CBod SBrt

Adesmia (*Papilionaceae*)

longipes	SPlb

Adiantum ✿ (*Pteridaceae*)

sp.	CMac
aethiopicum	XBlo
§ ***aleuticum*** ♀H6	CAby CLAP CMiW LCro LOPS NBro NLar SPlb WFib
- 'Imbricatum'	Widely available
§ - 'Japonicum'	CAby WFar
- 'Miss Sharples'	CAby CDTJ CLAP ECha GEdr LEdu LRHS MGos NLar NRHS SRms
§ - 'Subpumilum' ♀H5	CLAP NBro WCot WFib
- 'Tasselatum'	WCot
bonatianum	CExl
capillus-veneris	CBdn EBee ISha NBro WFib
- 'Mairisii'	see *A.* × *mairisii*
caudatum	CDoC EShb ISha
cuneatum	see *A. raddianum*
fulvum	CDoC
hispidulum	CBdn CCCN CDoC EBee LEdu LRHS MAsh NRHS
- 'Bronze Venus'	CCCN CDoC CRos EShb ISha LRHS NRHS SRms
§ × ***mairisii*** ♀H5	CLAP CRos EBee EShb ISha LEdu LRHS NRHS
pedatum misapplied	see *A. aleuticum*
pedatum ambig.	CTsd ISha
pedatum L.	CBcs CBct CDor CLAP ECha EFer ELon GAbr GMaP LEdu NBro NLar SPlb WCot WFar
- Asiatic form	see *A. aleuticum* 'Japonicum'
- 'Japonicum'	see *A. aleuticum* 'Japonicum'
- 'Roseum'	see *A. aleuticum* 'Japonicum'
- var. ***subpumilum***	see *A. aleuticum* 'Subpumilum'
peruvianum	CDoC ISha
poiretii	LEdu WCot
pubescens	ISha
§ ***raddianum*** ♀H1c	CDoC
- 'Fragrans'	see *A. raddianum* 'Fragrantissimum'
§ - 'Fragrantissimum'	EShb LCro LOPS
- 'Fritz Lüthi' ♀H1c	CDoC EShb
- 'Lisa'	EShb
reniforme	WCot
× ***tracyi***	ISha
venustum ♀H7	Widely available
- 'Texas' **new**	LEdu

Adlumia (*Papaveraceae*)

fungosa	CSpe LRHS NAts

Adonis (*Ranunculaceae*)

amurensis misapplied	see *A.* 'Fukujukai'
amurensis ambig.	CMea EBee GEdr GKev LEdu NHpl WPnP
amurensis Regel & Radde 'Pleniflora'	see *A. multiflora* 'Sandanzaki'
- 'Ryokuho' **new**	GEdr
- 'Sakhalin'	EBee
annua	SPhx
brevistyla	GEdr
'Chichibu-beni'	GEdr
§ 'Fukujukai'	ECha GEdr MBel XEll
multiflora 'Beni-nadeshiko'	GEdr
- 'Hakuju'	GEdr
- 'Hanazono' (d)	GEdr
§ - 'Sandanzaki' (d)	EBee GBin GEdr GKev LEdu
ramosa	GEdr

'Sado-no-maboroshi' (d)	GEdr
vernalis	CBod GPoy WCot

Adoxa (*Adoxaceae*)

moschatellina	CBre EBee EWld LEdu MNrw NGrd NRya WHer WSFF WShi WWtn

Adromischus (*Crassulaceae*)

cooperi ♀H2	CDoC SIvy
filicaulis **new**	SIvy
maculatus ♀H2	CDoC
schuldtianus **new**	CDoC

Aechmea ✿ (*Bromeliaceae*)

sp.	XBlo
'Blue Rain'PBR	CDoC
fasciata	WSFF XBlo
ramosa	XBlo
recurvata	NCft
victoriana	XBlo

Aegle (*Rutaceae*)

sepiaria	see *Citrus trifoliata*

Aegopodium (*Apiaceae*)

aff. ***handellii*** PAB 9003	SPhx
podagraria	CNat
'Dangerous' (v)	
- gold-margined (v)	EPPr
- 'Variegatum' (v)	EBee ECha ECrN EPPr EShb GKev GMaP GQue LRHS MBel MRav NBid NRHS NSti SEND SPer WCot WFar WHil XLum

Aeonium (*Crassulaceae*)

arboreum	CDTJ CDoC CKno CPbh CPla ELan EShb NCft SChr SEND SIvy WABo
- 'Albovariegatum' (v)	CDoC
- 'Atropurpureum'	CAbb CCCN CDTJ CPla CSde ELan EShb NCft NPer SEND SIvy
I - 'Magnificum'	EShb ESwi GBin SArc SIvy
- 'Variegatum' (v)	CPbh CPla NPer
'Ballecerina' **new**	SAll
balsamiferum	CBod CCCN CDTJ CDoC CPbh NCft SChr SIvy SSim WCot
'Black Cap'	CCCN
'Black Magic'	WOld
'Blush'	CKno
'Blushing Beauty' ♀H1c	CAbb SIvy SSim
'Bronze Medal'	WOld
'Bronze Teacup' **new**	WOld
canariense	CCCN CDTJ SIvy SVen
- Californian selection **new**	WOld
- var. ***palmense***	SVen
castello-paivae	SChr SIvy
ciliatum	SPlb
'Copper Kettle'	SIvy WAvo WOld
'Cornish Tribute'	CCCN CPbh SIvy SSim WOld
'Cristata Sunburst'	CDTJ WCot
cuneatum	CDTJ CPbh CSde SEND
- blue-leaved	SChr
'Cyclops'	CAbb CPbh NCft
* ***decorum*** 'Variegatum' (v)	WCot
'Dinner Plate'	CDTJ CPbh WOld
diplocyclum **new**	CPbh
'Du Rozzen'	CPbh
'Emerald Flame'	WOld
* ***escobarii***	SPlb
'Firecracker' **new**	WOld
glandulosum	SVen
'Goblin' **new**	WOld
gomerense	CPla
goochiae	SIvy
- 'Ballerina' (v)	SEdd SGro SIvy SSim WABo
haworthii ♀H1c	CDTJ CDoC NCft SEND SEdd SSim SVen
- 'Kiwi'	CCCN SEdd SIvy SSim WOld
- 'Variegatum' (v) ♀H1c	CDTJ CPbh EShb SIvy SVen
hierrense	CPbh SPlb
holochrysum Webb & Berth.	CAbb
lancerottense **new**	SIvy
leucoblepharum	EShb NCft SAll SIvy
lindleyi	SChr
'Logan Rock'	CPbh
'Merry Maiden'	CPbh
* ***multiflorum***	CDTJ
'Variegatum' (v)	
'Pen-du' **new**	WABo
'Phoenix Flame'	CTsd WOld
'Poldark'	CCCN CPbh
'Pomegranate' **new**	CCCN
rubrolineatum	SEdd
sedifolium	CPbh NCft SSim
'Simply Misty'	SSim
'Simply Scarlet'	SSim
simsii	CDTJ CPbh NCft
- variegated (v)	EShb
simsii × 'Zwartkop'	CBod CCCN CDoC CPbh CPla ELan MHer NCft SChr WOld
smithii **new**	SChr
spathulatum	CDTJ CPbh EDAr WCot
'Sunburst' (v) ♀H1c	CPbh SIvy WCot WOld
tabuliforme ♀H1c	CCCN CDTJ CDoC CPbh NCft SMad SPlb SSim WCot
'Torchbearer' **new**	CPbh
'Trewidden'	WCot WOld
undulatum	SChr SPlb
urbicum	EShb
valverdense	CTsd
'Velour'	CCCN CDTJ CDoC CPbh NCft NPer SIvy SSim
'Voodoo'	CAbb ELan SEdd SIvy SSim WCot WOld
'Zwartkop' ♀H1c	Widely available

Aeschynanthus ✿ (*Gesneriaceae*)

sp.	CDoC
Black Pagoda Group	WDib
'Fire Wheel'	WDib
'Hot Flash'	WDib
'Little Tiger'	WDib
longicalyx	WDib
§ ***longicaulis*** ♀H1a	CDoC WDib
marmoratus	see *A. longicaulis*
radicans ♀H1a	WDib
'Scooby Doo'	WDib
speciosus ♀H1a	WDib

Aesculus ✿ (*Sapindaceae*)

arguta	see *A. glabra* var. *arguta*
assamica WWJ 11886	WCru
'Autumn Splendor'	EPfP
§ × ***bushii***	MBlu
californica	CMCN EPfP SBrt WPGP
- 'Canyon Pink'	CMCN
× ***carnea***	SCob SGol
- 'Briotii'	CBcs CCVT CDoC CEnd CMac CSBt EBee ELan EPfP LMaj LRHS MGos MMuc NLar NOrn SCob

		SEND SEWo SGbt SPer SWeb WMat WTSh
*	- 'Variegata' (v)	CMCN
	chinensis	CBcs CMCN
	flava ♀H5	CMCN EBee ELan EPfP IArd LMaj SEND
	- f. ***vestita***	EPfP MBlu
	georgiana	see *A. sylvatica*
	glabra	CMCN
§	- var. ***arguta***	NLar
	- 'October Red'	EPfP
	glaucescens	see *A.* × *neglecta*
	hippocastanum	CBcs CCVT CMac CSBt CTri EBee ECrN ELan MGos MMuc MSwo NLar NOra SCob SEND SEWo SGol SPer WFar WMat WTSh
	- 'Aureomarginata' (v)	CMac
§	- 'Baumannii' (d)	CMCN ECrN ELan MGos MSwo SPer
	- 'Digitata'	CMCN
	- 'Flore Pleno'	see *A. hippocastanum* 'Baumannii'
	- 'Hampton Court Gold'	CMCN CMac
	- f. ***laciniata***	CMCN NLar
	- 'Wisselink'	CMCN
	indica	CLnd CMCN ECrN ELan EPfP EWTr LEdu LMaj MMuc SEND SGol SPtp WMou WTSh
	- 'Sydney Pearce' ♀H5	CBcs CEnd CMCN EPfP IArd MBlu MGos NLar NOra WMat
	× ***mississippiensis***	see *A.* × *bushii*
	× ***mutabilis*** 'Induta'	CMCN EPfP NOra WMat
§	× ***neglecta***	CMCN
	- 'Autumn Fire'	EBee EPfP NLar WMat
	- 'Erythroblastos' ♀H5	CBcs CEnd CMCN EPfP MBlu SCoo SPer WCot WMat
	parviflora ♀H5	CBcs CMCN CTri EBee ELan EPfP EWTr GKin IDee LMaj MBlu MGos MMuc MRav NLar NOra SEND SGol SMad SPer SWvt WMat
	pavia	CBcs CMCN
	- 'Atrosanguinea'	CEnd CMCN EPfP
	- var. ***discolor*** 'Koehnei'	CMCN ELan EPfP NLar NOra SPoG WMat
	- northern	SBrt
	- 'Purple Spring'	EPfP
	- 'Rosea Nana'	CMCN SMad
§	- Splendens Group	CMCN EPfP
	splendens	see *A. pavia* Splendens Group
§	***sylvatica***	CMCN
	turbinata	CBcs WMou
	wilsonii	CBcs CExl MBlu

Aethionema (*Brassicaceae*)

§	***grandiflorum*** ♀H5	CFis ELan EPot GJos GKev SRms
	- Pulchellum Group ♀H5	CSpe MMuc
*	***kotschyi*** hort.	WAbe
	pulchellum	see *A. grandiflorum*
	schistosum	SPlb
	'Warley Rose' ♀H5	CBor CRos EHyd ELan EPot EWTr LRHS MAsh MBel NBir NRHS SRms WIce WThu WTor XSen
	'Warley Ruber'	CMea EPot WAbe

Agapanthus ✿ (*Agapanthaceae*)

	'Adonis'	CPrp IBlr
	'African Moon'	CPrp IBal MAvo
	'African Skies'	CAbb CPrp IBal SFai WABo
	africanus misapplied	CBcs CElw CExl CTsd EBee ELan EPfP GKev IBal ILea LCro LOPS SArc SChr SCob SDeJ SPalm SPer SVic XLum XSen
	- 'Albus' misapplied	CBar CBcs CBod CExl EBee ELan EPfP GKev IBal ILea LCro LOPS LSRN MGos SCob SDeJ SEND SPalm SPer SRms WABo WSpi XLum XSen
	- hybrid	CBod
	'Aimee'	CBro IBal
	'Alan Street'	IBal MAvo
	'Albus' ambig.	GMaP
I	'Albus Nanus'	IBal
I	'Albus Roseus'	IBal
	'Alice Double' (d) **new**	CPbh
	'Allisio'	IBal
	'Amsterdam'	EBee EMor IBal IMou MAvo
	'Angela'	ELon IBal MAvo
	'Ankara'	IBal
	'Anneke'	IBal
	'Antibe'	IBal
	'Aphrodite'	IBlr
	'Aquamarine'	EPri IBal
	'Arctic Star'	CCCN CDoC CExl CKno CMac CPar CPou CPrp EBee ELon IBal LSRN LSou MAvo NHoy NLar SDys SFai SPoG WABo
	'Ardernei'	IBal
	'Ardernei Hybrid'	CExl ECha ECtt EWes GAbr IBal IBlr WCot WGwG
	'Ascona'	IBal
	'Atlas'	IBlr
	'Aureovittatus' (v)	IBal
	'Autumn Mist'	IBal
§	'B in B'PBR	CBro CCCN CExl CWCL ECha ELan EPfP EShb IBal MBNS MRav NBid NLar SCob SMad SPer WCot WFar
	'Baby Blue'	see *A.* 'Blue Baby' Rom.
	'Baby Pete'PBR	EBee IBal NHoy
	BACK IN BLACK	see *A.* 'B in B'
	'Ballerina'	CBdn CPne IBal
	'Ballyrogan'	IBlr
	'Bangor Blue'	IBlr
	'Barley Blue'	IBal
	'Barnfield Blue'	CPrp EBee IBal
	'Beatrice'	CPrp
	'Becky'	IBal
	'Beeches Dwarf'	IBal
	'Ben Hope'	CBro IBal IBlr NBPC
	'Berlin'	IBal
	'Beth Chatto'	see *A. campanulatus* 'Albovittatus'
	'Bethlehem Star'	EPri
	'Bicton Bell'	EPri IBal IBlr
	'Bicton Bride'	IBal
	'Big Ben'	IBal
	'Big Blue'	CBod CCCN CChe CMac CPrp CSde CWCL EBee SEND SLdr SRkn WABo WSMil WSpi
	'Black Beauty'	CBod CPrp EPfP IBal LSou WSpi
	'Black Buddhist'	CCCN CPrp CWCL EBee ECtt EPfP EPri IBal LSou MAvo NGdn NHoy NSti SPer XSen
	'Black Magic'	CAbb CPar CPrp EBee IBal LSou NHoy NSti SCob SFai SPoG WABo
	'Black Pantha'PBR	Widely available
	'Blitzza'	IBal
	'Bloemfontein'	IBal
§	'Blue Baby' Rom.	CCCN EHyd ELan ELon IBal
	'Blue Bayou'	IBal
	'Blue Brush'	CPrp EPfP SCoo

	'Blue Cascade'	IBlr
	'Blue Companion'	CPrp IBlr
	'Blue Diamond' ambig.	CMac
	'Blue Dot'	CPrp EPfP LSou SDys
	'Blue Flare'	IBal
	'Blue Flash'	IBal
	'Blue Formality'	IBal IBlr
	'Blue Giant'	CBro CCCN CChe CDor CPrp EBee ELan IBal MGos WAvo WSpi
	'Blue Globe'	CBod EBee EPri GMaP IBal MSCN
	'Blue Gown'	CSam
	'Blue Heaven' PBR	CBdn CPne CWGN EWes IBal ILea NHoy
	'Blue Horizons' PBR (v)	CCCN IBal
	'Blue Ice'	CPou CPrp EBee IBal NHoy SAko WABo WTyc
	'Blue Imp'	CBro IBal IBlr NWad
	'Blue Jay'	IBal
	'Blue Magic'	EBee IBal NHoy
	'Blue Moon'	CBro CPrp EBee ECha ECtt EPri IBal IBlr MAvo MHol SEND SEdd SLdr WCot
	'Blue Nile'	CBdn CPne CPrp IBal
	'Blue Pixie'	IBal
	'Blue Prince'	EBee ELon
	'Blue Rinse'	IBal
	'Blue Skies' ambig.	SDir
I	'Blue Skies' Dunlop	IBlr
	'Blue Steel'	IBal
	BLUE STORM ('Atiblu' PBR) (Storm Series)	CPrp EHyd EPfP IBal LBuc SArc
	'Blue Triumphator'	CBod CDor EPfP EWTr GKev GMaP IBal ILea NHoy SCob WSpi
	'Blue Umbrella'	CDor CPrp ELan SGsty SRkn WSpi
	'Blue Yonder'	EBee
	blue-flowered	WAvo WCFE
	'Bluety' PBR	IBal
	'Boleyn Blue' **new**	ECha
	'Bray Valley'	CBdn CPne CPrp
	'Bressingham Blue'	CAbb CBro CDoC CSam CTri EWes IBal IBlr LSou MAvo MRav NHoy SEdd SFai SMHy WABo WSpi
	'Bressingham Bounty'	EBee IBal
	'Bressingham White'	CDoC CPrp EPfP MRav
	'Bridal Bouquet'	EBee EPfP IBal LSRN LSou NHoy SAko SFai WABo
	'Bright Blue'	IBal
	BRILLIANT BLUE ('Aga0451')	CKno EBee IBal LSou MHol SFai WABo WHoo
	'Bristol'	IBal
	'Broadleigh Babe'	CBro
	'Brody'	CPrp
	'Buckingham Palace'	CBro EBee ECha ELon EWes GAbr IBal IBlr MAvo NChi WCot
	'Calimero'	IBal
	'Cally Blue'	GAbr IBal
	'Cally Large White'	GAbr
	'Cally Longstem'	EBee EPri
	'Cally Pale Blue'	IBal
	campanulatus	CBod CMac CPbh CPrp ELan ELon EPfP GKin IBal IBlr MRav NChi SGbt WAvo WFar WKif WSpi
	- var. ***albidus*** misapplied	see *A.* 'Franni'
	- var. ***albidus***	CBod CPrp ECha ELan EPfP GKev GKin IBlr MHer MMuc NBid NGdn NHoy SEND SPer WGwG WHoo WSHC WSpi
§	- 'Albovittatus' (v)	IBal
	- bright blue-flowered	IBal

	- 'Cobalt Blue'	CBod CPrp ELan EPri GKin IBal LSou MAsh MAvo MMuc NGdn SSut WHoo
	- dark blue-flowered	CPrp
	- 'Oxford Blue'	IBlr
	- subsp. ***patens*** ♀H4	CPrp EPfP IBal MRav
	- - deep blue-flowered	IBlr
	- 'Profusion'	CBro ECha EPri IBal IBlr NHoy
	- 'Ultramarine'	IBal
	- variegated (v)	EBee ECha NPer
	- 'Wedgwood Blue'	CPrp EBee IBal IBlr
	- 'Wendy'	EBee EPfP IBal IBlr
	- 'White Hope'	IBal IBlr
	'Castle of Mey'	CBro CCht CExl CPrp EBee ELon GAbr IBal IBlr LCro LOPS LSou MAvo NHoy SFai WABo WCAu WSpi
	'Catharina'	IBal
§	***caulescens*** ♀H3	CBdn CPne CPrp IBal IBlr SMHy
	- subsp. ***angustifolius***	ELon IBal IBlr MHol SEND
	- subsp. ***caulescens***	IBlr
	'Cedric Morris'	EPri IBal IBlr
	'Celebration'	CBdn CPne IBal SFai
	'Chandra'	IBal IBlr
	'Charlotte' PBR	CMac EBee ELan EPfP IBal LSou MHol SFai SPoG WABo WTor
	'Cheney's Lane'	SMHy
	'Cherbours'	IBal
	'Cherry Holley'	ELon IBal WSpi
	'Chika's Blue'	EBee IBal MAvo
	'Clarence House'	CBro IBal
	'Cloudy Days'	IBal
	coddii	CExl CPbh EPri IBal IBlr MHer WCot
	'Columba'	CPrp EBee ELon IBal NBid XSen
	comptonii	see *A. praecox* subsp. *minimus*
	'Corina'	EBee
	DANUBE	see *A.* 'Donau'
	'Dart Valley'	CPrp IBal
	'Dawn Star'	ECha
	'Debbie'	IBal
	'Delft'	EBee IBal IBlr
	'Delft Blue'	IBal MNHC NLar
	'Density'	IBlr
	'Dnjepr'	CBro EBee IBal
	'Dokkum'	IBal
	'Dokter Brouwer'	EWTr GKev ILea LSRN MCot SDir
§	'Donau'	CBro EBee EPri EShb IBal NBir
	DOUBLE DIAMOND ('Rfdd' PBR)	CCht EBee EHyd EPfP EPri EWes IBal LSRN LSou NHoy NWad SAko SCob SFai SPoG WFar WSpi XEll
	'Dublin'	IBal
	'Duivenbrugge Blue'	IBal
	'Durban'	IBal
	dwarf blue	NHoy
	dyeri	see *A. inapertus* subsp. *intermedius*
	'Early Blue'	ELon
	'Eggesford Sky'	CBdn CPne CPrp EBee IBal
	'Elaine'	IBal
	'Elisa'	IBal
	'Elizabeth Salisbury'	IBal
	'Ellamae'	IBal
	'Elsie's Sunshine' **new**	WFar
	'Enigma'	Widely available
	'Enigma Variations'	EBee
	'Ethel's Joy'	EBee EPri IBal
	'Eve'	IBlr
	'Evening Eclipse'	EPfP IBal
	'Evening Star'	EPri WABo
	EVER BLUE **new**	IBal

	'Exmoor'	IBal MAvo WABo
	'Findlay's Blue'	SMHy
	'Finnline' (v)	SRms
	'Flore Pleno' (d)	CExl CMac CPrp EBee ECha ECtt ELan GAbr GKin IBal IBlr LSou MHer MHol NGdn NHoy WCot WFar WPGP WSHC
	'Flower of Love'	CBdn CCht CPne CPrp IBal LCro LOPS LSou MHol NLar SFai SPoG WABo
I	'Forma' **new**	IBal
§	'Franni' **new**	WCav
	'Fulsome'	IBlr
	'Gail's Purple' **new**	IBal
	'Gayle's Lilac'	CBcs CBod CCCN CElw CExl CPrp ECtt ELan ELon EMor EPfP EWTr GKin LSou MPie MRav NGdn WGwG
	'Gem'	CPrp ELon
	'Genua'	IBal
	'Getty White'	ELan
	'Glacier'	IBal
	'Glacier Stream'	CBro CDor EPri IBal NLar SEdd XSen
	'Glen Avon'	CAbb CCCN CExl EBee EPfP IBal SCoo SFai SLon WABo
	'Gold Strike' PBR (v)	CPla IBal LSou NHoy SFai SPoG WABo WCot
	'Golden Drop' PBR (v)	CBcs CCht EHyd IBal LSou NHoy NSti SFai SPad SPeP SRms WABo
	'Golden Rule' (v)	IBlr
	'Gothenburg'	IBal
	'Greenfield'	EBee IBal
	'Hamar'	IBal
	'Hanneke'	IBal SFai
	'Hannover'	IBal
	'Happy Blue'	IBal
	'Harvest Blue'	CBdn CPne IBal
§	Headbourne hybrids	Widely available
	- dark blue-flowered	LPot
	'Headbourne White'	EPri
	'Heavenly Blue'	CCCN
	'Helen'	IBlr
	'Helsinki'	IBal
	'His Majesty'	IBal
	'Holbrook'	CSam
	'Hole Park Blue'	NHoy
	'Hoyland Blue'	CPrp IBal NHoy WFar
	'Hoyland Chelsea Blue'	NHoy
	'Ice Blue Star'	CBro IBal
	'Ice Lolly'	CBro EShb IBal
	ICICLES ('Duivenbrugge White')	CKno CPrp IBal LSou SFai WABo
	inapertus	CAby CBro CPbh CPrp CSpe EWes IBal WPGP WSHC
	- 'Avalanche'	EBee IBal SFai WSpi
	- 'Cascade Crystal' **new**	IBal
	- 'Cascade Diamond' **new**	IBal
	- 'Crystal Drop'	CAbb CExl CPou CPrp EBee EPri IBal LSou SFai WABo
	- dwarf	IBlr
	- subsp. ***hollandii***	IBal IBlr
	- - 'Sky'	CAbb CPrp EMor EPri EWTr IBal IBlr NBid SRms WABo
	- - 'Zealot'	IBlr
	- 'Ice Cascade'	CCCN EBee IBal
	- 'Icicle'	SPoG
	- subsp. ***inapertus***	IBlr
I	- - 'Albus'	IBlr
	- - 'Cyan'	IBlr

	- - 'White'	CPrp IBal
§	- subsp. ***intermedius***	CPrp IBal IBlr NHoy
	- - 'Long Tom'	CExl CPrp EBee EPri
	- - white-flowered	CPou
	- large	IBal
	- 'Margaret'	CCCN
	- 'Midnight Cascade'	CCCN CExl CPar CPrp CSpe EBee ECtt ELan IBal IPot LEdu NBid NHoy SEdd SRms WFar WTyc
	- 'Mood Indigo'	EBee EPri IBal NHoy
	- subsp. ***parviflorus***	IBlr
	- subsp. ***pendulus***	IBal IBlr
	- - 'Black Magic'	IBal
	- - 'Graskop'	CBcs CCCN CExl CSam EBee EHyd ELan EPfP EPri IBal IBlr MNrw NHoy NSti SEdd SFai SMHy SRms WTyc
	- - 'Violet Dusk'	IBlr
	- 'Sapphire Cascade'	LSRN
	- tall pale blue-flowered **new**	WPGP
	- 'Tempest'	WPGP
	- 'White Cloud'	IBal
	'Indigo Dreams'	CBdn CKno CPar CPne CPrp EBee IBal LPla MAvo NHoy SFai WABo
	'Inkspots'	CCCN CMac CPrp EHyd EPfP IBal LSou NHoy SEdd SFai SPoG
	'Intermedius' Leichtlin	IBal LEdu
I	'Intermedius' van Tubergen	IBal NBid
	'Isis'	CBro CPrp CSam CSde ECha ELon EPri IBal IBlr MAvo
	'Jacaranda'	CMac EBee IBal LSou NHoy SEdd SFai WABo
	'Jack Elliott'	MAvo
	'Jack's Blue'	CBro CDor CJun CSam EBee ECtt ELan ELon EMor EPri GMaP IBal LSRN MHol MNrw NGdn NHoy NLar SLdr SMad WCot WFar WSpi
	'Jersey Giant'	CPrp
	'Jodie'	ELon
	'Johanna'	EBee EMor IBal
	'Johannesburg'	IBal
	Johannesburg hybrids	ECha
	'Jolanda'	CPrp IBal
	'Jonie'	IBal
	'Jonny's White'	IBal
	'Kalmthout Blue'	IBal
	'Kew White'	SMHy
	'Kilmurry Blue'	IBal
	'Kilmurry White'	IBal
	'Kingston Blue'	IBlr NBid NHoy WSHC
	'Kobold'	CBro IBal WFar
	'Lady Edith'	IBlr
§	'Lady Grey'	IBlr
	'Lady Moore'	SMHy
§	'Lapis'	CBod CDoC CMac CPrp CSde EBee EPfP EPri IBal LSou MHol MPri NHoy NLar SEdd SFai SLdr WABo
	'Lapis Lazuli'	see *A.* 'Lapis'
	'Latent Blue'	IBlr
	'Lavender Haze'	CCCN CDoC CMac EBee EHyd EPfP IBal NHoy SEdd SFai WABo WSMil WSpi
	'Leanne'	IBal
	'Leicester'	IBal
	'Liam's Lilac'	CBdn CCCN CDoC CExl CKno CPou CPrp ELon IBal LCro LOPS LSou MAvo NHoy NLar SFai WABo WFar

	'Lilac Flash'	CBdn CPbh CPne IBal
	'Lilac Lullaby'	IBal
	'Lilac Time'	CExl CPrp IBal IBlr
	'Lilliput'	CBcs CBro CCCN CMac CMea CPrp CSpe EBou ECha ECtt ELan ELon EPfP EShb GKev GMaP IBal LSou MRav NGdn SPer SRms WCFE WFar XEll XSen
	'Lissabon'	IBal
	'Lisse'	IBal
	'Little Dutch Blue'	IBal WCot
	'Little Dutch White' PBR	IBal LEdu SEdd WCot
	'Little Frank'	NHoy
	'Little Sebastian'	NHoy
	'Little White'	IBal
	'Littlecourt'	CBro IBal MAvo
	'Loch Hope' ♀H6	CAby CBod CBro CPrp CSam EBee ECtt ELon EPfP IBal LPla MAvo MHol MRav SDix SLdr SPer WCot WSpi
	'Los Angeles'	IBal
	'Luly'	IBal MAvo MGos WFar
	'Luna'	EBee IBal
	'Lydenburg'	EBee EPri IBal IBlr LEdu MAvo WPGP
	'Lyn Valley'	CBdn CPne CPrp EBee IBal
	'Mabel Grey'	see *A.* 'Lady Grey'
	'Madurodam'	IBal
	'Magnifico'	CPrp IBlr
	'Malaga'	IBal
	'Malmo'	IBal
	'Marchants Cobalt Cracker'	SMHy
	'Marchants Midnight Blue'	SMHy
	'Marcus'	EBee IBal SDir
	'Margaret'	GKev IBal LSRN NHoy WFar
	'Maria'	CPrp
	'Marianne'	IBal
	'Mariètte'	EBee
	'Marijke'	IBal
	'Marjorie'	CBdn CPne WABo
	'Martine'	IBal
	'Maureen'	CPrp EBee IBal LSRN MAvo
	'Maurice'	IBal
	'May Snow' (v)	WCot
	'Medan'	IBal
	'Medusa'	IBal
	'Megan's Mauve'	CBdn CBro CKno CPne CPou CPrp EBee ELon EPri IBal LCro LOPS LSRN NSti SFai WABo
	'Meibont' (v)	IBal WCot
	'Melbourne'	SPad
	'Mercury'	IBlr
	'Messina'	IBal
	MI CASA ('Aaopr017')	IBal
	'Michelle'	IBal
	'Middleburg'	IBal
	MIDKNIGHT BLUE ('Monmid')	EWes WSHC
	'Midnight'	EWes IBal MAvo
	'Midnight Blue' ambig.	CDoC ELan EPfP EShb IBal MCot NWad SMHy WFar
	'Midnight Blue' P. Wood	IBlr
	'Midnight Dream'	EBee ECtt EPot IBal LEdu NHoy STPC WFar
	'Midnight Parade' **new**	MHtn
§	'Midnight Star'	Widely available
	'Mini Blue'	IBal
	'Misty Dawn' (v)	CBcs CBod CWGN EBee ECtt ELon EWhm IBal LSou MHol SLdr WCot WSMil

	'Mole Valley'	IBal
	'Molly Howick'	EBee
	'Monique'	IBal
	'Montreal'	IBal
	'Moonlight Star'	CCht EBee IBal IPot MHol NHoy SFai WABo
	'Moonshine'	IBal WFar
I	'Mooreanus' misapplied	EBee EPfP IBal NBid
	'Morning Star'	IBal
	'Mount Stewart'	IBal IBlr
	'Nancy'	IBal
	'Napoli'	IBal
	'Navy Blue'	see *A.* 'Midnight Star'
	'Newa'	EBee
	'Newcastle'	IBal
	'Nikki'	CBdn CMea CPne CPrp IBal
	'Norman Hadden'	IBlr
	'Northern Light'	IBal
	'Northern Star' PBR	CAbb CBdn CCht CDoC CExl CKno CPne CPrp CWGN EBee EHyd EMor EPot EPri EWes IBal LCro LOPS LSRN LSou MAvo MHol NHoy NLar NSti SFai SLon SPoG SRms WABo
	nutans	see *A. caulescens*
	'Nyx'	IBlr
	'Odessa'	IBal
	'Oslo'	IBal
	'Oxbridge'	IBlr
	'Oxford'	IBal
	'Pacific Blue' PBR	CDoC IBal SLdr
	Palmer's hybrids	see *A.* Headbourne hybrids
	'Patent Blue'	CPrp IBal IBlr
	'Patriot'	EPfP
	'Pavlova'	CBod IBal
	'Penelope Palmer'	CPrp IBal IBlr
	'Peter Franklin'	EBee IBal
	'Peter Pan' ambig.	CBcs CBod CCCN CDor CExl CKno CPrp CSBt EBee ECha ECtt EHyd ELan ELon EPfP IBal ILea MHer MNrw MTin NHoy SCob SFai SPoG SRms SSut WBrk WFar WKif WSpi
	'Peter Pan American'	GKev NHoy
	'Phantom'	CCht CPrp EBee IBal IBlr IMou MAvo NLar SAko SFai WABo WCot
	'Picton Blue'	WFar
	'Pinocchio'	EPot IBal IMou SDeJ
	'Pirame'	IBal
	PITCHOUNE BLUE ('Scrarey09' PBR)	IBal
	'Plas Merdyn Blue'	CPrp
	'Plas Merdyn White'	IBal IBlr
	'Podge Mill'	IBal IBlr
	'Polar Ice'	CPrp EBee ELon EPri GKev IBal ILea LSRN MAvo MNrw NHoy SDir WCAu WFar WSpi
	'Polar Star'	IBal
	'Porcelain'	IBal IBlr
	praecox ♀H2	CPrp GKev IBlr NHoy
	- 'Albiflorus' ♀H2	CBcs CBod CBro CPou CPrp CTri EPri GWyn MTin NHoy SEND SGsty
	- 'Maximus Albus'	CBod CPou IBal IBlr
§	- subsp. ***minimus***	CElw CPou IBal IBlr SEND
	- - 'Adelaide'	CPrp IBal
	- 'Neptune'	IBlr
§	- subsp. ***orientalis***	CBro CCCN IBlr
	- - 'Full Moon'	IBal SFai
	- - 'Royal Velvet'	CKno IBal LCro LOPS MHol SFai
	- - 'Silver Star' (v)	IBal

– subsp. ***praecox***	IBlr
– 'Saturn'	IBlr
– Slieve Donard form	IBlr
– 'Storms River'	IBal
– 'Uranus'	IBlr
– 'Venus'	IBlr
'Premier'	IBlr
'Pretty Heidy' **new**	LSou SFai
'Pretty Wendy'	IBal
'Princess Margaret'	CPrp IBal
§ 'Purple Cloud'	Widely available
'Purple Delight'	CPar CPbh CPrp EBee EPfP IBal LCro LOPS SAko SFai WABo WFar
'Purple Emperor'	IBal
'Purple Fountain'	IBal SRms
'Purple Haze'	IBal
'Purple Heart'	SFai
'Purple Magic'	IBal
'Purple Ripple'	IBal
'Purple Star'	CCCN
'Queen Anne'	CBod IBal
'Queen Mother'	CPrp IBal WSpi
QUEEN MUM ('Pmn06'PBR)	Widely available
'Queen of the Ocean'	IBal
'Quink Drops'	SMHy
'Radiant Star'	IBal
'Regal Beauty'	CBro CSBt EBee IBal LSRN NBid SAko SFai WABo
'Rhapsody in Blue'	CBdn CPne CPrp
'Rhone'	CBro IBal IBlr
'Robin'	IBal
'Rosewarne'	CBcs CBod CCCN CDoC CExl IBal IBlr
'Rotterdam'	IBal XSen
'Roxanne'	EBee IBal
'Royal Blue'	CBro CPrp GMaP IBal WCot WSpi
'Royal Knight'	IBal
'Ruan Vean'	CPrp
'Ruthie's Sunshine' **new**	WFar
'Sabang'	IBal
'Sally Anne'	CBdn CPne CPrp WABo
'San Remo'	IBal
'Sandringham'	CBcs CBod CPrp EBee ELon EPfP EPri EWes IBal LSRN MMuc NBid NHoy SEdd SFai WABo WFar
'Sandy'PBR	IBal LSou SFai
'Sapphire'	CPrp IBlr
'Sarah'PBR	CBod CCCN CWCL EBee IBal LSRN MTin NLar SFai SLdr
'Saville Blue'	CPrp MCot
'Sea Coral'	CBdn CBod CCCN CMac CPne CPrp EBee ECtt EMor EPri IBal MAvo NSti
'Sea Foam'	CMac XLum
'Sea Mist'	CBdn CCCN CPne CPrp EBee
'Sea Spray'	CCCN EBee EPri IBal WFar
'Sea Storm' (Storm Series) **new**	SPad
'Selma Bock'	CPbh IBal
'Semarang'	IBal
'Senna'PBR	CCCN CExl EBee GKev IBal
'Septemberhemel'	IBal
'Shooting Stars'	IBal
'Silberpfeil'	IBal
'Silver Anniversary'	IBal NHoy
'Silver Baby'	CAbb CBod CDoC CKno CPrp CWGN EBee EHyd EPfP EPri IBal LEdu LSou MHol NHoy SFai SRms WABo WTyc
'Silver Jubilee'	IBal
'Silver Lining'	CBdn CPne ECtt EMor IBal SFai
'Silver Mist'	CBdn CPne IBal IBlr
SILVER MOON ('Notfred'PBR) (v)	CBcs CBro CCCN EBee EHyd ELan EPfP GKev IBal LLWG LSou MCot MGos MHol NBPC NHoy NLar NSti SCob SEdd SFai SPoG WABo WCot
'Silver Sceptre'	IBlr
'Silver Stream'	NHoy
'Silver Suzy'	IBal
'Sky Rocket'	CPrp IBal IBlr WMal
'Sky Star'	IBal
'Skyscraper'	IBal
'Slieve Donard'	IBlr
'Snow Cloud'	CAbb CBro CExl CPne CPrp CTsd EBee EHyd EPfP LCro LOPS NLar SAko SEND SEdd SFai SLdr SLon WABo WSpi
'Snow Crystal'	SFai
'Snow Pixie'	CSpe EBee IBal LSRN NHoy SEdd SFai SLdr WABo WSpi
'Snow Princess'	ELon EPfP IBal
'Snow Shadows'	CBro IBal
'Snowball'	CBcs CExl WSpi
'Snowdrops'	CCCN EBee ELan
'Snowstorm'PBR (Storm Series)	EBee EPfP IBal LBuc SArc SPad
'Sofie'PBR	EBee STPC
'Sorento'	IBal
'Southern Cross'	EBee IBal NHoy SFai
'Southern Star'	IBal
'Star Quality'	EBee IBal LBuc LSou MNrw SFai WABo
'Starburst'	IBlr
'Starburst Blue'	IBal
'Starburst White'	IBal
'Stardust'	IBal LBuc
'Stargazer'	EBee IBal LBuc
'Stars and Stripes'	IBal
'Stellenbosch' **new**	WPGP
'Stéphanie Charm'	IBal
'Stockholm'	GAbr GKev IBal
'Storm Cloud' Reads	see *A.* 'Purple Cloud'
'Storm Cloud' (d)	CBro IBal
'Strawberry Ice'	CBro EBee IBal SFai WABo
'Streamline'	CBcs CBod CElw CKno CMea CPrp CSde EBee ECtt EHyd ELon EMor EPfP EShb GAbr GKin GMaP IBal MRav NHoy SDys SEND WSHC
'Su Casa'	IBal
'Summer Blue'	IBal
'Summer Clouds'	CPrp ELan
'Summer Days'	CBdn CPne CPrp IBal SFai WABo
'Summer Delight'	IBal
'Summer Skies'	CBdn CPne CPrp ELon IBal
'Summer Snow'	IBal
'Sunfield'	CDor CKno CPrp EPfP GKev IBal ILea MNrw NLar NPer
'Super Star'	CBro CPrp IBal
'Susan Elizabeth'	CPrp
'Sweet Surprise'	EBee IBal SEdd SFai
'Sylvia'PBR	IBal
'Sylvine'	CPrp IBal
'Tall Boy'	CPrp IBlr
'Tarka'	CBdn CExl CPne CPrp ELon EPfP EPri IBal LSou NHoy SDys WABo
'Taw Valley'	CKno CPrp EBee ELon IBal LCro LOPS MGos NHoy SEdd SMad WABo
'Thorn'	IBal

'Thumbelina'	CBro CMac EBee IBal LSou NHoy XLum
THUNDER STORM ('Dunaga02') (v)	IBal
'Timaru'	CBro CElw CPrp EBee ECha ECtt ELan ELon EPfP GAbr GMaP IBal MHol NGdn SLdr WCot
'Tinkerbell' (v)	CBcs CBdn CBor CBro CCCN CPne EBee ELan EPfP EPri EShb IBal MGos MHol MRav NHoy NPer SPoG SRms SWvt
'Tiny White'	EPri
'Titan'	IBlr
'Titch'	IBal
'Tom Thumb'[PBR]	CBod CDoC CExl CPrp CSde ECtt EHyd EPau EPfP GBin IBal NHoy SRkn
'Top Slice' (v)	WCot
'Torbay'	CBod CElw CPrp ECtt ELon EMor EPau EPfP EShb EWTr GAbr GKev GKin IBal MAvo MNrw NHol NLar SGbt WAvo WHoo
'Tornado'	CPrp EBee ECtt ELon IBal ILea NLar
'Triangle'	CPbh IBal
'Tsolo'	IBal
'Twilight Zone'	EBee IBal
TWISTER ('Ambic001'[PBR])	CBro CKno CPar CPla CPrp CSpe CTsd EPfP IBal LCro LLWG LOPS LSou NSti SEdd SFai SPad SPalm SPoG SRms WABo WTor
umbellatus Redouté	see *A. praecox* subsp. *orientalis*
'Underway'	EWes GKev IBal
Ventnor hybrid	SVen
'Volendam'	IBal
'Washington'	IBal
'Wavy Navy'	IBal
'Wedding Day'	CBdn CPne EBee IBal
'Wembworthy'	CBdn CPne CPrp EBee IBal
'White Dwarf'	see *A.* white-flowered, dwarf
'White Flash'	IBal
'White Giant'	CBod CSBt WSpi
'White Heaven'[PBR]	CAby CBod EBee ECtt ELon EPfP GAbr IBal IPot LCro LEdu LOPS LSun MAvo MHol NBPC NHoy NSti SCob SDix SEND SEdd SFai SLdr WCot WSpi
'White Ice'	CBcs CPbh IBal
'White Pixie'	IBal
'White Smile'	EPri
'White Superior'	CBod EBee EPfP GMaP MNHC MSCN
'White Umbrella'	EHyd ELan
'White Wings'	IBal
white-flowered	WAvo WCFE
§ - dwarf	CBro ECha EPfP EShb IBal MAsh MPie NBir NGdn NHol SGbt
'Whitney'[PBR]	IBal IBlr
'Windlebrooke'	CCCN EAJP ECha EPri IBal MAvo NLar SDeJ WCot
'Windsor Castle'	IBlr
'Windsor Grey'	Widely available
'Winsome'	IBlr
'Winter Sky'	IBal
'Wolga'	CBro EBee IBal
'Wolkberg' Kirstenbosch	IBal IBlr
'Yellow Tips'	IBal
'Yves Klein'	IBlr WABo
'Zachary'	CPou CPrp EBee ELon EPri WABo
'Zeal Thomas'	IBal
'Zigzag White'	WCot

Agapetes (*Ericaceae*)

'Ludgvan Cross' 𝕐[H2]	CBcs CCCN CTsd EShb MGil SPad
serpens 𝕐[H2]	CBcs CCCN CTsd SLon
- 'Scarlet Elf'	CCCN CTsd LRHS
smithiana var. ***major***	GGGa

Agastache (*Lamiaceae*)

'After Eight'	CSpe ECtt LRHS MBel
anethiodora	see *A. foeniculum* (Pursh) Kuntze
anisata	see *A. foeniculum* (Pursh) Kuntze
'Apricot Sunrise'	MCot
'Astello Indigo'	MNHC SPhx
aurantiaca	NGBl SPhx SPlb
- 'Apricot Sprite'	CSpe EMor EPfP MHol NGdn NRHS SRkn WCav WKif
'Blackadder'	Widely available
'Blaue Sangria'	NDov WGoo
'Blue Boa'[PBR]	CBod CDor CPla CWGN EBee ECtt GWyn LCro LOPS LRHS MAvo MBel MHol NCou NDov NLar NSti SEdd SIvy SMad SPoG SRms WCAu WSpi WTor
* 'Blue Bonnet'	CSpe
'Blue Fortune' 𝕐[H6]	CBcs CBod CRos ECha EHyd EPfP GWyn LCro LOPS LRHS MCot MRav NDov NLar NRHS SAko SCob SMad SPer SPhx SRms SWvt WCAu WSpi XSen
'Bolero'	CSpe LRHS MHol SPhx WSHC
§ ***cana***	SPhx
- 'Heatwave'[PBR]	EPfP NDov
- 'Purple Pygmy'	EPfP
'Cotton Candy'[PBR]	LCro LOPS
'Firebird'	CWGN EBee ECtt ELan EPfP SRms SWvt
'Fleur'	ECtt WGoo
foeniculum misapplied	see *A. rugosa*
§ ***foeniculum*** (Pursh) Kuntze	CBee CCBP CLau EBee ELan ENfk GPoy MCot MHer MNHC SPhx SRms WJek WTre XAbr
- 'Alabaster'	CBcs EBee EWes GWyn LCro LOPS NLar
- 'Alba'	NBre
- 'Blaustrahl'	SAko
'Globetrotter'	CBod EAJP ELan SPhx
'Kolibri'	ECtt WGoo
(Kudos Series) 'Kudos Ambrosia'[PBR]	ECtt EMor LRHS NRHS SPoG
- 'Kudos Coral'[PBR]	LRHS LSou MHol MNHC NRHS SRkn
- 'Kudos Gold'[PBR]	CKno EMor LRHS MHol SPoG SRkn
- 'Kudos Mandarin'[PBR]	CSpe EMor EPfP LRHS MMrt NLar NRHS SPoG
- 'Kudos Silver Blue'	ECtt LRHS MNHC NRHS
'Linda'	CWGN NDov WCot
§ ***mexicana***	WFar
- 'Champagne'	NWad
- 'Red Fortune'[PBR]	CBcs CWGN EBee ECtt EHyd EPfP ILea LCro LOPS LRHS MHol MPie NRHS SPad SPoG WCot WMal
- 'Rosea'	see *A. cana*
- 'Sangria'	CWGN ILea NGdn SBut SPhx SRms XLum XSen
nepetoides	EPPr NDov
ORANGE NECTAR (Nectar Series)	EBee MHol MPie WCot
'Painted Lady'	ECtt
pallidiflora var. ***neomexicana***	SPhx SPlb

- - 'Rose Mint'	CSpe
'Pink Pop'	ELan EPfP MHol
'Purple Haze'	CDoC LRHS NDov NRHS
'Raspberry Summer'PBR	CWGN ECtt EPfP LRHS MHtn NRHS WAul
§ ***rugosa***	CAby CBod CCBP ECha GPoy LEdu MNHC NAts SPer SPhx SPlb SRms WJek
- from Korea	IMou
- f. ***albiflora***	WCAu
- - 'Alabaster'	CDor NDov
- - 'Liquorice White'	CBod EBee ECha ELan EPfP GWyn MArl MBel NGBl SGbt SPer SPlb SPoG SRms WGwG
- 'Golden Jubilee'	CAby CBod CRos CSpe EBee EBou ECha ELan EPfP LRHS MAvo NGdn NLar NRHS NSti SGbt SRms SWvt WAul WJek WSMil XLum
- 'Heronswood Mist'	EBee
- 'Korean Zest'	WCru
- 'Liquorice Blue'	CBod CDor CTsd ELan EPfP LRHS MBel MSpe NAts NGBl NGdn SGbt SPer SPoG SRms SSut SWvt WHoo
- 'Little Adder'	CBod MHol
rupestris	CSpe SPhx XSen
- 'Apache Sunset'	SPlb XSen
'Serpentine'	ECtt EWes NLar WGoo
'Spicy'	NDov
'Summer Fiesta'PBR	EBee
'Summer Glow'PBR	CDor CSam CWGN ECtt EPfP LRHS MHol NDov NGBl NRHS SDys SPoG WCot
'Summer Love'PBR	ECtt NLar
'Summer Sky'PBR	ECtt LRHS
'Summer Sunset'PBR	CDor CWGN EBee ELan LCro LOPS LRHS MHol NRHS
'Tangerine Dreams' 🏆H3	CBod ECtt ELan EPfP LRHS MPie NRHS SCoo WAul
'Tutti-frutti'	ECtt
'Violet Vision'PBR	CWGN ECtt LCro LOPS MAvo MBel

Agathaea see *Felicia*

Agathis (*Araucariaceae*)

australis	SMad

Agathosma (*Rutaceae*)

ovata	CCCN
serpyllacea new	CCCN

Agave ✿ (*Asparagaceae*)

albomarginata	CDTJ
americana 🏆H2	CAbb CBcs CBen CBod CPla CTsd ELan EPfP EShb LRHS LSun SArc SChr SCob SEND SEdd SGsty SPalm SPlb SPre SVen SWeb SWvt WCot WGrn
- 'Marginata' (v) 🏆H2	CBrP CDTJ NQui SEND SVen WCot WSFF WSMil
- 'Mediopicta' misapplied	see *A. americana* 'Mediopicta Alba'
- 'Mediopicta' (v) 🏆H2	CDTJ SArc WGrn
§ - 'Mediopicta Alba' (v) 🏆H2	CAbb CBrP CCCN CDTJ CJun CPbh ELan SPalm SPlb WCot WGrn WSMil
- 'Mediopicta Aurea' (v)	WCot
- var. ***oaxacensis***	WPGP
- subsp. ***protamericana***	CDTJ
- - blue	SPlb
- subsp. ***protamericana*** × ***scabra*** F&M 310	WPGP
- 'Striata' (v)	CDTJ EShb WCot
- 'Variegata' (v) 🏆H2	CAbb CBcs CBen CBod CPbh CSde ELan EPfP EShb LRHS LSun MGos NPer SArc SChr SCob SGsty SPalm SPlb SWeb SWvt WBor
angustifolia	see *A. vivipara* var. *vivipara*
- var. ***marginata*** hort.	WCot
applanata	CJun SPlb WPGP
asperrima	CDTJ
§ - subsp. ***maderensis***	SPlb
atrovirens	WCot
- var. ***mirabilis***	CDTJ
- - F&M 245	WPGP
attenuata	CDTJ SPalm SPlb
beauleriana	SPalm
'Bloodspot'	WCot
'Blue Brian'	SArc
boldinghiana	WCot
bovicornuta	WCot
bracteosa	CCCN CDTJ WCot
celsii	see *A. mitis* var. *mitis*
cerulata subsp. ***nelsonii***	CDTJ
chrysantha	CCCN CDTJ WCot
- 'Black Canyon'	WCot
chrysoglossa	CDTJ
colimana	see *A. ortgiesiana*
colorata	CCCN CDTJ CJun WCot
'Cornelius'	WCot WGrn
cupreata	CDTJ
decipiens	SPlb
deserti	CDTJ CJun LRHS WCot
- var. ***simplex***	WCot
difformis	CDTJ
- NJM 05.034	WPGP
durangensis	SPlb
elongata	see *A. vivipara* var. *vivipara*
ensifera	CJun
felgeri	CDTJ
ferdinandi-regis	see *A. victoriae-reginae*
ferox	see *A. salmiana* var. *ferox*
filifera 🏆H2	CCCN CDTJ CDoC CJun CPbh SChr SPlb WCot
flexispina	SPlb
garciae-mendozae	CDTJ
geminiflora	CCCN CDTJ CJun CPbh EShb
gentryi	CDTJ SPlb WCot
ghiesbreghtii	CPbh
gigantea	see *Furcraea foetida*
guadalajarana	CDTJ CPbh
guttata	WCot
havardiana	CDTJ SPalm XSen
horrida	CDTJ CJun
- subsp. ***horrida***	SPlb
- 'Perotensis'	CDTJ EShb
hurteri	CDTJ
impressa	CDTJ WCot
isthmensis	SPlb
kerchovei	WCot
lechuguilla	CDTJ WCot XSen
lophantha	see *A. univittata*
- var. ***caerulescens***	see *A. univittata*
'Macha Mocha'	WCot
macroacantha 🏆H1c	CDTJ SPalm
maculosa	SBrt WCot
marmorata	CJun
maximilliana	SPlb
mckelveyana	WCot
- DJF 1575 from Bagdad, Arizona	WCot
mitis	CDoC

§	- var. ***mitis***	CDTJ SPlb SSim
	- var. ***mitis* × *variegata***	WCot
	montana	CCht CDTJ CTsd SArc SChr SPlb SPtp XSen
	multifilifera	XSen
§	***obscura***	CDTJ WCot
§	***ortgiesiana***	WCot
	ovatifolia	CDTJ CJun SMad SPalm SPlb WCot XSen
	- NJM 09.002	WPGP
	palmeri	CCCN CDTJ SPlb WCot XSen
	panamana	see *A. vivipara* var. *vivipara*
	parrasana 🏆H2	CDTJ SSim WCot
	parryi 🏆H2	CDTJ CPbh GKev SPlb SPtp WCot XSen
	- var. ***couesii***	CDTJ XSen
	- 'Cream Spike' (v)	CBcs CBod CTsd SEdd SIvy SPad SPalm WCot WGrn WSMil
	- var. ***huachucensis***	CDTJ WCot
	- subsp. ***neomexicana***	CCCN CDTJ SPlb WCot XSen
	- - SB 948 from W of Artesia, New Mexico	WCot
	- 'Ohi-kissho-ten-nishiki' (v)	WCot
	- subsp. ***parryi***	CDTJ WCot WPGP
	- var. ***truncata***	CDTJ SPlb
	- - variegated (v)	WCot
	parviflora 🏆H2	WCot
	polyacantha var. ***xalapensis***	see *A. obscura*
	potatorum 🏆H2	WCot
	- 'Gary Fisher'	WCot
	salmiana	CDTJ SPlb
	- subsp. ***crassispina***	SPlb
§	- var. ***ferox***	CDTJ SArc SChr SPalm SPlb
	scabra	CCCN WCot
	- subsp. ***maderensis***	see *A. asperrima* subsp. *maderensis*
	schidigera	WCot
	- 'Shira-ito-no-ohi' (v)	WCot
	schottii	CDTJ WCot
	'Sharkskin Shoes'	WCot
	shrevei subsp. ***magna***	SPlb
	sileri	WCot
	sisalana	CDTJ
	stictata	WCot
	striata subsp. ***falcata***	WCot
*	- 'Rubra'	CDTJ SPlb WCot
	stricta 🏆H2	CCCN CDTJ WCot
	- 'Nana'	CDTJ SMad
	- 'Rubra'	WCot
	tenuifolia	CPla
	titanota 🏆H1c	SPlb
	toumeyana 🏆H2	CPbh SPlb WCot
	- var. ***bella***	CDTJ
	triangularis	CDTJ
	undulata	WCot
	- 'Chocolate Chips'	WCot
§	***univittata***	CDTJ CJun WCot
	- 'Quadricolor' (v) 🏆H2	CBod CDTJ SMad SPlb WCot
	utahensis 🏆H3	CDTJ SEND SPlb WCot XSen
	- DJF 1521 from Peach Springs, Arizona	WCot
	- var. ***eborispina***	WCot
	- subsp. ***kaibabensis***	WCot
	variegata	WCot
	- B&SWJ 10234	WCru
§	***victoriae-reginae*** 🏆H2	CCCN CDTJ CJun CPbh EShb SChr SPalm SPlb SSim WCot XSen
	- dwarf	WCot
	virginica	WCot
§	***vivipara*** var. ***vivipara***	WCot
	wocomahi	WCot
	xylonacantha	CDTJ SChr SPlb WCot
	zebra	CDTJ

Ageratina (*Asteraceae*)

§	***altissima***	CDor CMac EBee
	- 'Braunlaub'	NBir NLar SHar WCAu
	- 'Chocolate'	Widely available
§	***aromatica***	SHar
§	***ligustrina***	CBcs CBod CCht CDoC CExl CRHN CSde CTri EBee ECha ELan LRHS MBlu NAts SDix SEND SPer SPoG SRkn SRms WLov WMal WSFF

Ageratum (*Asteraceae*)

	'Blue Champion'	MPri SCob
	corymbosum	CSpe EShb
	houstonianum 'Blue Danube' 🏆H2	LCro LOPS
	- 'High Tide Blue'	MPri
	petiolatum	LRHS SHar WFar

Aglaonema (*Araceae*)

	'Jubilee Compacta'PBR	LCro LOPS

Agrimonia (*Rosaceae*)

	eupatoria	CBod CHab ENfk GPoy MHer MNHC NAts NMir SRms WHer WWFP WWild
*	- var. ***alba***	NLar SBut
	- 'Cambridge Lace' (v)	MAvo WCot

Agropyron (*Poaceae*)

	glaucum	see *Elymus hispidus*
	magellanicum	see *Elymus magellanicus*
	pubiflorum	see *Elymus magellanicus*

Agrostemma (*Caryophyllaceae*)

	coronaria	see *Lychnis coronaria*
	githago	CHab LCro LOPS MBow MNHC NBir SRms
	- 'Ocean Pearl'	CSpe SPhx

Agrostis (*Poaceae*)

	calamagrostis	see *Stipa calamagrostis*
	capillaris	CHab
	nebulosa	SPhx WCot
	stolonifera 'Julia Ann' (v)	WCot

Aichryson (*Crassulaceae*)

	× ***aizoides*** var. ***domesticum*** 'Variegatum' (v) 🏆H1c	CDTJ CPbh EBak SIvy SSim WCot

Ailanthus (*Simaroubaceae*)

§	***altissima***	CBcs CCVT CExl ECrN EPfP SCob SPlb SWvt
§	- 'Hongye'	MBlu
	- 'Purple Dragon'	see *A. altissima* 'Hongye'
	- var. ***tanakae*** CWJ 12452	WCru
	- - NMWJ 14522	WCru
	glandulosa	see *A. altissima*

Ainsliaea (*Asteraceae*)

	apiculata	MAsh
	chapaensis B&SWJ 11720	WCru
	- B&SWJ 11732	WCru
	latifolia FMWJ 13426	WCru

nervosa B&SWJ 11344	WCru
petelotii FMWJ 13427	WCru
tonkinensis B&SWJ 11819	WCru

Ajania (*Asteraceae*)

§ ***pacifica***	CBor WFar
- 'Silver Edge'	XLum
trilobata	GKev

Ajuga (*Lamiaceae*)

genevensis	GWyn LRHS SPhx WOut
incisa	EWld
- 'Bikun' (v)	CBct EBee NEoE SPoG WCot WFar
- 'Blue Enigma'	CExl IMou NLar WFar
- 'Blue Ensign'	WSHC
'Little Court Pink'	see *A. reptans* 'Purple Torch'
lupulina	GEdr
'Pink Lightning' (v)	ELan LRHS LSou NHpl NRHS SRms WFar WHil
'Pink Spires'	WFar
pyramidalis 'Metallica Crispa'	CBre EBee ELan EWes GJos GWyn NBir NEoE NHol NHpl NLar SRms SWvt WCav WFar WTor
reptans	CHab CTri ECtt ENfk EPed GKev GPoy LCro LOPS MBel MHer MNHC NAts SRms WOut XLum
- f. ***albiflora***	CDor WFar
- - 'Alba'	CBre EBee ELon GWyn MBel MRav NBro SRms WFar
- 'Arctic Fox' (v)	GEdr NBro SWvt
- 'Argentea'	see *A. reptans* 'Variegata'
§ - 'Atropurpurea'	CTri ECha EHyd ELan EPfP GAbr GWyn LCro LOPS LRHS MGos MMuc NWad SEND SGol SPlb SRms SWvt WBrk XLum
- BLACK SCALLOP ('Binblasca'^{PBR})	Widely available
- 'Blueberry Muffin'	ECtt EWTr LCro LOPS NHpl
- 'Braunherz'	CRos CTri ECtt EHyd ELan EPfP EShb GMaP LRHS MAsh MBros MCot MPri NBir NHpl NLar NRHS NSla SCob SGol SPer SRms SWvt WCav WFar
- 'Burgundy Glow' (v)	Widely available
§ - 'Catlin's Giant' ♀H7	Widely available
- 'Choc Ice'	EWTr
- 'Chocolate Chip'	see *A. reptans* 'Valfredda'
- 'Dixie Chip'	WFar
- 'Ebony'	LSRN
- 'Evening Glow'	GJos WIce
- 'Golden Beauty' (v)	SRms WFar WOut
- 'Golden Glow' (v)	ELan LRHS NRHS WFar
- 'Harlequin' (v)	SWvt
- 'John Pierpoint'	SHar
- 'Jumbo'	see *A. reptans* 'Jungle Beauty'
§ - 'Jungle Beauty'	MRav XLum
- 'Macrophylla'	see *A. reptans* 'Catlin's Giant'
- 'Mahogany'	NLar SRms
§ - 'Multicolor' (v)	CBcs ELan LRHS MAsh MPri NRHS SCob SPer SPlb SPoG SRms SWvt WFar WRHF
- 'Pink Elf'	GQue MRav NBro
- 'Pink Surprise'	MHer NRya WFar
- 'Purple Brocade'	NLar
§ - 'Purple Torch'	ELon MPie NLar SHar SRms SWvt
- 'Purpurea'	see *A. reptans* 'Atropurpurea'
- 'Rainbow'	see *A. reptans* 'Multicolor'
- 'Rosea'	GWyn MBel SBut WFar XLum
- 'Rowden Amethyst'	WHil
- 'Tricolor'	see *A. reptans* 'Multicolor'
§ - 'Valfredda'	EHyd EPfP GAbr GBin GKev GQue GWyn LLWG LRHS NLar NRHS SRms SWvt WBrk WFar
§ - 'Variegata' (v)	ECtt NHpl SPer SPoG SRms WFar WTor
'Rose Glow'	NHpl
'Sparkler' (v)	NHpl WFar WOut
SUGAR PLUM ('Binsugplu'^{PBR}) (v)	ECul ELan MCot

Akebia ✿ (*Lardizabalaceae*)

longeracemosa	CRHN EBee SBrt SChF
- B&SWJ 3606	CExl LEdu WCot WCru WPGP
× ***pentaphylla***	CBcs CRos EBee EHyd ELan EPfP LRHS MAsh MGil MRav SPer
quinata	Widely available
- B&SWJ 4425	WCru
- 'Amethyst Glow'	CDoC CRos CWCL CWld EHyd ELon EMil EPfP LRHS MHtn NLar SEle SMad SPer SPoG
- cream-flowered	CCCN CRHN EHyd EMil EPfP EWld LCro LOPS LRHS MGos MRav NLar SCob SPer SRms SSta SWvt WCru WLov WPGP
- 'Shirobana'	CBcs CMen CWGN MBlu MGil NOra WAvo
- 'Silver Bells'	LRHS
- 'White Chocolate' ♀H6	ESwi NLar WCru WSHC
trifoliata	CBcs CMen CRHN CRos EBee EHyd ELan EPfP LRHS MGil MGos NOra SEdd SLon
- B&SWJ 5063	WCru
- B&SWJ 14570	WCru

Alangium (*Cornaceae*)

platanifolium	CBcs CExl WPGP
- var. ***macrophyllum***	CCCN EPfP MGil WBor

Albizia (*Mimosaceae*)

chinensis	EPfP LRHS
distachya	see *Paraserianthes lophantha*
§ ***julibrissin***	CDTJ CTsd EBee EPfP IDee MGil
- NJM 13.018 **new**	WPGP
- CHOCOLATE FOUNTAIN ('Ncaj1')	ELan WHwl
- OMBRELLA ('Boubri'^{PBR})	CBcs ELan NOra WHwl WMat WPGP
- f. ***rosea*** ♀H4	CBcs CExl CMCN CRos CWGN ELan EPfP LEdu LRHS MGil SArc SEND SEdd SEle SLim SPad SPlb SPoG WPGP
I - 'Rouge Selection'	EPfP LRHS SPoG
- 'Shidare'	EBee ELan NOra WHwl WMat
- 'Summer Chocolate'^{PBR} ♀H3	CBcs CRos CWGN EHyd ELan EPfP IDee LRHS MAsh NOra NRHS SCoo SPer SPoG WHwl WMat
kalkora	SPlb
lophantha	see *Paraserianthes lophantha*

Albuca ✿ (*Asparagaceae*)

JCA 15856	WHil
angolensis	CPou
'Ausgrabies Hills'	WHil
canadensis (L.) F.M. Leight.	CPou
'Dirk Wallace'	CExl
flaccida	WHil
glauca	EBee MPie
humilis	CExl EPot MHer WAbe WHil
nelsonii	CAvo CPrp EBee MPie SChr

shawii	CAvo CBod CBor CBro CPou CPrp CWld EAJP EBee EPri ERCP EWld GBin MHer MPie NBPC NSla SChr SPoG SRms WAbe WAvo WGwG WHil
spiralis	CBor GKev WHil
- 'Frizzle Sizzle'	CDoC
wakefieldii	WHil

× *Alcalthaea* (*Malvaceae*)

suffrutescens 'Freedom'	ELan MCot WFar
- 'Parkallee' (d)	CBod EBee ECha ECtt ELan ELon EPPr GMaP GWyn LRHS MAvo MCot MHol MNrw NLar SPhx WBrk WCot XLum
- 'Parkfrieden' (d)	ECha ECtt ELon LRHS MAvo MCot MNrw NLar SPhx XLum
- 'Parkrondell' (d)	ECha ECtt ELan ELon LRHS MAvo MNrw SHar SPhx WCot XLum
- 'Poetry'	ECtt ELan ELon LRHS MCot

Alcea (*Malvaceae*)

'Apple Blossom' (d)	EPfP
ficifolia	MHer WFar WSpi
froloviana	EBee
'Las Vegas'	WFar
pallida	XSen
§ ***rosea***	WFar
- 'Blacknight' (Spotlight Series)	CBod ELan EPfP GKev MHer NLar
- Chater's Double Group (d)	EPfP SCob SPoG SRms SVic WFar
- - chamois (d)	EPfP
- - chestnut-brown-flowered (d)	EPfP
- - maroon-flowered (d)	SPoG
- - pink-flowered (d)	ELan EPfP
- - red-flowered (d)	ELan EPfP SCob SPoG
- - salmon-pink-flowered (d)	EPfP
- - scarlet-flowered (d)	EPfP SPoG
- - violet-flowered (d)	EPfP
- - white-flowered (d)	ELan EPfP LCro LOPS SPoG
- - yellow-flowered (d)	EPfP SPoG SRms
- 'Crème de Cassis'	ELan EPfP LRHS
- Halo Series	WFar WHil
- - 'Halo Apricot'	CRos EHyd EPfP LRHS NRHS SPoG WHoo
- - 'Halo Blush'	CRos EHyd EPfP LRHS NRHS SPoG
- - 'Halo Cerise'	CRos EHyd EPfP LRHS NRHS SPoG WHil
- - 'Halo Cream'	CRos EHyd EPfP LRHS NRHS SPoG
- - 'Halo Red'	EPfP LRHS NRHS SPoG
- - 'Halo White'	EHyd EPfP LRHS NRHS SPoG
- 'Mars Magic' (Spotlight Series)	CBod EBee ELan EPfP LRHS MHer
- 'Nigra'	CSpe ECtt ELan EPfP LCro LOPS LRHS LSRN NGdn SCob SPer SRms WCAu XEll
- 'Polarstar' (Spotlight Series)	CBod EBee ELan LRHS
- 'Radiant Rose' (Spotlight Series)	CBod ELan LRHS MHer
- single-flowered	MMuc SEND SRms
- (Spring Celebrities Series) 'Spring Celebrities Crimson' (d)	LRHS
- - 'Spring Celebrities Lemon' (d)	NRHS
- - 'Spring Celebrities Pink' (d)	LRHS
- - 'Spring Celebrities White' (d)	NRHS
- Summer Carnival Group	SRms
- 'Sunshine' (Spotlight Series)	CBod EBee EPfP LRHS NLar
- 'The Watchman'	WHil
§ ***rugosa***	CBod EBee EPPr LEdu MCot SHar XSen

Alcea × *Althaea* see × *Alcalthaea*

Alchemilla ✿ (*Rosaceae*)

abyssinica	EBee
alpina misapplied	see *A. conjuncta*, *A. plicatula*
alpina ambig.	MCot
alpina L.	EBee ELan EPfP GPoy LEdu LRHS MBel MMuc MRav NBir NChi SEND SRms WFar WPGP WSHC
§ ***conjuncta***	CCBP CDor CMac CSam EBee ECha ELan EPfP GAbr GLog GMaP GWyn MHer MRav NBid NGrd NRya NSti SPer SPlb SRms WCAu WHoo
ellenbeckii	GAbr IMou NChi WTor
epipsila	EBee ELan EPfP EShb LRHS LSun NLar SPhx WSHC
erythropoda ♀H7	Widely available
- (Cepa Group) 'Alma'	LSun
- Turkish form	ECha
faeroensis	XLum
- var. ***pumila***	EBee GKev
fissa	EBee
§ ***fulgens***	WPGP
glaucescens	CNat
hoppeana misapplied	see *A. plicatula*
hoppeana (Reichenb.) Dalla Torre	EBee
iniquiformis	EBee
'Irish Silk'	CBod
mollis ♀H7	Widely available
I - 'Auslese'	SWvt
- 'Robustica'	GQue LSun MMuc SEND SPlb WFar WPnP
- 'Thriller'	CBod CRos EHyd EPfP LRHS LSun NRHS WFar
- 'Variegata' (v)	CNat
'Mr Poland's Variety'	see *A. venosa*
pedata	EBee NChi
peristerica	EBee
§ ***plicatula***	NLar WCav
saxatilis	CBod EBee EBou LRHS NLar SHar
sericata 'Gold Strike'	EBee ECtt ELan EMor EPfP GLog IMou LRHS NRHS SHar SWvt
splendens misapplied	see *A. fulgens*
straminea	EBee MRav
valdehirsuta	EBee
§ ***venosa***	EBee SHar
vetteri	EBee LRHS WHrl
vulgaris misapplied	see *A. xanthochlora*
§ ***xanthochlora***	GPoy NLar SRms WHer

alecost see *Tanacetum balsamita*

Alectorurus (*Liliaceae*)

yedoensis var. ***platypetalus***	EBee

Alectryon (*Sapindaceae*)

excelsus	CBcs

Alisma (*Alismataceae*)

lanceolatum	XBlo
plantago-aquatica	CBen CHab CWat MWts NPer WMAq WWtn XBlo
- var. ***parviflorum***	SPlb WWtn

Allagoptera (*Arecaceae*)

	arenaria	SPalm

Allamanda (*Apocynaceae*)

	cathartica	CCCN

Alliaria (*Brassicaceae*)

	petiolata	GPoy MNHC WHer WOut WSFF

Allium ✿ (*Alliaceae*)

	RCB AM 21	WCot
	SSSE 250	GEdr
I	***acuminatum*** 'Album'	LRHS
	acutiflorum	GKev
	aflatunense misapplied	see *A. hollandicum*
	aflatunense ambig.	LRHS LSRN SCob SDeJ SEND
	albidum	see *A. denudatum*
	albopilosum	see *A. cristophii*
	altissimum 'Goliath'	GKev LRHS NRHS WCot
	amabile	see *A. mairei* var. *amabile*
	'Ambassador' 🏆H5	CAvo CMea CRos CWCL ECul ERCP GKev ILea LCro LOPS LRHS NRHS SDir SDix WCot WFar WPhe
	amethystinum	GKev
	- 'Red Mohican'PBR	EBee ERCP LEdu MBriF SDeJ WCot WPhe
	ampeloprasum	ECha GKev SDix SPlb WHer WShi
	- var. ***babingtonii***	CAgr GPoy LEdu SRms WHer WKor WPGP WShi
	- - 'Green Drops' **<u>new</u>**	GKev
§	- 'Elephant'	LCro LEdu LOPS WCot
	- 'Pink Lady'	GKev
	- 'Purple Mystery'	GKev WCot
	amphibolum	GKev
	amplectens 'Graceful Beauty'	EBee EPot ERCP LCro LOPS MBow MWat SDeJ SDir SPer SPhx XEll
§	***angulosum***	CAvo CMiW GKev LEdu NHpl SDix WCot WMal XSen
	- 'Sara'	GKev
	aschersonianum	EBee SDeJ WCot
	atropurpureum	EBee ECha ECul ELan EPot ERCP GBin GKev GWyn LCro LOPS LRHS NRHS SDeJ SDir SMad SPhx WCot
	atroviolaceum W&B BG A-5	WCot
	auctum	EBee
	azureum	see *A. caeruleum*
	backhousianum	GKev
	- 'Green Craze' **<u>new</u>**	GKev
	'Beau Regard' 🏆H7	CWCL EBee ELan ERCP GKev LCro LOPS LRHS NLar SDir
	beesianum misapplied	see *A. cyaneum*
	beesianum W.W.Sm. 🏆H5	CMiW EBee GRum NBir NHpl
	bodeanum	see *A. cristophii*
	bolanderi	GKev
	'Bolero'	EBee LRHS
	brevicaule	GKev
	brevistylum	GKev
	bulgaricum	see *Nectaroscordum siculum* subsp. *bulgaricum*
§	***caeruleum***	CAvo CBor CDor EBee EPot ERCP GKev LCro LOPS LRHS MGos MNrw MWat NBir NLar NPer NRHS NRya SDeJ SDir SDix SPhx WCot
	- ***azureum***	see *A. caeruleum*
	caesium 🏆H5	EBee ERCP GKev WCot
	- 'Pskem's Beauty'	WCot
	callimischon subsp. ***callimischon***	EPot GKev
	- subsp. ***haemostictum***	WCot
	'Caméléon'	EBee ERCP GKev LCro LOPS LRHS NRHS WCot
	canadense	CAvo SHar WKor
§	***carinatum***	WHer
§	- subsp. ***pulchellum*** 🏆H5	CBro CSpe EBee ECha EPot GKev LRHS MHer MMuc MNrw NBir SDeJ SPhx WThu XEll
	- - f. ***album*** 🏆H5	CBro CSpe EBee ECha GKev LEdu LSun MNrw NBir SPhx
	- - 'Bill Baker'	LEdu
	- - 'Olympic Mist'	GKev
	cepa	CBod SVic
	- Aggregatum Group	CLau GPoy SRms
	- Proliferum Group	CAgr CLau EWhm GPoy LEdu MHer MNHC SRms WGwG WHer WJek WKor XAbr XLum
	- var. ***viviparum***	GKev
	cernuum	CAvo CBor CBro CDor CMea CRos CSpe ECha ELan EPot ERCP EWhm GKev GMaP LCro LEdu LOPS LRHS MBow MCot MNrw NHpl NQui NRHS SDeJ SPhx SRms WKor XSen
§	- 'Hidcote' 🏆H6	CSam EBee EDAr WKif XSen
	- 'Major'	see *A. cernuum* 'Hidcote'
	- pink-flowered	CLau
I	- 'Purple King' **<u>new</u>**	GKev
	- 'White Dwarf'	CBor CMea GKev
	- 'White Master' **<u>new</u>**	CAvo GKev
	chinense	CAgr GPoy LEdu WFar
	- 'October Mist'	LEdu
	cirrhosum	see *A. carinatum* subsp. *pulchellum*
	cowanii	see *A. neapolitanum* Cowanii Group
§	***cristophii*** 🏆H5	Widely available
	cupanii	GKev
	cupuliferum	GKev
	curtum RCB RL 13	WCot
§	***cyaneum*** 🏆H5	CMiW EPot GEdr GKev LBee LRHS MHer NHpl NRya WCot WFar
	cyathophorum	CBor
§	- var. ***farreri***	CBro EPot GKev LEdu LRHS MHer MNrw NHpl NRya WCot WThu XEll
	daghestanicum **<u>new</u>**	GKev
	darwasicum	WCot
§	***denudatum***	GKev
§	***drummondii***	LRHS NRHS
	elatum	see *A. macleanii*
	ericetorum	GKev WCot
	- PAB 1009	LEdu
	'Eros'	CBor EBee LCro LOPS SDir WRHF
	falcifolium	GKev WCot
	farreri	see *A. cyathophorum* var. *farreri*
	'Firmament'	CAby ECha ERCP GKev LRHS SDeJ WCot XEll
	fistulosum	CAgr CHby CLau ENfk EWhm GKev GPoy LCro LOPS MHer MNHC MPri SRms SVic WCot WGwG WJek XLum
	flavum 🏆H5	CBor CBro EAJP ECha EPot ERCP EWTr LRHS NHpl NSla SDeJ SPhx WGwG WThu
	- subsp. ***flavum***	GKev MBow SPhx
	- - var. ***minus***	MMuc SEND
	- var. ***nanum***	EPot
	- subsp. ***tauricum***	CSpe GKev SPhx WCot
	'Forelock'	ERCP GBin MNrw WCot XEll
	forrestii	WCot

	geyeri	EBee
	giganteum	CAvo CBcs CRos CWCL EBee ELan ERCP GBin GPoy LCro LEdu LOPS LRHS LSRN MArl MBros MCot MNHC MWat NLar NRHS SCob SDeJ SPoG SRms SWvt WFar
	- 'Twinkling Stars'	ERCP GKev
	'Gladiator' ♀H6	CAvo CRos CWCL EBee ERCP GKev GMaP ILea LCro LOPS LRHS LSun NRHS SDeJ SDir WPhe
	glaucum	see *A. senescens* subsp. *glaucum*
	'Globemaster' ♀H6	Widely available
	'Globus'	EBee GKev
	guttatum subsp. ***dalmaticum***	GKev
	- subsp. ***sardoum***	GKev
	haemanthoides	WCot
	'Hair'	see *A. vineale* 'Hair'
*	***hirtifolium*** var. ***album***	EBee GKev
§	***hollandicum***	CArg CAvo ECha GKev LCro LOPS SCob SPlb WFar
	- 'Purple Sensation' ♀H6	Widely available
	- 'Purple Surprise'	NBir WCot
	hookeri	LEdu
	- ACE 2430	LEdu WCot
	- var. ***muliense***	GEdr LEdu
	- 'Zorami'	CAgr ELan LEdu WMal WPGP
	huber-morathii	CBor EBee
	humile	GEdr
	hyalinum	CAvo
	- pink-flowered	WCot
§	***insubricum*** ♀H5	CSpe EDAr GBin GEdr LRHS MNrw NBir NHpl NRHS NRya SChF XEll
	'Jackpot'	CWCL EBee ERCP
	jesdianum	GKev
	- 'Akbulak' ♀H5	EBee LRHS SPhx
	- 'Early Emperor' ♀H5	CAvo CRos CWCL EBee ERCP GKev LRHS NRHS
	- 'Michael Hoog'	see *A. rosenorum* 'Michael H. Hoog'
	- 'Purple King'	GKev LRHS NRHS
	- 'Shing'	GKev
	- 'White Empress'PBR	EBee LRHS
	'Judith' new	WCot
	'Judith's Findling' new	WCot
	kansuense	see *A. sikkimense*
	karataviense	CAby CAvo EBee ECha ELan EPot GAbr LCro LOPS LRHS LSun MBow NBir NHpl NLar NRHS SCob SDeJ SWvt WCAu
	- 'Ivory Queen'	CAby CAvo EBee ECha EMor ERCP GKev LCro LOPS LRHS LSRN NHpl NLar NRHS SDeJ SDir SPlb
	- pink-flowered new	GKev
	- red- and pink-flowered	GKev
	kokanicum new	GRum
	komarovianum	see *A. thunbergii*
	komarovii	GKev
	ledebourianum	GKev
	lenkoranicum	CAvo WCot
	litvinovii	EBee GKev SPhx WCot WFar
	longifolium new	GKev
	loratum	EBee GKev
	'Lucy Ball'	ERCP LRHS NBir NLar NRHS SDeJ
§	***lusitanicum***	CBor CBro CCBP CLau ECha ERCP EShb GKev GMaP LEdu MHol NBre NDov SDix SRms WGoo XSen
§	***macleanii***	EBee LRHS NRHS
	- 'His Excellency'	CAvo CWCL EBee ERCP GKev
	macranthum	CSpe EBee GKev NHpl SBrt

	macrostemon	GKev
	var. ***uratense*** new	
	mairei	EHyd LRHS MMuc NRHS NRya
§	- var. ***amabile***	GEdr LEdu NRya NSla WThu
	- - dark-flowered	CBor
	maximowiczii	GKev NHpl
	membranaceum new	GKev
	'Mercurius'PBR	EBee GKev LRHS NRHS SDeJ SPhx WCot
	'Metallic Shine'	ERCP GKev SDir SPhx
	meteoricum	GKev WCot
	'Miami'	CRos EBee ECul ERCP GKev LRHS NRHS SDeJ SPhx
	'Millennium'	CBod LCro LOPS MHol NDov SHar WCot WGoo WMal
	moly	CAgr CWCL GKev GQue LCro LOPS MBow MRav NRya SDeJ SRms WCav XLum
	- 'Jeannine' ♀H6	EBee EPot GKev LRHS NRHS SDix
	'Mont Blanc'	CMea CRos EBee ELan ERCP GBin GKev ILea LRHS NLar NRHS SDir
	moschatum	GKev
	multibulbosum	see *A. nigrum*
	murrayanum misapplied	see *A. unifolium*
	narcissiflorum misapplied	see *A. insubricum*
§	***narcissiflorum*** Vill.	CSpe LEdu MNrw NSla NWad
	neapolitanum	CAgr CRos EPot GKev LRHS NRHS SRms WGwG WKor
§	- Cowanii Group	CFis GKev LCro LOPS LRHS NRHS SDeJ SPhx WCot WOut
§	***neriniflorum***	NSla
	nevskianum	EPot GKev
§	***nigrum***	CArg CAvo CBro CRos ECha EPot ERCP GKev GWyn LCro LOPS LRHS MCot MWat NBir NPer NRHS SDeJ SDir SPhx WCot WPhe
	- f. ***roseum***	CBro
	nutans	EWhm GKev LEdu MHer SRms WHal WJek
	- 'Caroline'	GKev WGoo
	nuttallii	see *A. drummondii*
§	***obliquum***	CAvo CBor CBro CSpe ECha EPri ERCP GEdr GKev LCro LOPS MBriF SDeJ SPhx WCot WMal
	ochotense	LPla WCot
	odorum L.	see *A. ramosum* L.
	oleraceum	WHer
	olympicum	GKev
§	***oreophilum***	CCBP CRos CSam ECha GJos GKev LCro LOPS LRHS NRHS SRms
	- 'Samur'	WCot
	- 'Zwanenburg' ♀H6	EPot
	orientale	GKev
	'Ostara'	ERCP GKev
	ostrowskianum	see *A. oreophilum*
	ovalifolium	GEdr
	var. ***leuconeurum***	
	pallasii	GKev
	pallens	CBre NBir
§	***paniculatum***	GKev WCot
*	- var. ***minor***	GKev
	paradoxum	LEdu NBir
	- var. ***normale***	CBro EPot EWld GKev NBir WCot
	parciflorum	GKev
	pedemontanum	see *A. narcissiflorum* Vill.
	pendulinum	GKev
	'Pinball Wizard'	CAvo CRos EBee ECul EHyd EMor ERCP GKev LCro LOPS LRHS NRHS
	'Ping Pong'	EBee ECul GKev NLar
	'Pink Jewel'	CAvo EBee ERCP GKev SDeJ WCot

	platycaule	WCot
	plummerae	EBee GKev XEll
	'Powder Puff' ♀H5	CAvo EBee GKev
	prattii	EBee WCot
	przewalskianum	SGro
	pskemense	WCot
	pulchellum	see *A. carinatum* subsp. *pulchellum*
	'Purple Rain' ♀H5	CAvo CRos CWCL ECha ELan ERCP LCro LOPS LRHS NRHS SDeJ WCot WHoo WPhe
	pyrenaicum misapplied	see *A. angulosum*
	pyrenaicum ambig.	SEND
	pyrenaicum Costa & Vayr.	XSen
	ramosum Jacq.	see *A. obliquum*
§	***ramosum*** L.	GKev LEdu
	'Red Eye'	LCro LOPS
	'Rien Poortvliet'	GKev
	roborowskianum	GKev
	rosenbachianum misapplied	see *A. stipitatum*
	rosenbachianum Regel	CBro LRHS NRHS
	- 'Album'	CRos GBin GKev LRHS NRHS WCot
	- 'Michael Hoog'	see *A. rosenorum* 'Michael H. Hoog'
§	***rosenorum*** 'Michael H. Hoog' ♀H5	EPot GKev LRHS
	roseum	CMea CRos GKev LCro LOPS LRHS MBow MWat NRHS SDeJ XLum
	rotundum	GKev
	'Round 'n' Purple' ♀H5	EMor ERCP GKev LCro LOPS LRHS
	sativum	ENfk LOPS MPri SPoG SRms
	- 'Elephant'	see *A. ampeloprasum* 'Elephant'
	- var. ***ophioscorodon***	GPoy SPlb WKor
	saxatile	GKev WCot
	- pink-flowered	GKev
	schmitzii	GKev LEdu WPGP
	schoenoprasum	Widely available
	- f. ***albiflorum***	CCBP CLau ECha EWhm GKev LEdu MHer NBir SRms
	- 'Black Isle Blush'	EBee EMor GPoy LEdu MBriF MHer WGoo WPGP
	- 'Cha Cha'	MBriF WJek
	- 'Colesbourne Giant'	EBee LEdu
	- 'Corsican White'	LEdu XSen
	- dwarf, white-flowered	CBre SRms
	- 'Elbe'	LEdu
	- fine-leaved	CLau GQue
	- 'Forescate'	ECha EWhm GKev LEdu LRHS LSou MHer MRav NBir NRHS SRms WJek XLum
	- 'Glowing Amethyst' new	GKev
	- 'Grande' new	CLau
	- medium-leaved	CLau MPri
	- 'Pink Bere'	LEdu
	- 'Pink Perfection'	GPoy LEdu MHer
	- 'Polar Bere'	LEdu
	- 'Polyphant'	CBre
	- 'Polyvert' new	CLau
	- 'Profusion'	see *A. schoenoprasum* 'Sterile'
	- 'Rising Star'	XSen
	- 'Shining Silver'	LEdu
	- var. ***sibiricum***	SDix WShi
	- 'Silver Chimes'	CBor EWhm MRav
	- 'Staro' new	CLau
§	- 'Sterile'	LEdu
	- thick-leaved	CLau SRms
	schubertii	CAvo CBod CSpe CWCL EHyd ELan EPot ERCP GKev LCro LOPS LRHS MNHC NRHS SDeJ SPer SPhx WCot WFar WPhe

	- 'Magic'	EWhm
	scorodoprasum 'Art'	CRos ERCP GKev LRHS NRHS
	- 'Passion'	CRos GKev LRHS NRHS
	- 'Purple Caila'	GKev
	senescens ♀H6	CBod CBro CTri EBee EPot GKev IMou LEdu LRHS MBel MRav NRHS SGro SRms WBrk WCAu XLum XSen
§	- subsp. ***glaucum***	CAvo CMea CPBP CSpe EBee ECha EDAr EWTr GKev LEdu LRHS MHer NBPC NDov NGdn NLar NRya SEND WCot WHoo XSen
	- 'Lisa Blue'	GKev
	- subsp. ***senescens***	GKev LEdu WPGP
	shelkovnikovii	EPot GKev
	sibthorpianum	see *A. paniculatum*
	siculum	see *Nectaroscordum siculum*
§	***sikkimense***	CBor EBee EDAr EWTr GEdr GKev GQue LRHS MHer MMuc NHpl NSla WAbe WCot WFar
	'Silver Spring'	EPot ERCP GKev LCro LOPS MNrw SDeJ
	sphaerocephalon ♀H6	Widely available
	- subsp. ***arvense***	WCot
	'Spider'	CWCL EBee EPot ERCP GBin GKev ILea LRHS SPhx WCot WHoo
I	***splendens*** var. ***kurilense***	GEdr
	stamineum W&B BGF-2	WCot
	staticiforme new	GKev
	'Statos'	EBee GKev LRHS NRHS WCot WPhe
	stellatum	LRHS NRHS SPhx WGwG
	stellerianum	GKev
	- var. ***kurilense***	NRya WThu
§	***stipitatum***	GKev WCot
	- 'Glory of Pamir'	GKev
	- 'Mars'	EBee LRHS NRHS SDix
	- 'Mount Everest' ♀H5	CAvo CBod CBro CRos ECul EPot ERCP GBin GKev GMaP GWyn ILea LCro LOPS LRHS LSRN MHtn MWat NLar NRHS SDeJ SDir SDix SPer SPhx WPhe
	- 'Violet Beauty' ♀H5	CRos CWCL EWhm LCro LOPS LRHS MHtn NLar NRHS WCot WPhe WRHF
	- 'White Giant'	CRos CWCL EBee ERCP GKev LEdu LRHS NRHS SArc
	stracheyi	WCot
	strictum Schrad.	ITim
	subhirsutum	GKev XLum
	subvillosum	EPot GKev
	'Summer Beauty'	see *A. lusitanicum*
	'Summer Drummer'	ECha ERCP GKev LRHS MBros SDeJ SDir SPer SPhx WCot
	taquetii	see *A. thunbergii*
	tardans new	GKev
	tauricola	GKev
	texanum	GKev
§	***thunbergii*** ♀H5	MHer NBir NRya SPhx WAbe
	- PAB 3821	LEdu
	- 'Album'	LEdu NRya WAbe
	- 'Ozawa'	GEdr SRms WCot WFar
	tibeticum	see *A. sikkimense*
	tripedale	CAvo CBro EPot ERCP GKev
	triquetrum	ELan EPot GKev LEdu MBow NBir SEND WCot WFar WHer XLum
	tschimganicum	EBee
	tuberosum	Widely available
	- B&SWJ 8881	WCru
	- purple/mauve-flowered	CHby CLau

	- 'White Dwarf'	SPhx WCot
	tuncelianum	GKev WCot
§	***unifolium*** 🏆H5	CAvo CWCL EBee EPot ERCP GKev GWyn LCro LOPS MRav NBir NPer NQui SDeJ SEND SPhx SRms WCot WGwG
	ursinum	CAby CHab CHby CLau CWld EMor ENfk EWhm GKev GPoy LCro LEdu LOPS MBow MHer MPri NAts NPoe SPlb SRms SVic WFar WKor WSFF WShi XAbr XEll XLum
	- 'Golden Fleece'	WCot
	validum NNS 06-41	WCot
	victorialis 'Cantabria'	GKev
	vineale	GQue WHer WJek
	- PAB 2763	LEdu
	- 'Dready'	ERCP GKev
§	- 'Hair'	CRos ELan ERCP LRHS NBir NPer NRHS SDeJ
	violaceum	see *A. carinatum*
	virgunculae	CMea EDAr GEdr
	- f. ***albiflorum***	GEdr
	wallichii	CSpe EBee EPot EWes GKev LEdu NBir NChi WCot XLum
	- CLD 1500	LEdu NBid
	- PAB 2976	LEdu WPGP
	- PAB 9191	LEdu
	- dark-flowered	GBin LPla WCot WFar
	'White Cloud'	EBee ELan GKev XEll
	zaprjagajevii	WCot
	zebdanense	GKev

almond see *Prunus dulcis*

Alniphyllum (*Styracaceae*)

eberhardtii FMWJ 13121	WCru
fortunei FMWJ 13013	WCru

Alnus ✿ (*Betulaceae*)

	cordata 🏆H6	CBcs CCVT CLnd CMCN CMac CSBt CTho CTri ECrN ELan EPfP EWTr LBuc LMaj MGos MMuc SCob SEND SEWo SGol SPer SPlb WMat WMou WTSh
	cremastogyne	EBtc
	fauriei	GKev
	formosana	IArd
	glutinosa	CArg CBcs CCVT CHab CLnd CMac CSBt CTho CTri ECrN EPfP GBin LBuc LMaj MGos SCob SEWo SGol SPer WMat WMou WSFF WTSh
	- 'Aurea'	CEnd MGos WCot
	- 'Imperialis' 🏆H7	CCVT CEnd CLnd CMac CTho EBee ELan EPfP EWTr IDee MBlu MMuc NLar NOra NOrn SCob SGol SMad SPer WMat WMou WTSh
	- 'Laciniata'	CCVT CTho ECrN GKev MGos NLar SCob
	incana	CBcs CCVT CLnd CMCN CTho ECrN LBuc LMaj MGos NLar SCob SGol SPer WMat WTSh
	- 'Aurea' 🏆H7	CBcs CCVT CEnd CLnd CMac CTho EBee ECrN ELan EPfP GBin IArd LMaj MBlu MGos MRav NLar NOra NOrn NPoe SCob SEWo SGol SPer SPoG WMat
	- 'Laciniata'	ELan NLar NOrn SCoo WFar WMou
	- 'Pendula'	CTho WMou
	japonica	MBlu
	maximowiczii	GKev
	- from Ulleungdo, South Korea	WCru
	nitida	EBtc
	oregana	see *A. rubra*
	pendula B&SWJ 10895	WCru
	rhombifolia	EBtc
§	***rubra***	CMCN CTho ELan MCoo WMat WTSh
	- f. ***pinnatisecta***	CMCN MBlu
	serrulata	CMCN
	sieboldiana	GKev LRHS WCru
	× ***spaethii***	LMaj MBlu
	subcordata NJM 13.009	EBee WPGP
	viridis	CAgr MCoo WTSh
	- subsp. ***sinuata***	CAgr

Alocasia (*Araceae*)

× ***amazonica*** 🏆H1a	XBlo
- 'Bambino Arrow' **new**	CDoC
- 'Polly'	CDoC LCro LOPS
'Calidora'	CDTJ
cucullata	XBlo
'Dragon Scale' **new**	LCro LOPS
lauterbachiana	CDoC LCro LOPS
macrorrhiza	CDTJ CTsd
odora	XBlo
plumbea	XBlo
'Portodora'	CDTJ
wentii	CDTJ

Aloe ✿ (*Asphodelaceae*)

arborescens	CDTJ CDoC CPbh CTrC EShb SEND SPlb WABo
- 'Variegata' (v) 🏆H1c	EShb SRms
aristata 🏆H3	CBcs CBen CDoC SArc SChr SEND SPad SPalm SPlb SSim WABo WOld XLum
- 'Cathedral Peak'	SChr
- COSMO ('Green Pearl'PBR)	SMad SPad
barbadensis	see *A. vera*
barberae	CCCN CPbh
brevifolia 🏆H2	EShb SArc SSim
broomii	CCCN CPbh SPlb
buettneri	EShb
camperi 'Maculata'	SEND
ciliaris	EShb SChr
'Cleopatra'	LSun SEdd WCot
cooperi	CCCN CDTJ WSMil
dichotoma	CAbb SPlb
ecklonis	CCCN SPlb
ferox	CAbb CBod CCCN CDTJ CPbh CTrC
fosteri	CDTJ
greatheadii var. ***davyana***	SChr SPlb
humilis	CDoC SChr SEND
juvenna	SRms
kedongensis	SEND
maculata	CDTJ
marlothii	CAbb CCCN SPlb
melanacantha	CAbb
microstigma	CCCN
mitriformis	NGBl SChr SEND SPalm
mutabilis	SChr SEND
peglerae	SRms
petricola	CAbb
plicatilis 🏆H2	CCCN CDTJ EShb
pluridens	CAbb
polyphylla 🏆H3	CCCN CDTJ CPbh MHer WPGP

pratensis	CCCN CDTJ
rauhii 🏆^{H1b}	CPbh SSim
reitzii	CAbb CPbh SPlb
'Snowflake'	EShb
speciosa	CAbb
× ***spinosissima***	SChr
squarrosa new	CDoC
striata	CBcs CCCN CPbh EShb SPlb SPtp SSim
striatula 🏆^{H3}	CBrP CDTJ CDoC CSam CSde CTrC IBlr LEdu SArc SChr SEND SPlb SVen WABo WCot WMal WPGP WSMil
- var. ***caesia***	WPGP
succotrina	CAbb
suprafoliata	CAbb
tenuior	EShb
variegata (v) 🏆^{H1c}	CBen EShb LSun SSim
§ ***vera*** 🏆^{H1c}	CCBP CCCN ELan GPoy LCro LOPS MHer MNHC MPri NPer SChr SEND SMad SPad SPalm SPlb SPre SRms SSim SVic WSFF XAbr
'White Beauty'	EShb SPad
wickensii	SPlb
yavellana	SPlb

Aloe × *Haworthia* see × *Alworthia*

Aloinopsis (*Aizoaceae*)

lueckhoffii	SSim
rosulata	SSim
spathulata	CPBP

Aloinopsis × *Nananthus* see × *Nananopsis*

Alonsoa (*Scrophulariaceae*)

'Bright Spark'	CSpe
incisifolia	CCCN CSpe
meridionalis	CBod CCCN
- 'Rebel'	CPla ECtt SRkn
- 'Shell Pink'	CBod
'Pink Beauty'	CPla CSpe
warscewiczii	CCCN
- 'Peachy-keen'	CSpe

Alopecurus (*Poaceae*)

alpinus	see *A. magellanicus*
§ ***magellanicus***	ELan GBin
pratensis	CHab
- 'Aureovariegatus' (v)	CTri EShb GMaP NBid SPer SRms
- 'Aureus'	NBro SPlb
- 'No Overtaking' (v)	EPPr

Alophia (*Iridaceae*)

lahue	see *Herbertia lahue*

Aloysia (*Verbenaceae*)

chamaedryfolia	EPfP LRHS
citriodora	see *A. citrodora*
§ ***citrodora*** 🏆^{H3}	Widely available
- 'Spilsbury Mint'	ELan MHer
gratissima	WJek
triphylla	see *A. citrodora*

Alpinia (*Zingiberaceae*)

japonica	CExl LEdu
- B&SWJ 8889	ESwi WCru
- PAB 6441	LEdu
nutans misapplied	see *A. zerumbet*
speciosa	see *A. zerumbet*
§ ***zerumbet***	XBlo
- 'Variegata' (v)	XBlo

Alsobia see *Episcia*

Alstroemeria ✿ (*Alstroemeriaceae*)

'Adonis'^{PBR}	WViv
'Aimi'	ELan MNrw SWvt WViv
'Alexis'^{PBR}	WViv
'Amarillo'	WViv
'Angelina'	CTsd SWvt
'Anne' (Midi Series)	SPer
'Apollo' 🏆^{H4}	CTsd EHyd ELan LRHS MNrw NBir NBre NRHS SWvt WViv
'Athena'	WViv
aurantiaca	see *A. aurea*
§ ***aurea***	CBod CPla GWyn MRav NWad SRms XLum
- 'Cally Apricot' new	WMal
- 'Lutea'	GKev NLar SDeJ SPlb WPav
- 'Orange King'	ELan EPfP GKev NLar SDeJ
'Avanti'	EHyd ELan LRHS NRHS WViv
'Blushing Bride'	CTsd SWvt WMal WViv
'Bodega'^{PBR}	WViv
'Bolero'	WViv
'Bonanza'	WViv
brasiliensis	CTsd SBrt SHar WCot WSHC WViv XLum
- 'Cally Star' (v)	EBee NLar
'Cahors' (Planet Series) 🏆^{H4}	LCro LOPS
'Candy'	WViv
'Catherine' (Little Miss Series)	WViv
'Charm'	CTsd SWvt WSpi WViv
'Chi Chi'	WCot
§ 'Christina'^{PBR} (Little Miss Series)	ELan LRHS NRHS SWvt WViv
'Christine Marsh'	WViv
'Cindy'	WViv
'Coronet' 🏆^{H4}	WViv
'Dandy Candy'	CBod ECtt EHyd LRHS MCot MHol NGdn NLar SPad WBrk WCot
'Davina'^{PBR} (Little Miss Series)	EHyd LRHS NLar NRHS WViv
'Dayspring Delight' (v)	MNrw
§ DIANA, PRINCESS OF WALES ('Stablaco')	EHyd LRHS NRHS
'Diane' (Midi Series)	CBod
Doctor Salter's hybrids	SRms
'Eleanor'	WViv
'Eleanor' (Little Miss Series)	EHyd LRHS NRHS WViv
'Elvira'	WViv
'Emily'^{PBR}	WViv
'Etna'^{PBR}	WViv
'Evening Song'	EHyd LRHS SWvt WViv
exserens	WCot
'Flaming Star'	WGwG WViv
'Flirt'	LOPS
'Frances' (v)	CAvo CBro WFar
'Freedom'	CBod CWGN ECtt ELon LSou MHol NLar NSti SCob SHar SPoG WCot
'Friendship' 🏆^{H5}	CTsd EHyd ELan LRHS NBre NRHS SWvt WGwG WMal WViv
'Gina'^{PBR} (Little Miss Series)	ELan LRHS NRHS WViv
'Gloria'	ELan LRHS NRHS SWvt WViv
'Glory of the Andes' (v)	CWGN NLar
'Golden Delight'	EHyd ELan LRHS NRHS WViv
§ H.R.H. PRINCESS ALICE ('Staverpi')	LRHS NRHS
'Hawera'	GBin
hookeri	WFar

(Inca Series) INCA ADORE ('Koadore')	CExl
- INCA AVANTI ('Koncavanti'PBR)	CWGN LBuc WViv
- INCA AZURE ('Konazur'PBR)	WViv
- INCA BANDIT ('Koncaband')	WViv
- INCA BATTLE **new**	WViv
- INCA BLUE HEAVEN **new**	WViv
- INCA CLASSIC ('Konclassic')	WViv
- INCA CORAL ('Konocoral')	WViv
- INCA DEVOTION ('Konevotio'PBR)	NLar
- INCA DREAM ('Kodream')	WViv
- INCA EXOTICA ('Koexotica')	WViv
- INCA FIRE **new**	WViv
- INCA FLAMINGO **new**	WViv
- INCA GLOW ('Koglow')	CExl CWGN EHyd ELon LRHS MHol NLar SDeJ SRms WViv
- INCA GOAL ('Koncagoal')	CBcs CBod CPla WViv
- INCA HUSKY ('Koncahusky'PBR)	CBcs CBod CPla CWGN LRHS MHol WViv
- INCA ICE ('Koice')	CWGN NLar WViv
- INCA JOLI ('Koncajoli'PBR)	WViv
- INCA LAKE ('Koncalake')	CWGN LBuc WViv
- INCA LOLLY ('Koncalolly'PBR)	WViv
- INCA MAMBO ('Koncamambo'PBR)	WViv
- INCA MILK ('Koncamilk')	WViv
- INCA MOONLIGHT ('Komolight')	NLar
- INCA NOBLE ('Koncanoble')	WViv
- INCA OBSESSION ('Koobsion')	WViv
- INCA PRETTY **new**	WViv
- INCA PULSE ('Konpulse'PBR)	CWGN ELon NLar SDeJ WViv
- INCA ROCKY ('Konyrock')	WViv
- INCA SERIN ('Koserin'PBR)	CWGN WViv
- INCA SMILE ('Koncasmile'PBR)	CWGN WViv
- INCA SUNDANCE ('Koncasuna') **new**	SPad
- INCA SWEETY ('Koncasweet'PBR)	WViv
- INCA TOTO ('Koncatoto'PBR)	WViv
- INCA TROPIC ('Kotrop')	CExl CWGN WViv
- INCA VITO ('Koncavito'PBR)	CBcs CBod CWGN LRHS MHol NLar SPoG
- INCA YUKO ('Koncayuko'PBR)	CBod CWGN ELon LBuc MHol WSpi WViv
INDIAN SUMMER ('Tesronto'PBR)	CBod CRos CWGN ECtt EHyd EPfP LCro LOPS LRHS LSou MHol MHtn MPri NRHS NSti SEdd SMad SPoG SWvt WCot WFar WHil WViv WWFP
(Inticancha Series) INTICANCHA ANTARCTICA ('Tesantarc'PBR)	WViv
- INTICANCHA BRYCE ('Tesbryce'PBR)	LSou MHol NLar SCob WFar WViv
- INTICANCHA CABANA ('Tescaban')	CBod CRos EHyd LSou MHol NRHS SCob SNig
- INTICANCHA CREAMY DARK PINK ('Tescreda')	SDeJ WViv
- INTICANCHA DARK PURPLE ('Tesdarklin'PBR)	CRos LRHS MHol NLar NRHS WFar WViv
- INTICANCHA IMALA ('Tesima'PBR)	EHyd
- INTICANCHA INDIGO ('Tesindie')	CBod MHol
- INTICANCHA KANIKA ('Tesikani')	EHyd
- INTICANCHA MACHU ('Tesmach'PBR)	WFar WViv
- INTICANCHA MAGIC WHITE ('Tesmaghwi') **new**	CBod LSou MHol
- INTICANCHA MAYA ('Tesmaya'PBR)	CRos CWGN ECtt EHyd LRHS NRHS SCob WFar WViv
- INTICANCHA MOONLIGHT ('Tesmoonli') **new**	NLar
- INTICANCHA NAVAYO ('Tesnava'PBR)	ECtt LSou MHol WFar
- INTICANCHA PASSION ('Tespassion'PBR)	ECtt EHyd LRHS LSou SNig WViv
- INTICANCHA PURPLE ('Tespurplin'PBR)	CWGN WFar WViv
- INTICANCHA RED ('Tesrobin'PBR)	CBod CRos CWGN LRHS MHol NRHS WFar WViv
- INTICANCHA SUNDAY ('Tessunday'PBR)	WViv
- INTICANCHA SUNLIGHT ('Tessunlight'PBR)	ECtt NLar WFar WViv
- INTICANCHA SUNSHINE ('Tesshine'PBR)	CBod LSou MHol
- INTICANCHA VALENTINO ('Tesvalen'PBR) **new**	CRos
- INTICANCHA WHITE PINK BLUSH ('Tesblushin'PBR)	EHyd LRHS NRHS WFar WViv
- INTICANCHA WHITE PINK HEART ('Tesheartin')	NLar
'Isabel' (Little Miss Series)	LRHS WFar WViv
ISABELLA ('Stalis')	LSRN
§ ***isabellana***	SBrt WCru WMal
'Jessica'PBR	LRHS WViv
'Junon' (Planet Series)	LCro LOPS
'Laguna'	WViv
LAURA ('Stalauli'PBR)	ECtt
'Leonie'	SPer
ligtu hybrids	CAvo ECha EPfP GKev LCro LOPS MNrw NPer SDeJ SRms SWvt WBrk XLum
- var. ***ligtu***	SMHy
'Little Miss Natalie'	see *A.* 'Natalie'
'Louise' (Midi Series)	LSRN
'Lucca'	WViv
'Lucinda'	SWvt WViv
'Lucy' (Little Miss Series)	WViv
'Maestro'PBR	WViv
'Marissa'	GMaP
'Mars' (Planet Series)	EHyd LRHS
'Mathilde' (Midi Series)	NLar
'Matilda' (Little Miss Series)	WViv
'Mauve Majesty'	ECtt ELon ILea LRHS MHol NLar SPoG WCot WHoo WViv
'Miranda' (Little Miss Series)	WViv
'Moulin Rouge'	WViv
§ 'Natalie'PBR (Little Miss Series)	EHyd LRHS NRHS WViv
'Neptune'	LCro LOPS
'Orange Glory' ♀H4	EHyd ELon LRHS MNrw SWvt WMal WViv
'Orange Supreme'	EHyd LRHS NRHS WViv
'Oriana' ♀H4	SWvt WViv
pallida	SPlb
'Pandora'PBR	LRHS NRHS WViv

'Perfect Orange' WViv
philippii WCot
- F&W 8699 WCot
'Phoenix' (v) ♀H4 SWvt WViv
'Pink Lady' WViv
'Pink Perfection' NLar
'Pink Sensation' LRHS NRHS WViv
'Polka' WViv
presliana RB 94103 WCot
(Princess Series) PRINCESS ALICE see *A.* H.R.H. PRINCESS ALICE
- PRINCESS AMINA ('Zapriamin'PBR) CBcs SPoG WViv
- PRINCESS ANOUSKA ('Zaprinous'PBR) NLar WViv
- PRINCESS ARIANE ('Zapriari'PBR) WViv
- PRINCESS BEATRIX ('Stadoran') SChr
- PRINCESS CAMILLA ('Stapricamil') SPoG
§ - PRINCESS CHARLOTTE ('Staprizsa'PBR) SPer
- PRINCESS CLAIRE ('Zapriclair'PBR) CBcs CRos CWGN EHyd EPfP LRHS NRHS
- PRINCESS DANIELA ('Stapridani') SCoo
- PRINCESS DIANA see *A.* DIANA, PRINCESS OF WALES ('Stablaco'), *A.* PRINCESS DIANA ('Zapridapal')
§ - PRINCESS DIANA ('Zapridapal'PBR) CBcs CWGN WViv
- PRINCESS ELIANE ('Zaprielia'PBR) CBcs CRos EHyd LRHS NRHS WViv
- PRINCESS FABIANA ('Zaprifabi'PBR) CRos EHyd LRHS NLar NRHS SPoG WViv
- PRINCESS FREDERIKA ('Stabronza') MCot
- PRINCESS ISABELLA ('Zapribel'PBR) EHyd LRHS LSRN WViv
- PRINCESS IVANA ('Staprivane'PBR) SPoG
- PRINCESS JULIETA ('Zaprijul'PBR) NLar
- PRINCESS KATE ('Zaprikate'PBR) CBcs CRos CWGN EHyd EPfP LRHS NRHS WViv
- PRINCESS LETIZIA ('Zaprilet'PBR) EHyd EPfP LRHS SPoG
- PRINCESS LILIAN ('Zaprilian'PBR) CRos EHyd EPfP LRHS NRHS WViv
- PRINCESS LISA ('Zaprilisa') **new** CWGN
- PRINCESS LOUISE ('Zaprilou'PBR) CBcs EHyd LRHS LSRN WViv
- PRINCESS MARGARET ('Staprimar') NLar
- PRINCESS MARY ('Zaprimary'PBR) NLar
- PRINCESS MATHILDE ('Zaprimat'PBR) WViv
- PRINCESS PAOLA ('Stapripal'PBR) CBcs CRos CWGN EHyd LRHS NRHS SCoo SPoG WViv
- PRINCESS SARA ('Staprisara'PBR) CBcs CRos EHyd EPfP LRHS NRHS SPoG
- PRINCESS SUSANA ('Staprisusa') SCoo
- PRINCESS TAMARA ('Zapritama') **new** CBcs CWGN
- PRINCESS THERESA ('Zapriteres'PBR) EPfP NLar
- PRINCESS ZAVINA ('Staprivina'PBR) NLar SPoG
- PRINCESS ZSA ZSA see *A.* PRINCESS CHARLOTTE
pseudospathulata CPla WCot
§ ***psittacina*** CBro CMea CSam CTsd ECha EPfP GBin MCot MHer SHar SMHy SRms WAvo WFar WGwG WViv XLum
- 'Mona Lisa' CBod XLum
- 'Royal Star' (v) CAby CBod CBro CExl CWCL EHyd ELan EPPr EPfP EPri EShb EWTr LRHS MPie NRHS SHar SPoG SRms WBrk WCot WFar WHoo WSHC WSpi XLum
pulchella Sims see *A. psittacina*
'Purple Rain' ELan SWvt WViv
'Red Beauty' (v) see *A.* 'Spitfire'
'Red Beauty' EHyd ELan GMaP LRHS NRHS SWvt WViv
'Red Elf' ♀H4 SMHy SWvt WViv
'Rhubarb and Custard' ELan
ROCK 'N' ROLL ('Alsdun01'PBR) (v) CDor EBee ELan ELon GAbr LCro LOPS LSou MHol MHtn MNrw MSCN SMad SPoG SRms WCot WFar WViv
'Rosanna' (Little Miss Series) WViv
§ 'Roselind' (Little Miss Series) ELan LRHS NRHS SWvt WViv
'Saturne' (Planet Series) LCro LOPS
'Selina' EHyd LRHS MNrw NBre WViv
'Serenade' WViv
'Sirius' (Planet Series) ♀H4 LCro LOPS
'Sonata' ♀H4 WViv
§ 'Sophie'PBR (Little Miss Series) ELan LRHS SWvt WViv
§ 'Spitfire' (v) ♀H4 EHyd LCro LOPS LRHS SWvt WCot WViv
'Strawberry Lace' ELan
'Summer Breeze' CBod CRos ECtt EHyd LRHS NRHS SPoG WFar WViv
(Summer Paradise Series) SUMMER BREAK ('Tessumbreak') **new** CBod ECtt LSou MHol
- SUMMER PARTY ('Tessumpar') CRos ECtt EHyd LRHS NRHS WFar
- SUMMER SKY ('Tessumsky') **new** MHol
'Summer Saint' ECtt LSou WViv
SUMMER SNOW ('Gasumsnow') LSou
'Summertime' LRHS NRHS WViv
'Sunstar' GMaP
'Sweet Laura'PBR CBod ECtt ELan ELon LRHS LSRN MHol MNrw MPie NGdn NLar NSti SEdd SMad SPoG WCot WSpi WViv
'Tangerine Tango' WViv
'Tanya' MNrw WViv
§ 'Tara'PBR (Little Miss Series) ELan LRHS NLar NRHS SWvt WViv
'Tessa' ♀H4 EHyd LRHS NBre WViv
'Uranus' LCro LOPS
'Ventura' WViv
'Venus' (Planet Series) LCro LOPS
'Veronica' (Little Miss Series) WViv
'Yellow Friendship' ♀H4 MNrw NLar SWvt WViv

Alternanthera (*Amaranthaceae*)

ficoidea 'Versicolor' **new** XBlo
reineckii XBlo
- 'Lilacina' XBlo
I - 'Rosaefolia' XBlo
sessilis **new** XBlo

Althaea (*Malvaceae*)

	armeniaca	EBee MAvo WCot
	cannabina	CCBP CFis CSam CSpe ECha ELan EPPr IPot MAvo MBel MHer MNrw NGBl SBut SHar SPhx WBor WCav WCot WHal WHil WOld WSHC
	officinalis	CBee CBod CCBP CHab CTsd EBou ELan ENfk EPPr GPoy MAvo MBow MHer MMuc MNHC NLar SRms SVic WHer WJek WSpi XAbr XLum XSen
§	- 'Romney Marsh'	MAvo MRav
	rosea	see *Alcea rosea*
	rugosostellulata	see *Alcea rugosa*

Altingia (*Hamamelidaceae*)

	poilanei B&SWJ 11756	WCru

× *Alworthia* (*Asphodelaceae*)

	'Black Gem'	EBee EShb SRms SSim WOld

Alyogyne (*Malvaceae*)

§	***huegelii***	CCCN CSpe EShb SEle SPlb
	- 'Santa Cruz'	CCCN CSam
	MAGIC MOMENTS ('Hutwow'PBR)	CCCN CWGN ELan SPoG SRkn

Alyssum (*Brassicaceae*)

	caespitosum	WAbe
	cuneifolium	GJos
	montanum	ECha SPlb SRms
§	- 'Berggold'	EBou ELan EPfP XLum
	- MOUNTAIN GOLD	see *A. montanum* 'Berggold'
	oxycarpum	EPot
	saxatile	see *Aurinia saxatilis*
	- 'Summit'	GJos SRms
	spinosum	CPla
	- 'Roseum' ♀H5	CMea CSpe CTri ECha ELan EPot WAbe
*	- 'Roseum Variegatum' (v)	EPot
	- 'Rubrum'	EPot
	'Takara Yellow'	GWyn
	tortuosum	SEND
	wulfenianum	GJos WIce XLum

Amaranthus (*Amaranthaceae*)

	'Autumn Palette'	CSpe
	caudatus	LCro LOPS
	cruentus **new**	CLau
	- 'Velvet Curtains' ♀H2 **new**	LCro LOPS
	hypochondriacus 'Pygmy Torch' ♀H2	CSpe
	tricolor	CLau SRms

× *Amarcrinum* (*Amaryllidaceae*)

	'Dorothy Hannibal'	WCot
	memoria-corsii	CPrp
	- 'Howardii'	EPri GKev LEdu SDeJ WCot

× *Amarine* (*Amaryllidaceae*)

	tubergenii	CAvo
	- Belladiva Series	CBro EBee ELan ERCP GKev LCro LOPS LRHS NHoy SDir
	- - 'Anastasia'PBR	CBro ERCP GKev NHoy SMad
	- - 'Aphrodite'PBR	CBro GKev NHoy SDir WFar
	- - 'Elvi'	NHoy
	- - 'Emanuelle'PBR	CAvo CBro ELan ERCP GKev NHoy
	- - 'Smilla'	GKev NHoy
	- - 'Tomoka'PBR	CBro ELan GKev
	- 'Fletcheri'	WCot
	- 'Zwanenburg'	CSpe GKev WCot

× *Amarygia* (*Amaryllidaceae*)

§	***bidwillii*** 'Alba'	CAvo CBro CPrp
	- 'Rosea'	WCot

Amaryllis (*Amaryllidaceae*)

§	***belladonna*** ♀H4	CBcs CBro CPrp CTri EBee EPfP ERCP EShb GKev LCro LOPS MPie SDeJ SDir SEND SEdd SPeP WCot
	- 'Hathor'	CBro SMHy
	- 'Johannesburg'	CBro WCot
	- 'Major'	SChr
	- 'Parkeri Alba'	see × *Amarygia bidwillii* 'Alba'
	- 'Purpurea'	WCot
	- white-flowered	SDeJ

Amaryllis × *Brunsvigia* see × *Amarygia*

Amaryllis × *Crinum* see × *Amarcrinum*

Amaryllis × *Nerine* see × *Amarine*

Ambrosina (*Araceae*)

	bassii	WCot

Amelanchier ✿ (*Rosaceae*)

	alnifolia	MGil NGrd WKor
	- 'Forestburg'	MBlu NLar
	- 'Honeywood'	MBlu MCoo NOra
	- 'Jb30' (F)	CAgr MCoo NOra
	- 'Martin' (F)	CAgr NOra
	- 'Northline' (F)	CAgr LCro LOPS LRHS MCoo NLar NOra
	- 'Obelisk'PBR	CAgr CDoC CRos CTho EBee EHyd ELan EPfP GKin LBuc LRHS LSRN MAsh MCoo MGos MPri MRav MSwo NLar NOra NOrn SCoo SGsty SPer SPoG WHwl WMat
	- pink-fruited	NLar
§	- var. ***pumila***	MMrt WCot
	- 'Regent' (F)	CAgr NLar
	- 'Smokey'	CAgr LRHS MBlu MCoo NLar NOra SPoG WKor
	- 'Thiessen'	MCoo NLar
	arborea TRADITION ('Trazam')	NLar SAko
	'Autumn Glory'	EPfP
	bartramiana	SSta
	- 'Eskimo'	NLar
	canadensis K. Koch	see *A. lamarckii*
	canadensis ambig.	CTsd ILea LPot MMuc MPri NOra SEND SEWo SPoG WFar WHwl WKor
	canadensis (L.) Medik.	CAgr CLnd CMac CRos CSBt CTho CTri EBee ECrN ELan EPfP LEdu LRHS MGos MRav MSwo SArc SPer WMat
§	- 'Glenn Form'	CEnd EPfP LRHS NOra SGol SLim SPer SPoG WMou
	- 'Prince William'	CAgr MBlu MCoo SGol
	- RAINBOW PILLAR	see *A. canadensis* 'Glenn Form'
	× ***grandiflora***	SCob
	- 'Autumn Brilliance'	CEnd CJun EPfP MBlu NHol NLar NOrn NRHS SGol
	- 'Ballerina'	Widely available
	- 'Cole's Select'	CAby EBee LRHS NLar SWvt
	- 'Princess Diana' ♀H7	NLar SCoo

§ - 'Robin Hill' 🏆H7	Widely available
- 'Rubescens'	CEnd CJun EBee NLar SLon SWvt
'La Paloma' 🏆H6	EBee EPfP LRHS LSRN MGos NOra NOrn SCoo SLim WHwl WMat
laevis	CBcs CTri EPfP LMaj
- 'Prince Charles'	NLar
- 'R.J. Hilton' 🏆H7	EBee EPfP LRHS NLar NOra SCoo WHwl WMat
- 'Snow Cloud'	EPfP
- 'Snowflakes'	CEnd CSBt EBee LRHS LSRN MAsh NOra NOrn SCob SEWo SLim SPer SPoG SWvt WHwl WMat WMou
§ ***lamarckii*** 🏆H7	Widely available
ovalis misapplied	see *A. spicata* (Lam.) K. Koch
ovalis Medik.	SPlb
- 'Edelweiss'	IArd MRav NLar SCoo
pumila	see *A. alnifolia* var. *pumila*
rotundifolia ambig.	CAgr MCoo
sanguinea 'Chimney Rock'	NLar
§ ***spicata*** (Lam.) K. Koch	CAgr MCoo
stolonifera	CTri

Amelanchier × *Sorbus* see × *Amelasorbus*

× *Amelasorbus* (*Rosaceae*)

raciborskiana	MBlu NLar

Amellus (*Asteraceae*)

asteroides	MAsh

Amicia (*Papilionaceae*)

zygomeris	CDTJ CDow CSde CSpe EBee EPfP EShb EWes IPot LEdu LRHS MGil SDix SEle SPhx SPoG WCot WPGP
- 'John's Big Splash' (v)	WCot

Ammi (*Apiaceae*)

majus 🏆H6	CBod CSpe LCro LEdu LOPS LRHS MAvo MNHC SDix SPhx WSFF
visnaga	see *Visnaga daucoides*

Ammobium (*Asteraceae*)

calyceroides	GBin

Ammocharis (*Amaryllidaceae*)

coranica	WCot
longifolia	WCot

Ammophila (*Poaceae*)

arenaria	CKno EBee IMou WABo XLum XSen
breviligulata	EBee IMou XLum

Amomum (*Zingiberaceae*)

sp.	SDir
subulatum	SDir SPre

Amomyrtus (*Myrtaceae*)

§ ***luma***	CBcs CTri CTsd EBee ELan ELon IDee LEdu MMuc SEND SPoG WJek WPGP WPav
meli new	WPGP

Amorpha (*Papilionaceae*)

canescens	CBod EBee LRHS SPlb
fruticosa	MBlu MGil MMuc SEND SPlb
nana	XLum

Amorphophallus ✿ (*Araceae*)

albus	CDTJ LEdu SPlb WCot
bulbifer	CDTJ ESwi LRHS SDeJ SDir SPlb XLum
dunnii	CDTJ LEdu
henryi	WCot
kerrii	CExl WCot
kiusianus B&SWJ 4845	WCru
konjac	CDTJ CExl CSpe LEdu LRHS NGKo SChF SChr SDeJ SPlb WCot XLum
napalensis	SDir WCot XLum
stipitatus	LEdu WCot
yuloensis	WCot

Ampelaster (*Asteraceae*)

§ ***carolinianus***	XEll

Ampelocissus (*Vitaceae*)

sikkimensis HWJK 2066	WCru

Ampelodesmos (*Poaceae*)

mauritanicus 🏆H3	CKno CSam CSpe ECha EShb EWes MAvo SDix SEND SPlb WCot XCre
- white-flowered	SMHy

Ampelopsis (*Vitaceae*)

aconitifolia	NLar WCru
- 'Chinese Lace'	EBee EShb ESwi MRav NLar WBor
arborea	WCru
brevipedunculata	ELan MGil MMrt SCoo SLim SPer WAvo
- 'Citrulloides'	WCru
- 'Elegans' (v)	CBcs CDoC CMac CRos CWld EBee ELan ELon EPfP EShb LRHS MGil MGos MRav SNig SPer SPoG SWvt WAvo WCot WLov
delavayana	EShb MGil MMuc
glandulosa var. ***hancei*** B&SWJ 1793	WCru
henryana	see *Parthenocissus henryana*
megalophylla	EShb NLar
sempervirens hort. ex Veitch	see *Cissus striata*
tricuspidata 'Veitchii'	see *Parthenocissus tricuspidata* 'Veitchii'

Amphicome see *Incarvillea*

Amsonia (*Apocynaceae*)

'Blue Ice'	Widely available
ciliata	IPot LEdu MCot MMrt NLar SHar WPGP XLum
§ ***elliptica***	EBee EPPr
'Ernst Pagels'	EPPr MAvo WCot WGoo
hubrichtii	CBod CKno CSpe EBee ECha EMor EPPr EPfP EWTr IPot LEdu LRHS LSun MBel NLar NRHS SBut SDix SMHy SMad SPhx SWvt WCAu WPGP WSHC
illustris	CRos EPPr LEdu LRHS NLar NRHS SBut SHar SMHy SPhx WHoo
§ ***orientalis***	CMea CRos CSpe CTri EBee ECha EMor GBin GWyn IPot LEdu LRHS MAvo MCot MRav NDov NLar NRHS SBut SPhx SVen SWvt WCot WFar WKif XEll XLum
- from Turkey	LEdu SMHy

- 'Cally Dark Stem'	LPla
sinensis	see *A. elliptica*
tabernaemontana	Widely available
- 'Montana'	SPer SWvt
- var. ***salicifolia***	EBee IMou IPot LCro LEdu LOPS LPla LRHS MCot NRHS SCob WCAu WPGP
- 'Stella Azul'	EBee MNrw
- 'Storm Cloud' **new**	IPot
tomentosa var. ***stenophylla***	EBee

Amygdalus see *Prunus*

Anacyclus (*Asteraceae*)

pyrethrum	GPoy
- var. ***depressus*** ♀H4	EBou ELan EPfP GKev MAsh MMuc SPlb
- - 'Garden Gnome'	CTri SRms
- - 'Silberkissen'	CMea EDAr WRHF

Anagallis (*Primulaceae*)

monellii 'Gentian Blue' ♀H3 **new**	LCro LOPS
- subsp. ***linifolia*** 'Blue Light'	CSpe
- 'Skylover'	CCCN LCro LOPS
tenella	LLWG
- 'Studland'	WAbe

Ananas (*Bromeliaceae*)

comosus (F)	CCCN SPre
- 'Champaca' (F) ♀H1a	CCCN LCro LOPS SPre

Anaphalioides (*Asteraceae*)

§ ***bellidioides***	CTri

Anaphalis (*Asteraceae*)

alpicola	EBee
margaritacea	CBcs ECha GMaP NBid NLar SRms WCAu WFar
§ - 'Neuschnee'	GJos LPla NBre NLar WFar XLum
- NEW SNOW	see *A. margaritacea* 'Neuschnee'
- var. ***yedoensis***	CTri SDix
§ ***nepalensis*** var. ***monocephala***	EBee MCot NSti SRms
nubigena	see *A. nepalensis* var. *monocephala*
transnokoensis	EWes
§ ***trinervis***	CExl LSun XLum
triplinervis ♀H7	CRos ELan EPfP EShb EWTr EWld GAbr GKev GMaP LRHS MRav NBid NLar NRHS SBut SCob SPer WCAu WFar WHoo
- CC 1620	EPPr NBir
- 'Silberregen'	SAko
§ - 'Sommerschnee' ♀H7	CBod CMac EAJP ECha ECtt EPfP GWyn LPot LRHS MCot MHol MRav NLar NRHS NWad SCob SGbt SPer WGwG WWtn
- SUMMER SNOW	see *A. triplinervis* 'Sommerschnee'

Anchusa (*Boraginaceae*)

§ ***azurea***	CBod NLar
- 'Dropmore'	EBee EBou EPfP LCro LOPS LRHS MRav NLar SCob SRms
- 'Feltham Pride'	CDor EBee ELan LRHS NRHS SRms SWvt WHoo
- 'Little John'	SRms
- 'Loddon Royalist'	Widely available
- 'Opal'	CBod CNor ECtt LRHS NRHS WCAu
capensis	GKev
- 'Blue Angel'	SWvt
cespitosa	ELan EWes WAbe WIce
italica	see *A. azurea*
laxiflora	see *Borago pygmaea*
myosotidiflora	see *Brunnera macrophylla*
officinalis	MNHC SRms
sempervirens	see *Pentaglottis sempervirens*

Ancylostemon (*Gesneriaceae*)

convexus B&SWJ 6624	WCru
- B&SWJ 7182	WCru

Andrachne (*Phyllanthaceae*)

colchica	see *Leptopus chinensis*

Andromeda (*Ericaceae*)

polifolia	SPlb
- 'Alba'	CRos EHyd LRHS MAsh SPer SWvt
- 'Alisa'	GKev
- 'Blue Ice'	CDoC CRos EHyd ELan GBin IDee LRHS LSRN MAsh NBir NLar SPer SPoG WFar
- 'Blue Lagoon'	CDoC NLar
- 'Compacta' ♀H6	CBor CDoC CRos EHyd GEdr LRHS LSRN MAsh NLar NWad SWvt WFar
- 'Grandiflora'	GKev
- 'Kirigamine'	CRos LRHS MAsh
- 'Macrophylla' ♀H6	GEdr ITim WAbe WThu
- 'Nikko'	CMac NLar

Andropogon (*Poaceae*)

gerardii	CKno EBee LRHS NWsh XLum
- 'Prairie Sommer'	NDov
- 'Weinheim Burgundy'	IPot
ischaemum	see *Bothriochloa ischaemum*
'JS Purple Konza'	IPot
scoparius	see *Schizachyrium scoparium*

Androsace (*Primulaceae*)

sp.	MAsh
adenocephala	GKev
alpina	WAbe
* ***bayanharshanensis***	WAbe
bulleyana	CPla GKev WAbe
carnea subsp. ***brigantiaca***	GKev NHar NHpl NSla WAbe
- var. ***halleri***	see *A. carnea* subsp. *rosea*
- subsp. ***laggeri*** ♀H5	NHar NSla WAbe
§ - subsp. ***rosea*** ♀H5	NHpl NSla
carnea × pyrenaica	CPBP ELan EPot WAbe WIce
ciliata	WAbe
cylindrica	CRos EPot ITim LRHS NRHS
cylindrica × hirtella	CRos EHyd EPot LRHS NRHS
delavayi	GKev WAbe
- ACE 1786	WAbe
elatior	WAbe
geraniifolia	EBee ECha SRms
globifera	WAbe
halleri	see *A. carnea* subsp. *rosea*
hedraeantha	NSla WAbe
helvetica hybrid	CPBP
himalaica	CPBP EPot GEdr WAbe
hirtella	ITim WAbe
idahoensis	WAbe
idahoensis × laevigata	WAbe
jacquemontii	see *A. villosa* var. *jacquemontii*
kosopoljanskii	CPBP EPot
lactea	CSpe WAbe
laevigata	ITim

- 'Gothenburg'	WFar
lanuginosa 🏆H5	CBod CMea CSpe EBou ECtt EDAr EPot GBin MMuc NHol NHpl SBut SGro SRms WAbe WIce WOld
lehmanniana	WAbe
- 'Gotëborg Yellow'	WAbe
limprichtii	see *A. sarmentosa* var. *watkinsii*
× ***marpensis***	EPot WAbe
mathildae	NSla WAbe
microphylla	see *A. mucronifolia* G.Watt
§ ***mollis***	CPBP
montana	WAbe
mucronifolia misapplied	see *A. sempervivoides*
§ ***mucronifolia*** G.Watt	EPot WAbe
mucronifolia G.Watt × ***sempervivoides***	EPot WAbe
muscoidea	WAbe
- SEP 132	CPBP
- 'Breviscapa'	EPot
- 'Dolpo Lilac'	WAbe
- Schacht's form	EPot WAbe
nivalis	SPlb
ochotensis	WAbe
primuloides	see *A. studiosorum*
pubescens	CPla CRos EHyd EPot ITim LRHS NRHS
pyrenaica	CRos EHyd EPot ITim LRHS NRHS SPlb WAbe
rigida	EPot WAbe
robusta	WAbe
subsp. ***purpurea***	
- - 'Dolpo Dwarf'	EPot WAbe
rotundifolia	GKev
sarmentosa misapplied	see *A. studiosorum*
sarmentosa ambig.	NHpl SPlb XLum
sarmentosa Wall.	EBou GKev SRms WHoo
- from Namche, Nepal	EPot WAbe
- Galmont's form	see *A. studiosorum* 'Salmon's Variety'
- 'Sherriffii'	SRms WHoo WIce
§ - var. ***watkinsii***	EPot
- var. ***yunnanensis*** misapplied	see *A. studiosorum*
- var. ***yunnanensis*** Knuth	see *A. mollis*
selago	WAbe
- 'Red Eye'	WAbe
§ ***sempervivoides*** 🏆H5	CRos EBou EDAr EHyd ELan EPot GBin GKev GMaP LRHS MBel NHol NRHS NSla SGro SPlb SRms WIce WOld
- 'Susan Joan'	EPot NHar WAbe WOld
septentrionalis	CSpe
- 'Stardust'	ELan MHol
spinulifera	EPot GKev
stenophylla	MAsh
strigillosa	GKev NHpl
§ ***studiosorum*** 🏆H5	EPot GAbr GKev WAbe
- 'Chumbyi'	CBor EPot NHpl SRms WIce WThu
- 'Conwy Gem'	WAbe
- 'Conwy Jewel'	WAbe
- 'Doksa'	EPot WAbe WIce
§ - 'Salmon's Variety'	CMea CTri EDAr
tapete	WAbe
vandellii	ITim NSla WAbe
villosa	NSla WAbe
§ - var. ***jacquemontii***	WThu
- - lilac-flowered	EPot WAbe
- - pink-flowered	EPot WAbe
vitaliana	see *Vitaliana primuliflora*
wardii	WAbe
watkinsii	see *A. sarmentosa* var. *watkinsii*
yargongensis	WAbe
zambalensis	WAbe

Andryala (*Asteraceae*)

agardhii	GKev WAbe
glandulosa	WCot
lanata	see *Hieracium lanatum*

Anemanthele (*Poaceae*)

§ ***lessoniana*** 🏆H4	Widely available
- 'Buffalo Gold' **new**	LSun
- 'Gold Hue'	ELon
- 'Sirocco'	CBod CSpe WCot WFar

Anemarrhena (*Asparagaceae*)

asphodeloides	SBrt WCot

Anemia (*Schizaeaceae*)

mexicana	ISha WPGP
tomentosa	ISha LEdu LRHS

Anemone ✿ (*Ranunculaceae*)

aconitifolia Michx.	see *A. narcissiflora*
altaica	GKev NLar SRms
amurensis	CExl
apennina 🏆H6	CAvo GEdr LEdu WShi
- var. ***albiflora***	EPot MAvo
- 'Petrovac'	CBor EPot GKev LEdu
baldensis	SRms WOut XEll
barbulata	CExl CPla EBee EMor EWes GKev GPSL LEdu
blanda 🏆H6	CAby CRos LCro LOPS LRHS MBow NLar NRHS SEND SRms WBor WFar WShi
I - 'Alba'	CRos EHyd LRHS NRHS
- blue-flowered	CAvo CCBP CMea CRos CTri EHyd ELan EPfP EPot ERCP GAbr GKev GMaP ILea LCro LOPS LRHS MWat NRHS SCob SDeJ SDir SPer SPhx SPoG SRms WCot
- 'Charmer'	CCBP CGrW EPot GKev ILea NHpl SDeJ WCot
- 'Ingramii'	EPot WCot
- var. ***rosea***	CRos EHyd LRHS NRHS SDeJ SPoG
- - 'Pink Star'	CAvo ERCP GKev NBir
- - 'Radar' 🏆H6	CBor EPot ERCP GKev MNrw NBir NHpl SDeJ
- 'Violet Star'	GKev SDeJ
- 'White Splendour' 🏆H6	CAby CAvo CBor CCBP CMea CTri ELan EPfP EPot ERCP GAbr GKev ILea LCro LEdu LOPS LRHS NBir NLar SDeJ SDir SPhx SPoG SRms WCot WWFP
- white-flowered	CRos LRHS MWat NRHS
'Bowles's Mauve'	GEdr
caerulea	LEdu
canadensis	EMor EPPr GEdr LEdu WCot
caroliniana	GKev
caucasica	EPot
chapaensis HWJ 631	WCru
'Cinderella'PBR (Fantasy Series)	EBee EHyd LRHS WSpi
coelestina var. ***linearis***	GKev
coronaria	EPfP SVic
- De Caen Group	CCBP CRos EHyd EPfP GKev LOPS LRHS NRHS SPoG
- - 'Bicolor'	GKev SDeJ
- - blue-flowered	CRos LRHS NRHS

	- - 'Bordeaux'	LCro LOPS
§	- - 'Die Braut'	ERCP EShb GKev LCro LOPS NBir SDeJ
	- - 'His Excellency'	see *A. coronaria* (De Caen Group) 'Hollandia'
§	- - 'Hollandia'	GKev SDeJ WRHF
	- - 'Mister Fokker'	ERCP EShb GBin GKev ILea LCro LOPS SDeJ
	- - pink-flowered	CRos LRHS NRHS
	- - red-flowered	CRos LRHS NRHS
	- - THE BRIDE	see *A. coronaria* (De Caen Group) 'Die Braut'
	- - 'The Governor'	ERCP GKev ILea SDeJ
	- (Harmony Series) 'Harmony Orchid'	CRos EHyd EPfP LRHS NRHS
	- - 'Harmony Pearl'	CRos EHyd LRHS NRHS
	- - 'Harmony Scarlet'	CRos EHyd LRHS NRHS
	- Saint Bridgid Group (d)	CRos EHyd GKev LRHS NRHS
	- - 'Lord Lieutenant' (d)	ERCP GKev NBir SDeJ
	- - 'Mount Everest' (d)	ERCP GKev ILea NBir SDeJ
	- - 'The Admiral' (d)	GKev NBir SDeJ
	- 'Sylphide' (Mona Lisa Series)	ERCP EShb GKev ILea LCro LOPS NBir SDeJ
	cylindrica	EPPr GEdr NDov NLar XEll
	'Dainty Swan'	CWGN EBee IPot LRHS MNrw MPri
	'Danish White'	MNrw WCot
	decapetala	MHer XEll
	demissa	XEll
	- var. ***major***	EBee
	'Dreaming Swan'	CMiW CPar CWGN EBee ELan EMor EPfP GBin GEdr GMaP IPot LRHS LSou MBNS MBel MHol MNrw MPnt MPri NLar NSti SEdd SHar SPoG SWvt WNPC
	drummondii	CPla CWCL EBee GKev
	'Elfin Swan'	CPar CWGN EPfP LRHS MBel MNrw NLar NRHS SPoG
	fasciculata	see *A. narcissiflora*
	filisecta	EBee MBel MHol MTis SDix WCot WRHF
	flaccida	CAby CBro EHyd EPPr GEdr LEdu LPla LRHS MAvo MNrw NRHS SHar WCot WHal WSHC
	- 'Futabazuru' (d)	GEdr WFar
	- 'Ginpai' (d)	GEdr WFar
	globosa	see *A. multifida* Poir.
	'Guernica'	EWes
	'Hatakeyama Double' (d)	LPla WSHC
	'Hatakeyama Single'	LPla
	hepatica L.	see *Hepatica nobilis*
§	***hortensis***	EBee
§	***hupehensis***	CExl EBee EBou GMaP LSun NDov
	- BWJ 8190	WCru
	- NJM 11.068	WPGP
	- f. ***alba***	CExl CSpe
§	- 'Bowles's Pink' ♀H7	CDor CElw CExl LCro LOPS
	- 'Crispa'	see *A.* × *hybrida* 'Lady Gilmour' Wolley-Dod
	- 'Eugenie'	ECtt EPfP LRHS NBir
	- 'Hadspen Abundance' ♀H7	CBar CExl CMac ECha ECtt ELan ELon EPfP GAbr GKin GMaP LCro LOPS LRHS LSRN MAvo MBNS NBir NChi NRHS NSti SCob SPer SPhx SRms SWvt WCAu WFar WSpi XLum
	- var. ***hupehensis***	WFar
§	- var. ***japonica***	CPou SRms XLum
	- - B&SWJ 4886	WCru
	- - PAB 8884	LEdu

	- - 'Bodnant Burgundy'	EBee LRHS SWvt
§	- - 'Bressingham Glow'	CExl CMac ECtt ELan EPfP EPot EShb GKin ILea LRHS NBir NLar SPer WBrk WCAu WFar WHil
§	- - 'Pamina' ♀H7	Widely available
	- - 'Pink Saucer'	CBod EBee WFar WHil
	- - PRINCE HENRY	see *A. hupehensis* var. *japonica* 'Prinz Heinrich'
§	- - 'Prinz Heinrich'	Widely available
§	- - 'Rotkäppchen' ♀H7	CBod CDor ECtt EShb GKin GQue LRHS LSun MHol MMuc NHol NLar NSti SPad SWvt WCot WRHF WSHC
	- - 'Splendens'	CMea CRos EHyd ELan EPfP LCro LOPS LRHS MCot NLar NRHS SCob SPer SPoG SRms SWvt WHal WSpi XLum
	- - 'Tiki Sensation' PBR **new**	CWGN LCro LOPS
	- 'Little Princess' PBR	EBee ECtt EShb MNrw
	- 'Ouvertüre'	ECtt
	- 'Pocahontas' PBR (Fantasy Series)	ECtt EHyd EPfP GBin LRHS MNrw NRHS
	- 'Praecox'	CBod CMea CRos EPfP LRHS MBNS MBros NBir NRHS SGbt SRms SWvt WCAu WGwG
	- 'Red Riding Hood' (Fantasy Series)	LRHS NRHS WSpi
	- 'September Charm'	see *A.* × *hybrida* 'September Charm'
	- 'Superba'	WSpi
§	× ***hybrida***	NChi
	- 'Alba' misapplied (UK)	see *A.* × *hybrida* 'Honorine Jobert'
	- 'Alba Dura'	see *A. tomentosa* 'Albadura'
	- 'Albert Schweitzer'	see *A.* × *hybrida* 'Elegans'
	- 'Andrea Atkinson'	Widely available
	- 'Bowles's Pink'	see *A. hupehensis* 'Bowles's Pink'
	- 'Bressingham Glow'	see *A. hupehensis* var. *japonica* 'Bressingham Glow'
	- 'Carmen'	LPla LSou NLar
	- 'Coupe d'Argent'	EBee ECtt LRHS MBel NLar
§	- 'Elegans' ♀H7	CSam ECtt GMaP LCro LOPS LRHS MMuc NBir SEND SWvt WFar
	- 'Frau Marie Maushardt'	WBrk
§	- 'Géante des Blanches'	LPla
§	- 'Honorine Jobert' ♀H7	Widely available
	- 'Josephine'	WFar
§	- 'Königin Charlotte' ♀H7	Widely available
	- 'Lady Gilmour' misapplied	see *A.* × *hybrida* 'Montrose'
	- 'Lady Gilmour' ambig.	GWyn SGbt XLum
§	- 'Lady Gilmour' Wolley-Dod	CSpe EBee ECtt EPfP LEdu LRHS MRav NBir NChi NRHS SRms WSpi XLum
	- 'Loreley'	CBod EPfP LPla MCot NLar SWvt WCot
	- 'Luise Uhink'	CPou
	- 'Märchenfee'	MNrw
	- 'Margarete' misapplied	see *A.* × *hybrida* 'Montrose'
	- 'Margarete' Kayser & Seibert	CExl ECrN ECtt ELan EPfP LRHS MHol WHil
	- 'Max Vogel'	see *A.* × *hybrida* 'Elegans'
	- 'Monterosa'	see *A.* × *hybrida* 'Montrose'
§	- 'Montrose'	CPou EBee ECha ELan EWes GMaP LCro LOPS LPla LRHS NBir NLar SRms WCAu
	- 'Pamina'	see *A. hupehensis* var. *japonica* 'Pamina'
	- PINK KISS ('Pkan' PBR)	EBee ELon LPla
	- Pretty Lady Series	SCob
	- - 'Pretty Lady Diana' PBR	ECtt LBuc LCro LRHS NLar SCob SWvt WTyc

	- - 'Pretty Lady Emily'PBR	EPfP LBuc LRHS NLar SCob SWvt WHil
	- - 'Pretty Lady Julia'PBR	EBee NLar WHil
	- - 'Pretty Lady Maria'	EBee LRHS NLar SCob
	- - 'Pretty Lady Susan'	CWGN EBee LBuc LCro LOPS LRHS NLar SWvt WHil
	- PRINCE HENRY	see *A. hupehensis* var. *japonica* 'Prinz Heinrich'
	- 'Profusion'	CTri EBee LBuc LRHS WHal
	- QUEEN CHARLOTTE	see *A.* × *hybrida* 'Königin Charlotte'
	- 'Richard Ahrens'	CRos ECtt EPfP EShb GBee GMaP LRHS LSRN MGos NGdn NLar NRHS SWvt WGwG
§	- 'Robustissima'	CBod CRos EBee EMor EPfP GMaP LRHS LSRN MCot MHol MMuc MNrw NBir NGdn NLar NRHS NSti SEND SPer SRms SWvt WAvo WCAu WFar
	- 'Rosea'	CBod
	- 'Rosenschale'	EWes LRHS MNrw NRHS
	- 'Rotkäppchen'	see *A. hupehensis* var. *japonica* 'Rotkäppchen'
§	- 'September Charm' ♀H7	Widely available
	- 'Serenade'	CRos CSam ECtt ELan EMor EPfP LRHS LSRN MRav NBir NLar NRHS SPoG WCAu XLum
	- TOURBILLON	see *A.* × *hybrida* 'Whirlwind'
§	- 'Whirlwind'	Widely available
	- 'White Queen'	see *A.* × *hybrida* 'Géante des Blanches'
	- WIRBELWIND	see *A.* × *hybrida* 'Whirlwind'
	japonica	see *A. hupehensis*, *A. hupehensis* var. *japonica*, *A.* × *hybrida*
	- 'Crustata'	CMac
§	× ***lesseri***	CSpe ECha ELan GEdr GKev MBel SRms
	leveillei	Widely available
	- BWJ 7919	WCru
§	× ***lipsiensis***	CAby CBro CMea CPBP EBee ECtt EPot GAbr GEdr GKev GMaP LEdu MBel MCot MNrw NHpl NLar SPer WCru WFar WHal WHoo WPGP WSHC WSpi
	- 'Pallida' ♀H5	CBor CElw CMiW CSam CSpe ELon GEdr GKev LEdu MAvo MCot NLar WCot WFar WIce WShi XEll
	- 'Schwefelfeuer'	LEdu MAvo NDry
	- 'Stiby' **new**	NDry
	- 'Vindobonensis'	EBee GEdr MAvo WCot
	lithophila	GEdr GKev
	lyallii	GKev
	magellanica hort. ex Wehrh.	see *A. multifida* Poir.
	'Majestic'	MHol
	matsudae B&SWJ 1452	WCru
	- NMWJ 14517	WCru
	multifida misapplied red-flowered	see *A.* × *lesseri*
§	***multifida*** Poir.	CTsd ECha EHyd GKev LRHS NBir NRHS NSti SPer WFar WHoo
	- Annabella Series	GKev
	- - 'Annabella Deep Rose'	GJos WHil
	- - 'Annabella White'	GJos
	- var. ***globosa***	GKev
	- 'Major'	CMea CSpe EPfP GPSL SPhx WIce
	- 'Rubra'	CBod EPfP GBin GEdr GKev GWyn LRHS MPie MSCN NBir NLar NRHS SPoG WBor WFar
	- yellow-flowered	GEdr
§	***narcissiflora***	CSpe EBee GKev NBir NChi SPhx
	nemorosa	Widely available
	- 'Alba'	CMiW LRHS WFar
	- 'Alba Plena' (d)	CSam ECha ECtt EPPr EPfP GKev MAvo NBPC NGdn NLar WFar WSHC
	- 'Allenii' ♀H5	CBor CBro CElw CMiW CRos ELon EPPr EPot GEdr GKev GMaP ITim LRHS MAvo MRav NRHS NRya WFar WShi
	- 'Amy Doncaster'	CLAP
	- 'Apuseni'	LEdu
	- 'Atley'	EBee GEdr MAvo WCot WFar
	- 'Atrocaerulea'	NLar
	- 'Atrorosea'	EPPr
	- 'Ballyrogan Blue'	MAvo
	- 'Behemoth Blue'	LEdu MAvo
	- 'Bill Baker's Pink'	CLAP LEdu
	- 'Blue Beauty'	EBee ELon GMaP MAvo
	- 'Blue Bonnet'	CAby EPot ITim LEdu MAvo
	- 'Blue Eyes' (d)	CAby CElw CLAP CWCL EBee GAbr GBin GEdr GKev GMaP IPot ITim LEdu MAvo NBir NHpl NLar SMHy SPVi WFar WSHC WTyc
	- 'Blue Queen'	ELon
	- blue-backed double (d) **new**	CBro
	- 'Blush'	LEdu
	- 'Bohemia'	MAvo
	- 'Bowles's Purple'	CAby CMiW EBee EMor EPot GEdr GMaP LRHS MAvo MHol NBid NHpl NRya WBor WCot WFar WSHC
	- 'Bracteata'	CAby CBro CMiW GEdr GKev MMrt SDir
	- 'Bracteata Pleniflora' (d)	CLAP CMiW EBee ELon EPot GKev GMaP LEdu MAvo MNrw NBir SDeJ WCot WHal WShi XEll
	- 'Buckland'	EBee EPfP EPot MAvo SPVi
	- 'Caerulea'	EPot ITim
	- 'Cedric's Pink'	CMiW EPPr MAvo WFar
	- 'Celestial'	ELan EPPr MAvo
	- 'Dark Leaf' **new**	MAvo
	- 'Dee Day'	EBee LEdu MAvo
	- 'Dell Garden'	EPPr
	- 'Evelyn Meadows'	MAvo WSHC
	- 'Explosion' (d) **new**	NDry
	- 'Flash' **new**	NDry
	- 'Flore Pleno' (d)	CAby CPla EBee GAbr NBir WBor WFar
	- 'Flushing'	GEdr MAvo WFar
	- 'Frenzy'	MAvo WCot
	- 'Frühlingsfee'	MAvo
	- 'Frühlingsfest'	EBee
	- 'Gerda Ramusen'	ELan ELon EPot EShb EWes LEdu
	- 'Gerry'	MAvo
I	- 'Gigantea Rubra'	MAvo WCot
	- 'Glyncock Gold'	MAvo
	- 'Green Dream'	MAvo WSHC
	- 'Green Fingers'	EPPr GEdr GKev GMaP ITim MMrt NHar WSHC XEll
	- 'Hakumane Senjuizaki'	WCot WSHC
	- 'Hall Farm Blue' **new**	MAvo
	- 'Hannah Gubbay'	EPot
	- 'Hilda'	EBee ECtt GEdr GKev IPot LEdu NBir NLar NRya
	- 'Ice and Fire'	EPot GKev LEdu
	- 'Jack Brownless'	LEdu
	- 'Kentish Pink'	GBin GMaP SPVi
	- 'Knightshayes Vestal' (d)	CExl CLAP CMiW MRav WSHC
	- 'La Rochanne'	MAvo MNrw
	- 'Lady Doneraile'	EPot LEdu NBir WFar WSHC

	- 'Lapis' **new**	NDry
	- 'Latvian Pink'	EPot GEdr LEdu MAvo WFar
	- 'Leeds' Variety'	CMiW EPot GKev GMaP LEdu MAvo SPVi
	- 'Lehna' (d)	MAvo
	- 'Lionel Bacon'	LEdu MAvo
	- 'Lismore Blue'	EBee EPPr EPot
	- 'Lismore Pink'	GEdr LEdu
	- 'Lucia'	EPot GEdr GKev LEdu MAvo WCot WFar
	- 'Lychette'	CBor EPPr EPot GAbr GEdr GKev MAvo WSHC
	- 'Maret' (d) **new**	NDry
	- 'Marie Rose'	EPot WFar
	- 'Mart's Blue'	CBor EBee EPfP EPot GKev WCot WFar
	- 'Monstrosa'	EPot GKev MAvo
	- 'New Pink'	MAvo
	- 'Noémie'	XEll
	- 'Parlez Vous'	CExl EPPr GEdr LEdu MAvo MNrw NHpl WFar WPnP WSHC XEll
	- 'Pat's Pink'	WShi
	- 'Pentre Pink'	EPot MAvo
	- 'Pink Carpet'	GEdr LEdu
	- 'Pink Delight'	LEdu
	- pink-flowered	MMuc
	- 'Ploeger de Bilt' **new**	MAvo
	- 'Ploeger's Plena' (d)	MAvo
	- 'Robinsoniana' 🏆H5	Widely available
	- 'Rosea'	CBor LEdu MAvo NLar
	- 'Royal Blue'	CAby CBro CMiW EBee ECtt EPPr GAbr GEdr GKev GMaP IPot LEdu MAvo NDov NHpl NLar SDir WCot WFar WPnP
	- 'Salt and Pepper'	LEdu NDry
	- 'Slack Top Pink'	MAvo
	- 'Slenaken'	MAvo
§	- 'Stammerberg' (d)	EPPr MAvo WSHC
	- 'Stammheim'	see *A. nemorosa* 'Stammerberg'
	- 'Tilo'	MAvo
	- 'Tinney's Blush'	CLAP
	- 'Tomas'	CLAP EAJP ELon EPot GEdr LEdu NHpl NRya WFar
	- 'Tups'	LEdu NDry
	- 'Vestal' (d) 🏆H5	Widely available
	- 'Virescens' 🏆H5	CAvo CMiW CPBP CWCL ELon EMor EPPr GEdr GKev GMaP LEdu MAvo NBir NLar WShi
	- 'Viridiflora'	CExl CLAP EPfP GAbr GBin MAvo MNrw NBir WCot WSHC
	- 'Westwell Pink'	EPPr MAvo MNrw SPVi WCot WFar WSHC WShi
	- white-flowered	CRos LRHS NRHS
	- 'Wilks' Giant'	MAvo
	- 'Wilks' White'	ELon EPPr GEdr MAvo
	- 'Wisley Pink'	EPot LEdu MAvo WFar
I	- 'Wisley White Form'	MAvo NLar WHoo
	- 'Wyatt's Pink'	ELon EPot GKev LEdu MAvo SPVi
	- 'Yerda Ramusem'	EPPr LEdu MAvo MNrw WSHC
	nemorosa* × *ranunculoides	see *A.* × *lipsiensis*
	obtusiloba	GBin GEdr NHpl WAbe WHal
	- CLD 1549	GEdr
	- 'Alba'	GEdr WAbe
	- 'Large Blue'	EPot GEdr LEdu NSla WAbe
	- 'Pradesh'	GEdr NHar NHpl WFar
I	- 'Sulphurea'	GEdr WAbe
	palmata	GEdr LEdu WKif
	parviflora	GKev XEll
	patens	see *Pulsatilla patens*

	pavonina	CAby CMea CMiW CSpe ECha LPla MAvo MHol NBir SLon SMHy SPoG WFar WOut
	polyanthes	CRos EBee EPfP GEdr GKev LRHS NRHS
	prattii	CExl EPPr GEdr LEdu NHpl
	pseudoaltaica	LEdu
	- 'Yuki-no-sei' (d)	GEdr WFar
	pulsatilla	see *Pulsatilla vulgaris*
*	***raddeana*** f. ***rosea***	GEdr
	ranunculoides 🏆H6	CAby CBro CMiW CPBP CSam CWCL EBee ELon EMor EPot GAbr GEdr GMaP LEdu LRHS MAvo MBel NBid NHol NHpl NLar NRya NSti SDeJ WFar WHil WPnP WSHC WShi
	- 'Anne' (d) **new**	NDry
	- 'Ants' (d) **new**	NDry
	- 'Aureus' (d) **new**	NDry
	- 'Bill Baker'	LEdu MAvo
	- 'Crazy Vienna'	WCot
	- 'Dagerort' (d) **new**	NDry
	- 'Dagö' (d) **new**	NDry
	- 'Ellen' (d) **new**	NDry
	- 'Ferguson's Fancy'	EPPr
	- 'Frank Waley'	MAvo WCot
	- 'Fuchsis Traum'	LEdu WCot WSHC
	- 'Golden Dream' (d) **new**	NDry
	- 'Hiiumaa' (d) **new**	NDry
	- 'Kahar' (d) **new**	NDry
	- 'Kreet' (d) **new**	NDry
*	- ***laciniata***	MAvo WCot
	- 'Leena' (d) **new**	NDry
	- 'Leida' (d) **new**	NDry
	- 'Linda' (d) **new**	NDry
I	- 'Linearis' **new**	NDry
	- 'Orange' **new**	NDry
	- 'Orjaku' (d) **new**	NDry
	- 'Papa' (d) **new**	NDry
	- 'Pisi' (d) **new**	NDry
	- 'Pleniflora' (d) 🏆H6	CAvo ECha GKev LRHS MAvo NBPC NLar NRHS WFar
	- subsp. ***ranunculoides***	GKev
	- 'Sääre' (d) **new**	NDry
	- 'Semi-Plena'	GEdr GKev LEdu
	- 'Siil' (d) **new**	NDry
	- 'Sirje' (d) **new**	NDry
	- 'Star 1' (d) **new**	NDry
	- 'Tafka' (d) **new**	NDry
	- 'Tapio' (d) **new**	NDry
	- 'Virve' (d) **new**	NDry
	- 'Vulkaan' (d) **new**	NDry
	- subsp. ***wockeana***	CSam EBee LEdu MAvo
	reflexa	EBee GKev
	rivularis	CAvo CPar CSde CSpe CTsd EMor EWTr GEdr GKev GPoy ILea IPot ITim LRHS MBriF MNrw NBir NLar NRHS SBrt SPer SRms WCru WFar WKif WSpi XEll
	- B&SWJ 13944	WCru
	- BWJ 7611	WCru
	- CC 4588	CExl
	- 'Glacier'	CCBP CWCL EBee MHol SBut WHil
	aff. ***rivularis*** 'Ruffled Swan'	CPar CWGN EMor GBin IPot LRHS LSun MBNS MNrw NLar NRHS NSti SEdd SLon SPoG WTyc
	rupicola	GEdr GKev NBir WCot XEll
	× ***seemannii***	see *A.* × *lipsiensis*
*	***sherriffii***	GKev

stellata Lam. — see *A. hortensis*
stolonifera double-flowered (d) — EBee LEdu LPla WCot WSHC
sulphurea misapplied — see *Pulsatilla alpina* subsp. *apiifolia*
sumatrana B&SWJ 11265 — WCru
sylvestris — Widely available
- 'Elise Fellmann' (d) — EBee WHal
- 'Madonna' — LSun
- 'Snow White' — CBod
tenuifolia — NHpl
tetrasepala — WCot XEll
§ **tomentosa** — CBod LRHS NRHS SDix SRms
§ - 'Albadura' — EBee MCot NLar
- 'Robustissima' — see *A.* × *hybrida* 'Robustissima'
trifolia L. — CMiW EBee EPPr EPot GKev LEdu NBid NLar WCot XEll
trullifolia — GBin NHar
- var. **linearis** — WAbe
udensis — GEdr WCot
vernalis — see *Pulsatilla vernalis*
virginiana — EBee LEdu MNrw WHrl
vitifolia misapplied — see *A. tomentosa*
vitifolia Buch.-Ham. ex DC.WJC 12743 — WCru
WILD SWAN ('Macane001'[PBR]) — Widely available

Anemonella (*Ranunculaceae*)

thalictroides — CBor CElw EMor EPot GEdr GKev MAvo MBel NHpl NLar NRya SPVi WAbe WFar WPnP WSHC WSpi XLum
- 'Amelia' — CElw GEdr NBro NHpl
- 'Babe' — WCot
- 'Betty Blake' (d) — CBor CElw EBee GBin GEdr GKev MAvo MMrt NBro NHpl NRya NSla SDir SPVi WCot WFar
- 'Blushing Bride' (d) — NBro WCot
- 'Cameo' — GEdr GKev MNrw NHpl NRya SDir WCot WFar
- 'Charlotte' — GEdr
- 'Dark Pink' — EBee GBin MAvo NHpl
- 'Diamante' — CElw MAvo WCot
- 'Double Diamante' (d) — WCot
- 'Full Double White' (d) — NHpl
- 'Green Hurricane' (d) — GEdr GKev NRya SDir SPVi WCot WFar
- 'Hakikomi-fu' (v) — GEdr
- 'Kikuzaki Pink' (d) — GEdr GKev WFar
- 'Kikuzaki White' (d) — CBor GEdr GKev WFar
- 'Nadine A.' (d) — XEll
- 'Pink Fairy' — SMHy
- f. **rosea** — CAby CElw ELan NLar WAbe
- - 'Oscar Schoaf' (d) — CElw GEdr GKev MAvo NHpl SPVi WAbe WCot WFar
- - semi-double pink-flowered (d) — CElw MAvo
- 'Rosea Plena' (d) — EMor SDir
- semi-double white-flowered (d) — CElw WAbe
- 'Shiozaki' (d) new — GEdr
- 'Snowflake' (d) — MAvo
- 'Spring Nymph' — SMHy
- 'Tairin' — CBor GEdr GKev NHpl WCot WFar

Anemonopsis (*Ranunculaceae*)

macrophylla — CExl CMiW CPBP CSpe EBee EPfP EWes GEdr LEdu MNrw MRav NHpl NLar WCru WFar WOld WPGP WSHC
- double-flowered (d) — GKev WSHC
- 'White Swan' — CMiW EWld GEdr WCru WSHC

Anemopsis (*Saururaceae*)

californica — EBee EWat LCro LLWG LOPS MWts SBrt WCot

Anethum (*Apiaceae*)

graveolens — EMor ENfk GPoy LCro LOPS MBow MBros MHer MNHC MPri SPhx SRms SVic XAbr
- 'Dukat' — CLau LCro LOPS
- 'Vierling' — SPhx

angelica see *Angelica archangelica*

Angelica (*Apiaceae*)

acutiloba — WFar
- var. **iwatensis** B&SWJ 11197 — WCru
anomala B&SWJ 10886 — ESwi LEdu WCru
archangelica — Widely available
- subsp. **decurrens** new — WPGP
arguta — EBee
- B&SWJ 14115 new — WCru
- B&SWJ 14162 — WCru
atropurpurea — EPfP LRHS MNrw MRav SWvt
brevicaulis — LEdu WPGP
breweri B&SWJ 14083 — WCru
cartilaginomarginata B&SWJ 12663 — WCru
cyclocarpa WJC 13658 — WCru
dahurica — SPhx WFar WHil
decursiva B&SWJ 5746 — WCru
edulis — WHer WPGP
- B&SWJ 10968 — WCru
genuflexa B&SWJ 14109 — WCru
gigas — Widely available
- B&SWJ 4170 — WCru
grayi — SPhx
hendersoni — SPhx
hispanica — see *A. pachycarpa*
japonica B&SWJ 11480 — WCru
montana — see *A. sylvestris*
morii RWJ 9802 — WCru
nubigena WJC 13763 — WCru
§ **pachycarpa** — CBod CRos CSam EBee EPPr GBin GMaP LRHS MHer MRav NBir NGBl NLar NRHS SPhx WCot WFar
pubescens — NDov
- B&SWJ 5593 — LEdu WCru
sinensis — LEdu
'Summer Delight' — see *Ligusticum scoticum*
§ **sylvestris** — CBre CHab LLWG NAts WOut
- 'Burgundy' — NGBl
- 'Ebony' 𝕐H5 — CBct CBod CPla ECtt GAbr IPot LEdu LRHS MBNS MHer MHol NSti SEdd SMad SPad SPhx SPoG WCot WPGP
* - 'Purpurea' — CDor CSam EWes GMaP
- 'Vicar's Mead' — EBee ECha LEdu LRHS MBel NBir NDov SPer SPhx SWvt WCAu WHil
taiwaniana — CBre CDTJ EBee ELan ESwi IMou LRHS MMuc NLar SPhx
ursina — NGBl WCru

Angelonia (*Plantaginaceae*)

ARCHANGEL DEEP ROSE ('Balarcrose') — CRos EHyd LRHS NRHS

Anigozanthos (*Haemodoraceae*)

sp.	CDoC
(Bush Gems Series)	SEle
BUSH BONANZA ('Rambubona'PBR)	
- BUSH DIAMOND ('Rambodiam'PBR)	SEle
- 'Bush Inferno'PBR	SEle
- 'Bush Ranger'	CCCN
flavidus	SPlb
- 'Ember'	CCCN
- 'Illusion'	CCCN
- 'Opal'	CCCN
- 'Pearl'	CCCN
- red-flowered	SPlb
- 'Splendour'	CCCN
- 'Yellow Gem'	CCCN
manglesii	SPlb
rufus	SEle

anise see *Pimpinella anisum*

Anisodontea (*Malvaceae*)

§ ***capensis***	CCCN ELan EPri SChF SEle SLim SPlb SRkn SRms SVen SWvt WABo WLov
- 'Elegans Princess'	CCCN
'Crystal Rose'	EPfP MGos XLum
'El Rayo'	CBod CSde CWGN ECtt LPla MHol MNrw MPie NCou SCob SDys SEdd SEle SMad SPad SPoG SRkn WAvo WBor WBrk WCot WFar WMal WSHC WTre XLum
'Elegant Lady'	SEle
huegelii	see *Alyogyne huegelii*
× ***hypomadara*** misapplied	see *A. capensis*
§ × ***hypomadara*** (Sprague) D.M.Bates	SEle
julii	SVen
LADY IN PINK ('Nuanilaninp')	CBod MBros NCou SEle
'Large Magenta'	CMac EBee ELon ILea LRHS SWvt

Anisodus (*Solanaceae*)

carnioliciodes BWJ 7501	WCru

Anisotome (*Apiaceae*)

imbricata var. ***imbricata***	WAbe
lyallii	GKev

Annona (*Annonaceae*)

cherimola (F)	CCCN XBlo
squamosa (F)	SPlb

Anoiganthus see *Cyrtanthus*

Anomalesia see *Gladiolus*

Anomatheca (*Iridaceae*)

cruenta	see *Freesia laxa*

Anredera (*Basellaceae*)

§ ***cordifolia***	CRHN EShb GKev LEdu

Antennaria (*Asteraceae*)

aprica	see *A. parvifolia*
dioica	CPla CTri ECtt GAbr GBin GPoy SPlb SRms WAbe XLum
- 'Alba'	GQue MCot
- 'Alex Duguid'	GPSL NWad
- 'Aprica'	see *A. parvifolia*
- 'Minima'	EPot GMaP NBro NSla WAbe
- 'Nyewoods Variety'	SRms
- var. ***rosea***	see *A. rosea*
- 'Rotes Wunder'	CMea ECha EPot NSla WAbe
* - 'Rubra'	ECha ECtt EDAr MBel NBir SRms WCav WIce XLum
microphylla 'Pink Pussy Toes'	EBou
§ ***parvifolia***	CTri SRms
- 'Alba'	EDAr
plantaginifolia	EBee
§ ***rosea*** ♀H5	CRos EBou EHyd EPfP GKev GMaP LRHS MAsh NRHS SPlb SRms WHal WHoo WIce

Antenoron see *Persicaria*

Anthemis ✿ (*Asteraceae*)

from Turkey	ECtt EWes
arvensis	CHab MBow MNHC SRms
- subsp. ***sphacelata*** **new**	WCot
§ 'Beauty of Grallagh'	WSpi
'Cally Cream'	ELon GWyn LRHS SDix SMHy SPhx WMal
'Cally White'	GAbr GBin WBrk
carpatica	MMuc NBro
- 'Karpatenschnee'	EHyd EPfP LRHS NRHS SAko SRms
cretica subsp. ***leucanthemoides***	WAbe
- subsp. ***tenuiloba***	EWes
frutescens Voss	see *Argyranthemum frutescens*
'Grallagh Gold' misapplied, orange-yellow	see *A.* 'Beauty of Grallagh'
'Grallagh Gold'	ECtt NPer SPhx
§ ***marschalliana***	EBou EDAr EPot LRHS NHpl NRHS SPlb SRms WAbe WCot
nobilis	see *Chamaemelum nobile*
'Orange Dream'	CBcs
punctata	Widely available
subsp. ***cupaniana*** ♀H4	
- - 'Nana'	NBir NPer SEdd SHar WCot
rudolphiana	see *A. marschalliana*
sancti-johannis	CRos EPfP LRHS NPer NRHS SAko SRms
SUSANNA MITCHELL ('Blomit')	CDor CRos EBee ECtt ELon GAbr GMaP LRHS LSRN MBel MHol MNrw NDov NLar NRHS NWad SWvt WMal WSHC XLum
'Tetworth'	ECha ELan EPfP GBee LRHS SAko
tinctoria	CBod CHby CMac EBee ENfk GPoy MHer MNHC MRav NAts NPer SRms SWvt WSFF XLum
- 'Alba'	CRos EBee LRHS NRHS NWad WFar
- 'Charme'PBR	LRHS NLar SPoG SRms SWvt
- 'Compacta'	EWes XLum
- 'E.C. Buxton' ♀H6	Widely available
- 'Eva'	NDov
- 'Hall Farm Frilly'	ECtt ELon
- 'Kelwayi'	CRos EBou EMor EPfP GLog GQue GWyn LRHS NLar NPer NRHS SPer SRms WFar XLum
- 'Lemon Ice'	EBee GBin GWyn MBel NLar
- 'Lemon Maid'	ECtt ELon
- 'Sauce Hollandaise'	Widely available
- 'Wargrave Variety'	CElw CMac CSam ECha ECtt ELan EPfP GBin GWyn LRHS MHol NBir NChi NGdn NRHS NWad SDix SPhx SWvt WCAu WFar

'Tinpenny Sparkle'	EBee ECtt EMor EWes EWhm GWyn MHol NLar WFar WHoo
triumfettii	EBee NDov NPer
tuberculata	NChi

Anthericum (*Asparagaceae*)

algeriense	see *A. liliago*
* ***bovei***	CBro
§ ***liliago***	CSpe ELan EWld GKev GMaP LRHS MCot MPie MRav NLar SMad SPer WAul XEll
- 'Major' ♀H5	CAvo CBro ECha LEdu SPhx
plumosum	see *Trichopetalum plumosum*
ramosum	CFis CSpe ECha EPPr EPot EPri EWes GKev LEdu LRHS MBrN NBid NBir NLar NSla SPhx WCot WSHC

Antholyza (*Iridaceae*)

coccinea	see *Crocosmia paniculata*
paniculata	see *Crocosmia paniculata*

Anthoxanthum (*Poaceae*)

odoratum	CHab GPoy GQue XLum

Anthriscus (*Apiaceae*)

cerefolium	CHby CLau ENfk GPoy LCro LOPS MBow MHer MNHC SEdi SRms SVic WSFF XAbr
nemorosa new	LEdu
sylvestris	CBre CHab GQue LCro LOPS LRHS NMir SPhx WFar WOut WSFF
- 'Going for Gold'	EPPr EWes MAvo MNrw NChi WCot WHil WMal WOut
- 'Golden Fleece' new	CBod SMad SPad
- 'Kabir'	LRHS SPhx
- 'Ravenswing'	Widely available
- yellow-leaved	GBin

Anthurium (*Araceae*)

andraeanum 'Glowing Pink'	XBlo
- RED HEART ('Rijn200469')	XBlo
- Tivoli ('Anthilap'PBR)	XBlo
'Aztec'	XBlo
BALENO ('Anthauf4'PBR)	XBlo
CARIBO ('Antvelonk'PBR)	XBlo
crenatum	XBlo
'Crimson'	XBlo
'Magenta'	XBlo
'Mikra'	XBlo
OCTAVIA ('Anthblafur')	XBlo
PICO BELLO ('Anthcupcup'PBR)	XBlo
PINK CHAMPION ('Antinkeles'PBR)	LCro LOPS XBlo
'Porcelaine White'	XBlo
RED CHAMPION ('Anthbnena'PBR)	LCro LOPS XBlo
VITARA ('Anthbnem'PBR)	XBlo
WHITE CHAMPION ('Anthefaqyr'PBR)	XBlo

Anthyllis (*Papilionaceae*)

hermanniae	LRHS
- 'Compacta'	see *A. hermanniae* 'Minor'
§ - 'Minor'	ELan EPot ITim WAbe
montana	XSen
- subsp. ***atropurpurea***	LRHS NRHS
- 'Rubra' ♀H5	CSpe EDAr EPot SPhx
vulneraria	CHab GJos LRHS NAts NMir NRya SPhx WSFF WWFP
- var. ***coccinea***	CBod EAJP ELan EWld GJos GKev LCro LOPS MBel NAts NSla SPhx WCFE WIce WOut
- dark red-flowered	CSpe

Antirrhinum (*Plantaginaceae*)

asarina	see *Asarina procumbens*
barrelieri	SEND
braun-blanquetii	CBod WCot
charidemi	EBee
glutinosum	see *A. hispanicum* subsp. *hispanicum*
hispanicum 'Avalanche'	ECtt
§ - subsp. ***hispanicum***	CSpe
- subsp. ***mollissimum***	EPot
latifolium	EBee
majus 'Admiral White'	LCro LOPS
- APPEAL BICOLOUR MIX	LOPS SCob
- 'Black Prince'	CSpe ECtt ELan LPla SPhx
- 'Night and Day'	CSpe
- 'Rocket White' (Rocket Series)	CSpe
- Sonnet Series, formula mixed	MBros MPri
molle	CSpe EBee GKev MCot NPer SChF
- pink-flowered	MCot SBut
- white-flowered	EBee SBut
PRETTY IN PINK ('Pmoore07'PBR)	CBod CSBt IPot LCro LOPS LRHS LSou MHol SHar SLon
sempervirens	CFis WAbe
siculum	EBee

añu see *Tropaeolum tuberosum*

Anubias (*Araceae*)

barteri new	XBlo

Aphelandra (*Acanthaceae*)

squarrosa	EShb
- 'Citrina'	XBlo

Aphyllanthes (*Asparagaceae*)

monspeliensis	SBrt XLum XSen

Apios (*Papilionaceae*)

§ ***americana***	EWes LEdu NBir SBrt WCot WCru WKor WSHC
- 'Nutty'	CAgr MCoo
tuberosa	see *A. americana*

Apium (*Apiaceae*)

graveolens	CHab CLau CTsd ENfk GPoy MHer MNHC SRms SVic WJek
- var. ***dulce*** 'Aurora'	LOPS
- - 'Brydon's Prize Red'	SVic
- - 'Celebrity' ♀H2	LRHS MCtn NRHS
- - 'Golden Self-blanching'	LCro LOPS SVic
- - 'Victoria' ♀H2	EKin MBros
- 'Giant Pink' - Mammoth Pink ♀H4	NRob
- var. ***rapaceum*** 'Prinz' ♀H4	CHby EKin LCro LOPS MCtn SVic
- (Secalinum Group) 'Par-cel'	MHer SRms
- - 'Zwolsche Krul'	MBow

Apium × *Petroselinum* (*Apiaceae*)

hybrid, misapplied	see *A. graveolens* Secalinum Group

Apocynum (*Apocynaceae*)

	cannabinum	GPoy

Aponogeton (*Aponogetonaceae*)

	desertorum	EWat LLWG
	distachyos	CBen CWat EWat LCro LLWG LOPS MWts NPer SVic WMAq XLum

apple see *Malus domestica*; also AGM Fruit Section

apricot see *Prunus armeniaca*

Aptenia (*Aizoaceae*)

	cordifolia	CCCN NPer SChr SPlb SVen
	- 'Variegata' (v)	CCCN

Aquilegia (*Ranunculaceae*)

	akitensis misapplied	see *A. flabellata* var. *pumila*
	'Alaska' (State Series) ♀H5	EBee EMor LRHS NRHS
	alpina	CMea EBee EBou EPfP LCro LOPS LRHS MAsh MBel MNHC NGdn SCob SPer SRms WHoo WSpi XEll XLum
	amaliae	see *A. ottonis* subsp. *amaliae*
	'Apple Blossom'	NBir
	aragonensis	see *A. pyrenaica*
§	***atrata***	CPou EBee GKev GQue
	aurea Janka	GKev
	barnebyi	CWCL
	bernardii	GKev
	bertolonii ♀H5	CMea EWld GKev LRHS NRHS NSla SRms WHoo WIce
	Biedermeier Group	CRos EPfP GJos LRHS NGdn NRHS WHil
	'Blackcurrant'	CWCL
	'Blue Star' (Star Series)	CWCL ELan EPfP GMaP GWyn LRHS NRHS SGbt SPtp WGwG
	'Bluebird' (Songbird Series) ♀H5	LBuc LRHS NBir NPer WFar
	'Bob Hares'	WAvo
	buergeriana	CBod GKev SPhx
	- 'Calimero'	EBee MBNS NLar
	- var. ***oxysepala***	see *A. oxysepala*
	'Bunting' (Songbird Series) ♀H5	SGbt
	canadensis ♀H5	CBod CSpe EBou ELan GAbr GKev GLog ITim NBir NBro SPhx SRms WFar WSpi XEll XLum
	- 'Little Lanterns'	EDAr GKev NHpl NLar WIce
	- 'Nana'	GKev
	- 'Pink Lanterns'	EDAr
	'Cardinal' (Songbird Series)	LBuc LRHS
	chaplinei	GKev NBir
	chrysantha	GJos GWyn MCot SRms SWvt WKif XSen
	- 'Denver Gold'	EShb SPhx WHil
	- 'Yellow Queen' ♀H5	CExl CWCL EMor EPPr EPfP GBin GMaP LCro LOPS LRHS MBel NGdn SDix SGbt SPhx SWvt WCFE WHil WTor XEll XLum
	clematiflora	see *A. vulgaris* var. *stellata*
	Clementine Series	EPfP
	coerulea ♀H5	GKev SRms XEll
	- var. ***coerulea***	SPhx
	- 'Rotstern'	CBod
	'Colorado' (State Series)	LRHS NRHS
	'Crimson Star'	CRos CWCL ELan EMor EPfP EShb LRHS MBel NRHS SPoG
	desertorum	GKev
	discolor	GAbr WThu XEll
	'Double Rubies' (d)	ELan
	'Dove' (Songbird Series) ♀H5	LBuc LRHS MHer SGbt SHar
I	'Dragonfly'	CBcs CRos EAJP ELan EPfP LRHS NRHS SPoG
	ecalcarata	see *Semiaquilegia ecalcarata*
	elegantula	GKev
	eximia B&SWJ 14053	WCru
	flabellata 'Blackcurrant Ice'	CWCL
	- (Cameo Series) 'Cameo Blue and White'	SRms
	- - 'Cameo Rose and White'	MHer
	- 'Georgia' (State Series) ♀H5	CRos LRHS NRHS
	- 'Ministar'	CWCL EDAr GWyn MHol XLum
	- 'Nana Alba'	see *A. flabellata* var. *pumila* f. *alba*
§	- var. ***pumila*** ♀H5	CWCL EAJP ECha EDAr EPfP GEdr GKev LRHS LSun NGdn NRHS SRms
§	- - f. ***alba*** ♀H5	ECha GKev LRHS LSun NRHS
	- - 'Atlantis'	MHol
I	- - f. ***kurilensis*** 'Rosea'	WAbe
	- 'Vermont' (State Series)	EBee EMor
	flavescens	GKev
	'Florida' (State Series) ♀H5	CRos EMor LRHS NRHS
	formosa	EPPr GQue NChi
	- var. ***formosa*** B&SWJ 13543	WCru
	- var. ***truncata*** B&SWJ 14072	WCru
§	***fragrans***	EBee
	'Fruit and Nut Chocolate'	EBee MHol WCot WMal
	glandulosa	GWyn
	glauca	see *A. fragrans*
	'Goldfinch' (Songbird Series)	LBuc LRHS NBir SGbt
	grahamii	EWTr
	'Heavenly Blue'	CBod CDor EBee GWyn LRHS
	'Hensol Harebell'	MBriF SHar SPtp SRms WSpi
	'Honeydew'	GWyn
	japonica	see *A. flabellata* var. *pumila*
	jonesii	GKev SPlb
	jonesii* × *saximontana	GKev
	'Kansas' (State Series)	CRos
	karelinii	EBee
	'Koralle'	CBod CDor GWyn WHil
	'Kristall'	CBod EShb MBel
*	***kuhistanica***	CBor EBee GWyn
	laramiensis	CPBP GKev
	'Leprechaun Gold' (v)	EMor EPfP MHol NGdn SDix
	'Lime Sorbet'	LRHS SRms
	longissima	GQue MHer SHar WCav WHoo
	'Louisiana' (State Series) ♀H5	CRos LRHS NRHS
	'Magpie'	see *A. vulgaris* 'William Guiness'
	× ***maruyamana***	EBee
	McKana Group	CBod CTri ELan EPfP GAbr GJos LRHS MGos NGdn NHol NLar SCob SPer SPlb SPoG SRms SVic SWvt WFar XLum
	'Montana' (State Series)	CRos
	Mrs Scott-Elliot hybrids	CBod CSBt EPfP MHol
	Music Series	SRms
	'Nightingale' (Songbird Series)	SGbt
	nigricans	see *A. atrata*
	olympica	LSun
	'Oregon' (State Series)	EMor
	'Origami Yellow' (Origami Series) ♀H5	WHil
§	***ottonis*** subsp. ***amaliae***	CPBP WAbe

§	***oxysepala***	CExl GLog MMrt
	- B&SWJ 4775	WCru
	- var. ***kansuensis***	GKev
	Perfumed Garden Group	WFar
§	***pyrenaica***	GKev XEll
	- dwarf	WAbe
	'Red Hobbit'	CSpe CTsd CWCL ELan EPfP LRHS MBel MBros MHol NGdn NHpl NLar WFar
	'Red Star' (Star Series)	CWCL EAJP EPfP EShb SGbt SHar SPoG WGwG
	'Rhubarb and Custard'	EMor
	'Robin' (Songbird Series)	SGbt
	rockii	EBee EWld GKev SBrt
	'Rose Queen'	CDor CWCL EPfP EShb GWyn SPtp
	saximontana	GEdr GKev
§	'Schneekönigin'	CWCL EBee LRHS NRHS WCFE
	scopulorum	GKev
	sibirica	EBee GKev
	'Silver Queen'	ELan EWTr GBin
	skinneri	CExl ELan GLog NWad WMal
	- 'Tequila Sunrise'	CSpe CWCL ELan EMor LRHS MHer NRHS
	SNOW QUEEN	see *A.* 'Schneekönigin'
	Spring Magic Series	MPri WCav
	- SPRING MAGIC BLUE AND WHITE	LRHS SCob
	- SPRING MAGIC WHITE	NRHS SCob
	stellata	see *A. vulgaris* var. *stellata*
	'Sunburst Ruby'	CWCL
	(Swan Series) 'Swan Lavender'	SCob WFar
	- 'Swan Pink and Yellow'	CBod SCob
	- 'Swan Red and White'	CBod SCob WFar
	- 'Swan Violet and White'	SCob WFar
	triternata	GWyn
	'Virginia' (State Series)	EMor LRHS NRHS
	viridiflora	CBod CBor EBee EMor LRHS SPhx WCot WHil XEll
	- 'Chocolate Soldier'	CCBP CSpe SPeP
	(Volcano! Group) 'Volcano!' (mixed)	GQue WHil
	vulgaris	CBod CHab EPfP GBin GKev GPoy GQue GWyn LCro LOPS LRHS MBow MHer MNHC NBro NGdn NGrd SCob SPlb WCAu WShi XSen
	- 'Adelaide Addison'	ECha
	- var. ***alba***	CBod CMea EPfP LRHS MMuc NRHS SCob
	- 'Altrosa'	GWyn
	- 'Aureovariegata'	see *A. vulgaris* Vervaeneana Group
	- 'Blackbird' (Songbird Series) (d)	CWCL
	- ***clematiflora***	see *A. vulgaris* var. *stellata*
	- Clementine Series	CBod
	- - 'Clementine Blue' (d)	CRos EPfP LRHS NRHS SPoG WCot
	- - 'Clementine Dark Purple' (d)	CRos EPfP LRHS NRHS SPoG
	- - 'Clementine Red' (d)	EPfP LRHS NRHS
	- - 'Clementine Rose' (d)	CRos GQue LRHS NRHS SPoG
	- - 'Clementine Salmon Rose' (d)	CRos CWCL EPfP LRHS NRHS SPoG
	- - 'Clementine White' (d)	CRos CWCL EPfP LRHS NRHS SPoG WSpi
	- 'Crystal Star'	EPfP LRHS NRHS
	- 'Eyecatcher'	WCot
	- var. ***flore-pleno*** bicoloured (d)	XAbr
	- - black-flowered (d)	MMuc SEND WCot
	- - 'Dorothy Rose' (Dorothy Series) (d)	SPtp
	- - 'Double Pleat' (d)	EPfP
	- - 'Double Pleat' pink/white-flowered (d)	CWCL
	- - 'Jane Hollow' (d)	CPou
	- - pink-flowered (d)	CWCL
	- - 'Strawberry Ice Cream' (d)	NBro
*	- - 'White Bonnet' (d)	CWCL
	- 'Heidi'	GWyn MMuc SEND
	- 'Mellow Yellow'	GPSL LRHS SDix
	- MUNSTEAD WHITE	see *A. vulgaris* 'Nivea'
§	- 'Nivea' ♀H7	CDor CPou CSpe EBee ECha ELan EPfP LCro LOPS NChi SEND SPoG SPtp WCot WSpi
	- Pom Pom Series	WSpi
	- - 'Pom Pom Crimson'	NBro WCot
§	- var. ***stellata***	CDor ELan EMor GKev GWyn NBir NBro
	- - (Barlow Series) 'Black Barlow' (d)	Widely available
	- - - 'Blue Barlow' (d)	CBod CDor CRos CSpe EBee ECtt EMor EPfP GMaP ILea LCro LOPS LRHS LSRN MPri NRHS SCob SEdd SPer SPhx STPC SWvt WCot WSpi XLum
	- - - 'Bordeaux Barlow' (d)	CBod LRHS NRHS STPC
	- - - 'Christa Barlow' (d)	CRos EBee EMor EPfP LRHS NLar NRHS SHar
	- - - 'Nora Barlow' (d)	Widely available
	- - - 'Rose Barlow' (d)	CBod CCBP CRos EPfP LRHS LSRN NRHS SCob WSpi
	- - - 'White Barlow' (d)	CDor CRos EPfP GMaP LCro LOPS LRHS MBel MPri NRHS SCob SPer STPC SWvt
	- - black-flowered	ITim
	- - blue-flowered	MMuc NBir SEND
	- - 'Greenapples' (d)	CBod CDor CWCL EAJP EMor EPfP EWhm GKev GQue LRHS SCob WHoo WRHF
*	- - 'Iceberg'	WSpi
	- - 'Royal Purple' (d)	NBro
	- - 'Ruby Port' (d)	CBcs CBod CDor CWCL ECha ECul ELan EMor EPfP GMaP GWyn ILea LCro LOPS LRHS LSRN MBel MNrw NChi NGdn NLar NRHS SCob SEdd SGbt SPer SPhx WCAu WTyc XLum
	- - 'Touchwood Dreamtime'	WHil
	- - white-flowered	CSpe NBir NBro SEdd
	- variegated foliage	see *A. vulgaris* Vervaeneana Group
§	- Vervaeneana Group (v)	CDor CSpe CWCL EPfP GAbr LRHS NBir NPer SPlb SRms WHoo
	- - 'Woodside Blue' (v)	NWad
	- - 'Woodside White' (v)	NBir WBrk
§	- 'William Guiness'	Widely available
	- 'William Guiness Doubles' (d)	GWyn
	'White Star' (Star Series)	CDor CWCL EBee ELan EPfP GMaP LRHS SGbt SPoG
	'White Swan'	WFar
	Winky Series	ELan GJos GQue SWvt WFar
	- 'Winky Blue-White'	CRos GBin LRHS NLar NRHS
	- 'Winky Purple-White'	LRHS NRHS
	- 'Winky Red-White'	LRHS NRHS SWvt
	- 'Winky Rose-Rose'	CRos LRHS NRHS
	yabeana	GKev SPhx
	'Yellow Star' (Star Series) ♀H5	CBod CDor ECtt EPfP LRHS NRHS SGbt

Aquilegia × *Semiaquilegia* (*Ranunculaceae*)

blue-flowered	NGdn

Arabis (*Brassicaceae*)

alpina	MAsh SPlb
- subsp. ***caucasica***	NWad WCot WHoo
'Arctic Joy' (v)	
- - 'Corfe Castle'	ECtt
- - 'Douler Angevine' (v)	ECtt ELon NHpl SPoG SRms WIce
- - 'Flore Pleno' (d) ♀H6	CElw CSpe CTri ECtt ELan EWld GAbr GMaP SGro SRms WBrk WHoo XLum
- - 'Little Treasure White'	GWyn
- - 'Lotti Deep Rose'	CBod MHol
- - 'Lotti White'	CBod MHol
- - 'Pink Pearl'	WFar
- - 'Pinkie'	SBut
- - 'Pixie Cream'	ECtt MHol NGdn SRms WRHF
- - 'Rosea'	GJos LRHS NBir SRms
§ - - 'Schneehaube' ♀H6	CPla CTri EPfP GMaP GWyn LRHS NBir NGdn SPoG SRms
- - SNOWCAP	see *A. alpina* subsp. *caucasica* 'Schneehaube'
- - 'Snowdrop'	WFar
- - 'Variegata' (v)	ELan SPoG SRms
androsacea	CPla GKev SRms
× ***arendsii*** 'Compinkie'	GJos SPlb SRms WHil
blepharophylla	MHol MPri
§ - 'Frühlingszauber' ♀H5	CTri EAJP ELan EPfP GJos MAsh NBir NGdn SPoG SRms WCav
- 'Rose Delight'	GJos LRHS NRHS
- 'Rote Sensation'	ELan NGdn
- SPRING CHARM	see *A. blepharophylla* 'Frühlingszauber'
carduchorum	XLum
ferdinandi-coburgi	NHol SRms WCav
- 'Aureovariegata' (v)	CMea CTri ECtt ELan SWvt
- 'Old Gold'	EBou EPfP GQue GWyn LPot MAsh MHer NHol NRya SPoG SRms SWvt WCFE WCav WFar WRHF
- 'Variegata'	see *A. procurrens* 'Variegata'
koehleri **new**	GJos
procurrens	WCot XLum XSen
- 'Glacier'	GJos
§ - 'Variegata' (v) ♀H6	CTri ECtt ELan EPfP EWes GAbr GPSL MAsh MBrN MHer SPlb SRms WCot WFar
pumila	GKev
purpurea	GJos
SNOW CAP	see *A. alpina* subsp. *caucasica* 'Schneehaube'
soyeri	GKev

Arachniodes (*Dryopteridaceae*)

aristata	LEdu
davalliaeformis	CLAP CRos EBee ISha LRHS MAsh NRHS SPlb WPGP
rhomboidea	CBdn CLAP
simplicior	CBdn CCCN CLAP EBee EShb ISha LBuc LEdu LLWG LRHS MAsh NRHS SIvy SPlb WCot WPGP
standishii	CLAP CRos EBee EShb ISha LEdu LRHS MAsh NRHS SPlb WCot WPGP

Araiostegia (*Davalliaceae*)

faberiana	CExl
hymenophylloides	WCot
parvipinnata	see *A. perdurans*
§ ***perdurans***	LEdu WPGP
- B&SWJ 1608	EBee WCru
pulchra HWJ 1007	ESwi WCru

Aralia ✿ (*Araliaceae*)

NJM 13.033 **new**	EBee
apioides	IMou
- EDHCH 9720	SBrt WCru
armata B&SWJ 6916	WCru
bipinnata Blanco CWJ 12407	WCru
- RWJ 10101	WCru
cachemirica	CDTJ ESwi EWld NBid SDix SMad SPlb WCru WHal
californica	CSam ESwi GPoy LEdu NLar WCru
castanopsidicola CWJ 12411	WCru
chapaensis B&SWJ 11812	WCru
- HWJ 1013	WCru
chinensis misapplied	see *A. elata*
chinensis L. BWJ 8102	WCru
continentalis	LEdu NLar WHoo
- pink-flowered B&SWJ 8437	WCru
cordata Thunb.	CAgr LEdu
- B&SWJ 5596	WCru
- B&SWJ 8524 from Ulleungdo, South Korea **new**	WCru
- var. ***sachalinensis***	NLar
- - B&SWJ 4773	WCru
- 'Sun King'	CAby CBct CBod CCht EBee ECtt EPfP ESwi LCro LOPS LRHS LSou MHol MNrw NBid NEoE NLar NSti SDix SPad SPeP SPoG SWvt WBor WFar WLov
dasyphylla	LEdu
decaisneana B&SWJ 6794	WCru
- NMWJ 14531	WCru
- NMWJ 14542	WCru
- RWJ 9910	WCru
§ ***elata***	CAby CBcs CDoC CExl CMac CRos EBee ELan EPfP LRHS MBlu MGos MHtn MMuc SArc SGol SPoG SWvt WFar WSpi
- B&SWJ 5480	WCru
- 'Albomarginata'	see *A. elata* 'Variegata'
- 'Aureo-marginata' (v)	WSpi
- 'Aureovariegata' (v) ♀H5	CBcs EWes NLar
- 'Golden Umbrella' (v)	NLar
- 'Silver Umbrella' (v)	NLar WSpi
§ - 'Variegata' (v) ♀H5	CBcs NLar SWvt
foliolosa B&SWJ 8360	WCru
- NJM 13.033	WPGP
- NJM 13.061	WPGP
kansuensis B&SWJ 9515 **new**	ESwi
- BWJ 7650	WCru
- CD&R 2289	WCru
leschenaultii B&SWJ 9515	WCru
- B&SWJ 11789	WCru
nudicaulis L.	GPoy
papyrifera	see *Tetrapanax papyrifer*
racemosa	CBod GPoy LEdu SPhx SRms WJek
- B&SWJ 9570	WCru
searelliana B&SWJ 11736	WCru
sieboldii de Vriese	see *Fatsia japonica*
spinosa L.	MBlu NChi SPlb
subcordata HWJK 2385	WCru
verticillata B&SWJ 11797	WCru

vietnamensis B&SWJ 12349E	WCru

Araucaria (*Araucariaceae*)

sp.	MAsh
angustifolia	CDTJ WPGP
§ ***araucana***	Widely available
bidwillii	MMuc SEND
excelsa misapplied	see *A. heterophylla*
§ ***heterophylla*** 🏆^{H2}	CCCN CDoC LCro SEND
imbricata	see *A. araucana*

Araujia (*Apocynaceae*)

sericifera	CBcs CRHN EShb LRHS SVen WSHC

Arbutus ✿ (*Ericaceae*)

andrachne	CDow LRHS WHwl WSpi
× ***andrachnoides*** 🏆^{H4}	CBcs CRos CTho ELan EPfP LEdu LRHS LSRN MAsh MRav NRHS SPer SPoG WPGP WSpi
× ***androsterilis***	WPGP
menziesii	MBlu MGil MHid
× ***reyorum*** 'Marina'	CJun ELan EPfP LRHS MAsh MBlu MPkF SMad SPoG WPGP
× ***thuretiana***	WPGP
unedo	Widely available
- 'Atlantic' 🏆^{H5}	CCCN CDoC CJun CRos EBee EPfP LRHS LSRN MAsh MGos MPkF SCob SGbt SGol SGsty SWvt WHwl WLov
- 'Compacta'	CBcs CCCN CRos EBee ELan EPfP LRHS MAsh NLar SCob SGol SLon SWvt WFar WTyc
- 'Elfin King'	CRos ELan EPfP LRHS MAsh SLon SPoG SWvt
- 'Quercifolia'	CCCN CJun EBee ELan LEdu LRHS MAsh NLar
- ROSELILY ('Minlily'^{PBR})	CDoC EMil LRHS LSRN SMad
- f. ***rubra*** 🏆^{H5}	CAgr CBcs CCCN CJun CRos CSBt ELan EPfP LRHS LSRN MAsh MBlu MGil MMuc MRav NLar NRHS SEND SGol SPer SPoG SSta SWvt WLov WMat WPGP
xalapensis	SPlb

Archontophoenix (*Arecaceae*)

cunninghamiana	SPalm XBlo

Arctanthemum (*Asteraceae*)

§ ***arcticum***	ECha MMuc NLar XLum
- 'Polarstern'	MNrw WFar
- 'Roseum'	EBee ELon WFar
- 'Schwefelglanz'	EBee WFar

Arcterica see *Pieris*

Arctium (*Asteraceae*)

lappa	GPoy SEdi SRms SVic WHer WSFF
minus	GQue

Arctostaphylos (*Ericaceae*)

uva-ursi	GPoy GQue NLar SPlb
- 'Snowcap'	MAsh
- 'Vancouver Jade'	CMac CRos EBee ELan GKin LRHS LSRN MAsh NRHS SCoo SLon SPer SPoG SSta SWvt

Arctotheca (*Asteraceae*)

calendula	EBee WMal WSHC

Arctotis (*Asteraceae*)

acaulis	WSMil
§ HANNAH ('Archnah'^{PBR}) (The Ravers Series)	CAby CCht CPla ECtt MBNS
HAYLEY ('Archley'^{PBR})	CCCN CCht ECtt MBNS
'Heidi'	CCht MBNS
'Holly'	CCht
× ***hybrida*** hort. 'Apricot'	CCCN ECtt
- 'Flame' 🏆^{H2}	CAby CCCN CCht ECtt MBNS SCoo WABo
- 'Harlequin'	XAbr
- 'Red Devil'	CCCN MBNS SCoo WABo
- 'Wine'	CCCN MBNS SCoo SRkn WABo
PUMPKIN PIE (The Ravers Series)	see *A.* HANNAH

Ardisia (*Primulaceae*)

crenata BOSPREMIUM	see *A. crenata* 'Queen Star'
§ - 'Queen Star' **new**	LCro LOPS
japonica	WCot
- B&SWJ 1032	SMad WCru
- var. ***angusta***	WCot
- 'Houkan' (v)	WPGP
- 'Ito Fukurin' (v)	CDTJ EBee WPGP
- var. ***minor***	GEdr
- - B&SWJ 1841	WCru
- - B&SWJ 3809	WCru

Areca (*Arecaceae*)

triandra	XBlo

Arecastrum see *Syagrus*

Arenaria (*Caryophyllaceae*)

§ ***alfacarensis***	EPot NLar SPlb WAbe WOld
balearica	EWes GKev LLWG MAsh NAts NSla SPlb SRms WFar
capillaris	CTri
festucoides	CPBP GKev WAbe
grandiflora	XLum
hookeri subsp. ***desertorum***	WAbe
kansuensis	NLar
ledebouriana	NLar SBrt
montana 🏆^{H5}	CAby CMea CTri ECha EDAr EPfP LCro LOPS LRHS MBel MGos NRHS NSla SPlb SRms WAbe WCav WFar WIce WKif
- 'Avalanche'	CBod ECtt LSun MHol
pulvinata	see *A. alfacarensis*
purpurascens	CPla EPot EWes GKev LLWG NLar SRms WAbe
* ***scopolina***	EWes
tetraquetra subsp. ***amabilis***	EPot

Argania (*Sapotaceae*)

spinosa	WPGP XAbr

Argemone (*Papaveraceae*)

grandiflora	CSpe EPPr
mexicana	IMou LRHS
platyceras **new**	WFar

Argyranthemum ✿ (*Asteraceae*)

canariense hort.	see *A. frutescens* subsp. *canariae*
CHERRY LOVE ('Supacher') (Daisy Crazy Series) (d) 🏆^{H2}	CCCN

'Citronelle'	CBcs
'Cornish Gold' ♀H2	CBcs CCCN ECtt MCot
double pink-flowered (d)	SVen
'Everest'	CRos LRHS NRHS SPoG
'Flamingo'	see *Rhodanthemum gayanum*
foeniculaceum misapplied, pink-flowered	see *A.* 'Petite Pink'
§ ***foeniculaceum*** (Willd.) Webb & Sch.Bip.	MCot
- 'Royal Haze' ♀H2	CCCN NPer
§ ***frutescens***	LCro LOPS SEND WKif
- (Aramis Series) 'Aramis Ice' **new**	LSou
- - 'Aramis Lemon' **new**	LSou
- - 'Aramis Rose' **new**	LSou
- - 'Aramis Wine Red' **new**	LSou
§ - subsp. ***canariae*** ♀H2	CCCN
gracile 'Chelsea Girl' ♀H2	CCCN CSpe MBNS MCot WABo WKif
Grandaisy Series	SCob
- GRANDAISY PINK HALO ('Bonmax 9163') ♀H3	MBros SCob WHil
- GRANDAISY RED ('Bonmax 1472') **new**	CWCL MBros SCob WHil
- GRANDAISY YELLOW ('Bonmax 1228') **new**	MBros SCob
GYPSY ROSE ('M9/18d')	CCCN
'Jamaica Primrose' ♀H2	CSpe CTri SDix WABo
aff. 'Jamaica Primrose'	CDow
LARITA BANANA SPLIT ('Kleaf10067') (LaRita Series) ♀H2	CRos LRHS NRHS SPoG
'Levada Cream' ♀H2	CSpe
'Lolly' **new**	CWCL
(Madeira Series) MADEIRA CRESTED HOT PINK ('Bonmad 11277')	LSou WHil
- MADEIRA CRESTED IVORY ('Bonmadcivy') (d)	SPoG
- MADEIRA CRESTED PINK ('Bonmadcink'PBR)	SPoG
- MADEIRA CRESTED YELLOW ('Bonmadcrel'PBR)	SPoG
- MADEIRA PRIMROSE ('Bonmadprose'PBR) **new**	MBros
- MADEIRA RED ('Bonmadre'PBR)	SPoG
- MADEIRA WHITE IMPROVED ('Bonmadwitim'PBR)	MBros SPoG
- MADEIRA WHITE ('Ohmadleva')	MBros
'Mary Wootton' (d)	ECtt
mawii	see *Rhodanthemum gayanum*
METEOR RED ('Supa742') (Daisy Crazy Series)	CBcs CWGN MBNS WHil
MOLIMBA XL PASTEL YELLOW ('Argyrayesi'PBR) (Molimba Series)	SPoG
PACIFIC GOLD ('Pacargone'PBR) (d)	CWGN
§ 'Petite Pink' ♀H2	CCCN
PING-PONG ('Innping'PBR) (d)	CCCN
'Pink Delight'	see *A.* 'Petite Pink'
POLLY ('Innpolly'PBR)	CBcs
'Powder Puff' (d)	ECtt
'Raspberry Ruffles' (d)	CBcs MCot WHil
SOLE MIO ('Supa3047') (d)	CWCL
'Sugar and Ice' (d)	CCCN
'Sugar Baby' (d)	CCCN
'Summer Melody' (d)	CCCN
'Summer Pink'	CCCN
'Vancouver' (d) ♀H2	CCCN ECtt
'Vera'	CCCN
'White Spider'	CCCN ELan

Argyrocytisus (*Papilionaceae*)

§ ***battandieri***	Widely available
- 'Yellow Tail' ♀H5	CEnd ELan EMil EPfP LRHS MGos MPri NLar NOra NOrn SPoG SSta WAvo WMat

Arisaema (*Araceae*)

CC 4904	CExl
CC 5511	CExl
album	XLum
amurense	CBor CElw WThu
§ - subsp. ***robustum***	WBor
angustatum var. ***peninsulae*** B&SWJ 8639	WCru
brachyspathum	see *A. heterophyllum*
brevipes	CExl
candidissimum ♀H4	CBor CDor CSpe ECha ELon EPPr EPfP EPot GEdr GKev LRHS MRav NLar NRHS NSla SDeJ SDir WBor WCot WHal WPnP
- pink-flowered	NGKo
- white-flowered	GEdr
ciliatum ♀H4	CPla CWCL EBee EPot GEdr NLar WTyc
- var. ***liubaense***	CWCL EPfP GKev ITim SPtp WCot
- - CT 369	CExl SDys WSHC
- - GG 97091	WCot
aff. ***ciliatum***	CPla
concinnum	GBin GKev NGKo WPnP XLum
consanguineum	CAby CBcs CExl EBee EPfP GBin GEdr GKev MBel SPtp WCot WFar WPGP WPnP XLum
- subsp. ***kelung-insulare*** B&SWJ 256	WCru
- 'The Perfect Wave'	CAby WCot
- variegated (v)	GKev WCot
costatum	CCCN EBee EPfP EPot GKev NGKo SDir WCot WFar WPGP XLum
dracontium	XLum
erubescens	XEll
exappendiculatum	CExl WPnP WTyc
fargesii	CExl EPot GKev XLum
flavum	CMiW CWCL EBee EPfP ESwi GBin GKev NGKo SDir SPlb SPtp WHil
- CC 6303	ITim
- subsp. ***abbreviatum***	GBin GKev MBel
- - CC 6300	ITim
formosanum B&SWJ 280	WCru
§ ***franchetianum***	CExl GKev
galeatum	GKev WCot XLum
grapsospadix B&SWJ 7000	WCru
§ ***griffithii***	EMor GBin GKev NBid NLar SDeJ SDir XLum
- var. ***pradhanii***	CAby GBin GKev XLum
- - WJC 13660	WCru
aff. ***griffithii***	SDir
helleborifolium	see *A. tortuosum*
§ ***heterophyllum***	GKev ITim
intermedium	MNrw XLum
jacquemontii	CAby GKev GLog NLar SDir XLum

- CC 5184	ITim
japonicum Blume	see *A. serratum* var. *mayebarae*
japonicum Komarov	see *A. serratum*
jinshajiangense	CExl
kishidae	GEdr
kiushianum	GKev SDir WCot
§ ***lobatum***	CExl
§ ***nepenthoides***	CAby EPot GBin GEdr GKev SDir WPnP WTyc XLum
ochraceum	see *A. nepenthoides*
onoticum	see *A. lobatum*
ovale	SDir
petelotii B&SWJ 9706	WCru
propinquum	GKev XLum
purpureogaleatum	see *A. franchetianum*
quinatum	GKev
ringens misapplied	see *A. amurense* subsp. *robustum*
ringens ambig.	CDTJ EPfP GEdr GKev
ringens (Thunberg) Schott	LEdu
- green-flowered	GKev SDir
- f. ***sieboldii*** B&SWJ 551	WCru
aff. ***ringens***	NHpl
robustum	see *A. amurense* subsp. *robustum*
sazensoo	GEdr
§ ***serratum***	GKev
- B&SWJ 14607	WCru
§ - var. ***mayebarae***	GEdr GKev
sikokianum	CMiW EPot GEdr GKev LRHS NHpl NLar SDir WPnP WTyc
- variegated (v)	GEdr NHpl
speciosum	CExl GEdr GKev NGKo SDeJ SPlb WCot WPnP XLum
* - var. ***magnificum***	CAby CBcs GEdr GKev NLar XLum
- var. ***mirabile***	GKev XLum
taiwanense	GEdr GKev
- B&SWJ 269	WCru
- NMWJ 14541	WCru
- f. ***cinereum*** NMWJ 14530	WCru
- silver-leaved	WFar
thunbergii	GEdr WBor
- subsp. ***autumnale*** B&SWJ 1425	WCru
- subsp. ***urashima***	GKev SDir WTyc
§ ***tortuosum***	CExl ECha EPfP GKev LEdu NGKo NLar SDir SPtp WFar WPnP XLum
- var. ***helleborifolium***	NBid XLum
triphyllum	CElw CExl EMor GKev GPoy NLar SPlb
§ ***utile***	EPot GKev XLum
verrucosum	see *A. griffithii*
- var. ***utile***	see *A. utile*

Arisarum (*Araceae*)

proboscideum	Widely available
vulgare	GKev

Aristea (*Iridaceae*)

§ ***capitata***	CCtw CDoC
- pink-flowered	CCtw
ecklonii	CBcs CExl CPou CPrp EBee EPri EShb GBin MHer SBrt
- GWJ 9469	CDoC MHol WCru
ensifolia	ELan
thyrsiflora	see *A. capitata*

Aristolochia (*Aristolochiaceae*)

baetica	CExl SBrt WCru
- B&SWJ 14001	WCru
californica	LEdu
chilensis	CCCN SPlb
clematitis	GPoy LEdu
contorta	EBee WPGP
cucurbitifolia B&SWJ 7043	WCru
durior	see *A. macrophylla*
elegans	see *A. littoralis*
fimbriata	CPla SBrt
- B&SWJ 13612	WCru
gigantea ♀H1b	CCCN
grandiflora	CCCN
griffithii B&SWJ 2118	WCru
kaempferi	CCCN
- B&SWJ 293	WCru
- B&SWJ 14674	WCru
- NMWJ 14565	WCru
kanukuensis NMWJ 14577	WCru
× ***kewensis***	CCCN
§ ***littoralis***	MGil
§ ***macrophylla***	CBcs CCCN MRav WSpi
manshuriensis	EBee
- B&SWJ 12557	WCru
paucinervis	EWld
sempervirens	LEdu SBrt WCru WSHC
- B&SWJ 13600	ESwi WCru
sipho	see *A. macrophylla*
trilobata	SBrt

Aristotelia (*Elaeocarpaceae*)

§ ***chilensis***	LEdu MGil WKor WPav
- 'Variegata' (v)	CCCN CMCN CMac WAvo
macqui	see *A. chilensis*
peduncularis	CExl
serrata	CTsd ESwi GBin MGil SVen

Armeria (*Plumbaginaceae*)

§ ***alliacea*** (Cav.) Hoffmanns. & Link	ECha GKev SPhx
- f. ***leucantha***	SPhx SRms
'Avalanche'	MHol
Bees' hybrids	SBut
'Brutus'	MAvo MHCG
caespitosa	see *A. juniperifolia*
- 'Bevan's Variety'	see *A. juniperifolia* 'Bevan's Variety'
cinerea **new**	GKev
§ ***curvifolia***	GAbr
§ ***girardii***	EPot
(Joystick Series) 'Joystick Lilac Shades'	EBee ELan EPfP LRHS NRHS SPoG
- 'Joystick Red'	ELan EPfP EShb LRHS NRHS SPoG
- 'Joystick White'	ELan EPfP LRHS NRHS SPoG
§ ***juniperifolia*** ♀H5	CMea ELan EPfP GJos LRHS MAsh MHer NRHS NSla SPlb SRms WIce XLum
- 'Alba'	CMea ELan EPfP EPot GBin GJos GKev GMaP ITim MHer NHpl SRms WHoo
§ - 'Bevan's Variety' ♀H5	EBou ECha ELan ELon EPfP EPot GEdr GMaP MMuc NLar NRya SIvy SPoG SRms WCav WHoo
- dark-flowered	WAbe
- 'New Zealand Form'	see *A. juniperifolia* 'Sugar Baby'
- rose-flowered	ITim
- spiny, dwarf	EPot
§ - 'Sugar Baby'	SRms
juniperifolia × ***maritima***	SRms
§ ***maritima***	CHab ECtt ELan EPfP GJos LPot LRHS MBel MBow NAts NRHS SWvt WBrk WCFE WWild
§ - 'A Little in the Red'	EPot GEdr WFar

- 'Alba'	CAby CBcs CTri ECha ELan EPfP GJos GMaP LPot LSun MAsh MBel MCot MHol MMuc NHpl NRHS NRya SEND SPlb SPoG SRms WBrk WCFE WCav
- subsp. ***andina***	see *A. curvifolia*
- 'Armada Rose'	CRos EPfP GKev LRHS NRHS SRms
- 'Bloodstone'	CTri ELan
- 'Corsica'	CMea CTri ECha NBir
- DÜSSELDORF PRIDE	see *A. maritima* 'Düsseldorfer Stolz'
§ - 'Düsseldorfer Stolz'	CBod CElw EBou ECha ECtt EDAr ELan EPfP EPot GKev GMaP LRHS MBros NRHS SPoG SWvt WIce XLum
- 'Glory of Holland'	EPot
§ - 'In the Red'	CAby CBod CMea ECha ELon EPPr EShb GEdr GKev GMaP LPot MAvo MBel MHer MMuc NHol NHpl NRya NSla SEND SEdd SPad SRms SWvt WCav WFar WHoo WIce WRHF WSMil
- 'Laucheana'	WCav WHoo
- 'Ministicks Rose'	LRHS
- 'Ministicks White'	LRHS
- 'Morning Star Deep Rose'	LSun
- 'Morning Star White'	CBod CMea MBros
- 'Nifty Thrifty' (v)	CBod CTri EBou ECtt MHer MHol SPoG SRms WFar WSMil
- 'Rubrifolia'	see *A. maritima* 'In the Red'
- 'Rubrifolia Compacta'	see *A. maritima* 'A Little in the Red'
- 'Ruby Glow'	CTri
- 'Schöne von Fellbach'	XLum
- subsp. ***sibirica*** **new**	GKev
- 'Splendens'	CBcs CRos CTri EDAr EPfP GMaP LRHS MAsh MHer MHol MMuc NHpl NMir NRHS NRya SPhx SPoG SSut XLum
- 'Splendens Alba'	XLum
- 'Vindictive' ♀H5	CMea
plantaginea misapplied	see *A. alliacea* (Cav.) Hoffmanns. & Link
pseudarmeria	ELan EPfP MHol WMal XLum
- (Ballerina Series) 'Ballerina'	NBir
- - 'Ballerina Lilac'	CBod CRos LRHS NRHS WBrk WFar
- - 'Ballerina Red'	CBod CRos EShb LRHS NRHS SRms WFar WTor
- - 'Ballerina White'	CBod CRos EPfP LRHS NRHS WBrk WFar
setacea	see *A. girardii*
splendens 'Perfecta'	LRHS NRHS
'Vesuvius'	XLum
vulgaris	see *A. maritima*

Armoracia (*Brassicaceae*)

§ ***rusticana***	CBod CCBP CHby CLau CTri EBou EMor ENfk GAbr GPoy LOPS MHer MNHC NPer SPoG SRms SVic WHer WHrl WSpi XAbr
- 'Horwood'	LCro
- 'Variegata' (v)	ELan LEdu NSti SRms WHer

Arnica (*Asteraceae*)

angustifolia subsp. ***iljinii***	NBir
chamissonis Less.	CBod CHby ENfk MNHC NLar SRms
montana	GPoy MGil MHer MNHC SRms

Arnoglossum (*Asteraceae*)

§ ***plantagineum***	SPhx

Aronia ✿ (*Rosaceae*)

arbutifolia	EPfP LSRN MBlu SGol SLon SPlb
- 'Erecta'	CBod CCVT CRos CTho EBee ELan EPfP LRHS MBlu MGil MMuc SPoG SRms SWvt WCFE
melanocarpa	CCVT CMCN CPla CRos CSpe CTsd ELan EPfP EWld GKin LRHS MAsh NRHS WKor
- var. ***grandifolia***	CJun
- 'Hugin'	CAgr CJun IDee LEdu MCoo MMuc MPkF NLar SVic WPGP
* - 'Red Viking'	NOra
× ***prunifolia***	WKor
- 'Aron' (F)	CAgr CJun MCoo
- 'Autumn Magic'	CBcs CJun CTho EBee ELan LRHS MAsh
- 'Brilliant'	CBcs CRos CTri EBee ELan EPfP LRHS MGil SGol SPer WAvo WMat
- 'Karhumäki' (F)	NLar
- 'Nero' (F)	CAgr CBcs CBod GBin LEdu MCoo NLar WMat WPGP
- 'Serina' (F)	CJun
- 'Viking' (F)	CAgr CDoC CJun EBee ECrN EPfP EPom GBin IDee LBuc LCro LEdu LOPS LRHS MBlu MMuc MNHC NLar SGol WFar WHwl WPGP

Aronia × *Pyrus* see × *Sorbaronia*

Arrhenatherum (*Poaceae*)

elatius	CHab
- var. ***bulbosum*** 'Variegatum' (v)	EBee ELan EPPr GBin GKev GMaP GQue MMuc NBid NWad SEND

Artemisia ✿ (*Asteraceae*)

RBS 0207	CExl
from Taiwan	WHer
§ ***abrotanum***	Widely available
- 'Courson'	ECha XSen
absinthium	CBod CEls CHab CLau ELan ENfk GJos GPoy GQue MGil MHer MNHC NLar SRms SVic WHer WTre XSen
- 'Lambrook Giant'	CEls
- 'Lambrook Mist'	CEls CFis CMac ECtt ELan EPfP GQue LRHS MRav SCob WCAu XLum
- 'Lambrook Silver'	CEls CExl EBee ECha ELan EPfP GMaP LRHS LSRN MHer MRav NBro SCob SEdd SPer SRms SWvt
- 'Persian Lace' **new**	CEls
- 'Silver Ghost'	CEls
afra	CEls XSen
§ ***alba***	CBod CEls GPoy SRms WJek XAbr XSen
§ - 'Canescens' ♀H5	CEls CSam EBee ECha ELan EPfP GMaP MAsh MHer MRav NLar SBrt XSen
annua	CEls
anomala	CEls
§ ***arborescens*** ♀H4	CEls GAbr SPer SRms
- 'Brass Band'	see *A.* 'Powis Castle'
- 'Faith Raven' ♀H3	CBod CEls GBin MBNS NLar SMad WLov
- 'Porquerolles'	CEls
arbuscula	CEls
argentea misapplied	see *A. arborescens*
argentea L'Hér.	CEls

	argyi	CEls
§	***armeniaca***	CEls WHer
	assoana	see *A. caucasica*
	atrata	CEls
	barrelieri	CEls
	caerulescens	CEls WCot
	subsp. ***cretacea***	
	- subsp. ***gallica***	CEls
	californica	CEls WHer
	- 'Canyon Gray'	CEls
	- 'Montara'	CEls
	campestris	XLum XSen
	- subsp. ***borealis***	CEls
	- subsp. ***campestris***	CEls
	- subsp. ***maritima***	CEls
	- - from Wales	CEls
	camphorata	see *A. alba*
	cana	CEls
	canariensis	see *A. thuscula*
	canescens misapplied	see *A. alba* 'Canescens'
	canescens Willd.	see *A. armeniaca*
	capillaris	CEls XLum
	carruthii	CEls
§	***caucasica*** ♀^{H7}	CEls EWes MHer SPhx SRms
	- var. ***caucasica***	EBou
	chamaemelifolia	CBod CEls SRms
	cretacea	see *A. nutans*
	discolor Dougl. ex Besser	see *A. michauxiana*
	douglasiana	CEls
	- 'Valerie Finnis'	see *A. ludoviciana* 'Valerie Finnis'
	dracunculus	ECha EWTr GQue LCro LOPS MNHC MRav SDix SPhx SPlb SRms SVic WBrk XAbr XSen
	- French	CBod CCBP CEls CHby CLau CTsd EBou ENfk EWhm GJos GPoy LCro LEdu LOPS MBow MBros MHer MPri NGrd SEND WFar WGwG WJek XLum
	- Russian	CEls EBou ENfk LCro LOPS SVic
	- 'Thüringen'	IMou
	ferganensis	CEls
	filifolia	CEls
	fragrans	CEls
	frigida ♀^{H5}	CEls
	genipi	CEls XAbr
	glacialis	CEls
	gmelinii	CEls
	gnaphalodes	see *A. ludoviciana*
	gorgonum	CEls SEND
	'Hausserman'	XLum
	herba-alba	CEls XSen
	indica var. ***momiyamae***	CEls EBee ECha WCot
	japonica	CEls
	kitadakensis 'Guizhou'	see *A. lactiflora* Guizhou Group
	laciniata	CEls
	lactiflora ♀^{H7}	CEls CElw EBee ECha ELan GMaP MRav NDov NGdn SDix SPer SRms WWtn XLum
	- NJM 11.010	CEls WPGP
	- 'Elfenbein'	CEls EBee EPPr IMou MNrw MRav NDov SMHy
§	- Guizhou Group	Widely available
	- - 'Dark Delight'	CEls EBee ECtt EWes LEdu SPhx
	- 'Jim Russell'	CDor CEls CElw EBee EWes LEdu MPie SPhx
	- ***purpurea***	see *A. lactiflora* Guizhou Group
	- 'Weisse Dame'	CEls MNrw
	- 'Weisses Wunder'	CEls EBee
	lanata Willd.	see *A. caucasica*
	lanata Lam.	XSen
	laxa	see *A. umbelliformis*
	'Little Mice'	CEls NLar
§	***ludoviciana***	CEls GBee NLar NPer SRms WCFE WFar XLum
	- subsp. ***ludoviciana***	CEls
	var. ***incompta***	
	- - var. ***latiloba***	CEls NBro SWvt
	- subsp. ***mexicana***	CEls
	var. ***albula***	
	- 'Silver Queen'	Widely available
	- 'Valerie Finnis' ♀^{H6}	Widely available
	maritima 'Coca-Cola'	CEls EBee LCro LOPS SRms
	- var. ***maritima***	CEls
	mauiensis	CEls
§	***michauxiana***	CEls EBee
	molinieri	CEls
	mutellina	see *A. umbelliformis*
	niitakayamensis	CEls
	nova	CEls
§	***nutans***	CEls MRav
	ORIENTAL LIMELIGHT ('Janlim') (v)	CBod CEls EBee NLar SDix SWvt WHrl WPnP
	palmeri hort.	see *A. ludoviciana*
	aff. ***parviflora*** CLD 1531	CEls
	pedemontana	see *A. caucasica*
	pontica	CEls EBee ELan GMaP GPoy GQue MNHC MRav NBro NSti SEND SRms WFar WHoo WPGP
§	'Powis Castle' ♀^{H3}	Widely available
	princeps	CEls EBee GPoy LEdu
	procera Willd.	see *A. abrotanum*
	purshiana	see *A. ludoviciana*
	pycnocephala	CEls
	- 'David's Choice'	CEls
	ramosa	CEls
	'Rosenschleier'	CEls EPPr GQue WWtn
	schmidtiana ♀^{H5}	CEls ECha SDix SRms
	- 'Nana' ♀^{H5}	CBcs CEls CMea CRos EBee ECtt ELan EPfP EPot GMaP LRHS MAsh MCot MHer MRav MSwo NLar NRHS SCob SEdd SPer SPlb SPoG SRms WCFE WCav WFar XLum XSen
	- 'Nana Attraction'	GJos NLar
	selengensis	CEls
	somai var. ***batakensis*** NMWJ 14559 **new**	WCru
	splendens misapplied	see *A. alba* 'Canescens'
	stelleriana	CEls CTri ECha GBee GKev NBro NLar SRms
	- RBS 0207	CEls
	- from Alaska	WCot
	- 'Boughton Silver'	CDor CEls CMea EBee ECtt ELan EPfP EShb GMaP LRHS MAsh MHer NLar NRHS NSti SCob SPer SRms SWvt
	- 'Mori'	see *A. stelleriana* 'Boughton Silver'
	- 'Nana'	CEls SWvt
	- 'Prostrata'	see *A. stelleriana* 'Boughton Silver'
	- 'Shemya'	CEls
	- 'Silver Brocade'	see *A. stelleriana* 'Boughton Silver'
	suksdorfii	CEls
	taurica	CEls
§	***thuscula***	CEls
	tridentata	EBee WHer
	- subsp. ***tridentata***	CEls
	- subsp. ***wyomingensis***	CEls
§	***umbelliformis***	CEls
	vallesiaca	CEls
	verlotiorum	CEls

vulgaris	CBod CEls GJos GPoy MGil MNHC WHer
- 'Variegata' (v)	CEls ELan SRms XLum
× ***wurzellii***	CEls

Arthropodium (*Asparagaceae*)

candidum 'Capri'	LPot
- 'Little Lilia' (v)	CBct CBod MHol WCot
- 'Maculatum'	MPie NHpl SPlb
- 'Purpureum'	GEdr NWsh
cirratum	CSpe CTsd GKev MHer MPie SVen WFar WSMil
- 'Matapouri Bay'	CBcs SEND
milleflorum	SBrt
minus	CExl

artichoke, globe see *Cynara cardunculus* Scolymus Group

artichoke, Jerusalem see *Helianthus tuberosus*

Arum (*Araceae*)

byzantinum	GKev
'Chameleon' ♀H7	CDor EPri GRum LEdu NBir NLar SEND SMad SPer WBrk WCot
§ ***concinnatum***	GKev
- 'Mount Ida'	LEdu
concinnatum × ***cyrenaicum***	GKev
cornutum	see *Sauromatum venosum*
creticum	CBro EBee EPot GKev MAvo MNrw MRav WBor XEll
- 'Karpathos'	CExl GKev WCot
- 'Marmaris White'	EBee WCot
- white-flowered	CMea
- white-spotted	EWes
cyrenaicum	GKev
dioscoridis	GKev
- var. ***syriacum***	GKev
dracunculus	see *Dracunculus vulgaris*
euxinum	GKev
gratum	GKev
hygrophilum	GKev LEdu
italicum	CTri GAbr GBin GWyn LCro LOPS MHol SDeJ WCot WShi
- 'Angelique'	WCot
- 'Edward Dougal'	MAvo WCot WFar
- 'Green Marble'	LEdu MAvo WFar
- subsp. ***italicum***	GKev MHer WBrk
§ - - 'Marmoratum' ♀H6	Widely available
- - 'Spotted Jack'	WCot
- - 'Tiny'	CExl SMHy SWvt WRHF
- - 'Uniquity'	WCot
§ - - 'White Winter' ♀H6	LEdu WBrk WCot
- subsp. ***neglectum***	SChr
- - 'Miss Janay Hall' (v)	MAvo WCot
- 'Pictum'	see *A. italicum* subsp. *italicum* 'Marmoratum'
- 'Sandy McNabb'	WCot
- 'Yarnells'	WCot
aff. ***italicum***	CMiW SDir
italicum × ***maculatum***	WHer
korolkowii	WCot
maculatum	EPot GKev GPoy MBow MHer MRav NLar WHer WShi
- 'Painted Lady' (v)	WCot
- 'Pleddel'	MRav
- Tar Spot Group	SEND
nickelii	see *A. concinnatum*
§ ***nigrum***	GKev LEdu SBrt
petteri misapplied	see *A. nigrum*
pictum	CAby CExl CMac EWes GKev LEdu
- 'Taff's Form'	see *A. italicum* subsp. *italicum* 'White Winter'
purpureospathum	GKev LEdu
rupicola var. ***virescens***	LEdu
'Streaked Spectre'	LEdu
'The Patch' new	WCot

Aruncus ✿ (*Rosaceae*)

aethusifolius ♀H7	Widely available
- 'Filigran'	EBee
- 'Little Gem'	WCru
- 'Opulenz' new	GBin
- 'Porzellan'	EBee
asiaticus B&SWJ 8624	WCru
'Bastei'	IMou
dioicus	Widely available
§ - (m) ♀H6	CBar CBen CMac ELan MBNS MRav MWts NBro NSti SMad SPer SRms WHil
- CHILD OF TWO WORLDS	see *A. dioicus* 'Zweiweltenkind'
- 'Glasnevin'	ECtt MRav NHol WFar
- var. ***kamtschaticus***	EWes NLar NWad WHrl
- - RBS 0208	NGdn
- 'Kneiffii'	CBod CRos EBee ECha ECtt ELan EPfP GAbr GKin GMaP LRHS MHol MPnt MRav NBPC NChi NRHS SCob SMad SPad SPer SPlb SPoG SRms SWvt WCAu WFar
- 'Whirlwind'	EWhm LPla
§ - 'Zweiweltenkind'	EWTr LPla LRHS NLar SMad WCot XLum
'Guinea Fowl'	CBod ECtt ELon GQue LEdu LLWG MBel MCot MHol NBid NBir NGdn NLar WCAu WWtn
'Horatio'	Widely available
'Johannifest'	EBee ECtt IMou IPot MAvo MCot WCot
'Misty Lace'	CBod CSpe EBee ECtt NBPC NGdn NLar SAko
'Netzwerk'	IMou
'Noble Spirit'	LSun NGdn NLar
'Perlehuhn'	EBee IMou
plumosus	see *A. dioicus*
* ***sinensis***	CBod NBre
sylvestris	see *A. dioicus*
- 'Sommeranfang'	IMou
'Woldemar Meier'	ILea IMou MAvo MCot NLar SAko WCot

Arundinaria (*Poaceae*)

anceps	see *Yushania anceps*
angustifolia	see *Pleioblastus chino* 'Murakamianus'
auricoma	see *Pleioblastus viridistriatus*
disticha	see *Pleioblastus pygmaeus* 'Distichus'
falconeri	see *Himalayacalamus falconeri*
fargesii	see *Bashania fargesii*
fastuosa	see *Semiarundinaria fastuosa*
fortunei	see *Pleioblastus variegatus*
§ ***gigantea***	CDTJ
- subsp. ***tecta***	CBcs
hindsii	see *Pleioblastus hindsii*
hookeriana misapplied	see *Himalayacalamus falconeri* 'Damarapa'
hookeriana Munro	see *Himalayacalamus hookerianus*
japonica	see *Pseudosasa japonica*

jaunsarensis	see *Yushania anceps*
maling	see *Yushania maling*
marmorea	see *Chimonobambusa marmorea*
murielae	see *Fargesia murielae*
nitida	see *Fargesia nitida*
oedogonata	see *Oligostachyum oedogonatum*
palmata	see *Sasa palmata*
pumila	see *Pleioblastus argenteostriatus* f. *pumilus*
pygmaea	see *Pleioblastus pygmaeus*
quadrangularis	see *Chimonobambusa quadrangularis*
simonii	see *Pleioblastus simonii*
tessellata	see *Bergbambos tessellata*
vagans	see *Sasaella ramosa*
variegata	see *Pleioblastus variegatus*
veitchii	see *Sasa veitchii*
viridistriata	see *Pleioblastus viridistriatus*
'Wang Tsai'	see *Bambusa multiplex* 'Floribunda'

Arundo (*Poaceae*)

donax	CAbb CKno CPla EBee ELan ELon EWes GMaP IDee MAvo MBlu MNrw MRav SArc SCob SDix SEND SMad SPlb SPoG SSut WHal
- 'Golden Chain' (v)	CKno EPPr EWes LRHS SMad WSMil
- 'Macrophylla'	CExl CKno LEdu WPGP WSMil
- 'Variegata'	see *A. donax* var. *versicolor*
§ - var. ***versicolor*** (v)	CAbb CBcs CBen CKno CPla EBee ELan ELon EWes LRHS MRav NRHS NWsh SArc SCob SDix SEND SMad SPer SPlb SPoG SSta WAvo WSMil XCre XLum
I - - 'Aureovariegata' (v)	CBod CDTJ SEND
formosana	CKno EPPr
- 'Golden Showers'	ESwi

Asarina (*Plantaginaceae*)

barclayana	see *Maurandya barclayana*
erubescens	see *Lophospermum erubescens*
lophantha	see *Lophospermum scandens*
lophospermum	see *Lophospermum scandens*
§ ***procumbens***	CTri CWld GAbr GKev NBir NRya SBut SPhx SRms WBrk WKif XAbr
scandens	see *Maurandya scandens*

Asarum (*Aristolochiaceae*)

arifolium	EBee EPPr GKev MBriF
- 'The Giant'	EBee NLar
- white-flowered	EBee
canadense	CDor EBee EMor GEdr GKev GPoy LEdu MBriF
caudatum	EBee ECha EMor ESwi GEdr GKev LEdu LPla MBriF NBro NLar SMad SRms WCot WCru WSpi
- 'Little Murphy'	WCot
caulescens	EPPr
delavayi	WCot
- giant	EBee XEll
epigynum	CDTJ CDor EBee MNrw NLar WCot
- 'Silver Web'	WCot
europaeum 🏆H6	Widely available
- PAB 4377	LEdu WPGP
- Pontic **new**	WPGP
lemmonii	LEdu
longirhizomatosum	GEdr WCru
maculatum	GKev
- B&SWJ 1114	WCru
maximum	CBor GKev
- 'Green Panda'	CDTJ
- 'Silver Panda'	CAby CBct CDTJ CExl EMor ESwi MNrw NGBl SMad WCot
pulchellum	ESwi
sieboldii	WCru
splendens	CAby CBct CBor CBro CDTJ ELan EMor EPfP GKev ILea LEdu MBriF MHol MNrw NGKo NLar NSti SDir SDix SPlb SPoG WCot WFar XLum
wulingense	CExl

Asclepias ✿ (*Apocynaceae*)

cordifolia	SBrt
curassavica	CCCN EShb SRkn XLum
exaltata	EBee SBrt SPhx
fruticosa	see *Gomphocarpus fruticosus*
hallii	EBee
incarnata	LRHS MRav SBrt SPhx SPlb WOld XLum
- 'Ice Ballet'	CBod NLar SPer
- 'Soulmate'	CBod EBee EPfP MSCN SPer
latifolia	SPhx
physocarpa	see *Gomphocarpus physocarpus*
purpurascens	EBee
speciosa	CBod EBee MMuc NBre SBrt SBut
sullivantii	IMou SPhx
tuberosa	CBcs CBod CBor CSpe EBee EMor EShb GPoy LRHS MBel MHer MNHC MSCN NRHS SMad SPad SPhx SPoG SRms WGwG XLum XSen
- 'Hello Yellow'	EShb
- subsp. ***interior***	EPPr MHol

Asimina (*Annonaceae*)

triloba (F)	CAby CBcs CCCN CDTJ IBal MBlu NLar SGol SPlb WKor
- 'Sunflowers'	CCCN SAko

asparagus see also AGM Vegetables Section

Asparagus (*Asparagaceae*)

acutifolius	XSen
asparagoides 🏆H3	EShb
densiflorus	WCot
- 'Mazeppa'	EShb
- 'Myersii' 🏆H1c	EShb LCro LOPS SEND
- 'Myriocladus'	EShb
- Sprengeri Group 🏆H1c	EShb LCro LOPS NGBl SEND
falcatus	CDoC EShb SEND
filicinus	XBlo
- NJM 12.024	WPGP
- var. ***giraldii***	WCot
aff. ***meioclados*** B&SWJ 8309	WCot WCru
plumosus	see *A. setaceus*
pseudoscaber 'Spitzenschleier'	EBee SDix WCot
retrofractus	WCot
scandens	EShb WCot
schoberioides	LEdu
- B&SWJ 8814	WCru
§ ***setaceus*** 🏆H2	CDoC EShb LCro LOPS
- 'Pyramidalis' 🏆H1c	CDoC XBlo
tenuifolius	WPGP
umbellatus	SEND
virgatus	EBee EShb LEdu SMad SPlb WPGP

Asperula (*Rubiaceae*)

aristata subsp. ***scabra***	CSpe ECha MMuc WCot

- subsp. ***thessala***	see *A. sintenisii*
boissieri	EPot SPlb WAbe
daphneola	ELan EPot EWes
gussonei	CPBP EPot WAbe WHoo WOld
lilaciflora var. ***caespitosa***	see *A. lilaciflora* subsp. *lilaciflora*
§ - subsp. ***lilaciflora***	EBou ELan
nitida	EPot WIce
- subsp. ***puberula***	see *A. sintenisii*
odorata	see *Galium odoratum*
§ ***sintenisii***	CMea CPBP EPot WAbe WHoo
taurina subsp. ***caucasica***	NLar WBor
tinctoria	GPoy MHer SRms

Asphodeline (*Asphodelaceae*)

§ ***brevicaulis***	XSen
liburnica	CBro CFis CMea CPla CSam ECha ELan EPri IMou LCro LOPS MMuc SEND SPhx XSen
§ ***lutea***	Widely available
§ - 'Gelbkerze'	EBee WAvo
- YELLOW CANDLE	see *A. lutea* 'Gelbkerze'

Asphodelus (*Asphodelaceae*)

acaulis	WCot
§ ***aestivus***	EBee EWes MBel WCot
albus	CAvo CBro CMea CSam CSpe ECha EPPr EPfP GAbr GBin NBid NGBl SPlb SRms XLum XSen
brevicaulis	see *Asphodeline brevicaulis*
cerasiferus	see *A. ramosus*
fistulosus	CBro LEdu SVen XSen
lusitanicus	see *A. ramosus*
luteus	see *Asphodeline lutea*
microcarpus	see *A. aestivus*
§ ***ramosus***	CPar LPla MCot WCot

Aspidistra (*Asparagaceae*)

B&SWJ 6645 from Thailand	WCru
Chen Yi 135	ESwi WCot
attenuata	IMou
- B&SWJ 377	WCru
- B&SWJ 2001	WCru
- B&SWJ 3727	WCru
- 'Dungpu Dazzler'	WCru
- 'Small 'n' Smart'	WCru
- 'Xitou Starlet'	WCru
caespitosa 'Jade Ribbons'	see *A. hainanensis* 'Jade Ribbons'
'China Star'	ESwi SMad WCot WCru
daibuensis B&SWJ 312b	ESwi WCru
- B&SWJ 1949	WCru
- B&SWJ 3236	WCru
- B&SWJ 6863	WCru
- B&SWJ 6866	WCru
- 'Taiwan Stars'	ESwi WCru
- 'Tidy Trim'	ESwi WCru
- 'Totally Dotty' (v)	ESwi WCru
- 'Yuli Yummy'	ESwi WCru
elatior ♀H3	CBct CDTJ CTsd EBak EBee EShb ESwi LCro LEdu LOPS MRav SAko SEND SMad WCot
- 'Akebono' (v)	WCot
- 'Asahi' (v)	ESwi WCot
- 'Hoshi-zora' (v)	WCot
- 'Lennon's Song' (v)	ESwi WCot
- 'Milky Way' (v)	EBee EShb ESwi SAko SEND XLum
- 'Okame' (v)	WCot
- 'Variegata' (v) ♀H3	EShb NBir
- 'Variegata Exotica' (v)	XBlo
- var. ***vietnamensis*** new	WCru
fasciaria new	WCru
aff. ***geastrum*** B&SWJ 6563	WCru
- 'Opium Hit'	WCru
§ ***hainanensis*** 'Jade Ribbons'	EShb ESwi WCot WCru
linearifolia new	WCru
- 'Leopard' (v)	ESwi WCot WCru
- 'Skinny Dippin''	WCru
lurida	EShb
- 'Ginga'	see *A. sichuanensis* 'Ginga'
- 'Ginga Giant' (v)	ESwi WCot WCru
minutiflora	ESwi WCot
- 'Spangled Ribbons'	WCru
mushaensis B&SWJ 315	WCru
- B&SWJ 1953	WCru
- 'Purple Picket'	WCru
- 'Wushe Wacky'	WCru
aff. ***mushaensis*** 'Spotty Dotty' (v)	ESwi WCru
omeiensis	WCot
punctata	WCru
retusa 'Nanjing Green' new	WCru
saxicola 'Uan Fat Lady'	see *A. zongbayi* 'Uan Fat Lady'
sichuanensis	WCru
§ - 'Ginga' (v)	ESwi WCot
subrotata B&SWJ 5252	WCru
- 'Chiang-dao Chace'	WCru
sutepensis B&SWJ 5216	WCru
- B&SWJ 6645	WCru
- 'Pha-Hom Pok-adot'	WCru
tonkinensis	ESwi WCot WCru
typica 'China Sun'	ESwi WCot
zongbayi	WCot
§ - 'Uan Fat Lady'	EBee ESwi WCot WCru

Asplenium ✿ (*Aspleniaceae*)

antiquum	EShb
- 'Osaka'	LRHS
bulbiferum misapplied	see *A.* × *lucrosum*
bulbiferum ambig. × ***oblongifolium***	GBin
bulbiferum Forst.f.	EShb ESwi GBin
§ ***ceterach***	CLAP ISha NHar SMad WBrk WCot WHer WHoo XLum
dareoides	ITim
daucifolium	NWad WCot
× ***ebenoides*** ♀H4	CBdn EMor ISha LEdu NBro NHar SPlb
§ × ***lucrosum*** ♀H1c	EShb ESwi IMou
'Maori Princess'	GBin WFib
nidus ♀H1b	LCro LOPS XBlo
- 'Crispy Wave'PBR	CDoC EShb LCro LOPS
'Parvati' new	CDoC
§ ***scolopendrium*** ♀H6	Widely available
- 'Angustatum' ♀H6	Widely available
- Crispum Group ♀H6	CLAP EFer ELan NBid SRms WAbe WFar WFib
- - 'Crispum Bolton's Nobile'	WFib
- - 'Golden Queen'	CDor MAvo
- Crispum Cristatum Group	MMuc SCob
- Crispum Fimbriatum Group	CLAP
- - 'Drummondiae'	CLAP
- Cristatum Group	CAby CBdn CDor CLAP CRos CWCL EBee ECtt ELan ELon EMor EPfP LRHS MGos MRav NBro NLar NRHS SPer SRms WFib WHoo
- Fimbriatum Group	LRHS MHost
- 'Fimbriatum Cristatum'	CLAP

- 'Furcatum'	CBdn CDTJ EBee ELan ELon EMor MMuc NLar SPad
- 'Kaye's Lacerated' ♀H5	EFer WFib
- Marginatum Group	CBdn EFer
- 'Muricatum'	ELan MRav NBid WFib WHoo
- 'Sagittatocristatum'	CLAP
- 'Sagittatoprojectum Sclater'	WFib
- Undulatum Group	CDTJ CRos EBee ECha EPfP GBin GQue LRHS MMuc NBir NLar NRHS SRms WCot WFar WGwG XLum
trichomanes ♀H6	CBcs CBdn CBod CLAP CRos CWCL EBee EFer ELan EMor EPfP GAbr GEdr GMaP LRHS MAsh MAvo MGos MHost NLar NRHS SCob SPer SPlb SWvt WAbe WFar WFib WHoo XLum
- Cristatum Group	CLAP CRos LRHS NRHS
- Incisum Group ♀H6	CLAP EFer WAbe

Astelia (*Asteliaceae*)

banksii	CBcs CBct CPbh CPla CRos CTrC CTsd EPfP IBal LRHS LSRN MCot MGos NCou NRHS SCoo SEdd WCot
§ ***chathamica*** ♀H3	CAbb CAby CBcs CBct CCCN CCht CSpe CTrC CTsd ELan EPfP LRHS LSRN MGos MHol SAko SArc SCob SCoo SEND SPer SPlb SPoG SWvt WCot WSpi
- 'Silver Spear'	see *A. chathamica*
fragrans	LEdu
grandis	LEdu WPGP
nervosa	LSRN SArc
- 'Westland'	CBcs CBct CBod CCCN CPla CRos CTrC CTsd ELan EShb GAbr GBin GWyn ILea LEdu LRHS LSRN MGos NRHS SCob SEND SWvt
'Red Devil'	CBcs CBct CBod CPla CSpe CTrC GWyn MGos MHol SCob SEdd SPoG WHer WPav
'Silver Shadow' PBR	CBcs CRos EPfP LCro LOPS LRHS MMrt NRHS SCob SPad SWvt WCot WFar WSpi

Aster ✿ (*Asteraceae*)

acris	see *Galatella sedifolia*
ageratoides	see *A. trifoliatus* subsp. *ageratoides*
§ ***albescens*** WJC 13657	WCru
alpinus ♀H5	EBou EPfP GKev LCro LOPS MAsh MHol SRms WFar
- var. ***albus***	EDAr EPfP GKev WCot XSen
- 'Antje'	MNrw
- DARK BEAUTY	see *A. alpinus* 'Dunkle Schöne'
§ - 'Dunkle Schöne'	EDAr MBel SRms WFar XSen
- 'Goliath'	EDAr ELan EPfP SPlb WFar
- 'Happy End'	CRos EPfP LRHS NRHS SRms WCAu XLum XSen
- 'Pinkie'	EBou EDAr ELan EPfP ITim
- 'Trimix'	LPot NBir SRms
amelloides	see *Felicia amelloides*
amellus	CPla ELon
- 'Blue King'	EWes IPot NWsh SWvt WFar WSpi
- 'Breslau'	ELon
- 'Brilliant'	CBod ECha ECtt ELon EPPr LRHS LSou MBNS MRav NLar NRHS NWsh SAko SEND SGbt SPer SPhx SRms WCAu WHoo WOld WSpi
- 'Butzemann'	ELon NLar WCot WFar
- 'Danzig'	NLar XLum
- 'Doktor Otto Petschek'	ELon NLar WCot
- EMPRESS	see *A. amellus* 'Glücksfund'
- 'Forncett Flourish' ♀H7	ECtt MAvo MHCG SMHy WCot WHoo WOld
- 'Framfieldii' ♀H7	SMHy WCot WFar WOld
§ - 'Glücksfund'	SAko XSen
- 'Gründer'	IMou MAvo MHCG WCot WOld
- 'Jacqueline Genebrier' ♀H7	MHCG WOld
- 'King George' ♀H7	Widely available
- 'Kobold' ♀H7	WOld
- 'Lac de Genève'	WCot XLum
- 'Lady Hindlip'	CSam IMou WCot
- 'Louise'	MBrN MHCG
- 'Mira'	ELon GBin SAko
- 'Moerheim Gem'	ECtt IMou WCot WOld
- 'Mrs Ralph Woods'	WOld
- 'Nocturne'	ELon WCot WOld
- 'Peach Blossom'	WOld
- PINK ZENITH	see *A. amellus* 'Rosa Erfüllung'
§ - 'Rosa Erfüllung' ♀H7	CBod CDor CMac EBee ECtt ELan ELon EPPr EPfP EWes GMaP LRHS MAvo MNrw MRav NLar NRHS SCob SGbt SMad SPhx SPoG SWvt WCAu WOld WSpi
- 'Rotfeuer'	ELon WSpi
- 'Rudolph Goethe'	CBod EBee ECtt ELan ELon EMil EPfP GJos LRHS NLar NRHS SCob WCAu WOld WSpi
- 'September Glow'	SHar WOld
- 'Silbersee' ♀H7	CSam IMou SAko
- 'Sonia'	ECtt ELon LRHS NRHS SWvt WOld
- 'Sonora' ♀H7	CMea MNrw SHar SPhx WKif WOld
- 'Sternkugel'	ELon WOld
- 'Ultramarine'	WOld
- 'Vanity'	WOld
§ - 'Veilchenkönigin' ♀H7	Widely available
- VIOLET QUEEN	see *A. amellus* 'Veilchenkönigin'
- 'Weltfriede'	ECtt WOld
× ***amethystinus***	see *Symphyotrichum* × *amethystinum*
'Anita Pfeiffer'	LRHS
asperulus misapplied	see *A. peduncularis*
'Betel Nut'	ECha SDix
capensis 'Variegatus'	see *Felicia amelloides* variegated
carolinianus	see *Ampelaster carolinianus*
'Cheavers'	LRHS NRHS
'Chilly Fingers'	MAvo MNrw MTis
ciliolatus	see *Symphyotrichum ciliolatum*
'Climax' misapplied	see *Symphyotrichum laeve* 'Arcturus', *S. laeve* 'Calliope'
coelestis	see *Felicia amelloides*
coloradoensis	see *Xanthisma coloradoense*
'Connecticut Snow Flurry'	see *Symphyotrichum ericoides* var. *prostratum* 'Snow Flurry'
cordifolius	see *Symphyotrichum cordifolium*
corymbosus	see *Eurybia divaricata*
'Cotswold Gem'	MHCG MNrw WCot WOld
diffusus	see *Symphyotrichum lateriflorum*
diplostephioides	EWhm GEdr GKev GLog LRHS MMrt SPlb WOld
divaricatus	see *Eurybia divaricata*
dumosus	see *Symphyotrichum dumosum*
'Dwarf Barbados'	EPfP LRHS NRHS
'Eleven Purple' PBR	MNrw
ericoides	see *Symphyotrichum ericoides*
falcatus	see *Symphyotrichum falcatum*
'Fanny's Fall'	see *Symphyotrichum oblongifolium* 'Fanny's'

	'Fingers and Thumbs'	MAvo
	× ***frikartii***	CMac EPfP MRav SGbt SWvt WSHC
	- 'Eiger'	WOld
	- 'Flora's Delight'	CBod CMea CRos CTsd ECtt ELon EMor LRHS MArl MRav NLar NRHS SPoG SRms WCAu WHoo WSpi
	- 'Jungfrau'	CRos CWGN EBee EPPr GMaP LRHS MRav NLar NRHS SPhx SRms WOld WSHC
	- 'Mönch' 🏆H7	Widely available
	- WONDER OF STAFA	see *A.* × *frikartii* 'Wunder von Stäfa'
§	- 'Wunder von Stäfa' 🏆H7	CBod CEnd CExl CKno EBee ECtt ELan ELon EPPr EPfP GMaP LCro LOPS LRHS MBNS MBel MCot MHol MWat NBir NLar SWvt WCAu WCot WFar WHoo WOld WSpi XLum
	furcatus	see *Eurybia furcata*
	glehnii	WCAu
	- 'Aglenii'	IMou MNrw NDov SMad
	greatae	see *Symphyotrichum greatae*
	× ***herveyi***	see *Eurybia* × *herveyi*
	himalaicus	NSla
	hybridus luteus	see *Solidago* × *luteus*
	'Ice Cool Pink'	SMHy
	'Ivy House'	ECtt
*	***kotarimus***	XLum
	laevis	see *Symphyotrichum laeve*
	lateriflorus	see *Symphyotrichum lateriflorum*
	laterifolius 'Snow Flurry'	see *Symphyotrichum ericoides* var. *prostratum* 'Snow Flurry'
	linosyris	see *Galatella linosyris*
	macrophyllus	see *Eurybia macrophylla*
	mongolicus	see *Kalimeris mongolica*
	'Moody Blue'	MAvo
	'Mrs Dean'	ECtt
	natalensis	see *Felicia rosulata*
	'Natasha'	LSRN
	novae-angliae	see *Symphyotrichum novae-angliae*
	novi-belgii	see *Symphyotrichum novi-belgii*
	oblongifolius	see *Symphyotrichum oblongifolium*
	OCTOBERLIGHT	see *Symphyotrichum* 'Oktoberlicht'
	oolentangiensis	see *Symphyotrichum oolentangiense*
	pappei	see *Felicia amoena*
§	***peduncularis***	CBod CKno CPou EBee EMor EPPr GBee IMou MAvo MHol MMuc MTis NCou NSti WCot WFar WHoo WMal WOld
	petiolatus	see *Felicia petiolata*
	pilosus	see *Symphyotrichum pilosum*
	ptarmicoides	see *Solidago ptarmicoides*
	puniceus	see *Symphyotrichum puniceum*
	pyrenaeus 'Lutetia'	CBod CKno CSam ECha EPPr GMaP LRHS MAvo MBow MNrw MPie MWat NLar NRHS SBut SPhx SRms WCAu WCot WFar WKif WOld XLum
	radula	see *Eurybia radula*
	rotundifolius 'Variegatus'	see *Felicia amelloides* variegated
	rugulosus 'Asrugo'	CKno
	× ***salignus***	see *Symphyotrichum* × *salignum*
§	***scaber***	WCot
	scandens	see *A. carolinianus*
	schreberi	see *Eurybia schreberi*
	sedifolius	see *Galatella sedifolia*
	sericeus	see *Symphyotrichum sericeum*
	sibiricus	see *Eurybia sibirica*
	'Small-Ness'	EShb GKev MAvo NWad
	'Snow Flurry'	see *Symphyotrichum ericoides* var. *prostratum* 'Snow Flurry'
	souliei	CPBP EBee
	spathulifolius	WCot XLum
	spectabilis	see *Eurybia spectabilis*
	stracheyi	GKev
	subcaeruleus	see *A. tongolensis*
	tataricus 'Jindai'	CSpe EBee WCAu
	thomsonii	GBin SHar WCot WOld WSpi
	- 'Nanus'	CAby EBee GBin GMaP ILea LRHS MCot MRav SPhx SPoG WOld WSHC WSpi
§	***tongolensis***	GKev NHpl
	- 'Berggarten'	LRHS MHol MNrw NRHS WHil WOld
	- 'Napsbury'	LRHS
	- 'Wartburgstern'	CBod EMor EPfP LRHS SGbt WHil XLum
	tradescantii misapplied	see *Symphyotrichum pilosum* var. *pringlei*
	tradescantii L.	see *Symphyotrichum tradescantii*
§	***trifoliatus*** subsp. ***ageratoides***	CPou WCot WOld
	- - 'Ashvi'	CBod CKno CMil ECtt GBin MBel MHol MTis NSti SDix SEdd SPoG WCAu WCot WFar WOld WRHF WSHC
	- - 'Asran'	CBod EBee ECtt EPPr EWes EWhm IMou LEdu MMuc MPie NLar SEND WBor WBrk WCAu WCot WFar WOld XLum
	- - 'Ezo Murasaki'	CSpe ELon LEdu MAvo MNrw NDov SAko SPoG WCot XLum
	- - var. ***firmus***	WPGP
	- - 'Harry Smith'	CBod MAvo MHol MTis NDov NSti SAko SHar SPoG WCot WFar WHil WOld
	- - 'Little Theo'	CKno EBee
	- - 'Stardust'	WHoo WOld
	- - 'Starshine'[PBR]	CBcs CBod CKno CWGN EBee ECtt EPfP MTis WCot
	trinervius var. ***harae***	WFar WOld
	tripolium	see *Tripolium pannonicum*
	'Triumph'	WCot
	turbinellus	see *Symphyotrichum turbinellum*
	vahlii	CPla
	vimineus Lam.	see *Symphyotrichum lateriflorum*
	- 'Ptarmicoides'	see *Solidago ptarmicoides*
	'Yvonne'	CBre

Asteranthera (*Gesneriaceae*)

ovata	CExl GGGa SLon WAbe WPGP WSHC

Asteriscus (*Asteraceae*)

'Gold Coin'	see *Pallenis maritima*
maritimus	see *Pallenis maritima*

Asteromoea (*Asteraceae*)

mongolica	see *Kalimeris mongolica*
pinnatifida	see *Kalimeris pinnatifida*

Asteropyrum (*Ranunculaceae*)

cavaleriei	GEdr
peltatum	GEdr

Asterotrichion (*Malvaceae*)

discolor	SPlb SVen

Astilbe ✿ (*Saxifragaceae*)

	CC 5201	CExl
	'Alive and Kicking'	LSou
	'Amerika' (× *arendsii*)	CSBt NBPC SRms
	'Amethyst' (× *arendsii*)	CMac EPfP LBuc LRHS MBel MRav NBPC NBir NHol SPer WFar
	'Angel Wings' (× *arendsii*)	NEoE
	'Anita Pfeifer' (× *arendsii*)	NLar XLum
	'Aphrodite' (*simplicifolia* hybrid)	CBcs XLum
	× ***arendsii***	EPfP LBuc NBre XLum
	(Astary Series) 'Astary Pink' (× *arendsii*)	LRHS NRHS
	- 'Astary Red' (× *arendsii*)	LRHS NRHS
	- 'Astary White' (× *arendsii*)	CRos LRHS NRHS
	astilboides	SWvt
	'Avalanche'	CAby NEoE NHol WBrk WSpi
§	'Beauty of Ernst' (× *arendsii*)	CBod EBee EMor EPfP LRHS MNrw SRms
§	'Beauty of Lisse' (× *arendsii*)	MNrw SPad
	'Betsy Cuperus' (*thunbergii* hybrid)	NBre WCAu
	'Bonn' (*japonica* hybrid)	CWCL CWat NLar SCoo SRms
§	'Brautschleier' (× *arendsii*) ♀H7	CBod CExl CMac ECtt EPfP GBin GKev GWyn LCro LOPS LRHS LSRN MHol NGdn NLar NQui NRHS WPnP XLum
	'Bressingham Beauty' (× *arendsii*) ♀H7	CAby CBod CExl CRos CWCL EBee ECtt ELan EPfP GBin GKev GMaP ILea LCro LOPS LRHS MHol MRav NEoE NHol NRHS SRms SWvt WFar
	BRIDAL VEIL (× *arendsii*)	see *A.* 'Brautschleier'
§	'Bronce Elegans' (*simplicifolia* hybrid) ♀H7	ECha GLog GMaP GWyn NHol NLar SRms WFar WSpi
	'Bronze Sprite' (*simplicifolia* hybrid)	WFar
*	***bumalda*** 'Bronze Pygmy'	NHol
	'Bumalda' (× *arendsii*)	CSBt CWCL GBin GLog GMaP LRHS NChi NGdn NRHS SPlb WFar WWtn
	'Bunter Zauber' (× *arendsii*)	XLum
	'Burgunderrot' (× *arendsii*)	MNrw NLar SRms
	'Cappuccino' (× *arendsii*)	CBcs EMor ILea MBel MSCN SPad
	'Catherine Deneuve'	see *A.* 'Federsee'
	'Cattleya' (× *arendsii*)	GWyn LRHS NLar NRHS SAko WSpi XLum
	'Cherry Ripe'	see *A.* 'Feuer'
	chinensis	GBin LRHS WSHC
	- B&SWJ 8178	WCru
	- var. ***davidii***	XLum
	- - B&SWJ 8583	WCru
	- - B&SWJ 8645	WCru
	- 'Diamonds and Pearls'PBR	CWGN ECtt LSou NLar WFar WSpi
	- 'Finale'	NHol WOut
	- 'Intermezzo'	GMaP NLar
	- 'Little Vision in Pink'PBR	CBod EPfP WFar
	- 'Milk and Honey'PBR	CWGN ECtt MBNS NBPC WFar WSpi
§	- var. ***pumila*** ♀H7	Widely available
	- - 'Serenade'	CMac LRHS NGdn
I	- - 'Tiny Form'	GRum
	- 'Purple Glory'	ECtt
	- var. ***taquetii***	CMac ELan EPfP LRHS NSti SRms XLum
	- - PURPLE LANCE	see *A. chinensis* var. *taquetii* 'Purpurlanze'
§	- - 'Purpurlanze' ♀H7	CKno CRos CSam EBee ECha ECtt EMor EShb EWTr GBin GMaP LRHS LSRN MRav NBir NBro NChi NDov NGdn NHol NLar SCob SPoG SWvt WBor WFar WHoo WSpi WWtn
§	- - 'Superba' ♀H7	CMac ECha LRHS NBro NWad SDix SPer SRms WFar
	- 'Veronika Klose'	GBin NLar
	- 'Vision in Pink'PBR	CWCL ELan EPfP MBNS MHol MNrw NBPC NDov SCob WFar
	- 'Vision in Red'PBR	CBod CWCL CWat ECtt ELan EPfP LSou MBNS MHol MNrw NBPC NDov NLar SAko SCob SGbt SPoG WAul WCAu WFar
	- 'Vision in White'	EPfP LCro LOPS NBPC NEoE SAko SCob SPoG WFar
	- 'Visions'	CMac EPfP LRHS MBNS NBro NEoE NGdn NRHS SCob WSMil
	- 'White Cloud'	NQui
	'Chocolate Shogun'	CAby CBcs CWGN EBee ECtt EMor LSou LSun MAvo MBNS MNrw MThu NCou SPad SPoG WCot WFar
	'Close Harmony'	LRHS
	COLOGNE	see *A.* 'Köln'
	COLOR FLASH	see *A.* 'Beauty of Ernst'
	COLOR FLASH LIME	see *A.* 'Beauty of Lisse'
	'Country and Western'PBR (× *arendsii*)	NEoE
	'Crimson Feather'	see *A.* 'Gloria Purpurea'
	× ***crispa*** 'Lilliput'	ECtt GBee NBir NEoE NLar NRya NWad
§	- 'Perkeo' ♀H5	CBcs ECtt ELan EPfP GMaP LRHS NBir NEoE NHpl NLar NRHS SRms WFar
	- 'Peter Pan'	see *A.* × *crispa* 'Perkeo'
	- 'Red Rog'	NEoE
	- 'Snow Queen'	NBir NEoE
	'Darwin's Dream'	MHol MNrw NEoE NLar WFar
	'Darwin's Favourite' (× *arendsii*)	CWCL
	'Delft Lace'	CAbb EBee LBuc LRHS MBel NRHS SRms
	'Deutschland' (*japonica* hybrid) ♀H7	CAby CBcs EBee ECtt EMor EPfP GBin GKev GLog GMaP ILea LRHS LSRN MBNS MGos MMuc MRav NBPC NBir NEoE NHol NLar NRHS SAko SCob SPer SPoG SRms WSpi
§	'Diamant' (× *arendsii*)	LSRN MMuc MNrw NBir NGdn NHol SEND WFar
	DIAMOND	see *A.* 'Diamant'
	'Drayton Glory' (× *arendsii*)	see *A.* × *rosea* 'Peach Blossom'
	'Drum and Bass'PBR	LSou NLar
	'Dunkelachs' (*simplicifolia* hybrid)	EBee
	'Dusseldorf' (*japonica* hybrid)	CWCL EBee LRHS NRHS
	'Eden's Odysseus'	NHol NWad
	'Eden's Twinkle'	EBee
	'Elegans' (*simplicifolia* hybrid)	CMac
	'Elisabeth' van Veen (× *arendsii*)	NBir
	ELIZABETH BLOOM ('Eliblo'PBR) (× *arendsii*)	GAbr LLWG LRHS MAsh MHol MRav NGdn NHol NRHS
	'Ellie' (× *arendsii*)	CMac CWCL ECtt EPfP EShb GBee LLWG LRHS LSRN MBNS MBel NGdn NHol NLar SPoG WFar
	'Else Schluck' (× *arendsii*)	ECha
	'Erica' (× *arendsii*)	CAby CExl CTri GLog NEoE NLar WBrk WFar
	'Etna' (*japonica* hybrid)	CBcs ECtt LRHS NBPC NGdn NLar NRHS SRms WFar WHoo

	'Europa' (*japonica* hybrid)	CMac ECtt EMor GBin GWyn LRHS MGos NGdn NLar NRHS SPoG SRms WCAu WFar
	'Fanal' (× *arendsii*) ♀H7	Widely available
§	'Federsee' (× *arendsii*)	CBcs CRos CWCL EBee ECha ECtt ELan LRHS MBNS NBro NEoE NGdn NRHS SPer WFar WWtn XLum
§	'Feuer' (× *arendsii*)	CMac ECtt ELan NEoE NGdn NHol NLar WFar
	FIRE	see *A.* 'Feuer'
	'Fireberry'PBR (Short 'n' Sweet Series)	EBee MSCN NLar
	'Flamingo'PBR (× *arendsii*)	ECtt MBNS MBel NLar
§	***formosa*** B&SWJ 10946	WCru
	'Freya' (× *arendsii*)	MAsh
	'Gertrud Brix' (× *arendsii*)	CWat MMuc NBir NGdn SEND XLum
§	***glaberrima***	NBid
§	- var. ***saxatilis*** ♀H5	GBin GEdr WAbe WFar
	- - 'Candy Floss'	NEoE
	- ***saxosa***	see *A. glaberrima* var. *saxatilis*
	'Gloria' (× *arendsii*)	CMac CTri ECtt
§	'Gloria Purpurea' (× *arendsii*)	NQui
	GLOW	see *A.* 'Glut'
§	'Glut' (× *arendsii*)	CWCL ECtt LRHS MMuc NGdn NHol SAko SEND SGbt SRms WFar WWtn
	'Granat' (× *arendsii*)	CMac NBir NGdn NHol NLar
*	Grande Group (× *arendsii*)	NBre
	grandis	WHer
	- BWJ 8076A	NLar
	'Grete Püngel' (× *arendsii*)	ECha GBin SRms WFar
	'Happy Spirit' **new**	LLWG MHol NLar
	'Heart and Soul'PBR	CWGN EPfP LSou
	'Hennie Graafland' (*simplicifolia* hybrid)	CBcs CBod CWCL NBPC NLar WFar
	'Henry Noblett'	LRHS
	'Holden Clough' (*japonica* hybrid)	NHol
	HYACINTH	see *A.* 'Hyazinth'
§	'Hyazinth' (× *arendsii*)	CExl CRos EBee GMaP LRHS NBir NHol NRHS
	'Icecream' (× *arendsii*)	CBod
	'Inshriach Pink' (*simplicifolia* hybrid)	CBcs ELan GBee LRHS NBir NHol NLar NRHS SGro SRms
	'Irrlicht' (× *arendsii*)	CMac CMea EBee ELan EPfP EShb LRHS NWad SPer SRms WHoo WPnP WWtn
	'Isa Hall'	NEoE NWad
	japonica	CExl
*	- 'Catherine Gladstone'	LRHS
*	- 'Pumila'	NBir NGdn
	- var. ***terrestris***	see *A. glaberrima*
	'Jo Ophorst' (*davidii* hybrid)	LRHS NGdn NLar
	'Jump and Jive'PBR	LLWG WFar
	'Juno'	XLum
	'Key West' (*simplicifolia* hybrid)	CPla
§	'Köln' (*japonica* hybrid)	CRos CWat LRHS NRHS
	koreana	WCot
	- B&SWJ 8611	WCru
	- B&SWJ 8680	WCru
	'Kvële' (× *arendsii*)	CRos LRHS NRHS WFar
	'Lilli Goos' (× *arendsii*)	GBin
	'Little Vision in Purple'PBR	CBod
	'Lollipop'	ECtt MBNS NEoE NLar SRms
	longicarpa B&SWJ 6711	WCru
	'Look at Me'PBR (× *arendsii*)	CBod CWGN ECtt LCro LOPS LSou MBel MHol MNrw NBPC SPoG
	'Maggie Daley'	NBro NEoE SRms
	'Mainz' (*japonica* hybrid)	CRos EBee ECtt LRHS NRHS
	microphylla B&SWJ 11085	WCru
	'Mighty Chocolate Cherry'	ILea LCro LOPS
	'Mighty Pip' (× *arendsii*)	CBod SPeP
	'Moerheim Glory' (× *arendsii*)	GBin NBre NGdn NLar
	'Montgomery' (*japonica* hybrid) ♀H7	CBod CRos CWCL EBee EMor EPfP EShb GAbr ILea LRHS LSRN LSou MBNS MBel MNrw NGdn NHol NLar NRHS SPoG
	'Nemo'	CBod MAsh
	'New Wave'	LLWG
	'Nikki'	NEoE NLar
§	***okuyamae*** B&SWJ 10975	WCru
	OSTRICH PLUME	see *A.* 'Straussenfeder'
	'Peaches and Cream'	NBro NLar
	'Peter Barrow' (*glaberrima* hybrid)	SRms
	'Pink Lightning'PBR (*simplicifolia* hybrid)	CWCL EShb GAbr LLWG MBNS NLar WFar
	PINK PEARL (× *arendsii*)	see *A.* 'Rosa Perle'
	'Poschka'	NEoE
	'Professor van der Wielen' (*thunbergii* hybrid)	EBee ECha GBin LRHS NHol NLar NWad SAko SRms WSpi
	pumila	see *A. chinensis* var. *pumila*
	'Purple Rain'PBR (× *arendsii*)	ILea MAsh
	'Radius'	CBod MAsh NGdn NLar WPnP
	'Red Baron'	CAby NEoE SPad WBrk
	RED LIGHT	see *A.* 'Rotlicht'
	'Red Sentinel' (*japonica* hybrid)	CBcs CBod CWCL CWat EBee EMor EPfP GMaP GWyn LRHS LSun MHol NBro NEoE NGdn NHol NLar NWad WFar WWtn
	'Rheinland' (*japonica* hybrid) ♀H7	CBcs CWCL GWyn LRHS MAsh MBel NBPC NGdn NLar NRHS SCob SEND WPnP
	'Rhythm and Blues'PBR	ECtt NLar
	rivularis	SDix WCot
	- CC 5201	GKev
	- CC 6857	NWad
	- GWJ 9366	WCru
	- PAB 7353	LEdu
	- PAB 9763	LEdu
I	- 'Grandiflora'	GBin
§	- var. ***myriantha***	EBee WPGP
	- - BWJ 8076a	WCru
	- - SICH 757	CExl
	'Robinson's Pink'	NGdn
	'Rock and Roll'PBR	CAby LSRN MAvo
§	'Rosa Perle' (× *arendsii*)	NHol NWad
§	× ***rosea*** 'Peach Blossom'	CBcs EMor EPfP EWTr ILea LLWG LRHS NBir NEoE NGdn SCob SPoG SWvt WFar WHil WHoo
	- 'Queen Alexandra'	XLum
	'Rosea' (*simplicifolia* hybrid)	NHol
	'Rot Straussenfeder' (× *arendsii*)	CBod
§	'Rotlicht' (× *arendsii*)	CMac CRos GBin LRHS NEoE NGdn NHol NLar NRHS
	'Salland'	LRHS
	'Saxosa'	see *A. glaberrima* var. *saxatilis*
	'Sheila Haxton' (*chinensis*)	LRHS
	Showstar Group (× *arendsii*)	SRms WWtn
	simplicifolia ♀H5	CAby CMea WFar
	- BRONZE ELEGANCE	see *A.* 'Bronce Elegans'
	- 'Darwin's Snow Sprite'	CMac NHol NLar SCob WFar
	- 'Jacqueline'	NHol

*	- 'Nana Alba'	NEoE
	- 'Rose of Cimarron'	NEoE NWad
	- 'White Sensation'PBR	CRos EBee ELan GQue LRHS NLar NRHS SAko
	'Snowdrift' (× *arendsii*)	CRos CWat GMaP LRHS MAsh MBNS MBel MMuc NBir NEoE NRHS SEND
	'Spartan' (× *arendsii*)	see *A.* 'Rotlicht'
	'Spinell' (× *arendsii*)	NBre WFar WPnP
	'Spotlight'PBR	CBod GBin MSCN
	'Sprite' (*simplicifolia* hybrid) 🏆H7	Widely available
§	'Straussenfeder' (*thunbergii* hybrid) 🏆H7	CAby CMac EBee ECtt EPfP GMaP GQue LRHS NBir NBro NGdn NHol NLar NRHS SPer SPoG SRms WCAu WWtn
	'Sugar Plum' (*simplicifolia* hybrid)	NGdn
	'Sugarberry'PBR (Short 'n' Sweet Series)	NLar
	'Superba'	see *A. chinensis* var. *taquetii* 'Superba'
	thunbergii	CExl LRHS NRHS
	- var. ***congesta*** B&SWJ 10961	WCru
	- var. ***formosa***	see *A. formosa*
	- var. ***hachijoensis***	EBee
	- - B&SWJ 5622	WCru
	- var. ***okuyamae***	see *A. okuyamae*
	- var. ***sikokumontanum*** B&SWJ 11164	WCru
	- - B&SWJ 11534	WCru
	- var. ***terrestris*** B&SWJ 6125	WCru
	'Thunder and Lightning' (*chinensis* hybrid)	NEoE
	'To Have and To Hold'	MNrw
	'Venus' (× *arendsii*)	ECtt GMaP MBNS MCot MMuc NGdn NHol SEND WFar
	'Vesuvius' (*japonica* hybrid)	CBcs ECtt NBro NLar
	virescens	see *A. rivularis* var. *myriantha*
	'Vision Inferno'PBR (× *arendsii*)	CBod NDov
	'Walter Bitner'	LRHS NBre NHol NRHS
	'Washington' (*japonica* hybrid)	EMor LRHS NBre NGdn WPnP
§	'Weisse Gloria' (× *arendsii*)	CMac ECha EMor EWTr GBin LRHS NBro NHol NRHS SCoo SGbt WCAu WFar WWtn
	'White Diamond' (× *arendsii*)	WFar
	WHITE GLORIA	see *A.* 'Weisse Gloria'
	'William Reeves' (× *arendsii*)	NHol NWad
	'Willie Buchanan' (*simplicifolia* hybrid)	CBcs CBod CRos GAbr GBin GKev GMaP LRHS NHol NHpl NRHS NWad SPer SRms WAbe WCFE WFar WHoo
	YOUNIQUE CARMINE ('Verscarmine'PBR)	ILea LLWG LSou
	YOUNIQUE CERISE ('Verscerise'PBR)	ILea
	YOUNIQUE SILVERY PINK ('Versilverypink'PBR)	WFar
	YOUNIQUE WHITE ('Verswhite'PBR)	ILea
	'Zuster Theresa' (× *arendsii*)	CRos LRHS MBNS MNrw NRHS

Astilboides (*Saxifragaceae*)

§	***tabularis***	Widely available

Astragalus (*Papilionaceae*)

canadensis	EBee LRHS NRHS
crassicarpus	SPhx
glycyphyllos	GJos NAts SPhx WCot
macrocarpus new	SPhx
neglectus	SPhx
odoratus	EBee

Astrantia ✿ (*Apiaceae*)

	'Atomic Sunburst'	GQue
	bavarica	GKev WFar
	'Berendien Stam'	CElw MNrw NLar WFar
	'Bloody Mary'	EBee GLet MAvo MNrw NGdn NLar
	'Bright and Breezy' new	MAvo
	'Buckland'	Widely available
	'Burgundy Manor'	CBod IPot NLar SHar
	'Bury Court'	NDov
	carniolica major	see *A. major*
	- 'Rubra'	CBcs GMaP WSpi
	- 'Variegata'	see *A. major* 'Sunningdale Variegated'
	'Censation Milano'	CWGN NLar
	'Clear Pink'	NDov
	'Dark Shiny Eyes'	CExl ECtt GLet ILea MTis NLar NSti SWvt
	'Good Pink'	LRHS MAvo
	'Hadspen Blood'	Widely available
	'Harvington Adrian's Choice Pink'	LRHS NRHS
	'Harvington Selected Red'	LRHS NRHS
	'Helen'	NLar
	helleborifolia	see *A. maxima*
	'Larch Cottage Clear Pink'	NLar WFar
	'Larch Cottage Magic'	MAvo WFar
	'Madeleine'	see *A. major* 'Madeleine van Bennekom'
§	***major***	Widely available
	- 'Abbey Road'PBR	CExl CWCL ECtt ELan EMor EPfP EWTr IPot LRHS LSou MHol MPnt NLar NRHS SAko SMad SRkn SRms
I	- 'Alba'	CBcs GKev GLet LRHS MCot MRav NBir NGdn NPer SCob SPer WPnP WSpi
	- 'April Love'	GLet
	- 'Berdien'	EBee
	- subsp. ***biebersteinii***	LRHS NBir
	- 'Bo-Ann'	NLar WFar
	- 'Can Candy'	MAvo MNrw
	- 'Celtic Star'	SWvt
	- 'Claret'	Widely available
	- 'Côte d'Azur'	WSpi
	- 'Cottage Herbery'	MNrw
	- 'Dark Desire'	GLet LEdu MAvo NDov
	- 'Elaine's Pink'	WHoo
	- 'Elmblut'	IMou MAvo WFar
	- 'Florence'PBR	CBct CBor CKno CNor CRos CWCL CWGN EBee ECtt EMor EPfP GLet LRHS MHol MHost MNrw MPri NDov NLar NRHS SAko SEdd SPeP SPoG SWvt WSpi
	- Gill Richardson Group	Widely available
	- 'Gracilis'	EBee EMor EPfP WFar
	- 'Green Tapestry' (v)	WCot
	- 'Gwaun Valley'	WFar
	- subsp. ***involucrata***	CElw LRHS WGoo
	- - 'Barrister'	CSam MAvo NLar
	- - 'Canneman'	EBee MNrw NLar SMHy WCot
	- - 'Jumble Hole'	EBee MAvo NDov WFar WGoo

	- - 'Margery Fish'	see *A. major* subsp. *involucrata* 'Shaggy'
	- - 'Moira Reid'	CExl CSam ECtt GLet GMaP MRav SHar WGoo
	- - 'Orlando'	MAvo MNrw WFar
§	- - 'Shaggy' Y^{H7}	Widely available
	- - 'Snape Cottage'	EBee WFar
	- 'Jade Lady'	WFar
	- 'Jitse'	WFar
	- 'Large White'	LCro LOPS SRms
	- 'Lars'	CExl ECtt GLet LRHS MHol MNrw NGdn NLar SPer SPoG SRms SWvt WCAu
	- 'Little Snowstar'	CWCL
	- 'Lola'	CDor EBee GLet MTis NLar
§	- 'Madeleine van Bennekom'	CNor EBee ECha ECtt GLet WFar
	- 'Midnight Owl'	CBcs ECtt MAsh MHol MNrw NBPC NSti
	- 'Penny's Pink'	EBee EWhm GLet LCro LOPS MAvo MNrw WSpi
	- 'Pink Crush'	CRos EPfP LRHS NRHS
	- 'Pink Pride'	GLet GWyn MHol MTis WCAu WFar WHil
	- 'Pink Sensation'	EBee GLet
	- 'Pink Surprise'	GLet MNrw NLar
	- 'Primadonna'	CBod CRos EBee EBou EPfP EPri GLet GMaP LRHS MHol MTis NLar NRHS SEdd SPlb SRms
	- 'Princesse Sturdza'	CWCL EBee WFar
	- 'Red Joyce'	CBod NLar WCAu
	- 'Reverse Sunningdale Variegated' (v)	WFar
	- 'Rosa Lee'	CElw CWCL WGoo
	- var. ***rosea***	CBod CRos CWCL EPfP GKev GLet GWyn LRHS MRav NGdn NRHS SHar WCAu WFar
	- - George's form	EPPr LSRN
	- 'Rosensinfonie'	CWCL EBee GLet GMaP GWyn NBro WPnP
§	- 'Rubra'	CRos CTsd CWCL EMor EPfP GKev GKin LCro LOPS LPot LRHS MCot MGos MHol NBir NChi NPer NRHS SRms WBor WCAu WHal
	- 'Ruby Cloud'	CBod CWCL ECtt ELan EMor EPri GLet LSou NBro NGdn NLar NRHS SPad WFar WSpi
	- 'Ruby Giant'	EBee EWTr GKin SHar SMad
	- 'Ruby Wedding'	Widely available
	- 'Silver Glow'	EBee ECtt
	- Sparkling Stars Series **new**	CWCL
	- - 'Sparkling Stars Pink'	GLet MBel MHol MNrw NBPC
	- 'Star of Beauty'^{PBR}	CKno CRos CWCL ECtt ELan EMor EPfP GLet GWyn LEdu LRHS MHost MNrw MPri NLar NRHS NSti SAko SCob SPoG SRms SWvt WSpi
	- 'Star of Billion'^{PBR}	CBod EBee ECtt ELan EPfP GLet LRHS MBros MHol MHost MNrw MPri NBPC NLar NRHS SCob SEdd SPoG SWvt WCAu WCot
	- 'Star of Fire'^{PBR}	CWGN EBee ECtt GLet LRHS MAsh MBel MBros MNrw NBPC NLar SCob WFar WHil
	- 'Star of Love' **new**	CKno GLet MHol MPnt WSpi
	- 'Star of Magic'^{PBR} (v)	GLet LRHS MAvo MNrw SPoG WCAu WTor
	- 'Star of Royals'^{PBR}	CWCL ECtt GLet LRHS NRHS SPoG WFar
	- 'Star of Summer'	EBee
	- 'Starburst'	EBee MNrw WFar
	- 'Sue Barnes' (v)	MNrw NLar
§	- 'Sunningdale Variegated' (v) Y^{H7}	Widely available
	- 'Titoki Point'	WCot
	- 'Venice'^{PBR}	Widely available
§	***maxima*** Y^{H7}	Widely available
	- 'Mark Fenwick'	MNrw NBir
I	- 'Rosea'	CDor ECtt MNrw MTis NBir NGdn
	'Millwood Crimson' **new**	CMiW
	minor	CBod LRHS
	'Moulin Rouge'^{PBR}	Widely available
§	'Mrs MacGregor'	MAvo MNrw WFar
	'Old Warwickshire Pink'	see *A.* 'Mrs MacGregor'
	'Queen's Children'	CDor GLet
	'Rainbow'	NLar
	'Roma'^{PBR} Y^{H7}	Widely available
	rubra	see *A. major* 'Rubra'
	'Ruby Star'^{PBR} Y^{H7}	Widely available
	'Sheila's Red'	LSRN MNrw
	'Snow Star'^{PBR}	CAby CRos CWCL EBee EPfP GLet LRHS MBNS MNrw MPri NLar NRHS STPC
	'Star of Heaven'	NLar
	'Star of Passion'^{PBR}	EBee ECtt ELan EPfP GLet NRHS SCob
	'Star of Treasure'^{PBR}	EBee ELan EMor GLet NLar NRHS
	'Superstar'^{PBR}	CAvo CBod CDor CTsd CWCL EBee ECtt ELon EMor EPfP EWTr GLet IPot LRHS MAvo MBNS MHol MHost MNrw MRav NBPC NDov NLar NSti SEdd SPer SWvt WCot WSpi XEll
	'Warren Hills'	EBee GMaP MNrw NLar WFar
	'Washfield'	CWCL MTis NDov NEoE
	'Whirling Dervish' **new**	MAvo

Astrodaucus (*Apiaceae*)

	littoralis	LEdu SPhx
	orientalis	SPhx

Astrolepis (*Pteridaceae*)

	sinuata	ISha SPlb

Asyneuma (*Campanulaceae*)

	campanuloides	SGro
	canescens	LRHS
	pulvinatum	CPBP WAbe

Asystasia (*Acanthaceae*)

	bella	see *Mackaya bella*

Athamanta (*Apiaceae*)

	cretensis	SPhx SPtp
	turbith	CPla CSpe MNrw SBrt
	- subsp. ***haynaldii***	SPhx
	vestina	LRHS SBrt SPhx

Athanasia (*Asteraceae*)

§	***parviflora***	SPlb

Athrotaxis (*Cupressaceae*)

	cupressoides	CBcs WThu
	laxifolia	LRHS

Athyrium ✿ (*Woodsiaceae*)

	auriculatum	CBdn
	'Branford Beauty'	CLAP CRos ISha LEdu LRHS NRHS
	'Branford Rambler'	CBdn CLAP EBee ISha LEdu
	filix-femina Y^{H6}	Widely available
§	- subsp. ***angustum*** Y^{H6}	CRos EMor LRHS MRav NGdn NRHS

- - f. ***rubellum*** 'Lady in Red' 🏆H6	CBdn CBod CLAP CRos CTsd CWCL EBee ELan EPfP ESwi IBal ISha LCro LRHS LSRN MAvo MGos NBPC NLar NRHS SPoG WCot WLov
- 'Clarissimum Jones'	WCot
- 'Crispum Grandiceps Kaye'	NGdn
- Cristatum Group	CLAP EFer ELan LSRN NGdn SMHy WCot WFib
- 'Dre's Dagger'	CBdn CLAP CMiW EBee EMor LEdu SPoG WPGP
- 'Fieldii'	CLAP EFer
- 'Frizelliae' 🏆H6	Widely available
- 'Frizelliae Capitatum'	CLAP WFib
- 'Frizelliae Cristatum'	CLAP
- 'Howardii'	NBro
- 'Lady-in-Lace' 🏆H6	EBee
- 'Minutissimum'	EBee ELan ISha LRHS NRHS WCot
- Plumosum Group	EShb MRav WFib XLum
- 'Plumosum Axminster'	CLAP EFer EShb WCot WFar
- 'Plumosum Cristatum Drueryi' **new**	WCot
- 'Plumosum Drueryi'	EFer
- 'Plumosum Percristatum'	WCot
- RED STEM	see *A. filix-femina* 'Rotstiel'
§ - 'Rotstiel'	CDTJ CLAP EBee EMor NBro
- 'Rotstiel Grandiceps'	ISha
- 'Setigerum Cristatum'	WFar
- 'Vernoniae' 🏆H6	CLAP ISha MRav
- 'Vernoniae Cristatum'	CLAP WFib
- 'Victoriae'	CAby CBdn CDTJ CRos CWCL EBee ECtt EFer ELan EPfP GMaP IBal ISha LLWG LRHS MAsh NBid NLar NRHS WFar WSpi XLum
- aff. 'Victoriae'	CLAP EWTr WFar
- aff. Victoriae Group	see *A. filix-femina* subsp. *angustum*
'Ghost' 🏆H5	CAby CBdn CLAP CRos EBee EMor ESwi ISha LEdu LRHS MAsh MGos NBro NLar NRHS NSti SPlb SPoG WCot
goeringianum 'Pictum'	see *A. niponicum* var. *pictum*
minimum	CAby CBdn CLAP EMor LEdu NBro NLar WCot WPGP
niponicum	CLAP LRHS WHal
- 'Godzilla'	CBdn CLAP EBee ISha
- f. ***metallicum***	see *A. niponicum* var. *pictum*
§ - var. ***pictum*** 🏆H5	Widely available
- - 'Apple Court'	CBdn CLAP CRos EBee ESwi ISha LEdu LRHS MAsh NRHS
- - 'Burgundy Lace'	CAby CBdn CLAP CMiW EBee ECtt ESwi MPnt NBro NLar SEdd WCot
* - - 'Cristatoflabellatum'	CLAP EBee LRHS
- - 'Pearly White'	CBdn CLAP
- - 'Pewter Lace'	CBdn CLAP CMiW EBee ECtt EMor LEdu NBro NLar
- - 'Red Beauty'	CBcs CBod CDTJ CRos CSpe ECha ECtt ELan EMor EPfP GBin IBal LRHS LSRN MAsh MMuc NLar NRHS SCob SEdd SPalm SRkn WCot WFar
- - 'Regal Red'	CBdn CLAP CRos EBee ISha LRHS MAsh NRHS
- - 'Silver Falls' 🏆H5	CBcs CLAP CRos EBee EShb ESwi LLWG LRHS NRHS SPoG WCot
- - 'Soul Mate'	CLAP
- - 'Ursula's Red'	CBod CLAP CMiW EBee ELan ELon EMor EPot EShb LCro LLWG LOPS LRHS LSun MHol NBPC NBid NHpl NLar SCob SPoG WCot WFar WPGP
'Ocean's Fury'	CAby CBdn CLAP EBee ECtt EFer EShb ESwi LPla SPoG WCot
otophorum 🏆H4	ISha MRav NBid WPGP
- var. ***okanum*** 🏆H4	Widely available
vidalii	CBdn CBod CLAP CRos EBee EMor IBal ISha LLWG LRHS NBro NLar NRHS SCob WFar WFib XLum
wardii	CBdn

Atractylodes (*Asteraceae*)

japonica	LEdu

Atragene see *Clematis*

Atriplex (*Amaranthaceae*)

canescens	CAgr
halimus	CAgr CBcs CCoa CLau CSde EBee ECha EPPr MRav NLar SDix SLon SPer SPlb WCot XAbr
- 'Cascais'	WCot
- 'Limelight' (v)	EPPr
hortensis	ENfk
- var. ***rubra***	CSpe ELan MNHC SRms
portulacoides	see *Halimione portulacoides*

Atropa (*Solanaceae*)

belladonna	GPoy SEND
mandragora	see *Mandragora officinarum*

aubergine see AGM Vegetables Section

Aubrieta (*Brassicaceae*)

'Agnetta'	ECtt
'Alba'	see *A.* 'Fiona'
albomarginata	see *A.* 'Argenteovariegata'
'Alix Brett'	CMea CPBP
§ 'Argenteovariegata' (v) 🏆H6	CRos ELan LRHS NRHS
'Audrey Blue' (Audrey Series)	GWyn
§ 'Aureovariegata' (v) 🏆H6	CMea NPer XLum
(Axcent Series) AXCENT BLUE WITH EYE ('Audelbley'PBR)	LRHS
- AXCENT DARK RED ('Audeldare')	LRHS WIce
- AXCENT DEEP PURPLE ('Audelpur'PBR)	LRHS
- AXCENT DEEP RED ('Abrz0001'PBR)	SRms
- AXCENT LIGHT BLUE ('Abrz0002'PBR)	CRos EPfP LRHS NRHS
- AXCENT LILAC ('Audelip'PBR)	CRos LRHS NRHS
- AXCENT MAGENTA ('Audelmag'PBR)	LRHS
bicoloured	CMea
BLAUE SCHÖNHEIT	see *A.* 'Blue Beauty'
'Blaumeise'	CBod EBou LRHS MHol
§ 'Blue Beauty'	CBod CMea EBou ECtt EPfP GBin GMaP NHpl NLar WHoo
'Blue Emperor'	ECtt
'Blue Whale'	CBod CPla ECtt GAbr LBuc MHol NLar SRms SWvt
§ 'Bob Saunders' (d)	CMea ECtt
'Boundary Haze'	EBou
'Boundary Purple'	EBou
'Bressingham Pink' (d) 🏆H6	ECtt SRms
'Bressingham Red'	ECtt ELan EPfP GMaP SRms
canescens	CPBP

Cascade Series	SPoG
- 'Blue Cascade'	CTri EBou EPfP GMaP MBNS MBel SPlb SPoG SRms
- 'Lilac Cascade'	SPoG SRms
- 'Purple Cascade'	CTri EBou LCro LOPS LSRN MAsh MBNS MBel SPlb SPoG SRms
- 'Red Cascade' 🏆H6	CTri EBou ECtt ELan EPfP LSRN MBNS SPlb SPoG
× ***cultorum***	LSun SVic XSen
deltoidea	WCFE
- Variegata Group (v)	CBod MAsh MHol WFar
- - 'Golden Variegata' (v)	EBou
- - 'Nana Variegata' (v)	CMea
'Doctor Mules' 🏆H6	ECtt SRms WCav
'Doctor Mules Variegata' (v)	ECtt ELan ELon EPfP GMaP GWyn MHer NLar SPoG SWvt WHoo WIce
double pink-flowered (d)	CBod ELan GAbr GMaP MBros MHol
'Elsa Lancaster'	NHpl
§ 'Fiona'	EWes
glabrescens	CMea CPBP EPot NHpl WAbe WTor
'Gloria'	CMea EBou ECtt NHpl NLar WHoo WIce
'Golden King'	see *A.* 'Aureovariegata'
gracilis 'Kitte Rose'	CRos EPfP LBuc LRHS MHol NRHS
'Greencourt Purple' 🏆H6	ECtt MHer
'Hamburger Stadtpark'	CWCL ECtt ELan ELon EPfP GMaP SRms
'Hemswell Purity'	see *A.* 'Snow Maiden'
'Ida'	ECtt WIce
'Kati'	GMaP LRHS
'Kitte'	CSma EBou ECtt ELan EPfP LRHS MHer NLar SPoG SRms
'Kitte Blue'	CRos EPfP LBuc LRHS MHol MPri NRHS SPoG SRms WIce
'Kitte Purple'	ELan EPfP SPoG
'Kitte White'	CRos EPfP LRHS MHer NRHS
'Leichtlinii'	XLum
'Lime Variegated' (v)	NHpl WCav
'Oakington Lavender'	ECtt
pinardii	GKev WAbe
'Pink Beauty'	ECtt
'Purple Charm'	SRms
'Red Carpet'	ELan EPot MAsh MHer SRms
'Rose Queen'	CMea ECtt
Royal Series 🏆H6	LCro LOPS
- 'Royal Blue'	CTri ELan EPfP MBros NLar SRms WFar
- 'Royal Lilac'	CTri WFar
- 'Royal Red'	CTri ELan EPfP GBin GWyn SRms WCav
- 'Royal Violet'	ELan EPfP SBut WFar
'Schofield's Double'	see *A.* 'Bob Saunders'
'Silberrand' (v)	ECha LBuc
§ 'Snow Maiden' PBR	NHpl
'Somerfield Silver'	ELan
'Somerford Lime' (v)	ELan EPfP SRms WIce
'Swan Red' (v)	CPBP CPla EBou ECtt ELon EPot NHpl NSla WTor
'Valerie' (v)	EWes GRum
'Westacre Gold' (v)	CBod ECtt EWes MAsh MHol
'Whitewell Gem'	XLum
'Winterberg'	ECtt

Aucuba ✿ (*Garryaceae*)

chlorascens B&SWJ 11815	WCru
himalaica	CDTJ GBin SBrt
var. ***dolichophylla***	
- - Og 95038	WCru
japonica	CCVT CDoC NLar SEWo WCru WFar
- B&SWJ 14602 **new**	WCru
- var. ***borealis*** (f) CWJ 12898	WCru
- 'Clent Wortley Hall' (m)	WCFE
- 'Crassifolia' (m)	ELon SArc
- 'Crotonifolia' (f/v) 🏆H5	Widely available
- 'Crotonifolia' (m/v)	CMac EBou MAsh SDix SGol SGsty SRms
- 'Dentata' (f)	SRms WAvo WCru
- 'February Star' (f/v)	ESwi SDix
- 'Golden Girl' (v)	CBod CRos LRHS MAsh NRHS SLon
- 'Golden King' (m/v) 🏆H5	CBod CDoC CMac CRos EBee ELan ELon EPfP LRHS MAsh MGos NLar NRHS SCob SGol SGsty SLim SMad WFar WRHF
- 'Golden Spangles' (f/v)	CBcs EMil EPfP LRHS SWvt
- 'Leucocarpa' (f)	SPer
- f. ***longifolia***	CMac EPfP NLar SArc SDix WCru
- - 'Salicifolia' (f) 🏆H5	EBee ELon ESwi MRav NLar WCru WFar WPGP
- 'Maculata' misapplied	see *A. japonica* 'Variegata'
- 'Marmorata' (v)	CRos LRHS MAsh NRHS
- 'Mr Goldstrike' (m/v)	CBod EPfP LRHS MAsh SGbt
- PEPPER POT ('Shilpot') (m/v) 🏆H5	CRos CTsd EPfP LRHS MAsh SLon WCFE
- 'Picturata' (m/v)	CBod CMac CRos ELan ELon ESwi LRHS MAsh MMuc NLar SEND WFar
- 'Rozannie' (f/m) 🏆H5	CBar CBcs CBod CBrac CDoC CEnd CMac CRos ECrN ELan ELon EPfP EShb LCro LOPS LRHS LSRN MAsh MBlu MGos MRav MSwo NLar NRHS SCob SLim SPer SPoG SWvt WFar
- 'Sulphurea Marginata' (f/v)	CMac CRos CTri EShb ESwi LRHS NLar NRHS SPer WFar WRHF
§ - 'Variegata' (f/v)	CBod CBrac CCVT CMac CRos CSBt CTho CTri EBee ECrN ELan ELon EPfP LBuc LRHS MAsh MGos NHol NRHS SCob SGbt SLim SLon SPer SRms SWeb WAvo
- 'Variegata' white-flowered (m/v)	SGbt
omeiensis	CBcs CDTJ CExl
- B&SWJ 2864	ESwi WCru
- BWJ 8048	WCru
- L 614	WPGP

Aulax (*Proteaceae*)

cancellata	CCCN SPlb

Aurinia (*Brassicaceae*)

§ ***saxatilis*** 🏆H5	ELan EPfP MMuc SHar SPlb WFar XSen
- 'Citrina' 🏆H5	ECha SRms
- 'Compacta'	ECtt GJos WIce
- 'Dudley Nevill'	WFar
- 'Dudley Nevill Variegated' (v)	ECha EWes
- GOLD BALL	see *A. saxatilis* 'Goldkugel'
- 'Gold Dust'	GJos SRms
§ - 'Goldkugel'	CBod CMea EPfP GJos GWyn MHol SPoG SRms WFar
- 'Variegata' (v)	SPoG SRms WHoo

Austrocedrus (*Cupressaceae*)

§ ***chilensis***	CKen SLim

Avena (*Poaceae*)

candida	see *Helictotrichon sempervirens*

Avenula see *Helictotrichon*

Averrhoa (*Oxalidaceae*)

carambola (F) CCCN SVic

avocado see *Persea americana*

Azadirachta (*Meliaceae*)

indica XAbr

Azalea see *Rhododendron*

Azara ✿ (*Salicaceae*)

dentata	CBcs CMac WFar WPav
- 'Variegata'	see *A. integrifolia* 'Variegata'
integrifolia	CCCN IDee MGil WPav
- 'Uarie'	CCCN
§ - 'Variegata' (v)	CCCN LRHS
lanceolata	CBcs CExl CTri CTsd LEdu NSti WPav
microphylla ♀H4	CBcs CCCN CDoC CExl CMac CRos CTri EBee ELan ELon EPfP LRHS LSRN MAsh MGil MGos MMuc NQui SArc SEND SPer SPlb WFar WPGP WPav WSpi
* - 'Albovariegata' (v)	CTri WPav
- 'Gold Edge' (v)	WFar WPav
- 'Variegata' (v)	CBcs CBct CExl CMac CRos CTsd EBee ELan EPfP LRHS MAsh MGil MMuc NLar SEND SPoG WAvo WFar WPav
* **patagonica**	MBlu WPav
petiolaris	CTri MGil WPav
serrata ♀H4	CBcs CBrac CCCN CEnd CRos CTsd ELan EPfP EShb GBin LRHS MGil NLar SDix SEND SGol SPer SPoG SRms SVen WBor WFar WKif WPav WSpi
uruguayensis	CCCN CExl CTsd GBin WPav

Azorella (*Apiaceae*)

filamentosa	EPot GEdr
glebaria misapplied	see *A. trifurcata*
glebaria A. Gray	see *Bolax gummifer*
gummifer	see *Bolax gummifer*
lycopodioides	SPlb WAbe
patagonica	SPlb
§ **trifurcata**	CPar CSpe CTri GAbr GKev MMuc NBir SPlb WAbe
- 'Nana'	GEdr GMaP XLum

Azorina (*Campanulaceae*)

§ **vidalii** EShb NWad SPlb

B

Babiana (*Iridaceae*)

nana 'Halley' new	GBin
patersoniae	SPlb
stricta ♀H2	CCCN CCtw GKev SDeJ
- Kew hybrids	GKev
- 'Purple Star'	CBor CExl
thunbergii	CPbh
'Zwanenburg's Glory'	CPrp

Baccharis (*Asteraceae*)

genistelloides	MPkF
patagonica	CRos EHyd LRHS MMuc SArc SVen

Backhousia (*Myrtaceae*)

citriodora GPoy MHer

Bacopa (*Plantaginaceae*)

misapplied	see *Chaenostoma cordatum*
caroliniana	XBlo

Baeckea (*Myrtaceae*)

gunniana	CExl
linifolia	SPlb
virgata	SPlb

Balbisia (*Ledocarpaceae*)

peduncularis CCCN

Baldellia (*Alismataceae*)

ranunculoides	EWat WMAq
- f. **repens**	LLWG

Ballota (*Lamiaceae*)

acetabulosa	ECha EWes WCot
'All Hallow's Green'	see *Marrubium bourgaei* var. *bourgaei* 'All Hallows Green'
hirsuta	XSen
nigra	GPoy NMir SRms
pseudodictamnus ♀H4	CBcs CBod CCBP CMac CRos EBee ECha EHyd ELan EPfP GMaP LRHS LSRN MPie MRav NPer NRHS NSti SCob SDix SEND SLon SPer WAvo XLum XSen
- B&M 8119	WCot WPGP
- from Crete	ECha
- 'Candia'	SHar
- compact	CBct EBee XSen
rupestris 'Frogswell Carolyn' (v)	XSen

Baloskion (*Restionaceae*)

§ **tetraphyllum**	CCtw CPbh CTsd GBin LRHS SEdd SPlb SPoG WSMil
§ - 'Cornish Gold' (v)	CPbh

Balsamita see *Tanacetum*

Balsamorhiza (*Asteraceae*)

rosea new GEdr

Bambusa (*Poaceae*)

glaucescens	see *B. multiplex*
§ **multiplex**	XBlo
- 'Alphonso-Karrii'	XCre
- 'Elegans'	see *B. multiplex* 'Floribunda'
- 'Fernleaf'	see *B. multiplex* 'Floribunda'
§ - 'Floribunda'	EShb XBlo XCre
- 'Golden Goddess'	XBlo
- 'Silverstripe'	see *B. multiplex* 'Variegata'
§ - 'Variegata' (v)	XBlo
- 'Wang Tsai'	see *B. multiplex* 'Floribunda'
oldhamii	XCre
pubescens	see *Dendrocalamus strictus*
tuldoides	XCre
ventricosa	XBlo XCre
- 'Striata'	XCre
vulgaris	XBlo
- 'Vittata'	XBlo

banana see *Ensete*, *Musa*

Banksia ✿ (*Proteaceae*)

canei SPlb
ericifolia CPbh
- var. **ericifolia** CCCN
- var. **macrantha** SPlb
'Giant Candles' new CTrC
grandis CCCN
integrifolia CBcs CCCN CDTJ CPbh CTrC SPlb
marginata CTrC CTsd LRHS SPlb
media SPlb
menziesii shrubby new CCCN
oblongifolia SPlb
paludosa CTrC SPlb
praemorsa CCCN
- yellow-flowered CCCN
prionotes CCCN
robur CBcs CCCN SPlb
serrata CCCN SPlb
speciosa SPlb
spinulosa CPbh CTrC
- 'Birthday Candles' CPbh
- var. **collina** SPlb
- var. **spinulosa** CCCN
violacea SPlb

Baptisia (*Papilionaceae*)

§ **alba** ILea LPla MBel MNrw SCob SPhx
- var. **alba** IPot NLar WCAu
§ - var. **macrophylla** EHyd EWes LRHS MNrw NRHS SPhx
australis ♀H7 Widely available
- 'Blueberry Sundae' CSpe CWGN EBee EWTr ILea MSCN SPer
- 'Caspian Blue' CExl GMaP LEdu
- 'Exaltata' ♀H7 EBee ECtt EPau LPla MBNS MHol MSCN NBPC NLar SEdd SHar WCot WRHF
- var. **minor** CSpe MMrt SPhx
× **bicolor** 'Starlite' (Prairieblues Series) MNrw
§ **bracteata** var. **leucophaea** SPhx
'Carolina Moonlight' EBee ECtt EWes GBin MNrw NSti SCob SHar SPer
'Cherries Jubilee' CWGN EBee ILea LCro LOPS MSCN WHil
'Chocolate Chip' MCot SHar
'Dutch Chocolate' (Decadence Series) CBcs CBod CWGN EBee ECtt ELan EMor EWes ILea IPot LCro LOPS LRHS MAvo NDov NSti SPad SPer SPoG WHil XEll
'Grape Taffy' new LCro LOPS MSCN
'Indigo Spires' EBee ILea MBel
lactea see *B. alba* var. *macrophylla*
'Lemon Meringue' CBod EBee ELan LCro LOPS MSCN NDov SPoG
leucantha see *B. alba* var. *macrophylla*
leucophaea see *B. bracteata* var. *leucophaea*
pendula see *B. alba*
'Pink Lemonade' new LCro LOPS
'Pink Truffles' (Decadence Series) LCro LOPS NSti SHar WHil
'Purple Smoke' CBcs CExl CSpe EBee ECtt ILea IPot LCro LEdu LOPS LRHS MBel MCot MHol MNrw SMHy SPhx WAul WHil WPGP
'Solar Flare' (Prairieblues Series) ILea
'Sparkling Sapphires' (Decadence Series) IPot
sphaerocarpa LPla SPhx SPlb
tinctoria SPhx
'Vanilla Cream' EWTr IPot LCro LOPS WHil
× **variicolor** 'Twilite' (Prairieblues Series) EBee EPfP GBin LRHS MMrt SCob

Barbarea (*Brassicaceae*)

praecox see *B. verna*
rupicola 'Sunnyola' CBor
§ **verna** GPoy MHer SRms SVic
vulgaris 'Variegata' (v) NBro

Barleria (*Acanthaceae*)

oenotheroides CCCN
suberecta see *Dicliptera sericea*

Barnardia (*Asparagaceae*)

japonica WCot

Barosma see *Agathosma*

Bartlettina (*Asteraceae*)

§ **sordida** CCCN

Basella (*Basellaceae*)

rubra CLau SPre

Bashania (*Poaceae*)

§ **fargesii** MMuc MRav MWht SEND XCre
I **qingchengshanensis** MWht XCre

basil see *Ocimum basilicum*; also AGM Vegetables Section

Bauhinia (*Caesalpiniaceae*)

* **lutea** CCCN
natalensis SPlb
purpurea L. CCCN SPlb
tomentosa CCCN
'White Lady' CCCN
yunnanensis SBrt SPlb

Baumea see *Machaerina*

bay see *Laurus nobilis*

beans see AGM Vegetables Section

Beaucarnea (*Asparagaceae*)

recurvata ♀H1c CDoC LCro LOPS SPad SPlb

Beaufortia (*Myrtaceae*)

sparsa CTrC
squarrosa SPlb

Beckmannia (*Poaceae*)

eruciformis XLum

Bedfordia (*Asteraceae*)

linearis SPlb

Beesia (*Ranunculaceae*)

§ **calthifolia** CBct CDTJ CDor CSpe EBee EPfP ESwi EWld GEdr IMou LEdu SChF SMad WCot WCru WPGP WSHC
- DJHC 98447 CExl
deltophylla misapplied see *B. calthifolia*

beetroot see AGM Vegetables Section

Begonia ✿ (Begoniaceae)

	'Abel Carrière' (R)	WDib
	aconitifolia (C)	EShb
	albopicta (C)	EBak
	- 'Rosea' (C)	EShb WDib
	AMOUR ('Yamour') (Million Kisses Series)	MBros
	'Angela Jane' (T)	WFib
	aff. ***angularis***	SPlb
§	***annulata*** ♀H1b	LEdu
	- HWJK 2424	ESwi WCru WFar
	'Apricot Delight' (Fragrant Falls Improved Series) (T)	WFib
	'Apricot Nectar' (Fragrant Falls Improved Series) (T)	EHyd LRHS NRHS
I	'Apricot Shades Improved'	SDeJ
	'Argentea' (R)	EBak
	'Argenteo-guttata'	EShb
	'Aya' (C)	WDib
	balansana	CBct
	'Beatrice Haddrell'	CBct
	BELEAF INCA NIGHT ('Krbelin02'PBR) (R) **new**	SCob
	'Benitochiba' (R) ♀H1b	CBcs CBct CBod CDTJ CExl CSpe ECtt ESwi GBin MHol SEdd SPoG WCot WDib
	'Beryl Rhodes' (T)	WFib
	'Bethlehem Star'	NWad WDib
	'Billy Langdon' (T)	WFib
	'Black Fang' ♀H1b	WDib
	'Black Knight' (R)	WDib
	'Blackberry Swirl' (R)	WDib
	'Blazing Star' (T)	LCro LOPS
	BLISSFUL (Million Kisses Series)	MBros
	'Blushing Star' (T)	CPla LCro LOPS
	'Bokit' × ***imperialis***	WDib
	boliviensis (T)	ESwi
	- 'Firecracker'	WDib
	BONFIRE ('Nzcone'PBR) ♀H1b	SPoG
	'Bouton de Rose' (T)	SDeJ
	'Buttermilk' (T)	WFib
	'Can-can' (T)	WFib
	'Candy Floss'	WCru WFar
	carolineifolia ♀H1b	WDib
	× ***carrierei***	see *B.* Semperflorens Cultorum Group
	'Cascade Florence'	SDeJ
	'Cascade Sunray'	SDeJ
	'Casey Corwin' (R)	WDib
	cathayana	EBee
	'Champagne'	LCro LOPS
	'Chantilly Lace'	NWad
I	***chapaensis*** HWJ 642	WCru
	'China Curl' (R) ♀H1b	WDib
	chitoensis B&SWJ 1954	WCru
	'Christmas Candy'	WFar
	'Cleopatra' ♀H1b	WDib
	coccinea (C)	WPav
	'Comte de Lesseps' (C)	WDib
	'Connee Boswell' ♀H1b	WDib
§	***corallina*** (C)	EBak
	cucullata var. ***arenosicola*** (S)	ECtt ESwi
	'Curly Fireflush' (R) ♀H1b	WDib
	'David Blais' (R) ♀H1b	WDib
	'Dawnal Meyer' (C)	WDib
I	'De Elegans'	WDib
	Devil Series (S)	SCob
	- 'Devil White' (S)	SCob
	DEVIL'S DELIGHT (mixed) (S) **new**	LCro LOPS MBros SCob
	DEVOTION ('Yadev') (Million Kisses Series) ♀H1b	MBros
	'Dewdrop' (R) ♀H1b	WDib
	'Dibleys Pink Showers' ♀H1b	WDib
	discolor	see *B. grandis* subsp. *evansiana*
	'Down Home' (C)	WDib
	DRAGON WING RED ('Bepared'PBR) ♀H1b	EShb MBros
§	***dregei*** (T) ♀H1b	EShb
	ELEGANCE ('Yagance'PBR) (Million Kisses Series) ♀H1b	MBros
	emeiensis	CBct WFar WPGP
	'Emerald Giant' (R)	WDib
	'Erythrophylla' ♀H1b	EShb
	'Escargot' (R) ♀H1b	WDib
	'Fairy Lights' (T)	WFib
	Fimbriata Group (T)	SDeJ
	'Fireworks' (R) ♀H1b	WDib
	'Flamenco' (T/d)	MPri
	'Flo'Belle Moseley' (C)	WDib
§	***foliosa*** var. ***miniata*** ♀H1b	CTsd EBak EShb MArl SDix WCot WDib
	- - pink-flowered	CCCN
	formosana	WCru
	f. ***albo-maculata*** B&SWJ 6881 **new**	
	Fragrant Falls Improved Series	SCob SPoG
	fuchsioides	see *B. foliosa* var. *miniata*
	'Funky Pink' (Funky Series) (T/d)	MPri SCob
	fusca	WMal WPGP
	'Garden Angel Blush' (Garden Angel Series)	CAbb CBct CBod SEdd WCot
	'Gay Gordon' (T)	WFib
	'Glowing Embers' ♀H1b	ECtt LBuc LSou MBros NWad SCob SPoG
	grandis (T)	IDee XLum
§	- subsp. ***evansiana*** ♀H2	CAby CBct CTsd EPPr EShb LEdu SDix SEND SPlb WCot WCru WFar
	- - B&SWJ 11188	WCru
	- - var. ***alba*** hort. ♀H2	CAby EBee EPPr EShb ESwi EWld GPSL LEdu SDix SGro WCot WPGP XLum
	- - 'Claret Jug'	CExl EBee ECtt ESwi MSCN WGrn WSMil
	- - 'Pink Parasol'	ESwi WCru
	- - pink-flowered	WFar
	- - 'Simsii'	EBee WFar
	- - 'Sublime'	LEdu
	- 'Heron's Pirouette' **new**	EPPr
	- subsp. ***holostyla*** 'Nanjiang Silver'	EPPr
	- 'Sapporo'	EBee ESwi SChr WCru WFar
§	- subsp. ***sinensis*** (T)	NWad
	- - BWJ 8133	WCru WFar
I	- - 'Red Undies'	ESwi WCru WFar
	- - 'Snowpop'	WFar WPGP
	'Green Gold' (R) ♀H1b	WDib
	'Green Valleyleaf'	NWad
	griffithii	see *B. annulata*

	haageana hort. ex W.Watson	see *B. scharffii*
	(Hanging Basket Series) 'Hanging Basket Orange' (T) **new**	SDir
	- 'Hanging Basket Pink' (T) **new**	SDir
	- 'Hanging Basket Red' (T) **new**	SDir
	- 'Hanging Basket Salmon' (T) **new**	SDir
	- 'Hanging Basket White' (T) **new**	SDir
	hatacoa	LEdu
	- silver-leaved	WDib
	HEAVEN DELIGHT (mixed) **new**	LCro LOPS
	Heaven Series (S)	SCob
	- 'Heaven Red' (S) **new**	SCob
	- 'Heaven White' (S) **new**	MBros
	'Helen Teupel' (R)	WDib
	'Helena Hall' (T)	WFib
	'Hilo Holiday' (R) ♀^{H1b}	WDib
	homonyma	see *B. dregei*
	HONEYMOON ('Yamoon'^{PBR}) (Million Kisses Series)	MBros
	Illumination Series (T/d)	LCro LOPS MBros
	- 'Illumination Apricot' (T/d)	SCoo
	- 'Illumination Rose' (T/d)	SCoo
	- 'Illumination Salmon Pink' (T/d) ♀^{H2}	SCoo
	- 'Illumination White' (T/d)	SCoo
	× ***intermedia*** 'Bertinii' (T)	LCro LOPS SDeJ
	'Jennifer Wilson' (T)	WFib
	'Jessie Cruickshank' (T)	WFib
	'John Smith' (T)	WFib
*	***koelzii*** NJM 12.077 **new**	WPGP
	'La Paloma' (C)	WDib
	Large-flowered Double Group (T/d)	SDeJ
	'Lianne' (T)	WFib
	'Limeade' ♀^{H1b}	WDib
	'Linda Jackson' (T)	WFib
	listada ♀^{H1b}	WDib
	'Little Brother Montgomery' ♀^{H1b}	EShb NWad WDib
	'Lois Burks' (C)	WDib
	'Lucerna' (C)	EBak ELan EShb WDib
	luxurians ♀^{H1b}	CAbb CBct CBod CDTJ CSpe EBee ECtt ELan ESwi GBin MNrw SDix SIvy SMad SPlb WCot WGrn WPGP WSMil
	macduffieana	see *B. corallina*
	maculata (C)	LCro LOPS
	- 'Wightii' (C)	CSpe WDib
	'Madame Butterfly' (C)	NWad
	(Majestic Series) 'Majestic Pink' (T)	SCob
	- 'Majestic Red' (T)	SCob
	- 'Majestic Sunburst' (T) **new**	SCob
	- 'Majestic Yellow' (T)	SCob
	'Majesty' (T)	WFib
	Marginata Group (T)	SDeJ
*	'Marginata Crispa White'	SDeJ
	'Marmaduke' ♀^{H1b}	WDib
	'Marmorata' (T)	SDeJ
	'Martin Johnson' (R) ♀^{H1b}	WDib
	masoniana ♀^{H1b}	ESwi WDib WSFF

I	'Matador' (T)	WFib
	'Matisse' (Impressionist Series)	CRos EHyd LRHS NRHS
	'Melissa' (T)	WFib
	'Merry Christmas' (R)	WDib
	'Metallic Mist'^{PBR}	ESwi
	'Midnight Magic' (R) ♀^{H1b}	WDib
	Million Kisses Series	LBuc MBros MPri
	'Mishmi Silver'	CBct LEdu WPGP
	'Monet' (Impressionist Series)	CRos EHyd LRHS NRHS
	'Mother's Day' (T)	LCro LOPS
	'Mrs E. McLaughlan' (T)	WFib
	'Mrs Peters' (T)	WFib
	'Munchkin' ♀^{H1b}	WDib
	'My Best Friend'	WDib
	'Namur' (R) ♀^{H1b}	WDib
	natalensis	see *B. dregei*
	'Nick Woodfield'	WFib
	Nonstop Series (T/d)	MBros SCob SDeJ
	- 'Nonstop Pink' (T/d)	SDeJ
	- 'Nonstop Red' (T/d)	MBros SDeJ
	- 'Nonstop Rose Petticoat' (T/d)	MBros
	- 'Nonstop Salmon' (T/d)	SDeJ
	- 'Nonstop White' (T/d)	MBros SCob SDeJ
	- 'Nonstop Yellow' (T/d)	MBros SCob SDeJ
	'Northern Lights' (R)	MBros SCob
	(Northern Lights Series) 'Northern Lights Pink' (T) **new**	MBros SCob
	- 'Northern Lights Scarlet Burst' (T)	MBros MPri SCob
	'Odorosa'	SDeJ
	'Ollykey' (T)	WFib
	'Orange Rubra' (C)	WDib
	'Orangeade' (c)	NWad
	'Organdy' (mixed)	MBros
	palmata	CBct CDTJ CExl WFar
	panchtharensis	SPlb
	- B&SWJ 2692	WCot WCru
	partita	see *B. dregei*
	'Peardrop'^{PBR}	MBros
	pedatifida DJHC 98473	ESwi EWld WCru WFar
	- 'Apalala' **new**	WPGP
	Pendula Group (T)	SDeJ
	- 'Pink Giant' (T)	LCro LOPS
	- 'Red Giant' (T)	LCro LOPS
	- 'White Giant' (T)	LCro LOPS
	'Picasso' (Impressionist Series)	CRos EHyd LRHS NRHS
	'Picotee' (T)	SDeJ
	'Pink Cascade'	SDeJ
	'Pink Champagne' (R) ♀^{H1b}	WDib
	'Pink Flamingo' (T)	LCro LOPS
	'Pink Gin' (R) **new**	WDib
	'Pink Spirit' (R) **new**	WDib
	'Pink Twist'	WDib
	'Pollux' ♀^{H1b}	WDib
	'Powder Puff' (T)	WFib
	'Président Carnot' (C) ♀^{H1b}	NWad
	'Princess Alice' (T)	WFib
	'Princess of Hanover' (R) ♀^{H1b}	WDib
	putii B&SWJ 7245	WCru
	'Queen Olympus'	WDib
	'Quinebaug'	CPla
	'Raspberry Swirl' (R)	WDib
	ravenii (T)	CDTJ

	'Ray Peters'	WFib
	'Red Admiral' (T)	WFib
	'Red Glory' (T)	LCro LOPS
	'Red Robin' (R) Υ^{H1b}	WDib
	'Red Tempest'	WDib
	'Red Undies' (*grandis*)	see *B. grandis* subsp. *sinensis* 'Red Undies'
	'Regal Minuet' (R) Υ^{H1b}	WDib
	'Renoir' (Impressionist Series)	CRos EHyd LRHS NRHS
	'Richmondensis' (S)	EShb
	'Rocheart' (R) Υ^{H1b}	WDib
	'Rosy Jewel' (R)	WDib
	'Roy Hartley' (T/d)	WFib
	'Ruby Slippers'^{PBR} (R)	ELan
	'Sal's Comet' (R) Υ^{H1b}	WDib
	'Sandra Haynes' (T)	WFib
	'Satin Starburst' (R)	WDib
	'Sceptre' (T)	WFib
	'Sceptre Cross' (T)	WFib
§	***scharffii***	EBak SDix
	'Scherzo'	WDib
	'Sea Urchin'	WDib
	semperflorens hort.	see *B.* Semperflorens Cultorum Group
§	Semperflorens Cultorum Group (S)	SCob
	'Senator White' (Senator Series) new	MBros
	serratipetala Υ^{H1b}	EBak WDib
	'Shamus'	WDib
*	***shepherdii***	WDib
	SHERBET BON BON ('Yabon') Υ^{H1b}	MBros
	sikkimensis	ESwi
	silletensis	WCot
	- subsp. ***mengyangensis***	WCot
	'Silver Cloud' (R) Υ^{H1b}	WDib
	'Silver Jewell' Υ^{H1b}	WDib
	'Silver Lace'	WDib
	'Silver Spirit' (R)	WDib
	'Silver Splendor'	CSpe ECtt ESwi XEll
	sinensis	see *B. grandis* subsp. *sinensis*
	sizemoreae	WDib WPGP
	'Snow Storm'	WDib
I	'Snowcap' (C) Υ^{H1b}	EShb WDib
	solananthera A.DC. Υ^{H1b}	WDib
	'Solid Silver' (R)	WDib
	soli-mutata	WDib
	'Stained Glass'	WDib
	'Star Bright'	WDib
	'Star Light'	WDib
	STARSHINE MIXED	LSou
	'Sugar Candy' (T/d)	WFib
	'Sugar Plum'	MAsh
	(Summerwings Series) SUMMERWINGS DARK ELEGANCE ('Insumdaele'^{PBR})	CSpe SPoG
	- SUMMERWINGS WHITE ('Innbolwhi'^{PBR})	CSpe ESwi
	'Sunset Yellow Champagne'	LCro LOPS
	'Susan' (T)	WFib
	sutherlandii (T) Υ^{H2}	CAvo CCCN CExl EBak EBee EShb ESwi EWld GQue NPer SAdn SDix SGro SIvy WCot WDib WGrn WHer WMal WPGP
	- 'Papaya' (T)	CSpe
	'Sweet Dreams' (T/d)	WFib
	(Sweet Spice Series) SWEET SPICE CITRUS ('Kerbespicit') (T/d)	LSou MPri SCob
	- SWEET SPICE ENGLISH ROSE (T/d)	LSou MPri SCob
	'Switzerland' (T)	SDeJ
	'Tahiti' (T)	WFib
	taliensis EDHCH 042	WCot WCru WFar
	tapatia (T) F&M 337 new	WPGP
	'Tapestry'	NWad
	'Tessa Robinson' (T)	WFib
	'Thurstonii' Υ^{H1b}	EShb
	'Tiger Paws' Υ^{H1b}	EShb
	'Tiny Gem'	WDib
*	***tripartita*** (T)	WDib
	'Truffle Cream'	MBros
	'Two Face'	WDib
	'Tye Dye'	CBct
	'Van Gogh' (Impressionist Series)	CRos EHyd LRHS NRHS
	'Vera Coates' (T)	WFib
	'Vesuvius' (R)	WDib
	'Vibrant Star' (T)	LCro LOPS
	'Wavy Green'	CBct EBee WPGP
	'Whispers' (T)	WFib
	'Wild Swan'	WCru WFar
*	***wynn-jonesiae*** 'Pink Lady'	WCru
	'Ziggy' (T)	WFib

Belamcanda see *Iris*

chinensis	see *Iris domestica*

Bellevalia (*Asparagaceae*)

	atroviolacea	GKev
	'Cream Pearl'	WCot
	desertorum JCA 0.227.690	WCot
	dubia	GKev WCot
	forniculata	WCot
	hyacinthoides	WCot
	longistyla	GKev
§	***paradoxa***	CAby CMea ERCP GBin GKev MNrw SDeJ WCot
	pycnantha misapplied	see *B. paradoxa*
	pycnantha ambig.	SDeJ
	pycnantha (K.Koch) Losinsk. 'Green Pearl'	CAby ERCP GKev SDeJ
	romana	ERCP GKev SDeJ WCot
	sarmatica	GKev
	tabriziana	WCot

Bellis (*Asteraceae*)

§	***caerulescens***	CMiW ECtt GAbr
	perennis	SPhx WWild
	- 'Alice'	ECtt GAbr
	- Bellissima Series	LCro LOPS MBros
	- 'Big Bob' (d)	ECtt WCot
	- 'Dresden China'	WCot
	- HEN AND CHICKENS	see *B. perennis* 'Prolifera' single-flowered
	- 'Miss Mason'	CMiW WCot
	- old strain	WCot
	- 'Prolifera' double-flowered (d)	WCot
§	- 'Prolifera' single-flowered	CFis ECtt
	- 'Single Blue'	see *B. caerulescens*
	- 'The Pearl'	GAbr WCot
	- 'Upper Seagry'	CNat
	rotundifolia 'Caerulescens'	see *B. caerulescens*

Bellium (*Asteraceae*)

	bellidioides	GQue

Belloa (*Asteraceae*)

	chilensis	SPlb

Beloperone see *Justicia*

Bensoniella (*Saxifragaceae*)

	oregona	CExl

Benthamiella (*Solanaceae*)

	patagonica	EPot SPlb WAbe
	- F&W 9345	WAbe
	- white-flowered	WAbe
	- yellow-flowered	WAbe

Berberidopsis (*Berberidopsidaceae*)

	corallina	CBcs CBod CDoC CMac CRHN CRos ELan EPfP IArd IDee IMou LRHS MGil MGos MRav NLar NOra SCob SDix SLim SPer SPoG SWvt WPav WSHC

Berberis (*Berberidaceae*)

	CC 4730	CExl
	CC 7810	CMCN
	aggregata	NBir SRms WKor
	amurensis var. ***latifolia*** B&SWJ 8539	WCru
	aquifolium	see *Mahonia aquifolium*
	- 'Fascicularis'	see *Mahonia* × *wagneri* 'Pinnacle'
	aristata misapplied	see *B. glaucocarpa*
	asiatica	CExl WPGP
	bealei	see *Mahonia bealei*
	buxifolia 'Nana' misapplied	see *B. microphylla* 'Pygmaea'
	calliantha	WFar
	candidula C.K. Schneid.	LRHS MMuc MSwo NLar SEND SPer
	- 'Jytte'	see *B.* 'Jytte'
	× ***carminea*** 'Buccaneer'	WSpi
	- 'Pirate King'	CRos CSBt EBee EHyd EPfP LRHS MAsh SPer SPoG SWvt WAvo
	chilensis	WPav
	darwinii ♀H5	Widely available
I	- 'Compacta'	CBod CDoC CMac CRos CSBt EBee ELan EPfP LBuc LRHS MAsh MGos NLar NRHS SCob SLim SNig SPad SPoG SWvt WCot WFar WPav
	densa B&SWJ 14873 (new)	WCru
	aff. ***densa*** B&SWJ 14880	WCru
	dictyophylla	ELan EPfP LRHS MMuc NLar SPer WSpi
	dulcis 'Nana'	see *B. microphylla* 'Pygmaea'
	empetrifolia	WPav WSpi
	× ***frikartii*** 'Amstelveen' ♀H5	CBod CCVT CDoC ELan EPfP MBNS MMuc MRav SCob SEND
	- 'Telstar'	SCob
	gagnepainii misapplied	see *B. gagnepainii* var. *lanceifolia*
	gagnepainii C.K. Schneid.	CMac
§	- var. ***lanceifolia***	MMuc NLar SEND SGol
	- - 'Fernspray'	EBee EPfP MRav SRms
	- 'Purpurea'	see *B.* × *interposita* 'Wallich's Purple'
	'Georgei' ♀H6	EPfP SPtp
§	***glaucocarpa***	SPtp
	'Goldilocks'	CAby EBee EPfP MBlu SPoG
	goudotii B&SWJ 10769	WCru
	- B&SWJ 14721	WCru
	- B&SWJ 14892	WCru
	hamiltoniana H&M 1919	EBee GKev SPtp
	heterophylla	GKev
	× ***hybridogagnepainii*** 'Chenault'	ELan
	hypokerina	CMac IDee SPtp
	insignis	IDee
	- subsp. ***insignis*** var. ***insignis*** B&SWJ 2432	WCru
§	× ***interposita*** 'Wallich's Purple'	CCVT CRos EPfP LRHS MRav MSwo SGol SPer
	jamesiana	SPtp
	julianae	CArg CBcs CBrac CMac ELan EPfP MGos MMuc MSwo SCob SEND SGol SPer SRms SWvt WFar WSHC WSpi
§	'Jytte'	EBee
	koehneana	SPtp
	koreana	EPfP NLar
	kumaonensis (new)	GLog
	linearifolia 'Orange King'	see *B. trigona* 'Orange King'
	'Little Favourite'	see *B. thunbergii* f. *atropurpurea* 'Atropurpurea Nana'
	× ***lologensis*** 'Apricot Queen' ♀H5	CBcs CMac CRos EPfP MAsh MGos NLar SPer SPoG SWvt
	- 'Mystery Fire'	IArd MAsh MGos NLar SGol SWvt WRHF
	- 'Stapehill'	CBrac CMac CRos EHyd ELan EPfP MAsh SPoG
	malipoensis (new)	GRum
	× ***media*** PARK JEWEL	see *B.* × *media* 'Parkjuweel'
§	- 'Parkjuweel'	CMac IArd MRav SRms
	- 'Red Jewel' ♀H6	CMac CRos EPfP LRHS MAsh MGos MMuc MRav SEND SPoG WCFE WFar
	microphylla	GKev WCFE
	- SDR 7027	GKev
§	- 'Pygmaea'	CBod CRos EBee EHyd EPfP LRHS MGos MMuc MRav SLim SPer WPav
	mitifolia	NLar
	montana	WPGP
	× ***ottawensis*** 'Auricoma'	SGol SWvt
	- f. ***purpurea***	CCVT CMac
§	- - 'Silver Miles' (v)	MRav WFar WLov
§	- - 'Superba'	CBar CBcs CBod CDoC CSBt CTri CTsd EBee ECrN ELan ELon EPfP MGos MMuc MRav MSwo NLar SCob SEND SLim SPer SRms SWvt WFar
§	***panlanensis*** 'Cally Rose'	EBee GBin WPGP
	poiretii	CExl
	polyantha	CTri
	var. ***polyantha***	
	'Red Tears'	MAsh MRav SPer WFar
	× ***rubrostilla*** 'Cherry Ripe'	CMac
	- 'Wisley'	CRos EHyd LRHS
	sibirica (new)	GBin
	sieboldii	LEdu MAsh MRav WCFE WLov WPav WSpi
	× ***stenophylla*** Lindl. ♀H5	CCVT CMac CSBt CTri EPfP GBin LBuc MMuc MRav SGol SPer SRms
	- 'Claret Cascade'	EBee ELan MRav SPer SPoG
	- 'Corallina Compacta' ♀H5	CMac CMea CRos EHyd ELan EPfP EPot GKev LRHS MAsh MHer SPer SPoG SRms
	- 'Cornish Cream'	see *B.* × *stenophylla* 'Lemon Queen'
	- 'Crawley Gem'	GAbr
	- 'Cream Showers'	see *B.* × *stenophylla* 'Lemon Queen'

- 'Etna'	CRos EHyd ELan LRHS MAsh SCoo SPoG
- 'Irwinii'	CMac LRHS SPer
- 'Lemon Queen'	WSpi
- 'Nana'	CRos EHyd LRHS
subacuminata FMWJ 13290	WCru
- NJM 09.165	WPGP
sublevis PAB 8943	LEdu
taliensis	CExl
temolaica ♀H5	CBcs EPfP EWes IDee MGos NLar SPer WAvo WPGP WSpi
thunbergii	CArg CBcs CMac EPfP LBuc SCob SPer SWvt WFar
- 'Anna'PBR **new**	GBin
- f. ***atropurpurea***	CBcs CBod CBrac CCVT CDoC CMac CSBt CTri EBee ECrN ELan EPfP LBuc LCro LOPS MGos MRav MSwo NLar SCob SGol SGsty SPer SPlb SRms WAvo WMou WTSh
- - 'Admiration'PBR ♀H7	CBcs CDoC CRos CSBt ECrN EHyd ELan EPfP LBuc LCro LOPS LRHS LSRN MAsh MGos MMrt MRav NHol NLar NRHS SCob SCoo SGbt SLim SLon SPer SPoG SWvt WFar WLov
§ - - 'Atropurpurea Nana' ♀H7	CBar CBcs CBrac CDoC CMac CRos CSBt CTri EBee EHyd ELon EPfP EShb LRHS MAsh MGos MRav MSwo NHol NLar NRHS SCob SGol SLim SPer SPoG SWvt
- - 'Bagatelle'	CDoC CRos ELan EPfP IArd LRHS LSRN MAsh MGos MRav NLar SCob SLim SPer SWvt WLov
- - 'Concorde' ♀H7	CRos EHyd ELan EPfP LRHS MAsh NRHS SCob
- - 'Dart's Red Lady' ♀H7	CDoC CExl CRos CSBt EHyd ELan EPfP LRHS MAsh NLar NRHS SCob SPer SWvt WAvo WFar
- - 'Golden Ring' (v) ♀H7	CBcs CBod CDoC CMac CRos EHyd ELan EPfP LRHS MAsh MGos MRav NRHS SGbt SPer SPoG SWvt WAvo WFar
- - 'Harlequin' (v) ♀H7	CBrac CChe CDoC CRos EHyd ELan EPfP LCro LOPS LRHS LSRN MAsh MGos NRHS SEle SGol SPer SPoG SRms SWvt WFar
- - 'Helmond Pillar'	CBod CDoC CMac CRos CSBt CTri EBee EHyd ELan ELon EPfP LCro LOPS LRHS LSRN MAsh MGos MRav NHol NLar NRHS SCob SGol SLim SPer SPoG SWvt WCFE WLov
- - 'Maja'PBR **new**	CBod
- - 'Pink Queen' (v)	ELan EPfP LRHS MAsh WFar
- - 'Red Chief'	CBcs CBod CMac CRos ELan EPfP LRHS MAsh MGos MSwo NRHS SGol SLim SLon SPoG SRms SWvt WFar
- - 'Red Pillar'	CChe CDoC CMac ELan EPfP MAsh MGos SGbt SNig SWvt WFar WLov
- - 'Red Rocket'	CRos EBee ELan LRHS NLar NRHS SCob SCoo SPer
- - 'Rose Glow' (v) ♀H7	Widely available
- - 'Rosy Rocket'PBR (v)	CWGN EBee ELan EPfP LRHS MRav NHol NLar SPad SPer SPoG WFar
- 'Atropurpurea Superba'	see *B.* × *ottawensis* f. *purpurea* 'Superba'

- 'Aurea'	CBcs CBrac CDoC CMac CRos EHyd ELan EPfP LRHS LSRN MBlu MGos MRav NLar NRHS SCob SGbt SLim SPlb SRms SWvt
- BONANZA GOLD ('Bogozam'PBR)	CBcs CRos EHyd ELan EPfP LRHS MAsh NLar SLim SPer
- 'Crimson Pygmy'	see *B. thunbergii* f. *atropurpurea* 'Atropurpurea Nana'
- 'Diabolic'	CBod EHyd LRHS MAsh NHol NRHS SPer SPoG
- 'Erecta'	CMac EPfP MRav SPer WCFE
- 'Fireball'PBR ♀H7	CRos EHyd EPfP LRHS MAsh
- FLAMINGO ('Hoho 1'PBR)	NLar SGol
- 'Golden Rocket'PBR	CRos EBee EHyd ELan EPfP LRHS MAsh MGos MRav NLar NRHS SCoo SPer SPoG WFar
- GOLDEN RUBY ('Goruzam') (v)	LCro LOPS
- 'Golden Torch'	CBod CRos CSBt EHyd ELan EPfP LRHS MAsh MRav NHol NRHS SLim SWvt WLov
- 'Green Carpet'	CMac LRHS MBlu NLar SGol SPoG SWvt
- 'Green Mantle'	see *B. thunbergii* 'Kelleriis'
- 'Green Marble'	see *B. thunbergii* 'Kelleriis'
- 'Green Ornament'	NHol
§ - 'Kelleriis' (v)	CRos EHyd LRHS MRav
- 'Kobold'	CMac EHyd EPfP LRHS MGos NLar SPer
- 'Lutin Rouge'PBR	LCro LOPS NLar
- 'Maria'PBR ♀H7	CRos CWGN EHyd ELon EPfP LRHS MGos MRav NLar NRHS SCob SGol SPoG WGrn
- 'Orange Dream'PBR	CDoC EBee
- 'Orange Rocket'PBR	CDoC CRos EBee EHyd ELan EPfP LCro LOPS LRHS MAsh MGos MRav NHol NRHS SCob SCoo SEle SPer SPoG WFar WLov
- 'Orange Sunrise'PBR (v)	CBod LCro LOPS
- 'Pow-wow'	CRos EHyd ELan LRHS MGos NLar NRHS SCoo SGol SLim SPoG SWvt WLov
- 'Redtorch'PBR	CRos EHyd LRHS NRHS
- 'Silver Mile'	see *B.* × *ottawensis* f. *purpurea* 'Silver Miles'
- 'Smaragd'	WFar
- 'Somerset'	CMac
- 'Starburst'PBR (v)	CBod CRos CSBt EBee EHyd EPfP LRHS MGos NEoE NHol NRHS SCoo SLim SLon SRms SWvt
- 'Tiny Gold'PBR	CRos EHyd ELan LCro LOPS LRHS MAsh MGos SLim SLon SWvt WFar
* - 'Tricolor' (v)	CMac MRav WFar
triacanthophora 'Cally Rose'	see *B. panlanensis* 'Cally Rose'
§ ***trigona*** 'Orange King'	CBcs CMac CRos CTri ELan EPfP GBin MAsh MGos NLar SPer SPoG
valdiviana ♀H5	CBcs CExl CJun EPfP GBin IArd IDee IMou SChF SMad WPGP
verruculosa ♀H5	CBcs CBrac CRos LRHS MBlu MGos SPer SRms SWvt WFar
aff. ***verticillata*** B&SWJ 10672	WCru
virescens B&SWJ 2646D	WCru
vulgaris	CAgr CNat GPoy MCoo WKor
- 'Wiltshire Wonder' (v)	CNat
wilsoniae	CBcs CMac CTri ELan ELon EPfP GLog SPer SRms WAvo WFar WSpi
- blue-leaved	WFar

- var. ***guhtzunica***	EWes
aff. ***wilsoniae*** **new**	CBrac
xanthoclada NJM 11.007	WPGP

Berberis × *Mahonia* see × *Mahoberberis*

Berchemia (*Rhamnaceae*)

racemosa	NLar

bergamot see *Citrus* × *limon* Bergamot Group

Bergbambos (*Poaceae*)

§ ***tessellata***	MMuc MWht SEND

Bergenia ✿ (*Saxifragaceae*)

'Abendglocken'	CMac ECha ECtt EPfP MWat NSti WCot WFar
§ 'Abendglut'	Widely available
'Admiral'	CBct CMac ECha WCot
afghanica	XLum
* ***agavifolia***	CBct XLum
'Andrea'	WCot
'Angel Kiss' (Dragonfly Series)	CWCL ECtt ELan GBin LCro LOPS MNrw NLar SCob SWvt WCot
'Apple Blossom'	CRos EHyd EPfP LRHS MAsh NRHS
'Apple Court White'	CBct
'Autumn Magic'	CBct CBod ELon EPfP LRHS NCou WFar
'Baby Doll'	Widely available
'Bach'	CBct CDor CRos EBee ECtt EHyd EPfP GAbr LPla LRHS LSun MBel MCot MMuc NGBl NLar NRHS NSti SCob SGbt SRms SWvt WCAu WCot WFar WWtn
§ 'Ballawley' clonal	CRos ECha EHyd IMou LRHS MRav NRHS WCot XLum
'Ballawley Guardsman'	CBct
§ Ballawley hybrids	CMac SWvt WSpi
'Ballawley' seed-raised	see *B.* Ballawley hybrids
'Bartók'	CBct ECtt ESwi GAbr LLWG NRHS WCAu WCot WPGP
beesiana	see *B. purpurascens*
'Beethoven'	CBct ECha GBin NBir WCAu WCot
BELL TOWER	see *B.* 'Glockenturm'
'Biedermeier' ♀H7	ECha
'Bizet'	CBct XLum
'Borodin'	CBct
'Brahms'	CBct
'Bressingham Bountiful'	CBct
'Bressingham Ruby'	CBct CBod CRos CWCL EBee ECha ECtt ELon EPed EPfP LRHS LSRN MBel MGos MHol MRav NBir NRHS SPer SWvt WCAu WCot WHoo WSpi
'Bressingham Salmon'	CBct EBee ECha ECtt ELon GMaP MRav NLar SRms WCot
'Bressingham White' ♀H6	Widely available
'Britten' ♀H7	CBct CMac GBin IMou
ciliata	CBct CDor CMac ECha EPri EShb GMaP LEdu LRHS MBriF MRav NHol NLar SDix SPer WAvo WFar WPGP WSHC WSpi XLum
- 'Dumbo'	CAbb CBct GBin IBal LEdu NLar WCAu
- f. ***ligulata***	see *B. pacumbis*
- 'Wilton'	CBct EWld LEdu MAvo SHar WCot WSHC
ciliata × ***crassifolia***	see *B.* × *schmidtii*
'Claire Maxine' ♀H7	CBct ECtt EPPr GBin GQue LRHS MPie NLar NWad SHar SPad SRms WCAu WCot WSHC
cordifolia	CBar CMac CRos CSBt CTri EBee EHyd ELan EPfP GKev GMaP LPot LRHS MBel MBros MGos MMuc MSwo NGrd NLar NRHS SCob SEND SPer SPlb SRms SWvt WWtn XLum XSen
- 'Flore Pleno' (d)	CBct
- 'Jelle'	CBct EBee WCAu
- 'Lunar Glow'	EBee ECtt ELan EPfP ESwi SRms WFar
- 'Purpurea'	CBcs CBod CMac CRos CWCL EBee ECha EHyd ELan EPed EPfP GBin GQue LBuc LCro LOPS LRHS NBir NRHS SCob SPer SRms SWvt WFar XLum
- 'Rosa Schwester'	CBct ECha
- 'Rosa Zeiten' ♀H7	CBct GBin IMou
- 'Tubby Andrews' (v)	CBct CMac ECha EShb LEdu LRHS MAvo MBel NEoE NLar SRms WHil WHrl
- 'Vinterglöd'	CBod EBou ELan ELon EPfP GMaP LRHS LSun MBel MGos NLar SRms SWvt XLum
crassifolia	EPfP SRms XLum
- DF 90028	CBct GBin
- 'Autumn Red'	CBct ECha
- 'Orbicularis'	see *B.* × *schmidtii*
I - var. ***pacifica***	XLum
'Croesus'	GBin
* ***cyanea***	WCot
'Dark Damsel'	CBct IBal
'David'	CBct EBee ECha
'Delbees'	see *B.* 'Ballawley' clonal
'Diamond Drops'	IBal
'Eden's Dark Margin'	CBct CBod ECtt ELan ELon EPed GBin MHol MNrw NLar WCot
'Eden's Magic Giant' ♀H7	CBct ECtt ELan ELon EShb GBin GQue LRHS MPie NLar SDix SRms WCot WFar XSen
emeiensis	CBct CDor IMou LEdu WCot WPGP WSHC
- hybrid	MWat
'Eric Smith' ♀H7	ECha SWvt WCAu
'Eroica' ♀H7	Widely available
'Evening Glow'	see *B.* 'Abendglut'
§ 'Glockenturm'	CBct
'Godfrey Owen'	EBee
'Harzkristall'	CBct CBod CDor CMac CMea CPla CRos EHyd ELan EPfP GBin GWyn LRHS NCou NRHS SCob SHar SPoG STPC SWvt WSpi
'Hellen Dillon'	see *B. purpurascens* 'Irish Crimson'
'Herbstblute'	EPfP GBin WCAu
'Ice Queen'	EBee ELan EWTr GBin LCro LOPS LPla MBel NLar SWvt WCAu WCot
'Jo Watanabe'	CBct ECha MRav
'Kashmir'	XLum
'Lambrook'	see *B.* 'Margery Fish'
'Little Pine'	WCot
§ 'Margery Fish'	CBct CFis ECha
milesii	see *B. stracheyi*
§ 'Morgenröte' ♀H6	CBcs CBct CBod CMac CRos ECha ELon EPfP GMaP LRHS LSRN MRav NHol NLar NSti SAko SPer SRms SWvt WCAu WCFE WCot XSen
MORNING RED	see *B.* 'Morgenröte'
'Mrs Crawford'	ECha
'Oeschberg'	CBct GBin

'Opal' CBct EBee GBin
'Overture' Widely available
§ ***pacumbis*** EBee EWld NBid NSti
- B&SWJ 2693 WCru
- CC 1793 SGro WCot
- CC 3616 CBct WSHC
'Pink Dragonfly' CBct CMac CRos ECtt EHyd ELon EPfP LPla LRHS MAsh NLar NRHS SCob SWvt WCAu WCot WFar
'Pink Ice' CBct CDor EBee WSHC
'Pinneberg' CBct EBee
'Pugsley's Pink' 🏆H7 CBct ECha MAvo
§ ***purpurascens*** 🏆H5 CBod CMac EBee EPfP GMaP LPot SPer WSpi
- SDR 4548 GKev
- var. ***delavayi*** 🏆H5 EHyd LRHS NLar NRHS SRms
§ - 'Irish Crimson' 🏆H7 CBct ECha GBin WCot
aff. ***purpurascens*** NGdn
'Purpurglocken' ECtt WCAu
'Red Beauty' CPla EPfP
'Red Rush' EBee
'Rietheim' CBct EBee GBin
'Rosenkristall' CRos EHyd EPfP LRHS NRHS
'Rosi Klose' CBct CDor CRos EBee ECha ECtt EHyd ELon EPfP EWes GBin LRHS MAsh MHol NGdn NRHS WCot WFar WHoo
'Rosi Ruffles' EBee
'Rotblum' CBct ELon EPfP GMaP LBuc NBir NGdn NGrd NRHS SRkn SRms
'Sakura' (Dragonfly Series) CWCL EBee GBin MNrw NHar SCob
§ × ***schmidtii*** CBct CMac MRav NBir NLar
'Schneekissen' CBct CMac ECtt EHyd EPri LRHS MCot WCAu WGwG
§ 'Schneekoenigin' CBct ECha SWvt WCot
§ 'Silberlicht' 🏆H6 Widely available
SILVERLIGHT see *B.* 'Silberlicht'
'Simply Sweet' WCot
SNOW QUEEN see *B.* 'Schneekoenigin'
'Spring Fling'PBR (Dragonfly Series) CRos GBin
§ ***stracheyi*** CExl ECha GBin GKev NBid NLar WCot
- Alba Group ECha
'Sunningdale' 🏆H7 CBcs CBct CMac ECha EHyd ELan EPfP GMaP LRHS MRav NBir NGdn NRHS SWvt WCAu
'Walter Kienli' GBin
WINTER FAIRY TALES see *B.* 'Wintermärchen'
§ 'Wintermärchen' 🏆H7 CBct CChe CRos ECha ELan ELon EPfP EShb GWyn LRHS MCot MMuc MRav NHol NRHS SEND SPoG SRms SWvt WCot
'XXL' LSun WCot

Bergenia × *Mukdenia* see × *Mukgenia*

Bergera (*Rutaceae*)

§ ***koenigii*** EOHP GPoy SCit SPre WJek WSFF

Bergeranthus (*Aizoaceae*)

vespertinus XLum

Berkheya (*Asteraceae*)

cirsiifolia EBee SPhx
macrocephala SPlb
multijuga EHyd LRHS
purpurea CAby CBcs CBod CDor CRos CSpe ECha EHyd ELon EPfP LRHS MHol MNrw NRHS SPlb SRms WCot WKif WSHC
- 'Silver Spike' EPfP MSCN NGdn
- 'Zulu Warrior' CMac
radula EBee

Berlandiera (*Asteraceae*)

lyrata CBod EHyd GEdr LRHS

Berula (*Apiaceae*)

erecta NPer

Berzelia (*Bruniaceae*)

galpinii SPlb
intermedia LRHS

Beschorneria (*Asparagaceae*)

albiflora WCot
calcicola CBod SEdd WCot
'Red Bells' WCot
rigida WCot
septentrionalis CAby CBod CCht CDTJ EBee ESwi GBin LRHS MBNS MHol NGBl SEdd SPad SPeP WCot WGrn
- variegated (v) WCot
tubiflora CDTJ WSMil
wrightii WCot
yuccoides 🏆H3 CAbb CBcs CExl CPla SEND SPlb
- 'Quicksilver' CBcs CCCN CEnd CExl ELan EPfP LRHS MHtn SPoG WGrn WPav

Bessera (*Asparagaceae*)

elegans CGrW EPot GKev SDeJ SDir WCot WHil

Besseya (*Plantaginaceae*)

wyomingensis EBee GKev

Beta (*Amaranthaceae*)

vulgaris WHer
- 'Barbietola di Chioggia' see *B. vulgaris* 'Chioggia'
- subsp. ***maritima*** CAgr

Betonica see *Stachys*

Betula ✿ (*Betulaceae*)

alba see *B. pendula*, *B. pubescens*
albosinensis misapplied see *B. utilis*
albosinensis Burkill CBrP CLnd CMCN MMuc SEND
- 'Bowling Green' CExl CJun EBee MBlu WPGP
§ - 'China Rose' 🏆H7 CBcs CJun EBee EPfP WMat WPGP
- 'China Ruby' K.Ashburner see *B. albosinensis* 'China Rose'
- 'China Ruby' ambig. CJun CLnd EPfP
- 'Chinese Garden' CJun EBee MBlu WPGP
- 'Chris Lane' CJun WPGP
- 'Chris Sanders' **new** WPGP
- clone F see *B. albosinensis* 'Ness'
- 'Joseph Rock' CJun
- 'K.Ashburner' CJun CTho
§ - 'Ness' CJun
- 'Pink Champagne' CBcs CJun EPfP LEdu MBlu WPGP
- 'Red Panda' 🏆H7 CJun EBee LRHS WHwl WMat WPGP
- 'Rhinegold' MBlu
- 'Sable' SLim
- var. ***septentrionalis*** CCVT CEnd CLnd CMac CTho EBee ECrN ELan ELon EPfP GBin MBlu MGos MMuc MRav MSwo

	NOrn SCob SGol SLim SPer WHwl WMou WPGP WSpi
- - PDM 752	WPGP
- - 'Kansu'	CJun EBee MBlu NLar NOra WMat
- - 'Purdom'	CJun CLnd
§ ***alleghaniensis***	CBcs CMCN EPfP GKev MMuc NLar SEND WCru
bomiensis	GKev
chichibuensis	CJun GKev MMrt SPtp
chinensis	CMCN GKev
'Cobhay Cream Spire' **new**	CJun
'Cobhay Snow Spire' **new**	CJun
'Conyngham'	CJun MBlu SLau
costata misapplied	see *B. ermanii* 'Grayswood Hill'
costata ambig.	CMCN LMaj SGol
costata Trautv.	MSwo
- 'Daleside'	EBee NDal NOra WMat
- 'Fincham Cream'	see *B. ermanii* 'Fincham Cream'
'Crimson Frost'	EBee GBin
cylindrostachya	WPGP
dahurica Pall.	CBrP
- 'Maurice Foster'	CJun EBee MBlu WPGP
- 'Stone Farm'	CJun
delavayi	GKev
ermanii	CBcs CCVT CMCN CMac ECrN ELan GBin LMaj MBlu MGos MMuc MRav NOrn SGol
- B&SWJ 8801 from South Korea	WCru
- B&SWJ 10852 from Aomori, Japan	WCru
- B&SWJ 12600 from South Korea	WCru
- 'Blush'	CJun EPfP MBlu SCoo WMou
§ - 'Fincham Cream'	CJun
§ - 'Grayswood Hill' ♀H7	CEnd CJun CLnd CMCN CSBt CTho EBee EPfP GBin LRHS MBlu SCob SCoo SWvt WHwl WPGP
- 'Hakkoda Orange'	CJun CTho EBee SCoo WPGP
- 'Holland'	IArd LMaj
- 'Kwanak Weeping'	CJun EBee MBlu
- 'Mount Zao'	CJun EBee WPGP
- 'Polar Bear'	CJun CLnd EBee EPfP MAsh MBlu NLar NOrn SCoo WMat
'Fascination' ♀H6	CBcs CCVT CJun CLnd CMCN CMac EBar EBee EPfP IArd LMaj MBlu MGos NOra NOrn SCoo SLim SPer SSta WHCr WHwl WMat WMou WSpi
'Fetisowii'	CJun EBee MBlu NOra WMat
globispica	CJun
gmelinii	see *B. ovalifolia*
grossa	IDee
'Hergest' ♀H6	CJun EBee ECrN EPfP MGos NOra WHCr WHwl WMat
insignis	CJun EBee WPGP
- subsp. ***fansipanensis***	IArd IDee SAko
- - B&SWJ 11751	WCru
- - FMWJ 13149	WCru
jacquemontii	see *B. utilis* var. *jacquemontii*
lenta	CMCN IArd IDee MBlu MMuc
luminifera	EBee IArd WPGP
lutea	see *B. alleghaniensis*
maximowicziana	CMCN MBlu NLar SGol WSpi
medwediewii	CJun CMCN EBee EPfP GKev NLar WPGP
- 'Gold Bark' ♀H7	CJun CMCN EPfP MBlu
megrelica	GKev
michauxii	EBee NLar WCru
'Mount Apoi'	CJun MAsh

nana 'Glengarry'	EPot GEdr
nigra	CBcs CCVT CEnd CLnd CMCN EBee ELan LMaj MMuc NLar SCob SEWo SGol SGsty WMou WTSh
- 'Black Star'	EBee MAsh NOra WMat
§ - 'Cully'	CMCN EBee ECrN LMaj LRHS MBlu NOra NOrn SGol WHCr
- HERITAGE	see *B. nigra* 'Cully'
- 'Little King'	CMCN
- 'Peter Collinson'	CJun
- 'Shiloh Splash'	SSta
- 'Summer Cascade' PBR	EBee LSRN MAsh NOra NOrn SLon WHwl WMat
- TECUMSEH COMPACT ('Studetec')	SGol
- Wakehurst form	EPfP SPer SPoG WPGP WSpi
§ ***ovalifolia*** MF 357	GKev
papyrifera	CBcs CCVT CLnd CMCN CMac CTri EBee ECrN ELan EPfP LBuc MGos MMuc MSwo NOra SEND SGol SPer WMat WTSh
- 'Belle Vue'	EBee
- var. ***cordifolia*** 'Clarenville'	CJun
- 'Saint George'	CJun CTho EBee WHCr WMat
§ ***pendula***	Widely available
- 'Black Prince'	WHCr
- f. ***crispa***	see *B. pendula* 'Laciniata'
- 'Dalecarlica' misapplied	see *B. pendula* 'Laciniata'
- 'Dalecarlica' ambig.	ECrN LRHS MRav NOra SWvt WFar WHCr WMat WTSh
- 'Dark Prince'	NOrn
- 'Fastigiata'	CCVT CJun CLnd CSBt CTho EBee ECrN ELan LRHS MAsh MGos NOrn SCoo SGol SPer WHwl
- FASTIGIATA JOES ('Jolep 1')	EBee ELan MAsh NOra NOrn SPer SPoG
- 'Golden Beauty'	CMac MAsh MGos NOra NOrn SGol SLim WMat
§ - 'Laciniata' ♀H7	CBcs CMCN CMac EBee ELan LMaj MAsh MBlu MGos MSwo NOrn SCob SCoo SGol SPer WCFE WMou WTSh
- 'Long Trunk'	CBrac EBee MBlu NOrn SGol SLim
- 'Obelisk'	LMaj
- 'Purpurea'	CCVT CMCN CMac CSBt ECrN ELan GKin IDee LSRN MGos MSwo NOrn SCoo SGol SPer WFar WTSh
- 'Silver Grace'	CJun LSRN MBlu
§ - 'Spider Alley' PBR	EBee GBin LRHS SLon WHwl WMat
- 'Swiss Glory'	LMaj
- 'Tristis' ♀H7	CBcs CCVT CEnd CLnd CMCN CMac CTho CTri EBee ECrN EPfP LMaj LRHS LSRN MGos MRav MSwo NOra NOrn SCob SGol SLim SPer WFar WMat
- 'Youngii'	Widely available
- 'Zwitsers Glorie'	CJun WHwl
platyphylla misapplied	see *B. platyphylla* subsp. *mandshurica*
platyphylla Sukaczev DAKOTA PINNACLE ('Fargo')	NOra SCoo WMat
§ - subsp. ***mandshurica***	MMuc
populifolia	EBtc
potaninii	GKev
§ ***pubescens***	CCVT CHab CTho CTri EBee LMaj MMuc SCob SEND WTSh
- 'Armenian Gold'	CLnd

	× ***purpusii*** new	GKev
	raddeana	EBtc GKev
	'Royal Frost'	CBcs EBee GQue LMaj LSRN MBlu NLar SGol WHwl WMat
	'Silver Trestles'	see *B. pendula* 'Spider Alley'
	szechuanica 'Liuba White'	CJun MBlu
§	***utilis***	CMCN ECrN LMaj SSta
	- GWJ 9259	WCru
	- HWJK 2250	WCru
	- HWJK 2345	WCru
	- Sch 2168	EBee
	- 'Bhutan Sienna'	CJun EBee WPGP
	- 'Buddha'	CJun EBee MBlu WPGP
	- 'China Bronze'	WPGP
	- 'Cobhay Amber'	CJun
	- 'Cobhay Sentinel'	CJun
	- 'Dark-Ness'	CJun MBlu NOra SLon WHCr WMat WPGP
*	- 'Fastigiata'	CJun CLnd NOrn SSta
	- 'Forest Blush' 🏆H7	CJun EBee EPfP WPGP
	- 'Himalayan Pink'	CJun WSpi
§	- var. ***jacquemontii***	Widely available
	- - Polunin	WPGP
§	- - 'Doorenbos' 🏆H7	Widely available
	- - 'Grayswood Ghost' 🏆H7	CBcs CEnd CJun CLnd CMCN CTho CTri EBee EPfP LCro LOPS LRHS MBlu NLar NOra NOrn SCob SLau SLim SPer SSta WHwl WMat WPGP WSpi
§	- - 'Inverleith'	CJun SCoo WPGP
	- - 'Jermyns' 🏆H7	CBcs CEnd CJun CLnd EBee EPfP LRHS LSRN MBlu NOra NOrn SCob SCoo SLim SPer SSta SWvt WHCr WMat WPGP
	- - 'Moonbeam'	CJun CLnd CSBt EBee EHyd MAsh SCoo SEWo SLim SPoG SWeb WHCr WMat
	- - 'Silver Shadow' 🏆H7	CEnd CJun CLnd CMCN CTho EBee EPfP LRHS LSRN MAsh MBlu NLar NOra NOrn NRHS SCob SCoo SGbt SLau SLim SPer SPoG SSta WHCr WMat WSpi
	- - 'Snow Leopard'	CJun WPGP
	- - 'Snow Queen'	see *B. utilis* var. *jacquemontii* 'Doorenbos'
	- - 'Trinity College'	CJun EBee LRHS MAsh MSwo SCoo WHwl WLov WMat WPGP
	- 'Jim Russell'	WPGP
	- 'Knightshayes'	CJun CTho EBee WPGP
	- 'Mount Luoji'	CJun EBee WPGP
	- 'Nepalese Orange'	CJun EBee EPfP WPGP
	- var. ***occidentalis*** new	WPGP
	- - 'Kyelang'	CJun
	- 'Park Wood' 🏆H7	CJun CTho EPfP WPGP
	- 'Polar Bear'	MBlu
	- var. ***prattii***	CJun CTho MBlu
	- 'Ramdana River'	CJun MBlu WPGP
	- 'Schilling'	CJun
	- 'Sichuan Red'	CJun
	- 'Silver Queen'	WSpi
	- subsp. ***utilis*** 'Edinburgh'	CJun CLnd LRHS MBlu WMat
	- 'Wakehurst Place Chocolate' 🏆H7	CJun CSBt EBee GBin MBlu NLar SCoo SGbt SLim WSpi
	- 'White-Ness'	MBlu
	cf. ***utilis***	CTri SGol
	verrucosa	see *B. pendula*

Biarum ✿ (*Araceae*)

S&L 604	WCot
SB&L 597	WCot
carratracense from Spain	WCot
davisii	WCot
dispar SB&L 294	WCot
ditschianum from Turkey	WCot
marmarisense	EPot WCot
rhopalospadix	GKev
tenuifolium	WCot
- LB 295	WCot
- PB 357	WCot
- S&L 174	WCot
- subsp. ***abbreviatum***	SBrt
- - MS 974	WCot
- subsp. ***arundanum***	WCot
- subsp. ***galianii*** PB 435	WCot
- subsp. ***zelebori***	WCot
- - CRL 502	WCot
- - LB 300	WCot
- - PB 224	WCot
- - PB 334	WCot

Bidens (*Asteraceae*)

	atrosanguinea	see *Cosmos atrosanguineus*
§	***aurea***	CCBP CFis EAJP ECtt EMor EPPr EWes LEdu MHol MSpe NPer SIvy WBor WFar WMal WPGP XLum
	- cream-flowered	CWld MNrw SPeP WMal
	- 'Hannay's Lemon Drop'	CFis CKno EAJP ECtt ELan ELon EMor EPPr EPfP ILea LEdu LPot MAsh MNrw MSpe SDix SGbt SPeP SPoG SPtp SRms WBor WFar WMal WPGP
	- 'Mellow Yellow'	WCot
	- 'Rising Sun'	ECtt EWes
	- 'Super Nova'	EPPr
	- white-flowered	EBee ELon EMor EPPr GPSL NSti WFar
	'Compact Bicolour Star' (Hawaiian Flare Series) new	LSou
	ferulifolia	NPer
	- 'Bee Alive' (Bee Series)	MBros WHil
	- BEEDANCE PAINTED RED ('Sunbidevb 2'PBR)	SPoG
	- BEEDANCE PAINTED YELLOW ('Sunbidevb4'PBR)	SPoG
	- 'Golden Eye'	ECtt MBros SPoG
	- 'Golden Glory'	MPri
	- SUN DROP ('Danbid7346')	LSou
	'Firelight'	WHil
	'Giant Yellow Red Tip' (Hawaiian Flare Series) new	LSou
	heterophylla Ortega	see *B. aurea*
	heterophylla misapplied	ECtt MAsh MCot MHol MMuc MRav MWat SBut WFar WHal XLum
	'Pirate's Treasure'	ECtt
	'Rockstar'	CPla
	'Yellow Red Star' (Hawaiian Flare Series) new	LSou

Bignonia (*Bignoniaceae*)

capreolata	CCCN CRHN ECre WSHC XSen
lindleyana	see *Clytostoma calystegioides*
tweedieana	see *Dolichandra unguis-cati*
unguis-cati	see *Dolichandra unguis-cati*

Bijlia (*Aizoaceae*)

tugwelliae new	SSim

Bilderdykia see *Fallopia*

Billardiera (*Pittosporaceae*)

cymosa	CTsd
longiflora ♀H3	CBcs CRos CSBt CTri EBee EHyd ELan EPfP GKev IArd LRHS MAsh MGil MGos MMuc MRav NOra SCob SLim SNig SPer SPoG SWvt
- 'Cherry Berry'	CBcs CRos EHyd ELan EPfP LRHS NOra SMad SNig SPer SPoG SRms SWvt
- 'Fructu-albo'	CBcs CRos EHyd ELan EPfP EWes GKev LRHS NLar NOra SLon SPer SPoG SWvt

Billbergia ✿ (*Bromeliaceae*)

nutans	CCCN EBak EShb LEdu NGBl SChr SEND SPlb WSFF
- var. ***schimperiana***	EShb
* - 'Variegata' (v)	CCCN CPla EShb NCft SChr WCot
pyramidalis	XBlo
'Santa Barbara' (v)	SChr
× ***windii*** ♀H1b	EBak NCft

Biophytum (*Oxalidaceae*)

sensitivum new	CDoC

Bismarckia (*Arecaceae*)

nobilis	CCCN SPalm

Bistorta see *Persicaria*

Bituminaria (*Papilionaceae*)

bituminosa	WCot

blackberry see *Rubus fruticosus*; also AGM Fruit Section

blackcurrant see *Ribes nigrum*; also AGM Fruit Section

Blechnum ✿ (*Blechnaceae*)

alpinum	see *B. penna-marina* subsp. *alpinum*
brasiliense ♀H1a	EShb ESwi ISha SPlb
- 'Volcano'	CBcs CBdn CMiW CTsd IBal LBuc LCro LLWG LOPS LRHS SIvy SPad SPalm SPoG WPGP
§ ***chilense*** ♀H4	CBcs CBdn CDTJ CLAP CTsd EBee EHyd EPfP EShb EWes GAbr GBin IBal IBlr LEdu LRHS NBro NRHS SArc SDix SMad SPlb SRms WCru WSMil
discolor	CTsd
- 'Silver Lady'	CDoC
fluviatile	CDTJ CTsd
gibbum	CDoC EShb SPlb
- 'Silver Lady'	EShb
magellanicum misapplied	see *B. chilense*
magellanicum (Desv.) Mett.	CTsd SPlb
minus	CBdn
§ ***niponicum***	GEdr
novae-zelandiae	CTrC CTsd
nudum	CBdn CDTJ
penna-marina	Widely available
§ - subsp. ***alpinum***	EBee ECha EPfP GEdr GKev NWad SBrt
- - BR 68	GEdr
- 'Cristatum'	CLAP GAbr GEdr GWyn NBro NWad
spicant ♀H6	Widely available
- ***incisum***	see *B. spicant* 'Rickard's Serrate'
§ - 'Rickard's Serrate'	CLAP
- Serratum Group	WAbe
tabulare misapplied	see *B. chilense*
tabulare (Thunb.) Kuhn	CBcs CBdn CDTJ CTsd WCot
wattsii	EBee

Blepharocalyx (*Myrtaceae*)

§ ***cruckshanksii***	CCCN CExl CSde ELon IDee LRHS MGil SEND SVen WLov WPGP
- 'Heaven Scent'	see *B. cruckshanksii*

Blephilia (*Lamiaceae*)

ciliata	SPhx

Bletilla (*Orchidaceae*)

sp.	NDav
hyacinthina	see *B. striata*
ochracea	CExl GKev SDir
sinensis	CExl
§ ***striata*** ♀H4	CAby CBct CDoC CExl CTri CTsd EBee EPot GAbr GKev LCro LEdu LOPS LRHS MBel MHer MNrw MSCN NBPC NRHS SDeJ SDir SIvy SPer SPlb WCot WFar WPGP WSMil XLum
- ***alba***	see *B. striata* f. *gebina*
- 'Albostriata'	CBct CExl ELan MAvo WCot XLum
- BLUE DRAGON	see *B. striata* 'Soryu'
§ - f. ***gebina***	CBod CExl CTri EBee ELan GKev LCro LEdu LOPS LRHS MBel NRHS SDeJ SDir SPeP SPer WCot WPGP
- - variegated (v)	EBee GKev LEdu
- 'Kuchi-beni'	EBee GKev SEdd
- 'Lips'	GKev SDir
- purple-flowered	GKev
- 'Shi-ran'	EBee MSCN SEdd
§ - 'Soryu'	CBor GKev LLWG MHol MSCN SDir SEdd SPeP
- variegated (v)	GKev
- yellow-flowered	GKev
Yokohama gx 'Sweet Lips' new	GKev

blueberry see *Vaccinium corymbosum*; also AGM Fruit Section

Blumea (*Asteraceae*)

balsamifera	CHab

Bocconia (*Papaveraceae*)

cordata	see *Macleaya cordata* (Willd.) R. Br.
frutescens B&SWJ 10654	WCru
microcarpa	see *Macleaya microcarpa*

Boehmeria (*Urticaceae*)

nivea	WCot
platanifolia	IMou MNrw
sieboldiana	EBee EPPr SBrt WFar
tricuspis	IMou SBrt SMad

Boenninghausenia (*Rutaceae*)

albiflora B&SWJ 1479	WCru
- from China	ITim
- pink-flowered B&SWJ 3112	WCru

Bolax (Apiaceae)

glebaria	see *B. gummifer*
§ ***gummifer***	EPot GEdr GKev WAbe WFar

Boltonia (Asteraceae)

asteroides	CCBP GQue MMuc NGrd NWsh SPer XLum
- var. ***latisquama***	CMea GMaP MHol MRav NLar SHar WBor WHal
- - JIM CROCKETT ('Masbolimket'PBR)	EBee LRHS
- - 'Nana'	LPla NChi
- - 'Snowbank'	CAby ELan WCAu WGoo
decurrens	CBod EBee EPPr IMou WBor
incisa	see *Kalimeris incisa*

Bomarea (Alstroemeriaceae)

acuminata	see *B. andreana*
acutifolia	EBee WCot
- B&SWJ 14291	WCru
- F&M 104	WPGP
§ ***andreana*** B&SWJ 14310	WCru
- B&SWJ 14376	WCru
aff. ***andreana*** B&SWJ 10617	WCru
boliviensis misapplied	see *Alstroemeria isabellana*
boliviensis Baker	WCot
aff. ***bredemeyerana*** B&SWJ 14706	WCru
- B&SWJ 14725 new	WCru
caldasii	see *B. multiflora*
costaricensis	EBee
- B&SWJ 10467	WCru
distichifolia	CExl WCru
§ ***edulis*** ♀H3	CAvo CRHN EWld MGil SBrt WAvo WCot WPav
- B&SWJ 9017	WCru
- F&M 104	CExl
'Fiesta'	WCot
frondea	see *B. multiflora*
hirsuta B&SWJ 14442	WCru
- B&SWJ 14902	WCru
hirtella	see *B. edulis*
§ ***multiflora*** ♀H2	CBcs CCCN CExl CTsd EBee WCru WSHC
- B&SWJ 14347	WCru
- B&SWJ 14354	WCru
- B&SWJ 14406	WCru
- B&SWJ 14419	WCru
- B&SWJ 14847	WCru
aff. ***multiflora*** B&SWJ 14730	WCru
- B&SWJ 14946 new	WCru
ovallei	CCCN
patacocensis JCA 13987	WCot
patinii B&SWJ 14213 new	WCru
- B&SWJ 14310	WCru
- B&SWJ 14895	WCru
puracensis B&SWJ 14705	WCru
- B&SWJ 14729 new	WCru
salsilla ♀H3	CAvo CCCN CPla SBrt
setacea B&SWJ 10681 new	WCru
- B&SWJ 14875	WCru

Bombax (Malvaceae)

ceiba	SPlb

Bongardia (Berberidaceae)

chrysogonum	CAvo EHyd GKev LRHS NRHS

Bonia (Poaceae)

§ ***solida***	CBdn MMuc MWht SEND XCre

Boquila (Lardizabalaceae)

trifoliolata	WCru

borage see *Borago officinalis*

Borago (Boraginaceae)

laxiflora	see *B. pygmaea*
officinalis	CCBP CHby CLau ENfk EPfP GPoy LCro LOPS MBow MHer MNHC MPri NBir SEdi SRms SVic XAbr
- 'Alba'	CBre CLau ENfk LCro LOPS MBow SEdi SRms WJek
- 'Bill Archer' (v)	CNat
§ ***pygmaea***	CExl CSpe ELan EWld MHer MNrw NBir NChi NSti SPhx SRms WHer WJek XAbr

borecole see AGM Vegetables Section

Borinda (Poaceae)

KR 5287	MWht
KR 5600	MWht
KR 6438	MWht
KR 6439	MWht
KR 7346	MWht
KR 7613	MWht
KR 7662	MWht
albocerea ♀H4	EPfP MWht
- Yunnan 2	CDTJ
- Yunnan 3a	CDTJ
- Yunnan 4	see *B. lushuiensis* Yunnan 4
angustissima	CDTJ CExl EPfP MMuc MWht XCre
boliana	SSut
frigida	CDTJ
- KR 4059	MWht
fungosa	XCre
grossa	CDTJ
- KR 5931	MWht
§ ***lushuiensis*** Yunnan 4	CDTJ MWht
macclureana KR 5051	MWht
- KR 5177 from Gyala, Nepal	ESwi MWht
- KR 6236	ESwi
- KR 6400 from Show La	ESwi
- KR 6438 from Pasm Tso	ESwi
aff. ***macclureana*** KR 6900	MWht
nujiangensis	CDTJ WPGP
papyrifera	WPGP XCre
- CS 1046	CBdn CJun MWht
perlonga Yunnan 6	MWht
scabrida	see *Fargesia scabrida*
Yunnan 4	see *B. lushuiensis* Yunnan 4

Boronia (Rutaceae)

anemonifolia 'Pink Star' new	LCro LOPS
crenulata	CBcs CCCN
heterophylla	CAbb CBcs CBod CCCN CSde CTsd ECre EPfP LRHS MPkF SEle WCot
- 'Ice Charlotte'	CCCN SEle

Bossiaea (Papilionaceae)

riparia	SPlb
scolopendria	SPlb

Bothriochloa (Poaceae)

§ ***bladhii***	CKno EBee EPPr SRms

caucasica see *B. bladhii*
§ ***ischaemum*** EPPr

Bougainvillea (*Nyctaginaceae*)

'Alexandra' CCCN SPre SWeb
'Brilliant' misapplied see *B.* × *buttiana* 'Raspberry Ice'
§ × ***buttiana*** 'Raspberry Ice' (v) EShb
glabra ♀H2 EShb SPre
§ - 'Sanderiana' SWeb
'Sanderiana' see *B. glabra* 'Sanderiana'
'Sentimento' CCCN
'Tropical Rainbow' see *B.* × *buttiana* 'Raspberry Ice'
Vera Series CCCN

Boussingaultia (*Basellaceae*)

baselloides Hook. see *Anredera cordifolia*

Bouteloua (*Poaceae*)

curtipendula CBod
§ ***gracilis*** CBod EHyd LRHS MBel SMad

Bouvardia (*Rubiaceae*)

× ***domestica*** EShb
ternifolia CWGN EBee ESwi WCot

Bowiea (*Asparagaceae*)

volubilis GKev SPlb

Bowkeria (*Stilbaceae*)

sp. CCCN
cymosa SPlb SVen
verticillata CBcs

Boykinia (*Saxifragaceae*)

aconitifolia CElw CMac GEdr GKev GLog IMou NRya SMad WCru
elata see *B. occidentalis*
heucheriformis see *B. jamesii*
§ ***jamesii*** GKev
lycoctonifolia NLar
§ ***occidentalis*** MBriF WCru XLum
rotundifolia EPPr NBir WCru
tellimoides see *Peltoboykinia tellimoides*

boysenberry see *Rubus* 'Boysenberry'

Brachychilum see *Hedychium*

Brachychiton (*Malvaceae*)

acerifolius SPlb
populneus CBcs SPlb
§ ***rupestris*** EShb

Brachyglottis (*Asteraceae*)

§ ***bidwillii*** WCot WPGP
- 'Basil Fox' WAbe
§ ***compacta*** CRos EHyd ELan EPfP LRHS MAsh SPer
(Dunedin Group) 'Drysdale' CRos EHyd ELan EPfP ILea LRHS NRHS SLon SWvt
§ - 'Moira Reid' (v) CExl
§ - 'Sunshine' ♀H4 CAgr CBar CBod CRos CSBt CTri EBee EHyd ELan EPfP LCro LOPS LRHS MGos MMuc MRav MSwo NPer NRHS SCob SEND SLim SPer SPlb SRms SWvt WAvo
'Frosty' CBod
greyi misapplied see *B.* (Dunedin Group) 'Sunshine'
§ ***greyi*** (Hook. f.) B. Nord. CMac SGol
huntii SVen
huntii × ***stewartii*** SEND
laxifolia misapplied see *B.* (Dunedin Group) 'Sunshine'
'Menthe Glaciale' **new** ILea
§ ***monroi*** CBcs CMac CRos CSBt EHyd ELan EPfP LRHS MAsh MRav SGol SLon SVen WFar
repanda 'Purpurea' CBcs
§ ***rotundifolia*** CCCN EBee ELan
'Silver Waves' CBod
I 'Sunshine Improved' CBcs CBrac MAsh SGbt
'Sunshine Variegated' see *B.* (Dunedin Group) 'Moira Reid'
WALBERTON'S SILVER DORMOUSE ('Walbrach'[PBR]) ♀H4 CBcs CBod CCht CRos CSBt EBee EHyd ELan EPfP GBin LRHS MGos MRav NCou NRHS SCob SPoG SWvt WNPC

Brachypodium (*Poaceae*)

pinnatum EPPr
sylvaticum CHab MMuc SEND

Brachyscome (*Asteraceae*)

'Magenta Delight' LSou
rigidula CPBP
'Royal Blue' MPri
SURDAISY STRAWBERRY PINK ('Bonbrapi'[PBR]) WHil

Brachystachyum (*Poaceae*)

densiflorum XCre

Bracteantha see *Xerochrysum*

Brahea (*Arecaceae*)

armata ♀H1c CBrP CDTJ CPHo SPalm SPlb WCot WSMil
dulcis SPalm
edulis CCCN CPHo SChr SPalm WSMil
'Super Silver' CPHo WCot

Brassaia see *Schefflera*

Brassica (*Brassicaceae*)

japonica see *B. juncea* var. *crispifolia*
juncea SVic
§ - var. ***crispifolia*** MNHC
- f. ***juncea*** **new** MBros
oleracea CAgr CLau SVic WHer
- var. ***ramosa*** LEdu NGrd
- - 'Cotswold Cream' (v) WCot
- - 'D'Aubenton Panaché' (v) WCot
rapa SVic
* - var. ***japonica*** MNHC
- subsp. ***nipposinica*** var. ***laciniata*** LCro LOPS MBros SVic

× *Brigandra* (*Gesneriaceae*)

calliantha WAbe

Briggsia × *Opithandra* see × *Brigandra*

Brighamia (*Campanulaceae*)

insignis CCCN

Brillantaisia (*Acanthaceae*)

kirungae CCCN
owariensis CSpe

Brimeura (*Asparagaceae*)

§ ***amethystina*** ♀H5	CExl GBin LEdu SBrt SDeJ SPhx WPGP WThu
- 'Alba'	SDeJ SPhx

Briza (*Poaceae*)

maxima	LPot NGdn NSti NWad SHar SPhx
media	Widely available
- 'Golden Bee'	CKno CRos EHyd EPPr EPfP EWes LEdu LRHS MMrt NLar NRHS SMad SPhx WMal WPGP
- 'Limouzi'	CElw CKno CWCL EHyd ELon EPPr LEdu LRHS MAvo NSti SMad SMea SPoG WPGP XCre XLum
- 'Romany Silver'	LEdu
- 'Russells'PBR	CBod CKno EBee EHyd ELan ELon EPfP LEdu LPot LRHS MGos NRHS NWsh SCob SMea SPer SPoG SRms SWvt
subaristata	EPPr
triloba	EAJP EHyd LRHS NWsh SPhx

broccoli see AGM Vegetables Section

Brodiaea (*Asparagaceae*)

§ ***californica***	EBee ERCP GKev WCot
- NNS 00-109	WCot
- 'Babylon'	ERCP GKev
'Corrina'	see *Triteleia* 'Corrina'
ida-maia	see *Dichelostemma ida-maia*
laxa	see *Triteleia laxa*
peduncularis	see *Triteleia peduncularis*

Bromus (*Poaceae*)

erectus	CHab
- W&B BG B-5	WCot
inermis 'Skinner's Gold' (v)	EBee EPPr NLar WCot

Broussonetia (*Moraceae*)

kazinoki	EBee
papyrifera	CBcs CMCN ELan ESwi LMaj MGil SPer WAvo WBor WCot WKor WLov
- 'Laciniata'	EBee IDee SMad

Browallia (*Solanaceae*)

from Sikkim	CSpe
americana	SPhx

Bruckenthalia see *Erica*

Brugmansia (*Solanaceae*)

'Angels Phenomenal' (d)	NGKo
'Angels Showtime' (d) **new**	NGKo
'Angels Sunbeam' (d)	ELan
§ ***arborea***	CBcs CDTJ NGKo
§ - 'Knightii' (d) ♀H1c	CDTJ CDow
- 'Rosea' variegated (v)	ELan
- variegated (v)	ELan
aurea	CCCN SAdn SGsty
× ***candida***	CCCN
- 'Chartreuse' **new**	CDow
- double-flowered (d) **new**	SAdn
§ - 'Grand Marnier' ♀H1c	CSam NGKo
- 'Plena'	see *B. arborea* 'Knightii'
§ - 'Variegata' (v)	CCCN CDTJ CSam NGKo
'Creamsickle' (d)	NGKo
× ***cubensis*** 'Charles Grimaldi'	NGKo
× ***insignis*** 'Pink'	NGKo
§ - pink-flowered	SEND
'Jamie' (v) **new**	NGKo
'Madame Foster' **new**	NGKo
'Miner's Claim' (v) **new**	NGKo
§ ***sanguinea***	CCCN CDow SEND SPlb
- red-flowered	SAdn
- 'Rosea'	see *B.* × *insignis* pink-flowered
§ ***suaveolens*** ♀H1c	CBcs
- ***rosea***	see *B.* × *insignis* pink-flowered
- 'Variegata' (v)	EShb
- yellow-flowered	EShb
'Variegata Sunset'	see *B.* × *candida* 'Variegata'
versicolor misapplied	see *B. arborea*
§ ***versicolor*** Lagerh.	CCCN
- yellow-flowered **new**	SAdn
'Vulcsa Red' **new**	NGKo
'Wildfire' (d)	NGKo
* 'Yellow Trumpet'	ELan

Brunfelsia (*Solanaceae*)

americana	CCCN WFib
australis	WFib
calycina	see *B. pauciflora*
lactea	CCCN
§ ***pauciflora*** ♀H1c	CCCN EShb SPer

Brunia (*Bruniaceae*)

albiflora	SPlb

Brunnera ✿ (*Boraginaceae*)

§ ***macrophylla***	Widely available
- 'Agnes Amez'	IMou
- 'Alba'	see *B. macrophylla* 'Betty Bowring'
- 'Alexanders Great'PBR	Widely available
§ - 'Betty Bowring'	Widely available
- 'Blaukuppel'	EWes NBir
- 'Dawson's White' (v)	CBcs CDor CRos CWCL ECha ECtt ELan ELon EMor EPfP GKev GMaP LRHS MBel MRav NBid NBir NHpl NLar NRHS SPer SRms SWvt WBor WCAu WCot WFar
- 'Diane's Gold'PBR	EBee ECha ECtt MGos MHol MNrw MPnt NLar SHeu
- 'Emerald Mist'PBR (v)	CBod EBee ECtt EMor GBin MGos MTin NLar SWvt WSpi
- 'Golden Jack Frost'	CBcs CBct CBod MPnt
- 'Gordano Gold' (v)	NBir WCot
- 'Green Gold' (v)	EMor IMou WFar
- 'Hadspen Cream' (v) ♀H6	Widely available
- 'Henry's Eyes'	EBee EPfP
- 'Jack Frost'PBR ♀H6	Widely available
- 'Jack's Gold'	ILea MBel MSCN SMad WHil
- 'Jennifer'	WCAu
- 'King's Ransom'PBR (v)	CBct CWGN ECtt GPSL NLar NSti SCob WFar
- 'Langford Hewitt' (v)	MNrw
- 'Langtrees'	CBct CMac EBee ECha EHyd GBin LRHS MCot MHol MMuc NBir NGdn SEND SPer WCFE WSpi
- 'Little Jack' (v)	CRos EBee EHyd EMor LRHS LSou NRHS SPoG
- 'Looking Glass'PBR ♀H6	Widely available
- 'Marley's White'	ELan
§ - 'Mister Morse'PBR (v) ♀H6	Widely available
- 'Sea Heart'PBR	CMea CSpe EBee ECtt EWTr GBin IPot LSou MBel NLar SCob SHeu WCAu WPnP
- 'Silver Heart'PBR	CBct CWGN ECtt EMor LSou MCot MTis SCob SHeu SPad WBor

- 'Silver Spear'	EBee LSun MHol MSCN NGBl WCAu WCot WHoo WRHF
- 'Silver Wings'	CElw CWCL EBee ECtt EHyd EMor EPfP GKev LRHS MBel MGos NBir NGdn NLar NSti NWad WCAu WFar
- 'Spring Yellow'	ECtt WCAu
- 'Starry Eyes'	IPot MCot MTis
'Mrs Morse'	see *B. macrophylla* 'Mister Morse'
sibirica	CElw EBee EPPr EWes NBid WCAu

Brunsvigia (*Amaryllidaceae*)

bosmaniae	WCot
- white-flowered	WCot
elandsmontana	WCot
grandiflora	WCot
gregaria	WCot
josephinae	WCot
- LAV 30394	WCot
litoralis	WCot
marginata	WCot
multiflora	see *B. orientalis*
§ ***orientalis***	WCot
pulchra	WCot
radulosa	WCot
rosea 'Minor'	see *Amaryllis belladonna*

Brussels sprouts see AGM Vegetables Section

Bryonia (*Cucurbitaceae*)

dioica	GPoy

Bryophyllum see *Kalanchoe*

Buddleja ✿ (*Scrophulariaceae*)

agathosma	CExl SLon WCFE WKif WLav WSHC
albiflora	SLon WLav
alternifolia 🏆H6	Widely available
- 'Argentea'	CBcs CDoC CRos EHyd ELan EPfP LRHS MBNS MRav NLar SLon SPer SPoG SWvt WCot WLav WWFP XSen
- UNIQUE ('Pmoore12')	CDoC LCro LOPS SLon SPoG
asiatica 🏆H3	EShb SLon WLav
- B&SWJ 11278	WCru
asiatica × lindleyana	WSpi
auriculata	CBcs CExl CMCN CRos CSde CTrC ELan EPfP IArd IDee LRHS MGil NSti SDix SLon SPlb SVen WGwG WLav
'Bel Argent'	EBee WPGP
'Blue Chip Junior' (Lo and Behold Series)	SLon SPoG
'Blue Chip'^{PBR} (Lo and Behold Series)	EHyd EPfP LBuc LRHS LSou MAsh MGos NLar SGol SLim SLon SRms SWvt WCot WFar WLav
* 'Blue Trerice'	CExl
caryopteridifolia	EBtc SEND SLon
colvilei	CAby CBcs CCCN ELan EPfP GBin GKin IArd LRHS SBrt SLon SWvt WBor WSpi
- B&SWJ 2121	WCru
- GWJ 9399	WCru
- WJC 13760	WCru
- 'Kewensis'	CBod CExl CRHN CSde ELan EPfP EWes MGil NLar SLon SVen WCFE WCru WLav WLov WSHC
- large-leaved	SBrt
- pink-flowered	GBin MGil NLar
cordata	SLon SVen
- B&SWJ 10433	WCru
coriacea	SLon
CRAN RAZZ ('Boseranz')	CBod SPad WNPC WTyc
§ ***crispa***	CBct CDoC CDow CExl CRos EBee ECha EHyd ELan EPfP LRHS SLon SPer SVen SWvt WFar WKif WPGP WSHC WSpi
- var. ***farreri***	MGil SLon SPoG
- 'Stone House Cottage'	WSHC
crotonoides subsp. ***amplexicaulis***	SLon
davidii	CCVT CDoC NPol WTSh
- B&SWJ 8083	WCru
- ADONIS BLUE ('Adokeep'^{PBR})	CBcs CSBt ECul EHyd LRHS MAsh SCob SLon SPoG WLav
- 'African Queen'	SLon WLav
- 'Apollonaria' **new**	WLav
§ - 'Autumn Beauty'	SLon WLav
- 'Autumn Delight'	SLon
- 'Beijing'	see *B. davidii* 'Autumn Beauty'
- 'Billy's Blue' **new**	WLav
- 'Black Knight' 🏆H6	Widely available
- 'Blue Eyes'	WLav
- 'Blue Horizon' 🏆H6	NLar SLon WCot WLav WRHF
- 'Border Beauty'	SLon WLav
- 'Butterfly Heaven'^{PBR}	WLav
- Buzz Series	LBuc NHol SLon
- - BUZZ CANDY PINK ('Tobudsopin')	CDoC CRos ECul EHyd ELan GJos LRHS NRHS SLon SPad SPoG WHil WLav
- - BUZZ HOT RASPBERRY	CNor ECul ELan NPer SLon WHil WLav
- - BUZZ INDIGO	CBod CDoC CRos ECul EHyd ELan EPfP LRHS NRHS WHil WLav
- - BUZZ IVORY ('Tobudivory'^{PBR})	CEnd CMac CRos EBee ECul EHyd ELan EPfP LRHS LSRN MGos NHol NLar NRHS SCob SLim SLon SPer SPoG WCot WHil WLav WSpi
- - BUZZ LILAC	ELan MGos NHol SLon
- - BUZZ MAGENTA IMPROVED ('Tobudmagen') **new**	MBros
- - BUZZ MAGENTA ('Tobudpipur'^{PBR})	CChe CDoC CEnd CMac CMea CRos EHyd ELan LRHS LSRN MGos MPri NHol NLar NRHS SCob SLon SPoG SRms SWvt WFar WLav WSpi
- - BUZZ SKY BLUE ('Tobudskybl'^{PBR})	CDoC CMac CRos ECul EHyd EPfP LRHS MBros MGos MPri NHol NLar NRHS SLon SPer SPoG SRms WFar WHil WLav
- - BUZZ VELVET ('Tobudvelve'^{PBR})	CBod CRos ELan LRHS NRHS SLon SPer
- - BUZZ VIOLET ('Tobudviole')	CDoC CRos ECul EHyd ELan LRHS MGos MPri NHol NLar NRHS SCob SLim SLon SPer SPoG SWvt WLav
- CAMBERWELL BEAUTY ('Camkeep') (English Butterfly Series) 🏆H6	LSRN SLon WLav
- 'Castle Blue'	CRos SLon
- 'Castle School'	CSam WLav
- 'Clive Farrell'	see *B. davidii* 'Autumn Beauty'
- 'Corinne Tremaine'	WHer
- 'Cotswold Blue'	WLav
- 'Cotswold Twilight' **new**	WLav
- 'Darent Valley' 🏆H6	SLon
- 'Dartmoor' 🏆H6	Widely available
- 'Dart's Ornamental White'	MRav SLon WLav

- 'Dart's Papillon Blue'	SLon WLav
- 'Dart's Purple Rain'	CRos SLon WLav
- 'Dubonnet'	SLon WLav
- 'Ecolonia'	SLon WLav
- 'Empire Blue'	CBcs CDoC CRos CSBt ECtt ECul EHyd EPfP GKin LRHS LSRN MGos NBir NPer NRHS SPer SPlb SPoG SRms SWvt XSen
- 'Fair Lady'	WLav
- 'Fascinating'	MRav NBir SLon WLav
- 'Flaming Violet'	SLon WLav
- FLORENCE ('Watflor')	LSRN NLar SCob SLon WFar
- 'Foxtail'	WLav
- 'Glasnevin Hybrid'	NLar SLon WLav
- 'Gonglepod'	CRos SLon WLav
- 'Greenway's River Dart'	SLon
- 'Grey Dawn'	WLav
- 'Griffin Blue'	MAsh WLav
- 'Gulliver'PBR	CRos EHyd LRHS NLar NRHS SCob SGol SLon WFar WLav
- 'Harlequin' (v)	CBcs CBod CMac CRos CTsd ECrN ELan EPfP LRHS MAsh MGos MSwo NLar NRHS SEND SGol SLim SPer SPlb SPoG SRms SWvt WAvo WFar WLov XSen
- 'Île de France'	NLar SLon SRms WLav
- 'Leela Kapila'	SLon
- 'Les Kneale'	SLon WLav WMal
- 'Lilac Moon'	WLav
- 'Loganberry Jam' **new**	WLav
- MARBLED WHITE ('Markeep') (English Butterfly Series)	ECul EHyd EShb LRHS NEoE SLon WLav
- MASQUERADE ('Notbud') (v)	MRav SLon
- MOONSHINE ('Buddma'PBR)	CBod MTin NEoE WFar
§ - NANHO BLUE ('Mongo')	CBcs CBrac CMac CRos CSBt EBee ECrN ECul EPfP GBin GKev GKin LRHS MAsh MGos MRav MSwo NBir NLar NRHS SGol SLim WSpi XSen
- 'Nanho Petite Indigo'	see *B. davidii* NANHO BLUE
- 'Nanho Petite Plum'	see *B. davidii* NANHO PURPLE
- 'Nanho Petite Purple'	see *B. davidii* NANHO PURPLE
§ - NANHO PURPLE ('Monum') ♀H6	CBcs CMac CRos CTri EPfP LRHS LSRN MGos MRav NLar NRHS SGol SLim SLon SPer SPlb SRms XSen
- NANHO WHITE ('Monite') ♀H6	CMac CRos EPfP LRHS SGol SLon SRms XSen
- var. ***nanhoensis***	SGol WFar WLav
- - blue-flowered	EPfP NWad SLon SPer
- 'Orchid Beauty'	SLon WLav
- 'Orpheus'	SLon WLav
- 'Panache'	CRos EHyd EPfP LRHS MAsh NRHS SLon WLav
- 'Party Girl' **new**	SLon
- 'Peace'	CMac CTri CWCL LSRN MRav NLar SLon SPoG WLav
- PEACOCK ('Peakeep'PBR) (English Butterfly Series)	CSBt MAsh SCob WLav
- 'Persephone'	SLon WLav
- 'Petite Indigo'	see *B. davidii* NANHO BLUE
- 'Pink Beauty'	LSRN MBlu WFar
- 'Pink Pearl'	SEND SLon WLav
- 'Pink Spreader'	SLon WLav
- 'Pixie Blue'	LBuc LRHS MAsh NLar WLav
- 'Pixie Red'	LBuc LRHS MAsh NLar WLav
- 'Pixie White'	LBuc MAsh NLar SCob SGol WLav
- PURPLE EMPEROR ('Pyrkeep') (English Butterfly Series)	ECul NBir SLon WLav
- 'Purple Friend'	SLon WLav
- 'Red Admiral'	SLon
- RÊVE DE PAPILLON BLUE ('Minpap3')	WLav
- RÊVE DE PAPILLON ('Minpap')	CRos EHyd LRHS MAsh NRHS SGsty WLav
- RÊVE DE PAPILLON WHITE ('Minpap2')	SGsty
- 'Royal Purple'	SLim SWvt
- 'Royal Red' ♀H6	Widely available
- 'Saith Ffynnon Early'	WSFF
- 'Santana' (v)	CBod CMac CRos EHyd ELon EPfP EWes LRHS MGos MRav MSCN NHol NLar NRHS NWad SCob SGol SPoG SRms SWvt WAvo WHil WSpi XSen
- 'Shire Blue'	WLav
- 'Son of Orpheus' **new**	WLav
- 'Southcombe Splendour'	CRos
- 'Summer Beauty'	MBlu SLon WLav
- 'Summer House Blue'	SLon WLav
- 'Twotones'	WLav
- 'Variegata' (v)	MAsh SLon SWvt WLav
- 'White Ball'	ELan NLar SLon WLav
- 'White Bouquet'	CCVT CSBt ECul EPfP GKin MSwo NLar SEND SPer SWvt WLav XSen
- 'White Cloud'	EPfP SLon SRms WGwG
- 'White Harlequin' (v)	SLon WCFE
- 'White Profusion' ♀H6	Widely available
- 'White Wings'	CRos SLon WLav
- 'Wisteria Lane'	LCro LOPS LRHS
davidii* × *fallowiana	WSpi
§ ***delavayi***	CExl ECre GBin SEND WCru
DREAMING LAVENDER ('Hinebud1'PBR)	SLon WNPC
DREAMING ORANGE	CBod SLon
DREAMING PURPLE ('Hinebud4')	LSou WNPC
DREAMING WHITE ('Hinebud3'PBR)	LSou WNPC
'Ellen's Blue'	CExl CRos NLar WLav
fallowiana misapplied	see *B.* 'West Hill'
fallowiana Balf.f. & W.W.Sm.	CRos EHyd ELan LRHS WLav
- ACE 2481	LRHS
- BWJ 7803	WCru
- var. ***alba*** ♀H5	CMac CRos ECrN EHyd ELan EPfP LRHS MBNS MRav NLar NRHS SDix SLon SPer WLov
- 'Bishop's Violet'	CTsd
'Flower Power'	see *B.* × *weyeriana* 'Bicolor'
FLUTTERBY FLOW LAVENDER ('Podaras 12'PBR) (Flutterby Flow Series)	LCro LOPS
FLUTTERBY PEACE ('Podaras 6'PBR) (Flutterby Series)	LBuc
(Flutterby Petite Series)	CBod CMea LCro LOPS MThu NLar
FLUTTERBY PETITE BLUE HEAVEN ('Podaras 8'PBR)	SLon
- FLUTTERBY PETITE DARK	LCro LOPS NLar
- FLUTTERBY PETITE SNOW WHITE ('Podaras 15'PBR)	CBod LCro LOPS NLar SLon
- FLUTTERBY PETITE TUTTI FRUITTI PINK ('Podaras 13'PBR)	CBod LBuc LCro LOPS SLon SRms
forrestii	WCru
- BWJ 8020	EBee WCru

globosa ♀H5	Widely available
- RCB/Arg C-11	WCot
- 'Cally Orange'	GBin WGwG
- cream-flowered HCM 98.017	WPGP
- 'Lemon Ball'	MBlu NPer SLon WLav
glomerata	CCht EShb MGil SLon SPlb
- 'Silver Service'	CBod CDow EPfP LRHS
heliophila	see *B. delavayi*
indica	SLon WLav
INSPIRED PINK	see *B.* × *weyeriana* 'Pink Pagoda'
japonica	SLon
- B&SWJ 8912	WCru
× ***lewisiana*** 'Margaret Pike'	SLon
'Lilac Chip' (Lo and Behold Series)	CDoC LRHS NLar SGol
limitanea	CMCN SLon SPtp
- from Cangshan, Yunnan, China	SBrt
lindleyana	Widely available
- 'Little Treasure'	NEoE SLon
aff. ***lindleyana***	GWyn WLov WSpi
- B&SWJ 11478	WCru
'Lochinch' ♀H5	Widely available
longifolia	EBee SLon
'Longstock Gem'	SLon
'Longstock Silver'	SLon
loricata	CExl CMCN CRos CTsd CWld EHyd EPfP GBin GWyn IDee LRHS MGil SEdd SLon SPlb WLav WSpi
macrostachya HWJ 602	WCru
- WWJ 12016	WCru
§ ***madagascariensis*** ♀H2	CRHN EShb NLar SLon SPlb SVen
megalocephala B&SWJ 9106	WCru WPGP
'Miss Ruby'[PBR] ♀H5	CDoC CRos EBee EPfP LBuc LRHS LSRN MAsh NRHS SGol SLon WLav
§ 'Morning Mist'[PBR]	CBcs CBod CDoC CExl CMac CRos CSBt CWGN EPfP GBin LCro LOPS LRHS LSRN NHol NRHS SGol SLon SRms SWvt WCot WFar
myriantha	CExl SLon WPGP
nappii	SLon
nicodemia	see *B. madagascariensis*
nivea	CExl MGil SLon WLav XSen
- B&SWJ 2679	WCru
- pink-flowered	SLon
aff. ***nivea***	WSpi
officinalis ♀H3	CExl CSde SLon WLav
paniculata	SLon WPGP
- GWJ 9286 from Sikkim	WCru
parvifolia	SLon
- MPF 148	WLav
× ***pikei*** 'Hever'	SRms XSen
'Pink Delight' ♀H5	Widely available
'Pink Micro Chip' (Lo and Behold Series)	SLon SPoG
'Pink Perfection'	WFar
'Pride of Hever'	SDys
'Pride of Longstock'	SLon SPoG
pterocaulis	EBee
'Purple Chip' (Lo and Behold Series)	LRHS
'Red Chip' (Lo and Behold Series)	SGol
saligna	SLon
'Salmon Spheres'	CBcs SLon WLav
salviifolia	CBcs CBct CExl CMac CRos CSde CTrC CTsd CWld EBee ELan IDee LRHS MBlu MGil NLar SBrt SEND SPlb SVen WAvo WCFE WGwG WHer WKif WLav WLov WPGP
- white-flowered	EBee SLon WPGP
SILVER ANNIVERSARY	see *B.* 'Morning Mist'
speciosissima	WPGP
stachyoides	WLav
stenostachya	CExl SLon
sterniana	see *B. crispa*
SUGAR PLUM ('Lonplum'[PBR])	CRos CSBt EHyd EMil EPfP LBuc LCro LOPS LRHS MAsh NRHS SLon SPoG
tibetica	see *B. crispa*
tubiflora	SLon WLav
venenifera	SLon
- B&SWJ 895 **new**	EBee
- B&SWJ 6036	WCru
× ***wardii***	WCFE
- KR 4881	EBee WPGP
§ 'West Hill' ♀H5	CRos EHyd EPfP LRHS NRHS SLon WLav
× ***weyeriana***	CMac ECtt EWTr GJos MBNS MGil MNrw MSwo NBir SIvy SPad SPlb SWvt WAvo WOut
§ - 'Bicolor'	EBee EPPr EPfP IDee LCro LOPS LSRN MNrw NLar NQui SCob SLon SRms WLav WMal
- 'Boy Blue'	SLon WLav
- 'Golden Glow'	CTri CWCL GBin GWyn LSRN NLar SLon SWvt WLav WSFF
- 'Honeycomb'	EShb MGos MMrt NLar WLov
- 'Lady de Ramsey'	SEND
- 'Moonlight'	CBcs CDoC CExl ELan EPPr GBin GWyn SLon SPer WCot WLav WSpi XSen
§ - 'Pink Pagoda'[PBR]	CBcs CSBt EPfP NLar SLon SPoG
- pink-flowered **new**	XSen
- 'Sungold' ♀H6	Widely available
'White Chip' (Lo and Behold Series)	LRHS LSou SGol
'Winter Sun'	SLon
'Yeti White' **new**	SPad
yunnanensis	CBcs NLar SBrt SLon
- B&SWJ 8146	WCru

Buglossoides (*Boraginaceae*)

§ ***purpurocaerulea***	ECha ELan EWld LPla MNrw NBid SPhx WCot WFar XLum

Bukiniczia (*Plumbaginaceae*)

cabulica	GKev XEll

Bulbine (*Asphodelaceae*)

annua misapplied	see *B. semibarbata*
bulbosa misapplied	see *B. semibarbata*
caulescens	see *B. frutescens*
§ ***frutescens***	CBod CCBP MHer MNHC NChi SRms SVen WSMil
- 'Hallmark'	CCCN
latifolia	CCCN GKev
§ ***semibarbata***	CCCN

Bulbinella (*Asphodelaceae*)

angustifolia	GKev MHer
gibbsii var. ***balanifera***	GKev
hookeri	CExl EBee EHyd GBee GBin GEdr GKev ITim LRHS SMad SRms WCot WHal
latifolia subsp. ***latifolia***	IBlr
nutans	EBee

Bulbinopsis see *Bulbine*

Bulbocodium (*Colchicaceae*)

	vernum	EPot GKev SDeJ

bullace see *Prunus insititia*

Bunias (*Brassicaceae*)

	orientalis	CAgr LEdu

Bunium (*Apiaceae*)

	bulbocastanum	CAgr IMou LEdu LRHS SPhx WPGP
	ferulaceum	CBod MHol MPie SEdd SMad WRHF
	- W&B BG B-10	WCot

Buphthalmum (*Asteraceae*)

	salicifolium	EBee ELan EMor EPfP MMuc NBro NGdn SPer SRms WCot WFar XLum
	- 'Alpengold'	CSam ECha GMaP NLar
	- 'Dora'	ECtt WCot WFar
	- 'Sunwheel'	CBod MHol SRms
	speciosum	see *Telekia speciosa*

Bupleurum (*Apiaceae*)

	angulosum	NBir
	- copper-leaved	see *B. longifolium*
	candollei	LEdu WSHC
	falcatum	CSpe ECha LRHS NDov SDix SPhx WCot WKif
	fruticescens	XSen
	fruticosum	CBcs CCCN CCht CRos CSpe EBee ECre EHyd ELan EPfP EWes GBin LRHS NRHS SCob SDix SEND SLon SMad SPer SPoG SPtp WCot WLov XSen
	- bronze-leaved	LRHS
	gibraltaricum	XSen
§	***longifolium***	CElw CFis CSpe EBee ECre EWes LEdu LRHS MNrw NAts NBPC NBir NChi WBor WFar WPGP
	- subsp. ***aureum***	LEdu LPla LRHS SPhx
	- 'Bronze Beauty'	GEdr MBriF MMrt SPtp
	ranunculoides	LPla SPhx XLum
	rotundifolium	CSpe IMou LEdu SPhx WCot
	- 'Copper'	NDov

Bursaria (*Pittosporaceae*)

	spinosa	CCCN

Butia (*Arecaceae*)

	capitata ♀H1c	CCCN CDTJ CPHo SArc SPalm
§	- var. ***odorata***	SPlb
	eriospatha	CPHo SPalm
	odorata	see *B. capitata* var. *odorata*

Butomus (*Butomaceae*)

	umbellatus	CBen CSpe CWat ECha EWat GBin MNrw MRav MWts NBir NPer WMAq WWtn XLum
	- 'Rosenrot'	EWat LLWG
	- 'Schneeweisschen'	EWat LLWG MWts

butternut see *Juglans cinerea*

butternut squash see AGM Vegetables Section

Buxus (*Buxaceae*)

	aurea 'Marginata'	see *B. sempervirens* 'Marginata'
	balearica	EBtc WSpi
	bodinieri	LTop
	'Green Gem'	NWad
	harlandii misapplied	CMen SRiv
	japonica 'Nana'	see *B. microphylla*
	macowanii	LTop
	macrophylla	WSpi
§	***microphylla***	NWad SGol
	- 'Asiatic Winter'	see *B. microphylla* var. *japonica* 'Winter Gem'
§	- 'Compacta'	CMen MHer SRiv WCot
	- 'Faulkner' ♀H6	ELan EPfP LBuc LMaj MGos SCob SGol SGsty SPer SRiv SRms SWeb WSpi
	- 'Golden Triumph'PBR	NLar
	- 'Green Pillow'	MHer SRiv WSpi
	- 'Herrenhausen'	WSpi
	- var. ***insularis***	see *B. sinica* var. *insularis*
	- var. ***japonica***	SGol
	- - 'National'	WSpi
§	- - 'Winter Gem'	MRav
	- 'John Baldwin'	SRiv
	- var. ***sinica***	LTop WSpi
	sempervirens	Widely available
§	- 'Angustifolia'	MRav NWad SMad
	- 'Arborescens'	LMaj
	- 'Argenteo-variegata' (v)	SGol WFar
	- 'Aurea'	see *B. sempervirens* 'Aureovariegata'
	- 'Aurea Maculata'	see *B. sempervirens* 'Aureovariegata'
	- 'Aurea Marginata'	see *B. sempervirens* 'Marginata'
§	- 'Aureovariegata' (v)	EPfP EShb LTop MGos MRav NLar NWad SRiv SRms
	- 'Bentley Blue'	LTop
	- 'Blauer Heinz'	ELan GQue LTop MHer MRav SRiv WAvo WSpi
	- 'Bowles's Blue'	WCFE
	- 'Bullata'	LMaj
	- clipped ball	EPfP LSRN LTop MGos NLar SRiv SRms
	- clipped bird	LTop SRiv
	- clipped cone	LSRN LTop SRiv SRms
	- clipped pyramid	EPfP LSRN LTop MGos NLar SRiv SRms
	- clipped spiral	LSRN LTop NLar SRiv SRms
	- 'Elegans'	LTop
§	- 'Elegantissima' (v) ♀H6	CBrac CExl CJun CTri ECrN ELan EPfP EShb LMaj LSRN LTop MAsh MGos MHer MMuc MPri MRav NLar SCob SEND SGol SGsty SPer SPoG SRiv SRms WAvo WCFE WSpi
	- 'Fiesta'	SRms
	- 'Gold Tip'	see *B. sempervirens* 'Notata'
§	- 'Graham Blandy' ♀H6	MHer SAko SGol SRiv WSpi
	- 'Green Balloon'	EPfP LBuc
	- 'Greenpeace'	see *B. sempervirens* 'Graham Blandy'
	- 'Handsworthensis'	CTri LTop SEND SRms WCFE WSpi
	- 'Ickworth Giant'	WSpi
	- 'Japonica Aurea'	see *B. sempervirens* 'Latifolia Maculata'
	- 'Kensington Gardens'	WSpi
	- 'King Midas'	SAko
	- 'Kingsville'	see *B. microphylla* 'Compacta'
	- 'Kingsville Dwarf'	see *B. microphylla* 'Compacta'
	- 'Latifolia' **new**	WMou
§	- 'Latifolia Maculata' (v) ♀H6	EPfP LRHS LTop MMuc NPer SEND SPoG SRiv WRHF WSpi

	- 'Longifolia'	see *B. sempervirens* 'Angustifolia'
§	- 'Marginata' (v)	LTop SGol WSpi
	- 'Memorial'	LTop NWad SRiv WSpi
	- 'Myosotidifolia'	SRiv WCot WSpi
	- 'Myrtifolia'	WSpi
§	- 'Notata' (v)	WSpi
	- 'Pendula'	WSpi
	- 'Prostrata'	NWad WSpi
	- 'Pylewell'	WSpi
	- 'Raket'	SGsty
	- 'Rosmarinifolia'	MRav
	- 'Rotundifolia'	ELan LTop MMuc SEND WSpi
	- 'Silver Variegated'	see *B. sempervirens* 'Elegantissima'
	- 'Suffruticosa'	CArg CBcs CBrac CSBt CTri ELan EPfP EShb GPoy LSRN LTop MGos MHed MRav MSwo NHol NLar SCob SEND SEWo SGol SPer SRiv SRms SWvt WCFE WSpi
	- 'Suffruticosa Variegata' (v)	SRms SWvt
	- 'Twisty'	WFar
	- 'Vardar Valley'	NWad SRiv WSpi
*	- 'Variegata' (v)	CBrac CPla MSwo NBir SArc
	- 'Wisley Blue'	LTop WSpi
§	***sinica*** var. ***insularis***	LTop WAvo
	- - 'Filigree'	NWad WSpi
	- - 'Justin Brouwers'	LPla MHer SRiv WSpi
	- - 'Tide Hill'	LTop SRiv WFar WSpi
	wallichiana	LTop

C

cabbage see AGM Vegetables Section

Cacalia (*Asteraceae*)

plantaginea	see *Arnoglossum plantagineum*
suaveolens	see *Hasteola suaveolens*

Cachrys (*Apiaceae*)

alpina	LEdu SBrt SPhx WHil

Caesalpinia (*Caesalpiniaceae*)

gilliesii ♀H3	CBcs EBee LRHS SPlb WCot
pulcherrima ♀H3	CCCN
spinosa	SPlb WPav

Caiophora (*Loasaceae*)

coronata	GEdr

calabrese see AGM Vegetables Section

Caladium (*Araceae*)

'Aaron' (v)	SDir
'Candidum' (v)	SDeJ SDir
'Carolyn Whorton'	SDeJ
'Florida Cardinal' (v)	SDeJ
'Frieda Hempel'	SDeJ SDir
praetermissum 'Hilo Beauty'	XBlo
'White Christmas' (v)	SDeJ

Calamagrostis (*Poaceae*)

	× ***acutiflora***	XLum
	- 'Avalanche'	CKno CRos EBou ECha ECtt EHyd ELon EPPr EPed EPfP EShb EWes GQue GWyn IMou LRHS MAsh MAvo MTis NDov NRHS NWsh SGbt SPoG
	- 'Eldorado' (v)	CKno ECha MAsh MMuc WCot
	- 'England' (v)	EPPr GBin MNrw
	- 'Karl Foerster'	Widely available
	- 'Overdam' (v)	Widely available
	- 'Stricta'	EPPr GMaP
	- 'Waldenbuch'	CKno EMor SMea
	argentea	see *Stipa calamagrostis*
	arundinacea	CElw CExl CMac EPed SPlb XSen
§	***brachytricha*** ♀H6	Widely available
	- 'Mona'	NDov
	canadensis	SPhx
	emodensis	CMea CSpe EAJP ECha NBid SPhx WGrn
	epigejos	CKno LEdu WPGP
	'Glenorchy Fireworks'	EPPr
	'Kyrgyz Giant' **new**	WPGP
	ophitidis	SPlb
	splendens misapplied	see *Stipa calamagrostis*
	splendens Trin.	LPla
	varia	CKno ELon EMor GBin LPla WHrl

Calamintha (*Lamiaceae*)

	alpina	see *Clinopodium alpinum*
	clinopodium	see *Clinopodium vulgare*
	cretica	SPhx
§	***grandiflora***	CBod CCBP ECha ELan GPoy MNHC MNrw MRav NBir NLar NPer SPer SPhx SPlb SRms WCAu WCav XSen
	- 'Elfin Purple'	EBee EPfP SBut
	- 'Variegata' (v)	EBee ELan ENfk EPfP MPie SRms WCAu
	'Harrogate'	WGoo
§	***nepeta***	CBod CCBP CHab CMea CRos EBou ECha EHyd EMor ENfk EWTr GBin LCro LOPS LRHS MHer MNHC NBro SEND SPhx SPlb SPoG SRms WCAu WHer WOut XAbr XSen
	- subsp. ***glandulosa***	SBut
	- - ACL 1050/90	WHoo
	- - 'White Cloud'	CFis EBee ECtt ELan EPfP MBel MBriF MPie MRav NBir SBut SRms WCAu
	- 'Gottfried Kuehn'	LPla MRav
§	- subsp. ***nepeta***	ELan ELon EPfP GMaP IMou MHer MMuc MRav NDov SPer WFar WHal XLum
	- - 'Blue Cloud'	CCBP CSam CSpe EBee EBou ECha ECtt EMor EPfP EPri GMaP GWyn MBel MBriF MRav NBir NDov SPhx SPoG SPtp SRms WCAu WFar
	- 'Triumphator'	IPot WGoo
	- 'Weisse Riese'	CMea EBee NDov
	nepetoides	see *C. nepeta* subsp. *nepeta*
	sylvatica	see *Clinopodium menthifolium*
	vulgaris	see *Clinopodium vulgare*

calamondin see *Citrus* × *microcarpa*

Calandrinia (*Portulacaceae*)

sibirica	see *Claytonia sibirica*
umbellata	EDAr MAsh WIce
- 'Ruby Tuesday'	XLum

Calanthe (*Orchidaceae*)

bicolor	see *C. striata*
discolor	EBee GKev SDir
- var. ***flava***	see *C. striata*

Kozu gx GKev LEdu WPGP
reflexa SDir
sieboldii see *C. striata*
§ ***striata*** EBee SDir
tricarinata SDir

Calathea (*Marantaceae*)

crocata see *Goeppertia crocata*
majestica see *Goeppertia majestica*
makoyana see *Goeppertia makoyana*
roseopicta see *Goeppertia roseopicta*
rufibarba see *Goeppertia rufibarba*
stromata see *Ctenanthe burle-marxii*
zebrina see *Goeppertia zebrina*

Calceolaria (*Calceolariaceae*)

andina EDAr
arachnoidea EDAr EWes GEdr SPlb WPav
§ ***biflora*** EDAr EWes GKev
- 'Goldcrest Amber' SPlb
'Camden Hero' CBcs CBod CSpe EShb
cavanillesii SPlb
corymbosa EBee GKev GLog
- subsp. ***floccosa*** GKev
falklandica EWld GKev
filicaulis EBee GKev
- subsp. ***luxurians*** GKev
fothergillii GLog WAbe
'Goldcrest' EWld LRHS
integrifolia ♀H2 CAbb CBcs CBod CDTJ CExl CFis CTri ECtt ELan MGil MSCN SAdn SPer SPoG SRms WBor WHer
- bronze-flowered MSCN SPer
'John Innes' EWld GKev
'Kentish Hero' EDAr MGil MHer SDys WAbe WMal
lagunae-blancae GKev
pavonii MGil SBrt
aff. ***pavonii*** CRHN
perfoliata B&SWJ 14722 **new** WCru
plantaginea see *C. biflora*
rugosa see *C. integrifolia*
tenella NSla WAbe
aff. ***tomentosa*** B&SWJ 14896 **new** WCru
uniflora var. ***darwinii*** GKev NHpl WAbe
'Walter Shrimpton' EPot WAbe

Calendula ✿ (*Asteraceae*)

arvensis CCCN
'Bronze Beauty' CSpe
officinalis CCBP CLau EBou ENfk GPoy LCro LOPS MGil MHer MNHC SRms SVic SWvt WSFF XAbr
- 'Apricot Twist' LSou
- Fiesta Gitana Group ♀H5 LCro LOPS SCob
- 'Indian Prince' (Prince Series) LCro LOPS SPhx
- 'Lemon Twist' (d) **new** LSou
POWERDAISY TANGO (PowerDaisy Series) **new** MHol
'Tarifa' SEND
(Winter Wonders Series) WINTER WONDERS AMBER ARCTIC ('212372D') LCro LOPS
- WINTER WONDERS BANANA BLIZZARD ('2012357d'PBR) LCro LOPS
- WINTER WONDERS GOLDEN GLAZE ('2012329d') LCro LOPS
- WINTER WONDERS PEACH POLAR ('2012391D'PBR) LCro LOPS

Calibrachoa (*Solanaceae*)

Cabaret Series SCob
- CABARET BRIGHT RED ('Balcabrite'PBR) ♀H2 MBros MPri
- CABARET DEEP BLUE ('Balcabdebu'PBR) MBros MPri SCob
- CABARET DEEP YELLOW ('Balcabdepy'PBR) MBros MPri
- CABARET HOT PINK ('Balcabhopi') MBros MPri
- CABARET PURPLE ('Balcabpurp') LSou
- CABARET WHITE ('Balcabwit') MBros MPri
(Can-can Series) CAN-CAN BLACK CHERRY LSou MBros
- CAN-CAN CHERRY BLOSSOM **new** LSou
- CAN-CAN CORAL REEF ('Balcanoree') LSou MBros
- CAN-CAN DOUBLE BLUE (d) MBros
- CAN-CAN DOUBLE DARK YELLOW (d) MBros
- CAN-CAN DOUBLE PINK (d) **new** LSou
- CAN-CAN DOUBLE PROVENCE BLUE (d) LSou
- CAN-CAN NEON PINK ('Balcaneoni') LSou
Kabloom Series MBros
- KABLOOM DEEP PINK ('Pas1020305') MBros
- KABLOOM WHITE ('Pas1020307') MBros
'Starlight Blue' MPri
'Starlight Pink' MPri
(Superbells Series) SUPERBELLS STRAWBERRY PINK ('Uscali47') CPla
- SUPERBELLS STRAWBERRY PUNCH ('Uscal58205') MBros

Calla (*Araceae*)

aethiopica see *Zantedeschia aethiopica*
palustris CWat EWat LLWG NPer SRms WMAq

Callerya (*Papilionaceae*)

§ ***reticulata*** CExl

Calliandra (*Mimosaceae*)

'Dixie Pink' CCCN
portoricensis CCCN
surinamensis CCCN
tweediei ♀H1b CCCN

Callianthemum (*Ranunculaceae*)

anemonoides GEdr WAbe WCot
coriandrifolium GEdr
kernerianum GEdr WAbe

Callicarpa (*Lamiaceae*)

CW&T 6228	CMCN
americana	CExl
- var. ***lactea***	CMCN
bodinieri	SavN
- var. ***giraldii***	CBrac LMaj MRav NLar SGol
- - 'Profusion' ♀^{H6}	Widely available
- 'Imperial Pearl'	EPfP LRHS
'Cardinal'	CJun
cathayana	NLar
dichotoma	CBcs CExl LRHS NLar
- 'Issai'	EBee EPfP ILea LRHS MBlu NLar
formosana NMWJ 14553 **new**	WCru
japonica	CExl CMen NLar SBrt SMad
- B&SWJ 12621	WCru
- f. ***albibacca***	LRHS NLar
- 'Heavy Berry'	NLar
- 'Koshima-no-homate'	NLar
- 'Leucocarpa'	CBcs CBod CExl CMac EBee ELan EPfP NLar SPer SPoG WGob WLov
- var. ***luxurians*** B&SWJ 8521	WCru
kwangtungensis	CBcs NLar
mollis	CExl
psilocalyx NJM 13.057	WPGP
shikokiana	NLar
× ***shirasawana***	NLar
aff. ***tikusikensis*** B&SWJ 7127	WCru
Van den Broek selection	NLar
yunnanensis	NLar

Callirhoe (*Malvaceae*)

bushii	EBee
involucrata	LPla WSHC XLum
- var. ***tenuissima***	EBee

Callisia (*Commelinaceae*)

elegans	EShb
fragrans	EOHP EShb
- 'Melnickoff' (v)	EShb
§ ***navicularis***	SSim
repens	EShb
'Turtle' **new**	CDoC

Callistemon (*Myrtaceae*)

acuminatus	CCCN
brachyandrus	SVen
citrinus	CTri EPfP EPri SEle SPlb WGrn
- 'Albus'	see *C. citrinus* 'White Anzac'
- 'Firebrand'	CRos LRHS
- 'Splendens' ♀^{H3}	Widely available
§ - 'White Anzac'	CBrac CDoC CMac CSBt CSde ELan EPfP LRHS SEND SIvy SPoG
comboynensis	CCCN
* 'Country Park'	CTrC
glaucus	see *C. speciosus*
'Inferno'	CAbb CTrC SPad
laevis hort.	see *C. rugulosus*
linearifolius	LSRN
linearis ♀^{H2}	CAby CBrac CMac CRos CSde CTrC CTri ELan EPfP LRHS LSRN MGos MHer SCob SEND SIvy SLim SLon SPlb SWvt WSHC
macropunctatus	SPlb SVen
'Masotti'^{PBR}	EHyd SPoG
'Mauve Mist'	CAbb CBod CCCN CCht CDoC CRos ELan EPfP EWTr LRHS SAko SPad SPoG SVen WGrn
pallidus	CBcs CBrac CCCN CDoC CMCN CMac CRos CTrC CTsd EHyd ELan EPfP EWTr LRHS MMuc MRav NRHS SAko SEND SEle SIvy SPer SPlb SVen
paludosus	see *C. sieberi* DC.
'Perth Pink'	CAbb CBcs CBod CCCN CDoC CSBt CSde ELan EPfP LRHS SEle SIvy SPad SVen WGrn
pinifolius	SPlb SVen
§ ***pityoides***	CExl CTsd NLar SEle SIvy SVen
'Red Clusters'	CBcs CBrac CDoC CMac CRos CSde CTrC ELan EPfP LRHS MAsh SNig SWvt WFar
rigidus	CBcs CBod CChe CDoC CRos CTri CTsd EHyd ELan EPfP IArd LRHS LSRN MGos MMuc MRav NLar NRHS SAko SEle SPer SVen SWvt
§ ***rugulosus***	CBrac CCCN CTrC LRHS SGbt SVen SWvt
salignus ♀^{H2}	CBcs CBod CCCN CMac CTrC CTri EPfP MHer MRav NLar SEle SLim SPer SVen
sieberi misapplied	see *C. pityoides*
§ ***sieberi*** DC.	CBcs CBod CDoC CMCN CTsd EBee ELan EPfP LRHS MGil MMuc NLar SLim SPlb
§ ***speciosus***	NLar SEND SPlb
subulatus	SArc SPlb
- 'Crimson Tail'	CTrC MGil MMuc SPtp
viminalis	CCCN CMCN SPlb
- 'Captain Cook'	CMac ECrN LRHS LSRN SVen SWvt WFar
- 'Endeavour'	CCCN
- 'Hannah Ray'	WFar
- HOT PINK ('Kkho1'^{PBR})	CTrC LRHS MGos SCob SLim
- 'Little John'	CBcs CBrac CCht LSRN SEND SPad SWvt
'Violaceus'	NLar SPlb SVen
viridiflorus	CMCN CTrC CTsd MMuc SEND SPlb SPtp WGwG
'White Anzac'	see *C. citrinus* 'White Anzac'

Callistephus (*Asteraceae*)

chinensis	SVic

Callitriche (*Plantaginaceae*)

sp.	WSFF
brutia subsp. ***hamulata***	LLWG
§ ***palustris***	CBen
stagnalis	EWat WMAq
verna	see *C. palustris*

Callitris (*Cupressaceae*)

endlicheri	CBrP
rhomboidea	WPav

Callitropsis see *Chamaecyparis*

× ***leylandii***	see × *Cuprocyparis leylandii*
nootkatensis	see *Xanthocyparis nootkatensis*

Calluna ✿ (*Ericaceae*)

vulgaris	NAts SWhi WOut
- 'Aberdeen'	SWhi
- 'Adrie'	CFst SWhi
- 'Agnes'^{PBR} (Garden Girls Series) **new**	SWhi

	- f. ***alba***	SWhi
	- 'Alba Aurea'	SWhi
	- 'Alba Carlton'	SWhi
	- 'Alba Elata'	SWhi
	- 'Alba Elegans'	SWhi
	- 'Alba Elongata'	see *C. vulgaris* 'Mair's Variety'
	- 'Alba Erecta'	SWhi
	- 'Alba Jae'	SWhi
	- 'Alba Minor'	SWhi
	- 'Alba Multiflora'	SWhi
	- 'Alba Pilosa'	SWhi
§	- 'Alba Plena' (d)	GPer SWhi
	- 'Alba Praecox'	SWhi
	- 'Alba Pumila'	SWhi
§	- 'Alba Rigida'	CFst GPer SWhi
	- 'Alex Warwick'	GPer SWhi
	- 'Alexandra'^{PBR} (Garden Girls Series)	SCoo SPoG SWhi
	- 'Alicia'^{PBR} (Garden Girls Series) 🏆^{H7}	CFst SCoo SPoG SWhi
	- 'Alieke'	SWhi
	- 'Alison Yates'	SWhi
	- 'Allegretto'	SWhi
	- 'Allegro'	GPer SCoo SWhi
	- 'Alportii'	GPer SWhi
	- 'Alportii Praecox'	SWhi
	- 'Alys Sutcliffe'	SWhi
	- 'Amanda Wain'	SWhi
	- 'Amethyst'^{PBR} (Garden Girls Series)	SPoG SWhi
	- 'Amilto'	CFst SWhi
	- 'Andrew Proudley'	SWhi
	- 'Anette'^{PBR} (Garden Girls Series)	SCoo SWhi
	- 'Angela Wain'	SWhi
	- 'Angie' (Garden Girls Series)	CFst SWhi
	- 'Anna'	SWhi
	- 'Annabel' (d)	CFst SWhi
	- 'Annegret'	see *C. vulgaris* 'Marlies'
	- 'Anneke'	SWhi
	- 'Annemarie' (d) 🏆^{H7}	CFst GPer SCoo SPlb SWhi
	- 'Anne's Goldzwerg'	CFst SWhi
	- 'Anne's Zwerg'	CFst SWhi
	- 'Anthony Davis'	SWhi
	- 'Anthony Wain'	SWhi
	- 'Anton'	SWhi
	- 'Antrujo Gold'	SWhi
	- 'Aphrodite'^{PBR} (Garden Girls Series)	SWhi
	- 'Apollo'	CFst SWhi
	- 'Applecross' (d)	SWhi
	- 'Arabella'^{PBR}	SWhi
	- 'Argentea'	SWhi
	- 'Ariadne'	SWhi
	- 'Arina'	GPer SCoo SWhi
	- 'Arran Gold'	SWhi
	- 'Ashgarth Amethyst'	SWhi
	- 'Ashgarth Shell Pink'	SWhi
	- 'Asterix'	SWhi
	- 'Atalanta'	SWhi
	- 'Athene'^{PBR} (Garden Girls Series)	CFst SWhi
	- 'Atholl Gold'	CFst SWhi
	- 'August Beauty'	GPer SWhi
	- 'Aurea'	SWhi
	- 'Aurelia' (Garden Girls Series) **new**	SWhi
	- 'Baby Ben'	CFst SWhi
	- 'Baby Wicklow'	SWhi
	- 'Barbara Fleur'	SWhi
	- 'Barnett Anley'	SWhi
	- 'Battle of Arnhem'	SWhi
	- 'Beechwood Crimson'	SWhi
	- 'Ben Nevis'	SWhi
	- 'Beoley Crimson'	GPer SCoo SWhi
	- 'Beoley Gold' 🏆^{H7}	CTri GPer MAsh NHol SCoo SWhi
	- 'Beoley Silver'	SCoo SWhi
	- 'Bernadette'	SWhi
	- 'Berta'^{PBR} (Garden Girls Series) **new**	SWhi
	- 'Betty Baum'	SWhi
	- 'Blazeaway'	CTri GPer MAsh SCoo SWhi
	- 'Blueness'	SWhi
	- 'Bonfire Brilliance'	GPer NHol SWhi
	- 'Bonita'^{PBR} (Garden Girls Series)	CFst SWhi
	- 'Boskoop'	CFst GPer MAsh NHol SWhi
	- 'Bradford'	SWhi
	- 'Braemar'	SWhi
	- 'Bray Head'	SWhi
	- 'Bronze Beauty'	SWhi
	- 'Bunsall'	SWhi
	- 'C.W. Nix'	GPer SWhi
	- 'Caerketton White'	GPer SWhi
	- 'Caleb Threlkeld'	SWhi
	- 'Calf of Man'	SWhi
	- 'Californian Midge'	SWhi
	- 'Carmen'	CFst SWhi
	- 'Carmen Neu' **new**	SWhi
	- 'Carngold'	SWhi
	- 'Cassa'	SWhi
	- 'Catherine'	SWhi
	- 'Catherine Anne'	SWhi
	- 'Charles Chapman'	SWhi
§	- 'Chernobyl' (d)	SWhi
	- 'Chindit'	SWhi
	- 'Christina'	SWhi
	- 'Claire' (Garden Girls Series) **new**	SWhi
	- 'Clare Carpet'	SWhi
	- 'Coccinea'	SWhi
	- 'Con Brio'	CFst GPer SCoo SWhi
	- 'Connemara Colleen'	CFst SWhi
	- 'Copper Glow'	SWhi
	- 'Corrie's White'	GJos GPer
	- 'Cottswood Gold'	GJos GPer SCoo SWhi
	- 'County Wicklow' (d) 🏆^{H7}	CFst CTri ELan GPer NHol SCoo SWhi
	- 'Craig Rossie'	SWhi
	- 'Crail Orange'	SWhi
	- 'Cramond' (d)	GPer SWhi
	- 'Cream Steving'	SWhi
	- 'Crimson Glory'	SWhi
	- 'Crinkly Tuft'	SWhi
	- 'Crowborough Beacon'	SWhi
	- 'Cuprea'	SCoo SWhi
	- 'Dainty Bess'	SWhi
	- 'Dark Beauty'^{PBR} (d) 🏆^{H7}	CBcs CFst ELan GPer LCro LOPS MAsh NHol SCoo SWhi
	- 'Dark Star' (d) 🏆^{H7}	CFst GJos GPer MAsh NHol SCoo SWhi
	- 'Darkness' 🏆^{H7}	CBcs CFst CTri GPer SCoo SWhi
	- 'Darleyensis'	SWhi
	- 'Dart's Amethyst'	SWhi
	- 'Dart's Flamboyant'	SWhi
	- 'Dart's Gold'	SWhi
	- 'Dart's Hedgehog'	SWhi
	- 'Dart's Parrot'	SWhi
	- 'Dart's Silver Rocket'	SWhi
	- 'Dart's Squirrel'	SWhi

	- 'David Eason'	CFst SWhi
	- 'David Hagenaars'	CFst SWhi
	- 'Desiree'	SWhi
	- 'Diana'	SWhi
	- 'Dirry'	CFst SWhi
	- 'Disco Queen'	GPer SWhi
	- 'Douglas Innes' **new**	SWhi
	- 'Drum-ra'	GPer SWhi
	- 'Dunkeld White'	SWhi
	- 'Dunnet Lime'	SPlb
	- 'Dunwood'	SWhi
§	- 'Durford Wood'	SWhi
	- 'E.F. Brown'	SWhi
	- 'E. Hoare'	SWhi
	- 'Easter-bonfire'	SCoo SWhi
	- 'Eckart Miessner'	SWhi
	- 'Elaine'	SWhi
	- 'Elegant Pearl'	SWhi
	- 'Elegantissima'	SWhi
	- 'Elkstone White'	SWhi
	- 'Ellen'	SWhi
	- 'Ellie Barbour'	SWhi
	- 'Else Frye' (d)	SWhi
	- 'Elsie Purnell' (d) 𝕐H7	CFst ELan GPer NHol SCoo SPlb SWhi
	- 'Emerald Jock'	SWhi
	- 'Emma Louise Tuke'	SWhi
	- 'Eric Easton'	SWhi
	- 'Fairy'	SWhi
	- 'Falling Star'	SWhi
	- 'Feuerwerk'	SCoo SWhi
§	- 'Finale'	SWhi
	- 'Firebreak'	SWhi
	- 'Firefly' 𝕐H7	CFst GPer NHol SCoo SPer SWhi
	- 'Flamingo'	GPer SCoo SWhi
	- 'Flore Pleno' (d)	SWhi
	- 'Floriferous'	SWhi
	- 'Florrie Spicer'	SWhi
	- 'Forest Fire'	CFst SWhi
	- 'Fort Bragg'	SWhi
	- 'Foxhollow Wanderer'	SWhi
	- 'Foxii'	SWhi
	- 'Foxii Floribunda'	SWhi
	- 'Foxii Lett's Form'	see *C. vulgaris* 'Mousehole'
	- 'Foxii Nana'	CFst NHol SWhi
	- 'Fred J. Chapple'	GPer SWhi
	- 'French Grey'	SWhi
	- 'Freya' (Garden Girls Series) **new**	SWhi
	- 'Fritz Kircher'PBR	SWhi
	- 'Galaxy'PBR	CFst SWhi
	- 'Gina'PBR (Garden Girls Series)	SWhi
	- 'Glen Mashie'	SWhi
	- 'Glencoe' (d)	SWhi
	- 'Glendoick Silver'	SWhi
	- 'Glenfiddich'	GPer SWhi
	- 'Glenmorangie'	SWhi
	- 'Gloucester Boy'	SWhi
	- 'Gnome Pink'	SWhi
	- 'Gold Finch'	SWhi
	- 'Gold Flame'	GPer SWhi
	- GOLD HAMILTON	see *C. vulgaris* 'Chernobyl'
	- 'Gold Haze'	CTri MAsh NHol SCoo SWhi
	- 'Gold Knight'	ELan SCoo SWhi
	- 'Gold Kup'	SWhi
	- 'Gold Mist'	SWhi
	- 'Gold Spronk'	CFst SWhi
	- 'Gold Turret'	SWhi
	- 'Goldcarmen'	SWhi

	- 'Golden Angie' (Garden Girls Series)	CFst SWhi
	- 'Golden Blazeaway'	SWhi
	- 'Golden Carpet'	CFst GJos GPer MAsh NHol SWhi
	- 'Golden Dew'	SWhi
	- 'Golden Feather'	SWhi
	- 'Golden Fleece'	CFst SWhi
	- 'Golden Wonder' (d)	SWhi
	- 'Goldsworth Crimson'	SWhi
	- 'Goldsworth Crimson Variegated' (v)	SWhi
	- 'Grasmeriensis'	SWhi
	- 'Great Comp'	SWhi
	- 'Grey Carpet'	CFst SWhi
	- 'Grizzly'	SWhi
	- 'Guinea Gold'	CFst GPer SWhi
§	- 'H.E. Beale' (d)	CTri GPer MAsh NHol SCoo SWhi
	- 'Hamlet Green'	SWhi
	- 'Hammondii'	SWhi
	- 'Hammondii Aureifolia'	GPer SPlb SWhi
	- 'Hammondii Rubrifolia'	SWhi
	- 'Hannover'	CFst SWhi
	- 'Harry Gibbon' (d)	SWhi
	- 'Harten's Findling'	SWhi
	- 'Hatje's Herbstfeuer' (d)	SWhi
	- 'Hayesensis'	SWhi
	- 'Heidberg'	SWhi
	- 'Heidepracht'	SWhi
	- 'Heidesinfonie'	CFst SWhi
	- 'Heideteppich'	SWhi
	- 'Heidezwerg'	SWhi
	- 'Heike' (d)	CFst SWhi
	- 'Helena' (Garden Girls Series)	CFst SWhi
	- 'Hera'PBR	SWhi
	- 'Herbert Mitchell'	SWhi
	- 'Hetty'	SWhi
	- 'Hibernica'	SWhi
	- 'Hiemalis'	SWhi
	- 'Hiemalis Southcote'	see *C. vulgaris* 'Durford Wood'
	- HIGHLAND CREAM	see *C. vulgaris* 'Punch's Dessert'
	- 'Highland Rose'	CFst SPlb SWhi
	- 'Hilda'PBR (Garden Girls Series)	CFst SWhi
	- 'Hilda Turberfield'	SWhi
	- 'Hillbrook Limelight'	SWhi
	- 'Hillbrook Sparkler'	SWhi
	- 'Hinton White'	SWhi
	- var. ***hirsuta***	SWhi
	- 'Hirsuta Albiflora'	SWhi
	- 'Hirsuta Typica'	SWhi
	- 'Hollandia'	SWhi
	- 'Hookstone'	SWhi
§	- 'Hugh Nicholson'	GPer SWhi
	- 'Humpty Dumpty'	SWhi
	- 'Hypnoides'	SWhi
	- 'Ide's Double' (d)	SWhi
	- 'Inchcolm'	SWhi
	- 'Ineke'	SWhi
	- 'Ingrid Bouter' (d)	SWhi
	- 'Inshriach Bronze'	SWhi
	- 'Islay Mist'	SWhi
	- 'Isobel Frye'	SWhi
	- 'Isobel Hughes' (d)	SWhi
	- 'J.H. Hamilton' (d)	CTri ELan GPer MAsh NHol SCoo SWhi
	- 'Jan'	SWhi
	- 'Jan Dekker'	GPer SWhi
	- 'Jana' (d)	CFst SWhi
	- 'Janice Chapman'	SWhi

	- 'Janina' (Garden Girls Series) **new**	SWhi
	- 'Japanese White'	SWhi
	- 'Jill'	SWhi
	- 'Jimmy Dyce' (d)	CFst SWhi
	- 'Joan Sparkes' (d)	SWhi
	- 'John F. Letts'	SWhi
	- 'Johnson's Variety'	SCoo SWhi
	- 'Josefine'	CFst SWhi
	- 'Joseph's Coat'	SWhi
	- 'Josi' (d) **new**	SWhi
	- 'Joy Vanstone'	GJos GPer SWhi
	- 'Julia'	CFst SWhi
	- 'Julie Ann Platt'	SWhi
	- 'Jysk Naturform' **new**	SWhi
	- 'Katja'^{PBR} (Garden Girls Series) **new**	SWhi
	- 'Kermit'	SWhi
	- 'Kerstin' ♀^{H7}	CFst GPer NHol SCoo SPer SPlb SWhi
	- 'Kinlochruel' (d) ♀^{H7}	CBcs CFst CTri GJos GPer MAsh NHol SPlb SWhi
	- 'Kiran'	CFst SWhi
	- 'Kirby White'	MAsh SPlb SWhi
	- 'Kit Hill'	SWhi
	- 'Klaudine'^{PBR} (Garden Girls Series)	CFst SWhi
	- 'Kuphaldtii'	SWhi
	- 'Kynance'	SWhi
	- 'Lady Maithe'	SWhi
	- 'Lambstails'	SWhi
	- 'L'Ancresse'	SWhi
	- 'Late Crimson Gold'	SWhi
	- 'Lemon Gem'	SWhi
	- 'Lemon Queen'	CFst SWhi
	- 'Lena'^{PBR} (Garden Girls Series) **new**	SWhi
	- 'Leprechaun'	CFst SWhi
	- 'Leslie Slinger'	SCoo SWhi
	- 'Liliane'^{PBR} (Garden Girls Series)	SWhi
	- 'Lilli'^{PBR} (Garden Girls Series)	SWhi
	- 'Lime Glade'	SWhi
	- 'Lisbeth'^{PBR} (Garden Girls Series) **new**	SWhi
	- 'Little John'	LSRN
	- 'Loch Turret'	GPer SWhi
	- 'Loch-na-Seil'	SWhi
	- 'Loki'^{PBR} (Garden Girls Series)	SWhi
	- 'London Pride'	SWhi
	- 'Long White'	SWhi
	- 'Low White' **new**	SWhi
	- 'Luisa'^{PBR} (Garden Girls Series)	CFst SWhi
	- 'Lyle's Late White'	SWhi
	- 'Lyle's Surprise'	SWhi
	- 'Lyndon Proudley'	SWhi
	- 'Macdonald of Glencoe'	SWhi
	- 'Madonna'^{PBR} (Garden Girls Series)	SWhi
§	- 'Mair's Variety'	GPer SCoo SWhi
	- 'Mallard'	SWhi
	- 'Manitoba'	SWhi
	- 'Marcelita' (d)	CFst SWhi
	- 'Marie'	SWhi
	- 'Marion Blum'	SWhi
	- 'Marleen'	SWhi
§	- 'Marlies'	CFst SWhi

	- 'Martha Hermann'	SWhi
	- 'Mary Rose' (Garden Girls Series) **new**	SWhi
	- 'Melanie' (Garden Girls Series)	NHol SCoo SWhi
	- 'Mick Jamieson' (d)	SWhi
	- 'Mickkle-Dickkle'	SWhi
	- 'Minima'	SWhi
	- 'Molecule'	CFst SWhi
§	- 'Mousehole'	SWhi
	- 'Mrs Alf'	SWhi
	- 'Mrs E. Wilson' (d)	SWhi
	- 'Mrs Pat'	MAsh SWhi
	- 'Mrs Ronald Gray'	SWhi
	- 'Mullach Mor'	SWhi
	- 'Mullion'	SWhi
	- 'Multicolor'	MAsh NHol SWhi
	- 'Murielle Dobson'	SWhi
§	- 'My Dream' (d)	SCoo SWhi
	- 'Nana Compacta'	CFst GPer SWhi
	- 'Natasja'	SWhi
	- 'Nelly' (Garden Girls Series) **new**	SWhi
	- 'Nico'	SWhi
	- 'Nora' (Garden Girls Series)	SWhi
	- 'October White'	CFst SWhi
	- 'Olive Turner'	SWhi
	- 'Olympic Gold'	CFst SWhi
	- 'Orange and Gold'	SWhi
	- 'Orange Max'	GPer
	- 'Orange Queen'	SWhi
	- 'Öxabäck'	SWhi
	- 'Oxshott Common'	SWhi
	- 'Pallida'	SWhi
	- 'Parsons Gold'	SWhi
	- 'Pearl Drop'	SWhi
	- 'Penhale'	SWhi
	- 'Penny Bun'	SWhi
	- 'Pennyacre Gold'	SWhi
	- 'Pennyacre Lemon'	CFst SWhi
	- 'Pepper and Salt'	see *C. vulgaris* 'Hugh Nicholson'
	- 'Perestrojka'	SWhi
	- 'Peter Sparkes' (d) ♀^{H7}	CBcs CFst GPer MAsh NHol SCoo SWhi
	- 'Petra'	SWhi
	- 'Pewter Plate'	CFst SWhi
	- 'Pink Angie' (Garden Girls Series) **new**	SWhi
	- 'Pink Beale'	see *C. vulgaris* 'H.E. Beale'
	- 'Pink Gown'	SWhi
	- 'Plantarium'	SWhi
	- 'Platt's Surprise' (d)	SWhi
	- 'Prizewinner'	SWhi
	- 'Prostrata Flagelliformis'	SWhi
	- 'Prostrate Orange'	SWhi
§	- 'Punch's Dessert'	SWhi
	- 'Purple Passion'	ELan SCoo SWhi
	- 'Pygmaea'	SWhi
	- 'Pyramidalis'	SWhi
	- 'Pyrenaica'	SWhi
	- 'Radnor' (d)	GPer SWhi
	- 'Radnor Gold' (d)	SWhi
	- 'Ralph Purnell'	ELan SCoo SWhi
	- 'Ralph Purnell Select'	SWhi
	- 'Ralph's Pearl'	SWhi
	- 'Ralph's Red'	SWhi
	- 'Red Beauty'	CBcs CFst SPer SWhi
	- 'Red Carpet'	SWhi
	- 'Red Favorit' (d)	CFst GJos GPer SWhi
	- 'Red Fred'	SCoo SWhi

– 'Red Haze'	GPer NHol SCoo SWhi
– 'Red Max'	SWhi
– 'Red Pimpernel'	CFst ELan SCoo SWhi
– 'Red Rug'	SWhi
– 'Red Star' (d)	CFst NHol SWhi
– 'Redbud'	CFst SWhi
– 'Rena' (Garden Girls Series) **new**	SWhi
– 'Rica'	SWhi
– 'Richard Cooper'	SWhi
– 'Rigida Prostrata'	see *C. vulgaris* 'Alba Rigida'
– 'Robert Chapman' ♀H7	CFst CTri MAsh NHol SPer SWhi
I – 'Rock Spray'	SWhi
– 'Roland Haagen'	SWhi
– 'Roma'	CFst SWhi
– 'Romina'	SWhi
– 'Ronas Hill'	SWhi
– 'Roodkapje'	SWhi
– 'Rosalind, Crastock Heath'	SWhi
– 'Rosalind, Underwood's'	NHol SWhi
– 'Rosann' (Garden Girls Series)	SWhi
– 'Rosita'PBR (Garden Girls Series)	CFst SWhi
– 'Ross Hutton'	SWhi
– 'Roter Oktober'	CFst SWhi
– 'Ruby Slinger'	NHol SWhi
– 'Ruth Sparkes' (d)	NHol SWhi
– Saint Kilda Group	SWhi
– 'Saint Nick'	SWhi
– 'Sally Anne Proudley'	SWhi
– 'Salmon Leap'	GPer SWhi
– 'Sam Hewitt'	SWhi
– 'Sampford Sunset'	SWhi
– 'Sandwood Bay'	SWhi
– 'Sandy'PBR (Garden Girls Series)	CFst SPoG SWhi
– 'Sarah'PBR (Garden Girls Series) **new**	SWhi
– 'Schneewittchen'	CFst
– 'Scholje's Rubin' (d)	SWhi
– 'Scholje's Super Star' (d)	SWhi
– 'Schurig's Sensation' (d)	SWhi
– 'Scotch Mist'	SWhi
– 'Sellingsloh'	SWhi
– 'Selma'PBR (Garden Girls Series) **new**	SWhi
– 'Serlei'	SWhi
– 'Serlei Aurea'	SWhi
– 'Serlei Grandiflora'	SWhi
– 'Serlei Purpurea'	SWhi
– 'Serlei Rubra'	SWhi
– 'Sesam'	CFst SWhi
– 'Shirley'	SWhi
– 'Silvana'PBR (Garden Girls Series)	CFst SWhi
– 'Silver Cloud'	SWhi
– 'Silver Fox'	CBcs CFst SWhi
– 'Silver King'	CFst SWhi
– 'Silver Knight'	ELan GJos GPer MAsh NHol SCoo SPlb SWhi
– 'Silver Queen' ♀H7	CFst GPer MAsh NHol SWhi
– 'Silver Rose'	SWhi
– 'Silver Sandra'	SWhi
– 'Silver Stream'	SWhi
– 'Sir John Charrington'	CFst GPer NHol SWhi
– 'Sister Anne' ♀H7	CFst GPer SCoo SWhi
– 'Skipper'	SWhi
– 'Snow White'	CFst SWhi
– 'Snowball'	see *C. vulgaris* 'My Dream'
– 'Snowflake'	SWhi
– 'Soay'	SWhi
– 'Sonning' (d)	SWhi
– 'Spicata'	SWhi
– 'Spicata Aurea'	SWhi
– 'Spitfire'	CFst GPer SWhi
– 'Spring Cream' ♀H7	CBcs CFst GPer MAsh NHol SCoo SWhi
– 'Spring Glow'	SWhi
– 'Spring Torch'	CBcs CFst GPer MAsh NHol SCoo SWhi
– 'Stefanie'	SWhi
– 'Stranger'	SWhi
– 'Strawberry Delight' (d)	ELan SCoo
– 'Summer Elegance'	SWhi
– 'Summer Orange'	GJos GPer
– 'Sun Sprinkles'	CFst SWhi
– 'Sunningdale'	see *C. vulgaris* 'Finale'
– 'Sunrise'	SWhi
– 'Sunset'	CFst GJos GPer SWhi
– 'Tenuis'	SWhi
– 'Terrick's Orange'	SWhi
– 'Theresa' (Garden Girls Series)	SWhi
– 'Tib' (d) ♀H7	GPer MAsh SWhi
– 'Tijdens Copper'	SWhi
– 'Tom Thumb'	CFst SWhi
– 'Tomentosa Alba'	SWhi
– 'Tom's Fancy'	SWhi
– 'Torogay'	SWhi
– 'Torulosa'	SWhi
– 'Tremans'	SWhi
– 'Tricolorifolia'	SCoo SWhi
– 'Trinklet'	SWhi
– 'Underwoodii'	SWhi
– 'Velvet Fascination' ♀H7	CFst GPer SCoo SWhi
– 'Visser's Fancy'	SWhi
– 'Waquoit Brightness'	SWhi
– 'Westerlee Green'	SWhi
– 'Westphalia'	SWhi
– 'White Angie' (Garden Girls Series)	SWhi
– 'White Bouquet'	see *C. vulgaris* 'Alba Plena'
– 'White Carpet'	SWhi
– 'White Coral' (d) ♀H7	CFst ELan SCoo SWhi
– 'White Gold'	SWhi
– 'White Gown'	SWhi
– 'White Lawn'	CFst GPer NHol SWhi
– 'White Mite'	SWhi
– 'White Princess'	see *C. vulgaris* 'White Queen'
§ – 'White Queen'	SWhi
– 'Whiteness'	SWhi
– 'Wickwar Flame' ♀H7	CBcs CFst ELan GPer MAsh NHol SCoo SPlb SWhi
– 'Wingates Gem'	SWhi
– 'Wingates Gold'	SWhi
– 'Winter Chocolate'	CFst MAsh NHol SCoo SWhi
– 'Winter Fire'	SWhi
– 'Wollmer's Weisse' (d)	SWhi
– 'Wood Close'	SWhi
– 'Yellow Basket'	CFst SWhi
– 'Yellow Beauty'PBR	CFst SWhi
– 'Yvette's Gold'	CFst SWhi
– 'Yvette's Silver'	CFst SWhi
– 'Zelia'PBR (Garden Girls Series) **new**	SWhi
– 'Zeta'PBR (Garden Girls Series)	CFst SWhi
– 'Zora'PBR (Garden Girls Series) **new**	SWhi

	- 'Zulu'^{PBR} (Garden Girls Series) **new**	SWhi

Calocedrus (*Cupressaceae*)

§	***decurrens*** 𝕐^{H7}	CBcs CLnd CTho EPfP LMaj MBlu MGil SPtp WTSh
	- 'Aureovariegata' (v) 𝕐^{H7}	CBcs
	- 'Berrima Gold' 𝕐^{H7}	NLar
§	- 'Depressa'	CKen
	- 'Maupin Glow' (v)	NLar SLim
	- 'Nana'	see *C. decurrens* 'Depressa'
	- 'Pillar'	CKen

Calocephalus (*Asteraceae*)

	brownii	see *Leucophyta brownii*

Calochortus (*Liliaceae*)

	'Cupido'^{PBR}	CExl EPot GKev SDeJ
	luteus 'Golden Orb'^{PBR}	CExl SDeJ
	splendens 'Violet Queen'	SDeJ
	superbus	SDeJ
	'Symphony'^{PBR}	CExl SDeJ
	venustus	SDeJ
	- 'Burgundy'	SDeJ

Calomeria (*Asteraceae*)

§	***amaranthoides***	WJek

Calonyction see *Ipomoea*

Caloscordum see *Allium*

Calothamnus (*Myrtaceae*)

	validus	SPlb
	villosus	SPlb

Calpurnia (*Papilionaceae*)

	aurea	SPlb

Caltha ✿ (*Ranunculaceae*)

	howellii	see *C. leptosepala* subsp. *howellii*
	laeta	see *C. palustris* var. *palustris*
	leptosepala	EBee EMor EWat GEdr GKev GMaP LLWG NLar
	- SDR 8134	GKev
§	- subsp. ***howellii*** NNS 07-87	GKev
	natans	LLWG
	palustris	Widely available
	- var. ***alba***	Widely available
	- 'Auengold'	LLWG
	- 'Auenwald'	LLWG
	- var. ***barthei***	GEdr
	- 'Flore Pleno' (d) 𝕐^{H7}	CAby CBen CMac CMea CWld EBee ECha ELan EWat GAbr GKin GMaP GQue MMuc MRav NBir NChi NGdn NHol NLar NPer NRya SEND SPer SPlb SRms WFar WMAq WPnP XLum
	- 'Girls Eyes'	MNrw
	- 'Himalayan Snow'	EBee LLWG WFar
	- 'Honeydew'	CAby ELon EWat LLWG MNrw WCot WSHC
	- var. ***laeta*** **new**	LLWG
	- 'Marilyn'	LLWG
	- 'Multiplex' (d)	CDor ECtt EMor
	- Newlake hybrid	LLWG
§	- var. ***palustris***	CBen CBre ECha EWat LLWG WWtn
	- - 'Plena' (d)	CRos CSam CWat EHyd EWat LRHS MTin NRHS SGol
	- var. ***radicans***	EWat GEdr
	- - 'Flore Pleno' (d)	WWtn
	- 'Stagnalis'	MWts
	polypetala Hochst. ex Lorent	CWat MSCN NPer SMad WMAq
	sagittata	WSHC
	scaposa	GKev

Calycanthus (*Calycanthaceae*)

	'Aphrodite'	CBcs CMCN
	chinensis	CBcs CCCN CJun CMCN CRos EBee EHyd EPfP LRHS MBlu MGil MPkF NLar SPtp
	fertilis	see *C. floridus* var. *glaucus*
	floridus	Widely available
	- 'Athens'	CJun WPGP
§	- var. ***glaucus***	EPfP
	- - 'Purpureus'	CJun MBlu NLar
	- var. ***laevigatus***	see *C. floridus* var. *glaucus*
	- 'Michael Lindsay'	CJun NLar WPGP
	mohrii	NLar
	occidentalis	CBcs CMCN MAsh MBlu MGil SBrt
	× ***raulstonii*** 'Hartlage Wine' 𝕐^{H5}	CBcs CDoC CJun CMCN CRos EHyd ELan ELon EPfP GKin IArd IDee LCro LOPS LRHS LSRN MAsh MBlu MGos NLar SMad SPoG SavN WKif
	'Venus'	CBcs CJun CMCN ELan EPfP LCro LOPS MAsh MBlu NLar SMad SavN

Calystegia (*Convolvulaceae*)

§	***hederacea*** 'Flore Pleno' (d)	SMad
	japonica 'Flore Pleno'	see *C. hederacea* 'Flore Pleno'
	soldanella NNS 99-85	WCot

Calytrix (*Myrtaceae*)

	tetragona	SPlb

Camassia ✿ (*Asparagaceae*)

	'Blue Candle'	EPfP EPot GKev NHsp SPhx
	'Blue Heaven'	CAvo CMea CRos EPfP ERCP LRHS LSun MAvo NHsp NLar NRHS SDeJ SPhx
	Broadleigh Belle Group	CBro
	cusickii	CAby CBro CExl CRos CTri CWCL EBee ECtt EHyd ELan EPfP EPot ERCP EWhm GBin GKev LCro LOPS LRHS MCot NBir NLar NRHS SDeJ SDix WPnP
	- 'Crystal Star' **new**	NHsp
	- white-flowered	CBod
	- 'Zwanenburg'	CRos EHyd ERCP GKev IPot LRHS NHpl NHsp NRHS WCot
	esculenta Lindl.	see *C. quamash*
	leichtlinii misapplied	see *C. leichtlinii* subsp. *suksdorfii*
	leichtlinii (Baker) S.Watson	MArl
	- 'Alba' misapplied	see *C. leichtlinii* subsp. *leichtlinii*
*	- 'Alba Plena'	LSun MNrw NBir NHpl
	- Avon's Stellar Group **new**	CAvo
	- BLUE DANUBE	see *C. leichtlinii* subsp. *suksdorfii* 'Blauwe Donau'
	- 'Blue Wave'	NHsp NWad
	- 'Harlequin' (v)	NHsp
§	- subsp. ***leichtlinii***	Widely available
	- 'Magdalen'	MAvo
	- pale pink-flowered	GKev NHsp
	- 'Plena' (d)	ECha
	- 'Sacajawea' (v)	CAvo CMea CRos ECha EHyd EPfP ERCP GKev LRHS MAvo NHsp NRHS SDeJ WCot WFar WTor

- 'Semiplena' (d)	CAvo CBro CMea CRos EBee ECtt EHyd EPfP EPot ERCP GKev LRHS MBel MBow MBriF MNrw NRHS NSti SPhx WBor WCot WPnP WShi
§ - subsp. ***suksdorfii***	LCro LOPS MBriF NPoe WCot
- - 'Alba'	CAby CAvo CRos EHyd EPot GBin GMaP ITim LCro LOPS LRHS NRHS NSti SCob SEdd SPtp
§ - - 'Blauwe Donau'	ILea
- - Caerulea Group	Widely available
- - - 'Maybelle'	CAvo CMea ERCP GKev IPot MBriF MPri NHsp
- - 'Electra'	CAvo CMea ECha MAvo WCot
- - 'Lady Eve Price'	MAvo WCot
§ ***quamash***	CAvo CCBP CSpe CWCL EBee ECha EHyd ELan EPot ERCP GAbr GKev LCro LEdu LOPS LRHS NBir NLar NRHS SDeJ SDix SRms WCav WFar WPnP WShi XLum
- 'Blue Melody' (v)	CMea CRos CSam EBee EHyd EPot ERCP GMaP LEdu LRHS NHsp NRHS SDeJ WOut WRHF
- 'Orion'	CRos EBee EHyd ERCP GKev LRHS NHsp NRHS WCot
- var. ***quamash***	CBcs

Camellia ✿ (*Theaceae*)

'Adorable' (*pitardii* hybrid)	LRHS LSRN
'April Blush'	WFar
'Auburn White'	see *C. japonica* 'Mrs Bertha A. Harms'
azalea	SReu SavN
'Barbara Clark' (*reticulata* × *saluenensis*)	LRHS LSRN MAsh NRHS
'Bertha Harms Blush'	see *C. japonica* 'Mrs Bertha A. Harms'
'Black Lace' ♀H5	CBcs CBod CDoC CRos CTrh CTri EPfP LCro LOPS LRHS LSRN MAsh MMuc MPri NRHS SArc SWeb SWvt
'Blissful Dawn'	CBcs CTrh
'Bonnie Marie'	CBcs SCam
'Canterbury'	CDoC SCam
'Christmas Daffodil' (*japonica* hybrid)	CBcs LRHS
'Cinnamon Cindy'	LRHS SCam
'Congratulations'	CSBt LSRN
'Contessa Lavinia Maggi'	see *C. japonica* 'Lavinia Maggi'
'Cornish Snow' (*cuspidata* × *saluenensis*) ♀H4	CBcs CDoC CMac CTri CTsd SCam SWvt WFar
'Cornish Spring' (*cuspidata* × *japonica*) ♀H4	CBcs CBod CCCN CSBt CTrh LRHS NRHS SCam
'Crimson Candles' ♀H5	LRHS
'Delia Williams'	see *C.* × ***williamsii*** 'Citation'
'Diamond Head' (*japonica* × *reticulata*)	CBcs LSRN
'Diana's Charm'	CDoC
'Doctor Clifford Parks' (*japonica* × *reticulata*) ♀H4	CBcs
'Donckelaeri'	see *C. japonica* 'Masayoshi'
'Extravaganza' (*japonica* hybrid) ♀H5	CTrh IArd SCoo
'Fairy Blush'	LRHS
'Fascination'	SWvt
'Faustina Lechi'	see *C. japonica* 'Faustina'
'Felice Harris' (*reticulata* × *sasanqua*)	SCoo
forrestii	GKev IDee WPGP
'Forty-niner' (*japonica* × *reticulata*)	LRHS NRHS
'Fragrant Pink'	SCam
'Francie L' ♀H4	CBcs CMac
'Frau Minna Seidel'	see *C. japonica* subsp. *rusticana* 'Ōtome'
'Free Spirit'	CDoC CTrh
'Freedom Bell' ♀H5	CDoC CTrh EPfP GKin LRHS MPri NRHS SCam SCob
'Frosted Star'	LRHS
'Gay Baby'	CDoC
'Golden Anniversary'	see *C. japonica* 'Dahlohnega'
grijsii	CBcs CExl CTrh LRHS
handelii	CExl
'Happy Anniversary'	CSBt LSRN SWvt
§ ***hiemalis*** 'Bonanza'	CTrh LRHS
- 'Chansonette'	SCam
§ - 'Dazzler'	CBcs LRHS NRHS SCam
- 'Elfin Rose'	LRHS
- 'Kanjirō'	MHtn SCam SWeb
- 'Shishigashira'	CTrh
- 'Shōwa-no-sakae'	MHtn
'Hooker'	LRHS MAsh NRHS
'Imbricata Rubra'	see *C. japonica* 'Imbricata'
'Inspiration' (*reticulata* × *saluenensis*) ♀H5	CDoC CMac CTrh EPfP LRHS LSRN MGos NLar SCam
japonica	LMaj LRHS SEWo SPre
- 'Aaron's Ruby'	ELon LRHS NRHS
- 'Ace of Hearts'	SCoo
- 'Ada Pieper'	CTrh
- 'Adelina Patti' ♀H5	CBcs CDoC CTrh SCam XLot
- 'Adeyaka'	LRHS NRHS XLot
- 'Adolphe Audusson' ♀H5	CBcs CBod CDoC CSBt CTrh CTri ELon EPfP LCro LMil LOPS LRHS LSRN MAsh MGos MMuc MPri MSwo NRHS SCam SCob SGol SLim SPer SPoG SRms SSta SWvt WFar XLot
§ - 'Akashigata' ♀H5	CBcs ELon EPfP LRHS LSRN NRHS SCam SSta
- 'Alba Plena' (d) ♀H5	CSBt CTrh LRHS SCob SWvt
- 'Alba Simplex'	CMac CTrh EPfP LMaj MPri SSta XLot
§ - 'Albertii'	XLot
- 'Alexander Hunter' ♀H5	LRHS NRHS SCam
§ - 'Althaeiflora'	CBcs CDoC ELon LRHS NRHS SCam
- 'Anemoniflora'	EPfP LRHS NRHS
- 'Angel'	LSRN WBor
- 'Angello'	LRHS NRHS
- 'Ann Sothern'	CBcs
- 'Annie Wylam' ♀H5	CTrh SCoo
- 'Apollo' ambig.	CBcs LRHS MAsh NRHS
§ - 'Apollo' Paul, 1911	MSwo SCam
§ - 'Apple Blossom'	CBcs LRHS NRHS
- 'April Blush'	XLot
- 'April Kiss'	XLot
- 'April Remembered'	WFar XLot
- 'April Rose'	WFar XLot
- 'Arajishi' misapplied	see *C. japonica* subsp. *rusticana* 'Beni-arajishi'
- 'Augustine Supreme'	CMac
- 'Ave Maria' ♀H5	CDoC CTrh LMaj LRHS MGos NRHS
- 'Baby Pearl'	LSRN SCam
- 'Baby Sis'	LRHS NRHS
- 'Ballet Dancer' ♀H5	ELon LSRN SCam
- 'Bambino'	CDoC
- 'Baron Gomer'	see *C. japonica* 'Comte de Gomer'
- 'Baronne Leguay'	SCam
- 'Beau Harp'	LRHS NRHS SCam
- 'Bella Romana'	LMaj SCam XLot
- 'Berenice Boddy' ♀H5	CTrh LRHS NRHS

	– 'Betty Foy Sanders'	CTrh
	– 'Betty Robinson'	LRHS NRHS
	– 'Betty Sheffield'	LRHS MAsh NRHS
	– 'Betty Sheffield Pink'	LRHS NRHS SCam
	– 'Betty Sheffield Supreme'	CBcs SCam
	– 'Billie McCaskill'	SCam
	– 'Black Magic'	CDoC CTrh LRHS MAsh NRHS
	– 'Black Tie'	CBcs CDoC CTrh ELon LRHS MAsh MGos NRHS SCam WFar
	– 'Blackburnia'	see *C. japonica* 'Althaeiflora'
§	– 'Blood of China'	CBcs CSBt LRHS LSRN MGos NLar NRHS SCam SCoo SWvt XLot
	– 'Blush Tinsie'	LRHS NRHS
	– 'Bob Hope' $\mathbb{Y}^{H5}$	CDoC CTrh CTri LRHS NRHS SCam
	– 'Bob's Tinsie' $\mathbb{Y}^{H5}$	CBcs CSBt ELon EPfP LRHS LSRN MGos NRHS SPoG
§	– 'Bokuhan' $\mathbb{Y}^{H5}$	SCam
	– 'Bonomiana'	XLot
	– 'Bright Buoy'	LRHS NRHS
	– 'Brushfield's Yellow'	CBcs CDoC CRos CSBt CTrh CTsd ELan ELon EPfP IArd LRHS LSRN MAsh MGos NLar NRHS SCam SCoo SPer SSta WSpi XLot
	– 'Bush Hill Beauty'	see *C. japonica* 'Lady de Saumarez'
§	– 'C.M. Hovey' $\mathbb{Y}^{H5}$	CMac LRHS MAsh NRHS XLot
	– 'C.M. Wilson'	CMac
	– 'Campsii Alba'	SCam SCoo
	– 'Can Can'	CDoC ELon XLot
	– 'Cara Mia'	LRHS NRHS SCam SCoo
	– 'Cardinal's Cap'	XLot
	– 'Carolyn Tuttle'	LRHS NRHS
	– 'Carter's Sunburst' $\mathbb{Y}^{H5}$	CBcs ELon
	– 'Cassandra'	EPfP
	– 'Centifolia Alba'	LMaj
	– 'Chandleri Elegans'	see *C. japonica* 'Elegans'
	– 'Charlotte de Rothschild'	CTrh CTri
	– 'Cinderella'	LRHS NRHS
	– CLASSIQUE ('Kerguelen'^{PBR}) (v)	CDoC LRHS MAsh WFar
	– 'Colonel Firey'	see *C. japonica* 'C.M. Hovey'
	– 'Commander Mulroy' $\mathbb{Y}^{H5}$	CBcs SCoo
	– 'Compton's Brow'	see *C. japonica* 'Gauntlettii'
§	– 'Comte de Gomer'	ELon EPfP LRHS MPri NRHS SCam
	– 'Conspicua'	CBcs
	– 'Contessa Samailoff'	CDoC
§	– 'Coquettii' $\mathbb{Y}^{H5}$	LRHS MAsh NRHS
	– 'Covina' (d) **new**	XLot
	– 'Curly Lady'^{PBR}	CDoC MPri WFar XLot
§	– 'Dahlohnega'	CBod CDoC CRos CSBt CTrh ELon LMil LRHS LSRN MAsh MGos MHtn NRHS WFar
	– 'Dainty'	CBcs
	– 'Daitairin'	see *C. japonica* 'Dewatairin'
	– 'Daphne du Maurier'	CDoC LRHS NRHS
	– 'Dark of the Moon'	LRHS NRHS
	– 'Dear Jenny'	CBcs
	– 'Debutante'	CBcs CMac ELon LMaj SCam SGsty
	– 'Desire' $\mathbb{Y}^{H5}$	CBcs CBod CDoC CPla CSBt CTrh EPfP LCro LMil LOPS LRHS LSRN MAsh MGos NRHS SCam SPoG WFar
	– 'Devonia'	CBcs
§	– 'Dewatairin' (Higo)	CBcs CDoC SCam
	– 'Diddy's Pink Organdie'	LRHS NRHS
	– 'Dixie Knight'	LRHS NRHS SCam
	– 'Dobreei'	CMac
	– 'Doctor Burnside'	CBcs CTrh LMaj LRHS SCam SGsty SWeb
	– 'Doctor King'	CDoC EPfP LRHS MAsh MPri NRHS SCob SCoo SPoG WFar
	– 'Doctor Tinsley' $\mathbb{Y}^{H5}$	CDoC CRos EPfP LRHS MAsh MPri NRHS SCam SWeb
	– 'Dona Herzilia de Freitas Magalhães'	CBcs CDoC
	– 'Donckelaeri'	see *C. japonica* 'Masayoshi'
	– 'Donnan's Dream'	CDoC CTrh
	– 'Drama Girl' $\mathbb{Y}^{H5}$	CBcs LMaj LRHS NRHS SCam XLot
	– 'Duchesse Decazes'	CBcs
	– 'Edelweiss'	ELon SCam
§	– 'Elegans'	CBcs ELon EPfP LCro LMil LOPS LRHS MGos NRHS SCam SLim SPer SPoG SWvt
	– 'Elegans Splendor'	CDoC
	– 'Elisabeth'	LRHS NRHS
	– 'Elizabeth Cooper'	CTrh LSRN
	– 'Elizabeth Hawkins'	CTrh LRHS MAsh NRHS SCam
	– 'Elizabeth Weaver' **new**	CTrh
	– 'Emmett Pfingstl'	SCam
	– 'Emperor of Russia'	CBcs LRHS NRHS
	– 'Eric Baker'	SCam
	– 'Eugène Lizé'	SCam
	– 'Eximia'	LRHS NRHS
	– 'Faith'	CBcs
	– 'Fanny'	MHtn
	– 'Fashionata'	CDoC
§	– 'Faustina'	LRHS MAsh NRHS
	– 'Finlandia Variegated' (v)	ELon SCam
	– 'Fire Dance'	CDoC
	– 'Firebird'	CBcs CTsd
	– 'Flashlight'	EPfP LRHS NRHS
§	– 'Fleur Dipater'	CBcs CRos LRHS NRHS SCam
	– 'Frans van Damme'	CBcs
	– 'Fred Sander'	CDoC LRHS NRHS
	– 'Frosty Morn'	CDoC
§	– 'Gauntlettii'	CBcs
	– 'General George Patton' (d) **new**	XLot
§	– 'Gigantea'	ELon LRHS NRHS
	– 'Giuditta Rosani'	CDoC LRHS NRHS
	– 'Glen 40'	see *C. japonica* 'Coquettii'
	– 'Gloire de Nantes' $\mathbb{Y}^{H5}$	CTrh XLot
	– 'Gold Tone'	CDoC ELon SCam
	– 'Grace Bunton'	CBcs ELon
	– 'Grand Prix' $\mathbb{Y}^{H5}$	ELon LSRN NLar SWeb
	– 'Grand Slam' $\mathbb{Y}^{H5}$	MAsh SCam
	– 'Grandiflora Alba'	CBcs
	– 'Guest of Honor'	LRHS NRHS
	– 'Guilio Nuccio' $\mathbb{Y}^{H5}$	CBcs CTri ELon LRHS LSRN MPri NRHS SCam SLim SWeb
	– 'Gus Menard'	SCam
	– 'Gwenneth Morey'	CDoC
	– 'H.A. Downing'	CDoC SCam
§	– 'Hagoromo' $\mathbb{Y}^{H5}$	CBcs CSBt CTrh LMaj LRHS NRHS SWeb XLot
§	– 'Hakurakuten' $\mathbb{Y}^{H5}$	CTrh CTri SCam SCoo
	– 'Hanafūki'	LRHS MAsh NRHS SCam
	– 'Happy Birthday'	LSRN
	– 'Happy Higo'	SCam
	– 'Haru-no-utena'	CDoC CTrh
	– 'Hatsuzakura'	see *C. japonica* 'Dewatairin'
	– 'Hawaii'	CMac CTrh ELon LRHS NRHS SCam
	– HERME	see *C. japonica* 'Hikarugenji'
	– 'High Hat'	CBcs
	– 'High, Wide 'n' Handsome'	CDoC
§	– 'Hikarugenji'	LRHS NRHS
	– 'Hinomaru'	CMac
	– 'Holly Bright'	CDoC CTrh LRHS

§	– 'Imbricata'	CDoC CTrh LRHS MAsh NRHS
	– 'Imperator'	CDoC
	– 'Incarnata'	SCam
	– 'Italiana Vera'	CDoC LRHS MAsh NRHS
	– 'J.J. Whitfield'	CMac
	– 'Janet Waterhouse'	CBcs
§	– 'Japonica Variegata' (v)	LRHS NRHS
	– 'Joseph Pfingstl' ♀H5	CDoC CTri EPfP LRHS MAsh MMuc NLar NRHS SCam
	– 'Jovey Carlyon'	CBcs LRHS NRHS
	– 'Joy Sander'	see *C. japonica* 'Apple Blossom'
	– 'Jules Verne'	CDoC
	– 'Juno'	LRHS NRHS
	– 'Jupiter' Paul, 1904 ♀H5	CBcs CDoC CMac CTri EPfP LSRN MAsh SCam
	– 'Kellingtoniana'	see *C. japonica* 'Gigantea'
	– 'Kenny'	CBcs
	– 'Kentucky'	LRHS NRHS
	– 'Kick-off'	CBcs CTrh LRHS SCam
	– 'Kimberley'	CBcs CTsd LSRN SCam XLot
	– 'King Size'	CDoC
	– 'King's Ransom'	LRHS NRHS
	– 'Kingyoba-shiro-wabisuke'	SCam
	– 'Kingyo-tsubaki'	SCam SSta
	– 'Kitty Berry'	CTrh
	– 'Kokinran'	SCam
§	– 'Konronkoku' ♀H5	LRHS NRHS
	– 'Kouron-jura'	see *C. japonica* 'Konronkoku'
	– 'Kramer's Supreme' ♀H5	CBcs CBod CCCN CDoC ELon LRHS LSRN MAsh MGos NRHS SCam SCob SCoo SGol XLot
§	– 'Kumasaka'	CTri LRHS MAsh NRHS
	– 'Kuro Delight' (d) **new**	XLot
	– 'L.T. Dees' (d) **new**	XLot
	– 'La Pace Rubra'	SCam
	– 'Lady Campbell'	CPla CTri EPfP LRHS MPri SCam SCoo WFar
	– 'Lady Clare'	see *C. japonica* 'Akashigata'
§	– 'Lady de Saumarez'	CBcs CMac CTsd
	– 'Lady Erma'	CBcs
	– 'Lady Kay'	LRHS
	– 'Lady Loch'	CTrh
	– 'Lady Marion'	see *C. japonica* 'Kumasaka'
	– 'Lady McCulloch'	LRHS NRHS
	– 'Lady Vansittart'	CBod CDoC CRos CTrh EPfP LCro LMil LOPS LRHS LSRN MAsh MGos NRHS SCam SCob SLim SPer SPoG SSta XLot
§	– 'Lady Vansittart Pink'	CMac
	– 'Lady Vansittart Red'	see *C. japonica* 'Lady Vansittart Pink'
	– 'Lady Vansittart Shell'	see *C. japonica* 'Yours Truly'
	– 'Latifolia'	SCam
	– 'Laurie Bray'	SCoo SWeb
§	– 'Lavinia Maggi' ♀H5	CBcs CTri ELon EPfP LMaj LRHS LSRN MAsh MGos MPri NRHS SCam SCob SCoo SGsty SPoG SRms SSta
	– 'Lavinia Maggi Alba' (d) **new**	XLot
	– 'Lavinia Maggi Rosea'	LMaj
	– 'Lemon Drop'	CBcs CTrh
	– 'Leonora Novick'	CDoC
	– 'Lily Pons'	CTrh LRHS
	– 'Lipstick'	CDoC LRHS
	– 'Little Bit'	ELon SCam SSta
	– 'Little Man'	LRHS NRHS
	– 'Lotus'	see *C. japonica* 'Gauntlettii'
	– 'Lovelight' ♀H5	CDoC CTrh LRHS NRHS
	– 'Lucy Hester'	CDoC
	– 'Ludgvan Red'	LRHS NRHS
	– 'Lulu Belle'	CBcs
	– 'Mabel Blackwell'	SCam
	– 'Madame de Strekaloff'	CMac CSBt SCam
	– 'Madame Lebois'	SCam
	– 'Madge Miller'	LRHS MAsh NRHS
	– 'Magnoliiflora'	see *C. japonica* 'Hagoromo'
	– 'Maiden's Blush'	CMac
	– 'Margaret Davis' ♀H5	CBod CCCN CDoC CRos CSBt CTrh ELan ELon EPfP LCro LOPS LRHS LSRN MAsh MGos NRHS SCam SCoo SGol SLim WFar XLot
	– 'Margaret Davis Picotee'	CBcs SPer
	– 'Margaret Rose'	SCam
	– 'Margherita Coleoni'	CBcs XLot
	– 'Marguérite Gouillon' Drouard-Gouillon	SSta
	– 'Marian Mitchell'	SCam
	– 'Mariana'	ELon
	– 'Marie Bracey'	XLot
	– 'Mariottii Rubra'	CMac
	– 'Marjorie Magnificent'	CDoC LRHS MAsh
	– 'Mark Alan'	CDoC LSRN SCam
	– 'Maroon and Gold'	LRHS NRHS
	– 'Mars' ♀H5	CBcs SCam
	– 'Marshmallow'	LRHS
	– 'Mary Costa'	CDoC CTrh SCam
	– 'Mary J. Wheeler'	LSRN
§	– 'Masayoshi' ♀H5	CBcs CSBt LRHS NRHS
	– 'Mathotiana'	XLot
	– 'Mathotiana Alba'	CMac CTri EPfP LSRN MGos SCam WSpi
§	– 'Mathotiana Rosea'	CBcs CMac NLar
	– 'Mathotiana Supreme'	CDoC SCam
	– 'Matilija Poppy'	CTrh SCam
	– 'Matterhorn'	CTrh
	– 'Mattie Cole'	SCam
	– 'Mercury' ♀H5	CBcs CMac EPfP GGGa
	– 'Mermaid'	LRHS NRHS SCam
	– 'Midnight'	CBcs CTsd LRHS MAsh NRHS
	– 'Midnight Magic'	CBcs CDoC CTrh CTri LRHS NRHS
	– 'Midnight Serenade'	LRHS NRHS
	– 'Midsummer's Day'	CBcs
§	– 'Mikenjaku'	CBcs EPfP LRHS NRHS
	– 'Miriam Stevenson'	SCam
	– 'Miss Charleston'	CBcs
	– 'Monstruosa Rubra'	see *C. japonica* 'Gigantea'
	– 'Monte Carlo'	SCam
	– 'Moshe Dayan'	CDoC CTsd LRHS MAsh NRHS
§	– 'Mrs Bertha A. Harms'	LRHS NRHS
	– 'Mrs Charles Cobb'	CDoC LMaj LRHS SGsty
	– 'Mrs D.W. Davis'	CBcs CDoC EPfP
	– 'Mrs Sander'	see *C. japonica* 'Gauntlettii'
	– 'Mrs Tingley' (d)	XLot
	– 'Mrs William Thompson'	LRHS NRHS SCam
	– 'Myorenji'	CDoC
	– 'Nagasaki'	see *C. japonica* 'Mikenjaku'
	– 'Nancy Bird'	SCam
	– 'Nigra'	see *C. japonica* 'Konronkoku'
	– 'Nina Avery'	SCam
	– 'Nobilissima' ♀H5	CBcs CDoC CMac CTrh CTri LCro LMil LOPS MAsh MBlu MMuc SCam SCob SPer SPoG WFar XLot
	– 'Nuccio's Cameo' ♀H5	CBcs CDoC CTrh EPfP LRHS MAsh MPri NRHS SCob
	– 'Nuccio's Gem' ♀H5	CBcs CDoC LCro LOPS LRHS NRHS SGol SWeb XLot
	– 'Nuccio's Jewel' ♀H5	CBcs CDoC CSBt EPfP LMaj LRHS LSRN MAsh NRHS SCam SWeb XLot

	- 'Nuccio's Pearl' ♀H5	CBcs CBod EPfP LMaj LRHS LSRN MPri NRHS SArc SCam SWeb XLot
	- 'Nuccio's Pink Lace'	CBcs CDoC CTri LRHS MAsh NRHS
	- 'Nuova Iride' (d) **new**	XLot
	- 'Onetia Holland'	CBcs LSRN SCam SLim WFar
	- 'Oo-La-La'	CDoC CTrh
	- 'Optima'	ELon LRHS NRHS SCam
	- 'Orandakō'	LRHS SCob
	- 'Patricia Ann'	LSRN
	- 'Paulette Goddard'	SCam
	- 'Paul's Apollo'	see *C. japonica* 'Apollo' Paul, 1911
	- 'Peachblossom'	see *C. japonica* 'Fleur Dipater'
	- 'Pearl Harbor'	SCam
	- 'Pearl Maxwell'	XLot
	- 'Pensacola Red'	CDoC
	- 'Pink Chiffon'	LRHS NRHS
	- 'Pink Clouds'	CBcs
	- 'Pink Perfection'	see *C. japonica* subsp. ***rusticana*** 'Ōtome'
	- 'Pope John Paul XXIII'	SCam
	- 'Preston Rose'	CBcs
	- 'Primavera'	CDoC CTrh SCam
	- 'Prince Albert'	see *C. japonica* 'Albertii'
	- 'Prince Murat'	LRHS NRHS
	- 'Princess Baciocchi'	SCam SReu
	- 'Princess du Mahe'	CMac
	- 'Princesse Baciocchi'	CBcs
	- 'Professor Sargent' (d)	XLot
	- 'R.L. Wheeler' ♀H5	CBcs CDoC CSBt CTri EPfP LMaj LRHS LSRN MGos MPri NRHS SCam SCoo
	- 'Red Dandy'	SCam
	- 'Red Red Rose'	LRHS NRHS SCam
	- 'Roger Hall'	CBcs CDoC CTrh LRHS LSRN MAsh NRHS SPoG
	- 'Rōgetsu'	CBcs
	- 'Rosa Baroveira Nella'	NLar
	- 'Rosularis'	ELon
	- 'Royal Velvet'	CTrh
	- 'Rubescens Major'	CBcs
	- 'Ruddigore'	CTrh
	- subsp. ***rusticana*** 'Arajishi' misapplied	see *C. japonica* subsp. ***rusticana*** 'Beni-arajishi'
	- - 'Arajishi' Ko'emon	SCam
§	- - 'Beni-arajishi'	LRHS NRHS SCam
§	- - 'Ōtome'	SCam
	- - 'Reigyoku' (v)	CBcs CDoC
	- 'Sabiniana'	LRHS NRHS
	- 'Sacco Nova'	LMaj XLot
	- 'Saint André'	CMac LRHS MAsh NRHS
	- 'San Dimas' ♀H5	CDoC CTrh LRHS NRHS SCam SWeb
	- 'Saturnia'	CDoC CRos ELon LRHS MAsh NRHS
	- 'Scentsation' ♀H5	CTri LRHS NRHS
	- 'Sea Foam'	LRHS NRHS SCam
	- 'Sea Gull'	SCam
	- 'Shikibu'	CTrh SCam
	- 'Shintsukasa-nishiki' **new**	XLot
	- 'Shiragiku'	LMaj XLot
	- 'Shiro Chan'	ELon SCam
	- 'Shirobotan'	ELon LRHS NRHS SCam
	- 'Silver Anniversary' ♀H5	CBcs CDoC CRos CSBt CTri ELon EPfP LCro LMil LOPS LRHS LSRN MAsh MGos MHtn MPri NLar NRHS SCam SCob SCoo SLim SPoG SWvt WFar XLot
	- 'Silver Ruffles'	CDoC CTrh ELon LRHS NRHS SCam
	- 'Snow White' (d) **new**	XLot
	- 'Something Beautiful'	SCam
	- 'Souvenir de Bahuaud-Litou' ♀H5	CBcs SCam
	- 'Souvenir de Hubert Thoby' (d) **new**	XLot
	- 'Splendens Carlyon'	LRHS MAsh NRHS
	- 'Spring Fever'	SCam
	- 'Spring Fling'	CTrh SPoG
	- 'Spring Formal'	CTrh
	- 'Spring Frill'	SCam
	- 'Spring Sonnet'	XLot
	- 'Stacy Susan'	CDoC
	- 'Strawberry Parfait'	CBcs
	- 'Strawberry Swirl'	CBcs
	- 'Sugar Babe'	CTrh LRHS NRHS SCam
	- 'Sylva' ♀H5	GGGa
	- 'Sylvia'	CMac
	- 'Takanini'	CBcs CTrh LRHS SCam
	- 'Tama-no-ura'	CDoC SCam
	- 'Tammia'	LRHS NRHS
	- 'Teresa Ragland'	SCam
	- 'The Mikado'	LRHS NRHS
	- 'Tiffany'	CBcs ELon LRHS NRHS SCam XLot
	- 'Tiki'	SCoo
	- 'Tinker Bell'	ELon SCam
	- 'Tom Thumb' ♀H5	CTrh ELon LRHS NRHS SRms
	- 'Tomorrow'	CDoC SCam
	- 'Tomorrow's Dawn'	SCam
	- 'Tregye'	CBcs CDoC
	- 'Trewithen White'	CDoC LRHS MAsh NRHS
§	- 'Tricolor' ♀H5	CBcs CMac CSBt CTrh ELon LRHS MGos MMuc NRHS SCam
	- 'Tricolor Red'	see *C. japonica* 'Lady de Saumarez'
	- 'Triphosa'	SWeb
	- 'Victor Emmanuel'	see *C. japonica* 'Blood of China'
	- 'Ville de Nantes'	LRHS NRHS
	- 'Virginia Carlyon'	CBcs
	- 'Virginia Robinson'	SCam
	- 'Visconti Nova'	LRHS NRHS
	- 'Vittorio Emanuele II'	CDoC CTrh LRHS NRHS
	- 'Volcano'	CDoC
	- 'Volunteer'	LCro LOPS LRHS
	- 'Wheel of Fortune'	LRHS NRHS
	- 'White Nun'	CBcs LMaj
	- 'White Swan'	CMac CSBt LRHS NRHS
	- 'Wildfire'	LRHS NRHS
	- 'William Bartlett'	CDoC CTrh SCoo
	- 'William Honey'	CTrh
	- 'Wisley White'	see *C. japonica* 'Hakurakuten'
	- 'Witman Yellow'	CTrh
§	- 'Yours Truly'	CDoC CMac CRos CTrh CTsd LRHS LSRN NRHS
	'Jury's Yellow'	see *C.* × *williamsii* 'Jury's Yellow'
	'Lasca Beauty' (*japonica* × *reticulata*)	CBcs
	'Lavender Queen'	see *C. sasanqua* 'Lavender Queen'
	'Leonard Messel' (*reticulata* × (× *williamsii*)) ♀H5	CBcs CDoC CMac CTrh CTri EPfP LRHS MGos NLar NRHS SCam
	lutchuensis	LRHS MPkF
	'Magic Mum'	LSRN
	'Maud Messel' (*reticulata* × (× *williamsii*))	SCam
	'Minato-no-haru' **new**	XLot
	'Nicky Crisp' (*japonica* × *pitardii*)	CTrh LRHS NRHS SPoG
	oleifera	CExl CTrh
	'Pink Goddess' (*hiemalis* hybrid)	LRHS MPkF

	'Pink Icicle' (*oleifera* hybrid)	CBcs SCam
	'Pink Spangles'	see *C. japonica* 'Mathotiana Rosea'
	pitardii WWJ 11925 from Vietnam	WCru
	'Polar Ice'	CBcs
	'Portuense'	see *C. japonica* 'Japonica Variegata'
	'Quintessence' (*japonica* × *lutchuensis*)	LRHS
	'Red Fellow' (*japonica* × *oleifera*) (d) **new**	XLot
	reticulata 'Mary Williams'	SCob SPoG XLot
	rosthorniana CUPIDO	see *C. rosthorniana* 'Elina'
§	- 'Elina'[PBR]	ELan IDee LCro LOPS LRHS NRHS SPoG
	'Royalty' (*japonica* × *reticulata*) ♀H5	CBcs
	saluenensis* × *japonica	see *C.* × *williamsii*
	sasanqua Thunb.	MHid
I	- 'Alba'	CMac CTri
	- 'Baronesa de Soutelinho'	ELon SCam
	- 'Bonanza'	see *C. hiemalis* 'Bonanza'
	- 'Cleopatra'	EPfP SCob SEWo
	- 'Cotton Candy'	CDoC SCam
	- 'Crimson King' ♀H4	CTrh LRHS NRHS
	- 'Dazzler'	see *C. hiemalis* 'Dazzler'
	- 'Dwarf Shishi'	CTrh
	- 'Early Pearly'	SCam
	- 'Flamingo'	see *C. sasanqua* 'Fukuzutsumi'
	- 'Fragrans'	ELon SCam
	- 'Fuji-no-mine'	ELon SCam
§	- 'Fukuzutsumi'	CSBt
	- 'Gay Border'	LRHS
	- 'Gay Sue'	CTrh SCam
	- 'Hinode-gumo'	SEWo
	- 'Hiryū'	LRHS MHtn NRHS SCam SEWo
	- 'Hugh Evans' ♀H4	CDoC CTrh ELan ELon EPfP LRHS NRHS SCam SSta
	- 'Jean May' ♀H4	ELon EPfP LRHS NRHS SCam WCot
	- 'Jennifer Susan'	CTrh CTri
	- 'Kenkyō'	CDoC ELon SCam SSta
§	- 'Lavender Queen'	SCam
	- 'Maiden's Blush'	LRHS NRHS SCam WCot
	- 'Mignonne'	CTrh
	- 'Mine-no-yuki'	CTrh
	- 'Narumigata' ♀H4	CBcs CDoC CMac CTrh EPfP LCro LOPS LRHS MBlu MGos NRHS SCam SPoG SSta WSHC
	- 'Navajo'	CTrh
	- 'New Dawn'	SCam
	- 'Nyewoods'	CMac
	- 'Papaver'	SCam
	- 'Paradise Audrey'	LMil LRHS LSRN SPoG
	- 'Paradise Belinda'	EPfP LMil LRHS SPoG
	- 'Paradise Blush'	CBcs LRHS SWvt
	- 'Paradise Glow'	LMil
	- 'Paradise Helen'	LRHS LSRN
	- 'Paradise Hilda'	LRHS
	- 'Paradise Pearl'	CBcs EPfP LMil LRHS
	- 'Paradise Venessa'	EPfP SCam
	- 'Plantation Pink'	CTrh LCro LOPS LRHS NRHS SCob SPer SRkn WCot
	- 'Rainbow'	CBcs CDoC CTrh ELan ELon EPfP LRHS NRHS SCoo SPer SSta
	- 'Rosea'	CMac ELon LRHS NRHS SCam
	- 'Sasanqua Rubra'	CMac SCam
	- 'Sasanqua Variegata' (v)	CTrh SCam
	- 'Sekiyō'	LRHS
	- 'Snowflake'	SCam SSta
	- 'Sparkling Burgundy'	see *C.* 'Sparkling Burgundy'
	- 'Tanya'	CTrh SCam
	- 'Versicolor'	LCro LOPS LRHS NRHS
	- 'Winter's Joy'	CBcs SCam
	- 'Winter's Snowman'	CDoC LCro LOPS LRHS NRHS SCam
	'Satan's Robe' (*reticulata* hybrid)	CDoC
	'Scented Sun'	CTrh
	'Scentuous' (*japonica* × *lutchuensis*)	CBcs
	'Show Girl' (*reticulata* × *sasanqua*) ♀H4	SCam
§	***sinensis***	CBcs CCCN CTrh CTsd EShb GPoy LRHS MHtn NLar NRHS SCam SPlb SPre SWeb SWvt
	- var. ***assamica***	CCCN CDoC SPre
	- var. ***sinensis***	CCCN LCro LOPS
	'Snow Flurry'	CTrh LRHS NRHS XLot
§	'Sparkling Burgundy' ♀H4	LCro LOPS LRHS MGos NRHS SCam
	'Spring Festival' (*cuspidata* hybrid) ♀H4	CBcs CSBt CTrh EPfP LCro LMil LOPS LRHS MGos MPri NRHS SCam XLot
	'Spring Mist' (*japonica* × *lutchuensis*)	CDoC CTrh
	'Sugar Dream'	CTrh SCam
	'Superscent'	CTrh
	'Swan Lake'	EPfP LMil LRHS MPri NRHS
	'Sweet Jane'	LRHS SCam
	'Tarōkaja' (wabisuke)	SCam
	thea	see *C. sinensis*
	'Tinsie'	see *C. japonica* 'Bokuhan'
	'Tiny Princess' (*fraterna* × *japonica*)	CBcs
	'Tom Knudsen' (*japonica* × *reticulata*) ♀H4	CTrh LRHS NRHS SCam
	transnokoensis ♀H4	CExl CTrh LRHS
	'Tricolor Sieboldii'	see *C. japonica* 'Tricolor'
	'Tristrem Carlyon' (*reticulata* hybrid)	CDoC CTri CTsd EPfP LRHS MAsh MPri NRHS
	tsaii	LRHS
	'Usu-ōtome'	see *C. japonica* subsp. *rusticana* 'Otome'
	'Valley Knudsen' (*reticulata* × *saluenensis*)	CBcs
	× ***vernalis*** 'Yuletide'	CBcs CDoC CRos CTrh LCro LOPS LRHS LSRN NRHS SCam SCob SWeb
§	× ***williamsii***	SWeb
	- 'Angel Wings'	LRHS NRHS
	- 'Anticipation' ♀H5	CBcs CBod CDoC CMac CRos CSBt CTrh ELan EPfP GGGa GKin LCro LMil LOPS LRHS MAsh MGos MSwo NRHS SCob SLim SPer SPoG SWvt WFar
	- 'Anticipation Variegated' (v)	CBcs LRHS NRHS
	- 'Ballet Queen'	CBcs CSBt SCam
	- 'Ballet Queen Variegated' (v)	ELon
	- 'Bartley Number Five'	CMac
	- 'Beatrice Michael'	CBcs CMac
	- 'Blue Danube'	CBcs SCoo
	- 'Bow Bells'	CTri
	- 'Bowen Bryant' ♀H5	CTrh EPfP LRHS NRHS
	- 'Brigadoon' ♀H5	CBcs CTrh CTri EPfP GGGa LRHS MAsh NRHS SCam
	- 'Burncoose'	CBcs
	- 'C.F. Coates'	SCam

- 'Caerhays' CBcs
- 'Carolyn Williams' CBcs
- 'Celebration' CBcs CSBt LSRN
- 'Charles Colbert' CDoC LRHS SCam
- 'Charles Michael' CBcs
- 'China Clay' ♀H5 CBcs LRHS LSRN NRHS
§ - 'Citation' CMac
- 'Contribution' CTrh
- 'Crinkles' SCam
- 'Debbie' ♀H5 Widely available
- 'Debbie's Carnation' LRHS NRHS SCam
- 'Donation' ♀H5 Widely available
- 'E.G. Waterhouse' CSBt CTrh CTri CTsd ELan GKin LRHS MAsh MGos NRHS SCam SSta WFar XLot
- 'E.T.R. Carlyon' ♀H5 CBcs CBod CDoC CRos CTrh CTri EPfP LMil LRHS MAsh MGos NLar NRHS SLim
- 'Elegant Beauty' ♀H5 CDoC CTrh ELon LRHS MAsh NLar NRHS SCam
- 'Elizabeth Anderson' CTrh CTsd
- 'Ellamine' CBcs
- 'Elsie Jury' ♀H5 CBcs CMac CTri ELan ELon GKin LRHS MAsh MGos NLar NRHS SCam SGol
- 'Exaltation' SCam
- 'Fiona Colville' SCam
- 'Francis Hanger' CBcs CDoC CTrh LRHS NRHS SCam
- 'Galaxie' CBcs SCam
- 'Gay Time' LRHS NRHS
- 'George Blandford' ♀H5 CBcs CMac
- 'Glenn's Orbit' ♀H5 NLar SCam
- 'Golden Spangles' (v) CBcs CBod CMac ELan EPfP LRHS MGos MMuc NRHS SCam SPer SPoG
- 'Grand Jury' CDoC ELon LRHS NRHS
- 'Gwavas' CBcs CCCN CDoC CTrh LRHS NRHS SCam
- 'Hilo' SCam
- 'Hiraethlyn' CBcs
- 'J.C. Williams' ♀H5 CBcs CMac CTri LRHS
- 'Jenefer Carlyon' CBcs
- 'Jennifer Trehane' **new** CTrh
- 'Jill Totty' CTrh
- 'John Pickthorn' CBcs
- 'Julia Hamiter' ♀H5 CBcs CDoC LRHS NRHS
§ - 'Jury's Yellow' ♀H5 CBcs CBod CCCN CDoC CRos CSBt CTrh CTri ELan EPfP GGGa LCro LMil LOPS LRHS LSRN MAsh MGos MPri SCam SCob SLim SPer SPoG SSta SWvt
- 'Lady's Maid' CBcs SCam
- 'Laura Boscawen' CBcs CDoC CTrh SCam
- 'Les Jury' ♀H5 CBcs CSBt CTrh LMil LRHS LSRN MGos NRHS SLim WFar
- 'Lucky Star' (d) LRHS
- 'Margaret Waterhouse' CBcs SCam
- 'Marjorie Waldegrave' LRHS NRHS
- 'Mary Jobson' CBcs
- 'Mary Larcom' CBcs
- 'Mary Phoebe Taylor' ♀H5 CBcs LMaj NLar SCam SLim
- 'Mirage' CDoC CTrh
- 'Monica Dance' CBcs CDoC
- 'Muskoka' ♀H5 CBcs EPfP
- 'Night Rider' SCam WPGP
- 'November Pink' CBcs SCam
- 'Philippa Forward' CBcs CMac
- 'Pink Wave' LRHS NRHS
- 'Red Dahlia' CBcs
- 'Rendezvous' CDoC CTrh SCam
- 'Rosemary Williams' CBcs CMac
- 'Ruby Wedding' (d) ♀H5 CBcs CDoC CRos CSBt CTrh EPfP LMil LRHS LSRN MAsh MGos MHtn MPri NRHS SCam SCoo SLim SPoG SWvt WFar
- 'Saint Ewe' ♀H5 CBcs CDoC CSBt CTrh CTri EPfP LRHS MGos NRHS SCam XLot
- 'Saint Michael' CBcs
- 'Sayonara' CDoC LMaj
- 'Senorita' ♀H5 ELon LRHS MAsh NLar NRHS SCam
- 'Shocking Pink' LRHS NRHS
- 'The Duchess of Cornwall' LRHS NRHS SCam
- 'Tiptoe' CDoC CTrh SCoo
- 'Toni Finlay's Fragrant' CTrh
- 'Twinkle Star' LRHS NRHS
- 'Water Lily' ♀H5 CBcs CDoC CTri ELon LRHS NLar NRHS SCam
- 'Wilber Foss' CBcs CDoC LRHS NRHS SCam
- 'William Carlyon' LRHS NRHS
- 'Winter Gem' LRHS

'Winter's Charm' CBcs LRHS NRHS
'Winter's Dream' CBcs
'Winter's Fancy' (d) **new** XLot
'Winter's Interlude' CBcs LRHS NRHS
'Winter's Joy' XLot
'Winter's Rose' **new** XLot
'Winter's Toughie' CBcs LRHS NRHS SCam
'Yoimachi' (*fraterna* × *sasanqua*) CTrh LRHS

Camissonia (*Onagraceae*)

bistorta 'Sunflakes' CSpe

Campanula ✿ (*Campanulaceae*)

RCB AM 13 WCot
alata CCBP XLum
'Albert Kirkham' EBee WCot
§ ***alliariifolia*** CDor CMea CSam CWld EBee ECha ECtt EHyd ELan EMor EPfP GKev GLog LRHS LSRN MRav NBro NGdn NRHS NSti SBut SEND SPer SRms WCAu WCot WFar WGwG WSpi
- DHTU 0126 WCru
- 'Ivory Bells' see *C. alliariifolia*
- 'Ivory Towers' EBee
americana WFar XLum
arvatica EACa EHyd LRHS NRHS NSla SRms WAbe WFar WIce
aucheri see *C. bellidifolia* subsp. *aucheri*
'Barbara Valentine' EBee EWTr WCAu
barbata EACa EBee EPfP GKev
bayerniana GKev
'Belinda' CPBP
bellidifolia CPla NSla
§ - subsp. ***aucheri*** GEdr GKev
§ - subsp. ***besenginica*** GEdr
- subsp. ***saxifraga*** GEdr
bellidifolia* × *tridentata GKev
besenginica see *C. bellidifolia* subsp. *besenginica*
§ ***betulifolia*** ♀H5 GEdr NSla WCot
biebersteiniana GEdr ITim NSla
'Birch Hybrid' EACa ECtt EHyd ELan ELon EPot GBee LRHS MMuc NRHS SAko SRms WFar XLum
'Blue Octopus' CWGN EHyd ELon EMor LRHS LSou MPnt SRms WSpi

'Blue Pearl'	WAbe
bononiensis	SRms
'Burghaltii'	NLar
calaminthifolia	ITim
* ***campanulata***	MCot
'Cantata'	WAbe
carpatha	CPBP
carpatica ♀^{H5}	CPla EPfP NGdn SPlb SRms WFar XLum
- f. ***alba***	EHyd LRHS NGdn NRHS SPlb XLum
§ - - 'Weisse Clips'	CBar EHyd ELan EPfP GJos GMaP LCro LOPS LRHS MAsh NGdn NHol NRHS SPer SPoG SRms SWvt WFar
§ - 'Blaue Clips'	CBar CBcs ECtt EHyd ELan EPfP GJos GMaP LCro LRHS MAsh MGos NGdn NRHS SPer SPoG SRms SWvt WFar
- Blue Clips	see *C. carpatica* 'Blaue Clips'
- 'Blue Moonlight'	EACa EHyd LRHS NRHS
- blue-flowered	ECrN
- 'Chewton Joy'	EACa EHyd LRHS NRHS
- 'Pearl Deep Blue' **new**	MTin
- 'Pearl White'	MHol
- 'Rapido Blue'	MHol
- 'Rapido White' **new**	CBod
- var. ***turbinata***	SRms
- - 'Foerster'	EHyd LRHS NRHS XLum
- - 'Isabel'	EHyd LRHS NRHS XLum
- - 'Jewel'	EHyd LRHS NRHS
- White Clips	see *C. carpatica* f. *alba* 'Weisse Clips'
§ ***cashmeriana***	WAbe
cephallenica	see *C. garganica* subsp. *cephallenica*
§ ***chamissonis***	EPot GEdr NWad
- 'Major'	EWes
- 'Oyobeni'	EACa
§ - 'Superba' ♀^{H5}	EACa NHpl WAbe WIce
'Chloe'	EBee EWTr WFar WHil
choruhensis	EWes GEdr SPlb
ciliata	GEdr
§ ***cochlearifolia*** ♀^{H5}	CSpe EBee EBou EHyd EPfP GAbr GJos GKev GMaP LRHS MAsh MMuc NHpl NRHS NWad SPoG WFar WHoo XLum
- var. ***alba***	CSpe CTri EBou EDAr ELan MMuc NHpl NRya SRms WAbe WFar XLum
- - 'Advance White' **new**	WFar
- - double white-flowered (d)	WFar
- - 'White Baby' (Baby Series)	EACa EHyd EPfP EPot LRHS NRHS NWad SPoG SRms WFar XLum
- 'Bavaria Blue'	NHol XLum
- 'Bells Blue'	MHol
- 'Blue Baby' (Baby Series)	EPfP LRHS NHpl SPoG SRms WIce
- 'Blue Wonder'	ECtt
- 'Elizabeth Oliver' (d) ♀^{H5}	CMea EACa ECtt EDAr EHyd ELan GEdr GMaP LRHS MHer MHol MSCN NBir NHar NHpl NRHS SPlb SRms WAbe WFar WHoo WIce
- 'Flore Pleno' (d)	WFar
- 'R.B. Loder' (d)	EHyd LRHS MHer NRHS
- 'Silver Bells' **new**	LSou
- 'Tubby'	EACa EHyd EPot LRHS MHer SGro SRms
- 'Warleyensis'	see *C.* × *haylodgensis* W. Brockbank 'Warley White'
collina	EACa EBee EHyd GEdr LRHS NRHS XLum

'Constellation'	EACa
'Covadonga'	CMea EACa EHyd LRHS NRHS WAbe WThu
'Cremewit' **new**	EPot
cretica	MHol
'Crystal'	CFis ECtt MAvo MCot MSpe NLar WCot WFar
cymbalaria	GKev
dasyantha	see *C. chamissonis*
dolomitica	CPla EACa
'E.K. Toogood'	CElw CPBP EACa EBou ECtt SRms WFar XLum
'Faichem Lilac'	WCot
fenestrellata	EACa XLum
§ - subsp. ***istriaca***	GKev
finitima	see *C. betulifolia*
garganica ♀^{H5}	EACa EBou EDAr EHyd EPfP GMaP GWyn LRHS MAsh MMuc MRav NRHS SRms SVic SWvt WFar XLum
- 'Aurea'	see *C. garganica* 'Dickson's Gold'
- 'Blue Diamond'	EACa EBou ELon NLar
§ - subsp. ***cephallenica***	EACa
§ - 'Dickson's Gold'	Widely available
- 'Erinus Major'	EACa XLum
- 'Filigree'	WBrk WCot WFar
- subsp. ***istriaca***	see *C. fenestrellata* subsp. *istriaca*
- 'Major'	SPoG WFar
- 'Mrs Resholt'	CTri ECtt EPau MHer NBir NLar SEdd SRms SWvt WFar WIce
- 'Senior'	EWTr
- 'W.H. Paine' ♀^{H5}	EACa ECtt NLar NSla WAbe WBrk WFar WHoo
'Glandore'	EACa SAko XLum
glomerata	CBee CExl CWld GAbr GJos GKev LSRN MBow MHer NAts NBir NGBl NGrd NMir WFar
- var. ***acaulis*** hort.	EPfP NGrd NLar SCob SRms WFar XLum
- var. ***alba***	CBcs CBod CNor CRos CSpe EACa ECtt EHyd ELan EMor EPfP GJos GMaP LRHS MBel NRHS SBut SCob SGbt SPer SPlb SPoG WCAu WGwG
§ - - 'Schneekrone'	ECha LCro LOPS WFar
- Bellefleur White (Bellefleur Series)	EWTr
- 'Caroline' ♀^{H7}	Widely available
- Crown of Snow	see *C. glomerata* var. *alba* 'Schneekrone'
- var. ***dahurica***	CSpe EAJP EBee EHyd EMor LRHS NLar SBut SHar XLum
- 'Emerald'	CBod EBee EHyd EPfP LRHS MHer MSCN NLar NRHS SCob SPad SRms WFar XSen
- 'Freya'^{PBR} ♀^{H7}	EACa EBee ECtt EPfP LPla MHol MNrw NLar SPad WCot WFar WHil WMal
- (Genti Series) Genti Blue ('Allgentibl'^{PBR})	MPri WFar
- - Genti Twisterbell ('Allgentitwist'^{PBR})	EMor MHol MSCN NEoE SCob WHil
- - Genti White ('Allgentiw'^{PBR})	CWGN MPri NLar WFar
- 'Joan Elliott'	CSam EBee ECha ECtt EPfP LEdu MPie SGbt WGwG XSen
- 'Purple Pixie'	LRHS SRms
- 'Stevie's Wonder' **new**	CRos
- 'Superba' ♀^{H7}	Widely available
grossekii	EBee EHyd LRHS

	Name	Suppliers
	'Hannah'	EHyd LRHS NRHS
	× ***haylodgensis*** misapplied	see *C.* × *haylodgensis* 'Plena'
§	× ***haylodgensis*** W. Brockbank 'Marion Fisher' (d)	WAbe WFar WHoo
§	- 'Plena' (d)	EACa ECtt EHyd LRHS NRHS SRms WAbe WFar WKif
§	- 'Warley White' (d)	XLum
	- 'Yvonne'	ECtt ELan NHpl WFar
	hercegovina	CPBP
	- 'Nana'	CPBP WAbe
	hofmannii	GJos GKev NWad
	hypopolia	WAbe
§	***incurva***	CSpe CWCL EACa GEdr GJos GKev WAbe
	IRIDESCENT BELLS ('Iribella'PBR)	CWGN EACa EBee EMor EWTr EWes LCro LRHS LSou MBel MHol MNrw MSCN NSti SCob SPad SPer WCAu WHil WPnP WTyc
	isophylla 🏆H2	EPot
	JENNY ('Harjen'PBR)	CWGN IPot SHar
	'Joan Beeston' **new**	WAbe
	'Joe Elliott'	WAbe
	kemulariae	EDAr WCot XLum
	'Kent Belle' 🏆H7	Widely available
	kirpicznikovii	EBee GEdr GKev
	komarovii	WCot
	lactiflora	CAby CElw CMac CPla CSpe EACa EBee ECha EHyd EPfP GAbr LRHS MCot MNrw NRHS SPer WCAu WFar WSpi WWtn XLum
	- ***alba***	see *C. lactiflora* white-flowered
	- 'Alba' 🏆H7	CAby CBod EBee ECha EPfP GBin GMaP MAvo MBel MHol MMuc SEND WBrk WCAu WCot WSpi
	- 'Assendon Pearl' 🏆H7	EACa LPla SHar SPhx WCot
	- AVALANCHE ('Camblo')	EACa EBee ECtt LCro LOPS MTis
	- 'Border Blues'	ECtt ELon EPfP MHol MNrw NDov NLar WFar
	- 'Dixter Presence'	LPla SMHy
	- dwarf pink-flowered	EACa EAJP EPfP
	- 'Favourite' 🏆H7	ECtt NGdn SHar
	- 'Lidie's Choice'	CSam
	- 'Loddon Anna' 🏆H7	Widely available
	- 'Macrantha'	CBod
	- 'Marchants Nimbus'	GBin
	- 'Platinum' 🏆H7	LPla SMHy
	- 'Pouffe'	CRos EACa EBee ECtt EHyd EPfP GMaP GWyn LRHS MHol MNrw NGdn NLar NRHS SGbt SPer SWvt
	- 'Prichard's Variety' 🏆H7	Widely available
	- 'Superba' 🏆H7	EACa ECtt
	- 'Violet'	WSpi
	- 'White Pouffe'	CRos EACa ECtt EHyd EPfP GMaP LRHS NChi NLar NRHS SCob SGbt SPer SPoG WFar WGwG
§	- white-flowered	ECha NBir SPer WCAu WCav
	lasiocarpa	EPot
	latifolia	EACa GJos GQue MCot NBid NChi NMir SPer SRms WCAu WShi WSpi
	- var. ***alba***	CRos EBee EHyd EPfP GJos GWyn LRHS MBel MMuc NGdn NRHS SEND SPer SRms WHal WSpi
*	- 'Amethyst'	WSpi
	- blue-flowered	SEND
	- 'Brantwood'	CDor EHyd EPfP GAbr LRHS MRav WSpi
	- 'Gloaming'	EBee ECtt EHyd LRHS WSpi
	- var. ***macrantha***	CDor CFis CMea EBee EHyd ELan EPfP GMaP LRHS MBel NRHS NSti SWvt
	- - 'Alba'	CMea EWTr GLog GMaP MHol MRav NLar NWad WCAu
	latiloba	WCot WKif
§	- 'Alba'	EBee MCot MNrw NLar WBrk WRHF
	- 'Hidcote Amethyst'	CDor CWGN ECtt EHyd ELan ELon LRHS MBriF MCot MHol NBid NBir NGdn SEND SPer WCAu WCot WKif WSpi
	- 'Highcliffe Variety' 🏆H7	EACa EBee ECtt EHyd ELan EPfP LRHS MBriF MPie NLar NRHS SPoG WCAu WCot WRHF WSpi WWtn
	- 'Percy Piper' 🏆H7	CRos EACa EBee EHyd LRHS MPie MRav NLar NRHS WCAu WSpi
	- 'Splash'	MNrw
	'Linda'	IPot
	'Lynchmere'	CMea NWad WAbe WMal
	makaschvilii	EACa EWhm GKev GWyn
	makaschvilii × ***trachelium***	WCot
	'Margaret Brine'	WAbe
	'Marion Fisher'	see *C.* × *haylodgensis* W. Brockbank 'Marion Fisher'
	medium 'Alba'	CBod
	- 'Caerula' **new**	CBod
§	- var. ***calycanthema*** hort.	WSpi
	- 'Cup and Saucer'	see *C. medium* var. *calycanthema* hort.
	- 'Rosea'	CBod GQue
	'Mevr. V. Vollenhove'	CSpe EBee ECtt MAvo MHol NSti
	'Misty Dawn' 🏆H7	MAvo NLar WCot
	moesiaca	GKev
	muralis	see *C. portenschlagiana*
	myrtifolia	WAbe
	nitida	see *C. persicifolia* var. *planiflora*
	ochroleuca	CMea EBee GBin IMou WCFE WCot
	odontosepala	NWad WFar
	- from Iran	EMor EPPr NLar
	olympica misapplied	see *C. rotundifolia* 'Olympica'
	orphanidea	IMou
	ossetica	EBee ECtt WBor
	pallida subsp. ***tibetica***	see *C. cashmeriana*
	patula	EACa GKev WKif XLum
	'Paul Furse'	ECtt NSti SHar WCot WHrl
	'Pearlescent Pink'	EWes LSou
	'Pearlescent White'	EWes LSou
	pendula	GJos LSun SBut
	persicifolia	Widely available
	- var. ***alba***	Widely available
§	- 'Alba Coronata' (d)	GAbr SRms
	- 'Alba Flore-Pleno' (d) **new**	SGbt
	- 'Alba Plena'	see *C. persicifolia* 'Alba Coronata'
	- 'Azure Beauty'	EBee ECtt NLar WCot WSpi XSen
	- 'Beau Belle'	EWld NLar
§	- 'Bennett's Blue' (d)	MRav
	- blue and white-flowered	SRms
	- 'Blue Bell'	GWyn
	- 'Blue Bloomers' (d)	CDor EACa ECtt EHyd EPri EWes LRHS MRav MSCN NQui NWad SRms WCFE WCot WHal XLum
	- 'Blue-eyed Blonde'PBR (v)	NLar
	- blue-flowered	MBow SPlb SRms
	- 'Boule de Neige' (d)	CDor WSpi
§	- 'Chettle Charm'PBR	CDor CTri CWCL ECtt EHyd EPfP EShb GAbr LRHS MBriF MCot MRav NBPC NBir NLar NRHS SCob SRms SWvt WCot WFar

	- 'Cornish Mist'	CExl EBee ELan EPfP MHol MPie NLar WCAu WSpi
	- 'Fleur de Neige' (d)	MRav
	- 'Frances' (d)	WCot
	- 'Gawen'	CMac EACa ECtt EHyd LRHS NBre SGbt WCAu WCot
	- 'George Chiswell'	see *C. persicifolia* 'Chettle Charm'
	- 'Grandiflora'	CDor EAJP
	- 'Grandiflora Alba'	EAJP GBin NLar NWad SDix
	- 'Hampstead White' (d)	WSpi
	- 'Kelly's Gold'	MHol SRms
	- 'La Belle' (d)	EBee EHyd LRHS MNrw NLar
	- 'La Bello'PBR	EBee EHyd LRHS MNrw WPnP
	- 'La Bonne Amie' (d)	EBee EPfP MNrw NLar SPoG XEll
	- 'Moerheimii' (d)	WSpi
	- 'Perry's Boy Blue'	NPer
§	- var. ***planiflora***	CPBP WAbe
	- - f. ***alba***	CPBP NHpl WAbe WCot
	- 'Powder Puff' (d)	EPfP GBin GWyn MHol NLar XEll
	- 'Pride of Exmouth' (d) ♀H7	CDor CMiW MHer MRav WSpi
	- subsp. ***sessiliflora*** 'Alba'	see *C. latiloba* 'Alba'
	- 'Snow White' (d)	SGsty
	- 'Snowdrift'	SRms
	- (Takion Series) 'Takion Blue'	CBod EHyd ELan GWyn LRHS NRHS SPoG SRms
	- - 'Takion White'	EHyd ELan EPfP GWyn LRHS NRHS SPoG SRms
	- 'Telham Beauty' ambig.	CBod MCot NGBl SCob SGbt SWvt WCFE WSpi XLum
	- 'Telham Beauty' misapplied	CSBt EBee EHyd ELan EPfP LRHS MRav NRHS SPer SRms SWvt
	- 'Telham Beauty' D.Thurston	MBow NLar
	- 'Tinpenny Blue'	WCot
	- 'Wortham Belle' misapplied	see *C. persicifolia* 'Bennett's Blue'
	- 'Wortham Belle' ambig.	CBod LPot MRav SGbt WCAu
	- 'Wortham Belle' Blooms	ECtt EHyd LRHS NRHS WGwG
	'Peter Nix'	EACa
	petrophila	WAbe
	pilosa	see *C. chamissonis*
	- 'Superba'	see *C. chamissonis* 'Superba'
	'Pink Octopus'PBR	CAby CBor CRos CWGN ECtt EHyd ELan ELon EMor EPfP LPot LRHS LSou MBNS MHol MSCN MTis NGdn NLar NRHS SCob SEle SPad SPoG SRkn SRms STPC WSpi XLum
	planiflora	see *C. persicifolia* var. *planiflora*
	pollinensis	WCot
§	***portenschlagiana*** ♀H5	Widely available
	- 'Alba' **new**	WFar
	- 'Biokovo'	XLum
	- 'Catharina'	EACa ECtt EHyd EPPr EShb LRHS MBros MHol NRHS SPoG SRms
	- 'Lieselotte'	CElw CMea CPBP EACa ECtt SAko WFar
	- 'Major'	EACa NCou
	- 'Resholdt's Variety'	CBar CMea CSam CTri EACa EAJP EBou ECtt EDAr EHyd ELan EPfP GKev LRHS MBel MHol MRav NRHS SAko SRms WAbe WCot XLum XSen
	- 'Sago'	MHol
	poscharskyana	Widely available
	- 'Blauranke'	EACa EWes SAko WFar XLum
	- 'Blue Gown'	EACa ECtt SAko XLum
	- 'Blue Rivulet'PBR	ECtt
	- BLUE WATERFALL ('Camgood')	CWGN EACa ECtt MBNS NDov SPoG WBrk WCot XLum
	- 'E.H. Frost'	CBre CElw EACa ECtt ELan EPPr EPfP EShb EWTr GBin GKev GMaP LPot MCot MMuc NLar NRya SAko SEND SPer SRms SWvt WBrk WFar WSpi XLum
	- 'Erich G.Arends'	SAko
I	- 'Freya'	EACa SAko XLum
	- 'Frühlingszauber'	WCot
	- 'Hirsch Blue'	SRms
	- 'Lilacina'	EACa EPPr
	- 'Lisduggan Variety'	CBre CElw EACa EBee ECtt EPPr EWes GMaP MHer NLar SAko SRms WBrk WFar WIce XLum XSen
	- 'Nana Alba'	EACa EPPr SAko WBrk
	- 'Pinkins'PBR	CSma EACa ECtt WIce
	- 'Schneeranke'	XSen
	- 'Silberregen'	SAko
	- 'Stella' ♀H5	ECha ECtt EHyd ELan EPfP GBin GMaP IPot LRHS LSRN MRav NDov NRHS SAko SPer SWvt WBrk WCav WCot WHoo XLum
	- 'Trollkind'	EACa EPPr SAko WFar XLum
	- variegated (v)	EBee EPPr
	- 'Weissranke' **new**	WFar
	- white-flowered	CTri WFar
	× ***pseudoraineri***	EACa EHyd EWes LRHS NRHS
	pulla	EACa EBou ECtt EHyd ELan LRHS NHpl NRHS NSla SCob SPoG SRms WAbe WIce
	- 'Alba'	EACa EHyd LRHS NRHS NSla WAbe WIce
	× ***pulloides*** 'G.F.Wilson' ♀H5	EACa ECtt GEdr GMaP IPot NLar SRkn WFar
	- 'Jelly Bells'PBR	NLar
	punctata	GJos MCot NBro NSti WCAu WFar WGwG
	- f. ***albiflora***	WFar
	- 'Alina's Double' (d)	NLar
	- dwarf	CPBP
	- var. ***hondoensis***	GKev
	- hose-in-hose (d)	WGwG
	- 'Hot Lips'	CMac MHol
*	- var. ***howozana***	GKev
	- 'Kurokawa'	WFar
	- var. ***microdonta*** B&SWJ 5553	WCru
	- 'Milky Way'	EMor LSou NEoE WHil
*	- 'Nana'	WFar
	- 'Pantaloons' (d)	CMac CWGN EWes NLar SCob SRms
	- 'Pink Chimes'	CDor MHol NLar SEle
	- 'Plum Wine'	NWad
	- purple-flowered	EHyd ELan LRHS
	- f. ***rubriflora***	CBod CDor CRos CSpe EBee EBou ECtt EHyd ELan EMor EPfP LRHS MBel MCot MHol MNrw NRHS SCob SPer SRms WCAu WGwG
	- - 'Beetroot'	CWCL EMor GBee GBin GKev GWyn MHer MHol NLar WFar
	- - 'Bowl of Cherries'	ECtt EHyd LRHS MMrt NLar SRms
	- - 'Cherry Bells'	CDor ECtt EHyd EPfP LRHS LSRN NRHS
	- - 'Vienna Festival'	CSBt
	- - 'Wine 'n' Rubies'	EBee ECtt MHol
I	- 'Silver Bells'	CBod ECtt EHyd EMor EPfP LRHS NLar NSti SRms WFar
	- 'Wedding Bells'	CDor EACa EBou EHyd EMor EPfP EPri LPot LRHS LSRN MBel MBriF MHer MHol MSpe MTis NLar NRHS SCob SRms WCAu WGwG WHil WWtn

	- white hose-in-hose (d)	XLum
	'Purple Sensation'[PBR]	CWGN EBee EPfP LSou MBel MHol MNrw MSCN NLar WCot
	pusilla	see *C. cochlearifolia*
	pyramidalis	CCBP CSpe EACa EBee ELan EPfP GJos MMuc NGBl SDix SEND SPlb WBor WBrk XLum
	- 'Alba'	CSpe EACa ELan EPfP GJos NGBl SDix SPlb XLum
	- variegated (v) **new**	CRos
	raddeana	CPla EACa GKev SBrt WBrk
	raineri	NSla WAbe
	- 'Nettleton Gold'	EACa EHyd LRHS NRHS
§	***rapunculoides***	SRms WCFE XLum
§	- 'Afterglow'	MAvo WFar
	- 'Alba'	EPPr MAvo WFar XLum
	rapunculus	MNHC WOut XLum
	recurva	see *C. incurva*
	rhomboidalis Gorter	see *C. rapunculoides*
	rhomboidalis L.	WCot XLum
	rigidipila	GJos WHer
	(Ringsabell Series) 'Ringsabell Indigo Blue'	EBee ELan EMor EPfP SPoG
	- 'Ringsabell Mulberry Rose'	CBod ELan EPfP SRms WCAu
	- 'Ringsabell Opal White'	ELan
	rotundifolia	CMac CWld EACa EBou EHyd ELan EMor EPfP GAbr GJos GLog MBow MCot MHer SPhx SPlb SRms WBrk WWild
	- var. ***albiflora***	CElw EWes
	- 'Jotunheimen'	EACa WAbe
§	- 'Olympica'	EACa EBee ECtt WHoo
	- 'White Gem'	CBod EACa EBee EHyd ELan EMor EPfP LRHS NBre NRHS WHoo
	'Royal Wave'	EBee ECtt IPot MHol NLar
	rupicola	CPBP
	'Samantha'	CWCL CWld EACa EBee ECtt ELon GKev LRHS LSRN MCot NHpl SHar WFar XEll
	'Sarastro'	Widely available
	sarmatica	EACa EBee EPfP SGro SRms WFar
	- 'Hemelstraling'	MAvo MCot
	- subsp. ***woronowii*** **new**	ITim
	sartorii	GEdr WAbe
	scheuchzeri	WAbe
	'Senior'	EACa ECtt EPPr MHol SAko WBrk WCot WGoo
	'Snow Dune' **new**	WCAu
	'Spring Bell White'	MHol
	'Stansfieldii'	EACa EHyd LRHS NRHS
	stevenii	see *C. stevenii* subsp. *beauverdiana*
§	- subsp. ***beauverdiana***	SBrt
	subramulosa	see *C. cochlearifolia*
	'Summer Pearl'	ECtt LLWG
	'Summertime Blues'[PBR]	EACa EBee ECtt EHyd ELan EMor LRHS NLar NRHS WCot WMal
§	'Swannables'	CPou EHyd LRHS MAvo MRav WFar WOut
	takesimana	CRos CSpe ECtt EHyd ELan EPfP GKev GKin LEdu LRHS NGrd NLar NRHS SPer SRms SWvt XLum
I	- 'Alba'	EMor WFar
	- 'Elizabeth'	CBod CRos CWld EACa EBee ECtt EHyd EMor EPPr EPfP GMaP GWyn LPot LRHS LSRN MBel MSpe NGdn NRHS SCob SGbt SPer SPlb SWvt WCAu WFar WGwG WHil WKif XLum
	- 'Elizabeth II' (d)	EPPr SHar WFar
	- 'Feenrock JP'	XLum
	- 'White Giant'	SHar
	thyrsoides	CSpe EBee GJos
	'Timsbury Chimes'	WAbe
	'Timsbury Perfection'	WAbe
	tommasiniana ♀H6	SBrt WAbe
	trachelium	EACa EBee EHyd ELon GJos GKev LRHS MBow MHer MNHC MRav NAts NGrd NMir WCot WFar WHer WOut WShi WSpi XLum
	- f. ***alba***	EBee EHyd ELan GJos IMou LRHS NLar SGbt WCot WFar
	- - 'Alba Flore Pleno' (d)	LEdu LPla SMHy
	- 'Bernice' (d)	CBod CDor EACa EBee ECtt ELan EPfP GMaP LRHS MAvo MCot MHol MNrw MPie MTin NLar NSti SCob SPer WBor WCAu WCot WFar WSpi XSen
	- 'Purple Break'	EBee MHol WCot
	- 'Snowball'	CMac
	trachyphylla **new**	CPBP
	troegerae	GKev
	'Van-Houttei'	CDor NLar WCot
	versicolor	CPBP SRms
	vidalii	see *Azorina vidalii*
	'Viking'[PBR]	EHyd LRHS SRms
	waldsteiniana	WAbe
	wanneri	EDAr GJos
	'Warley White'	see *C.* × *haylodgensis* W. Brockbank 'Warley White'
	'Warleyensis'	see *C.* × *haylodgensis* W. Brockbank 'Warley White'
	'White Octopus'	ECtt LSou SEle
	× ***wockei*** 'Puck'	CPBP EACa ECtt EHyd LRHS NRHS WAbe WOld
	zangezura	CFis EACa EBou EDAr ELan GJos GKev SGbt XLum
	zoysii	WAbe

Campanula × *Symphyandra* see *Campanula*

Campanumoea see *Codonopsis*

Campsis (*Bignoniaceae*)

	grandiflora	CBcs CRos CWGN EHyd ELan EPfP LRHS LSRN SPer SWvt WCFE
	radicans	CBcs CBod CMac CRHN CRos CWCL ECrN EHyd ELan EPfP LRHS MGil MSwo NRHS SLon SNig SPer SPlb
	- 'Atrosanguinea'	SVen
	- 'Flamenco'	CBcs CDoC CMac CRos CWCL EBee EHyd ELan EPfP LRHS LSRN MGil SAdn SCob SCoo SLim SNig SPoG SVen SWvt WLov
§	- f. ***flava*** ♀H4	CBcs CMac CRos CTri CWCL EBee EHyd ELan EPfP LRHS MBlu MGil MGos NOra NRHS SCob SGbt SLim SNig SPer SPoG SVen SWvt
	- 'Stromboli'	EBee EPfP
	- 'Yellow Trumpet'	see *C. radicans* f. *flava*
	× ***tagliabuana*** DANCING FLAME ('Huidan'[PBR])	CRos CWCL CWGN EHyd LRHS NOra SAdn
	- INDIAN SUMMER ('Kudian'[PBR])	CBcs CDoC CRos CWCL CWGN EHyd ELon EPfP LRHS LSRN MGil MGos NOra NRHS SCoo
	- 'Madame Galen' ♀H4	CBcs CDoC CRos CTri CWCL CWGN EBee ECrN EHyd ELan ELon EPfP LRHS LSRN MAsh

	MBlu MGos MPri NOra SCob SEND SGbt SLim SPer SPoG SRms SSta SVen SWvt
– 'Takarazuka Yellow'PBR (Summer Jazz Series)	CRos EHyd LRHS NRHS
– 'Takarazuka Zujin'PBR (Summer Jazz Series)	CRos EHyd LRHS NRHS

Camptosorus see *Asplenium*

Campylandra see *Tupistra*

Campylotropis (*Papilionaceae*)

macrocarpa	WSHC

Canarina (*Campanulaceae*)

canariensis ♀H2	CCCN CMCN CTsd SBrt SVen
– from Los Silos, Tenerife	WCot

Candollea see *Hibbertia*

Canna ✿ (*Cannaceae*)

'Adam's Orange'	XBlo
'Alberich'	SHaC
altensteinii	CDTJ SHaC SPlb XBlo
'Ambassador'	SDeJ
'Ambassadour'	SHaC
'Annaeei' ♀H3	SHaC SPlb
'Anthony and Cleopatra' (v)	WCot
I 'Aphrodite' van Klaveren	CBod MBros
'Argentina'	SHaC
'Assaut'	SHaC
'Atlantis'	XBlo
'Australia'	CDTJ SHaC XBlo
'Baron Seguier'	XLum
'Bird of Paradise'	SHaC
'Black Knight'	SCob SDeJ SHaC XBlo
'Bonfire'	CDTJ CTsd
brasiliensis	CPla SHaC WSMil XBlo
'Brillant'	SDeJ SHaC
'Burbank'	CDTJ
'Caballero'	SHaC XLum
'Caliméro'	SHaC
'Canary'	XBlo
Cannova Series	SHaC
– CANNOVA BRONZE ORANGE **new**	CCht SHaC
– CANNOVA BRONZE SCARLET	CCht SHaC
– CANNOVA LEMON	SHaC
– CANNOVA MANGO	CCht SHaC
– CANNOVA ORANGE SHADES	SHaC
– CANNOVA RED SHADES	CCht SHaC
– CANNOVA ROSE	SHaC
– CANNOVA YELLOW	CCht SHaC
'Carnaval'	SHaC
'Centenaire de Rozain-Boucharlat'	SDeJ SHaC XLum
'Champion'	SHaC
'Chocolate Sunrise'	LCro LOPS
'Chouchou'	SHaC
I 'Citrina'	XBlo
§ 'City of Portland'	SDeJ
§ 'Cleopatra'	CCCN SDeJ SHaC XBlo
coccinea	SArc
compacta	SHaC
'Corrida'	XLum
'Creamy White'	XBlo
'Di Bartolo'	XBlo
'Durban' Hiley, orange-flowered	see *C.* 'Phasion'
'Durban' ambig.	CBod CCht CWGN SArc SEdd SHaC WSMil
'E. Neubert'	ELan SHaC
edulis	CDTJ
§ × ***ehemanii*** ♀H3	CAvo CDTJ SBrt SHaC
'Emblème'	SHaC
'En Avant'	SHaC SPlb
'Endeavour'	SHaC
'Erebus' ♀H3	SHaC
'Ermine'	SHaC
'Étoile du Feu'	XBlo
'Extase'	SHaC
'Fatamorgana'	SHaC
'Feuerzauber'	SHaC
'Fiesta'	SHaC
FIREBIRD	see *C.* 'Oiseau de Feu'
'Firebird'	SHaC
flaccida	SHaC
'Flame'	XBlo
'General Eisenhower' ♀H3	SHaC
× ***generalis*** × ***indica***	SHaC
glauca	SHaC
'Gnom'	SDeJ
'Golden Girl'	MBros
'Golden Lucifer'	SDeJ
'Golden Orb'	SHaC
'Grand Duc'	SHaC
'Grande'	NGKo SHaC SPlb XLum
'Grandiose'	SHaC
'Happy Carmen' (CannaSol Series)	SHaC
'Happy Cleo' (CannaSol Series)	SHaC
'Happy Emily' (CannaSol Series)	SHaC
'Happy Isabel' (CannaSol Series)	SHaC
'Happy Julia' (CannaSol Series)	SHaC
'Happy Wilma' (CannaSol Series)	SHaC
Henlade hybrids	CDTJ
'Herman'	SHaC
'Hossegor'	XLum
'Indiana'	SHaC
indica	CAbb CDTJ CPla CTsd NGKo SArc SHaC SMHy SPlb WSMil
– 'Purpurea'	CDTJ SHaC SPlb
– 'Red King Rupert'	CCCN
– 'Russian Red' ♀H3	SHaC
– TROPICANNA GOLD ('Mactro'PBR)	CCCN CPla ELan LCro LOPS
'Intrigue'	SHaC
iridiflora misapplied	see *C.* × *ehemanii*
iridiflora Ruiz & Pav.	CDTJ CSpe SArc
'Italia'	CDTJ
jacobiniflora	SHaC
jaegeriana	SHaC
'Jivago'	SHaC
'Kalimpong'	CDTJ
I 'King Humbert' (blood-red)	CBcs CDTJ SDeJ XBlo
KING HUMBERT (orange-red)	see *C.* 'Roi Humbert'
'King Midas'	see *C.* 'Richard Wallace'
§ 'Königin Charlotte'	SDeJ SHaC
latifolia	SHaC

'Lesotho Lil'	SHaC
'Libération'	XLum
'Liberté'	see *C.* 'Wyoming'
'Lion Rouge'	XLum
'Lolita'	SHaC
'Louis Cayeux' ♀H3	SHaC
'Louis Cottin'	CBcs CCCN CDTJ NBPC
'Lucifer'	CCCN MBros NBPC NPer SDeJ XLum
'Lucy Steele' **new**	SHaC
lutea	SHaC XBlo
'Madame Angèle Martin'	XBlo
'Madame Paul Casaneuve'	SHaC
'Madeira' (Island Series)	SHaC
'Malawiensis Variegata'	see *C.* 'Striata'
'Marlena'	SHaC
'Marshmallow'	SHaC
'Mirizia'	SHaC
'Montaigne'	SHaC
'Moonshine'	CCCN LCro LOPS
'Mrs Oklahoma'	SDeJ
'Musifolia' ♀H3	CDTJ EWes NGKo SHaC XBlo
'Mystique' ♀H3	SHaC
'Ointment Pink'	XBlo
§ 'Oiseau de Feu'	XLum
'Oiseau d'Or'	SHaC XLum
'Orange Chocolate'	SHaC
'Orange Punch'	SHaC
'Orchid'	see *C.* 'City of Portland'
'Panache'	CDTJ SHaC
'Panama'	SHaC
paniculata	SHaC
'Peach Pink'	XBlo
'Pearlescent Pink'	XBlo
'Perkeo'	SHaC
§ 'Phasion' (v) ♀H3	CAbb CBod CCCN CSpe ELan LCro LOPS NPer SHaC SPalm SPoG WCot WSMil XBlo
'Picasso' ♀H3	CBcs CCCN CDTJ CExl SHaC XBlo
'Pink Champagne'	XBlo
'Pink Futurity' (Futurity Series)	CCCN SPad
'Pink Perfection'	SHaC
'Plaster Pink'	XBlo
'President'	SDeJ SHaC WSMil XBlo XLum
'Pretoria'	see *C.* 'Striata'
'Pretoria Variegata'	see *C.* 'Striata'
'Prince Charmant'	SHaC
'Pringle Bay' (v)	XBlo
'Professor Lorentz'	see *C.* 'Wyoming'
'Puck'	SHaC
'Queen Charlotte'	see *C.* 'Königin Charlotte'
'Ra' ♀H3	SHaC
'Red Cherry'	SDeJ
§ 'Richard Wallace'	CExl SDeJ SHaC SPlb XBlo
'Robert Kemp'	SHaC
§ 'Roi Humbert'	SHaC
'Roi Soleil'	SHaC XLum
'Roma'	SHaC
'Rosemond Coles'	SDeJ SHaC XBlo
'Saladin'	SHaC XLum
'Salsa'	SHaC
'Sémaphore'	SHaC WCot XBlo
'Shenandoah' ♀H3	SHaC
'Singapore Girl'	SHaC
'Snow-white'	XBlo
'Society Belle' ♀H3	SHaC
'Soudan'	CDTJ
'South Pacific'	SHaC
speciosa	CDTJ SPlb XBlo
'Strasbourg'	NPer XLum
'Strawberry Pink'	XBlo
'Striata' misapplied	see *C.* 'Stuttgart'
§ 'Striata' (v) ♀H3	CBod CCCN CCht CDTJ CTsd CWGN SEND SEdd SHaC SPalm WCot XBlo
'Striped Beauty' (v)	CCCN CDTJ CTsd
§ 'Stuttgart' (v)	CDTJ ESwi EWes SHaC SPad
'Summer Gold'	XBlo
'Sunset'	WCot
'Tali'	SHaC
'Talisman'	XBlo
'Taney'	SHaC
'Taroudant'	SHaC XLum
'Triomphe'	SHaC
(Tropical Series) 'Tropical Bronze Scarlet'	SHaC
- 'Tropical Red'	SHaC
- 'Tropical Rose'	SHaC
- 'Tropical Salmon'	SHaC
- 'Tropical White'	SHaC
- 'Tropical Yellow'	SHaC
TROPICANNA	see *C.* 'Phasion'
TROPICANNA BLACK ('Lon01'PBR)	CAbb CPla ELan EPfP LCro LOPS SPoG
tuerckheimii	SHaC
'Valentine'	WCot
'Vanilla Cream'	SDeJ
'Vanilla Pink'	XBlo
* 'Variegata' (v)	SPalm
'Verdi' ♀H3	SHaC
warscewiczii	CDTJ CExl SHaC
'Weymouth'	CDTJ
'Whithelm Pride' ♀H3	SDeJ SHaC
'Wintzer's Colossal'	SHaC
'Woodbridge Pink'	XBlo
§ 'Wyoming' ♀H3	CBcs CCCN CDTJ LCro LOPS NBPC SCob SDeJ SEND SHaC XBlo
'Yara'	SDeJ SHaC
'Yellow Humbert' misapplied	see *C.* 'Cleopatra', *C.* 'Richard Wallace'
'Yellow Humbert'	SDeJ

Cannomois (*Restionaceae*)

grandis	CCtw CPbh SPlb

Cantua (*Polemoniaceae*)

buxifolia ♀H3	CBcs CBod CCCN CExl CTsd ECre EShb LRHS MGil SIvy
- 'Alba'	CBcs CBod CCCN EShb
- 'Dancing Oaks'	SVen

Cape gooseberry see *Physalis peruviana*

Capeochloa (*Poaceae*)

§ ***cincta***	WCot

Capnoides see *Corydalis*

Capparis (*Capparaceae*)

spinosa	CCCN WJek
- subsp. ***rupestris***	SPlb

Capsicum (*Solanaceae*)

annuum	CCCN SVic
- 'Ancho'	SVic
- var. ***annuum*** 'Blondy'	LRHS NRHS
- - (Cerasiforme Group) 'Piccante Calabresé'	SVic

- - (Conioides Group) 'Super Chili' ♀H1c	SPre SVic
- - 'Demetra' ♀H1c **new**	EKin
- - (Grossum Group) 'Almapaprika'	SVic
- - - 'Bell Boy'	LCro LOPS LRHS NRHS
- - - 'Bendigo' **new**	MBros
- - - 'Corno di Toro Rosso' ♀H1c	CHby LCro LOPS
- - - 'Mini Bell Red'	SVic
- - - 'Mini Bell Yellow'	SVic
- - - 'Mohawk' ♀H1c	CRos EHyd EKin LRHS MBros NRHS
- - - 'Redskin' ♀H1c	CRos EHyd EKin LCro LOPS LRHS NRHS
- - - 'Thor'	LRHS
- - (Longum Group) 'Bolivian Rainbow' ♀H1c	SVic
- - - cayenne	CCCN LCro LOPS
- - - 'Filius Blue' ♀H1c	NRob
- - - 'Fish'	SVic
- - - 'Golden Cayenne'	SVic
- - - jalapeño	EHyd LCro LOPS LRHS NRHS SVic
- - - 'Hot Thai' ♀H1c	CRos EHyd LRHS NRHS
- - - 'Joe's Long Cayenne'	SVic
- - - 'Loco' ♀H1c	CRos EHyd LRHS NRHS
- - - 'Piccante Di Cayenna' **new**	LCro LOPS
- - - 'Ring of Fire'	SEdi SVic
- - - 'Serrano'	SVic
- - - 'Tokyo Hot'	SVic
- - 'Marconi Rosso'	LOPS SVic
- - 'Prairie Fire' ♀H1c	CCCN CRos EHyd LCro LOPS LRHS NRHS NRob SVic
- - 'Purple Mavros'	LRHS NRHS
- 'Apache' ♀H1c	CCCN CRos EHyd EKin LRHS MBros MPri NRHS NRob SPre
- 'Basket of Fire' ♀H1c	CRos EHyd EKin LRHS NRHS SPre SVic
- 'Britney'	LRHS
- 'Bulgarian Carrot'	SVic
- 'Cayenne Red'	SEdi SPre SVic
- 'Cayenne Sweet'	SVic
- 'Cheyenne'	CRos EHyd LRHS NRHS
- 'Cow Horn'	SVic
- 'Demon Red' ♀H1c	CRos EHyd EKin LRHS MCtn NRHS SPre SVic
- 'Etna' ♀H1c	CRos EHyd LRHS MCtn NRHS
- 'Explosive Ember'	SVic
- 'Fresno' ♀H1c	LRHS NRHS
- var. ***glabriusculum***	SVic
- 'Holy Mole'	SVic
- 'Hungarian Hot Wax' ♀H1c	CHby EKin LCro LOPS MCtn NRob SVic
- 'Hungarian Yellow Wax'	SVic
- 'Jalapeno Fooled You'	SVic
- 'Jericho'	CRos EHyd LRHS NRHS
- 'Krakatoa' ♀H1c	CRos EHyd LRHS NRHS
- 'Las Cruces Cayenne'	SVic
- 'Masquerade'	CRos EHyd LRHS NRHS
- 'Medina'	LRHS
- 'Medusa'	CRos EHyd LRHS NRHS
- 'Nosferatu'	SVic
- 'Numex Garnet'	SVic
- 'Numex Piñata'	SVic
- 'Numex Primavera'	SVic
- 'Numex Twilight'	CRos EHyd LRHS NRHS SPre SVic
- 'Padron'	LCro LOPS SVic
- 'Paper Lantern'	CRos EHyd LRHS NRHS
- 'Pasilla Bajio'	SVic
- 'Peter Pepper'	SVic
- 'Pinocchio's Nose'	SVic
- 'Pot Black' ♀H1c	SVic
- 'Razzamatazz'	CRos EHyd LRHS NRHS
- 'Red Cherry Small' **new**	SEdi
- 'Tricolor Variegatum' (v) ♀H1c	NRob
- 'Trinidad Perfume'	LRHS
- 'Vampire'	SVic
- 'Zimbabwe Black'	LRHS
baccatum 'Aji Limon'	SVic
- 'Aji Omnicolor'	SVic
- 'Brazilian Starfish'	SVic
- 'Christmas Bell'	SVic
- 'Lemon Drop'	SPre
chinense 'Bhut Jolokia'	SVic
- 'Carolina Reaper'	SVic
- 'Cheiro Roxa'	SVic
- Habanero Group ♀H1c	EKin
- - 'Habanero Caribbean Red'	SVic
- - 'Naga Morrich'	SVic
- - 'Caribbean Antillais' ♀H1c	SVic
- 'Hot Paper Lantern'	SVic
- 'Numex Suave Orange'	SVic
- 'Numex Suave Red'	SVic
- 'Peito de Moca'	SVic
- 'Scotch Bonnet'	CRos EHyd LRHS MBros NRHS SPre
- 'Trinidad Moruga Scorpion'	LRHS SVic
frutescens 'Adorno' **new**	LCro LOPS
- Tabasco Group	SVic
'Rodeo'	SVic

Caputia (*Asteraceae*)

§ ***scaposa***	EShb WSMil
§ ***tomentosa*** ♀H1c	EShb

Caragana (*Papilionaceae*)

CC 3945	CExl
arborescens	CAgr CMCN EBee ELan EPfP NLar SPer SPlb
- PAB 13.376	LEdu
- 'Lorbergii'	CEnd MBlu NLar SPer
- 'Pendula'	CMac ELan GBin MAsh MBlu NLar NOrn SCoo SPer
- 'Walker'	CEnd ELan MAsh MBlu MGos NHol NLar SCoo SPer
aurantiaca	NLar SBrt

carambola see *Averrhoa carambola*

caraway see *Carum carvi*

Cardamine (*Brassicaceae*)

asarifolia misapplied	see *Pachyphragma macrophyllum*
bipinnata	WCot
bulbifera	EBee ELon EPPr GBin GEdr LEdu MAvo NAts NRya WCru
californica	EBee EPPr LEdu MAvo NRya WCru
concatenata	WCru
digitata	EBee EMor
diphylla	CAby EBee LEdu WCot WCru
- 'American Sweetheart'	CExl
- 'Eco Cut Leaf'	CExl EBee MAvo WCru
- 'Eco Moonlight'	WCru
enneaphylla	EWld GWyn NBid NLar
glanduligera	CElw EBee ECha ELon EPPr EPri GEdr LEdu MAvo MNrw SBrt WCot WCru WFar

§ ***heptaphylla***	CAby CMiW ECha ELon GEdr GKev GQue ILea WCru WSHC
- from the Pyrenees	NLar
- 'Big White'	EBee EPPr GAbr GBin MNrw NLar WFar WPnP
- Guincho form	EPPr MAvo WCot
- 'Helen Myers' **new**	GEdr
§ ***kitaibelii***	CAby CMiW EMor EPPr LEdu MNrw NLar SBrt WCot WCru WFar
latifolia Vahl	see *C. raphanifolia*
macrophylla	EBee GEdr LEdu WCot WSHC
- 'Bright and Bronzy'	CExl IMou MAvo WCru
maxima	MAvo SHar WCru
microphylla	GKev
pentaphylla 🏆^{H5}	CSpe EBee EPPr EPot GAbr GBin GKev GMaP LEdu MCot NHpl SPhx WCru WSHC
pratensis	CBcs CBre CDor CWat GAbr GJos LCro LOPS MBow MHer MNHC NAts NMir SPhx SRms WHer WSFF WShi
- 'Diane's Petticoat'	MAvo
- 'Edith' (d)	LPot
- 'Flore Pleno' (d)	CBre CDor CSpe ECha GQue LEdu MHer MNrw NBid NBir NBro NLar SHar WSFF
- 'Flore Pleno' white-flowered (d)	LEdu
- white-flowered	CDor
- 'William' (d)	LEdu
quinquefolia	CAby CElw CMea CMiW ECha EHyd ELon EPfP ILea LEdu LRHS MAvo MBel MNrw MPie NLar SDix SDys WBrk WCot WCru WFar WPnP
- PAB 9992	LEdu
§ ***raphanifolia***	CBre CExl EBee GAbr IMou LLWG NBid NBro NRya NSti SHar WBor WFar
- PAB 204	LEdu
trifolia	CAby CElw CMac EBee ECha ELon EMor EPPr EWld GBin GEdr GMaP ILea IMou LEdu MAvo MNrw MRav NBir NBro NLar NRya SBut WCot WCru WFar
waldsteinii	CElw CExl EBee EPPr GEdr ILea LEdu MAvo NLar SMHy WCru WFar WPGP WSHC
yezoensis	GBin
- B&SWJ 4659	EBee EPPr WCru

cardamon see *Elettaria cardamomum*

Cardiandra (*Hydrangeaceae*)

alternifolia B&SWJ 5719	WCru
- B&SWJ 5845	WCru
- B&SWJ 6177	WCru
- B&SWJ 6354	WCru
- subsp. ***moellendorffii***	CExl WPGP
- 'Pink Geisha'	WCru
amamiohshimensis	WCru
formosana	CExl WPGP
- B&SWJ 2005	WCru
- 'Crûg's Abundant'	WCru
- 'Hsitou'	WCru
- 'Hsitou Splendour'	WCru

Cardiocrinum ✿ (*Liliaceae*)

cordatum	GKev
- B&SWJ 2812	WCru
- B&SWJ 4841	WCru
- B&SWJ 5427	WCru
- B&SWJ 6336	WCru
- B&SWJ 11069	WCru
- var. ***glehnii***	CCCN GEdr
- - B&SWJ 10827	WCru
- - B&SWJ 10843	WCru
- red-veined	SBrt
giganteum	CAby CBcs CBor CCCN CPla CRos EBee EHyd GAbr GBin GEdr GKev LRHS MNrw NBid NHpl NLar NRHS SDir SMad WCru WPnP WTyc
- B&SWJ 2419	WCru
- GWJ 9219 from Sikkim	WCru
- HWJK 2158 from Nepal	WCru
- WJC 13661 from Sikkim	WCru
- WJC 13698 from Sikkim	WCru
- var. ***giganteum*** **new**	CSpe
- pure white-flowered	GKev
- var. ***yunnanense***	EBee EPfP GEdr ITim NBid WCru WPGP
- - NJM 11.023 from Guizhou	WPGP
- - PAB 8347	LEdu
aff. ***giganteum*** NJM 12.060 from Nagaland, India	WPGP

cardoon see *Cynara cardunculus*

Carduus (*Asteraceae*)

defloratus subsp. ***argemone***	SBrt
- subsp. ***defloratus***	SBrt

Carex (*Cyperaceae*)

from Kyoto, Japan	EBee EPPr SMHy
acuta	CHab
- 'Variegata' (v)	CBen CMac CWat EShb GMaP LLWG NBro
alba	WCot
'Amazon Mist'	CRos LRHS NLar NRHS SCob SRms SWvt WFar
arenaria	CKno
§ ***atrata*** subsp. ***pullata*** KEKE 494	EBee
aurea	CBod GWyn
baccans	CExl SBrt
berggrenii	CSde GBin SPlb
boottiana	MHost
brizoides	IMou
brunnea	CMac
- 'Jenneke' (v)	EBee EHyd LRHS SWvt
- 'Jubilo'PBR	EBee
- 'Variegata' (v)	WHoo WSpi
buchananii	Widely available
- 'Firefox'	CBod
- 'Green Twist'	CBod EHyd EShb LRHS NRHS
- 'Red Rooster'	EBee LBuc LSun NWsh SCob
- 'Viridis'	CBod XLum
chathamica	CPla LRHS SVen WABo WCot
ciliatomarginata 'Treasure Island' (v)	EBee
colchica	XLum
comans	EPfP NBro
- 'Bronze Perfection'	CBod WRHF
- bronze-leaved	CBod CCBP CDoC CPla CRos CSBt EHyd ELan EPfP GBin LPot LRHS MAsh MHost NBir NRHS NSti NWad NWsh SCob SLim SPer SRms SWvt WCAu WSMil XCre

	- 'Bronzita'	WFar
	- 'Dancing Flame'	CWCL ELon
	- 'Frosted Curls'	Widely available
	- 'Phoenix Green' **new**	NWsh
	- red-leaved	NLar SRms
	- 'Small Red'	see *C. comans* 'Taranaki'
§	- 'Taranaki'	SCoo
	conica 'Hime-kan-suge'	see *C. conica* 'Snowline'
§	- 'Snowline' (v)	CMac ELan EShb GMaP LEdu NBro NLar NWsh SWvt XBlo XLum
	davalliana	EBee
	dioica	LLWG
	dipsacea	CKno CMac CRos CWCL EHyd EShb GMaP LRHS MHost NLar NRHS NWad NWsh WHal
	- 'Dark Horse'	CPla MMuc
	divulsa	CKno
	- subsp. ***leersii***	EPPr
§	***dolichostachya*** 'Kaga-nishiki' (v)	LEdu LRHS SLim
	duthiei	see *C. atrata* subsp. *pullata*
§	***elata*** 'Aurea' ♀H6	Widely available
	- 'Bowles's Golden'	see *C. elata* 'Aurea'
	- 'Knightshayes'	CKno WCot WFar
	elongata	CHab
	'Evergold'	see *C. oshimensis* 'Evergold'
	'Feather Falls' (v)	CDoC
	firma 'Green Dragon' **new**	GEdr
	- 'Variegata' (v)	EPot GEdr WAbe
	flacca	CHab CKno EPPr GBin WBor XCre XLum
	- 'Blue Zinger'	CBod CKno ELan WFar XSen
§	- subsp. ***flacca***	EBee NSti
	flagellifera	CBcs CBod CMac CRos CSpe CTri CWCL EBee EHyd ELan ELon EPfP EShb GMaP LRHS MHost MMuc NBir NRHS SCob SDix SEND SPlb SPoG WSMil
	- 'Auburn Cascade'	ELan NWsh
	- 'Kiwi'	EHyd NRHS NWsh
	folliculata	EPPr
	glauca Scop.	see *C. flacca* subsp. *flacca*
	'Gold Fountains'	see *C. dolichostachya* 'Kaga-nishiki'
	grayi	EHyd GBin LEdu LRHS MBlu NLar NRHS SPlb WBor WHoo WPGP
	'Ice Dance' (v)	Widely available
	kaloides	XLum
	laxiculmis 'Bunny Blue'PBR	NLar
*	***leformeri***	XLum
	limosa	LLWG
	lupulina	GBin
	lurida	XLum
	melanocephala	EBee
	MILK CHOCOLATE ('Milchoc'PBR) (v)	CBod ECtt ELan EPed EPfP MAsh SGbt SRms
	morrowii misapplied	see *C. oshimensis*
I	***morrowii*** Boott 'Fisher's Form' (v)	CTri ELan EPPr MRav SWvt WAvo WBrk
	- 'Gilt' (v)	EPPr NWad
	- 'Irish Green' **new**	CBod WFar
	- 'Nana Variegata' (v)	CTri
	- 'Pinkie'	CPla MHost
	- var. ***temnolepis***	IMou
	- 'Variegata' (v)	CBod ELan EPPr GMaP MMuc NBir NSti SRms WAvo XLum
	muskingumensis	CExl CKno CWCL ELan EPPr EPfP EShb GBin LEdu LLWG MHost NBro NLar SCob SDix SLim SMad WPnP WSMil XCre
	- 'Little Midge'	CKno CMac EShb GBin LEdu LPla NLar
	- 'Oehme' (v)	CKno CWCL EBee EHyd EPPr LLWG LRHS NBid NHol NWad
	- 'Silberstreif' (v)	CKno EPPr EShb GBin LEdu MMuc XCre XLum
	nigra (L.) Reichard	GQue WAvo XLum
§	- 'On-line' (v)	EPPr
	- 'Variegata'	see *C. nigra* 'On-line'
	No 4, Nanking (Greg's thin leaf)	EPPr
	obnupta	CKno
	ornithopoda 'Aurea'	see *C. ornithopoda* 'Variegata'
§	- 'Variegata' (v)	GBin NHol NWsh
§	***oshimensis***	EPPr WCot
	- EVEREST ('Fiwhite'PBR) (v)	CBcs CBod CKno CSBt EBee EPfP EShb GBin GWyn LCro LOPS LRHS LSRN LSun MAsh MBel MCot NEoE NWad NWsh SCob SPoG SRms WCot WFar WHoo WSHC
§	- 'Evergold' (v) ♀H7	Widely available
	- 'Evergreen'	SCob
	- (Evercolor Series) 'Everillo'PBR	CBcs CBct CBod CKno EBee EMor ESwi GBin LBuc LRHS MAsh NGBl NLar NWad NWsh SCob SPeP SPoG SRms WCot
	- - 'Everlime'PBR (v)	CBct CBod CKno EMor LRHS MAsh
	- - 'Everlite' (v) **new**	CKno LCro LOPS
	- - 'Everoro' (v)	CKno LSun WCot WRHF
	- - 'Eversheen'PBR (v)	LRHS
	- 'Variegata' (v)	NBir
	otrubae	CHab XLum
	panicea	CWCL EBee EPPr EShb LLWG
	paniculata	XLum
	pendula	CBcs CBen CHab CKno CTri ECha ELan EPfP GAbr GMaP MHost MMuc NBid NBir NBro NLar SCob SEND SLim SMad XLum XSen
	- 'Cool Jazz' (v)	EPPr
	- 'Moonraker' (v)	ESwi MHost WCot
	petriei	EBee ECha ELon XLum
	phyllocephala	EShb
	- 'Sparkler' (v)	ELon LRHS SCob SPad SPoG SWvt XLum
	plantaginea	EPPr EShb GBin LEdu WPGP WSHC
	praegracilis	CKno
	pseudocyperus	GBin NPer NWsh WPnP
	punctata	XLum
	remota	CKno EPPr EShb LPla
	riparia	CHab MMuc MWts NPer WShi
	- 'Bowles's Golden'	see *C. elata* 'Aurea'
	sabynensis	see *C. umbrosa* subsp. *sabynensis*
	scaposa	ESwi
	- KWJ 12304	LEdu WCru
	secta	CKno CRos EHyd EPPr EPfP GMaP IMou LRHS NRHS SRms
	- from Dunedin, New Zealand	EPPr
	siderosticta	WMal WSHC
	- 'Banana Boat'	see *C. siderosticta* 'Golden Falls'
§	- 'Golden Falls' (v)	SMad
	- 'Kisokaido' (v)	EShb
	- 'Shima-nishiki' (v)	EBee LRHS
	- 'Variegata' (v)	CTri CTsd ELan EShb LEdu NBir NLar NSti NWsh SLim WBor XCre
	'Silver Sceptre' (v)	CBod EHyd EMor EShb GKev GMaP LRHS MBNS MBel MGos NRHS NSti NWad NWsh SLim SPlb SWvt WBrk WFar

solandri	CKno XLum
spicata	CHab
spissa	MNrw
stricta Gooden. 'Bowles's Golden'	see *C. elata* 'Aurea'
stricta Lam.	MMuc SEND
sylvatica	CHab WOut
tenuiculmis	CWCL EBee EHyd LRHS NRHS NSti NWad SPtp WCot XLum
testacea	Widely available
- 'Limeshine'	EWes GBin WFar
- 'Old Gold'	SMad SPlb
- 'Prairie Fire'	CSpe EBou EPfP GMaP LCro LOPS LRHS NLar NRHS SCob SPtp SRms WGrn WSMil
texensis	EPPr
'The Beatles'	NBir
'Triffid'	MHost
trifida	CKno MHost
- 'Chatham Blue'	CBod GBin MMuc
- 'Rekohu Sunrise'^{PBR} (v)	CBod CKno EBee ELon EPfP LRHS LSun MMuc NEoE NSti SLon WCot
umbrosa	EShb XCre
subsp. ***sabynensis*** 'Thinny Thin' (v)	
vulpina	MHost

Carica (*Caricaceae*)

papaya (F)	SPre SVic XBlo
- 'Babaco'	CCCN
pubescens	see *Vasconcellea pubescens*

Carissa (*Apocynaceae*)

grandiflora	see *C. macrocarpa*
§ ***macrocarpa*** (F)	CCCN SVic WKor

Carlina (*Asteraceae*)

acanthifolia	SPhx
acaulis	ELan SPlb
- var. ***caulescens***	see *C. acaulis* subsp. *simplex*
§ - subsp. ***simplex***	ECha EHyd ELon LRHS NRHS
- - bronze-leaved	SPhx
vulgaris	GKev GPoy
- 'Silver Star'	SPhx

Carmichaelia (*Papilionaceae*)

odorata	CExl
stevensonii	CBcs CCCN EBee ELan IArd IMou MBlu NLar WPGP

× *Carmispartium* see *Carmichaelia*

Carpenteria (*Hydrangeaceae*)

californica	CCBP CCCN CRos CSBt CTri EBee EHyd ELan EPfP ESwi EWTr GBin IDee LCro LOPS LRHS MGil MGos NRHS SCob SPer SWvt WFar WHwl WSpi
- 'Bodnant' 🏆H4	CBcs CBod CCCN CRos EBee EHyd ELan LRHS LSRN MAsh MGos NLar NRHS SEle SPer SWvt WFar WGob WPGP WSpi
- 'Elizabeth' 🏆H4	CSBt CWGN EPfP LRHS LSRN MAsh NLar SPoG SSta
- 'Eskimo'	CBcs CCCN CDoC EMil LRHS SWvt
- 'Ladhams' Variety'	CBcs CMac CRos EHyd EPfP LRHS MRav SMad SPer SRkn SWvt WHwl WKif WSpi

Carpinus ✿ (*Betulaceae*)

betulus 🏆H7	Widely available
* - 'A. Beeckman'	CLnd SGol
- 'Columnaris'	CLnd CTho EBee
* - 'Columnaris Nana'	MPkF WCot WLov
§ - 'Fastigiata' 🏆H7	CBcs CCVT CEnd CLnd CMCN CMac CSBt CTho EBar ECrN ELan EPfP EWTr LBuc LMaj MGos NOrn SArc SCob SCoo SEWo SGol SGsty SSta SWeb SWvt WMat WMou WTSh
I - 'Folis Argenteovariegatis Pendula' (v) new	MBlu
- 'Frans Fontaine'	CCVT CEnd CLnd CMCN CMac CTho EBee EPfP EWTr IArd LMaj LSRN MBlu MGos NLar NOra SCob SCoo SEWo SGol SLim SPer SPoG WLov WMat WMou
- 'Globus'	MBlu
- 'Incisa'	WMou
- 'Lucas'	CCVT EBee MBlu NOra SGol WMat
- 'Monument'	MPkF
I - 'Monumentalis'	NLar
- 'Pendula'	CEnd CTho EBee LMaj MBlu SWvt WMou
- 'Purpurea'	CEnd CLnd MBlu
- 'Pyramidalis'	see *C. betulus* 'Fastigiata'
- 'Rockhampton Red'	MBlu WMat WMou
- 'Stegemanns Primus'^{PBR}	EBee
caroliniana	CLnd CMCN EPfP
- from Mexico new	WPGP
- 'Red Fall'	EPfP LRHS MBlu WMou
- 'Sentinel Dries'	LRHS MBlu WMou
cordata	MBlu SSta
coreana	SMad
fangiana	CBcs CEnd CExl CJun CLnd CMCN CTho EBee EPfP MBlu WPGP
fargesiana	EBee SMad WPGP
- KR 8780	WPGP
fargesii	see *C. viminea*
henryana	CExl CMen
- var. ***simplicidentata***	CMCN MBlu
japonica 🏆H6	CBcs CEnd CLnd CMCN CMen CTho EBee EPfP MBlu NOra SAko SCoo SEWo SMad SSta WMat WMou
- B&SWJ 10803	WCru
- B&SWJ 11072	WCru
- 'Chinese Lantern'	SGol
kawakamii	CMCN
- CWJ 12412	WCru
- CWJ 12449	WCru
laxiflora	CExl CMen
- B&SWJ 10809	WCru
- B&SWJ 11035	WCru
- var. ***longispica*** B&SWJ 8772	WCru
- var. ***macrostachya***	see *C. viminea*
omeiensis	EBee
- KR 280	WPGP
orientalis	CMCN
polyneura	EBee SSta WPGP
pubescens	WPGP
rankanensis	SSta
- NMWJ 14544 new	WCru
- RWJ 9839	WCru
× ***schuschaensis***	EBtc LRHS
shensiensis	EBee WPGP

tschonoskii	EBee
- B&SWJ 10800	WCru
- BBJMT 297	WPGP
turczaninowii	CMCN CMen MBlu NLar SSta
- var. ***turczaninowii*** new	WPGP
§ ***viminea***	CEnd CExl CMCN SSta WCot

Carpobrotus (*Aizoaceae*)

acinaciformis	SVen
§ ***edulis***	CCCN CDTJ SArc SEND SVen WHer XLum
- 'Gugh Dawn' (v)	SVen
- var. ***rubescens***	CCCN
- white-flowered new	CCCN
muirii	CCCN SVen
sauerae	CCCN

Carrierea (*Salicaceae*)

calycina	CBcs EBee IArd WPGP

carrot see *Daucus carota* for species; also AGM Vegetables Section for cultivars

Carthamus (*Asteraceae*)

dianius	SBrt
mitissimus	GEdr
tinctorius	MNHC SRms SVen

Carum (*Apiaceae*)

carvi	CBod CLau ENfk GPoy MHer MNHC SRms SVic WJek XAbr
petroselinum	see *Petroselinum crispum*

Carya ✿ (*Juglandaceae*)

cordiformis	MBlu
glabra	CBcs CMCN
illinoinensis (F)	CAgr CBcs CLnd MBlu
- 'Carlson No 3' seedling (F)	CAgr
- 'Colby' seedling (F)	CAgr
- 'Cornfield' (F)	CAgr
- 'Lucas' (F)	CAgr
laciniosa (F)	EPfP
- 'Henry' (F)	CAgr
- 'Keystone' seedling (F)	CAgr
ovata (F)	CAgr CBcs CMCN EPfP MBlu WPGP
- 'Grainger' seedling (F)	CAgr
- 'Neilson' seedling (F)	CAgr
- 'Weschcke' seedling (F)	CAgr
- 'Yoder No 1' seedling (F)	CAgr
tomentosa	NLar WPGP

Caryophyllus see *Syzygium*

Caryopteris (*Lamiaceae*)

× ***clandonensis***	CMac ECtt MGil NBir
- 'Arthur Simmonds' 🏆^{H4}	ECha
- BLUE BALLOON ('Korball')	NLar SGol
- 'Dark Knight'	CBod CDoC CRos CSpe EBee ECtt EHyd ELan EPfP LBuc LCro LOPS LRHS MAsh MCot NRHS SCob SEdd SEle SPer SPoG STPC SWvt WFar WHil WHoo
- 'Ferndown'	NLar SEND SRms
- 'First Choice' 🏆^{H4}	CBrac CRos EHyd ELan EPfP LRHS LSRN MAsh MGil MGos NRHS SLim SPer SRkn SWvt
- 'Gold Giant'	CRos EHyd EPfP LRHS MAsh NRHS
- GRAND BLEU ('Inoveris'^{PBR})	CMac EBee EHyd ELan EPfP LRHS LSRN MGos NLar SAko SGbt SGol SGsty SWvt SavN WLov
- 'Heavenly Baby' 🏆^{H4}	CRos EHyd EPfP LRHS MAsh SLon
- 'Heavenly Blue'	Widely available
- 'Hint of Blue'	SGol
- HINT OF GOLD ('Lisaura'^{PBR}) 🏆^{H4}	CRos CSBt EHyd ELan EPfP LCro LOPS LRHS MAsh MCot NLar NRHS SCob
- 'Kew Blue'	CBcs CRos CSBt EBee EHyd ELan EPfP EShb LRHS LSRN MAsh MGos MHer MSwo NLar NRHS SCoo SGbt SGol SLim SLon SPer SRms SSta SWvt XSen
- 'Longwood Blue'	CRos EPfP
- 'Pershore'	WAvo
- PETIT BLEU ('Minbleu'^{PBR})	EBee LRHS MPkF
- PINK PERFECTION ('Lisspin')	CBod CRos EHyd ELan LRHS NEoE NRHS SEle SPoG
- STEPHI ('Lissteph'^{PBR})	CBcs CRos EHyd ELan EPfP LRHS NRHS SPoG
- STERLING SILVER ('Lissilv'^{PBR}) 🏆^{H4}	CMac CRos EBee EHyd EPfP LRHS LSRN MAsh NEoE NRHS SCob SPer SPoG SRms SSta
- 'Summer Gold'	CMac MAsh
- 'Summer Sorbet'^{PBR} (v) 🏆^{H4}	CBod CMac CRos CWGN EBee ELan EPfP EWes LRHS MAsh MGos NLar SCob SCoo SEND SGbt SGol SLim SNig SPer SRms SWvt WFar WHil
- weeping	ELan EPPr WFar
- 'White Surprise'^{PBR}	CBod CMac CRos CWGN EHyd ELan EMil EPfP LRHS MGos NRHS SCob SGol SGsty SPer SPoG WFar WHil
- 'Worcester Gold' 🏆^{H4}	CBcs CMac CRos CSBt CTri ECha ECtt EHyd ELan EPfP LRHS MAsh MGos MHer MRav MSwo NRHS SEND SGol SLim SPer SPlb SRms SWvt WAvo WFar
- aff. 'Ferndown'	CBrac
divaricata	CMCN LPla SBrt
- 'Electrum'	WCot WFar WSHC
- 'Jade Shades'	WSHC
- pink-flowered	WFar
- 'Snow Fairy' (v)	MGil
incana 'Blue Cascade'	ELan EPfP LRHS MRav NLar SRms WAvo WGrn
- 'Delft Blue'	EBee LRHS
§ - 'Jason'^{PBR}	CBcs NLar SPoG WFar WHil
- SUNSHINE BLUE	see *C. incana* 'Jason'

Caryota (*Arecaceae*)

mitis	CCCN

Cassandra see *Chamaedaphne*

Cassia (*Caesalpiniaceae*)

corymbosa Lam.	see *Senna corymbosa*
fistula	CDow
marilandica	see *Senna marilandica*
nemophila	SPlb

Cassinia (*Asteraceae*)

fulvida	CBcs SVen
leptophylla	CBcs
vauvilliersii	SVen

Cassinia × *Helichrysum* (*Asteraceae*)

hybrid	WKif

Cassiope ✿ (*Ericaceae*)

'Askival Snowbird'	ITim

'Askival Snow-wreath'	see *C.* Snow-wreath Group
'Askival Stormbird'	ITim
'Badenoch'	GKev
'Edinburgh' ℽH6	EPot GBin ITim WThu
lycopodioides ℽH6	ITim
- 'Beatrice Lilley'	EPot GKev GRum WThu
- 'Jim Lever'	WAbe
- 'Rokujō'	ITim
mertensiana var. ***gracilis***	ITim WThu
'Muirhead' ℽH6	WThu
'Randle Cooke' ℽH6	EPot GBin
selaginoides LS&E 13284	EPot WAbe WThu
§ Snow-wreath Group	ITim
tetragona	ITim
wardii	EPot

Castanea ✿ (*Fagaceae*)

'Bouche de Bétizac' (F)	CAgr
crenata	CAgr
henryi	CMCN
'Maraval' (F)	CAgr WMat
'Maridonne' (F)	CAgr
'Marigoule' (F)	CAgr EPom SPer WMat
'Marsol' (F)	CAgr ECrN WMat
'Précoce Migoule' (F)	CAgr
sativa	Widely available
§ - 'Albomarginata' (v) ℽH6	CEnd EPfP NOra SPoG WMat
- 'Anny's Summer Red'	SPer
- 'Argenteovariegata'	see *C. sativa* 'Albomarginata'
- 'Aureomarginata'	see *C. sativa* 'Variegata'
- 'Belle Epine' (F)	CAgr
- 'Bournette' (F)	CAgr
* - 'Doré de Lyon'	CAgr
- 'Marlhac' (F)	CAgr NOra WMat
- 'Marron Comballe' (F)	CAgr
- 'Marron de Goujounac' (F)	CAgr
- 'Marron de Lyon' (F)	CAgr CEnd CHab EPfP EPom SVic
- 'Regal' (F)	EPom
§ - 'Variegata' (v)	CMCN ELan SCob SPer
seguinii	WPGP

Castilleja (*Orobanchaceae*)

applegatei	GKev
subsp. ***pinetorum***	
integra	SPlb
latifolia	GKev
miniata	SPlb WAbe
scabrida	GKev
sessiliflora	SPlb

Casuarina (*Casuarinaceae*)

cunninghamiana	EBtc SPlb
glauca	SVen

Catalpa ✿ (*Bignoniaceae*)

bignonioides ℽH6	CBcs CBee CCVT CHab CLnd CMCN CTho CTri EBee ECrN ELan EPfP EWTr LMaj MMuc MRav MSwo NOra NOrn SCob SEND SGol SGsty SPer SPlb SWvt WHwl WMat WMou WTSh
- B&SWJ 15090 **new**	WCru
- 'Aurea' ℽH6	Widely available
- 'Nana'	ELan SGsty WLov
- 'Purpurea'	see *C.* × *erubescens* 'Purpurea'
- 'Variegata' (v)	EBee ELon EPfP WLov
bungei	CCVT CMCN MBlu SArc SGol
§ × ***erubescens*** 'Purpurea' ℽH6	CBcs CCVT CEnd CMCN CMac CTho EBee ELan ELon EPfP EWTr LMaj MBlu MGil MRav MSwo NLar NOra NOrn SMad SPer SPoG SWvt WHwl WLov WMat WMou WPGP
fargesii f. ***duclouxii*** ℽH6	CBcs CEnd CLnd EBee EPfP MBlu SAko SChF WLov WPGP
ovata	CMCN SPad
speciosa ℽH6	CMCN GBin SVen
- 'Frederik'	NLar
- 'Pulverulenta' (v)	EBee MBlu SMad WLov

Catalpa × *Chilopsis* see × *Chitalpa*

Catananche (*Asteraceae*)

caerulea	CBod CMea CSBt CSpe CTri EBee ECha EHyd ELan EPfP EShb EWTr GQue LRHS MBel MNHC NRHS SCob SEdd SGbt SPer SPhx SPoG SWvt WCAu WCav WFar WHoo WSMil XSen
- 'Alba'	CBod CRos CSpe EAJP EBee ECha EHyd ELan EPfP GQue LRHS MBel MNrw NRHS SCob SEdd SGbt SPer SPoG SWvt WCAu XSen
- 'Amor Blue'	CRos EHyd EPfP LRHS NRHS SPoG
- 'Major' ℽH5	CRos EHyd LCro LOPS LRHS NRHS SEdd SRms

Catha (*Celastraceae*)

edulis	GPoy

Cathcartia (*Papaveraceae*)

§ ***chelidoniifolia***	EHyd LRHS NBid
§ ***villosa***	GGGa

Catopsis (*Bromeliaceae*)

morreniana	NCft

cauliflower see AGM Vegetables Section

Caulokaempferia (*Zingiberaceae*)

petelotii B&SWJ 11818	WCru
- HWJ 541	WCru

Caulophyllum (*Berberidaceae*)

thalictroides	CAby EMor EPPr GKev IMou LEdu MMrt WCru WHil WPGP WPnP WSHC
- subsp. ***robustum***	EBee WCru

Cautleya ✿ (*Zingiberaceae*)

cathcartii	CExl LEdu
- 'Tenzing's Gold'	EBee ESwi EWld LEdu WCru WPGP WSHC
§ ***gracilis***	CAby CBod CDTJ CExl
- BWJ 7843	WCru
- from Manipur, India	WPGP
- 'Crûg Gold'	WCru WPGP
- 'Dzoukou'	LEdu
lutea	see *C. gracilis*
spicata	CAby CBct CCCN CDTJ CSpe GKev MHid NGKo
- CC 3676	CExl
- 'Arun Flame'	CBct ESwi LEdu MNrw WCru WPGP
- 'Bleddyn's Beacon'	ESwi WCru
- 'Crûg Canary'	LEdu MHid WCru WPGP
- 'Crûg Compact'	WCru
* - var. ***lutea***	CBct CDTJ LEdu MHid WBor WPGP
- 'Robusta'	CAvo CBcs CExl EBee ELan EPfP LEdu MNrw SMad WBor WCot WCru WPGP

Cayratia (*Vitaceae*)

	japonica B&SWJ 6636	WCru
§	***thomsonii*** BWJ 8123	EPPr WCru

Ceanothus ✿ (*Rhamnaceae*)

	'A.T. Johnson'	SGol SRms
	arboreus	SArc
	- 'Trewithen Blue' ♀H4	Widely available
	'Autumnal Blue' ♀H4	CBcs CBrac CDoC CExl CMac CRos CSBt CTri EBee EHyd ELan EPfP LCro LOPS LRHS MAsh MGos MRav MSwo NLar NRHS SCob SGbt SGol SLim SPer SRms SSta SWvt WAvo
	'Blue Cushion'	CRos CTri EPfP LRHS MAsh MGos NLar NRHS SLon SWvt
	'Blue Diamond'PBR	LSRN
	'Blue Jeans'	CBcs MMuc NLar
	'Blue Mound' ♀H4	CBcs CBod CBrac CDoC CMac CRos CSBt CTri EHyd ELan EPfP LRHS MAsh MGos MRav MSwo NHol NLar NRHS SCob SGbt SGol SLim SPer SPoG SRms SWvt WAvo WFar
	'Blue Sapphire'PBR	CWGN ELan EPfP LRHS LSRN MAsh MGos NOra SPoG SRms SWvt WTyc
	'Blue Sensation'	NLar
	'Burkwoodii' ♀H4	CBcs CRos CSBt ELan EPfP LRHS MAsh MGos MRav SCob SPer SRms SWvt
	'Cascade' ♀H4	CBcs LSRN SPer SPlb WAvo
	'Concha' ♀H4	Widely available
	'Cynthia Postan'	CBod CRos EHyd EPfP LRHS MHer NLar NOra
	'Dark Star' ♀H4	CBcs CRos CSBt CTri CWGN EHyd ELan ELon EPfP LRHS LSRN MAsh MGos NHol NRHS SPoG SSta SWvt
	'Delight'	CBcs
	× ***delileanus*** 'Gloire de Versailles' ♀H4	CBcs CTri ELan EPfP EWTr ILea MGos MRav MSwo NLar SCob SCoo SGol SPer SPoG SWvt WKif WSpi
	- 'Henri Desfossé'	ELan EPfP LSRN MRav MSwo NLar SPer SPoG WKif
	- 'Topaze' ♀H4	ELan EPfP LRHS MRav NLar SGol SLon WKif
	dentatus Torr. & A. Gray	SPlb
	'Diamond Heights'	see *C. griseus* var. *horizontalis* 'Diamond Heights'
	EL DORADO ('Perado') (v)	CSBt ELan SGol WAvo
	'Eleanor Taylor'	WRHF
	gloriosus 'Emily Brown'	CBcs CBod CBrac ELan MRav NLar
§	***griseus*** var. ***horizontalis*** 'Diamond Heights' (v)	CBod LSRN MAsh NLar NOra SCob SPer
	- - 'Silver Surprise'PBR (v)	LBuc LSRN MPri NLar NOra SRms
	- - 'Yankee Point'	CBcs CDoC CMac CRos CSBt EHyd EPfP EShb LRHS LSRN MGos MRav MSwo NLar NRHS SCob SCoo SEND SGol SLim SPlb SPoG SWvt
	impressus	CTri MAsh SWvt WFar
	'Italian Skies'	CBcs CBrac CRos CSBt ECrN EHyd ELan EPfP LRHS LSRN MAsh MGos MSwo NLar NOra NRHS SCob SCoo SGol SLim SLon SPer SPlb SPoG SWvt
	'Julia Phelps'	SGol WAvo
	'Lemon and Lime'PBR	LBuc LRHS
	'Madagascar'	SCoo SPoG
	MARIE-ROSE ('Minmarose')	EPfP
	× ***pallidus*** 'Marie Simon'	CRos EHyd ELan EPfP LRHS LSRN MAsh MGos SGol SPer SPoG SRms SWvt WCFE WKif
	- 'Perle de Jade' **new**	ILea
	- 'Perle Rose' ♀H4	CBcs EPfP MGos SPer WKif
	papillosus	IArd WPav
§	'Pershore Zanzibar'PBR (v)	CBcs CBod CChe CMac CRos CTri EHyd LRHS MGos MRav MSwo NRHS SGbt SGol SPer SPoG SRms WAvo
	'Pin Cushion'	CDoC CRos EHyd EPfP LRHS MAsh
	'Point Millerton'	see *C. thyrsiflorus* 'Millerton Point'
	'Popcorn'	LRHS
	prostratus	SMad
	'Puget Blue' ♀H4	CBar CBcs CBod CBrac CDoC CMac CRos EHyd ELan ELon EPfP LCro LOPS LRHS LSRN MAsh MGos MPri MSwo NRHS SCob SGbt SGol SLim SPer SPoG SRms SWvt WFar WKif
	'Puget Blue' × ***thyrsiflorus*** var. ***repens***	LOPS
	'Ray Hartman'	NLar
	repens	see *C. thyrsiflorus* var. *repens*
	'Skylark' ♀H4	CBar CBcs CBod CBrac CChe CDoC CMac CRos EHyd ELan EPfP GBin GWyn LCro LOPS LRHS LSRN MAsh MGos NRHS SCob SEND SGol SLim SPer WAvo WFar
	'Snow Flurries'	see *C. thyrsiflorus* 'Snow Flurry'
	'Snow Showers'	CBcs
	'Southmead' ♀H4	CRos CTri ECrN EHyd ELan EPfP LRHS MGos MSwo NRHS
	thyrsiflorus	CTri NOra SRms SWvt WAvo
§	- 'Millerton Point'	CBod CCCN CDoC ELan EPfP LRHS MNHC NLar SGol
	- 'Mystery Blue' ♀H4	CRos EHyd LRHS NRHS SWvt
§	- var. ***repens*** ♀H4	Widely available
§	- 'Snow Flurry'	ELan MSwo SCob SGol
	'Tilden Park'	CRos EHyd LRHS
	'Tuxedo'PBR	LRHS MAsh MRav NLar SCob SGol
	× ***veitchianus***	CSBt EPfP LRHS SPer
	'Victoria'	CDoC CEnd EBee LRHS LSRN MSwo NLar SGol SRms
	'Zanzibar'	see *C.* 'Pershore Zanzibar'

Cedrela (*Meliaceae*)

sinensis	see *Toona sinensis*

Cedronella (*Lamiaceae*)

§	***canariensis***	CBod ENfk GPoy MNHC SRms WJek WOut XAbr
	mexicana	see *Agastache mexicana*
	triphylla	see *C. canariensis*

Cedrus (*Pinaceae*)

atlantica	LMaj SCob SGol WMat WTSh
- 'Aurea' ♀H6	LRHS NLar SLim SSta
- 'Fastigiata'	LRHS NLar SLim
- Glauca Group	CCVT CMac CMen CTho EBee ECrN ELan EPfP EWTr LRHS MBlu MGos NLar SCob SEWo SGol SPer SPlb SPoG SSta SWeb WMat WMou
- - 'Glauca' ♀H6	CLnd LMaj MAsh NOra SAko SGsty WTSh
- - 'Glauca Pendula' ♀H6	CCVT CLnd LRHS MBlu MGos NLar SGol SLim SSta WMat XLot

- - 'Silberspitz' CKen NLar
- 'Pendula' NOra
- 'Pyramidalis' LMaj
- 'Sapphire Nymph' CKen MAsh NLar SLim

brevifolia EBtc LRHS NLar
- 'Hillier Compact' CKen NLar
- 'Jade Medusa' LRHS
- 'Kenwith' CKen NLar

deodara ♀H6 Widely available
- 'Albospica' (v) SWvt
- 'Aurea' ♀H6 CCVT CKen EPfP LMaj MGos NHol NOra NOrn SGol WFar WMat XLot
- 'Blue Dwarf' CKen
* - 'Blue Mountain Broom' CKen
- 'Blue Snake' CKen
- 'Blue Surprise' SLim
- 'Bush's Electra' LRHS MBlu NLar
- 'Deep Cove' SLim
- 'Devinely Blue' CKen
- 'Eisregen' LRHS
- 'Feelin' Blue' ♀H6 CKen ELan EWTr LMaj LRHS MAsh NLar SLim SMad SWeb SWvt WFar XLot
- FEELIN' SUNNY ('Monkinn') NLar
- 'Gold Cascade' SLim
- 'Golden Horizon' CKen CMen ELan LRHS MAsh NLar SCob SLim SPoG WFar XLot
- 'Golden Jubilee' SGol
- 'Karl Fuchs' LRHS NLar XLot
- 'Kelly Gold' EBee
- 'Klondyke' MAsh
- 'Lime Glow' CKen SLim
- 'Mr Blue' SPoG
- 'Nana' CKen
- 'Pendula' ♀H6 CKen SLim
- 'Pygmy' CKen
- 'Robusta' LMaj WPGP
- 'Scott' CKen
- 'Silver Mist' CKen

libani ♀H6 CBrac CCVT CLnd CMCN CMac CTho ECrN ELan EPfP LMaj LRHS MBlu MMuc NLar NOra NOrn SCob SEND SGol SPlb SWvt WFar WMou WTSh XLot
- 'Alibaba' NLar
- 'Blue Angel' SLim
- 'Blue Fountain' NLar NOrn XLot
- 'Comte de Dijon' LRHS NLar
- 'Fontaine' NLar
- 'Glauca' XLot
- 'Golden Dwarf' **new** CKen
- 'Green Prince' NLar
- 'Hedgehog' CKen NLar
- 'Home Park' CKen NLar
- 'Italie' NLar
- 'May' LRHS NLar SLim
- 'Minitaur' NLar
- Nana Group CKen ELan
- 'Pendula' CKen NLar
- 'Sargentii' LRHS MBlu NLar XLot
- 'Taurus' NLar

Ceiba (*Malvaceae*)

pentandra SPlb

Celastrus (*Celastraceae*)

dependens CWJ 12478 WCru
- NMWJ 14556 WCru

flagellaris B&SWJ 8572 WCru
hookeri B&SWJ 11667 WCru
kusanoi CWJ 12445 WCru
orbiculatus CBcs MRav SLon SPer WHer
- Hermaphrodite Group ♀H6 MGil SDix
- var. **papillosus** B&SWJ 591 WCru
- var. **punctatus** CWJ 12439 WCru

scandens CMac SPhx SPlb
stephanotiifolius B&SWJ 4727 WCru
stylosus WJC 13746 WCru

celeriac see *Apium graveolens* var. *rapaceum*; also AGM Vegetables Section

celery see *Apium graveolens* var. *dulce*; also AGM Vegetables

Celmisia (*Asteraceae*)

allanii GKev WAbe
angustifolia ♀H5 WAbe
argentea EPot NHar WAbe
bellidioides EPot NSla WAbe
coriacea misapplied see *C. semicordata*
densiflora GKev
'Eggleston Silver' NBir
gracilenta GKev WAbe
haastii × viscosa NSla
hectorii WAbe
ramulosa ITim NHar WAbe
- var. **tuberculata** NSla

§ **semicordata** ITim NHpl
sessiliflora EPot WAbe
I 'Wooley Hybrid' **new** EPot

Celosia (*Amaranthaceae*)

argentea var. **cristata** LSou
(Plumosa Group) 'Dragon's Breath' ♀H2 **new**
- - - Kimono Series MBros SPoG

Celsia see *Verbascum*

× *Celsioverbascum* see *Verbascum*

Celtica see *Stipa*

Celtis (*Cannabaceae*)

australis CBcs CMCN EBee LEdu MBlu WKor
biondii NLar
caucasica GKev
choseniana B&SWJ 12774 WCru
occidentalis EBtc EWTr WKor
sinensis CMen

Cenolophium (*Apiaceae*)

denudatum ♀H6 Widely available

Centaurea ✿ (*Asteraceae*)

HH&K 271 NBid
RCB AM 6 WCot
W&B BGB-1 WCot
affinis EBee GKev
alpestris NLar SPhx
'Amethyst on Ice' ELan LBuc LRHS SRms WCav
§ **atropurpurea** CBod CSpe EBee EHyd ELan EPfP EWes LPot LRHS MBNS MBel MHol

	NBid NGBl NLar NSti SEdd SHar SPhx SPlb WCot WHil WMal
babylonica RCB/TQ 18	WCot
bella	CBod CRos EBee ECtt EHyd ELon LRHS MBel MRav MSpe NBro NGrd NRHS NSti SBut SMHy SPhx WFar WGwG WKif XLum XSen
benoistii misapplied	see *C. atropurpurea*
benoistii ambig.	MRav
benoistii ambig. × ***orientalis***	SPhx
'Big Purple'	WCot
candidissima misapplied	see *C. cineraria*
candidissima Lam.	see *C. rutifolia*
'Caramia'	CBcs CBod EBee ECtt EHyd ELan EPfP LEdu LRHS MAvo MHol MNrw MSpe NBPC NBid NHpl NRHS WCAu WHil
carniolica	SHar
- SDR 5443	EBee
cheiranthifolia	CFis CMea EPPr MHol MNrw NBid NBir NLar SBut SEdd SHar
§ ***cineraria***	CSpe ECre WSpi
- subsp. ***cineraria*** 🏆H3	SEND WCot WMal
clementei	EBee
cyanoides	LRHS SPhx
cyanus	CHab CSpe LCro LOPS MBow MHer MNHC MPri SVic
- 'Black Ball'	CSpe LCro LOPS LRHS MNHC SPhx
- 'Blue Ball'	CSpe
- 'Blue Boy'	LRHS
- 'Blue Diadem'	SPhx
- 'Florence Blue' (d)	LRHS SPhx
- 'Pinkie' (d)	MNHC SPhx
- 'Snowman'	SPhx
cynaroides Link	see *Rhaponticum centaureoides*
dealbata	CBod CMac CRos EAJP EBee EHyd ELon EMor EPfP LRHS MBel MHol MMuc NBro NGrd NLar NMir NRHS SCob SEND SRms STPC XLum
- 'Steenbergii'	CMac MBel NBid NBir NGdn NPer NSti SPer SPoG WCAu WCot
declinata RCB UA 18	WCot
gigantea	WHer
glastifolia	EBee
grinensis	WOut
gymnocarpa	see *C. cineraria*
jacea	ELon EWTr GAbr GWyn NBid NLar SBut SPhx WCot WOut WPGP
- PAB 8821	LEdu
'John Coutts'	Widely available
'Jordy'	Widely available
karabaghensis	EBee GKev MSpe
macrocephala	CBod CRos ECha ECtt EHyd ELan ELon EMor EPfP EShb GAbr LEdu LPot LRHS MBel MHol NBid NBro NChi NGBl NLar NRHS SDix SPer SPoG SRms WCAu XLum
mollis	NBid
montana	Widely available
- 'Alba'	Widely available
- 'Amethyst Dream' PBR	CRos EBee EHyd EMor EPfP LRHS MNrw NLar NRHS SPoG WCAu
- 'Amethyst in Snow'	CBod CElw CRos EAJP EBee ECtt EHyd EMor EPfP LEdu LRHS MBNS MHol NBPC NHol NLar NRHS NWad SCob SPoG WBor WCAu WTor

- 'Black Sprite'	CAby CBod CSpe CWGN EAJP EBee ECtt EHyd ELon EPfP GMaP ILea LRHS MBNS MNrw NBPC NLar NRHS NSti SPoG WBor WBrk WFar WHil
- 'Blewit'	EBee ELon NLar WCAu
§ - 'Carnea'	CElw CSam ELon EPPr GMaP LRHS MCot NBir NChi NLar SHar SPhx WBrk WCAu WFar WOut
- 'Elworthy Glacier'	CElw WMal
- 'Gold Bullion'	CRos CSpe CWGN EBee ECtt EHyd EWes GMaP LRHS MHol MRav NBid NLar NRHS WSHC
- 'Grandiflora'	CCBP EBee ELon MPie
- 'Joyce'	CElw MTis NBid NLar SCob SHar WCAu WSHC
- 'Lady Flora Hastings'	CElw CSam CSpe EBee ELon EPPr LRHS NBid WBrk
- 'Lavender Mist'	CBod MHol NRHS
- lilac-flowered	NBid NLar
- 'Ochroleuca'	CElw NBid
- 'Parham'	CBod CElw CRos ECtt EHyd ELon GAbr GQue LRHS MNrw MRav NBPC NLar NRHS NSti SPer SPlb WSHC
- 'Purple Heart'	CAby CBcs CBod CMea CWGN EBee ECtt ELon EPfP EWTr GBin LCro LOPS LSun MAvo MBNS MBel MCot MHer MNrw MSpe NGBl NLar SEdd SPad SPer SRms WCAu WCot
- 'Purple Prose'	CElw EPPr LPla
- 'Purpurea'	CElw
- 'Rosea'	see *C. montana* 'Carnea'
I - 'Violacea'	NBid
- 'Violetta'	CElw ELon LCro LOPS MSpe NBid NBir WBrk WCAu
nervosa	NBid NBro XLum
nigra	CBod CDor CHab ELan ELon EPfP GJos LCro LOPS MBow NLar NMir SPhx SRms WOut WSFF WWild
- var. ***alba***	CBre NBid WOut
- 'Mardi Gras' (v)	ECtt
- subsp. ***rivularis***	NBid XLum
- 'Waterfall White' **new**	MAvo
orientalis	CSpe EHyd EWes LRHS MBel MHol MSpe NGBl SGbt SPhx WHoo
pannonica	EPPr
- subsp. ***pannonica*** HH&K 259	NBid
phrygia	CBod MMuc NLar SPhx
pulcherrima	MNrw
'Pulchra Major'	see *Rhaponticum centaureoides*
pullata	EHyd LRHS
rupestris	EBee EPfP SPhx
ruthenica	CDor CFis SPhx SPlb WGoo
§ ***rutifolia***	WMal
salicifolia	NBir
salonitana RCB AM 1	WCot
scabiosa	CBre CCBP CDor CHab LCro LOPS MHer MNHC MSpe NBid NBir NGrd NMir SPhx SRms
'Silver Feather'	CKno EBee EHyd LRHS MHol NRHS NSti SBut SPoG SRkn SRms WNPC
simplicicaulis	CSam ELon MAsh NBir NChi NHpl SHar SRms WCav WHoo XSen
thracica	EBee WCot
triumfettii 'Hoar Frost'	EBee ELon NDov
- subsp. ***stricta***	SHar

Centaurium (*Gentianaceae*)

erythraea	GPoy
scilloides	EBou GKev NSla WAbe

Centella (*Apiaceae*)

§ ***asiatica***	GPoy LCro LEdu LOPS WJek XAbr

Centradenia (*Melastomataceae*)

inaequilateralis	CCCN
- 'Cascade' ♀H2	MBros

Centranthus (*Caprifoliaceae*)

§ ***lecoqii***	ECha ECtt EPPr EWes LRHS MBel NDov SPhx WCot WGoo
macrosiphon	CMac
§ ***ruber***	Widely available
* - 'Alba Pura'	GAbr
§ - 'Albus'	Widely available
- 'Atrococcineus'	ECha MMuc SGbt
- var. ***coccineus***	CBcs CBod CRos EAJP EBee EHyd ELan EPfP EWTr GAbr GBin GJos GKin GMaP LPot LRHS LSun MRav NRHS SBut SCob SEND SPer SPhx SSut WCot WFar WGwG XSen
- mauve-flowered misapplied	see *C. lecoqii*
- 'Roseus'	EHyd EPfP LRHS
- 'Rosy Red'	CBod
- 'Snowcloud'	EBee ECtt EHyd ENfk EPfP MBow MNHC SBut SRms WHil
'White Cloud'	SPad

Centropogon (*Campanulaceae*)

ferrugineus B&SWJ 10665	WCru

Cephalanthus (*Rubiaceae*)

'Magical Moonlight'	LCro LOPS LRHS NLar
occidentalis	CAby CBod EBee LRHS MAsh MBNS MBlu NLar NQui SLim SPhx SPoG WCFE
- SUGAR SHACK ('Smcoss')	LRHS

Cephalaria (*Caprifoliaceae*)

§ ***alpina***	CBod EHyd EMor EPPr EPfP LRHS MAsh MNrw NRHS SDix SHar SPhx SRms WBrk WFar XLum
caucasica	see *C. gigantea*
dipsacoides	LRHS MSpe SPhx SRms WGoo
§ ***flava***	EHyd LRHS
galpiniana	SPlb
§ ***gigantea***	Widely available
graeca	see *C. flava*
leucantha	CFis EMor MMuc NLar SEND SPhx WBrk
litvinovii	SPhx
radiata	NDov SPhx
tatarica hort.	see *C. gigantea*
tchihatchewii	ILea IMou NLar WCot
transsylvanica	SPhx
- W&B BGJ-1	CSpe WCot

Cephalotaxus (*Taxaceae*)

fortunei	LEdu WCru WKor
harringtonii	CMCN LEdu WKor
- 'Fastigiata'	IArd LRHS MAsh MGos SLim SPoG XLot
- 'Gimborn's Pillow'	MAsh NLar
- 'Korean Gold'	LRHS SLim

Cephalotus (*Cephalotaceae*)

follicularis ♀H2	CHew SHmp

Cerastium (*Caryophyllaceae*)

alpinum	SRms
- var. ***lanatum***	EWes GKev XLum
biebersteinii	XLum
candidissimum	EWes
fontanum	CHab
tomentosum	CBar CBod CSBt CTri ELan EPfP GWyn MHol MMuc NBir SEND SPer SPlb SPoG WFar
- var. ***columnae***	ECha EWes GMaP WIce XLum XSen

Ceratonia (*Caesalpiniaceae*)

siliqua	SEND SPlb SVic

Ceratophyllum (*Ceratophyllaceae*)

demersum	CBen CWat EWat LCro LOPS MWts SVic WMAq WSFF XBlo
submersum	LLWG

Ceratopteris (*Pteridaceae*)

thalictroides new	XBlo

Ceratostigma (*Plumbaginaceae*)

abyssinicum	CBcs ELan ESwi EWTr SIvy
asperrimum B&SWJ 7260	WCru
'Autumn Blue'	EPfP LRHS
capensis	CMac
griffithii	Widely available
§ ***plumbaginoides*** ♀H5	Widely available
willmottianum ♀H4	Widely available
- BWJ 8140	WCru
- DESERT SKIES ('Palmgold'PBR)	CMac EPfP NLar SCob SLim SWvt
- FOREST BLUE ('Lice'PBR) ♀H4	CDoC CMac CRos CSBt EHyd ELan EPfP LCro LOPS LRHS LSRN MAsh MGos MPri MRav NRHS SAko SCoo SEle SLim SPer SPoG SSta SWvt
- SAPPHIRE RING ('Lissbrill'PBR)	CBcs CCCN CDoC CRos EBee EHyd ELan EPfP LRHS LSRN MAsh NRHS SCoo SPoG WFar WHil

Cercidiphyllum ✿ (*Cercidiphyllaceae*)

japonicum ♀H5	Widely available
- 'Boyd's Dwarf'	CDoC CJun CRos EHyd ELan EPfP LRHS MBlu NLar SPoG SSta WCot
- 'Chameleon' (v)	MBlu NLar
- GLOWBALL ('Jww4'PBR)	IArd LRHS MBlu
- 'Herkenrode Dwarf'	MBlu NLar
- 'Heronswood Globe' ♀H5	CJun CMCN EPfP MBlu NLar SSta WHwl
- 'Kreukenberg Dwarf'	CJun NLar SSta
- 'Morioka Weeping'	CJun CTho EBee MPkF NLar SSta
- 'Peach'	CJun NLar
§ - f. ***pendulum*** ♀H5	Widely available
- - 'Amazing Grace'	CTho MBlu NLar SGbt SSta
- 'Raspberry'	CJun MBlu NLar
- RED FOX	see *C. japonicum* 'Rotfuchs'
§ - 'Rotfuchs'	CBcs CEnd CJun CMCN CMac CRos CTho EBee EHyd ELan EPfP EWTr LRHS MBlu MGos MPkF NLar NOra SAko SChF SGsty SPoG SSta WFar WHwl WMat
- 'Ruby'	CJun EBee MBlu
- 'Strawberry'	CBcs CJun MBlu NLar SSta
- 'Tidal Wave'	CJun LRHS MBlu NLar SSta
- 'Titania'	NLar SSta

magnificum	CBcs CEnd CExl CLnd CMCN MBlu NLar
- f. ***pendulum***	see *C. japonicum* f. *pendulum*

Cercis ✿ (*Caesalpiniaceae*)

canadensis	CAgr CMCN CTsd CWGN LMaj MGil MGos NLar SCob SavN XSen
- f. ***alba***	CBcs CMCN LSRN
- - 'Royal White'	EPfP MBlu SPer
- 'Appalachian Red'	CJun CTho MBlu MGos
- 'Cascading Hearts'	CRos EHyd LRHS NRHS
- 'Flame'	CJun SSta
- 'Forest Pansy' ♀H5	Widely available
- 'Hearts of Gold'PBR	CWGN EBee LRHS MGos MRav NLar NOra NOrn SLon SPoG WHwl WMat
- LAVENDER TWIST ('Covey')	CMac CRos EBee EHyd ELan EPfP LCro LMaj LOPS LRHS LSRN MBlu MGos NLar NOra NOrn NRHS SGol SLon SPer SPoG SRms WHwl WMat WMou
- LITTLE WOODY ('Litwo'PBR)	MGos NLar SGol
- 'Melon Beauty'	MBlu NLar WHwl WLov
- 'Merlot'	ELan MGos SGsty WHwl WMat
- 'Pauline Lily'	ESwi NLar
- 'Pink Heartbreaker'	NLar SGol
- 'Pink Pom Poms'	EBee LRHS MPri NLar WHwl
- RED FORCE ('Minrouge3'PBR)	CDoC LSRN NLar SGsty WCot
- 'Ruby Falls'PBR ♀H5	CBcs CMac CRos EBee EHyd ELan EPfP EWTr LCro LMaj LOPS LRHS MGos NOra NRHS SPoG WHwl WMat
- 'Rubye Atkinson'	NLar
- var. ***texensis*** 'Oklahoma'	CJun EBee EPfP LRHS MGos WMat WPGP
- - 'Texas White'	CEnd CMac CTho EBee EPfP LRHS NLar NOrn WMat
- - 'Traveller'	SGol
- 'The Rising Sun'	MGos
- 'Vanilla Twist'PBR	EBee NLar SPoG WHwl
chinensis	EWTr GKev LMaj NLar SPer SavN WMou
- B&SWJ 12665	WCru
- NJM 11.047	WPGP
- f. ***alba***	CTho MGos
- 'Avondale' ♀H5	CBcs CEnd CJun CMac CTho EBee EHyd ELan EPfP EWes IArd LCro LMaj LOPS LRHS LSRN MAsh MBlu MGil MGos NLar NOra NOrn SCoo SPer SPoG SWvt WHwl WMat WMou
- 'Diane'	SSta
- 'Don Egolf' ♀H5	CJun MBlu MGos NLar SGol
- 'Shirobana'	GKev WMat
chingii	CExl
gigantea	NLar WPGP
griffithii	CMCN LEdu NLar SSta WPGP
occidentalis	LEdu SSta
racemosa	CExl WPGP
siliquastrum	Widely available
- f. ***albida***	CRos CTho EHyd ELan EPfP EWes GKev LRHS SSta
- 'Bodnant' ♀H5	CMac CTho EPfP EWes IArd LRHS LSRN MBlu MGos NLar NOra SSta WHwl WMat
- 'White Swan'	CJun CTho

Cerinthe (*Boraginaceae*)

major	SWvt
- 'Purpurascens'	CSpe ELan EPfP LCro LOPS MNHC SPer SPhx SPoG WKif

Ceropegia (*Apocynaceae*)

§ ***linearis***	CDoC EShb
subsp. ***woodii*** ♀H1c	
sandersonii ♀H1c	CCCN CDoC ELan EShb
woodii	see *C. linearis* subsp. *woodii*

Cestrum (*Solanaceae*)

aurantiacum	EShb SEND
buxifolium B&SWJ 14395	WCru
× ***cultum*** 'Cretan Pink'	CCCN
- 'Cretan Purple'	CBcs CCCN CRos EBee EHyd ELan ELon EPfP EShb IDee LRHS MGil SWvt WKif
diurnum × ***nocturnum***	EShb
§ ***elegans***	CBod CExl CSde EBee ELon EPfP EWld IDee LRHS MGil NQui SEND SIvy SLon SPad SWvt WCFE
fasciculatum	SDix
'Newellii' ♀H3	CBcs CCCN CExl CRos EBak EBee EHyd ELan ELon EPfP LRHS SPlb SVen SWvt WKif
nocturnum	CBcs CCCN EBak EShb WCFE
parqui ♀H3	CAbb CBcs CCCN CMCN CTsd EBee ELan EPfP IDee MGil SDix SEND SIvy SLon SMad SWvt WKif WSHC
- purple-tinged	SBrt
psittacinum	CExl
purpureum (Lindl.) Standl.	see *C. elegans*
roseum	CExl
- B&SWJ 10255 from Oaxaca State, Mexico	WCru
- 'Ilnacullin'	CCCN CSde

Ceterach see *Asplenium*

officinarum	see *Asplenium ceterach*

Chaenomeles (*Rosaceae*)

cathayensis	CAgr EPfP LEdu NLar WCru WFar WHer WKor WLov WPGP
§ ***japonica***	CCCN MMuc SCob SEND SPre WKor
- 'Chojubai'	CMen
- 'Cido'	CAgr LEdu MCoo
- 'Orange Beauty'	LRHS NHol SCob SPer
- 'Rising Sun'	NLar
- 'Sargentii'	MBlu NLar SGol
MADAME BUTTERFLY ('Whitice')	CBod CRos EBee EHyd ELan EPfP LRHS LSRN MAsh MRav NRHS SCob SEND SGol SLim SPoG SRms
maulei	see *C. japonica*
'Orange Star'	CEnd
sinensis	see *Pseudocydonia sinensis*
speciosa 'Apple Blossom'	see *C. speciosa* 'Moerloosei'
- 'Contorta'	LRHS MAsh WFar
- 'Eximia'	LRHS SGsty
- 'Falconnet Charlet' (d)	CRos EHyd LRHS MRav NRHS SRms
- 'Flocon Rose'	EPfP LRHS SGol
- 'Friesdorfer'	CDoC LRHS SGsty
- 'Geisha Girl' (d) ♀H6	CBcs CBod CDoC CEnd CMac CRos EBee EHyd ELan EPfP LCro LOPS LRHS LSRN MAsh MGos MRav MSwo NOra NRHS SGbt SGol SLim SPer SPoG SRms SWvt WFar
- HOT FIRE ('Minvesu')	CDoC CRos EPfP LRHS SGsty WCot
- 'Kinshiden'	EMil EPfP LRHS LSRN NLar SGol SGsty

- MANGO STORM ('Mincha01'PBR) **new**	CRos SGsty
§ - 'Moerloosei' 🏆H6	Widely available
- 'Nivalis'	Widely available
- 'Orange Storm'PBR	CRos LCro LOPS LRHS LSRN SGol
- 'Pink Storm'PBR	CRos LCro LOPS SGol
- RED KIMONO ('Ainoomoi'PBR)	LRHS SGol
- 'Rubra Grandiflora'	LRHS SGsty
- 'Scarlet Storm'PBR	CRos LRHS SGol
- 'Simonii' (d)	CBcs MRav SPer
- 'Snow'	MAsh MSwo SRms
- 'Umbilicata'	MBlu SPer SRms
- 'Yukigotan' (d)	CDoC CRos LEdu LRHS NLar SGol SWvt
× ***superba*** 'Boule de Feu'	CTri MCoo
- 'Cameo' (d)	CBrac CEnd ELon EPfP IArd LEdu LRHS MBNS MRav NLar SCob SGbt SGol SIvy SRms WCot WFar
- 'Coquelicot'	NLar
- 'Crimson and Gold' 🏆H6	Widely available
- 'Elly Mossel'	CMac NLar SRms WFar
- 'Ernst Finken'	NLar
- 'Etna'	WFar
- 'Fire Dance'	CTsd MSwo NLar SGol SPer WCot WLov
- 'Fusion'	CAgr
- 'Hollandia'	SRms
- 'Issai White'	MRav
- 'Jet Trail'	CBcs CMac CRos EHyd ELan EPfP LRHS LSRN MAsh MGos MRav MSwo NLar NRHS SCob SGbt SGol SLim SRms SWvt WFar
- 'Knap Hill Scarlet'	CBod CRos EBee EHyd ELan EPfP LRHS MAsh MGos NOra NRHS SCob SLim SPer SPoG SRms SWvt WCot
- 'Lemon and Lime'	CBcs CBod ELan LRHS MAsh MGos MRav NLar NOra SLon SPer SRms
- 'Nicoline' 🏆H6	CBcs CRos LRHS MGos
- 'Pink Lady' 🏆H6	Widely available
- 'Pink Trail'	NLar SGbt SRms
- 'Red Joy'	EBee EPfP LRHS MRav NLar SRms
- 'Red Trail'	MRav
- 'Rowallane' 🏆H6	CBod ELan MRav
- 'Salmon Horizon'	IArd NLar
- 'Texas Scarlet'	SRms WMou
- 'Tortuosa'	CBod LRHS MBNS NLar WCot WGrn
'Toyo-nishiki'	MBlu

Chaenorhinum (*Plantaginaceae*)

glareosum	NHpl
§ ***origanifolium***	SPlb
- 'Blue Dream'	CSpe EBou EPfP EWTr GKev MAsh SBut SPoG SWvt WFar WHoo WIce

Chaenostoma (*Scrophulariaceae*)

cordatum (Abunda Series) ABUNDA COLOSSAL BLUE ('Balabolue')	LSou MBros
- - ABUNDA COLOSSAL PINK	MBros
- - ABUNDA COLOSSAL WHITE ('Balabowite'PBR)	LSou MPri
- COPIA GULLIVER WHITE ('Dangul14'PBR) (Copia Series)	MPri
- 'Olympic Gold' (v)	SCoo
- (Scopia Series) SCOPIA GOLDEN LEAVES WHITE ('Dancop15')	MBros MPri
- - SCOPIA GREAT REGAL BLUE ('Dancop30')	MPri
- - SCOPIA GULLIVER DYNAMIC WHITE ('Dancop40'PBR)	MCot
§ - 'Snowflake'	MBros NPer SCoo SPoG SWvt
§ ***neglectum***	WPGP

Chaerophyllum (*Apiaceae*)

aromaticum **new**	LEdu
aureum **new**	NAts
azoricum	LEdu LPla MAvo WOut WPGP
coloratum **new**	SPtp
creticum **new**	SPtp
hirsutum	IMou
- 'Roseum'	Widely available

Chamaecyparis ✿ (*Cupressaceae*)

lawsoniana	CBrac LMaj SCob WMou WTSh
- 'Allumii Aurea'	see *C. lawsoniana* 'Alumigold'
- 'Allumii Magnificent'	MAsh
§ - 'Alumigold'	LRHS MAsh NOra NOrn
- 'Alumii'	CBrac NOrn
- 'Aurea'	CBrac
- 'Aurea Densa' 🏆H6	CKen CSBt CTri MGos
- 'Bleu Nantais' 🏆H6	CKen LBee LRHS MGos SCoo SPoG WCFE
- 'Blom'	CKen
- 'Blue Surprise'	CKen
- 'Brégéon'	CKen NLar
- 'Broomhill Gold' 🏆H6	CSBt LBee MGos NOra NOrn SCoo SLim SPoG SVic
- 'Caudata'	CKen
§ - 'Chilworth Silver' 🏆H6	CBrac CSBt LBee LRHS MAsh
- 'Columnaris'	EPfP LBee SCoo SPoG SReu XLot
- 'Columnaris Aurea'	see *C. lawsoniana* 'Golden Spire'
- 'Columnaris Glauca'	CBrac CMac MGos NOrn SCob SCoo SPer
- 'Cream Glow'	CKen CSBt LRHS
- 'Dik's Weeping' 🏆H6	NLar SLim
- 'Drooping Solo'	CKen NLar
- 'Dutch Gold'	MAsh
- 'Dwarf Blue'	see *C. lawsoniana* 'Pick's Dwarf Blue'
- 'Eclipse'	CKen
- 'Elegantissima' ambig.	CMac SLim
- 'Ellwoodii' 🏆H6	CBod CBrac CMac CSBt CTri ELan EPfP LRHS MAsh MGil MGos MPri SCob SCoo SGsty SLim SPer XLot
I - 'Ellwoodii Glauca'	SPlb
- 'Ellwood's Gold' 🏆H6	CBcs CBrac CMac CSBt ELan EPfP LBee LRHS MAsh MGos MPri NOrn SCob SGsty SLim SPer SPlb SPoG SVic XLot
- 'Ellwood's Gold Pillar' 🏆H6	LBee LRHS MAsh NHol SLim
§ - 'Ellwood's Nymph'	CKen MAsh
- ELLWOOD'S PILLAR ('Flolar') 🏆H6	CMac LBee LRHS MAsh MGos NLar NOrn SCoo SLim
- 'Ellwood's Pygmy'	CMac
- 'Ellwood's Silver Threads'	CMac LBee
- 'Ellwood's Variegata'	see *C. lawsoniana* 'Ellwood's White'
§ - 'Ellwood's White' (v)	CMac SPoG
- 'Emerald Spire'	MAsh NOra
- 'Erecta Viridis'	CBrac CMac
- 'Filip's Golden Tears'	ELan NLar SLim
- 'Fleckellwood'	MAsh NOrn

- 'Fletcheri' ♀H6	CBrac CMac
- 'Fletcheri Aurea'	see *C. lawsoniana* 'Yellow Transparent'
- 'Forsteckensis'	NLar
- 'Gimbornii' ♀H6	NLar
- 'Globosa'	XLot
- 'Gnome'	CKen CMac NHol SCoo SPoG
§ - 'Golden Pot'	CSBt LBee
§ - 'Golden Spire'	NOra
- 'Golden Wonder' ♀H6	MAsh SCoo SLim
- 'Grayswood Feather' ♀H6	LBee MAsh SCob SPlb
- 'Green Globe' ♀H6	CKen CMen CSBt LBee LRHS MGil SLim
§ - 'Green Hedger'	CSBt
§ - 'Green Pillar'	LBee SLim
- 'Green Spire'	see *C. lawsoniana* 'Green Pillar'
- 'Imbricata Pendula' ♀H6	CKen IDee MBlu NLar SLim SMad WPGP
- 'Intertexta'	SLim
- 'Ivonne' ♀H6	EPfP LRHS MGos NOra SLim SPoG SReu XLot
- 'Jackman's Green Hedger'	see *C. lawsoniana* 'Green Hedger'
- 'Jackman's Variety'	see *C. lawsoniana* 'Green Pillar'
- 'Jeanette'	CKen
- 'Kilmacurragh' ♀H6	CMac WCFE
- 'Kilworth Column'	LRHS NLar
- 'Knowefieldensis'	CMac
- 'Lane' misapplied	see *C. lawsoniana* 'Lanei Aurea'
- 'Lane' den Ouden	CBrac
§ - 'Lanei Aurea' ♀H6	LMaj
- 'Little Spire' ♀H6	LRHS NLar XLot
§ - 'Lutea Nana'	CBrac CMac
- 'Luteocompacta'	LBee
- 'Magnifica Aurea'	LRHS
- 'Mason's Pillar' **new**	CKen
- 'Minima Argentea'	see *C. lawsoniana* 'Nana Argentea'
- 'Minima Aurea' ♀H6	CBod CBrac CKen CMac CSBt EPfP LBee LRHS MAsh MGil MGos SLim SPoG WCFE
- 'Minima Glauca' ♀H6	CBrac CMac SCoo SLim WFar
- 'Moonsprite' ♀H6	CKen NLar SCoo SLim SPoG
- 'Nana'	CBrac
- 'Nana Albospica' (v)	LBee
§ - 'Nana Argentea'	CKen CMac EPfP SPoG
- 'Nana Lutea'	see *C. lawsoniana* 'Lutea Nana'
- 'Nicole'	MAsh SCoo
- 'Nyewoods'	see *C. lawsoniana* 'Chilworth Silver'
- 'Nymph'	see *C. lawsoniana* 'Ellwood's Nymph'
- 'Pearly Swirls' (v)	LRHS NLar SPoG
§ - 'Pelt's Blue'	CBcs CSBt NLar
- 'Pembury Blue' ♀H6	CBrac CCVT EPfP LBee LRHS MGos NLar NOrn SCob SCoo SLim SPoG
§ - 'Pick's Dwarf Blue'	CBrac
- 'Pina Colada' PBR	LRHS
- 'Pitt Lane' **new**	CKen
- POT OF GOLD	see *C. lawsoniana* 'Golden Pot'
- 'Pottenii'	CBrac LBee NLar NOrn
- 'Pygmaea Argentea' (v) ♀H6	CBrac CKen CMac CSBt ELan MAsh MGos SLim SPoG
- 'Pygmy'	CMen
- 'Rijnhof'	LBee
- 'Rimpelaar'	CKen NWad
- 'Silver Queen' (v)	CKen
- 'Silver Threads' (v)	ELan LBee LRHS SLim SPoG
- 'Snow Flurry' (v)	CKen
- 'Snow White' (v) ♀H6	LBee LRHS MAsh MGos NHol NOrn SCoo SLim SPoG SVic XLot
- 'Springtime' PBR	CSBt LBee LRHS SLim
- 'Stardust' ♀H6	CBcs CSBt ELan LRHS MAsh MGos MPri NOra NOrn SCob
- 'Summer Snow' (v) ♀H6	NHol SCoo
- 'Sunkist'	SLim XLot
- 'Tamariscifolia'	WCFE
- 'Treasure' (v)	MAsh
- 'Van Pelt'	see *C. lawsoniana* 'Pelt's Blue'
- 'Westermannii' (v)	NOra NOrn
- 'White Spot' (v)	NOra
- 'Winston Churchill'	CMac NOra NOrn
- 'Wisselii' ♀H6	CKen CMac MGos NLar SLim WCFE XLot
- 'Wisselii Nana'	CKen
- 'Wissel's Saguaro' ♀H6	CKen NLar SLim
- 'Witzeliana'	NLar
- 'Yellow Spire'	NLar SLim
§ - 'Yellow Transparent'	CMac
× ***leylandii***	see × *Cuprocyparis leylandii*
nootkatensis	see *Xanthocyparis nootkatensis*
obtusa 'Albovariegata' (v)	CKen
- 'Arneson's Compact'	CKen
- 'Aurora' ♀H7	CKen ELan LRHS SLim SPoG
- 'Bambi'	CKen CMen WAbe
- 'Barkenny'	CKen
- 'Bartley'	CKen
- 'Bassett'	CKen
- 'Bess'	CKen
- 'Blizzard' (v)	NLar
- 'Brigitt'	CKen
- 'Bronze Pygmy'	LRHS
- 'Butterball'	CKen CMen LRHS
- 'Caespitosa'	WAbe
- 'Chilworth'	CKen NWad
- 'Chima-anihiba'	CKen
- 'Chirimen'	CKen CMen MGil NLar
- 'Clarke's Seedling'	CKen LRHS
- 'Confucius'	LSRN NOra
§ - 'Coralliformis'	CBod
§ - 'Crippsii' ♀H7	CMac
- 'Crippsii Aurea'	see *C. obtusa* 'Crippsii'
- 'Dainty Doll'	CKen NHol NWad
- 'Densa'	see *C. obtusa* 'Nana Densa'
- 'Draht'	LRHS NLar XLot
- 'Draht Hexe'	CKen
- 'Elf'	CKen NLar
- 'Ellie B'	CKen CMen
- 'Ericoides'	CKen
- 'Fernspray Gold' ♀H7	CCVT CTri EPfP LRHS MGos MMrt NLar NOra SCoo SMad SPoG
- 'Flabelliformis'	CKen NWad
- 'Gemstone'	NLar
- 'Gitte'	SLim
- 'Gnome'	CKen CMen
- 'Gold Fern'	CKen
- 'Golden Brigitt'	NLar
- 'Golden Fairy'	CKen
- 'Golden Filament' (v)	CKen
- 'Golden Nymph'	CKen
- 'Golden Sprite'	CKen WAbe
- 'Gracilis Aurea'	CKen CMac CMen
- 'Green Cushion'	CKen NLar
- 'Green Diamond'	CKen
- 'Hage'	CKen
- 'Hannah'	NLar
- 'Hypnoides Nana'	CKen
- 'Intermedia'	CKen WAbe
- 'Ivan's Column'	CKen
- 'Junior'	CKen
- 'Juniperoides'	CKen

	- 'Juniperoides Compacta'	WAbe
	- 'Kamarachiba' 🏆H7	CKen CSBt LBee LSRN MAsh NOrn SCoo SLim SPoG
	- 'Kerdalo'	LRHS
	- 'Kosteri' 🏆H7	CKen CMac ELan LBee NHol SCoo
	- 'Kyoto Creeper'	CKen
	- 'Leprechaun'	WAbe
	- 'Limerick'	CKen
	- 'Little Markey'	CKen CMen
	- 'Lucas' [PBR]	LRHS
	- 'Marian'	CKen
§	- 'Mariesii' (v)	CKen LRHS
	- 'Melody'	CKen NLar
	- 'Meroke'	MGil NLar
	- 'Minima'	CKen
	- 'Nana' 🏆H7	CKen CMac CMen LBee NHol NWad
	- 'Nana Aurea' 🏆H7	CBrac CMac CSBt EPfP LRHS MAsh NHol XLot
§	- 'Nana Densa'	CKen CMac LRHS
	- 'Nana Gracilis' 🏆H7	CBrac CKen CMen CSBt ELan EPfP LRHS MAsh MGos NOra NWad SCob SCoo SLim SMad SPoG XLot
I	- 'Nana Gracilis Aurea'	CMen
I	- 'Nana Lutea' 🏆H7	CKen CMen ELan LBee LRHS MAsh MGos NHol NWad SLim
	- 'Nana Rigida'	see *C. obtusa* 'Rigid Dwarf'
	- 'Nana Variegata'	see *C. obtusa* 'Mariesii'
	- 'Oregon Crested'	MGil NLar
	- 'Pillnitz'	NLar
	- 'Pygmaea'	CBrac CSBt SCoo SLim
	- 'Rashahiba'	LRHS
	- 'Rezek Dwarf'	CKen CMen
§	- 'Rigid Dwarf'	CKen LBee LRHS SLim
	- 'Saffron Spray'	LRHS NLar SLim
	- 'Snowflake' (v)	CKen ELan LRHS NWad
	- 'Snowkist' (v)	CKen
	- 'Sparkles'	NLar
	- 'Spiralis'	CKen
	- 'Stoneham'	CKen CMen
	- 'Strangman'	CKen
	- 'Suiroya-hiba'	SLim
	- 'Tempelhof'	CKen SCoo SLim
	- 'Tetragona Aurea'	CMac NWad
	- 'Timothy'	CMac
	- 'Tonia' (v)	CKen MAsh SLim
	- 'Torulosa'	see *C. obtusa* 'Coralliformis'
	- 'Tsatsumi Gold' 🏆H7	CKen CMen ELan EPfP LRHS SCoo SLim SPoG
	- 'Verdon'	CKen
	- 'Wiels Baby'	NLar
	- 'Wyckoff'	CKen
	- 'Yellowtip' (v)	CKen EPfP MAsh
	pisifera 'Baby Blue'	CKen ELan EPfP LRHS SCoo SLim SPoG XLot
	- 'Blue Bun' **new**	CKen
	- 'Blue Globe'	CKen
	- 'Blue Moon' [PBR] **new**	LCro LOPS
	- 'Boulevard' 🏆H7	CBcs CBod CBrac CMac CSBt ELan EPfP LBee LRHS MAsh MGos SCob SLim SPer WBor XLot
	- 'Compacta'	LRHS
	- 'Curly Top' 🏆H7	EPfP NHol SCoo SLim SPoG
	- 'Filifera'	CMac CSBt
	- 'Filifera Aurea' 🏆H7	CKen CMac ELan EPfP LBee LMaj LRHS MAsh MGos NHol SCob SCoo WCFE XLot
	- 'Filifera Nana'	EPfP LRHS SLim XLot
	- 'Filifera Nana Aurea'	see *C. pisifera* 'Golden Mop'
	- 'Filifera Sungold'	see *C. pisifera* 'Sungold'
	- 'Fuiri-tsukomo'	CKen
	- 'Gold Cushion'	CKen
	- 'Gold Dust'	see *C. pisifera* 'Plumosa Aurea'
	- 'Gold Spangle'	CBrac CKen
§	- 'Golden Mop'	CBrac CKen
	- 'Green Pincushion'	CKen CMen
	- 'Hime-himuro'	CKen
	- 'Hime-sawara'	CKen CMen
	- 'Lime Pie'	CKen
	- 'Nana'	CBrac CKen CMen NHol
	- 'Nana Aurea'	NRya
	- 'Nana Aureovariegata' (v)	CSBt LBee
I	- 'Nana Compacta'	CMac
	- 'Nana Variegata' (v)	CMac LBee
I	- 'Parslorii'	CKen
	- 'Pici'	CKen
§	- 'Plumosa Aurea'	CKen MAsh
	- 'Plumosa Aurea Compacta'	CKen NWad
	- 'Plumosa Aurea Nana'	MAsh
I	- 'Plumosa Aurea Nana Compacta'	CMac
	- 'Plumosa Aurescens'	CMac
§	- 'Plumosa Compressa' 🏆H7	CBrac CKen NWad
	- 'Plumosa Densa'	see *C. pisifera* 'Plumosa Compressa'
I	- 'Plumosa Juniperoides'	CKen
	- 'Pygmy'	see *C. pisifera* 'Tsukumo'
	- 'Silver Lode' (v)	CKen
	- 'Snow' (v)	CKen
	- 'Snowflake'	CKen
	- 'Spaan's Cannon Ball'	CKen CMen
	- 'Squarrosa Dumosa'	CKen
I	- 'Squarrosa Lombarts'	CMac CSBt
	- 'Squarrosa Lutea'	CKen
	- 'Squarrosa Sulphurea'	CSBt ELan
§	- 'Sungold' 🏆H7	CKen CSBt ELan EPfP LRHS MAsh MGos SCoo SLim SPoG SRms XLot
	- 'Tama-himuro'	CKen
	- 'Teddy Bear'	SMad
	- 'True Blue'	CKen ELan
§	- 'Tsukumo' **new**	CKen
	thyoides 'Andelyensis'	CMac CSBt
	- 'Blue Rock'	SLim
	- 'Conica'	MAsh
	- 'Ericoides'	CTri LBee SPlb
	- 'Little Jamie'	CKen
	- 'Red Star'	see *C. thyoides* 'Rubicon'
§	- 'Rubicon'	CMac CSBt EPfP LBee LRHS MAsh NOra SPoG
	- 'Top Point'	LBee MAsh SCoo SLim SPoG

Chamaecytisus see *Cytisus*

Chamaedaphne (*Ericaceae*)

	calyculata	CBcs

Chamaedorea (*Arecaceae*)

	metallica misapplied	see *C. microspadix*
§	***microspadix*** 🏆H1a	CPHo SPalm
	radicalis	CBrP CPHo SPalm

Chamaemelum (*Asteraceae*)

§	***nobile***	CBod CHby CLau CTri EBou ENfk EPfP GPoy LCro LOPS MBow MHer MMuc MNHC MPri NGdn SPlb SRms SVic WSpi WTre XAbr
	- dwarf	SMor SVic

- dwarf, double-flowered (d) LEdu
- 'Flore Pleno' (d) CBod CBre CElw CLau CMea CPrp CTri ECha ENfk EPfP GPoy MHer MHol MNHC MRav NBro NGdn NGrd SGro SPer SRms WFar WHal WJek WTre
- 'Treneague' CBod CBre CCBP CPrp CTri EBou ECha EHyd ELan ENfk EPfP EWhm GAbr GPoy GQue LRHS MBow MCot MHer MNHC NRHS SMor SPer SPlb SRms WFar WHal WHer WJek WTre

Chamaenerion (*Onagraceae*)

§ ***angustifolium*** SEdd WSFF
§ - 'Album' Widely available
- 'Hullavington Fire' CNat
- 'Isobel' MRav WCot
- 'Stahl Rose' CMea EPfP EWes LEdu MBel MBriF NSti SGbt SMad SPhx WCot WHrl WSHC
§ ***dodonaei*** EWes IMou MHer SBut SPhx WCot
§ ***fleischeri*** CPla

Chamaepericlymenum see *Cornus*

Chamaerops (*Arecaceae*)

excelsa misapplied see *Trachycarpus fortunei*
excelsa Thunb. see *Rhapis excelsa*
humilis ♀H4 CAbb CBcs CBod CBrP CDoC ELan EPfP LRHS MGos SArc SChr SEND SGsty SIvy SPlb SPoG SWeb WLov
§ - var. ***argentea*** CBrP CDTJ CPHo MGos SChr SPalm SPlb SWeb WCot
- var. ***cerifera*** see *C. humilis* var. *argentea*
- var. ***humilis*** SPalm
- 'Vulcano' CDTJ LRHS SChr SGsty SPalm

Chamaespartium see *Genista*

Chamaesphacos (*Lamiaceae*)

ilicifolius misapplied see *Siphocranion macranthum*

Chamelaucium (*Myrtaceae*)

uncinatum CCCN EShb
- 'Snowflake' CCCN EBee

Chamerion see *Chamaenerion*

chard see AGM Vegetables Section

Charybdis (*Asparagaceae*)

§ ***maritima*** CBod GKev WCot

Chasmanthe (*Iridaceae*)

aethiopica CPbh EPri SChr
bicolor CExl CPrp EPri EWld WOut
floribunda CPrp EPri GKev SDeJ
- var. ***duckittii*** CPla CPrp GKev SDeJ SPeP
- - 'Golden Wave' CPrp GKev
- 'Saturnus' GKev SPeP WABo WCFE

Chasmanthium (*Poaceae*)

§ ***latifolium*** CBod CKno CRos CSde CSpe EBee ECha EHyd ELan ELon EPPr EPfP EShb LEdu LRHS MBel MMuc NRHS NWsh SCob SDix SGol SMad SPad SPoG SRms WCot WPnP XCre XLum
- 'River Mist' (v) ELan SPoG

Chasmatophyllum (*Aizoaceae*)

sp. EDAr

Cheilanthes ✿ (*Pteridaceae*)

argentea ISha
distans WCot
eatonii WAbe
ecklomiana WAbe WCot
farinosa LEdu
grisea WCot
lanosa CBdn CBod CCCN CCht CDoC CMiW CSpe CTsd EBee EHyd EMor EWes LBuc LRHS MPie NRHS SEdd SPlb SPoG WCot
lindheimeri WCot
myriophylla WAbe WCot
sieberi ISha
tomentosa CAby CCCN CRos EHyd ISha LEdu LRHS MAsh NRHS WAbe
wootonii SPlb WAbe WCot

Cheiranthus see *Erysimum*

Cheirolophus (*Asteraceae*)

benoistii misapplied see *Centaurea atropurpurea*
benoistii (Humb.) Holub MRav WSHC

Chelidonium (*Papaveraceae*)

hylomeconoides GEdr
japonicum see *Hylomecon japonica*
majus GPSL GPoy NBir NMir WHer WHil WSFF XAbr
- 'Flore Pleno' (d) CBre GJos NBid NBir NBro
- var. ***laciniatum*** WCot

Chelone (*Plantaginaceae*)

barbata see *Penstemon barbatus*
§ ***glabra*** CBod CMac EBee ECha ELan EMor GMaP GWyn LRHS MMuc MPie NBid NBro NGdn NHol NLar SPeP SPer SPlb SRms WFar WPnP WSHC WWtn
lyonii EBee NLar WShi
- 'Hot Lips' WHil WPnP
- 'Pink Temptation' EBee GEdr
- TINY TORTUGA ('Armitpp02') new SPad
obliqua Widely available
- var. ***alba*** see *C. glabra*
- 'Ieniemienie' CBod
- 'Pink Sensation' WFar

Chelonopsis (*Lamiaceae*)

moschata EBee EMor EWld GEdr LEdu MBel MHer SBrt SPlb WHil
yagiharana CMea SHar WFar

Chengiopanax (*Araliaceae*)

sciadophylloides WCru

Chenopodium (*Amaranthaceae*)

ambrosioides SEdi SVic
bonus-henricus CAgr CHab CHby ENfk EWhm GPoy GQue MCoo MHer MNHC SRms SVic WHer WJek WTre XAbr
capitatum CSpe SVic
giganteum CLau MNHC SRms WJek

cherimoya see *Annona cherimola*

cherry, Duke see *Prunus* × *gondouinii*

cherry, sour or morello see *Prunus cerasus*; also AGM Fruit Section

cherry, sweet see *Prunus avium*; also AGM Fruit Section

chervil see *Anthriscus cerefolium*

chestnut, sweet see *Castanea sativa*

Chiastophyllum see *Umbilicus*

simplicifolium	see *Umbilicus oppositifolius*

chicory see *Cichorium intybus*; also AGM Vegetables Section

Chiliotrichum (*Asteraceae*)

diffusum	CCCN GAbr MMuc
- 'Siska'	CBcs GBin

chilli pepper see *Capsicum*; also AGM Vegetables Section

Chimonanthus ✿ (*Calycanthaceae*)

fragrans	see *C. praecox*
nitens	CMCN NLar
§ ***praecox***	Widely available
- 'Brockhill Goldleaf'	NLar
- 'Grandiflorus' ♀H5	CEnd CJun CRos EHyd ELan EPfP EWTr LRHS MAsh SPer SPoG WCot
- 'Luteus' ♀H5	CEnd CJun CRos EHyd ELan EPfP LEdu LRHS MAsh MGos NLar SChF SPer SPoG WCot
- 'Red Heart' **new**	NLar
- 'Sunburst'	CJun
- 'Trenython' ♀H5	CEnd CJun

Chimonobambusa (*Poaceae*)

KR 7592	MWht
hookeriana misapplied	see *Himalayacalamus falconeri* 'Damarapa'
macrophylla f. ***intermedia***	XCre
§ ***marmorea***	CDTJ MMuc XCre
- 'Variegata' (v)	CDTJ ESwi XCre
§ ***quadrangularis***	CBcs CDTJ EPfP ESwi IMou MWht XCre
- 'Joseph de Jussieu' **new**	XCre
- 'Suow' (v)	CDTJ XCre
sichuanensis	XCre
tumidissinoda	CBcs CBdn CDTJ ESwi IMou MWht WFar XCre

Chinese cabbage see AGM Vegetables Section

Chinese chives see *Allium tuberosum*

Chiogenes see *Gaultheria*

Chionanthus (*Oleaceae*)

retusus	CBcs CCCN CRos EBee EHyd EPfP EWTr LMaj LRHS MPkF NLar SPer
- 'Arnold's Pride'	WPGP
virginicus	CBcs CCCN CMCN CRos EHyd ELan EPfP EWTr GBin LRHS MBlu MGil MRav NLar SPer SPlb WSpi

Chionochloa (*Poaceae*)

conspicua	CBod CElw EAJP EBee EPfP GAbr GBee GBin GKev MAvo NBid NBir WPGP
- subsp. ***conspicua***	WCot
- 'Rubra'	see *C. rubra*
flavescens	CTsd EBee EMor EPfP MAvo WPGP
flavicans	CBod CSpe EPfP GBin IMou
rigida	GBin IMou MAvo
§ ***rubra*** ♀H7	CCht CElw CSpe EBee ELan EPfP EWes GBin IMou MRav WBor WCot WPGP
- PAB 67	EHyd LEdu LRHS
- subsp. ***cuprea***	CAby

Chionodoxa see *Scilla*

gigantea	see *Scilla. luciliae* Gigantea Group

Chionographis (*Melanthiaceae*)

japonica	GEdr

Chionohebe (*Plantaginaceae*)

§ ***densifolia***	EPot
pulvinaris	WAbe
'Vera Cox'	WAbe

Chionophila (*Plantaginaceae*)

jamesii **new**	GEdr

× *Chionoscilla* see *Scilla*

Chiranthodendron (*Malvaceae*)

pentadactylon	SPlb

Chirita (*Gesneriaceae*)

'Aiko'	WDib
'Candy'	WDib
'Chastity'	WDib
'Diane Marie'	WDib
'Erika'	WDib
flavimaculata	WDib
heterotricha	WDib
'Keiko'	WDib
linearifolia	WDib
linearifolia × ***sinensis***	WDib
longgangensis	WDib
'New York'	WDib
sinensis ♀H1c	WDib
- 'Hisako'	WCot WDib
speciosa 'Crûg Cornetto'	WCru
'Stardust'	WDib
'Sweet Dreams'	WDib
tamiana	WDib

Chironia (*Gentianaceae*)

baccifera	SPlb

× *Chitalpa* (*Bignoniaceae*)

tashkentensis	CBcs CEnd EPfP ESwi MMrt SBrt
- 'Morning Cloud'	MBlu
- 'Pink Dawn'	CBcs ESwi MBlu SMad
- SUMMER BELLS ('Minsum')	CCCN CSpe EBee ELan ELon WCot WLov

chives see *Allium schoenoprasum*

Chlidanthus (*Amaryllidaceae*)

fragrans	CCCN GKev SDeJ

Chloranthus (*Chloranthaceae*)

fortunei CMiW ESwi WCot
glaber GPoy
glaber B&SWJ 11102 WCru
henryi GEdr SIvy WCot
japonicus GEdr WCru
oldhamii WPGP
- B&SWJ 2019 GEdr LEdu WCru
serratus GEdr WCru
sessilifolius 'Domino' ESwi WCot

Chloris (*Poaceae*)

distichophylla see *Eustachys distichophylla*

Chlorogalum (*Asparagaceae*)

pomeridianum 'Berkeley Hills' SBrt
- tall, from Siskiyou Mountains, Oregon SBrt

Chlorophytum (*Asparagaceae*)

chinense new SBrt
comosum EShb SEND SVic
- 'Aureomarginata' (v) SEND
- 'Bonnie'^{PBR} (v) EShb
- 'Variegatum' (v) $\mathbb{Y}^{H2}$ EShb LCro LOPS NGBl SEND SPre WSFF
- 'Vittatum' (v) $\mathbb{Y}^{H2}$ CDoC EShb NGBl
graminifolium EBee
krookianum WCot
macrophyllum EShb
nepalense WPGP
- B&SWJ 2528 WCru
- PAB 13.034 LEdu
saundersiae CExl EPPr
- 'Starlight' (v) new LCro LOPS

Choisya (*Rutaceae*)

× **dewitteana** APPLE BLOSSOM ('Pmoore09') CBcs CBod CSBt LCro LOPS MAsh SLon SPad SPoG
- 'Aztec Gold'^{PBR} CBcs CRos EHyd EPfP LRHS MAsh MGos NLar NRHS SCob
- 'Aztec Pearl' $\mathbb{Y}^{H4}$ Widely available
- GOLDFINGERS ('Limo'^{PBR}) CBar CBcs CBod CMac CRos CWGN EBee EHyd ELan EPfP EShb LRHS LSRN MGos MPri MRav NHol NLar NRHS SCob SGbt SLon SPer SPoG SRms SWvt
- SNOW FLURRIES ('Lisflurry'^{PBR}) CRos EHyd ELan EPfP LRHS MAsh MRav NRHS SPoG
- WHITE DAZZLER ('Londaz'^{PBR}) $\mathbb{Y}^{H4}$ Widely available
dumosa var. **arizonica** 'Whetstone' new WPGP
ROYAL LACE ('Pmoore06'^{PBR}) LBuc LRHS SLon
ternata $\mathbb{Y}^{H4}$ Widely available
- MOONSHINE ('Walcho'^{PBR}) CBcs EBee NLar
- MOONSLEEPER see *C. ternata* SUNDANCE
§ - SUNDANCE ('Lich') $\mathbb{Y}^{H4}$ Widely available

Chondrosum (*Poaceae*)

gracile see *Bouteloua gracilis*

Chordospartium see *Carmichaelia*

Chorisia (*Malvaceae*)

speciosa CCCN SPlb

Chorizema (*Papilionaceae*)

cordatum $\mathbb{Y}^{H2}$ SVen
dicksonii SPlb

Chronanthus see *Cytisus*

Chrysalidocarpus see *Dypsis*

Chrysanthemopsis see *Rhodanthemum*

Chrysanthemum ✿ (*Asteraceae*)

E.H.Wilson s.n. ECre EShb EWes MHCG MNrw NWad SMHy WCot
'Action Bronze' (22) NWsh
'Action Yellow' (22) $\mathbb{Y}^{H3}$ WFar
'Agnes Ann' (21d) MNrw NWad
'Ahlemer Rote' (21) MHCG MNrw NWad
'Alan Brown' (25a) MCms
'Alan Foxall Yellow' (3b) MCms
'Alec Bedser' (25a) NHal
'Alex Young' (25b) MCms
'Alfredo Mauve' (12) MCms
'Alfredo Orange' (12) MCms
'Alice Jones' (24b) MCms
'Aline' (21) MHCG
'Alison' (29c) ELon MNrw WFar
'Alison's Dad' MNrw NWad
'Allouise' (25b) $\mathbb{Y}^{H3}$ NHal
'Allouise Orange' (25b) MCms NHal
'Allouise Pink' (25b) MCms
'Allyson Peace' (14a) MCms NHal
alpinum see *Leucanthemopsis alpina*
'Alyece Shaw' (29d) NHal
'Amber Gigantic' (1) NHal
'Amber Matlock' (24b) MCms
'American Beauty Lemon' (5b) MCms
'American Beauty Snowball' (5b) MCms
'American Beauty White' (5b) MCms
'Anastasia' ambig. SAko
'Anastasia' (21c) CRos EBee EHyd ELon LRHS MNrw MRav NRHS SRms WRHF
'Anderton' (6b) MCms
'Angela Blundell' (19b) MNrw WCot WFar
'Angelic' (21b) $\mathbb{Y}^{H4}$ EBee ELon WBrk
'Ann Dickson' (25a) MCms
'Anne Ratsey' (21) CSam MNrw WBrk WFar
'Anne, Lady Brocket' (21d) ECtt MNrw
'Anthony Peace' (25b) MCms
'Antigua'^{PBR} MCms
'Apollo' H. Shoesmith MNrw
'Apollo' (21) MHCG SPhx WFar WHoo
'Apricot' see *C.* 'Cottage Apricot'
'Apricot Chessington' (25a) MCms
'Apricot Courtier' (24a) MCms NHal
'Apricot Enbee Wedding' see *C.* 'Bronze Enbee Wedding'
'Apricot Mundial' (6b) MCms
'Arctic Beauty' (4b) MCms
'Arctic Cream' (29b) MCms
'Arctic Queen'^{PBR} (23a) MCms
'Arctic Queen Yellow' (23a) MCms
'Arctic White' (9c) MCms
'Arctic Yellow' (9c) MCms
arcticum L. see *Arctanthemum arcticum*
argenteum see *Tanacetum argenteum*

'Arthur Ellis' (25b)	MCms
'Astro' (25b)	MCms NHal
'Aunt Millicent' (21d) ♀H4	ECre MHCG NHal WCot
'Balcombe Perfection' (5a)	MCms NHal
balsamita	see *Tanacetum balsamita*
'Barbara Dakin' (25b) new	MCms
BARBARA ('Yobarbara') (22)	NHal
'Barca'	MCms
'Beacon' (5a) ♀H2	MCms NHal
'Beechcroft' (29Rub)	MNrw WFar
'Belle' (21d)	EShb MHCG MNrw NWad WMal
'Beppie Bronze' (29e)	MCms
'Beppie Purple' (29e)	MCms
'Beppie Red' (29e)	MCms
'Beppie Rose' (29e)	MCms
'Beppie Yellow' (29e)	MCms
'Best Man' (29d)	MCms
'Bienchen'	ELon SAko WFar
'Bill Holden' (14a)	MCms NHal
'Bill Wade' (25a)	MCms NHal
'Billy Bell' (15a)	MCms NHal
'Blanche Poitevene' (5b)	EMal MCms
'Bob Green' (13b)	MCms
'Bobby Swinburn' (13b)	MCms
boreale	WCot
'Boulou Pink' (12)	MCms
'Boulou White' (12)	MCms
'Boulou Yellow' (12)	MCms
BRAVO ('Yobra') (22c) ♀H3	NHal
* 'Breitner's Supreme'	ECtt MHCG MNrw WFar
'Brennpunkt'	MNrw NWad
'Bretforton Road'	ECtt MHCG MNrw WBrk WCot WFar WMal WOld
'Brightness' (21)	MNrw
'Bronze Cassandra' (5b) ♀H2	MCms NHal
'Bronze Dee Gem' (29c)	MCms NHal
§ 'Bronze Elegance' (21b) ♀H4	CDor CRos CTri ECtt EHyd EPPr LRHS MNrw NBir NGdn NRHS NWsh SHar SRms WBor
§ 'Bronze Enbee Wedding' (29d) ♀H3	MCms NHal
'Bronze Gigantic' (1)	NHal
'Bronze Matlock' (24b)	MCms NHal
'Bronze Max Riley' (23b) ♀H3	MCms NHal
'Bronze Mayford Perfection' (5a) ♀H2	MCms
'Bronze Mei-kyo'	see *C.* 'Bronze Elegance'
'Bronze Talbot Parade' (29c) ♀H3	MCms
'Bronze William Florentine' (15a)	MCms
'Brooke Farm Red'	NWsh
'Brown Eyes' (21b) ♀H4	MNrw
'Bryony Wade' (13b)	MCms NHal
'Bryony Wade White' (13b)	MCms
'Buff William Florentine' (15a)	MCms
'Bunty' (28)	SMad
burnt orange-flowered	CDor CFis MNrw WFar
'Burntwood Belle' (3b)	MCms
'Buxton Ruby'	MNrw NWad
'Candy John Wingfield' (14b)	MCms
'Capel Manor'	EBee MHCG MNrw WCot
'Capella' (10a)	MCms
'Cardinal Red'	EHyd LRHS
'Carlene Welby' (25b)	MCms
'Carmine Blush' (21d) ♀H4	GAbr MHCG MNrw WBrk WCot WFar
'Casablanca' (25a)	MCms NHal
'Cassandra' (5b) ♀H2	MCms NHal
'Cawthorne' (29d)	WFar
'Cerisa' (29d)	NHal
'Charles Tandy' (5a)	MCms
'Charles Tandy Primrose' (15a)	MCms
'Charles Tandy Yellow' (15b)	MCms
'Charlie' (24b)	MCms
'Chatsworth' (29c)	NHal
'Chelsea Physic Garden'	EBee ELon GAbr MHCG MNrw SPhx WCot WFar
'Chempak Rose' (14b)	MCms
'Cherry Chessington' (25a)	MCms
'Cherry Tracey Waller' (24b)	MCms
'Chesapeake Primrose' (10a)	MCms
CHESAPEAKE ('Yochesapeake'PBR) (10a)	MCms NHal
'Chessington' (25a)	MCms
'Chessington Oyster' (25a)	MCms
'Chestnut Talbot Maid' (29c)	MCms
'Chestnut Talbot Parade' (29c) ♀H3	MCms WFar
'Chloe Ball' (13b)	MCms
'Christmas'	MNrw NWad WFar
'Christopher Lawson' (24b)	MCms NHal
cinerariifolium	see *Tanacetum cinerariifolium*
'Citronella'	MNrw
'Clapham Delight' (23a)	MCms NHal
'Clara Curtis' (21d)	CBod CDor CMac CRos ECha ECtt EHyd ELan EPfP LRHS MHol MNrw MPie MRav NPer NRHS NWsh SGbt SPoG SRms WAul WBor WCAu WFar WSHC XLum
'Clare Louise' (24b)	MCms
'Clarksdale' (15b)	MCms NHal
coccineum	see *Tanacetum coccineum*
'Colsterworth'	MHCG MNrw NWad WFar
'Coral Reef' (10b)	MCms NHal
'Coral Rynoon' (9d)	MCms
'Corinna' (21d)	GBin MNrw NWad
'Cornetto' (25b)	MCms NHal
'Corsair' (9d)	MCms
corymbosum	see *Tanacetum corymbosum*
§ 'Cottage Apricot' (21)	CDor CRos EBee EHyd EPfP LRHS MBNS MRav NRHS SMHy SRms WFar
'Cottage Bronze'	MNrw NWad
'Cottage Lemon'	MHCG MNrw NWad WFar
'Cottage Pink'	see *C.* 'Emperor of China'
'Courtier' (24a)	NHal
'Cousin Joan' (21d) ♀H4	ELon MHCG MNrw SPhx WBor WCot WFar WMal WOld
'Cream Dorridge Crystal' (24a)	MCms
'Cream Elegance' (9c)	NHal
'Cream John Hughes' (3b)	MCms
'Cream Patricia Millar' (14b)	NHal
'Cream Ryski' (9d)	MCms
'Cream Talbot Maid' (29c)	MCms
'Cream Talbot Parade' (29c) ♀H3	MCms
'Cream West Bromwich' (14a)	MCms

'Cricket' (25b)	MCms
'Crimson Purple Glow' (5a)	MCms
DANA ('Yodana') (25b) ♀H3	NHal
DANCE ('Fidance'PBR) (9f)	MCms
'Dance Red' (9f)	MCms
DANCE SALMON ('Fidancesal') (9f)	MCms
'Dance Sunny' (9f)	MCms
'Dance White' (9f)	MCms
'Daniel Cooper' (21d) ♀H4	EBee MNrw SGro WFar
'Daphne Davis' (29d)	NHal
'Darren Pugh' (3b)	MCms NHal
'Darren Pugh Primrose' (3b)	MCms
'David Shoesmith' (25a)	MCms
'Dawn Charlton' (14a)	MCms
'Dee Gem' (29c) ♀H3	MCms NHal WFar
'Delta' (5b)	NHal
'Delta Copper Bronze' (9d)	NHal
'Delta Crimson' (29d)	NHal
'Delta Yellow' (29)	NHal
'Denise Oatridge' (5a)	MCms
'Dernier Soleil'	EBee MNrw XLum
'Deva Glow' (25a)	NHal
'Disco Club'	MCms
'Dixter Orange'	EBee EWes MHCG SMad SPhx WMal
'Dixter Pink'	WMal
§ 'Doctor Tom Parr' (21c)	CExl ELan MNrw
'Domingo' (14b)	MCms
'Doreen Hall' (15a)	NHal
'Doreen Statham' (4b)	MCms NHal
'Doris Ozols' (25a)	MCms NHal
'Dorothy Stone' (25b)	NHal
'Dorridge Crystal' (24a)	MCms NHal
'Dorridge King' (4b)	MCms
'Downpour' (10a)	MCms
'Dublin' (9f)	MCms
'Duchess of Edinburgh' (21d)	CRos EBee ECtt EHyd ELan ELon EPfP GBin LRHS MHer MNrw NLar NRHS SPhx WCAu WFar WMal XLum
'Dulwich Pink' (21d) ♀H4	MHCG MNrw NWad WCot WFar
'Early Yellow'	EBee ELon MNrw WCot WFar
'Edelweiss' (21)	EShb MNrw NWad
'Edina' (29d)	NHal
'Edmund Brown'	MNrw WCot WFar
'Egret' (23b)	MCms NHal
'Elaine's Hardy White'	MHCG MNrw WCot WFar WMal
'Elegance' (9c)	NHal
'Eliška'	MNrw
'Elizabeth Lawson' (5b)	NHal
'Elizabeth Shoesmith' (1)	NHal
§ 'Emperor of China' (21)	CDor ECtt MHer MNrw MRav NHal SMad SPhx SRms WBor WFar WOld XLum
'Enbee Wedding' (29d) ♀H3	MCms NHal
'Energy'PBR (9)	MCms
'Erntekranz' **new**	MNrw WMal
'Esther' (21d)	EBee EShb LEdu MHCG MHer MNrw SMad WFar
'Etta Dakin' (25b)	MCms
'Fairweather' (3b)	MCms
'Fairweather Cream' (3b)	MCms
'Fairweather Peach' (3b)	MCms
'Fanfare Cherry'	EHyd LRHS
'Fanfare Claret'	EHyd ELan LRHS
'Fanfare Flame'	EHyd ELan LRHS

'Fanfare Glowing Embers'	EHyd LRHS
'Fanfare Orange'	EHyd LRHS
'Fanfare Pink Blush'	EHyd LRHS
'Fanfare Pink Pastel'	EHyd LRHS
'Fanfare Rosetta'	EHyd LRHS
'Fanfare Ruby'	EHyd LRHS
'Fanfare Sunset'	EHyd LRHS
'Feeling Green Dark'PBR	MCms
'Feeling Sunny'PBR	MCms
'Fleur de Lis' (10a)	MCms
foeniculaceum (Willd.) Desf.	see *Argyranthemum foeniculaceum* (Willd.) Webb & Sch Bip.
'Folk Song' (4b)	MNrw
'Fondant'	NHal
'Fred's Yellow'	NWad
'French Rose'	WFar
'Frizbee' (29d) **new**	NHal
'Froggy'PBR (9)	MCms
frutescens	see *Argyranthemum frutescens*
'Gambit' (24a)	MCms NHal
'Geoff Amos' (3b)	MCms
'Geoff Brady' (5a)	MCms NHal
'George Griffiths' (24b) ♀H3	MCms NHal
'Gillette' (23b)	MCms
'Ginger Nut' (25b)	MCms
'Ginger Nut Yellow' (25b)	MCms
I 'Gladys' (12a)	NHal
'Gladys Emerson' (3b)	MCms NHal
'Gold Enbee Wedding' (29d) ♀H3	MCms
'Gold Mundial' (6b) ♀H2	MCms
'Golden Cassandra' (5b) ♀H2	MCms NHal
'Golden Chalice' (12a)	MCms NHal
'Golden Courtier' (24a)	MCms NHal
'Golden Masons' (7b)	MCms
'Golden Mayford Perfection' (5a) ♀H2	MCms
'Golden Rain' (10a) ♀H2	MCms NHal
'Golden Roy Coopland' (5b)	MCms
'Golden Seal' (7b)	MCms
'Golden Shoesmith Salmon' (4a)	MCms
'Golden Splendour' (10a)	MCms NHal
'Golden William Florentine' (15a)	MCms
'Golden Woolman's Glory' (7a)	NHal
'Goldengreenheart' (21d) ♀H4	ECtt ELon EPPr EShb MHCG MNrw SPhx SRms WBrk WFar WHoo
'Goldmarianne' (21)	GBin WFar XLum
'Goodlife Sombrero' (29a) ♀H3	MCms
'Goshu Penta' (10a)	MCms
'Grace Riley' (24a)	MCms
'Grand Cherry'	MCms
'Grand Pink'	MCms
'Grand Salmon'	MCms
'Grandchild' (21c) ♀H4	MNrw NHal
'Green Goddess' (2)	MCms
'Hanenburg' (25b)	MCms NHal
haradjanii	see *Tanacetum haradjanii*
'Harold Lawson' (5a)	NHal
'Harry Gee' (1)	NHal
* 'Harry Lawson'	MCms
'Harry Woolman' (13b)	MCms
'Heather James' (3b)	MCms NHal
'Hebe' (21d)	EBee MNrw
'Heda'	MNrw

	'Heide' (29c) 🏆^{H3}	NHal
	'Helen Harrison' **new**	MAvo
	'Helen Louise' (25b)	MCms NHal
	'Helen Ward'	MNrw
	'Herbie McCauley' (24b)	NHal
	'Herbstbrokat'	GBin WFar XLum
	'Herbstfeuer' (21)	MNrw NWad
	'Hillfield Apricot'	EShb
	'Hillside Apricot'	ECtt
	'Hoagy' (29d)	MCms NHal
	'Holly Elizabeth' (14a)	MCms
	HOLLY ('Yoholly') (22b) 🏆^{H3}	NHal
	'Honey Enbee Wedding' (29d)	MCms NHal
	hosmariense	see *Rhodanthemum hosmariense*
	indicum	SVic
	'Innocence' (21d) 🏆^{H4}	CDor CFis CSam ECtt ELan ELon MBNS MNrw MRav NGdn SHar WFar WHoo
	'Jan Wardle' (5a)	MCms
	'Janet South'	MNrw
	'Jante Wells' (21b) 🏆^{H4}	MNrw
	'Jasoda Dark Orange'^{PBR} **new**	LCro LOPS
	'Jasoda Mauve'^{PBR} **new**	LCro LOPS
	'Jasoda Pink'^{PBR} **new**	LCro LOPS
	'Jasoda White'^{PBR} **new**	LCro LOPS
	'Jasoda Yellow'^{PBR} **new**	LCro LOPS
	'Jenny Wren' (12a)	NHal
	'Jessie Cooper' misapplied	see *C.* 'Mrs Jessie Cooper' (21d)
	'Jimmy Tranter' (14b)	NHal
	'John Harrison' (25b)	MCms NHal
	'John Hughes' (3b)	MCms NHal
	'John Lowry' (24a)	NHal
	'John Riley' (14a)	NHal
	'John Wingfield' (14b)	MCms NHal
	'John Wingfield Honey' (14b)	MCms
	'John Wingfield Pearl' (14b)	MCms
	'Jolie Rose'	WCot WFar
	'Joyce Fountain' (24a)	MCms NHal
	'Joyce Frieda' (13b)	MCms NHal
	'Julia' (28)	MNrw
	'Julia Arnold'	WHoo
	'Julia Peterson'	MHCG MHer MNrw SRms WCot WFar WHoo
	JULIA ('Yojulia')	NLar
	'Julie Lagravère' (28)	MHCG MNrw WFar XLum
	'Karen Taylor' (29c) 🏆^{H3}	NHal
	'Kath Stephenson' (7b)	MCms NHal
	'Kath Stephenson Honey' (7b)	MCms
	'Kath Stephenson Peach' (7b)	MCms
	'Kath Stephenson Primrose' (7b)	MCms NHal
	'Kath Stephenson Rose' (7b)	MCms NHal
	'Kath Stephenson Salmon' (7b)	MCms
	'Kay Woolman' (13b)	MCms NHal
	'Kay Woolman Cream' (13b)	MCms
	'Kay Woolman Primrose' (13b)	MCms
	'Kay Woolman Yellow' (13b)	MCms
	'Killerton Tangerine'	MHCG MNrw WFar WMal
	'Kimberley Marie' (15b)	MCms NHal
	'Kiyomi-no-meisui'	MCms NHal
	'Kleiner Bernstein'	MNrw
	'La Damoiselle'	WCot
§	'Lady in Pink' (21)	MNrw MPie NWad
	'Lakelanders' (3b)	MCms NHal
	'Laura Jayne' (25a)	MCms
	'Lava' (10a)	MCms
	leucanthemum	see *Leucanthemum vulgare*
	'Lexy'^{PBR} (9)	MCms
	'Lexy Red'^{PBR} (9)	GBin MCms
	'Lighthouse'	NHal
	'Lilac Chessington' (25a)	MCms
	'Lilian Shoesmith' (5b)	MCms
	LINDA ('Lindayo') (22c) 🏆^{H3}	NHal
	'Liverpool Festival' (23b)	MCms
	'Lollipop'^{PBR} (9e)	MCms
	LOLLIPOP PURPLE ('Filollipop Purple'^{PBR}) (9e)	MCms
	'Lorna Wood' (13b)	MCms NHal
	'Lucy' (29a)	MCms NHal
	'Lynn Johnson' (15a)	MCms
	LYNN ('Yolynn') (22c) 🏆^{H3}	NHal
	macrophyllum	see *Tanacetum macrophyllum* (Waldst. & Kit.) Sch.Bip.
	'Malcolm Perkins' (25a)	NHal
	'Mancetta Comet' (29a)	MCms NHal
	'Mancetta Symbol' (5a)	MCms
I	'Mandarin'	MNrw
	'Mandarin' (5b)	SAko
	'Manito'	MNrw
	maresii	see *Rhodanthemum hosmariense*
	'Margaret Dear' (25a)	MCms
	'Margaret Lawson' (14b)	NHal
	'Margery Fish'	MNrw WFar
	'Marion' (25a)	MNrw WCot WFar
	'Martin Bell' (29d)	WFar
	'Martina' (24b)	MCms
	'Mary' (21f)	MHCG NHal
	'Mary Stoker' (21d)	CDor CRos CSam CTri EBee ECtt EHyd ELan LRHS MNrw MPie MRav NHal NLar NRHS NWsh WAul WCAu XLum
	'Mason's Bronze' (7b)	MCms
	'Matlock' (24b)	NHal
	'Mauve Gem' (21f) 🏆^{H3}	NHal
	'Mavis' (21) 🏆^{H3}	MHCG MNrw
	'Mavis Smith'	MNrw
	mawii	see *Rhodanthemum gayanum*
	'Max Riley' (23b) 🏆^{H3}	MCms NHal
	maximum misapplied	see *Leucanthemum* × *superbum*
	maximum Ramond	see *Leucanthemum maximum* (Ramond) DC.
	'Maxine Charlton' (24b)	NHal
	'Maxine Johnson' (25b)	MCms
	'May Shoesmith' (5a) 🏆^{H2}	MCms
	'Mayford Perfection' (5a) 🏆^{H2}	MCms
	'Mei-Kyō' (28b) 🏆^{H4}	CDor CFis CMea CTri ECre ECtt EHyd EPPr LRHS MHCG MNrw MPie NRHS SRms WBor WBrk WCAu WFar
	'Membury' (24b)	MCms NHal
	'Mezzo Bronze Red' (Poppins Series)	MCms
	'Mezzo Gold' (Poppins Series)	MCms
	'Mezzo Magenta' (Poppins Series)	MCms
	'Mezzo Pink' (Poppins Series)	MCms
	'Migdale' (24b) **new**	MCms

'Millennium' (25b) ♀H3	MCms NHal
'Misty Cream' (25b)	MCms
'Misty Golden' (25b)	MCms
'Misty Lemon' (25b)	MCms
'Moonlight' (29d/K)	MNrw MRav NWad
'Morning Star' (12a)	NHal
'Mount Fuji' (10b)	MCms
§ 'Mrs Jessie Cooper' (21d) ♀H4	EBee ELon EPPr GBee GQue MNrw NLar NWad SDys SRms WCot WFar WHoo
'Mrs Jessie Cooper No 1'	WOld
'Mrs Jessie Cooper No 2'	MNrw
'Mundial' (6)	MCms
'Mundial Peach' (6b/9a)	MCms
'Mundial Rose' (6b)	MCms
'Mundial Ruby' (6b)	MCms
'Muriel Odell' (7b)	MCms
'Music' (23b)	MCms NHal
'Muxton Sable' (10a)	MCms
'Myss Debbie' (29e)	NHal
'Myss Dorothy' (29c)	MCms NHal
'Myss Eliza' (29c)	MCms
'Myss Goldie' (29c)	MCms
'Myss Rihanna' (29c)	MCms NHal
'Myss Saffron' (29c) ♀H3	MCms NHal
'Nancy Perry' (21d)	CSam MRav XLum
'Nantyderry Sunshine' (28b) ♀H4	CDor CRos ECre EHyd ELon LRHS MHCG MNrw MPie NRHS NWsh SPhx SRms WCot WFar WOld
'Naru' (9c)	NHal
'Naru Crimson' (9c)	NHal
'Natalie Sarah' (29d) ♀H3	NHal
'Nell Gwynn' (21d)	MNrw NHal
'New Stylist' (24b)	MCms
NICOLE ('Yonicole') (22c) ♀H3	NHal
nipponicum	see *Nipponanthemum nipponicum*
'Nora Brook' (25b)	MCms
'Nutcracker' (23b)	MCms
'Old Norwell'	WMal
'Orange Enbee Wedding' (29d)	NHal
'Orchid Helen'	MNrw
'Pacific Lady' (29d)	NHal
pacificum	see *Ajania pacifica*
'Paloma Redeye' (29d)	NHal
'Paloma Regent' (29d)	NHal
'Paloma Sands' (29d)	NHal
parthenium	see *Tanacetum parthenium*
'Pat Bahn' (29c)	NHal
'Patricia Millar' (14b)	MCms NHal
'Patricia Millar Cerise' (14b)	MCms
'Patricia Millar Coral' (14b)	MCms
'Patricia Millar Orange' (14b)	MCms
'Patricia Millar Yellow' (14b)	MCms NHal
'Paul Boissier' (30)	CDor CFis ECtt MNrw SPhx WFar
'Pauline White' (15a)	MCms
'Peach Courtier' (24a)	NHal
'Peach Enbee Wedding' (29d) ♀H3	MCms NHal
'Peach John Wingfield' (14b)	MCms NHal
'Peach Patricia Millar' (14b)	MCms
'Peach Rynoon' (9d)	MCms
'Peach Southway Sheeba' (29d)	NHal
'Pearl Celebration' (24a)	MCms
'Pearl Enbee Wedding' (29d)	MCms
'Pennine Bullion'	NHal
'Pennine Gambol' (29a)	MCms
'Pennine Jude' (29a)	MCms
'Pennine Marie' (29a) ♀H3	MCms
'Pennine Oriel' (29a) ♀H3	MCms NHal
'Pennine Point' (19c)	NHal
'Pennine Polo' (29d) ♀H3	NHal
'Pennine Swan' (29c)	MCms NHal
'Penny's Yellow'	WBrk
'Percy Salter' (24b)	NHal
'Perry's Peach' (21d) ♀H4	ELon MHCG MNrw NHal NPer SPhx
'Peter Jolley' (25b)	MCms
'Peter Rowe' (23b)	MCms NHal
'Peterkin'	CMac EBee ECtt EHyd ELon LRHS XLum
'Picasso'	EShb GAbr MHCG MNrw SEdd WCot WFar
'Pink John Wingfield' (14b)	NHal
'Pink Progression'	see *C.* 'Lady in Pink'
'Pocahontas' (10a)	MCms
'Poesie'	MNrw SAko WCot WFar WMal
'Polar Gem' (3a)	MCms NHal
'Pomander' (25b)	MCms
'Pot Black' (14b)	MCms
'Prelude Apricot' (Poppins Series)	MCms
'Prelude Autumn Bronze' (Poppins Series)	MCms
'Prelude Popcorn' (Poppins Series)	MCms
'Prelude Rose Pink' (Poppins Series)	MCms
'Prelude White' (Poppins Series)	MCms
'President Osaka'	MNrw
'Primrose Allouise' (24b) ♀H3	MCms NHal
'Primrose Chessington' (25a)	MCms
'Primrose Courtier'	see *C.* 'Yellow Courtier'
'Primrose Cricket' (25b)	MCms
'Primrose Dorothy Stone' (25b)	NHal
'Primrose Dorridge Crystal' (24a)	MCms
'Primrose Egret' (23b)	MCms
'Primrose Enbee Wedding' (29d) ♀H3	MCms NHal
'Primrose Fairweather' (3b)	MCms
'Primrose John Hughes' (3b)	MCms
'Primrose Mayford Perfection' (5a) ♀H2	MCms
'Primrose Pauline White' (15a)	MCms
'Primrose Pennine Oriel' (29a)	MCms
'Primrose West Bromwich' (14a)	MCms
'Princess' (21d)	MNrw
'Promise' (25a)	MCms NHal
'Purleigh White' (28b)	ELon EPPr MNrw NWsh WFar
'Purple Chempak Rose' (14b)	MCms
'Purple Dee Gem' (29c)	NHal
'Purple Glow' (5a)	MCms
'Purple Haze' (7b) **new**	MCms
'Raquel' (21)	MNrw
'Ray's Red'	MHCG MNrw
'Red Balcombe Perfection' (5a)	MCms NHal

'Red Chempak Rose' (14b)	MCms
'Red Goodlife Sombrero' (29a)	MCms
'Red Mayford Perfection' (5a)	MCms
'Red Pennine Gift' (29c)	NHal
'Red Regal Mist' (25b)	MCms NHal
'Red Shirley Model' (3a)	MCms NHal
'Redbreast' (12a)	NHal
'Regal Mist' (25b)	NHal
'Regal Mist Purple' (25b)	MCms
'Regent' (5b)	MCms
'Rejoyce'	GBin
I 'Rhumba'	MNrw WCot
'Rihanna'	MCms
'Riley's Dynasty' (14a)	MCms
'Ringdove' (12a)	NHal
'Rita Fox' (25b)	MCms
'Rita McMahon' (29d) 🏆H3	NHal
'Robeam' (9c) 🏆H2	MCms
ROBIN ('Yorobi') (22c)	NHal
'Roblush' (9c)	MCms
'Roen Sarah' (29c)	NHal
'Romantica'	MNrw NWad WOld
'Roscene' (9c)	MCms
'Rose Enbee Wedding' (29d)	MCms NHal
'Rose Madder'	GAbr MNrw WCot WFar
'Rose Mayford Perfection' (5a) 🏆H2	MCms
'Rose Patricia Millar' (14b)	MCms NHal
'Rose Talbot Parade' (29c)	MCms
'Rosedew' (25a) **new**	MCms
'Rosetta'	MHCG MNrw
roseum	see *Tanacetum coccineum*
'Rosie Lyttle' (29c)	NHal
'Roter Spray'	MNrw NWad
'Roy Bevan' (29d)	MCms
'Roy Coopland' (5b) 🏆H2	MCms
'Royal Command' (21a)	MHCG MNrw WCot WHoo
'Royal Sport'	MNrw
rubellum	see *C. zawadzkii*
'Ruby Enbee Wedding' (29d) 🏆H3	MCms WFar
'Ruby Glow' (7b)	MCms
'Ruby Mound' (21c) 🏆H3	GAbr MHCG MNrw NHal SDys SHar SPhx WBrk WCot WFar WMal WOld
'Ruby Raynor' (21c) 🏆H4	MNrw NHal WFar
'Rumpelstilzchen' (21d)	CFis CMea ECtt ELon MHer MNrw NWsh WMal
'Ryflare' (9c)	MCms
'Ryflash' (9d)	MCms
'Rynoon' (9d)	MCms
'Ryski' (9d)	MCms
'Salhouse Dream' (10a)	MCms NHal
'Salhouse Joy' (10a)	MCms NHal
'Salmon Allouise' (25b)	MCms NHal
'Salmon Enbee Wedding' (29d) 🏆H3	NHal
'Salmon Fairweather' (3b)	MCms
'Salmon John Wingfield' (24b)	MCms
'Salmon Patricia Millar' (14b)	MCms
'Salmon Pauline White' (15a)	MCms
'Salmon Talbot Maid' (29c)	MCms
'Salmon Talbot Parade' (29c) 🏆H3	MCms WFar
'Salmon Tracey Waller' (24b)	MCms
'Salmon Venice' (24b)	MCms
'Sam Vinter' (5a)	NHal
'Samba'	WCot WFar
'Samson'	MCms
'Samson Bronze'	MCms
'Samson Orange'	MCms
'Samson Purple'	MCms
'Sarah Louise' (25b)	NHal
'Savanna Charlton' (25a)	MCms NHal
'Schaffhausen'	WFar
'Schweizerland' **new**	WFar
'Sea Urchin' (21f) 🏆H3	NHal
'Seaton's Galaxy' (10a)	MCms NHal
'Senkyo Karyu' (10a)	MCms
'Senkyo Kenshin' (10a)	MCms NHal
'Shamrock' (10b)	MCms
'Sheffield'	XLum
'Sheila Coles' (7b)	NHal
'Sheila Harris' (3b)	MCms
'Shining Light' (21f)	WCot WFar
'Shoesmith Salmon' (4a)	MCms
'Shoesmith Salmon Bright Bronze' (4a)	MCms
'Shoesmith Salmon Crimson' (4b)	MCms
'Shoesmith Salmon Purple' (4a)	MCms
'Skomer' (9f)	MCms
'Skomer Pink' (9f)	MCms
'Skomer Yellow' (9f)	MCms
'Soir d'Orient'	WFar
'Sonya' (21)	MNrw
'Sound' (9d)	MCms
'Southway Semtex' (29d)	MCms
'Southway Sheba' (29d) 🏆H3	MCms NHal
'Southway Sheba Bronze' (29d)	MCms NHal
'Southway Shimmer' (29d)	MCms NHal WFar
'Southway Shiraz' (29d)	MCms WFar
'Southway Sloe' (29d)	MCms NHal
'Southway Spectacular' (29d)	MCms
'Southway Spritzer' (29d)	MCms NHal
'Southway Strontium' (29d)	MCms NHal
'Southway Sunbeam' (29d)	MCms
'Spartan Display'	ECre EWes MNrw
'Spartan Seagull' (21d)	MNrw
'Spencer's Cottage' (13b)	MCms
'Stallion' (9)	GBin MCms
'Stallion Yellow'	MCms
'Starlet' (21f) 🏆H4	NHal
'Steve Packham' (23b)	NHal
'Stockton' (3b) 🏆H2	MCms
'Stratford Pink' (21d)	MNrw NWad
'Suffolk Pink'	ECtt EShb MNrw NWsh
'Sunny John Wingfield' (14b)	MCms
'Super-Bronze Shoesmith Salmon' (4a)	MCms
'Susan Kate' (25b)	MCms
'Swan Cream'	MCms
SWAN ('Fiswan' PBR) (9)	MCms
'Swan Sunny'	MCms
'Sweetheart Pink'	MHCG MNrw WMal
'Syllabub' (21f) 🏆H3	ECtt MNrw
'Symphony' (10a)	MCms NHal
'Talbot Maid' (29c)	MCms

'Talbot Parade' (29c) 🏆H3	MCms
'Talbot Parade Pink' (29c)	MCms
'Tapestry Rose' (21d)	CMea MNrw NWsh SPhx SRms WBrk WFar WHoo WOld
'Thoroughbred' (24a)	NHal
'Tickle Pink' (29f/K)	MNrw NWad
'Tom Parr'	see *C.* 'Doctor Tom Parr'
'Tom Snowball' (3b)	MCms
'Topsy' (21d) 🏆H4	MHCG
'Tracey Waller' (24b)	MCms
TRIUMPH ('Yotri') (22)	NHal
uliginosum	see *Leucanthemella serotina*
'Uri'	CFis EBee ELon MHCG MNrw SPhx WFar
'Vagabond Prince'	ELon MHCG MNrw SRms WBor WBrk WFar WHoo WOld
'Venice' (24b)	MCms NHal
'Venice Peach' (24b)	MCms
'Venice Rose' (24b)	MCms
'Venus' (21)	WCot WMal
'Venus One'	ECtt MNrw NHal
'Vibrant' (9c) 🏆H2	NHal
'Viking' (9)	MCms
'Vysočina'	MNrw
'Wedding Day' (29k)	MNrw NWad
'Wedding Sunshine' (21)	MNrw NWad WFar
welwitschii	see *Glebionis segetum*
'Wembley' (24b)	MCms
'Wendy Tench' (21d)	EBee MNrw NWsh
'West Bromwich' (14a)	MCms
weyrichii	CTri CTsd EBou EHyd GPSL LEdu LRHS MNrw NHpl SGro SRms WFar WIce
'White Allouise' (25b) 🏆H3	MCms NHal
'White Beppie' (29e)	MCms WFar
'White Bouquet' (28)	WFar
'White Cassandra' (5b)	MCms NHal
'White Denise Oatridge' (5a)	MCms
'White Enbee Wedding' (29d)	MCms NHal
'White Fairweather' (3b)	MCms
'White Gem' (21f)	NHal
'White Gloss' (21e)	MNrw SPhx
'White Pearl Celebration' (24a)	MCms
'White Tower' (27)	MNrw MPie NWad
'Wilder Charms'	MNrw NWad
'William Florentine' (15a)	MCms NHal
'Wills Wonderful' (21d) 🏆H4	MHCG MNrw WMal
'Win' (9c)	NHal
'Wind Dancer' (10a)	MCms
'Winning's Red' (21)	MHCG SMad WCot WFar
'Winter Queen' (5b)	MCms
'Winter Queen Yellow' (5b)	MCms
'Woolley Globe' (15b)	MCms
'Woolman's Glory' (7a)	MCms NHal
'Woolman's Glory Red' (7a)	MCms
'Woolman's Star' (3a)	MCms NHal
'Woolman's Venture' (14b)	MCms NHal
'Woolman's Venture Red' (14b)	MCms
'Xiang'	NWad
'Yellow Allouise' (25b)	MCms
'Yellow American Beauty' (5b) 🏆H2	MCms
'Yellow Billy Bell' (15a)	NHal
'Yellow Chessington' (25a)	MCms
'Yellow Clapham Delight' (23a)	MCms NHal
§ 'Yellow Courtier' (24a)	MCms NHal
'Yellow Egret' (23b)	MCms
'Yellow Enbee Wedding' (29d)	MCms NHal
'Yellow Goodlife Sombrero' (29a)	MCms
'Yellow Heide' (29c) 🏆H3	NHal
'Yellow Jewel' (Poppins Series)	MCms
'Yellow John Harrison' (25b)	MCms
'Yellow John Hughes' (3b) 🏆H2	MCms NHal
'Yellow John Wingfield' (14b)	MCms
'Yellow Mayford Perfection' (5a) 🏆H2	MCms
'Yellow Pennine Oriel' (29a) 🏆H4	MCms NHal
'Yellow Ryski' (9d)	MCms
'Yellow Spider' (10a)	MCms
'Yellow Spray' (12b) **new**	SCob
'Yellow Talbot Parade' (29c)	MCms
'Yellow Woolman's Glory' (7a)	MCms
yezoense	CDor MNrw SRms
– B&SWJ 10872	WCru
– 'Roseum'	ECtt
aff. ***yezoense*** **new**	MHol
'Yvonne Arnaud' (24b)	MCms
'Yvonne's Rot-Goldene'	SAko
§ ***zawadzkii***	CMac SRms WFar

Chrysogonum (*Asteraceae*)

virginianum	CMea EBee EWes SBrt SPer WFar
– var. ***australe***	EHyd LRHS SBrt
– 'Golden Acres'	ECtt

Chrysopogon (*Poaceae*)

gryllus	NDov WPGP

Chrysosplenium (*Saxifragaceae*)

alternifolium	EBee GEdr
davidianum	CBre CSam EBee EPot EWld GJos GKev IMou NHpl NLar WBor WCru WSHC
– SBEC 233	CExl
aff. ***hebetatum*** B&SWJ 9835	NWad
lanuginosum var. ***formosanum***	GEdr
– – B&SWJ 6979	ESwi WCru
macrophyllum	CExl EBee EPPr EWld GBin GKev GMaP IMou LEdu MAvo MNrw MPie NLar SDix SHar WBor WCot WCru WSHC
oppositifolium	ECha WSFF WShi

Chusquea (*Poaceae*)

culeou 🏆H4	CBcs EPfP LEdu MAvo MGos MWht SPlb SSta XCre
– 'Purple Splendour'	CDTJ
– weeping	CDTJ
delicatula from Machu Picchu, Peru	CExl
gigantea 🏆H3	CBcs CDTJ CExl EPfP ESwi MAvo MWht WPGP XCre
macrostachya	XCre
montana	CDTJ
mulleri F&M 104A from Mexico	CExl

Cicerbita (Asteraceae)

§	***alpina***	GAbr GBee NBid SPlb
	bourgaei	CFis MMuc
	macrophylla new	MBow
	plumieri	GAbr WCot WSHC
	- 'Blott' (v)	WCot

Cichorium (Asteraceae)

	endivia 'Pancalieri' 🏆H3	CHby EKin MCtn
	intybus	CHby CLau CSpe CWld ELan ENfk GAbr GPoy LSun MCot MHer MNHC NBir NGBl NMir SBut SPer SPlb SPoG SRms WFar WHrl WSHC WTre WWild
	- f. ***album***	CBod ECha ECtt EHyd LRHS MPie NBPC NRHS SBut SPer
	- 'Brussels Witloof'	SVic
	- 'Indigo' 🏆H5	LRHS NRHS
	- 'Palla Rossa' 🏆H5	CHby MCtn SRms
	- 'Pan di Zucchero' 🏆H5	CHby
	- 'Red Rib'	SRms
	- 'Roseum'	CBod CWld ECha ECtt EHyd ELan LRHS MBel MPie NBPC NRHS SBut SPer SPoG WHrl

Cimicifuga see *Actaea*

	acerina	see *Actaea japonica*
	americana	see *Actaea podocarpa*
	cordifolia (DC.) Torrey & A.Gray	see *Actaea cordifolia*
	cordifolia Pursh	see *Actaea podocarpa*
	foetida	see *Actaea cimicifuga*
	racemosa var. ***cordifolia***	see *Actaea cordifolia*
	- 'Purpurea'	see *Actaea simplex* Atropurpurea Group
	ramosa	see *Actaea simplex* 'Prichard's Giant'
	rubifolia	see *Actaea cordifolia*
	simplex var. ***matsumurae***	see *Actaea matsumurae*

Cineraria (Asteraceae)

	× ***hybrida***	see *Pericallis* × *hybrida*
	maritima	see *Jacobaea maritima*

Cinnamomum (Lauraceae)

	camphora	CBcs CExl IArd
	japonicum B&SWJ 14627 new	WCru

Circaea (Onagraceae)

	lutetiana	WHer
	- 'Caveat Emptor' (v)	NBid WCot

Cirsium (Asteraceae)

	arvense	WSFF
	canum	CSpe GQue SEdd
	diacantha	see *Ptilostemon diacantha*
	eriophoroides	GEdr
	helenioides	see *C. heterophyllum*
§	***heterophyllum***	CDor EBee EWld LEdu LRHS MAvo MHol NAts NChi NLar SHar
	- PAB 067	LEdu WMal WPGP
	- 'Pink Blush'	CWCL EMor GBin LCro LOPS MPri NSti WNPC
	japonicum 'Pink Beauty'	EMor SBut
	- 'Rose Beauty'	WSpi
	'Mount Etna'	CBod CFis CSam EBee EHyd ELan EPfP GKin LRHS MBNS MBel MBriF MMuc MSpe NBPC NDov NGdn NRHS SEND SGbt WCAu WWtn
	oleraceum	EBee LEdu NBid NLar SBrt
	rivulare	Widely available
	'Atropurpureum' 🏆H7	
	- FROSTED MAGIC ('Lowcir')	CBcs CKno ECul GMaP IPot LBuc LCro LOPS LRHS LSou MAvo MBNS MBel NSti SMad WCAu WNPC WTor
	- 'Trevor's Blue Wonder'	see *C. rivulare* 'Trevor's Felley Find'
§	- 'Trevor's Felley Find'PBR	Widely available
	tuberosum	ECha LEdu LPla LRHS SDix SPhx WCot
	vulgare	WSFF

Cissus (Vitaceae)

	antarctica 🏆H1c	CCCN EShb SEND
	pedata B&SWJ 2371	WCru
	rhombifolia 🏆H1c	EOHP EShb
	- 'Ellen Danica' 🏆H1c	EShb
§	***striata***	CBcs CDoC CMac CWCL EBee EHyd EShb LRHS MGil MRav NChi SBrt SEND SLim SNig SWvt

Cistus ✿ (Cistaceae)

	acutifolius misapplied	see *C.* × *pulverulentus*
	× ***aguilarii***	CTri MRav
	- 'Maculatus' 🏆H4	CAby CBcs CBod CDoC CExl CRos CSBt CSam ELan EPfP LRHS LSRN MMuc NLar SEle SPer SPoG SWvt WKif WPGP WSpi
	albidus	WSpi XSen
	algarvensis	see *Halimium ocymoides*
	'Anne Palmer'	see *C.* × *fernandesiae* 'Anne Palmer'
	× ***argenteus*** 'Blushing Peggy Sammons'	CAby CRos EHyd ELan EPfP LRHS NLar NRHS SWvt WAvo
	- 'Paper Moon'	CBod EWTr LSRN NLar
§	- 'Peggy Sammons'	CBod CBrac CRos ECha ELan EPfP EWTr LRHS LSRN MAsh MGos NLar SAko SCob SGbt SLim SPer SWvt XSen
	- 'Silver Ghost'	CAby CDoC LRHS SWvt
	- 'Silver Pink' ambig.	Widely available
	'Blanche'	see *C. ladanifer* 'Blanche'
	× ***bornetianus*** 'Jester' 🏆H4	CBod CBrac CRos CSBt EHyd ELan EPfP LRHS MAsh NLar NRHS SWvt
	× ***canescens*** f. ***albus***	XSen
	clusii subsp. ***multiflorus***	XSen
	× ***corbariensis***	see *C.* × *hybridus*
	creticus	CAby CBcs CDoC CExl CPla CRos CSam EHyd GPoy LRHS MAsh MGos SLon SPoG SRms SWvt WSpi
	- subsp. ***corsicus***	XSen
§	- subsp. ***creticus***	EBee ELan EPfP MRav SCoo SPer
§	- subsp. ***incanus***	WCot
§	× ***crispatus*** 'Warley Rose'	GMaP WKif XLum
	crispus misapplied	see *C.* × *pulverulentus*, *C.* × *purpureus*
§	***crispus*** L.	ELan XSen
	- 'Prostratus'	see *C. crispus* L.
	- 'Sunset'	see *C.* × *pulverulentus* 'Sunset'
§	× ***cyprius*** 🏆H4	CBrac CRos EBee EHyd ELan EPfP LRHS NRHS SDix SRms SWvt WKif WSpi
§	- var. ***ellipticus*** 'Elma' 🏆H4	CRos EHyd ELan EPfP LRHS MAsh NLar NRHS SPer WAvo WCot
§	× ***dansereaui***	CMac CSBt LRHS SWvt WSpi
	- 'Decumbens' 🏆H4	CBod CDoC CRos CSde CTri EBee EHyd ELan EPau EPfP LRHS MAsh MBNS MRav MSwo NLar NRHS

	SArc SCob SCoo SGbt SPer SPhx SPoG SWvt WFar WPGP WSpi
- 'Jenkyn Place' ♀H4	CBod CDoC EBee ELan GMaP LSRN MBNS MMuc NLar SPer SPoG WKif
'Elma'	see *C.* × *cyprius* var. *ellipticus* 'Elma'
§ × ***fernandesiae*** 'Anne Palmer'	CDoC EBee EHyd LRHS MAsh NLar
× ***florentinus*** misapplied	see × *Halimiocistus* 'Ingwersenii'
× ***florentinus*** ambig.	WSpi XLum
§ × ***florentinus*** Lam.	GMaP XSen
* - 'Tramontane'	XSen
'Gordon Cooper' ♀H4	LSRN MMrt MMuc NLar SPoG WSpi
× ***heterocalyx*** 'Chelsea Bonnet'	CBod CBrac EWTr GMaP MBNS NLar SCoo SPoG
'Highlights'	MAsh
§ × ***hybridus***	Widely available
- 'Gold Prize' (v)	CWGN NLar SCob SWvt WGrn
- LITTLE MISS SUNSHINE ('Dunnecis'^{PBR}) (v)	MAsh MGos NHol NLar SRms SWvt
- ROSPICO ('Rencis'^{PBR}) (v)	EPfP LRHS NLar
incanus	see *C. creticus* subsp. *incanus*
ingwerseniana	see × *Halimiocistus* 'Ingwersenii'
'Jessamy Beauty'	WAvo
'Jessamy Charm'	SPhx
ladanifer misapplied	see *C.* × *cyprius*
ladanifer ambig.	CMac ECha WKif
ladanifer L.	CBcs CSBt CSde CTri ELan EPfP GPoy LRHS MRav MSwo SCob SWvt WSpi XSen
§ - 'Blanche'	EPfP LSRN NLar SPer SWvt WKif WSpi
- var. ***maculatus***	MNHC
- Palhinhae Group	see *C. ladanifer* var. *sulcatus*
- 'Pat'	CDoC CRos EHyd ELan EPfP LRHS LSRN MAsh NLar NRHS SPoG SWvt
- var. ***petiolatus*** 'Bennett's White'	WAvo
§ - var. ***sulcatus***	CRos CTsd ELan LRHS
lasianthus	see *Halimium lasianthum*
laurifolius	EPfP LRHS MGos SWvt WSpi XSen
- subsp. ***atlanticus***	XSen
× ***laxus*** 'Snow White' ♀H4	CBod CBrac CWGN EBee EPfP LRHS MGos NLar NPer SAko SLon
§ × ***lenis*** 'Grayswood Pink' ♀H4	CBod CBrac CDoC CExl CRos CTri EBee ELan EPfP LRHS LSRN MAsh MGos MMuc MSwo NLar SAko SCob SEND SLim SPer SPhx SPlb SPoG SWvt XLum XSen
× ***loretii*** misapplied	see *C.* × *dansereaui*
× ***lusitanicus*** Maund	see *C.* × *dansereaui*
'McGuire's Gold'	ELan
'Merrist Wood Cream'	see × *Halimiocistus wintonensis* 'Merrist Wood Cream'
'Mickie' (v)	ELan
monspeliensis	CMac CRos EPfP LRHS MAsh MBNS SLon SPer SPoG WLov XSen
- 'Vicar's Mead'	CCCN CRos EHyd LRHS
monspeliensis* × *salviifolius	see *C.* × *florentinus* Lam.
× ***oblongifolius***	SWvt XSen
× ***obtusifolius*** ambig.	EBou ELan LRHS
× ***obtusifolius*** Sweet	WPGP
§ - 'Thrive' ♀H4	CRos EHyd EPfP LRHS MGos NRHS SCoo
ocymoides	see *Halimium ocymoides*
palhinhae	see *C. ladanifer* var. *sulcatus*
parviflorus misapplied	see *C.* × *lenis* 'Grayswood Pink'
'Peggy Sammons'	see *C.* × *argenteus* 'Peggy Sammons'
× ***platysepalus***	SDix SPhx
populifolius	CMac CRos ECha EHyd EPfP EWTr LRHS NLar SPer SWvt
- var. ***lasiocalyx***	see *C. populifolius* subsp. *major*
§ - subsp. ***major***	CRos LRHS LSRN WPGP WSpi
§ × ***pulverulentus***	CExl CTri ECha XSen
§ - 'Sunset' ♀H4	Widely available
- 'Warley Rose'	see *C.* × *crispatus* 'Warley Rose'
§ × ***purpureus*** ♀H4	Widely available
- 'Alan Fradd'	CBcs CBod CDoC CMac CRos EHyd ELan EPfP LCro LOPS LRHS LSRN MAsh MCot MGos MMuc MSwo NRHS SCob SCoo SEND SGbt SLim SPoG SWvt WFar XLum XSen
- 'Betty Taudevin'	see *C.* × *purpureus*
- f. ***stictus***	LRHS WAvo
× ***rodiaei*** 'Jessabel'	EPfP LRHS MAsh MRav NLar SPer SWvt WPGP
'Ruby Cluster'	CBod CCCN CDoC LRHS NLar
sahucii	see × *Halimiocistus sahucii*
salviifolius	CCCN XSen
- 'Avalanche'	WAbe
- 'Gold Star'	CDoC NLar
- 'May Snow'	LRHS MAsh
- 'Prostratus'	CAby CDoC CRos CSde ELan EPfP LRHS SWvt WSpi
× ***argenteus*** 'Silver Pink' misapplied	see *C.* × *lenis* 'Grayswood Pink'
× ***skanbergii***	CBod CDoC CMac CSam CTri ELan EPfP MGos MHol MMuc MRav NBir NLar SCob SDix SEND SPer WCFE WSpi XLum XSen
'Snow Fire' ♀H4	CAby CCCN CRos EBee ELan EPfP LRHS LSRN MAsh MGos MMuc NLar SAko SCoo SWvt WAvo WGrn
'Thrive'	see *C.* × *obtusifolius* 'Thrive'
tomentosus	see *Helianthemum nummularium* subsp. *tomentosum*
× ***verguinii***	XSen
villosus	see *C. creticus* subsp. *creticus*
wintonensis	see × *Halimiocistus wintonensis*

Cistus × *Halimium* see × *Halimiocistus*

Citharexylum (*Verbenaceae*)

quadrangulare Jacq.	see *C. spinosum*
spicatum	CCCN CExl
§ ***spinosum***	CBcs EBee

citrandarin see *Citrus reticulata* × *C. trifoliata*

citrange see *Citrus* × *insitorum*

citrangequat see *Citrus* × *georgiana*

× *Citrofortunella* see *Citrus*

limequat	see *Citrus* × *floridana*
mitis	see *Citrus* × *microcarpa*

citron see *Citrus medica*

Citronella (*Icacinaceae*)

§ ***gongonha***	IArd SVen
mucronata	see *C. gongonha*

Citrullus (*Cucurbitaceae*)

lanatus 'Charleston Gray'	SVic

Citrus (*Rutaceae*)

§ × ***aurantiifolia*** (F)	CCCN EPfP SCit SPre
- key lime	see *C.* × *aurantiifolia*

§	× ***aurantium*** (F)	SCit
	- 'Aber's Narrowleaf' (F)	SCit
	- subsp. ***bergamia***	see *C.* × *limon*
	- 'Bergamot de Versailles' (F)	EPfP
	- 'Bouquet de Fleurs'	see *C.* × *aurantium* (Sour Orange Group) 'Bouquet'
	- 'Gou-tou Cheng' (F)	SCit
§	- Grapefruit Group (F)	CCCN SPre SWeb
	- - 'Foster' (F)	SCit
	- - 'Golden Special' (F)	SCit
	- - 'Marsh' (F)	SCit
	- - 'Oroblanco' (F)	SCit
	- - 'Red Blush' (F/S)	SCit
	- - 'Star Ruby' (F/S)	CCCN SCit SPre SVic
	- - 'Wheeny'	see *C. maxima* 'Wheeny'
	- var. ***myrtifolia***	see *C.* × *aurantium*
	- 'Pursha' (F)	SPre
	- 'Robinson' (F)	SCit
§	- (Sour Orange Group) 'Bouquet' (F)	SCit
	- - 'Bouquetier de Nice' (F)	SCit
	- - 'Chinotto' (F)	SCit SPre SWeb
	- - 'Seville' (F)	LSRN SCit SPre
	- - 'Smooth Flat Seville' (F)	SCit
§	- Sweet Orange Group (F)	CCCN CDoC SCit SPre SVic SWeb
§	- - 'Baia' (F/S)	SCit SPre
	- - 'Embiguo' (F)	SCit
	- - 'Fukumoto' (F)	CCCN
	- - 'Jaffa'	see *C.* × *aurantium* (Sweet Orange Group) 'Shamouti'
	- - 'Lane Late' (F)	CCCN SCit SPre
§	- - 'Malta Blood' (F)	SCit
	- - 'Maltaise Sanguine'	see *C.* × *aurantium* (Sweet Orange Group) 'Malta Blood'
	- - 'Navelate' (F)	SCit
	- - 'Navelina' (F/S)	CCCN SCit SPre
	- - 'Newhall' (F/S)	NLar SCit
	- - 'Salustiana' (F/S)	SCit
§	- - 'Sanguinelli' (F)	CCCN SCit SPre SVic
§	- - 'Shamouti' (F)	SCit
	- - 'Spanish Sanguinelli'	see *C.* × *aurantium* (Sweet Orange Group) 'Sanguinelli'
	- - 'Succari' (F)	SCit
	- - 'Tarocco' (F)	SCit
	- - 'Valencia' (F)	CCCN SCit SPre
	- - 'Washington'	see *C.* × *aurantium* (Sweet Orange Group) 'Baia'
	- - 'Washington Navel'	see *C.* × *aurantium* (Sweet Orange Group) 'Baia'
§	- (Tangelo Group) 'Minneola' (F)	SCit
§	- - 'Nova' (F/S)	CCCN SCit SVic
	- - 'Orlando' (F)	SCit
	- - 'Seminole' (F)	SCit
	- - 'Ugli' misapplied	see *C.* × *aurantium* (Tangelo Group) 'Minneola'
	- - 'Ugli' (F)	SCit
	- (Tangor Group) 'Dweet' (F)	SCit
	- - 'Ellendale' (F)	SCit
	- - 'Murcott' (F)	SCit
	australasica (F)	SCit SPre SVic
	australasica × (× ***floridana*** 'Eustis') (F)	SPre
	bergamia	see *C.* × *limon*
	- bergamot	see *C.* × *limon* Bergamot Group
	- 'Castagnaro' (F)	SCit
	'Buddha's Hand'	see *C. medica* 'Fingered'
	calamondin	see *C.* × *microcarpa*
§	***cavaleriei*** (F)	WPGP
	citrandarin	see *C. reticulata* × *trifoliata*
	deliciosa	see *C. reticulata* 'Willowleaf'
§	× ***floridana***	SWeb
	- 'Eustis' (F)	SCit SPre
	- 'Lakeland' (F)	SCit SPre
	× ***georgiana*** 'Thomasville' (F)	SCit
§	***hystrix***	CCCN CDoC ELan LSRN NLar SCit SPre SWeb
	Ichang lemon	see *C. cavaleriei*
	ichangensis	see *C. cavaleriei*
	× ***insitorum*** 'C-35' (F)	SCit
	- 'Carrizo' (F)	SCit
	- 'Citromon' (F)	SCit
	- 'Curafora' (F)	SCit
	- 'Swingle' (F)	SCit
	- 'Us119' (F)	SCit
	- 'Venasca' (F)	SCit
	jambhiri	see *C.* × *taitensis*
§	***japonica*** (F) ♀H1c	CBcs ELan EPfP LCro LOPS SCit SPre SVic
	- Hong Kong kumquat (F)	SCit
	- 'Nagami' (F)	SPre SWeb
	- 'Reale' PBR (F)	SPre
§	× ***junos***	SCit SPre SVic
	kinokuni	see *C. japonica*
	kotokan	see *C.* × *aurantium*
	'Kucle' (F)	SCit SPre
	'Kulci' (F)	CCCN
	kumquat	see *C. japonica*
	'La Valette' (F)	CCCN SPre
	× ***latifolia*** (F/S)	CCCN CDoC EPfP SCit SPre SWeb
	- 'Bearss' (F)	SCit SVic
	- variegated (F/v)	SPre
	latipes Hook. f. & Thomson ex Hook. f.	see *C. hystrix*
	limetta (F)	CCCN SPre SVic SWeb
	limettioides (F)	SCit SPre
§	× ***limon*** (F)	LSRN SCit SGsty SPre SVic WKor
§	- Bergamot Group (F)	SPre
	- - 'Fantastico' (F)	SCit
	- 'Eureka'	see *C.* × *limon* 'Garey's Eureka'
	- 'Eureka Variegated' (F/v)	SCit
	- 'Fino' (F)	CCCN SCit
	- 'Four Seasons'	see *C.* × *limon* 'Garey's Eureka'
§	- 'Garey's Eureka' (F)	CCCN ELan EPfP LCro LOPS NLar SCit SPre
	- 'Imperial' (F)	SCit SPre
	- 'Improved Meyer'	see *C.* × *limon* 'Meyer'
	- 'Lemonade' (F)	SCit
	- 'Lisbon' (F)	SCit
	- 'Lunario' (F)	SCit SPre
§	- 'Meyer' (F) ♀H2	CBcs CCCN CDoC CTri CTsd ELan EPfP LSRN NLar SCit SGsty SPer SPre SWeb
	- 'Ponderosa' (F)	SCit
	- 'Quatre Saisons'	see *C.* × *limon* 'Garey's Eureka'
	- 'Rangpur' (F)	SCit SPre
	- 'Romana' (F)	SCit
	- 'Sfusato d'Amalfi' (F)	SCit
	- 'Siracusano' (F)	SCit
	- 'Variegata' (F/v) ♀H2	CCCN ELan SCit SPre
	- 'Verna' (F)	CCCN SCit
	- 'Villa Franca' (F)	SCit
	- 'Yen Ben' (F)	SCit
	- 'Zagara Bianco' (F)	SCit
	× ***limonia***	see *C.* × *limon*
	'Lipo' (F)	CCCN SCit SPre

	macrophylla (F)	SCit
	madurensis	see *C. japonica*
	maxima (F)	SWeb
§	- 'Wheeny' (F)	SCit
§	***medica*** (F)	SWeb
	- 'Cedra' (F)	SPre
	- 'Cidro Digitado'	see *C. medica* 'Fingered'
	- var. ***digitata***	see *C. medica* 'Fingered'
	- 'Ethrog' (F)	SCit SPre
§	- 'Fingered' (F)	SCit SPre SWeb
*	- 'Rubra'	SPre
	- var. ***sarcodactylis***	see *C. medica* 'Fingered'
	× ***meyeri***	see *C.* × *limon*
§	× ***microcarpa*** (F) 🏆H3	CCCN CDoC NLar SCit SPre SWeb
	- Philippine lime	see *C.* × *microcarpa*
§	- 'Tiger' (F/v)	SCit SPre SVic
	- 'Variegata'	see *C.* × *microcarpa* 'Tiger'
	× ***mitis***	see *C.* × *microcarpa*
	natsudaidai	see *C.* × *aurantium*
	'Nippon'	SCit
	× ***nobilis*** Lour.	see *C. reticulata* 'Willowleaf'
	- var. ***inermis***	see *C. japonica*
	- Ortanique Group	see *C.* × *aurantium* Sweet Orange Group
	× ***obovata*** (F)	SPre
	- 'Fukushu' (F)	CCCN SCit
	× ***paradisi***	see *C.* × *aurantium* Grapefruit Group
	- 'Wheeny'	see *C. maxima* 'Wheeny'
	'Pursta' (F)	CCCN
	reshni	see *C.* × *aurantium*
§	***reticulata*** (F)	CCCN SCit SPre SWeb
	- 'Clausellina' (F/S)	SCit
	- var. ***deliciosa***	see *C. reticulata* 'Willowleaf'
	- 'Fina' (F/S)	SCit
	- 'Hashimoto' (F/S)	SCit
	- 'Hernandina' (F)	CCCN
	- Mandarin Group (F)	EPfP SPre SWeb
	- - 'Clementine' (F)	EPfP SPre SWeb
	- - 'Encore' (F)	SCit
	- - 'Esbal' (F)	CCCN
	- - 'Fortune' (F)	SCit
	- - 'Fremont' (F)	SCit
	- - 'Nules' (F/S)	CCCN SCit SPre
	- 'Marisol' (F/S)	SCit
	- 'Miyagawa' (F)	CCCN SCit
	- 'Nour' (F)	SCit
	- 'Nova'	see *C.* × *aurantium* (Tangelo Group) 'Nova'
	- 'Okitsu' (F/S)	CCCN SCit
	- 'Owari' (F/S)	SCit
	- Satsuma Group	see *C. reticulata*
	- (Tangerine Group) 'Dancy' (F)	SCit
§	- 'Willowleaf' (F)	SCit
§	***reticulata*** × ***trifoliata***	SCit
	sinensis	see *C.* × *aurantium* Sweet Orange Group
	- 'Jaffa'	see *C.* × *aurantium* (Sweet Orange Group) 'Shamouti'
	- 'Washington'	see *C.* × *aurantium* (Sweet Orange Group) 'Baia'
	sudachi	see *C. medica*
§	× ***taitensis*** (F)	SCit SPre
	- 'Otaheite' (F)	CCCN SCit SPre
§	- rough lemon (F)	SCit
	- Schaub rough lemon	see *C.* × *taitensis* rough lemon
§	***trifoliata***	CAgr CBcs CCCN CDoC EBee EHyd ELan ELon EPfP IDee LRHS MBlu MGil MMuc MRav SCit SMad SPer SPlb WFar WKor WSHC
	- 'Flying Dragon'	SCit
	unshiu	see *C. reticulata*
	volkameriana	see *C.* × *limon*
	wilsonii	see *C.* × *junos*

Cladium (*Cyperaceae*)

	mariscus	XLum

Cladrastis (*Papilionaceae*)

§	***kentukea***	CBcs CLnd CMCN CTho EBee ELan EPfP ESwi EWTr LMaj MBlu NLar NOra WMat WPGP
§	- 'Perkins Pink'	MBlu
	- 'Rosea'	see *C. kentukea* 'Perkins Pink'
	lutea	see *C. kentukea*
	sinensis	CExl EBee EPfP MBlu WPGP
	wilsonii	WPGP

Clarkia (*Onagraceae*)

	CROWN DOUBLE MIXED **new**	SVic

Claytonia (*Portulacaceae*)

	alsinoides	see *C. sibirica*
§	***perfoliata***	GPoy MNHC WHer
§	***sibirica***	CAgr IMou LPot WKor XLum
	- f. ***albiflora***	EWld MPie WCot
	virginica	CBor EBee EPot GKev WFar

Clematis ✿ (*Ranunculaceae*)

	BWJ 7630 from China	WCru
	CC 711	CExl
	CC 4710	CExl
	'Abigail' (Vt)	NHaw
	ABILENE ('Evipo027'PBR) (EL)	CRos CWGN EHyd ELan EPfP ETho LRHS MAsh NRHS SNig SPoG
	'Abundance' (Vt) 🏆H6	CArg CBcs CRHN CWCL ELan EPfP ETho LCro LRHS LSRN MAsh NHol NOra SPer WFar
	ACROPOLIS ('Evipo078'PBR) (Boulevard Series)	CBod CWGN ELan LSou
	addisonii	NHaw WSHC
	'Advent Bells' (C)	CWGN ETho LCro LOPS WSpi
	'Akaishi' (EL)	ETho XLot
	akebioides	GKev
	ALABAST ('Poulala'PBR) (EL) 🏆H6	ETho LRHS SCoo WSpi
	ALAINA ('Evipo056'PBR) (EL)	CRos EHyd LRHS NRHS SLon SPoG
	'Alba Luxurians' (Vt)	CBcs CDoC CRHN CRos CTri CWCL EHyd ELan EPfP EShb ETho LCro LOPS LRHS LSRN MAsh MGos NHol NOra NRHS SCob SLim SPer SPoG XLot
	'Albina Plena' (A/d)	EPfP ETho XLot
	'Alice Fisk' (EL)	ETho LSRN MSwo
	'Alionushka' (I) 🏆H6	CRHN CRos CWCL EHyd ELan EPfP ETho LRHS LSRN NLar NOra XLot
	ALITA ('Evipo070'PBR) (Vt)	CWCL EBee EHyd LRHS SLon SNig
	'Allanah' (LL)	CWCL ETho LRHS LSRN SCoo WSpi
	alpina	GKev GLog LCro LOPS LRHS LSRN MAsh MCot MRav NPer SEWo SPlb SPre SWvt WFar XLot
	- 'Albiflora'	see *C. sibirica*
	- 'Columbine White'	see *C.* 'White Columbine'
§	- 'Pamela Jackman' (A) 🏆H6	CMac CRos CWCL EHyd ELan LRHS LSRN MAsh MMuc NOra NRHS SCob SCoo SLim SPer SPoG SRkn SWvt WFar

- pink-flowered (A)	GKev
- 'Stolwijk Gold' (A)	CWGN EBee ETho MBlu SRms
alternata	CWGN EBee NHaw
'Amethyst Beauty' (A)	EHyd EPfP LRHS
AMETHYST BEAUTY ('Evipo043'PBR) (LL)	ETho MAsh SLon SPoG
'Andante' (I)	CWGN WSpi
'Andromeda' (EL)	CDoC CRos EBee EHyd EPfP ETho IPot LRHS NHaw NLar NRHS XLot
ANETA ('Evipo055'PBR) (Vt)	CWGN SLon
ANGELA ('Zoang'PBR) (EL)	ETho LSRN
ANGELIQUE ('Evipo017') (EL)	CRos CWGN EHyd ELan EPfP ETho LRHS MAsh MGos NRHS SCoo SLon SNig SPer
'Anissa' (V)	NHaw
'Anita' (Ta)	EBee EPfP ETho LSRN NHaw NOra
ANNA LOUISE ('Evithree'PBR) (EL) ♀H6	CRos CWCL EHyd EPfP ETho LRHS LSRN MGos SCoo SLim SLon SNig
'Annabel' (EL)	LSRN MAsh
ANNABELLA ('Zo08169') (V)	ETho
ANNIVERSARY ('Pynot') (EL)	LSRN SCoo
'Aotearoa' (LL)	ETho IPot NHaw
'Aphrodite' (I)	MAsh
'Aphrodite Elegafumina' (I)	CRHN CWGN EHyd LRHS NHaw
apiifolia	NHaw WSpi
'Apollonia'	CWGN
'Apple Blossom' (Ar) ♀H4	CBcs CDoC CRos CTri CWCL ELan EPfP ETho LBuc LCro LOPS LRHS LSRN MAsh MGos MRav MSwo NLar NOra NRHS SCob SLim SPer SPoG SRkn SRms SWvt XLot
'Arabella' (I) ♀H6	CRHN CRos CWCL CWGN EHyd ELan ELon EPfP EShb ETho LRHS LSRN MAsh MGos NLar NOra NRHS SLim SNig SPer SRkn SWvt WBor WFar WSpi XLot
§ ARCTIC QUEEN ('Evitwo'PBR) (EL) ♀H6	CRos EHyd EPfP ETho LBuc LRHS LSRN MAsh MPri NRHS SCoo SLon SPoG
armandi	Widely available
- 'Enham Star' (Ar)	CRos EHyd EPfP LRHS MGos NRHS
§ - 'Little White Charm' (Ar)	CRos EBee EHyd ELan EPfP LBuc LRHS NRHS
- 'Meyeniana'	see *C. armandii* 'Little White Charm'
§ - 'Snowdrift' (Ar)	CBcs CRos EBee EHyd ELan EPfP ETho LCro LOPS LRHS LSRN MAsh MGos MSwo NLar NRHS SEle SPer SPoG SRms XLot
× ***aromatica***	CRos CWGN EBee EHyd ELan EPfP EShb ETho IPot LRHS MMrt WSpi
'Asao' (EL)	CArg CRos EHyd EPfP ETho LRHS SCoo SNig SPoG XLot
'Ascotiensis' (LL) ♀H6	CRHN CRos EBee EHyd EPfP ETho LRHS NHaw SCoo SLon
'Ashva' (LL)	CWGN SNig XLot
ASTRA NOVA ('Zo09085'PBR) (Vt)	CWGN IPot WSpi
'Aureolin' (Ta)	NOra
AVANT-GARDE ('Evipo033'PBR) (Vt)	CDoC CRos CWCL CWGN EHyd ELan EPfP ETho LRHS SLon
§ AZTEK ('Daihelios') (Ta)	CRos ETho LRHS NOra
BABY DOLL ('Zobadol'PBR) (EL)	CWGN EBee ETho WSpi
'Baby Pink' (I)	NHaw
BABY STAR ('Zobast'PBR) (EL)	CWGN ETho
§ 'Bagatelle' (LL)	EHyd ETho LRHS NHaw SNig XLot
'Bal Maiden' (Vt)	CRHN NHaw
'Bałtyk' (EL)	XLot
'Barbara' (LL)	LSRN
'Barbara Dibley' (EL)	CTri CWCL EHyd ETho LRHS MAsh NHaw NOra SCoo SNig
'Barbara Harrington'PBR (LL)	EHyd LRHS LSRN NOra SNig
'Barbara Jackman' (EL)	CArg CRos CWCL EHyd ETho LRHS LSRN MAsh MGos MSwo NOra SCob SCoo SLon XLot
'Beata' (LL)	CWCL NHaw
'Beautiful Bride'PBR (EL)	ETho LCro LOPS XLot
'Beauty of Worcester' (EL)	CDoC CRos CWCL ELan ELon EPfP ETho LRHS LSRN MAsh MSwo NOra SCoo SLim
'Bees' Jubilee' (EL)	CArg CBcs CMac CRos CWCL EBee EHyd ELan EPfP ETho LCro LOPS LRHS LSRN MAsh MGos MSwo NLar NOra SLim SNig SPer SPoG SWvt XLot
'Bella' (EL)	LSRN
'Belle Nantaise' (EL)	CRos EHyd LRHS NRHS SRms
'Belle of Woking' (EL)	CRos CWCL EHyd ELan ELon LRHS LSRN NOra SCoo SNig SWvt
BERNADINE ('Evipo 061'PBR) (EL)	CBod CPla CRos CWGN EHyd ETho LRHS LSou NRHS SNig
'Berry Red' (A)	CWGN
'Best Wishes'	CRos EHyd ETho LRHS LSRN NOra NRHS SNig WSpi
§ 'Beth Currie' (EL)	EHyd EPfP LRHS SNig
'Betty Corning' (Vt)	CRHN CRos CWGN EBee EHyd ELan EPfP ETho LRHS LSRN MGos NRHS SCoo SLon SPoG SRms SWvt
'Betty Risdon' (EL)	NOra
BIJOU	see *C.* THUMBELINA
'Bill MacKenzie' (Ta) ♀H6	CArg CBcs CDoC CMac CRos CSam CTri EHyd ELan EPfP ETho GKev IPot LRHS LSRN MGos MPri MRav NHol NOra NRHS SLim SNig SPer SPoG SRms SWvt WSHC XLot
'Black Prince' (Vt)	CRHN CRos CWGN EHyd ELan EPfP ETho IPot LCro LRHS LSRN NLar NRHS SLim SLon SPer SPoG SRms XLot
'Black Tea' (LL)	CRos EHyd EPfP IPot LRHS LSRN NOra NRHS SLim SLon
§ 'Błękitny Anioł' (LL) ♀H6	CRHN CRos CWCL CWGN EBee EHyd ELan ELon EPfP ETho LCro LOPS LRHS MAsh NLar NOra NRHS SCoo SLon SPoG WBor
BLUE ANGEL	see *C.* 'Błękitny Anioł'
'Blue Belle' (Vt)	CRHN ELan IPot LRHS NLar SLon WFar
'Blue Bird' (A/d)	CArg CBcs CWCL EBee ELan LRHS SRms
BLUE BLOOD	see *C.* 'Königskind'
'Blue Boy' (EL)	see *C.* 'Elsa Späth'
'Blue Boy' (I)	see *C.* × *diversifolia* 'Blue Boy' (I)
'Blue Dancer' (A)	CBcs CDoC CRos EHyd EPfP ETho LRHS MGos NLar SNig
'Blue Eclipse' (A)	CRos CWGN EHyd ETho LRHS NHaw NHol NOra NRHS SPoG
'Blue Eyes' (EL)	ETho LSRN NLar
§ 'Blue Light'PBR (EL/d)	CWGN ELan ETho LRHS NLar
BLUE MOON ('Evirin'PBR) (EL)	CRos CWCL EHyd EPfP ETho LRHS LSRN NLar SCoo SLon SNig
BLUE OCEAN ('Zo09045'PBR) (I)	EBee IPot
BLUE PIROUETTE ('Zobluepi'PBR) (I)	CWCL ELan ETho IPot

BLUE RAIN	see *C.* 'Sinii Dozhd'
'Blue Ravine' (EL)	EPfP LRHS NLar NOra SCoo
BLUE RIVER ('Zoblueriver'PBR)	CWCL CWGN ELan ETho
'Blue Sensation' (I)	XLot
'Bolam Belle' (Vt)	NHaw
BONANZA ('Evipo031'PBR) (Vt)	CRos EHyd EPfP LRHS NLar SCoo SLon SNig SPoG
× ***bonstedtii*** 'Crépuscule' (H)	ECtt MCot WSpi
BOURBON ('Evipo018'PBR) (EL)	CRos CWCL EHyd ELan EPfP ETho LRHS SCoo SLon SNig
'Brianna' (Vt)	NHaw
'Brocade' (Vt)	CRHN NHaw
'Broughton Bride' (A)	CDoC CRos CWCL CWGN EHyd EPfP ETho LRHS NHol NLar NOra NRHS SRms XLot
'Broughton Star' (M/d) ♀H5	Widely available
'Brunette' (A)	EHyd ELan EPfP ETho LRHS NLar SLon XLot
buchananiana Finet & Gagnep.	see *C. rehderiana*
'Buckland Beauty' (V)	CWCL CWGN NHaw
'Buckland Pixie' (Vt)	NHaw
'Burford Bell' (V)	NHaw WSHC
'Burford Princess' (Vt)	CRHN NHaw
'Burford White' (A)	NLar
'Burma Star' (EL)	CWCL CWGN EPfP ETho SNig
BURNING LOVE ('Vitiwester'PBR) (Vt) **new**	ETho XLot
CADDICK'S CASCADE	see *C.* 'Semu'
calycina	see *C. cirrhosa* var. *balearica*
§ ***campaniflora***	ETho NHaw
- dark-flowered	CMea
campestris	EBee GKev
'Candleglow' (A)	NOra
'Candy Stripe'	EHyd LRHS NOra SCoo SNig SPoG
'Capitaine Thuilleaux'	see *C.* 'Souvenir du Capitaine Thuilleaux'
'Cardinal Wyszyński'	see *C.* 'Kardynał Wyszyński '
'Carlien' (Vt) **new**	CRHN
'Carlotta' (Vt)	NHaw
'Carmencita' (Vt)	CRHN EBee LRHS LSRN NHaw SCoo SLon
'Carnaby' (EL)	CArg CRos CWCL EHyd ELan EPfP ETho LRHS LSRN MAsh NOra SCoo SNig SWvt WSpi
'Carol Klein' (I)	NHaw
'Carol Leeds' (Vt)	NHaw
'Caroline' (LL)	CWGN LSRN
× ***cartmanii*** 'Avalanche'PBR (Fo/m)	CRos EHyd ELan EPfP ETho LRHS MGos MPri NLar NRHS SCob SCoo SLon SNig SPoG SWvt
- 'Joe' (Fo/m) ♀H4	CBcs CDoC CRos CWCL EHyd ELan EPfP ETho EWes ITim LCro LOPS LRHS LSRN NOra NRHS SCob SCoo SPoG SWvt WIce
- 'Joe' × ***cirrhosa*** **new**	CWCL
- 'Joe' × ***marmoraria*** (Fo)	MAsh
- 'Joe' × 'Sharon' (Fo)	LSRN
- MICHIKO ('Evipo044'PBR) (Fo)	CRos EBee EHyd EPfP ETho LRHS NRHS SNig SPoG
- 'White Abundance'PBR (Fo/f)	EHyd LRHS NLar
CASSIS ('Evipo020'PBR)	EHyd ETho LRHS LSRN MAsh SCoo SLon SNig SPer
'Catherine Clanwilliam' (T)	CWGN
'Catherine Penny' (VT)	NHaw
'Celebration' Caddick	see *C.* 'Pink Celebration'
'Celebration'PBR Godfrey (EL)	ETho
CÉZANNE ('Evipo023'PBR) (EL)	CRos CWCL EHyd ELan EPfP ETho LRHS MAsh MGos NLar NOra NRHS SCoo SLon SNig
'Chacewater' (Vt)	CRHN
'Chalcedony' (EL)	CWGN ETho NOra
CHANTILLY ('Evipo021'PBR) (EL)	CRos EHyd ELan EPfP ETho LRHS LSRN NOra NRHS SCoo SLon SNig
'Charissima' (EL)	CWGN EHyd LRHS NLar NOra SCoo
'Charlie Brown' (LL)	CRHN NHaw
CHARMAINE ('Evipo022'PBR) (EL)	CRos CWGN EHyd EPfP ETho LRHS NRHS SNig SPoG
'Chatsworth' (Vt)	CRHN CWGN ETho NHaw SLon
CHELSEA ('Evipo100'PBR)	CRos EHyd EPfP ETho LRHS NRHS SLon SNig
CHEROKEE	see *C.* OOH LA LA
CHEVALIER ('Evipo040'PBR) (EL)	CRos EHyd ELan EPfP ETho LRHS MAsh NRHS SLon SNig SPoG
chinensis misapplied	see *C. terniflora*
CHINOOK ('Evipo013'PBR)	EHyd LRHS SRms
chrysantha	see *C. tangutica*
chrysocoma misapplied	see *C. spooneri*
chrysocoma Franch.	WSpi
'Cicciolina' (Vt)	CRHN ETho NHaw
cirrhosa	CRos CTri EHyd LRHS MAsh NOra
§ - var. ***balearica***	CBcs CDoC CMac CRos CTri CWCL EHyd ELan EPfP ETho LCro LOPS LRHS LSRN MAsh MGos MRav MSwo NOra SCob SEND SLim SPer SPoG SWvt
- 'Jingle Bells' (C)	CDoC CMac CRos CWCL EBee EHyd ELan EPfP ETho LCro LOPS LRHS LSRN MAsh MGos NLar NOra NRHS SCoo SLim SLon SNig SRms
- 'Ourika Valley' (C)	CWGN EBee ELon ETho MAsh NLar NOra
- var. ***purpurascens*** 'Freckles' (C) ♀H4	Widely available
- - 'Lansdowne Gem' (C)	CMac CRos CWCL CWGN EHyd ETho LBuc LRHS NLar NOra SPoG SWvt WSpi
- 'Winter Parasol' (C)	EBee LBuc
- 'Wisley Cream' (C) ♀H4	CBcs CDoC CMac CRos CWCL EBee EHyd ELan EPfP ETho LCro LOPS LRHS LSRN MAsh MCot MSwo NLar NOra NRHS SCoo SLim SNig SPer SPoG SRms SWvt
cirrhosa × 'Early Sensation' **new**	CWCL
clarkeana misapplied	see *C. urophylla* 'Winter Beauty'
'Cloudburst' (LL)	ETho
coactilis	NHaw SBrt
columbiana	GKev
- var. ***tenuiloba*** 'Ylva' (A)	WAbe
'Columbine' (A)	EBee EHyd EPfP LRHS MSwo SPer
'Columella' (A)	CWGN EBee NLar XLot
'Comtesse de Bouchaud' (LL) ♀H6	CArg CRos CTri CWCL EBee EHyd ELan EPfP EShb ETho LCro LOPS LRHS LSRN MAsh MGos MPri MRav NOra NRHS SCob SLim SNig SPer SPoG WBor
CONFETTI ('Evipo036'PBR) (Vt)	EHyd EPfP LRHS LSRN
'Congratulations' (EL)	CRos EHyd LRHS LSRN NOra NRHS SPoG
aff. ***connata*** HWJK 2176 from Nepal	WCru

'Consort' (LL) **new**	CWGN
'Constance' (A) 🏆^{H6}	CArg CRos CWCL EBee EHyd EPfP ETho LRHS LSRN NLar NRHS SCoo SNig SPre SRms WFar
'Continuity' (M)	CWGN NOra
'Cora' (I)	CWGN
'Coralie' (T) **new**	NHaw
CORINNE ('Evipo063'^{PBR}) (EL)	CRos EHyd ETho LRHS NRHS SNig SPoG
'Cornish Spirit' (Vt)	CRHN
'Corona' (EL)	EPfP LRHS SCoo
'Côte d'Azur' (H)	CExl ELan LRHS MNrw NLar WSFF
'Countess of Lovelace' (EL)	CBcs ELan EPfP ETho LRHS LSRN NOra SCoo
COUNTRY ROSE ('Zocoro'^{PBR}) (A)	EPfP WSpi
'Cragside' (A)	CRos EHyd LRHS NRHS
§ 'Crimson King' (LL)	ETho NLar
'Crinkle'^{PBR} (M)	CCCN
§ ***crispa***	CWGN NHaw
§ CRYSTAL FOUNTAIN ('Evipo038'^{PBR}) (EL)	CDoC CRos CWCL CWGN EHyd ELan EPfP ETho LBuc LCro LOPS LRHS LSRN MGos NOra SCoo SLon SNig SPer SPoG SRms
'Danae' (Vt)	NHaw
DANCING QUEEN ('Zodaque'^{PBR}) (EL)	ETho WSpi
DANCING SMILE ('Zodasmi'^{PBR}) (EL)	EBee
'Daniel Deronda' (EL) 🏆^{H6}	CArg CDoC CRos CWCL CWGN EBee ELan EPfP ETho IPot LRHS LSRN MAsh NOra NRHS SCob SCoo SLim SNig SPoG
'Darius' (EL)	SNig
'Dark Eyes' (Vt)	CWGN ETho IPot LCro LOPS SNig XLot
'Dark Secret' (A)	NHol NOra
dasyandra NJM 11.075	WPGP
'Dawn' (EL)	CCCN CRos CWCL EHyd ETho LRHS LSRN SCoo WSpi
'Dazzle' (EL)	ETho
'De Vijfhoeven' (Vt)	NHaw
'Débutante' (EL)	NHaw
'Denny's Double' (EL/d)	CWCL CWGN LRHS SNig
'Destiny' (EL)	CWGN XLot
DIAMANTINA ('Evipo039'^{PBR}) (EL)	CRos CWCL EBee EHyd EPfP ETho LRHS NRHS SLon SNig
'Diamond Anniversary' (A)	EPfP ETho LCro LOPS
'Diamond Ball'^{PBR} (EL)	ETho
'Diana' (LL)	LSRN NHaw
DIANA'S DELIGHT ('Evipo026'^{PBR}) (EL)	CRos CWCL EHyd EPfP ETho LRHS LSRN MAsh NRHS SLon SPoG
dioscoreifolia	see *C. terniflora*
§ × ***diversifolia***	CRHN LRHS NHaw SWvt WCot XLot
- 'Benedikt' (I)	CWGN WSpi
§ - 'Blue Boy' (I)	CRHN NHaw WSpi
- 'Heather Herschell' (I)	CRHN CTsd XLot
§ - 'Hendersonii' (I)	CBod CRos CWCL EHyd ELan EMor GAbr GKev LRHS LSRN MRav SMHy SPer SWvt WCot
§ - 'Olgae' (I)	CExl NHaw
'Doctor Mary' (V)	NHaw
'Doctor Ruppel' (EL)	CArg CDoC CMac CRos CWCL EHyd ELon EPfP ETho LCro LOPS LRHS LSRN MAsh MSwo NOra NRHS SCob SLim SNig SPer XLot
'Dominika' (LL)	NHaw
'Dorath'	CRos CWGN EHyd EPfP LRHS NHaw NOra SNig
'Dorothy Tolver' (EL)	ETho
'Dorothy Walton'	see *C.* 'Bagatelle'
'Double Delight' (M)	CWGN
'Duchess of Albany' (1897) (T)	CArg CDoC CRos CTri CWCL EHyd ELan EPfP ETho LRHS LSRN MAsh MGos NHol NOra SPer SRkn
'Duchess of Edinburgh' (EL)	CBcs CDoC CMac CWCL EHyd ELan EPfP ETho LRHS LSRN MAsh MGos MSwo NHol NOra NRHS SCob SLim SNig SPoG SWvt XLot
× ***durandii*** 🏆^{H6}	CBcs CRHN CRos CSpe CWCL EHyd ELan EPfP ETho IPot LRHS LSRN MAsh MGos MRav NRHS SCob SCoo SPer SPoG SWvt WSpi
'Dutch Sky' (LL)	CWGN ETho XLot
'Early Sensation' (Fo/f)	CBcs CDoC CRos CTri CWCL EHyd ELan EPfP ETho LCro LOPS LRHS LSRN MAsh NOra NRHS SCoo SLim SPer SPoG SPre SWvt
EAST RIVER ('Zoeastri'^{PBR}) (I)	ELan
'Eclipse' (H)	CRos LRHS
EDDA ('Evipo074'^{PBR}) (Boulevard Series) (EL)	CRos EHyd EPfP ETho LRHS MAsh NRHS SNig
'Edith' (EL) 🏆^{H6}	CWCL ETho LSRN NHaw NLar
'Édouard Desfossé' (EL)	ETho LRHS
'Edward Prichard'	EPfP
'Eetika' (LL)	CRHN NHaw
'Effie Dewey' (LL)	NHaw
'Ekstra' (LL)	NHaw
'Eleanor' (Fo/f)	GEdr
'Elf' (Vt)	CWGN
'Elgar'	see *C.* 'Sir Edward Elgar'
'Elizabeth' (M) 🏆^{H5}	Widely available
§ 'Elsa Späth' (EL)	CArg CExl CMac CRos CTri EHyd ELan EPfP ETho LRHS LSRN MAsh NOra NRHS SNig SPer SPoG SWvt
'Elten' (M)	XLot
'Elvan' (Vt)	CRHN NHaw NLar
'Ember' (I)	CWGN
'Emerald Dream'^{PBR} (Fo)	ELan LRHS
'Emilia Plater' (Vt)	CRHN CWGN EPfP ETho NHaw SLon
'Empress Amy Lai'	CWCL NHaw
EMPRESS ('Evipo011'^{PBR}) (EL)	EHyd ELan EPfP LRHS SLon SNig
ENDELLION ('Evipo076'^{PBR}) (EL)	CRos EHyd ETho LRHS NRHS SNig
'Entel' (Vt)	CRHN EBee NHaw
× ***eriostemon***	see *C. × diversifolia*
'Ernest Markham' (LL) 🏆^{H6}	CDoC CMac CRos CWCL EHyd ELan EPfP ETho LRHS LSRN MAsh MGos MPri MSwo NOra NRHS SLim SNig SPer SPoG SWvt WSpi XLot
ESME ('Evipo048'^{PBR})	CRos CWGN ETho SLon SNig
ESTHER ('Zo09143') (EL)	IPot
'Étoile de Malicorne' (EL)	XLot
ETOILE NACRÉE	see *C.* 'Sakurahime'
'Étoile Rose' (Vt)	CMac CRHN CRos CTri CWCL EBee EHyd ELan EPfP ETho IPot LRHS LSRN MAsh NHaw NHol NOra SCoo SLim SLon SPer WBor
'Étoile Violette' (Vt) 🏆^{H6}	Widely available
EVENING STAR ('Evista') (EL)	EPfP
'Everett' (V)	WSHC
'Fair Rosamond' (EL)	ETho NLar

FAIRY BLUE	see *C.* CRYSTAL FOUNTAIN
'Fairydust' (Vt)	NHaw
× ***fargesioides***	see *C.* 'Paul Farges'
fasciculiflora KWJ 12160	WCru
- L 657	WCru WPGP
'Fascination'^{PBR} (I)	CWCL CWGN WCot WSpi
'Fay' (Vt)	NHaw
'Fenna' (EL) **new**	CWGN
FILIGREE ('Evipo029'^{PBR}) (EL)	CRos EHyd ETho LBuc LRHS MAsh MGos NRHS SNig
'Filomae' (Vt)	NHaw
finetiana misapplied	see *C. paniculata* J.G. Gmel.
'Firefly' (EL)	XLot
'Fireworks' (EL)	CArg CRos CWCL CWGN EHyd EPfP ETho LRHS LSRN MAsh MRav NLar NOra SLim SPer SPoG
FLAMENCO DANCER ('Bfccfla'^{PBR}) **new**	LCro LOPS
flammula	CArg CDoC CRos EHyd ELan EPfP ETho LCro LOPS LRHS LSRN MAsh MBlu MRav NLar NRHS SPer SPoG SRms SWvt WSpi XSen
- 'Rubra Marginata'	see *C.* × *triternata* 'Rubromarginata'
FLEURI ('Evipo042'^{PBR}) (Boulevard Series) (EL)	CRos CWCL EHyd EPfP ETho LRHS LSRN NOra NRHS SCoo SLon SNig SPoG WSpi
florida	CWGN SWvt
- 'Bicolor'	see *C. florida* var. *florida* 'Sieboldiana'
- var. ***flore-pleno*** 'Plena' (d)	CCCN CRos CWCL EHyd ELan EPfP ETho IPot LRHS LSRN MAsh NRHS SNig SPoG XLot
§ - var. ***florida*** 'Sieboldiana' (d)	CBcs CRos CWCL CWGN EHyd ELan EPfP ETho LCro LOPS LRHS LSRN MAsh NRHS SCob SNig SPoG SWvt XLot
- var. ***normalis*** PISTACHIO ('Evirida'^{PBR}) (LL)	CCCN CRos CWGN EHyd ELan EPfP LRHS MAsh MGos NLar NOra SLon SNig SPoG
'Floris V' (I)	CWCL GKev MCot NHaw NLar
'Fluffy Duck' (Vt/d)	NHaw
'Fond Memories' (EL)	CRos CWCL CWGN EHyd EPfP ETho LCro LOPS LRHS LSRN NHaw NLar NOra NRHS SLon
FOREVER FRIENDS ('Zofofri'^{PBR}) (LL)	CRos CWGN EHyd EPfP ETho LRHS NRHS SLon
'Forget-me-not NLP1'	ETho LSRN NLar
forrestii	see *C. napaulensis*
§ ***forsteri***	WSHC
'Foxtrot' (Vt)	CRHN
'Foxy' (A) ♀H6	ETho LRHS NLar
FRAGRANT OBERON ('Hutbron'^{PBR}) (Fo)	ETho LCro LOPS SWvt
'Fragrant Spring' (M)	CDoC CSBt CWGN EHyd EPfP ETho LRHS NLar SLim XLot
'Frances Rivis' (A) ♀H6	CArg CDoC CMac CRos CWCL EHyd ELan EPfP ETho GBin LCro LOPS LRHS LSRN MAsh MBlu MCot MRav MSwo NLar NOra SCob SPer SPoG SRms XLot
'Francesca' (A)	LSRN
'Frankie' (A) ♀H6	CRos EHyd ELan EPfP ETho LCro LOPS LRHS LSRN MAsh MGos MHer SCoo
FRANZISKA MARIA ('Evipo008') (EL)	CRos EHyd EPfP LRHS MAsh MGos SCoo SLon
'Freda' (M) ♀H6	CRHN CRos CTri CWGN ELan EPfP ETho LCro LOPS LRHS LSRN MAsh MBlu MRav NHol NOra SLim SPer SRms XLot
fremontii	NHaw
'Fryderyk Chopin' (EL)	NLar
'Fudō' (V)	NHaw
'Fujimusume' (EL) ♀H6	CRos CWGN EHyd EPfP ETho IPot LRHS MAsh NHaw NOra NRHS SPoG XLot
'Fukuzono' (I)	CRos EHyd LRHS LSRN NHaw NRHS XLot
fusca misapplied	see *C. japonica*
fusca Turcz.	EWld
- dwarf	CWGN
- large-flowered B&SWJ 8431	WCru
'Fuyu-no-tabi' (EL)	ETho XLot
'Gabrielle' ambig.	LSRN
GALORE	see *C.* VESUVIUS
GAZELLE ('Evipo014'^{PBR}) (I)	EHyd LRHS MAsh SRms
'Generał Sikorski' (EL)	CBcs CDoC CRos CWCL EHyd ELan EPfP ETho LRHS LSRN MAsh MGos NOra NRHS SCoo SLim SNig SPer SWvt WSpi XLot
gentianoides	SBrt
'Geoffrey Tolver' (LL)	CWGN
'Georg Ots' (LL)	NHaw
GIANT STAR ('Gistar'^{PBR}) (M)	CRos EHyd EPfP LRHS NLar NPer NRHS SLim SPoG
'Gillian Blades' (EL) ♀H6	CRos EBee EHyd ELan EPfP ETho LBuc LRHS LSRN MAsh MGos NHaw NOra NRHS SCoo SNig SPoG SWvt XLot
GINA ('Evipo092') (Garland Series) (LL) **new**	CWGN
'Ginny' (V)	NHaw
§ 'Gipsy Queen' (LL) ♀H6	CArg CBcs CRos CWCL EHyd ELan ELon EPfP ETho LRHS LSRN MAsh MGos NOra SLim SNig SPer SPoG SWvt XLot
'Girėnas' (EL)	XLot
GISELLE ('Evipo051'^{PBR})	CRos EHyd EPfP ETho LRHS MAsh NRHS SLon SNig SPoG
'Gladys Picard' (EL)	NHaw
glauca Turcz.	see *C. intricata*
glauca ambig.	GKev SBrt
glaucophylla	NHaw SBrt
'Gojōgawa' (EL)	ETho
'Golden Harvest' (Ta)	EPfP ETho LSRN NLar
GOLDEN TIARA ('Kugotia'^{PBR}) (Ta) ♀H6	CWGN ETho LSRN NLar SRms WCot XLot
'Grace' (Ta)	EPfP NHaw NLar
gracilifolia BWJ 8002	WCru
grandiflora	LBuc SRms XLot
I 'Grandiflora' (F)	CDoC ETho WFar
'Grandiflora Sanguinea' (Vt)	NHaw
grata misapplied	see *C.* × *jouiniana*
'Gravetye Beauty' (T)	CDoC CRHN CRos CWCL EBee EHyd ELan EPfP ETho LRHS LSRN MAsh MGos NHol NOra SLon SNig SPoG SRms SWvt XLot
§ 'Grażyna' (LL)	ETho
GREEN PASSION ('Zo11050') (EL/d)	ETho LCro LOPS
GREFVE ERIK RUUTH ('Kbk02'^{PBR}) (EL) **new**	CWGN
'Guernsey Cream' (EL)	CDoC CRos CWCL EHyd EPfP ETho LCro LOPS LRHS LSRN MAsh MGos NLar NOra SCoo SNig SRkn XLot
GUIDING PROMISE ('Evipo053'^{PBR})	SLon SNig
'Guiding Star' (EL)	XLot

	'H.F.Young' (EL)	CRos EHyd ELan EPfP ETho LRHS LSRN MAsh MGos NLar NOra SCob SCoo SNig SPer SWvt
	'Hågelby Pink' (Vt) Υ^{H6}	CRHN CWGN ELan NHaw
	'Hågelby White' (Vt)	CRHN CWGN ELan NHaw
	'Hagley Hybrid' (LL)	CArg CMac CRos CWCL EBee EHyd ELan EPfP ETho LRHS LSRN MAsh MGos MRav NLar NOra NRHS SCob SLim SNig SPer SPoG SRms SWvt XLot
	'Hakuōkan' (EL)	EPfP ETho LRHS LSRN NLar NOra SCoo WSpi
	'Hanaguruma' (EL)	ETho LSRN NOra SNig XLot
	'Hanajima' (I)	ETho
	'Hania' (EL)	ETho
	'Happy Anniversary' (EL)	ETho LBuc LCro LOPS LSRN NLar
§	HAPPY BIRTHDAY ('Zohapbi'^{PBR}) (LL) Υ^{H6}	ETho LCro LOPS LSRN WSpi
	HARLOW CARR ('Evipo004'^{PBR})	CMac CRos EHyd EPfP LRHS NRHS SCoo SRms
	'Haru Ichiban' (EL)	ETho
	'Hayate'	CWGN
	'Helios'	see *C.* AZTEK
	'Helsingborg' (A) Υ^{H6}	CRos EHyd ELan EPfP ETho LRHS MAsh MPri NOra SCoo SNig SPoG SRms
I	'Hendersonii' (I)	LSRN MCot
	hendersonii Koch	see *C.* × *diversifolia* 'Hendersonii'
	hendersonii Stand.	see *C.* × *diversifolia*
I	'Hendersonii Rubra' (Ar)	LRHS
	'Hendryetta'^{PBR} (I)	EHyd LRHS SWvt
	henryi	EHyd EShb LSRN MAsh SNig
	- B&SWJ 3402	WCru
	- var. ***morii*** B&SWJ 1668	WCru
	'Henryi' (EL)	CDoC CMac CRos CTri CWCL EBee ELan EPfP LCro LOPS LRHS LSRN MRav MSwo NOra NRHS SPer SPoG XLot
	heracleifolia	CBod CMac CPou ECtt ELan GLog LRHS MCot NLar WBor WOld
	- ALAN BLOOM	see *C. tubulosa* ALAN BLOOM
	- 'Blue Dwarf' (H)	CWGN ETho WAbe
	- 'Cassandra' (H) Υ^{H5}	CRos CSpe CWCL CWGN ECtt EHyd ELan ELon EPfP ETho GLog LRHS LSRN MCot MHer MHol NRHS
	- 'China Purple' (H)	CExl CPou ECtt GBin ILea LRHS MCot MHol NLar
	- 'Pink Dwarf' (H)	CWGN NLar WAbe
	'Herbert Johnson' (EL)	NHaw
	hexapetala Forster	see *C. forsteri*
	hexasepala	see *C. forsteri*
	hirsutissima	SPhx
	- var. ***scottii***	EBee GKev
	'Honora' (LL)	CRos CWGN EHyd LRHS MAsh NOra NRHS SCoo
	'Horn of Plenty' (EL)	CRos EHyd LRHS NHaw
	'Hoshi-no-flamenco' (T)	CWGN IPot
	huchouensis	NHaw
	HUDSON RIVER ('Zo06137'^{PBR}) (I)	IPot
	'Huldine' (LL) Υ^{H6}	CBcs CRHN CRos CWCL ELan EPfP ETho LRHS LSRN MAsh MRav NOra SLon SNig SPer SWvt XLot
	'Huvi' (LL)	CWGN NHaw XLot
	'Hybrida Sieboldii' (EL)	SCoo
	HYDE HALL ('Evipo009'^{PBR}) (EL)	CMac CRos CWGN EHyd ELan EPfP LRHS MAsh MGos NRHS SCoo SLon SNig SPer SRms
	'Hythe Egret' (Fo)	WIce

	I AM A LITTLE BEAUTY ('Zolibe') (Vt)	CRHN EBee NHaw
	I AM HAPPY ('Zoiamha') (Vt)	CWGN ELan
	I AM LADY J ('Zoiamlj') (Vt)	ELan NHaw
	I AM LADY Q ('Zoiamladyq'^{PBR}) (Vt)	CWGN EBee ETho LRHS NHaw
	I AM RED ROBIN ('Zorero'^{PBR}) (A)	CWGN
	ianthina 'Josie's Midnight Blue' (V)	NHaw
	- var. ***kuripoensis*** B&SWJ 700	WCru
	'Ibi' (EL)	CWGN WSpi
	ICE BLUE ('Evipo003'^{PBR}) (Prairie Series) (EL)	CRos EHyd ELan EPfP LRHS MAsh SCoo SLon SNig
	'Ice Queen' (EL)	MAsh
	indivisa Willd.	see *C. paniculata* J.G. Gmel.
	INES ('Evipo059'^{PBR}) (Boulevard Series)	CRos EHyd ETho LRHS NRHS SNig
	'Ingrid Biedenkopf' (Vt)	NHaw
	'Innocent Blush'^{PBR} (EL)	ETho
	'Innocent Glance'^{PBR} (EL)	ETho
	INSPIRATION ('Zoin'^{PBR}) (I)	ELan NLar SCoo
	integrifolia	CBod CCBP CExl CFis ELan EMor EPfP GKev IPot LRHS MBriF MCot NChi NLar NPer SRms WHil WHoo WMal
I	- 'Alba' (I)	CRos ECtt EPfP ETho GKev LRHS LSRN NHaw NLar SCoo SRms
	- 'Baby Blue' (I)	NHaw
	- 'Blue Ribbons' (I)	CSpe MMrt NLar SPhx
	- dark blue-flowered (I)	GKev
	- 'Gletschereis' (I) **new**	CWCL
	- 'Hendersonii' Koch	see *C.* × *diversifolia* 'Hendersonii'
	- MONGOLIAN BELLS ('Psharlan') (I)	CSpe CWCL
	- 'Olgae'	see *C.* × *diversifolia* 'Olgae'
	- 'Ozawa's Blue' (I)	CWGN ETho MBNS WAvo
	- violet-flowered (I)	GKev
	- white-flowered (I)	see *C. integrifolia* 'Alba'
§	***intricata***	CExl
	- 'Harry Smith' (Ta)	WSpi
	ISABELLA ('Zo12220') (EL) **new**	IPot
	ispahanica	NHaw SBrt
	'Iubileinyi-70' (LL)	NHaw
	'Ivan Olsson' (EL)	CWCL ETho
	'Jackmanii' (LL) Υ^{H6}	CArg CBcs CMac CRos CTri EBee EHyd EPfP ETho LCro LOPS LRHS LSRN MAsh MGos NOra SCob SCoo SLim SNig SPoG SWvt XLot
	'Jackmanii Alba' (EL)	CRos CWCL EHyd ELan ELon EPfP ETho LRHS LSRN MAsh SCoo SLim SPoG XLot
	JACKMANII PURPUREA ('Zojapur'^{PBR}) (LL)	ETho
	'Jackmanii Rubra' (EL)	NOra
	'Jackmanii Superba' misapplied	see *C.* 'Gipsy Queen'
	'Jackmanii Superba' ambig. (LL)	CDoC CMac CRos CWCL EHyd ELan EPfP ETho LCro LOPS LRHS MAsh MGos MPri MRav MSwo NPer SCob SLim SNig SPer SPoG XLot
	'Jacqueline du Pré' (A) Υ^{H6}	CBcs CDoC EBee ELan EPfP ETho LRHS
	'James Mason' (EL)	ETho LSRN SNig
	'Jan Fopma'^{PBR} (I)	CWGN

	'Jan Lindmark' (A/d)	CDoC CRos EHyd EPfP LRHS MAsh NLar NRHS SCoo SPoG SPre XLot
§	'Jan Paweł II' (EL)	CRos EHyd ELan ETho LRHS NOra SCoo SNig SPer XLot
	'Jane Ashdown' (M)	NHaw
	'Janny' (A)	XLot
§	***japonica***	NHaw
	'Jasper' (V)	ETho
	'Jean Caldwell' (Vt)	NHaw
	'Jean Cumpston' (C)	NHaw
	'Jeanne's Pink' (EL)	CWCL EBee ETho
I	'Jenny' (Cedergren) (LL)	ETho NHaw
	'Jenny' (M/d)	CRos CWCL EHyd LRHS LSRN SPoG WSpi XLot
	'Jenny Caddick' (Vt)	NHaw
	'Jerzy Popiełuszko' (EL)	ETho
	JESSICA ('Evipo012'PBR) (I)	EHyd LRHS
	JEWEL OF MERK	see *C.* HAPPY BIRTHDAY
	'Jiska' (A) **new**	XLot
	'Joan Picton' (EL)	NOra
	JOHN HOWELLS ('Zojohnhowells'PBR) (Vt)	CWCL CWGN ETho LSRN SLon WSpi
	'John Huxtable' (LL)	CRos EHyd ETho LRHS SNig WSpi
	JOHN PAUL II	see *C.* 'Jan Paweł II'
	'John Treasure' (Vt)	CRHN NHaw NLar
	'John Warren' (EL)	CRos EHyd LRHS MAsh NHaw NOra NRHS SCoo
	JOSEPHINE ('Evijohill'PBR) (EL)	CDoC CRos CWCL CWGN EHyd EPfP ETho LCro LOPS LRHS LSRN MAsh MGos NLar NOra NRHS SCoo SLim SNig SPer SPoG SWvt WSpi
§	× ***jouiniana***	MRav NHaw SEND SHar SWvt WSHC
	'Julka' (EL)	CDoC CWCL ETho NHaw WSpi
	'Justa' (Vt)	NHaw XLot
	'Juuli' (I)	LSRN NHaw XLot
	'Kaaru' (LL)	CRHN
	'Kacper' (EL)	ETho NHaw
	'Kaen' (EL)	ETho
	'Kaiser'PBR	ETho
	'Kaiu' (V)	CWCL CWGN EHyd ETho LRHS NHaw
§	'Kakio' (EL)	CRos CWCL EHyd EPfP ETho LRHS LSRN MAsh MGos NOra SNig SPer XLot
I	'Kamilla' (EL)	CWGN
§	'Kardynał Wyszyński' (EL)	ETho
§	'Kasmu' (Vt)	NHaw
	'Kathleen Dunford' (EL)	LSRN SCoo
	'Kathryn Chapman' (Vt)	CRHN CWGN NHaw
	'Kaunitar' (LL)	NHaw
	'Ken Donson' (EL) 𝕐H6	LRHS SCoo
	'Kermesina' (Vt) 𝕐H6	CDoC CRHN CRos EBee EHyd ELan EPfP ETho LCro LOPS LRHS MAsh NOra SCoo SLim SNig SPer SPoG SRms WBor
	'Ketu Õde' (LL)	NHaw
	'Kiev' (Vt)	NHaw XLot
	'Killifreth' (Vt)	CRHN NHaw
	KIMIKO ('Evipo066'PBR) (Boulevard Series) (Fo)	CRos EHyd LRHS NRHS SPoG
	'King Edward VII' (EL)	LRHS
	KINGFISHER ('Evipo037'PBR) (EL)	CRos EHyd ELan EPfP ETho LRHS NOra SCoo SLon SPoG
	'Kinju Atarashi' (LL)	CWCL ETho
	'Kiri Te Kanawa' (EL)	CWCL ELon EPfP ETho LRHS LSRN NLar WSpi
	kirilowii	NHaw
	'Kirsten Creed'	NOra
	KITTY ('Evipo097') (EL)	CRos EHyd ETho LRHS NRHS SPoG WSpi
	'Kommerei' (LL)	NHaw
§	'Königskind' (EL)	ETho NLar XLot
	koreana	CPla LRHS MAsh WCru
	- AMBER ('Wit141205') (A)	CBcs CRos EHyd ELan ETho IPot LCro LOPS NRHS XLot
	- var. ***carunculosa***	WSHC
	- - B&SWJ 12725	WCru
	- - 'Lemon Bells' (A)	CRos EBee EHyd EPfP LRHS MAsh SCoo SLon SPoG
	'Kosmicheskaia Melodiia' (LL)	XLot
	'Krakowiak'PBR (Vt)	NHaw
	'Külli' (LL)	NHaw
	ladakhiana	EWld NHaw
	'Lady Betty Balfour' (LL)	CMac CRos EHyd ETho LRHS SCoo SNig SWvt
	'Lady Bird Johnson' (T)	CRos CWCL EHyd LRHS LSRN SCoo
	'Lady Caroline Nevill' (EL)	CRos EHyd LRHS NRHS
	'Lady Kyoko' (d) **new**	LCro LOPS
	'Lady Londesborough' (EL)	NHaw
	'Lady Northcliffe' (EL)	CTri CWCL EHyd EPfP ETho LRHS MAsh NOra SNig
	'Lambton Park' (Ta) 𝕐H6	CRHN CWCL ETho NHaw NLar
	'Lantern Light' (A)	NOra
	lasiandra	NHaw
	'Last Dance' (Ta)	CRHN EBee
	LASTING LOVE	see *C.* 'Grażyna'
	'Lasurstern' (EL) 𝕐H6	CArg CBcs CExl CMac CRos CTri EBee EHyd ELan EPfP ETho LCro LOPS LRHS LSRN MAsh NOra SCob SPer SPoG SWvt WFar XLot
	'Laura Denny' (EL)	ETho
	'Lavender Twirl' (Vt)	CRHN
	'Lawsoniana' (EL)	LRHS
	'Lech Wałęsa' (EL)	ETho
	'Lemon Chiffon' (EL)	CRos EHyd LRHS
	'Lemon Dream'PBR (A)	ETho
	LIANNE ('Evipo064') (EL)	SNig
	LIBERATION ('Evifive'PBR) (EL)	EHyd LRHS NLar SCoo SLon SNig WSpi
	LIBERTY ('Zo08095'PBR) (EL)	ETho IPot
	ligusticifolia	NHaw
	'Lilac Wine' (I) **new**	NHaw
	'Lily the Pink' (Vt)	NHaw
	'Lincoln Star' (EL)	CArg CMac CRos EHyd ELon LRHS MAsh NOra SLim SNig SPer SWvt
	'Lisboa' (Vt)	NHaw
	'Little Bas' (Vt)	CDoC CRHN CWGN ELan ETho NHaw NLar SLon XLot
	'Little Butterfly' (Vt)	CRHN NHaw
	'Little Mermaid' (EL)	CWCL LCro LOPS XLot
	'Little Nell' (Vt)	CCCN CRHN EBee ELan EPfP ETho LRHS LSRN MAsh NOra SCoo SLon XLot
	'Lord Herschell'	CWCL CWGN ETho
	'Lord Nevill' (EL)	CRos EPfP LRHS NOra
	'Louise Rowe' (EL)	CRos CWCL EHyd ELan ETho LRHS LSRN NOra SNig
	'Love Jewelry' (EL)	SNig
	LUCKY CHARM ('Zo09067') (LL)	CWGN IPot
	LULA ('Evipo057'PBR) (Boulevard Series)	CWGN SNig

	'Lunar Lass' (Fo/f)	EBee ETho LRHS NRHS
	'Luther Burbank' (LL)	XLot
	'Luxuriant Blue' (Vt)	CRHN ELan NHaw
	'M. Koster' (Vt)	CDoC CRHN ETho LRHS NHaw NOra SLon SRms XLot
	macropetala (d)	CDoC CRos EHyd ELan EPfP ETho GKev LRHS MAsh MGos MMuc MRav NRHS SNig SPer
	- 'Blue Lagoon'	see *C. macropetala* 'Lagoon' Jackman 1959
	- 'Lagoon' Jackman 1956	see *C. macropetala* 'Maidwell Hall' Jackman
	- 'Lagoon' ambig.	LSRN
§	- 'Lagoon' Jackman 1959 (A/d) $\mathbb{Y}^{H6}$	CRos EHyd ETho LCro LOPS LRHS LSRN MAsh MSwo NHol NOra NRHS SCoo
§	- 'Maidwell Hall' Jackman (A/d)	CTri EPfP LSRN MAsh
	- 'Maidwell Hall' Wyatt (A)	CBcs NOra SCob
	- 'Wesselton' (A/d) $\mathbb{Y}^{H6}$	CDoC CRos CTri CWCL EHyd EPfP ETho LCro LOPS LRHS MAsh NLar NOra NRHS SPoG SPre SRms
	- 'White Moth'	see *C.* 'White Moth'
	'Madame Baron-Veillard' (LL)	CRos EHyd LRHS SCoo
	'Madame Édouard André' (LL)	CRos CWCL EHyd EPfP ETho LRHS MAsh NOra NRHS SCoo SNig XLot
	'Madame Grangé' (LL)	CRos EHyd LRHS NHaw SCoo
	'Madame Julia Correvon' (Vt) $\mathbb{Y}^{H6}$	Widely available
	'Madame le Coultre'	see *C.* 'Mevrouw Le Coultre'
	'Majojo' (Fo)	GEdr
	MANON ('Evipo054'^{PBR}) (Boulevard Series) (EL)	CRos EHyd LRHS NRHS
	marata	WThu
	'Margaret Hunt' (LL)	ETho LSRN NHaw SNig XLot
	'Mari' (LL)	NHaw
	'Maria' Kivistik (LL)	NHaw
	'Maria Cornelia'^{PBR} (Vt)	CWGN ETho LCro LOPS SLon
	'Maria Skłodowska-Curie'^{PBR} (EL)	ETho
	'Marie Boisselot' (EL) $\mathbb{Y}^{H6}$	CArg CBcs CMac CRos CTri CWCL EHyd ELan EPfP ETho LRHS LSRN MAsh MGos MPri MSwo NLar NOra SCob SNig SPoG SWvt
	'Marinka'	CWGN
	'Marjorie' (M/d)	CArg CBcs CDoC CRos CTri EHyd ELan EPfP ETho EWTr GKin LRHS LSRN MAsh MGos MRav NOra NRHS SCob SLim SNig SPer SPoG SRms WFar XLot
	'Markham's Pink' (A/d) $\mathbb{Y}^{H6}$	CArg CBcs CDoC CRos CTri CWCL EHyd ELan EPfP LCro LOPS LRHS LSRN MAsh MGos MRav MSwo NHol NLar NOra NRHS SCob SLim SNig SPer SPoG SRms SWvt WFar
	marmoraria	CRos EHyd EPot LRHS NRHS SPlb SRms WAbe
	'Marmori' (LL)	CWGN ETho NHaw
	MARTA ('Evipo071'^{PBR}) (Garland Series)	SNig
	'Mary Habberley' (Vt)	NHaw
	'Mary Rose'	see *C. viticella* 'Flore Pleno'
	MASA ('Evipo089') (Garland Series) **new**	CWGN
	maximowicziana	see *C. terniflora*
	'Mayleen' (M) $\mathbb{Y}^{H4}$	CRos CTri EPfP ETho LRHS MAsh MRav NOra NRHS SCoo SLim SNig SPer SPoG SRms SWvt WFar XLot

I	'Melodie' (Vt)	NHaw
§	'Mevrouw Le Coultre' (EL)	XLot
	'Mia' (EL/d)	CWGN
	MIENIE BELLE ('Zomibel'^{PBR}) (T)	CWGN NHaw
	'Mikelite' (Vt)	NHaw XLot
	'Miniseelik' (LL)	NHaw
	'Minister' (EL)	XLot
	'Minuet' (Vt) $\mathbb{Y}^{H6}$	CDoC CRHN CRos EBee EHyd EPfP ETho LCro LOPS LRHS MAsh MGos NOra SCoo SLon SPer SPoG SWvt
	MIRABELLE ('Evipo072'^{PBR}) (Boulevard Series)	EHyd LRHS
	MIRANDA ('Floclemi'^{PBR}) (I)	CWGN
	'Miss Bateman' (EL)	CDoC CMac CRos CTri CWCL EBee EHyd ELan EPfP ETho LCro LOPS LRHS LSRN MAsh MGos NOra NRHS SCob SLim SNig SPer SPoG WBor XLot
	'Miss Christine' (M)	CDoC ELan ETho LCro LOPS LSRN SPoG SWvt
	MISSISSIPPI RIVER ('Zomisri') (I)	IPot
	'Mister Hans Horn' (Vt)	NHaw
	MON AMOUR ('Zomoa'^{PBR}) (EL)	CWGN
	MON CHERRY ('Zomonch') (EL)	CWGN IPot
	'Moniuszko' (EL)	CWGN
	montana	CExl CPla MAsh SCob SEWo SGbt
	- WJC 13713 from the Himalaya	WCru
	- var. ***alba***	see *C. montana* var. *montana*
	- 'Alexander' (M)	CRos EHyd EPfP LRHS NRHS SPoG
	- 'Da Yun' (M)	CWGN EBee
	- var. ***grandiflora*** (M) $\mathbb{Y}^{H5}$	CArg CBrac CChe CMac CRos CWCL EHyd ELan EPfP ETho EWTr GKin LBuc LCro LOPS LRHS MMuc MPri NRHS SCob SEND SLim SNig SPer SPoG SRms SWeb SWvt XLot
I	- 'Lilacina' (M)	NOra
§	- var. ***montana***	CBar CBcs CBod CSBt LCro LOPS LRHS MAsh NOra SPer SPoG WFar XLot
	- var. ***rubens*** misapplied	see *C. montana* var. *montana*
	- var. ***rubens*** Buch.-Ham. ex DC.	CDoC CRos CSBt CTri EHyd ELan LRHS NHol NRHS SPlb
I	- - 'Odorata' (M)	EPfP ETho GKin LRHS MRav SCoo XLot
	- - 'Pink Perfection' (M)	CDoC CMac CRHN CRos EHyd ELan EPfP GKin LCro LOPS LRHS LSRN MAsh NRHS SCoo SLim SNig SPer SPoG SWvt WFar
I	- - 'Rubens Superba' (M)	CTri ECtt GKin SRms WFar
	- - 'Tetrarose' (M) $\mathbb{Y}^{H5}$	Widely available
	- - 'Veitch' (M)	XLot
	- var. ***sericea***	see *C. spooneri*
	- var. ***wilsonii***	CRos CWCL ECtt EHyd ELan EPfP ETho GKin GLog LRHS LSRN MRav MSwo SPer SPoG SRms SWvt XLot
	'Monte Cassino' (EL)	CWGN SNig
	'Moonbeam' (Fo)	EPot GEdr ITim WIce
§	'Moonlight' (EL)	LRHS MAsh XLot
	MORNING CLOUD	see *C.* 'Yukikomachi'
	'Morning Heaven' (Vt)	CRHN NHaw
	MORNING STAR ('Zoklako'^{PBR}) (EL)	CWGN LRHS
	MORNING YELLOW ('Cadmy'^{PBR}) (M)	CCCN LRHS

'Mrs Cholmondeley' (EL) ♀H6	CRos CWCL EHyd ELan EPfP ETho LRHS LSRN MAsh MGos MPri MSwo NOra SCob SLim SNig SPer SPoG XLot
'Mrs George Jackman' (EL) ♀H6	CRos CWCL EBee EHyd ETho LRHS NLar NOra SCoo SNig WSpi XLot
'Mrs James Mason' (EL)	EBee
'Mrs N.Thompson' (EL)	CArg CDoC CMac CRos CTri CWCL EBee EHyd ELan ELon ETho LCro LOPS LRHS LSRN MAsh MGos NHol NOra NPer SLim SNig SPer XLot
'Mrs P.B.Truax' (EL)	EHyd EPfP ETho LRHS
'Mrs Robert Brydon' (H)	CWCL ECtt NLar SRms
'Mrs Spencer Castle' (EL)	NOra
§ 'Mrs T. Lundell' (Vt)	CRHN EPfP LRHS NHaw NLar
'Multi Blue' (EL)	CArg CBcs CRos CWCL EHyd ELan ELon EPfP LRHS LSRN MAsh MGos NOra SLim SNig SPer SPoG SRkn SRms WSpi XLot
'My Angel'PBR (Ta)	ELan IPot LCro LOPS NHaw NLar WSpi
'Myōjō' (EL)	LRHS
MYOSOTIS ('Zo08159') (EL) **new**	IPot
§ ***napaulensis***	CWCL ELan EPfP ETho LCro LOPS MNrw NHaw WCru
I 'Natacha' (EL)	EBee NHaw SCoo
'Natascha' (EL)	CWCL EHyd ETho LRHS LSRN SNig SWvt
'Negritianka' (LL)	LRHS LSRN NHaw NOra XLot
'Negus' (LL)	NHaw
'Nelly Moser' (EL) ♀H6	Widely available
NEVA ('Evipo050'PBR) (Boulevard Series) (EL)	CRos EHyd LRHS NRHS SNig
'New Dawn' (M)	XLot
'New Love'PBR (H)	CWGN ETho LCro LOPS LSRN NLar SPoG
'Night Veil' (Vt)	CDoC NHaw SLon
'Nikolai Rubtsov' (LL)	XLot
NINON ('Evipo052'PBR) (Boulevard Series)	CBod CWGN EPfP LSou SNig
'Niobe' (EL) ♀H6	Widely available
'Nirwana' (EL) **new**	XLot
NORTH STAR (LL)	see *C.* 'Põhjanael'
'North Star' (EL)	EPfP NOra
NUBIA ('Evipo079'PBR) (Boulevard Series) (LL)	CBod CWGN EPfP ETho LSou
nutans var. ***thyrsoidea***	see *C. rehderiana*, *C. veitchiana*
'Oberek' (Vt)	CRHN NHaw
'Ocean Pearl' (A)	LSRN NLar XLot
ochotensis	GKev
ochroleuca	NHaw
OCTOPUS ('Zooct'PBR) (A)	CWGN
'Odoriba' (V)	CRHN CWGN NHaw
'Olimpiada-80' (EL)	NHaw
'Omoshiro' (EL)	CWCL CWGN ETho IPot LRHS NHaw XLot
§ OOH LA LA ('Evipo041'PBR) (Boulevard Series) (EL)	CRos CWCL ECul EHyd EPfP ETho LRHS MAsh NRHS SCoo SNig SPer SPoG WSpi
orientalis misapplied	see *C. tibetana* subsp. *vernayi*
orientalis ambig.	SRms
orientalis L.	EBee EPfP SCoo SWvt
- PAB 13.731	LEdu
- from Kyrgyzstan	WPGP
- 'Orange Peel'	see *C. tibetana* subsp. *vernayi* var. *vernayi* 'Orange Peel'
- 'Sherriffii'	see *C.* 'Sherriffii'
orientalis × ***tangutica***	SWvt

'Oshikiri' (V)	NHaw
otophora	NHaw
'Ovation'PBR (Fo)	IBal LCro LOPS
'Pagoda' (Vt)	CRHN EPfP IPot LRHS SCoo SLon SRms
PALETTE ('Zo08111') (EL)	IPot
'Pamela' (F)	NHaw
'Pamela Jackman' (A)	see *C. alpina* 'Pamela Jackman'
'Pamiat Serdtsa' (I)	ELon ETho NHaw
'Pamina' (EL)	ETho XLot
'Pangbourne Pink' (I) ♀H6	CRos CWCL EHyd EPfP ETho LRHS NHaw NRHS SCoo
paniculata Thunb.	see *C. terniflora*
§ ***paniculata*** J.G.Gmel.	MNrw
- var. ***lobata***	WSpi
'Paola' (EL/d)	IPot
'Paradise Queen' (EL)	NLar
PARADISO ('Zo11154') (EL)	IPot LCro LOPS
PARISIENNE ('Evipo019'PBR) (Boulevard Series) (EL)	CRos CWCL CWGN ECul EHyd ELon EPfP ETho LRHS MAsh NOra NRHS SCoo SLon SNig SPoG
parviflora DC.	see *C. campaniflora*
parviloba var. ***bartlettii*** B&SWJ 6788	WCru
'Pat Coleman' (EL)	CWCL ETho
patens 'Korean Moon' (EL)	WCru
§ - 'Manshuu Ki' (EL)	CRos CWCL EHyd ETho LRHS XLot
- 'Yukiokoshi' (EL)	EBee ETho XLot
PATRICIA ANN FRETWELL ('Pafar') (EL)	ETho
§ 'Paul Farges' (Vb) ♀H6	CArg CDoC CWGN EPfP EShb ETho GLog IPot MNrw NHaw NLar XLot
'Pauline' (A/d) ♀H6	CBcs EHyd LRHS LSRN SCoo
'Peggy West' (LL)	NHaw
'Pendragon' (Vt)	CRHN NHaw
PEPPERMINT ('Evipo005'PBR) (d)	EHyd ELan EPfP LRHS SCoo SLon
'Perida' (LL)	CWGN
'Perle d'Azur' (LL) ♀H6	CBcs CDoC CRHN CRos CTri CWCL EBee EHyd ELan EPfP ETho LCro LOPS LRHS LSRN MAsh MGos MSwo NOra SCob SLim SPer SPoG SRms WFar WSpi
PERNILLE ('Zo09113'PBR) (Vt) **new**	CWGN ETho LCro LOPS
'Perrin's Pride' (Vt)	CRos EBee EHyd LRHS MGos NHaw NLar SCoo
PETIT FAUCON ('Evisix'PBR) (I) ♀H6	CRos CWCL EHyd EPfP ETho LRHS LSRN MGos MMrt NLar SCoo SNig SPer SRms SWvt
petriei	WThu
'Peveril Pristine' (Vt)	CWGN NHaw
PICARDY ('Evipo024'PBR) (EL)	CRos EHyd EPfP ETho LRHS MAsh NRHS SCoo SNig SPoG WSpi
PICOTEE ('Zo09124') (EL)	CWGN ETho IPot WSpi
I 'Picton's Variety' (M)	CTri
'Piilu' (EL)	CArg CDoC CRos CWCL CWGN EBee EHyd ELan ETho LRHS LSRN MAsh MBNS NLar NOra SCoo SNig SRkn XLot
§ 'Pink Celebration' (EL)	XLot
PINK CHAMPAGNE	see *C.* 'Kakio'
'Pink Fantasy' (LL)	CRHN CTri EHyd ETho LRHS MAsh NLar NOra SCoo SRkn XLot
'Pink Flamingo' (A) ♀H6	CRos CWCL EHyd ELan EPfP LRHS MGos NRHS SCoo SNig SPoG XLot
'Pink Ice' (I)	CWCL

	'Pirko' (Vt)	NHaw
§	***pitcheri***	CWGN NHaw WSHC
	'Pixie' (Fo/m)	CDoC EBee ELan ELon EPfP ETho ITim LCro LOPS LRHS MGos NLar NOra SCoo SPoG
§	'Plum Beauty' (A)	XLot
	pogonandra	NHaw
§	'Põhjanael' (LL)	NLar
	POLAR BEAR	see *C.* ARCTIC QUEEN
	'Poldice' (Vt) ♀H6	CRHN
	'Polish Spirit' (LL) ♀H6	Widely available
	'Polonez' (Vt)	NHaw
	potaninii	ETho GKev
	- 'Summer Snow'	see *C.* 'Paul Farges'
	'Praecox' (H) ♀H6	CDoC CRHN CRos CWCL EBee EHyd ELan EPfP ETho LRHS MCot NQui NSti SAdn WCot WGwG
	'Prairie River' (A)	WSpi
	PRETTY IN BLUE ('Zopre'^{PBR}) (F)	EBee SWvt
	'Primrose Star'	see *C.* 'Star'
	'Prince Charles' (LL) ♀H6	CDoC CRHN CTri CWCL ELan EPfP EShb ETho LCro LOPS LRHS LSRN MAsh NHaw NLar NOra SCoo SLim SPer SWvt XLot
	'Prince George' (LL)	CDoC CWCL EPfP ETho LCro LOPS LSRN NLar
	'Prince Philip' (EL)	ETho LCro LOPS
	PRINCE WILLIAM ('Zo08171') (EL) **new**	CWGN IPot LCro LOPS
I	'Princess' **new**	XLot
	'Princess Charlotte' (EL)	ETho LCro LOPS
§	'Princess Diana' (T) ♀H5	CBcs CRHN CTri CWGN EBee EHyd ELan EPfP ETho IPot LBuc LCro LOPS LRHS LSRN MAsh MBlu MSwo NHol SCoo SLim SNig SPer SPoG SRms SWvt XLot
	PRINCESS KATE ('Zoprika'^{PBR}) (T)	CRos CWGN EBee EHyd EPfP ETho EWTr IPot LCro LOPS LRHS MAsh MBlu NRHS SPer SPoG WBor WCot WSpi
§	'Princess of Wales' (1875) (EL)	CDoC CWCL LSRN NLar SLon SWvt XLot
	'Propertius' (A)	CArg CRos CWCL CWGN EHyd EPfP ETho LRHS MGos SPoG WSpi XLot
	'Prosperity' (M)	CRHN ETho
	'Proteus' (EL)	CRos EHyd ELan EPfP ETho LRHS MAsh MGos NOra SCoo SNig XLot
	'Pruinina'	see *C.* 'Plum Beauty'
	psilandra CWJ 12377	WCru
	'Purple Haze' (Vt)	CRHN NHaw
	'Purple Princess' (H)	CDoC SPoG
	'Purple Rain' (A)	CDoC NOra
	'Purple Spider' (A/d)	EPfP ETho LRHS MAsh MBlu NLar SCoo
	'Purpurea Plena Elegans' (Vt/d) ♀H6	CBcs CDoC CMac CRHN CRos CTri CWCL EBee EHyd ELan EPfP ETho IPot LCro LOPS LRHS LSRN MAsh MSwo NHol NOra NRHS SCob SLim SPer SPoG SWvt WBor XLot
	quadribracteolata	NHaw
	QUEEN MOTHER ('Zoqum') (Vt)	CWGN EPfP ETho LRHS
	'Radiance'	CWGN NHaw
	'Ragamuffin' (EL/d)	XLot
	'Rahvarinne' (LL)	SNig XLot
	'Ramona' (LL)	CRos EHyd LRHS LSRN NHaw
	ranunculoides	NHaw
	'Rapture' (T)	NHaw
	'Raspberry Ripple' (V) **new**	NHaw
	'Rasputin' (LL)	CWGN ETho XLot
	REBECCA ('Evipo016'^{PBR}) (EL)	CRos CWCL CWGN EHyd ELan EPfP ETho LCro LOPS LRHS LSRN MAsh NOra NRHS SCoo SLon SNig SPer SPoG WSpi
	recta	CWCL ECtt MNrw NHaw NLar
	- PAB 9005	LEdu
	- 'Lime Close' seedlings	IPot
	- 'Purpurea' (F)	CDor CRos EHyd ELan EMor EPfP ETho GKev GWyn IPot LRHS MAvo MBriF MMrt MNrw NChi NOra SEND SPer SPtp XLum
	- 'Velvet Night' (F)	CBod ECtt IPot LRHS MBNS MHol NLar NSti WCot
	'Red Ballon' (Ta)	IPot
	'Red Cooler'	see *C.* 'Crimson King'
	'Red Pearl' (EL)	CWCL EHyd LRHS LSRN NOra
I	'Red Star' (d)	XLot
	REFLECTIONS ('Evipo035') (LL)	CRos EHyd EPfP LRHS MAsh SLon
§	***rehderiana*** ♀H5	CCBP CDoC CRHN CWCL EBee ELan EPfP ETho IMou IPot MBlu NOra SWvt WCot WFar WPGP WSHC
	REIKO ('Evipo088') (Garland Series) **new**	CWGN
	'Reiman' (LL)	NHaw
	'Remembrance' (LL) ♀H6	CWCL EPfP ETho LSRN NHaw
	'Reverie' (T)	NHaw
	'Rhapsody' ambig.	CDoC EPfP IPot LBuc MAsh MGos NOra SCoo SNig
	'Rhapsody' B. Fretwell (EL)	CRos EHyd ETho LRHS LSRN NHaw
	'Ribble Red' (V)	NHaw
	'Richard Pennell' (EL) ♀H6	CDoC CRos EHyd LRHS NOra
	'Richard's Picotee' (Vt)	NHaw
	'Rising Star'	NHaw SNig
	'Ristimägi' (LL)	NHaw
	'Rituaal' (LL)	NHaw
	'Robud'^{PBR} (M/d)	NPer
	'Roelie' (Vt)	NHaw
	'Roko' (LL)	CWGN
	'Roko-Kolla' (LL) ♀H6	ETho NHaw
	'Romantika' (LL)	CRos EHyd ELan ELon ETho LCro LRHS LSRN MAsh NHaw NOra NRHS SCoo SNig XEll XLot
	'Rooguchi' (I)	CDoC CWCL CWGN ETho LRHS NHaw XLot
	'Rooran' (EL)	CWCL
	'Rosa Königskind' (EL)	ETho NLar
	ROSALYN ('Zo09087'^{PBR}) (Vt)	CWGN ETho IPot
I	'Rosea' (A/d)	EHyd
I	'Rosea' (I)	CWCL EPfP ETho GKev LRHS LSRN WHoo
I	'Rosea' Westphal. (Vt)	NHaw
	ROSEMOOR ('Evipo002'^{PBR}) (EL)	CRos CWCL CWGN EHyd EPfP LRHS MAsh NRHS SCoo SLon SNig SWvt
	'Rosy O'Grady' (A) ♀H6	MAsh NLar SRms
	'Rosy Pagoda' (A)	EHyd ELan ETho LRHS NLar
	'Rouge Cardinal' (LL)	CArg CBcs CDoC CRos EBee EHyd ELan ELon EPfP ETho LRHS LSRN MAsh MGos NOra NRHS SCob SLim SNig SPer SPoG SRms XLot
	'Royal Velours' (Vt)	CRHN CRos CTri CWCL ELan EPfP ETho IPot LCro LOPS LRHS LSRN MAsh MGos NHol NLar NOra

		NRHS SCob SCoo SLim SNig SPer SPoG WSpi XLot
	ROYAL VELVET ('Evifour'PBR) (EL)	CRos EHyd LRHS LSRN SCoo
	'Royalty' (EL)	CDoC CRos CWCL EHyd ELan EPfP ETho LRHS LSRN MAsh NOra SCoo WSpi
	'Rubens Superba'	see *C. montana* var. *rubens* 'Rubens Superba'
	'Rubra' (Vt)	IPot XLot
	'Ruby' (A)	CRos CWCL ELan EPfP ETho LRHS LSRN MAsh SCoo SPer SRms
	'Ruby Celebration' (A) **new**	CDoC
	'Ruby Glow' (EL)	CRos EHyd EPfP LRHS LSRN SCoo
	'Ruby Tuesday' (V)	NHaw
	'Ruby Wedding' Fretwell (T)	CWGN
	'Ruby Wedding NLP2' (EL)	CWCL EPfP ETho LBuc LCro LOPS LSRN SWvt
	'Rüütel' (EL)	CRos CWCL ELon ETho LRHS MAsh NHaw NOra SCoo SNig XLot
	'Saalomon' (LL)	NHaw
	SABINE ('Bfccsab'PBR) (LL) **new**	CWGN
	SACHA ('Evipo060') (EL)	CRos EHyd EPfP ETho LRHS NRHS SNig SPoG
	'Sakali' **new**	WSpi
§	'Sakurahime' (EL)	IPot XLot
	SALLY ('Evipo077') (EL)	CRos EHyd ELan EPfP ETho LRHS MAsh NRHS SNig SPoG
	'Samantha Denny' (EL)	XLot
	SAMARITAN JO ('Evipo075')	CRos CWGN EHyd EPfP ETho LRHS MAsh NRHS SNig SPoG
	'Sanssouci' (M)	EBee
	SARAH ELIZABETH ('Evipo098') **new**	CRos LRHS
	SAVANNAH ('Evipo015'PBR) (Vt)	MAsh
	'Scartho Gem' (EL)	EHyd LRHS SCoo SNig XLot
	SEA BREEZE ('Zo09063') (Vt)	CWGN ETho IPot LCro LOPS
§	'Semu' (LL)	CWGN ETho NHaw NOra XLot
	'Serafina' (EL) **new**	XLot
	serratifolia	CBcs CRHN ECtt GKev GLog SBrt SPlb
	- B&SWJ 8458 from Korea	WCru
I	'Sherriffii' (Ta)	NOra SWvt
	'Shikoo' (EL)	CWCL ETho LSRN
	SHIMMER ('Evipo028'PBR) (LL)	CRos EHyd EPfP LRHS MAsh NRHS SLon
	'Shirayukihime' (EL)	NLar
§	'Shiva' (A)	NOra
§	***sibirica***	CRos EHyd EPfP LRHS NRHS
	- var. ***tianschanica***	NHaw
	'Signe' (Vt)	see *C.* 'Kasmu'
	'Siirus' (EL)	NHaw
	'Silver Moon' (EL)	CWCL EPfP ETho LRHS MAsh NLar NOra SCoo WSpi
	'Simplicity' (A)	NOra
	simsii Small	see *C. pitcheri*
	simsii Sweet	see *C. crispa*
§	'Sinii Dozhd' (I)	CWCL
§	'Sir Edward Elgar' (A)	CRos LRHS NOra NOrn NRHS
	'Sir Eric Savill' (M)	ETho
	'Sir Garnet Wolseley' (EL)	NOra
	'Sir Trevor Lawrence' (T)	EHyd LRHS NHaw
	'Sizaia Ptitsa' (I)	XLot
	'Skyfall' (LL)	ETho
	smilacifolia NJM 10.094	WPGP
	'Snow Queen' (EL)	CDoC CRos EHyd ELon EPfP ETho LRHS SNig SRms XLot
	'Snowbird' (A/d)	CRos EHyd LRHS NOra SPoG
	'Snowdrift'	see *C. armandii* 'Snowdrift'
	SO MANY RED FLOWERS ('Zo06178') (EL) **new**	IPot
	socialis	NHaw
	'Södertälje' (Vt)	CRHN ETho NHaw SCoo XLot
	'Sokojiro' (EL)	EHyd ETho LRHS
	'Solidarność' (EL)	ETho
	'Solina' (Vt)	NHaw
	songarica	NHaw SBrt
	'Sonnette' (V)	CRHN CWGN NHaw
	'Sophie' (V)	NHaw
§	'Souvenir du Capitaine Thuilleaux' (EL)	ELon NOra
	'Special Occasion' (EL)	CRos CWGN EHyd EPfP ETho LRHS LSRN NLar NOra SCoo SNig XLot
§	***spooneri***	EPfP LRHS NOra SCoo SWvt WSpi
	'Sputnik' (I)	NHaw
	stans	CDoC CExl CPou EHyd ETho LRHS NLar
	- B&SWJ 5073	WCru
	- B&SWJ 6345	WCru
§	'Star'PBR (M/d)	CDoC EHyd EPfP ETho LRHS MSwo NLar SPer
	'Star of India' (LL)	CRos EHyd ELan EPfP ETho LRHS MGos NOra SCoo SNig XLot
	STAR OF PAKISTAN ('Zostapa') (LL)	CWGN
	STAR RIVER ('Zostarri'PBR) (I)	ELan IPot
I	'Starfish' (EL)	NHaw
	'Starlight' (M)	CWCL ELon NOra SNig
	'Stasik' (LL)	NHaw XLot
	'Stefan Franczak' (EL)	ETho
	STILL WATERS ('Zostiwa'PBR) (EL)	ETho
	'Strawberry Kiss' (V)	NHaw
	'Sue Reade' (V)	NHaw
	SUGAR CANDY ('Evione'PBR) (EL)	LRHS MAsh SCoo SNig
	SUMMER SNOW	see *C.* 'Paul Farges'
	'Sundance' (Ta)	NHaw
	SUNNY SKY ('Zosusk'PBR) (Vt)	ELan NHaw
	'Sunrise' (M/d)	CDoC EBee EPfP ETho MSwo NLar
	'Sunset' (EL) ♀H6	CArg CRos CWCL EHyd ELon LRHS LSRN MGos NLar SCoo SNig
	SUPER NOVA ('Zo09088') (Vt)	ELan ETho IPot
	'Swedish Bells' (I)	CWGN ETho
	'Sweet Scentsation' (F)	CDoC EPfP ETho NHaw NLar WSpi
	'Sweet Summer Love'PBR (F)	CDoC CWGN ETho IPot LCro LOPS NHaw XLot
	SWEETHEART ('Witswe'PBR) (I)	ELan EPfP ETho XLot
	'Sylvia Denny' (EL)	CArg EPfP ETho MAsh NOra SNig WSpi
	'Sylviorna' (V) **new**	NHaw
	szuyuanensis CWJ 12455	WCru
	'Tae'	see *C.* 'Toltae'
	'Tage Lundell'	see *C.* 'Mrs T. Lundell'
	'Taiga'PBR (d)	CBcs CWGN ELan ETho LCro LOPS SPad XLot
	'Tamakazura' (V)	CWGN NHaw
	'Tango' (Vt)	CRHN NHaw
§	***tangutica***	CBcs CDoC CExl CMac CRos CTri ECrN EHyd ELan EPfP GQue LCro LOPS LRHS LSRN MAsh

	MGos MSwo NPol NRHS SCob SPer SPlb SPoG SRms SWvt WBor WFar XLot XLum
'Tapestry' (I)	NHaw
'Tartu' (EL)	NHaw
tashiroi 'Yellow Peril'	WCru
TEKLA ('Evipo069'^{PBR}) (LL)	CRos CWCL EHyd LRHS NRHS SNig SPoG WSpi
'Teksa' (LL)	NHaw
TEMPTATION ('Zotemp'^{PBR}) (EL)	ETho
§ ***terniflora***	EPfP ETho NHaw SPtp
- B&SWJ 5751	WCru
- var. ***mandshurica***	EBee ETho GBin NHaw NLar WSpi XEll XLot
- - dwarf **new**	CWGN
texensis	NHaw WSHC
- 'The Princess of Wales'	see *C.* 'Princess Diana'
- 'Wellmax'^{PBR}	IPot NHaw
'The Bride' (EL)	CWCL CWGN ETho LRHS LSRN
THE COUNTESS OF WESSEX ('Evipo073') (EL)	CRos EHyd EPfP ETho LRHS MAsh NRHS SNig SPoG
'The First Lady' (EL)	CWCL ETho NOra XLot
'The President' (EL) 🏆H6	CArg CDoC CMac CRos CTri CWCL EHyd ELan EPfP ETho LCro LOPS LRHS LSRN MGos MPri MSwo NLar NOra NRHS SCob SLim SNig SPer SPoG SRms WFar WSpi XLot
'The Princess of Wales' (EL)	see *C.* 'Princess of Wales' (1875) (EL)
'The Princess of Wales' (T)	see *C.* 'Princess Diana' (T)
'The Vagabond' (EL)	CWCL CWGN ELan EPfP ETho LRHS LSRN MAsh NHaw NLar NOra SCoo WSpi XLot
§ THUMBELINA ('Evipo030'^{PBR}) (EL)	CRos CWCL EHyd EPfP ETho LRHS NRHS SNig SPoG
thunbergii misapplied	see *C. terniflora*
'Thyrislund' (EL)	SNig
'Tibetan Mix' (Ta)	NHaw
tibetana	NHaw
- CC 7447	GKev
- 'Black Tibet' (Ta)	CWGN NHaw
§ - subsp. ***vernayi***	SCob
- - 'Glasnevin Dusk' (Ta)	WSHC
- - 'Lorcan O'Brien' (Ta) **new**	IDee
§ - - var. ***vernayi*** 'Orange Peel' (Ta)	ETho LRHS XLot
'Tie Dye' (LL)	CWGN EBee ELan EPfP ETho SPoG SRms XLot
'Tim's Passion' (Vt)	CRHN
'Tinkerbell'	see *C.* 'Shiva'
'Titipu' (V)	NHaw
'Toki' (EL)	CWGN ETho XLot
§ 'Toltae'^{PBR} (EL)	CDoC CRos CWGN EHyd ETho LRHS NRHS
tongluensis	WPGP
tosaensis f. ***cremea***	NHaw
TRANQUILITE ('Evipo111') **new**	CRos LRHS
'Tranquility'	CWGN
'Triinu' (Vt)	NHaw
§ × ***triternata*** 'Rubromarginata'	CDoC CMac CRHN CRos CWCL CWGN EHyd ELan EPfP ETho LCro LOPS LRHS LSRN MAsh MGos MMrt MRav NLar NOra NRHS SCob SLim SLon SNig SPer SPoG SRms XLot
TSUKIKO ('Evipo110') (Garland Series) **new**	CWGN
'Tsunami Child' (M)	IMou
'Tsuzuki' (EL)	XLot
§ ***tubulosa*** ALAN BLOOM ('Alblo'^{PBR}) (H)	EHyd LRHS
- 'Wyevale' (H)	CMac CRos EHyd ELan EPfP ETho LRHS MCot MRav NLar NRHS SCoo SPer WAul
'Tuchka' (EL)	CWGN
'Tudor' (EL) **new**	XLot
'Twilight' (EL)	CRos EHyd EPfP LRHS MAsh NOra
TWINKLE ('Zotwi') (I)	CWGN ETho
uncinata	CBcs
'Uno Kivistik'^{PBR} (LL)	NHaw
urophylla	SPhx
§ - 'Winter Beauty'	CDoC CWCL EBee ELan EPfP ETho LCro LOPS LSRN NOra SCoo SPoG WPGP WSHC XLot
urticifolia B&SWJ 8651	WCru
- B&SWJ 8852	WCru
'Utopia' (EL)	CWGN
'Valge Daam' (LL)	CWGN NHaw XLot
'Valour' (Vt) **new**	ETho
'Van Gogh' (M)	CWGN ETho XLot
'Vanessa' (LL)	CRHN NHaw
'Vanso'	see *C.* 'Blue Light'
'Varenne' (EL) **new**	XLot
§ ***veitchiana***	EWld NHaw
'Venosa Violacea' (Vt) 🏆H6	CDoC CRHN CRos EHyd ELan EPfP ETho LRHS LSRN MAsh NHaw NHol NOra SCob SCoo SNig SPer SPoG SRms
'Vera' (M)	EPfP LRHS LSRN SCoo
vernayi	see *C. tibetana* subsp. *vernayi*
'Veronica's Choice' (EL)	CWCL ELan ETho SNig XLot
VERSAILLES ('Evipo025'^{PBR}) (EL)	EHyd EPfP LRHS SNig
§ VESUVIUS ('Evipo032'^{PBR}) (Vt)	EHyd LRHS SCoo SLon
VICTOR HUGO ('Evipo007'^{PBR}) (LL)	CRos EHyd LRHS NLar SCoo SNig
'Victoria' (LL)	CRos EHyd ETho LRHS LSRN NHaw
VIENNETTA ('Evipo006'^{PBR}) (d)	CRos CWGN EHyd EPfP LRHS MGos SCoo SLon SNig SRms
'Ville de Lyon' (LL)	CBcs CDoC CRHN CWCL EHyd ELan EPfP ETho LRHS LSRN MAsh MGos NOra NRHS SCob SLim SNig SPer SPoG XLot
vinacea	NHaw
'Vince Denny' (Ta)	EBee NHaw
VINO ('Poulvo'^{PBR}) (EL)	EHyd LRHS SCoo
'Viola' (LL)	CWGN ELon LSRN NHaw NOra XLot
'Violet Elizabeth' (EL)	XLot
viorna	CWGN EWld GKev NHaw WSHC
virginiana misapplied	see *C. vitalba*
§ ***vitalba***	CWld ECrN GKev NHaw SCob WHer WSFF WSpi
viticella	CRHN NHaw SCob SMHy WSHC XLot
- subsp. ***campaniflora***	see *C. campaniflora*
§ - 'Flore Pleno' (Vt/d)	CRHN CRos EHyd ELan EPfP ETho IPot LCro LOPS LRHS LSRN NHaw NRHS SLon SNig SPoG
- 'Hågelby Blue' (Vt)	NHaw
- 'Hanna' (Vt)	CRHN IPot LSRN NHaw
- 'Mary Rose'	see *C. viticella* 'Flore Pleno'
'Viva Polonia'^{PBR} (EL)	XLot
'Vivienne'	see *C.* 'Beth Currie'

VOLCANO ('Mazowsze') (LL) new	SNig
'Voluceau' (Vt)	CRos CWCL EHyd ELan EPfP LRHS LSRN SNig SRms XLot
VOLUNTEER ('Evipo080') (EL)	CRos EHyd ETho LRHS NRHS
'Vostok' (LL)	NHaw XLot
'Vyvyan Pennell' (EL)	CArg CBcs CDoC CMac CRos CTri CWCL EHyd ELan EPfP ETho LRHS LSRN MAsh MSwo NLar NOra SCob SLim SNig SPer SPoG SWvt WFar WSpi XLot
'W.E. Gladstone' (EL)	CRos EHyd LRHS
WADA'S PRIMROSE	see *C. patens* 'Manshuu Ki'
'Walenburg' (Vt) ♀H6	CRHN CWGN ETho NHaw SLon XLot
'Walter Pennell' (EL)	EHyd LRHS SCoo
'Warsaw' (Ta)	NLar
'Warszawska Nike' (EL) ♀H6	CRHN CRos CWCL EHyd ELan EPfP ETho LCro LOPS LRHS MAsh MGos NOra SCob SCoo SNig SPoG XLot
'Warwickshire Rose' (M)	CDoC CMac CRHN CRos CTri CWGN EBee EHyd ELan EPfP ETho LRHS LSRN MAsh NOra SLim SNig SPoG XLot
'Wedding Day' (EL)	EPfP ETho LCro LOPS LSRN NLar
'Wee Willie Winkie' (M)	SRms
'Westerplatte' (EL)	CRos CWCL CWGN EHyd EPfP ETho LRHS MGos NHaw NOra SNig SPoG WSpi XLot
§ 'White Columbine' (A) ♀H6	ELan LRHS SPer
'White Heart' (Vt)	CRHN NHaw
'White Magic'PBR (Vt)	XLot
§ 'White Moth' (A/d)	LSRN MAsh NHol NOra
'White Prince Charles' (LL)	CWGN NHaw XLot
'White Satin' (A)	CRos EHyd EPfP LRHS SRms
'White Swan' (A/d)	ETho MAsh NHol NLar NOra SCoo
'White Wings' (A/d)	LSRN
'Whoopi' (EL) new	XLot
'Will Goodwin' (EL) ♀H6	CRos CWCL EHyd ELan EPfP LRHS SNig SRms
'William Kennett' (EL)	CWCL ELan ETho LRHS
'Willy' (A)	CArg CRos EHyd ELan EPfP ETho LRHS MAsh MGos NLar NOra NRHS SRms
WISLEY ('Evipo001'PBR) (Vt) ♀H6	EPfP MGos NLar SLon
WONDERFUL ('Zo09073') (Vt)	CWGN LCro LOPS
'Xerxes' misapplied	see *C.* 'Elsa Späth'
'Xerxes' C. Noble (EL) new	XLot
XIU ('Evipo065') (Boulevard Series) (Fo)	LRHS
'Yatsuhashi' ambig.	NOra
'Yellow Queen' Holland	see *C. patens* 'Manshuu Ki'
'Yellow Queen' Lundell/ Treasures	see *C.* 'Moonlight'
§ 'Yukikomachi' (EL)	ETho NHaw SNig WSpi XLot
yunnanensis	WPGP
ZARA ('Evipo062'PBR) (EL)	ETho MAsh SLon SNig
'Zephyr' (Vt)	NHaw

Clematopsis see *Clematis*

Clementsia see *Rhodiola*

Cleome (*Cleomaceae*)

hassleriana 'Helen Campbell' ♀H2	CSpe LCro LOPS
- 'Violet Queen'	LCro LOPS
SEÑORITA CAROLINA ('Inclesrcar')	CSpe
SEÑORITA ROSALITA ('Inncleosr'PBR)	CSpe MHol MPri

Clerodendrum (*Lamiaceae*)

CW&T 6506	CMCN
bungei	Widely available
- 'Diamond'	SGol
- 'Pink Diamond' (v)	CCCN CWGN ELan EPfP EWes LRHS LSRN MGos NLar SGbt SPer SPoG SWvt
§ ***chinense*** var. ***chinense*** (d) ♀H1b	CCCN
- 'Pleniflorum'	see *C. chinense* var. *chinense*
colebrookianum B&SWJ 6651	WCru
- PAB 7794	LEdu
fragrans var. ***pleniflorum***	see *C. chinense* var. *chinense*
myricoides 'Ugandense'	see *Rotheca myricoides* 'Ugandense'
paniculatum 'Starshine' new	CCCN
philippinum	see *C. chinense* var. *chinense*
aff. ***subscaposum*** WWJ 11735	WCru
thomsoniae ♀H1b	EShb WSFF
trichotomum	CAby CBcs CEnd CExl CMCN CRos CSam CSpe CTri EPfP EWTr IArd LRHS MAsh NLar SCob SLim SLon SPer WBor WMat
- var. ***fargesii*** ♀H5	Widely available
- - 'Carnival' (v) ♀H5	CBod CCCN CDoC CExl CMac CRos EBee EHyd ELan EPfP EWes LRHS MAsh NLar SEle SMad SPer SPoG SWvt WAvo WCot
- 'Purple Blaze'	CJun EBee
- 'Purple Haze'	NLar
- 'Shiro'	WCru
wallichii	EShb
- 'Prospero' new	CDoC

Clethra ✿ (*Clethraceae*)

CW&T 6497	CMCN
alnifolia	CBcs CExl SRms WFar
- 'Anne Bidwell'	MBlu NLar
- 'Creel's Calico' (v)	NLar
- 'Fern Valley Pink'	CCCN CDoC CMac EBee ELon EPfP LRHS NLar SRms WFar
- 'Hokie Pink'	ELon NLar
- 'Hummingbird' ♀H5	CCCN CEnd CExl CMac CRos ELan ELon EPfP LRHS MAsh MBlu MMrt NLar SChF SEle SPad SPoG SWvt WFar
- 'Paniculata'	CBod CRos ELon LRHS MGil MMuc WBor
- 'Pink Spice'	CRos LRHS
- 'Pink Spires'	CBcs CExl ECrN GKin LEdu MMuc MRav NLar SCoo SEle SPer WBor WLov
- 'Rosea'	CTri GKin
- 'Ruby Spice' ♀H5	CBcs CBod CCCN CDoC CEnd CExl CJun CMac CRos EHyd ELan ELon EWTr GBin GGGa GKin IDee LRHS LSRN MAsh MBlu NLar NQui SEle SPad SPer SPoG SWvt
- 'September Beauty'	CJun NLar

- 'Sixteen Candles'	GGGa LRHS MMrt MPkF NLar
- VANILLA SPICE ('Caleb')	CBcs
arborea	CBcs ECre MGil
barbinervis ♀H5	CBcs CExl CRos CTho EPfP GGGa IDee LRHS MBlu MGil NLar WPGP
- B&SWJ 11562	WCru
- GREAT STAR ('Minbarb')	EPfP IDee LRHS WPGP
- 'White Star'	CJun CMac EBee EPfP LRHS
delavayi Franch.	CBcs CCCN CDoC CMCN EBee EPfP GGGa IDee MGil MMrt WPGP
- SBEC 1513	CExl
fabri B&SWJ 11702	WCru
- FMWJ 13037	WCru
fargesii	CExl EPfP IDee IMou NLar SPtp WPGP
kaipoensis NJM 11.020	WPGP
- NJM 11.058	WPGP
- PAB 8571	LEdu
monostachya	CExl EBee GGGa MGil WPGP
pachyphylla new	WPGP
petelotii FMWJ 13401	WCru
pringlei	CBcs EBee IDee IMou NLar WPGP
tomentosa 'Cottondale'	CJun EWTr IDee NLar

Cleyera (*Pentaphylacaceae*)

fortunei	see *C. japonica* 'Fortunei'
- 'Variegata'	see *C. japonica* 'Fortunei'
§ ***japonica*** 'Fortunei' (v)	CCCN CMac EBee SSta
- var. ***japonica***	EBee WPGP
- 'Tricolor' (v)	IDee SAko
- var. ***wallichii***	WPGP

Clianthus ✿ (*Papilionaceae*)

maximus	CTsd
- 'Kaka King'	EWes MPkF
* ***pauciflorus***	CCCN
§ ***puniceus*** ♀H3	CAbb CBcs CBod CCht CExl CSpe CTsd EBee EHyd EPfP LRHS MGil MHtn SChF SEdd SEle SGbt SPer SPlb SPoG SWvt
§ - 'Albus' ♀H3	CBcs CCCN CExl CSpe CTsd EBee EHyd EPfP LRHS MGil SPer SPoG SWvt
- 'Flamingo'	see *C. puniceus* 'Roseus'
- 'Red Admiral'	see *C. puniceus*
- 'Red Cardinal'	see *C. puniceus*
§ - 'Roseus' ♀H3	CBcs CCCN CExl CPla CRos EHyd EPfP LRHS NRHS SMad SPer SPoG
- 'White Heron'	see *C. puniceus* 'Albus'

Clinanthus (*Amaryllidaceae*)

incarnatus apricot-flowered	WMal
§ ***variegatus***	WCot
- yellow-flowered	WCot

Clinopodium (*Lamiaceae*)

alpinum	EBou EDAr GJos SRms WJek XLum
calamintha	see *Calamintha nepeta*
corsicum	WHoo WKif
grandiflorum	see *Calamintha grandiflora*
§ ***menthifolium***	NBre NLar
§ ***vulgare***	CHab EBee EHyd GPSL LRHS MBow MHer MNHC NAts NMir SBut SRms WOut WWild
- PAB 7562	LEdu

Clintonia (*Liliaceae*)

andrewsiana	GAbr GBin

Clivia ✿ (*Amaryllidaceae*)

caulescens	NHoy WCot
- pink-flowered	NHoy WCot
× ***cyrtanthiflora***	NHoy
gardenii	NHoy WCot
miniata ♀H1c	CAbb CBcs CCCN CDoC CTsd LCro LOPS NHoy SAdn SEND SPlb WCot
- 'Anshan Variegated' (v)	WCot
- 'Arturo's Yellow'	NHoy WCot
- 'Aurea'	CSpe
- Belgian hybrids	NHoy WCot
- Belgian hybrids (improved strain)	NHoy
- 'Beverley's Delight'	NHoy WCot
- broad-leaved, variegated (v)	NHoy WCot
- 'Chubb's Peach' × 'Vico Yellow'	NHoy
- var. ***citrina*** ♀H1c	NHoy SDir
- - variegated (v)	NHoy WCot
- 'Connemara Flame'	NHoy
- 'Dancing Sisters' × 'Terracotta Green Throat'	NHoy WCot
- Daruma Group	WCot
- 'Florid White Lips'	NHoy
- fragrant yellow-flowered	NHoy
- green-centred	NHoy WCot
- green-centred, orange-flowered	NHoy
- historical clone	NHoy
- 'Hot Number One'	NHoy
- large strawberry orange-flowered	NHoy
- 'Light of Buddha' (v)	NHoy WCot
- 'Mitsuhashi Multipetal'	WCot
- 'Mrs P. Lofus'	NHoy
- Nakamura yellow-flowered	NHoy
- 'Pale Majesty'	NHoy
- pale yellow-flowered	NHoy
- pastel shades	NHoy WCot
- 'Pink Perfection'	NHoy WCot
- 'Queen of the Strawberries'	NHoy
- 'Strawberry Giant'	NHoy
- 'Striata' (v)	NHoy WCot
- 'Terracotta Treasure' (v)	NHoy WCot
- 'Vico Shima'	WCot
- 'Wide Leaf Monk'	WCot
nobilis ♀H1c	NHoy SPlb WCot
robusta	NHoy WCot
'San Marcos Yellow' × 'Solomone Yellow'	WCot
'Sweet Undress'	NHoy WCot

Clusia (*Clusiaceae*)

rosea	CCCN

Clytostoma (*Bignoniaceae*)

§ ***calystegioides***	CCCN CRHN

Cnidium (*Apiaceae*)

officinale	GPoy LEdu
silaifolium	LEdu SPhx

Cobaea (*Polemoniaceae*)

pringlei	CRHN EBee WPGP
- CD&R 1323	SBrt WCot

scandens ♀H2 — CCCN CDTJ CSpe EShb MGil SPhx
- f. ***alba*** — CSpe EShb LCro LOPS

cobnut see *Corylus avellana*; also AGM Fruit Section under hazelnut

Cocculus (*Menispermaceae*)

laurifolius — IArd
§ ***orbiculatus*** — CExl
- B&SWJ 535 — WCru
trilobus — see *C. orbiculatus*

Cochlearia (*Brassicaceae*)

armoracia — see *Armoracia rusticana*
officinalis — WHer

Cochliasanthus (*Papilionaceae*)

§ ***caracalla*** — CCCN

Cocos (*Arecaceae*)

plumosa — see *Syagrus romanzoffiana*

Codiaeum ✿ (*Euphorbiaceae*)

variegatum var. ***pictum*** 'Excellent' (v) — LCro LOPS

Codonanthe (*Gesneriaceae*)

gracilis — WDib
'Paula' — WDib

Codonanthe × *Nematanthus* see × *Codonatanthus*

× *Codonatanthus* (*Gesneriaceae*)

'Golden Tambourine' — WDib
'Sunset' — WDib
'Tambourine' — WDib

Codonopsis ✿ (*Campanulaceae*)

HWJK 2105 from Nepal — WCru
affinis — EBee
- HWJCM 70 — WCru
- HWJK 2151 — WCru
benthamii GWJ 9352 — WCru
bhutanica — WSHC
cardiophylla — EBee WSHC
clematidea — CDor CSpe EBee EBou ECha EPfP EPot EWld GAbr GKev MNrw NLar SPlb SWvt
convolvulacea misapplied — see *C. grey-wilsonii*
convolvulacea ambig. — CWCL GKev
- 'Alba' — see *C. grey-wilsonii* 'Himal Snow'
- Forrest's form — see *C. forrestii* Diels
'Dangshen' — see *C. pilosula*
aff. ***deltoidea*** SSSE 86 — EBee EWld
dicentrifolia — NLar
foetens — GKev
subsp. ***nervosa*** new
forrestii misapplied — see *C. grey-wilsonii*
§ ***forrestii*** Diels — EBee EWld GKev WCot
- BWJ 7847 — WCru
§ ***grey-wilsonii*** ♀H5 — CAby CBro EWld GEdr GKev WCot
- B&SWJ 7532 — WCru
§ - 'Himal Snow' — CAby EPot EWld GEdr GKev WCru
inflata GWJ 9442 — WCru
kawakamii — EBee EWld
- B&SWJ 1592 — WCru
- RWJ 10007 — WCru
§ ***lanceolata*** — CAby CPla EWld SBrt
- B&SWJ 562 — WCru
nepalensis Grey-Wilson — see *C. grey-wilsonii*
obtusa — EBee
ovata — EBee EWld GKev NBro NLar
§ ***pilosula*** — CDor EBee EWld GKev GPoy SBrt
- var. ***modesta*** — EBee
§ ***rotundifolia*** var. ***angustifolia*** — EBee GKev WCru
- var. ***grandiflora*** — EBee WSHC
silvestris — see *C. pilosula*
tangshen misapplied — see *C. rotundifolia* var. *angustifolia*
tangshen Oliv. — WSHC
ussuriensis — see *C. lanceolata*
vinciflora — EWld
viridis HWJK 2435 — WCru

coffee see *Coffea*

Coffea (*Rubiaceae*)

arabica — CCCN SPre

Colchicum ✿ (*Colchicaceae*)

agrippinum ♀H4 — CAvo ECha EPot MRav NBir WAbe WCot WHoo WThu
alpinum — GKev
'Antares' — ECha
asteranthum — GKev
atropurpureum — GKev
§ ***autumnale*** — CAvo CHab EPot GKev GPoy NRya SDeJ SEND WShi
- 'Alboplenum' — ERCP GKev NBir SDeJ
- 'Album' — CAvo ELan EPot GKev LCro LOPS NBir WShi
- var. ***major*** hort. — see *C. byzantinum* Ker Gawl.
- var. ***minor*** hort. — see *C. autumnale*
§ - 'Nancy Lindsay' ♀H5 — EPot GKev WShi XEll
- 'Pannonicum' — see *C. autumnale* 'Nancy Lindsay'
§ - 'Pleniflorum' (d) — GKev
- 'Roseum Plenum' — see *C. autumnale* 'Pleniflorum'
§ ***bivonae*** — EPot
- 'Apollo' — GKev
- 'Mount Giona' — GKev
§ ***boissieri*** — GKev
bornmuelleri misapplied — see *C. speciosum* var. *bornmuelleri* hort.
bornmuelleri Freyn — GKev
bowlesianum — see *C. bivonae*
§ ***byzantinum*** Ker Gawl. ♀H5 — ELan SDeJ WShi
- ***album*** — see *C. byzantinum* 'Innocence'
§ - 'Innocence' — GKev WCot
cilicicum 'Purpureum' — EPot
corsicum — GKev WThu
cupanii AH 9707 — GKev
davisii — GKev
'Dick Trotter' — EPot SDeJ WFar WOld
'Disraeli' — EPot GKev
§ ***giganteum*** — GKev
graecum — GKev
'Hannibal' — GKev
'Harlekijn' — ERCP
hungaricum — EPot
- 'Valentine' — GKev
- 'Velebit Star' — GKev
illyricum — see *C. giganteum*
laetum misapplied — see *C. parnassicum*
'Lilac Wonder' — ELan GKev LCro LOPS MRav SDeJ WCot WHoo

	longifolium	see *C. neapolitanum*
	'Lysimachus'	GKev
	macrophyllum	GKev WCot
	munzurense	GKev
§	***neapolitanum***	GKev
	'Oktoberfest'	EPot
	parlatoris	GKev
§	***parnassicum***	ECha GKev
	procurrens	see *C. boissieri*
	psaridis	GKev
	pusillum	GKev
	'Rosy Dawn' ♀H5	ECha GKev WOld
	sibthorpii	see *C. bivonae*
	'Spartacus'	GKev
	speciosum ♀H5	CAvo ELan EPot GBin GKev NBir WShi
	- 'Album' ♀H5	CAvo ECha EPot ERCP GAbr LEdu NBir SDeJ
	- 'Atrorubens' ♀H5	ECha EPot GKev
I	- var. ***bornmuelleri*** hort.	WHoo WOld
	- var. ***illyricum*** hort.	see *C. giganteum*
	szovitsii 'Snow White'	GKev
	tenorei ♀H4	EPot GKev NBir
	'The Giant'	EPot GKev LCro LOPS SDeJ WFar
	'Violet Queen'	EPot ERCP GAbr GKev SDeJ
	'Waterlily' (d) ♀H5	CAvo CBod CWCL ELan EPot ERCP GAbr GKev LCro LOPS MBow NBir NPoe SDeJ WCot WFar WHoo

Coleonema (*Rutaceae*)

§	***pulchellum***	CCCN CSpe SVen
	- 'Aureum' **new**	CSde
	- 'Breath of Gold' **new**	CCCN
§	- 'Pink Fountain'	CAbb CBod CCCN CRos CTsd ECre EHyd ELan EPfP LRHS MPkF NRHS SEle SPoG WCot
	pulchrum misapplied	see *C. pulchellum*
§	'Sunset Gold'	CAbb CBod CCCN CCht CDoC CPbh CRos CSBt EBee EHyd ELan EPfP LRHS MPkF NRHS SCoo SEle SPlb SPoG

Coleus see *Plectranthus, Solenostemon*

Colignonia (*Nyctaginaceae*)

	ovalifolia B&SWJ 10644	WCru

Colletia (*Rhamnaceae*)

	armata	see *C. hystrix*
	cruciata	see *C. paradoxa*
§	***hystrix***	CBcs CMac CTri CTsd ELon MGil WPav
	- RCB RA S3	WCot
	- 'Rosea'	CMac MBlu SArc WPav WSHC
§	***paradoxa***	CBcs CBod CCCN CMCN ELan EPfP IArd IDee SArc SMad SPlb SPoG WFar WPav
	paradoxa × ***spinosissima***	SMad
	spinosissima	WPav
	ulicina	SVen

Collinsonia (*Lamiaceae*)

	canadensis	LEdu WPGP

Collomia (*Polemoniaceae*)

	grandiflora	WCot

Colocasia (*Araceae*)

	antiquorum	see *C. esculenta*
§	***esculenta*** ♀H1b	CDTJ LCro LOPS SDir SPalm SPlb XBlo
	- B&SWJ 6909	ESwi WCru
	- 'Black Coral'	CAbb SPad
	- 'Black Magic'	CDTJ EHyd LRHS SDir XBlo
	- 'Blue Hawaii'	CAbb CDTJ CPla
	- burgundy-stemmed	CDTJ CTsd SPalm
	- 'Emerald'	SDir
	- 'Fontanesii'	CBct CDTJ SDix
	- 'Hawaiian Punch'	CAbb CDTJ
	- 'Illustris'	CAbb CDTJ
	- 'Jack's Giant'	CDTJ
	- 'Mammoth'	CDTJ
	- 'Mojito' (v)	CDTJ
	- 'Pink China'	CBct MPkF
	formosana	see *C. esculenta*
	gaoligongensis	CBct CDTJ CPHo SPlb

Colquhounia (*Lamiaceae*)

	coccinea	CBod CCCN CSde EShb ESwi LRHS MBlu MGil MRav NLar NOra NQui SBrt SEdd SIvy SLon SPoG WCot WLov
	- Sch 2458	EPfP WPGP
§	- var. ***mollis*** B&SWJ 7222	WCru
	- var. ***vestita*** misapplied	see *C. coccinea* var. *mollis*
	- var. ***vestita*** ambig.	CBcs EBee EPfP LRHS MBNS SEND

Columnea (*Gesneriaceae*)

	'Aladdin's Lamp'	WDib
	× ***banksii*** ♀H1c	WDib
§	'Broget Stavanger' (v) ♀H1c	WDib
	'Chanticleer' ♀H1a	WDib
I	'Firedragon'	WDib
	'Gavin Brown'	WDib
	gloriosa	EBak
	'Inferno'	WDib
	'Katsura'	WDib
	'Merkur'	WDib
I	'Midnight Lantern'	WDib
	'Rising Sun'	WDib
	schiedeana	WDib
	'Sherbert'	WDib
	'Stavanger' ♀H1a	WDib
	'Stavanger Variegated'	see *C.* 'Broget Stavanger'

Coluria (*Rosaceae*)

	geoides	WCot

Colutea (*Papilionaceae*)

	arborescens	CAgr CBcs CExl CRos EHyd ELan ESwi EWTr LRHS MBlu MGil MGos SEND SPer SPlb
	× ***media***	EWld
	- 'Copper Beauty'	CBcs ELan MMrt MPie NLar SPer
	orientalis	CCCN EBee

Colvillea (*Caesalpiniaceae*)

	racemosa	SPlb

Comarum see *Potentilla*

Combretum (*Combretaceae*)

	fruticosum	CCCN

Commelina (*Commelinaceae*)

	benghalensis	XBlo
	coelestis	see *C. tuberosa* Coelestis Group
	dianthifolia	EBee EHyd GEdr LEdu LRHS NHpl SBrt SBut WHil

	- 'Electric Blue'	ELan SVic
	robusta	WCot WFar
	tuberosa	GKev NWad
	- B&SWJ 10353	SBrt WCru
	- blue-flowered	SDeJ
§	- Coelestis Group	CAby CCBP CSpe ECha SDys SEdd WKif WSHC
	- - 'Hopleys Variegated' (v)	WFar
	- - 'Rhapsody' **new**	WFar

Comospermum (*Asparagaceae*)

	yedoense 'Kikuzaki White'	GKev

Comptonia (*Myricaceae*)

	peregrina	EBee WPGP

Conandron (*Gesneriaceae*)

	ramondoides B&SWJ 8929	WCru

Conicosia (*Aizoaceae*)

	pugioniformis	SVen

Coniogramme (*Pteridaceae*)

	emeiensis	LEdu WCot
	intermedia	WPGP
	japonica	MAvo WFib WPGP
	- 'Flavomaculata' 🏆H4	EBee LEdu MSCN SMad WCot WFar WPGP

Conoclinium (*Asteraceae*)

§	***coelestinum***	CBod CFis CRos EBee EHyd GJos LRHS NRHS SBrt XLum

Conopodium (*Apiaceae*)

	majus	CEls WOut WShi

Consolida (*Ranunculaceae*)

§	***ajacis***	CSpe LRHS
	- Giant Imperial Series	SVic
	ambigua	see *C. ajacis*

Convallaria ✿ (*Asparagaceae*)

	japonica	see *Ophiopogon jaburan*
	keiskei	EPPr EPot MAvo WFar
I	- 'Marginata' (v)	WCot
	- 'Shiro-shima-fu' (v)	GEdr WFar
	majalis 🏆H7	Widely available
	- 'Albostriata' (v)	CBct CRos EHyd ELan EPPr GKev GMaP LEdu LRHS MAvo MHer MHol MNrw MRav NBPC NBir NRHS WCot WFar WHer WHil WHoo WPnP
	- 'Aurea'	WFar
	- 'Berlin Giant'	EPPr MAvo NRya SDeJ WFar
	- 'Blush'	CAvo WFar
	- 'Bordeaux'	CBre CBro CExl CWCL CWld ELan EMor EPPr GPSL MBel NLar SEdd WCot WPnP WTyc
	- 'Bridal Choice'	EBee EPot GKev MAvo NLar WFar XEll
	- 'Cream da Mint' (v)	WFar
	- 'Dorien'	CBct EMor EPPr IMou MAvo WFar
	- 'Fernwood's Golden Slippers'	CAvo GEdr WCot WFar
	- 'Flore Pleno' (d)	EWld GEdr MMrt WFar
	- 'Géant de Fortin' 🏆H7	CAvo CBct CBro CExl EPot GEdr MRav NBir NLar WCot WFar
	- 'Gérard Debureaux'	see *C. majalis* 'Green Tapestry'
	- 'Golden Jubilee'	CBct LEdu MAvo MNrw WCot WFar
	- 'Grandiflora'	WFar
§	- 'Green Tapestry' (v)	CBct MAvo WCot WFar
	- 'Haldon Grange' (v)	CAby EPPr MAvo WFar
	- 'Hardwick Hall' (v)	CAvo CBct CDor CExl CWCL EBee GEdr GKev LEdu MAvo MBel NSti WAul WCot WFar XEll
	- 'Heitmann'	CWCL WFar
	- 'Hitscherberger Riesenperle'	WFar XLum
	- 'Hofheim' (v)	CAby CAvo CBct GEdr GKev LEdu WCot WFar WHal
	- 'Landgraaf' (v)	MAvo WFar
	- 'Lineata' (v)	WFar
	- 'Marcel' (v)	WFar
	- 'Mary Brooks'	WFar
	- POLISH BEAUTY	see *C. majalis* 'Polska Piękność'
§	- 'Polska Piękność' (v)	WFar
	- 'Prolificans'	CBct CBod EBee ECtt EPPr EPfP EPot GEdr GKev ILea LCro LOPS MRav NBPC NBir NLar NSti WCot WFar WPnP
	- var. ***rosea***	Widely available
	- 'Rosea Plena' (d)	NBPC SPeP
	- 'Silberconfolis' (v)	WCot WFar
	- 'Variegata' (v)	CPla EMor WFar WThu
	- 'Vic Pawlowski's Gold' (v)	CAby CBct CBro CExl CMac EPPr GEdr LEdu MAvo WFar WPGP WSHC
	- 'Vierländer Glockenspiel'	WFar
	- 'Viktor'	WFar
*	- 'Viridistriatus'	WFar
	transcaucasica	GKev

Convolvulus (*Convolvulaceae*)

	althaeoides	CFis ELan
§	- subsp. ***tenuissimus***	EWes WCot
§	***boissieri***	WAbe XEll
	cantabrica	EHyd LRHS SBut SPhx XLum
	chilensis	CCCN
	cneorum 🏆H4	Widely available
	- 'Snow Angel'	CRos LRHS SWvt
	elegantissimus	see *C. althaeoides* subsp. *tenuissimus*
	lineatus	EWes
	mauritanicus	see *C. sabatius*
	nitidus	see *C. boissieri*
§	***sabatius*** 🏆H3	CCCN CCht CSam CSpe CTri EBee EBou ECtt ELan EPfP EPot EShb MCot SEND SPer SPlb SPoG SVen SWvt WCFE WSHC XLum
	- dark-flowered	CCCN
	- 'Moroccan Beauty'PBR	ECtt
	- white-flowered	CCCN
	tricolor 'Blue Ensign' 🏆H3 **new**	CSpe LCro LOPS

× *Cooperanthes* see *Zephyranthes*

Cooperia see *Zephyranthes*

Coprosma (*Rubiaceae*)

	acerosa 'Hawera'	CTrC
	- 'Red Rocks'	CTrC
	baueri misapplied	see *C. repens*
	'Beatson's Gold' (f/v)	CBcs CCoa CDTJ CExl CTrC ELan EShb LRHS SEND SWvt
	'Black Cloud'	CTrC ELon SEND
	brunnea (f)	WThu

- (m)	WThu
'Cappuccino'	EShb SEle
'Clearwater Gold'	SIvy
'Coppershine'	CExl
× ***cunninghamii*** × ***macrocarpa*** (m)	CCoa
× ***cunninghamii*** × ***macrocarpa*** (f) **new**	CTrC
'Cutie' (f)	CTrC
depressa	WThu
'Evening Glow'PBR (f/v)	CBod CCCN CCht CDTJ CRos CSBt EHyd LRHS MGos NRHS SEle SIvy SLim SRms WNPC
'Fire Burst'PBR (f/v)	CAbb CBcs CBct CCCN EHyd LRHS MGos SEle SLim SRms WNPC
'Inferno'PBR (v)	CAbb CBcs CDoC SEle SPad
'Karo Red'PBR (v)	SRms
× ***kirkii*** 'Variegata' (f/v)	CSde CTrC CTsd ELan EPfP EShb GBin LRHS
'Lemon and Lime'PBR (v)	CBod CRos EBee EHyd LRHS MGos NRHS SEle SGbt SIvy SPoG SRms
macrocarpa **new**	CTrC
petriei	GAbr WThu
- 'White Pearls'	WThu
'Rainbow Surprise'PBR (v)	CCCN CDoC CExl CSBt EHyd LRHS MGos SRms WFar WNPC
§ ***repens***	CExl EShb SPlb SVen
- 'County Park Plum' (v)	CBcs SVen
- 'Inferno' **new**	CMCN
- 'Marble Queen' (m/v) ♀H3	EShb
- 'Midnight Martini' (v)	CBod CRos EHyd LRHS NRHS SEle WNPC
- 'Pacific Dawn'	CSBt SEle WNPC
- PACIFIC NIGHT ('Hutpac'PBR) (m)	CBod CCht CDoC CRos CSBt EHyd LRHS MGos SGbt SLon WNPC
- PACIFIC SUNSET ('Jwncopps') (m/v)	CDoC EBee LCro LOPS LSRN SEle SGbt
- 'Painter's Palette' (m)	SVen
- 'Picturata' (m/v) ♀H3	EShb
- 'Pina Colada'PBR (v)	CAbb CDoC CRos CSBt EHyd LRHS NRHS SEdd SEle SGbt SPoG
- 'Tequila Sunrise'	CAbb CBcs CBod CCht CDoC CRos CSBt EBee EHyd LRHS LSRN NRHS SEdd SEle
robusta	CTrC
'Roy's Red' (m)	CBod CCht CMac EShb LSRN
rugosa (f)	CExl
'Scarlet O'Hara'	CCht SEle SPoG
'Walter Brockie'	CCoa CSde CTrC

Coptis (*Ranunculaceae*)

chinensis B&SWJ 12865	WCru
japonica	GPoy WCru
- var. ***dissecta***	GEdr WCru
- var. ***major***	GEdr WCru WSHC
laciniata B&SWJ 12863	WCru
omeiensis	WCru
quinquefolia	GEdr
- B&SWJ 1677	WCru
ramosa B&SWJ 6000	WCru
- B&SWJ 6030	WCru
trifolia	WCru

Corallospartium see *Carmichaelia*

Cordyline ✿ (*Asparagaceae*)

australis ♀H3	Widely available
- 'Albertii' (v) ♀H3	CCCN SArc
- 'Atlantic Green'	CBrac EHyd LRHS SavN
- 'Atropurpurea'	CBrac CCCN
- 'Black Night'	CCCN
- CHARLIE BOY ('Ric01'PBR) (v)	CTsd ELon SPad
- 'Claret'	CBcs
- 'Karo Kiri'	CCCN
- 'Olive Fountain'	CCCN
- 'Peko'PBR	CCCN CDoC
- 'Purple Heart'	CCCN MSwo
- Purpurea Group	CBcs CDTJ CDoC ELan MGos SCob SEND SPlb SWeb WFar
- 'Red Sensation'	CCCN SWvt
- 'Salsa'	CRos EHyd NRHS
- 'Sparkler' (v)	CCCN EHyd EPfP
- 'Torbay Dazzler' (v) ♀H3	CAbb CBcs CBod CBrac CDoC CEnd CMac CPla CRos CSBt CTsd EHyd ELan EPfP LRHS LSRN MAsh MGos MPri NRHS SCob SGbt SLim SPalm SPer SPoG SWvt WFar
- 'Torbay Sunset'	CCCN
- 'Variegata' (v)	CDoC
'Autumn'	CCCN
banksii	CCCN CCht
'Can Can'PBR (v)	SCob SEND
'Cardinal'PBR	CBcs
'Cha Cha'PBR (v)	CCCN SEND WAvo WCot
'Cherry Sensation' (v)	CRos EHyd EPfP LRHS NRHS WFar
'Coffee Cream'	CCCN
'Dark Star'	CCCN CDTJ
'Eurostar' (v)	CCCN
'Firecracker'	CCCN
fruticosa 'Kiwi'	EHyd LRHS
- 'Red Edge' ♀H1b	XBlo
§ ***indivisa***	CCCN CDTJ CPbh CTsd SArc SPlb SWeb WPGP
'Jive'PBR (v)	LCro LOPS
kaspar	CCCN
mauritiana	WCot
obtecta	CCCN
'Pink Champagne' (v)	CCCN EHyd LRHS MPkF MSwo
PINK PASSION ('Seipin'PBR)	CBod CCCN CPla CRos ELan EPfP LBuc LRHS SPalm SPoG
'Pink Stripe' (v)	CCCN LSRN SLim SWvt
'Purple Sensation'	CBcs CCCN
'Red Bush'	XBlo
'Red Heart'	CCCN
'Red Star'	CAbb CBcs CBod CCCN CChe CDoC CEnd CRos CSBt EHyd EPfP LCro LOPS LRHS MSwo NPer NRHS SCob SGbt SPoG SWeb SWvt WFar
'Southern Splendour' (v)	CBcs CCCN CDoC CPla CRos EHyd EPfP LRHS MPri NRHS SPoG
'Sundance' ♀H3	CBcs EPfP LRHS MGos MSwo NPer SLim SPoG SRms SWvt WFar
'Sunrise' (v)	CPla EHyd LRHS
terminalis	see *C. fruticosa*
'Torbay Red' ♀H3	CBrac CCCN CMac CPla CRos EHyd EPfP LRHS LSRN MAsh MPri SCob SPalm SPer SPoG SWvt

Coreopsis (*Asteraceae*)

'Astolat'	CBod LSou MRav SGbt
auriculata CUTTING GOLD	see *C.* 'Schnittgold'
- 'Elfin Gold'	EBou EHyd ELan EPfP
- 'Nana'	MNrw NBre
- 'Zamphir'	CDor EBee EPfP WCot
'Baby Gold'	see *C. lanceolata* 'Sonnenkind' (unblotched)

	BABY SUN	see *C.* 'Sonnenkind' (red-blotched)
	'Calypso' (v)	SPoG XLum
	'Center Stage'	ELan LSou
	'Citrine'PBR (Hardy Jewel Series)	CWGN
	'Cosmic Evolution' (Big Bang Series)	EBee EHyd ELan EMor LRHS SPoG
	'Cosmic Eye' (Big Bang Series)	EBee EHyd ELan NRHS SPoG WFar
	'Cranberry Ice'	LRHS NRHS
	'Daybreak' (Li'l Bang Series)	EHyd NRHS
	'Enchanted Eve'PBR (Li'l Bang Series)	EHyd EPfP MHol NRHS WFar
	'Fool's Gold'	EBee
	'Fruit Punch'PBR (Punch Series)	EHyd
	'Full Moon'PBR (Big Bang Series)	EBee EHyd ELan LRHS NLar NRHS SPoG STPC WFar XLum
	'Galaxy' (Big Bang Series)	EBee EHyd ELan LRHS NRHS WFar
	gigantea	SPlb
	grandiflora	GQue
	- 'Bernwode' (v)	CMac EBee SWvt
	- 'Domino'	EBee EHyd LSun
	- 'Early Sunrise' ♀H5	CRos CSBt EAJP EBee EHyd EPfP LCro LOPS LRHS MBow MNHC NBir NGBl NPer NRHS SGbt SPoG SWvt WFar XLum
	- FLYING SAUCERS ('Walcoreop'PBR)	CRos EHyd EPfP LRHS NRHS SCoo SPoG
	- 'Illico'	EShb
	- 'Mayfield Giant'	CBod EBee ELan EPfP LPot SGbt SRms SWvt
	- 'Presto' (d)	ELan EMor MBros NGBl WFar WHil
	- 'Rising Sun'	EHyd ELan
	- Solena Series **new**	CRos
	- 'Sunburst'	ELan EPfP NBre XLum
	- 'Sunfire'	CRos EHyd LRHS MBros NRHS SCob WFar
	- SUNKISS ('M8867p'PBR)	MPri
	- 'Sunray'	CBcs CBod CChe CRos CSBt ECtt EHyd EMor EPfP LRHS MAsh NGdn NRHS SGbt SHar SPlb SPoG SRms SWvt XLum
	- 'Tetra Riesen'	NBre
	'Highland Blast' **new**	CRos
	'Imperial Sun'PBR	CBod ECtt ELan LSou
	'Jethro Tull'PBR	EBee
	'Jive'PBR (Coloropsis Series)	CWGN
	lanceolata	NBre
	- 'Goldfink'	MRav SRms
	- 'Goldteppich'	CRos EHyd EPfP LRHS NRHS
§	- 'Sonnenkind' (unblotched)	EPfP GMaP XLum
	- 'Walter'	EBee LSou SPoG WCot WFar WGwG XLum XSen
	'Limbo' (Coloropsis Series)	EAJP
	'Limerock Passion'PBR	EHyd EPfP LRHS NRHS SCob SRkn
	'Limerock Ruby'PBR	EHyd GMaP LRHS MHol NRHS SCob SPoG SRkn SWvt WFar XLum
	major	EBee WFar
	'Mambo' (Coloropsis Series)	SEle
	'Mango Punch' (Punch Series)	EBee MCot
	maximiliani	see *Helianthus maximiliani*
	'Mercury Rising'PBR (Big Bang Series)	EBee EHyd LEdu LPla LRHS LSou NRHS SHar
	palmata	SPhx
	'Pink Lady'PBR	WCav
	pubescens 'Sunshine Superman'	EHyd ELan
	'Red Elf'PBR (Li'l Bang Series)	CRos EHyd NRHS
	'Red Satin' (Permathread Series)	WTor
	'Redshift'	EBee EHyd EMor ILea LRHS NRHS SPoG
	rosea	NGBl
	- 'American Dream'	CBod CFis CRos EHyd ELan EPfP GMaP LRHS NBir NGdn NLar NRHS SBut SGbt SPer SPlb SRms SWvt WFar WGwG XLum
	- 'Heaven's Gate'PBR	CSBt EHyd LRHS MHol WFar
	- 'Nana'	XLum
	'Route 66'PBR	EBee WCAu WFar
	'Ruby Frost' (Hardy Jewel Series)	CBcs EBee SPoG
	'Salsa' (Coloropsis Series)	SEle
§	'Schnittgold'	EHyd LRHS NBre NRHS SHar
	'Show Stopper'PBR	ELan LSou
	'Sienna Sunset'	EBee EHyd ELan LRHS NRHS
	'Snowberry'	ELan LRHS NRHS
	SOLANNA GOLDEN SPHERE	CBod EPfP MHol MPri SPoG
	'Solar Dance'	CWGN EWTr NLar
I	'Sonnenkind' (red-blotched)	EHyd LRHS NBre NRHS
	'Star Cluster' (Big Bang Series)	CWGN EBee EHyd ELan EMor EPfP LEdu LSou MHol NRHS SMad SPoG WFar
	'Starlight' (Li'l Bang Series)	EHyd NRHS WFar
	'Sterntaler'	EBee EHyd ELon EPfP GWyn LPot LRHS LSou NCou NRHS SPad SWvt XLum
	SUN CHILD	see *C.* 'Sonnenkind' (red-blotched)
	SUNNY DAY ('Balcorsunay')	CBod WFar
	'Sweet Marmalade'PBR	EPfP NLar
	tinctoria	MNHC SRms XAbr
	tripteris	ELan EPPr EPfP XLum
	- 'Mostenveld'	EBee
	- 'Red November'	MNrw
	(UpTick Series) UPTICK CREAM & RED ('Balupteamed') **new**	CRos LSou
	- UPTICK CREAM ('Balupteam')	CBod
	- UPTICK GOLD AND BRONZE ('Baluptgonz')	LSou MHol
	- UPTICK YELLOW AND RED ('Baluptowed') ♀H3 **new**	CBod
	verticillata	CMac CTri ECha MBel MBrN MHer NLar NPer SCob SRms WCAu WHal WOld
	- 'Bengal Tiger'PBR	ELan LSou
	- CRÈME BRÛLÉE ('Crembru'PBR)	EHyd LRHS NLar SCoo SRkn SWvt
I	- 'Golden Gain'	CBod ECtt NGdn WFar
	- 'Golden Shower'	see *C. verticillata* 'Grandiflora'
§	- 'Grandiflora' ♀H5	CBcs CBod EHyd ELan ELon EMor EPfP GMaP LRHS MArl MRav NGdn NHol NRHS NWad SHar SPer WFar XLum
	- 'Limerock Dream'PBR	EBee EHyd LRHS NRHS
	- 'Moonbeam'	Widely available
	- 'Ruby Red'	CRos EHyd LRHS NRHS
	- 'Sunbeam'	ELon
	- 'Tweety'PBR	WFar
	- 'Zagreb' ♀H5	Widely available

coriander see *Coriandrum sativum*

Coriandrum (*Apiaceae*)

sativum	CLau ENfk EWhm GPoy LCro LOPS MBros MHer MNHC MPri SPoG SRms XAbr

	- 'Calypso'[PBR] 🏆[H2]	EKin MCtn
	- 'Confetti' 🏆[H2]	EKin LCro LOPS MCtn
	- 'Leisure'	LCro LOPS SVic
	- 'Slobolt'	SPhx

Coriaria ✿ (*Coriariaceae*)

	arborea	ESwi
	intermedia B&SWJ 019	WCru
	japonica	ESwi MMrt NLar SVen WCru
	- B&SWJ 2833	WCru
	- subsp. ***intermedia*** B&SWJ 3877	WCru
	kingiana	WCru
§	***microphylla***	WCru
	- B&SWJ 8999	WCru
	- B&SWJ 14702	WCru
	myrtifolia	EWld WCru
	- B&SWJ 14003	WCru
	nepalensis	NLar WCru
	pteridoides	WCru
	ruscifolia	WCru
	- HCM 98178	WCru
	sarmentosa	WCru
	terminalis f. ***fructu-rubro***	WCru
	- var. ***xanthocarpa***	SBrt WCru
	- - GWJ 9204	WCru
	- - HWJK 2112c	WCru
	thymifolia	see *C. microphylla*

Cornus ✿ (*Cornaceae*)

	NJM 12.048	WPGP
	alba L.	CArg CCVT CLnd ECrN MRav SEWo SRms WMou WTSh
	- 'Alleman's Compact'	LRHS
	- 'Argenteovariegata'	see *C. alba* 'Variegata'
	- 'Aurea' 🏆[H7]	Widely available
	- BATON ROUGE ('Minbat'[PBR])	CAby CBod CDoC CRos EBee EHyd ELan ELon EPfP LRHS LSRN MAsh MRav NRHS SGsty SPoG SWvt WFar
	- 'Cream Cracker'[PBR] (v)	MRav
	- 'Elegantissima' (v) 🏆[H7]	Widely available
	- 'Gouchaultii' (v)	CMac CRos EPfP GKin LRHS MGos MRav NLar NRHS SCob SGol SGsty SPer SRms SWeb WFar
	- 'Hessei' misapplied	see *C. sanguinea* 'Compressa'
	- IVORY HALO ('Bailhalo'[PBR])	EMil EPfP LRHS LSRN MAsh MRav NLar SPer
	- 'Kesselringii'	Widely available
	- RED GNOME ('Regnzam')	ELon EPfP MAsh
	- 'Siberian Pearls'	CBcs CRos EHyd ELan GKin LRHS MBlu NLar NRHS SPoG
§	- 'Sibirica' 🏆[H7]	Widely available
	- 'Sibirica Ruby' **new**	SavN
	- 'Sibirica Variegata' (v) 🏆[H7]	CMac CRos EBee EHyd ELon EPfP GKin LRHS LSRN MAsh MBlu MGos NRHS SCob SLim SPer SWvt
	- 'Spaethii' (v) 🏆[H7]	Widely available
§	- 'Variegata' (v)	WFar
	- 'Westonbirt'	see *C. alba* 'Sibirica'
	alternifolia	CCVT CMCN CTho SSta WMou
§	- 'Argentea' (v) 🏆[H6]	Widely available
	- 'Brunette'	CJun MBlu
	- GOLDEN SHADOWS ('Wstackman'[PBR]) (v)	CWGN IArd MMrt SGsty SMad
	- 'Golden Surprise'	CJun
	- 'Goldfinch' (v)	CJun MBlu
	- 'Illusion' (v)	CJun
	- 'Moonlight' (v)	CJun
	- PINKY SPOT ('Minpinky')	LSRN NLar
	- 'Silver Giant' (v)	CJun NLar WSpi
	- 'Variegata'	see *C. alternifolia* 'Argentea'
	- 'Yellow Spring'	CJun NLar
	amomum	EBtc NLar
	- 'Blue Cloud'	CBcs CBod CRos MBlu MMuc
	- 'Lady Jane'	NLar
	'Ascona'	CBcs CEnd CJun CLnd EWTr NLar SPer SSta WGob
	canadensis	Widely available
	candidissima Marshall	see *C. foemina* Mill.
	capitata	CAby CBcs CJun CLnd CMac CPla CRos CTsd EHyd EPfP ESwi EWTr GKev IArd IDee IMou LRHS MGil MGos NRHS SAko SEND SGol SPoG SReu WCru WFar WKor WPGP
	- subsp. ***emeiensis***	CJun
	- 'Foreness Fog' (v)	SEND
	- 'Kilmacurragh Rose'	IArd IMou
	aff. ***capitata*** NJM 13.046	WPGP
	'Celestial Shadow'	MPkF SGol
	chinensis	SSta SWvt
	controversa	CBcs CCVT CMCN CTri ELan EPfP EWTr LCro LMaj LOPS MBlu MGil NLar SEND SEWo SGol SReu SSta SWvt WMou XLot
I	- 'Aurea'	LRHS MAsh
	- 'Candlelight'	MBlu NLar SSta
	- 'Carpe Diem'	LRHS
§	- 'Frans Type' (v)	CJun
	- 'Gosia'[PBR] (v) **new**	XLot
	- 'Green Carpet'	NLar SSta
	- 'Laska'	CJun LMaj NLar
	- 'Lucia'	CJun LMaj NLar
I	- 'Marginata Nord'	NLar
	- 'Pagoda'	CJun MBlu NLar
	- 'Troya Dwarf'	CJun NLar
	- 'Variegata' (v) 🏆[H5]	Widely available
	- 'Variegata' Frans type	see *C. controversa* 'Frans Type'
	'Dorothy'	CJun
	'Eddie's White Wonder' 🏆[H5]	Widely available
	elliptica	WPGP
	- 'First Choice'	CJun
	- 'Full Moon'	CJun
	× ***elwinortonii*** VENUS ('Kn30 8'[PBR]) (Jersey Star Series)	CWGN EBee EPfP LCro LOPS LRHS MAsh MBlu NLar SGsty SLon SMad SSta WPGP
	excelsa F&M 57	WPGP
	florida	CBcs CMCN CTho ESwi GKev LCro LMaj MMuc NOra NOrn SCob SPer SReu WMat WMou WTSh
	- 'Appalachian Spring'	CJun
	- 'Apple Blossom'	GQue
	- 'Autumn Gold'	SSta
	- CHEROKEE BRAVE ('Comco No 1')	CBcs CRos EHyd LMil LRHS MAsh NRHS SGol SPoG SSta WGob
	- 'Cherokee Chief'	CBcs CEnd CJun CLnd CRos CTho CTri EHyd EWTr LRHS LSRN NLar NRHS SGol SPer WHwl WSpi
	- 'Cherokee Daybreak'	see *C. florida* 'Daybreak'
	- 'Cherokee Princess'	CJun CRos EHyd EWTr LRHS MAsh NOra NOrn SGol SSta WMat
	- 'Cherokee Sunset'	see *C. florida* 'Sunset'
	- 'Cloud Nine'	CBcs CTho EWTr GKin NLar NOrn SGsty WGob
	- 'Comanche Chief' **new**	CRos
§	- 'Daybreak' (v) 🏆[H5]	CBcs CRos EHyd LRHS LSRN MAsh NOra NOrn NRHS SPer SPoG WMat XLot

- 'Eternal Dogwood' (d)	SGol
- 'First Lady' (v)	WGob
- 'Fragrant Cloud'	SWvt
- 'Granary Gold'	SSta
- 'Junior Miss'	CEnd
- 'Pink Flame' (v)	SSta
- f. ***pluribracteata*** (d)	WHwl
- 'Rainbow' (v) ♀H5	CBcs CJun CRos EHyd LRHS MAsh NOra NOrn NRHS SGol SPer SPoG WMat XLot
- f. ***rubra***	ELan GKin LCro LMaj LOPS LRHS MMrt MRav NOrn SGsty SPer SPoG WGob WHwl WMat
- - 'Red Giant'	CBcs EWTr MPkF
- - 'Spring Song'	CJun CMac WGob
- 'Spring Day'	CMac WGob WHwl
- 'Springtime'	CJun
- 'Stoke's Pink'	CEnd CJun WGob
§ - 'Sunset' (v)	CEnd CRos EHyd ELan LCro LOPS LRHS MAsh MMrt NLar NOrn NRHS SSta SWvt WGob WMat
- 'Sweetwater'	CJun SAko WGob
- subsp. ***urbiniana***	CBcs WPGP
- 'Variegata' (v)	GKin
- 'White Cloud'	CJun NOra WMat
§ ***foemina*** Mill.	SBrt
'Gloria Birkett'	CJun CRos EHyd LMil LRHS MAsh WGob
hessei misapplied	see *C. sanguinea* 'Compressa'
hongkongensis	LMaj LRHS MPkF NLar WPGP
- B&SWJ 11700	WCru
- HWJ 1033	EPfP WPGP
- subsp. ***gigantea*** KWJ 12225	WCru
- subsp. ***melanotricha***	EBee
- subsp. ***tonkinensis*** B&SWJ 11791	WCru
'Jerry Mundy'	CMac
'Kelsey Dwarf'	see *C. sericea* 'Kelseyi'
'Kenwyn Clapp'	CJun
kousa	CBcs CCVT CDoC CMCN CMac CTho ELan EPfP GKev GKin LMaj NLar SCob SGol SPer SPlb SReu WKor WLov
- B&SWJ 12610 from Korea	WCru
- B&SWJ 14620 from Japan **new**	WCru
- 'Akabana'	CJun
- 'Akatsuki' (v)	CJun MPkF NLar SSta XLot
- 'All Summer'	CJun
- 'Autumn Rose'	CJun NLar SMad
- 'Beni-fuji'	CLnd CRos EHyd EWTr LRHS MBlu MPkF NLar NRHS WPGP XLot
- 'Big Apple'	CJun CRos EHyd EPfP LMil LRHS MAsh NLar SGsty WGob XLot
- 'Blue Shadow'	CBcs CJun LRHS MBlu NLar SSta
- 'Bonfire' (v)	NLar
- 'Bultinck's Beauty'	EWTr LRHS NLar
- 'Bultinck's Giant'	CLnd LRHS MBlu MPkF NLar WGob XLot
- 'Cappuccino'	CJun EWTr LRHS MPkF NRHS SGsty SMad XLot
- 'Cherokee'	CJun LRHS NLar XLot
- 'China Dawn' (v)	CJun SSta
- var. ***chinensis***	Widely available
- - 'Barmstedt'	SAko
- - 'Bodnant Form'	CAby CEnd CJun CTho EPfP ESwi NLar SChF SSta WBor WGob WHwl XLot
- - 'China Girl' ♀H5	Widely available
- - 'Claudia'	EPfP IArd LRHS SSta
- - 'Great Star'	LRHS LSRN MAsh SGsty
- - 'Greta's Gold' (v)	CJun SSta
- - 'Ikone'	SAko
- - 'PVG'	CJun
- - 'Snowflake'	CJun
- - 'Spinners'	CJun
- - 'Summer Stars'	CJun
- - 'Tri-Splendor'	NLar
- - 'White Dusted' (v)	CJun MBlu NLar SMad
- - 'White Fountain'	EPfP LSRN MPkF MPnt NLar NOra NOrn WMat
- - 'Wieting's Select'	CJun EWTr MBlu MPkF SAko XLot
- - 'Wisley Queen' ♀H5	CJun CRos EHyd EPfP LMil LRHS MAsh SPoG SSta WPGP
- - 'Xanthocarpa'	CBcs
- 'Claudine'	CJun
- 'Copacabana'	MBlu MPkF
- 'Daybreak'	SGol
- 'Doctor Bump'	CJun NLar
- 'Doubloon'	CJun
- 'Dwarf Pink'	CJun LRHS XLot
- 'Ed Mezitt'	CJun LRHS NLar XLot
- 'Elizabeth Lustgarten'	CJun MBlu MPkF SSta
- 'Eurostar'	ELan LRHS MBlu
- 'Fanfare'	CJun
- 'Fernie's Favourite'	CJun
- GALILEAN ('Galzam')	MThu WGob XLot
- 'Gay Head'	CJun
- giant-flowered	MPkF
I - 'Girard's Nana'	CJun
- 'Gold Cup' (v)	CJun SSta XLot
- 'Gold Star' (v)	CBcs CEnd CJun CMCN ELan LMil MAsh MBlu NLar SChF SGol SPoG SSta WGob WHwl XLot
- 'Greensleeves'	CJun CRos EHyd EPfP GKev LMil LRHS MAsh SSta WGob
- 'Heart Throb'	CJun NLar SGol WGob
- 'Highland'	CJun NLar
- 'John Slocock' ♀H5	CJun IArd NLar WGob
- 'Koree'	NLar
- 'Kreutzdame'	CJun MBlu XLot
- 'Laura'	CWGN ELon MBlu SGol SMad XLot
- 'Little Beauty'	CJun
- 'Lizzie P'	NLar
- 'Lustgarten Weeping'	CJun
- 'Madame Butterfly'	CJun CRos LRHS MBlu NLar SPoG
- 'Melanie' PBR	WMat
- 'Milky Way'	CBod CDoC CJun CLnd CMCN CTho EPfP EWTr LMaj LRHS LSRN MAsh MBlu MGos MPkF MRav NLar SGol SGsty WGob WHwl WSpi XLot
- 'Milky Way Select'	CBcs CJun CRos EHyd LRHS NRHS
- 'Miss Petty'	CJun NLar
- 'Miss Satomi' ♀H5	Widely available
- 'Moonbeam'	CJun EWTr NLar SMad
- 'Mount Fuji'	CJun MBlu NLar SSta
- 'National'	CDoC CJun ILea LMaj LMil LRHS MAsh NLar SSta WGob XLot
- 'Nicole'	LRHS WGob XLot
- 'Ohkan'	CJun MPkF
- 'Pévé Foggy'	LRHS MThu
- 'Pévé Limbo' (v)	CJun
- 'Pévé Satomi Compact'	CJun NLar
- 'Pink Lips'	NLar XLot
- 'Polywood'	CJun NLar
- RADIANT ROSE ('Hanros')	EPfP NLar SSta WGob

– 'Rasen'	CJun NLar
– 'Rel Whirlwind'	CJun NLar
* – 'Robert'	NLar
– 'Rosea'	CJun
– 'Rosemoor Pink'	CJun
– SAMARITAN ('Samzam') (v)	CBcs CEnd EWTr LRHS LSRN SGol SSta XLot
– 'Schmetterling'	CJun EWTr LRHS MBlu MPkF NLar WHwl XLot
– 'Sluis Slim'	MBlu
– 'Snowbird'	CJun LRHS
– 'Snowboy' (v)	CEnd CLnd MBlu SMad
– 'Snowflurries'	CJun
– 'Southern Cross'	CJun WGob
– 'Square Dance'	CJun NLar
– 'Steeple'	CJun
– 'Summer Fun' ♀H5	CJun CRos EHyd EWTr LMil LRHS SPoG SSta XLot
– 'Summer Majesty'	CJun
– 'Sunsplash' (v)	CJun LRHS SPoG SSta
– 'Temple Jewel' (v)	CJun
– 'Teresa'	LRHS XLot
– 'Teutonia' ♀H5	CJun ELan EWTr IArd MGos NLar SAko SSta WGob WHwl XLot
– 'Trinity Star'	CJun
– 'Triple Crown'	CJun
– 'Tsukubanomine'	CJun CLnd NLar
– 'Weaver's Weeping'	CJun MPkF NLar
– 'Weisse Fontäne'	CJun LRHS MBlu MPkF NLar XLot
– 'White Dream'	CJun LRHS NLar
– 'White Giant'	CJun SPer
– 'Willy Boy'	XLot
– 'Wolf Eyes' (v) ♀H5	CJun ELan EPfP LMil LRHS MAsh MBlu NLar SGol SPoG SSta XLot
macrophylla Wall.	CMCN IDee WCru WPGP
– MSF 821	WPGP
– var. ***macrophylla***	SSta
mas	Widely available
– 'Aurea' (v) ♀H6	CBcs CJun EPfP LMil LRHS MAsh MBlu MRav NLar SGol SSta WLov
§ – 'Aureoelegantissima' (v)	CJun CMac CRos EHyd LRHS NLar WCot WLov
– 'Elegant' (F)	CAgr
– 'Elegantissima'	see *C. mas* 'Aureoelegantissima'
– 'Elena' (v) **new**	NLar
– 'Golden Glory' ♀H6	CJun CLnd EPfP NLar XLot
– 'Gourmet' (F)	CAgr
– 'Hillier's Upright'	CJun
– 'Jolico' (F) ♀H6	CAgr CJun LEdu MBlu NLar WMat XLot
– 'Kasanlaker' (F)	CAgr LEdu NLar
– 'Nikolka' (F) **new**	NLar
– 'Pancharevo' (F)	CAgr
– 'Pioneer' (F)	CJun NLar
– 'Redstone' (F)	CJun
– 'Shan' (F)	CAgr
– 'Shumen' (F)	CAgr NLar
– 'Spring Glow'	CJun NLar
– 'Variegata' (v) ♀H6	CBcs CJun CMCN CRos CTho EHyd EPfP LRHS MAsh MBlu MGos NLar SGol
– 'Vraća Kaštel' (F)	CAgr
– 'Xanthocarpa' (F)	CAgr CJun
mas × officinalis	CJun
'Norman Hadden' ♀H5	Widely available
nuttallii	CLnd ELan EPfP EWTr SPer SWeb SWvt
– 'Colrigo Giant'	CJun
– 'Gold Spot' (v)	CJun
– 'Monarch'	CJun EWTr SPer
– 'North Star'	CJun NLar
– 'Portlemouth'	CEnd CJun
– 'Zurico'	CJun
oblonga	CExl EBee WPGP
officinalis	CAgr CJun CMCN CRos EBee EPfP IMou LEdu LRHS MBlu NLar NOra SWvt WSpi
– 'Kintoki' ♀H6	NLar WLov
'Ormonde' ♀H5	CJun EPfP NLar SMad SSta WGob WPGP
'Pink Blush'	CJun
'Porlock' ♀H5	CJun CMCN CRos EHyd EPfP LRHS NLar NRHS SWvt WGob
pumila	NLar
racemosa	EBtc NLar
rugosa	EBtc NLar
× ***rutgersensis***	LRHS
– (Stellar Series) AURORA ('Rutban')	CJun MBlu NLar SGol SMad
§ – – CELESTIAL ('Rutdan')	CJun CRos EHyd LMil LRHS NRHS SGol WGob
– – GALAXY	see *C.* × *rutgersensis* CELESTIAL
– – CONSTELLATION ('Rutcan')	CJun LMil SGol
– – RUTH ELLEN ('Rutlan')	CJun EWTr NLar
– – STELLAR PINK ('Rutgan')	CBcs CJun CLnd CRos EBee EHyd EWTr LRHS MGos MPkF NLar NRHS SAko SCob SGol WGob WPGP
sanguinea	CBcs CCVT CHab CLnd CMac CTho CTri ECrN EPfP LBuc MRav MSwo SCob SEWo SGol SPer SReu SVic WMat WMou WTSh
§ – 'Anny'	CJun MBlu
– 'Anny's Winter Orange' ♀H6	CJun CMac CRos EHyd ELan ELon EShb LRHS LSRN LSvl MAsh NRHS SGol SPoG WAvo WCot
§ – 'Compressa'	MBlu MGil MRav NLar WAvo
– 'Magic Flame' ♀H6	CDoC CJun CRos EHyd ELon EPfP LRHS MAsh NLar NRHS SPoG SWvt WCot
– 'Midwinter Fire'	Widely available
– 'Winter Beauty'	CJun CSBt EBee EPfP MBlu NLar SCob SEdd SLon SWvt WAvo
– 'Winter Flame'	see *C. sanguinea* 'Anny'
sericea 'Bud's Yellow'	CRos EHyd ELon EPfP LRHS MBlu NLar NRHS
– 'Cardinal'	CDoC CRos EBee EHyd ELon EPfP LRHS MAsh MGos NLar NRHS
– 'Flaviramea' ♀H7	Widely available
– 'Hedgerows Gold' (v) ♀H7	CDoC CRos EBee EHyd ELan ELon EMil EPfP LRHS MAsh MGos NEoE NRHS SPoG WFar WLov
§ – 'Kelseyi'	CMac EBee ELan EPfP ILea MRav NLar SBrt SCob SPoG
– KELSEY'S GOLD ('Rosco')	CRos LRHS MAsh NRHS SPoG WLov
– subsp. ***occidentalis*** 'Sunshine'	EPfP NEoE NLar
§ – 'White Gold' (v)	CBod EBee ELon EPfP MRav NLar SPer SPoG SRms WFar
– 'White Spot'	see *C. sericea* 'White Gold'
stricta	see *C. foemina* Mill.
walteri	EBtc
– B&SWJ 8776	WCru
wilsoniana	WPGP
'Winter Orange'	CDoC CJun NLar

Corokia ✿ (*Argophyllaceae*)

buddlejoides	CBcs CBod CCoa CSde CTrC CTsd EBee GBin NLar SEND WFar
'Coppershine'	CCoa
cotoneaster	CBcs CBrac CMac CRos CSBt CSde CTrC CTri EBee EHyd ELan EPfP EPot LRHS MGil MGos NLar SCob SEdd SEle SIvy SPer SPoG SWvt SavN WAvo WCot WFar WGrn WLov
- 'Geenty's Ghost'	CTrC
* ***parviflora***	CTrC
× ***virgata***	CChe CRos CTrC CTri ELan EPfP LRHS NLar SArc SPlb SWvt WKif WSHC
- 'Banana Royal' **new**	CDoC
- 'Bronze King'	CBrac CRos CTrC LRHS SPer SPlb SVen
- 'Frosted Chocolate'	CBod CCoa CDoC CRos CSde CTrC CTsd EBee ELan EPfP LRHS SEND SIvy SLim SPoG SSta SVen SWvt WAvo WFar WGrn WLov
- 'Geenty's Green'	CCoa CRos CTrC LRHS WGrn
- 'Limey' **new**	CBod
- 'Mangatangi'	CTrC
- 'Pink Delight'	CCht EPfP MRav
- 'Red Wonder'	CMac CRos CTrC EHyd ELan EPfP LRHS SEND SPoG SVen WAvo WGrn WLov
- 'Sunsplash' (v)	CBod CBrac CCoa CDoC CMac CRos CTrC CTsd EBee ELan EPfP LRHS NLar SEND SEle SPoG SSta SWvt WFar WGrn
- 'Welsh Whiskey' **new**	CDoC SEle
- 'Yellow Wonder'	CBcs CRos CTrC ELan LRHS NLar SEND SPlb SWvt

Coronilla (*Papilionaceae*)

cappadocica	see *C. orientalis*
comosa	see *Hippocrepis comosa*
coronata	EHyd LRHS
emerus	see *Hippocrepis emerus*
glauca	see *C. valentina* subsp. *glauca*
minima	WAbe
'Nan Hicks'	EWld
§ ***orientalis***	CPBP EPPr
valentina	CRHN MGil
- 'Cotswold Cream' (v)	CBod NSti SEdd SPoG WCot WMal
§ - subsp. ***glauca*** ♀H4	CDoC CMac CSBt CSde CTri CWld EBee ELan EPfP LRHS LSRN MNHC SEND SIvy SPer SRms SVen SWvt XSen
- - 'Brockhill Blue'	CAby EPfP LRHS SAko WCot
- - 'Citrina' ♀H4	Widely available
- - 'Lauren Stevenson'	MHol NCou WCot
* - - 'Pygmaea'	LRHS SEle SRms WAbe WCot WHwl
- - 'Variegata' (v)	CBcs CDoC CMac CRos CTri EBee ELan EPfP IDee LRHS MAsh MCot MGil MRav NQui SEle SLim SLon SPer SPoG SRms SVen WCot
- - 'XXS'	WCot
varia	see *Securigera varia*

Correa ✿ (*Rutaceae*)

alba	CCCN CExl CTrC EPfP
- 'Pinkie' ♀H3	CCCN CExl CTrC CTsd
alba* × *backhouseana	SEle
backhouseana ♀H3	CAbb CBcs CCCN CExl CRos CSde CTri CTsd EHyd ELan EPfP LRHS NLar SBrt SEle SVen WAvo WSHC
- 'Peaches and Cream'	CCCN SEle SRkn
decumbens	CTrC
'Dusky Bells' ♀H3	CAbb CBcs CCCN CRos CSde CTrC CTri CTsd EHyd ELan EPfP LRHS MAsh MGil SEle SPlb SPoG SRkn SVen WAvo
'Dusky Maid'	CCCN CExl
'Federation Belle'	CCCN SVen
glabra	CTrC SEle WAvo
'Harrisii'	see *C.* 'Mannii'
'Ivory Bells'	LRHS
lawrenceana	CExl CTsd EBee LRHS SEND SEle WPGP
- var. ***grampiana***	SVen
§ 'Mannii' ♀H3	CBcs CCCN CExl ELan EPfP LRHS MGil
'Marian's Marvel' ♀H3	CBcs CCCN CExl CSde CTrC ELan EPfP IArd IDee MAsh SEND SEle SRkn SVen
'Peachy Cream'	CAbb CCCN CSBt LRHS
'Poorinda Mary'	CCCN MHtn SEle
pulchella ♀H3	CExl CMac CTri IDee MGil SEle WAvo
- orange-flowered	WAbe
- 'Pink Mist'	CTrC WCot
reflexa ♀H3	CExl
- var. ***nummulariifolia***	MAsh MGil WAbe WCot WPGP
- var. ***reflexa***	CExl WCot
* - ***virens***	CExl
schlechtendalii	CCCN MGil SEle SVen

Cortaderia ✿ (*Poaceae*)

araucana **new**	ELan
argentea	see *C. selloana*
fulvida misapplied	see *C. richardii* (Endl.) Zotov
§ ***fulvida*** (Buchanan) Zotov ♀H5	IArd IDee WCot
richardii misapplied	see *C. fulvida* (Buchanan) Zotov
richardii ambig.	CBod CChe CExl CPla CTsd IMou MMuc NBir SPtp SWvt WSpi
§ ***richardii*** (Endl.) Zotov ♀H5	CAby CBcs CDoC CKno EHyd EWes IMou LRHS MAvo SArc SDix SRms WPGP
- Brown's strain	WCot
rudiuscula	EBee
§ ***selloana***	CBcs CBod EBee MGos MHtn NBir NGrd SGol SPlb
§ - 'Albolineata' (v)	CBcs ELon MWht SWvt
§ - 'Aureolineata' (v) ♀H6	CBcs CMac CSde EHyd ELan EPfP GMaP LRHS MWht NRHS SEND SGsty SPer SPoG SWvt
- 'Evita'PBR ♀H6	ECtt ELan NLar SPoG SWvt WCot
- 'Gold Band'	see *C. selloana* 'Aureolineata'
- 'Golden Goblin'PBR	CKno
- 'Icalma'	CSde EPPr
- 'Monstrosa' ♀H6	SEND SMad
- 'Patagonia' ♀H6	EPPr
- 'Pink Feather'	EHyd ELan EPfP MAsh SEND SPer WFar
- 'Pink Phantom'	EHyd LRHS
- 'Pointe du Raz'	EBee ELan SWvt
- 'Pumila' ♀H6	Widely available
- 'Rendatleri'	CBcs ELan SCoo SLim SWvt
- 'Rosea'	CBod EPfP NLar SCob SGol WFar
- 'Senior'	NLar
- 'Silver Comet'	ECtt
- SILVER FEATHER ('Notcort') (v) ♀H6	SCob
- 'Silver Fountain' (v)	EHyd ELan EPfP LRHS MAsh NRHS SPer SPoG

	- 'Silver Stripe'	see *C. selloana* 'Albolineata'
	- 'Splendid Star' PBR (v)	CRos EHyd LRHS MAsh MGos NRHS SCob SPoG SWvt
	- 'Sunningdale Silver' 🏆H6	CBcs CMac ECha EHyd ELan ELon EPfP LRHS LSRN MGos SCob SEND SMad SPer SPoG SWvt
*	- 'White Feather'	CBod EHyd NLar SPer WFar
	Toe Toe	see *C. richardii* (Endl.) Zotov

Cortusa (*Primulaceae*)

	altaica	CBor
	brotheri	EBee
*	***caucasica***	GKev
*	- 'Alba'	EBee
§	***matthioli***	GKev GPSL NHpl WFar
	- 'Alba'	GKev
	- var. ***congesta***	CWCL EBee
	- subsp. ***matthioli*** **new**	CWCL
	- subsp. ***pekinensis***	EBee GKev MPnt NBid WSHC WTyc
	- - var. ***sachalinensis***	EBee GKev
	turkestanica	NWad

Corydalis ✿ (*Papaveraceae*)

	'Ambigua' **new**	GKev
	angustifolia	WCot
	anthriscifolia	EWes LEdu MMrt
	'Blackberry Wine'	CExl CWCL EBee ECtt LCro LEdu LOPS MPnt SPoG
	BLUE LINE ('Couriblue')	CWGN EMor GBin LSou NHar SCob SPoG
	'Blue Panda'	see *C. flexuosa* 'Blue Panda'
	brunneovaginata	WCot
	bulbosa misapplied	see *C. cava*
	bulbosa (L.) DC.	see *C. solida*
	buschii	CAby CWCL EBee GEdr NRya
	calycosa	IPot MAvo
	'Canary Feathers' PBR	CRos EHyd LRHS NHpl NRHS
	cashmeriana	EHyd GKev LRHS NBid NRHS WAbe WHal
	- 'Kailash'	EBee EHyd LRHS
	cashmeriana* × *flexuosa	WAbe
	caucasica	GKev
	- var. ***alba*** misapplied	see *C. malkensis*
§	***cava***	EBee EMor GKev NHpl WShi
	chaerophylla	EWld
	cheilanthifolia	CExl CSpe EPfP EPot EWld IMou LEdu SRms WMal
	'Craigton Blue'	EBee EPPr EWld GBin GEdr GKev GMaP GQue IMou ITim MNrw NHar NSti WFar WMal
	'Craigton Purple' **new**	NHar
	curviflora	WAbe
	- subsp. ***rosthornii***	CExl
	- - 'Blue Heron'	CAby CBct CWCL CWGN ECtt EHyd EMor EWld GEdr GKev LRHS MBNS MHol MPnt NHar NLar NRHS SPad WFar WSHC
	davidii	CExl
	decipiens Schott, Nyman & Kotschy	see *C. solida* subsp. *incisa*
	decipiens misapplied	EPot GKev
	densiflora	GKev
	'Dzukou Mousse' **new**	WPGP
	elata	CMea CSpe EHyd EWes GAbr GWyn LRHS MArl MBel MBriF MCot MNrw NBid NBir NChi NRHS NSla SPoG SPtp WCru WHal WSHC
	- 'Blue Summit'	EHyd EPPr IMou LRHS MBel MPnt WFar
	elata* × *flexuosa	IMou
	elata* × *flexuosa clone 1	CExl GEdr
	flexuosa 🏆H5	CSpe EPfP GKev GWyn MNrw WSHC XLum
	- CD&R 528	NRya
	- 'Balang Mist'	CExl
	- 'Blue Dragon'	see *C. flexuosa* 'Purple Leaf'
§	- 'Blue Panda'	CExl EPPr EWes GMaP MPnt NLar WCru
	- 'Blue Panther' **new**	LEdu
	- 'Blue Skies'	MHol
	- 'Blue Summit' **new**	LEdu
	- 'China Blue'	Widely available
	- 'Golden Panda' (v)	NHpl
	- 'Hale Cat'	EPPr
	- 'Nightshade'	CExl EWld NBid WCot
I	- 'Norman's Seedling'	EPPr
	- 'Père David'	CDor CMac CRos CSBt CSam CSpe CWCL EBee ECha EHyd ELan EMor EPPr EPfP GKev GWyn LEdu LRHS MHer NBir SPlb SPoG SRms SWvt WCru WPnP XLum
§	- 'Purple Leaf'	Widely available
	fumariifolia var. ***azurea*** **new**	GKev
	glauca	see *C. sempervirens*
	'Heavenly Blue'	GKev
	henrikii	GEdr
	heterocarpa	IMou
	integra	GKev
	'Kingfisher'	CBor CSma LEdu NBir NLar NSla WAbe WSHC
	leucanthema DJHC 752	CExl
	- 'Silver Spectre' (v)	CExl ECha
	linstowiana CD&R 605	CExl
§	***lutea***	CBcs EPfP MMuc NBir NPer NWad SEND SRms WCot
§	***malkensis*** 🏆H5	CPla CWCL EBee EMor EPot GKev MAvo NRya WThu
	'Maya' (v)	XLum
	moorcroftiana	CExl
	nobilis	GKev SPhx
	ochotensis	EHyd IMou LRHS
§	***ochroleuca***	CSpe EPot NLar
	omeiana	EPPr SPtp WCot WFar
	ophiocarpa	ELan
	pachycentra	CExl WAbe
	paczoskii	EHyd GKev LRHS NRHS
	popovii	CWCL
	pseudofumaria alba	see *C. ochroleuca*
	'Rainier Blue'	WFar
	'Rukšāns Red'	CWCL
	'Sapphire'	CBro
	scandens	see *Dactylicapnos scandens*
	scouleri	NBir
§	***sempervirens***	GWyn
	shimienensis 'Berry Exciting' PBR	CBcs CDor EBee EMor MBNS MHol MPnt NPer SPoG WTor
	siamensis	IMou
	- B&SWJ 7200	WCru
§	***solida***	CAvo CElw CMea CPla EBee ECtt EHyd EMor EPfP EPot GKev LEdu LRHS MRav NLar NRHS NRya SDeJ SPhx WBrk WCot WShi
	- 'Advocet'	GEdr
	- 'Evening Shade'	GEdr
	- 'Fire Bird'	GEdr GKev
	- 'Firecracker'	CBor EHyd GKev LRHS NRHS SPhx
	- 'Gaviota'	GEdr
§	- subsp. ***incisa*** 🏆H5	EPot SDeJ SPhx

- - 'Giona'	GKev
- 'Lucky Bird'	GKev
- 'Purple Beauty'	CBor GKev SPhx WTor
- 'Purple Bird'	ERCP GKev SDeJ WFar
- 'Pussy'	EBee EMor
- RAINBOW (mixed)	GKev
- 'Robin' new	GKev
- 'Snowy Owl' new	GKev
§ - subsp. ***solida***	EPot GKev NBir NRya SPhx WCot
- - 'Alba'	NSla
- - 'Beth Evans'	CAvo CBcs CBro CWCL ECha EMor EPot ERCP GAbr GEdr LEdu MHer MNrw NBir NHpl NLar NWad SDeJ SPhx WCot WFar
- - 'Blushing Girl'	GEdr WFar
- - 'Dieter Schacht' ♀H5	EPot GEdr NLar
- - 'Evening Shade'	GEdr
- - 'George Baker' ♀H5	Widely available
- - 'Nettleton Pink'	GKev
- - Prasil Group	CBor GEdr GKev NHpl SPhx
- - 'White Knight'	GKev NHpl WCot
- f. ***transsylvanica***	see *C. solida* subsp. *solida*
- 'Turaco'	GKev
- 'White King'	WCot
- 'White Swallow'	CBor EPot GEdr GKev SDeJ
- 'Zwanenberg'	GKev
'Spinners'	CDor CElw CFis EBee ECtt ELon EMor EPPr GKev GLog GPSL IMou LEdu NQui WFar WPnP WSHC WTyc XLum
stipulata B&SWJ 2951	WCru
'Sylvia's Castle Haven'	MPie
taliensis	CExl EMor GKev GLog
tauricola	GEdr
temulifolia 'Chocolate Stars'	CBcs CBod CMiW CSpe CWGN EBee ECtt EMor EWld ILea LRHS MBNS MHol MPie SPoG WCot WSHC
tomentella	GKev
'Tory MP'	CDor CExl CMiW CRos CSam EBee EHyd EPPr EPfP GEdr LEdu LRHS MNrw MPie NBid NChi NRHS WFar WMal WPGP XEll
transsylvanica hort.	see *C. solida* subsp. *solida*
vivipara	EPPr
'Wildside Blue'	EPPr EWld NHar WSHC
wilsonii	CExl GKev

Corylopsis (*Hamamelidaceae*)

SDR 7921	GKev
glabrescens	CBcs CJun CRos EHyd EPfP LMil LRHS NLar WCFE
- B&SWJ 14636 new	WCru
- var. ***gotoana***	CJun CRos EHyd EPfP LRHS MAsh NLar
- - 'Chollipo'	CJun CRos EHyd LRHS NLar SSta
- 'Lemon Drop'	CJun NLar WPGP
glandulifera	CJun
pauciflora ♀H5	CBcs CBod CDoC CEnd CJun CRos CTho CTri EBee ELan EPfP IDee LCro LOPS LRHS LSRN MAsh MGil MPri MRav NLar SCob SGol SLim SPer SPoG WPGP
platypetala	see *C. sinensis* var. *calvescens*
- var. ***laevis***	see *C. sinensis* var. *calvescens*
sinensis	CBcs EBee EPfP GKev
§ - var. ***calvescens***	CBcs CJun CTho EPfP NLar WCFE
§ - - f. ***veitchiana*** ♀H5	CJun CRos EHyd EPfP IMou LRHS MAsh WCFE
§ - var. ***sinensis*** ♀H5	CCCN CDoC CJun CMCN CRos CTho EBee ELan ELon EPfP LRHS MAsh NLar SGol SLon WCFE WSpi
- - 'Spring Purple'	CBcs CEnd CJun CMac CRos EBee EPfP EWes IDee LRHS MGos NLar NRHS SChF SPoG WPGP
- 'Veitch's Purple'	CJun NLar
spicata	CBcs CJun CMCN IArd IDee LRHS MBlu MGil MRav NLar SGbt SGol SLim
- 'Golden Spring'	NLar
- 'Red Eye'	CJun NLar
veitchiana	see *C. sinensis* var. *calvescens* f. *veitchiana*
willmottiae	see *C. sinensis* var. *sinensis*

Corylus ✿ (*Betulaceae*)

avellana (F)	CArg CBcs CCVT CHab CLnd CMac CTho CTri ECrN EPfP EPom GAbr LBuc LCro LMaj LOPS MGos NGrd NLar SCob SEWo SGsty SPer SReu SRms SVic WMat WMou WTSh
- 'Anaconda'	MBlu
- 'Anny's Compact Red'	WHwl
- 'Anny's Purple Dream'PBR	IDee MBlu NLar
- 'Anny's Red Dwarf'	NLar
- 'Aurea'	CBcs CEnd CTri EBee ELan EPfP MAsh MBlu MGos NLar SLim SPer SPoG SSta SWvt WBor WFar
- 'Bollwylle'	see *C. maxima* 'Halle'sche Riesennuss'
§ - 'Butler' (F)	CAgr CMac CTri SRms
- 'Casina' (F)	CAgr
- 'Clark' (F) new	MCoo
- 'Contorta' ♀H6	Widely available
- 'Corabel' (F)	CAgr NOra SKee SRms WMat
- 'Cosford' (F)	CAgr CCVT CMac CSBt CTho CTri ECrN EPom IArd LBuc MBlu MGos NLar NOra NOrn SEWo SGol SKee SPer SRms SWvt WMat
- Emoa Series	WMat
§ - 'Ennis' (F)	CAgr NLar NOra
- 'Feriale' (F)	CAgr
- 'Fuscorubra' misapplied	see *C. avellana* 'Rotblättrige Zellernuss'
- 'Gustav's Zeller' (F)	NOra WMat
§ - 'Heterophylla'	EBee NLar SSta WLov
- 'Laciniata'	see *C. avellana* 'Heterophylla'
§ - 'Lang Tidlig Zeller' (F)	CAgr NLar NOra WMat
- 'Lewis' (F)	CAgr
- 'Merveille de Bollwyller'	see *C. maxima* 'Halle'sche Riesennuss'
- 'Nottingham Prolific'	see *C. avellana* 'Pearson's Prolific'
- 'Pauetet' (F)	CAgr
§ - 'Pearson's Prolific' (F)	CAgr CSBt LBuc SGol SSFr
- 'Pendula'	LMaj MBlu NOra SCoo SRms WCot WHwl
- 'Princess' (F)	SVic
- 'Purpurea'	see *C. avellana* 'Rotblättrige Zellernuss'
- 'Red Majestic'PBR ♀H6	Widely available
§ - 'Rotblättrige Zellernuss' (F) ♀H6	CEnd CHab CTho EPom EShb IArd MBlu MRav MWat NLar NOra SCoo SGol SGsty SKee SLim SPoG SRms SSta SWvt WCot WHwl WLov
- 'Rouge de Zeller'	see *C. avellana* 'Rotblättrige Zellernuss'

- 'Scooter' **new**	NLar
- 'Tonda di Giffoni' (F)	NOra SKee WMat
- 'Webb's Prize Cob' (F)	CAgr CTri ELan IArd MBlu NLar SGol SKee SSFr SVic
chinensis	EBee WPGP
colurna ♀H6	CAgr CCVT CLnd CMCN EBee ECrN ELan EPfP EWTr IArd LMaj MBlu MGos MPri NLar NOra NOrn SCob SCoo SGol SRms WMat WMou WPGP
× ***colurnoides*** 'Chinoka' (F)	CAgr WMat
- 'Freeoka' (F)	CAgr WMat
cornuta **new**	WMou
EARLY LONG ZELLER	see *C. avellana* 'Lang Tidlig Zeller'
fargesii	WPGP
ferox	CJun
maxima (F)	CLnd CTri EPom MSwo MWat
- 'Butler'	see *C. avellana* 'Butler'
- 'Ennis'	see *C. avellana* 'Ennis'
- 'Fertile de Coutard'	see *C. maxima* 'White Filbert'
- 'Frühe van Frauendorf'	see *C. maxima* 'Red Filbert'
- 'Grote Lambertsnoot'	see *C. maxima* 'Kentish Cob'
- 'Gunslebert' (F) ♀H6	CCVT CMac CTri NOra SPoG SRms SSFr WMat
- HALLE GIANT	see *C. maxima* 'Halle'sche Riesennuss'
§ - 'Halle'sche Riesennuss' (F)	CAgr ELan NLar NOra SKee SSFr WMat
§ - 'Kentish Cob' (F) ♀H6	CAgr CBcs CMac CSBt CTho CTri EBee ECrN ELan EPfP EPom IArd LBuc LRHS MGos MWat NLar NOrn SEWo SEdi SKee SLim SPer SPoG SRms SSFr SVic SWvt WMat WMou
- 'Lambert's Filbert'	see *C. maxima* 'Kentish Cob'
- 'Longue d'Espagne'	see *C. maxima* 'Kentish Cob'
- 'Monsieur de Bouweller'	see *C. maxima* 'Halle'sche Riesennuss'
- 'Nottingham Cobnut' (F)	SVic
- 'Purple Filbert'	see *C. maxima* 'Purpurea'
§ - 'Purpurea' (F)	Widely available
- 'Red Filbert' misapplied	see *C. avellana* 'Rotblättrige Zellernuss'
- 'Red Zellernut'	see *C. maxima avellana* 'Rotblättrige Zellernuss'
- 'Spanish White'	see *C. maxima* 'White Filbert'
§ - 'White Filbert' (F)	CHab
- 'White Spanish Filbert'	see *C. maxima* 'White Filbert'
- 'Witpit Lambertsnoot'	see *C. maxima* 'White Filbert'
'Nottingham Early' (F)	NLar
sieboldiana B&SWJ 11056	WCru
- var. ***mandshurica***	MBlu
'Te Terra Red'	CMCN EBee EPfP MAsh MBlu SLon SRms WMat WMou
tibetica	LEdu WPGP

Corymbia

§ ***citriodora***	MHer SKin SPlb
§ ***eximia***	SPlb
- 'Nana'	SPlb
§ ***ficifolia***	CDTJ IDee

Corynabutilon see *Abutilon*

Corynephorus (*Poaceae*)

canescens	NBir
- 'Spiky Blue'	CBod

Cosmos (*Asteraceae*)

§ ***atrosanguineus***	CBcs CMea CPla CSpe CWGN ECtt ELan EPfP LCro LOPS LSRN MBow MRav NLar SCob SDeJ SDir SPer SPoG SWvt WHoo
- CHOCAMOCHA ('Thomocha'[PBR])	CBcs CBod CCCN CChe CDor CPla CRos CSpe CWGN ECtt EHyd EPfP GMaP LCro LOPS LRHS LSou MBros MGos MPri NLar NRHS NSti SEle SGbt SPer SPoG
- ECLIPSE ('Hamcoec'[PBR])	CRos
- SPELLBOUND ('Hamcosp')	ECtt
bipinnatus 'Antiquity'	MBros MPri SBut SPhx
- (Casanova Series) 'Casanova Pink'	SCob SPoG
- - 'Casanova Red'	SCob SPoG
- - 'Casanova Violet'	SCob SPoG
- - 'Casanova White'	SCob SPoG
- 'Cupcakes White' (Cupcakes Series) **new**	CSpe
- 'Dazzler'	LCro LOPS SPhx
- (Double Click Series) 'Double Click Cranberries' (d)	CSpe SPhx
- - 'Double Click Snow Puff' (d)	SPhx
- 'Purity'	CSpe LCro LOPS LRHS SBut SPhx
- Razzmatazz Series **new**	LCro LOPS MBros
- 'Rubenza' ♀H3	CSpe LCro LOPS SPhx
- Sensation Series	SBut
- - 'Sensation Picotee'	LCro LOPS
- - 'Sensation Pinkie' ♀H3	LCro LOPS
- Sonata Series	MBros SCob SEle
- - 'Sonata Carmine'	MPri
- - 'Sonata Pink'	MPri SCob
- - 'Sonata White'	CSpe MBros MPri SCob
- 'Sweet Sixteen'	SPhx
- 'Xanthos'	CSpe LCro LOPS MBros MPri
peucedanifolius 'Flamingo'	CGrW SDeJ
sulphureus 'Bunte Lichter'	CSpe
- LADYBIRD MIXED	SVic
'Yellow Garden'	SPhx

Cosmos × *Dahlia* (*Asteraceae*)

'Mexican Black'	see *Dahlia* 'Mexican Black'

costmary see *Tanacetum balsamita*

Costus (*Costaceae*)

barbatus	NGKo
pulverulentus	LRHS

Cotinus ✿ (*Anacardiaceae*)

americanus	see *C. obovatus*
'Candy Floss'	CRos EHyd EPfP LRHS NRHS
§ ***coggygria***	CBcs CBrac CMCN CMac ELan EPfP MRav MSwo NLar NOra SCob SEND SGbt SGol SPer SRms SWvt SavN WFar WHwl XSen
- GOLDEN LADY ('Mincojau3') **new**	SGsty
- GOLDEN SPIRIT ('Ancot'[PBR]) ♀H5	Widely available
- GREEN FOUNTAIN ('Kolcot'[PBR])	EBee LRHS
- 'Kanari'	NLar
- 'Lilla'[PBR]	EPfP LRHS MAsh MBlu MPkF NLar NRHS SGsty

- 'Notcutt's Variety'	MRav
- 'Old Fashioned'PBR	CBod MPkF NEoE NLar WMou
- 'Pink Champagne'	NLar SSta
- Purpureus Group	EPfP SGol SRms
- 'Red Beauty'	NLar
- RED SPIRIT ('Firstpur')	NLar
- 'Royal Purple' ♀H5	Widely available
- Rubrifolius Group	CBcs EPfP SEND SGol SPer SWvt
- SMOKEY JOE ('Lisjo'PBR)	CBcs CBod CRos EHyd EPfP LRHS MAsh MPkF SLon SPoG SSta SWvt
- 'Velvet Cloak'	EPfP LRHS MGos NLar SLon SWvt
- 'Well Spotted'	EMil
- 'Westonbirt Orange'	NLar
- 'Young Lady'PBR ♀H5	CBcs CBod CDoC CMac ECrN ELan ELon EPfP EWes GBin LRHS MAsh MBlu MPkF MRav NLar SCob SCoo SGol SPer SRms SWvt SavN WFar
DUSKY MAIDEN ('Londus'PBR)	CRos CSBt CTsd EHyd ELan ELon EPfP LRHS MAsh MGos NEoE NLar NRHS SLon WFar
'Flame' ♀H5	CBcs CDoC CRos CTho EBee EHyd ELan ELon EPfP EWTr LRHS MAsh MGos MRav NRHS SGbt SGsty SPer SPoG SWvt WAvo WFar
'Grace'	Widely available
§ ***obovatus***	CMCN EPfP IArd LRHS MBlu MPkF MRav SSta WPGP
'Ruby Glow'	CRos EHyd EPfP LCro LOPS LRHS MGos NRHS

Cotoneaster ✿ (*Rosaceae*)

acuminatus	SRms
acutifolius	see *C. laetevirens*
var. ***laetevirens***	
§ ***adpressus*** 'Little Gem'	NHar NLar
- var. ***praecox***	see *C. nanshan*
- 'Tangstedt'	SGol
- 'Tom Thumb'	see *C. adpressus* 'Little Gem'
affinis	SPtp SRms
albokermesinus	SRms
ambiguus Rehder & E.H.Wilson	NLar
amoenus	NLar SRms
- ACE 1028	SPtp
§ ***apiculatus***	NLar SRms
§ ***ascendens***	SRms
assamensis	SRms
§ ***astrophoros***	CMac GRum MBlu NLar
atropurpureus	NLar SRms
§ - 'Variegatus' (v) ♀H6	CBcs CDoC CMac CRos EHyd ELan ELon EPfP LRHS MAsh MGos NLar NPer NRHS SCob SCoo SDix SLim SPer SPoG SRms SWvt WAvo WFar
aurantiacus	NLar SPtp
beimashanensis	ELan SPtp
boisianus	NLar SPtp SRms
bradyi	EBee GBin GKev SRms
brickellii	NLar
§ ***bullatus***	CTri EPfP NLar SPer SRms
- 'Firebird'	see *C. ignescens*
- f. ***floribundus***	see *C. bullatus*
- var. ***macrophyllus***	see *C. rehderi*
bumthangensis	NLar SRms
buxifolius blue-leaved	see *C. lidjiangensis*
- 'Brno'	see *C. marginatus* 'Brno'
- f. ***vellaeus***	see *C. astrophoros*
camilli-schneideri	SRms
canescens	NLar SRms
chadwelli	NLar
chuanus	NLar
- L 624 **new**	SPtp
chungtiensis	NLar
cinerascens	SPtp
cinnabarinus	SRms
§ ***cochleatus***	SPtp SRms
§ ***congestus***	CSBt ELan MSwo NLar SPer SPlb SRms XLum
- 'Nanus'	GEdr
conspicuus	CBcs EWTr SPtp SRms
- 'Decorus' ♀H6	CBrac CDoC CRos CSBt EHyd EPfP LRHS MGos MMuc MSwo SCob SGol SLim SNig SPer SPlb SPoG SWvt
- 'Leicester Gem'	SRms
- 'Red Glory'	CMac
cooperi	SRms
- 'Nicolette' **new**	NLar
* 'Coral'	ECrN
cordifolius	MBlu NLar SRms
- KW 13363	SPtp
cornifolius	SRms
- Og 93330	SPtp
§ 'Cornubia' ♀H6	Widely available
crispii	NLar
cuspidatus	MBlu NLar SPtp
dammeri	CBcs CBod CDoC CMac CRos CSBt CTri EBee ECrN EHyd ELan EPfP LRHS MAsh MGos MRav MSwo NHol NLar NRHS SCob SGol SLim SPer SPoG SRms SWvt WCFE WFar
§ - 'Major'	CBar LBuc SCob
§ - 'Mooncreeper'	CDoC
- 'Oakwood'	see *C. radicans*
- var. ***radicans*** misapplied	see *C. dammeri* 'Major'
- var. ***radicans*** (Dammer ex C.K. Schneid.) C.K. Schneid.	see *C. radicans*
dammeri × ***microphyllus***	CBrac
dielsianus	NLar SRms
divaricatus	NLar SPer SRms
duthieanus	NLar SPtp
- 'Boer'	see *C. apiculatus*
elatus	SRms
elegans	SPtp SRms
emeiensis	NLar SRms
encavei	NLar
- KEKE 1239	SPtp
'Erlinda'	see *C.* × *suecicus* 'Erlinda'
'Exburiensis'	CBcs CBod CBrac CCVT EBee EPfP MGos MMuc MRav NLar NOra NOrn SCob SEND SGol SPer WFar WMat
falconeri	SRms
fastigiatus	SPtp SRms
flinckii	NLar SRms
floccosus	IArd SEND SPtp
floridus	SRms
forrestii	GKev NLar SRms
franchetii	Widely available
frigidus	CMCN CTho SPtp SRms
§ - 'Pershore Coral'	WAvo
froebelii	SPtp
fulvidus	NLar
gamblei	SRms

	- KR 1576	SPtp
	ganghobaensis	CMCN GKev NLar SPtp SRms
	- B&L 12234	WCru
	glabratus	SRms
	- KR 232	SPtp
	glacialis	CPla SRms
	glaucophyllus	IArd SRms
§	***glomerulatus***	NLar SRms
	gracilis	SRms
	granatensis	NLar SRms
	'Green Fan'	SPtp
	harrovianus	SRms
	harrysmithii	NLar
	hebephyllus	NLar
	hedegaardii	SPtp
I	- 'Fructu Luteo'	SPtp SRms
	- yellow-fruited	SPtp
	henryanus	SRms
	- 'Corina'	SRms
	'Herbstfeuer'	see *C. salicifolius* 'Herbstfeuer'
	'Highlight'	see *C. pluriflorus*
	hillieri	NLar SPtp
§	***hjelmqvistii***	LBuc NLar SPtp SRms
	- 'Robustus'	see *C. hjelmqvistii*
	- 'Rotundifolius'	see *C. hjelmqvistii*
	hodjingensis	SRms
	horizontalis	Widely available
	- 'Variegatus'	see *C. atropurpureus* 'Variegatus'
	- var. ***wilsonii***	see *C. ascendens*
	huahongdongensis	ELan SPtp
	hualiensis	NLar SRms
	- B&SWJ 3143	WCru
	humifusus	see *C. dammeri*
	hummelii	SRms
	hupehensis	NLar
§	'Hybridus Pendulus'	CBcs CBrac CCVT CMac CTri EBee ECrN LCro LSRN MGos MPri MRav NLar NOra NOrn SCob SGbt SLim SPer SPoG SRms SWvt WJas WMat
§	***hylmoei***	ELan NLar SPtp SRms
	hypocarpus	SPtp SRms
	ignavus	SRms
§	***ignescens***	NLar SRms
	ignotus	SRms
	incanus	NLar
	induratus	SRms
	insculptus	SPtp SRms
	insolitus	NLar SPtp
	integerrimus	SRms
§	***integrifolius***	ELan SPtp SRms
	kangdingensis	SRms
	kingdonii	NLar
	kitaibelii	NLar
	konishii	NLar
	kuanensis SICH 56A	SPtp
	kweitschoviensis	NLar
	lacteus ♀H6	Widely available
	- F 10419	ELan SPtp
	- 'Milkmaid' (v)	NLar
§	***laetevirens***	NLar
	lancasteri	NLar SRms
	langei	SRms
	laxiflorus	SRms
§	***lidjiangensis***	NLar SRms
	lucidus	SRms
	ludlowii	SPtp SRms
	magnificus	SRms
§	***mairei***	NLar SPtp SRms
	marginatus Lindl. ex Loudon	SRms
§	- 'Blazovice'	NLar SRms
§	- 'Brno'	SRms
	marquandii	NLar SRms
§	***meiophyllus***	MBlu NLar
	melanocarpus	NLar
	melanotrichus misapplied	see *C. cochleatus*
	melanotrichus (Franch.) G. Klotz **new**	SPtp
	meuselii	NLar SRms
	- TSS 13864	SPtp
	microphyllus misapplied	see *C. purpurascens*
	microphyllus ambig.	CBcs EBee GBin SCob
	microphyllus Wall. ex Lindl.	CRos CTri LRHS MGos SPer
	- NICE 004	WCFE
	- var. ***cochleatus*** (Franch.) Rehder & E.H. Wilson	see *C. cochleatus*
	- var. ***cochleatus*** ambig.	EPot NSla
	- 'Donard Gem'	see *C. astrophoros*
	- 'Teulon Porter'	see *C. astrophoros*
	- var. ***thymifolius*** (Lindl.) Koehne	see *C. integrifolius*
	- var. ***thymifolius*** ambig.	CRos EHyd LRHS
	milkedandaensis	SRms
	miniatus	SRms
	mirabilis	NLar SRms
	monopyrenus	SRms
	- F 11422	GKev
	'Mooncreeper'	see *C. dammeri* 'Mooncreeper'
	morrisonensis	SRms
	moupinensis	SRms
	- BWJ 8167	WCru
	mucronatus	NLar SPtp SRms
	'My Pet'	GAbr
§	***nanshan***	SRms WAvo
	- 'Boer'	see *C. apiculatus*
	naoujanensis	EPfP NLar
	- 'Berried Treasure'	CRos EHyd EPfP LRHS NRHS
	nepalensis	NLar
	newryensis	SRms
	nitens	NLar SRms
	nitidifolius	see *C. glomerulatus*
	nohelii	NLar SRms
	notabilis	SRms
	nummularioides	SRms
	nummularius Fisch. & C.A. Mey.	SRms
	obscurus	SRms
	obtusus Wall. ex Lindl.	NLar SRms
	ogisui	EBee GBin LEdu
	- Og 95105	EBee GKev WPGP
	omissus	NLar
	pangiensis	SRms
	pannosus	SRms
	paradoxus	SRms
	parkeri	NLar SRms
	pekinensis	SRms
	permutatus	see *C. pluriflorus*
	perpusillus	SRms
	'Pershore Coral'	see *C. frigidus* 'Pershore Coral'
§	***pluriflorus***	SRms
	poluninii	NLar SPtp SRms
	polycarpus	SRms
	praecox 'Boer'	see *C. apiculatus*
	procumbens	SRms
	- 'Needham'	NLar
	- 'Queen of Carpets' ♀H6	CBod CBrac CDoC CRos EBee EHyd ELan EPfP LRHS LSRN MAsh MGos MRav NLar NRHS SCoo SLim SPoG SRms SWvt

	- 'Streib's Findling'	see *C.* 'Streib's Findling'
	prostratus	SRms
	- 'Arnold-Forster'	ELan SPtp
	przewalskii	SRms
	pseudo-obscurus	SRms
	psikangensis new	NLar
§	***purpurascens***	CRos CSBt EHyd LRHS NLar NRHS
	pyrenaicus misapplied	see *C. congestus*
	qungbixiensis	NLar SRms
	raboutensis	NLar
	racemiflorus	SRms
§	***radicans***	CMCN
§	***rehderi***	NLar SPtp SRms
	reticulatus	NLar
	rhytidophyllus	ELan GKev SPtp
	- Og 95102	SPtp
	rokujodaisanensis	NLar
	roseus	NLar SRms
	'Rothschildianus' ♀H6	CBcs CBod CCVT CMac CRos CSBt CTho CTri EBee EHyd ELan EPfP LRHS MBlu MGos MRav MSwo NLar NRHS SAko SCoo SGbt SLim SPer SRms SSta SWvt WJas
	rubens W.W.Sm.	NLar
	rugosus E. Pritz. ex Diels	NLar SPtp SRms
	'Saint Andrews Blaze' new	ELan SPtp
	'Saint Monica'	MBlu
	salicifolius	CTri MSwo NLar SCob SPtp SRms WFar
	- AUTUMN FIRE	see *C. salicifolius* 'Herbstfeuer'
§	- 'Avonbank'	CEnd NLar WAvo
	- 'Brno Orangeade'	SRms
	- 'Emerald Carpet'	SEND
	- 'Fructuluteo'	SPtp
	- 'Gnom' ♀H6	CChe CDoC CMac CRos EHyd ELan EPfP LRHS MAsh MGos NBir SCob SLim SPer SPoG SPtp SRms WAvo
§	- 'Herbstfeuer'	MRav MSwo SRms
	- 'Pendulus'	see *C.* 'Hybridus Pendulus'
	- 'Pink Champagne' ♀H6	CMac
	- 'Repens'	CBrac EPfP NOra SCob SGol SLim SPer SPoG SRms WMat
	- var. ***rugosus***	see *C. hylmoei*
	salwinensis	NLar SPtp SRms
	sandakphuensis	SRms
	scandinavicus	SRms
	schantungensis	NLar SRms
	schlechtendalii 'Blazovice'	see *C. marginatus* 'Blazovice'
	- 'Brno'	see *C. marginatus* 'Brno'
	schubertii	SRms
*	***sengorensis***	NLar
	serotinus misapplied	see *C. meiophyllus*
	serotinus Hutch.	SRms
	shannanensis	ELan SPtp SRms
	shansiensis	NLar SPtp SRms
	sherriffii	NLar SRms
	sikangensis	GBin SRms
	simonsii	CCVT CLnd CMac CRos EBee ECrN ELan GKev LBuc LRHS MGos MMuc NHol NWad SCob SGol SPtp SRms WFar
	- MF 904 new	SPtp
	soczavianus	NLar
§	***splendens***	ELan GKev SPtp SRms
	- 'Sabrina'	see *C. splendens*
	spongbergii	NLar SRms
	staintonii	SRms
	sternianus ♀H6	EPfP NLar SPtp SRms
	- ACE 2200	MSwo
	aff. ***sternianus*** Yu 15716	SPtp
§	'Streib's Findling'	EHyd LRHS MAsh NLar SGol SPtp
	suavis	SRms
	subacutus	SRms
	subadpressus	SRms
	submultiflorus	NLar
	× ***suecicus*** 'Coral Beauty' ♀H6	CBod CBrac CCVT CDoC CRos CTri EBee EHyd EPfP EShb LBuc LCro LOPS LRHS MAsh MGos MRav MSwo NHol NLar NOra NRHS SCob SGol SLim SPoG SRms SWvt WMat
§	- 'Erlinda' (v)	SPoG SRms
	- 'Ifor'	SRms
	- 'Juliette' (v) ♀H6	CMac CRos EHyd EShb LRHS LSRN MAsh MMrt MRav NLar NOra NOrn NRHS SCoo SLim SPer SPoG WMat
	- 'Skogholm'	CBcs CRos ELan EPfP LRHS MGos SCob SPer SRms
	svenhedinii	NLar
	taoensis	SPtp SRms
	taofuensis Sich 1878 new	SPtp
	tardiflorus	NLar SPtp SRms
	tauricus	SRms
	teijiashanensis	NLar SPtp SRms
	tengyuehensis	SPtp SRms
	thimphuensis	NLar SRms
	tomentellus	WCFE
	tomentosus	SRms
	transcaucasicus	NLar
	trinervis	GKev
	turbinatus	NLar SPtp SRms
	'Valkenburg'	SRms
	vandelaarii	ELan NLar SPtp SRms
	veitchii	NLar SRms
	verruculosus	SRms
	vestitus	NLar
	villosulus	SRms
	vilmorinianus	SPtp SRms
	wardii misapplied	see *C. mairei*
	wardii W.W.Sm.	SRms
	× ***watereri***	CBod CCVT ECrN ELon EPfP MSwo WJas
	- 'Avonbank'	see *C. salicifolius* 'Avonbank'
	- 'Cornubia'	see *C.* 'Cornubia'
	- 'John Waterer'	EPfP SPer SPoG
	- 'Pendulus'	see *C.* 'Hybridus Pendulus'
	wilsonii	SRms
	yalungensis	SRms
	yinchangensis	SRms
	zabelii	SRms

Cotula (*Asteraceae*)

	coronopifolia	CBen CWat NPer
	hispida ambig.	CPla EBou ECtt EPfP EWld
§	***hispida*** (DC.) Harv.	CTri CWCL EDAr GMaP MAsh MHer NPer NRya SPoG SRms WIce XLum
	lineariloba (DC.) Hilliard	ECha EWes
	pectinata	see *Leptinella pectinata*
	perpusilla	see *Leptinella pusilla*
	'Platt's Black'	see *Leptinella squalida* 'Platt's Black'
	potentilloides	see *Leptinella potentillina*
	pyrethrifolia	see *Leptinella pyrethrifolia*
	reptans	see *Leptinella scariosa*
	scariosa	see *Leptinella scariosa*
	squalida	see *Leptinella squalida*

Cotyledon (*Crassulaceae*)

	chrysantha	see *Rosularia chrysantha*
	oppositifolia	see *Umbilicus oppositifolius*

orbiculata	CPbh EShb SPlb WCot
- 'Cedric Morris' **new**	SChr
- var. ***oblonga***	CDoC EShb WCot
- 'Silver Waves'	MCot
pendens **new**	EShb
simplicifolia	see *Umbilicus oppositifolius*

courgette see AGM Vegetables Section

Crambe (*Brassicaceae*)

abyssinica	SPhx
cordifolia $\mathrm{♀}^{H5}$	Widely available
- 'Morning's Snow' **new**	NLar
maritima	Widely available
- 'Lilywhite'	CAgr LEdu SVic
orientalis	WHil

cranberry see *Vaccinium macrocarpon*, *V. oxycoccos*

Crassula ✿ (*Crassulaceae*)

	anomala	see *C. atropurpurea* var. *anomala*
	arborescens	EShb SChr SSim XAbr
	- subsp. ***undulatifolia*** **new**	CDoC
	argentea	see *C. ovata*
§	***atropurpurea*** var. ***anomala***	SChr
	- subsp. ***arborescens*** 'Blue Mist'	SEND
	'Buddha's Temple'	SSim
	coccinea	CPbh EShb SPlb WCot
	columnaris **new**	SSim
*	***coralloides***	CPBP SPlb
	cordata	EShb
	hystrix 'Variegata' (v) **new**	SAll
	lycopodioides variegata	see *C. muscosa* 'Variegata'
	muscosa	CBen EShb SChr SPlb
§	- 'Variegata' (v)	SSim
§	***ovata*** $\mathrm{♀}^{H2}$	EBak LCro LOPS NCft NGBl NPer SChr SEND SPlb SPre SSim SVen WThu
	- 'Gollum' $\mathrm{♀}^{H2}$	EShb NCft SEND
	- 'Hummel's Sunset' (v) $\mathrm{♀}^{H2}$	EShb NCft
	- 'Minima'	NCft
*	- ***nana***	SEND
	- 'Undulata'	WCot
	- 'Variegata' (v)	EBak EShb WCot
	pellucida subsp. ***marginalis***	CDoC
	- - f. ***rubra***	CDoC EShb
*	- - 'Variegata' (v)	SSim WOld
	perfoliata var. ***falcata*** $\mathrm{♀}^{H2}$	EShb SIvy WCot
	perforata $\mathrm{♀}^{H2}$	CDoC NCft
	- 'Variegata' (v)	CDoC EShb LLWG NCft NWad SSim
	portulacea	see *C. ovata*
	rupestris $\mathrm{♀}^{H2}$	CDoC SSim
	- subsp. ***marnieriana***	CDoC SIvy
§	***sarcocaulis*** $\mathrm{♀}^{H3}$	CBcs CMea CPla CTri EBou ELan ELon GMaP LLWG MAsh MCot NHpl SBrt SIvy SPlb SPoG SRms SVen WAbe WCav WHoo WIce WMal WSHC XSen
I	- 'Alba'	NHpl
	schmidtii	SSim
	- dark-flowered **new**	SSim
	- white-flowered **new**	SSim
	sedifolia	see *C. setulosa* 'Milfordiae'
	sediformis	see *C. setulosa* 'Milfordiae'
	sericea	WOld
	var. ***hottentotta*** **new**	
	setulosa	SPlb
§	- 'Milfordiae'	CTri NBir NHpl NRya WAbe
	tetragona	SEND
*	***tomentosa*** 'Variegata' (v)	EShb

+ *Crataegomespilus* (*Rosaceae*)

'Jules d'Asnières'	NLar

× *Crataegosorbus* (*Rosaceae*)

miczurinii 'Ivan's Belle'	CAgr

Crataegus (*Rosaceae*)

	arnoldiana	CAgr CLnd CTri EBee ECrN MAsh MCoo NLar SPoG WMat
	'Autumn Glory'	CEnd CLnd ECrN
§	***coccinea*** L.	CAgr CLnd LMaj WMat
	cordata	see *C. phaenopyrum*
	crus-galli misapplied	see *C. persimilis* 'Prunifolia'
	crus-galli L.	CCVT CLnd ECrN EPfP MAsh NLar SPer WJas
	douglasii	EBtc
	× ***durobrivensis***	CAgr CLnd EBee EPfP MBlu
	ellwangeriana	CAgr ECrN WCot
	- 'Fire Ball'	MBlu NLar
	eriocarpa	CLnd
	gemmosa	CAgr
	× ***grignonensis*** $\mathrm{♀}^{H7}$	CBcs CLnd CTho ECrN ELan MAsh MMuc NLar WJas
	harbisonii	IArd
	jonesiae	EPfP
	laciniata misapplied	see *C. orientalis*
§	***laevigata***	SCob
	- 'Coccinea Plena'	see *C. laevigata* 'Paul's Scarlet'
	- 'Crimson Cloud'	see *C. laevigata* 'Punicea'
	- 'Gireoudii'	CBod WJas
	- 'Mutabilis'	CTri SGol
§	- 'Paul's Scarlet' (d) $\mathrm{♀}^{H7}$	Widely available
	- 'Pink Corkscrew'	EPfP MAsh MBlu WCot WLov
	- 'Plena' (d)	CLnd CMac CSBt CTri EBee ECrN ELan EPfP MGos MRav MSwo NOra NOrn SCob SEWo SGol SLim SPer SWvt WMat
§	- 'Punicea' $\mathrm{♀}^{H7}$	CArg CBcs CBrac CCVT CEnd CLnd EBee ECrN ELan EPfP EWTr LSRN MGos MMuc MPri MSwo NLar NOra NOrn SCoo SEND SEWo SGbt SLim SLon SPer SPoG WMat WMou
	- 'Rosea'	GKin
	- 'Rosea Flore Pleno' (d) $\mathrm{♀}^{H7}$	Widely available
	× ***lavalleei***	CCVT CLnd CMCN CTri ECrN ELan MRav MSwo NOrn SCoo SLon WTSh
	- 'Aurora'	NLar
	- 'Carrierei' $\mathrm{♀}^{H7}$	CMac CTho EPfP EWTr LMaj LSRN SCob SCoo SEND SEWo SGsty SPoG WMat WMou
	mexicana	see *C. pubescens* f. *stipulacea*
	mollis	CAgr ECrN EPfP WSpi
	monogyna	Widely available
§	- 'Biflora'	CEnd CLnd CTho CTri MAsh MCoo MGos SLim WMat WSpi
	- 'Compacta'	MAsh MBlu WCot WLov
	- 'Praecox'	see *C. monogyna* 'Biflora'

	- 'Stricta'	CCVT CLnd CSBt ECrN EPfP IDee LMaj SCob SPer
	- 'Variegata' (v)	ECrN SWeb
	× ***mordenensis*** 'Toba' (d)	CLnd LRHS
§	***orientalis*** ♀H6	CCVT CEnd CLnd CMCN CTho CTri ECrN ELan EPfP EWTr IArd IMou MAsh MCoo MGos NLar NOrn SCoo SLim WJas WMat WMou WSpi
	oxyacantha misapplied	see *C. laevigata*
	pedicellata	see *C. coccinea* L.
	persimilis	LMaj
§	- 'Prunifolia' ♀H7	Widely available
	- 'Prunifolia Splendens'	CAgr CCVT EBar EBee EWTr LBuc LMaj NOra NOrn WMat
§	***phaenopyrum***	CLnd CTho EBee EPfP SPtp
	pinnatifida var. ***major***	CEnd ECrN EPfP LEdu MCoo NOrn
	- - 'Big Golden Star'	CAgr CTho EBee EPfP MBlu MCoo NLar NOra WMat WMou
	'Praecox'	see *C. monogyna* 'Biflora'
	prunifolia	see *C. persimilis* 'Prunifolia'
§	***pubescens*** f. ***stipulacea***	CTho ECrN EPfP
	punctata	EPfP
	- f. ***aurea***	EPfP MBlu
	pycnoloba	GKev
	sanguinea	EPfP
	schraderiana	CAgr CLnd CTho EBee EPfP EWTr NLar WMat
	submollis	CLnd
	succulenta 'Jubilee'PBR	CAgr EBee MCoo NLar NOra WMat
	- var. ***macracantha***	CMCN
	tanacetifolia	CAgr CTho EPfP MBlu
	viridis 'Winter King'	CAgr EPfP
	wattiana	CLnd EBee

Crataegus × *Mespilus* see × *Crataemespilus*

Crataegus + *Mespilus* see + *Crataegomespilus*

Crataegus × *Sorbus* see × *Crataegosorbus*

× *Crataemespilus* (*Rosaceae*)

	grandiflora	CLnd

Cremanthodium (*Asteraceae*)

	lineare	GKev

Cremnophila × *Sedum* see × *Cremnosedum*

× *Cremnosedum* (*Crassulaceae*)

§	'Little Gem'	WOld

Crenularia see *Aethionema*

Crepis (*Asteraceae*)

	aurea	CPla
	incana ♀H5	CBor CPla ECtt EWld GBin NChi NSla SRms WAbe WMal
	rubra	CSpe

Crinitaria see *Aster*

Crinodendron (*Elaeocarpaceae*)

	hookerianum ♀H4	Widely available
	- 'Ada Hoffmann'	CBcs CBod CBrac CCCN CEnd CExl CMac CPla CRos EHyd EPfP GKin LRHS MBlu MGil MGos MPkF NLar SEle SGol SWvt WHwl WPav
	patagua	CBcs CCCN CExl CMac CPla EBee EHyd ELan ELon EPfP ESwi GBin LRHS MGil NLar SEND SEle SPlb SVen WHwl WPav

Crinum (*Amaryllidaceae*)

	amoenum	CCCN EShb GKev
§	***bulbispermum***	CPrp
	capense	see *C. bulbispermum*
	'Carolina Beauty'	WCot
	'Cintho Alpha'	GKev SDeJ SPer
	'Elizabeth Traub'	WCot
	'Ellen Bosanquet'	CCCN EHyd ELan EPri GBin GKev LRHS SDir WCot
	'Emma Jones'	WCot
	'Hanibal's Dwarf'	WPGP
	moorei	CBro LEdu SChr WPGP
	- f. ***album***	CCCN EBee EPri GKev
	- hybrid **new**	WMal
	'Ollene'	WCot
§	× ***powellii***	CBcs CBro CExl CPrp CRos CTsd EBak ECha EHyd ELan ELon EPfP EShb GKev LEdu LRHS MNrw MRav NRHS NWad SDeJ SDir SEND SMad SPer SRms WCot
	- 'Album'	CAvo CBod CBro CPrp CTri EBee ECha EHyd ELan EPfP EShb EWes GKev LEdu LRHS MRav NRHS SDeJ SDir SEND SMad SPer SRms WAvo WCot WFar WPGP WSHC
	- 'Bak-madder'	EBee
	- 'Harlemense'	EBee
	- 'Krelagei'	EBee
	- 'Longifolium'	see *C. bulbispermum*
	- 'Roseum'	see *C.* × *powellii*
	'Sangria'	WCot
	'Summer Nocturne'	WCot
	'White Queen'	WCot
	yemense misapplied	GKev

Criogenes see *Cypripedium*

Crithmum (*Apiaceae*)

	maritimum	CEls GPoy LRHS MNHC SBrt SPhx SPlb SRms WABo WJek

Crocosmia (*Iridaceae*)

	'Abundant Joy'	EBee IBal
	'African Beauty'	ECtt IBal
	'Anna Marie'	EBee ECtt ELan GAbr GKev SDir WFar
	'Anniversary'	IBlr
	'Apricot'	IBal
	'Apricot Surprise'	ECtt IBal
	aurea misapplied	see *C.* × *crocosmiiflora* 'George Davison' Davison
	aurea ambig.	CPrp EHyd EShb LRHS
	aurea (Pappe ex Hook.f.) Planch.	CPou IBal IBlr LEdu
	- from Swaziland	IBal
	- subsp. ***aurea***	IBlr
	- - 'Maculata'	IBlr
	- 'Golden Ballerina'PBR	CWCL EBee ECtt EWes IBal MHol MWat SPoG
	- subsp. ***pauciflora***	IBlr
	'Auricorn'	IBal IBlr LEdu SMad WPGP
	'Auriol'	IBlr
	'Aurora'	NGdn
	'Ballyrogan Sundown'	IBlr
	'Baywalker'	MAvo
	'Beth Chatto'	IBal
	'Big Top'	IBal

	Name	Suppliers
	'Blaze'	IBal
	'Bowland Blaze'	IBal MAvo
	BRESSINGHAM BEACON ('Blos')	EHyd LRHS MSpe
	'Bressingham Blaze'	CBre CPrp CRos CSam EHyd IBal LRHS NGdn NHol NRHS
	BRIGHT EYES ('Walbreyes'^{PBR})	EHyd EPfP LRHS NRHS
	'Buttercups'	CMea ECul ELan SWvt WCAu WSpi
	'Cadenza'	IBal IBlr NWad
	'Caistor Sunset'	IBal
	'Cascade'	IBal
	'Chinatown'	IBal IBlr
	'Chrome'	CSam
	'Chrome Spray'	IBlr
	'Citronella' misapplied	see *C.* × *crocosmiiflora* 'Honey Angels'
	'Comet' Knutty	CRos EHyd IBal IBlr LRHS MAvo NRHS
	'Cornish Copper'	CPrp
	× ***crocosmiiflora***	CTri IBlr LCro LOPS SPlb SRms WBrk WShi
	- 'A.J. Hogan'	CPrp IBal NHol
	- 'African Glow'	EBee IBal
	- 'Amberglow'	CExl GWyn IBal NHol NPer WFar
	- 'Apricot Queen'	NHol
	- 'Baby Barnaby'	CBre EBee WFar
	- 'Babylon' ♀^{H4}	Widely available
	- 'Best of British'	ECtt
	- 'Bicolor'	CElw
	- 'Burford Bronze'	IBal NHol
	- 'Burnt Umber'	IBal
	- 'Buttercup'	CDor CRos CSam ECtt EHyd EPfP GKev IBal LRHS MAvo NHol NRHS SRkn WFar WSpi
	- 'Canary Bird'	CBro CSam ECtt ELon GAbr IBal NGdn NHol WBrk WSpi
§	- 'Carmin Brillant' ♀^{H4}	Widely available
	- 'Challa'	ECtt IBal
	- 'Citrina'	MNrw
	- 'Citronella' J.E. Fitt	CAby CBro CExl CSam EBee EHyd EPfP GMaP LRHS MBel NGdn NHol NRHS SDix
§	- 'Coleton Fishacre'	CExl CNor CSam CWCL ECha ECtt ELan ELon EPfP EPri GMaP IBal IBlr LRHS MMuc MNrw NBid NChi NHol SEND SPer WCot WFar WHoo WOld
§	- 'Columbus'	CAvo CBro CPrp CSam EHyd EPfP EPri EWhm IBal ILea LRHS MAvo MTis NHol NRHS SDir SMad SPer SRms WFar
	- 'Colwall'	IBal NWad WSHC
	- 'Comet'	EBee IBal
	- 'Constance'	CBro CDor CSam ECtt EHyd EPri GAbr IBal LRHS MAvo NBid NGdn NHol NRHS WBrk WFar
	- 'Corona'	CPrp IBal MAvo NHol
§	- 'Croesus'	IBal MAvo
	- 'Custard Cream'	CPrp EHyd LRHS NHol
	- 'Daisy Hill'	IBlr
	- 'David Fitt'	IBal MAvo WFar
	- 'Debutante'	CPrp EBee EPri IBal NHol SHar WHoo WSHC
§	- 'Diadème'	CWCL IBal
	- 'Dusky Maiden'	CMac ECtt ELon GKin GMaP IBal MMuc MSwo NHol SRms SWvt
	- 'Dwarf Gold'	IBal
§	- 'E.A. Bowles'	CPou
	- 'Eastern Promise'	CBre IBal MAvo
	- 'Elegans'	ECtt IBal
§	- 'Emily McKenzie'	Widely available
	- 'Fantasie'	IBal
	- 'Fire Jumper'	CBod EBee ECtt EMor GWyn IBal IPot MAvo MBel MSpe
	- 'Fireglow'^{PBR}	CRos ECtt EHyd GKev IBal LRHS NRHS
	- 'George Davison' misapplied	see *C.* × *crocosmiiflora* 'Golden Glory' ambig., *C.* 'Sulphurea'
§	- 'George Davison' Davison	Widely available
	- 'Gillian'	IBal
	- 'Gloria'	IBal MAvo SMad
	- 'Golden Glory' misapplied	see *C.* × *crocosmiiflora* 'Diadème'
§	- 'Golden Glory' ambig.	CBod CDor CExl CWCL ECul ELan ELon EShb GAbr GKev GWyn IBal LPot MSwo NBir SGbt SPer SRms WCFE
	- 'Goldfinch'	CPrp EBee
	- 'Goldie'	WFar
	- 'Hades'	IBal IBlr
	- 'Harlequin'	CBcs CBod CElw CPrp EBee EMor IBal ILea LRHS MAsh MAvo MBriF MHol MSCN MTis NBPC SPoG SWvt WFar WHoo WTor
	- 'Harvest Sun'	IBlr
	- 'His Majesty'	CBro CPrp IBal IBlr NHol WFar
	- 'Hoey Joey'	MAvo
§	- 'Honey Angels'	Widely available
	- 'Honey Bells'	WBrk WOld
	- 'Irish Dawn'	IBal IBlr NHol NWad
§	- 'Jackanapes'	CBor CMea CRos CWCL ECtt ELon IBal IBlr LRHS MNrw SCob SRms
	- 'Jackanapes VI'	IBal
	- 'James Coey' misapplied	see *C.* × *crocosmiiflora* 'Carmin Brillant'
	- 'James Coey' J.E. Fitt	CPrp ECha EPfP GKin IBal NDov NLar SPoG
§	- 'Jessie'	CElw
	- 'Judith'	IBal
	- 'Kiautschou'	CWCL IBal IBlr NHol
	- 'Lady Hamilton'	CExl ECtt EHyd IBal LRHS NHol WOut
	- 'Lady McKenzie'	see *C.* × *crocosmiiflora* 'Emily McKenzie'
	- 'Lady Oxford'	IBal NHol
	- 'Lady Wilson'	CRos EHyd LRHS NRHS
	- 'Lambrook Gold'	CAvo IBal
	- 'Lord Nelson'	CExl IBal NHol
	- 'Loweswater'	IBal
	- 'Lutea'	CPrp ECtt IBal
	- 'Marjorie'	IBal
	- 'Mars'	EWes IBal MAvo NGdn WOut
	- 'Mephistopheles'	CBor CPrp IBlr NHol WFar
	- 'Merryman'	IBal MAvo
	- 'Météore'	ECtt EHyd EPfP LRHS NRHS WFar
	- 'Morgenlicht'	IBal NHol WFar
	- 'Mount Usher'	CPrp IBal MNrw NHol WOut
§	- 'Mrs Geoffrey Howard'	EHyd GBin IBal LRHS NHol SHar SRms WCru
	- 'Mrs Morrison'	see *C.* × *crocosmiiflora* 'Mrs Geoffrey Howard'
	- 'Newry Seedling'	see *C.* × *crocosmiiflora* 'Prometheus'
	- 'Nimbus'	CPrp IBal
§	- 'Norwich Canary'	ECha ECtt EHyd EPri IBal LRHS MPie MRav NBir NGdn NHol NRHS SPer WSpi
	- 'Olympic Fire'	NHol

– 'Pepper'	IBlr
– 'Plaisir'	IBal NBid NHol
– 'Polo'	CPrp CSam CWCL ECtt EHyd IBal LRHS
– 'Princess'	see *C. pottsii* 'Princess'
– 'Prolificans'	IBal
§ – 'Prometheus'	EHyd IBal IBlr LRHS NHol
§ – 'Queen Alexandra' J.E. Fitt	CPrp ECha EWes WHal
– 'Queen Charlotte'	IBal
– 'Queen Mary II'	see *C.* × *crocosmiiflora* 'Columbus'
– 'Queen of Spain'	ELon IBal
– 'Rayon d'Or'	IBal
– 'Red David' **new**	WFar
– 'Red King'	CBro CDor CRos CWld EBee EHyd EPfP GKev IBal LRHS MPri NLar NRHS WBrk WFar WRHF
– 'Red Knight'	IBal
– 'Rheingold' misapplied	see *C.* × *crocosmiiflora* 'Diadème'
– 'Saint Clements'	IBal IBlr NHol
– 'Saracen' ♀H4	CBcs CBod CBro CMac CWCL EBee ECtt EMor EShb GKin IBal LEdu LRHS MAvo MHol MNrw NLar NSti SEdd SPoG SPtp WAul WCot WFar
– 'Severn Seas'	ECtt
– 'Sir Mathew Wilson'	IBal
– 'Solfatare' ♀H4	Widely available
– 'Solfatare Coleton Fishacre'	see *C.* × *crocosmiiflora* 'Coleton Fishacre'
– 'Star of the East' ♀H4	Widely available
– 'Sultan'	CExl WFar
– 'Sunglow'	CBod CPla EBee ECtt EPfP GKev IBal LRHS MNrw MPri NWsh SHar WHil WOut
– 'Twilight Fairy Gold'	CBod CPou EBee ECha ECtt EMor IBal MBNS MHol NHpl SPer WCot WFar WMal WSpi
– 'Venus'	CDor ECtt IBal MHer MSpe NHol
– 'Vesuvius'	IBal WSHC
– 'Vic's Yellow'	IBal
– 'Voyager'	CPrp ECtt EHyd GKev IBal LRHS NHol NLar SDeJ SDir
– Wasdale strain	IBal
– 'Zeal Tan'	CBod CExl CPrp CWCL EBee ECtt ELan ELon EMor EPfP EPri EWhm IBal LEdu LLWG LRHS MNrw NLar NRHS NSti SDix SEdd SGbt SPoG WAul WCAu WCot WFar WGwG WHoo
× ***crocosmioides*** 'Castle Ward Late'	CFis CPrp ECtt EHyd EPfP IBal IBlr LEdu LRHS NHol NLar NRHS SRms WCot WFar WOut
§ – 'Vulcan' Leichtlin	IBlr WHil WOut
'Darkleaf Apricot'	see *C.* × *crocosmiiflora* 'Coleton Fishacre'
'Doctor Marion Wood'	IBal
'Eldorado'	see *C.* × *crocosmiiflora* 'E.A. Bowles'
'Ellenbank Canary'	IBal MAvo
'Ellenbank Firecrest' ♀H4	CPrp EBee IBal IPot MAvo MHCG
'Ellenbank Goldcrest'	IBal WSHC
'Ellenbank Skylark'	IBal MAvo
'Emberglow'	Widely available
'Fandango'	IBal NHol
'Fernhill'	IBal
'Fire King' misapplied	see *C.* × *crocosmiiflora* 'Jackanapes'
'Fire King' ambig.	EHyd IBal LRHS NLar NRHS NSti SWvt
'Firebird'	CRos ECtt EHyd ELon IBal LRHS MHol NHol NRHS SRms WCot

'Firefly'	CPrp CRos EBee ECtt ECul EHyd EPfP LRHS MAsh NRHS
'Flaire'	IBlr
'Fleuve Jaune'	IBal
'Forest Fire'	IBal
fucata 'Jupiter'	see *C.* 'Jupiter'
fucata* × *paniculata	IBal
'Fugue'	IBal IBlr SMad
'Golden Dew'	ECtt IBal MBNS WCot WFar
GOLDEN FLEECE *sensu* Lemoine	see *C.* × *crocosmiiflora* 'Coleton Fishacre'
'Harmonia'	EPri
'Hellfire' ♀H5	Widely available
'Highlight'	IBal MAvo NHol NWad
'Jennine'	IBal
JENNY BLOOM ('Blacro'PBR)	EBee EHyd IBal LRHS
'John Boots'	ECtt ELon IBal LRHS MCot NBid NLar SRms
§ 'Jupiter'	CDor CSam CWCL IBal LRHS MAvo NBir NChi NHol NLar WHil
'Karin'	CRos EBee EHyd GKev LRHS MAsh NRHS SDir WFar
'Kathleen'	CPrp
'Krakatoa'	CPrp EBee IBal MBel MHer SWvt WFar
'Lady Ann'	CPrp EBee GKev MAsh
'Lady Jane'	CRos EBee EHyd EPfP GKev LRHS NRHS
'Lady Wilson' misapplied	see *C.* × *crocosmiiflora* 'Norwich Canary'
'Lana de Savary'	CPrp ECtt EWes IBal MNrw NBid NHol NWad SMad WCot
'Late Cornish'	see *C.* × *crocosmiiflora* 'Queen Alexandra' J.E. Fitt
'Late Lucifer'	CTri IBal IBlr MNrw
'Late Yellow'	IBal WSMil
'Lemon Spray'	IBal IBlr
'Limpopo'	Widely available
'Lucifer' ♀H5	Widely available
LUCIFER'S CHILDREN	ELan EPfP
'Malahide Castle Red'	SMad
'Marcotijn'	IBal
masoniorum ♀H4	Widely available
– from Satan's Nek, South Africa	IBal
– 'African Dawn'	EBee ECtt
– 'Amber'	IBlr
– 'Dixter Flame'	SDix SMHy WOut
– 'Golden Swan'	SRms
– 'Kiaora'	IBlr
– 'Moira Reid'	IBal
– 'Rowallane Apricot'	IBlr
– 'Rowallane Orange'	GBin IBal IBlr MSpe
– 'Rowallane Yellow' ♀H4	EBee EHyd GBin IBal IBlr IMou LRHS MNrw NHol SMHy WBor WMal WPGP WSHC
– 'Sherbert Orange'	IBal MAvo
– Slieve Donard selection	IBal
– 'Sunflare'	IBlr
– 'Tropicana'	IBlr
aff. ***mathewsiana***	IBal
'Mex'	IBal LEdu SMad WPGP
'Ministar'	CBod CPrp CRos EBee EHyd GKev LLWG LRHS MAsh NRHS WFar
'Minotaur'	IBal
'Miss Scarlet'	EHyd EPfP LRHS NRHS SAko
'Mistral'	CCCN CRos ECtt EHyd EPfP GAbr GKev IBal LEdu LRHS NHol NLar NRHS SCob WFar

	'Moorland Sunset'	IBal
	'Mount Stewart'	see *C.* × *crocosmiiflora* 'Jessie'
	'Mr Bedford'	see *C.* × *crocosmiiflora* 'Croesus'
	'Okavango'	CBcs CBor CBre CBro CMac CPrp ECtt ELon EMor EPfP EPot EPri EShb IBal IPot LPla LSun MAvo MBNS MHol MNrw MSCN NLar NSti SDix WBor WCAu WCot WFar
	OLD HAT	see *C.* 'Walberton Red'
	'Orange Devil'	CBre ECtt EHyd EPfP EWes GKin IBal LRHS MBNS MBel NRHS SGbt WGoo
	ORANGE PEKOE ('Pek Or'[PBR])	GBin IBal LCro LOPS NSti SMad WHil
	'Orange River'	WCot WFar
	'Orangeade'	ECtt IBal NHol SRms
	'Pageant'	IBal
§	***paniculata***	CMac CPou ECtt GAbr LEdu NBid WBrk WOut WPGP WShi
	- brown/orange-flowered	IBlr
	- 'Cally Greyleaf'	EBee GBin IBal MAvo MNrw SMHy WCot WMal
	- 'Cally Sword'	IBal
	- 'Major'	CTri IBlr
	- 'Natal'	CPrp ECtt IBal NHol
	- red-flowered	IBal IBlr SWvt
	- triploid	IBlr
	'Paul's Best Yellow' 🏆H4	Widely available
	'Peach Sunrise'	IBal
	'Phillipa Browne'	CSde ECtt EPot IBal MNrw NLar WCot
	'Plancheon'	IBal
	pottsii	CRos EHyd GWyn LEdu LRHS NRHS
	- CD&R 109	CPou
	- 'Culzean Pink'	CElw CExl CPrp EBee EPPr EWhm GBin IBal IBlr LPla MNrw MSpe NBid NBir NHol WFar WOut
	- 'Grandiflora'	IBal
§	- 'Princess'	EBee ECtt EHyd GKev IBal LRHS NRHS
	- tall	IBal
	'Pride of Plantion'	CPrp ILea
	'Prince of Orange'	CBro CRos EBee ECul EHyd EPfP ERCP GKev LRHS MSCN NRHS SDeJ WFar WWtn
	'Queen Alexandria'	CRos EHyd LRHS NRHS WFar
	'R.W. Wallace'	IBal
	'Raspberry Spray'	IBlr
	'Red Star'	IBal
	rosea	see *Tritonia disticha* subsp. ***rubrolucens***
	'Rowden Bronze'	see *C.* × *crocosmiiflora* 'Coleton Fishacre'
	'Rowden Chrome'	see *C.* × *crocosmiiflora* 'George Davison' Davison
	'Ruby Velvet'	IBlr
	'Saffron Queen'	IBlr
	'Sampford Yellow'	IBal
	'Saturn'	see *C.* 'Jupiter'
	'Scarlatti'	EBee ECtt IBal LRHS NHol NWad WOut
	'Severn Sunrise' 🏆H5	Widely available
	'Shocking'	IBal
	'Spitfire'	CExl CPrp CSam ECtt ELan GQue IBal MArl MAvo MRav NHol SWvt WFar WOld
§	'Sulphurea'	CExl CPou CRos CSam ECtt EPfP IBal LRHS MSpe NHol
	'Sunzest'	ECtt MAvo WHoo
	'Suzanna'	ECtt MAvo SDir
	'Tai Pan' **new**	IBal
	'Tamar Double Red'	SMad
	'Tamar Glow'	WOld
	'Tamar Peace'	SMad
	'Tangerine Dream'	IBlr
	'Tangerine Queen'	GAbr IBal IBlr NHol NWad
	'Tangerine Spray'	IBlr
	'Tiger'	CElw
	'Toccata'	IBlr
	'Twilight Fairy Crimson'	CWGN EBee ECtt EMor EPri GBin LEdu NHpl NLar WFar
I	'Vulcan' A. Bloom	IBal IBlr MAvo
	'Vulcan' Leichtlin	see *C.* × *crocosmioides* 'Vulcan' Leichtlin
§	'Walberton Red'	CSam EBee EWes IBal MAvo NWad SMad WOut
	WALBERTON YELLOW ('Walcroy'[PBR])	EHyd EPfP LRHS NRHS SMad
	'Zambesi'	CBro CMac ECtt ELon GBin IBal IPot MAvo MBNS MNrw MTis WCot
	'Zeal Giant' 🏆H4	ECtt EPfP IBal IBlr MAvo NHol WMal
	'Zeal Unnamed'	CPrp IBal NHol

Crocus ✿ (*Iridaceae*)

	adanensis	GKev
	'Advance'	EMor GKev LCro LOPS SDeJ SDir
	ancyrensis	EPot GKev SDeJ
	- 'Golden Bunch'	EHyd LRHS NRHS SDeJ SDir WShi
§	***angustifolius*** 🏆H6	EPot GKev SDeJ WShi
	- 'Berlin Gold'	GKev
	- 'Minor'	EPot
	antalyensis yellow-flowered	GKev
	'Ard Schenk'	CAby CRos EHyd GKev LRHS NRHS
	asturicus	see *C. serotinus* subsp. *salzmannii*
	asumaniae	EPot GKev
	'Aubade'	EPot GKev
	aureus	see *C. flavus* subsp. *flavus*
	banaticus 🏆H6	EPot GKev NDry NHar NHpl
	- 'Albus'	NDry
	- 'Snowdrift'	GKev NHar
	biflorus 'Blue Pearl' 🏆H6	CAvo EMor EPot ERCP GKev LCro LOPS NBir SDeJ SDir SPer SPhx WCot WShi
	- subsp. ***melantherus***	GKev NDry
	- 'Miss Vain'	EPot ERCP GKev
	- subsp. ***nubigena*** **new**	NDry
	- subsp. ***pulchricolor***	GKev
	- 'Serevan'	EPot
	- subsp. ***stridii***	EPot GKev
	- subsp. ***tauri***	EPot
	- subsp. ***weldenii*** 'Albus'	EPot GKev
	- - 'Fairy'	GKev
	'Blue Bird'	EPot
	blue-flowered	CRos EHyd LRHS NRHS
	boryi	CRos EHyd LRHS NRHS
	cancellatus	SDeJ
§	- subsp. ***cancellatus***	EPot GKev
	- var. ***cilicicus***	see *C. cancellatus* subsp. *cancellatus*
	- subsp. ***lycius***	EPot
	candidus var. ***subflavus***	see *C. olivieri* subsp. *olivieri*
	cartwrightianus 🏆H6	EHyd LRHS NRHS WShi
	- 'Albus' misapplied	see *C. hadriaticus*
	- 'Albus' Tubergen 🏆H6	EPot GKev SDeJ

	- 'Marcel'	GKev
	chrysanthus 🏆H6	CHab
	- 'Blue Peter'	EPot
	- 'Constellation'	EPot
	- 'Cream Beauty' 🏆H6	CAby CAvo EHyd EPot ERCP LCro LOPS LRHS MBros NBir NRHS SDeJ SDir WShi
	- var. ***fuscotinctus***	EPot GKev LCro LOPS SDeJ
	- 'Goldene Sonne'	EPot
	- 'White Beauty'	CWCL
	- 'Zwanenburg Bronze' 🏆H6	SDeJ
	'Cloth of Gold'	see *C. angustifolius*
	corsicus 🏆H6	EPot GKev
	dalmaticus	EPot
	- 'Petrovac'	GKev
	'Dorothy'	EPot MWat SDir WShi
	'Dutch Yellow'	see *C.* × *luteus* 'Golden Yellow'
	'Early Gold'	see *C.* × *leonidii* 'Early Gold'
	etruscus 🏆H6	GKev
	- 'Rosalind'	GKev
	- 'Zwanenburg'	CRos EHyd EPot GKev LRHS NRHS SDeJ SDir
	'Fantasy'	GKev WShi
§	***flavus*** subsp. ***flavus*** 🏆H6	EPot GKev WShi
	fleischeri	EPot GKev
	'Flower Record'	CArg GKev LRHS NBir SDeJ
	gilanicus	GKev
	'Gipsy Girl'	CAvo EMor EPot ERCP GKev LCro LOPS MWat SDir
	'Golden Mammoth'	see *C.* × *luteus* 'Golden Yellow'
	'Goldilocks' 🏆H6	GKev SDeJ
	goulimyi 🏆H6	EHyd EPot LRHS NRHS SDeJ WCot
	- 'Albus'	see *C. goulimyi* subsp. *goulimyi* 'Mani White'
§	- subsp. ***goulimyi*** 'Mani White' 🏆H4	EPot
	- subsp. ***leucanthus***	GKev
	'Grand Maître'	CAvo GKev SDeJ SDir
	'Haarlem Gem'	GKev
§	***hadriaticus*** 🏆H6	EHyd GKev LRHS NDry NRHS
	- 'Alepohori'	GKev
	- 'Annabelle'	GKev
	- var. ***chrysobelonicus***	see *C. hadriaticus*
	- subsp. ***hadriaticus*** f. ***lilacinus***	GKev
	- 'Jumbo'	NDry
	'Herald'	CAvo GKev SDeJ
§	***heuffelianus***	GKev WShi
	- 'Drina Marvel'	GKev
	- 'Graecus'	GKev
	- 'Krasno Polje'	GKev
	- 'Michael's Purple'	GKev
	- 'Shock Wave' **new**	CWCL
	- 'Snow Princess'	NDry
	- Uklin strain	GKev
	imperati subsp. ***suaveolens***	CWCL EPot
	- - 'De Jager'	CAvo ERCP GKev SDeJ
	'Jeanne d'Arc'	CAby CArg CAvo EPot GKev LCro LOPS LRHS NBir SDeJ WShi
	'Jeannine'	SDeJ
	× ***jessoppiae***	GKev
	karduchorum	EPot GKev
	'Karin'	EPot
	'King of the Striped'	GKev SDeJ SPer
	korolkowii	GKev
	- 'Golden Nugget'	GKev
	- 'January Gold'	CAvo
	- 'Kiss of Spring'	EPot GKev
	- 'Mountain Glory'	NDry

	kosaninii	GKev
	kotschyanus 🏆H6	GKev MBros SDeJ
	- 'Albus'	GKev SDeJ
§	- subsp. ***kotschyanus***	EPot GKev SDeJ
	- 'Reliance'	GKev
	'Ladykiller'	EMor EPot GKev SPhx WShi
	laevigatus 🏆H4	GKev NDry
	- CE&H 612	EPot
	- 'Fontenayi'	EPot ERCP GKev
	'Large Yellow'	see *C.* × *luteus* 'Golden Yellow'
	large-flowered blue	SDir
§	× ***leonidii*** 'Early Gold'	GKev SDir
§	***ligusticus*** 🏆H6	EPot GKev
	longiflorus 🏆H6	EHyd EPot GKev LRHS NRHS
§	× ***luteus*** 'Golden Yellow' 🏆H6	CArg CAvo EPot GKev LCro LOPS LRHS SDeJ SDir WShi
§	- 'Stellaris' 🏆H6	EPot
	malyi 🏆H6	CWCL GKev
	- 'Sveti Roc'	GKev
	mathewii	EPot GKev NDry NHpl
	- 'Dream Dancer'	EPot GKev NDry
	medius	see *C. ligusticus*
	minimus	EPot ERCP GKev
	- 'Bavella'	CAvo
	- 'Spring Beauty'	EMor ERCP LCro LOPS SDeJ
	'Negro Boy'	EPot
	niveus	EHyd EPot GKev LRHS NRHS
	nudiflorus	EPot GKev
	ochroleucus	EPot GKev SDeJ
	olivieri AH 0156	GKev
§	- subsp. ***balansae*** 'Orange Monarch'	ERCP
	- - 'Zwanenburg'	EPot
§	- subsp. ***olivieri***	GKev
	- - 'Little Tiger'	GKev
	'Orange Monarch'	see *C. olivieri* subsp. *balansae* 'Orange Monarch'
	pallasii VV KR.75	GKev
	- subsp. ***turcicus***	GKev
	paschei	GKev
	pestalozzae	GKev
	- var. ***caeruleus***	GKev
	- subsp. ***violaceus*** **new**	GKev
	'Pickwick'	CAby CArg CAvo GKev LCro LOPS LRHS NBir SDeJ WShi
	'Prins Claus'	CRos EHyd EPot ERCP GKev LCro LOPS LRHS MBros NBir NRHS SDeJ
	pulchellus 🏆H6	CAvo SDeJ WCot
	- 'Albus'	EPot
	- 'Inspiration'	GKev
	'Purple Heart'	NDry
	'Purpureus'	see *C.* 'Purpureus Grandiflorus'
§	'Purpureus Grandiflorus'	CAby SDeJ
	'Queen of the Blues'	CAvo EPot SDeJ
	'Rainbow Gold'	NDry
	'Remembrance'	CAby CArg EPot LCro LOPS LRHS NBir SDeJ WShi
	reticulatus	EPot
	'Romance'	EHyd EPot GKev LCro LOPS LRHS NBir NRHS SDeJ
	'Ruby Giant'	CAvo CRos EHyd EMor EPot ERCP LCro LOPS LRHS NBir NRHS SDeJ SPer SPhx WShi
	rujanensis	EPot
	salzmannii	see *C. serotinus* subsp. *salzmannii*
	sativus	CAvo CBod ELan EPot ERCP GAbr GKev GPoy ILea LCro LOPS MHtn NBir SDeJ SDir SVic XAbr
	'Saturnus'	EPot

scepusiensis	see *C. heuffelianus*
serotinus subsp. ***clusii*** 'Poseidon'	GKev
§ - subsp. ***salzmannii***	GKev
- - 'Atropurpureus'	WCot
- - 'Erectophyllus'	GKev
sibiricus	see *C. sieberi*
§ ***sieberi***	EPot
- 'Albus'	see *C. sieberi* 'Bowles's White'
- subsp. ***atticus*** 'Amfiklia'	GKev
- - 'Firefly'	EHyd EPot ERCP GKev LRHS MWat NRHS SDeJ
§ - 'Bowles's White' ♀H6	EPot SDeJ
- 'Hubert Edelsten' ♀H6	EPot GKev
- 'Ronald Ginns'	EPot
- subsp. ***sublimis***	GKev
- - 'Tricolor' ♀H6	CAby CArg CAvo EHyd EPot LCro LOPS LRHS NBir NRHS SDeJ WBrk WOld
'Snow Bunting' ♀H6	CAvo ELan EPot GKev LCro LOPS NBir SDeJ SDir SPer WShi
speciosus ♀H6	CAvo LCro LOPS NBir SDeJ WShi
- 'Aino'	GKev
- 'Aitchisonii'	EHyd GKev LRHS NRHS
- 'Albus' ♀H6	CAvo EPot ERCP GKev LCro LOPS NDry SDeJ WShi
- 'Artabir'	EHyd GKev LRHS NRHS SDeJ
- 'Cassiope'	EHyd GKev LRHS NRHS SDeJ
- 'Conqueror'	EHyd ELan ERCP GKev LCro LOPS LRHS NRHS SDeJ
- 'Oxonian'	EHyd ELan EPot GKev LRHS MCot NRHS WOld
- subsp. ***speciosus***	EPot GKev NBir SDeJ
aff. ***speciosus*** **new**	SDir
× ***stellaris***	see *C.* × *luteus* 'Stellaris'
susianus	see *C. angustifolius*
suterianus	see *C. olivieri* subsp. *olivieri*
thomasii	GKev
tommasinianus ♀H6	CArg CAvo CGrW CHab ELan EPot LCro LOPS MRav NBir SDeJ SDir SPhx SRms WShi
- 'Albus'	EPot GKev WShi
- 'Barr's Purple'	CAby EHyd EPot LCro LOPS LRHS NBir NRHS SDeJ
- 'Bobbo'	EHyd NDry
- 'Claret'	NDry
- 'Eric Smith'	EPot NDry
- 'Lilac Beauty'	EPot GKev
- 'Lyn's Pink' **new**	NDry
- 'Pictus'	EPot GKev NDry WShi
- 'Roseus'	EPot ERCP GKev SDeJ SPhx WCot WShi
- 'Rubinetta'	GKev
- 'Whitewell Purple'	CAvo EHyd EPot ERCP GKev LCro LOPS LRHS NBir NRHS SDeJ WCot WShi
tournefortii ♀H4	CAvo EHyd EPot GKev LRHS NRHS
'Twinborn'	EPot
'Vanguard' ♀H6	EPot GKev LCro LOPS SDeJ WCot
§ ***vernus***	GKev WShi
- subsp. ***albiflorus***	see *C. vernus*
- blue-flowered	GKev
- 'Lavender Symphony' **new**	GKev
- purple apex	GKev
- 'Purple Desire' **new**	GKev
- subsp. ***vernus*** 'Grandiflorus'	see *C.* 'Purpureus Grandiflorus'
versicolor JMH 8215	GKev
- 'Picturatus'	EPot GKev SDeJ WShi
vitellinus	EPot GKev
'Yalta'	CAvo GKev WCot
'Yellow Mammoth'	see *C.* × *luteus* 'Golden Yellow'
'Zenith'	EPot
'Zephyr' ♀H6	GKev SDeJ SPhx WOld
zonatus	see *C. kotschyanus* subsp. *kotschyanus*

Croomia (*Stemonaceae*)

heterosepala	WCru

Crossandra (*Acanthaceae*)

infundibuliformis ♀H1a	EShb

Crossyne (*Amaryllidaceae*)

flava	WCot

Crotalaria (*Papilionaceae*)

laburnifolia ♀H2	CCCN

Crowea (*Rutaceae*)

exalata × ***saligna***	CExl

Crucianella (*Rubiaceae*)

stylosa	see *Phuopsis stylosa*

Cruciata (*Rubiaceae*)

§ ***laevipes***	NAts NMir

Crusea (*Rubiaceae*)

coccinea	GEdr SBrt WCot
- 'Crûg Crimson'	WSHC

Cryptanthus (*Bromeliaceae*)

bivittatus	NCft

Cryptanthus × *Billbergia* see × *Cryptbergia*

× *Cryptbergia* (*Bromeliaceae*)

'Rubra'	SChr

Cryptocarya (*Lauraceae*)

alba	GBin SVen

Cryptocoryne (*Araceae*)

wendtii brown-leaved **new**	XBlo
- long-leaved **new**	XBlo
× ***willisii***	XBlo

Cryptogramma (*Pteridaceae*)

crispa	WHer

Cryptomeria ✿ (*Cupressaceae*)

fortunei	see *C. japonica*
§ ***japonica***	CMen CTho EPfP MBlu MMuc SCob SEND SWvt SavN WMou WTSh
- 'Antique Gold'	LRHS
- Araucarioides Group	SLim
- 'Atawai'	NLar
- 'Bandai-sugi' ♀H6	CKen CMac CMen IArd MGos NHol NLar SRms
- 'Barabits Gold'	LRHS SavN
- 'Bicton Broom' **new**	SLim
- 'Birodo'	CKen
- 'Black Dragon'	SLim
- 'Carmel' **new**	MBlu
- 'Compacta Nana' **new**	SLim
- 'Compressa'	CKen EPfP LBee LRHS MAsh NLar SLim SRms

§	- 'Cristata'	CMac ELan LRHS MGos MPkF SLim SRms SavN XLot
	- 'Dacrydioides'	LRHS MGil NLar
	- 'Dinger'	CKen NLar
	- 'Elegans Aurea'	CCVT ELan LRHS SPoG SWvt WFar
	- 'Elegans Compacta' 🏆H6	CMac CSBt ELan GBin LBee LRHS MAsh MMuc NLar NOra SCob SLim SPad SRms SWvt WHwl
	- Elegans Group	CBcs CMac CSBt ELan EPfP LRHS MGos NLar NOra SCoo SEND SLim SPer SPoG SRms WFar WMat
	- - 'Elegans' 🏆H6	CBrac MGil NOrn SGsty SLim
	- 'Elegans Nana'	MGil SRms WHwl
	- 'Elegans Viridis' 🏆H6	LRHS MGil NOra SGsty SLim WMat
I	- 'Elegantissima'	CCVT
	- 'Globosa Nana' 🏆H6	EPfP LBee MGos NHol NPoe SArc SCob SCoo SGsty SLim SPoG SWeb
	- 'Golden Promise' 🏆H6	CBcs CBod MAsh NHol NRya NWad SLim SWvt
	- 'HB Bandai' **new**	MBlu
	- 'Jindai-sugi'	NLar XLot
	- 'Kilmacurragh'	CKen
	- 'Kohui-yatsubusa'	CKen
	- 'Koshyi'	CKen
	- 'Little Champion'	LRHS SLim
	- 'Little Diamond'	CKen
	- 'Little Sonja'	CKen SLim
	- 'Little Yoko'	CKen NLar
	- 'Littleworth Dwarf'	see *C. japonica* 'Littleworth Gnom'
§	- 'Littleworth Gnom'	LRHS
	- 'Lobbii Nana' hort.	see *C. japonica* 'Nana'
	- 'Majiro-sugi'	NLar
	- 'Midare'	NLar
	- 'Monstrosa'	NLar
	- 'Mushroom'	SLim
§	- 'Nana'	SRms
	- 'Osaka-tama'	CKen
	- 'Pipo'	CKen
	- 'Pygmaea'	NHol NLar NWad SRms
	- 'Rasen-sugi'	IDee NLar XLot
	- 'Rein's Dense Jade'	SLim
	- 'Sekkan-sugi' 🏆H6	CBcs CBod CBrac CCVT CMac ELan EPfP ESwi GBin GKin IArd LBee LRHS MAsh MGos NLar NOrn NPoe SCoo SLim SPoG SWvt
	- 'Sekka-sugi'	see *C. japonica* 'Cristata'
§	- 'Spiralis' 🏆H6	CKen ELan EPfP LBee LRHS MAsh MGos NHol NLar SAko SCoo SLim SPoG SRms SWvt
§	- 'Spiraliter Falcata'	NLar
§	- 'Tansu'	CKen LRHS MGil
	- 'Tenzan-sugi' 🏆H6	CKen NHol NLar
	- 'Tenzan-yatsubusa'	CMen
	- 'Tilford Gold'	LSRN NHol NOra SLim
	- 'Toda'	CKen
	- 'Twinkle Toes'	CKen
	- 'Vilmorin Gold'	NHol
	- 'Vilmoriniana' 🏆H6	CKen CMen CTri ELan EPfP GKin LRHS LSRN MAsh MGil MGos NHol NLar NOra SCoo SLim SPer SPoG SWvt XLot
	- 'Winter Bronze'	CKen
	- 'Yatsubusa'	see *C. japonica* 'Tansu'
	- 'Yellow Twig'	NLar
	- 'Yore-sugi'	see *C. japonica* 'Spiralis', 'Spiraliter Falcata'
	- 'Yoshino'	CKen SLim
	sinensis	see *C. japonica*

Cryptostegia (*Apocynaceae*)

	grandiflora	CCCN

Cryptotaenia (*Apiaceae*)

	japonica	CAgr CHby CLau CPou GPoy MNHC SRms WHer WJek
	- f. ***atropurpurea***	CDor CSpe EBee EWhm LEdu LPla MNrw WBor WPGP

Ctenanthe (*Marantaceae*)

§	***burle-marxii***	CDoC XBlo
	lubbersiana 🏆H1b	XBlo
	oppenheimiana	NGBl XBlo

Cucubalus (*Caryophyllaceae*)

	baccifer	NLar

cucumber see AGM Vegetables Section

Cudrania see *Maclura*

cumin see *Cuminum cyminum*

Cuminum (*Apiaceae*)

	cyminum	SRms SVic

Cunninghamia (*Cupressaceae*)

	konishii	CExl
§	***lanceolata***	CBcs CKen CMCN CMac CTho EPfP IDee LRHS MGil SMad SSta WPGP
	- 'Glauca'	CExl CJun
	sinensis	see *C. lanceolata*
	unicaniculata	see *C. lanceolata*

Cunonia (*Cunoniaceae*)

	capensis	CExl

Cuphea (*Lythraceae*)

	caeciliae	WMal
	cyanea	CSpe SDix SEdd
	hyssopifolia 🏆H2	CTsd EShb SWvt WHil
	- 'Alba'	CCCN EShb SWvt
	- pink-flowered	CCCN
	- red-flowered	CCCN
	- 'Rosea'	SWvt
§	***ignea*** 🏆H2	CTsd ELan
	- 'Matchless'	SVic
	- 'Roxy' **new**	EPPr
	'Lilac Belle'	CSpe
§	***llavea*** 'Georgia Scarlet'	CCCN
	- 'Tiny Mice'	see *C. llavea* 'Georgia Scarlet'
	maculata	CCCN
	platycentra	see *C. ignea*
	'Torpedo'	MBros WHil
	viscosissima	CSpe ELan MCot

× *Cupressocyparis* see × *Cuprocyparis*

Cupressus (*Cupressaceae*)

	arizonica	SWeb
I	- 'Fastigiata Aurea'	SGsty SWeb
	- var. ***glabra*** 'Angaston'	SLim
	- - 'Aurea'	MAsh SGol SLim
	- - 'Blue Ice'	CMac CTho MAsh MGos SLim SWvt
	- - 'Compacta'	CKen

I	- - 'Fastigiata'	CCVT ECrN SCob SGsty
	- 'Pyramidalis' 🏆H5	SEND SGol
	cashmeriana 🏆H3 KR 8688A	WPGP
	dupreziana var. ***atlantica***	SLim WPav
	× ***leylandii***	see × *Cuprocyparis leylandii*
	lusitanica 'Brice's Weeping'	CKen SLim
	- 'Pygmy'	CKen
	macnabiana	GLog
	macrocarpa	CBcs CBod CCVT CTho SEND
	- 'Compacta'	CKen
	- 'Gold Spread'	SLim
	- 'Goldcrest' 🏆H4	CBcs CBod CCVT CMac ECrN ELan LRHS MGos MPri NBir SCob SEWo SGol SGsty SLim SWeb SWvt
	- 'Golden Pillar'	SWvt
	- 'Lohbrunner'	CKen
I	- 'Pendula'	SLim
	- 'Pygmaea'	CKen
	- 'Sulphur Cushion'	CKen
	- 'Wilma' 🏆H4	CSBt ELan LBee LRHS MAsh MGos SCoo SGol SLim SPoG SWeb SWvt
	- 'Woking'	CKen
	nootkatensis	see *Xanthocyparis nootkatensis*
	sempervirens	LRHS SPlb SWeb
	- 'Agrimed'	CCVT
	- 'Bolgheri'	LSRN
	- 'Green Pencil'	CKen
	- 'Pyramidalis'	see *C. sempervirens* Stricta Group
	- var. ***sempervirens***	see *C. sempervirens* Stricta Group
§	- Stricta Group	CBcs CBrac CCVT CTho LMaj LRHS NLar NOrn SArc SCob SEND SEWo SGol SGsty WCFE
	- 'Swane's Gold'	CKen MAsh
	- 'Totem Pole'	CCVT CKen CSBt CTho CTri ELan EPfP LBee LRHS MAsh MGos SCoo SGsty SLim SPad SPoG SWeb SWvt
	torulosa	CMCN

Cupressus × *Xanthocyparis*
see × *Cuprocyparis*

× *Cuprocyparis* ✿ (*Cupressaceae*)

§	***leylandii***	CArg CBcs CBrac CCVT CMac CTri ECrN EPfP LBuc LMaj LSRN MAsh MGos MPri SCob SGol SGsty SLim SPer SPoG SWeb SWvt WAvo WFar WMou
I	- '2001'	CBod CCVT SGol SLim
	- 'Blue Jeans'PBR	SEND
§	- 'Castlewellan'	CBcs CBod CCVT CMac CTri EPfP LBuc LSRN MAsh MGos MMuc MPri SCob SEND SGol SGsty SLim SPer SPoG SWeb SWvt WAvo WFar WTSh
	- EXCALIBUR GOLD ('Drabb'PBR)	SCob
	- 'Ferngold'	MAsh
	- 'Galway Gold'	see × *C. leylandii* 'Castlewellan'
	- 'Gold Rider' 🏆H6	CBod CMac ELan MAsh MGos SCoo SGol SGsty SLim SPer SPoG SWeb SWvt
§	- 'Harlequin' (v)	CMac SGsty SWvt
	- 'Leighton Green'	WTSh
	- 'Naylor's Blue'	CMac SEND
	- 'Olive's Green'	SWvt
	- 'Robinson's Gold'	CMac SGol
	- 'Silver Dust' (v)	WAvo
	- 'Variegata'	see × *C. leylandii* 'Harlequin'

Curculigo (*Hypoxidaceae*)

capitulata	XBlo
crassifolia B&SWJ 2318	WCru
- HWJ 683 from Vietnam	WCru
- NJM 10.123	WPGP

Curcuma ✿ (*Zingiberaceae*)

alismatifolia	SDeJ
longa	GPoy SPlb SPre
roscoeana	SDeJ
zedoaria 'Bicolor Wonder'	CCCN
- 'Pink Wonder'	CCCN
- 'White Wonder'	CCCN GBin SDeJ

Curio (*Asteraceae*)

§	***articulata***	EShb
§	***ficoides***	EShb NGBl
	- 'Mount Everest'	EShb
§	***repens***	CDoC EShb SSim
§	***rowleyanus***	EBak EShb LCro LOPS SSim WSMil
§	***talinoides*** subsp. ***mandraliscae***	WSMil
	- - 'Blue Finger'	WCot

Curtonus see *Crocosmia*

Cussonia ✿ (*Araliaceae*)

gamtoosensis	WCot
natalensis	WCot
paniculata	CDTJ CWGN SPlb
sphaerocephala	SPlb WCot
spicata	CDTJ SPlb
transvaalensis	CDTJ
zuluensis	WCot

custard apple see *Annona cherimola*

Cyananthus (*Campanulaceae*)

	incanus	GEdr GKev
	integer misapplied	see *C. microphyllus*
	lobatus 🏆H5	GKev WAbe
	- 'Albus'	NHar WAbe
	- giant	GEdr NHar
	lobatus × ***microphyllus***	EWld GEdr WAbe
	longiflorus	GKev
	macrocalyx	NHar
§	***microphyllus*** 🏆H5	EPot GEdr GKev NHar NSla WAbe
	microphyllus × 'Sherriff's Variety'	NHar
	sherriffii	WAbe
	spathulifolius	WAbe

Cyanastrum (*Tecophilaeaceae*)

cordifolium	GKev

Cyanotis (*Commelinaceae*)

beddomei 🏆H1b	EShb
somaliensis 🏆H1b	EShb

Cyathea ✿ (*Cyatheaceae*)

australis	CBdn CDTJ CTrC CTsd IDee SPlb
cooperi	CAbb CBcs CBct CBdn CBod CDTJ CTrC CTsd ESwi ISha NBro WFib
- 'Brentwood'	EBee ESwi ISha
dealbata	CBdn CDTJ CTrC

	dregei	SPlb
	medullaris	CBdn
	smithii	CDTJ
	tomentosissima	CDTJ

Cyathodes (*Ericaceae*)

	colensoi	see *Leucopogon colensoi*
	fraseri	see *Leucopogon fraseri*

Cycas (*Cycadaceae*)

	panzhihuaensis	CBrP SPlb
	revoluta ♀H2	CAbb CBcs CBrP CCCN CDoC CTsd EPfP EShb LCro LOPS SArc SChr SEND SGsty SPalm SPlb SWeb WSMil XBlo
	revoluta × taitungensis	CBrP
§	***rumphii***	CBrP
	taitungensis	CBrP
	thouarsii	see *C. rumphii*

Cyclamen ✿ (*Primulaceae*)

	abchasicum	see *C. coum* subsp. *caucasicum*
	africanum	CBro EHyd GKev LRHS MAsh NRHS XEll
§	***alpinum***	CRos EHyd EPot GKev LRHS MAsh NRHS SDeJ XEll
	- 'Nettleton White'	MAsh
	balearicum	EHyd EPot GKev LRHS MAsh NRHS
	cilicium ♀H3	CAby CBro EHyd EPot ERCP GKev LCro LOPS LRHS MAsh NHpl NRHS NSla WHoo WShi XEll
	- f. ***album***	EHyd EPot GKev LRHS MAsh NRHS XEll
	colchicum	MAsh
§	***coum*** ♀H5	Widely available
	- var. ***abchasicum***	see *C. coum* subsp. *caucasicum*
	- 'Ashwood Snowflake'	MAsh
§	- subsp. ***caucasicum***	MAsh
	- subsp. ***coum***	CBro
	- - f. ***albissimum***	GKev
	- - - 'George Bisson'	MAsh
	- - - 'Golan Heights'	MAsh
	- - - 'Lake Effect'	MAsh
	- - f. ***coum*** Nymans Group	GRum MAsh
	- - - Pewter Group ♀H5	GEdr GKev WCot XEll
	- - - - 'Maurice Dryden' ♀H5	CBro CRos EHyd EPot GKev LEdu LRHS MAsh NRHS WHoo
	- - - - 'Tilebarn Elizabeth'	GRum MAsh NBir WHoo
	- - - 'Roseum'	CAvo
	- - - Silver Group	CBro CRos EHyd EPot LRHS NRHS NRya WHoo
	- - - - red-flowered	WHoo
	- - magenta-flowered	WHoo
	- - f. ***pallidum*** 'Album'	CAvo CWCL EMor EWhm GEdr GKev GMaP GWyn LCro LOPS SDeJ SEND SEdd SPeP SPer WHoo WPnP WShi
	- dark pink-flowered	CAvo WHoo
	- hybrid	ERCP
	- marble-leaved	WHoo
	- 'Marianne'	SAko
	- 'Meaden's Crimson'	GRum
I	- 'Rubrum'	GKev GWyn LCro LOPS
	- silver speckled leaf	CAvo
	creticum	MAsh
	cyprium	EHyd GKev LRHS MAsh NRHS XEll
	- 'E.S.'	MAsh WThu
	- 'Galaxy'	MAsh
	× ***drydeniae***	MAsh
	elegans	MAsh
	europaeum	see *C. purpurascens*
	graecum	CBro EHyd EPot GKev LRHS MAsh NRHS WHoo WThu XEll
	- subsp. ***candicum***	MAsh
	- subsp. ***graecum*** f. ***album***	CBro EHyd GKev LRHS MAsh NRHS XEll
	- - f. ***graecum*** 'Glyfada'	GKev MAsh XEll
§	***hederifolium*** ♀H5	Widely available
	- S&L 175/1	WCot XLum
	- 'Amaze Me'	MHol WBrk WCot
	- var. ***hederifolium*** f. ***albiflorum*** ♀H5	CAby CAvo CBro CTsd EMor GKev LCro LEdu LOPS NWad SDeJ SEND SEdd SPeP WHoo WPnP XLum
	- - - 'Album'	CWCL SDeJ WShi
	- - - Bowles's Apollo Group	NWad
	- - - 'Discovery'	WCot
	- - - 'Nettleton Silver'	see *C. hederifolium* var. *hederifolium* f. *albiflorum* 'White Cloud'
	- - - 'Perlenteppich'	GMaP
	- - - silver-leaved	SDys
§	- - - 'White Cloud' ♀H5	MAsh NHpl WHoo
	- - f. ***hederifolium*** 'Fairy Rings'	MAsh
	- - - 'Rosenteppich'	CAby CTsd
	- - - 'Ruby Glow'	CRos CWCL EHyd LRHS MAsh NBir NRHS WThu
	- - - Silver Cloud Group ♀H5	CAby CBro MAsh NBir WHoo
	- - - 'Silver Shield'	MAsh
	- - - 'Stargazer'	MAsh
	- island scented strain	WCot
	- 'Lysander'	GKev MAsh
	- 'Pewter Mist'	SPeP
	- 'Red Sky'	CBro NWad
	- 'Rosenteppich' **new**	CMiW
	- 'Silver Leaf'	see *C. hederifolium* Silver-leaved Group
§	- Silver-leaved Group	CAvo CRos EHyd EPot GEdr GKev LRHS NRHS NSla WBor XEll
	- - 'Silver Leaf Pink'	GMaP NWad
	- - 'Silver Leaf White'	GMaP NWad
	ibericum	see *C. coum* subsp. *caucasicum*
	intaminatum	CBro CRos EHyd EPot GKev LRHS MAsh NRHS WHoo XEll
	- plain-leaved	WThu
	latifolium	see *C. persicum*
	libanoticum	CBro CRos EHyd GKev LRHS MAsh NRHS XEll
	maritimum	XEll
	mirabile ♀H4	CBro CRos EHyd EPot GKev LRHS MAsh NHpl NRHS NSla SDeJ
	- 'Alba'	GKev SDeJ XEll
	- f. ***mirabile*** 'Tilebarn Anne'	MAsh
	- - 'Tilebarn Nicholas'	MAsh
	- f. ***niveum***	SDeJ
	- - 'Tilebarn Jan'	MAsh
	neapolitanum	see *C. hederifolium*
	orbiculatum	see *C. coum*
	parviflorum	MAsh
§	***persicum***	CRos CWCL EHyd GKev LRHS MAsh NRHS WCot
	- f. ***albidum***	MAsh
	- Ashwood silver-leaved	MAsh
	- Metis Series	SCob
	- (Super Verano Series) VERANO NEON PINK **new**	LCro LOPS

- - VERANO RED **new**	LCro LOPS
- WINFALL WHITE ('Synwinfwhi') (Winfall Series) **new**	LCro LOPS
pseudibericum 🏆H4	CBro CRos EHyd EPot GKev LRHS MAsh NRHS SDeJ WCot
- AC&W 664	NWad
- f. ***roseum***	ITim MAsh
§ ***purpurascens***	CAby CBro GKev GRum MAsh NHpl NSla WHoo WThu
- 'Lake Garda'	MAsh
repandum	CAby CAvo CBro CRos EHyd EPot GKev LRHS MAsh NRHS WHer
- 'Pelops' misapplied	see *C. rhodium* subsp. *peloponnesiacum*
rhodium	GKev MAsh
§ - subsp. ***peloponnesiacum***	GKev MAsh
- subsp. ***vividum***	MAsh
rohlfsianum	CRos EHyd GKev LRHS MAsh NRHS XEll
× ***schwarzii***	MAsh
'Trena'	SDeJ
trochopteranthum	see *C. alpinum*
× ***wellensiekii***	MAsh

Cyclea (*Menispermaceae*)

polypetala KWJ 12157	WCru

Cyclosorus ✿ (*Thelypteridaceae*)

tottoides	CBdn WPGP

Cydonia ✿ (*Rosaceae*)

japonica	see *Chaenomeles japonica*
oblonga (F)	SGsty
- 'Agvambari' (F)	SKee
- 'Aromatnaya' (F)	MCoo NOra SKee WMat
- 'Champion' (F)	CAgr CHab EBee EPom LBuc MCoo NOra SEdi SKee SVic WMat
- 'Early Prolific' (F)	ECrN SEND SEdi
- 'Ekmek' (F)	SKee
- 'Gamboa' (F)	SKee
- 'Iranian' (F)	CAgr
- 'Isfahan' (F)	SKee WMat
- 'Krymsk' (F)	CAgr WWct
- 'Leskovac' (F)	CAgr EPom LMaj NOra WWct
§ - 'Lusitanica' (F)	CAgr CHab ELan EPom LRHS SKee SPer SSFr WMat
- 'Meech's Prolific' (F) 🏆H5	CAgr CHab CLnd CTri EBee ECrN EPom LCro LOPS LRHS MAsh MGos MRav NLar NOra SEdi SKee SLim SPer SSFT SSFr WMat WWct
- pear-shaped (F)	CHab SPer
- PORTUGAL	see *C. oblonga* 'Lusitanica'
- 'Rea's Mammoth' (F)	CHab NLar
- 'Seibosa' (F)	SKee
- 'Serbian Gold' (F)	CMac CTho EBee ECrN EPom GQue LRHS MAsh MWat NLar NOra SKee SSFT WMat
- 'Smyrna' (F)	NLar NOra SKee WMat
- 'Sobu' (F)	SKee
- 'Vranja' ambig. (F)	CBcs MAsh MWat SEdi SPoG WHwl
- 'Vranja' Nenadovic (F) 🏆H5	Widely available

Cydonia + *Pyrus* see + *Pyrocydonia*

Cydonia × *Pyrus* see × *Pyronia*

Cylindropuntia (*Cactaceae*)

imbricata	SPlb XLum XSen
leptocaulis	XSen
§ ***spinosior***	XLum
versicolor	XSen

Cymbalaria (*Plantaginaceae*)

aequitriloba 'Alba'	GAbr GEdr NRya
§ ***hepaticifolia***	CSma SBrt SPlb
§ ***muralis***	ECtt GAbr GJos LLWG MHer NRya WHer WIce WTor
- 'Albiflora'	see *C. muralis* 'Pallidior'
- 'Kenilworth White'	GJos WCot
- 'Nana Alba'	ECtt
§ - 'Pallidior'	SPhx
- 'Snow Wave'	ECtt MHol WCot WFar
§ ***pallida***	CPBP CSma MAsh MMuc SEND SGro SPlb WCav WFar
- 'Alba'	EPfP WFar
§ ***pilosa***	ECtt NLar

Cymbopogon (*Poaceae*)

citratus	CBod CCCN ENfk GPoy LCro LOPS MNHC SEdi SPlb SPre SRms SVic XAbr
flexuosus	CCCN MHer SRms WJek
nardus	GPoy

Cynanchum (*Apocynaceae*)

ascyrifolium	EBee LEdu
atratum **new**	GEdr

Cynara (*Asteraceae*)

cardunculus 🏆H5	Widely available
- 'Bianco Avorio'	SVic
- dwarf	SDix
- subsp. ***flavescens***	SBrt
I - 'Florist Cardy'	NLar
- 'Gobbo di Nizza'	SRms
- 'Porto Spineless'	CAgr
§ - Scolymus Group	CBcs CMea EHyd EPfP EWes GPoy LCro LOPS LRHS LSRN MNHC MRav NRHS SCob SEND SPhx SPoG WHer
- - 'Bere'	LEdu
- - 'Gros Camus de Bretagne'	MAvo WCot
- - 'Gros Vert de Lâon' 🏆H5	CBcs CLau ELan LRHS WCot
- - 'Monica Lynden-Bell'	WCot WMal
- - 'Purple Globe'	LEdu SRms
- - 'Romanesco'	CLau LCro LOPS SRms SVic
- - 'Rouge d'Alger'	CAgr WLov
- - 'Tavor'	CLau SVic
- - 'Vert Globe'	CLau CTsd ENfk LCro LEdu LOPS NLar NPer SRms SVic SWvt WHil
- - 'Violet de Provence'	CSBt MHer SRms
- - 'Violetto di Chioggia' 🏆H4	CLau WHil
cornigera	SPhx
* ***gomerensis***	WCot
humilis white-flowered	SBrt
scolymus	see *C. cardunculus* Scolymus Group
syriaca	SPhx

Cynodon (*Poaceae*)

aethiopicus	EBee EPPr NWsh

Cynoglossum (*Boraginaceae*)

amabile 🏆H5	LCro LOPS
grande	SBrt
nervosum	CBod CCBP EBee EPPr MBel MMrt MMuc SEND SPer WCAu WCot WTyc

Cynosurus (*Poaceae*)

	cristatus	CHab NMir WWild

Cypella (*Iridaceae*)

	aquatilis	EWat
§	***coelestis***	XEll
	plumbea	see *C. coelestis*

Cyperus (*Cyperaceae*)

§	***albostriatus***	CCCN EShb
	alternifolius misapplied	see *C. involucratus*
	alternifolius L.	CBen CCCN EPfP SArc WMAq XBlo
	- 'Compactus'	see *C. involucratus* 'Nanus'
	'Chira'	NWsh
	diffusus misapplied	see *C. albostriatus*
§	***eragrostis***	EPPr LPot MWts NSti SDix SPlb WGrn WMAq
	esculentus	CAgr EShb
	glaber	EHyd
	haspan misapplied	see *C. papyrus* 'Nanus'
	haspan L.	WCot
§	***involucratus*** 🏆H1c	EShb EWat MWts SEND WSMil
§	- 'Nanus'	EShb
	longus	CBen CWat EWat MMuc MWts NPer SEND SMad SPlb WMAq WWtn XLum
	papyrus 🏆H1c	CCCN CDTJ CDow EShb LCro LOPS LRHS LSun MHer SPlb WSMil XBlo
§	- 'Nanus' 🏆H1c	XBlo
	- 'Perkamentus'^{PBR}	CCCN EShb
	prolifer	EShb
	vegetus	see *C. eragrostis*
	'Zumila'	EShb

Cyphomandra see *Solanum*

Cyphostemma (*Vitaceae*)

	mappia	SPlb

Cypripedium (*Orchidaceae*)

	Achim gx	XFro
	Aki gx	XFro
	- 'Pastel'	XFro
	Anna gx	XFro
	× ***barbeyi***	see *C.* × *ventricosum*
	Birgit gx pastel-flowered	XFro
	calceolus	GBin GKev SDir XEll
	Chauncey gx	XFro
	Cleo Pinkepank gx	XFro
	Dietrich gx 🏆H5	XFro
	Emil gx	XFro
	Eurasia gx	XFro
	fasciolatum	LRHS
	formosanum 🏆H3	EPot EWld GEdr GKev SDir
	Gabriela gx 'Kentucky Maxi'	GKev NHpl
	Gisela gx	CAvo XFro
	Hank Small gx 🏆H5	XFro
	Hans Erni gx	XFro
	Inge gx	XFro
	Ingrid gx	XFro
	Irene gx	XEll
	kentuckiense 🏆H5	CCCN GBin GKev LRHS NHpl SDir XEll
	'Kentucky Pink'	see *C.* Philipp gx 'Kentucky Pink'
	Kristi Lyn gx	XFro
	Lucy Pinkepank gx	XFro
	- 'Kentucky Pink Blush'	LRHS NHpl
	macranthos	GKev
	- 'Album'	GKev
	- John Hagger Group	XFro
	Maria gx	XFro
§	**Michael gx** 🏆H5	XFro
	Monto gx	XFro
	Mops gx	XFro
	parviflorum	GKev SDir
§	- var. ***pubescens***	GKev
	'Parville'	LRHS NHpl SDir
	Paul gx	XFro
	Peter gx	XFro
	Philipp gx 🏆H5	XFro
§	- 'Kentucky Pink'	GBin GKev NHpl SDir
	Piccolo gx	GKev
	Pluto gx	XFro
	pubescens	see *C. parviflorum* var. *pubescens*
	'Pueblo'	GBin LRHS NHpl
	Rascal gx	XFro
	reginae 🏆H5	CCCN GKev LRHS NHpl SDir XEll
	- f. ***albolabium***	GBin NHpl
	- f. ***album***	GKev LRHS SDir XEll
	Renate gx pastel-flowered	XFro
	Sabine gx 🏆H5	GBin XFro
	- pastel-flowered	XFro
	Schoko gx	GBin
	Sebastian gx	XFro
	- 'Frosch's Mountain King'	XFro
	- 'Multiflower White'	NHpl
	Sunny gx	GBin XFro
	Tilman gx	XFro
	Ulla Silkens gx 🏆H5	GEdr GKev XEll XFro
	Ursel gx	XFro
§	× ***ventricosum***	GKev XFro
	- 'Frosch's Queen of the Mist'	XFro
	- 'Pastel'	XFro
	- white-flowered	GKev
	Victoria gx	XFro

Cyrilla (*Cyrillaceae*)

	racemiflora	CMac IArd

Cyrtanthus (*Amaryllidaceae*)

§	***brachyscyphus***	EShb
	breviflorus	CPbh WCot WPGP
	'Edwina'	CCCN
§	***elatus*** 🏆H2	CSam CTsd EShb GKev NSti SPtp WCot
	'Elizabeth'	CCCN
	epiphyticus	WCot
	falcatus 🏆H2	WCot
	mackenii	EShb WPGP
	- var. ***cooperi***	CAby
	- cream-white-flowered	CCCN EShb GKev
	- 'Himalayan Pink'	CCCN EShb GKev
	- orange-flowered	GKev
	- red-flowered	CCCN EShb GKev
	- yellow-flowered	GKev
	montanus	WCot
	parviflorus	see *C. brachyscyphus*
	purpureus	see *C. elatus*
	sanguineus	WCot
	speciosus	see *C. elatus*

Cyrtomium ✿ (*Dryopteridaceae*)

§	***caryotideum***	CLAP ISha
	devexiscapulae	CAby CBdn CLAP LEdu LLWG WPGP

§ ***falcatum*** ♀H3	CAby CBod CDoC CLAP CPla CRos EFer EHyd ELon EMor EPfP GMaP LEdu LRHS MAsh NLar NRHS SCob SDix SEND SPlb SPoG SRms WCot XBlo XLum
- 'Maritimum'	CBdn
- 'Rochfordianum'	CBdn CCCN CRos EHyd GBin ISha LEdu LRHS MRav NRHS WFib
§ ***fortunei*** ♀H3	CAby CBct CBdn CLAP CRos CSpe EFer EHyd ELon EMor EPfP LCro LOPS LRHS MAsh MGos MRav NBid NBro NLar NRHS SCob SPoG SRms WCFE WFib WPnP XLum
- var. ***clivicola***	CBdn CTsd EAJP EBee EHyd EMor EPfP EShb ISha LEdu LRHS MGos MRav NBro NGrd NLar NRHS SPad WBrk WCot XLum
macrophyllum	CLAP CRos EBee EHyd LEdu LRHS NRHS WPGP
tukusicola	EBee

Cystopteris ✿ (*Woodsiaceae*)

bulbifera	WCot
dickieana	WFib
fragilis	EFer GKev LEdu WFib
moupinensis B&SWJ 6767	WCot WCru

Cytisus (*Papilionaceae*)

'Andreanus'	see *C. scoparius* f. *andreanus*
battandieri	see *Argyrocytisus battandieri*
× ***beanii*** ♀H5	CRos EHyd ELan EPfP LRHS MAsh NLar SLon
'Boskoop Glory'	NLar
× ***boskoopii*** 'Apricot Gem'	CBod CSBt ELan NLar
- 'Boskoop Ruby' ♀H5	CBod CBrac CDoC CMac CRos CSBt ECrN EHyd ELan EPfP GKin LCro LOPS LRHS LSRN MAsh NHol NRHS SCob SGbt SPer SWvt
- 'Dukaat'	NLar
- 'Hollandia' ♀H5	CBcs CSBt ELan EPfP GKin MMuc MRav NLar SPer
- 'La Coquette'	CBod CDoC EPfP SPlb
- 'Windlesham Ruby'	CExl EHyd ELan EPfP LRHS LSRN NLar SLim WFar
- 'Zeelandia' ♀H5	CMac EBee EHyd ELan EPfP LRHS NHol NLar SCob SPer
'Burkwoodii' ♀H5	CBcs CBod EHyd ELan ELon EPfP LRHS LSRN MSwo SCob SNig SPoG WFar
canariensis	see *Genista canariensis*
'Daisy Hill'	WRHF
§ ***decumbens***	MAsh
demissus ♀H5	WAbe
'Golden Cascade'	CBcs CBod CRos EHyd ELan LRHS MAsh NRHS SLim
'Goldfinch'	CBrac CRos EHyd ELan LRHS MSwo NHol NLar NRHS SNig WFar
§ ***hirsutus***	CExl SBrt
× ***kewensis*** ♀H5	CRos EHyd ELan EPfP LRHS MAsh MGos MRav NLar NRHS SRms
- 'Niki'	EPfP MAsh NLar SPer WRHF
'Killiney Red'	ELan
'Killiney Salmon'	EMil GKin LSRN MRav
'Lena' ♀H5	CMac CRos CSBt ECrN EHyd ELan EPfP GKin LRHS LSRN MGos NBir NHol NLar NRHS SCob SGbt SLim SPoG WFar
'Luna'	EPfP SCob
'Maria Burkwood'	NLar
'Minstead'	EBee SPer
'Moyclare Pink'	LCro LOPS
'Mrs Norman Henry'	NLar
'Newry Seedling'	CMac
nigricans 'Cyni' ♀H5	CRos EHyd ELan LRHS MAsh SPer SPoG
'Palette'	SCob
'Porlock'	see *Genista* 'Porlock'
× ***praecox***	CMac CRos EHyd ELon EPfP LRHS MAsh NRHS SCob SPlb SPoG WFar
- 'Albus'	CBcs CBod CBrac CDoC CMac CRos EHyd ELan EPfP LRHS LSRN MAsh MGos MMuc MRav NHol NRHS SCob SEND SPer WFar
- 'Allgold' ♀H5	Widely available
- 'Frisia'	WFar
- 'Lilac Lady'	CRos EHyd LRHS
- 'Warminster' ♀H5	CBrac EPfP GKin MRav SEND SPer SRms
proliferus	CExl
purpureus	EBee EPfP LRHS MMrt MRav WSHC
- 'Atropurpureus'	EPfP
racemosus	see *Genista* × *spachiana*
'Red Wings'	CBrac
scoparius	SCob WTSh
§ - f. ***andreanus***	CTri EPfP
- - 'Splendens'	SPer
- 'Cornish Cream'	CSBt ELan EPfP
- 'Firefly'	CBcs CMac
- 'Fulgens'	EPfP
- 'Golden Sunlight'	CSBt MSwo
§ - subsp. ***maritimus***	CMac
- var. ***prostratus***	see *C. scoparius* subsp. *maritimus*
- 'Tiltstone Moonglow' **new**	GBin
- 'Vanesse'	NLar
× ***spachianus***	see *Genista* × *spachiana*
supinus	see *C. hirsutus*
'White Lion'	CMac

D

Daboecia ✿ (*Ericaceae*)

§ ***cantabrica*** f. ***alba***	NWad SWhi
- - 'Alba Globosa'	GPer SWhi
- - 'Alberta White'	CFst SWhi
- - 'Creeping White'	CFst SWhi
- - 'David Moss'	SWhi
I - - 'Early Bride'	SWhi
- - 'Snowdrift'	SWhi
- 'Amelie'PBR	CFst SWhi
- 'Andrea'	CFst SWhi
- 'Angelina'PBR	CFst SWhi
- 'Arielle'	CFst SWhi
- 'Atropurpurea'	CFst NWad SWhi
- 'Bicolor'	CFst SWhi
- 'Blueless'	SWhi
- f. ***blumii*** 'Pink Blum'	CFst SWhi
- - 'Pinky Perky'	CFst SWhi
- - 'Purple Blum'	CFst SWhi
- - 'White Blum'	CFst SWhi
- 'Bubbles'	CFst SWhi
- 'Celtic Star'	CFst
- 'Chaldon'	CFst SWhi

	– 'Charles Nelson' (d)	CFst SWhi
	– 'Cinderella'	CFst SWhi
	– 'Cleggan'	SWhi
	– 'Covadonga'	CFst
	– 'Cupido'	SWhi
§	– 'Donard Pink'	GJos GPer
	– 'Eskdale Baron'	SWhi
	– 'Glamour'	CFst SWhi
I	– 'Globosa Pink'	CFst NWad SWhi
	– 'Harlequin'	SWhi
	– 'Heather Yates'	CFst SWhi
	– 'Hookstone Purple'	SWhi
	– 'Lilac Osmond'	CFst SWhi
	– 'Pink'	see *D. cantabrica* 'Donard Pink'
	– 'Pink Lips'	CFst
§	– 'Polifolia'	CFst SWhi
	– 'Porter's Variety'	SWhi
	– 'Praegerae'	SWhi
	– 'Rainbow' (v)	CFst SWhi
	– 'Rodeo'	CFst SWhi
	– 'Romantic Muxoll' (d)	CFst SWhi
	– 'Rosella' PBR	CFst SWhi
	– subsp. ***scotica*** 'Barbara Phillips'	SWhi
	– – 'Bearsden'	SWhi
	– – 'Ben'	CFst
	– – 'Cora'	CFst SWhi
	– – 'Ellen Norris'	CFst SWhi
	– – 'Golden Imp'	CFst SWhi
	– – 'Goscote'	CFst MGos SWhi
	– – 'Jack Drake'	CFst SWhi
	– – 'Katherine's Choice'	CBcs CFst SWhi
	– – 'Red Imp'	CFst SWhi
	– – 'Robin'	CFst SWhi
	– – 'Sarah' **new**	SWhi
	– – 'Sid Brown' **new**	SWhi
	– – 'Silverwells' ♀H5	CBcs MAsh SWhi
	– – 'Tabramhill'	SWhi
	– – 'Thumbelina'	CFst
	– – 'William Buchanan' ♀H5	CFst GAbr GJos GPer MAsh NWad SCoo SWhi
	– – 'William Buchanan Gold' (v)	CFst
	– 'Stardust Muxoll'	CFst SWhi
	– 'Sun Seeker'	CFst SWhi
	– 'Tinkerbell'	CFst SWhi
	– 'Vanessa' PBR	CFst SWhi
	– 'Waley's Red' ♀H5	NWad SWhi

Dacrycarpus ✿ (*Podocarpaceae*)

§	***dacrydioides***	CBrP CTsd LEdu

Dacrydium ✿ (*Podocarpaceae*)

	cupressinum	SPlb WThu
	franklinii	see *Lagarostrobos franklinii*

Dactylicapnos (*Papaveraceae*)

	macrocapnos	CBcs CSpe GKev WBor WCru
	platycarpa	WPGP
§	***scandens***	CAby CRHN GEdr IRos SBrt WAvo
	– GWJ 9438	WCru
	– WJC 13793	WCru
	– 'Shirley Clemo'	CExl
§	***ventii*** GWJ 9376	WCru
	– WJC 13786	WCru

Dactylis (*Poaceae*)

	glomerata	CHab SVic WSFF
	– 'Variegata' (v)	MMuc NBid

Dactylorhiza (*Orchidaceae*)

§	***elata*** ♀H5	GBee GKev
	Foliorella gx	GBin
§	***foliosa*** ♀H4	CCCN ECha GKev MAvo NChi WSHC
§	***fuchsii***	CCCN CMil EMor EPot EWat GKev LEdu MNrw NBir NRya WHer WSFF
	– 'Bressingham Bonus'	GKev
	– 'Eleanor' **new**	MPhe
	× ***grandis***	IBlr
	– Blackthorn hybrid	CBor CJun IBlr
	'Harold Esslemont'	GKev
	hybrid	LEdu NRya
	incarnata	NBid
§	***maculata***	EHyd GKev LRHS WBor
	maderensis	see *D. foliosa*
§	***majalis***	EMor WSFF XEll
	mascula	see *Orchis mascula*
	praetermissa	CCCN LRHS
	purpurella	CMiW EPot GAbr GJos NRya

Dahlia ✿ (*Asteraceae*)

	'A la Mode' (D)	CWGr
	'Abbie' (D)	NHal
	'Abingdon Ace' (D)	SGbt
	'Abridge Ben' (D)	CWGr
	'Abridge Taffy' (D)	CWGr
	'AC Abby' (C) **new**	WPhe
I	'Acapulco' (S-c)	ERCP
	'Ace Summer Emotions' PBR (D)	SDeJ
	'Adelaide Fontane' (D)	CWGr
	'Admiral Rawlings' (D)	CWGr
	'After Dusk' (D) **new**	WPhe
	'Aggie White' (D) **new**	NHal
	'Aitara Caress' (C)	SGbt
	'Aitara Diadem' (D)	LSou
	'Aitara Majesty' (S-c)	GRid
	'Akita' (Misc)	CWGr ELan LCro LOPS SGbt
	'Aladdin's Lamp' (WL)	NJRG
	'Alauna Clair-Obscur' (Fim)	CWGr ERCP LCro LOPS SDir
	'Albert Schweitzer' (S-c)	CWGr SGbt
	'Alden Regal' (C)	CWGr
	'Alfred C' (S-c)	CWGr
	'Alfred Grille' (S-c)	LCro LOPS SDeJ SGbt
	'Alf's Mascot' (D)	NJRG WPhe
	'Alison Shingler' (S-c)	CWGr
	'Aljo' (S-c)	CWGr
	'Allan Snowfire' (S-c)	NHal
	'Allan Sparkes' (WL) ♀H3	CWGr MCot
	'Alloway Candy' (Misc)	ERCP
	'Alloway Cottage' (D)	CWGr NHal SGbt WPhe
	'Alltami Apollo' (S-c)	CWGr
	'Alltami Classic' (D)	CWGr
	'Alltami Corsair' (S-c)	CWGr
	'Alltami Ruby' (S-c)	CWGr
	'Almand's Climax' (D) ♀H3	CWGr GRid SGbt
	'Alpen Beauty' (Col)	CWGr
	'Alpen Fern' (Fim)	CWGr
	'Alpen Flame' (C)	CWGr
	'Alpen Fury' (Anem)	NJRG
	'Alpen Mildred' (S-c)	CWGr
	'Alpen Sun' (S-c)	CWGr
	'Alstergruss' (Col)	CWGr SDeJ
	'Alva's Doris' (S-c) ♀H3	CWGr LAyl
	'Alva's Lilac' (D)	CWGr
	'Alva's Supreme' (D) ♀H3	CWGr GRid LAyl NHal WPhe

'Amante' (D) **new** LCro LOPS
'Amaran Guard' (D) CWGr
'Amaran Relish' (D) CWGr GRid SGbt
'Amaran Return' (D) CWGr
'Amaran Royale' (D) CWGr
'Amaran Troy' (WL) CWGr
I 'Amazone' (Sin/DwB) LRHS SPoG
'Amber Banker' (C) CWGr SGbt
'Amberglow' (Ba) CWGr
'Amberley Joan' (D) CWGr
'Amberley Victoria' (D) CWGr
'Ambition' (S-c) CAvo CWGr ERCP LCro LOPS
'Amelia's Surprise' (D) CWGr
'American Copper' (D) CWGr
'American Dawn' (D) ERCP LCro LOPS SPer WPhe
'American Moon' (D) LOPS
AMERICAN PIE ('Vdtg26'PBR) (Dark Angel Series) (Sin) CWGr SDeJ
'American Sun' (D) ERCP
'Amethyst' (D) CWGr
'Amgard Coronet' (D) CWGr
'Amgard Delicate' (D) CWGr SGbt
'Amgard Rosie' (D) CWGr
'Amira' (Ba) CWGr GRid
'Amorangi Joy' (C) CWGr
'Amy Cave' (Ba) GRid NHal WPhe
'Amy Madison' (S-c) CWGr
'Andrea Clark' (D) GRid NHal WPhe
'Andrea Lawson' (Ba) GRid WPhe
'Andrew Mitchell' (S-c) CWGr GRid NHal
'Andries' Amber' (S-c) CWGr
'Andries' Orange' (C) ECtt
'Andries' Orange As' (S-c) CWGr
'Andy Murray' (Sin) CWGr
'Angora' (Fim) SGbt
'Angus McInns Walls' (S-c) CWGr
'Anita Summerhayes' (Misc) CWGr
'Ann Breckenfelder' (Col) ♀H3 CWGr ECtt ERCP GRid NHal NJRG WPhe
I 'Anna' (Sin) **new** WPhe
'Anna Lindh' (WL) GRid
'Anne Cornelia' (D) **new** WPhe
'Annika' (Sin) SDeJ
'Anniversary Ball' (Ba) CWGr
'Another Pet' see *D.* 'Mystic Enchantment'
'Antique'PBR (Sin) EHyd LRHS
'Apache' (Fim) CWGr ERCP SDeJ SGbt SPer
'Apache Blauw' (Fim) ERCP
'Apopa Sky' (Sin) NJRG
'Apple Blossom' (C) SGbt
I 'Appleblossom' (Col) CWGr
'Apricot Desire' (WL) ERCP
'Apricot Honeymoon Dress' (D) CWGr
'Apricot Jewel' (D) CWGr
I 'Apricot Parfait' (Fim) CWGr
'April Dawn' (D) CWGr
'April Heather' (Col) ♀H3 NHal WPhe
'Arabian Night' (D) CAby CAvo CBcs CWCL CWGr EBee ECtt ELan EPfP ERCP LAyl LCro LOPS LRHS LSRN LSun MHol NLar SDeJ SDir SEND SGbt WBrk WCot WPhe WSpi
'Arbatax' (D) ERCP SDir
'Arc de Triomphe' (D) CWGr
'Arlequin' (D) SGbt
'Arnhem' (D) CWGr
'Arthur Godfrey' (D) CWGr
'Arthur's Delight' (D) CWGr
'Asahi Chohje' (Anem) ♀H3 CWGr
'Askwith Edna' (D) **new** WPhe
'Askwith Josephine' (D) **new** WPhe
'Askwith Minnie' (D) NHal WPhe
'Askwith Rodger' (D) **new** WPhe
'Atilla' (D) CWGr
I 'Atlanta' (D) SGbt
atropurpurea CWGr
'Audacity' (D) CWGr LAyl SGbt
'Aurora's Kiss' (Ba) ERCP NHal SGbt
I 'Aurore' (C) CWGr
'Aurwen's Violet' (Pom) NHal WPhe
australis CSpe EBee SMad
– B&SWJ 10389 WCru
I 'Autumn Fairy' (S-c) SCob SDeJ
'Autumn Lustre' (WL) CWGr
'Avignon' (D) SDeJ
'Avoca Amanda' (D) NHal WPhe
'Avoca Comanche' (S-c) GRid NHal
'Avoca Salmon' (D) GRid
'B.J. Beauty' (D) GRid NHal NJRG WPhe
'Babette' (S-c) GRid
'Baby Fonteneau' (S-c) CWGr
'Babylon' (D) LRHS SGbt
§ 'Babylon Brons' (D) ERCP LRHS SGbt
'Babylon Bronze' see *D.* 'Babylon Brons'
'Babylon Lila' (D) SGbt
§ 'Babylon Paars' (D) ECtt LRHS SDeJ SGbt
'Babylon Purple' see *D.* 'Babylon Paars'
'Babylon Rose' (D) LRHS SGbt
'Bacardi' (D) ERCP
'Badger Twinkle' (S-c) CWGr GRid WPhe
'Bahama Lemon' see *D.* 'Lemon Cane'
'Balham' (Sin) WCot
'Ballego's Glory' (D) CWGr SGbt
'Balthasar' (D) **new** ERCP
'Bambino' (Lil) CWGr
'Banker' (C) CWGr
'Bantling' (Pom) CWGr ERCP SDir SGbt
'Barbara Schell' (D) CWGr
'Barbara's Pastelle' (S-c) CWGr NJRG SGbt
'Barbara's Yellow' (S-c) NJRG
'Barbarossa' (D) CWGr
'Barbarry Aleks' (D) **new** WPhe
'Barbarry Ball' (Ba) CWGr
'Barbarry Banker' (D) CWGr LAyl
'Barbarry Bluebird' (D) SGbt
'Barbarry Carousel' (Ba) CWGr
'Barbarry Civic' (D) GRid
'Barbarry Cosmos' (D) CWGr
'Barbarry d'Amour' (D) **new** NHal
'Barbarry Delegate' (D) **new** NHal
'Barbarry Dominion' (D) CWGr
'Barbarry Drifter' (D) CWGr
'Barbarry Drum' (D) **new** NHal
'Barbarry Flag' (D) CWGr
'Barbarry Gem' (Ba) CWGr
'Barbarry Maverick' (D) WPhe
'Barbarry Melody' (D) NHal
'Barbarry Monitor' (Ba) CWGr SGbt
'Barbarry Olympic' (Ba) CWGr
'Barbarry Oracle' (D) CWGr
'Barbarry Patriot' (Ba) **new** NHal
'Barbarry Pinky' (D) CWGr
'Barbarry Pip' (D) NHal WPhe
'Barbarry Primrose Hall' (D) **new** NHal WPhe
'Barbarry Red Devil' (D) GRid

'Barbarry Rover' (D) **new**	WPhe
'Barbarry Sultan' (D)	NHal
'Barbarry Token' (D)	GRid
'Barbarry Triumph' (D)	CWGr
'Barbarry Vintage' (D)	GRid
'Barbarry Vulcan' (D) **new**	WPhe
'Barbetta' (D)	SPer
'Barbette' (D)	CWGr
'Bareham's Beauty' (D)	CWGr
'Baret Joy' (S-c)	CWGr GRid WPhe
'Bargaly Blush' (D)	GRid NHal
'Baron Ray' (D)	CWGr
'Barry Williams' (D)	SGbt
'Bart' (D)	CWGr
'Barton Memory' (S-c)	GRid
'Bassingbourne Beauty' (D)	CWGr
'Bayou'PBR (Anem)	CAby CWGr ERCP LCro LOPS LSou NJRG SGbt WPhe
'Bedford Sally' (D)	CWGr
'Bednall Beauty' (Misc/ DwB) ♀H3	CRos CWGr ECtt ELan LRHS NJRG WSpi
'Belinda Appleyard' (Ba)	CWGr
'Bell Boy' (Ba)	SGbt
'Belle Epoque' (C)	CWGr
'Belle of Barmera' (D)	ERCP
'Ben Huston' (D)	GRid
'Bengale' (D)	CWGr
'Berger's Rekord' (S-c)	CWGr
'Bernice Sunset' (S-c)	CWGr
'Berolina' (D)	CWGr
'Berwick Banker' (Ba)	CWGr
'Berwick Wood' (D)	CWGr GRid NHal SGbt WPhe
'Bess Painter' (D)	CWGr
'Best Bett'	see *D.* MYSTIC SPIRIT
'Beth's Chaplet' (Sin)	WCot
'Betty Ann' (Pom)	CWGr
'Beving Beauty' (D) **new**	CWGr
'Biddenham Fairy' (D)	CWGr
'Biddenham Strawberry' (D)	CWGr SGbt
'Bilbao'PBR (Jumbo Collection) (D)	SDeJ
'Bill Holmberg' (D)	CWGr GRid SGbt WPhe
'Bingo' (D)	SGbt
'Birkenshaw Garden Friends' (Col)	NJRG
'Bishop of Auckland'PBR (Misc)	CAby CAvo CRos CWGN CWGr ECtt EHyd EPfP ERCP LCro LOPS LRHS MGos NJRG NRHS SDeJ SDir SGbt WCot
'Bishop of Cambridge' (Sin)	SDir
'Bishop of Canterbury'PBR (P)	CCht CRos CWGr ECtt EHyd ELan EPfP LCro LOPS LRHS LSou MBros MGos NHal NRHS SDeJ SDir SGbt SPer SPoG WPhe
'Bishop of Dover' (Sin)	CWGr EPfP LCro LOPS LRHS SDeJ SDir SGbt WBrk WPhe
'Bishop of Lancaster' (Misc)	NLar SDir
'Bishop of Leicester' (Misc)	CWGr EHyd ELan EPfP LCro LOPS LRHS NLar NRHS SDeJ SDir SGbt SHar WPhe
'Bishop of Llandaff' (P) ♀H3	Widely available
'Bishop of Oxford' (Misc)	CAby CCht CRos CWGr ELan EPfP ERCP LCro LOPS LRHS MBros MGos NJRG NRHS SDeJ SDir SGbt SPoG WPhe
'Bishop of York' (Misc)	CAby CAvo CRos CWGr ECtt EHyd ELan EPfP LAyl LCro LOPS LRHS LSou MBros MGos MSCN NGdn NLar NRHS SDeJ SGbt SPer SPoG WHil WPhe

'Bishop Peter Price' (Sin)	CWGr
'Bista' (Ba)	GRid
'Black Fire' (D)	CWGr ECtt
'Black Jack' (D)	ERCP NHal NJRG WPhe
'Black Monarch' (D)	CWGr NHal SGbt
'Black Narcissus' (C)	CWGr ERCP SGbt
I 'Black R. Jack' (Misc)	NJRG
'Black Spider' (S-c)	CWGr
'Black Star' (Sin)	EPfP
'Black Touch' (Fim)	CWGr ERCP
'Blackberry Ripple' (S-c)	CWGr SDir
'Blaze' (D)	CWGr
'Blithe Spirit' (D)	CWGr
'Bloemfontein' (D)	CWGr
'Bloodstone' (D)	CWGr SGbt
'Bloody Mary' (D)	ERCP
'Bloom's Graham' (S-c)	CWGr
'Bloom's Kenn' (D)	CWGr SGbt
'Blue Beard' (S-c)	CWGr
'Blue Bell' (D)	SPer
'Blue Boy' (D)	CWGr ERCP LCro LOPS LSou WBrk
'Blue Wish' (WL)	ERCP GRid LCro LOPS NJRG
'Blueberry Hill' (Col)	LAyl
'Bluesette' (D)	WPhe
'Blyton Everest' (D)	NHal
'Blyton Golden Girl' (D)	GRid NHal WPhe
'Blyton Lady in Red' (D)	GRid LAyl NHal WPhe
'Blyton Romance' (D)	NHal
'Blyton Royal Velvet' (D)	GRid
'Blyton Shiraz' (D) **new**	WPhe
'Blyton Softer Gleam' (D) ♀H3	CWGr GRid NHal NJRG SGbt WPhe
'Blyton Valentine' (D)	NHal
'Bob's Bonaventure' (D)	GRid WPhe
'Bodacious' (D)	CWGr
'Bokay' (WL)	CWGr
'Bonesta' (D)	CWGr
'Bonny Blue' (Ba)	CWGr
'Boogie Woogie' (Anem)	CWGr SDeJ WPhe
'Boom Boom White' (Ba)	ERCP
'Boom Boom Yellow' (Ba)	ERCP SDeJ
'Bora Bora' (S-c)	CWGr
'Border Princess' (C/DwB)	SGbt
'Boy Scout' (Ba)	CWGr
'Bracken Lorelei' (WL)	NJRG
'Brackenridge Ballerina' (WL)	CWGr GRid NJRG SGbt WPhe
'Brandaris' (S-c)	CWGr SGbt
'Brandon James' (D)	SDeJ
'Brandysnap' (D)	CWGr SGbt
'Brantwood' (Sin)	CWGr
'Brasilia' (Dalina Series) (D)	CWGr
BRAVEHEART ('Vdtg67'PBR) (Dark Angel Series) (Sin)	LCro LOPS SDeJ
'Brian's Dream' (D)	LAyl NHal
'Bride's Bouquet' (Col)	ERCP LRHS
'Bridge View Aloha' (S-c) ♀H3	CWGr SGbt
'Bright Diamond' (D)	SDeJ
'Bright Eyes' (Sin)	ERCP WOld
'Brindisii' (Anem)	SDeJ
'Bristol Petite' (D)	CWGr
'Brookfield Delight' (Sin/ Lil) ♀H3	CWGr
'Brookfield Rachel' (Ba)	CWGr
'Brookfield Snowball' (Ba)	CWGr
'Brookside Cheri' (C)	CWGr
'Brookside Snowball' (Ba)	CWGr
'Brown Sugar' (Ba) **new**	WPhe

	'Bryce B. Morrison' (D)	CWGr
	'Bryn Terfel' (D)	CWGr GRid GWyn NHal SGbt WPhe
	'Bull's Pride' (D)	CWGr
	'Burlesca' (Ba)	ERCP
	'Butch' (D)	CWGr
	'Butterball' (D/DwB)	SDeJ
*	'Buttercup' (Pom)	CWGr
	'By George' (D)	CWGr
	'Caballero' (WL)	CWGr GRid
	'Café au Lait' (D)	CAby CWCL CWGr ELan ERCP IPot LAyl LCro LOPS LRHS MSCN NHal SDeJ SDir SGbt SPer WPhe WSpi
	'Caitlin's Joy' (Ba) **new**	WPhe
	'Calgary' (D)	CWGr
	'California Sunset' (Misc)	CAby
	'Calin' (WL)	CWGr
	'Camano Ariel' (C)	CWGr
	'Camano Passion' (S-c)	CWGr
	'Camano Poppet' (Ba)	CWGr
	'Camano Regal' (S-c)	CWGr
I	'Cameo' (WL)	ELan LAyl NHal NJRG SGbt WPhe
	campanulata	CWGr
	'Campos Billy M' (S-c)	CWGr
	'Campos Hush' (S-c)	CWGr
	'Campos Philip M' (D)	CWGr
	'Canary Fubuki' (Fim)	CWGr ERCP SDeJ SGbt SPer
I	'Candlelight' (D)	GRid
	'Candy Cane CZ' (D)	CWGr
	'Candy Cupid' (Ba)	CWGr
	CANDY EYES	see *D.* 'Zone Ten'
	'Candy Hamilton Lillian' (D)	CWGr
	'Candy Keene' (S-c)	CWGr GRid NHal
	'Captain Bruce Bairnsfather' (C)	CWGr
	'Caribbean Fantasy' (D)	CWGr
	'Carlien' (WL) **new**	WPhe
	'Carol Klein' (Sin/DwB) **new**	CWGr
	'Carola' (S-c)	CWGr
	'Carole Chamberlain' (Col)	NJRG
	'Carolina Moon' (D)	CWGr GRid GWyn NHal SGbt
	'Carol's Spanish Dancer' (C)	LAyl NHal NJRG WPhe
	'Carstone Firebox' (Col)	LAyl WPhe
	'Carstone Ruby' (D)	NHal
	'Carstone Sunbeam' (D)	CWGr
	'Carstone Suntan' (C)	CWGr GRid
	'Carstone Valiant' (Ba)	NHal WPhe
	'Cartouche' (D)	CWGr ERCP
	'Catherine Deneuve' (Misc)	CWGN CWGr NJRG SGbt
	'Catherine Ireland' (D)	CWGr
	'Cerise Prefect' (S-c)	CWGr
	'Cha Cha' (S-c)	CWGr SGbt
	'Challenger' (D)	GWyn
	'Charles de Coster' (D)	CWGr
	'Charles Dickens' (Ba)	CWGr
	'Charlie Dimmock' (WL) ♀H3	CWGr GRid NHal NJRG SGbt WPhe
	'Charlie Two' (D)	CWGr GRid NHal WPhe
I	'Charlotte' (Sin)	CWGr
	'Charlotte Bateson' (Ba)	CWGr
	'Chat Noir' (S-c) ♀H3	CWGr ERCP IPot LAyl LCro LOPS LRHS SDir SGbt WPhe WTre
	'Chatsworth Splendour' (Sin/DwB) **new**	CWGr
	'Checkers' (D) **new**	CWGr WPhe
	'Chee' (WL)	CWGr
	'Cheerio' (S-c)	ECtt EHyd LRHS NRHS WGwG
	'Cherokee Beauty' (D)	CWGr
	'Cherry Wine' (D)	CWGr
	'Cherrywood Millfield' (S-c)	CWGr
	'Cherrywood Turnpike' (D)	CWGr
	'Cherrywood Wilderness' (D)	CWGr
	'Cherubino' (Col)	CWGr
	'Cherwell Goldcrest' (S-c)	CWGr GRid NHal SGbt WPhe
	'Cherwell Lapwing' (S-c)	GRid
	'Cherwell Linnet' (Ba)	GRid NHal WPhe
	'Cherwell Skylark' (S-c)	GRid
	'Cherwell Waxwing' (D)	GRid
	'Chessy' (Sin/Lil) ♀H3	CWGr
	'Chilson's Pride' (D)	CWGr SGbt
	'Chiltern Amber' (D)	CWGr
	'Chiltern Sylvia' (S-c)	CWGr
	'Chimacum Topaz' (S-c)	CWGr GRid
	'Chimborazo' (Col)	CWGr EWes LAyl SGbt
	'Chinese Lantern' (D)	CWGr
	'Chloe's Keene' (S-c)	CWGr
	'Chorus Girl' (D)	CWGr
	'Christie Snowy'	GRid
	'Christine' (D)	CWGr
I	'Christine' (WL)	SGbt
	'Christmas Carol' (Col)	CWGr ECtt GRid GWyn NHal NJRG WPhe
	'Christopher Nickerson' (S-c)	CWGr SGbt
	'Christopher Taylor' (WL)	NHal SGbt SHar WPhe
	'City of Leiden' (S-c)	LCro LOPS
	'Clair de Lune' (Col) ♀H3	CWGr ECtt ERCP GRid LRHS NHal NJRG SGbt WCot WPhe WSpi
	'Claire Diane' (D)	CWGr
	'Claire Louise Downting' (D) **new**	WPhe
	'Clara May' (Fim)	CWGr
	'Clarion' (S-c)	LRHS NRHS
I	'Clarion' (Sin)	CWGr WPhe
	'Classic A.1' (C)	CWGr
	'Classic Poème' PBR (Misc)	ERCP
	'Classic Rosamunde' PBR (Misc) ♀H3	ERCP NHal
	'Classic Summertime' (Misc)	CWGr
§	'Classic Swanlake' PBR (Misc)	CWGr ERCP LCro LRHS NJRG
	'Claudette' (D)	MHol
	'Clayt's Candy' (S-c)	GRid NHal WPhe
	'Clearview Arlene' (S-c)	GRid
	'Clearview Audrey' (S-c) **new**	NHal WPhe
	'Clearview Daniel' (Ba) ♀H3	NHal
	'Clearview Debby' (D) **new**	WPhe
	'Clearview Dorothy' (S-c) **new**	WPhe
	'Clearview Edie' (DblO)	GRid NHal WPhe
	'Clearview Irene' (S-c)	GRid NHal
	'Clearview Louise' (S-c)	NHal WPhe
	'Clearview Sundance' (C)	GRid NHal WPhe
	'Clearview Tammy' (S-c) **new**	NHal WPhe
	'Cleo Laine' (S-c)	CWGr NHal
	'Cloverdale' (D)	CWGr
	coccinea	CExl CSpe CWGr EShb MCot SGbt SMHy WPGP
	– NJM 05.072	WPGP
	– orange-flowered	CWGr
	– var. ***palmeri***	CAvo WPGP XEll
	– yellow-flowered	CWGr
	'Cocktail' (S-c)	CWGr
	'Color Spectacle' (S-c)	CWGr LRHS
	'Coltness Gem' (Sin/DwB)	CWGr

	'Comet' (Anem)	CWGr
	'Como Polly' (D)	CWGr
	'Contessa' (D)	SDeJ
	'Coral Jupiter' (S-c)	CWGr GRid WPhe
	'Coral Strand' (D)	CWGr
	'Cornel' (Ba)	CWGr ERCP NHal NJRG SGbt WPhe
	'Cornel Brons' (Ba)	ERCP WPhe
	'Cornell' (D)	GRid
	'Cornish Ruby' (Sin)	EBee EPfP
I	'Corona' (S-c/DwB)	SDeJ
	'Coronella' (D)	CWGr SGbt
	'Corson George' (S-c) **new**	NHal
	'Corson Gold' (S-c) **new**	NHal
	'Cortez Silver' (D)	CWGr
	'Cortez Sovereign' (S-c)	CWGr
	'Corton Bess' (D)	CWGr
	'Corton Olympic' (D)	CWGr
	'Corydon' (D)	CWGr
	'Cottontail' (Col)	CWGr
	'Country Boy' (S-c)	CWGr GRid
	'Coupe de Soleil' (D)	CWGr
	'Craigowan' (S-c)	GRid NHal WPhe
	'Crazy Legs' (DblO)	SGbt
	'Crazy Love' (D)	CWGr LCro LOPS SPer
	'Cream Alva's' (D) 🏆H3	CWGr GRid
I	'Cream Beauty' (WL)	CWGr
	'Cream Capella' (D)	GRid
	'Cream Diane' (D) **new**	NHal
	'Cream Klankstad' (C)	CWGr
	'Cream Linda' (D)	CWGr
	'Cream Moonlight' (S-c)	CWGr GRid NHal NJRG SGbt
	'Cream Reliance' (D)	CWGr
	'Cream Ruskin Diane' (D) **new**	WPhe
	'Crème de Cassis' (D)	CAvo CWGr ERCP LCro LOPS NHal WPhe
	'Crème de Cognac' (D) **new**	ERCP
	'Crève Coeur' (D)	CWGr GRid
	'Crichton Cherry' (D)	CWGr
	'Croesus' (S-c)	CWGr
	'Crossfield Anne' (D)	CWGr
	'Crossfield Festival' (D)	CWGr GRid
	'Croydon Ace' (D)	CWGr
	'Croydon Jumbo' (D)	CWGr
	'Croydon Snotop' (D)	CWGr
	'Croydon Superior' (D)	SGbt
	'Cryfield Harmony' (Ba)	CWGr WPhe
	'Cryfield Jane' (Ba)	CWGr
	'Cryfield Keene' (S-c)	CWGr
	'Cryfield Max' (C)	CWGr
	'Cryfield Rosie' (Ba)	CWGr
	'Culdrose' (D)	SGbt
	'Curate' (Misc)	CWGr
	'Curiosity' (Col)	GRid NJRG
	'Currant Cream' (Ba)	CWGr SGbt
	cuspidata	EBee
	'Cyclone' (D)	CWGr
	'Cycloop' (S-c)	CWGr
	'Cynthia Chalwin' (Ba)	CWGr
	'Cynthia Louise' (D)	CWGr
	'Czar Willo' (Pom)	CWGr
	(Dahlietta Surprise Series) DAHLIETTA BECKY (Col)	CWGr
	- DAHLIETTA JENNY	see *D.* 'Jenny'
	- DAHLIETTA LEANNE ('Dapacher') (Misc)	CWGr
	'Daily Mail' (D)	CWGr
	'Daisy Duke' (D)	ERCP
	DALAYA SHIVA ('Kledh13033'[PBR])	MPri
	DALAYA YOGI ('Kledh11031'[PBR])	MPri
	'Daleko Gold' (D)	CWGr
	'Daleko Jupiter' (S-c)	CWGr GRid NHal WPhe
	'Daleko National' (D)	CWGr
	'Daleko Tangerine' (D)	CWGr
	DALINA COZUMEL (Dalina Maxi Series) (D/DwB) **new**	CRos
	'Dame Deidre' (S-c)	CWGr
	'Dana Audrey' (C)	CWGr
	'Dana Dream' (S-c)	CWGr
	'Dana Iris' (S-c)	CWGr
	'Dana Sunset' (C)	CWGr
I	'Dandy' (Col)	SVic
	'Danjo Doc' (D)	SGbt
	'Dannevirke' (Sin)	CWGr
	'Danum Belle' (D)	CWGr
	'Danum Fancy' (D)	CWGr
	'Danum Gail' (D)	CWGr GRid
	'Danum Hero' (D)	CWGr
	'Danum Meteor' (S-c)	CWGr
	'Danum Rebel' (S-c)	CWGr
	'Danum Rhoda' (D)	CWGr
	'Danum Salmon' (S-c)	CWGr
	'Danum Torch' (Col)	CWGr ECtt SGbt
	'Dark Butterfly' (D)	CWCL CWGr ERCP LCro LOPS
	'Dark Desire' (Sin/DwB)	CSpe CWGr MCot
	'Dark Fubuki' (Fim)	ERCP
§	'Dark Side Of The Sun'[PBR] (Sin)	EHyd LRHS LSou NRHS SPoG WPhe
	'Dark Spirit' (D)	ECtt SDeJ SGbt WPhe
	'Dark Stranger' (C)	CWGr
	'Darkarin' (Misc)	CWGr ERCP
	'Darlington Diamond' (S-c)	CWGr
	'Darlington Jubilation' (S-c)	CWGr
	'Davenport Anita' (D)	CWGr
	'Davenport Honey' (D)	CWGr GRid
	'Davenport Lesley' (D)	CWGr
	'Davenport Sunlight' (S-c)	CWGr
	'Dave's Choice' (Ba)	GRid NJRG WPhe
	'Dave's Snip' (D)	CWGr
	'David Digweed' (D)	CWGr SGbt
	'David Howard' (D) 🏆H3	CAby CBod CWGr ECtt EHyd ELan EPfP ERCP GRid LAyl LCro LOPS LRHS LSou NHal NJRG NRHS SCob SGbt SPer SWvt WBrk WCot WFar WGwG WHoo WPhe WSpi
	'David's Choice' (D)	CWGr
	'Dawn Chorus' (D)	CWGr
	'Dawn Sky' (D)	LAyl
	'Dazzler' (D/DwB)	CWGr
	'Debora Renae' (WL)	ERCP
	'Deborah's Kiwi' (C)	CWGr GRid NHal SGbt
	'Debra Anne Craven' (S-c)	CWGr GRid NHal WPhe
	'Decorette' (D/DwB)	CWGr SGbt
	'Deepest Yellow' (Ba)	CWGr SDeJ SGbt
	'De-la-Haye' (S-c)	NHal
	'Demi Schneider' (Col)	CWGr
	'Dentelle de Venise' (C)	CWGr
	'Deuil du Roi Albert' (D)	CWGr
	'Deutschland' (D)	CWGr
	'Devon Elegance' (S-c)	CWGr
	'Devon Liam' (S-c)	CWGr
	'Devon Temptation' (C)	CWGr
	DIABLO MIXED (Misc/DwB) **new**	MBros

	'Diamond Rose' (Anem/ DwB)	CWGr
	'Diamond Wedding' (D)	SGbt
	'Diamond Years' (D)	SGbt
	'Diana Gregory' (Pom)	CWGr SGbt
	'Diana's Memory' (D)	LCro LOPS
	'Dikara Jodie' (D)	NHal WPhe
	'Dikara Moon' (D)	NHal
	'Dikara Superb' (D)	CWGr GRid NHal
	'Dilys Ayling' (Col)	NHal WPhe
	'Dinah Shore' (S-c)	CWGr
	'Dionne' (Misc) **new**	WPhe
I	'Disneyland' (Col)	SGbt
	dissecta	CExl CWGr EBee
	'Diva US' (D)	ERCP SDeJ
	'Dixieland' (D) **new**	CBod
	'Doc van Horn' (S-c)	CWGr
	'Doktor Hans Ricken' (D)	CWGr
	'Don Hill' (Col) ♀H3	GRid NJRG WPhe
	'Doris Bacon' (Ba)	CWGr
	'Doris Day' (C)	CWGr NHal SGbt
	'Doris Muldoon' (WL)	CWGr
	'Doris Rollins' (C)	CWGr
	'Dorothy Rose' (D)	WPhe
	'Dottie D.' (Ba)	CWGr
	'Double Dream Fantasy' (Dreamy Series) (Misc)	EHyd EPfP LRHS NRHS
	'Dovegrove' (Sin) ♀H3	CWGr
	'Downham Royal' (Ba)	CWGr ERCP LCro LOPS
	'Dr Caroline Rabbit' (D)	CWGr SGbt
	DRACULA ('Vdtg17'PBR) (Dark Angel Series) (Sin)	ERCP
	DRAGON BALL ('Vdtg31'PBR) (Dark Angel Series) (Sin)	SDeJ
	'Dream Seeker' (Col)	WPhe
	(Dreamy Series) DREAMY BLUSH WHITE (Misc)	EHyd
	- DREAMY EYES (Misc)	CRos NLar
	- DREAMY FANTASY (Misc)	CPla CWGr ELan MCot
	- DREAMY FUSION (Sin)	CWGr
	- DREAMY INSPIRE (Misc)	EHyd LRHS NLar
	- DREAMY KISS (P)	EHyd LRHS NLar NRHS
	- DREAMY LIPS (P)	NLar
	- DREAMY MOONLIGHT (Sin)	EHyd LRHS
	- DREAMY NIGHTS (Misc)	EHyd LRHS NRHS
	- DREAMY PASSION (Sin)	EHyd LRHS
	'Drummer Boy' (D)	GRid
	'Duddon Grace' (WL)	NHal
	'Duet' (D)	CWGr ELan SGbt
	'Dusky Harmony' (WL)	SGbt
	'Dutch Boy' (D)	CWGr
	'Dutch Explosion' (S-c)	ELan
	'Earl Haig' (D)	CWGr
	'Earl Marc' (C)	CWGr
	'Early Harvest' (D)	SGbt
	'East Anglian' (D)	CWGr
	'Eastwood Moonlight' (S-c)	CWGr GRid NHal SGbt WPhe
	'Eastwood Star' (S-c)	CWGr
	'Ebbw Vale Festival' (D)	CWGr
	'Edge of Gold' (D)	CWGr
	'Edge of Joy' (D)	LCro LOPS SRms
	'Edgeway Joyce' (Ba)	CWGr GRid
	'Edinburgh' (D)	CDoC CWGr ERCP GRid GWyn NHal SDeJ SDir SGbt WPhe
	'Edith Jones' (Col)	CWGr NHal NJRG
	'Edith Mueller' (Pom)	CWGr
	'Edmund' (Sin)	WCot
	'Edna C' (D)	CWGr
	'Edwin's Sunset' (WL) ♀H3	GRid NHal WPhe
	'Eileen Denny' (S-c)	CWGr GRid
	'El Cid' (D)	CWGr
	'El Paso' (D)	CWGr SDeJ
	'Elaine Beedle' (D)	CWGr
	'Elga-Bergerhoff' (C)	ERCP LRHS
	'Elgico Leanne' (C)	CWGr SGbt
	'Elizabeth Snowden' (Col)	GRid
	'Ella Britton' (D)	EHyd LRHS NRHS
	'Ellen Huston' (Misc/ DwB) ♀H3	CWGr ECtt ERCP GRid SGbt
I	'Elly' (WL) **new**	WPhe
	'Elma E' (D)	CWGr ERCP GRid NHal WPhe
	'Elmbrook Chieftain' (D)	CWGr
	'Elmbrook Rebel' (S-c)	CWGr GRid
	'Elmdon Superb' (Ba)	GRid
	'Elsie Merina' (D)	CWGr
I	'Embrace' (C)	NJRG WPhe
	'Emma's Coronet' (D)	CWGr WPhe
	'Emmaus' (Fim)	CWGr
	'Emmie Lou' (D)	CWGr
	'Emory Paul' (D)	CWGr ERCP
	'Emperor' (D)	CWGr
I	'Encore' (Fim)	CWGr ERCP
	'Engadin' (D)	CWGr
	'Engelhardts Matador' (D)	CBod ECtt ERCP LRHS MCot MHol NJRG SGbt WBrk WCot WRHF
	'Enid Adams' (D)	CWGr
	'Epping Forest' (D)	CWGr
	'Eric's Choice' (D)	CWGr
	'Esau' (D)	CWGr
	'Essex Chronicle' (D)	CWGr
	'Esther' (Col)	SDeJ
	'Esther Chamberlain' (Col)	NJRG
	'Etheral' (Sin)	CWGr
	'Eunice Arrigo' (S-c)	CWGr
I	'Eurydice' (Fim)	CWGr
	'Eveline' (D)	CAby CWGr ERCP LCro LOPS SDeJ SGbt
	'Evelyn Foster' (D)	CWGr GRid
	'Evelyn Rumbold' (D)	CWGr SGbt
	'Evelyn Taylor' (S-c)	NJRG
	'Evening Breeze' (D)	ERCP
	'Evening Lady' (D)	CWGr
	'Evening Mail' (S-c)	GRid
I	'Evita' (Anem)	NJRG
	excelsa (B)	NJRG
	- B&SWJ 10238 **new**	ESwi
	- 'Penelope Sky' (Sin)	ESwi WCru
	'Excentrique' (Misc)	CWGr ERCP NJRG
	'Exotic Dwarf' (Sin/Lil) ♀H3	NJRG
	'Explosion' (S-c)	CWGr
	'Extase' (S-c)	CWGr
	'Eye Candy' (Sin)	LRHS NJRG NRHS
	'Fabula' (Col)	CWGr
	'Fairway Pilot' (D)	CWGr NHal WPhe
	'Fairway Spur' (D)	CWGr GRid NHal WPhe
	'Fairy Queen' (C)	CWGr SGbt
§	'Famoso' (Col)	ERCP
	'Fantasie du Cap' (Fim)	ERCP
	'Fantastico' (Col)	CWGr ERCP
	'Fascination' (P) ♀H3	CAby CBcs CCht CWGr ECtt EHyd ERCP LAyl LRHS LSRN MCot MSCN NLar NRHS SCob SDeJ SGbt WHoo WSpi
	'Fashion Monger' (Col)	CAby CWGr ECtt ERCP GRid NHal NJRG SGbt WPhe
	'Fata Morgana' (Anem)	CWGr NJRG SGbt
	'Fern Irene' (WL)	CWGr
	'Fern Ridge Painted Lady' (D)	GRid

	'Ferncliff Illusion' (D)	CWGr ERCP SGbt
	'Ferncliff Inspiration' (S-c)	ERCP
	'Fernhill Champion' (D)	CWGr
	'Festivo' (Col)	CWGr
	'Feu Céleste' (Col)	CWGr
	'Fidalgo Blacky' (D)	CWGr
	'Fidalgo Bounce' (D)	CWGr
	'Fidalgo Climax' (Fim)	CWGr
	'Fidalgo Magic' (D)	CWGr
	'Fidalgo Snowman' (S-c)	CWGr
	'Fidalgo Supreme' (D)	GRid LAyl
I	'Fiesta' (Pom)	SDeJ
	Figaro Series (Misc/DwB)	MBros MPri SCob
	'Figurine' (WL) 🏆^{H3}	GRid NJRG SHar
	'Fille du Diable' (S-c)	CWGr SGbt
	'Finchcocks' (WL) 🏆^{H3}	CWGr LAyl
	'Fiona Stewart' (Ba)	CWGr GRid
	'Fire and Ice' (Misc)	CWGr SDeJ
	'Fire Magic' (S-c)	CWGr
	'Fire Mountain' (D)	GRid LAyl NHal NJRG WPhe
	'Firebird' (Sin)	CWGr
	'Firebird' (S-c)	see *D.* 'Vuurvogel'
	'Firebrand' ambig. (S-c)	CWGr SGbt
	'Firepot' (D)	ERCP SGbt SPer
	'First Lady' (D)	CWGr
	'Fleur'	see *D.* 'Fleurel'
§	'Fleurel'^{PBR} (Fim)	ERCP MSCN SDeJ
	'Floorinoor' (Anem)	ERCP GWyn LCro LOPS SGbt WPhe
	'Florence Vernon' (Ba)	CWGr
	'Flutterby' (WL)	CWGr
	'Fontmell Kaz' (Col)	NJRG SGbt
	'Formby Art' (D)	LAyl NHal WPhe
	'Formby Perfection' (D)	GRid
	'Formby Supreme' (D)	CWGr SGbt
	'Forrestal' (S-c)	CWGr
	'Fortuna' (Col/DwB)	ERCP
I	'Forty Niner' (WL) **new**	WPhe
	'Frank Holmes' (Pom)	CWGr GRid
	'Frank Hornsey' (D)	CWGr
	'Frank Lovell' (S-c)	CWGr
	'Franz Kafka' (Pom)	CAvo CWGr ERCP GRid NHal NJRG SDeJ SDir WPhe
	'Fred Wallace' (C)	CWGr
	'Freelancer' (C)	CWGr SGbt
	'Freestyle' (C)	CWGr GRid NJRG
§	'Freya's Paso Doble' (Anem) 🏆^{H3}	CWGr LAyl SGbt WPhe
	'Freya's Thalia' (Sin/Lil)	CWGr
	'Friendship' (C)	CWGr
	'Frigoulet' (C)	CWGr ERCP SGbt
	'Fripon' (C)	CWGr
	'Frost Nip' (D) **new**	CWGr
	'Funfair' (D)	CWGr
	'Fusion' (D) 🏆^{H3}	CWGr SGbt SHar WCot
	'G.F. Hemerik' (Sin)	CWGr
	'G.H. Lammerse' (D) **new**	ERCP
	'G.I. Joe' (D)	SGbt
	'Gale Lane' (Pom)	CWGr GRid
	(Gallery Series) 'Gallery Art Deco'^{PBR} (D) 🏆^{H3}	CRos CWGr ERCP LRHS NHal NRHS SGbt WPhe
	- 'Gallery Art Fair'^{PBR} (D) 🏆^{H3}	CWGr ERCP LCro LOPS LRHS SDeJ
	- 'Gallery Art Nouveau'^{PBR} (D) 🏆^{H3}	CWGr ERCP LRHS NHal NRHS SDeJ WFar WPhe
	- 'Gallery Bellini'^{PBR} (D)	CRos EHyd LRHS NRHS SDeJ
	- 'Gallery Cézanne'^{PBR} (D)	CWGr LRHS SDeJ SGbt
	- 'Gallery Cobra'^{PBR} (D)	ERCP
	- 'Gallery La Tour'^{PBR} (D) 🏆^{H3}	SDeJ

	- 'Gallery Leonardo'^{PBR} (D) 🏆^{H3}	CWGr LCro LOPS SDeJ
	- 'Gallery Pablo'^{PBR} (D) 🏆^{H3}	CWGr SGbt
	- 'Gallery Pinto'^{PBR} (D)	CRos CWGr EHyd LRHS NRHS
	- 'Gallery Rembrandt'^{PBR} (D) 🏆^{H3}	CWGr LCro LOPS
	- 'Gallery Renoir'^{PBR} (D) 🏆^{H3}	CWGr LRHS
	- 'Gallery Rivera'^{PBR} (D)	LRHS NRHS SDeJ
	- 'Gallery Salvador'^{PBR} (D)	ERCP SGbt
	- 'Gallery Singer'^{PBR} (D)	CWGr SDeJ
	- 'Gallery Valentin'^{PBR} (D)	CRos EHyd LRHS NRHS WFar
	- 'Gallery Vermeer'^{PBR} (D)	SGbt
	- 'Gallery Vincent'^{PBR} (D) 🏆^{H3}	CWGr
	'Gardaia' (Anem)	CWGr
	'Garden Festival' (WL)	CWGr ERCP GRid
	'Garden Miracle' (D)	NJRG
	'Garden Princess' (C/DwB)	SGbt
	'Garden Wonder' (D)	CWGr SDeJ SPer
	'Gargantuan' (S-c)	CWGr
	GATESHEAD FESTIVAL	see *D.* 'Peach Melba'
	'Gay Mini' (D)	CWGr
	'Gay Princess' (WL)	CWGr
	'Gay Triumph' (S-c)	CWGr
	'Geerlings Babette' (Ba)	CWGr ERCP
	'Geerlings Beatrice' (Ba)	CWGr
	'Geerlings Camelea' (Pom) **new**	WPhe
	'Geerlings Cupido' (WL)	SGbt
	'Geerlings Daydream' (D) **new**	WPhe
	'Geerlings Indian Summer' (S-c)	CWGr NHal
	'Geerlings Moonlight' (D)	CWGr
§	'Geerlings Sorbet' (S-c)	CAby NHal SGbt WPhe
	'Geerlings Yellow' (S-c)	CWGr
	'Gelber Vulkan' (S-c)	SGbt
	'Gemma Darling' (D)	CWGr GRid
	'Genova' (Ba)	CAvo ERCP SDeJ SGbt WPhe
	'George Marston' (D) **new**	NHal
	'Gerald Grace' (S-c)	CWGr
	'Gerlos' (D)	CWGr
I	'Geronimo' (S-c)	CWGr
	'Gerrie Hoek' (WL)	CWGr EHyd ERCP LRHS NJRG NRHS SDeJ SGbt WPhe WSpi
I	'Gerry Scott' (C) **new**	WPhe
	'Gill's Pastelle' (S-c)	GRid
	'Gilt Edge' (D)	CWGr
	'Gilwood Terry G' (C)	GRid WPhe
	'Gina Lombaert' (S-c)	CWGr
	'Ginger Willo' (Pom)	CWGr
	'Gipsy Boy' (D)	LAyl
	'Gipsy Night' (Ba)	ERCP SDeJ
	'Giraffe' (DblO)	CWGr ERCP SGbt
	'Gitty' (Ba)	CWGr
	'Gitty Up' (Anem) **new**	WPhe
	'Glamour Girl' (S-c)	ERCP
	'Glen Afton' (Pom)	CWGr
	'Glen Gharry' (Col)	CWGr
	'Glenbank Honeycomb' (Pom)	GRid
	'Glenbank Paleface' (Pom)	CWGr
	'Glenbank Twinkle' (C)	CWGr
	'Globular' (Ba)	CWGr
	'Glorie van Heemstede' (WL) 🏆^{H3}	CWGr ERCP LCro LOPS NHal NJRG SDeJ SGbt WPhe

'Glorie van Naardwijk' (D) CWGr
'Glorie van Noordwijk' (S-c) ERCP SDeJ SGbt
'Glow Orange' (Ba) CWGr
'Go American' (D) CWGr NHal WPhe
'Gold Crown' (S-c) SDeJ
'Goldean' (D) CWGr
I 'Golden Emblem' (D) CWGr ECtt SDeJ
'Golden Fizz' (Ba) CWGr
'Golden Heart' (S-c) CWGr
'Golden Impact' (S-c) CWGr GRid
'Golden Scepter' (D) CWGr ERCP SDeJ SGbt
'Golden Symbol' (S-c) CWGr
'Golden Turban' (D) CWGr
'Golden Vulcan' (S-c) **new** WPhe
'Goldfield' (D) CWGr
'Goldie Gull' (Anem) NJRG
'Goldilocks' (S-c) CWGr
'Goldorange' (S-c) CWGr
'Good Earth' (C) CWGr SDeJ
I 'Good Hope' (D) CWGr
'Good Intent' (Ba) CWGr
'Goshen Beauty' (WL) CWGr
'Goya's Venus' (S-c) CWGr
'Grace Kendall' (D) GRid
'Gracie S' (C) CWGr GRid NJRG
'Gramma's Lemon Pie' (D) CWGr
'Grand Finale' (S-c) SDeJ
'Grand Prix' (D) CWGr SDeJ SGbt
'Greenway Zoe' (S-c) NHal
'Grenadier' (D) 🏆H3 CWGr ECtt ERCP LRHS NJRG NLar SGbt WCot
'Grenidor Pastelle' (S-c) CWGr GRid NJRG WPhe
'Gretchen Heine' (D) CWGr
'Groovy' (D) **new** WPhe
'Gryson's Yellow Spider' (C) 🏆H3 ERCP WPhe
'Gunyuu' (D) CWGr
'Gurtla Twilight' (Pom) GRid NHal NJRG WPhe
'Gute Laune' (C) CWGr
'Gwyneth' (WL) GRid NHal NJRG WPhe
'Gypsy Girl' (D) CWGr SGbt
'Hadrian's Midnight' (Sin) NHal WPhe
'Hadrian's Sunlight' (Sin) 🏆H3 NHal
'Hadrian's Sunset' (Sin) NHal
'Hallmark' (Pom) GRid GWyn NJRG
'Hallwood Satin' (D) CWGr
'Hallwood Tiptop' (D) CWGr
'Hamari Accord' (S-c) 🏆H3 CWGr LAyl
'Hamari Bride' (S-c) 🏆H3 CWGr
'Hamari Girl' (D) CWGr GRid SGbt
'Hamari Gold' (D) 🏆H3 CWGr GRid NHal SGbt WPhe
'Hamari Katrina' (S-c) CWGr
'Hamari Rosé' (Ba) 🏆H3 CWGr GRid NHal SGbt SHar
'Hamari Sunshine' (D) SGbt
'Hamilton Amanda' (D) CWGr
'Hamilton Lillian' (D) 🏆H3 CWGr
'Hanny' (WL) **new** WPhe
'Hans Ricken' (D) CWGr
'Hapet Blue Eyes' (D) **new** WPhe
'Hapet Charmant' (WL) NJRG
'Hapet Duo' (D) **new** WPhe
'Hapet Ideal' (S-c) GRid
'Hapet Pearl' (Ba) WPhe
'Hapet Skyline' (S-c) **new** WPhe
'Hapet Vinete' (Pom) WPhe
'Happy Boy' (S-c) GRid
'Happy Butterfly' (D) **new** CWGr
'Happy Caroline' (D) CWGr
HAPPY DAYS NEON ('Hdne33'PBR) (Sin) **new** CRos ERCP MPri
HAPPY DAYS PINK ('Hdpi117'PBR) (Sin) 🏆H3 CRos ERCP WFar
HAPPY DAYS PURPLE ('Hdpu165'PBR) (Sin) 🏆H3 ERCP MPri WHil
HAPPY DAYS RED FLAME ('Hdrf155'PBR) (Sin) EPfP
'Happy Go Lucky' (D) SDeJ
'Happy Halloween' (D) CWGr
'Happy Hour'PBR (Ba) **new** ERCP
(Happy Single Series) HAPPY SINGLE DATE ('HS Date'PBR) (Sin) CWGr ERCP LRHS SDeJ
- HAPPY SINGLE FIRST LOVE ('HS First Love'PBR) (Sin) CWGr ERCP LRHS SDeJ WHil
- HAPPY SINGLE FLAME ('HS Flame'PBR) (Sin) 🏆H3 CAvo CWGr ERCP LRHS NJRG SDir
- HAPPY SINGLE JULIET ('HS Juliet'PBR) (Sin) CBod CWGr ERCP LRHS SDeJ
- HAPPY SINGLE KISS ('HS Kiss'PBR) (Sin) CAvo CWGr LRHS
- HAPPY SINGLE PARTY ('HS Party'PBR) (Sin) CWGr SDeJ
- HAPPY SINGLE PRINCESS ('HS Princess'PBR) (Sin) 🏆H3 CWGr ERCP LRHS SDeJ
- HAPPY SINGLE ROMEO ('HS Romeo'PBR) (Sin) CWGr LRHS SDeJ WFar WPhe
- HAPPY SINGLE WINK ('HS Wink'PBR) (Sin) 🏆H3 CWGr ERCP GRid LCro LOPS LRHS SDeJ SDir WPhe
'Haresbrook' (Sin) SHar WSpi
'Harpet Perfekt' (Fim) **new** WPhe
'Harriet G' (WL) NJRG
'Hartenaas' (Col/DwB) SDeJ
'Hart's Dr McMurray' (D) SPer
'Harvest' (Fim) CWGr
§ 'Harvest Samantha' (Sin/Lil) 🏆H3 CWGr NHal
'Haseley Goldicote' (D) CWGr
'Haseley Triumph' (D) CWGr
'Hawai'PBR (D) CWGr
'Hawaiian Dreams'PBR (Sin) EHyd LRHS WPhe
'Hayley Jayne' (C) CWGr ERCP LSou NJRG SGbt
'Heather Huston' (D) CWGr
'Heather Jean' (Col) NJRG
'Heather Linford' (Fim) CWGr NHal
'Helma Rost' (S-c) CWGr
'Hemera' (Sin) CWGr
'Henriette' (C) CWGr WPhe
'Herbert Smith' (S-c) CWGr
'Hexton Copper' (Ba) CWGr SGbt
'Highgate Torch' (S-c) CWGr
'Highness' (S-c) CWGr
'Highwarden Cliff' (S-c) GRid
'Hilary's Honour' (Fim) CWGr
'Hilda Clare' (Col) CWGr
'Hildepuppe' (Pom) CWGr
'Hillcrest Albino' (S-c) CWGr
'Hillcrest Amour' (D) CWGr GRid SGbt
'Hillcrest Aura' (D) GRid WPhe
'Hillcrest Bobbin' (Ba) CWGr
'Hillcrest Camelot' (S-c) CWGr
'Hillcrest Candy' (S-c) 🏆H3 CWGr GRid NHal NJRG SGbt WPhe
'Hillcrest Carmen' (D) GRid
'Hillcrest Chelsey' (D) GRid

'Hillcrest Contessa' (Ba)	CWGr
'Hillcrest Delight' (D)	GRid NHal SGbt
'Hillcrest Desire' (C) 🏆H3	GRid
'Hillcrest Divine' (D)	GRid
'Hillcrest Duncan Edwards' (S-c)	NHal WPhe
'Hillcrest Embers' (D)	GRid
'Hillcrest Fiesta' (S-c)	CWGr
'Hillcrest Firecrest' (D)	GRid NHal
'Hillcrest Hannah' (D)	GRid
'Hillcrest Harvest' (D)	GRid
'Hillcrest Heights' (S-c)	CWGr
'Hillcrest Hillton' (S-c)	GRid
'Hillcrest Jake' (S-c)	GRid WPhe
'Hillcrest Jersie' (S-c)	GRid NHal NJRG WPhe
'Hillcrest Jessica J' (C)	GRid WPhe
'Hillcrest Kismet' (D)	GRid NHal NJRG
'Hillcrest Liam' (S-c)	GRid
'Hillcrest Margaret' (D)	GRid
'Hillcrest Matt' (D)	GRid WPhe
'Hillcrest Millennium' (S-c)	GRid
'Hillcrest Pearl' (D)	CWGr
'Hillcrest Regal' (Col) 🏆H3	CWGr GRid SGbt
'Hillcrest Royal' (C) 🏆H3	CWGr ELan LAyl NHal SGbt WPhe
'Hillcrest Suffusion' (D)	CWGr NJRG WPhe
'Hillcrest Thomas J' (D)	GRid
'Hillcrest Ultra' (D)	GRid
'Hill's Delight' (S-c)	CWGr
'Hindu Star' (Ba)	CWGr
'Hockley Maroon' (D)	CWGr
'Holbrook Honey' (Sin)	CSam
'Holbrook Lilac' (Sin)	CSam
'Holbrook Magenta' (Sin)	CSam
'Holland Festival' (D)	CWGr GRid SDir SGbt
'Hollyhill Big Pink' (S-c)	SGbt
'Hollyhill Spiderwoman' (Misc)	CAby CWGr ERCP SPer
'Home Run' (Sin)	CWGr
'Homer T' (S-c)	CWGr
'Honest John' (C)	CWGr
'Honey' (Anem/DwB)	CWGr SDeJ
'Honeypot' (Ba)	SGbt
'Honka' (SinO) 🏆H3	CWGr ECtt ERCP LAyl LCro LOPS LRHS NHal NJRG SDeJ WCot WPhe
'Honka Black' (SinO) **new**	ERCP
'Honka Fragile' (SinO)	CAby CWGr ERCP IPot LCro LOPS SDeJ
'Honka Orange' (SinO)	ERCP NJRG
'Honka Pink' (SinO) **new**	WPhe
'Honka Pink Edge' (SinO)	NJRG
'Honka Red' (SinO)	CAby CWGr ERCP LCro LOPS SDeJ
'Honka Rose' (SinO)	ERCP NJRG SDeJ WPhe
'Honka Surprise' (SinO)	CAby CWGr EBee ECtt ERCP LCro LOPS NJRG SDeJ WCot
'Honka White' (SinO)	CWGr ERCP
'Honor Francis' (Misc)	WCot
'Hootenanny - Swan Island' (Col) 🏆H3	NJRG WPhe
'Hot Chocolate' (D)	CWGr NJRG SGbt
'Hugh Mather' (WL)	CWGr GRid
'Hulin's Carnival' (D)	CWGr
'Hy Clown' (D)	CWGr
'Hy Fire' (Ba)	CWGr
'Hy Totem' (D)	GRid
'Ian Hislop' (Sin)	CWGr
'Ice Crystal' (Fim)	ERCP LSou SPer
'Ice Cube' (D)	ERCP SDeJ
'Ice Queen' (WL)	CWGr

I 'Idylle' (S-c)	CWGr
'Ieda' (Sin)	NJRG
'Ike' (Fim)	CWGr
imperialis (B)	CDTJ CWGr ERCP ESwi EWes ILea LEdu LRHS NJRG SChr SDir SGbt XEll
- B&SWJ 8997	WCru
- B&SWJ 14341	WCru
- 'Alba' (B)	CWGr SDir
- pink double-flowered (B)	CExl
aff. ***imperialis***	CWGr XLum
'Impression Famosa'	see *D.* 'Famoso'
'Inca' (Anem)	SDeJ
'Inca Dambuster' (S-c)	CWGr NHal SGbt WPhe
'Inca Glamour' (D)	CWGr
'Inca Matchless' (D)	CWGr
'Inca Metropolitan' (D)	CWGr
'Inca Panorama' (D)	CWGr
'Inca Spectrum' (S-c)	CWGr
'Inca Vanguard' (D)	CWGr
'Inca Vulcan' (S-c)	CWGr
'Independence' (D)	SGbt
'Inglebrook Jill' (Col)	CWGr NJRG
'Inland Dynasty' (S-c)	CWGr GRid
'Inn's Gerrie Hoek' (D)	CWGr
'Irene Ellen' (D)	GRid
'Irene van der Zwet' (Sin)	CWGr
'Irene's Pride' (S-c)	GRid
'Iris' (Pom)	GRid GWyn
'Irish Glow' (Pom) **new**	WPhe
'Irish Pinwheel' (Misc) **new**	ERCP
'Isadora' (D) **new**	WPhe
'Islander' (D)	ERCP
'Ivanetti' (Ba)	CWGr ERCP GRid NHal SGbt WPhe
'Ivy Della' (D)	CWGr
'J Boy' (Ba)	GRid
'J.R.G.' (Misc) 🏆H3	NJRG
'Jack Hood' (D)	CWGr SGbt
'Jackie Magson' (S-c)	CWGr
'Jacqueline Tivey' (D)	CWGr
'Jake's Pastelle' (S-c)	GRid
'Jaldec Jerry' (S-c)	CWGr
'Jaldec Jolly' (C)	CWGr
'Jamaica' (D)	CWGr SGbt
'Jamie' (S-c)	CWGr
'Jan Lennon' (S-c)	CWGr
'Jan van Schaffelaar' (Pom)	ERCP SDeJ
'Janal Amy' (S-c)	CWGr GRid NHal SGbt WPhe
'Jane Cowl' (D)	CWGr
'Jane Horton' (Col)	CWGr GRid SGbt
'Janet Beckett' (C)	CWGr
'Japanese Waterlily' (WL)	CWGr
'Jazzy' (Col)	CWGr
'Je Maintiendrai' (D)	CWGr
'Jean Ellen' (Fim) **new**	WPhe
'Jean Fairs' (WL) 🏆H3	CWGr SGbt
'Jean Marie'^{PBR} (D)	CWGr
'Jean Melville' (D)	CWGr
'Jean Shaw' (D)	GRid NHal
'Jeanne d'Arc' (C)	CWGr
'Jeannie Leroux' (Fim)	CWGr
'Jean's Carol' (Pom)	CWGr
I 'Jennie' (Fim)	CWGr GRid
§ 'Jenny' (Dahlietta Select Series) (Misc)	SGbt
'Jersey Beauty' (D)	CWGr
'Jescot India' (D)	CWGr
'Jescot Jess' (D)	CWGr

	'Jescot Jim' (D)	CWGr
	'Jescot Julie' (DblO)	CWGr ERCP LAyl LCro LOPS NJRG
	'Jescot Lingold' (D)	CWGr SGbt
	'Jescot Redun' (D)	CWGr
	'Jessica' (S-c)	CWGr WPhe
	'Jessie G' (Ba)	CWGr ERCP
	'Jessie Ross' (D/DwB)	CWGr
	'Jet' (S-c)	CWGr
I	'Jet Fire' (D)	GRid
	'Jill Day' (C)	CWGr
	'Jill Doc' (D)	CWGr
	'Jill's Delight' (D)	CWGr
	'Jim Branigan' (S-c)	NHal
	'Jive' (Anem)	ELan ERCP SDeJ
	'Joan Beecham' (D)	GRid
	'Joan Walker' (D)	GRid WPhe
	'Jocondo' (D)	CWGr GRid NHal SGbt WPhe
	'Jodie Wilkinson' (Ba) ♈H3	NHal WPhe
	'Joe Swift' (Sin)	CWGr
	'Johann' (Pom)	CWGr GRid NHal
	'John Hill' (D)	GRid NHal
	'John Prior' (D)	CWGr
	'John Street' (WL)	CWGr WSpi
	'John's Champion' (D)	CWGr
	'Jolly Good' (Sin)	WPhe
	'Jomanda' (Ba) ♈H3	CWGr GRid NHal NJRG SGbt WPhe
	'Jorja' (S-c)	GRid
	'Jo's Choice' (D)	CWGr
	'José Maria' **new**	WPhe
	'Josie Gott' (Ba) ♈H3	NJRG SGbt WPhe
	'Josudi Aurora' (C) **new**	NHal
	'Josudi Hercules' (S-c)	NHal WPhe
	'Josudi Neptune' (S-c) **new**	NHal
	'Josudi Telstar' (C)	NHal
	'Jowey Frambo' (Ba) **new**	ERCP
	'Jowey Ingrid' (D)	GRid
	'Jowey Linda' (Ba)	ERCP
	'Jowey Mirella' (Ba) **new**	ERCP
	'Jowey Winnie' (Ba)	ERCP
	'Joy Donaldson' (C)	CWGr
	'Joyce Green' (S-c)	CWGr GRid SGbt
	'Joyce Margaret Cunliffe' (D)	CWGr
	'Joyful Investment' (Col) **new**	WPhe
	'JS Dorothy Rose' (D) **new**	NHal
	'Juanita' (S-c)	CWGr
	'Jules Dyson' (Misc)	SDys
	'Julie One' (DblO)	CWGr ECtt SGbt
	'Julie's Delight' (S-c)	CWGr
	'Julio' (Ba)	CWGr
	'Jura' (S-c)	CWGr
	'Kaga-komachi' (D)	LRHS NRHS
	'Kaiser Wilhelm' (Ba)	CWGr
	'Kaisha Lea' (D)	ERCP
	'Karen G' (Col)	NJRG
	'Karenglen' (D) ♈H3	GRid NHal NJRG SGbt
	'Kari Quill' (C)	CWGr
	'Karma Amanda'PBR (D)	CWGr
	'Karma Bon Bini'PBR (C)	CAby LSou SGbt
	'Karma Choc'PBR (D) ♈H3	CAby CBod CSpe CWGr EBee EHyd ERCP EWes LCro LOPS LRHS MHol NRHS SDir SEND SGbt SPer WBor WCot WFar WHoo WPhe
	'Karma Corona'PBR (C)	CAvo CWGr SGbt
	'Karma Fiesta'PBR (D)	ERCP
	'Karma Fuchsiana' (D)	CWGr ERCP LCro LOPS SGbt WPhe
	'Karma Irene'PBR (D)	CWGr ERCP
	'Karma Lagoon'PBR (D)	CWGr ERCP LRHS SGbt WPhe
	'Karma Maarten Zwaan'PBR (WL)	CWGr ERCP
	'Karma Naomi'PBR (D)	ERCP SGbt
	'Karma Pink Corona'PBR (C)	CWGr LCro LOPS
	'Karma Prospero'PBR (D)	ERCP LCro LOPS
	'Karma Red Corona'PBR (C)	SDeJ SGbt
	'Karma Sangria'PBR (C)	CWGr LCro LOPS SDeJ SGbt
	'Karma Serena'PBR (D)	SDeJ
	'Karma Yin Yang' (D)	CWGr LRHS SGbt
	'Karras 150' (S-c)	CWGr
	'Kate Mountjoy' (Col)	CWGr SGbt
	'Kate's Dream' (D) **new**	WPhe
	'Katie's Velvet' (Col)	NHal
	'Katisha' (D)	CWGr
	'Kayleigh Spiller' (Col)	SGbt
	'Kea Magic' (D)	GRid
	'Keith's Choice' (D)	GRid NHal SGbt WPhe
	'Kelsea Carla' (S-c) ♈H3	CWGr
	'Kelsey Annie Joy' (Col)	NJRG WPhe
	'Kelvin Floodlight' (D)	CBod CWGr SDeJ SGbt
	'Kennemerland' (S-c)	LCro LOPS SDeJ SGbt
	'Kenora Challenger' (S-c)	CWGr GRid NHal NJRG SGbt WPhe
	'Kenora Clyde' (S-c)	CWGr
	'Kenora Fireball' (Ba)	CWGr GRid
	'Kenora Frills' (Fim)	NHal
	'Kenora Jubilee' (S-c)	GRid GWyn SGbt WPhe
	'Kenora Lisa' (D)	CWGr
	'Kenora Macop-B' (Fim)	CWGr ECtt ERCP NHal SPer WPhe
	'Kenora Moonbeam' (D)	CWGr GRid
	'Kenora Ontario' (S-c)	CWGr
	'Kenora Sunset' (S-c) ♈H3	CWGr GRid NHal SGbt
	'Kenora Superb' (S-c)	CWGr GRid SGbt
	'Kenora Valentine' (D) ♈H3	CWGr NHal SGbt WPhe
	'Kenora Wildfire' (D)	CWGr GRid
	'Kenora Wow' (S-c)	NHal WPhe
	'Ken's Choice' (Ba)	GRid
	'Ken's Coral' (WL)	CWGr
	'Ken's Flame' (WL)	CWGr SGbt
	'Ken's Rarity' (WL)	NHal NJRG SGbt
§	'Kidd's Climax' (D) ♈H3	CWGr ERCP GRid WPhe
	'Kiev' (Jumbo Collection) (D)	LCro LOPS
	'Kikoski' (C)	SGbt
	'Kilburn Fiesta' (S-c)	GRid NHal WPhe
	'Kilburn Glow' (WL)	LAyl NHal NJRG WPhe
	'Kilburn Rose' (WL) ♈H3	NJRG WPhe
	'Kilmorie' (S-c)	GRid NHal WPhe
	'Kingston' (D)	CWGr SGbt
	'Kirsty G' (Col)	NJRG WPhe
	'Kismet' (Ba)	CWGr
	'Kit Kat' (C)	CWGr
	'Kiwi Brother' (S-c)	CWGr
	'Kiwi Gloria' (C)	CWGr GRid NHal NJRG WPhe
	'Kiwi Sister' (S-c)	CWGr
	'Klondike' (S-c)	CWGr NJRG WPhe
I	'Knockout'PBR (Sin) ♈H3	CAby CBcs CRos CWGr EHyd EPfP ERCP LRHS LSou LSRN NRHS SDys SPoG
	'Kochelsee' (Ba)	CWGr
	'Kogane Fubuki' (Fim)	CWGr
	'Kordessa' (D) **new**	SDir
	'Kotare Jackpot' (S-c)	CWGr
	'Kung Fu' (D)	CWGr
	'Kym Willo' (Pom)	CWGr
I	'Kyoto' (WL)	CWGr SGbt
	'L.A.T.E.' (Ba)	CWGr GRid NHal SGbt
	'La Gioconda' (Col)	CWGr GRid

	Name	Suppliers
	'La Recoleta' (D)	CWGr ERCP
	'Labyrinth' (D)	ERCP WPhe
	'Lady Darlene' (D)	CWGr ERCP LSou
	'Lady Kate' (D)	LCro LOPS
	'Lady Kerkrade' (C)	CWGr
	'Lady Liberty' (D)	ERCP
	'Lady Linda' (D)	CWGr GRid SGbt
	'Lady Orpah' (D)	CWGr
	'Lady Sunshine' (S-c)	CWGr
	'Laguna Beach' (Ba)	CWGr
	'Lake Carey' (D)	LCro LOPS
	'Lake Ontario' (D) **new**	CWGr
	'Lakeland Polly' (Pom)	NHal NJRG WPhe
	'Lambada' (Anem)	ELan ERCP
	'L'Ancresse' (Ba)	GRid LAyl NHal NJRG
	'Larkford' (D)	CWGr
	'Last Dance' (D)	CWGr
	'Laura's Choice' (D)	CWGr
	'Lavendale' (D)	CWGr
	'Lavender Chiffon' (S-c)	CWGr
	'Lavender Freestyle' (C)	CWGr
	'Lavender Leycett' (D)	CWGr
	'Lavender Line' (S-c)	GRid NHal SHar
	'Lavender Nunton Harvest' (D)	CWGr
	'Lavender Perfection' (D)	CWGr SDeJ
	'Lavender Ruffles' (D) **new**	CWGr
	'Lavengro' (D)	CWGr
	'Le Baron' (D)	ERCP MCot
	'Le Castel' (WL) 🏆^{H3}	CWGr SDeJ
	'Le Feu du Soleil' (Fim)	NHal
	'Le Patineur' (D)	CWGr
	'Le Vonné Splinter' (S-c)	CWGr GRid
	'Leander' (S-c)	CWGr
	'Lee Marshall' (C)	CWGr
	'Leila Savanna Rose' (S-c)	CWGr ERCP
§	'Lemon Cane' (D)	CWGr ECtt
	'Lemon Crest' (S-c) **new**	WPhe
	'Lemon Elegans' (S-c) 🏆^{H3}	CWGr GRid NHal NJRG
	'Lemon Meringue' (D)	CWGr ECtt SGbt
	'Lemon Puff' (Anem)	CWGr
	'Lemon Symbol' (S-c)	CWGr
	'Lemon Zing' (Ba)	GRid LAyl NHal SGbt
	'Leopold Chloe' (D)	GRid NHal WPhe
	'Leopold Sophie' (D)	GRid WPhe
	'Leslie Skinner' (Col) **new**	CWGr
	'Leslie's Willo' (Pom)	GRid
	'Lexington' (Pom)	CWGr
	'Leycett' (D)	CWGr
	'Libretto' (Col)	CWGr
	'Life Force' (D)	CWGr SGbt
	'Life Style' (Anem)	CWGr GWyn
	'Lifesize' (D)	GRid
	'Light Music' (S-c)	CWGr
	'Lilac Athalie' (C)	CWGr
	'Lilac Bull' (D)	ERCP LRHS
	'Lilac Marston' (D) 🏆^{H3}	NHal
	'Lilac Pathfinder' (Sin)	NJRG
	'Lilac Taratahi' (C) 🏆^{H3}	CSam
I	'Lilac Time' (D)	CWGr ERCP SDeJ SGbt
	'Lilac Willo' (Pom)	CWGr
	lilac-flowered B&SWJ 14942 from Colombia	WCru
	'Lilian Alice' (Col)	GRid
	'Lilian Marston' (D)	GRid
	'Lilianna W' (Sin/DwB)	NJRG
	'Linda's Baby' (Ba)	ERCP
	'Linda's Chester' (C)	CWGr
	'Linda's Diane' (D)	CWGr
	'Linda's Polly' (Pom)	NJRG
	'Lindsay' (WL)	GRid
	'Linz' (D)	WPhe
	'Lismore Carol' (Pom)	CWGr GWyn NHal WPhe
	'Lismore Moonlight' (Pom)	CWGr GRid NHal WPhe
	'Lismore Robin' (D)	NHal
	'Lismore Sunset' (Pom)	CWGr GRid SGbt
	'Lismore Willie' (WL) 🏆^{H3}	CWGr GRid NJRG
	'Lisonette' (C) **new**	WPhe
	'Little Beeswing' (C)	ERCP
I	'Little Darling' (S-c) **new**	WPhe
	'Little Dorrit' (Sin/Lil)	CWGr NJRG
	'Little Lamb' (S-c)	CWGr
	'Little Laura' (Ba)	CWGr
	'Little Matthew' (Pom)	CWGr SGbt
	'Little Robert' (D)	CWGr ERCP SDir SGbt
	'Little Sally' (Pom)	CWGr SGbt
	'Little Scottie' (Pom)	CWGr
	'Little Shona' (D)	CWGr
	'Little Snowdrop' (Pom)	CWGr SGbt
	'Little Sun' (WL) **new**	WPhe
	'Little Tiger' (D)	CWGr
	'Little Willem' (Pom)	SDeJ SGbt
	'Lloyd Huston' (S-c)	CWGr
	'Lois Walcher' (D)	CWGr
	'Loraine Mitchell' (WL)	NJRG
	'Loretta' (Ba)	GRid
	'Lorona Dawn' (SinO)	WPhe
	'Loud Applause' (C)	CWGr
	'Louie Meggos' (D)	NHal
	'Louis V' (Fim)	SGbt
*	'Louis Walchen' (D)	CWGr
	'Louise Bailey' (D)	CWGr
	'Louise'^{PBR} (Dahlietta Surprise Series) (D/DwB)	CWGr
	'Lovelife'^{PBR} (D)	SPer
	'Lubega Power Burgundy' (D/DwB) **new**	CRos
	'Lubega XL Burgundy' (D/DwB) **new**	CRos
	'Lucky Devil' (WL)	CWGr
	'Lucky Number' (D)	CWGr ERCP
	'Ludwig Helfert' (S-c)	CWGr
	'Lula Pattie' (D)	GRid
	'Lupin Dixie' (C)	CWGr
	'Lynn T' (Col)	GRid
	'Mabel Ann' (D)	CWGr GRid LAyl WPhe
	'Madaline Ann' (D)	CWGr
	'Madame Simone Stappers' (WL)	CWGr ECtt EHyd LAyl LRHS NRHS WSpi
	'Madame Vera' (D)	CWGr
	'Maddie Grace' (D)	CWGr
	'Magenta Magenta' (D)	LAyl SGbt
	'Magenta Magic' (Sin/DwB)	NHal
	'Magenta Star' (Sin) 🏆^{H3}	CWGr ERCP SGbt WPhe
I	'Magic Moment' (S-c)	CWGr
	'Maisha' (D)	CWGr
	'Maisie' (D)	CWGr
	'Maisie Mooney' (D)	CWGr
	'Majestic Kerkrade' (C)	CWGr
	'Majjas Symbol' (S-c)	CWGr
	'Malham Portia' (WL)	CWGr
	'Malvern Martha' (D)	GRid
	'Malvern Spring' (Sin/DwB) **new**	CWGr
I	'Mambo' (Anem)	CWGr ERCP SDeJ
	'Manhattan Island' (D)	CWGr MSCN SDeJ
	'Manuel' (D)	CWGr
	'Marble Ball' (D)	CWGr ERCP SDeJ SGbt SPer
	'Marcanti' (S-c)	SPer
	'Margaret Anne' (D)	CWGr

	'Margaret Brookes' (D)	CWGr
	'Marie' (D)	CWGr
	'Marie Schnugg' (SinO) 🏆H3	CWGr NJRG SGbt
	'Marissa' (WL)	GRid
	'Mark Damp' (S-c)	CWGr
	'Mark Hardwick' (D)	CWGr GRid WPhe
	'Mark Lockwood' (Pom)	CWGr
	'Market Joy' (S-c)	CWGr
	'Marla Lu' (C)	CWGr
	'Marlene Joy' (Fim)	CWGr SGbt
	'Marrakech' (WL)	CWGr
I	'Mars' (Col)	CWGr SGbt
	'Marston George' (Ba)	CWGr GRid NJRG WPhe
	'Marston Karen' (D) **new**	WPhe
	'Marston Suzanne' (D)	GRid NHal WPhe
	'Martina' (D)	GRid WPhe
	'Martin's Yellow' (Pom)	GRid NHal
	'Mary Anna Rosa' (S-c)	CWGr
	'Mary Crichton' (D)	GRid
I	'Mary Eveline' (Col)	ECtt NHal
	'Mary Evelyn' (C)	ERCP SDir SGbt
	'Mary Hammett' (D)	WSpi
	'Mary Layton' (Col)	CWGr
	'Mary McLelland' (Col)	GRid
	'Mary Pitt' (D)	CWGr SGbt
	'Mary Richards' (D)	CWGr
	'Mary's Jomanda' (Ba) 🏆H3	CWGr GRid GWyn NHal NJRG SGbt WPhe
	'MAS Robert' (Fim)	CWGr
	'MAS Sixty' (D)	CWGr
	'Mascot Maya' (D)	NJRG
	'Master Michael' (Pom)	CWGr
	'Matador' (D)	WPhe
	'Match' (S-c)	CWGr GRid WPhe
	'Matchless' (C)	CWGr
	'Matilda Huston' (S-c)	CWGr LAyl NHal
	'Matt Armour' (Sin)	CWGr
	'Maureen Hardwick' (D)	CWGr SGbt
	'Maureen Jones' (Col)	NJRG
	'Maxime' (D)	ERCP SDir WPhe
	'Maxine Bailey' (D)	CWGr
	'Mayan Blood' (DblO)	CWGr
	'Mayan Pearl' (DblO) 🏆H3	CWGr LAyl NHal SGbt WPhe
	'Mayan Swan' (S-c) 🏆H3	SGbt
	'Mayan Warrior' (S-c)	NJRG
	'Mediterranee' (D)	ERCP
	'Megan Dean' (Ba)	GRid NHal WPhe
	'Meiro' (D)	CWGr
	'Melanie Jane' (S-c)	CWGr
	'Melody Allegro'[PBR] (D)	ERCP LRHS MHol NRHS WFar
	'Melody Bolero'[PBR] (D)	CWGr SDeJ WFar
	'Melody Dixie'[PBR] (D)	ERCP WFar
	'Melody Dora'[PBR] (D)	CWGr GRid LCro LOPS LRHS
	'Melody Fanfare'[PBR] (D)	ERCP SDeJ
	'Melody Gipsy'[PBR] (S-c)	CWGr LRHS
	'Melody Harmony'[PBR] (D) 🏆H3	CWGr
	'Melody Latin'[PBR] (D)	CWGr
	'Melody Lizza'[PBR] (D)	LRHS NRHS WPhe
	'Melody Pink Allegro' (D)	ERCP
	'Melody Swing'[PBR] (D)	CWGr ERCP
	'Mel's Orange Marmalade' (Fim)	CWGr ERCP LCro LOPS WPhe
	'Menorca' (D)	ERCP
	merckii	CExl CSpe CWGr ECha EHyd EShb EWes LRHS MCot MMrt MNrw MRav NRHS SBut SEdd SHar SIvy SMHy WSHC
	– 'Alba' (B)	CExl CSpe WFar
	– dark-flowered	WPGP
	'Mevrouw Clement Andries' (Fim)	ERCP
§	'Mexican Black' (Misc)	CWGr EBee ECtt ERCP IPot NJRG WPGP
	'Mexican Star' (Sin) **new**	ERCP
	'Mexico Mogul' (D)	SGbt
	'Mi Wong' (Pom)	GRid
	'Miami' (D)	CWGr
	'Michael Haynes' (D)	CWGr
	'Michael J' (D)	CWGr
	'Michigan' (D)	CWGr
	'Mick' (C)	CWGr
	'Mick's American Dream' (S-c) **new**	WPhe
	'Mick's Peppermint' (S-c)	CAby CWGr SGbt WPhe
	'Midas' (S-c)	CWGr
	'Midnight' (Pom)	SGbt
	'Midnight Star' (SinO)	NJRG
	'Mies' (Sin)	CWGr
	'Milk Shake' (D)	CWGr NRHS
	'Mingus Alex' (S-c)	CWGr
	'Mingus Erik' (Fim)	GRid
	'Mingus Gregory' (S-c)	CWGr ERCP SDeJ
	'Mingus Heather' (WL)	GRid
	'Mingus Julie' (C)	GRid
	'Mingus Kyle D' (D)	CWGr
*	'Mingus Max'	ERCP
	'Mingus Nichole' (D)	CWGr
	'Mingus Randy' (S-c)	CWGr
	'Mingus Toni' (D)	ERCP
	'Mingus Tracy Lynn' (S-c)	CWGr GRid
	'Mingus Whitney' (S-c)	GRid
	'Mini Red' (S-c)	CWGr
	'Minley Carol' (Pom)	CWGr GRid NHal NJRG WPhe
	'Minnesota Migrant' (S-c)	CWGr
	'Miramar' (D)	CWGr
	'Miss Ellen' (Misc) 🏆H3	CWGr
	'Miss Rose Fletcher' (S-c)	CWGr
	'Miss Sophie' (S-c)	ERCP
	'Mister Frans' (D)	ERCP
	'Misterton' (D)	CWGr SGbt
	'Mistill Beauty' (C)	CWGr
	'Mistill Delight' (D)	CWGr
	'Mom's Special' (D)	CWGr
	'Monet Mystique' (WL)	SGbt
	'Monet Sunlight' (WL)	SGbt
	'Monk Marc' (C)	CWGr
	'Monkstown Diane' (C)	CWGr
	'Monrovia' (Ba)	CWGr
	'Moonfire' (Sin) 🏆H3	CAby CBcs CCht CRos CWCL CWGN CWGr ECtt EHyd ELan EPfP LRHS NHal NJRG NLar NRHS SGbt SPer WCot WHoo WPhe WSpi
	'Moonglow' (S-c)	CWGr ERCP LRHS
	'Moonlady' (D) **new**	ERCP
	'Moor Place' (Pom)	CWGr GRid NHal NJRG SGbt WPhe
	moorei	WPGP
	'Moray Susan' (WL)	CWGr
	'Moret' (S-c)	CWGr
	'Morley Lady' (D)	CWGr
	'Morna Whitlock' (S-c)	CWGr
	'Morning Dew' (WL)	CWGr
	'Motto' (D)	CWGr
	'Moulin Rouge' (C)	SPer
	'Mount Noddy' (Sin)	CWGr
	'Mr Sandman' (Fim)	MSCN
	'Mrs Black' (Pom)	CWGr

	'Mrs Eileen' (D)	ERCP SDeJ SGbt
	'Mrs H. Brown' (Col)	SGbt
	'Mrs McDonald Quill' (D)	CWGr GRid SGbt
	'Mrs Silverston' (D)	CWGr
	'Ms Kennedy' (Ba)	LAyl NHal WPhe
	'München' (D)	SDeJ SGbt
	'Murdoch' ambig. (D)	ECtt LRHS MHol WBrk WCot WSpi
	'Murillo' ambig. (Sin)	LAyl
	'Murray May' (WL)	CWGr
	'Murray Petite' (S-c)	CWGr
	'Musette' (D)	SGbt
	'Musson's Silverback' (Fim)	CWGr
	'My Irene' (WL)	NJRG
	'My Love' (S-c)	CWGr ECtt ERCP LCro LOPS SEND SGbt
	'My Neddy' (D)	SGbt
I	'My Pride' (D)	ERCP GRid
	'Myama Fubuki' (Fim)	ELan ERCP
	'My-nute Blend' (Misc) ♀H3	CWGr
	'Myrtle's Folly' (Fim)	ERCP SDeJ WPhe
	'Mystère' (Anem)	CWGr
	'Mystery Day' (D)	CWGr SDir
	MYSTIC DESIRE	see *D.* 'Scarlet Fern'
	MYSTIC DREAMER	see *D.* 'Zone Ten'
§	'Mystic Enchantment' PBR (Sin)	CRos EHyd ELan EPfP LRHS LSou NRHS SDys SPoG
	'Mystic Haze'	see *D.* 'Dark Side Of The Sun'
	MYSTIC ILLUSION	see *D.* 'Knockout' (Sin)
	MYSTIC MARS	see *D.* 'Scarlet Fern'
§	MYSTIC SPIRIT ('Hamspirit' PBR) (Sin)	EHyd ELan LRHS LSou NRHS WPhe
	'Mystic Wonder' (Sin)	CRos EHyd ELan LRHS NRHS WPhe
	'Nadia Ruth' (Fim)	ERCP
	'Nagano' (D)	CWGr SDeJ
	'Nancy H' (Ba)	CWGr
	'Nancy Margaret' (S-c)	GRid
	'Nargold' (Fim)	CWGr LAyl
	'Narrow's Tricia' (S-c)	GRid NJRG WPhe
	'Natal' (Ba)	CAvo ECtt SDeJ
	'Natalie G' (D)	ERCP NJRG
	'Nathalie's Wedding' (WL)	ERCP
	'Nationwide' (D)	CWGr
	'Neal Gillson' (D)	CWGr
	'Nelly Geerlings' (Sin)	CWGr
	'Nenekazi' (Fim)	GRid LAyl NJRG WPhe
	'Néo' (D)	CWGr
	'Nepos' (WL)	CWGr GRid GWyn NJRG SGbt WPhe
	'Nescio' (Pom)	CWGr ERCP LSou SDeJ
I	'New Baby' (Ba)	CWGr ERCP LCro LOPS SGbt
	'Newby' (D)	CWGr
	'Newquay' (Sin)	CWGr
	'Newsham Wonder' (D)	CWGr
	'Nicholas' (D)	CWCL ERCP SPer
	'Nick Sr' (D) **new**	WPhe
	'Nicola' (S-c)	CWGr
	'Nienke' (D)	NJRG
	'Night Butterfly' (Col)	CAby ERCP
	'Night Editor' (D)	CWGr
I	'Night Queen' (Ba)	ERCP
	'Nijinsky' (Ba)	CWGr
I	'Nina' (D) **new**	WPhe
	'Nina Chester' (D)	GRid
	'Nippon' (Sin)	EHyd EPfP LRHS
	'Nogent' (D)	CWGr
	'Nonette' (WL)	CWGr EBee ECtt SGbt WCot
	'Norbeck Dusky' (S-c)	CWGr
	'Noreen' (Pom)	CWGr GRid NHal NJRG WPhe
	'Norman Lockwood' (Pom)	CWGr
	'Normandie Frills' (Fim) **new**	NHal
	'Normandie Wedding Day' (Fim)	NHal WPhe
	'Northland Primrose' (C)	CWGr
§	'Nuit d'Eté' (S-c)	CAby CAvo CWGr ELan ERCP LCro LOPS LRHS SDeJ SGbt WPhe
	'Nuland's Josephine' (Ba)	LAyl NHal NJRG WPhe
	'Nunton Form' (D)	CWGr
	'Nunton Harvest' (D)	CWGr GRid
	'Nymphenburg' (WL)	CWGr
	'Oakwood Belle' (C)	CWGr
	'Oakwood Bridesmaid' (C)	CWGr
	'Oakwood Christina' (Ba)	CWGr
	'Oakwood Dazzle' (D)	CWGr
	'Oakwood Diamond' (Ba)	CWGr
	'Oakwood Duchess' (D)	CWGr
	'Oakwood Fire' (S-c)	CWGr WPhe
	'Oakwood Firelight' (S-c)	CWGr
	'Oakwood Goldcrest' (S-c)	GRid NHal WPhe
	'Oakwood Heather' (Ba)	CWGr
	'Oakwood Katie' (S-c)	CWGr
	'Oakwood Kim' (D)	CWGr
	'Oakwood Lyndon S' (S-c)	CWGr
	'Oakwood Marian S' (D)	CWGr
	'Oakwood Naranga' (D) ♀H3	CWGr
	'Oakwood Natasha' (Pom)	CWGr
	'Oakwood Royale' (D)	CWGr
	'Oakwood Tulisa' (D)	CWGr
	'Oakwood Vivian S' (S-c)	CWGr
	'Ocean Bird' PBR (D) ♀H3	ERCP
I	'Old Gold' (D)	CWGr SGbt
I	'Olivia' (Col)	CWGr GRid NJRG WPhe
	'Olivia Mari' (WL)	GRid NHal WPhe
	'Omo' (Sin/Lil) ♀H3	NJRG
	'Onesta' (D)	CWGr ERCP SDeJ
	'Only Love' (S-c)	CWGr
	'Onslow Michele' (D)	CWGr
	'Onslow Renown' (S-c)	CWGr
	'Opal' (Ba)	CWGr
	'Optic Illusion' (D)	CWGr ERCP
	'Opus' (D)	CWGr SGbt
	'Orange Chum' (D)	CWGr
	'Orange Cushion' (D)	CWGr
	'Orange Explosion' (Misc)	CWGr SGbt
	'Orange Fire' (S-c)	CWGr
	'Orange Fubuki' (D)	ERCP
	'Orange Keith's Choice' (D)	CWGr GRid WPhe
	'Orange Kiss' (Col)	NJRG WPhe
	'Orange Mullett' (D/DwB)	CWGr
	'Orange Nugget' (Ba)	CWGr SDeJ
	'Orange Pathfinder' (Misc)	CWGr NJRG
	'Orange Pekoe' (D) **new**	ERCP
I	'Orange Queen' (C)	CWGr SGbt
	'Orange Sun' (D)	CWGr
	'Orchid Lace' (C)	CWGr
	'Orel' (Col)	GRid SGbt
	'Oreti Bliss' (C)	GRid LAyl NHal
	'Oreti Classic' (D)	NHal
	'Oreti Duke' (Pom)	CWGr
	'Orfeo' (C)	CWGr ERCP LCro LOPS MNrw SDeJ SGbt
	'Ornamental Rays' (C)	CWGr
	'Osaka' (D)	CWGr
	'Osirium' (D)	ERCP
	'Ossie Latham' (Sin)	CWGr SGbt

	'Othello' (S-c)	CWGr GRid
	'Otto's Thrill' (D) 🏆H3	CWGr ERCP MSCN
	'Pacific Ocean' (WL)	ERCP
	'Paint Box' (S-c)	CWGr
	'Painted Girl' (D)	LSou
	'Paisley Gem' (Sin)	CWGr
	'Palmares' (D) **new**	LSou
	'Palomino' (D)	CWGr
	'Pam Howden' (WL)	NHal NJRG SGbt
	'Pamela' (D)	CWGr
	'Paradise City' (D)	ERCP
	'Pari Taha Sunrise' (S-c)	CWGr
	'Park Princess' (C/DwB)	CWGr NHal NRHS SDeJ SGbt
	'Park Record' (S-c)	LCro LOPS
	'Parkland Glory' (D) **new**	LSou
	'Parkland Rave' (S-c)	CWGr NHal
	'Paroa Gillian' (C)	CWGr
	'Paso Doble' misapplied	see *D.* 'Freya's Paso Doble'
	'Passion' (D)	CWGr
	'Pat Knight' (Col)	CWGr NJRG WPhe
	'Pat Mark' (S-c)	CWGr
	'Pat 'n' Dee' (D)	CWGr
	'Pat 'n' Perc' (Col)	NJRG SGbt WPhe
	'Pat Seed' (D)	CWGr
	'Paul Chester' (C)	CWGr
	'Paul Critchley' (C)	CWGr
	'Paul Smith' (Ba)	CWGr
	'Peace Pact' (WL)	CWGr
	'Peach Athalie' (C)	CWGr
	'Peach Delight' (S-c)	SGbt
§	'Peach Melba' (D)	NHal WPhe
	'Peaches and Cream' [PBR] (D)	CWGr ECtt
	'Peachette' (Misc/Lil)	CWGr
	'Pearl Hornsey' (D)	CWGr
	'Pearl of Heemstede' (D) 🏆H3	CWGr LAyl NHal NJRG
	'Pearl Sharowean' (S-c)	CWGr
	'Pearson's Ben' (S-c)	CWGr GRid NHal NJRG
	'Pearson's Melanie' (C)	CWGr
	'Pearson's Patrick' (S-c)	CWGr
	'Pembroke Levenna' (Ba)	LAyl
	'Penhill Autumn Shade' (S-c)	NJRG SGbt
	'Penhill Dark Monarch' (D)	ERCP
	'Penhill Watermelon' (D)	ERCP SDeJ
	'Pennsclout' (D)	CWGr
	'Penny Lane' (D)	SDir
	'Pensford Marion' (Pom)	CWGr GRid
	'Peppermint Splash' (D) **new**	WPhe
I	'Perfect' (D)	CWGr
	'Perfect Partner' (Sin)	CWGr
	'Perfectos' (C)	CWGr
	'Peter' (D)	CWGr SGbt
	'Petit Byoux' (Col/DwB)	CWGr
	'Petite Harvest' (Misc/DwB)	NJRG
	'Petite Lilliput' (Sin/Lil) **new**	WPhe
	'Petite Sunrise' (Sin)	NJRG
	'Petite Sunset' (Misc/Lil)	NJRG
	'Petra's Wedding' (Ba)	CWGr ERCP
	'Pfitzer's Joker' (C)	CAby
	'Philadelphia' (D)	CWGr
	'Pianella' (S-c)	CWGr SGbt
	'Pineapple Lollipop' (Ba)	CWGr
	'Pinelands Pam' (Fim)	CWGr GRid
	'Pinelands Princess' (Fim)	ERCP SGbt
	'Pink Attraction' (D)	CWGr
	'Pink Carol' (Pom)	CWGr GRid NJRG
	'Pink Giraffe' (DblO) 🏆H3	CWGr ERCP SGbt
	'Pink Isa' [PBR] (D)	CWGr
	'Pink Jean Fairs' (WL)	CWGr
	'Pink Jupiter' (S-c)	CWGr GRid NHal SGbt WPhe
	'Pink Katisha' (D)	CWGr
	'Pink Kerkrade' (C)	CWGr
	'Pink Leycett' (D)	CWGr
	'Pink Loveliness' (WL)	CWGr
	'Pink Pastelle' (S-c) 🏆H3	GRid SGbt
	'Pink Pat and Perc' (Col)	GRid NHal NJRG WPhe
	'Pink Perception' (WL) **new**	ERCP
	'Pink Preference' (S-c)	CWGr
	'Pink Robin Hood' (Ba)	CWGr
	'Pink Runner' (D)	ERCP
	'Pink Sensation' (C) 🏆H3	CWGr
	'Pink Shirley Alliance' (C)	CWGr
	'Pink Silk' (D)	ERCP
	'Pink Skin' (D)	ECtt LRHS SDeJ
	'Pink Spur' (D)	GRid
	'Pink Suffusion' (D)	GRid WPhe
	'Pink Sylvia' (D)	CWGr
	'Pink Worton Ann' (D)	CWGr
	'Pinkie Swear' (S-c)	ERCP
	pinnata B&SWJ 10240	WCru
	– B&SWJ 14901 from Colombia	WCru
	'Piperoo' (C)	CWGr SGbt
	'Piper's Pink' (S-c/DwB)	CWGr ECtt EHyd GRid LRHS NRHS SGbt
I	'Pippa' (WL)	CWGr
I	'Pippi' (D)	CWGr
	'Pitchoun' (Sin)	CWGr
	'Platinium Blonde' (Anem)	ERCP WPhe
	'Playa Blanca' (C/DwB)	SGbt
	'Playboy' (D)	CWGr
	'Plum Surprise' (Pom)	CWGr
	'Polar Ice' (D) **new**	CWGr
	'Polar Sight' (C)	CWGr
I	'Polka' (Anem)	CWGr NJRG SDeJ SGbt WPhe
	'Polly Peachum' (D)	CWGr
	'Polventon Kristobel' (D)	NHal WPhe
	'Polventon Supreme' (Ba)	CWGr WPhe
	'Pontiac' (C)	CWGr SGbt
	'Pooh' (Col)	see *D.* 'Pooh - Swan Island'
§	'Pooh - Swan Island' (Col) 🏆H3	CAby CBod CWGr EBee ECtt ERCP ESwi GRid LAyl NHal NJRG SPer WCot WPhe
	'Pop Willo' (Pom)	GRid NJRG
I	'Poppet' (Pom)	CWGr
	'Poppyscotland' (Sin)	CWGr
	'Popular Guest' (Fim)	CWGr
	'Porcelain' (WL)	WPhe WSpi
	'Pot Black' (Ba)	CWGr
	'Potgeiter' (Ba)	CWGr
	'Prefect' (S-c)	CWGr
	'Prefere' (Sin)	CWGr
	'Preference' (C)	CWGr ERCP SDeJ SGbt
	'Preston Park' (Sin/DwB) 🏆H3	CWGr LAyl NHal
	PRETTY WOMAN ('Vdtg43' [PBR]) (Dark Angel Series) (Sin) 🏆H3	ERCP LCro LOPS
	'Priceless Pink' (Misc)	ERCP
	PRIDE OF BERLIN	see *D.* 'Stolz von Berlin'
	'Prime Minister' (D)	CWGr
	'Primrose Diane' (D)	GRid WPhe
	'Primrose Pastelle' (S-c)	GRid
	'Primrose Rustig' (D)	CWGr
	'Prince Valiant' (D)	CWGr

I	'Princess' (Col)	SDeJ
	'Princess Amalia' (D) **new**	WPhe
	'Princess Beatrix' (D)	CWGr
	'Princess Marie José' (Sin)	CWGr
	'Princesse Gracia' (D)	ERCP
	'Procyon' (D)	CWGr SGbt
	'Profundo' (D) **new**	ERCP
	'Prom' (Pom)	CWGr
	'Promise' (Fim)	CWGr ECtt ERCP SDeJ
	pteropoda	CWGr
	aff. ***pteropoda***	CWGr
	- F&M 312	WPGP
	PULP FICTION ('Vdtg61'PBR) (Dark Angel Series) (Sin)	CWGr ERCP
	'Punky' (Pom)	CWGr
	'Purbeck Lydia' (S-c)	CWGr
	'Purpinca' (Anem)	CWGr
	'Purple Cottesmore' (WL)	CWGr
	'Purple Duncan Edwards' (S-c) **new**	NHal
	'Purple Flame'PBR (D)	CAvo ERCP
	'Purple Fox'PBR (Ba)	ERCP
	'Purple Gem' (S-c)	CWGr ERCP LCro LOPS MSCN SDeJ SGbt SPer
	'Purple Haze' (Misc)	ERCP LCro LOPS LSRN
	'Purple Pearl' (D)	ERCP NHal WPhe
	'Purple Petite' (Sin)	NJRG
	'Purple Puff' (Anem)	LAyl NHal NJRG WPhe
	'Purple Sensation' (S-c)	CWGr
	'Purple Splash' (WL)	CWGr
	'Purple Taiheyō' (D)	CWGr ERCP
	purpusii	CWGr
	aff. ***purpusii*** B&SWJ 10321	WCru
	'Pussycat' (D)	CWGr
	'Quel Diable' (S-c)	CWGr
	'Quinty' (D) **new**	WPhe
	'R. Mona' (WL)	NHal WPhe
	'Rachel de Thame' (Sin)	CWGr
	'Rachel's Place' (Pom)	CWGr
	'Radiance' (C)	CWGr
I	'Radjah' (Pom)	NRHS
	'Ragged Robin' (Misc)	CSpe CWGr ECtt ERCP LRHS
	'Raisa' (D) **new**	WPhe
	'Raiser's Pride' (C)	WPhe
	'Rancho' (WL) **new**	WPhe
	'Raspberry Valiant' (B)	NHal
*	'Raymond Guernsey'	ECtt
	'Razzle Dazzle' (D)	ERCP
	'Rebecca Lynn' (D)	CWGr
	'Rebecca's World' (D)	CWGr ECtt ERCP LCro LOPS SPer
	'Red and White' (D)	CWGr SGbt
	'Red Arrows' (D)	CWGr
	'Red Cap' (D)	CWGr
	'Red Carol' (Pom)	CWGr GRid
	'Red Diamond' (D)	NHal
	'Red Emperor' (D)	GRid
	'Red Fox'PBR (Ba)	LCro LOPS
	'Red Fubuki' (D)	SDeJ
	'Red Highlight' (S-c)	CWGr
	'Red Majorette' (S-c)	CWGr SDeJ
	'Red Pathfinder' (Sin)	NJRG
	'Red Pimpernel' (D)	WPhe
	'Red Pygmy' (S-c)	CWGr SDeJ
	'Red Riding Hood' (Sin)	CWGr
	'Red Schwieter's' (D)	CWGr
	'Red Sun' (D)	CWGr
	'Red Velvet' (WL)	CWGr GRid
	'Red Warrior' (Pom)	CWGr
	'Reddy' (Sin/Lil)	CWGr
	'Reedly' (D)	CWGr
	'Rees' Dream' (D)	CWGr
	'Reginald Keene' (S-c)	CWGr GRid NHal WPhe
	'Reliance' (Ba)	CWGr
	'Renato Tosio' (D)	WPhe
	'Reputation' (C)	CWGr SGbt
	'Requiem' (D)	CWGr ECtt ERCP NJRG
	'Reverend P. Holian' (S-c)	CWGr SGbt
	'Revive' (Misc)	CWGr
	'Rhanna Tammy' (D)	GRid
	'Rhonda' (Pom)	GRid NHal WPhe
	'Rhonda Suzanne' (Pom) ♀H3	GRid
	'Rhubarb and Custard' (Sweet Candy Series) (Col) **new**	WPhe
	'Richard Marc' (C)	CWGr
	'Richard S' (S-c)	NHal
	'Riisa' (Ba)	CWGr
	'Rip City' (S-c)	CWGr ERCP LCro LOPS LRHS MCot
	'Risca Miner' (Ba)	CWGr
	'Rising Sun' (S-c) **new**	WPhe
	'Rita Easterbrook' (D)	CWGr
	'Rita Rosina' (D)	CWGr
	'Rita Shrimpton' (Misc)	CWGr
	'Roan' (D)	CWGr
	'Robann Regal' (D)	CWGr
	'Robann Royal' (Ba)	CWGr
	'Robert Too' (D)	CWGr
	'Rocco' (Ba)	ERCP LCro LOPS LSou SGbt
	'Rockcliffe Billy' (S-c)	NJRG
	'Roger Turrell' (D)	NHal
	'Rokewood Opal' (C)	CWGr
	'Romance' (C)	CWGr
	'Ron's Dark Ember' (Fim)	GRid
	'Rosalinde' (S-c)	CWGr
	'Rose Jupiter' (S-c)	CWGr GRid NHal WPhe
	'Rose Tendre' (S-c)	CWGr
	'Rosella' (D)	CWGr SDeJ SGbt
	'Rosemary Webb' (D)	CWGr SGbt
I	'Rosita' (Col)	CWGr
	'Rossendale Flamenco' (D)	NHal
	'Rossendale Heide' (D)	NHal WPhe
	'Rossendale Hero' (Ba) **new**	NHal
	'Rossendale Izzy' (D)	GRid
	'Rossendale Joshua' (D)	GRid
	'Rossendale Lottie' (D)	GRid
	'Rossendale Luke' (D)	GRid
	'Rossendale Mollie' (D)	WPhe
	'Rossendale Natasha' (Ba)	NHal SGbt
	'Rossendale Parky' (D)	NHal
	'Rossendale Roxy' (D) **new**	WPhe
	'Rossendale Stephanie' (D)	GRid
	'Rossendale Tara' (D)	GRid
	'Rosy Cloud' (D)	CWGr
	'Rothesay Castle' (D/DwB)	CWGr
	'Rothesay Reveller' (D)	CWGr
	'Rothesay Robin' (D)	CWGr
	'Rothesay Rose' (WL)	CWGr
	'Rothesay Superb' (Ba)	CWGr
I	'Roxy' (Sin/DwB)	CAby CBcs CRos CWGr EBee ECtt EHyd ELan EPfP ERCP LAyl LRHS LSRN NCou NJRG NRHS SGbt WCot WPhe WSpi
	'Royal Amethyst' (D)	CWGr
	'Royal Blood' (Misc)	LAyl
	'Royal Mail' (D)	SGbt

	'Royal Visit' (D)	CWGr SGbt
	'Royal Wedding' (S-c)	CWGr
	'Ruby' (D)	GRid
	'Ruby Red' (Ba)	CWGr
	'Ruby Wedding' (D)	CWGr SGbt
	rudis	CExl EBee WPGP
	'Ruskin Andrea' (S-c)	GRid NHal WPhe
	'Ruskin Avenger' (S-c)	NJRG WPhe
	'Ruskin Belle' (S-c)	CWGr
	'Ruskin Buttercup' (D)	CWGr SGbt
	'Ruskin Charlotte' (S-c)	CWGr GRid
	'Ruskin Diane' (D)	CWGr GRid NHal NJRG WPhe
	'Ruskin Dynasty' (D)	CWGr
	'Ruskin Emile' (S-c)	CWGr
	'Ruskin Gypsy' (Ba)	CWGr
I	'Ruskin Harmony' (S-c)	CWGr
	'Ruskin Harmony' (Ba) **new**	WPhe
	'Ruskin Impact' (D)	GRid
	'Ruskin Lilactime' (Ba)	GRid
	'Ruskin Limelight' (C)	NHal
	'Ruskin Marigold' (S-c)	CWGr GRid NHal
	'Ruskin Mars' (D)	GWyn
	'Ruskin Michelle' (S-c)	GRid NHal WPhe
	'Ruskin Myra' (S-c)	CWGr GRid NHal WPhe
	'Ruskin Respectable' (S-c)	NJRG
	'Ruskin Sensation' (S-c)	NHal
	'Ruskin Splendour' (S-c)	GRid
	'Ruskin Sunshine' (S-c)	GRid
	'Ruskin Tangerine' (Ba)	NHal SGbt WPhe
	'Russell Turner' (S-c)	CWGr
	'Rustig' (D)	CWGr
I	'Rusty' (Sin)	CWGr
I	'Ruth Ann' (Ba)	NHal
	'Ruth Parker' (Col)	CWGr
	'Ryecroft Bella' (Ba) **new**	NHal
	'Ryecroft Blackberry' (Pom) **new**	NHal
	'Ryecroft Brenda T' (D)	GRid NHal NJRG
	'Ryecroft Claire' (D)	NHal
	'Ryecroft Gem' (Ba)	GRid
	'Ryecroft Helen' (S-c)	NHal
	'Ryecroft Huntsman' (D) **new**	NHal
	'Ryecroft Ice' (D)	GRid SGbt
	'Ryecroft Isobel' (D)	GRid
	'Ryecroft Jan' (Ba) 🏆H3	GRid NHal NJRG WPhe
	'Ryecroft Jim' (Anem)	LAyl NHal WPhe
	'Ryecroft Laura' (Ba)	NHal
	'Ryecroft Misty' (D) **new**	NHal
	'Ryecroft Pixie' (C)	GRid NHal
	'Ryecroft Rebel' (D)	WPhe
	'Ryecroft Sparkler' (C)	SGbt
	'Ryecroft Yellow Orb' (Ba)	NHal
	'Ryecroft Zoe' (S-c)	NHal
	'Ryedale Pinky' (D)	CWGr
	'Ryedale Prince' (D)	CWGr
	'Ryedale Rebecca' (S-c)	CWGr GRid
	'Ryedale Ria' (D)	GRid
	'Sabrina' (D)	WPhe
	'Safe Shot' (D)	CWGr
	'Sailor' (Fim)	CWGr
	'Saint Giles 150' (Misc)	GRid
	'Saint Martin' (WL)	ERCP
	'Saint-Saëns' (S-c)	SDeJ
	'Sakura Fubuki' (Fim)	ERCP
	'Salmon Hornsey' (D)	CWGr
	'Salmon Keene' (S-c)	GRid
	'Sam Hopkins' (D)	ERCP LAyl NHal WPhe
	'Sam Huston' (D)	CWGr SGbt
	'Samantha'	see *D.* 'Harvest Samantha'
	'Sandia Melody' (WL) 🏆H3	GRid
	'Sandia Serenity' (WL)	NHal
	'Sandra' (D)	ERCP LCro LOPS
	'Sans Souci' (C)	CWGr
	'Santa Claus US' (D)	SGbt WPhe
	'Sarabande' (S-c)	CWGr
	'Sarah' (S-c)	CWGr ECtt EHyd LRHS NRHS
	'Sarah Bryant' (D)	NHal
I	'Sarah Elisabeth' (WC) **new**	WPhe
	'Sarah G' (S-c)	CWGr
	'Sarah Louise' (WL)	CWGr
	'Sarah Thomas' (Col)	CWGr
	'Sarum Aurora' (D)	CWGr
	'Sascha' (WL) 🏆H3	GRid NHal
	'Sassy' (D)	SGbt
	'Satellite' (S-c)	CWGr
	'Scarborough Ace' (D)	CWGr
	'Scarlet Comet' (Anem)	CWGr
§	'Scarlet Fern' (Sin)	CWGr EHyd LRHS
	'Scarlet Kokarde' (D)	CWGr
	'Scarlet O'Hara' (D)	NJRG
	'Scarlet Rotterdam' (S-c)	CWGr
	'Scarlet Star' (S-c)	CWGr
	'Scarlett Claire' (Col)	CWGr
	'Scaur Blaze' (D)	GRid
	'Scaur Christine' (D)	GRid
	'Scaur Glen' (Pom)	GRid
	'Scaur Promise' (D)	GRid
	'Scaur Queen' (D)	GRid
	'Scaur Ruby' (D)	GRid
	'Scaur Saffron' (D)	GRid
	'Scaur Sunrise' (D)	NJRG
	'Scaur Sunset' (D)	GRid
	'Scaur Swinton' (D)	CWGr GRid NHal SGbt
	'Scaur Tango' (D)	GRid
	'Scaur Topper' (Ba)	GRid WPhe
	'Scaur Vale' (D)	GRid
	'Scaur Whisper' (D)	GRid
	'Schneeflocke' (Ba)	CWGr
	'Schweitzer's Kokarde' (D)	CWGr
	'Scottish Rhapsody' (S-c)	CWGr GRid
	'Scura' (Sin)	CWGr
	'Seattle' (D)	CBod CWGr
	'Seduction' (D)	CAvo ERCP
	'Sefton Silvertop' (D)	NHal
	'Seirō' (S-c)	SGbt
	'Senior Ball' (Ba)	CWGr
	'Senzoe Ursula' (D)	CWGr GRid
	'Shandy' (S-c)	CWGr LAyl SHar
	'Shannon' (D)	CWGr
I	'Sheila' (Ba)	GRid WPhe
	'Sheila Mooney' (D)	CWGr GRid
	'Shep's Memory' (WL) 🏆H3	NJRG
	sherffii	CWGr NJRG
	'Sherwood Monarch' (S-c)	CWGr
	'Sherwood Sunrise' (D)	CWGr
	'Sherwood Titan' (D)	CWGr
	'Sherwood's Peach' (D)	CWGr
	'Sheval Megan' (D)	NHal WPhe
	'Shining Star' (C)	CWGr
	'Shirley' (D)	CWGr
	'Shirley Pillman' (Misc)	CWGr
	'Shirley Westwell' (D) **new**	CWGr
	'Shirwell George' (D)	GRid
	'Shirwell Greta' (D)	GRid NHal WPhe
	'Shooting Star' (S-c)	CWGr
	'Show 'n' Tell' (Fim)	CWGr ERCP SGbt WPhe
	'Shy Princess' (C)	CWGr
	'Siedlerstolz' (D)	CWGr

	'Silver City' (D)	CWGr NHal SGbt WPhe
	'Silver Years' (D)	CWGr
	'Silvie's Queen' (D)	SDeJ
	'Sir Alf Ramsey' (D)	CWGr GRid LAyl NHal SDir SGbt WPhe
	'Skipper Rock' (D)	CWGr
	'Small World' (Pom) ♀H3	CWGr GRid LAyl NHal WPhe
	'Smokey' (D)	CWGr
	'Smoots' (Fim)	CWGr
	'Sneezy' (Sin/DwB)	CWGr
	'Snoho Peggy' (Ba)	GRid
	'Snoho Sonia' (Ba) **new**	WPhe
	'Snoho Tammie' (Ba)	CWGr
	'Snow Cap' (S-c)	SDeJ
	'Snow Fairy' (C)	CWGr
	'Snow White' (Sin/DwB)	CWGr
	'Snowbound' (D)	GRid SGbt
I	'Snowflake' (Pom)	ERCP SDeJ
I	'Snowstorm' (D)	CWGr LRHS SGbt
	'Snowy' (Ba)	CWGr
	'So Dainty' (S-c) ♀H3	CWGr
I	'Sofia' (WL)	CWGr
	'Soheim'	GRid
	'Sonia Henie' (Ba)	CWGr
	'Sophie Taylor' (SinO)	NJRG
	'Sorbet' (S-c)	see *D.* 'Geerlings Sorbet' (S-c)
	'Sorbet' (DwB)	LAyl
I	'Sorbet' (D)	NHal
	sorensenii	CWGr
	'Sorrento Flush' (D)	NJRG
	'Soulman' (Anem)	CWGr ERCP NJRG SGbt SPer WPhe
	'Souvenir d'Eté' (Pom)	CWGr SDeJ
	'Spanish Conquest' (D)	CWGr NHal SGbt
	'Spartacus' (D)	CWGr ERCP NHal
	'Spassmacher' (S-c)	CWGr
	'Spectacular' (D)	CWGr SGbt
	'Spencer' (D)	CWGr
	'Spennythorn Aristocrat' (Ba)	GRid
I	'Spike' (S-c)	SGbt
	'Spikey Symbol' (S-c)	CWGr
	'Sprinter' (C)	CWGr
	'Staleen Condesa' (S-c) ♀H3	GRid SGbt WPhe
	'Stan's Nirvana' (WL)	CWGr
	'Star Child' (SinO)	CWGr
	'Star Elite' (C)	CWGr
	'Star Surprise' (C)	SDeJ
	STAR WARS ('Vdtg14'PBR) (Dark Angel Series) (Sin)	ERCP LCro LOPS SDeJ SPer
	'Starlight Keene' (S-c)	CWGr
	'Starry Night' (S-c)	CWGr
	'Star's Favourite' (C)	SDeJ
	'Star's Lady' (C)	CWGr
	'Stephanie' (S-c)	CWGr
	'Steve Meggos' (D) **new**	WPhe
	'Stevie D' (D) ♀H3	CWGr SGbt
§	'Stolz von Berlin' (Ba)	CWGr ERCP SDeJ SGbt
	'Stoneleigh Joyce' (Pom)	CWGr
	'Storm Warning' (D)	CWGr
	'Storrs Julie' (Pom)	NJRG WPhe
	STRAWBERRY ICE	see *D.* 'Kidd's Climax'
	'Streets Ahead' (D)	GRid
	'Strike a Light' (C)	CWGr
	'Striped Ambition' (Fim)	CWGr ERCP
	'Striped Vulcan' (S-c)	CAby WPhe
	'Sue Mountjoy' (Col)	CWGr WOld
	'Sue Willo' (Pom)	CWGr
	'Sue's Kilmorie' (S-c)	NHal
	'Suffolk Fantasy' (D)	CWGr
	'Suffolk Punch' (D)	CWGr ELan LAyl
	'Sugar Diamond' (C)	SPer
	'Suitzus Julie' (Misc)	CWGr NJRG WPhe
	'Summer Festival' (D)	CWGr SGbt
	'Summer Gold' (D)	GRid
	'Summer Night' (S-c)	see *D.* 'Nuit d'Eté'
	'Summer Nights' (Misc)	NJRG
	'Sunlady' (D) **new**	LSou
	'Sunlight' (Ba)	CWGr
	'Sunlight Pastelle' (S-c)	CWGr GRid
	'Sunny Boy' (Ba)	CWGr SDeJ
	'Sunray Silk' (S-c)	CWGr
	'Sunshine Girl' (Col)	NHal NJRG
	'Super Trouper' (D)	CWGr
	'Superfine' (C)	CWGr
	'Susan Gilbert' (Col) ♀H3	NHal NJRG WPhe
	'Susan Gilliott' (S-c)	GRid NHal
	'Susan Willo' (Pom)	CWGr
	'Sutton Gem' (Ba)	GRid
I	'Suzanne' (Col)	NJRG
	'Suzette' (D/DwB)	SGbt
	'Swallow Falls' (D)	CWGr
	'Swan Lake'	see *D.* 'Classic Swanlake'
	'Swanvale' (D)	CWGr GRid SGbt
	'Sweet Content' (D)	CWGr SGbt
	'Sweet Love' (D)	ERCP
	'Sweet Surprise' (D)	ERCP
	'Sweetheart' (D)	CWGr NJRG SDeJ
	'Swiss Miss' (Ba)	CWGr
I	'Sylvia' (Ba)	CWGr ERCP LCro LOPS
	'Sylvia's Desire' (C)	CWGr
	'Symbol' (S-c)	CWGr
	'Sympathy' (WL)	CWGr GRid
	'Syston Harlequin' (D)	CWGr
	'Syston Sophia' (Ba)	CWGr
	'Table Dancer' (Fim) **new**	SDir
	'Tahiti Sunrise' (S-c)	LSou
	'Tahoma Moonshot' (SinO)	CWGr
	'Take Off' (Anem)	CWGr ERCP SDeJ
	'Tally Ho' (Sin) ♀H3	CWGr ECtt EHyd EPfP LRHS NJRG NRHS SDys WCot
	'Tally Ho Double' (P)	CWGr
	'Tam Tam' (Ba)	CWGr SPer
	'Tamburo' (S-c)	ERCP
	'Tangerine Pathfinder' (Misc)	NJRG
I	'Tapestry' (Sin)	CWGr SGbt
	'Taratahi Ruby' (WL) ♀H3	CWGr ERCP GRid NHal NJRG WPhe
	'Tartan' (D)	CWGr ERCP LSou WPhe
	'Tartarus' (P)	CWGr
	TAXI DRIVER ('Vdtg57'PBR) (Dark Angel Series) (Sin)	ERCP
	'Teesbrooke Audrey' (Col)	CAby CWGr ECtt GRid LCro LOPS NHal NJRG WPhe
	'Teesbrooke Red Eye' (Col)	CWGr ERCP NJRG SGbt WPhe
	'Temptress' (S-c)	CWGr
	'Tender Moon' (D)	CWGr
	tenuicaulis	CDTJ CExl
	'Terracotta' (Misc/DwB)	NJRG
	'Terrie Bandey' (Fim)	LAyl NHal WPhe
	'Thais' (Col)	NJRG
	'Thames Valley' (D)	CWGr
	'That's It!' (D)	CWGr
	'The Baron' (D)	CWGr
	'The Big Wow' (D) **new**	CWGr
	'The Phantom' (Anem)	ERCP NJRG SDeJ
I	'The Queen' (S-c)	CWGr
	'Thelma Clements' (D)	CWGr

	'Thelma Joyce' (D)	GRid
	'Theo Sprengers' (D)	CWGr
	'Thomas A. Edison' (D)	CWGr ERCP LCro LOPS MSCN SDeJ SGbt
	'Thoresby Jewel' (D)	CWGr
I	'Tiara' (D)	CWGr
	'Tiffany Lynn' (SinO)	CWGr
I	'Tiger' (Sin/DwB)	CWGr
	'Tiger Eye' (D)	SGbt
	'Tiger Tiv' (D)	CWGr
	'Timeless' (D)	SPer
	'Tinker's White' (D)	CWGr
	'Tioga Chantilly' (Fim)	GRid
	'Tioga Dawn' (Fim)	GRid
	'Tioga Seahawk' (Fim)	GRid
	'Tioga Spice' (Fim)	CWGr GRid
	'Toga' (WL)	CWGr
	'Tohsuikyoh' (Misc)	CWGr SGbt
	'Tom McLelland' (S-c)	NHal
	'Tommy Doc' (S-c)	CWGr
	'Tommy Keith' (Ba)	CWGr
	'Tomo' (D)	ELan LAyl NHal
	'Tom's August Bride' (S-c)	CWGr
	'Top Affair' (S-c)	CWGr
	'Top Choice' (S-c)	CWGr
	'Top Totty' (D)	GRid
I	'Topaz Puff' (Anem)	CWGr
	'Topmix' (Sin/DwB)	SDeJ
	'Topmix Mama' (Sin)	NJRG
	'Topmix Orange' (Sin)	NJRG SDeJ
	'Topmix Pink' (Sin/DwB)	CWGr SDeJ
	'Topmix Purple' (Sin)	NJRG
	'Topmix Red' (Sin/DwB)	NJRG SDeJ
	'Topmix Reddy' (Sin)	NJRG
I	'Topmix Rose' (Sin)	NJRG
	'Topmix Salmon' (Sin)	ERCP
	'Topmix White' (Sin/DwB)	ERCP SDeJ
	'Topmix Yellow' (Sin/DwB)	SDeJ
	'Totally Tangerine' (Anem)	CWGr ERCP WPhe
	'Toto' (Anem)	ERCP SDeJ
	'Tour du Monde' (WL)	CWGr
	'Towneley Class' (D)	CWGr
	'Tramar' (C)	CWGr
	'Trebbiano' (S-c) **new**	ERCP
	'Trelawny' (D)	CWGr
	'Trelissick Purple'	CWGr
	'Trelyn Amber' (Col) **new**	WPhe
	'Trelyn Crimson' (Col) 🏆^{H3}	WPhe
	'Trelyn Daisy' (Col) 🏆^{H3}	CWGr
	'Trelyn Kiwi' (S-c) 🏆^{H3}	GRid NHal NJRG SGbt WPhe
	'Trelyn Kristia' (Col) **new**	WPhe
	'Trelyn Rebecca' (Col)	WPhe
	'Trelyn Red Dragon' (SinO)	WPhe
	'Trelyn Rhiannon' (C) 🏆^{H3}	WPhe
	'Trelyn Seren' (SinO)	GRid LAyl NHal WPhe
	'Trendy' (D)	CWGr
	'Trengrove Autumn' (D)	CWGr SGbt
	'Trengrove Jill' (D)	CWGr
	'Trengrove Millennium' (D)	CWGr GRid NHal NJRG SGbt WPhe
I	'Trevor' (Col)	CWGr ECtt SGbt
	'Tricolor' ambig.	MSCN
	'Trooper Dan' (S-c)	GRid WPhe
	'Trotter's Jo-Anne' (S-c)	CWGr
	'Troy Dyson' (Misc)	SDys
	'Truly Scrumptious' (S-c)	SGbt
	'Tsuki-yori-no-shisha' (Fim)	LCro LOPS
	tubulata	EBee
	'Tudor 1' (Misc/DwB)	NHal
	'Tui Avis' (C)	CWGr NJRG
	'Tui Connie' (D)	GRid
	'Tui Orange' (S-c)	CWGr
	'Tula Rosa' (Pom)	CWGr
	'Tutankhamun' (Pom)	CWGr
	'Tu-tu' (S-c)	CWGr SGbt
	'Twiggy' (WL)	CWGr SGbt
	'Twilight Time' (D)	CWGr SDeJ WPhe
	'Twilite' (Anem)	CWGr
*	'Twinkle Stars'	SDeJ
	'Twyning's After Eight' (Sin) 🏆^{H3}	CAby CAvo CExl CRos CSpe CWGN CWGr ECtt EHyd ELan EPfP ERCP IPot LAyl LCro LOPS LRHS LSun NHal NJRG NRHS SDys SGbt SPer WBor WCot WGwG WHoo WPhe
	'Twyning's Aniseed' (Sin)	CWGr
	'Twyning's Black Cherry' (D)	CWGr ECtt
	'Twyning's Candy' (Sin)	CWGr
	'Twyning's Chocolate' (Sin)	CWGr
	'Twyning's Peppermint' (Sin)	CWGr
	'Twyning's Purple Cherry' (D)	CWGr
	'Twyning's Revel' (Sin) 🏆^{H3}	CWGr WMal
	'Twyning's Smartie' (Sin)	CAby CBod CWGr EBee ECtt LCro LOPS SPer WPhe
	'Twyning's Velvet' (Sin)	CWGr
	'Twyning's White Chocolate' (Sin)	CWGr ERCP
	'Uchuu' (D)	CWGr
	'Uncle Hankey' (D)	ERCP
	'Union Jack' (Sin)	CWGr
	'Uniquity' (Sin)	WCot
	'United' (D)	CWGr
	'Urchin' (C)	CWGr
	'Usugesho' (D)	CWGr
	'Vader Abraham' (D)	CWGr
I	'Valentino' (WL/DwB)	CWGr
	'Valerie Moody' (D)	CWGr
	'Val's Candy' (S-c)	GRid NHal WPhe
	'Vancouver' (Misc)	CBod CWGr ECtt LCro LOPS SDeJ WFar
	'Variace' (Ba)	CWGr
	'Vassio Meggos' (D)	CWGr ERCP NHal WPhe
	'Vera's Elma' (D)	CWGr
	'Veritable' (S-c)	CWGr LCro LOPS
	'Verrone's Obsidian' (SinO)	CAby CWGr ERCP LCro LOPS WBrk WPhe
	'Verwer's Heatwave' (D)	ERCP
	'Victory Day' (C)	CWGr
	'Vigor' (WL)	CWGr
	'Viking' (Pom)	CWGr
	'Vino' (Pom)	CWGr WPhe
	'Violet Davies' (S-c)	CWGr
	'Vivex' (Pom)	CWGr
	'Vivian Russell' (WL)	NHal NJRG WPhe
	'Volkskanzler' (Sin)	CWGr
	'Vulcan' (S-c)	CWGr ERCP SGbt WPhe
§	'Vuurvogel' (S-c)	CWGr SDeJ
	'Walter Hardisty' (D)	CWGr GRid
	'Walter James' (D)	CWGr
	'Waltzing Mathilda' (Misc) 🏆^{H3}	CWGr ERCP LCro LOPS WPhe
	'Wanborough Gem' (Ba)	CWGr
	'Wanda's Aurora' (D)	GRid
	'Wanda's Capella' (D)	CWGr GRid
	'Wanda's Moonlight' (D)	CWGr

	'Wandy' (Pom)	CWGr
	'War of the Roses' (D)	CWGr EWes SIvy WHer
	'Warkton Willo' (Pom)	CWGr
I	'Waterlily' (Sin)	EHyd LRHS NRHS
I	'Welcome Guest' (S-c)	CWGr
I	'Wendy' (Ba)	CWGr
	'Wendy's Place' (Pom)	GRid
	'Westerton Ella Grace' (D) **new**	NHal
	'Westerton Folly' (Ba) ♀H3	NHal WPhe
	'Westerton Harry' (D)	GRid NHal
	'Westerton J.W.H.' (D)	NHal WPhe
	'Westerton Lilian' (D)	GRid NHal WPhe
	'Westerton Southside' (D)	NHal
	'Weston Aramac' (S-c)	CWGr
	'Weston Buccaneer' (C)	NHal
	'Weston Corsair' (C)	NJRG WPhe
	'Weston Cream' (C)	GRid
	'Weston Forge' (C)	CWGr
	'Weston Kelpie' (C)	NJRG
	'Weston Melody' (S-c)	GRid
	'Weston Miss' (S-c)	CWGr GRid GWyn NJRG WPhe
	'Weston Nugget' (C)	CWGr
	'Weston Pirate' (C) ♀H3	CWGr GRid LAyl NHal NJRG WPhe
	'Weston Spanish Dancer' (C) ♀H3	CWGr ERCP NHal NJRG SGbt WPhe
	'Weston Stardust' (C) ♀H3	GRid NJRG WPhe
	'Wheels' (Col)	GRid NJRG
	'White Alva's' (D) ♀H3	CWGr GRid LAyl NHal SGbt WPhe
	'White Aster' (Pom)	CWGr ERCP
	'White Ballerina' (WL)	NHal SGbt
	'White Ballet' (D) ♀H3	CWGr LAyl SGbt
	'White Cameo' (WL)	CWGr
	'White Charlie Two' (D)	GRid NHal
	'White Hallelujah' (Sin)	CWGr
	'White Hamari Katrina' (S-c) **new**	WPhe
	'White Hunter' (D)	CWGr
	'White Klankstad' (C)	CWGr
	'White Knight' (D)	GRid NHal
	'White Lace' (Fim)	GRid WPhe
	'White Linda' (D)	CWGr GRid
	'White Magenta Star' (Sin)	CWGr
	'White Moonlight' (S-c)	CWGr GRid NHal WPhe
	'White Nettie' (Ba)	CWGr SGbt
	'White Onesta' (D)	ERCP SDeJ
	'White Pastelle' (S-c)	CWGr GRid WPhe
	'White Perfection' (D)	CWGr ECtt ERCP SDeJ SDir WSpi
	'White Rustig' (D)	CWGr
	'White Seedling' (Sin)	CWGr
	'White Star' (S-c)	CWGr ERCP LCro LOPS LRHS SDeJ
	'White Swallow' (S-c)	NHal
	white-flowered B&SWJ 14340 from Colombia	WCru
	'Who Dun It' (D)	CWGr ERCP
	'Wicky Woo' (D)	CWGr
	'Wildwood Marie' (WL)	CWGr NJRG
	'William John' (Pom)	CWGr
	'Williamsburg' (S-c)	CWGr
	'Willo's Borealis' (Pom)	CWGr NHal
	'Willo's Flecks' (Pom)	CWGr
	'Willo's Night' (Pom)	CWGr
	'Willo's Surprise' (Pom)	CWGr SGbt
	'Willo's Violet' (Pom)	CWGr GRid NHal NJRG SGbt WPhe
	'Willowfield Matthew' (D)	GRid
	'Willowfield Mick' (D)	CWGr
	'Will's Ringwood Rosie' (Pom)	GRid
	'Wilma McCulloch'	GWyn
	'Wine and Roses' (WL)	SGbt
	'Wine-eyed Jill' (Ba) **new**	ERCP
	'Winholme Diane' (D)	GRid NHal WPhe
	'Winkie Colonel' (D)	CWGr GRid
	'Winkie Lambrusco' (Pom)	NHal NJRG WPhe
	'Winnie' (Pom)	CWGr
	'Winsome' (WL)	CWGr
	'Winston Churchill' (WL)	CWGr WSpi
	'Wise Guy' (D)	CWGr
	'Wishes n Dreams' (Sin)	NJRG
	'Wisk' (Pom)	CWGr
	'Wittem' (D)	CWGr SDir
	'Witteman's Best' (S-c)	CWGr ERCP MCot SGbt
	'Witteman's Superba' (S-c) ♀H3	CWGr NHal
	'Wizard of Oz' (Ba)	CWGr ERCP LCro LOPS
	'Woodbridge' (Sin)	CWGr SGbt
	'Woodside Finale' (D)	NHal
	'Wootton Carnival' (C)	CWGr
	'Wootton Cupid' (Ba) ♀H3	CWGr
	'Wootton Impact' (S-c) ♀H3	GRid NHal WPhe
	'Wootton Phebe' (D)	CWGr
	'Wootton Tempest' (S-c)	CWGr
	'Wootton Windmill' (Col)	CWGr
	'Worton Blue Streak' (S-c)	CWGr SGbt
	'Worton Revival' (D)	CWGr
	'Worton Superb' (D)	CWGr
	'Wyndal Horizon' (S-c)	CWGr
	'X Factor' (D) **new**	CWGr SDir
	'XXL Grand Central' (D)	CWGr
	'Yamabiraki' (D)	CWGr
I	'Yellow Bird' (Col)	CWGr
	'Yellow Bulldog' (Sin)	CWGr
	'Yellow Galator' (C)	SGbt
	'Yellow Hammer' (Sin/DwB) ♀H3	CWGr NHal NJRG SGbt
	'Yellow Lakeland Sunset' (C)	GRid
	'Yellow Linda's Chester' (C)	CWGr
	'Yellow Pages' (D)	CWGr
	'Yellow Passions' (D)	ERCP
	'Yellow Perception' (WL)	ERCP SDeJ
	'Yellow Pet' (D)	CWGr
	'Yellow Present' (D)	GRid
	'Yellow Sneezy' (Sin/Lil)	SDeJ WHil
	'Yellow Spiky' (S-c)	CWGr
	'Yellow Star' (S-c)	CWGr ERCP SDeJ
	'Yellow Vulcan' (S-c)	CWGr
	'Yelno Enchantment' (WL)	CWGr
	'Yelno Petite Glory' (D)	CWGr
	'York and Lancaster' (D)	CWGr EBee SGbt WAvo WBrk
	'Yukino' (Col)	CWGr
I	'Yvonne' (WL)	WPhe
	'Zagato' (D)	CWGr
	'Zakuro-hime' (D)	CWGr
I	'Zelda' (D)	CWGr GRid
	'Zest' (D)	CWGr
	'Zingaro' (D)	LCro LOPS
	'Zippity Do Da' (Pom)	ERCP
	'Zirconia' (D)	ERCP
	'Zoey Rey' (D) **new**	WPhe
§	'Zone Ten'PBR (Sin/DwB)	CWGr EHyd EPfP LRHS LSou NRHS SDys SPoG WPhe
	'Zorro' (D) ♀H3	CWGr ERCP GRid NHal SGbt
	'Zundert Mystery Fox'PBR (Ba)	ERCP
	'Zurich' (S-c)	CWGr

Dais (*Thymelaeaceae*)

cotinifolia	EShb

Daiswa see *Paris*

Dalea (*Papilionaceae*)

purpurea	EBee SBut
- 'Stephanie' **new**	CSpe

damson see *Prunus insititia*; also AGM Fruit Section

Danae (*Asparagaceae*)

§ ***racemosa*** ♀H5	CBcs CMac CTri EBee EPfP EWes LEdu MGil MGos MMuc MRav SEND SPer SRms SWvt WCot WCru WPGP WSpi

Daphne (*Thymelaeaceae*)

acutiloba	GKev WSpi
- 'Fragrant Cloud'	CExl CJun CTrC EWes SChF WPGP
albowiana	CBcs CCCN CJun GKev LRHS SChF WSpi
alpina	GKev WThu XEll
altaica	CJun
arbuscula ♀H5	EPot
arisanensis B&SWJ 6983	WCru
aurantiaca	EPot
- 'Gang-ho-ba'	CJun
bholua	CCCN CJun ECre GKev LRHS SChF SReu SavN WSpi
- B&SWJ 8275 from Fansipan, Vietnam	WCru
- GWJ 9436 from India	WCru
- NJM 13.115	WPGP
I - 'Alba'	GKev SSta WPGP WSpi
- 'Cobhay Coral' **new**	CJun
- 'Cobhay Debut'	CJun
- 'Cobhay Pink Delight' **new**	CJun
- 'Cobhay Snow'	CJun
- 'Darjeeling'	CCCN CExl CJun CTho EBee WPGP WSpi
- 'Garden House Enchantress'	WPGP
- 'Garden House Ghost'	WPGP
- 'Garden House Red Stem'	WPGP
- 'Garden House Sentinel'	WPGP
- var. ***glacialis*** 'Gurkha' ♀H4	CExl CJun WPGP
- - 'Gurkha' × ***mezereum***	WSpi
- 'Hazel Edwards'	LRHS
- 'Heale House'	WPGP
- 'Jacqueline Postill' ♀H4	CCCN CDoC CExl CJun CRos CTho CTri ECre EHyd EPfP GBin GKev LCro LOPS LRHS LSRN MBlu MGil MGos NLar NOra NRHS SChF SLim SReu SSta WHwl WPGP WSpi
- 'Limpsfield'	CJun LRHS SChF SSta WPGP
- 'Penwood'	CJun
- 'Peter Smithers'	CExl CJun SSta WPGP
blagayana	GKev SRms
- 'Brenda Anderson'	CJun EPot WAbe
'Bramdean'	see *D.* × *napolitana* 'Bramdean'
× ***burkwoodii***	LSRN
- 'Albert Burkwood'	CJun
- 'Astrid' (v)	CBcs ELon LRHS MGil SGol
§ - 'Carol Mackie' (v)	CJun
- 'G.K. Argles' (v)	CJun
I - 'Gold Sport'	CJun
- 'Golden Treasure'	CCCN CJun LRHS
- 'Lavenirii'	CJun
- 'Marjolein'PBR	LRHS
- 'Somerset' ♀H4	CBcs CCCN CDoC CJun ELan LCro LOPS LRHS MGil MGos MSwo WSpi
§ - 'Somerset Gold Edge' (v)	CJun
§ - 'Somerset Variegated' (v)	EPot
- 'Variegata' broad cream edge	see *D.* × *burkwoodii* 'Somerset Variegated'
- 'Variegata' broad gold edge	see *D.* × *burkwoodii* 'Somerset Gold Edge'
- 'Variegata' narrow gold edge	see *D.* × *burkwoodii* 'Carol Mackie'
caucasica	CJun GKev
circassica	SChF
cneorum	CBcs GKev MGil
- 'Eximia' ♀H5	GKev
- 'Grandiflora'	see *D.* × *napolitana* 'Maxima'
- 'Major'	EPot
- var. ***pygmaea***	EPot
- 'Variegata' (v)	EWes GEdr
- var. ***verlotii***	EPot
collina	see *D. sericea* Collina Group
domini	GKev
× ***eschmannii*** 'Jacob Eschmann'	CJun
§ ***gemmata***	CBcs LRHS NLar
- 'Royal Crown'	CCCN WSpi
genkwa	CJun LRHS
aff. ***giraldii***	WSpi
glomerata	GKev
gnidium	CMCN
- PAB 8371	LEdu
× ***hendersonii*** 'Aymon Correvon'	WThu
- 'Bonnie Glen'	EPot
- 'Ernst Hauser'	WIce WThu
- 'Fritz Kummert'	WAbe WThu
- 'Jeanette Brickell'	WThu
- 'Kath Dryden'	EPot GEdr
- 'Marion White'	EPot XEll
- 'Rosebud'	EPot WThu
'Hinton'	CJun
× ***houtteana***	CJun
japonica 'Striata'	see *D. odora* 'Aureomarginata'
jasminea upright	EPot
jezoensis	SSta
'Kilmeston Beauty'	CJun
kosaninii	GKev
kurdica	GKev
× ***latymeri*** 'Spring Sonnet'	SChF
laureola	CJun EPfP GKev GPoy MMrt NBid NBir NLar NPer WSpi
- 'Margaret Mathew'	EPot NLar SChF WSpi
- subsp. ***philippi***	CBcs CCCN CJun CMac EBee EPfP EWes IDee LCro LOPS LRHS MAsh MBlu MGil MGos NLar NOra WCot WPGP WSpi
longilobata	EBee GKev
× ***mantensiana*** 'Audrey Vockins'	CJun
- 'Manten'	CJun
× ***mauerbachii*** 'Perfume of Spring'	CJun
'Meon'	see *D.* × *napolitana* 'Meon'
mezereum	GKev GPoy LRHS MAsh MGos SChF SCob SGol SWvt WCot WFar WHwl WPGP
- f. ***alba***	GAbr GBin GKev GLog MAsh MGos SRms SWvt WSpi
- - 'Bowles's Variety'	EPot
I - var. ***alpina*** hort.	GKev
- 'Rosea'	MAsh SRms

	- var. ***rubra***	CBcs CCCN CDoC ELan GKin LRHS MGil MGos MRav MSwo SPer WFar WSpi
	modesta	WAbe XEll
	× ***napolitana*** 🏆H4	CJun
§	- 'Bramdean'	CJun SChF
§	- 'Maxima'	MAsh
§	- 'Meon'	CJun ELan EPot GEdr LRHS SChF WThu
	odora	CBcs CCCN CJun CRos CSBt EPfP GKev LCro LOPS LRHS MSwo NOra NRHS SCob SEle SGbt SGol SavN WPGP WSpi
§	- f. ***alba***	CCCN LRHS NLar NOra
	- - 'Sakiwaka'	CCCN CExl WLov
§	- 'Aureomarginata' (v)	Widely available
I	- 'Aureomarginata Alba' (v)	SEle WSpi
	- 'Cameo' **new**	CCCN CRos NLar
	- 'Double Cream' (v)	CJun
	- 'Geisha Girl' (v)	CCCN LRHS SReu
	- var. ***leucantha***	see *D. odora* f. *alba*
	- 'Mae-jima' (v)	CBcs CExl CRos LRHS MAsh MGos NOra SLon
	- 'Marginata'	see *D. odora* 'Aureomarginata'
	- MARIANNI ('Rogbret') (v)	CBcs CCCN CDoC CTho CTrC LRHS MRav NLar SGol SWvt
	- REBECCA ('Hewreb') (v)	CBct CBod CMea CRos EBee ECre EHyd ELan EPfP LBuc LCro LOPS LRHS LSRN MAsh MBNS MGos NRHS SLon SPoG WSpi
	- var. ***rubra***	CCCN CMac GKev LRHS SGol
	- 'Sweet Amethyst'	CCCN LCro LOPS
	- 'Walberton' (v)	CRos EHyd EPfP LRHS NRHS
	oleoides	GKev
	- var. ***buxifolia***	GKev
	papyracea	CExl
	PERFUME PRINCESS ('Dapjur01')	CBcs CCCN ECul ESwi GBin ILea LRHS LSRN MThu NLar NRHS SPer WSpi
	petraea	WAbe XEll
	pontica	CBcs CCCN CJun CMac CRos EPfP GBin LRHS NLar NRHS SChF SPer SPoG SavN WPGP WSpi
	retusa	see *D. tangutica* Retusa Group
	'Richard's Choice'	CJun
	× ***rollsdorfii*** 'Arnold Cihlarz'	CJun SChF WAbe
	- 'Wilhelm Schacht' 🏆H5	CJun EPot MAsh NOra SChF WThu
	rosmarinifolia **new**	EPot
	'Rosy Wave'	CJun SChF
	× ***schlyteri*** 'July Glow'	EPot GEdr SChF
	- 'Lovisa Maria'	EPot GEdr
	sericea	CJun XEll
§	- Collina Group	SChF WIce
	'Spring Beauty'	CCCN CJun CRos EPfP GBin IDee LRHS LSRN MAsh NOra SChF SPer WPGP WSpi
	'Spring Herald'	CCCN CJun CTho SChF SPer WPGP WSpi
	× ***suendermannii*** 'Franz Suendermann'	WOld
	× ***susannae*** 'Anton Fahndrich'	GKev NLar WSpi WThu
	- 'Cheriton' 🏆H5	CJun ELan EPot SChF WCot WThu
	- 'Tichborne'	EPot GEdr SChF WIce WThu
	tangutica 🏆H5	CBcs CBor CExl CJun CRos CSpe CTri EPfP GKev LCro LOPS LRHS LSRN MAsh MGos NHol NLar SReu SRkn SRms WKif WOld WPGP WSpi
	- 'Aureomarginata' (v)	CDoC
§	- Retusa Group 🏆H5	CExl CJun EPot EWes EWld GBin GEdr GKev SRms WSpi
	× ***transatlantica*** 'Beulah Cross' (v)	CJun SChF
	- ETERNAL FRAGRANCE ('Blafra'^{PBR}) 🏆H5	Widely available
§	- PINK FRAGRANCE ('Blapink'^{PBR})	CBcs CDoC CRos EBee EHyd ELan EPfP GBin GKev ILea LCro LOPS LRHS MAsh MMrt MRav NOra NRHS SGol SPer SPoG WSpi XEll
	- SPRING PINK ETERNAL FRAGRANCE	see *D.* × *transatlantica* PINK FRAGRANCE
	- 'Summer Ice' (v)	SChF
	'Valerie Hillier'	CJun GBin GKev WSpi
	velenovskyi 'Weber's Findling'	SChF
	'White Queen'	CCCN LCro LOPS LRHS NLar SavN WSpi
	× ***whiteorum*** 'Beauworth'	EPot WAbe WOld
	wolongensis	GKev
	- 'Guardsman'	CCCN CJun GBin LRHS
	- ex 'Guardsman' **new**	GKev
	- 'Kevock Star'	CExl GKev

Daphniphyllum (*Daphniphyllaceae*)

	aff. ***angustifolium*** B&SWJ 8225	WCru
	- B&SWJ 11804	WCru
	- WWJ 12020	WCru
	chartaceum KWJ 12244	WCru
	- KWJ 12313	WCru
	glaucescens subsp. ***oldhamii*** var. ***kengii*** B&SWJ 6872	
	- - - B&SWJ 7119	WCru
	- - var. ***oldhamii*** B&SWJ 7056	WCru
	- - - CWJ 12351	WCru
	himalaense	IDee
	humile	see *D. macropodum* var. *humile*
	aff. ***longeracemosum*** B&SWJ 11788	WCru
	- NJM 10.147	WPGP
	macropodum	CBcs CBct CCCN EBee ELan EPfP IArd IMou LRHS NLar SArc SDix SPer SVen WCru WPGP
	- B&SWJ 581	WCru
	- B&SWJ 2898	WCru
	- B&SWJ 6809 from Taiwan	WCru
	- B&SWJ 8507 from Ulleungdo, South Korea	WCru
	- B&SWJ 8763 from Jejudo, South Korea	WCru
	- B&SWJ 11489 from Yakushima, Japan	WCru
	- B&SWJ 12691	WCru
	- dwarf	WCru
§	- var. ***humile*** B&SWJ 11232	WCru
	majus B&SWJ 11744	WCru
	paxianum B&SWJ 9755	WCru
	pentandrum B&SWJ 6888	WCru
	- B&SWJ 7056	WCru
	- CWJ 12393	WCru
	- RWJ 9836	WCru
	teysmannii B&SWJ 11110 from Japan	WCru
	- B&SWJ 11112	WCru
	- B&SWJ 11358 from Japan	WCru
	- B&SWJ 14626 from Japan	WCru

aff. ***teysmannii*** CWJ 12350 from Taiwan — WCru

Darlingtonia (*Sarraceniaceae*)

californica ♀H3 — CHew SHmp SPlb WSSs WTyc

Darmera (*Saxifragaceae*)

peltata ♀H6 — Widely available
- 'Nana' — EBee ECha EPfP MBel NBid NHol NLar WFar

Dasylirion (*Asparagaceae*)

§ ***acrotrichum*** — CDTJ CExl EShb SArc
berlandieri — CExl
cedrosanum — CDTJ CJun SPlb
glaucophyllum — CCht CJun
gracile Planchon — see *D. acrotrichum*
leiophyllum — SPlb XSen
longissimum — CCCN EShb XSen
miquihuanense — CCht XSen
quadrangulatum — SPlb
wheeleri ♀H2 — CBrP SPlb XSen

Dasyphyllum (*Asteraceae*)

diacanthoides — EBee WPGP

date see *Phoenix dactylifera*

Datisca (Datiscaceae)

cannabina — CDTJ CSpe ECha IMou LEdu LRHS SBrt SMad WHer WSHC

Datura (*Solanaceae*)

arborea — see *Brugmansia arborea*
cornigera — see *Brugmansia arborea*
metel — SAdn
rosea — see *Brugmansia* × *insignis* pink-flowered
rosei — see *Brugmansia sanguinea*
sanguinea — see *Brugmansia sanguinea*
stramonium — EBtc
suaveolens — see *Brugmansia suaveolens*
versicolor — see *Brugmansia versicolor* Lagerh.
- 'Grand Marnier' — see *Brugmansia* × *candida* 'Grand Marnier'

Daucus (*Apiaceae*)

carota — CHab LRHS SPhx SRms SVic WHer WSFF WWild

Davallia ✿ (*Davalliaceae*)

canariensis ♀H1c — CMen
mariesii ♀H2 — ISha
tasmanii — CMen
trichomanoides — CLAP CMen
- f. ***barbata*** — CMen

Davidia (*Nyssaceae*)

involucrata ♀H5 — Widely available
- 'Crimson Spring' — NLar
- 'Lady Dahlia' (v) **new** — NLar
- 'Sonoma' — CLnd LRHS MBlu NLar SWeb
- var. ***vilmoriniana*** ♀H5 — CBcs CRos EHyd ELan EPfP LMaj LRHS MAsh MBlu MGos NOrn SLim SPtp WHwl

Daviesia (*Papilionaceae*)

cordata — SPlb
* ***ovalifolia*** — SPlb
pectinata — SPlb

Debregeasia (*Urticaceae*)

longifolia — SVen
- WWJ 11686 — ESwi WCru

Decaisnea (*Lardizabalaceae*)

fargesii — Widely available
- B&SWJ 8070 — WCru
insignis WJC 13740 — WCru

Decumaria (*Hydrangeaceae*)

barbara — CMac NLar WCru
- 'Vicki' — NBro NLar
sinensis — CRos EBee EHyd EPfP LRHS NRHS SLon SPoG WCru WSHC

Degenia (*Brassicaceae*)

velebitica — WAbe

Deinanthe ✿ (*Hydrangeaceae*)

bifida — CBct CExl CMil EBee EHyd EPfP EWes GEdr LRHS MMrt WCru WPGP
- B&SWJ 5436 — WCru
- B&SWJ 5551 — WCru
- B&SWJ 5655 — LEdu NLar
- 'Pink-Kii' — WCru
- 'Pink-Shi' — CMil IPot WCru WSHC
bifida × ***caerulea*** — WCru
'Blue Blush' — WCru
caerulea — CMil GEdr GKev IMou LEdu LRHS NLar WCru WSHC
- 'Blue Wonder' — CExl IPot
- white-flowered — IMou

Delairea (*Asteraceae*)

§ ***odorata*** — CCCN CExl WPGP

Delonix (*Caesalpiniaceae*)

decaryi — SPlb
* ***grandiflora*** **new** — SPlb
regia — SPlb

Delosperma (*Aizoaceae*)

from Graaf Reinet, South Africa — EPot NSla XLum XSen
from Ouberg Pass, South Africa — CPBP
§ ***aberdeenense*** ♀H3 — SAko SSim XLum XSen
alpinum — see *Ectotropis alpina*
ashtonii — CCCN EWes NSla WThu XLum
basuticum — MAsh NHpl NSla
'Beaufort West' — CRos EDAr EHyd EPot EWes LRHS NRHS NSla XLum
congestum **new** — CPBP CTsd EPot SMad WIce
congestum misapplied — see *Malotigena frantiskae-niederlovae*
cooperi — CCCN CRos CTri ECtt EHyd ELan EPfP EPot GBin GKev ITim LRHS MHer NHpl NRHS SChr SEdd SIvy SPlb SSim SVen WIce XLum XSen
- (Jewel of Desert Series) — SEdd SPad
JEWEL OF DESERT GRENADE ('Dsaa13-1')
- - JEWEL OF DESERT AMETHYST ('Dsam13-1') **new** — EWTr
- - 'Jewel of Desert Garnet'PBR — CCCN CRos ECtt EHyd LCro LOPS LRHS NHpl NRHS SPad SPoG

- - 'Jewel of Desert Moon Stone'[PBR]	CCCN CRos ECtt EHyd LRHS NHpl NRHS WIce
- - 'Jewel of Desert Peridott'[PBR]	CCCN CRos CWGN ECtt EHyd LRHS NHpl NRHS SPad SPoG WIce
- - JEWEL OF DESERT ROSEQUARTZ ('12Rosk1')	CCCN CRos EHyd LRHS NRHS SPoG
- - 'Jewel of Desert Ruby'[PBR]	CCCN CWGN LRHS NHpl SEdd WIce
- - 'Jewel of Desert Topaz'[PBR]	CCCN CRos CWGN ECtt EHyd EWTr LRHS NHpl NRHS SEdd SPad SPoG WIce
- (Wheels of Wonder Series) GOLDEN WONDER ('Wowd20111'[PBR])	CCCN LCro LOPS SPoG
- - HOT PINK WONDER ('Wowdry1'[PBR])	LCro LOPS
- - ORANGE WONDER ('Wowdoy3'[PBR])	CCCN SPoG
- - VIOLET WONDER ('Wowdrw5'[PBR])	CCCN MPri SPoG
- - WHITE WONDER ('Wowdw7'[PBR])	CCCN MPri SPoG
dyeri RED MOUNTAIN ('Psdold')	CRos EHyd LRHS NRHS SAko WIce XLum
ecklonis	GKev
FIRE SPINNER ('P001s')	EDAr WIce XLum
floribundum 'Starburst'	MHol SSim
- 'Stardust'	EWes
jansei	NSla
§ 'John Proffitt'	CCCN EDAr GKev SAko SPlb WMal XLum
lavisiae	ELon NSla SPlb
'Lesotho Pink'	EWes
lineare	XLum
MESA VERDE ('Kelaidis')	ECtt SAko XLum
nubigenum	CSma CTri EBou ECtt ELan EPot GAbr GKev NHpl SPlb SSim XSen
'Ruby Coral'	CRos ECtt EHyd LRHS NRHS
sphalmanthoides	CPBP EPot GEdr NHpl NSla SPlb SSim
sutherlandii ♀H3	CCCN CSma EDAr GBin NHpl SEdd SIvy XLum
- 'Peach Star'	CCCN EDAr NHpl SSim WIce
TABLE MOUNTAIN	see *D.* 'John Proffitt'

Delphinium ✿ (*Ranunculaceae*)

'After Midnight'	LHom
albocoeruleum new	GKev
'Alice Artindale' (d)	CMea EWes LHom MAvo WCot
ambiguum	see *Consolida ajacis*
'Ann Woodfield'	CNMi LHom
'Apollo'	WSpi
'Ariel' ambig.	LRHS
Astolat Group	CBcs CBod CTri CWCL EHyd ELan EMor EPfP EWTr GMaP LCro LOPS LRHS MGos MHol MNHC NHol NLar NRHS SCob SGbt SPer SPoG SWvt WCAu
'Atholl' ♀H5	CNMi
(Aurora Series) 'Aurora Deep Purple'	LCro LOPS
- 'Aurora Lavender'	LCro LOPS
'Bambi'	CNMi
Belladonna Group	ELan EPfP
- 'Atlantis'	ECha EHyd LRHS NLar NRHS WCot WSpi
- 'Bellamosum'	EPfP GMaP LRHS MNrw WSpi
- 'Casa Blanca'	EPfP GMaP LRHS NLar WSpi
- 'Cliveden Beauty'	EPfP LRHS NLar WSpi
- 'Gute Nacht'	LRHS
§ - 'Janny Arrow'	LRHS
- 'Moerheimii'	WSpi
- 'Piccolo'	ECha NLar
- 'Pink Sensation'	see *D.* × *ruysii* 'Pink Sensation'
- 'Völkerfrieden'	LRHS MCot MNrw NLar WCot WSpi
'Berghimmel'	LRHS
'Beryl Burton'	CNMi
Black Knight Group	Widely available
'Black Pearl'	ECtt
'Black-eyed Angels' (New Millennium Series)	EHyd ELan IPot LRHS NRHS SGbt
'Black-eyed Beauty'	MHol
'Blauwal'	LRHS WSpi
'Blue Arrow'	see *D.* (Belladonna Group) 'Janny Arrow', *D.* 'Blue Max Arrow', *D.* 'Kings Blue Arrow'
Blue Bird Group	CBcs CBod CTri EHyd ELan EMor EPfP GMaP LRHS MGos MWat NRHS SCob SGbt SPer SPoG WCAu
'Blue Butterfly'	see *D. grandiflorum* 'Blue Butterfly'
'Blue Dawn' ♀H5	CNMi LHom
Blue Fountains Group	EPfP LSRN SPoG SRms
Blue Jade Group	LHom
'Blue Jay'	EPfP LSRN WSpi
'Blue Lace'	CNor EHyd SGbt
I 'Blue Lace' (New Millennium Series)	ECtt EPfP LCro LOPS LRHS NLar SHar WSpi
§ 'Blue Max Arrow'	LRHS
'Blue Nile' ♀H5	CNMi LHom LRHS NRHS SPoG
'Blue Oasis'	CNMi
Blue Springs Group	NGdn
'Blue Tit'	CNMi ECtt LHom
'Bolero'	CMiW ECtt EHyd EPfP LRHS MPri NRHS SPoG WCot
'Boudicca'	CNMi
'Bruce' ♀H5	CNMi LHom
brunonianum	GKev
'Butterball'	CNMi LHom WSpi
Cameliard Group	CBcs CRos ELan EPfP LCro LOPS LRHS NLar NRHS SPer SPoG
'Cameliard' (Pacific Hybrid Series)	CBod
carolinianum	SBrt
cashmerianum	EBee GKev GRum
'Cassius'	LHom
caucasicum	see *D. speciosum*
(Centurion Series) 'Centurion Sky Blue' ♀H5	LCro
- 'Centurion White'	LCro LOPS
'Cha Cha'	CBcs EBee EHyd EPfP LRHS MPri NLar NRHS SPad WCot WTor
'Chelsea Star'	LHom LRHS
'Cherry Blossom'	CBod EHyd EPfP NLar
'Cherub' ♀H5	CRos EHyd LRHS NRHS
chinense	see *D. grandiflorum*
'Christel'	LRHS LSRN MCot NLar
'Claire'	CNMi
'Clifford Sky' ♀H5	CRos EHyd LRHS NRHS
confusum	EBee
'Conspicuous' ♀H5	LHom
'Constance Rivett'	LHom
'Cranberry Delight'	CNMi
'Crown Jewel'	EWes LRHS
'Cupid'	LHom
'Dark Blue Black' (Excalibur Series)	EPfP
'Dark Blue Black Bee' (Excalibur Series)	SPoG

	'Dark Blue White Bee' (Excalibur Series)	CWCL EMor LRHS SPoG
	'Darling Sue'	CNMi LHom
	'Diamant'^{PBR}	LRHS
	'Dreaming Spires'	SRms
	'Dunsden Green'	CNMi LHom
	Dusky Maidens Group	EHyd ELan LCro LOPS LRHS MHol NLar SGbt SPoG
	elatum (Aurora Series) 'Aurora Blue' new	LCro LOPS
	- - 'Aurora Light Blue' new	LCro LOPS
	- - 'Aurora White' new	LCro LOPS
	- 'Blushing Brides' (New Millennium Series)	EBee EHyd EPfP LRHS SPoG
	- 'Dasante Blue'	LRHS MHol
	- 'Double Innocence' (New Millennium Series) (d)	CPla ECtt EHyd ELan EPfP IPot LRHS MHol NLar NRHS
	- 'Morning Lights' (New Millennium Series)	ECtt EHyd EPfP IPot LRHS MHol NLar NRHS SPoG
	- 'Sweethearts' (New Millennium Series) 🏆H5	EBee ECtt EPfP LCro LOPS
	'Elizabeth Cook' 🏆H5	CNMi LHom
	'Elmfreude'	LRHS WSpi
	'Emily Hawkins' 🏆H5	CNMi LHom
	exaltatum	CSpe LPla
	'Fanfare'	LHom
	'Faust' 🏆H5	CNMi CRos EHyd LHom LRHS MCot NRHS SPoG WSpi
	'Fenella' 🏆H5	CNMi CRos EHyd LHom LRHS NRHS
	'Finsteraarhorn'	LRHS MAvo MCot WSpi
	'Flamenco'	CBcs CMiW EBee ECtt EHyd LRHS MBriF MPri NLar NRHS SCob SPad SPoG WCAu WCot
	'Foxhill Nina' 🏆H5	LHom
	Galahad Group	CBcs CWCL ECtt EHyd ELan EMor EPfP EWTr GMaP LRHS MWat NGdn NHol NRHS SCob SGbt SPer SPlb SPoG WCAu
	'Galahad' (Pacific Hybrid Series)	CBod GQue LCro LOPS LSun MGos MHol MNHC NLar
	'Gemini'	CNMi LHom
	'Gemma'	CNMi LHom
	'Gillian Dallas'	LHom LRHS
	glaciale HWJK 2299	WCru
	glaucum	EBee
	'Gordon Forsyth'	LHom
	'Gossamer'	CNMi ECtt NLar
§	***grandiflorum***	CPla EBee
§	- 'Blue Butterfly'	CMea CRos CSpe EPfP LRHS NRHS SPlb SPoG
	- Delfix Series	LRHS
	- - 'Delfix Rose'	EPfP
	- (Summer Series) 'Summer Blues'	LRHS
	- - 'Summer Nights'	EHyd EPfP NRHS SPoG
	- 'White Butterfly'	CRos EHyd LRHS NRHS
	'Green Twist' (New Millennium Series)	ECtt EHyd EPfP LRHS NRHS SCob
	Guardian Series	WFar
	- 'Guardian Blue'	CRos LRHS MHol NRHS SPoG
	- 'Guardian Lavender'	CRos LRHS MHol NRHS SPoG
	- 'Guardian White'	CRos LRHS NRHS SPoG
	Guinevere Group	CBcs ECtt EMor EPfP SPer SPoG
	- 'Lady Guinevere'	CBod GQue
	'Guy Langdon'	CNMi
	hansenii	SPhx
	'Highlander Blueberry Pie'	ECtt LRHS SCob SPad SPoG WCot WSpi

	'Highlander Crystal Delight'	ECtt EHyd LRHS MBriF MHol MPri NLar NRHS SCob SPad SPoG WCot
	'Highlander Morning Sunrise'	SCob SPoG WCot
	himalayae	GKev
	hotulae	EBee
I	'Independence'	LRHS
	'Innocence'	LRHS SCob WSpi
	ithaburense	SPhx
	'Jill Curley' 🏆H5	CRos EHyd LRHS NRHS
	'Kennington Classic' 🏆H5	LHom
	'Kestrel' 🏆H5	CNMi LHom
	King Arthur Group	CBcs CBod CTsd CWCL ELan EMor EPfP LCro LOPS LSRN LSun MGos MHol MWat SCob SHar SPer SPoG
§	'Kings Blue Arrow'^{PBR}	LRHS
	'La Bohème'	CWCL WSpi
	'Langdon's Orpheus'	LHom
§	'Langdon's Royal Flush'	CRos EHyd LRHS NRHS
	'Lanzenträger'	LRHS
	'Leonora'	CNMi
	'Light Blue' (Excalibur Series)	EPfP
	'Light Blue White Bee' (Excalibur Series)	SPoG
	'Lillian Basset'	LHom
	'Loch Leven'	CNMi
	'Loch Nevis'	LHom
	'Lord Butler' 🏆H5	CNMi EBee EWes LHom LRHS
	'Lucia Sahin' 🏆H5	CNMi LHom
	maackianum	WCot
	Magic Fountains Series	LRHS MBros SPlb SPoG SVic
	- 'Magic Fountains Blue/ White Bee'	CBod MBros
	- 'Magic Fountains Cherry Blossom'	CBod CWCL EPfP SPoG
	- 'Magic Fountains Dark Blue'	CBod EPfP GMaP LSRN NLar SPoG WFar
	- 'Magic Fountains Deep Rose/White Bee'	MBros
	- 'Magic Fountains Lavender'	EPfP NLar NRHS
	- 'Magic Fountains Lilac Pink'	EPfP SPoG WFar
	- 'Magic Fountains Lilac Rose'	LRHS NRHS
	- 'Magic Fountains Pure White'	EPfP LRHS MBros NRHS WFar
	- 'Magic Fountains Sky Blue'	EPfP MHol SPoG WFar
	'Margaret' 🏆H5	LHom
	'Marilyn Clarrissa'	CNMi
	'Melanie Avery'	LHom
	'Merlin' ambig.	LRHS
	'Michael Ayres' 🏆H5	CNMi LHom
	'Mighty Atom'	CNMi LHom LRHS
	'Min' 🏆H5	CNMi LHom
	'Misty Mauves' (New Millennium Series) (d)	EHyd EPfP LRHS NRHS WSpi
	'Molly Buchanan'	CNMi NLar
	'Moon Light'^{PBR} (Highlander Series) (d)	CRos ECtt EPfP LBuc LRHS MHol MPri SCob SPoG WCot WSpi
	'Moonbeam'	LRHS SPoG
	'Moonlight Blues' (New Millennium Series)	EHyd LPla LRHS LSun SGbt
	'Morgentau'	LRHS NLar
	'Morning Sunrise'^{PBR}	LPla SCob
	'Mrs Newton Lees'	LRHS
	'Mydark'	LHom

'Ned Rose' MAvo
New Zealand hybrids WFar
nudicaule GKev SPlb
- 'Laurin' LRHS
'Olive Poppleton' ♀H5 LHom
'Oliver' ♀H5 LHom
'Our Deb' ♀H5 LHom
'Ouvertüre' LRHS
Pacific hybrids EPfP LCro LOPS LSRN MHer SRms SWvt WCav
'Pagan Purples' (New Millennium Series) (d) ECtt EHyd EPfP LCro LOPS LRHS NRHS WSpi
'Patricia Johnson' CNMi
Percival Group CBod EPfP
'Pericles' LHom
'Pink' (Excalibur Series) EPfP SPoG
'Pink Punch' (New Millennium Series) ELan EPfP LRHS
'Pink Ruffles' LHom
'Plagu Blue' PBR NLar WSpi
PRINCESS CAROLINE ('Odabar') CBcs
'Pure White' CBod
'Pure White' (Excalibur Series) EPfP SPoG
'Purple Passion' (New Millennium Series) EHyd ELan EPfP LRHS NLar SPoG
'Red Caroline' CBcs SPeP
requienii CBgR CCBP CSpe LEdu NSti SPhx WKif
'Rose Butterfly' (d) EHyd LRHS NRHS
'Rosemary Brock' ♀H5 LHom
'Royal Aspirations' (New Millennium Series) EHyd ELan EPfP LRHS SGbt SPoG
'Royal Flush' see *D.* 'Langdon's Royal Flush'
'Ruby' CNMi
'Ruby Tuesday' CNMi
'Ruby Wedding' CNMi LHom
§ × ***ruysii*** 'Pink Sensation' LRHS NLar SGbt WSpi
'Sandpiper' CNMi LHom
'Schildknappe' LRHS
'Schönbuch' LRHS
'Secret' PBR LRHS WCot
'Shieldbearer' LRHS
'Sky Sensation' LRHS
'Snow Queen Arrow' LRHS
'Sommerabend' LRHS
'Sooty' CNMi
§ ***speciosum*** EBee
'Spindrift' ♀H5 CNMi CRos EHyd LHom LRHS NRHS
staphisagria XAbr
'Starlight' PBR LRHS WSpi
'Strawberry Fair' LRHS NLar NRHS SPoG
Summer Skies Group CBcs CBod CCBP CTsd CWCL ELan EMor EPfP LCro LOPS LRHS MGos MMrt MWat SCob SPer SPoG WCAu
'Summerfield Diana' CNMi
'Summerfield Oberon' LHom WCot
'Sungleam' ♀H5 ECtt EWes LHom LRHS NRHS WSpi
'Sunkissed' ♀H5 CNMi LHom
'Sunny Skies' (New Millennium Series) EHyd ELan LRHS
sutchuenense EWld
'Sweet Sensation' PBR (Highlander Series) (d) ECtt EHyd EPfP LPla LRHS LSun NLar NRHS SCob SPoG WCot WSpi WTor WTyc
'Sweetheart' EHyd LRHS NRHS
'Tiger Eye' LHom
'Titania' LHom
'Trudy' CNMi
'Turkish Delight' LHom
uliginosum SPlb
'Vanessa Mae' CNMi LHom
vestitum SBut
'Walton Benjamin' LHom
'Walton Gemstone' ♀H5 LHom
'White Swan' EPfP
'Wishful Thinking' PBR MHol
'Yvonne' LRHS
'Zauberflöte' LRHS

Dendranthema see *Chrysanthemum*

pacificum see *Ajania pacifica*

Dendriopoterium see *Sanguisorba*

Dendrobenthamia see *Cornus*

Dendrocalamus (*Poaceae*)

asper XBlo
giganteus XBlo
§ ***strictus*** XBlo

Dendromecon (*Papaveraceae*)

rigida CRos LRHS WPGP

Dendropanax ✿ (*Araliaceae*)

cf. ***kwangsiensis*** FMWJ 13274 WCru
trifidus WPGP
- B&SWJ 11230 WCru

Dendroseris (*Asteraceae*)

litoralis CCCN

Dennstaedtia ✿ (*Dennstaedtiaceae*)

punctilobula EHyd LRHS NRHS

Dentaria see *Cardamine*

pinnata see *Cardamine heptaphylla*
polyphylla see *Cardamine kitaibelii*

Dermatobotrys (*Scrophulariaceae*)

saundersii ECre WCot

Derwentia see *Parahebe*

Deschampsia ✿ (*Poaceae*)

cespitosa CBod CKno CNat EPPr EPfP GKev LCro LOPS LRHS MBel SEdd SPhx SPlb WCot WHwl XLum
- BRONZE VEIL see *D. cespitosa* 'Bronzeschleier'
§ - 'Bronzeschleier' CBod CDor CWCL EBee EHyd ELan ELon EMor EPPr EPed EPfP GBin GMaP GWyn LRHS MAsh NGdn NRHS NWsh SCob SPer SPhx SRms SWvt WFar WHwl XCre XLum
- 'Cabana Buta' LEdu SPhx WPGP
- 'Coral Cloud' GQue
- 'Fairy's Joke' see *D. cespitosa* var. *vivipara*
- 'Garnet Schist' GQue LEdu LRHS SPhx
- GOLD DUST see *D. cespitosa* 'Goldstaub'
- GOLDEN DEW see *D. cespitosa* 'Goldtau'
- GOLDEN PENDANT see *D. cespitosa* 'Goldgehänge'
- GOLDEN SHOWER see *D. cespitosa* 'Goldgehänge'
- GOLDEN VEIL see *D. cespitosa* 'Goldschleier'
§ - 'Goldgehänge' CSam NBir XLum

§ - 'Goldschleier' ♀H6 — CBar CBod CRos CSam CWCL EBee ECha EHyd ELon EMor EPPr EPed EPfP GBin GMaP LRHS NGdn NRHS NWsh SCob SPer SPhx SWvt WFar WHwl WSpi XCre XLum
§ - 'Goldstaub' — EPPr
§ - 'Goldtau' — Widely available
- 'Mill End' — CKno LEdu WPGP
- 'Morning Dew' — WFar
- 'Northern Lights' (v) — CSBt ELan EPfP LRHS MBel SLim SPer SPoG SRms SWvt WPnP XLum
- 'Pixie Fountain' — CBod EHyd GQue LRHS MNrw NDov NWsh
- 'Schottland' — CKno EBee ECha ELon EPPr GBin LEdu
- 'Tardiflora' — EBee EPPr
- 'Tauträger' — EBee ELon EPPr GQue SMHy XLum
§ - var. ***vivipara*** — EPPr GBin NBro
- 'Waldschatt' — EBee ECha EPPr
- 'Willow Green' — SCoo
- 'Yunnan' — EPPr
flexuosa — CKno EHyd LRHS NBir NRHS NWsh SPhx
- 'Tatra Gold' ♀H6 — CBod CWCL ECha ECtt EHyd ELan EMor EPed GMaP LRHS MAsh MBel MRav NBir NBro NGdn NLar NRHS NSti SCob SLim SPer SPoG SWvt

Desfontainia (*Loganiaceae*)

§ ***spinosa*** ♀H4 — CAbb CAby CBcs CDoC CMac CPla CTri EBee EHyd ELan ELon EPfP GAbr GKin IArd LRHS MAsh MBlu MGil NLar SLim SPer SPoG SRms WFar WPav WSHC
- 'Harold Comber' — CMac
- f. ***hookeri*** — see *D. spinosa*

Desmodium (*Papilionaceae*)

callianthum — CMac EHyd LRHS SBrt SMad WSHC
canadense — EBee IMou MNrw NLar SBrt SPhx XAbr
§ ***elegans*** — CBcs CExl EBee ELan EPfP LRHS NLar SBrt SChF SMad SPhx SVen WPGP WSHC
- dark-flowered — SMad WPGP
glutinosum — EBee
praestans — see *D. yunnanense*
tiliifolium — see *D. elegans*
§ ***yunnanense*** — CExl WSHC

Deuterocohnia (*Bromeliaceae*)

sp. — WCot
brevifolia ♀H2 — NCft WCot WPGP
lotteae — WCot

Deutzia ✿ (*Hydrangeaceae*)

CC 4548 — CExl
CC 4550 — CExl
bhutanensis HWJK 2180 — WCru
'Bright Eyes' — WPGP
calycosa BWJ 8007 — WCru
- 'Dali' — CBcs CExl IArd IDee NLar SDys SMad
chunii — see *D. ningpoensis*
compacta — CBcs CMCN SLon WPGP
- 'Lavender Time' — CDoC CExl CMac EBee ELan EPfP LRHS MAsh NLar SWvt
cordatula B&SWJ 3720 — WCru
- B&SWJ 6917 — WCru
corymbosa — MRav
- GWJ 9202 — WCru
- GWJ 9203 — WCru
- GWJ 9339 — WCru
- var. ***corymbosa*** — WSpi
crenata B&SWJ 8886 — WCru
- B&SWJ 8896 — WCru
- B&SWJ 8924 — WCru
- 'Flore Pleno' — see *D. scabra* 'Plena'
- var. ***heterotricha*** B&SWJ 5805 — WCru
- - B&SWJ 8879 — WCru
- var. ***nakaiana*** B&SWJ 11184 — WCru
- - 'Nikko' — see *D. gracilis* 'Nikko'
§ - 'Pride of Rochester' (d) ♀H5 — CBcs CBod CDoC CMCN ECrN ELan EPfP GKin LRHS MBlu MGil MRav NLar SCob SEND SEle SGol SPoG SReu SWvt WGrn WLov
aff. ***crenata*** — SReu
'Dark Eyes' — CExl SAko SMad
discolor 'Major' — CExl WCru WPGP
× ***elegantissima*** — SRms
- 'Fasciculata' — CRos EHyd ELan EPfP EWTr LRHS MGil NLar SPer SWvt WBor WSpi
- 'Rosealind' ♀H5 — CBcs CCCN CDoC CExl CMac CRos CTri EBee ELan EPfP GKin IArd LRHS LSRN MGil MRav SPer SRms SWvt WCFE WKif WSpi
glabrata B&SWJ 617 — WCru
- B&SWJ 8427 — WCru
glomeruliflora BWJ 7742 — WCru WPGP
gracilis — CBod CSBt ELan EPfP GKin LRHS MAsh MGil MGos MRav MSwo NLar SPer WFar WSpi
- B&SWJ 8927 — WCru
- 'Aurea' — CMac EPfP LRHS
- 'Carminea' — see *D.* × *rosea* 'Carminea'
§ - 'Marmorata' (v) — WAvo WLov
§ - 'Nikko' ♀H5 — Widely available
- var. ***ogatae*** B&SWJ 8911 — WCru
- 'Rosea' — see *D.* × *rosea*
- 'Variegata' — see *D. gracilis* 'Marmorata'
grandiflora — WPGP
hookeriana — CRos EBee EHyd EPfP LRHS NRHS SWvt
× ***hybrida*** 'Contraste' ♀H5 — CMac WLov
- 'Iris Alford' — CExl CRos EHyd EPfP LRHS MGos NRHS SLon WPGP
- 'Joconde' ♀H5 — CExl WFar
- 'Magicien' misapplied — see *D.* × *hybrida* 'Strawberry Fields'
- 'Magicien' ambig. — CBod CPla WAvo WSpi
- 'Magicien' Lemoine — CExl CMac CRos CSBt EBee ECrN EHyd ELan EPfP LRHS MAsh MRav MSwo NBir SLon SPer SRms SWvt WFar WKif WLov WSpi
- 'Mont Rose' ♀H5 — Widely available
- 'Reuthe's Pink' **new** — SReu
§ - 'Strawberry Fields' ♀H5 — Widely available
× ***kalmiiflora*** — CBod CBrac CExl CMac CSBt CTri EBee ELan GKin MAsh MGil MMrt MRav NLar SChF SPer SRms WFar WLov
× ***lemoinei*** — EPfP
longifolia — CMCN WPGP
- 'Veitchii' — CSBt EPfP MGil MRav

- 'Vilmoriniae'	MRav
× ***magnifica***	MMrt NLar SCob SGbt SRms
- 'Rubra'	see *D.* × *hybrida* 'Strawberry Fields'
maximowicziana B&SWJ 11567	WCru
monbeigii ♀H5	CExl ELan EPfP LRHS MRav SWvt WKif
- BWJ 7728	WCru
multiradiata	CExl EBee WPGP
§ ***ningpoensis***	CBod CExl EBee ELan EPfP LEdu MGil SMad WCFE WPGP WSpi
paniculata B&SWJ 8592	ESwi WCru
parviflora var. ***barbinervis*** B&SWJ 8478	WCru
'Pink Pompon'	see *D.* 'Rosea Plena'
prunifolia B&SWJ 8588	WCru
pulchra	CAby CBcs CDoC CMCN CRos EBee EHyd ELan EPfP EWTr LRHS MGil MRav SBrt SLon SPer SPoG WLov WPGP WSpi
- B&SWJ 1738	WCru
- B&SWJ 3870	WCru
- B&SWJ 3948 from the Philippines	WCru
- B&SWJ 6908	WCru
- pink-tinged	WPGP
purpurascens	GKev
- BWJ 7859	WCru
- 'Alpine Magician'	WKif
§ × ***rosea***	CRos EHyd EPfP LRHS MAsh NRHS SRms WKif
- 'Campanulata'	CExl MSwo
§ - 'Carminea'	ILea MGil SDix SPlb SRms WFar WLov
§ 'Rosea Plena' (d)	CExl CMac CRos CSBt EHyd ELan EPfP GKin LBuc LRHS MAsh MGos NLar NRHS SEle SLim SPoG SRms SWvt WFar
× ***rosea*** YUKI CHERRY BLOSSOM ('Ncdx2')	CBcs CRos LRHS
- YUKI SNOWFLAKE ('Ncdx1')	CRos LRHS
scabra	CBrac CTri
- B&SWJ 11127	WCru
- B&SWJ 11168	WCru
- B&SWJ 11178	WCru
§ - 'Candidissima' (d) ♀H5	MGil MMuc MRav SEND SPer WLov
- 'Codsall Pink' ♀H5	MRav
§ - 'Plena' (d)	CBrac CExl ECrN EPfP GKin NLar SPer SPoG WCFE
- 'Pride of Rochester'	see *D. crenata* 'Pride of Rochester'
- 'Punctata' (v)	MAsh SEND SRms
- 'Robert Fortune'	SPlb
- 'Variegata' (v)	CMac
setchuenensis	CMac MRav WSHC
- PAB 7449	LEdu
- var. ***corymbiflora*** ♀H5	CBcs CExl CMCN CRos CTri EBee ECre EHyd ELan EPfP EWTr LRHS MMuc MSwo NLar NOra SAko SChF SEle SPoG SWvt WFar WKif WLov WPGP WSpi
- - NJM 11.096	WPGP
- - 'Kiftsgate'	WPGP
taiwanensis	EBee EPfP SChF SGol WPGP
- B&SWJ 6858	WCru
- CWJ 12443	WCru
- CWJ 12459	WCru
× ***wellsii***	see *D. scabra* 'Candidissima'
× ***wilsonii***	SRms

Dianella ✿ (*Hemerocallidaceae*)

caerulea	CBcs CMac EBee EPri IMou NBir NLar
- CASSA BLUE ('Dbb03'PBR)	CCht EHyd LRHS NRHS
- LITTLE JESS ('Dcmp01'PBR)	CExl EBee
- 'Variegata'	see *D. tasmanica* 'Variegata'
nigra	CBcs CExl CTsd IMou LEdu
- 'Margaret Pringle' (v)	CExl
revoluta	CBor
§ - 'Allyn Citation'PBR	LRHS
- COOLVISTA	see *D. revoluta* 'Allyn Citation'
- LITTLE REV ('Dr5000'PBR)	CCht EBee EPfP SEle WSHC
'Silver Streak' (v)	EHyd LRHS
'Streetscape'	EBee
tasmanica	CAbb CBcs CBor CElw CExl CKno CMac CTri CTsd ECre ELan EPfP EShb GBin LEdu SEle SMad SRms SVen WAvo WSHC WSMil
- DESTINY ('Tas100')	CBct CCht MCot
- 'Emerald Arch'	LEdu
- 'Little Devil' **new**	SPad
- 'Splice'	CDTJ
- TASRED ('Tr20'PBR)	CBod CExl ELan EPfP MBNS SCob
§ - 'Variegata' (v)	CCCN CDTJ CExl ELan NLar WSMil

Dianthus ✿ (*Caryophyllaceae*)

'Alan Titchmarsh' (p)	ECtt EHyd EPfP LRHS LSRN MGos SPoG SWvt
'Alice' (p)	CCal LSRN
'Alice Lever' (p)	WAbe
'Allspice' (p)	CFis MRav WHoo
Allwoodii Alpinus Group (p)	NGdn SRms XLum
(Allwoodii Group) CHERRY DAIQUIRI ('Wp15 Pie42') (Cocktails Series) (p)	CCal EHyd LRHS MTis NRHS WCot
- 'Doris' (p) ♀H6	CAby CBcs CBod CCal EAJP ECtt EHyd EPfP GJos GMaP GQue LCro LOPS LRHS LSRN MGos MHer MRav MTis NGdn NRHS SCob SEND SPer SPlb SPoG SWvt WCAu WCFE
- 'Hope' Allwood, 1946 (p)	CCal
- SHIRLEY TEMPLE ('Wp15 Pie44') (Cocktails Series) (p)	CCal EHyd LRHS MTis NRHS
- TEQUILA SUNRISE ('Wp15 Pie45') (Cocktails Series) (p)	CCal CRos EHyd LRHS MTis NRHS
alpinus ♀H6	GJos MMuc NSla
- 'Albus' (p)	NWad
- 'Darcie's Love' (p)	EDAr
- 'Joan's Blood' (p) ♀H6	LSRN NHpl
- 'Millstream Salmon'	WFar
- red-flowered	NSla
amurensis	EPPr SPhx WSHC XLum
- 'Siberian Blue' (p)	EPPr
anatolicus	CCal CRos EBou EDAr EHyd GJos LRHS MHer NGdn NRHS XLum
'Anders Irene Ann' (pf)	CNMi
'Anders Patricia Griffiths' (p)	CNMi
'Anders Supernova' (p)	CTri
'Angela Carol' (pf)	CNMi
'Ann Franklin' (pf) ♀H2	CNMi

	'Annette' (p)	CCal CMea CRos EDAr EHyd GKev LRHS LSRN MAsh NGdn NHol NRHS SWvt
	'Annie Claybourne' (pf)	CNMi
	ARCTIC STAR	see *D.* 'Devon Arctic Star'
	arenarius	GKev NGdn SPlb XLum
	- 'Little Maiden' (p)	CCal CSpe EDAr GWyn NGdn
	- 'Snow Flurries' (p)	ITim
	armeria	CBgR CFis CSpe NAts WHer WOut
	arpadianus	EPot
	var. ***pumilus***	
	'Arthur Holmes' (pf)	CNMi
§	× ***arvernensis*** (p) 🏆H6	ECha SGro
	'Ashley Reay' (p)	CNMi
	'Audrey Robinson' (pf)	CNMi
	'Auvergne'	see *D.* × *arvernensis*
	'Averiensis'	see *D.* 'Berlin Snow'
	'Badenia' (p)	ECha
	'Bailey's Celebration' (p)	CCal MTis
	barbatus	MPri
	- 'Black Adder' (p,a)	CSpe
	- Dash Series (p,a)	MHol
	- - 'Dash Crimson' (p,a)	MHol SPhx
	- - 'Dash Magician' (p,a)	MHol SCob SPhx
	- (Diabunda Series) 'Diabunda Purple Picotee' (p,a)	SCob
	- - 'Diabunda Red' (p,a)	SCob
	- - 'Diabunda Rose' (p,a) **new**	SCob
	- Festival Series (p,a) **new**	MBros
	- - 'Festival Raspberry' (p,a) **new**	SCob
	- - 'Festival Red' (p,a) **new**	SCob
	- - 'Festival White Flame' (p,a) **new**	SCob
	- GREEN TRICK ('Temarisou'[PBR]) (p,a)	LCro LOPS WNPC
	- 'Heart Attack' (p,a)	WCot
	- 'Indian Carpet' (p,a)	LCro LOPS MBros
	- Messenger Group (p,a)	SVic
	- 'Monksilver Black' (p,a)	CBod CSpe CWld EBee ECtt LSun MAvo MBNS MHol MPie NCou NSti SIvy SMad SPad WBrk WCot WMal WSHC WTyc
	- Nigrescens Group (p,a) 🏆H7	CBre CSpe SPhx WHil
	- - 'Sooty' (p,a)	GJos GWyn WCFE WFar WHer
	- 'Oeschberg' (p,a)	GWyn SAko
	- 'Red Romance' (p,a)	CPla
*	- 'Roseus' (p,a)	GWyn
	'Becky Robinson' (p) 🏆H6	CNMi
§	'Berlin Snow' (p)	CPBP CRos EHyd EPot ITim LRHS NRHS
	'Betty Morton' (p) 🏆H6	EHyd LRHS NRHS WKif
	'Betty's Choice' (pf)	CNMi
	'Bill Smith' (pf)	CNMi
	'Binsey Red' (p)	SBut SGro
	'Black and White Minstrels' (p,a) **new**	CCal
	'Blue Hills' (p)	GKev
	'Blush'	see *D.* 'Souvenir de la Malmaison'
	'Bob's Highlight' (pf)	CNMi
	'Bombardier' (p)	ECtt GMaP
	'Bouquet Purple' (p)	CSpe WMal
	'Bramdean' (pf)	CNMi
	brevicaulis	CCal GJos
	'Bridal Veil' (p)	CCal SBut SGro WHer
	'Brilliant'	see *D. deltoides* 'Brilliant'
	'Brilliant Star' (p) 🏆H6	CRos ECtt EHyd LRHS NRHS SWvt WIce
	'Brockenhurst' (pf)	CNMi
	'Brympton Red' (p)	CCal CFis ECha
	BUBBLEGUM ('Wp15val12') (p)	CCal
§	'Caesar's Mantle' (p)	EPPr
	caesius	see *D. gratianopolitanus*
	callizonus	NSla
	'Calypso Star' (p)	ECtt SPoG
	'Can-can' (pf)	ECtt MHol
	CANDY FLOSS	see *D.* 'Devon Flavia'
	'Candy Spice' (p)	MRav
§	'Carmine Letitia Wyatt'[PBR] (p) 🏆H6	CCal CRos ECtt EHyd LRHS NRHS SPoG
	CARMINE VALDA	see *D.* 'Devon Louise'
	carthusianorum	Widely available
	- W&B BGL-1	WCot
I	- 'Rupert's Pink' (p)	CCal EBee NGdn SHar SWvt
	- tan-flowered (p) **new**	SMHy
	caryophyllus	CLau ENfk SVic WSFF
	'Casser's Pink' (p)	NWad
	'Charles Musgrave'	see *D.* 'Musgrave's Pink'
	'Chastity' (p)	CCal ECtt WHoo
	Cheddar pink	see *D. gratianopolitanus*
	'Cherly'	LSRN
	'Cheryl'	see *D.* 'Houndspool Cheryl'
	'Chetwyn Ruth Gillies' (pf)	CNMi
	CHILI	see *D.* CRACKER
	chinensis 'Black and White' (p,a)	CCal CSpe
	cintranus subsp. ***cintranus*** **new**	WCot
	'Claret Joy' (p) 🏆H6	ECtt MMuc SEND
	'Cleopatra' (pf)	EMal
	'Clifford Pipperoo' (pf)	WCot
§	'Cockenzie Pink' (p)	CCal SGro WHer
	COCONUT SUNDAE ('Wp 05 Yves'[PBR]) (Scent First Series) (p)	CCal CRos ECtt EHyd ELan ELon EPfP LRHS LSRN MCot NRHS SCob
	'Constance Finnis'	see *D.* 'Fair Folly'
	'Conwy Silver' (p)	WAbe
	'Conwy Star' (p)	EPot WAbe
	'Coral Reef'[PBR] (Scent First Series) (p)	CCal ECtt EHyd ELan LRHS NRHS SPoG
	'Corona Iceberry Magic' (p,a)	EHyd NRHS
	'Corona Strawberry Magic' (p,a) **new**	CRos
	corsicus	XSen
	COSMOPOLITAN ('Wp15 Pie43') (p)	CCal CRos EHyd LRHS MTis NRHS
	'Coste Budde' (p)	WSHC
§	CRACKER ('Wp10 Sab06'[PBR]) (Early Bird Series) (p)	CCal EHyd LRHS NRHS
	'Cranberry Crush' (pf)	CNMi
	'Cranmere Pool' (p) 🏆H6	CBcs CCal CRos ECtt EHyd ELan EPfP LCro LOPS LRHS NRHS SEND SPoG SWvt WBrk WCAu WFar
	'Crimson Chance' (p)	NSla
	'Crimson Warrior' (pf)	CNMi
	'Crompton Classic' (pf)	CNMi
	'Crompton Princess' (pf)	CNMi
	cruentus	CAby CPla CSpe CWld EBee EDAr ELan EPPr EWTr EWes LCro LEdu LOPS LRHS MBel MCot NDov SBut SDix SHar SPhx SPtp SWvt WCAu WCot WMal

	'Cumbria' (pf)	CNMi
	'D.D.R.'	see *D.* 'Berlin Snow'
	'Dad's Favourite' (p)	SBut
	'Dainty Dame' (p) ♀H4	CRos CSpe CTri ECtt EHyd EPfP LRHS MNHC NRHS SGro
	'Dancing Geisha'	EDAr
	'David' (p)	LSRN SCob
	'Dawn's Delight' (pf)	CNMi
	'Dedham Beauty' (p)	MPie SEND WCot
	deltoides ♀H6	ECha ENfk EPfP EWld GQue LCro LEdu LOPS MAsh MBel MBow MNHC NAts SCob SDix SPlb SRms WFar WMal WWild
	- 'Albus' (p)	ECha EPfP GWyn NGdn
	- 'Arctic Fire' (p)	CBod CCal EPfP GWyn MBel MHol NGdn NHol WFar
	- 'Bright Eyes' (p)	CCal
§	- 'Brilliant' (p)	CCal CChe GJos GWyn NGdn NHol SRms SVic
	- FLASHING LIGHT	see *D. deltoides* 'Leuchtfunk'
§	- 'Leuchtfunk' (p)	CCBP CCal EHyd GPSL NRHS NSla SPoG WFar WTor
I	- 'Luneburg Heath Maiden Pink' (p)	NGdn
	- 'Nelli' (p)	NGdn
	- 'Roseus' (p)	GJos
	- 'Shrimp' (p)	ECtt NGdn
	- 'Zing Rose' (p)	GJos
	'Dennis' (p)	LSRN
	'Desmond'	ELon
§	'Devon Arctic Star' (Early Bird Series) (p)	CCal CMea CTri EHyd ELan GMaP LRHS NRHS SPoG SWvt WIce
	'Devon Cream' (p)	CCal ELan LRHS
	'Devon Dove'PBR (p) ♀H6	CAby CCal CTri ECtt EHyd ELan EPfP LRHS MBel MRav MSpe MTis NDov NRHS SGbt
	'Devon Esther'	see *D.* POP STAR
	'Devon Fatima'	see *D.* ICED GEM
§	'Devon Flavia'PBR (Scent First Series) (p) ♀H6	CCal EHyd LRHS MTis NRHS SCob SEdd SPad SPoG
	'Devon Flores'	see *D.* SHOOTING STAR
	'Devon General'PBR (p)	CCal MWat
§	'Devon Louise'PBR (p)	WFar
	'Devon Magic'PBR (p)	CCal ECtt
	'Devon Sapphire'	see *D.* MYSTIC STAR
§	'Devon Winnie'PBR (p)	CCal MTis
	'Devon Wizard' (p) ♀H6	CAby CCal ECtt EHyd EPfP LCro LOPS LRHS MBel MRav MSpe MTis NDov NRHS SGbt WCAu
§	'Devon Xera' (p) ♀H6	CCal MTis SEND
§	'Devon Yolande'PBR (Scent First Series) (p)	CCal EHyd EPfP LRHS LSRN NRHS SPoG
	'Dewdrop' (p)	CCal CMea EHyd EWTr MAsh MMuc NBir SEND WHal
	'Diana'	see *D.* DONA
	'Diana Lavender Picotee' (p,a)	EHyd LRHS
	'Diane' (p) ♀H6	EAJP ELon EPfP SPoG SWvt WFar
	DIANTICA DARK RED PINK EYE (pt)	EHyd
	DIANTICA STRAWBERRY CREAM ('Kledg15176') (pt) **new**	CRos
	DIANTICA WHITE WITH EYE ('Kledg11116') (pt)	EHyd NRHS
§	DONA ('Brecas') (pf)	LSRN
	'Dora' (p)	EHyd LRHS NRHS
	'Doreen Hodgson' (p)	ECtt
	'Doris Allwood' (pf)	CNMi EMal
	'Doris Ruby'	see *D.* 'Houndspool Ruby'
	'Double Lace' (b)	ECtt
	'Double North' (p)	CTri
	'Duchess of Roxburghe' (pf)	EMal
	'Duchess of Westminster' (M)	EMal
	'Duke of Norfolk' (pf)	EMal
	'Dunkirk Spirit' (pf)	CNMi
	'Dusky Janelle' (pf)	CNMi
	'Earl Kelso' (pf)	EMal
	'Earl of Essex' (p)	SBut
	'Eileen Lever' (p)	CPBP WAbe WHoo
	'Eira Wen' (p)	WAbe
	'Eleanor Parker' (p)	WAbe
	'Eleanor's Old Irish' (p)	ECtt ELon LRHS MHol WAvo WBrk WCot WHer
	'Elizabethan' (p)	CFis CMea CSpe GBin MCot SGro SRms WTor
*	'Elizabethan Pink' (p)	CCal
	'Elsie Ketchen' (pf)	CNMi
	'Emmeline Pankhurst' (pf)	CNMi
	erinaceus	EPot GJos
	- var. ***alpinus***	EPot ITim NSla
	- Duguid's	WAbe
	'Evelyn Berry' (p)	CNMi
	'Evening Star' (p) ♀H6	CCal CRos CTri EHyd LRHS NRHS SPoG SWvt WIce
	'Eve's Holly' (pf)	CNMi
§	'Fair Folly' (p)	CCal WHer
	ferrugineus	EPPr SBrt SPhx
	'Fettes Mount' (p)	WAvo WBrk WCot WMal
	'Feuerhexe' (p)	ECtt XLum
	'Fimbriatus' (p)	WHoo
	FIRE STAR	see *D.* 'Devon Xera'
	'Firestar' (p)	CCal CRos CTri EHyd ELan GMaP LRHS MAsh NRHS SWvt
	FIZZY ('Wp08 Ver03'PBR) (Early Bird Series) (p)	CRos EHyd ELan LRHS MHol MWat NRHS
	'Flashdance' (pf)	CNMi
	'Fleur' (p)	CCal
	'Florence Franklin' (pf)	CNMi
	'Fragrant Ann' (pf) ♀H6	EMal
	'Frank Bruno' (pf)	CNMi
	'Freda Woodliffe' (p)	CPBP ECtt SGro WAbe WHoo
	freynii	EPot EWes GKev
*	- var. ***nana***	GKev
	FRILLY ('Wp08 Ulr03'PBR) (Early Bird Series) (p)	CCal EHyd LRHS
	fringed pink	see *D. superbus*
	'Fusilier' (p)	CCal CRos CTri EBou ECtt EHyd EPfP GMaP LRHS MAsh NRHS SHar SWvt WIce WRHF
	'Garland' (p)	CMea
	giganteus	SPhx
	'Gingham Gown' (p)	CCal ECtt EPot NBir
	glacialis	CCal
*	- ***elegans***	GKev
	'Gold Dust' (p)	CPBP ECtt EPot EWTr SGro
	'Gold Embrace' (pf)	CNMi
	'Gran's Favourite' (p) ♀H6	CBcs CCal EAJP ECtt EHyd ELan EPfP LCro LOPS LPot LRHS LSRN MCot MGos MHol MMuc MTis MWat NGdn NRHS SEND SPer SPlb SPoG SWvt WHer
§	***gratianopolitanus*** ♀H6	CBod CCal CTri EDAr ENfk EPfP GJos GQue LEdu MBow MHer MRav NBid
	- from Cheddar	WWild
	- 'Albus' (p)	MHer
	- dwarf	WAbe

* - 'Karlik' (p)	GQue
§ - 'Tiny Rubies' (p)	EDAr WAbe
Grenadin Group **new**	CCal
'Gypsy Star' (p)	SPoG
haematocalyx	GJos
- 'Alpinus'	see *D. haematocalyx* subsp. *pindicola*
§ - subsp. ***pindicola***	NSla WAbe
'Hamish Berry' (p)	CNMi
'Hampshire' (pf)	CNMi
'Hayden' (pf)	CNMi
HAYTOR	see *D.* 'Haytor White'
'Haytor Rock' (p) ♀H6	CCal EPfP MTis
§ 'Haytor White' (p) ♀H6	CBcs CCal CTri EAJP EPfP LCro LOPS SCob WFar
'Helen' (p)	ELon LSRN
'Helena Allwood' (pf)	EMal
'Herbert's Pink' (p)	SPhx
'Hercules' (pf)	CNMi
'Hereford Butter Market' (p)	EBee SBut
'Hidcote' (p)	CTri EHyd LRHS NRHS
'Highland Fraser' (p)	WKif
'Hot Spice' (p)	SPoG
§ 'Houndspool Cheryl' (p) ♀H6	CBcs CCal ECtt EHyd EPfP GJos LRHS NRHS WCAu WFar
§ 'Houndspool Ruby' (p) ♀H6	CBcs CCal EPfP GQue LSRN
hyssopifolius	CCal EDAr GKev GQue WOut
'Ian' (p)	LSRN
§ ICED GEM ('Wp06 Fatima'PBR) (Scent First Series) (p)	EHyd ELan ELon LRHS LSRN MTis SPoG
'Icomb' (p)	WHoo
'Inchmery' (p)	CCal LRHS WHer WHoo
'India Star'PBR (p) ♀H6	CCal CTri EHyd EPfP LRHS MTis NRHS NWad WIce
'Inshriach Dazzler' (p) ♀H6	CCal CPBP CPla ECtt EPot GMaP MAsh MHer NHol NSla WAbe WHal WTor
'Inshriach Startler' (p)	CMea
'James Muir' (M)	EMal
'Janelle Welch' (pf)	CNMi
'Janet Walker' (p)	GMaP
'Jess Hewins' (pf)	CNMi
'Joan Schofield' (p)	CPBP
'Joanne' (pf)	CNMi
'Joanne's Highlight' (pf)	CNMi
'John Ball' (p)	SBut
'Josephine' (pf) **new**	CNMi
'Joy' (p) ♀H6	CCal EPfP SPoG
'Julie Martin' (pf)	CNMi
'Just Jodie' (pf)	CNMi
'Kelly's Kiss' (p)	CNMi
'Kent' (pf)	CNMi
'Kessock Rose Blush' (p)	CCal
'Kesteven Kirkstead' (p) ♀H6	GAbr MNrw
knappii	CCBP EDAr GWyn LRHS SBut SDix SHar SPhx WSHC XLum
- 'Yellow Harmony' (p,a)	CCal GQue
'Kristina' (pf) ♀H2	CNMi
'La Bourboule' (p) ♀H6	CCal CMea ECtt EHyd GAbr GMaP LRHS NRHS
'La Bourboule Alba' (p) ♀H6	CTri ECtt MAsh
'Laced Monarch' (p)	CBcs CCal ECtt EHyd ELan EPfP LRHS MCot NRHS SPlb SPoG WGwG WHer
'Laced Mrs Sinkins' (p)	CCal WHer
'Laced Treasure' (p)	CCal
'Lady Granville' (p)	CCal SBut
LADY IN RED ('Wp04 Xanthe'PBR) (p)	CCal ECtt EHyd ELan EPfP LRHS MTis NBir NRHS
'Lady Windermere' (M)	EMal
'Lancing Supreme' (p)	WHer
'Langford Manor' (pf)	CNMi
'Langport Lady' (pt)	CNMi
'Lavastrom' (p)	CPBP
'Layla Jane' (p)	CNMi
'Leatham Pastel' (pf)	CNMi
'Lemsii' (p) ♀H6	NGdn
'Letitia Wyatt' (p) ♀H6	CCal CRos EHyd ELan EPfP LRHS MCot MWat NRHS SPoG
'Leuchtkugel' (p)	CPBP EPot WAbe
LILY THE PINK ('Wp05 Idare'PBR) (p) ♀H6	CCal EHyd LRHS NRHS
'Lime Crush' (pf)	CNMi
'Linfield Annie's Fancy' (pf)	CNMi
'Linfield Pink Margaret' (p)	CNMi
'Little Jock' (p)	CCal ECtt EHyd EPot GEdr GQue LRHS MAsh NRHS SPlb SRms
'London Lovely' (p)	SBut
'London Poppet' (p)	ECtt
lumnitzeri	XLum
'Maggie' (p)	LSRN MBel
'Manon des Sources' (pf)	CNMi
'Marian Allwood' (pf)	EMal
'Marilyn's Highlight' (pf)	CNMi
'Marmion' (pf)	EMal
'Matthew' (p)	WHoo
'Maxine' (pf)	CNMi
'Maybush' (pf)	CNMi
MEMORIES ('WP11 Gwe04'PBR) (Scent First Series) (p)	CCal CRos EBee EHyd ELan EPfP LBuc LRHS MCot MHol MTis MWat NCou NRHS SCob SPoG WCot WFar WTor WWFP
MENDLESHAM MINX ('Russmin'PBR) (p)	CCal EHyd ELan EPfP LRHS NRHS SWvt
'Messines Pink' (p)	WHer
microlepis	EDAr EPot NGdn NSla
- f. ***albus***	NSla
- ED 791562	NGdn
- 'Rivendell' (p)	WAbe
'Miss Farrow' (p)	EHyd EWes LRHS SPhx
'Miss Sinkins' (p)	CTri
MOJITO ('Wp15 Pie41') (p)	CCal EHyd LRHS MPri MTis NRHS WCot
'Monica Wyatt' (p) ♀H6	CBcs CCal ECtt EHyd ELan EPfP LRHS NRHS SPoG
'Montrose Pink'	see *D.* 'Cockenzie Pink'
'Monty's Pink' (pf)	EMal
'Moor Editha' (p)	CNMi
MORNING STAR	see *D.* 'Devon Winnie'
'Morrissey' (pf)	CNMi
'Mottisfont Pink'	NWad
'Moulin Rouge' (p) ♀H6	CBod CCal CRos CTri ECtt EHyd ELan EPfP LCro LOPS LRHS MBow MTis NRHS SPoG
'Mrs Sinkins' (p)	Widely available
'Murray Douglas' (p)	SBut
'Murray's Laced Pink' (p)	SBut
'Musgrave's Pink' (p)	CFis ECha MRav WHer
'Musgrave's White'	see *D.* 'Musgrave's Pink'
myrtinervius	CCal EDAr GPSL NGdn WAvo
§ MYSTIC STAR ('WP 05 Saphire') (p) ♀H6	CCal CMea ELan MTis WIce
'Napoleon III' (p)	WMal
nardiformis	XLum
neglectus misapplied	see *D. pavonius*
'Neon Star'PBR (p) ♀H6	CCal CRos CTri EHyd ELan GKev LRHS MTis NRHS SEdd SPoG

	'Night Star' (p) $\mathbb{Y}^{H6}$	CCal CPla CRos EHyd ELan EPfP GMaP GWyn LPot LRHS MHol NRHS NSla SEND
	nitidus	EPot
	noeanus	see *D. petraeus* subsp. *noeanus*
	'Nomie' (pf)	CNMi
	'Northland' (pf)	CNMi EMal
	'Nyewoods Cream' (p)	CMea EPot GMaP MHer NGdn NWad SGro
	'Oakwood Erin Mitchell' (p)	CNMi
	'Odessa Red' (Odessa Series) (pt)	SRms
	'Old Blush'	see *D.* 'Souvenir de la Malmaison'
	'Old Dutch Pink' (p)	NWad
	'Old French Red' (pf)	EMal
	'Old Mother Hubbard' (p)	SGro
	'Old Red Clove' (p)	ECtt GBee MBel MHol MPie SDix SPer WCot
	'Old Rose' (pf)	EMal
§	'Old Square Eyes' (p)	CCal EPPr MNrw SHar WHer
	'Old Velvet' (p)	CCal WHoo
	OLIVIA SWEET ('Hilbealoswee') (Beauties Series) (pt) **new**	CBod
	'Oscar' (b)	EWld SCob
	'Paisley Gem' (p)	SBut
	PASSION ('Wp Passion'^{PBR}) (Scent First Series) (p)	CCal CRos EBee ECtt EHyd ELan EPfP GBin LRHS MBel MHol MTis NCou NRHS SCob SEND SPoG WCot WRHF
§	***pavonius***	CCal EDAr EHyd EWes LRHS NGdn NRHS
	'Peach' (p)	SEND
§	***petraeus***	EWes NGdn
§	- subsp. ***noeanus***	WHal
	'Pheasant's Eye' (p)	WHer
*	'Picton's Propeller' (p)	EPPr NWad WSHC
	PIERROT ('Kobusa') (pf)	CNMi
	'Pike's Pink' (p) $\mathbb{Y}^{H6}$	CRos CSpe CTri EHyd ELan EPfP EPot LRHS MAsh MMuc NBir NGdn NRHS SEND
	PINBALL WIZARD ('Wp15mow08') (p)	CCal EHyd LRHS MTis NRHS
	pindicola	see *D. haematocalyx* subsp. *pindicola*
	pinifolius	EDAr SBrt
	'Pink Doris' (pf)	CNMi
	PINK FIZZ ('Wp10 Xav04'^{PBR}) (Scent First Series) (p)	LRHS
	'Pink Jewel' (p)	CMea CPBP ECha EPot GKev MAsh MNHC XLum
	PINK KISSES ('Kledg12163') (pt)	CRos EHyd LCro LOPS LRHS NRHS SPoG
	'Pink Mrs Sinkins' (p)	CCal
	'Pixie' (b)	CPBP EPot
	'Pixie Star'^{PBR} (p) $\mathbb{Y}^{H6}$	CCal EPfP SPoG
	plumarius	SBut XLum
	- 'Albiflorus' (p)	XLum
	- Ipswich Pinks Group (p)	CCal
§	POP STAR ('Wp04 Esther'^{PBR}) (p)	CCal MTis SGbt WIce
	'Pretty' (p)	ECtt
	PRETTY FLAMINGO	see *D.* 'Carmine Letitia Wyatt'
	'Prince Charming' (p)	MAsh
	'Princess of Wales' (M)	EMal
	'Pudsey Prize' (p)	CPBP EPot
	'Purple Frosted' (pf)	EMal
	pygmaeus NMWJ 14561	WCru
	'Queen of Hearts' (p)	SEND
§	'Queen of Henri' (p)	CRos EHyd LRHS NRHS
	'Queen of Sheba' (p)	WHer WKif
	'Rachel' (p)	ELon
	'Rainbow Loveliness' (p,a)	CCal WOut
	RASPBERRY SUNDAE	see *D.* 'Devon Yolande'
	REBEKAH ('Wp09 Mar05'^{PBR}) (Early Bird Series) (p)	CCal CMea CPla CRos EHyd ELan LRHS NRHS
	'Red Dwarf'	see *D.* 'Red Star'
§	'Red Star'^{PBR} (p) $\mathbb{Y}^{H6}$	CCal EHyd GAbr GJos LRHS NRHS WIce WTor
	'Reine de Henri'	see *D.* 'Queen of Henri'
	repens	GKev
	'Ringwood Belle' (pf)	CNMi
	'Rizalene' (p)	CNMi
	'Robert Allwood' (pf)	EMal
	'Robin Ritchie' (p)	WHoo
	'Robina's Daughter' (p)	GAbr
	ROMANCE ('Wp09 Wen04'^{PBR}) (Scent First Series) (p)	CCal CRos EHyd EPfP LRHS MTis NRHS SCob
	'Romsey' (pf)	CNMi
	'Roodkapje' (p)	XLum
	'Rose de Mai' (p)	CFis CNMi CSam SBut WHer WHoo
	'Rose Joy' (p) $\mathbb{Y}^{H6}$	EPfP
	ROSEBUD ('Wp08 Ros03'^{PBR}) (Early Bird Series) (p)	CCal EHyd LRHS NRHS
	'Rötkappchen' (p)	ELon
	'Royal Crimson' (pf)	EMal
	'Royal Salmon' (pf)	EMal
	'Ruby'	see *D.* 'Houndspool Ruby'
	'Ruby Doris'	see *D.* 'Houndspool Ruby'
	'Ruby Wedding' (p)	LSRN
	rupicola	WCot
	'Saint Nicholas' (p)	WThu
	'Seraphina' (pf)	CNMi
	'Seren Wen' (p)	WAbe
	serotinus	EPot WCot
	SHERBET ('Wp08 Nik03'^{PBR}) (Early Bird Series) (p)	WIce
§	SHOOTING STAR ('Wp04 Flores'^{PBR}) (p)	CCal ELan MTis SRms WIce
	'Shot Silk' (pf)	EMal
	'Show Aristocrat' (p)	CCal
	SHOW GIRL ('Hilshow') (pt)	EHyd LRHS
	SILVER STAR ('Wp10 Hel01'^{PBR}) (p)	CCal CTri EHyd EPfP LRHS NRHS
	'Sir David Scott' (p)	SBut
*	'Six Hills' (p)	NWad
	SLAP 'N' TICKLE ('Wp 05 Pp 22'^{PBR}) (Scent First Series) (p)	CRos ECtt EHyd ELon EPfP LRHS LSRN NRHS SPoG
	'Solomon' (p)	CCal
	'Somerset' (pf)	CNMi
	'Sops-in-wine' (p)	CCal CFis CSam ECha ECtt MSCN
§	'Souvenir de la Malmaison' (M)	EMal
	spiculifolius	EPot MMuc
	Spooky Group (p)	CCal
	'Spring Star' (p)	ECtt
	'Square Eyes'	see *D.* 'Old Square Eyes'
	squarrosus	CPBP EPot
	- 'Nanus'	see *D.* 'Berlin Snow'
	'Starburst'^{PBR} (p)	CCal MTis

	STARGAZER ('Wp13 Gil05'^{PBR}) (Whetman Stars Series) (p)	CCal MTis MWat
	'Starlette'^{PBR} (Star Double Series) (p)	CCal EHyd LRHS NRHS WIce
	STARLIGHT ('Hilstar') (pf)	CCal CMea SRms
	STARLIGHT ('Wp 06 Parnia'^{PBR}) (p)	CCal
	'Starry Eyes' (p) 🏆^{H6}	CCal CRos EHyd ELan GMaP LRHS NRHS SRms SWvt WIce
	'Storm' (pf)	EMal
	'Strawberries and Cream' (p)	ECtt SPoG
	strictus	WCot
*	- subsp. ***pulchellus***	GEdr NSla
	subacaulis	EDAr SBut XLum
	- subsp. ***brachyanthus***	GJos
	- - 'Murray Lyon' (p)	WThu
	suendermannii	see *D. petraeus*
	SUGAR PLUM ('Wp08 Ian04'^{PBR}) (Scent First Series) (p)	CCal EBee ECtt EHyd ELan LRHS MTis NRHS SCob
	'Summerfield Jo' (p)	CFis
	SUNFLOR CHARMY ('Hilcharm') (Sunflor Series) (pt)	LRHS
§	***superbus***	CCal EPPr EWld LRHS SBrt SPhx WHer
	- 'Crimsonia' (p)	WOut
I	- 'Primadonna' (p)	SHar
	SUPERNOVA ('Wp11 Tyr04'^{PBR}) (pf)	CCal MTis
	'Susan' (p)	CCal
	'Sweet Cecille' (pf)	CNMi
	SWEETNESS MIXED (p)	CCal
	sylvestris	GJos WOut
	'Tatra' (pf)	NQui
	'Tatra Blush' (p)	EPPr
	'Tatra Fragrance' (p)	EPPr
	'Tayside Red' (M)	EMal
	the Bloodie pink	see *D.* 'Caesar's Mantle'
	THE WESSEX PINK ('Wp15val11') (p)	CCal ECtt EHyd EPfP LRHS MTis MWat
	'Thora' (M)	EMal
	'Thunderstorm' (pf)	CNMi
	tianschanicus	GKev SPhx
	TICKLED PINK ('Devon Pp 11'^{PBR}) (Scent First Series) (p)	CCal CRos CTri ECtt EHyd ELan ELon EPfP LRHS LSRN NRHS SPoG
	'Tiny Rubies'	see *D. gratianopolitanus* 'Tiny Rubies'
	'Tony's Choice' (pf)	CNMi
	tristis	XLum
	'Tropic Butterfly' (p)	LPot
	'Tudor'	ELon MHCG MNrw
	'Tudor Rose' (b)	MNrw
	turkestanicus	WMal
	'Unique' (p)	CCal
	'Valda Wyatt' (p) 🏆^{H6}	CBcs CCal ELan EPfP MCot SEND SPoG SWvt WFar
	'Velvet Pelargonium' (pf)	EMal
	'Vic Masters' (p)	SGro
	'Violet Yates' (pf)	CNMi
	'W.A. Musgrave'	see *D.* 'Musgrave's Pink'
	'Waithman Beauty' (p)	CCal CFis WHoo
	'Waithman's Jubilee' (p)	CCal SGro
	'Warden Hybrid' (p)	CCal CRos CTri ECtt EHyd EPfP LRHS MNHC NRHS NWad SHar SPoG SWvt
	'Waterloo Sunset'^{PBR} (p)	CCal MTis
	webbianus **new**	WMal
	'Weetwood Double' (p)	SGro
	'Wessex' (pf)	CNMi EHyd LRHS NRHS
	'Whatfield Anona' (p)	CCal
	'Whatfield Beauty' (p)	ECtt
	'Whatfield Cancan' (p) 🏆^{H6}	CCal CRos ECtt EHyd ELan EPfP EPot GMaP LRHS MHol MNHC NGdn NHol NRHS NRya NSla SGro SPoG SWvt WCAu
	'Whatfield Cyclops' (p)	CCal
	'Whatfield Dorothy Mann' (p)	CCal
	'Whatfield Gem' (p)	CCal CFis CPla ECtt ELan ELon EPfP MNHC NGdn SWvt WCav WIce
	'Whatfield Joy' (p)	CCal CPBP CRos ECtt EHyd ELan EPfP LRHS NGdn NRHS
	'Whatfield Magenta' (p) 🏆^{H6}	CRos ECtt EHyd ELan EPot EWTr LRHS NRHS SPoG SRms WAbe
	'Whatfield Misty Morn' (p)	ECtt
	'Whatfield Peach' (p)	CCal
	'Whatfield Ruby' (p)	ECtt
	'Whatfield White' (p)	CCal ECtt
	'Whatfield Wisp' (p)	CPBP EPfP EPot MRav NBir
	'White Joy'^{PBR} (p) 🏆^{H6}	MRav
	'White Ladies' (p)	MRav
	'Widecombe Fair' (p) 🏆^{H6}	CCal EPfP MTis SPoG

Diarrhena (*Poaceae*)

japonica	MAvo
obovata	EBee EPPr

Diascia (*Scrophulariaceae*)

	'Andrew'	SGro
	'Aurora Apricot' (Aurora Series)	EHyd LRHS NRHS
	barberae 'Belmore Beauty' (v)	EWes
	- 'Blackthorn Apricot' 🏆^{H4}	EBee ECha EHyd ELan EPfP GWyn LRHS LSRN MBow NDov NLar NRHS SPer SPlb SPoG SRms SWvt XEll
§	- 'Fisher's Flora' 🏆^{H4}	WFar
§	- 'Ruby Field' 🏆^{H4}	EBee ECha EHyd EPfP LRHS LSRN NRHS SPer SPoG SRms SWvt
	BLUE BONNET ('Hecbon')	SWvt
	'Bluebelle' (Maritana Series)	NDov NLar
	'Blush'	see *D. integerrima* 'Blush'
	(Breezee Series) BREEZEE APPLE BLOSSOM	LSou NLar
	- BREEZEE APRICOT ('Diaspritwo'^{PBR})	NLar
	- BREEZEE PLUS PINK	MPri
	- BREEZEE RED	NLar
	- BREEZEE SNOW ('Inndiabzsno'^{PBR})	ELan NLar
	'Coldham'	LPla WGoo WMal
	CORAL BELLE ('Hecbel'^{PBR}) 🏆^{H3}	CRos EHyd LRHS NRHS
	cordata misapplied	see *D. barberae* 'Fisher's Flora'
	cordata ambig.	WFar
	cordifolia	see *D. barberae* 'Fisher's Flora'
	'Denim Blue'	EDAr WFar
	'Diamond Fuchsia' **new**	LSou
	'Divara Pink' **new**	LSou
	elegans misapplied	see *D. fetcaniensis*, *D. vigilis*
	'Emma'	LPla NDov SMHy SWvt WGoo
	felthamii	see *D. fetcaniensis*
§	***fetcaniensis***	CMea CPrp EBee EPfP LEdu LPla LRHS MCot MMuc NDov NLar SIvy SWvt WHal WSHC
	- 'Daydream'	LBuc MNrw MPie SGro WCFE WFar

flanaganii misapplied	see *D. vigilis*
(Flying Colours Series) FLYING COLOURS ANTIQUE ROSE ('Diastu'PBR)	SPoG
- FLYING COLOURS APPLEBLOSSOM ('Diastara')	SPoG
- FLYING COLOURS APRICOT ('Diastina')	SPoG
- FLYING COLOURS DEEP SALMON IMPROVED ('Dala Depsam'PBR)	SPoG
- FLYING COLOURS RED ('Diastonia')	SPoG
'Hector Harrison'	see *D.* 'Salmon Supreme'
§ 'Hopleys'	CRos ECha EHyd EWes LRHS MAvo MHCG MPie MSCN NLar NRHS SMHy SWvt WAvo WFar WOut WWtn
ICE CRACKER ('Hecrack')	CMea CRos EHyd ELan LRHS NRHS SRms
ICEBERG ('Hecice')	NDov SWvt
§ ***integerrima*** ♀H4	ECha MCot
- 'Alba'	see *D. integerrima* 'Blush'
§ - 'Blush'	CSpe EBee NDov WGoo
- 'Ivory Angel'	see *D. integerrima* 'Blush'
integrifolia	see *D. integerrima*
'Jacqueline's Joy'	CMea NPer
'Joyce's Choice' ♀H3	CRos EHyd LRHS NRHS SRms
'Katherine Sharman' (v)	EWes
'Lilac Belle' ♀H3	EDAr EHyd ELan EPfP LRHS NBir NRHS SPlb SPoG SRms
'Lilac Mist' ♀H3	NPer
LITTLE DANCER ('Pendan'PBR)	ELan NLar
LITTLE DREAMER ('Pender'PBR)	NLar
LITTLE DRIFTER ('Pendrif'PBR)	NLar
LITTLE MAIDEN ('Penmaid'PBR)	NLar
LITTLE TANGO ('Pentang'PBR)	NLar SRms
personata	Widely available
- 'Hopleys'	see *D.* 'Hopleys'
- orange-flowered new	WMal
'Peter'	NDov WGoo
PINK PANTHER ('Penther')	SWvt
RED ACE ('Hecrace')	EPfP MBow NPer SWvt
REDSTART ('Hecstart')	SWvt
rigescens ♀H3	CBod CCBP CWCL ECtt ELan EPfP GBin GWyn LRHS MBow NLar NPer SChF SPer SPlb SPoG SWvt WAbe WAvo WCFE WSHC WSpi
§ - 'Anne Rennie'	LRHS SWvt
- pale-flowered	see *D. rigescens* 'Anne Rennie'
'Ruby Field'	see *D. barberae* 'Ruby Field'
'Rupert Lambert' ♀H3	NDov
§ 'Salmon Supreme'	CRos EHyd EPfP LRHS NPer NRHS SPoG SRms
(Sundiascia Series) SUNDIASCIA BLUSH PINK ('Sunjodipi'PBR)	CBod
- SUNDIASCIA ORANGE ('Sunjodiora'PBR)	CBod
- SUNDIASCIA ROSE PINK ('Sunjodiropi'PBR)	CBod
- SUNDIASCIA UPRIGHT BRIGHT PINK ('Sunjodiblupi'PBR) new	CWCL
TOWERS OF FLOWERS AURORA CHERRY BLOSSOM new	ELan
TOWERS OF FLOWERS AURORA DARK PINK new	ELan
TOWERS OF FLOWERS AURORA LIGHT PINK new	ELan
'Twinkle' ♀H3	CRos EHyd LRHS NBir NPer NRHS SRms
§ ***vigilis*** ♀H3	CExl CMea EBee EHyd EMor EPot LRHS MHol NBro NRHS SRms WHal

Dicentra ✿ (*Papaveraceae*)

CC 4452	CExl
'Adrian Bloom'	CExl ECtt EPfP GLet SPer SWvt WFar
(Amore Series) 'Amore Pink'	CMiW CWGN LPla NLar WHil
- 'Amore Rose'PBR	CWGN GBin NBPC NHpl
'Aurora'	CBcs CBod CMac CMiW EBee ECtt EHyd ELon EMor EPfP GMaP GWyn ILea LCro LOPS LRHS MRav NBPC NGdn NLar NRHS SCob SPer SPoG SWvt WCAu
'Boothman's Variety'	see *D.* 'Stuart Boothman'
'Bountiful'	CMac EBee ECtt EHyd GLet LRHS MRav NGdn NRHS SWvt WGwG
'Burning Hearts'PBR	CAby CMiW CWCL CWGN ECtt EPot GEdr LRHS MPnt SPer SPoG WCAu WHil
canadensis	CAby CMiW EBee LEdu MAvo MNrw WAbe WFar WHal
'Candy Hearts'PBR	EBee ECtt ELan MHol SCob SGol WHil
cucullaria	CAby CElw CMea CMiW CWCL EBee EHyd ELon EMor EPPr EPot GAbr GEdr GKev GLet ITim LEdu LRHS MNrw MRav NHpl NLar NRHS WAbe WFar WMal XEll
- 'Little Angels' (d) new	WFar
- 'Pink Punk'	CWCL EBee ELon EMor EPPr EPot LEdu NLar WFar WMal
- 'Pittsburg'	CAby EBee EPPr LEdu MNrw WSpi
eximia misapplied	see *D. formosa*
eximia ambig.	CMac CPla GPSL MHol WFar
eximia (Ker Gawl.) Torr. 'Alba'	see *D. eximia* (Ker Gawl.) Torr. 'Snowdrift'
§ - 'Snowdrift'	SRms WFar
'Filigree'	CSpe ECha SPVi
'Firecracker'	ECtt MPnt
§ ***formosa***	CBcs CBod CTri ECha EHyd ELan EPfP GKev LRHS NBro NGdn NRHS SPlb SRms WCAu
- f. ***alba***	CTri GAbr GLet GLog NBir SRms WCru WFar WKif
- 'Bacchanal' ♀H5	Widely available
- 'Cox's Dark Red'	CExl EWes GAbr GBin GKev GLet IMou NHpl
- 'Langtrees' ♀H5	CMac CRos ECha EHyd EPfP GKev LEdu LRHS MRav NBro NLar NRHS SRms SSut SWvt WCru WFar WSpi
- 'Moorland Mist' new	WFar
- 'Moorland Pearl'	WFar
- subsp. ***oregana***	EPPr WHal
- SNOWFLAKES ('Fusd')	MRav

- 'Spring Gold'	CBod ECha EHyd ELon EPPr LRHS LSou NLar WFar
- 'Spring Magic'	CRos ECtt EHyd EPPr EPfP GBin GWyn LRHS LSou MRav NLar NRHS WSpi
'Ivory Hearts'PBR	CWGN EBee ELan MAvo MCot NLar NSti SCob SPer WHil
§ 'Katie'	EPPr
'Katy'	see *D.* 'Katie'
'King of Hearts'	Widely available
'Love Hearts'PBR	MHol
'Luxuriant' ♀H5	CBcs CBod CRos CSBt ECtt EHyd ELan EMor EPfP EShb GKev LRHS LSRN MCot MGos MHol MRav NBPC NRHS SPer SPoG SRms SWvt WCAu WFar
macrantha	see *Ichthyoselmis macrantha*
'Pearl Drops'	EHyd GKev GLog GMaP GWyn LRHS MCot MHCG MMrt NBid NLar NRHS SRms WFar
peregrina alba	GEdr
'Red Fountain'PBR	MPnt NLar SMad
scandens	see *Dactylicapnos scandens*
'Silver Beads'	ELon
spectabilis	see *Lamprocapnos spectabilis*
'Spring Morning'	CElw ECtt EMor EPPr GLet LEdu NGdn WSpi
§ 'Stuart Boothman' ♀H5	CMac CWCL ECtt EPfP GBin GLet GMaP ILea LEdu LRHS MCot MHol MRav NBro NGdn NLar NQui SPoG SRms SWvt WCAu WFar WKif
thalictrifolia	see *D. scandens*
ventii	see *Dactylicapnos ventii*

Dichelostemma (*Asparagaceae*)

congestum	CAvo CBor GKev SDeJ WCot
§ ***ida-maia***	CAby CAvo CBor CGrW CWCL EPot GKev SDeJ
- 'Pink Diamond'	CBor EBee GKev SDeJ
volubile	GKev
- 'Pink Giant'	SDeJ

Dichondra (*Convolvulaceae*)

argentea 'Silver Falls'	CPla EShb MBros MPri SCoo SPer SPoG WSMil
§ ***micrantha***	EShb
repens misapplied	see *D. micrantha*

Dichopogon (*Asparagaceae*)

strictus	WSFF

Dichroa ✿ (*Hydrangeaceae*)

from Guizhou, China	WPGP
cyanea NJM 13.104	EBee WPGP
febrifuga B&SWJ 9734	WCru
- B&SWJ 9753	WCru
- NJM 10.042	WPGP
- PAB 8639	LEdu
hirsuta B&SWJ 8207 from Vietnam	WCru
- NJM 10.051	WPGP
aff. ***hirsuta*** B&SWJ 8371 from Laos	WCru
- NJM 10.051	WPGP
aff. ***yunnanensis*** B&SWJ 9734	WCru

Dichroa × *Hydrangea* see × *Didrangea*

Dichromena see *Rhynchospora*

Dichrostachys (*Mimosaceae*)

cinerea	SPlb

Dicksonia ✿ (*Dicksoniaceae*)

antarctica ♀H3	Widely available
fibrosa ♀H3	CDTJ CTrC
sellowiana	CDTJ
squarrosa ♀H3	CBdn CCCN CDTJ
youngiae	CDTJ

Dicliptera (*Acanthaceae*)

§ ***sericea***	CCCN ECtt EShb SEND SGro SRkn XSen
suberecta	see *D. sericea*

Dictamnus (*Rutaceae*)

albus	CBcs CBod CRos CSpe CWCL EBee ECha EHyd ELan EMor EPfP EWTr LPla LRHS LSun MBel MCot MNrw MRav NRHS SMHy SPer SPoG SWvt WCAu WSpi XAbr
- var. ***albus*** ♀H6	SWvt
§ - var. ***purpureus*** ♀H6	CPla CSpe ECha EHyd ELan EMor EPfP GBin ILea LRHS LSun MBel MNrw MRav NGBl NRHS SPer SPoG SRms SWvt WCAu WKif WSpi
* - var. ***roseus***	IMou
caucasicus	WSHC
fraxinella	see *D. albus* var. *purpureus*

× *Didrangea* (*Hydrangeaceae*)

B&SWJ 6605 from Thailand	WCru
versicolor	CAbb CBcs CBod CDoC CExl CMCN EBee EHyd EMdy EPfP ESwi LRHS MGil SBrt SEdd SIvy SPoG SWvt WPGP
- B&SWJ 6565	WCru
ytiensis B&SWJ 11790	WCru

Didymochlaena (*Dryopteridaceae*)

lunulata	see *D. truncatula*
§ ***truncatula***	CDoC EShb XBlo

Dierama ✿ (*Iridaceae*)

CD&R 192	CElw
adelphicum	GAbr
ambiguum	CElw EBee GAbr XLum
argyreum	CBcs CBct CBod CBor CCCN CElw CMac CMiW CTsd CWCL EBee EMor EPri GEdr GKev GPSL ITim NLar SEdd SPad SPoG WGob WHil XLum
atrum	EBee WHil
'Autumn Dazzler'	CPla
Barr hybrids	CBro
'Black Knight'	CExl
'Blackberry Bells'	CBct CBor CPla CWCL CWGN EBee EHyd ELan ELon EMor EPfP GPSL GWyn LRHS MAvo MHol NLar NWad SPoG WSpi
'Blood Drops' **new**	GAbr
BLUE BELLE ('Rowblu'PBR)	CBor CWCL EBee ECtt GBin IBal LRHS
'Candy Stripe'	EBee IBal
'Carmine'	CWCL
'Cinnamon Fairy'	EBee EHyd EPfP IBal LRHS
cooperi	CBor CPou EBee EPfP NBir
'Coral Belle'	EBee IBal LRHS

'Coral Bells'	CCCN IBal MNrw WPGP
'Cosmos'	CBcs CExl CPla CWCL ELon EPri LRHS MMrt NBPC NWad SEdd WFar
§ ***dracomontanum***	Widely available
dracomontanum* × *pulcherrimum	SMad
ensifolium	see *D. pendulum*
erectum	CBcs CBct CBor CCCN CMac CTsd CWCL EBee EMor EPri GPSL NBPC NLar SEdd SPeP WGob
formosum	EBee
galpinii	CCCN CPla CWCL EBee EPri SEdd
grandiflorum	CPou WSHC
'Guinevere'	CBor CDor CExl CWCL CWGN EBee GMaP GWyn IBal LEdu LRHS MRav NBir NChi NGdn NQui SCob SEdd SPoG SVen WFar WGwG WHoo WSHC XEll
igneum	Widely available
- CD&R 278	CExl CPou
insigne	CCCN CWCL EBee EHyd LRHS MMrt NLar NWad SEdd WCot WHil
jucundum	CWCL EBee EMor EWes LRHS SEdd WCot WSMil
'Kilmurry White'	IBal
'Lancelot'	CBcs CExl EBee ECtt IBal LRHS NBir SCob SWvt WCot WFar WKif WSHC
latifolium	WGob
luteoalbidum	GKev
'Milkmaid'	CExl
'Miranda'	CBcs CWCL EBee ECtt ELan EMor EPri IBal LRHS LSRN NLar SEdd
mossii	CBcs CBor CCBP CCCN CExl CRos CWCL EMor EPfP EPri LRHS MSCN NLar NQui NWad SEdd SPeP SPlb SPoG SVen WGob WHil XLum
'Painted Lady'	EBee EHyd EPfP IBal LRHS SLon
'Pale Pink'	CWCL
pallidum	CExl
'Pamina'	CExl CPrp
pauciflorum	CCCN CExl CPrp CRos CWCL EBee EMor EPri LRHS NBir NLar NSla SEdd SPer WCot WGob WSHC
§ ***pendulum***	CBro LRHS MRav SWvt WCot WFar WGob
'Pink Rocket'	CBct CBod CBor CMiW CPla CWCL EMor GEdr MHer MHol MHtn NHol SPad SPeP
Plant World hybrids	ELon WFar
PLANT WORLD JEWELS	CBct CWCL NWad WFar
'Pretty Flamingo'	CExl CPrp
'Puck'	EBee MRav
pulcherrimum	Widely available
- var. ***album***	CCCN CWCL GAbr GKev MAvo MHer MNrw NQui WHil
- 'Blackbird'	CBcs CCCN CExl CPla CWCL EBou ELan EMor EPri GAbr GEdr LRHS LSRN MAvo MHer MSCN NBPC NHol NLar SChF SEdd SPeP SPoG SWvt WFar WGob WHoo WPGP
- 'Flaring Tips'	GKev LRHS
- 'Merlin'	CDor CExl CWCL EBee ECtt ELon GEdr IBal LRHS NBir SCob SVen SWvt WFar
- pale-flowered	ECha
- purple-flowered	CSpe CWCL
- Slieve Donard hybrids	CWCL EMor WFar WHil
pumilum misapplied	see *D. dracomontanum*
reynoldsii	CBod CBor CCCN CExl CPla CTsd CWCL EMor EPri GBin GEdr MBel NBPC NWad SBrt SEdd SPlb SPoG SRkn SVen WFar WHer WKif WSpi
robustum	CAbb CCCN CExl CPou CWCL EMor EWes LRHS WCot WFar WPGP
'Sarastro'	CExl
'Snowgoose'	CPla
'Spring Dancer'	CPla CWCL EBee MHer NHol SPlb
'Tiny Bells'	EBee EDAr IBal SMHy WSHC
'Titania'	GBin IBal
trichorhizum	CBod CCCN CElw CExl CWCL EMor EPri GKev LPla LRHS NWad SEdd
tyrium	GAbr WHil
white-flowered	MBel
Wildside hybrids	WSHC

Diervilla ✿ (*Caprifoliaceae*)

middendorffiana	see *Weigela middendorffiana*
rivularis HONEYBEE ('Diwibru01'PBR)	CBod CSBt LCro LOPS NEoE SGol SPoG WHil
- 'Troja Black'	EPPr EPfP MBlu NLar SGol
§ ***sessilifolia***	CBrac CFis CMac EBee EPPr MBlu MRav SLon WCot
- 'Butterfly'	CMac EPPr LCro LOPS NLar WFar
- COOL SPLASH ('Lpdc Podaras'PBR) (v)	CMac EBee ELan LRHS NEoE SPoG SWvt
× ***splendens***	CBrac CExl EBee EHyd ELan EPPr EPfP IDee LRHS MBNS MBlu MGil MSwo NLar SIvy SPer SPoG SWvt
- DIVA	see *D.* × *splendens* 'El Madrigal'
§ - 'El Madrigal'PBR **new**	MMrt SPad

Dietes (*Iridaceae*)

sp.	XBlo
bicolor	CAbb CAby CBod CExl CPbh CPrp CSpe EBee EPri ESwi LEdu SBrt SChr SPoG WCFE WSHC
grandiflora	CAbb CAby CBod CExl CPbh CSpe CTsd ESwi SVen WCFE WCot
§ ***iridioides***	CPrp EPri ESwi WGob XLum
robinsoniana	WCot

Digitalis ✿ (*Plantaginaceae*)

NJM 13.013	WPGP
'Albino'	CRos EHyd EPfP LRHS NRHS
ambigua	see *D. grandiflora*
apricot hybrids	see *D. purpurea* 'Sutton's Apricot'
canariensis	CAbb CCCN CDTJ CPla CSpe CTsd LRHS MEch MGil MMrt SEle SIvy SPad SPlb SVen WCFE
ciliata	GKev
davisiana	CExl GLog MNHC
'Elsie Kelsey'	ECtt EPfP SWvt
eriostachya	see *D. lutea*
ferruginea ♀H6	CDor CSpe ECha ECtt ELan EPPr EPfP EWTr GKev GQue LEdu LRHS MRav NBir NDov NGdn NRHS SCob SPer SRms SVen WCAu WKif
- 'Gelber Herold'	CDor EMor GMaP LRHS MWat SCob WFar WSpi
- 'Gigantea' ♀H7	ECtt ELan EMor EPfP LBuc LEdu MBNS SPlb WPGP

	'Foxtrot'	EPfP
	× ***fucata*** 'Miranda'	SWvt
	- 'Pink Chapel'	ECtt
	- 'Red Skin'	NLar NWad
	'Glory of Roundway' ♀H6	CBod CDor EBee ECtt EShb LCro LOPS MHol MNrw MPie NCou SCob SPer STPC WCAu WCot WMal
§	GOLDCREST ('Waldigone'PBR)	CRos CWGN EHyd LRHS LSou MHol NRHS SHar SPoG WNPC
§	***grandiflora*** ♀H6	Widely available
	- 'Carillon' ♀H5	CBod EBee EHyd ELan EMor EPfP GJos ITim MBros WCav
	- 'Cream Bell'	CBod EPfP LRHS MHol
	Illumination Series	see *D.* × *valinii* Illumination Series
	isabelliana	CBod CCCN
	'John Innes Tetra'	MBriF MMrt MNrw SPtp WHoo
	kishinskyi	see *D. parviflora* Jacq.
	laevigata	EBee LEdu NBro SEND
	- white-flowered	WCot
	lamarckii misapplied	see *D. lanata*
§	***lanata***	CBod CRos EBou ECtt EHyd ELan EPfP LRHS MBNS MNHC MPie NGdn NRHS NWad SGbt SPlb SRms WGwG
	- 'Café Crème'	CDor EMor
§	***lutea*** ♀H6	Widely available
	'Martina' ♀H5	WMal
	× ***mertonensis*** ♀H5	Widely available
	- 'Summer King'	CChe CDor ECtt ELan GJos LSRN MBow MHol MPri MWat SPtp WFar
	minor	CPla
	obscura	CCCN EAJP IMou SBrt SEdd SPlb SVen WHer
	- 'Sunset'	GJos SBut
	orientalis	see *D. grandiflora*
§	***parviflora*** Jacq. ♀H5	CBod CSam ECha ECtt EPPr EPfP LCro LRHS MBNS MMrt MMuc NBro NChi SEND SEdd WWtn
	- 'Milk Chocolate' ♀H5	CAbb CDor CSpe CWCL ECtt ELan EMor EPfP LRHS LSRN MBros MHer NBir NHpl NLar NWad SPtp
	(Polkadot Series) 'Polkadot Petra' **new**	EAJP
	- 'Polkadot Polly'	MBriF
	purpurea	CBod CHab CWld EBou EHyd ELan ENfk EPfP GPoy LCro LOPS LRHS LSun MBow MHer MNHC MPri NMir SCob SPlb SPoG WBrk WOut WSFF WWild
	- 'Alba'	see *D. purpurea* f. *albiflora*
§	- f. ***albiflora***	Widely available
	- - 'Anne Redetzky'PBR	CSpe LRHS
	- 'Apricot Delight'	EBee SBut WCAu
	- 'Berggold'	LSun
	- Camelot Series	SHar SVic
	- - 'Camelot Cream' ♀H5	CRos EHyd ELan EPfP LRHS SWvt
	- - 'Camelot Lavender' ♀H5	CRos EHyd ELan EPfP LRHS SWvt
	- - 'Camelot Rose' ♀H5	CRos EHyd ELan EPfP LRHS SWvt
	- - 'Camelot White' ♀H5	EHyd ELan EPfP
	- - 'Cream Carousel'	EBee EHyd LRHS NRHS
	- Dalmatian Series	SCob
	- - 'Dalmatian Crème' ♀H7	CRos EPfP LRHS MAsh NRHS SCob
	- - 'Dalmatian Peach' ♀H5	CBod CRos ELan EPfP MAsh MBros MHer
	- - 'Dalmatian Purple' ♀H5	CBod CRos ELan EPfP LCro LOPS MAsh MHol SCob
	- - 'Dalmatian Rose' ♀H5	CBod CRos ELan EPfP LCro LOPS LRHS MAsh MBros MHol NRHS SCob
	- - 'Dalmatian White' ♀H5	CBod CRos EAJP ELan EPfP LCro LOPS LRHS MBros SCob
	- Excelsior Group	CBcs CDor CMac CRos CSBt CTri ECtt EHyd EPfP GJos GMaP LCro LOPS LRHS NHol NMir NRHS SCob SGbt SPer SPoG SRms SVic SWvt XLum
	- - (Suttons; Unwins)	ECtt MRav
	- - white-flowered	CTri
	- Foxy Group	CBod EHyd EPfP LRHS MNHC SPoG
	- Giant Spotted Group	CRos ECtt EHyd EPfP LRHS NRHS SPoG
	- subsp. ***heywoodii*** 'Silver Fox'	CBcs CBod MHol NRHS SCob WHil
	- 'Lavender Carousel' (Carousel Series)	EHyd LRHS NRHS
	- 'Monstrosa'	CBod
	- 'Orchid Carousel' (Carousel Series)	EHyd LRHS NRHS
	- 'Pam's Choice' ♀H7	CBod CChe CDor CExl CRos CSpe EAJP ECtt EHyd ELan EPPr EPfP LCro LOPS LRHS LSRN MPri NHol NLar NRHS SCob SPer WBor WCAu
	- 'Pam's Split'	MHol MWat SCob
	- 'Primrose Carousel' (Carousel Series)	NLar SCob
	- 'Purple Carousel' (Carousel Series)	EHyd LRHS NRHS
	- 'Serendipity'	CRos EHyd EPfP LRHS NRHS
	- 'Snow Thimble'	CBod CDor EHyd ELan EPfP LRHS LSun MHol NCou NLar NRHS STPC
§	- 'Sutton's Apricot'	CBcs CBod CDor CRos ECha ECtt EHyd ELan EPfP GMaP GQue LCro LOPS LRHS MBriF MPri MRav NBir NGdn NLar NRHS SCob SGbt SPer SPoG SWvt WCot XLum
	- (Virtuoso Series) 'Virtuoso Cream' **new**	CRos
	- - 'Virtuoso Lavender' **new**	CRos
	- - 'Virtuoso Rose Compact' **new**	CRos
	- - 'Virtuoso White' **new**	CRos
	- 'White Carousel' (Carousel Series)	CRos EHyd LRHS NRHS
	sceptrum	CCCN CExl MGil SIvy SPlb SVen
	'Spice Island'	CBod CDor EBee ECtt EPfP EShb LCro LOPS LRHS LSou MHol MNrw NLar SEdd SPad SPer STPC WCot WRHF WSpi
*	***stewartii***	EWes NWad
	thapsi	EPPr EPfP
	- white-flowered	EPPr
	trojana	CFis GKev WWtn
	- 'Helen of Troy'	WHer WSpi
	× ***valinii*** 'Berry Canary'	CRos SPad SPoG WHil
	- FOXLIGHT PLUM GOLD ('Takfoplgo'PBR)	CWGN LCro LOPS
	- FOXLIGHT RUBY GLOW ('Takforugl'PBR) **new**	LSou WHil
§	- Illumination Series	EHyd LRHS SCob
§	- - 'Harkstead Apricot'	CCCN EBee EPfP MNHC NDov NHpl SEle
§	- - 'Harkstead Flame'PBR	EHyd LRHS MAvo MHol NHpl NRHS SPoG
	- - 'Harkstead Red' **new**	CCCN CSpe LSun MAvo MHol
	- - ILLUMINATION APRICOT	see *D.* × *valinii* 'Harkstead Apricot' (Illumination Series)
	- - ILLUMINATION CHERRY BRANDY	see *D.* × *valinii* ILLUMINATION RUBY SLIPPERS

- - ILLUMINATION FLAME — see *D.* × *valinii* 'Harkstead Flame' (Illumination Series)
- - ILLUMINATION PINK ('Tmdgfp001'PBR) — CAbb CDor EBee EPfP LBuc LCro LOPS MBros MHol MSCN NHpl NLar SPoG WCot
§ - - ILLUMINATION RUBY SLIPPERS ('Tmdg1204'PBR) — EBee EHyd EPfP LBuc LRHS MHol MNHC NDov NHpl NLar NRHS
viridiflora — CExl CSam CSpe GQue
'Walberton's Goldcrest' — see *D.* GOLDCREST

dill see *Anethum graveolens*

Dionaea ✿ (*Droseraceae*)

muscipula — CHew EECP LCro LOPS SHmp SPlb WSSs WTyc
- 'Akai Ryu' ♀H3 — SHmp WSSs
- 'All Green' — EECP
- 'B52' — EECP WSSs
- 'Big Mouth' — EECP
- 'Bimbo' — EECP
- 'Bohemian Garnet' — EECP WSSs
- 'Coquillage' — EECP
- 'Cross Teeth' **new** — CHew
- 'Darwin' — WSSs
- (Dentate Traps Group) 'Dentate Traps' — CHew WSSs
- 'Green Sawtooth' — EECP
- 'Harmony' — EECP
- 'Louchapates' — EECP
- 'Mk1979' — WSSs
- 'Red Piranha' — CHew
- 'Red Shark Teeth' — EECP
- 'Royal Red' — CHew WSSs
- 'Sawtooth' — EECP WSSs
- shark-toothed — EECP
- 'South West Giant' ♀H3 — WSSs
- 'Spider' — EECP
- 'Tiger Fangs' — WSSs
- 'Trichterfulle' — EECP

Dionysia (*Primulaceae*)

'Annielle' — EPot WAbe
aretioides ♀H4 — WAbe
- 'Alan Furness' — EPot
- 'Bevere' — EPot WAbe
bryoides — WAbe
'Charlson Emma' — EPot WAbe
'Charlson Gem' — EPot
'Charlson Jake' — WAbe
'Charlson Petite' — WAbe
'Charlson Pip' — WAbe
'Charlson Thomas' — EPot
'Corona' — WAbe
curviflora — WAbe
'Eric Watson' — WAbe
'Geist' — WAbe
'Inka Gold' **new** — WAbe
iranica **new** — EPot
janthina — WAbe
'Judith Bramley' — WAbe
'Mike Bramley' — WAbe
'Monika' — WAbe
'Pascal' — WAbe
sarvestanica — WAbe
tapetodes — EPot WAbe
- 'Brimstone' — WAbe
'Tess' — EPot WAbe
'Zdeněk Zvolánek' — WAbe

Dioon (*Zamiaceae*)

argenteum — CBrP
califanoi — CBrP
caputoi — CBrP
edule ♀H1b — CBrP SPlb
- var. ***angustifolium*** — CBrP
merolae — CBrP
rzedowskii — CBrP
spinulosum — CBrP CCCN

Dioscorea (*Dioscoreaceae*)

araucana — CPla
bulbifera **new** — SPlb
deltoidea — CExl
japonica — CAgr CLau LEdu
polystachya — CAgr CRHN GPoy LEdu
villosa — LEdu

Diosma (*Rutaceae*)

ericoides L. — SWvt
hirsuta 'Silver Flame' — CBod
'Pink Fountain' — see *Coleonema pulchellum* 'Pink Fountain'
'Sunset Gold' — see *Coleonema* 'Sunset Gold'

Diosphaera (*Campanulaceae*)

asperuloides — see *Trachelium asperuloides*

Diospyros (*Ebenaceae*)

austroafricana — SPlb
glabra — SVen
* ***hyrcanum*** — NLar
kaki (F) — CBcs CMCN ECrN IDee NLar WCot
- 'Fuyu' (F) — CAgr
- 'Kostata' (F) — CAgr
- 'Mazelii' (F) — CAgr WPGP
- 'Rojo Brillante' (F) — SVic
lotus — CAgr CBcs CMCN EBee LEdu NLar SPlb WKor WMat
- FMWJ 13164 — WCru
- PAB 10032 — LEdu WPGP
- (f) — IDee LMaj
- 'Albert' (m) — CAgr
- 'Browny' (f/F) — CAgr
lycioides — CPbh SPlb
'Mount Goverla' (F) — CAgr
'Nikita's Gift' (F) — CAgr
'Nikita's Russian' (F) — CAgr
'Nikshoo' (F) — CAgr
ramulosa — SPlb
rhombifolia — NLar
'Russian Beauty' (F) — CAgr
'Russian Red' (F) — CAgr
virginiana (F) — CBcs CMCN EBee IDee NLar SPlb WKor
- 'Morris Burton' (F) — CAgr
- 'Nc-10' (F) — CAgr

Dipelta (*Caprifoliaceae*)

floribunda ♀H5 — CBcs CExl CMCN EHyd ELan EPfP IArd IDee LRHS MBlu MGil SWvt WPGP
ventricosa — CBcs CExl EHyd EPfP IDee LRHS MBlu MGil NLar NOra SBrt SPoG WPGP
yunnanensis — CBcs CCCN CExl CTho EBee EHyd EPfP IArd IDee IMou LRHS MBNS NLar SMad SPoG SWvt WPGP WPav

Diphylleia (*Berberidaceae*)

cymosa	CAby ECha GEdr GKev LEdu LPla MNrw MRav SPhx WCot WCru
grayi	GEdr LEdu WCru
sinensis	CExl WCru

Diplacus see *Mimulus*

Dipladenia see *Mandevilla*

Diplarrena (*Iridaceae*)

§ ***latifolia***	CNor IBlr LRHS
moraea	CAby CElw CMac CSpe CTsd CWCL EBee GAbr IBlr ITim LEdu MBel WSHC
- ***minor***	IBlr
- 'Slieve Donard'	IBlr
- West Coast form	see *D. latifolia*

Diplopanax (*Cornaceae*)

stachyanthus B&SWJ 11803	WCru

Diplotaxis (*Brassicaceae*)

muralis	CLau
tenuifolia	CAgr CLau ENfk EWhm LCro LOPS MNHC SRms

Dipsacus (*Caprifoliaceae*)

asper PAB 8884	LEdu
dipsacoides new	LEdu WPGP
§ ***fullonum***	CBod CHab ENfk EPfP LCro LOPS MBow MNHC MPri NGrd NMir SDix SEdd SRms WHer WSFF WWild
inermis	CSam ECha NBid
japonicus HWJ 695	SPhx WCru
laciniatus	EBee
pilosus	CBgR NDov
pinnatifidus PAB 2845	LEdu
sativus	CWld
strigosus	SPhx
sylvestris	see *D. fullonum*

Dipteracanthus see *Ruellia*

Dipteronia (*Sapindaceae*)

sinensis	CBcs CMCN MBlu SMad WLov

Disa (*Orchidaceae*)

aurata	NDav
Bride's Dream gx	NDav
Child Safety Transvaal gx	NDav
- 'Sonia'	NDav
Colette Cywes gx 'Blush'	NDav
Constantia gx	NDav
Diores gx	NDav
- 'Inca City'	NDav
- 'Inca Gold'	NDav
- 'Inca Princess'	NDav
- 'Inca Warrior'	NDav
Diorosa gx	NDav
Foam gx	NDav
- 'Zoe'	NDav
Glasgow Orchid Conference gx	NDav
Ivan Watson gx	NDav
Kalahari Sands gx	NDav
- 'Tina'	NDav
Kewbett gx	NDav
- 'Pink Gem'	NDav
Kewdior gx	NDav
Kewensis gx 'Alice'	NDav
- 'Ann'	NDav
- 'May'	NDav
- 'Milkmaid'	NDav
- 'Ruth'	NDav
Reheat gx	NDav
Riette gx	NDav
Robert Parkinson gx	NDav
Sealord gx	NDav
Tracey Parkinson gx	NDav
tripetaloides	NDav
Unidiorosa gx 'Tracey'	NDav
uniflora	NDav SPlb
- carmine-flowered	NDav
- pink-flowered	NDav
- red-flowered	NDav
Unifoam gx	NDav
- 'Firebird'	NDav
Unilangley gx	NDav
Watsonii gx 'Bramley'	NDav
- 'Candy'	NDav
- 'Don'	NDav
- 'Sandra'	NDav

Disanthus (*Hamamelidaceae*)

cercidifolius ♀H5	CBcs CMCN CMac CRos EHyd EPfP GBin GKin IArd IMou LRHS MBlu MPkF NLar SPoG WMat WPGP
- 'Ena-nishiki' (v)	MBlu NLar WPGP
ovatifolius B&SWJ 11706	WCru
- FMWJ 13365	WCru
- WWJ 11933	WCru
- WWJ 11994	WCru

Discaria (*Rhamnaceae*)

chacaye	WPav

Dischidia (*Apocynaceae*)

ruscifolia	CDoC EShb

Diselma (*Cupressaceae*)

archeri 'Read Dwarf'	CKen

Disepalum (*Annonaceae*)

petelotii FMWJ 13375	WCru

Disporopsis (*Asparagaceae*)

sp.	WBor
B&SWJ 229 from Taiwan	WCru
B&SWJ 1864 from Taiwan	WCru
aspersa	CAvo CBro EPPr EPot ESwi EWld ITim LEdu MAvo MBriF MNrw NBir WCru WFar WPGP
- tall	CBct CExl ESwi WCru
bodinieri FMWJ 13457	WCru
- KWJ 12277	ESwi WCru
fuscopicta	CBct EPPr LEdu MAvo WCru
longifolia	IMou
- B&SWJ 5284	WCru
luzoniensis	IMou
- B&SWJ 3891	CBct CExl EPPr ESwi GEdr LEdu WCru
'Min Shan'	CExl ELon
* ***nova***	EPPr MAvo
§ ***pernyi***	Widely available
- B&SWJ 1864	EPPr GEdr
- 'Bill Baker'	CBct EBee EPPr ESwi LEdu MAvo WSHC

aff. ***pernyi*** MBriF NBPC WHil
'Shina-no-tsuki' see *Disporum bodinieri* 'Shina-no-tsuki'
taiwanensis CAvo EBee IMou LEdu
- B&SWJ 3388 CBct GEdr WCru
undulata CBct CSpe EMor EPPr EPot ESwi ILea IMou LEdu NBid SHar WCru WPGP

Disporum (*Colchicaceae*)

austrosinense IMou
bodinieri CBod CExl EMor EPfP GKev ILea
- DJHC 765 WCru
§ - 'Shina-no-tsuki' (v) IPot
cantoniense CBct IMou LEdu SDir WCru WFar WHil WPnP
- B&L 12512 CExl
- B&SWJ 1424 WCru
- B&SWJ 9715 WCru
- DJHC 98485 LEdu WPGP
- PAB 8339 LEdu
I - 'Aureovariegata' CBct EPfP ESwi LEdu WCot
- 'Blueberry Bere' LEdu
- var. ***cantoniense*** f. ***brunneum*** B&SWJ 5290 WCru
- 'Leigong' WPGP
- 'Moonlight'PBR (v) new CBct
- var. ***multiflorum*** B&SWJ 11252 WCru
- - B&SWJ 11291 WCru
- var. ***sikkimense*** B&SWJ 2337 WCru
- - B&SWJ 2358 LEdu WCru
- - PAB 13.1711 LEdu
- var. ***y-tiense*** HWJ 1045 WCru
hookeri see *Prosartes hookeri*
kawakamii B&SWJ 350 WCru
- RWJ 10103 CBct WCru
lanuginosum see *Prosartes lanuginosa*
leschenaultianum B&SWJ 9484 WCru
- B&SWJ 9505 WCru
leucanthum EBee ECha WCru
- B&SWJ 2389 WCru
longistylum EBee LEdu
- B&SWJ 2859 WCru
- BWJ 8128 WCru
- L 1564 CBct ESwi EWld LEdu WCru
- 'Green Giant' CBct CExl CMiW EBee EPfP GEdr GKev IDee ILea LEdu LPla LRHS MAvo MBel NHar NLar SHar WFar WSHC
- 'Night Heron' ♀H6 CDor CExl EHyd GKev IMou IPot LEdu LPla LRHS MAvo NRHS SHar WCot WFar
- 'Night Heron' seedlings CSpe
aff. ***longistylum*** NJM 11.011 WPGP
lutescens EBee EPot WCru WPGP
maculatum see *Prosartes maculata*
megalanthum CBct CBod CExl EMor GKev ILea LEdu NHar WCru WPGP
- CD&R 2412B CExl EBee
menziesii see *Prosartes smithii*
nantouense B&SWJ 359 LEdu WCru
- B&SWJ 6812 WCru
oreganum see *Prosartes hookeri* var. *oregana*
sessile EBee LEdu NBir WCru
- B&SWJ 2824 WCru
I - 'Aureovariegatum' (v) WCru
- 'Awa-no-tsuki' (v) GEdr
- 'Kinga' (v) GKev LEdu
- f. ***macrophyllum*** IMou
- - B&SWJ 4316 WCru
- 'Snow Stream' (v) GEdr WFar
- 'Variegatum' (v) CAby CDor CExl EBee ECha EHyd ELan ELon EMor EPPr EPfP ESwi IMou LEdu LRHS MNrw NBir NHpl NLar NQui NRHS SMad SPhx WCru WFar WPGP WSHC
- var. ***yakushimense*** LEdu
- yellow-margined variegated (v) GKev
shimadae B&SWJ 399 WCru
smilacinum NLar WCru
- B&SWJ 713 CBct WCru
* - 'Aureovariegatum' (v) EPot LEdu WCru
- 'Ki-naka-fu' (v) new WFar
- 'Kogane-tsuki' (v) GEdr
- 'Koutei' (v) new WFar
- pink-flowered CBct ESwi LEdu WCot WCru WSHC
- 'Roseum' GKev IPot
smithii see *Prosartes smithii*
taiwanense B&SWJ 1513 WCru
- B&SWJ 2018 WCru
tonkinense B&SWJ 11814 WCru
trabeculatum CBct CDor WCru
- 'Nakafu' EBee IMou WCru
trachycarpum see *Prosartes trachycarpa*
uniflorum CAby CAvo CBct CBor CRos EHyd EMor EPfP GKev LEdu LRHS MHid MHol MMrt MNrw NBid NRHS WSHC
- B&SWJ 651 CBct LEdu WCru
- B&SWJ 872 WCru
- B&SWJ 4100 WCru
- MSF 800 LEdu
viridescens CBct EBee EMor EPPr IMou LEdu WCru WPnP
- B&SWJ 4598 EPot ESwi WCru

Distyliopsis (*Hamamelidaceae*)

tutcheri CJun

Distylium (*Hamamelidaceae*)

myricoides NLar
racemosum CCCN CMac EBee EPfP MBlu NLar SSta WSHC

Dittrichia (*Asteraceae*)

viscosa WCot

Diuranthera see *Chlorophytum*

Dizygotheca see *Schefflera*

Docynia (*Rosaceae*)

delavayi new SPtp

Dodecatheon (*Primulaceae*)

alpinum GKev NHar
- subsp. ***alpinum*** EBee
amethystinum GKev
'Aphrodite'PBR ECtt MHol NLar
austrofrigidum GEdr SBrt WFar
clevelandii GEdr GKev WAbe
- subsp. ***insulare*** GKev
- subsp. ***patulum*** EHyd LRHS NRHS
'Comet' CBor WFar

conjugens GKev XEll
cusickii see *D. pulchellum* subsp. *cusickii*
dentatum 🏆H5 CPBP EBee GEdr LEdu NHar NRya SBrt WAbe WFar
- subsp. ***utahense*** GEdr NHar NRya WFar
frigidum GEdr GKev WAbe
§ ***jeffreyi*** CBod ECtt EHyd EPPr EPfP GEdr GKev LRHS MBNS MNrw NBPC NLar SRkn WFar
- subsp. ***pygmaeum*** EBee GKev
- 'Rotlicht' EHyd LRHS NRHS
§ ***meadia*** 🏆H5 Widely available
- from Cedar County, USA WAbe
- f. ***album*** 🏆H5 CBro CRos EHyd ELan EMor EPot GKev LEdu LRHS MBel NHol NHpl NRHS SDir SPer SWvt WFar WPnP WSpi WTyc
- 'Aphrodite' WFar
- 'Goliath' GAbr GWyn
- membranaceous WAbe
- 'Queen Victoria' LEdu NLar WFar
'Meteor' CBor WFar
pauciflorum misapplied see *D. pulchellum*
pauciflorum (Dur.) E. Greene see *D. meadia*
poeticum SPlb
§ ***pulchellum*** 🏆H5 EBee EHyd EWld GEdr GKev LLWG LRHS MNrw NRHS NRya WIce
- ***album*** GKev WCav
§ - subsp. ***cusickii*** LEdu
- subsp. ***pulchellum*** GKev
- - 'Red Wings' CBor ELan EPot GWyn LRHS NHpl NLar SPad WCav WTyc
- Radicatum Group **new** CRos
- 'Sooke Variety' WAbe
radicatum see *D. pulchellum*
'Stellar Pink' **new** GEdr
tetrandrum see *D. jeffreyi*

Dodonaea (*Sapindaceae*)

viscosa EPfP SPlb
- 'Purpurea' CBcs CBod CCht CExl CTsd EBee LRHS MGil MHtn SEdd SGsty SIvy SPoG SVen
- 'Red Wings' (f) SRkn

Doellingeria (*Asteraceae*)

scabra see *Aster scaber*
umbellata CBod CBre CKno ECha EPPr GQue LEdu MMuc MTis NBir NDov NLar WCot WOld WSpi
- 'Weisser Schirm' MNrw

Dolichandra (*Bignoniaceae*)

§ ***unguis-cati*** 🏆H3 CCCN CRHN EShb

Dolichos (*Papilionaceae*)

purpureus see *Lablab purpureus*

Dombeya (*Malvaceae*)

wallichii CCCN

Dondia see *Hacquetia*

Doodia ✿ (*Blechnaceae*)

aspera CAby CLAP NBro
- 'Rough Ruby' CAbb CMiW CTsd NBro SIvy SPad
§ ***caudata*** NBro
media CAbb CAby CBct CLAP CMiW CRos EBee EHyd EShb ISha LEdu LLWG LRHS MAsh NBro NRHS SPalm SPlb WCot
squarrosa see *D. caudata*

Dorema (*Apiaceae*)

ammoniacum **new** SPhx

Doronicum (*Asteraceae*)

austriacum CBod MSCN NBid
caucasicum see *D. orientale*
§ ***columnae*** CBcs
cordatum see *D. columnae*
§ × ***excelsum*** 'Harpur Crewe' EBee LEdu MRav NPer SHar
'Finesse' CRos EPfP GJos LRHS NRHS SRms
'Little Leo' CBod ELan EMor EPfP GJos GMaP LSRN NLar SCob SPoG SRms WFar
§ ***orientale*** EPfP GJos MBel MPri SPoG
- 'Leonardo' CBod CRos EHyd EPfP LRHS NGrd NRHS
- 'Magnificum' CBod CRos CSBt EHyd EMor EPfP GMaP LRHS NGBl NRHS SCob SPoG SRms WCAu WFar
pardalianches CFis CMea GAbr GJos WBrk WRHF
- 'Goldstrauss' EBee
plantagineum MMuc
- 'Excelsum' see *D.* × *excelsum* 'Harpur Crewe'

Doryanthes (*Doryanthaceae*)

palmeri CBrP CTsd

Dorycnium see *Lotus*

Douglasia see *Androsace*

vitaliana see *Vitaliana primuliflora*

Dovyalis (*Salicaceae*)

caffra (F) XBlo

Doxantha see *Macfadyena*

Draba (*Brassicaceae*)

acaulis WAbe
aizoides CRos EBou EHyd GJos LRHS NRHS SPlb SRms
aizoon see *D. lasiocarpa*
alpina **new** GKev
§ ***aspera*** GJos
athoa ITim
aurea var. ***leiocarpa*** ITim
bertolonii Boiss. see *D. loeseleurii*
bertolonii Nyman see *D. aspera*
breweri GJos
bruniifolia NSla
subsp. ***heterocoma***
var. ***heterocoma***
- subsp. ***olympica*** GJos
'Buttermilk' WAbe
compacta see *D. lasiocarpa* Compacta Group
* ***condensata*** GJos
cretica GJos ITim
cusickii GKev
cuspidata GJos
dedeana EPot GJos ITim
densifolia CPBP
gilliesii GJos
hispanica ITim
'John Saxton' EPot WAbe
kotschyi SPlb
§ ***lasiocarpa*** GJos XLum

§ - Compacta Group ITim
§ ***loeseleurii*** GJos
longisiliqua ♀H5 EPot WAbe
mollissima EPot SPlb WAbe
- 'Göteborg' EPot
nivalis GJos SPlb
norvegica GJos ITim
oligosperma EDAr GJos WAbe
ossetica WAbe
parnassica GJos
paysonii ITim
polytricha NSla
rigida var. ***bryoides*** compact EPot WAbe
* - var. ***imbricata*** NSla
rosularis EDAr EPot GJos WAbe
scardica see *D. lasiocarpa*
sphaeroides GJos NSla SPlb
yunnanensis WAbe

Dracaena ✿ (*Asparagaceae*)

aletriformis XBlo
cochinchinensis SPlb
draco ♀H1c CCCN CMCN EShb SPlb XBlo
fragrans (Compacta Group) 'Compacta' XBlo
- - 'White Jewel'PBR (v) new LCro LOPS
- Deremensis Group XBlo
- - 'J.A. Truffaut' XBlo
- - 'Lemon Lime' (v) ♀H1b LCro LOPS
- - 'Souvenir d'August de Schrijver' (v) XBlo
- 'Janet Craig' LCro LOPS
- 'Janet Lind' (v) new LCro LOPS
indivisa see *Cordyline indivisa*
'Lemon Lime Tips' XBlo
marginata (v) ♀H1b LCro LOPS XBlo
- 'Tricolor' (v) ♀H1b XBlo

Dracocephalum (*Lamiaceae*)

sp. XAbr
argunense GBin SPhx SRms
- 'Blue Carpet' NLar
- 'Fuji Blue' CExl EDAr EPfP EWes SBut SPoG WMal
- 'Fuji White' CExl EDAr SPhx
botryoides CPBP EDAr EPot SPhx
calophyllum GKev
forrestii GKev
grandiflorum CPla SPhx WCot XLum
moldavica SPhx
nutans SPhx
peregrinum 'Blue Dragon' SPhx
prattii see *Nepeta prattii*
rupestre CSpe SPhx
ruyschiana CFis MMrt SPhx XLum
- 'Blue Moon' CWCL
sibiricum see *Nepeta sibirica*
* ***tataricum*** EHyd LRHS
virginicum see *Physostegia virginiana*

Dracunculus (*Araceae*)

canariensis CBod ESwi WCot
muscivorus see *Helicodiceros muscivorus*
§ ***vulgaris*** CAby CRos EBee EHyd EPfP EPot ESwi GKev LRHS NRHS SEND SPlb WCot WHil
- white-flowered WCot

Dregea (*Apocynaceae*)

sinensis CBcs CCCN CRHN CRos EBee ECre ELan EPfP EShb EWes LRHS MRav NOra SEND SPer SPoG SWvt WPGP WSHC
- 'Brockhill Silver' EPfP LRHS SPoG SWvt
- 'Variegata' (v) EShb EWes

Drepanostachyum (*Poaceae*)

falconeri J.J.N. Campbell. ex D. McClintock see *Himalayacalamus falconeri*, *H. falconeri* 'Damarapa'
hookerianum see *Himalayacalamus hookerianus*
§ ***khasianum*** CExl

Drimiopsis (*Asparagaceae*)

maculata EShb GKev

Drimys (*Winteraceae*)

andina CExl MGil MMuc
aromatica see *Tasmannia lanceolata*
colorata see *Pseudowintera colorata*
granadensis var. ***grandiflora*** B&SWJ 10777 WCru
winteri ♀H4 CBcs CMac CRos CSBt CSde CTri EBee EHyd ELan EPfP GBin GKin LEdu LRHS LSRN MBlu MGil MGos MNrw NQui SArc SEle SGol SMad SPer SPlb SPoG SWvt WFar WPav
§ - var. ***chilensis*** CBcs CExl EHyd EPfP LRHS WCru WPGP
- Latifolia Group see *D. winteri* var. *chilensis*
- var. ***winteri*** SRms

Drosanthemum (*Aizoaceae*)

eburneum SSim
flammeum new SSim
floribundum SSim
hispidum CRos EHyd ELan EPot LRHS MAsh NRHS SPlb SPoG SSim
micans SSim

Drosera ✿ (*Droseraceae*)

adelae CHew
admirabilis CHew
aliciae ♀H3 CHew EECP SHmp
'Andromeda' new CHew
ascendens CHew
binata CHew EECP SHmp
§ - subsp. ***dichotoma*** ♀H3 SHmp
capensis CHew LCro LOPS SHmp SPlb
- 'Albino' ♀H3 CHew EECP SHmp
cuneifolia CHew
dichotoma see *D. binata* subsp. *dichotoma*
dichrosepala EECP
filiformis var. ***filiformis*** CHew EECP SHmp SPlb
- var. ***floridana*** new CHew
hamiltonii CHew
latifolia new CHew
madagascariensis SHmp
nidiformis CHew
regia new CHew
rotundifolia SHmp
schizandra new CHew
scorpioides EECP SHmp
slackii ♀H3 CHew
spatulata CHew SHmp

Drosophyllum (*Drosophyllaceae*)

	lusitanicum	CHew

Dryandra (*Proteaceae*)

	formosa	CPbh SPlb
	quercifolia	SPlb

Dryas (*Rosaceae*)

	drummondii	GAbr
§	***integrifolia***	WAbe
	- 'Greenland Green'	WAbe
	octopetala ♀H7	CMea CPla CRos EHyd GKev LRHS NChi NRHS SPoG SRms SWvt WAbe WHoo
§	- 'Minor' ♀H7	EPot WAbe
	× ***suendermannii*** ♀H7	EPot GBin GMaP NHar SGro WAbe
	tenella misapplied	see *D. octopetala* 'Minor'
	tenella Pursh	see *D. integrifolia*

Drynaria (*Polypodiaceae*)

	sp.	XBlo
	baronii	WCot

Dryopteris ✿ (*Dryopteridaceae*)

	aemula	CBdn EFer LEdu
§	***affinis*** ♀H5	CBdn CDor CLAP CMac CRos CWCL ECha EHyd EMor EPfP GMaP LBuc LRHS MAsh MCot MGos MMuc NRHS SCob SPer SPoG SRms WCot WFib WShi WSpi XLum
	- 'Angustata Crispa'	EBee MAsh SRms
	- subsp. ***cambrensis***	ISha
	- - 'Insubrica'	EFer
	- 'Congesta Cristata'	CWCL ECtt EFer GMaP SCob
	- Crispa Group	CBdn CBod CLAP EAJP EHyd EMor EPfP LRHS NRHS WBrk
§	- 'Crispa Gracilis' ♀H5	CAby CBod CLAP CMiW EHyd ELan ISha LRHS NBir NHol NLar NRHS
*	- 'Crispa Gracilis Congesta'	EMor LLWG MRav NGdn NWad WCot WFib
§	- 'Cristata' ♀H5	Widely available
	- 'Cristata Angustata' ♀H5	CLAP EFer ELan EMor EPfP LLWG NBid NBro NGdn NHol SCob WFib
	- 'Cristata Beeches'	EBee
	- 'Cristata The King'	see *D. affinis* 'Cristata'
	- 'Grandiceps Askew'	GBin WFib
	- 'Pinderi'	CAby CBdn CLAP EBee EMor EPfP ISha LEdu LPla MPie MPnt NLar NRHS SCob WCot WSpi
	- Polydactyla Group	SPlb
	- - 'Polydactyla Dadds'	CBdn CLAP EBee EMor NLar
	- - 'Polydactyla Mapplebeck' ♀H5	CLAP NBid WFib
	- 'Revolvens'	EFer
	atrata misapplied	see *D. cycadina*
	atrata (Wall. ex Kunze) Ching	CAby CDTJ CWCL EHyd ELan LLWG LRHS NLar NRHS SPoG XLum
	× ***australis***	CBdn CLAP EBee ISha
	austriaca	see *D. dilatata*
	buschiana	EBee EMor MRav NLar WCot
	carthusiana	EBee EFer NLar WSpi XLum
	- 'Cristata'	EFer
	celsa	EBee ISha
	championii	CBdn CCCN CLAP EBee EHyd ELan EMor ISha LRHS NBro NLar NRHS
	clintoniana	EBee ECtt EFer EHyd GQue ITim LPla LRHS MPie NRHS
	× ***complexa***	CLAP ISha
	- 'Stablerae' ♀H7	CLAP EFer GBin WFib
	- 'Stablerae' crisped ♀H7	WFib
	coreanomontana	EMor NLar
	crassirhizoma ♀H6	CCCN CLAP CRos EBee ECtt EHyd ELan EMor EPfP GAbr ISha LEdu LPla LRHS LSun NLar NRHS SEdd SMad SPoG WCot WRHF WSpi
	cristata	CLAP CWCL EBee EPfP XLum
§	***cycadina*** ♀H4	CBcs CBdn CLAP CRos CTsd EBee EFer EHyd ELan EMor EPfP EShb ISha LEdu LRHS MAsh MGos NBid NBir NRHS SCob SPlb WCot WFib WLov
§	***dilatata*** ♀H6	CLAP CRos ECha EFer EHyd ELan EPfP LRHS MAsh MMuc MRav NRHS WFib WHal WShi
	- 'Crispa Whiteside' ♀H6	CAby CBdn CDor CLAP CMiW CRos CWCL EBee EFer EHyd ELan EMor EPfP EShb LRHS MAsh MHost MRav NBro NLar NRHS SPlb SPoG WFib WLov
	- 'Cristata'	LSun
	- 'Grandiceps'	CMac EFer WFib
	- 'Jimmy Dyce'	CBdn CLAP CRos EBee EHyd ISha LEdu LRHS NRHS
I	- 'Lepidota Crispa'	EHyd NRHS
	- 'Lepidota Crispa Cristata'	CLAP EBee
	- 'Lepidota Cristata' ♀H6	CBdn CMiW CWCL ELan EMor GKev LEdu NBro WFib
*	- 'Recurvata'	CLAP NLar
	erythrosora ♀H4	Widely available
	- from Guizhou, China	WPGP
	- 'Brilliance' ♀H5	CAby CBcs CBct CBdn CBod CCCN CDoC CLAP CRos EBee ECtt EHyd EPot GQue ISha LEdu LLWG LPla LRHS LSun MAsh MAvo MHol MPie NCou NRHS SEdd WCot WRHF
	- dwarf **new**	CBod CMiW LEdu
	- var. ***koidzumiana***	CLAP EHyd LEdu LRHS MAsh NRHS WCot
	- var. ***prolifica***	CBdn CBod CLAP CRos EBee EHyd ELan EMor EPfP GMaP ISha LEdu LRHS MAsh MGos NBir NLar NRHS SPoG WFar WFib WLov
	- 'Radiance'	ISha
	filix-mas ♀H7	Widely available
	- 'Barnesii'	CLAP CRos CWCL EFer EHyd ELan ISha LRHS NLar NRHS SEND SPlb WFar
	- 'Crispa'	CRos EHyd EPfP LEdu LRHS MAsh MPnt NRHS WFib
	- 'Crispa Congesta'	see *D. affinis* 'Crispa Gracilis'
	- 'Crispa Cristata' ♀H7	CBod CChe CLAP CRos CWCL EBee ECtt EFer EHyd ELan EPfP GMaP GWyn LLWG LRHS MAsh NBid NBir NBro NRHS SCob SPoG WFib XLum
	- 'Crispatissima'	EBee
	- 'Cristata' ♀H7	CLAP EBee ECtt EFer ELan EMor LCro LLWG LOPS NBro SEND
	- Cristata Group	EFer
*	- - 'Cristata Grandiceps'	EFer
	- - 'Cristata Jackson'	SPlb
	- - 'Cristata Martindale'	CLAP EBee NBid WFib
	- - 'Fred Jackson'	WFib
	- 'Depauperata'	CLAP

	- 'Furcans'	CBdn CRos EBee ECtt EHyd ELan LRHS NRHS
	- 'Grandiceps Wills' 🏆H7	NBid WFib
	- 'Linearis'	EFer EHyd ELan ISha LRHS MCot MGos NRHS WFib
	- 'Linearis Polydactyla' 🏆H7	CAby CBdn CBod CDor CLAP CMac CRos CWCL EFer EHyd ELan EPPr EPfP EShb EWTr LEdu LRHS MMuc MRav NHol NLar NRHS SCob SEND SPoG WPnP XLum
	- 'Parsley'	CLAP EBee ISha
*	- Polydactyla Group	ECha MRav
I	- 'Revolvens'	WFib
	formosana	CBdn WPGP
	goldieana	CDTJ CLAP CRos EBee ECha ECtt EFer EHyd ELan EMor EWTr GMaP ISha LLWG LRHS MAsh NBid NBir NLar NRHS WFar WFib WPnP WSpi XLum
	hirtipes misapplied	see *D. cycadina*
	intermedia	CBdn EBee ISha
	kuratae	CBdn NBro NLar WPGP
	labordei	CLAP EBee EHyd ISha LRHS
	lacera	ISha
	lepidopoda	CAby CBcs CBdn CDoC CDor CLAP CRos ECtt EHyd EMor ITim LEdu LPla LRHS MAsh MPie NBro NRHS SPoG WCot WPGP WRHF WSpi
	ludoviciana	CRos EHyd ISha LRHS MAsh NLar NRHS WSpi
	marginalis	CDTJ EHyd EMor LRHS NLar NRHS SCob
	namegatae	WCot
	oreades	WCot
	pseudofilix-mas	ISha
	pseudomas	see *D. affinis*
	pulcherrima	CLAP CRos EHyd LRHS NRHS
	pycnopteroides	CLAP
	× ***remota***	CLAP EBee EFer ISha
	× ***separabilis***	ISha
	sieboldii 🏆H6	Widely available
	stewartii	CAby CBdn CLAP EMor NBro NLar
	subarborea	EBee
	submontana	CRos EHyd LRHS MAsh NRHS
	tokyoensis 🏆H6	CDTJ CLAP EHyd ISha LRHS NLar NRHS WSpi
	uniformis	CLAP EFer
	wallichiana 🏆H5	Widely available

Duchesnea (*Rosaceae*)

	chrysantha	see *D. indica*
§	***indica***	GJos MRav SEND WOut XLum
§	- 'Harlequin' (v)	CExl
	- 'Variegata'	see *D. indica* 'Harlequin'

Dudleya (*Crassulaceae*)

	calcicola	SPlb
	cymosa	SPlb
	lanceolata	SPlb

Dugaldia (*Asteraceae*)

	hoopesii	see *Hymenoxys hoopesii*

Dulichium (*Cyperaceae*)

	arundinaceum	LLWG
	- 'Tigress'	LLWG

Dunalia (*Solanaceae*)

	australis	see *Iochroma australe*

Duranta (*Verbenaceae*)

§	***erecta***	CCCN
§	- 'Geisha Girl'	CCCN EShb
	- 'Sapphire Swirl'	see *D. erecta* 'Geisha Girl'
	- 'Variegata' (v)	CCCN
	- white-flowered	SVen
	plumieri	see *D. erecta*
	repens	see *D. erecta*
	serratifolia	CCCN

Duvernoia see *Justicia*

Dyckia (*Bromeliaceae*)

	brevifolia	WCot
	'Burgundy Ice'	WCot
	'Cherry Coke'	WCot
	floribunda	EShb
	frigida	WCot WGrn
	goehringii	WCot
	jonesiana	WCot
	leptostachya	SEND SPlb WCot WGrn
	'Morris Hobbs'	WCot
	remotiflora	SChr

Dypsis (*Arecaceae*)

§	***decaryi***	CCCN SPlb XBlo
	lutescens 🏆H1a	LCro LOPS XBlo

Dysosma see *Podophyllum*

Dystaenia (*Apiaceae*)

	takesimana	EBee LEdu SPhx

E

Ecballium (*Cucurbitaceae*)

	elaterium	CDTJ LEdu WCot WPGP
	- 'Lahij'	WPGP

Eccremocarpus (*Bignoniaceae*)

	scaber	CBcs CWCL ELan EShb NPer SPlb SPoG
	- 'Carmineus'	EPfP
	- cream-flowered	NLar
	- red-flowered	CWCL NLar
	- 'Tangerine'	CSpe

Echeveria ✿ (*Crassulaceae*)

	sp.	LCro LOPS
	affinis	CDTJ MHer SEdd
	agavoides 🏆H2	CDTJ CDoC LCro LOPS MRav SIvy
	- 'Ebony'	WCot WOld
	- 'Lipstick'	WCot
	- 'Red Edge'	SSim
	albicans	SPlb
	alpina	see *E. secunda*
	ballsii	WCot
	bicolor B&SWJ 14388	WCru
	- B&SWJ 14849 **new**	WCru
*	'Black Knight'	MCot SEdd SSim
*	'Black Prince'	CDTJ CDoC ELan LCro LOPS NPer SPlb WCot WOld
	'Blue Bird' **new**	CDoC
	'Blue Waves'	WCot
*	***cana***	CDTJ NCft SEdd SIvy SSim
	cante 🏆H2	SPlb

chihuahuaensis 'Raspberry Dip' **new**	WOld
coccinea	ELan
'Corymbosa'	WCot
'Curly Locks'	ECtt SEdd SIvy WCot WGrn
cuspidata* × *setosa var. ***ciliata***	SSim
derenbergii 🏆H2	MHCG
× ***derosa***	CDTJ
'Duchess of Nuremberg'	SEdd SIvy SPlb SSim
'Easter Bonnet'	SSim
'Echoc' **new**	SPad
elegans 🏆H2	CDTJ CDoC EPfP EWes LSun NCft NWad SEND SIvy SPlb SSim WSMil
'Fireball' **new**	WOld
'Frida Kahlo' **new**	WOld
'Ghost Buster'	WPGP
'Giant Blue' **new**	CDoC
* × ***gilva*** 'Red'	LSun MHol SEdd WCot
glauca Baker	see *E. secunda* var. *glauca*
'Green Pearl' PBR **new**	LCro LOPS
lilacina 🏆H2	CDoC EShb LCro LOPS NCft SEdd SPlb SSim
'Mahogany'	WCot WGrn
'Mauna Loa'	SEdd WCot WGrn
maxonii B&SWJ 10396	WCru
'Mexecensis' **new**	WOld
minima 🏆H2	SPlb
montana B&SWJ 10277	WCru
nodulosa	SIvy WCot
- 'Nicolas Bravo'	SSim
peacockii	MHer SPlb
'Perle von Nürnberg' 🏆H2	CAbb CCBP CDoC EShb LCro LOPS SMad
prolifica	SPlb
pulidonis 🏆H2	MHer SSim
pulvinata 🏆H2	MHCG
I - 'Rubra'	SPlb
purpusorum	CDoC SPlb
quitensis B&SWJ 14393	WCru
'Ramillette'	WMal
'Red Prince' **new**	CDoC
rosea 🏆H2	MHer SPlb SSim WCot WMal
runyonii 🏆H2	CDoC
- 'Topsy Turvy' 🏆H2	CDTJ MHer SEdd SIvy SSim WCot
'Scorpio'	WOld
§ ***secunda***	CAbb SPlb WOld
§ - var. ***glauca***	CDTJ CDoC ELan EShb GAbr NCft SIvy WCav WPGP
- - 'Compton Carousel' 🏆H2	SIvy SSim WCot WOld
* - - 'Gigantea'	NPer
setosa 🏆H2	CDTJ NCft SIvy
- var. ***ciliata***	EShb
shaviana 🏆H2	CDTJ SPlb SSim WCot
subsessilis	WCot
'Tarantula' **new**	WOld
'Violet Queen'	EShb
'Zodiac' **new**	WOld

Echeveria × *Pachyphytum* see × *Pachyveria*

Echeveria × *Sedum* see × *Sedeveria*

Echinacea (*Asteraceae*)

§ 'Adam Saul'	EHyd LRHS
§ 'After Midnight' PBR (Big Sky Series)	ECtt
'Aloha' PBR	EMor IPot LRHS NLar NRHS SPad SPoG WCAu
'Amazing Dream' PBR	CAbb CWGN EBee ECtt LCro LOPS LRHS NRHS
angustifolia	EMor ENfk EPfP GPoy LRHS SPhx XAbr
'Big Kahuna' PBR	CAbb CBcs CWGN EBee ECtt IPot LRHS SCob SPad
'Buttercream'	EBee
'Butterfly Kisses' PBR (d)	CPla LCro LOPS
'Caribbean Green'	EBee
'Cherry Fluff' (Cone-fections Series) (d)	CWGN
CHEYENNE SPIRIT (mixed)	CDor EAJP ELan EMor EPfP LEdu MBros MHol SPhx WFar WHil WTor
'Chiquita' PBR (Prairie Pixie Series)	CKno EHyd LRHS LSou SPoG
CHUNKY PURPLE **new**	MHtn
'Cinnamon Cupcake' PBR	EBee SPoG
'Cleopatra' PBR	CBod CWGN EBee EPfP NLar SPoG WCot
'Colorburst Orange' (Colorburst Series) (d)	CWGN
CRAZY PINK	see *E.* 'Adam Saul'
CRAZY WHITE	see *E.* 'Noam Saul'
'Daydream' PBR	CWGN EBee WSpi
DELICIOUS CANDY ('Noortdeli' PBR)	CWGN LPla NLar WCot WHil WTor WTyc
(Dixie Series) 'Dixie Belle'	CAbb
- 'Dixie Scarlet' PBR	CAbb
(Double Scoop Series) DOUBLE SCOOP BUBBLEGUM ('Balscblum' PBR) (d)	EBee MHol
- DOUBLE SCOOP LEMON CREME ('Balsclemc') (d)	MHol
- DOUBLE SCOOP MANDARIN ('Balscandin') (d)	EBee
- DOUBLE SCOOP ORANGEBERRY ('Balscoberr' PBR) (d)	CBod EBee
- DOUBLE SCOOP RASPBERRY ('Balsceras' PBR) (d)	EBee MHol
'Eccentric' PBR (d)	CWGN EWTr LRHS SMad WSpi WTor
'Eccentric Yellow' (d) **new**	CWGN
'Emily Saul'	see *E.* 'After Midnight'
'Evan Saul'	see *E.* 'Sundown'
EVENING GLOW ('Eglow' PBR)	CWGN EBee WSpi WWtn
'Ferris Wheel' (Carnival Series)	WSpi
'Flame Thrower' PBR	EWTr LCro LOPS
'Fourth of July' PBR	EHyd NRHS
'Funky White' **new**	CWGN WTor
'Funky Yellow'	CAby CBod CWGN WCot
'Gemini Pink'	EHyd LRHS
'Golden Skipper'	ECtt EHyd LRHS MAvo NRHS
'Green Envy' PBR	CBcs CWGN EBee EHyd ELan ELon EMor EPfP GMaP LCro LOPS LRHS MBel MNrw NLar NRHS SMad WCAu WTor
'Greenline' PBR	EBee
'Guava Ice' PBR	CDor CWCL EMor WSpi
§ 'Harvest Moon' PBR (Big Sky Series)	EBee ECtt EPfP EWTr LRHS MBNS SWvt
'Honeydew' PBR	EBee
'Hot Lava' PBR	CWGN EBee EHyd EWTr LCro LRHS NRHS SCob
'Hot Papaya' PBR (d)	CWCL CWGN ECtt ELan EMor EPfP LCro LOPS SCob SMad SPoG SWvt

'Hot Summer'PBR	CBcs CWCL CWGN EBee EHyd LEdu LRHS SGbt
'Indian Summer'	EBee
'Irresistible'PBR (d)	CWGN EBee EHyd LCro LOPS LRHS
'Julia'PBR	ECtt
'Jupiter' (Big Sky Series)	ECtt
'Katie Saul'	see *E.* 'Summer Sky'
'Leilani'PBR	CAbb WCAu
'Mac 'n' Cheese'PBR	EBee LRHS SCob
'Mama Mia'PBR	CAbb CWGN LCro LOPS LRHS SGbt
MANGO MEADOWBRITE ('CBG Cone3')	EHyd LRHS
'Marmalade'PBR	CBcs CDor CWCL CWGN EBee EMor EWTr SCob SPad SPoG WCAu
'Matthew Saul'	see *E.* 'Harvest Moon'
'Maui Sunshine'PBR	CAbb EBee NLar
'Meditation'PBR	WCot
'Meteor Red'PBR (Meteor Series)	CPla CRos ECtt EHyd LRHS NRHS
(Mooodz Series) MOOODZ AWAKE ('Hilmoooawak')	NRHS
- MOOODZ COSY ('Hilmooocosy') **new**	CRos
- MOOODZ SATISFY ('Hilmoosati') **new**	CRos
- MOOODZ SHINY ('Hilmoooshin')	LRHS NRHS
'Mozzarella' (d)	EBee
§ 'Noam Saul'	EHyd LRHS
'Now Cheesier'PBR	EHyd LCro LOPS LRHS SMad
ORANGE PASSION ('Orpass'PBR)	CWGN EBee EWTr LRHS NLar WCAu
'Orange Skipper' (Butterfly Series)	CRos EHyd MAvo NRHS
'Pacific Summer'	CWGN WSpi
pallida	CCBP CKno CRos CSam CSpe EAJP EBee EHyd ELan EMor EPfP EShb EWTr GPoy GQue LCro LOPS LRHS MBel MGos NDov NGdn NRHS SPer SPhx SRms SWvt WCAu WSpi XLum
- 'Hula Dancer'	CDor EAJP GWyn NGdn SPeP SPhx
'Papallo Compact White' (Papallo Series)	NLar
paradoxa	CBcs CRos EHyd ELan EMor EPfP LPla LRHS MBel MCot NDov NGdn NRHS NSti SPer SPhx SPlb SWvt WCAu XLum
PICCOLINO ('Noortpicco'PBR)	LRHS
'Pineapple Sundae'PBR	CWGN EBee
'Pink Tip' **new**	LPla
PIXIE MEADOWBRITE ('CBG Cone 2')	CWGN
'Postman' (Butterfly Series)	SPad SPoG WTor
'Purple Emperor'PBR	ECtt
§ ***purpurea***	Widely available
- 'Alaska'PBR	NGdn
I - 'Alba'	CRos EHyd EPfP LRHS NRHS WCot WFar XLum
- 'Amber Mist'PBR (Mistical Series)	EBee
- 'Augustkönigin'	CKno EBee LRHS WCAu WCot
- 'Avalanche'PBR	CBod CWGN EBee EMor LPla
- 'Baby Swan Pink'	CBod CRos EHyd LRHS NLar NRHS
- 'Baby Swan White'	CBod CRos EHyd ELan EPfP LRHS NLar NRHS
- Bressingham hybrids	CBod CRos EHyd LRHS MArl MRav NRHS SGbt SPer
- 'Catharina'PBR	CWGN EBee ECtt
- 'Coconut Lime'PBR	CWGN ECul EPfP LCro LOPS WCAu WTor
- DOPPELGANGER	see *E. purpurea* 'Doubledecker'
§ - 'Doubledecker'	CBod CNor EBee ELan EPfP GWyn NGdn SGbt XLum
- ELTON KNIGHT ('Elbrook'PBR) ♀H5	LRHS STPC SWvt WCot
- 'Fancy Frills'	WCot
- 'Fatal Attraction'PBR	CBcs CBod CPar CRos CWGN ECtt EHyd ELan EMor EPfP EWTr GMaP LEdu LPla LRHS LSRN LSou LSun MBNS MBel MRav NLar NRHS SCob SEdd SPad SPoG SWvt WCot
- 'Firebird'PBR	CBcs ECtt LEdu LRHS SGbt SPoG
- 'Fragrant Angel'PBR	ECtt LRHS MBNS MBel NLar SWvt
- 'Green Eyes'	EBee
- 'Green Jewel'PBR	CBcs CBod CDor CPar CWGN EBee ECul EHyd EMor EPfP LCro LOPS LPla LRHS MBel MCot MNrw NLar NRHS NSti SEdd SGbt SPad WCAu WCot
- 'Green Twister' **new**	CBod CWGN EAJP EWTr
- 'Gum Drop'PBR	LRHS
- 'Happy Star'	CDor CRos EAJP EBee EHyd LRHS NRHS SGbt SPhx
- 'Hope'PBR	EBee EHyd LPla LRHS MBel NLar WCAu
- 'Jade'	EBee LSRN MBNS NLar
- 'JS Purple Prairie'	IPot
- 'Kim's Knee High'PBR	CKno ELan EPfP GMaP LRHS MBel MTin NGdn NLar SPer SPoG SWvt
- 'Kim's Mop Head'	CRos EPfP LRHS MRav NLar WCot
§ - 'Leuchtstern'	CKno EHyd ELan EPfP LRHS NBir NGdn NRHS XLum
- 'Lilliput'PBR	NLar
- 'Little Magnus'PBR	EHyd LRHS SCob SPoG
- 'Lucky Star'	EHyd ELan EPfP LRHS SPhx
- 'Magnus'	Widely available
- 'Magnus Superior'	CBod CDor CKno CMea CRos CSpe EAJP EBee EHyd LRHS LSou LSun MBel MHer MNrw NDov NRHS SBut SGbt SPhx SWvt
- 'Maxima'	LRHS
- 'Merlot'PBR	LRHS NLar
- 'Milkshake'PBR	CWGN EBee ECul EMor LRHS WSpi
- MISTRAL ('Echmis'PBR)	EHyd LRHS
- 'Pica Bella'	CRos CWGN EHyd EPfP LRHS MNHC NRHS SPad
- 'Pink Double Delight'PBR	LCro LOPS MRav NGdn
- 'Pink Glow'	NDov
- 'Pink Poodle'PBR	EBee
- 'Pink Sorbet'PBR	SCob
- (PowWow Series) POWWOW WHITE ('Pas709018')	CBod CWGN LRHS SCob SPoG WTor
- - POWWOW WILD BERRY ('Pas702917'PBR)	CBod CRos CWGN EHyd EPfP LRHS MBros MHol NRHS SPoG WFar WTor
- 'Prairie Splendor'	EPfP LRHS MWat SPhx
- 'Primadonna Deep Rose'	ELan LEdu NGBl SVic
- 'Primadonna White'	CSpe EHyd EPfP LRHS SRms
- 'Purity'PBR	ECtt LRHS SPoG

- 'Razzmatazz'PBR (d)	CMac EBee ECtt ELan MRav NGdn NSti SWvt WCot
- 'Red Knee High'PBR	NLar
- 'Robert Bloom'	NBir SWvt WSpi
- 'Rubinglow'	ECtt LCro LOPS LSou MGil NBir NDov NLar SWvt
- 'Rubinstern'	Widely available
- 'Ruby Giant' ♀H5	CDor CKno ECtt EHyd ELan GBin GMaP GQue LEdu LRHS LSRN LSou LSun MBel MTis NLar NRHS SEdd SGbt WCot
- 'Sensation Pink'PBR	CAby CPar CWGN EHyd IPot LRHS LSou MHol NRHS
- 'Southern Belle'PBR	CDor CNor CWCL CWGN ELan EMor IPot MBNS SMad WSpi
- 'Summer Salsa'PBR	CWGN EBee WCot
- 'The King'	CRos EHyd LRHS NGdn NLar NRHS WSpi
- 'Tom Thumb'	EBee
- 'Vintage Wine'PBR	CRos ECtt ELan EPfP LCro LOPS LRHS NLar NSti SPer SPoG SWvt WCAu
- 'Virgin'PBR	EBee LCro LOPS MAvo MBel NDov NLar SCob WCAu
- 'White Double Delight'PBR (d)	SPad
- 'White Lustre'	ECha SRms
- WHITE NATALIE ('Norwhinat'PBR)	EBee
- 'White Swan'	Widely available
'Quills and Thrills'PBR (Prairie Pillars Series)	MMrt
'Raspberry Truffle'PBR	EBee EPfP EWTr
ROBIN HOOD ('JS Roho') **new**	IPot
(Secret Series) 'Secret Affair' **new**	EHyd
- 'Secret Passion'PBR (d)	CWGN EBee LRHS SGbt
- 'Secret Romance'PBR	LRHS WCAu
simulata	EAJP EBee
'Solar Flare'PBR (Big Sky Series)	EBee
(Sombrero Series) SOMBRERO ADOBE ORANGE ('Balsomador'PBR)	CBod
- SOMBRERO BAJA BURGUNDY ('Balsombabur'PBR)	MHol
- SOMBRERO BLANCO ('Balsomblanc')	CRos LSou MHol
- SOMBRERO FLAMENCO ORANGE ('Balsomenco'PBR)	LRHS
- SOMBRERO HOT CORAL ('Balsomcor'PBR)	NLar
- SOMBRERO LEMON YELLOW ('Balsomemy'PBR)	CBod
- SOMBRERO SALSA RED ('Balsomsed'PBR)	CBcs CBod LRHS
'Starlight'	see *E. purpurea* 'Leuchtstern'
'Strawberry Shortcake'	EBee
'Summer Cloud'	CRos CWGN EHyd LCro LOPS LRHS LSou NRHS SMad WTor
'Summer Cocktail'PBR	CWGN EHyd ELan LCro LOPS LRHS SPoG WHil WTor
'Summer Passion'	CWGN
§ 'Summer Sky'PBR (Big Sky Series)	EHyd EPfP LRHS
'Summer Sun'PBR	LRHS SPoG
§ 'Sundown'PBR (Big Sky Series)	CPar EBee EHyd EMor EPfP EWTr LCro LOPS LRHS NLar NSti SCob SGbt SWvt WCAu
'Sunrise'PBR (Big Sky Series)	EBee EHyd ELan EMor EPfP GMaP LRHS MBNS NLar NSti SCob SGbt SPoG SWvt WCAu WSpi
(SunSeekers Series) SUNSEEKERS ORANGE ('Apecssior'PBR)	EBee WTor
- SUNSEEKERS PURPLE ('Apecssipu') **new**	CRos
- SUNSEEKERS RED ('Apecssired') **new**	CRos MHtn
- SUNSEEKERS WHITE ('Apecssiwh')	EBee
- SUNSEEKERS YELLOW ('Apecssiye'PBR)	CRos EBee
'Sunset'PBR (Big Sky Series)	ELan LSRN SWvt WSpi
'Supreme Cantaloupe' (d)	CWGN SPad
'Tangerine Dream'PBR	EBee EHyd EMor EPfP LRHS SCob WCAu WSpi
tennesseensis 'Rocky Top'	EHyd GAbr LRHS MBNS MGos SBut
'Tiki Torch'PBR	CBcs EHyd LCro LOPS LRHS SCob SEdd SPer SPoG SWvt WCot WTor
'Tomato Soup'PBR	CBcs CBod CDor CRos CSpe CWGN EBee ECtt ELan EMor EPfP EWTr GMaP LCro LEdu LOPS LPla LRHS MNrw NLar SCob SEdd SGbt SPoG SWvt WCAu WCot WHil
'Twilight'PBR (Big Sky Series)	LRHS
'White Meditation'PBR	CBcs EHyd EMor EPfP LRHS NRHS SPoG
'Yellow Spider'	EBee

Echinodorus (*Alismataceae*)

grandiflorus **new**	XBlo
'Harbich' **new**	XBlo
palifolius **new**	XBlo
'Rosé' **new**	XBlo
'Ruben' **new**	XBlo
subalatus **new**	XBlo
uruguayensis **new**	XBlo

Echinops (*Asteraceae*)

albus	see *E.* 'Nivalis'
§ ***bannaticus***	CBcs CMac CPla NBid WWtn
* - 'Albus'	WCAu
- 'Blue Globe'	CRos CWld EHyd ELan EPfP GBin LRHS LSRN MBel MBriF MCot MGos MHol NGdn NHol NRHS SCob SGbt SPoG WCAu WFar WHoo
- 'Blue Glow'	CBod NLar SPhx
- 'Star Frost'	CBod CRos EBee EHyd ELan EPfP LRHS NLar NRHS SCob SPhx SRms WFar
- 'Taplow Blue'	Widely available
- 'The Giant' **new**	CBod
giganteus	CWld
maracandicus	LPla WCot
§ 'Nivalis'	CBre EHyd LRHS
ritro misapplied	see *E. bannaticus*
§ ***ritro*** L. ♀H7	Widely available
- 'Blue Cloud'	EBee
- subsp. ***ruthenicus*** ♀H7	GKev MRav WCot
- - 'Platinum Blue'	CRos ECtt ELan ELon EMor LRHS NLar SPhx SRms

	- 'Veitch's Blue' misapplied	see *E. ritro* L.
	- 'Veitch's Blue'	Widely available
	sphaerocephalus	NBir NDov SPlb
	- 'Arctic Glow'	CRos CWld EBee ECha ECtt EHyd ELan EMor EPfP GMaP LRHS MBriF MCot MPri MTis NDov NGdn NLar NRHS SCob SGbt SPeP SPer SPlb SPoG SWvt WFar
	tjanschanicus	CPla CRos EBee EHyd GPSL LRHS MMuc NLar NRHS SEND

Echium ✿ (*Boraginaceae*)

	aculeatum	MEch
	amoenum	CSpe EHyd LRHS MEch NRHS SPhx
	angustifolium Mill.	MEch SPhx
	asperrimum	MEch
	bethencourtianum	MEch SVen
	'Blue Steeple'	CPla CWCL MEch
	boissieri	CCCN MEch
	brevirame	MEch
	callithyrsum	MEch
	candicans ♀H1c	CAbb CBcs CBod CCCN CPbh CPla CSde CTrC CTsd ECre ELan MEch SEND SVen WOut WSMil
	- 'Dwarf Blue'	CCCN
	decaisnei	MEch SVen
	subsp. ***decaisnei***	
	fastuosum	CCht CDoC SArc SEdd WABo WSMil
	gentianoides	MEch SPlb SVen
	giganteum	MEch
	hierrense	MEch
	italicum	CCCN MEch
	lusitanicum	CCCN
	nervosum	MEch
	onosmifolium	MEch SVen
	'Pearce's Grey' **new**	SVen
	pininana ♀H3	CAbb CBcs CBod CCht CPbh CPla CTrC CTsd ECre ELan MEch SArc SChr SEND SMad SPhx SVen WABo WSMil
	- 'Snow Tower'	CBod CCCN CDTJ CPla CTrC CWCL ELan LRHS MEch
	pininana × 'Red Rocket'	CPla
	pininana × ***wildpretii***	CPla CTrC MEch
	'Pink Fountain'	CBod CCCN CDTJ CPla CTrC CWCL ELan GJos LRHS MEch
	'Red Rocket'	CBcs CBod CCCN CDTJ SMad
	rosulatum	CCCN
	russicum	CBod CCCN CSpe EHyd ELan LPot LRHS MEch MNHC SBut SPad SPhx SPlb XEll
	sabulicola	MEch
	simplex ♀H1c	MEch
	strictum	CCCN MEch
	sventenii	MEch SPlb
	tuberculatum	EWld LRHS MEch SPhx
	virescens	MEch SVen
	vulcanorum	MEch
	vulgare	CBod CCCN CHab CSpe ELan ENfk LCro LOPS MEch MHer MNHC NGrd NMir SBut SPhx WABo WOut WSFF WTre WWild
	- from Armenia	WCot
	- 'Blue Bedder' ♀H7	CSpe MEch SPhx WSFF
	- 'Pink Bedder'	MEch
	- 'White Bedder'	MEch
	webbii	MEch MMrt SVen
	wildpretii ♀H2	CCCN CDTJ CDoC CPla CTsd MEch SPhx SPlb SVen WABo WSMil
	- subsp. ***wildpretii***	MEch

Ectotropis (*Aizoaceae*)

§	***alpina***	EHyd EWes GEdr LRHS
	seanii-hoganii	ECtt EPot EWes GEdr NSla WAbe

Edgeworthia (*Thymelaeaceae*)

§	***chrysantha***	CBcs CCCN CExl CRos EBee EHyd ELan EPfP LCro LEdu LMaj LOPS LRHS MGos NLar NRHS SArc SavN SCob SEdd SGsty SPer SPoG SWeb WHwl
	- 'Frederic' **new**	CDoC
I	- 'Grandiflora'	CBcs CDoC EBee ELon ESwi GBin IDee LRHS MGos MPkF NLar SMad WHwl WPGP
	- 'Nanjing Gold'	MPkF
§	- 'Red Dragon'	IMou LCro LOPS LRHS MPkF NLar SMad SPer SavN WHwl
	- f. ***rubra*** hort.	see *E. chrysantha* 'Red Dragon'
	- 'Winter Liebe'	LRHS NLar WHwl
	papyrifera	see *E. chrysantha*

Edraianthus (*Campanulaceae*)

	croaticus	see *E. graminifolius*
	dalmaticus	GKev
	- ***albus***	GKev
	dinaricus	GKev
	glisicii	GKev
§	***graminifolius***	GEdr GKev
	- from Durmitor, Montenegro	NSla
	- subsp. ***graminifolius***	GKev
	niveus	GKev NSla
§	***pumilio*** ♀H5	EPot GEdr GJos GKev NSla SRms WAbe
	- silver-leaved	EPot GKev
	serbicus	GKev
§	***serpyllifolius***	EPot GKev
	- 'Major'	GKev
	sutjeskae	GKev
	tenuifolius	GKev
	wettsteinii	GKev
	zogovicii	see *E. graminifolius*

Egeria (*Hydrocharitaceae*)

§	***densa***	CBen

Ehretia (*Boraginaceae*)

	anacua	CBcs
	rigida	SPlb

Elaeagnus (*Elaeagnaceae*)

	angustifolia	CAgr CArg CBcs EPfP IDee LMaj MCoo MGos NLar SPer SRms WKor XSen
	- Caspica Group	see *E.* 'Quicksilver'
	argentea Pursh	see *E. commutata*
§	***commutata***	CBcs CMac ECrN EPfP MBlu MCoo NLar SPer
I	- 'Aurea'	NLar
	- 'Zempin'	EPfP LRHS NLar
	× ***ebbingei***	see *E.* × *submacrophylla*
	macrophylla	EBee EPfP LRHS
	multiflora	MBlu NLar WPGP
	- 'Sweet Scarlet'	CAgr
	parvifolia	CCCN ELan
	pungens 'Argenteovariegata'	see *E. pungens* 'Variegata'
	- 'Aureovariegata'	see *E. pungens* 'Maculata'
	- 'Dicksonii' (v)	EHyd LRHS NLar SLon SPer SRms WFar

	- 'Forest Gold' (v)	EHyd EPfP LRHS
	- 'Frederici' (v)	CBcs CCCN CDoC CMac EBee EHyd ELan LRHS MAsh MRav NLar SCob SPer SWvt WAvo
	- 'Hosoba-fukurin' (v)	EBee ELan EPfP NLar NOra SLon
§	- 'Maculata' (v)	Widely available
§	- 'Variegata' (v)	CBcs CMac SPer SavN
§	'Quicksilver'	Widely available
§	× ***submacrophylla*** ♀H5	Widely available
	- 'Coastal Gold' (v)	CBcs CBod CCoa CDoC CSde EBee EPfP LSRN MGos SGol SRms WAvo WFar WRHF
I	- 'Compacta'	CBod CCCN CCoa EBee ECrN ELan LSou MGos SCob SGsty
	- 'Gilt Edge' (v) ♀H5	Widely available
	- GOLD SPLASH ('Lannou') (v)	CMac EPfP SGol SWvt
	- 'Limelight' (v)	Widely available
	- 'Moonlight'	EPfP MAsh
	- 'Salcombe Seedling'	CCCN
	- 'Svelte Edge'	NLar
	- 'Viveleg'PBR (v)	CCVT CDoC CRos EHyd ELan EPfP LMaj LRHS NLar NRHS SCob SEWo
	umbellata	CBcs CExl EBee EPfP IDee LEdu MBlu NLar SPer WKor WLov WSHC
	- 'Amber' (F)	CAgr NLar
	- 'Big Red' (F)	CAgr
	- var. ***borealis*** 'Polar Lights'	NLar
	- 'Brilliant Rose' (F)	CAgr
	- 'Garnet' (F)	CAgr
	- 'Hidden Springs' (F)	CAgr LEdu
	- 'Jewel' (F)	CAgr
	- 'Late Scarlet' (F)	CAgr
	- 'Newgate' (F)	CAgr
	- 'Red Cascade' (F)	CAgr LEdu MBlu NLar
	- var. ***rotundifolia*** CWJ 12835	WCru
	- 'Ruby' (F)	CAgr LEdu NLar
	- 'Sweet 'n' Tart' (F)	CAgr LEdu WLov

Elaeocarpus (*Elaeocarpaceae*)

sylvestris var. ***ellipticus***	LEdu WPGP

elderberry see *Sambucus nigra*

Elegia (*Restionaceae*)

capensis	CCCN CCtw CDTJ CExl CPbh CTrC MPkF SPlb WPGP
cuspidata	CCtw
elephantina	CCht CCtw CPbh CTrC LRHS
equisetacea	CCtw CPbh
fistulosa	CCtw
grandis	CCtw SPlb
macrocarpa	CCCN CPbh SPlb
mucronata	CCtw
tectorum ♀H2	CBod CCtw CPbh CTrC LRHS SPlb SPoG WSMil
- dwarf	CPbh
- 'Fish Hoek'	CCtw CPbh

Eleocharis (*Cyperaceae*)

acicularis	LLWG
palustris	LLWG
vivipara	XBlo

Elettaria (*Zingiberaceae*)

cardamomum	EShb GPoy LEdu SPre WJek

Eleutherococcus ✿ (*Araliaceae*)

	from Manipur, India	WPGP
	divaricatus B&SWJ 5027	WCru
	giraldii BWJ 8091	WCru
	hypoleucus B&SWJ 5532	WCru
	aff. ***leucorrhizus*** PAB 8119	WPGP
	pictus	see *Kalopanax septemlobus*
	senticosus	GPoy LEdu
	- B&SWJ 4568	WCru
	septemlobus	see *Kalopanax septemlobus*
	sessiliflorus B&SWJ 4528	WCru
	- B&SWJ 8457	WCru
	- B&SWJ 8618	WCru
	sieboldianus	MRav SEND
	- 'Variegatus' (v)	CCCN ELan ELon EPfP EShb ESwi LRHS MGil MRav NLar SPoG WCFE WSHC
	trifoliatus PAB 7113	LEdu
	- RWJ 10108	WCru

Ellisiophyllum (*Plantaginaceae*)

pinnatum B&SWJ 197	LEdu WCru

Elodea (*Hydrocharitaceae*)

canadensis	LLWG NBir WMAq
densa	see *Egeria densa*

Elsholtzia (*Lamiaceae*)

flava PAB 13.012	WPGP
stauntonii	CBcs CBod EBee ECha ELan GPoy LEdu LRHS MGil MHer MNrw NLar NQui SPhx SRms SWvt WBor WHer WHil WJek XLum

Elymus (*Poaceae*)

	arenarius	see *Leymus arenarius*
	canadensis	EPPr
	- 'Icy Blue' **new**	SMea
	cinereus from Washington State, USA	SPeP
	glaucus misapplied	see *E. hispidus*
§	***hispidus*** ♀H6	CBod EPPr MBlu NDov SCob SPer WCot
§	***magellanicus***	Widely available
	- 'Blue Sword'	EHyd ELan LRHS MGos NRHS SPtp SRkn SRms
	riparius	EPPr
	villosus	EPPr
	- var. ***arkansanus***	EPPr
	virginicus	EPPr SPhx

Embothrium ✿ (*Proteaceae*)

coccineum	CBcs CPla EHyd EPfP GBin LRHS MGil SPlb WAbe WPGP WPav
- Lanceolatum Group	CBcs CEnd CTrC CTsd EBee EHyd EPfP LRHS MBlu SAko SArc SIvy SSta SWvt WLov
- - 'Inca Flame'	CBrac CCCN CDoC CJun CTrC EHyd EPfP LRHS SWvt
- Longifolium Group	CCCN EPfP IBlr WPGP

Emilia (*Asteraceae*)

coccinea	CSpe

Emmenopterys (*Rubiaceae*)

henryi	CBcs CMCN EPfP IMou MBlu NLar

emperor's mint see *Micromeria*

Empetrum (*Ericaceae*)

nigrum	GPoy WKor
rubrum	MGil

Empodium (*Hypoxidaceae*)

plicatum	CBor

Encephalartos ✿ (*Zamiaceae*)

altensteinii	CBrP
ferox	CBrP
horridus	CBrP
lebomboensis	CBrP
lehmannii	CBrP
natalensis	CBrP

endive see AGM Vegetables Section

Endymion see *Hyacinthoides*

Engelmannia (*Asteraceae*)

peristenia	WHil

Enkianthus ✿ (*Ericaceae*)

campanulatus 🏆H5	Widely available
- var. ***campanulatus*** f. ***albiflorus***	CBcs GKin NLar SEdd
- 'Miyama-beni' **new**	NLar
I - 'Pagoda'	CBcs IArd IDee NLar SAko SReu
- var. ***palibinii***	CBcs CRos EHyd EPfP GGGa GKin LRHS MAsh MMrt NLar
- 'Red Bells'	CBcs EPfP GKin MAsh NLar SGol SWvt WFar
- 'Red Velvet'	CBcs GKin NLar
- 'Ruby Glow'	CBcs CDoC NLar SAko
- 'Showy Lantern'	NLar
- var. ***sikokianus***	NLar
- 'Sinsetu'	NLar
- 'Tokyo Masquerade' (v)	CRos EHyd LRHS SPoG
- 'Venus'	CBcs GKin NLar
- 'Victoria'	CBcs IArd NLar
- 'Wallaby'	CBcs IDee NLar
cernuus f. ***rubens*** 🏆H5	CBcs GGGa NLar
chinensis	CBcs CRos EHyd EPfP LRHS MAsh SPoG
deflexus	CBcs CRos EHyd IArd IDee LRHS WPGP
I 'Pagoda Red'	LRHS
perulatus 🏆H5	CBcs CCCN EBee EPfP MGil MGos SPer
serrulatus	GGGa

Ennealophus (*Iridaceae*)

fimbriatus	CBor GKev

Ensete (*Musaceae*)

gilletii	XBlo
- from Malawi	XBlo
- from Mozambique	XBlo
glaucum	CDTJ CTsd
§ ***ventricosum*** 🏆H2	CCCN CDTJ XBlo
§ - 'Maurelii' 🏆H2	CCCN CCht CDTJ CDoC CSBt CTsd ESwi LCro LOPS SChr SDix SEND SGsty SPoG WSMil
- 'Rubrum'	see *E. ventricosum* 'Maurelii'
- 'Tandarra Red'	CAbb

Entelea (*Malvaceae*)

arborescens	EShb SPlb

Eomecon (*Papaveraceae*)

chionantha	CBor CExl CMiW CPla CSam EBee EWld GAbr GEdr LEdu MAvo MPie MRav NBro NHpl NQui SBrt WCru WFar WPGP WPnP XLum

Epacris (*Ericaceae*)

serpyllifolia	WThu

Ephedra (*Ephedraceae*)

sp.	MPie SArc
andina	IMou
chilensis	GKev
distachya	GPoy WKor
equisetina RCB/TQ K-1	WCot
fedtschenkoi	GKev
fragilis	XSen
gerardiana	CRos LEdu LRHS
- CC 3925	WCot
- var. ***sikkimensis***	WOld
§ ***major***	XSen
monosperma	WThu
nebrodensis	see *E. major*
nevadensis	GPoy

Epilobium (*Onagraceae*)

angustifolium	see *Chamaenerion angustifolium*
- f. ***leucanthum***	see *Chamaenerion angustifolium* 'Album'
californicum misapplied	see *Zauschneria californica*
canum	see *Zauschneria cana*
dodonaei	see *Chamaenerion dodonaei*
fleischeri	see *Chamaenerion fleischeri*
garrettii	see *Zauschneria californica* subsp. *garrettii*
glabellum misapplied	NSla
glabellum G. Forst.	MMuc WKif
microphyllum	see *Zauschneria cana*
rosmarinifolium	see *Chamaenerion dodonaei*
septentrionale	see *Zauschneria septentrionalis*
villosum	see *Zauschneria californica* subsp. *mexicana*
'White Wonder Bells' PBR	GWyn

Epimedium ✿ (*Berberidaceae*)

from Jian Xi, China	GEdr
from Yunnan, China	WPGP
acuminatum	CAby CSam CWCL ESMi GEdr GPSL LEdu MNrw NLar WFar WPGP WSHC
- CC 031207	XPou
- L 575	CElw CExl
- 'Galaxy'	CExl CJun CMil LEdu
- 'Night Mistress'	ESMi GPSL IMou LEdu SPVi WPGP XPou
- 'Quinquin'	IMou
- yellow-flowered	WPGP
- - CC 011415	CSta XPou
'Akebono'	Widely available
ALABASTER ('Conalba')	EBee ELan GPSL MAvo MBel MTis
alpinum	CBod CFis CMac CWCL EBee EHyd EPfP EPot GBin GKev GLog LEdu LRHS MHer NChi NRHS SHar SPer SRms WFar XLum
- 'Samobor' **new**	LEdu
'Amanogawa'	CAby CJun CMil GEdr LEdu XPou
'Amber Queen' PBR	CBcs CBod CMil CSpe CSta CWCL CWGN EBee EMor EPfP EWTr GEdr GGGa IMou LSun

	MBel MMrt MNrw NLar NSti NWad SEdd SPVi SPoG SWvt WCAu WCot WFar WPnP XLum
'André Charlier' **new**	CElw CSta
'Anju'	GEdr
'Arctic Wings'PBR	CMil CSta CWCL EBee EPfP GEdr NGdn SMHy SPVi SWvt
'Asiatic Hybrid'	CJun WHal
'Autumn Raspberry'	CJun
baojingense	XPou
'Beni-goromo'	GEdr
'Beni-kujaku'	CAby CJun EBee EMor GEdr GGGa GPSL MHol WFar
'Beni-yushima'	GEdr
'Bieke'	SMHy
'Black Sea'	CAby CElw CJun CMil CSpe CWCL EBee EMor EPPr EPot ESMi EWTr GBin GPSL IMou LEdu LPla LRHS MAvo MBriF MNrw MPnt NLar SPVi WBor WFar WHil WHoo XPou
brachyrrhizum	CAby CExl CJun GPSL NLar
- CPC 940447	XPou
brevicornu	GEdr WPGP
- Og 82.010	CAby CExl CJun XPou
- Og 88.010	CJun SPVi XPou
'Buckland Buzz'	EBee
'Buckland Spider'	CBor CFis CSta EBee EPPr MNrw WCot WFar WPGP
'Buff Beauty' **new**	ESMi
'Buttered Popcorn'	EBee
campanulatum	CAby
- Og 93.087	CExl CJun EBee
× ***cantabrigiense***	CBro CDor CMac CWCL ECtt EHyd EPPr GGGa GKev GMaP GPSL ILea LPla LRHS MRav NHpl NLar SRms XLum
chlorandrum	CAby EBee LEdu WPGP
- Og 94.003	XPou
creeping yellow	EBee EMor EWTr MNrw WHil
cremeum	see *E. grandiflorum* subsp. *koreanum*
'Dark Secret'	ESMi
'Darrell's Pink'	EBee
davidii	CBor CMil EBee EMor EPPr ESMi GEdr LEdu MNrw NLar SPVi WHal WHoo WPGP WSHC
- CPC 960079	CExl XPou
- EMR 4125	CElw CExl CJun XPou
- dwarf	CAby CExl
diphyllum	CExl CTsd EBee EPfP GEdr WHal WPGP XPou
- dwarf white	CSam
- pink-flowered	XPou
- 'Roseum' **new**	SEdd
dolichostemon	CBod CElw GPSL IMou
- Og 81.010	CJun WPGP XPou
'Domino'	CMil ESMi GPSL LEdu SPVi WPGP XPou
ecalcaratum	CAby CMil EBee LEdu WPGP
- Og 93.082	CExl CJun XPou
- spurred	XPou
'Egret'	CAby CMil CSta EBee LEdu SMHy WPGP
elongatum	IMou
- CC 012906	XPou
'Emperor'	see *E.* 'Phoenix'
'Enchantress'	CElw CJun CMiW CMil EMor ESMi EWld MBel MNrw NLar SPVi WHal

epsteinii	CAby CDor CMil EBee EPPr ESMi EWld GEdr LEdu MNrw SBrt WCot WPGP WSHC
- CPC 940347	CElw CExl CJun XPou
fangii	CExl
- CC 022008	XPou
- Og	XPou
fargesii	CAby CExl EBee GEdr LEdu MNrw WCAu WPGP WSHC
- 'Pink Constellation'	CAby CExl CJun CMil CSta EBee GEdr ITim LEdu MNrw SGro WPGP XPou
'Fire Dragon'PBR	CBor CWCL ECtt EPfP GEdr MBNS MNrw NLar SPoG WFar
flavum	EBee WPGP
- Og 92.036	CExl CJun EBee XPou
'Flowers of Sulphur'PBR	CSta EBee EMor EPfP GEdr SPVi WFar
franchetii	CAby CElw CExl CTsd ELon GEdr
- 'Brimstone Butterfly'	CAby CBor CExl CFis CJun EPPr ESMi GEdr GPSL LEdu NLar SPVi WCot WHoo WPGP WSpi XPou
'Fukujuji'	GEdr
'Golden Eagle'	CElw CExl CJun EBee EWes MNrw SPVi
§ ***grandiflorum*** 𝕐H5	CBcs CElw CRos CTri CTsd CWCL ELan ELon EMor EPfP EWTr GLog LRHS NBir NHpl NLar SPVi SPer WCAu WPnP
- 'Agaki-Zakura' **new**	CSta SPVi XPou
- 'Akakage'	CExl
- 'Beni-chidori'	CJun GEdr
- 'Bicolor Giant'	XPou
- 'Bronze Trim' **new**	SMHy
- 'Circe'	SPVi XPou
- var. ***coelestre***	XPou
- 'Cranberry Sparkle'	EBee
- 'Crimson Beauty'	CAby CJun ECha NLar WHal WHoo WSHC
- 'Dark Beauty'	SMad WHil
- dwarf, pink-flowered **new**	SMHy
- 'Elfenkönigin'	EBee LRHS NLar
- f. ***flavescens*** Aomori forms	XPou
- - Number 1	XPou
- 'French Braid'	EBee
- 'Freya'	CExl EBee SMHy WSHC XPou
- 'Freya Mk II'	SMHy
- subsp. ***grandiflorum***	GGGa
§ - var. ***higoense***	CJun GEdr WHal WPGP
- - 'Bandit'	CWCL GEdr GPSL SPVi XPou
- - 'Saturn'	CMil XPou
- 'Jennie Maillard'	ELon ESMi WCot
- 'Koji'	EBee NLar WHil WSHC
§ - subsp. ***koreanum***	ECha ESMi GEdr
- 'Kotobuki'	XPou
- 'Kourin'	CSta GEdr
- 'La Rocaille'	CAby CElw EWld SMHy SPVi XPou
- lilac-flowered	CAby WHal
- 'Lilafee'	Widely available
- 'Lilipes' **new**	SEdd
- 'Mount Kitadake'	SPVi WAbe XPou
- 'Mugawa-gen-pan'	XPou
- 'Nanum' 𝕐H5	CAby CJun EBee EMor EPot ESMi EWTr MCot MNrw NHar NWad SMHy WAbe WPGP XPou
- pink-flowered	MCot
- 'Princess Susan'	XPou

- 'Purple Pixie'[PBR]	CBod CDTJ CWCL ECtt EMor EPed GPSL LSou MBel MHol NLar SCob WCAu WFar WHil
- 'Purple Prince'	CExl CMil EBee WPGP XPou
- 'Queen Esta'	CAby CExl CJun CMil EBee ESMi LEdu MNrw MRav WPGP WSHC XPou
- 'Red Beauty'	Widely available
- 'Red Queen'	WCAu
- 'Rose Queen' ♀[H5]	CAby CSam CWCL EBee ELan ELon EMor EPfP ESMi LEdu LRHS MNrw MRav NBir NSti SPVi SWvt WFar WPGP
- 'Roseum'	CBod CMac CMil GMaP GPSL SWvt
- 'Rubinkrone'	CWCL GMaP IMou LRHS MNrw
- 'Sayuri' **new**	XPou
- 'Sirius'	CAby CJun
- 'Tancho'	XPou
- var. ***thunbergianum*** **new**	CSta
- f. ***violaceum***	CElw CJun EBee WCFE
- 'Waterfall' **new**	CSta
- 'White Beauty'	WSHC
- 'White Queen' ♀[H5]	CElw CJun EBee EPPr ESMi LRHS MBel SMHy WCot WHal XPou
- 'White Winkie' **new**	SMHy
- 'Wildside Red'	CJun
- 'Yellow Princess'	CAby CElw CJun EBee XPou
- 'Yubae'	CSta GEdr
'Hagoromo'	GEdr
'Hakubai'	GEdr
'Harugasumi'	GEdr
'Heavenly Purple'	CJun
higoense	see *E. grandiflorum* var. *higoense*
'Hina Matsuri'	GEdr
hunanense	XPou
ilicifolium	CAby CJun LEdu WPGP XPou
'Jean O'Neill'	CAby CMil CSta EPPr EPri LEdu WCot WPGP WSHC
'Jenny Pym'	EBee
'Jujisei'	XPou
'Kaguyahime'	CElw CJun CMil EPPr GPSL LEdu WSHC
'Kibana Genpei'	XPou
'King Prawn'	CSta LEdu SMHy WPGP
'Knight Star'	CSta ESMi
'Kodai Murasaki'	XPou
'Koki'	CBor GEdr
koreanum 'Harold Epstein'	XPou
'Korin'	SPVi XPou
'Koshino-Shina' **new**	XPou
'Kotobuki'	GEdr
latisepalum	CMil EBee ESMi GEdr LEdu MNrw WCot WSHC XPou
- Og 91.002	CJun
'Lemon Meringue Pie'	CJun
'Lemon Zest'	EBee ESMi XPou
leptorrhizum	CAby CDor CElw CExl CJun CWCL EBee ELon EPPr ESMi EWld GEdr IMou LEdu MNrw NLar SBrt WCot WHal
- Og Y44	CExl WSHC XPou
- 'Mariko'	CAby CExl CJun CMil LEdu MNrw XPou
lishihchenii	CExl CJun CMiW GEdr WPGP
- CC 96024	SPVi XPou
'Little Shrimp'	CJun CTri EBee EHyd ELon GMaP GPSL LRHS MNrw NLar WSHC
macranthum	see *E. grandiflorum*
macrosepalum	CElw GEdr GPSL WPGP XPou
'Mandarin Star'	CWCL EBee EMor ESMi GEdr GPSL
'Marchant's Sulphur Queen'	SMHy
'Marchant's Twin Set'	SMHy
membranaceum	CMil EBee ESMi GEdr LEdu WHal WPGP XEll XPou
- Og 93.047	CExl CJun EPPr GEdr LEdu
mikinorii	CExl GEdr
- CC 990001	LEdu WPGP XPou
'Milky Way'	MNrw
'Mine-no-fubuki'	GEdr
'Miyako'	XPou
'Moonlight'	XPou
'Myojo'	EBee GEdr
myrianthum	CAby CJun EBee GEdr GPSL LEdu WPGP XPou
'Never the Red Rooster' **new**	CSta
ogisui	CAby CDor CElw CMil ESMi IMou LEdu MRav SMHy SPVi WPGP XPou
- Og 91.001	CExl CJun EBee MNrw
- 'Diane'	LEdu SPVi XPou
§ × ***omeiense*** 'Akame'	CAby CExl CJun CMil EPPr GEdr LEdu MNrw SPVi XPou
- 'Emei Shan'	see *E.* × *omeiense* 'Akame'
- 'Myriad Years'	SPVi XPou
- 'Pale Fire Sibling'	CJun CMil GEdr
- 'Stormcloud'	CAby CElw CExl CJun CMiW CMil EBee EPPr IMou LEdu XPou
'Pathfinder'	EBee ESMi
pauciflorum	EBee EPPr GEdr LEdu LPla WPGP XPou
- Og 92.123	CExl CJun
× ***perralchicum***	CAby CBro CJun CTri ECha GKev NLar WSHC
- 'Fröhnleiten'	Widely available
- 'Lichtenberg'	EBee EWes
- 'Nachfolger'	SPVi
- 'Wisley'	CDor CElw CJun EWes SPVi
perralderianum	CMac CSam CSta CWCL EBee GMaP MBel MCot MNrw SRms WHal WPnP
- 'Weihenstephan'	CRos CWCL LRHS NLar WPnP
aff. ***perralderianum***	MPnt
'Perrine's Pink' (Magique Elfes Series)	WCot
'Persian Carpet'	CMil
§ 'Phoenix'	CAby CExl CMil CSta ESMi WCot
'Pink Champagne'	CSta EPfP ESMi GEdr LEdu NBPC SCob SMad SPVi WCot WFar WPGP XPou
'Pink Elf'[PBR]	CMil CSta CWCL CWGN EBee EMor EPfP GBin GEdr GPSL MBNS MBriF MNrw NGdn NLar NSti SMad SPVi SRms WCAu WFar WPnP
pinnatum	CBod EBee GMaP MBel WHal XLum
§ - subsp. ***colchicum*** ♀[H7]	CJun CWCL ELan EMor EPfP EWTr GLog GQue LEdu LRHS MCot MRav NGdn NLar SCob SDix SPer WCAu WCot WFar WPnP WSpi XEll
- - L 321	WPGP
- - 'Thunderbolt'	EBee
- ***elegans***	see *E. pinnatum* subsp. *colchicum*
platypetalum	CAby ESMi IMou SBrt WCot
- Og 93.085	CExl CJun EBee XPou
'Prince Shrimp'	SMHy
pubescens	CAby
- CC 022556 from Shaanxi, China	XPou

- Og 91.003	CExl CJun EBee WPGP
pubigerum	CAby CDor CJun CRos CSam CWCL EBee EMor ESMi GGGa GLog ILea LEdu LPla LRHS MAsh MMuc NHpl NLar SEND SIvy SRms SWvt WCAu WHal WSpi XEll
qingchengshanense 03124	XPou
'Red Maximum'	ESMi LEdu SPVi WCot WPGP XPou
reticulatum	GEdr
rhizomatosum	CAby CDor EPPr ESMi GEdr GMaP WPGP WSHC
- Og 92.114	CJun LEdu WCot WPGP XPou
'Rhubarb and Custard' new	ESMi
'Royal Purple'	XPou
× ***rubrum*** ♀H7	Widely available
- 'Galadriel'	CBor EMor ESMi GBin WCAu WHil WHoo
- 'Sweetheart'	GEdr
sagittatum 'Warlord'	WPGP XPou
'Sakura-maru'	CBor GEdr
'Sam Taylor' new	SPVi XPou
'Sasaki'	CBor CWCL EPot ESMi GBin GPSL NLar WHil XEll XPou
sempervirens	CAby CJun WHal
- 'Candy Hearts' new	WCot
- 'Creamsickle' (v)	GEdr
- 'Mars'	XPou
- 'Okuda's White'	EBee XPou
- 'Violet Queen'	XPou
× ***setosum***	CJun ESMi NLar WHal
'Shiho'	CWCL EBee GEdr GPSL MAvo NLar
shuichengense CC 030175	XPou
'Simple Beauty' new	CSta
'Sphinx Twinkler'	see *E.* 'Spine Tingler'
§ 'Spine Tingler'	Widely available
'Spinners'	EBee ESMi WCot
'Starcloud'	EBee
stellulatum	GEdr
- long-leaved	ESMi XPou
- 'Wudang Star'	CExl CJun CMil CRos EBee EPot EWes GPSL IMou ITim LEdu LRHS MCot SPVi WFar WSHC XPou
- 'Yukiko'	XPou
'Sunshowers'	CSta
sutchuenense CC 990394	XPou
'Suzuka'	GEdr LEdu WPGP
'Tama-no-genpei'	CJun CSta GEdr LEdu WCot
'Tanima-no-yuki'	GEdr
'The Giant'	SPVi WCot WPGP XPou
'Togen'	WCot XPou
'Tokiwa-gozen'	GEdr
'Totnes Turbo'	CSta EBee ESMi
trifoliolatobinatum CC 950046	LEdu XPou
truncatum CC 030557	XPou
'Valor' new	WCot
× ***versicolor***	CExl EShb SSut
- 'Cherry Tart'	EBee ESMi XPou
- 'Cupreum'	CFis CJun CWCL EMor LEdu LRHS SPVi WCAu WHil
§ - 'Discolor'	CAby CElw CFis CMiW CSta ECha EPPr NBir SMHy WCot XPou
- 'Neosulphureum'	CAby CBro CWCL EBee EPPr LRHS WFar WPGP WSHC WThu
- 'Sulphureum' ♀H7	Widely available
- 'Versicolor'	see *E.* × *versicolor* 'Discolor'
× ***warleyense***	Widely available
- 'Orangekönigin'	Widely available
'Wildside Amber' new	CSta
'Wildside Ruby'	CMil ESMi
'William Stearn'	CExl CJun CSta GEdr SPVi WCot WPGP XPou
'Windfire'	EBee
wushanense	CAby EBee EPPr ESMi GEdr LEdu XPou
- CC 14193 new	WPGP
- Og 93.019	CExl CJun WPGP XPou
- 'Caramel'	CAby CExl CJun CMil CSta EBee GEdr GPSL LEdu WCAu WCot WSHC XPou
- 'Cardiff Star' new	CSta
- 'Sandy Claws'	CSta SPVi WCot
- spiny-leaved	CMil EBee ESMi SPVi WCot WFar
- - CC 014631	WPGP XPou
'Yachimata-hime'	GEdr
'Yokihi'	CSta GEdr SPVi XPou
× ***youngianum*** 'Beni-kujaku'	EWTr WFar XPou
- 'Capella'	XPou
- 'Fairy Dust'	EBee
- 'Grape Fizz'	EBee
- 'Marchacos Sprite'	EBee
- 'Merlin'	CDor CElw CJun CMil CWCL EBee EMor EPPr EPfP ESMi GEdr GGGa GPSL LSou MBel NLar NSti WHal WSHC
- 'Niveum' ♀H5	Widely available
- 'Roseum'	CDor CRos CSta CWCL EMor EPfP EShb GKev GKin LRHS LSRN MAsh MBel MCot MRav NHpl NLar NRHS NSti SCob SEdd SPer SPlb SRms SWvt WPnP
- 'Ruby Tuesday'	EBee
- 'Shien'	XPou
- 'Shikinomai'	CExl CJun
- 'Tamabotan'	CAby CMil GEdr MNrw MRav XPou
§ - 'Typicum'	CElw MCot WSHC
- 'Yenomoto'	CJun
- 'Youngianum'	see *E.* × *youngianum* 'Typicum'
zhushanense	CAby EBee ESMi LEdu WCot WPGP
- CC 02885	XPou
- CC 022403	SPVi XPou

Epipactis (*Orchidaceae*)

Catalina gx	CJun MNrw
gigantea	CJun CPla EBee ECha ELan EWld GBin GEdr LRHS MHer MNrw MRav NDav WPGP
- 'Serpentine Night'	CJun
gigantea × ***palustris***	see *E.* Sabine gx
helleborine	WHer
Lizzy Lou gx	CJun
Lowland Legacy gx	CJun
- 'Edelstein'	MNrw WFar
palustris	ECha EWat GBin IPot LRHS MBNS MNrw WHer WPnP
Passionata gx Light Royals Group	CJun
Renate gx	CJun
royleana	CJun GEdr
§ **Sabine gx**	CAby CJun
- 'Frankfurt'	MNrw WFar

Epipremnum (*Araceae*)

§ ***aureum*** ♀H1b	LOPS
pinnatum 'Marble Queen' (v)	XBlo

Episcia (*Gesneriaceae*)

dianthiflora	WDib
'San Miguel'	WDib

Equisetum ✿ (*Equisetaceae*)

'Bandit' (v)	CNat MAvo SMad WPGP
× ***bowmanii***	CNat
* ***camtschatcense***	CBod EShb SArc SMad SPlb WSMil XLum
fluviatile	CNat
giganteum	LLWG
hyemale	CBen CTsd EWat GQue LLWG LRHS MAvo MMuc NBro NPer NSti SPlb WCot WWtn XLum
§ - var. ***affine***	CBdn CNat EBee ELan LEdu WMAq WPGP
- var. ***robustum***	see *E. hyemale* var. *affine*
ramosissimum var. ***japonicum***	WPGP
scirpoides	EFer LLWG MWts NPer NWad WMAq XLum
sylvaticum	CNat
telmateia	LEdu SMad
variegatum	EBee EFer

Eragrostis (*Poaceae*)

curvula	CBod CElw CKno CMea CWCL ECha EHyd EPPr EPfP EWTr IMou LRHS MAvo MBel NBir NGdn NWsh SEND SPhx XLum
- S&SH 10	CElw EPPr SMHy WPGP
- 'Totnes Burgundy'	CAby CExl CKno CRos CSde ECha EHyd EMor EPPr EPfP EShb LRHS MAsh MAvo NRHS SPhx SRms WPGP
elliottii	CKno CSpe ECha ELan EPPr EShb LRHS MAvo SEND SMea WCot XCre
- 'Wind Dancer'	CSde EBee SRms XSen
spectabilis	CBod CKno CSde EBee EHyd ELan EPfP NGdn SMea XCre XLum XSen
trichodes	CBod CKno LEdu NWsh SEND SEdd SMea XCre XSen

Eranthemum (*Acanthaceae*)

pulchellum ♀H1b	ECre

Eranthis (*Ranunculaceae*)

albiflora	GKev
cilicica	see *E. hyemalis* Cilicica Group
§ ***hyemalis*** ♀H6	CArg CBro CMea CRos CWCL EHyd ELan ELon EMor EPfP GKev LCro LOPS LRHS MBow MPri NHpl NRHS SDeJ SDir SPhx SWvt WCot WHoo WShi
§ - Cilicica Group	EHyd EPot GEdr GKev GMaP LRHS NBir NLar NRHS SDeJ SDir SPer SPhx WBor WCot WShi
- 'Flore Pleno' (d)	EPot GEdr GKev WCot
- 'Grünling'	CAvo EPot WCot
- 'Grünspecht'	EPot GEdr
- 'Orange Glow'	EPot GEdr
- 'Schwefelglanz'	CAvo CBro EPot GEdr GKev WCot
§ - Tubergenii Group	EPot GKev
- - 'Guinea Gold' ♀H6	CMea
pinnatifida	GEdr GKev
× ***tubergenii***	see *E. hyemalis* Tubergenii Group

Ercilla (*Phytolaccaceae*)

volubilis	CBcs CExl CRHN CWGN EPfP EShb EWld LRHS MGil SBrt WCru WSHC WSpi

Eremophila (*Scrophulariaceae*)

longifolia	SPlb

Eremostachys (*Lamiaceae*)

laciniata	SPhx

Eremurus (*Asphodelaceae*)

bungei	see *E. stenophyllus* subsp. *stenophyllus*
'Emmy Ro'	GKev LRHS NLar
'Foxtrot'	GKev SDeJ
fuscus	LRHS
'Helena'	LRHS SDir SPhx
himalaicus	ELan EPot ERCP GBin GKev GMaP ILea LRHS NLar SDeJ SDir SPhx
'Image'	EHyd LRHS
× ***isabellinus*** 'Cleopatra'	CMea EHyd EPfP EPot ERCP EWhm GKev GMaP LCro LOPS LRHS MBNS MHer NLar SDeJ SPad SPhx SPoG WCot
- 'Obelisk'	EHyd LRHS
- 'Pinokkio'	EHyd LCro LOPS LRHS NLar SDeJ
- Ruiter hybrids	EHyd ELan EPfP GKev GMaP LRHS MGos NLar SCob SDeJ SPer
- Shelford hybrids	CBcs EHyd GKev LRHS MBros SDeJ
- 'Tropical Dream'	GKev LRHS
'Jeanne-Claire'	LRHS SDir
'Joanna' ♀H6	LCro LOPS LRHS NLar SDir SPhx
'Lemon Fizz'	NLar SDir SPhx
'Line Dance'	EHyd LRHS NRHS
'Moneymaker'	LRHS
'Oase'	EHyd LRHS SDeJ
'Pink Persuasion'	NLar
'Rexona'	GKev SDeJ
robustus ♀H6	CBcs EHyd ELan EPot ERCP GKev LRHS NLar SDeJ SDir SPeP SPhx SPlb WCot
'Romance'	EHyd ERCP LRHS NRHS SDeJ
'Rumba'	SDir
'Sarah Cato'	GKev SPhx
stenophyllus ♀H6	CBod EHyd EPot ERCP GKev LCro LOPS LRHS NLar SCob SDeJ SDir SPhx SPoG
§ - subsp. ***stenophyllus***	CBcs CBod EPfP GMaP MHer MNrw NPer SPer
'Tap Dance'	EHyd GKev LRHS NLar SPhx
'White Beauty Favourite' PBR	ERCP GKev LCro LOPS MHer SDeJ SPeP
'White Sensation'	LRHS SDir
'Yellow Giant'	GKev
zenaidae JCA 0.444.409	WCot

Erepsia (*Aizoaceae*)

lacera	SPlb

Erianthus see *Saccharum*

Erica ✿ (*Ericaceae*)

aestiva	SPlb
alopecurus	SPlb
andevalensis	SWhi
- f. ***albiflora***	CFst
arborea	SPlb SWhi
- var. ***alpina*** ♀H4	CTri EPfP GAbr SWhi
§ - - f. ***aureifolia*** 'Albert's Gold' ♀H4	CBcs CDoC CFst CRos CSBt CTri ELan EPfP GAbr LRHS MGos MMrt NHol NOra NRHS SCoo SPer SPoG SWhi

- 'Arbora Gold'	see *E. arborea* var. *alpina* f. *aureifolia* 'Albert's Gold'
- 'Arnold's Gold'	see *E. arborea* var. *alpina* f. *aureifolia* 'Albert's Gold'
- f. ***aureifolia*** 'Golden Joy'	CFst SWhi
- 'Estrella Gold' ♀H4	CBcs CDoC CFst CRos CSBt CTri EHyd ELan EPfP LRHS MAsh NHol NOra NRHS SCoo SPer SPoG SWhi
- 'Spring Smile'	SWhi
× ***arendsiana*** 'Charnwood Pink'	CFst SWhi
- 'Ronsdorf'	CFst SWhi
australis	SWhi
- f. ***albiflora*** 'Holehird White'	CFst
- - 'Mr Robert' ♀H4	CFst SWhi
- - 'Polar Express'	CFst SWhi
- 'Holehird'	CDoC CFst NOra
- 'Riverslea' ♀H4	CDoC CFst CRos CTri EHyd LRHS NOra NRHS SPoG SWhi
- 'Trisha'	CFst NOra
azorica	SWhi
bauera	CPbh
caffra	CPbh SPlb
canaliculata ♀H3	CBcs
carnea 'Accent'	CFst SWhi
- 'Adrienne Duncan' ♀H6	GPer SCoo SRms SWhi
- 'Alan Coates'	SWhi
- f. ***alba*** 'Cecilia M. Beale'	SWhi
- - 'Golden Starlet' ♀H6	CFst CSBt CTri MAsh NHol SCoo SRms SWhi
- - 'Ice Princess' ♀H6	ELan MAsh SCoo SRms SWhi
- - 'Isabell' ♀H6	CBcs CFst CSBt MAsh SCoo SRms SWhi
- - MADAME SEEDLING	see *E. carnea* f. *alba* 'Weisse March Seedling'
- - 'Romance'	SWhi
- - 'Rosalinde Schorn'	SRms SWhi
- - 'Schneekuppe'	SWhi
- - 'Schneesturm'	CFst SRms SWhi
- - 'Snow Queen'	SRms SWhi
- - 'Snowbelle' **new**	SWhi
- - 'Springwood White' ♀H6	CFst CSBt CTri ELan MAsh MMuc NHol SRms SWhi
§ - - 'Weisse March Seedling'	CFst SWhi
- - 'Whitehall'	CFst LCro LOPS MAsh SCoo SRms SWhi
- - 'Winter Snow' ♀H6	CFst CSBt ELan SCoo SPer SRms SWhi
- 'Amy Doncaster'	see *E. carnea* 'Treasure Trove'
- 'Ann Sparkes' ♀H6	CBcs CFst CSBt CTri ELan GPer MAsh NHol SCoo SRms SVic SWhi
- 'Antje'	SWhi
- 'Atrorubra'	SWhi
- f. ***aureifolia*** 'Altadena'	SWhi
- - 'Aurea'	MAsh SCoo SRms SWhi
- - 'Barry Sellers'	SRms SWhi
§ - - 'Bell's Extra Special'	SRms SWhi
- - 'Dorset Sunshine'	CFst SWhi
- - 'Foxhollow' ♀H6	CBcs CFst CTri IArd MAsh NHol SCoo SRms SVic SWhi
- - 'Gelber Findling'	SRms SWhi
- - 'Hilletje'	SRms SWhi
- - 'January Sun'	SRms SWhi
- - 'Moonlight'	SWhi
- - 'Sunshine Rambler'	SWhi
- - 'Tybesta Gold'	SWhi
- - 'Westwood Yellow' ♀H6	CSBt MAsh NHol SRms SWhi
- 'Aztec Gold'	CFst SPer SWhi
- 'Beoley Pink'	SRms
- 'Branton Bamford'	CFst SWhi
- 'C.J. Backhouse'	SRms SWhi
- 'Carnea'	SWhi
- 'Challenger' ♀H6	ELan GPer MAsh SCoo SRms SVic SWhi
- 'Christine Fletcher'	SWhi
- 'Clare Wilkinson'	SRms SWhi
- 'Claribelle'	CFst SWhi
- 'Corinna' PBR	CFst SWhi
- 'David's Seedling'	SWhi
- 'December Red'	CFst ELan MAsh MMuc SCoo SEND SRms SVic SWhi
- 'Diana Young'	CFst SCoo SWhi
- 'Dømmesmoen'	CFst SRms
- 'Duncan' **new**	SWhi
- 'Early Red'	SRms SWhi
- 'Eileen Porter'	CFst MMuc SWhi
- 'Eva' ♀H6	CBcs CFst SRms SWhi
- 'Foxhollow Fairy'	SPer SRms SWhi
- 'Gracilis'	SRms SWhi
- 'Heathwood'	MAsh SRms SWhi
- 'James Backhouse'	CFst CTri SWhi
- 'Jason Attwater'	SRms SWhi
- 'Jennifer Anne'	CFst SRms SWhi
- 'John Kampa'	SRms SWhi
- 'John Pook'	SCoo SRms SVic SWhi
- 'Kathy'	SWhi
- 'King George'	CFst CTri SRms SWhi
- 'Late Pink'	SWhi
- 'Lena'	see *E.* × *darleyensis* 'Lena'
- 'Lesley Sparkes'	CFst SWhi
- 'Little Peter'	SWhi
- 'Lohse's Rubin'	SRms SWhi
- 'Loughrigg' ♀H6	CTri MAsh NHol SCoo SRms SVic SWhi
- 'March Seedling' ♀H6	CFst MAsh NHol SCoo SRms SWhi
- 'Margaret Benson'	SWhi
- 'Margery Frearson'	SRms SWhi
I - 'Martin'	SRms SWhi
- 'Memory'	SWhi
- 'Mrs Sam Doncaster'	SWhi
- 'Myretoun Ruby' ♀H6	CBcs CFst CSBt CTri GPer LCro LOPS MAsh NHol SCoo SRms SWhi
- 'Nadja'	SWhi
- 'Nathalie' ♀H6	CFst CSBt MAsh SCoo SRms SWhi
- 'Oriënt'	SWhi
- 'Pink Beauty'	see *E. carnea* 'Pink Pearl'
- 'Pink Cloud'	CFst
- 'Pink Mist'	SRms SWhi
§ - 'Pink Pearl'	CFst
- 'Pink Spangles' ♀H6	CBcs CFst CSBt CTri MAsh SCoo SPer SRms SWhi
- 'Pirbright Rose'	SRms SWhi
- 'Polden Pride'	SRms SWhi
- 'Porter's Red'	SWhi
- 'Praecox Rubra'	NHol SCoo SRms SWhi
- 'Prince of Wales'	SWhi
- 'Queen Mary'	SRms SWhi
- 'Queen of Spain'	CFst SRms SWhi
- 'R.B. Cooke'	MAsh SCoo SRms SWhi
- 'Red Rover'	SWhi
- 'Robert Jan'	SRms
- 'Rosalie' ♀H6	CFst IArd MAsh SCoo SPer SRms SWhi
- 'Rosantha'	CFst SRms SWhi
- 'Rosea'	SPlb SWhi

	- 'Rosy Gem'	SWhi
	- 'Rosy Morn'	SRms SWhi
	- 'Rotes Juwel'	SRms SWhi
	- 'Rubens' Palette'	SWhi
	- 'Rubinette'	SWhi
	- 'Rubinteppich'	SRms
	- 'Rubra'	SWhi
	- 'Ruby Glow'	NHol SWhi
	- 'Sally'	CFst
	- 'Saskia'	CFst SWhi
	- 'Scatterley'	SRms
	- 'Schatzalp'	SRms SWhi
	- 'Sherwood Creeping'	SRms SWhi
	- 'Smart's Heath'	SRms
	- 'Spring Day'	SWhi
	- 'Springwood Pink'	CSBt CTri GPer MAsh NHol SRms SWhi
I	- 'Startler'	SWhi
	- 'Tanja'	CFst SWhi
§	- 'Treasure Trove'	CFst SWhi
	- 'Viking'	MAsh
	- 'Vivellii' ♀H6	CFst CTri GPer MAsh NHol SCoo SRms SWhi
	- 'Vivellii Aurea'	SWhi
	- 'Walter Reisert'	SRms SWhi
	- 'Wanda'	SWhi
	- 'Wentwood Red'	SRms SWhi
	- WHISKY	see *E. carnea* f. *aureifolia* 'Bell's Extra Special'
	- 'Winter Beauty'	NHol SWhi
	- 'Winter Rubin'	CFst SRms
	- 'Winterfreude'	SWhi
	- 'Wintersonne' ♀H6	CFst MMuc SRms SWhi
	cerinthoides ♀H2	CPbh
	ciliaris 'Alba'	SWhi
	- f. ***albiflora*** 'Stoborough'	CFst SWhi
	- - 'White Wings'	CFst SWhi
	- f. ***aureifolia*** 'Aurea'	SWhi
	- 'Bretagne'	SWhi
	- 'Camla'	SWhi
	- 'Corfe Castle'	CFst SWhi
	- 'David McClintock'	CFst SWhi
	- 'Globosa'	SWhi
	- 'Mawiana'	SWhi
	- 'Mrs C.H. Gill'	SWhi
	- 'Rotundiflora'	SWhi
	- 'Stapehill'	SWhi
	- 'Wych'	CFst SWhi
	cinerea	SWhi
	- f. ***alba***	SWhi
	- - 'Alba Major'	CFst SWhi
	- - 'Alba Minor'	CFst MAsh SWhi
	- - 'Celebration'	SWhi
	- - 'Domino'	SWhi
	- - 'Hookstone White'	CFst SWhi
	- - 'Snow Cream'	SWhi
	- - 'White Dale'	CFst
	- 'Alfred Bowerman'	SWhi
	- 'Angarrack'	SWhi
	- 'Anja Blum'	SWhi
	- 'Apple Blossom'	SWhi
	- 'Aquarel'	SWhi
	- 'Ashgarth Garnet'	SWhi
	- 'Atropurpurea'	SWhi
	- 'Atrorubens'	CFst SWhi
	- 'Atrorubens, Daisy Hill'	SWhi
	- 'Atrosanguinea Reuthe's Variety'	SReu SWhi
	- 'Atrosanguinea Smith's Variety'	CFst SWhi

	- f. ***aureifolia*** 'Anne Berry'	SWhi
	- - 'Apricot Charm'	SWhi
	- - 'Constance'	SWhi
	- - 'Fiddler's Gold'	MAsh SWhi
	- - 'Golden Charm'	SWhi
	- - 'Golden Drop'	CFst SWhi
	- - 'Golden Hue'	SWhi
	- - 'Golden Sport'	CFst SWhi
	- - 'Golden Tee'	SWhi
	- - 'Goldilocks'	CFst
	- - 'John Eason'	SWhi
	- - 'Summer Gold'	SWhi
	- - 'Windlebrooke'	SWhi
	- 'Baylay's Variety'	SWhi
	- 'Blossom Time'	SWhi
	- 'Bucklebury Red'	CFst
	- 'C.D. Eason' ♀H7	CFst CTri GPer SCoo SWhi
§	- 'C.G. Best'	SWhi
	- 'Caldy Island'	SWhi
	- 'Cevennes'	GPer SWhi
	- 'Champs Hill'	CFst SWhi
	- 'Cindy'	SWhi
	- 'Coccinea'	SWhi
	- 'Colligan Bridge'	SWhi
	- 'Contrast'	SWhi
	- 'Creepy Crawly'	CFst SWhi
	- 'Discovery'	CFst SWhi
	- 'Duncan Fraser'	SWhi
	- 'Eden Valley'	CFst GPer SCoo SWhi
	- 'Felthorpe'	SWhi
	- 'Flott' **new**	SWhi
	- 'Foxhollow Mahogany'	SWhi
	- 'Frances'	SWhi
	- 'Fred Corston'	SWhi
	- 'G. Osmond'	SWhi
	- 'Glasnevin Red'	SWhi
	- 'Glencairn'	GPer SWhi
	- 'Graham Thomas'	see *E. cinerea* 'C.G. Best'
	- 'Grandiflora'	SWhi
	- 'Guernsey Lime'	SWhi
	- 'Hardwick's Rose'	SWhi
	- 'Harry Fulcher'	SWhi
	- 'Heatherbank'	CFst SWhi
	- 'Heidebrand'	SWhi
	- 'Iberian Beauty'	SWhi
	- 'Janet'	SWhi
	- 'John Ardron'	CFst SWhi
	- 'Joseph Murphy'	CBcs CFst SWhi
	- 'Josephine Ross'	SWhi
	- 'Joyce Burfitt'	CFst SWhi
	- 'Katinka'	CBcs CFst GPer SWhi
	- 'Kerry Cherry'	SWhi
	- 'Knap Hill' **new**	SWhi
	- 'Knap Hill Pink'	SWhi
	- 'Lady Skelton'	CFst SWhi
	- 'Lavender Lady'	SWhi
	- 'Lilac Time'	CFst GPer SWhi
	- 'Lilacina'	SWhi
	- 'Lime Soda'	SWhi
	- 'Margaret Bowerman' **new**	SWhi
	- 'Michael Hugo'	SWhi
	- 'Miss Waters'	CFst SWhi
	- 'Molly Rose'	SWhi
	- 'Mrs Dill'	SWhi
	- 'Mrs E.A. Mitchell'	GPer SPlb SWhi
	- 'Mrs Ford'	SWhi
	- 'My Love'	CFst SWhi
	- 'Nellie Dawson'	SWhi
	- 'Newick Lilac'	SWhi

- 'Next Best'	SWhi
- 'Novar'	SWhi
- 'Ockham'	CFst SWhi
- 'Old Rose'	SWhi
- 'P.S. Patrick'	SWhi
- 'Pallas'	CFst SWhi
- 'Pallida'	SWhi
- 'Pentreath'	GPer SWhi
- 'Pink Foam'	SWhi
- 'Pink Ice' ♀H7	CFst CTri GPer MAsh NHol SWhi
- 'Plummer's Seedling'	SWhi
- 'Prostrate Lavender'	SWhi
- 'Providence'	CFst SWhi
- 'Purple Beauty'	GPer SWhi
- 'Purple Robe'	SWhi
- 'Purple Spreader'	SWhi
- 'Purpurea'	SWhi
- 'Pygmaea'	SWhi
- var. ***rendlei*** **new**	SWhi
- 'Rock Pool' **new**	SWhi
- 'Rock Ruth'	SWhi
- 'Romantic Scotland'	GPer
- 'Romiley'	SWhi
- 'Rose Queen'	SWhi
- 'Rosea'	GPer
- 'Rosita'	CFst
- 'Rosy Chimes'	SWhi
- 'Rote Rosita' **new**	SWhi
- 'Roter Kobold'	SWhi
- 'Rozanne Waterer'	SWhi
- 'Ruby'	SWhi
- 'Sandford Heritage'	CFst SWhi
- 'Sandpit Hill'	CFst SWhi
- 'Schizopetala'	CFst
- 'Sherry'	NHol SWhi
- 'Spicata'	SWhi
- 'Splendens'	SWhi
- 'Startler'	SWhi
- 'Stephen Davis' ♀H7	CFst GPer NHol SCoo SWhi
- 'Ted Oliver'	CFst SWhi
- 'Velvet Night' ♀H7	GPer MAsh NHol SWhi
- 'Victoria'	SWhi
- 'Violacea'	SWhi
- 'Vivienne Patricia'	CFst
- 'Wine'	SWhi
coccinea	CPbh
cooperi	SPlb
curviflora	SPlb
× ***darleyensis*** 'Alba'	see *E.* × *darleyensis* f. *albiflora* 'Silberschmelze'
- f. ***albiflora*** 'Ada S. Collings'	MAsh SRms SWhi
- - 'Bing'	SCoo SWhi
- - 'Dunreggan'	SWhi
- - 'N.R. Webster'	SRms SWhi
§ - - 'Silberschmelze'	CSBt CTri GJos MAsh MMuc SCoo SRms SWhi
- - 'Snow Surprise'	SWhi
- - 'White Glow'	CTri MAsh SRms SWhi
- - 'White Perfection' ♀H5	CBcs CDoC CFst IArd MAsh NHol SCoo SPoG SRms SWhi
- - 'White Spring Surprise'	SWhi
- 'Archie Graham'	SRms SWhi
- 'Arthur Johnson' ♀H5	CFst CTri MAsh SRms SWhi
§ - f. ***aureifolia*** 'Eva Gold'PBR	CFst SWhi
- - 'Golden Perfect'	CFst SWhi
- - 'Jack H. Brummage'	CSBt CTri MAsh SRms SWhi
- - 'Mary Helen'	CSBt MAsh NHol SCoo SRms SWhi
- - 'Moonshine'	CFst SRms SWhi
- - 'Tweety'	CBcs CFst CSBt SRms SWhi
- 'Aurélie Brégeon'	CFst SRms SWhi
- 'Bert'	SCoo SWhi
- 'Cherry Stevens'	see *E.* × *darleyensis* 'Furzey'
§ - 'Darley Dale'	CFst CSBt ELan GJos GPer MAsh MMuc SCoo SPoG SRms SWhi
- 'Epe'	CFst SRms SWhi
- 'Eva'	see *E.* × *darleyensis* f. *aureifolia* 'Eva Gold'
§ - 'Furzey' ♀H5	CSBt GPer LCro LOPS MAsh NHol SCoo SRms SWhi
- 'George Rendall'	CTri MAsh SCoo SRms SWhi
- 'Ghost Hills' ♀H5	CSBt LCro LOPS MAsh SCoo SPoG SRms SWhi
- 'Irish Treasure'	CFst SWhi
- 'J.W. Porter' ♀H5	MAsh MMuc SCoo SRms SWhi
- 'James Smith'	SRms SWhi
- 'Jenny Porter' ♀H5	ELan SCoo SWhi
- 'Katia'PBR (Winter Belles Series)	CFst SPer SWhi
- 'Kramer's Rote' ♀H5	CFst CSBt CTri ELan NHol SCoo SPoG SRms SWhi XLum
§ - 'Lena'	CFst SWhi
- 'Lucie'PBR (Winter Belles Series)	CFst GJos SWhi
- 'Margaret Porter'	CFst SCoo SWhi
- MOLTEN SILVER	see *E.* × *darleyensis* f. *albiflora* 'Silberschmelze'
- 'Mrs Parris' Red'	SWhi
- 'Phoebe'PBR (Winter Belles Series)	CBcs CFst SWhi
- 'Pink Harmony'PBR **new**	SWhi
- 'Pink Perfection'	see *E.* × *darleyensis* 'Darley Dale'
- 'Red Summersnow' (v) **new**	SWhi
- 'Rubina'PBR	CFst SWhi
- 'Spring Surprise'PBR ♀H5	CFst SCoo SWhi
- 'W.G. Pine'	SRms
- 'Winter Surprise'	CFst SWhi
- 'Winter Treasure'	CFst SWhi
discolor	CPbh
erigena f. ***alba*** 'Brian Proudley'	SWhi
- - 'Hibernica Alba'	SWhi
- - 'Mrs Parris' White'	SWhi
- - 'Nana Alba'	SWhi
- - 'Nana Compacta'	SWhi
- - 'W.T. Rackliff' ♀H5	CBcs CSBt GPer MAsh NHol SCoo SRms SWhi
- f. ***aureifolia*** 'Golden Jubilee'	CFst SWhi
- - 'Golden Lady'	CSBt MAsh NHol SCoo SRms SWhi
- - 'Thing Nee'	CFst SRms SWhi
- 'Brightness'	CSBt NHol SCoo SWhi
- 'Ewan Jones'	SWhi
- 'Glauca'	SWhi
- 'Hibernica'	SWhi
- 'Irish Dusk' ♀H5	CBcs CSBt CTri GPer MAsh MMuc SCoo SRms SWhi
- 'Irish Salmon'	SWhi
- 'Irish Silver'	SWhi
- 'Mrs Parris' Lavender'	SWhi
- 'Rosea'	SWhi
- 'Rosslare'	SWhi
- 'Rubra'	SWhi
- 'Superba'	SRms SWhi
erigena × ***lusitanica*** 'Lucy Gena' **new**	SWhi
× ***factitia*** 'Heidedorf Lüllingen' **new**	SWhi

	formosa	CPbh
	glandulosa	CPbh
	glauca var. ***glauca***	SPlb
	gracilis	CDoC
	× ***griffithsii*** 'Ashlea Gold'	CFst SWhi
	- 'Elegant Spike'	CFst SWhi
§	- 'Heaven Scent'	CFst SWhi
	- 'Jacqueline'	CFst SWhi
	- 'Valerie Griffiths'	CFst GPer NHol SWhi
	'Heaven Scent'	see *E.* × *griffithsii* 'Heaven Scent'
	× ***krameri*** 'Rudi'	SWhi
	lusitanica ♀H4	CFst SWhi
	- f. ***aureifolia*** 'George Hunt'	CFst CRos EHyd ELan LRHS SPer SWhi
	- GREAT STAR	see *E. lusitanica* 'La Vasterival'
§	- 'La Vasterival'	CFst
	- 'Sheffield Park'	CFst CRos EHyd LRHS NOra NRHS SPer SPoG SWhi
	mackayana new	SWhi
	- 'Donegal'	SWhi
	- f. ***eburnea*** 'Doctor Ronald Gray'	CFst SWhi
	- - 'Shining Light'	CFst SWhi
	- 'Errigal Dusk'	CFst SWhi
	- 'Galicia'	CFst SWhi
	- f. ***multiplicata*** 'Plena' (d)	SWhi WHer
	mammosa ♀H2	CPbh SPlb
	- cream-flowered	CPbh
	- pink-flowered	CPbh
	- red-flowered	CPbh
	- white-flowered	CPbh
	manipuliflora	SWhi
	- 'Bert Jones' new	SWhi
	- 'Corfu'	SWhi
	- 'Elegant Spike'	CFst
	- 'Korçula'	CFst SWhi
	mediterranea misapplied	see *E. erigena*
	multiflora	XSen
	nana new	SWhi
	× ***oldenburgensis*** 'Ammerland' ♀H5	CFst NOra SCoo SRms SWhi
	- 'Oldenburg'	NOra
	'Pat Turpin'	CFst
	patersonii	SPlb
	perspicua	CPbh SPlb
	platycodon	CFst SWhi
	subsp. ***maderincola*** f. ***aureifolia*** 'Levada Gold'	
	- - - 'Madeira Gold'	SWhi
	plukenetii	CPbh
	scabriuscula	CPbh
	scoparia	SWhi
§	- 'Minima'	CCCN SWhi
	- 'Pumila'	see *E. scoparia* 'Minima'
	sessiliflora	CPbh
	spiculifolia	SWhi
	- f. ***albiflora*** 'Raika' new	SWhi
	- 'Balkan Rose'	CFst SWhi
	- 'Branka' new	SWhi
	- 'Graf Dracula' new	SWhi
	- 'Manja' new	SWhi
	- 'Mila' new	SWhi
	straussiana	SPlb
	× ***stuartii*** 'Connemara'	SWhi
	- 'Irish Lemon' ♀H5	CFst GPer NHol SWhi
	- 'Irish Orange'	GPer NHol SWhi
	- 'Nacung'	SWhi
	- 'Stuart's Original'	SWhi
	terminalis	SWhi
	- 'Golden Oriole'	SWhi
	- 'Thelma Woolner'	CFst SWhi
	tetralix	SWhi
	- f. ***alba*** 'Alba Mollis' ♀H6	CFst GPer MAsh SWhi
	- - 'Alba Praecox'	SWhi
	- - 'Melbury White'	CFst
	- - 'White House'	SWhi
	- 'Allendale Pink'	SWhi
	- f. ***aureifolia*** 'Ruth's Gold'	NHol SWhi
	- 'Con Underwood'	CFst GPer SWhi
	- 'Daphne Underwood'	SWhi
	- 'Delta'	SWhi
	- 'Foxhome'	SWhi
	- 'George Fraser'	SWhi
	- 'Gratis'	SWhi
	- 'Hookstone Pink'	CFst
	- 'Humoresque'	SWhi
	- 'Ken Underwood'	CFst SWhi
	- 'L.E. Underwood'	SWhi
I	- 'Mollis' new	SWhi
	- 'Morning Glow'	see *E.* × *watsonii* 'F. White'
	- f. ***racemosa*** 'Terschelling'	SWhi
	- 'Riko'	CFst SWhi
	- 'Rosea'	SWhi
	- 'Rubra'	SWhi
§	- 'Ruby's Variety'	SWhi
	- 'Ruby's Velvet'	see *E. tetralix* 'Ruby's Variety'
	- 'Salmon Seedling'	SWhi
	- 'Samtpfötchen'	CFst
	- 'Silver Bells'	SWhi
	- 'Stardome'	SWhi
	- f. ***stellata*** 'Pink Star' ♀H6	CFst NHol SWhi
	- 'Tina'	CFst SWhi
	vagans f. ***alba***	SWhi
	- - 'Cornish Cream' ♀H5	GPer NHol SWhi
	- - 'Diana's Gold'	SRms
	- - 'French White'	SWhi
	- - 'Golden Triumph'	CFst SWhi
	- - 'Kevernensis Alba' ♀H5	GPer SWhi
	- - 'Leucantha'	SWhi
	- - 'Lyonesse' ♀H5	MAsh MMuc NHol SWhi
	- - 'White Spire'	SWhi
	- f. ***aureifolia*** 'Valerie Proudley' ♀H5	GPer MAsh NHol SWhi
	- - 'Yellow John'	CFst CSma SRms SWhi
	- 'Birch Glow' ♀H5	CFst CSma SWhi
	- 'Charm'	SWhi
	- 'Chittendenii'	SWhi
	- 'Diana Hornibrook'	SWhi
	- 'Fiddlestone'	SWhi
	- 'George Underwood'	SWhi
	- 'Grandiflora'	SWhi
	- 'Hookstone Rose'	SWhi
	- 'Ida M. Britten'	SWhi
	- 'J.C. Fletcher'	SWhi
	- 'Keira'	CFst CSma SRms SWhi
	- 'Lilacina'	SWhi
	- 'Miss Waterer'	SWhi
	- 'Mrs D.F. Maxwell' ♀H5	CBcs CFst GPer MMuc NHol SWhi
	- 'Mrs Donaldson'	CFst SWhi
	- 'Pallida'	SWhi
	- 'Peach Blossom'	SWhi
	- 'Pyrenees Pink'	SWhi
	- 'Rubra'	SWhi
	- 'Saint Keverne'	CFst IArd MAsh MMuc NHol SWhi

	- 'Summertime'	CFst SWhi
	- 'Valerie Smith'	SWhi
	- 'Viridiflora'	SWhi
	- 'White Giant'	SWhi
	× ***veitchii***	SWhi
	- 'Exeter' 🏆^{H4}	CDoC CFst CRos CSBt EHyd ELan LRHS MAsh NOra NRHS SPer SPoG SWhi
	- 'Gold Tips' 🏆^{H4}	CFst CSBt NOra SWhi
	- 'Pink Joy'	SWhi
	- 'Westbourne Grove' **new**	SWhi
	versicolor 🏆^{H2}	CPbh SPlb
	verticillata	CPbh
	× ***watsonii*** 'Cherry Turpin'	CFst SWhi
	- 'Claire Elise'	CFst SWhi
	- 'Dawn'	SWhi
	- 'Dorothy Metheny'	CFst SWhi
§	- 'F. White'	SWhi
	- 'Gwen'	CFst SWhi
	- 'H. Maxwell'	SWhi
	- 'Mary'	CFst SWhi
	- 'Pink Pacific'	CFst SWhi
	- 'Rachel'	SWhi
	- 'Truro'	SWhi
	× ***williamsii*** 'Cow-y-Jack'	SWhi
	- 'David Coombe'	SWhi
	- 'Gew Graze'	SWhi
	- 'Gold Button'	SWhi
	- 'Gwavas'	SWhi
	- 'Ken Wilson'	CFst GPer SWhi
	- 'Lizard Downs'	SWhi
	- 'Marion Hughes'	SWhi
	- 'P.D. Williams'	SWhi
	'Winter Fire'	CDoC CPbh
I	'Winter Fire' (*oatesii* hybrid)	NOra
	woodii	SPlb

Erigeron (*Asteraceae*)

	'Adria'	CRos EHyd ELon LRHS MBel MMuc NRHS
	annuus	CSpe MMuc MNrw NDov SDix SPhx WBrk WMal WSHC WTre
	aurantiacus	CBcs CBor CSpe ELan SMad
	aureus 'Canary Bird' 🏆^{H4}	EPot NSla WAbe
	- 'The Giant'	WAbe
	AZURE FAIRY	see *E.* 'Azurfee'
§	'Azurfee'	CBod CSBt ELan EPfP GKev GMaP MHol NBir NLar SPer SPoG SWvt WFar
	BLACK SEA	see *E.* 'Schwarzes Meer'
	'Blue Beauty'	CMac CRos EHyd EPfP LRHS NRHS SRms
	'Charity'	MHCG MRav
	chrysopsidis	GKev
	- 'Grand Ridge'	EHyd LRHS NRHS WAbe
	compositus	GKev SRms WCav
§	- var. ***discoideus***	CMea NSla SPlb WHal WOld
	- 'Rocky'	MMuc NSla
	DARKEST OF ALL	see *E.* 'Dunkelste Aller'
	'Dignity'	CBod EHyd ELan LRHS MBel MBrN MMuc MPie MRav NHol SWvt WBrk
	'Dimity'	ECha NBir NBre WFar WHal
	'Dominator'	CWGN WCot WFar
I	'Dunkelste Aller'	CAby CBcs CBod CSam EHyd ELan EPfP GLog GMaP LRHS LSou MBel MRav NLar NRHS NSti SGbt SPoG SRms SWvt WCAu WFar WHoo
*	***ereganus***	NBre
	flettii	GKev
	'Foersters Liebling' 🏆^{H5}	EBee MBel MTis
	'Four Winds'	ECtt ELan EWes GKev LRHS NGdn NHpl WBrk WIce
	'Gaiety'	NBre
	glaucus	CCCN CSBt GQue LRHS MMuc MRav NGdn SEND SMad WBrk
	- 'Albus'	ELon LRHS NLar WBor WFar
	- 'Elstead Pink'	CTri ECtt ELan WFar
	- large-flowered	ELon LRHS
	- 'Roger Raiche'	CFis MRav
	- 'Rose Purple'	CFis
	- 'Roseus'	CBcs SEND
	- 'Sea Breeze'	Widely available
	- 'Sennen'	MHCG WBrk
	- 'Viewpoint Blue'	ELon LRHS
	'Karminstrahl' **new**	ELon
§	***karvinskianus*** 🏆^{H5}	Widely available
	- 'Kew Profusion'	CRos EHyd LRHS MHol NRHS WHil
	- 'Lavender Lady' **new**	WCot
	- 'Sea of Blossom'	CCht LSou NCou
	- 'Stallone'	CBod LSou LSun MHol NLar
	leiomerus	GEdr GKev
	'Mrs F.H. Beale'	GBin WCot
	mucronatus	see *E. karvinskianus*
	'Nachthimmel'	NBre NGdn
	philadelphicus	CElw MNrw NBir NBro WFar
	PINK JEWEL	see *E.* 'Rosa Juwel'
	PINK TRIUMPH	see *E.* 'Rosa Triumph'
	'Professor Korodi' (d)	EBee
	'Profusion'	see *E. karvinskianus*
	pulchellus	WBrk
	pumilus	WGoo
	pyrenaicus Rouy	see *Aster pyrenaeus*
	'Quakeress'	CAby CBod CMea ECtt ELon EPri GMaP GQue LSou MBel MMuc MNrw MRav NGdn SDix SWvt WBrk WFar WGwG
§	'Rosa Juwel'	CBod CSBt ECtt EHyd ELan EPfP GMaP LRHS MHol MRav NBir NRHS SPer SPoG SRms SWvt WCAu WFar
§	'Rosa Triumph'	EBee
	'Rotes Meer'	CMac EBee MRav
	rotundifolius 'Caerulescens'	see *Bellis caerulescens*
	salsuginosus misapplied	see *Eurybia sibirica*
§	'Schneewittchen' 🏆^{H5}	CBod CCBP CRos CSam EBee ELan ELon LRHS MBNS MBel MPie MRav NRHS SRms SWvt WGwG
§	'Schwarzes Meer'	EBee ELon WCot
	scopulinus	ITim WAbe WOld
	simplex	EHyd LRHS NRHS
	'Sincerity'	XLum
	'Snow Queen'	SWvt
	SNOW WHITE	see *E.* 'Schneewittchen'
	'Sommerneuschnee'	EBee MTis NDov SHar WCAu
	speciosus 'Grandiflora'	CBod
	'Strahlenmeer'	NBre
	'Synehurst'	WCot WFar
	trifidus	see *E. compositus* var. *discoideus*
	uniflorus	MAsh SRms
	'Violetta'	SPoG
	'Wayne Roderick'	CBod CRos EHyd ELan EPfP LRHS NRHS WFar
	'White Quakeress'	CFis CMea MHCG MRav WCot WFar

Erinacea (*Papilionaceae*)

§	***anthyllis*** 🏆^{H5}	WAbe WThu XEll
	pungens	see *E. anthyllis*

Erinus (*Plantaginaceae*)

alpinus ♀H6	CPBP ECtt EDAr GAbr GJos GKev MAsh NBir NGrd SRms XLum
- var. ***albus***	GMaP SRms WHoo XLum
- 'Doktor Hähnle'	EDAr GJos GMaP MBel SRms WHoo XLum

Eriobotrya (*Rosaceae*)

'Coppertone'	see × *Rhaphiobotrya* 'Coppertone'
japonica (F) ♀H4	CAbb CBcs CCCN CDoC CRos CTsd EHyd ELan EPfP LRHS MGos MMuc NLar SArc SCoo SEND SEdd SGsty SPer SPlb SSta SVic SWeb WHer WKor WLov WPGP
- 'Gold Nugget' (F)	XBlo
- 'Mrs Cookson' (F)	WMat
- 'Oliver' (F)	WMat
- 'Rose-Anne' (F)	SGol WPGP

Eriobotrya × *Rhaphiolepis*

see × *Rhaphiobotrya*

Eriocapitella see *Anemone*

Eriocephalus (*Asteraceae*)

africanus	CBod SPlb WJek

Eriogonum (*Polygonaceae*)

alleni 'Little Rascal'	ELan
cespitosum	WAbe
chrysops new	GKev
grande var. ***rubescens***	EBee
umbellatum	EPot GKev
- var. ***porteri***	GKev
- var. ***torreyanum***	CMea
wrightii var. ***subscaposum***	GKev

Eriophorum (*Cyperaceae*)

angustifolium	CBen CWat EWat LLWG MWts SPlb WMAq WPnP WWtn XLum
chamissonis	MWts
latifolium	LLWG XLum
rousseauianum	LLWG
vaginatum	EWat LLWG XLum

Eriophyllum (*Asteraceae*)

lanatum	EBee ECha ELan EPfP MMuc NBid NGBl SHar

Eriostemon (*Rutaceae*)

myoporoides	see *Philotheca myoporoides*

Eritrichium (*Boraginaceae*)

aretioides	SPlb

Erodium (*Geraniaceae*)

absinthoides	EHyd EPot LRHS NRHS XSen
- var. ***amanum***	see *E. amanum*
§ ***acaule***	EPPr
'Almodovar'	WCot WFar
§ ***amanum***	CSpe EWes GMaP
'Ardwick Redeye'	EPot
balearicum	see *E.* × *variabile* 'Album'
'Caroline'	CMea WHoo
carvifolium	GKev
§ ***castellanum***	NLar SPtp
celtibericum	EPot
- 'Peñagolosa'	XSen
chamaedryoides	see *E. reichardii*
- 'Roseum'	see *E.* × *variabile* 'Roseum'
chrysanthum	CTri EBou ECha ECtt EDAr ELan EPfP EPot EWTr MMuc MPnt NChi NLar SEND SPtp SWvt WKif XLum XSen
- (f)	WFar
- (m)	NRya
- 'Arcadia'	CMea SPhx
- pink-flowered	CSpe ECtt MMuc
'County Park'	ECha SBut SHar SRms WFar XSen
daucoides misapplied	see *E. castellanum*
daucoides ambig.	GKev
'Eileen Emmett'	EPot
'Fran's Delight'	CMea CPBP ECtt EPot SGro WAbe WFar WHoo
'Freedom'	CBor MHol WFar WIce XEll
'Fripetta'	WIce
'Gini's Choice'	WCot
glandulosum ♀H5	CCBP EBee ELan EPfP MAsh MMuc NLar SEND SRms WFar WSHC XLum XSen
'Grey Blush'	WKif
gruinum	SPhx
guttatum misapplied	see *E.* 'Katherine Joy'
guttatum (Desf.) Willd.	CWGN EPot EWTr GMaP SRms
hymenodes L'Hér.	see *E. trifolium*
'Julie Ritchie'	WHoo
§ 'Katherine Joy'	CBor ECtt EPot EWes MCot MHer NRya WFar
× ***kolbianum***	WAbe WCot WFar WHoo
- 'Natasha'	CBor ECtt ELan EPot EWes MHer MMuc WIce WKif
'Las Meninas'	ECtt WCot
× ***lindavicum***	MHer NChi
macradenum	see *E. glandulosum*
manescavii ♀H5	Widely available
'Marchants Mikado'	WKif
'Maryla'	CBor CMea WFar WIce
'Merstham Pink'	SRms XLum
'Mesquita'	CMea
'Milly'	CMea
pelargoniiflorum	CPla CRos CSpe EBee EHyd ELan EMor EPfP LRHS MCot MNHC NRHS SAko SRms SWvt WCAu WFar WHil WKif
'Peter Vernon'	MHer
petraeum subsp. ***petraeum***	EPot
'Purple Haze'	EHyd ELan EMor SRms WFar
§ ***reichardii***	CRos CTri ECtt EHyd LRHS MBrN NRHS SPoG SRms WCFE WCav
- 'Album'	CRos EHyd LRHS MAsh MHol MMuc NHpl NRHS SPoG WFar WHoo
- 'Bianca'	ELan EMor EPfP
- 'Jenny'	NHpl
- 'Rubrum'	MAsh
'Robertino'	WAbe
'Special Rose'	CSpe
rodiei	EWes
romanum	see *E. acaule*
§ ***rupestre***	SRms WIce
'Spanish Eyes'	CDor EBee ECtt LRHS LSou MHol SMad SWvt WCot WFar WKif
'Stephanie'	CBor ECtt ELan EPot EWes MHer MMuc NLar WIce XSen
supracanum	see *E. rupestre*
'Tiny Kyni'	WFar
trichomanifolium L'Hér.	EWes

§ ***trifolium***	ELan MHer SGro SPhx WBrk
× ***variabile***	LLWG WFar
§ - 'Album'	CMea CRos EHyd EPfP EPot GKev GMaP LRHS MHer NGrd NRHS SRms SWvt WBrk WFar WTor
- 'Candy'	ECtt MHer NHpl
- dwarf white **new**	CBod
- 'Flore Pleno' (d)	CRos CTri EBou EHyd ELan EPfP EWes LLWG LRHS MHer NHpl NRHS SPoG SRms WBrk WFar
- 'Red Rock'	CTri
§ - 'Roseum' ♀H5	ECtt ELan LLWG MMuc NCou SEND SPlb SRms WBrk
- 'William Bishop'	CBod CMea CRos ECtt EHyd EPfP EPot GJos GMaP LLWG LRHS MAsh MBel MHol NQui NRHS NRya SPoG SRms SWvt WBrk WCFE WFar WHoo WIce WLov

Erpetion see *Viola*

Eruca (*Brassicaceae*)

vesicaria	ENfk
- subsp. ***sativa***	CSpe GPoy MHer MNHC SRms SVic

Eryngium (*Apiaceae*)

from Mexico	SBrt
§ ***agavifolium***	Widely available
- giant	SMad WPGP
alpinum	CBod CSpe ECha GKev GMaP MGos MSCN NBir SPer SPhx SRms WCAu WFar
- 'Amethyst'	LRHS
- 'Blue Star'	CAby CExl CSpe EBee ECtt ELan ELon NLar WFar WSpi
- 'Slieve Donard'	see *E.* × *zabelii* 'Donard Variety'
- 'Superbum'	ECtt EHyd GLog LRHS MBriF SRms
amethystinum	EPri EWes LRHS SPhx
'Blue Jackpot'	CBod EBee ECtt EPfP EWes MBel MHol MNrw
bourgatii	Widely available
- Graham Stuart Thomas's selection	CBod CDor CEnd CExl CRos CSpe ECtt EHyd ELan EPPr EWes GAbr GMaP LRHS MBel MHol NBid NBir NRHS SEdd SPad SPer SRms WCAu WCot WHoo WKif WSpi
- 'Oxford Blue' ♀H5	LRHS NLar NSla SPtp SWvt
- 'Picos Amethyst'	CBcs CBct CMac EBee EHyd EMor IPot LCro LOPS LRHS MHol NLar SCob SCoo SEdd SMad SPtp SRkn SRms WABo WNPC WSHC
- 'Picos Blue' PBR ♀H5	Widely available
bromeliifolium misapplied	see *E. agavifolium*, *E. eburneum*
bromeliifolium F. Delaroche	EHyd LRHS
campestre	SPhx WOut
'Cobalt Star'	GWyn MAvo MRav SMHy
creticum	MNrw
cymosum B&SWJ 10267	WCru
decaisneanum misapplied	see *E. pandanifolium*
deppeanum F&M 54	WPGP
Dove Cottage hybrid	MAvo
ebracteatum	CSpe LEdu
- var. ***poterioides***	ELan EMor ILea IPot LCro LOPS LPla LRHS MBel NDov SEdd SPhx SPtp
§ ***eburneum***	ECha ELan EPfP EWes GMaP ILea LRHS SMad SPtp
aff. ***eburneum***	CMac
'Electric Haze'	CSam
§ ***giganteum*** ♀H6	Widely available
- 'Silver Ghost' ♀H6	CAby CBod CExl CPla CSam CSpe ECtt GMaP LCro LOPS LRHS MHol NChi NDov NGdn NLar NSti SPhx SWvt WAvo WCot WFar WSpi
gracile B&SWJ 10441	WCru
'Green Jade'	LRHS NRHS
guatemalense B&SWJ 10397	ESwi WCru
heterophyllum	SPhx
horridum misapplied	see *E. eburneum*
horridum ambig.	EWes NLar SArc
horridum Malme	WCot
humboldtii B&SWJ 14342	WCru
aff. ***humboldtii*** B&SWJ 14367	WCru
humile B&SWJ 10464	WCru
- var. ***brevibracteatum*** B&SWJ 14735	WCru
'Indigo Star'	MAvo
leavenworthii	EHyd LRHS
- 'Purple Sheen'	LSun
longifolium B&SWJ 14786	WCru
maritimum	CEls CPla CPou CSpe GPoy MNHC SPhx SPlb SRms
Miss Willmott's ghost	see *E. giganteum*
× ***oliverianum*** ♀H5	CBod CDor CMea CTri ECtt ELan EPfP GAbr GKev LRHS MAvo MCot MRav NBir NCou NLar SPoG SWvt WCot WKif
§ ***pandanifolium*** ♀H4	CKno ELan EWes MNrw SArc SEND SMHy SMad SPlb SPoG SWvt
- 'Physic Purple'	CAby CDor CSpe ELan LRHS MAvo SDix SPtp WCot
paniculatum B&SWJ 14367	WCru
- B&SWJ 14826	WCru
'Pen Blue'	CAby CAvo CDor CMea CSam CSpe ECha ECtt ECul EPfP LRHS MGos MHol MNrw NDov SAko SPoG WCAu WCot WHoo WTor
planum	Widely available
§ - 'Blauer Zwerg'	GMaP LRHS NLar WFar
- 'Blaukappe'	CBod CExl CMea CRos EAJP EBee EHyd ELan ELon EMor EPfP LRHS LSun MMuc NLar NRHS SEND SPhx SRms WFar
- BLUE DWARF	see *E. planum* 'Blauer Zwerg'
- 'Blue Glitter'	CCBP CDor EBee ELon LRHS NLar SPhx SWvt
- 'Blue Hobbit'	CBod CExl CMea EBee ECtt EHyd ELan ELon EPfP GEdr LBuc LRHS LSun MGos MHer MTin NGdn NLar NQui NWad SCob SPad SRms SWvt WCAu WFar
- 'Flüela'	EHyd EPfP EWes LRHS LSRN MAvo NRHS
- 'Jade Frost' PBR (v)	CBcs CBct CBod CDor CExl CWCL CWGN EBee EHyd ELan EMor EPfP EWes LCro LOPS LRHS LSou MBNS MHol MNrw MPri MTis NLar SCob SEdd SPad SPoG SRms SWvt WCot
- 'Little Blue Wonder' PBR	NHol
- MAGICAL PURPLE FALLS ('Kolmapufa' PBR) **new**	IPot
- 'Naughty Jackpot' (v)	NLar
- 'Paradise Jackpot' PBR	SRms
- 'Seven Seas'	EHyd LRHS MBNS NRHS

- 'Silver Salentino'	CBod GPSL
- 'Silver Stone'	SRms
- 'Tetra Petra'	LRHS SRms
- 'Tiny Jackpot'	CWGN GEdr GMaP NLar
- 'White Glitter'	EBee ELan EPfP
proteiflorum	CBod LRHS NDov SPlb WFar
serbicum	MAvo SDix
serra	EHyd EWes LRHS
tricuspidatum	CDoC CRos EBee ECtt EHyd LRHS NRHS
× ***tripartitum*** ♀H5	CBcs CBod CTri EBee ECha ECtt EHyd ELan EMor EPfP EWTr GMaP LRHS LSRN MBel MNrw MRav NBro NLar NRHS SDix SWvt
variifolium	Widely available
- 'Miss Marble'	EPfP LPot LSun NGrd SIvy SRms WFar WSHC
venustum	EHyd LRHS SDix SMad SPhx SPtp
yuccifolium	CBod CSpe EBee EMor EPfP EWes LRHS SPeP SPhx SPlb SPtp SWvt XLum
- 'Kershaw Blue'	WPGP
× ***zabelii***	CDor ECha EMor
- 'Big Blue' ♀H5	Widely available
§ - 'Donard Variety'	EHyd ILea LRHS MAvo MCot NLar
- 'Forncett Ultra'	MNrw
- 'Jos Eijking'	Widely available
- 'Neptune's Gold'PBR	Widely available
- 'Violetta'	CAby CSpe EBee EHyd ELon EMor EPfP IPot LEdu LRHS MAvo MCot NLar NRHS WCAu WFar WTor

Erysimum ✿ (*Brassicaceae*)

allionii misapplied	see *E.* × *marshallii*
'Apricot Delight'	see *E.* 'Apricot Twist'
§ 'Apricot Twist'	CBcs CBod CRos CSpe CWCL CWGN EAJP ECtt EHyd ELan ELon EPfP LRHS MAsh MCot MHol NLar NRHS SCoo SPer SPoG SRms SWvt WFar WHoo WMal
arkansanum	see *E. helveticum*
'Audrey's Pink'	CCBP WHoo
bonanianum	WCot
'Bowles's Mauve' ♀H4	Widely available
'Bowles's Purple'	SRms SWvt
'Bowles's Yellow'	MHCG NWad WCot
'Bredon'	NPer WKif WMal
cheiri	MHer MPri NGrd
- 'Baden-Powell' (d)	EPPr
- 'Blood Red'	CSpe LCro LOPS SPhx
- 'Bloody Warrior' (d)	CElw ECtt
- 'Fire King'	LCro LOPS
- 'Harpur Crewe' (d)	NPer SRms WHer
- 'Persian Carpet' (mixed) ♀H5 **new**	LCro
- Sunset Series **new**	MBros
'Constant Cheer'	CElw CMea CSBt EAJP ECtt EHyd ELan EPfP MCot MMuc NLar NPer SEND SRkn SRms SWvt WHoo WSpi
'Cotswold Gem' (v)	ELon MHer MMuc NPer SWvt
'Desert Island'	ECtt
'Dorothy Elmhirst'	see *E.* 'Mrs L.K. Elmhirst'
'Golden Jubilee'	ECtt EHyd LRHS SRms WCav WIce
§ ***helveticum***	SRms
'Jacob's Jacket'	ECha MHer NPer
'John Codrington'	GBin NPer WSpi
'Joseph's Coat'	MHCG
kotschyanum	CBor EBou NSla SRms WHal
'Lemon Light'	WHoo
linifolium	SRms
§ - 'Variegatum' (v)	CCCN CSBt ECtt ELan EPfP LRHS MHol MPri NPer SHar SPer SPoG WCav WHer XLum
- 'Variegatum' peach-flowered (v)	MBros NQui
§ × ***marshallii***	SPhx
'Moonlight'	GMaP MRav NBir SRms WHoo
§ 'Mrs L.K. Elmhirst'	NPer
mutabile	CTri EHyd EPfP WHal
'Orange Flame'	CBor CMea ECha MHer NPer SEND WHoo
'Orange Zwerg'	MMuc WIce
'Paint Box' (Artist Series)	SCob WCav
'Parish's'	CCBP CElw CFis CSpe CWld WGoo WHoo
'Parkwood Gold'	NHpl WIce
'Pastel Patchwork'	CSpe ECtt EPfP LCro LOPS LRHS NRHS WCot WFar
Perry's hybrid	NPer
'Perry's Peculiar'	NPer
'Perry's Surprise'	NPer
'Perry's Variegated' (v)	NPer
'Plant World Lemon'	CDor CWCL EAJP NLar
§ ***pulchellum***	ECha GKev
pumilum DC.	see *E. helveticum*
'Red Jep'	CDoC CSpe EHyd ELan EPfP LRHS NLar NRHS SAdn WCot WNPC WTor
rupestre	see *E. pulchellum*
'Ruston Royal'	CElw ECha WMal
RYSI COPPER	CRos EHyd EPfP LRHS MAsh NRHS SPoG
scoparium	ECha
'Sissinghurst Variegated'	see *E. linifolium* 'Variegatum'
'Spice Island'	ECtt SCob
'Sprite'	CMea CTri NPer
'Stars and Stripes' (v)	CBod ECtt LRHS SRkn WCFE
Sugar Rush Series	MBros
SUNBURST ('Listrace')	CDor ECtt WCot
'Sweet Sorbet'	MBNS NLar SRkn SWvt
WALBERTON'S FRAGRANT STAR ('Walfrastar'PBR) (v)	EHyd EPfP LRHS MAsh NRHS SPoG SRms
WALBERTON'S FRAGRANT SUNSHINE ('Walfrasun')	CRos EHyd EPfP LRHS NRHS SCoo SPoG
'Wenlock Beauty'	CFis SRms
'Winter Joy'	ELan EPfP LRHS MBNS NLar SHar
WINTER ORCHID	CWGN NLar
'Winter Passion'	CWCL EHyd EPfP LRHS MBNS SPoG
WINTER SORBET ('Inneryws'PBR)	ECtt ELan EPfP LRHS

Erythraea see *Centaurium*

Erythrina (*Papilionaceae*)

abyssinica	SPlb
amazonica	SPlb
arborescens	SPlb
× ***bidwillii***	CCCN WPGP
crista-galli ♀H3	CBcs CCCN CDTJ CRos CSpe EBee EHyd ELan EPfP LRHS SPlb WCot WPGP
- 'Compacta'	LRHS
flabelliformis	SPlb
guatemalensis	SPlb
herbacea	SBrt SPlb
§ ***humeana***	SPlb
latissima	SPlb
lysistemon	SPlb

princeps	see *E. humeana*
rubrinervia	SPlb
speciosa	SPlb
vespertilio	SPlb

Erythronium ✿ (*Liliaceae*)

albidum	GEdr IBlr
americanum	IBlr MNrw WAbe
'Apple Blossom' ♀H4	IBlr
'Ballyrogan's Blaze'	IBlr
'Beechpark'	IBlr
'Blush'	IBlr
'Bronze Beauty'	IBlr
'Bryn Meifod'	WAbe
'Californian Star'	IBlr
'Californian Sunshine'	IBlr
californicum	CWCL EBee EHyd GKev IBlr LRHS MAvo MNrw NRHS
- 'Ballyrogan Bronze Bounty'	IBlr
- 'Brimstone'	IBlr
- 'Brocklamont Inheritance' ♀H5	IBlr
- 'Bronze Edge'	IBlr
- 'Dark Delight'	IBlr
- Plas Merdyn form	IBlr
- 'Stellar'	IBlr
- 'White Beauty' ♀H5	Widely available
'Carol Scott'	IBlr
caucasicum	EPot
'Citronella'	GKev IBlr MAvo
cliftonii hort.	see *E. multiscapideum* Cliftonii Group
'Craigton Beauty'	IBlr
'Craigton Cover Girl'	IBlr
'Craigton Cream'	IBlr
'Delicacy'	IBlr
dens-canis	CBod CBro CTri CWCL ELan EMor EPot ERCP GAbr GEdr GKev GMaP IBlr ILea LCro LEdu LOPS MNrw NBir NHol NRya SCob WAbe WPnP WShi
- 'Charmer'	GEdr MNrw
- dark **new**	CBor
- 'Frans Hals'	EPot GEdr GKev LEdu WAbe
- 'Lilac Wonder' ♀H5	EBee EPot GEdr GKev GMaP LEdu MNrw SDeJ
* - 'Moerheimii' (d)	GEdr GKev IBlr
- var. ***niveum***	GEdr
- 'Old Aberdeen' ♀H5	CAvo CRos CWCL EHyd IBlr LRHS MAvo NRHS WAbe
- 'Pink Perfection'	EBee GEdr GKev LEdu MNrw SDeJ WAbe
- 'Purple King'	EBee EPot GEdr GKev GMaP LEdu MNrw NHol NHpl SDeJ WAbe
- 'Rose Queen'	EPot GEdr GKev GMaP LEdu MAvo MNrw SDeJ
- 'Snowflake'	CAvo CRos EHyd EPot GEdr GKev LEdu LRHS MNrw NBir NHol NHpl NRHS SDeJ WAbe
- 'Valerie Wollaston'	MAvo
- 'White Splendour'	EPot GEdr IBlr LEdu MAvo MNrw
'Eirene'	IBlr
elegans	NHpl
'Flaire'	IBlr
'Flash'	IBlr NHar
§ ***grandiflorum***	CWCL EBee EMor
- subsp. ***chrysandrum***	see *E. grandiflorum*
'Harvington Snowgoose'	CRos EHyd LRHS MAvo NHar NRHS
'Harvington Sunshine' **new**	NHar
helenae	MNrw
hendersonii ♀H5	EHyd IBlr LRHS NRHS SPlb WAbe XEll
- 'Pacific Skies'	IBlr
- 'Pacific Sunshine'	IBlr
'Hidcote Beauty'	CRos EHyd LRHS MAvo NRHS
'Janice' ♀H5	IBlr WAbe
japonicum	CMiW EPot GKev MNrw
'Jeanette Brickell'	IBlr
'Jeannine'	IBlr
'Joanna' ♀H5	GEdr IBlr MAvo MNrw NHar
'John Brookes'	IBlr
'Kinfauns Pink'	CBor CWCL EBee ELon EMor EPot GBin GEdr GKev GMaP IBlr
'Kondo'	CBcs CBod CTri EHyd EPfP GMaP IBlr LRHS NBir NHol NLar SCob SDeJ
'Lavender Eye'	IBlr
'Margaret Mathew'	IBlr WAbe
'Minnehaha'	IBlr
§ ***multiscapideum***	EMor MAvo MNrw WSHC
§ - Cliftonii Group ♀H4	MAvo WAbe
'Oregon Encore'	IBlr
oregonum	CRos CWCL EHyd EMor GBin GKev LRHS MNrw NHpl NRHS WAbe
'Pagoda' ♀H5	Widely available
purdyi	see *E. multiscapideum*
'Purple Heart'	IBlr
revolutum	CAvo CBro EBee EHyd ELon EMor GBin GEdr GKev GMaP IBlr LRHS MNrw NHar NHpl NLar NRHS SChF
- from God's Valley, Oregon	IBlr MNrw
I - 'Album'	IBlr
- 'Ballyrogan White Blusher'	IBlr
- 'Dark Dapple'	IBlr
- 'Guincho Splendour'	IBlr
- 'Inferno'	IBlr
I - 'Inshriach Form'	IBlr
- Johnsonii Group	EPot WAbe WCru
- 'Knightshayes'	CRos EBee EHyd LRHS MAvo NRHS
- 'Knightshayes Pink'	CAvo NBir WShi
- 'Pink Beauty'	CPla GKev
- 'Wild Salmon'	EBee EHyd LRHS MAvo NHar NRHS
'Rippling Waters'	IBlr
'Rosalind'	IBlr NHar WAbe
rostratum	GKev
sibiricum	GKev NHpl
'Spring Fresh'	IBlr
'Sundisc' ♀H4	ECha IBlr WAbe
'Sunshine'	IBlr
'Susannah'	EHyd IBlr LRHS NRHS
tuolumnense	CWCL EBee EMor GEdr GKev GMaP IBlr MCot MNrw NHpl SDeJ WAbe
- EBA clone 2	IBlr
- EBA clone 3	IBlr
- Plas Merdyn form	IBlr
- 'Spindlestone'	CRos EHyd GEdr IBlr LRHS NHar NRHS WAbe
umbilicatum	EPot GEdr NHpl
'White Star'	IBlr
'Winifred Loraine'	IBlr

Escallonia (*Escalloniaceae*)

'Alice'	SPer
angustifolia	WPav
var. ***coquimbensis***	

'Apple Blossom' ♀H4 Widely available
§ ***bifida*** ♀H3 CRos EBee EHyd ELan EPfP LRHS MAsh NRHS WPGP
'C.F. Ball' CBcs CBrac CTri EHyd ELan EPfP IArd LRHS MAsh MSwo SGol SRms
'Compacta Coccinea' LRHS
'Donard Beauty' CBrac SRms
'Donard Brilliance' SGol SRms
'Donard Radiance' ♀H4 CBcs CBrac CMac CSBt EPfP EShb NLar NWad SCob SGbt SGol SLim SPer SPoG SRms SWvt WFar
'Donard Seedling' CBcs CBrac CCVT CRos ECrN EHyd ELan EPfP LRHS MAsh MGos MMuc MSwo NPer NRHS SCob SGol SLim SPer SRms SWvt WFar
'Donard Star' EPfP NLar NWad WCFE
'Donard White' CBod EPfP NLar SPoG
'Edinensis' EPfP NLar SRms WSpi
'Everest' EHyd LRHS MMuc SLon
× ***exoniensis*** SRms
'Glowing Embers' **new** MAsh
GOLDEN CARPET ('Alcaura'PBR) CBod CRos EHyd ELan GBin LRHS MAsh MTin NRHS SCob SHar SLon SPoG WNPC
'Hopleys Gold' see *E. laevis* 'Gold Brian'
illinita NLar WPav
'Iveyi' ♀H4 Widely available
'Jamie'PBR LSRN
§ ***laevis*** LRHS
§ - 'Gold Brian' CMac CRos EHyd EPfP LRHS LSRN MAsh MGos NLar NRHS SGol SPer
- 'Gold Ellen' (v) CBrac CDoC CRos CSBt CTri EHyd ELan EPfP LRHS LSRN MAsh MGos MRav MSwo NHol NLar NRHS SCob SCoo SEND SLim SPer SPoG SRms SWvt
- PINK ELLE ('Lades'PBR) CDoC CRos CSBt EBee EHyd EPfP LCro LOPS LRHS MAsh MGos NRHS SCob SPoG WFar WNPC
'Langleyensis' ♀H4 CMac CTri SGol SRms
× ***mollis*** SPer
montevidensis see *E. bifida*
myrtilloides B&SWJ 14329 WCru
organensis see *E. laevis*
'Peach Blossom' ♀H4 CBar CBcs CDoC CRos EBee EHyd ELan EPfP LRHS MAsh MMuc MSwo NHol NRHS SCob SCoo SGbt SGol SLim SPer SRms WFar
'Pride of Donard' ♀H4 CSBt EPfP MGos SCob SGsty SRms
pulverulenta WPav
punctata see *E. rubra*
RED CARPET ('Loncar'PBR) CBcs GBin LRHS SCob SLon WNPC
'Red Dream' CSBt EHyd EPfP GBin LRHS MAsh MGos MSwo NLar SCob SCoo SGsty SPoG SRms SWvt WAvo WFar
'Red Elf' CMac CRos EBou EHyd ELan EPfP GKin LRHS MGos SPer SPlb SRms SWvt WFar
'Red Hedger' CBod CSBt CTsd ECrN ELan MRav SRms
'Red Knight' CRos EHyd LRHS MAsh NHol NRHS WNPC
resinosa CExl CMCN CTsd SPlb SRms SVen WPav
revoluta CTri MGil WPav
§ ***rubra*** GKev
- 'Crimson Spire' ♀H4 CBar CBcs CBod CBrac CSBt CTri ECrN EPfP GKin LRHS LSRN MAsh MGos MMuc MRav NBir SCob SEND SGbt SLim SNig SPer SPlb SRms
- 'Ingramii' SEND
- var. ***macrantha*** CBar CBcs CBod CBrac CCVT CDoC CMac CRos CSBt CTri ECrN EHyd ELan EPfP GKin IArd LRHS MHed NBir NLar NRHS SCob SCoo SLim SNig SPer SPoG SRms WAvo
- 'Pygmaea' see *E. rubra* 'Woodside'
§ - 'Woodside' CMCN NWad SGol SRms
'Silver Anniversary' MSwo
'Slieve Donard' CBrac CMac MRav SRms
tucumanensis SPlb
'Ventnor' SPlb SVen
virgata WPav

Eschscholzia (*Papaveraceae*)

caespitosa 'Sundew' SPhx
californica MBel
- 'Alba' CSpe
- 'Apricot Chiffon' (Thai Silk Series) ♀H3 **new** LCro LOPS
- 'Ivory Castle' SPhx
- var. ***maritima*** CSpe SPhx
- subsp. ***mexicana*** ' Sun Shades' SPhx
- 'Mission Bells' LCro
- 'Orange King' **new** SPhx
- 'Red Chief' CSpe LRHS SPhx

Espeletia (*Asteraceae*)

argentea B&SWJ 14322 WCru
killipii B&SWJ 14319 WCru
aff. ***killipii*** WCru
aff. ***lopezii*** B&SWJ 14374 WCru
aff. ***summapacis*** WCru
uribei B&SWJ 14339 WCru

Esterhuysenia (*Aizoaceae*)

alpina CPBP SPlb

Eucalyptus ✿ (*Myrtaceae*)

aggregata SArc SKin
alpina SPlb WPav
amygdalina SPlb
approximans SKin
archeri CDTJ CDoC CTsd ELan EPfP LRHS MGos MHtn MMuc NLar SKin
caesia ♀H2 SPlb
camaldulensis LMaj SPlb
camphora CCCN SKin
cinerea CTsd SKin SPlb SWeb
citriodora see *Corymbia citriodora*
coccifera CBcs CDoC CSBt CTsd EBee MMuc NPer SKin SPlb
cordata EPfP IDee SKin WPGP
crenulata EBee SKin
crucis subsp. ***crucis*** SPlb
cypellocarpa SPlb
dalrympleana ♀H5 CDoC CRos EPfP LRHS LSRN MGos MMuc NPer SEND SKin SLim SPer SPlb WPGP
debeuzevillei see *E. pauciflora* subsp. *debeuzevillei*
delegatensis NPer
divaricata see *E. gunnii* subsp. *divaricata*
erythrocorys SPlb
eximia see *Corymbia eximia*
ficifolia see *Corymbia ficifolia*

	fraxinoides	SPlb
	gamophylla	SPlb
	glaucescens	CAbb LRHS SArc SKin SPer
	globulus	SPlb
§	***gregsoniana***	SKin SPlb
	gunnii ♀H5	Widely available
	- AZURA ('Cagire'PBR)	IBal LCro LOPS LSRN NLar SCob SEWo SLim WMat
§	- subsp. ***divaricata***	SKin
*	- 'Silver Drop'	WFar
	johnstonii	ELan SKin SPer
	kitsoniana	SKin
	kruseana	SPlb
	kybeanensis	SKin
	leucoxylon	SKin SPlb
	subsp. ***megalocarpa***	
	ligustrina	SKin
	macrocarpa	SPlb
	mitchelliana	SKin
	moorei var. ***nana***	CDTJ
	neglecta	SKin
	nicholii	CAbb CBcs CDoC CSpe CTsd EBee EPfP EWes LRHS MGos MMuc SCoo SEdd SKin SPoG WPGP
	niphophila	see *E. pauciflora* subsp. *niphophila*
	nitens	CDTJ SKin SPlb
§	***nitida***	SKin
	parviflora	SKin
	parvula ♀H5	CCCN CMac CTsd EPfP MMuc SEND
	pauciflora	CCCN EBee SCob SPer
§	- subsp. ***debeuzevillei*** ♀H5	CAbb CTsd EPfP NOrn SArc SKin WPGP
	- var. ***nana***	see *E. gregsoniana*
§	- subsp. ***niphophila*** ♀H5	CAbb CBcs CMac CSBt CTho CTsd EHyd ELan EPfP LRHS LSRN MBlu MGos MHtn MMuc MPri MRav MSwo NOrn SCob SKin SPer SPlb SPoG SWvt WCot WFar WMat WPGP
	perriniana	CBcs ECrN ELan EPfP LRHS MGos MHtn NOrn SKin SPer SPlb SPoG SWvt WFar WMat
	pulverulenta	CMac SPlb WFar
	- 'Baby Blue'	CTsd SKin SPer SWvt WFar
	regnans	IDee SKin
	rossii	SPlb
	rubida	CCCN SKin
	saxatilis new	SKin
	sideroxylon	SPlb
	- 'Rosea'	SPlb
	simmondsii	see *E. nitida*
	stellulata	SKin
	stricta	SKin
	subcrenulata	CDoC CTsd EPfP SKin
	tetraptera	SPlb
	torquata	SPlb
	urnigera	CTsd SMad
	vernicosa	SKin
	viminalis	IDee SKin

Eucharidium see *Clarkia*

Eucharis (*Amaryllidaceae*)

§	***amazonica*** ♀H1b	CCCN EShb SDeJ SDir
	grandiflora misapplied	see *E. amazonica*

Eucomis ✿ (*Asparagaceae*)

	ALOHA	see *E.* 'Leia'
	autumnalis misapplied	see *E. zambesiaca*
§	***autumnalis*** (Mill.) Chitt. ♀H4	CBod CBro EPot ERCP GKev LRHS SDeJ SDir SPer SPlb WCot
	- subsp. ***amaryllidifolia***	CBro
	bicolor ♀H4	Widely available
	- 'Alba'	CBro CExl GKev
§	***comosa***	CAvo CBro CPrp CSam EBee EHyd ERCP EShb GKev LRHS NGKo SDeJ SDir WCot
	- 'Cherry Blossom'	CBro
	- 'Cornwood'	CAvo GKev
	- 'Johannesburg'	EBee GKev
	- 'Kilimanjaro'	EBee
	- 'Oakhurst'	CAby CChe CCht CPla ECtt ESwi LRHS WABo WCot
	- purple-leaved	CAvo EShb
	- 'Sparkling Burgundy' ♀H4	Widely available
	- 'Sparkling Rosy'	CAvo CBro ERCP GKev IPot NGKo SDir WFar
	- var. ***striata***	CAby EBee
	'Dark Star'	ECtt IPot MNrw
	'Freckles'	CAby CPla NGKo SPoG SRms
	'Glow Sticks'	CWGN ECtt WHil
	humilis	XEll
	- 'Twinkle Stars'	ERCP SDeJ WFar WSMil
	'John Treasure'	SMHy
	'Joy's Purple'	CBro CPar EPri
§	'Leia'PBR (Aloha Lily Series)	CAvo CBro ERCP EShb GKev LRHS LSou
	MAUI ('Gsalkele'PBR) (Aloha Lily Series)	LSou
	'Mini Tuft Cherry Blossom' new	WHil
	montana	CBro CPla CPrp EBee EPot ERCP GKev SDeJ SDir WCot
	NANI ('Gsalipol'PBR) (Aloha Lily Series)	LSou
	pallidiflora ♀H3	CAvo LEdu NGKo WPGP
	'Pink Gin'	CAvo GKev IPot
	'Playa Blanca'	EBee EShb GKev
§	***pallidiflora*** subsp. ***pallidiflora***	CBro CExl CPar ELan EPPr EPri EShb GKev MRav NGKo SDeJ SDir WAvo WSHC WSMil
	- - dark	GKev
	- - pink-flowered	CPar
I	- - 'Purpurea'	CExl
	- subsp. ***pole-evansii*** misapplied	see *E. pallidiflora* subsp. *pallidiflora*
	pole-evansii	see *E. pallidiflora* subsp. *pole-evansii*
	punctata	see *E. comosa*
	regia JCA 3.230.709	WCot
	'Swazi Pride'	NGKo WHil
	undulata	see *E. autumnalis* (Mill.) Chitt.
	vandermerwei ♀H3	CBro EBee EPot LEdu NGKo NWad SDeJ SDir SPlb WGwG
	- 'Octopus'	CCCN CExl CPrp ELan EPfP GKev WCot WFar WSMil
§	***zambesiaca***	CAvo CBro CPla GKev NGKo SMHy WPGP
	- JCA 3.230.709	WCot
	- JCA 3.231.010	WCot
	- 'White Dwarf'	CBcs SPer WFar WGwG
	'Zeal Bronze'	WAvo WCot
	'Zulu Flame' new	IPot

Eucommia (*Eucommiaceae*)

	ulmoides	CMCN NLar

Eucryphia ✿ (*Cunoniaceae*)

	cordifolia	CMac IDee MBlu MGil NLar WPav
§	***cordifolia*** × ***lucida***	CCCN

	glutinosa ♀H4	CCCN CRos EHyd EPfP GGGa GKev IDee LRHS MAsh MGil SAko SCob WPav
	- 'Miniature'	EPfP WPGP
	× ***hillieri***	WSpi
	- 'Winton'	CBct EBee WPGP
	× ***intermedia***	CCCN CDoC CExl CMac NLar SRms SSta
	- 'Rostrevor' ♀H4	CBcs CExl CJun CMac CRos CTho EHyd ELan EPfP GGGa IArd IMou LRHS LSRN MAsh MBlu NLar SSta WPGP
	'Leatherwood Cream'	WSpi
	lucida	CBcs CCCN CRos EHyd LRHS MMuc NLar NRHS WSpi
	- 'Ballerina' ♀H4	CBcs CJun CMac CRos CTho EBee EHyd ELan EPfP GKin LRHS MAsh NRHS SAko SChF SCoo SMad SPoG WPGP
I	- 'Chaplin's Variety'	EBee WPGP
	- 'Dumpling'	CExl EBee WPGP
	- 'Gilt Edge' (v)	CBcs CRos EHyd LRHS NRHS SPoG
	- 'Leatherwood Cream' (v)	ELon
	- 'Pink Cloud'	CBcs CEnd CExl CJun CMac CRos CTho EHyd ELan EPfP GKin IArd LRHS LSRN MBlu MGil MGos NLar NRHS SWvt WPGP
	- 'Spring Glow' (v)	CExl CRos EHyd LRHS MAsh NRHS
	milliganii	CDoC CMac CRos EHyd ELon EPfP LRHS MBlu MRav SPer SRms SSta WPGP WSpi
	moorei	CCCN CExl CMac IDee SAko WPGP
	× ***nymansensis***	CHab SArc SRms WSpi
	- 'George Graham'	GGGa IArd WPGP
	- 'Nymans Silver' (v)	CBcs CDoC CJun CLnd CMac CRos CTho EHyd ELan EPfP GGGa LRHS MAsh SPer SPoG SSta
	- 'Nymansay' ♀H4	Widely available
	'Penwith' misapplied	see *E. cordifolia* × *lucida*
	'Penwith' ambig.	IDee MGos NLar

Eugenia (*Myrtaceae*)

uniflora	CCCN

Eumorphia (*Asteraceae*)

sericea	GBin

Eunomia see *Aethionema*

Euodia (*Rutaceae*)

daniellii	see *Tetradium daniellii*
hupehensis	see *Tetradium daniellii* Hupehense Group

Euonymus ✿ (*Celastraceae*)

	B&L 12543	EWes
	CC 4522	CExl
	NJM 09.109	CRHN
	NJM 10.106	WPGP
	from Kachin, Burma	WPGP
	alatus	Widely available
	- B&SWJ 8794	WCru
	- var. ***apterus***	EPfP WGrn
	- 'Blade Runner'	CRos EHyd EPfP ESwi LRHS MBlu MGos NLar NRHS SGol
	- CHICAGO FIRE	see *E. alatus* 'Timber Creek'
	- 'Ciliodentatus'	see *E. alatus* f. *striatus*
	- 'Compactus' ♀H6	Widely available
	- 'Fastigiata'	CJun
§	- 'Fire Ball'	CJun
*	- 'Macrophyllus'	CJun
	- 'Rudy Haag'	CJun EPfP
	- 'Select'	see *E. alatus* 'Fire Ball'
	- 'Silver Cloud'	NLar
§	- f. ***striatus***	CJun
	- - B&SWJ 11051	ESwi WCru
§	- 'Timber Creek'	CJun EPfP MBlu
	americanus	EPfP MBlu NLar
	- var. ***angustifolius*** B&SWJ 12905	ESwi WCru
	'Benkomoki'	SGsty
	bungeanus	EPfP WLov
	- B&SWJ 8782 from South Korea	WCru
	- 'Dart's Pride'	CJun EPfP NLar
	- 'Fireflame'	CJun NLar WCot
	- 'Pendulus'	MBlu
	- var. ***semipersistens***	CJun WCru
§	***carnosus***	CJun CMCN
	- CWJ 12425	WCru
	- 'Red Wine'	CJun EPfP LEdu LRHS MBlu NLar NOra WCot WLov
	- 'Trompenburg Lustre' **new**	NLar
	chibae B&SWJ 11159	WCru
§	***clivicola***	CJun EBee WCru
	aff. ***clivicola*** HIRD 103 **new**	SBrt
	cornutus	SPtp WPGP
	- var. ***quinquecornutus*** ♀H6	CJun CMCN CSpe ELan EPfP ESwi IArd MBlu MMrt SBrt SPoG WPGP
	'Den Haag'	CJun EPfP LRHS
	echinatus	IDee
	europaeus	Widely available
	- from Slovakia	WCru
	- f. ***albus***	EPfP LRHS SMad SPoG
	- 'Atropurpureus'	CMCN CTho EPfP NLar
	- 'Atrorubens'	CJun
	- 'Aucubifolius' (v)	CMac
*	- 'Aureus'	CNat
	- 'Brilliant'	CJun EPfP LRHS NLar
	- 'Chrysophyllus'	EPfP MBlu
	- var. ***intermedius***	CJun EPfP MBlu
	- 'Miss Pinkie'	CEnd NOrn
	- 'Red Cascade' ♀H6	Widely available
	- 'Scarlet Wonder'	CJun IArd MAsh NLar WMat
	- 'Thornhayes'	CTho EPfP
	farreri	see *E. nanus*
	fimbriatus	CJun
	fortunei	SavN
	- BLONDY ('Interbolwi'PBR) (v)	CBcs CDoC CRos CTri EHyd ELan EPfP LRHS MAsh MGos MMuc MSwo NLar NRHS SCob SCoo SGol SLim SPer SPoG SRms SavN
	- 'Canadale Gold' (v)	CMac CRos EHyd EPfP LRHS MAsh NHol NRHS SGsty SLon SPer WAvo
	- 'Coloratus'	EPfP MBlu MSwo SEND
	- 'Country Gold'	WFar
	- DAN'S DELIGHT ('Dandel'PBR) (v)	LCro LOPS MGos MThu SGol SPoG
	- 'Dart's Blanket'	CBod EBee ELan EPfP MRav SCob SGol SavN
	- 'Emerald Gaiety' (v) ♀H5	Widely available
*	- 'Emerald Green'	SavN
	- 'Emerald 'n' Gold' (v) ♀H5	Widely available
	- 'Gold Spot'	see *E. fortunei* 'Sunspot'
	- 'Gold Tip'	see *E. fortunei* 'Golden Prince'
	- GOLDEN HARLEQUIN ('Hoogi'PBR) (v)	CBcs EPfP LRHS MAsh MThu NWad SPoG SWvt

§	- 'Golden Prince' (v)	CMac MRav MSwo NLar SRms
	- GOLDY ('Waldbolwi'PBR)	EPfP NLar SGol SPoG
	- 'Harlequin' (v)	CBcs CBrac CMac CRos CSBt EHyd ELan EPfP LBuc LRHS LSRN MAsh MBlu MGos MRav NBir NRHS SCob SGol SLim SPer SPoG SRms SWvt SavN WFar
	- 'Heins Silver'PBR	EBee LRHS MGos SGol
	- 'Hort's Blaze'	EBee
	- 'Kewensis' ♀H5	CMac EHyd ELan LRHS SArc SPoG WCFE WCru
	- 'Kewensis Variegatus' (v)	MRav
	- 'Longwood'	LRHS
	- 'Minimus'	CSpe EPPr MSwo SMad WBor WPGP XLum
*	- 'Minimus Variegatus' (v)	EPPr SPlb
	- 'Perrolino'	SavN
	- 'Prince John'	CSBt
	- 'Sheridan Gold'	MRav
	- 'Silver Gem'	see *E. fortunei* 'Variegatus'
	- 'Silver Queen' (v)	Widely available
	- 'Silverstone'PBR (v)	EMil EPfP LRHS SGol SPoG
	- 'Sunshine' (v)	CRos EHyd ELan EPfP LRHS MAsh SLon SPoG WAvo
§	- 'Sunspot' (v)	CBcs CBod CMac EBee ELan MMuc MSwo SGol SRms
§	- 'Variegatus' (v)	SRms
	- 'Wolong Ghost' ♀H5	CDoC CExl CMCN CRos EHyd ELan EPPr LRHS MBlu MGos MMuc NLar NRHS SGol SWvt WCot WLov
	frigidus KWJ 12275	WCru
	- var. ***elongatus*** GWJ 9378	WCru
	grandiflorus misapplied	see *E. carnosus*
§	***grandiflorus*** Wall.	CJun EPfP IArd NLar SCoo
	- 'Ruby Wine' **new**	CBcs WMat
	- f. ***salicifolius*** misapplied	see *E. grandiflorus* Wall.
	hamiltonianus	CMCN ECrN EPfP LRHS MMuc SMad
	- 'Fiesta'	CJun NLar
	- subsp. ***hians***	see *E. hamiltonianus* subsp. *sieboldianus*
	- 'Indian Summer'	CJun CRos CTho EHyd EMil EPfP EWTr LRHS MAsh NLar NOra SPoG WMat
	- 'Koi Boy'	CJun EPfP LSRN MAsh NOra SPoG WMat
	- 'Miss Pinkie'	CJun NLar WLov
	- 'Pink Delight'	CJun
	- 'Poort Bulten'	CJun
	- 'Popcorn'	CJun EPfP LRHS WLov
	- 'Rainbow'	CJun EPfP MMrt
	- 'Red Chief'	CJun
	- 'Red Elf'	CJun NLar
	- 'Rising Sun'	CBod CJun EPfP NLar
§	- subsp. ***sieboldianus***	CExl CTho EPfP MRav WLov
	- - B&SWJ 10941	SAko WCru
	- - PAB 5337	LEdu
	- - 'Calocarpus'	CJun EPfP
	- - 'Coral Charm'	CBcs CJun EPfP NLar WLov
	- 'Snow' (v)	WCot WLov
	- 'Winter Glory'	CJun LRHS
§	***huangii***	CJun WLov
	- B&SWJ 3700	WCru
	japonicus	CBcs CBod CCoa CDoC CMac ECrN EPfP LMaj SArc SCob SEND SEWo SGsty SPer SWeb SavN
	- 'Albomarginatus' (v)	CBcs CTri EPfP MPri SCob SEND SRms
§	- 'Aureomarginatus' (v)	CBrac CCVT GBin MPri SWeb
	- 'Aureopictus'	see *E. japonicus* 'Aureus'
	- 'Aureovariegatus'	see *E. japonicus* 'Ovatus Aureus'
§	- 'Aureus' (v)	CBcs CDoC CSBt EPfP LRHS MPri NRHS SCob SCoo SEND SLon SPer
	- 'Benkomasaki'	LSRN
	- 'Bravo' (v)	CBar CCVT CDoC CRos EHyd EPfP LMaj LRHS MAsh MGos MPri NRHS SArc SCob SCoo SEWo SGsty SLim SPer SPoG SWeb SWvt WCot WFar
	- 'Carnival Candle'	SEND
	- 'Charles'PBR	SPoG
	- 'Chollipo' (v) ♀H5	EBee ELan EPfP LRHS SEND SPoG WAvo
	- 'Compactus'	SCoo
	- 'Duc d'Anjou' misapplied	see *E. japonicus* 'Viridivariegatus'
	- 'Duc d'Anjou' Carrière (v)	EBee ELan EPfP EWes MRav SEND SPoG
	- 'Elegantissimus Aureus'	see *E. japonicus* 'Aureomarginatus'
	- EXSTASE ('Goldbolwi'PBR) (v)	WCot
	- 'Francien' (v)	EHyd EPfP LRHS NLar NRHS
	- 'Gold Queen'PBR	NLar
	- 'Golden Maiden' (v)	CRos EHyd ELan EPfP LRHS MAsh SLim SLon SPoG SRms SWvt
	- GREEN MILLENIUM ('Minmil'PBR)	LRHS
	- 'Green Rocket'	CBod CCVT CCoa CRos EBee EHyd EPfP GBin LRHS LSRN MGos MRav NRHS SGol SLim SPoG SSta WCot WFar
	- 'Green Spider'	SPoG
	- 'Green Spire'	CDoC LRHS NLar
	- 'Happiness'PBR	MTin NEoE
	- 'Kathy'PBR	CRos EHyd ELan ELon EPfP LRHS LSRN MAsh NLar NRHS SPoG SavN
§	- 'Latifolius Albomarginatus' (v)	ELan EPfP MRav MSwo SPer SWvt
	- 'Luna'	see *E. japonicus* 'Aureus'
	- 'Macrophyllus'	SavN
	- 'Macrophyllus Albus'	see *E. japonicus* 'Latifolius Albomarginatus'
	- 'Maiden's Gold'	CSBt
	- 'Marieke'	see *E. japonicus* 'Ovatus Aureus'
	- 'Microphyllus'	CMac MRav SArc SGol SRms
§	- 'Microphyllus Albovariegatus' (v)	CMac CSBt CTri EHyd ELan EPfP LRHS MGos SCob SLim SRms SWvt WAvo WFar WLov
§	- 'Microphyllus Aureovariegatus' (v)	CMac CRos CSBt EHyd ELan ELon EPfP LRHS MAsh MMuc NLar NRHS
	- 'Microphyllus Aureus'	see *E. japonicus* 'Microphyllus Pulchellus'
	- 'Microphyllus Gold Dust'	CBod
§	- 'Microphyllus Pulchellus' (v)	CBcs CDoC CMac CSBt EPfP LRHS MGos MMuc SPoG SWvt
	- 'Microphyllus Variegatus'	see *E. japonicus* 'Microphyllus Albovariegatus'
§	- 'Ovatus Aureus' (v) ♀H5	CBar CDoC CExl CMac CRos CSBt CTri ELan ELon EPfP LMaj LRHS MGos MRav NLar NRHS SCob SEND SGbt SGol SGsty SLim SPer SPlb SPoG SRms SWeb SWvt SavN WFar
	- PALOMA BLANCA ('Lankveld03'PBR)	CRos EHyd EPfP LCro LOPS LRHS NRHS SCoo SPoG SavN WFar
	- 'Président Gauthier' (v)	CDoC EBee ELan LRHS SCob SCoo SGsty SLim SPer SWeb SWvt
	- 'Pulchellus Aureovariegatus'	see *E. japonicus* 'Microphyllus Aureovariegatus'
	- 'Robustus'	CBod

- 'Rokujo'	GEdr
- 'Silver King'	CMac SGsty
- 'Silver Krista' (v)	NLar
- 'Susan' (v) 🏆^{H5}	CMac MAsh SGsty
§ - 'Viridivariegatus' (v)	LRHS WAvo
kachinensis B&SWJ 11668	WCru
kiautschovicus	NLar
'Berry Hill'	
- 'Manhattan'	NLar
latifolius	CJun CMCN CTho EPfP IDee IMou LEdu WCru
aff. ***latifolius*** NJM 13.024 new	WPGP
§ ***laxiflorus*** GWJ 9351	WCru
- HWJ 890	WCru
lucidus	CBcs CExl
macropterus	CJun IArd IMou
- B&SWJ 12591	WCru
morrisonensis	see *E. huangii*
myrianthus	CJun ELan EPfP EWTr IArd IDee MBlu MPkF NLar SPtp
aff. ***myrianthus*** slim-leaved NJM 11.016	WPGP
§ ***nanus***	CTri NLar
- var. ***turkestanicus***	LRHS SBrt SLon SRms
'Ogisu'	GKev
oresbius	IArd
oxyphyllus 🏆^{H6}	CJun CMCN EPfP LRHS MMuc NLar SPtp WCru
- 'Waasland'	CJun NLar
phellomanus 🏆^{H6}	CBcs CTho EBee EPfP GKin IDee LRHS MBlu MGil MGos MMuc MPkF MRav MSCN NLar NOra NOrn SCoo SPer SPoG SWvt WMat WPGP
- 'Silver Surprise' (v)	CJun
PIERROLINO ('Heespierrolino'^{PBR})	MRav NLar SCoo
§ ***planipes***	CAby CBcs CCVT CDoC CExl CMCN CRos CTho CTri EBee ECrN EHyd ELan EPfP EWTr GKin LRHS MAsh MBlu MGil MMuc MRav NLar NOra SLim SPer SPoG WLov WMat
- B&SWJ 8660	WCru
- 'Dart's August Flame'	CJun
- 'Sancho' 🏆^{H6}	CJun EPfP LRHS NLar WMat
porphyreus B&SWJ 13914	WCru
- GWJ 9377	WCru
quelpaertensis	CJun
'Rokojō Variegated' (v)	WCot
rongchuensis 'Cliuicolus'	see *E. clivicola*
rosmarinifolius	see *E. nanus*
rubescens	see *E. laxiflorus*
sachalinensis misapplied	see *E. planipes*
sachalinensis (F. Schmidt) Maxim. B&SWJ 10835	WCru
sacrosanctus	CJun MBlu
sanguineus	NLar
semenovii new	WPGP
sieboldianus var. ***sanguineus*** B&SWJ 11140	WCru
- - B&SWJ 11386	WCru
spraguei	SBrt
- CWJ 12446	WCru
tingens	CJun CMCN SPtp WPGP
trapococcus	EPfP SPtp
vagans Wall.	WCot
velutinus	SPtp
verrucosus	CJun NLar
wilsonii	LRHS NLar
yedoensis	see *E. hamiltonianus* subsp. *sieboldianus*

Eupatoriadelphus see *Eupatorium*

Eupatorium ✿ (*Asteraceae*)

B&SWJ 9052 from Guatemala	WCru
FMWJ 13428 from Northern Vietnam	WCru
album misapplied	see *Ageratina altissima*
album L.	NBid
altissimum	SRms
amabile NMWJ 14456	WCru
aromaticum	see *Ageratina aromatica*
atrorubens	see *Bartlettina sordida*
cannabinum	CBod CHab ELan GPoy LLWG MBNS MHer MMuc MNHC MWts NAts NBir NMir NPer SEND SPhx WHer WSFF
§ - f. ***albiflorum***	SPhx
- 'Album'	see *E. cannabinum* f. *albiflorum*
- f. ***cannabinum*** 'Flore Pleno' (d)	CMac ECtt ELan ELon MBel MHer MRav NBir NGdn NLar SDix WCot WFar WSFF WWtn XLum
- - 'Spraypaint' (v)	WSFF
capillifolium 🏆^{H3}	EBee ECtt ESwi EWes MBel MNrw MPie SDix SHar SMad
- 'Elegant Plume'	EBee MNrw
coelestinum	see *Conoclinium coelestinum*
dubium 'Baby Joe'^{PBR}	CAby CBod CWGN EBee ECtt EHyd ELan IPot LRHS MBNS MNHC MNrw NLar NRHS SEdd SHar SPad SPeP WNPC WSFF
- 'Little Joe'	EBee GBin LEdu MTis WCAu WSFF
fistulosum	EBee
- f. ***albidum***	ECha EWhm MMuc
- - 'Bartered Bride'	CKno EBee ECtt EPPr EWes LPla MBel NLar SPeP WCot WSFF
- - 'Ivory Towers'	CBod CDor CRos EBee EHyd GJos LRHS NRHS SPtp WCot WSFF
- - 'Massive White' 🏆^{H7}	ELon GBee MNrw NBir NSti
- 'Berggarten'	WSFF
- 'Carin'	WSFF
fortunei 'Capri' (v)	WHil
- 'Fine Line' (v)	WSFF
- 'Pink Elegance' (v)	CAby CBod EBee ECtt EHyd EMor EShb LRHS LSou MNrw MPie NBPC NRHS SDix SGbt SPoG SRms WWtn
- 'Pink Frost' (v)	EWTr MWts NGdn SCob SPeP
japonicum	GPoy
ligustrinum	see *Ageratina ligustrina*
lindleyanum	LEdu WSFF
- var. ***trisectifolium*** B&SWJ 12742	WCru
maculatum	NGdn NLar WHrl
- Atropurpureum Group	Widely available
- - 'Ankum's August'	EBee IMou LPla SMHy
- - 'Gateway'	CBod CKno EBee ECtt EHyd ELon EPPr EWTr LEdu LRHS MBel NBid NLar SWvt WSFF
- - 'Glutball'	CKno EHyd ELon IMou LPla LRHS LSun MNrw NChi SMad SPeP
- - 'Little Red'	WSFF
- - 'Orchard Dene' 🏆^{H7}	LEdu SMHy
- - 'Phantom'^{PBR}	CRos EBee ECtt EHyd ELon EMor GBin LRHS MHol NBPC NLar NRHS SAko SMad SPoG WSFF

- - 'Prairie Giant' **new**	NDov
- - 'Purple Bush' 🏆[H7]	CDor CKno EBee ECtt EHyd ELon GQue ILea LCro LOPS LRHS MHer MTis NDov NGrd SDix SWvt WSFF
- - 'Red Dwarf'	CBod ECtt EHyd ELon EMor EShb EWTr GQue LEdu LRHS MCot MHol MPie NRHS SPoG SWvt WHil WHoo WPGP
- - 'Riesenschirm' 🏆[H7]	Widely available
- 'J.S. Humble'	IPot MNrw
- 'Snowball'[PBR]	CBod EPfP MCot MTis
makinoi	WCru
var. ***oppositifolium*** B&SWJ 8449	
'Mask'	IPot MNrw NLar
micranthum	see *Ageratina ligustrina*
perfoliatum	EMor GPoy IPot NBre NLar WSFF
purpureum	CBcs CBod CHby ECtt ELon GMaP GPoy LLWG MHer MNHC MWat NBro NChi NGdn SCob SPer SPlb SRms WCAu WHer WOld WSFF
- 'Album'	CTri SWvt
rugosum	see *Ageratina altissima*
* 'Snowball'	LSou NDov SPoG
weinmannianum	see *Ageratina ligustrina*
yakushimaense **new**	GEdr

Euphorbia ✿ (*Euphorbiaceae*)

'Abbey Dore' 🏆[H7]	GBin MAvo SPhx WCot WSHC
amygdaloides	ECtt SWvt WOut XSen
- 'Bob's Choice'	WSHC
- 'Craigieburn'	EHyd LRHS MRav NRHS
§ - 'Purpurea'	Widely available
§ - var. ***robbiae*** 🏆[H6]	Widely available
- - dwarf	EWes
- - 'Redbud'	EWes
- 'Rubra'	see *E. amygdaloides* 'Purpurea'
- Ruby Glow ('Waleuphglo')	CBod CSpe
baselicis	EWes
biglandulosa Desf.	see *E. rigida*
Blackbird ('Nothowlee'[PBR])	CBcs CExl CMac CWCL CWGN ECtt ELan EPfP EWTr LCro LOPS LRHS MBel MGos MRav NLar SCob SEdd SLim SWvt WHil WSpi XEll XSen
'Blue Dome'	CSpe
'Blue Haze'	LPla WCot WFar WMal WSHC WSpi
cactus **new**	CDoC
capitulata	SBrt
cashmeriana CC&McK 607	EWes
ceratocarpa 🏆[H4]	CSpe ECtt EWes GMaP LRHS SPhx WAvo WCot WSHC WSpi WTor XSen
characias	CBcs CMac ECtt EHyd EPfP LRHS MCot MRav NPer NRHS SPer SRms SWvt WBrk WCot WSMil XSen
- 'Ascot Moonbeam'	SPoG
- 'Black Pearl'	CAbb CBcs CBod CRos ECtt EHyd ELan EPfP LRHS MAvo MBel MPri NLar NRHS SCob SGbt SLim SPer SPoG SRkn SWvt WSpi
- 'Blue Wonder'	CBod CExl CSam ECtt EHyd ELan EPfP EWes GMaP LRHS NLar SCob WCot WNPC XSen
- 'BQ'	WCot
- subsp. ***characias***	CAby EPfP NLar SEND
- - 'Blue Hills' 🏆[H4]	ECtt
- - 'Burrow Silver' (v)	CDor EPfP MRav SWvt WNPC
- - 'Humpty Dumpty'	CBod CExl CRos EBee ECtt EHyd ELan EPfP GMaP GWyn LRHS LSRN MPri NGdn NLar NPer NRHS SCob SPer SRms SWvt WFar
- - 'Joshua'	WCot
- 'Eye-catcher'	WCot
- 'Forescate'	EBee EHyd EPfP NRHS
- 'Glacier Blue'[PBR] (v)	CBct CPla CRos CSpe CTsd CWGN EBee ECha EHyd ELan EMor EPfP LRHS LSRN MAsh MBel MCot MHol NHpl NLar NRHS SCob SEdd SHeu SPeP SPoG SRms WCot WNPC
- 'Goldbrook'	EPfP LRHS MBriF MRav NRHS
- 'Kestrel' (v)	WCot
- 'Portuguese Velvet'	CBct CBod CExl CRos ECtt EHyd ELan EPfP GWyn LRHS MCot MRav NLar NRHS SArc SLim WCot XSen
- 'Silver Edge' (v) **new**	LSou MHol NSti WNPC
- Silver Swan ('Wilcott'[PBR]) (v)	CBcs CBod CRos CWGN EBee EHyd ELan EPfP EWes GKin LBuc LRHS LSRN MGos MPri MRav NLar SCob SEle SGbt SLim SPer SPoG SRkn SRms STPC SWvt XSen
- 'Tasmanian Tiger'[PBR] (v) 🏆[H4]	CBcs CRos CWGN ECtt EPfP EWTr EWes GMaP LRHS LSRN MGos MHol NHpl NLar NRHS SCob SEle SHeu SPoG SRms SWvt WCot WNPC WSpi
- subsp. ***wulfenii***	Widely available
- - 'Bosahan'	CExl
- - 'Emmer Green' (v)	CExl ECtt EWes LSou MHol NSti WCot
- - 'Jayne's Golden Giant'	SMad
- - 'Jimmy Platt' 🏆[H4]	SRms WCot
§ - - 'John Tomlinson'	EWes MRav SPtp WAvo WSpi
- - Kew form	see *E. characias* subsp. *wulfenii* 'John Tomlinson'
- - 'Lambrook Gold'	MRav NLar NPer SCob WCot WSpi
- - 'Lambrook Gold' seed-raised	see *E. characias* subsp. *wulfenii* Margery Fish Group
§ - - Margery Fish Group	EHyd EPfP LRHS MCot NBir NRHS SPer
- - 'Perry's Tangerine'	EWes NPer
§ - - 'Purple and Gold'	ECtt EWes NLar SWvt XSen
- - 'Purpurea'	see *E. characias* subsp. *wulfenii* 'Purple and Gold'
- - 'Shorty'	EBee ECtt EHyd EPfP LRHS NLar NRHS SPoG XSen
- - 'Silver Shadow' (v)	EBee MHol NGBl WCot
- - 'Thelma's Giant'	MAvo
- - 'Westacre Giant'	EWes
clavarioides	WAbe
- var. ***truncata***	WCot
'Copton Ash'	CBcs CSpe EBee ECtt EMor IPot LRHS SPhx XSen
corallioides	CBod ECha EPfP GWyn LPla LSun NLar NPer NSti WHer WNPC
§ ***cornigera*** 🏆[H5]	CDor EBee ECha EHyd LRHS MMuc NBid NGdn NLar NRHS NSti SEND SPhx WCru WFar
- 'Goldener Turm'	ECtt EHyd EPfP LCro LOPS LRHS LSou SMHy SPer SPhx
corollata	IPot
cyparissias	CBcs ECha ELan GQue MRav NBir NGdn NLar SRms WBrk WFar XLum XSen
- 'Betten'	see *E.* × *gayeri* 'Betten'

	Name	Suppliers
	- 'Clarice Howard'	see *E. cyparissias* 'Fens Ruby'
	- clone 2	WCot
§	- 'Fens Ruby'	Widely available
	- 'Orange Man'	CBcs CBod CRos ECtt EHyd ELan EPfP EWes LRHS LSou MCot NGdn NLar NRHS SPoG SVen SWvt WAul WBrk WFar WSMil
	- 'Purpurea'	see *E. cyparissias* 'Fens Ruby'
	- 'Red Devil'	CDor
	- 'Tall Boy'	EBee EWes
	deflexa	EBee EWes MAvo NLar
	dendroides	LRHS SPtp
	'Despina'^{PBR}	LRHS
§	***donii***	ECha EWes MAvo WSpi XEll
	- HWJK 2405	WCru
	- 'Amjillasa'	ECha LPla SDix SMHy
	dulcis	CBre NBro
	- 'Chameleon'	CDor ECtt ELan ELon EPfP GQue GWyn MGos MRav NBid NBir NLar NPer SCob SPlb SWvt WBrk WCAu WCot WFar WSpi
	'Efanthia'^{PBR}	CDor CRos EWes GBin LRHS NRHS
§	***epithymoides***	Widely available
	- 'Bonfire'^{PBR}	CBod ECha LSun MAvo MBNS MBel NGBl NLar SAko SEdd SPer SPoG WCot WHil
§	- 'Candy'	CWCL ECha EMor LPla MHol MNrw NLar SIvy WFar
	- 'First Blush' (v)	MNrw NLar WCot WFar
	- 'Geisha'	EWes
	- 'Golden Fusion'	EPfP
§	- 'Lacy' (v)	EWes NBir WFar
§	- 'Major' 🏆^{H6}	CExl EBee SDix WKif
	- 'Midas'	GBin MNrw SEdd SMHy
	- 'Senior'	CRos EHyd EPfP LRHS MNrw NLar NRHS SEdd
	EXCALIBUR ('Froeup'^{PBR})	CExl CMac CWCL ELan ELon LSRN MBNS MMuc MNrw MRav NBir NLar NRHS NSti SEND SWvt
	fischeriana B&SWJ 8575	WCru
§	× ***gayeri*** 'Betten'	EBee EWes LPla NLar
	'Golden Foam'	see *E. stricta*
	griffithii	GQue LEdu NBro WFar WWtn
	- 'Dixter'	Widely available
	- 'Fern Cottage'	EWes MSpe
	- 'Fireglow'	Widely available
	- 'King's Caple'	EMor EWes LRHS NLar SPoG WCru
	- 'Wickstead'	EMor LRHS NLar
	'Helena'^{PBR} (v)	CExl LSRN NLar SWvt
	heptagona	SEND
	hierosolymitana	SBrt
	horrida 🏆^{H2}	SPlb
	hypericifolia DIAMOND FROST ('Inneuphe'^{PBR})	CSpe ESwi LCro LOPS LSou SRkn WCot
	- 'Diamond Star'	LSou WCot
	- 'Silverfog'^{PBR} **new**	LSou MCot
	jacquemontii	MRav NLar WCot
	'Jade Dragon'	LRHS SWvt
	'Jessie'	NLar
	jolkinii	CExl
	KALIPSO ('Innkalff')	EPfP NLar
	'Lambrook Silver'	SRkn
	lathyris	CBre NLar NPer SRms SVic
	longifolia misapplied	see *E. cornigera*
	longifolia D. Don	see *E. donii*
	longifolia Lam.	see *E. mellifera*
	margalidiana 🏆^{H4}	EWes WCot
	× ***martini***	Widely available
	- 'Aperitif'	SPoG
	- 'Ascot Rainbow'^{PBR} (v) 🏆^{H5}	Widely available
	- 'Baby Charm'	CBod CRos EBee EPfP LRHS LSRN MBel MGos NLar NRHS SCob WNPC XSen
	- 'Helen Robinson' 🏆^{H5}	WCot
	- 'Kolibri'	EHyd LRHS NRHS SWvt
	- 'Rudolph'^{PBR}	CBod ECtt ELan NLar SPoG
	- TINY TIM ('Waleutiny')	CRos EBee ECtt EHyd EPfP LRHS LSRN MPri NRHS SWvt
	- 'Walberton's Red Flush'	CRos EHyd LRHS NRHS
	mauritanica	EShb
§	***mellifera*** 🏆^{H3}	Widely available
	milii 🏆^{H1b}	EBak
	myrsinites 🏆^{H5}	Widely available
	- 'Washfield'	WSHC
	nereidum 🏆^{H5}	EWes
	nicaeensis	EBee LRHS SPhx WCot XSen
	oblongata	CSpe LRHS NLar SEND SPhx WCot
	palustris 🏆^{H7}	Widely available
	- 'Teichlaterne'	GBin SAko
	- 'Walenburg's Glorie'	CWCL EBee ECha ELan ELon EWTr GBin LCro LOPS LRHS MNrw MRav NLar NSti SMad WKif
	- 'Woodchippings'	WCot
	- 'Zauberflöte'	SRms
	paralias	WHer
§	× ***pasteurii***	CBct CBod CDTJ CSam ELan EPfP EWes GMaP GWyn MBNS MNrw MRav NBir NLar SPhx WCot WMal WPGP
	- Brown's strain	CAby CBod ELan EMor LSun MBNS MNrw SEdd SMad WCot WRHF
	- 'John Phillips' 🏆^{H4}	CBct CExl EBee EPfP LRHS MAvo SChF WPGP
	- 'Phrampton Phatty' 🏆^{H4}	LRHS MAvo WCot WPGP
	- 'Roundway Titan' 🏆^{H6}	EMil EPfP LRHS SAko SWvt
	- 'Skinny Bere'	LEdu
	pentagona	SVen
	pilosa 'Major'	see *E. epithymoides* 'Major'
	pithyusa	CPla ECha ELan SEND SPlb WSHC XSen
	polychroma	see *E. epithymoides*
	- 'Purpurea'	see *E. epithymoides* 'Candy'
	- 'Variegata'	see *E. epithymoides* 'Lacy'
	portlandica	SVen WHer
	REDWING ('Charam'^{PBR})	CBcs CMac ELan EMor GWyn LBuc LRHS MHol MNrw MRav NCou NLar NSti SLim SPoG SWvt WCot
	reflexa	see *E. seguieriana* subsp. *niciciana*
§	***rigida*** 🏆^{H6}	CBro ELan EWes SHar SPhx WCot WSpi XSen
	robbiae	see *E. amygdaloides* var. *robbiae*
	sarawschanica	ECha LPla LRHS SMad SPhx
	schillingii 🏆^{H5}	CDor CRos EBee ELan EPfP EWTr GMaP GWyn IPot LRHS LSRN MMuc MRav NLar SMad SPhx SPlb SPoG SPtp SRms SWvt WCAu WCru WFar WSpi
	schoenlandii	SPlb
	seguieriana	ECha EWes
§	- subsp. ***niciciana***	EWTr IMou LCro LOPS LRHS MAvo SMHy SPhx WCAu WHoo XSen
	serrulata Thuill.	see *E. stricta*
	sikkimensis 🏆^{H5}	CExl CMea ECha EHyd ELan EWes GLog GWyn IMou LPla LRHS NLar NPer NRHS SRms WCru WFar

	- 'Crûg Contrast'	WCru WFar
	spinosa	SPlb
§	***stricta***	CBgR GWyn NWad WSpi
	stygiana	CAbb CAby CBod CDTJ CExl ELan ELon EPfP EWes GBin LPla LRHS MCot SAko SDix SMad SPlb SPtp WCot WCru WPGP WSHC
	- subsp. ***santamariae***	CDTJ WMal WPGP WSHC
	- subsp. ***stygiana***	EBee WPGP
	- 'Torridge' 🏆^{H4}	WCot
	tirucalli	EShb
	valdevillosocarpa	GWyn LPla NLar SPhx WFar
	'Velvet Ruby'	GWyn LSRN SWvt WNPC XSen
	wallichii misapplied	see *E. donii*
	wallichii Kohli	see *E. cornigera*
	wallichii ambig.	CBod LOPS MCot MRav NSti
	wallichii Hook. f.	CExl EPfP LCro LOPS MNrw SPhx WCot
	'Whistleberry Garnet' 🏆^{H7}	CBar CMac EBee ELan EPfP EWTr GBin LRHS MMuc SPhx SWvt WNPC

Euptelea (*Eupteleaceae*)

	franchetii	see *E. pleiosperma*
§	***pleiosperma***	CBcs NLar
	polyandra	EBee EPfP NLar SBrt WPGP

Eurya (*Pentaphylacaceae*)

	japonica 'Moutiers' (v)	CBcs
	- 'Variegata' misapplied	see *Cleyera japonica* 'Fortunei'

Eurybia (*Asteraceae*)

§	***divaricata***	Widely available
§	- 'Eastern Star'	WCot WFar WOld WSpi
	- Raiche form	see *E. divaricata* 'Eastern Star'
	- 'Snow Heron'	MNrw
	- 'Tradescant'	IMou MNrw NLar SMad
§	***furcata***	XLum
§	× ***herveyi***	Widely available
§	***macrophylla***	CFis EHyd ELan GQue LRHS MMuc NLar NRHS SPhx WFar WOld
	- 'Albus'	EPPr WFar WOld
	- 'Twilight'	see *E.* × *herveyi*
§	***radula***	CSam EPPr EWes IMou MAvo MNrw NLar NWsh WOld WSHC
	- 'August Sky'	CBod CKno EBee EMor EPPr ITim LRHS MTis NDov SHar SPhx WCot WFar WHoo WRHF
§	***schreberi***	CDor ECha EPPr EWes LEdu LPla MAvo MNrw MPie MSpe NWsh WCot WFar WHoo WOld WPGP
§	***sibirica***	EBou NLar WOld
§	***spectabilis***	EBou EHyd IMou LRHS WFar
	- 'JS Macho Blue'	IPot MNrw WFar

Euryops (*Asteraceae*)

	abrotanifolius	CCCN SVen
§	***acraeus*** 🏆^{H4}	CMea ECtt ELan EPot EWes GEdr WAbe
	brachypodus	SVen
§	***chrysanthemoides***	CBcs CCCN CSde EShb SEND SVen
	evansii Schltr.	see *E. acraeus*
	lateriflorus	SPlb
	pectinatus 🏆^{H3}	CBcs CBod CCCN CCht CDTJ CDoC CExl CRos CSBt CSde CTri EHyd ELan EPfP EShb LRHS MGil MSCN SEND SVen SWvt WWFP
	- double-flowered (d) <u>**new**</u>	CCCN
	tenuissimus	SVen
	tysonii	ELon EWes SPlb SVen
	virgineus	CCCN CExl SPlb SVen

Euscaphis (*Staphyleaceae*)

	japonica	SPtp
	- B&SWJ 11359	WCru
	- B&SWJ 12739	WCru

Eustachys (*Poaceae*)

§	***distichophylla***	EHyd LRHS NWsh

Eustephia (*Amaryllidaceae*)

	coccinea	WCot

Eutrema (*Brassicaceae*)

§	***japonicum***	CExl EMor GPoy LEdu
	- 'Monzen'	GPoy

Eutrochium see *Eupatorium*

Ewartia (*Asteraceae*)

	planchonii	SPlb WAbe

Exbucklandia (*Hamamelidaceae*)

	populnea <u>**new**</u>	WPGP
	tonkinensis KWJ 12209	WCru

Exochorda (*Rosaceae*)

	alberti	see *E. korolkowii*
	giraldii var. ***wilsonii***	CExl CMac EBee ELan EMil EPfP LRHS MBlu MMuc MRav NLar SWvt WCFE
§	***korolkowii***	LRHS MAsh
	× ***macrantha***	ILea LRHS
	- 'Irish Pearl'	CExl
§	- 'Niagara'PBR	CBcs CDoC CMac CRos EBee EHyd EPfP EShb LCro LOPS LRHS LSRN MGos NLar NRHS SCob SGol SPoG SavN
	- SNOW DAY SURPRISE	see *E.* × *macrantha* 'Niagara'
	- 'The Bride' 🏆^{H6}	Widely available
	MAGICAL SPRINGTIME ('Kolmaspirit')	LRHS NLar
	racemosa	EPfP NLar SPer
	serratifolia	CBcs EBee ELan EPfP LRHS SPoG
	- 'Snow White'	CEnd CJun EWes GKin IArd IDee ILea IMou LRHS MAsh MBlu NLar NOrn SGsty SLon SWvt

F

Fabiana (*Solanaceae*)

	foliosa 'Cliftonville Limelight'	WAbe
	imbricata	CPbh CRos LRHS MGil SLon SPlb WPav
	- 'Prostrata'	CBod CRos ELan LRHS SVen WPav
	- f. ***violacea*** 🏆^{H4}	CExl CMac CRos CSBt CTri ELan EPfP LRHS MMuc SPad SWvt WAvo WKif WPav WSMil
	- - dark-flowered	CBcs
	nana	WAbe

Fagopyrum (*Polygonaceae*)

	cymosum	see *F. dibotrys*
§	***dibotrys***	CSpe EBee ECha EWld LEdu MMuc XLum
I	- 'Cally Form'	ESwi

Fagraea (*Gentianaceae*)

	ceilanica FMWJ 13099	WCru

Fagus ✿ (*Fagaceae*)

	from Guangxi, China	WPGP
	from Vietnam	WPGP
§	***crenata***	CMCN CMen MBlu
	- 'Mount Fuji'	CMen
	engleriana	CExl LRHS
	grandifolia	WPGP
	subsp. ***mexicana***	
	longipetiolata	CBcs CExl CMCN WPGP
	- NJM 11.036	WPGP
	lucida	CExl CMCN MBlu
	orientalis	CMCN
	- 'Iskander'	EBee IArd IDee MBlu SGol SMad
	sieboldii	see *F. crenata*
	sylvatica 🏆H6	Widely available
	- 'Albovariegata' (v)	CLnd
	- 'Aniek'	SGol
	- 'Asterix'	LRHS MBlu
	- Atropurpurea Group	Widely available
	- - 'Purpurea Pendula'	CBcs CCVT CEnd CMCN CMac CSBt CTri EBee ELan EPfP GKin MAsh MGos NOrn SCoo SGol SLau SLim SPer SPoG WFar WMat WTSh
	- - 'Riversii' 🏆H6	CBcs CEnd CLnd CMCN CTho CTri ELan EPfP GKin MGos NOrn SGsty SPer WMat
	- - 'Swat Magret'	EPfP
	- 'Aurea Pendula'	CEnd CMCN MBlu SMad
	- 'Bicolor Sartini'	MBlu
	- 'Birr Zebra'	CEnd
	- 'Black Swan'	CLnd CMCN EBee ELan LSRN MAsh MBlu MGos NHol NOra NOrn SLon SPer SPoG WMat WMou
	- 'Bornyensis'	MBlu
	- 'Brathay Purple'	MBlu SMad
	- 'Cochleata'	CMCN
	- 'Cockleshell'	MBlu
	- 'Cristata'	MBlu
§	- 'Dawyck' 🏆H6	CBcs CLnd CMac CTho ECrN ELan EPfP LMaj MGos NLar SCob SGol SLau SPer
	- 'Dawyck Gold' 🏆H6	CBcs CEnd CLnd CMCN CMac CRos CSBt CTri ELan GKin LMaj MAsh MBlu MGos NLar NOra NOrn SCob SGol SLau SPer WMat WMou
	- 'Dawyck Purple' 🏆H6	CBcs CEnd CLnd CMCN CMac CRos CSBt CTho CTri ELan EPfP GKin LMaj LSRN MAsh MBlu MGos NLar NOra NOrn NRHS SCob SGol SPer SPoG WMat WTSh
	- 'Fastigiata' misapplied	see *F. sylvatica* 'Dawyck'
	- 'Franken' (v)	MBlu SMad
	- 'Grandidentata'	LMaj
	- 'Green Obelisk'	MBlu
	- 'Greenwood'	MBlu
	- var. ***heterophylla***	CLnd CTho
	- - 'Aspleniifolia' 🏆H6	CBcs CEnd CMCN CMac EBee ECrN ELan EPfP EWTr GBin GKin LMaj MBlu MGos SCoo SGol SLau SPer SPoG WMat WMou
	- - (Atropurpurea Group) 'Ansorgei'	CEnd MBlu
	- - 'Incisa'	MBlu
	- - f. ***laciniata***	MBlu
	- - 'Mercedes'	CMCN MBlu SMad WLov
	- 'Horizontalis'	MBlu
	- 'Pendula' 🏆H6	CBcs CCVT CEnd CMCN CMac CSBt CTho ECrN ELan MGos MSwo NOra SGol SLau SPer WMat WMou WTSh
	- 'Purple Fountain' 🏆H6	CEnd CMCN ELan LMaj MAsh MBlu MGos NLar NOra NOrn SLau SWeb WMat
	- Purple-leaved Group	see *F. sylvatica* Atropurpurea Group
§	- 'Purpurea Tricolor' (v)	CEnd CMCN CMac EBee LMaj MBlu MGos NOra SCoo WMat WMou
	- 'Red Obelisk'	see *F. sylvatica* 'Rohan Obelisk'
	- 'Rohan Gold'	CEnd CMCN SGol
§	- 'Rohan Obelisk'	CEnd CMCN EBee ELan LMaj MBlu NLar
I	- 'Rohan Pyramidalis'	CEnd CMCN
	- 'Rohan Trompenburg'	CMCN MBlu
	- 'Rohan Weeping'	MBlu
	- 'Rohanii'	CBcs CEnd CMCN CTri ELan EPfP GKin MGil MGos SLau
	- 'Roseomarginata'	see *F. sylvatica* 'Purpurea Tricolor'
	- 'Rotundifolia'	LMaj MBlu
	- 'Silver Wood'	SMad
	- 'Spaethiana'	GKin
	- f. ***tortuosa***	MBlu MPkF
	- 'Tricolor' misapplied (v)	see *F. sylvatica* 'Purpurea Tricolor' (v)
	- 'Tricolor' ambig. (v)	SLau
	- 'Tricolor' (v)	CBcs CLnd ECrN NHol NOra SGol
	- 'Tur'	SMad
	- 'Zlatia'	CLnd CMCN ELan MBlu MGil MGos NLar SGol SLau

Fallopia (*Polygonaceae*)

	aubertii	see *F. baldschuanica*
§	***baldschuanica***	Widely available
§	***japonica*** var. ***compacta***	XLum
	- - 'Fuji Snow'	see *F. japonica* var. *compacta* 'Milk Boy'
§	- - 'Milk Boy' (v)	EShb
	- - 'Variegata' misapplied	see *F. japonica* var. *compacta* 'Milk Boy'
§	***multiflora***	LEdu
	- var. ***hypoleuca***	CSde SCoo SPoG
	- - B&SWJ 120	WCru

Farfugium (*Asteraceae*)

§	***japonicum***	SBrt WSMil
	- B&SWJ 884	WCru
	- B&SWJ 14699	WCru
	- 'Argenteum' (v)	EMil SMad WCot
§	- 'Aureomaculatum' (v) 🏆H3	ECtt
	- 'Bumpy Ride'	WCot
	- 'Crispatum'	LEdu
	- double-flowered (d)	WCru
	- var. ***formosanum*** NMWJ 14574	WCru
	- 'Kaimon Dake' (v)	WCot
	- 'Kinkan' (v)	WCot
I	- 'Tsuwa-buki'	WCot
	'Last Dance'PBR	EBee ECtt NLar
	tussilagineum	see *F. japonicum*

Fargesia (*Poaceae*)

	from Jiuzhaigou, China	CDTJ MAvo MMuc MWht NLar WPGP XCre
	from Taibashan, China	XCre
	adpressa	CBdn MWht

conferta	XCre
confusa	CDTJ
denudata	CBct CBdn CDTJ ESwi NLar XCre
- L 1575	CExl MWht
- Xian 1	CBdn CDTJ XCre
dracocephala	CBdn CExl GBin MAvo MBrN MMuc MWht XCre
- 'White Dragon'	CDTJ CExl
ferax	XCre
'Green Dragon'	XCre
'Jiuzaighou 9'	GBin XCre
§ ***murielae*** 🏆H5	CAgr CBcs CBdn CDoC ELan EPau EPfP LCro LOPS LRHS MGos MMuc MWht SArc SCob SPlb WFar XCre
- 'Bimbo'	CBdn CBod CDoC EPfP LRHS MAvo MWht NLar SWvt
- 'Dana Jumbo'	CRos EHyd LRHS NRHS
- 'Grüne Hecke'	MWht
- 'Harewood'	MWht SWvt
- 'Joy'	CBct CBod GBin NLar
- 'Jumbo'	CBod CDoC CSBt ELon EPfP MAvo MGos MWht NGdn NLar NRHS SGsty SPer SRms SWvt
- 'Mae'	CDTJ MWht
- 'Panda'PBR	CRos EHyd LRHS NRHS
- 'Simba'	CBct CBdn CBod CExl CRos EHyd EPfP GBin GMaP LMaj LRHS LSRN MAvo MBrN MGos MMuc MWht NGdn NLar NRHS SCob SGsty SPer SPlb SPoG SWeb SWvt WFar WPGP
- 'Vampire'	LRHS
murieliae BLUE DRAGONSCALE	see *F. murieliae* BLUE LIZARD
§ - BLUE LIZARD ('Japo 72'PBR)	ELan MWht
- RED ZEBRA ('Japo 51'PBR)	MWht
- 'Superjumbo'PBR	CBdn
§ ***nitida***	CAbb CBcs CEnd CRos EHyd ELan EPfP LRHS MAsh MGos MWht NRHS SCob SPoG SRms SWvt WPGP
- 'Black Pearl'	WPGP XCre
- 'Chennevières'	XCre
- 'Ghanzu II'	XCre
- 'Great Wall'	CBod CDTJ CDoC CSBt ELan GBin MMuc MWht NLar XCre
- Jiuzhaigou 1	see *F.* RED PANDA
- 'Jiuzhaigou 2'	MWht
- 'Jiuzhaigou 4'	CDTJ CExl WPGP
- 'Jiuzhaigou 8'	CDTJ
- 'Jiuzhaigou Genf'	CDTJ MWht NLar WPGP
- 'Volcano'	XCre
§ RED PANDA ('Jiu') 🏆H4	CExl LCro LOPS SPoG SWvt
robusta 🏆H5	CAbb CBct CDTJ CSBt ELan EPfP MAvo MBrN MMuc MWht NGdn SCob SSut
- 'Campbell'	CBdn CDoC NLar SGsty XCre
- 'Ming Yunnan'	LEdu WPGP
- 'P. King'	MWht
- 'Pingwu'	CBdn CBod CDTJ CDoC MGos MWht SGsty XCre
- 'Red Sheath'	CDTJ CExl MWht WPGP
- 'Wenchuan'	XCre
- 'Wolong'	CBdn CExl MWht WPGP XCre
rufa 🏆H4	CAbb CBcs CBdn CBod CDoC CExl CSBt ELan ELon EPfP EShb LCro LOPS LSRN MBlu MBrN MGos MMuc MWht NLar SCob SWeb WFar WPGP XCre
§ ***scabrida*** 🏆H4	CBdn CDTJ MAvo MWht SSut WPGP XCre
- 'Asian Wonder'	CBod ECrN LCro LOPS LRHS NLar SGsty
similaris KR 4175	MWht
spathacea misapplied	see *F. murielae*
'Tom 1'	XCre
utilis	MMuc MWht SEND XCre
'Winter Joy'	XCre
yulongshanensis	MWht XCre

Fascicularia (*Bromeliaceae*)

andina	see *F. bicolor*
§ ***bicolor***	Widely available
- subsp. ***bicolor***	CDoC CMac SMad
- subsp. ***canaliculata***	ELon LEdu MNrw SChr SIvy SMad SPad WPGP
kirchhoffiana	see *F. bicolor*
litoralis	see *Ochagavia litoralis*
pitcairniifolia misapplied	see *F. bicolor*
pitcairniifolia (Verlot) Mez	see *Ochagavia litoralis*

× *Fatshedera* ✿ (*Araliaceae*)

lizei 🏆H3	CBcs CMac CRos CSde CTri EBee ECrN ELon EPfP GBin LRHS MAsh MRav SArc SDix SEND SGol SPer SPlb SPoG SRms SWvt WAvo
§ - 'Annemieke' (v) 🏆H3	CBcs CBod CRos EHyd ELan ELon EPfP LRHS MMuc MRav SEND SEle SPer SPoG WAvo
- compact	EPfP
- 'Lemon and Lime'	see × *F. lizei* 'Annemieke'
- 'Maculata'	see × *F. lizei* 'Annemieke'
- 'Variegata' (v) 🏆H3	CSde EBee ELan ELon EPfP LRHS SDix SEND SPer SWvt WAvo
- 'Variegata' compact (v)	SPoG

Fatsia ✿ (*Araliaceae*)

§ ***japonica*** 🏆H5	Widely available
- 'Annelise' (v)	SEND SMad
- 'Annemie' (v)	WSMil
- 'Moseri'	CBod CExl ELan ESwi MBNS MHol SWvt WCot
- 'Spider's Web' (v)	Widely available
- 'Variegata' (v) 🏆H5	CMac CRos ELan EPfP LRHS MAsh MGos MRav SCob SEND SGsty SLon SPer SPoG WCot
I 'Megafatsia'	CDTJ
papyrifera	see *Tetrapanax papyrifer*
polycarpa	CDTJ CExl IMou
- B&SWJ 1776	WCru
- B&SWJ 3467	WCru
- B&SWJ 7144	CExl WCru
- RWJ 10133	WCru
§ - deeply cut leaf	CBct CCht GBin MBNS SMad WCot WPGP
- Needham's form	see *F. polycarpa* deeply cut leaf

Fatsia × *Hedera* see × *Fatshedera*

Faucaria (*Aizoaceae*)

tuberculosa 🏆H2	CBod SSim

Feijoa see *Acca*

Felicia (*Asteraceae*)

aethiopica	CPbh
§ ***amelloides***	CCCN SPlb
- 'Santa Anita'	CTri NWad SVen

§	- variegated (v)	CCCN ECtt NPer
§	***amoena***	CTri
	- 'Variegata' (v)	CCCN CTri
	capensis	see *F. amelloides*
	coelestis	see *F. amelloides*
	echinata	CCCN
	FELICITARA BLUE ('Wigetablue'[PBR])	SPoG
	filifolia blue-flowered	SVen
	'Forever Blue' **new**	CWCL
	natalensis	see *F. rosulata*
	pappei	see *F. amoena*
§	***petiolata***	CFis CTri EBee EWes MMuc MNrw
§	***rosulata***	CAby CSma GAbr GEdr MAsh MHol NBro NLar SBrt WFar WIce
	tenella	WSpi
	uliginosa	EWes SBrt SPlb WIce
	wrightii	GEdr

Fenestraria (*Aizoaceae*)

	rhopalophylla subsp. ***aurantiaca*** ♀H2	SSim

fennel see *Foeniculum vulgare*

fenugreek see *Trigonella foenum-graecum*

Ferraria (*Iridaceae*)

§	***crispa***	CBor CPBP WCot
	- var. ***nortieri***	WCot
	divaricata	WCot
	schaeferi	WCot
	undulata	see *F. crispa*
	variablis	WCot

Ferula (*Apiaceae*)

	assa-foetida	WJek
	chiliantha	see *F. communis* subsp. *glauca*
§	***communis***	CCBP CMea CRos CSpe ECha ELan EWes GBin LEdu LRHS NDov SDix SEND SPad SPhx SPlb SPoG SPtp WJek
	- 'Cretan Giant'	WPGP
	- 'Gigantea'	see *F. communis*
§	- subsp. ***glauca***	EBee ECha EWes SDix SPhx SSut WCot
	- - B&SWJ 12999	WCru
	- - NJM 13.001	WPGP
	'Giant Bronze'	see *Foeniculum vulgare* 'Giant Bronze'
	linkii	SPhx
	tingitana B&SWJ 14005	WCru
	- 'Cedric Morris'	ECha SDix SPhx WCot

Ferulago (*Apiaceae*)

	cassia	WCot
	stellata	WCot
	sylvatica	SPhx
	- PAB 2875	LEdu WPGP

Festuca (*Poaceae*)

	actae	XLum
	amethystina	CBod CKno EShb LCro LOPS LRHS MBel MMuc NGdn SCob SEND SMea SPhx XCre XLum
	- 'Aprilgrün'	XLum
	arundinacea	CHab MMuc SEND
	californica	CKno IMou
	curvula subsp. ***crassifolia***	EShb
	durissima	XLum
	elegans	EPPr XLum
	eskia	IMou XLum
	filiformis	CHab
	gamisansii	XLum
§	***gautieri***	CBod LRHS NWsh WSpi XLum
	- 'Pic Carlit'	NLar XLum
	gigantea	CHab MMuc SEND XLum
	glacialis	XLum
	- 'Czakor'	XLum
	glauca Vill.	CBcs CBod EShb GMaP GWyn MBNS MGos MRav NGdn SLim SPer SPlb SRms XSen
I	- 'Auslese'	CBod CExl EShb NGdn
	- 'Azurit'	EWes NLar NWad SCob SPoG SRms
§	- 'Blaufuchs'	CRos CSBt EHyd ELan EPfP EWes GMaP LRHS MBlu MGos NLar NRHS NWad NWsh SCob SLim SPer SPlb SWvt WFar WSpi XLum
§	- 'Blauglut'	EBee EHyd LRHS MRav SCob SRms
	- BLUE FOX	see *F. glauca* 'Blaufuchs'
	- BLUE GLOW	see *F. glauca* 'Blauglut'
	- 'Blue Select'	LSun
	- 'Elijah Blue'	Widely available
	- 'Golden Toupee'	ECha EHyd ELan EPfP LRHS MAsh MBlu MGos NLar NRHS SLim SPer SPlb SWvt XLum
	- 'Harz'	XLum
	- INTENSE BLUE ('Casblue'[PBR])	CKno CRos EBee EHyd ELan EPfP EWes GBin LCro LOPS LRHS LSRN MAsh MGos MPkF NRHS NWsh SMad SPeP SPoG SRms
*	- ***minima***	CCCN NWsh
	- SEA URCHIN	see *F. glauca* 'Seeigel'
§	- 'Seeigel'	LRHS NRHS NWad
	- SELECT	see *F. glauca* 'Auslese'
	- 'Seven Seas'	see *F. valesiaca* 'Silbersee'
	- 'Solling'	XLum
	- 'Uchte'	ECha
	idahoensis	EShb
	- 'Tomales Bay'	CKno
	liviensis	XSen
	mairei	CBod CKno ECha IMou LPla NWsh SEdd SPhx XCre XLum
	ovina	CHab WSFF
	- var. ***gallica***	NWsh
*	- 'Tetra Gold'	SWvt
	paniculata	CKno XLum
	- subsp. ***spadicea***	XLum
	pratensis	CHab
	punctoria	MMuc
	rubra	CHab CKno WSFF XLum
	scoparia	see *F. gautieri*
	tatrae	MBel MMuc SEND
	valesiaca	XLum
	- var. ***glaucantha***	NGdn XLum
§	- 'Silbersee'	SRms
	- SILVER SEA	see *F. valesiaca* 'Silbersee'
	vivipara	NBid XLum
*	'Willow Green'	SPlb

Fibigia (*Brassicaceae*)

I	***clypeata*** 'Select'	CSpe
	eriocarpa	LRHS

Ficaria (*Ranunculaceae*)

	fascicularis	GKev MNrw NRya WCot
	verna	MMuc
	- Alba Group	CSam LEdu NRya
	- anemone-centred	see *F. verna* 'Collarette'

§ - Aurantiaca Group CDor ECha NLar NRya SPhx
- var. ***aurantiacus*** see *F. verna* Aurantiaca Group
- 'Bowles's Double' see *Ficaria verna* 'Double Bronze'
- 'Brambling' ECha LEdu NBPC
- 'Brazen Child' SHar
- 'Brazen Hussy' Widely available
- subsp. ***bulbilifer*** see *F. verna* subsp. *verna*
§ - subsp. ***chrysocephala*** EBee ECha MNrw WCot
- 'Coffee Cream' ECul
§ - 'Collarette' (d) ECul ELan EMor LEdu MHer NBir NLar NRya WFar
- 'Coppernob' CDor CFis WCot
- 'Cracked Parchment' CNat
- 'Cupreus' see *F. verna* Aurantiaca Group
§ - 'Double Bronze' (d) LEdu NBir NRya WFar
§ - 'Double Mud' (d) CWCL EPPr LEdu NLar NRya SHar WFar WHal
- double, cream-flowered see *F. verna* 'Double Mud'
- double, green-eyed (d) LEdu
- double, yellow-flowered see *F. verna* Flore Pleno Group
- 'Dusky Maiden' NLar NRya WFar
- 'E.A. Bowles' see *F. verna* 'Collarette'
- 'Edna' WOut
§ - Flore Pleno Group (d) CBod CDor CMac CTri ECha ELan EPPr EPfP NRya SRms WCot WFar
- 'Fried Egg' WFar
- 'Green Petal' (d) ECul EPPr NBir NRya WFar WHal WHer
- 'Green Rim' CNat
- 'Hyde Hall' NLar WCot
- 'Ken Aslet Double' (d) EPPr MHer WHal
- 'Kingscot' **new** CNat
- 'Lambrook Variegated' (v) CFis
- 'Lemon Dazzler' **new** EBou
- subsp. ***major*** see *F. verna* subsp. *chrysocephala*
- 'Martin Gibbs' Progeny' CNat
- 'Montacute' (d) CDor CFis
- 'Old Master' WCot
- 'Orange Sorbet' (d) WFar
- 'Petrol Spillage' CNat
- 'Primrose' NRya
- 'Randall's White' CDor EPfP SHar WFar
- 'Richard and Val' WCot
- 'Rita Pirouet' WCot
- 'Salmon's White' EPPr NBir NRya SHar WFar WHal
- 'Silver Collar' (d) LEdu
- 'Suffusion' CNat
- 'Tortoiseshell' EPPr
§ - subsp. ***verna*** CTri WHer WOut WSFF WShi
- - 'Chedglow' WCot
- 'Wisley Double' see *Ficaria verna* 'Double Bronze'

Ficinia (*Cyperaceae*)

§ ***nodosa*** SPlb
truncata WCot
- 'Ice Crystal' (v) EHyd ELan LRHS NRHS SPoG

Ficus (*Moraceae*)

afghanistanica 'Silver Lyre' EBee EPfP IArd SMad SVen WPGP
benjamina 'Danielle'PBR **new** LCro LOPS
carica (F) CCCN CDoC LMaj SArc SEWo SGsty SLon SPad
- 'Adam' (F) CCCN LEdu NLar SEND SMad SVen
I - 'Bauern Feige' (F) SRms
- 'Beall' (F) CCCN
- 'Black Ischia' (F) CCCN SDix
- 'Bornholm' (F) CCCN LSRN SPre SWeb
- 'Bourjassotte Grise' (F) CAgr XSen
- 'Brown Turkey' (F) ♀H4 Widely available
- 'Brunswick' (F) CAgr CCCN CRHN CTri ELan ELon EPfP EPom EShb LEdu LRHS NLar NRHS SDix SEND SKee SLim SNig SRms SVen WCot WFar WMat
- 'Califfo Blue' (F) SRms
- 'Cambridge Builder' (F) **new** SVen
- 'Castle Kennedy' (F) CCCN
- 'Celeste' (F) SRms
- 'Col de Dame Blanc' (F) XSen
- 'Col de Dame Noir' (F) XSen
- 'Colummaro Black Apulia' (F) CCCN
- 'Colummaro White Apulia' (F) CCCN
- 'Dalmatie' (F) CAgr CCCN ELan EPfP LRHS MGos NOra SEND SGsty SRms WMat WPGP XSen
I - 'Digitata' (F) MBlu
- 'Dorée' (F) EPom XSen
- 'Dorée de Porquerolles' (F) CCCN
- 'Filacciano' (F) CCCN
- 'Fiorone Verde' (F) **new** SVen
- 'Flanders' (F) CCCN
- 'Gianchetta' (F) **new** SVen
- 'Goutte d'Or' (F) CAgr CCCN EPfP EPom
- 'Green Ischia' (F) CCCN
- 'Grise de Marseille' (F) CCCN
- 'Grise de Saint Jean' (F) CCCN XSen
- 'Ice Crystal' (F) ♀H5 CBod CDoC CRos EBee ECrN ELan EPfP EShb LRHS MBlu SCoo SMad SPoG SRms SVen WCot WMat WPGP
- 'Jordan' (F) LRHS
- 'Kadota' (F) CCCN SVen
- 'Longue d'Août' (F) XSen
- 'Lupo' (F) **new** SVen
- 'Madeleine des Deux Saisons' (F) EPom SEND SKee XSen
- 'Marseillaise' (F) EPfP XSen
- 'Melanzana' (F) CCCN
- 'Morena' (F) SRms
- 'Negretta' (F) **new** SVen
- 'Negrétte de Porquerolles' (F) CCCN
- 'Newlyn Harbour' (F) ELon
- 'Noire de Barbentane' (F) XSen
- 'Noire de Caromb' (F) CAgr CCCN EPfP LRHS SKee SRms WMat XSen
- 'Noire de Provence' see *F. carica* 'Reculver'
- 'Osborn's Prolific' (F) EPfP SEND SGol SWvt
- 'Panachée' (F) CCCN EPom LRHS SMad SRms
- 'Pastilière' (F) XSen
- 'Perretta' (F) LRHS
- 'Précoce de Dalmatie' (F) CCCN CTho EPfP EShb LEdu NLar SRms
- 'Quinta' (F) CCCN
§ - 'Reculver' (F) SEND
- 'Ronde de Bordeaux' (F) CCCN EPfP SEND SWeb XSen
- 'Rouge de Bordeaux' (F) CCCN CTsd EPom SKee SPlb SRms SSta
- 'Rubado' (F) **new** SVen
- 'Safi' (F) CCCN
- 'San Piero' (F) **new** SVen
- 'Sultane' (F) CAgr EPom IDee SVen WPGP XSen
- 'Tayip 1' (F) CAgr
- 'Tayip 2' (F) CAgr
- 'Verte d'Argenteuil' (F) CCCN

- 'Violette Dauphine' (F)	EPfP LEdu SEND SKee SMad
- 'Violette de Sollies' (F)	SVic XSen
- 'Violette Normande' (F)	SEND
- 'White Adriatic' (F)	NLar SRms
- 'White Genoa'	see *F. carica* 'White Marseilles'
§ - 'White Marseilles' (F)	CAgr CCCN CMac CRHN ECrN LRHS SEND SKee SRms WMat WPGP
- 'Zamoreica' (F)	SEND
- 'Zidi' (F)	CCCN
elastica	XAbr
- 'Robusta'	LCro LOPS
- 'Tineke' (v)	LCro LOPS
lyrata 'Bambino'PBR **new**	LCro LOPS
aff. ***oligodon***	SVen
- NJM 13.084 **new**	WPGP
pubigera	CExl
pumila ♀H2	CDoC EShb
- 'Sonny' (v)	NWad
- 'Variegata' (v) ♀H2	EShb
punctata	EShb
retusa (F)	NGKo
tikoua	IArd

fig see *Ficus carica*; also AGM Fruit Section

filbert see *Corylus maxima*

Filipendula (*Rosaceae*)

alnifolia 'Variegata'	see *F. ulmaria* 'Variegata'
camtschatica	CPla EBee ECha ELan IMou MMuc NBid NLar WPGP WWtn
- B&SWJ 10987	WCru
- RBS 0224	NLar
digitata 'Nana'	see *F. multijuga*
hexapetala	see *F. vulgaris*
- 'Flore Pleno'	see *F. vulgaris* 'Multiplex'
'Kahome'	CRos EHyd ELon EShb EWhm GLog GMaP ILea LRHS MHol NBid NBir NGdn NLar NRHS NSti SCob SPer SPhx WFar WPnP
kiraishiensis	EBee
- B&SWJ 1571	WCru
koreana	CRos EBee EHyd LRHS NRHS
§ ***multijuga***	EBee EWhm NHol NLar NWad WBor
- B&SWJ 10950	WCru
- 'Hjördis'	CBod ELon MAvo MBel MHol MNrw MPie SMad SPad WHil WHoo WWtn
- var. ***yezoensis*** B&SWJ 10828	IMou WCru
palmata	ECha EHyd LRHS NBre WFar
- 'Digitata Nana'	see *F. multijuga*
- dwarf	GRum
- 'Elegantissima'	see *F. purpurea* 'Elegans'
- 'Göteborg'	EBee IMou NLar
- 'Nana'	see *F. multijuga*
- 'Rosea'	CMac NBir
- 'Rubra'	CRos EBee EHyd LRHS MRav NGdn NRHS
purpurea	CKno EBee ECha ELon GQue ILea LCro LLWG MMuc SCob SEND SRms WCru WFar WTyc
- f. ***albiflora***	ILea
§ - 'Elegans'	EBee EHyd ELon EWTr ILea IMou LRHS NBid NHol NWad SCob SPer SRms WFar WPnP WTyc
- 'Pink Dreamland'	SPhx
* - 'Plena' (d)	NLar
'Queen of the Prairies'	see *F. rubra*
§ ***rubra***	WSFF
§ - 'Venusta' ♀H5	Widely available
- 'Venusta Magnifica'	see *F. rubra* 'Venusta'
rufinervis B&SWJ 8469	WCru
- B&SWJ 8611	WCru
§ ***ulmaria***	Widely available
- 'Aurea'	CBod CDor CMac CTri CWCL EBee ECha ECtt EHyd ELan EMor EWhm GBin GMaP LEdu LRHS MRav NBid NLar SPer SRms WCot WFar WSHC
- 'Corinne Tremaine'	WHer
- 'Flore Pleno' (d)	CBod EBee LRHS MAvo MRav NBid SPer WCot WFar WHrl
- 'Rosea'	EHyd LEdu LLWG LRHS MHer
§ - 'Variegata' (v)	CWCL EBee ECtt EHyd ELan EWhm GQue LRHS MHol NBid NGdn NLar NRHS SPer SRms WBor WFar WHer
§ ***vulgaris***	CDor CHab EMor GLog LEdu MBow MMuc MNHC NBro NGrd NMir NQui SPhx WHer
- 'Devon Cream'	MAvo
- 'Flore Pleno'	see *F. vulgaris* 'Multiplex'
- 'Grandiflora'	CBre
§ - 'Multiplex' (d)	CDor CMac CSpe ECha EHyd ELan GMaP LLWG LPot LRHS MHer MMrt MMuc MNHC MRav MSCN NBid NBir NLar NRHS NRya NSti SCob SEdd SRms WFar XLum
- 'Plena'	see *F. vulgaris* 'Multiplex'
- 'Rosea'	NBre

Firmiana (*Malvaceae*)

simplex	CBcs EBee EShb ESwi LEdu MBlu SMad WPGP

Fitzroya (*Cupressaceae*)

cupressoides	CBcs IArd IDee SLim WPav

Florence fennel see *Foeniculum vulgare*; also AGM Vegetables Section

Flueggea (*Phyllanthaceae*)

suffruticosa	SBrt

Foeniculum (*Apiaceae*)

vulgare	Widely available
- 'Bronze'	see *F. vulgare* 'Purpureum'
- var. ***dulce***	ENfk
§ - 'Giant Bronze'	EMor GWyn LCro LEdu LOPS LRHS MAvo SCob SPhx WGrn WSpi XSen
- 'Orion' ♀H2	EKin
§ - 'Purpureum'	Widely available
- 'Smoky'	ECha MRav
- 'Sweet Florence'	LCro SVic
- 'Zefa Fino' ♀H2	EKin MCtn NRob

Fontanesia (*Oleaceae*)

fortunei	EBtc

Fontinalis (*Fontinalaceae*)

antipyretica	XBlo

Forsythia (*Oleaceae*)

'Arnold Dwarf'	ECrN NBir SRms
'Beatrix Farrand' ambig.	CTri SEND SRms
'Beatrix Farrand' K. Sax	MMuc NLar
'Fiesta' (v)	CBod ELon EPfP MAsh MHer MRav MSwo NLar SPer WCot WFar

giraldiana	MSwo SRms
GOLD TIDE	see *F.* MARÉE D'OR
'Golden Nugget'	CMac ELan EPfP MAsh SLon SPoG WCFE WFar
'Golden Times' (v)	CMac CRos EHyd LRHS LSRN MAsh MSwo NEoE NHol NRHS SPoG SWvt WAvo WCot WFar
'Goldstream' (v)	NWad
× ***intermedia***	EShb
- 'Arnold Giant'	MBlu
- 'Goldrausch'	CRos EHyd LCro LOPS LRHS NLar NRHS SAko
- 'Goldzauber'	CBrac
- 'Lynwood Variety' ♀H5	Widely available
- 'Lynwood Variety' variegated (v)	CMac
- MINIGOLD ('Flojor')	CBrac CMac CSBt ELan MSwo NLar SRms
- 'Nimbus'PBR	CBod EBee LRHS NLar WFar
- SHOW OFF ('Mindor'PBR)	LBuc LRHS
- 'Spectabilis'	CBrac EPfP LBuc SCoo SGol SLim WFar
- 'Spectabilis Variegated' (v)	NEoE
- 'Spring Glory'	CDoC MHer WAvo WLov WSpi
- 'Susan Gruninger' (v)	WCot
- 'Variegata' (v)	CBrac SRms
- WEEK END ('Courtalyn') ♀H5	CBod CDoC CEnd CRos EHyd EPfP LBuc LCro LOPS LRHS MAsh MMuc NHol NLar NRHS SCob SEND SGol SLon SPlb SavN WFar
'Kanarek'	NLar
× ***mandschurica***	CBcs IMou SAko
- 'Vermont Sun' **new**	IArd
§ MARÉE D'OR ('Courtasol') ♀H5	CRos EPfP LRHS MAsh MRav NLar NRHS SLon SPer SPoG WFar
MÊLÉE D'OR ('Courtaneur')	SGol WBor
'Northern Gold'	MBlu
ovata 'Ottawa'	WLov
'Paulina'	WCot
suspensa	CMac CTri EPfP ESwi SPlb SRms WSpi
- f. ***atrocaulis***	WSpi
- 'Nymans'	EPfP EWTr MRav NLar NSti SBrt SEND SPer
§ - 'Taff's Arnold' (v)	CExl WSpi
- 'Variegata'	see *F. suspensa* 'Taff's Arnold'
'Tremonia'	ECrN
viridissima 'Bronxensis'	EPot MAsh NBir WAbe WCot
- CITRUS SWIZZLE ('Mckcitrine'PBR)	NLar WCot
- var. ***koreana*** 'Kumsom' (v)	CRos EBee LRHS NLar SAko
- 'Weber's Bronx'	NLar

Fortunella see *Citrus*

Fothergilla (*Hamamelidaceae*)

gardenii	CBcs CJun CRos EHyd EPfP LRHS MBlu MRav NLar SPer SWvt
- 'Blue Mist'	CBod CCCN CEnd CExl CJun CRos EBee EHyd ELan EPfP LRHS MAsh NLar SPer SPoG SSta WFar
- 'Glaucophylla'	NLar
- 'Suzanne'	CJun NLar
- 'Zundert'	NLar
× ***intermedia*** BEAVER CREEK ('Klmtwo')	NLar
- 'Blue Shadow'	CBcs CBod CCCN CJun EHyd IDee LRHS MGos MPkF MRav NLar NRHS SGol
- 'Mount Airy' ♀H5	CJun CMCN CRos EPfP LRHS MPkF NLar SSta
- 'Red Licorice'	CJun EPfP NLar
- 'Sea Spray'	CJun NLar
- 'Windy City'	CJun NLar
major ♀H5	CBcs CBod CDoC CJun CRos EBee EHyd ELan EPfP LCro LOPS LRHS MAsh MBlu MGil MGos MRav NLar SPer SWvt WFar WMat WTSh
- 'Bulkyard'	CJun
- Monticola Group	CEnd CJun CRos CTho EHyd EPfP LRHS MAsh MMuc SCob SGbt SLim SSta
- - 'Huntsman'	CCCN CJun CTho EPfP SPer SSta

Fouquieria (*Fouquieriaceae*)

columnaris	SPlb
splendens	SPlb

Fragaria ✿ (*Rosaceae*)

alpina	see *F. vesca* 'Semperflorens'
- 'Alba'	see *F. vesca* 'Semperflorens Alba'
× ***ananassa*** 'Albion'PBR (F)	CArg CMac LCro LOPS LRHS LSRN
- 'Alice'PBR (F) ♀H6	CAgr CMac EPom
§ - 'Anablanca' (F)	LRHS
- 'Aromel' (F)	CTri MMuc
- Bubbleberry (F) **new**	LCro LOPS
- 'Buddy'PBR (F)	CArg EPom
- 'Cambridge Favourite' (F) ♀H6	CAgr CArg CMac CRos CSBt CTri EHyd EMil EPfP EPom LBuc LCro LOPS LRHS MGos MMuc MPri NRHS SEdi SPlb
- 'Cambridge Vigour' (F)	LRHS NRHS
- 'Charlotte'PBR (F)	LRHS
- 'Christine' (F)	CAgr CArg EPom
- 'Cupid'PBR (F)	CArg EPom LCro LOPS
- 'Darselect'PBR (F)	EPom
- 'Delia' (F)	CRos EHyd LRHS NRHS
- DELIZZ ('Liza'PBR) (F)	EHyd NRHS
- 'Elan'PBR (F)	LRHS NRHS
- 'Elegance'PBR (F)	CArg EPom
- 'Elsanta' (F)	CArg CRos CSBt CTri ECrN EHyd EMil EPfP EPom IArd LBuc LRHS MPri NRHS SEdi SPer WMat
- 'Everest'PBR (F)	LRHS NRHS
- 'Fenella'PBR (F)	CArg CMac EMil EPom LCro LOPS
- 'Finesse' (F)	LRHS NRHS
- 'Flamenco'PBR (F)	CArg EPom LEdu
- 'Florence'PBR (F)	CAgr CArg CRos CSBt CTri EHyd EPom LBuc LRHS NRHS SPer
- 'Florian' (F)	LEdu
- (Fragoo Series) FRAGOO DEEP ROSE ('Tarpan') (F)	CRos EHyd LRHS NRHS
- - FRAGOO PINK ('Pikan') (F)	CRos EHyd LRHS NRHS
- - FRAGOO WHITE ('Belton') (F)	CRos EHyd LRHS NRHS
- Fraise des Bois	see *F. vesca*
- 'Framberry' (F)	EPom LEdu LRHS
- 'Frau Mieze Schindler' (F)	LEdu
* - 'Fresca' (F)	EHyd LRHS NRHS
- 'Gariguette' (F)	EPom LRHS
- 'Gorella' (F)	LRHS
- 'Hapil' (F) ♀H6	CTri EMil EPfP EPom LBuc LRHS
- 'Honeoye' (F) ♀H6	CAgr CArg CMac CSBt EMil EPfP EPom LBuc LCro LEdu LOPS LRHS MMuc SPer

- 'Korona'PBR (F)	CMac EPom
- 'Leo Alba' (F)	CArg
- 'Loran' (F)	LRHS MBros
- 'Lucy'PBR (F)	CMac
- 'Mae'PBR (F)	CArg LEdu
- 'Malling Centenary'PBR (F)	EPom
- 'Malling Opal'PBR (F)	EPom
- 'Malwina'PBR (F)	EPom SVic
- 'Manille' (F)	EPom
- 'Merlan'PBR (F)	LRHS
- 'Mount Everest' (F)	LCro LRHS
- 'Pandora' (F)	LEdu
- 'Pegasus' (F) ♀H6	CAgr CRos CSBt EHyd EPfP EPom LRHS NRHS
- pineberry (F)	LEdu
- PINK PANDA ('Frel') (F)	CBod CMac CTri EBee EHyd ELan LRHS MBel MHer MRav NGdn NLar NRHS SGbt SPer SPoG WBor WCAu WCav WSMil
- pink-flowered (F)	GAbr
- 'Red Dream' (F)	LCro LOPS
- 'Red Glory'PBR (F)	LRHS NRHS
- 'Red Princess'PBR (F)	LRHS NRHS
- RED RUBY	see *F.* × *ananassa* 'Samba'
- 'Redgauntlet' (F)	CRos EHyd EPfP LRHS NRHS
- 'Rhapsody' (F) ♀H6	CRos EHyd LRHS LSRN NRHS
- 'Roman' (F)	LRHS
- 'Royal Sovereign' (F)	CMac CTri EPom NBir SVic
§ - 'Samba'PBR (F)	CBod EHyd ELan GLog LEdu LRHS MBel MNrw NGdn NLar NRHS SGbt
- 'Senga Sengana' (F)	SVic
- SNOW WHITE ('Hansawhit'PBR) (F)	EPom LEdu SVic
- 'Sonata'PBR (F)	ELan EPom LRHS
- 'Sweet Ann'PBR (F)	LRHS
- 'Sweetheart' (F)	EPfP EPom LCro LOPS
- 'Symphony'PBR (F) ♀H6	CAgr CRos EHyd EPfP EPom LBuc LRHS LSRN NRHS
- 'Temptation' (F)	CRos EHyd LRHS NRHS SVic
§ - 'Variegata' (v)	CMea MRav SGbt SPer SPoG
- 'Vibrant'PBR (F)	EMil EPom
- 'White Dream' (F)	LCro LOPS
'Bowles's Double'	see *F. vesca* 'Multiplex'
chiloensis (F)	LEdu WKor
- 'Chaval' (F)	ECha EPPr IMou MRav NChi WMal
- 'Variegata' misapplied	see *F.* × *ananassa* 'Variegata'
indica	see *Duchesnea indica*
'Lipstick'	EBee NLar WSpi
moschata	CAgr CLau WKor
nubicola	CAgr GPoy
'Variegata'	see *F.* × *ananassa* 'Variegata'
§ ***vesca*** (F)	Widely available
* - var. ***albescens***	CLau
- 'Alexandria' (F)	CLau ENfk NPol
- 'Alpina Scarletta' (F)	ENfk
- 'Ana Blanca'	see *F.* × *ananassa* 'Anablanca'
- 'Baron Solemacher' (F)	NPol SPhx WHer
- 'Capron Royale' (F)	CAgr
- 'Flore Pleno'	see *F. vesca* 'Multiplex'
- 'Fructu Albo' (F)	CAgr CBre
- 'Golden Alexandra' (F)	ECha EWes EWhm NPol NWad
- 'Mara des Bois' (F)	EPom EShb LRHS SPer SVic
- 'Mignonette'	CLau EWhm NPol
- 'Monophylla' (F)	NPol WHer
§ - 'Multiplex' (d)	EPPr NPol WBor WHer WOut
§ - 'Muricata'	CBre LEdu
- 'Patchwork'	NPol
- 'Pineapple Crush' (F)	NPol WHer
- 'Plymouth Strawberry'	see *F. vesca* 'Muricata'
- 'Reine des Vallées' (F)	LRHS
- 'Rügen' (F)	NPol
- 'Scarlet Beauty' (F)	EPom MNHC NPol
§ - 'Semperflorens' (F)	ECrN
§ - 'Semperflorens Alba' (F)	CAgr NWad
- 'Variegata' misapplied	see *F.* × *ananassa* 'Variegata'
- 'White Soul' (F)	NPol
- 'Yellow Wonder' (F)	NPol
virginiana	CAgr WKor
- subsp. ***glauca***	EPPr
viridis	CAgr WKor

Francoa (*Francoaceae*)

appendiculata	ILea MGil NBir NWad SHeu WHer WPav
Ballyrogan strain	IBlr
'Confetti'	CExl CMea
* dwarf purple	CElw
'Purple Spike'	see *F. sonchifolia* Rogerson's form
ramosa	CPla CTri EBee GKev IBlr ILea NBir NBro SDix WKif
* - 'Alba'	CSpe
sonchifolia	Widely available
- 'Alba'	EBee
- 'Cally Dwarf Purple'	SHeu
- 'Petite Bouquet'	CKno EWes GKev LRHS SHar SRms WNPC
- 'Pink Bouquet'	CAbb CKno CMac CWGN EBee LRHS LSRN MHol NBPC SHar SHeu SIvy SRkn WFar
- 'Pink Giant'	CAby CBod CPla CSpe CWld EHyd EPau EWhm GAbr GKev LPot LRHS MBel MPie NBPC NRHS NWad SHeu SPhx WFar
§ - Rogerson's form	CElw CMiW CRos CTri EHyd ELon EShb GBin IMou LRHS NBPC NBir NChi NRHS SDix SHeu WBrk WFar

Frangula (*Rhamnaceae*)

§ ***alnus***	CArg CCVT CHab CTri EWTr LBuc MBlu MGos SavN SCob SEWo SavN WFar WMou WSFF WTSh
- 'Aspleniifolia'	CSpe CTho ELan EPfP IDee LRHS MBlu MGil MMuc MRav NLar WCFE WGrn WLov
- 'Fine Line'	CRos EHyd ELan LRHS NLar NRHS SPoG SavN
- 'Minaret'	MBlu
- 'Ron Williams'	MBlu WMat
californica B&SWJ 14057	WCru

Frankenia (*Frankeniaceae*)

laevis	SRms
thymifolia	CTri EBou ECtt MAsh MHer MMuc SPlb WHoo WRHF XLum

Franklinia (*Theaceae*)

alatamaha	CBcs IDee LRHS MBlu MGil WPGP

Franklinia × *Gordonia* see × *Gordlinia*

Fraxinus ✿ (*Oleaceae*)

americana 'Autumn Purple'	SCob
angustifolia 'Raywood'	ECrN GBin MGos MMuc MSwo SCob
chiisanensis B&SWJ 12719	WCru
excelsior	CHab ECrN MGos MMuc NGrd SCob

- 'Crispa'	NLar
- 'Jaspidea'	ECrN MGos MMuc MSwo
- 'Pendula'	ECrN SCob
- 'Westhof's Glorie'	SCob
ornus	ECrN MMuc MSwo SEND WTSh
- 'Arie Peters'	SCob
uhdei **new**	GKev

Freesia (*Iridaceae*)

sp.	EShb
alba Foster	see *F. lactea*
alba (G.L. Mey.) Gumbl.	CPbh
'Blue Moon'	LCro LOPS
'Delta River'	EPfP SPoG
'Fragrant Sunburst'	EPfP SPoG
fucata	CPbh
'Gold River'	SPoG
grandiflora	CExl
§ ***lactea***	CBor XEll
§ ***laxa*** 🏆H3	CExl CPbh CSpe CTri EPri GKev LEdu LRHS NHpl SChF SChr WFar
- var. ***alba*** 🏆H3	CExl CPbh EPri GKev WFar
- blue-flowered	SBrt
- 'Joan Evans'	SChF WFar
- red-spotted	CExl
(Lovely Series) 'Lovely Blue' **new**	CRos
- 'Lovely Cream' **new**	CRos
- 'Lovely White' **new**	CRos
'Red River'	SPoG
refracta	CPbh
viridis	CExl
'White River'	EPfP SPoG

Fremontodendron (*Malvaceae*)

'California Glory' 🏆H4	CBcs CDoC CMac CRos EHyd EPfP IDee LRHS LSRN MAsh MBlu MGil MGos MHol NRHS SArc SCob SEle SGbt SGol SIvy SMad SPer SPoG SVen SWvt WSMil
californicum	CTri EBee ELan NLar SEND SNig SPlb WFar
'Pacific Sunset'	LRHS MGos MRav SGol
'Tequila Sunrise' 🏆H4	CWGN LRHS

Freylinia (*Scrophulariaceae*)

cestroides	see *F. lanceolata*
§ ***lanceolata***	CBcs CCCN EBee SPlb SVen
tropica	MGil
visseri	SVen

Fritillaria ✿ (*Liliaceae*)

acmopetala 🏆H4	CAby CAvo CBor CMiW CWCL ELon EMor EPot ERCP GKev ITim MBow MNrw SDeJ SDir SHar WCot WSHC
affinis	CWCL EMor GKev NHpl
§ - var. ***tristulis***	ELon EMor
- yellow-flowered	CWCL
amana	CWCL ELon EMor ERCP GKev WCot
- 'Cambridge'	WCot
arabica	see *F. persica*
assyriaca	EPot
aurea 'Golden Flag'	SDeJ
ayakoana	GKev
'Beethoven' (Rascal Series)	GKev WCot
biflora 'Martha Roderick'	SDeJ
§ ***bithynica***	ITim
bucharica	EPot GKev
camschatcensis	CWCL EHyd ELon EMor EPot ERCP GBin GEdr GKev GMaP LRHS NBir NHpl SDeJ SPhx WCot
- 'Alaska'	NHar
- 'Aurea'	GRum NHar
- black-flowered	CAby NHar
- double-flowered (d)	GKev
- dwarf **new**	GRum
- f. ***flavescens***	GEdr GKev
carduchorum	see *F. minuta*
carica	GKev
citrina	see *F. bithynica*
crassifolia subsp. ***crassifolia***	GKev
§ - subsp. ***kurdica***	ITim
davidii	NDry
davisii	EPot GKev SDeJ
eduardii	GKev
- 'Castor'	EPot GKev
- 'Pollux'	GKev
elwesii	CAvo EPot ERCP GKev ITim SDeJ SDir
* ***glauca*** 'Golden Flag'	SDeJ
- 'Goldilocks'	SDeJ
graeca	SDeJ
- subsp. ***ionica***	see *F. graeca* subsp. *thessala*
§ - subsp. ***thessala***	GKev
hispanica	see *F. lusitanica*
imperialis 🏆H7	MWat
- 'Aureomarginata' (v)	SDir
- 'Aureovariegata' (v) **new**	SDir
- 'Aurora'	CRos EHyd EPot ERCP GKev LRHS NLar NPer NRHS SCob SDeJ SPer SPhx WPhe
- 'Bach' (Rascal Series)	GKev
- 'Brahms' (Rascal Series)	GKev
- 'Chopin' (Rascal Series)	CAvo GKev
- 'Early Fantasy'	GKev
- 'Early Magic'	GKev
- 'Early Passion'	GKev SDir
- 'Garland Star'	CRos EHyd GKev LRHS LSun NLar NRHS SDeJ SDir SPhx
- var. ***inodora***	GKev
- 'Lutea'	CAvo CRos EHyd ERCP LRHS NRHS SCob SPoG WPhe
- 'Mahler' (Rascal Series)	GKev
- 'Maxima'	see *F. imperialis* 'Rubra Maxima'
- 'Maxima Lutea' 🏆H7	CRos CWld EHyd ELan EPot ERCP LRHS NLar NRHS SDeJ SPhx SPoG
- 'Orange Beauty'	CRos EHyd GKev LRHS NRHS SDeJ WPhe
- 'Prolifera'	GKev SDeJ SPeP
- 'Rubra'	CBod CRos CWld EHyd ERCP LCro LOPS LRHS NLar NRHS SCob WFar WPhe
§ - 'Rubra Maxima'	CRos EHyd ELan EPot ERCP LRHS LSun NRHS SDeJ SPhx
- 'Satie' (Rascal Series)	GKev
- 'Striped Beauty'	EPot SDeJ SDir WPhe
- 'Sunset'	GKev
- 'The Premier'	GKev SDeJ
- 'Vivaldi' (Rascal Series)	GKev
- 'William Rex'	CAvo CRos CWCL EHyd EPot ERCP GKev LBuc LRHS NRHS SDir SPhx SPoG
involucrata	WCot
ionica	see *F. graeca* subsp. *thessala*
karadaghensis	see *F. crassifolia* subsp. *kurdica*

koidzumiana	GKev
lanceolata	see *F. affinis* var. *tristulis*
latakiensis	EPot GKev
§ ***lusitanica***	ITim
meleagris ♀H5	Widely available
- var. ***unicolor*** subvar. ***alba*** ♀H5	ERCP GKev ILea LCro LOPS NHol SDeJ SPer SPhx WPnP WShi
- - - 'Aphrodite'	EPot NBir WCot
messanensis subsp. ***gracilis***	GKev
michailovskyi	CAvo CRos EHyd EPot ERCP EWhm GKev LRHS MNrw NHpl NRHS SDeJ SRms WFar WPhe
- 'Multiflorum'	GKev
§ ***minuta***	EPot ERCP SDeJ
olivieri	GKev
pallidiflora ♀H5	CAvo CMiW ELon EMor EPot ERCP GKev NBir NHpl SDeJ SPhx WCot
- yellow-flowered	ITim
§ ***persica***	CPla CWld ECha EHyd EPot ERCP EWhm IPot LCro LOPS LRHS MWat NChi NRHS SPeP SPhx WCot WPhe
- 'Adiyaman' ♀H4	ELan SDeJ
- 'Alba'	GKev SDeJ SPeP SPhx
- 'Green Dreams'	GKev NLar
- 'Ivory Bells'	EPot ERCP GKev LCro LOPS LRHS NLar SDeJ WPhe
- 'Midnight Bells'	GKev
* - 'Senkoy'	GKev
- 'Twin Towers Tribute'	GKev NLar
pontica ♀H4	CAvo CWCL EMor EPot ERCP GKev ITim NHpl SDeJ SPhx WCot
pudica 'Giant'	SDeJ
raddeana	CAvo ELon EMor EPot ERCP GBin NLar SDeJ SPhx WCot
rubra major	see *F. imperialis* 'Rubra Maxima'
sewerzowii	EPot WCot
- 'Black Bear'	GKev
sibthorpiana	EPot
stenanthera	EPot
thunbergii	WCot
uva-vulpis	CAby CAvo CRos EAJP ECtt EHyd ELon EPot ERCP GWyn LRHS MBow MNrw NBir NRHS SDeJ WFar
verticillata	CMea ECha

Fuchsia ✿ (*Onagraceae*)

'A.M. Larwick'	EBak SLBF
'A.W. Taylor'	EBak
'Abbé Farges' (d)	CLoc CRos EBak EHyd EPts LRHS NRHS SLBF SVic
'Abundance'	EHDe
'Achievement' ♀H4	CLoc LCla MJac SVic
'Adinda' (T) ♀H1c	EPts LCla MHer
'Adrienne' (d)	EPts
'Ailsa Garnett' (d)	EBak
'Alan Titchmarsh' ♀H2	EPts LCla SLBF
'Alaska' (d)	CLoc
'Albertus Schwab'	LCla
'Alderford'	SLBF
'Alfonso' (d)	SLBF
'Alice Ashton' (d)	EBak
'Alice Doran'	LCla
'Alice Hoffman' (d) ♀H4	CCCN CLoc CMac CRos CSBt EBak EBee EHDe EHyd ELan EPfP EPts LRHS MAsh MGos MJac NLar NRHS SCob SEND SLBF SLim SPer SPoG SVic WFar WLov WOld
'Alicia Sellars'	SLBF
'Alison Ewart'	CLoc SVic
'Alison Patricia' ♀H2	EBak LCla MJac SLBF SVic
'Alison Ruth Griffin' (d)	MJac
'Alison Ryle' (d)	EBak
'Alison Sweetman' ♀H2	MJac
'All Summer Beauty' (T) **new**	SLBF
'Allen Jackson'	LCla SLBF
alpestris	EBak LCla
'Alyce Larson' (d)	EBak
'Alyssa May Garcia' (d)	EPts MJac SLBF
'Amazing Maisie' (d)	SLBF
'Amelia Rose'	SLBF
'Amelie Aubin'	CLoc EBak
§ ***ampliata***	LCla
'Amy'	MJac
'Amy Lye'	CLoc EHDe SVic
§ 'Andenken an Heinrich Henkel' (T)	CLoc EBak
'André Le Nostre' (d)	EBak
'Andreas Schwab'	LCla
andrei	LCla
'Andrew Carnegie' (d)	CLoc
'Angela Leslie' (d)	EBak SVic
'Angel's Flight' (d)	EBak
'Angel's Kiss' (E)	SLBF
'Anita'	CLoc EPts MJac SLBF
'Ann Allen'	SLBF
'Ann Howard Tripp'	CLoc EPts MJac SVic
'Ann Reid'	SLBF
'Anna Sunshine' (T)	EPts
'Annabel' (d) ♀H4	CLoc CTri EBak EPts LCla MJac SLBF SVic
'Annie Earle'	EHDe
'Annie M.G. Schmidt'	EPts LCla
'Anthea Day' (d)	CLoc
'Antigone'	SLBF
'Aphrodite' (d)	CLoc
'Applause' (d)	CLoc EBak EPts SLBF
aprica misapplied	see *F.* × *bacillaris*
aprica Lundell	see *F. microphylla* subsp. *aprica*
'Apricot Ice'	CLoc SVic
'Arabella Improved'	EHDe
arborea	see *F. arborescens*
§ ***arborescens***	CBcs CBod CLoc CWCL EBak ECre EHDe EWld IDee LCla MCot MHer SDys SIvy SVic
- B&SWJ 10475	WCru
'Arcady'	CLoc
'Ariel' (E)	SVic
'Arkie'	MJac
'Army Nurse' (d) ♀H4	CBod CLoc CRos EHyd ELan ELon EPfP EPts LRHS MGos NBir NLar NRHS SGol SLBF SVic WLov
'Ashley'	LCla
'Ashtede'	SLBF
'Ashville'	SLBF
'Atlantic Star'	MJac
'Aubergine'	see *F.* 'Gerharda's Aubergine'
'Auenland'	MJac
'Auntie Doris' (d) **new**	SLBF
'Auntie Jinks' ♀H2	EBak MJac
'Aurora Superba'	CLoc EBak SLBF
'Autumnale' ♀H2	CLoc EBak EHDe EPts NWad SLBF SPoG
'Avalanche' ambig. (d)	CLoc EBak SLBF
'Avocet'	CLoc
'Avon Celebration' (d/v)	CLoc
'Avon Gem'	CLoc

	'Avon Glow' (d)	CLoc
	'Avon Gold'	CLoc
	'Awake Sweet Love' (T)	EPts
	ayavacensis	LCla
	'Aylisa Rowan' (E)	SLBF
	'Azure Sky' (d)	MJac
	'Baby Blue Eyes' ♀H4	CLoc CRos EHDe EHyd ELan ELon LRHS LSRN MAsh NRHS SLBF SVic
	'Baby Thumb' (v)	EPts
§	× ***bacillaris*** (E)	CAbb CChe CDoC EPPr ESwi EWes LRHS SEle SIvy SLBF SPoG WHer XLum
§	- 'Cottinghamii' (E)	EWld ILea WSHC
§	- 'Reflexa' (E)	CCCN CTrC
	'Bagworthy Water'	CLoc
	'Baker's Tri' (T)	EBak
	'Balkonkönigin'	CLoc
	'Ballerina Girl' (E)	SLBF
	'Ballet Girl' (d) ♀H2	CLoc EBak SLBF
	'Bambini'	EPts
	'Banks Peninsula'	GBin
	'Barbara'	CLoc EBak EPts LCla MJac SVic
	'Barbara Evans'	SLBF
	'Barbara Windsor'	MJac
	'Barry's Queen'	see *F.* 'Golden Border Queen'
	'Bashful' (d)	EPts LCla SVic
	'Beacon'	CLoc CMac CRos EBak EHyd EPfP EPts LCla LRHS MJac NRHS SGol SLBF SPoG SVic
	'Beacon Rosa' ♀H4	CLoc CRos EHyd EPfP EPts LCla LRHS MJac NRHS SLBF SPoG SVic
	'Beauty of Bath' (d)	CLoc
	'Beauty of Clyffe Hall' Lye	EBak EHDe
	'Beauty of Exeter' (d)	EBak LCla
	'Beauty of Prussia' (d)	CLoc
	'Beauty of Swanley'	EHDe
	'Beauty of Trowbridge'	EHDe LCla
	'Bella Rosella' (California Dreamers Series) (d) ♀H2	CLoc EPts MBros MJac SCoo
	'Belvoir Beauty' (d)	CLoc
	'Ben de Jong'	LCla SLBF
	'Ben Jammin'	CDoC CLoc EPfP EPts SVic
	'Ben-Ben'	SLBF
	'Berliner Kind' (d)	EBak
	'Bernice Elizabeth' (d)	SLBF
	'Bernie's Big-un' (d)	SLBF
	'Bernisser Hardy' ♀H4	EPts LCla NQui SLBF SLim XLum
	'Bessie Kimberley' (T)	LCla
	'Betsy Huuskes'	SLBF
	'Beverley'	EBak EPts
	'Bicentennial' (d)	CLoc EBak EPts MBros MJac SLBF
	'Billy Green' (T) ♀H2	CLoc EBak EHDe EPts LCla MHer MJac SVic
	'Blacky' (d)	CCCN EBak GBin SDix SDys SEND
	'Bland's New Striped'	EBak EPts SLBF
§	'Blauer Engel' (d)	MJac
	'Blaze Away' (d)	MBros MJac
	BLUE ANGEL	see *F.* 'Blauer Engel'
	'Blue Bush'	EPts MJac SVic XLum
	'Blue Gown' (d)	CLoc EBak SVic
	'Blue Lace' (d)	SVic
	'Blue Mirage' (d)	CLoc SVic
	'Blue Pearl' (d)	EBak
	'Blue Pinwheel'	EBak
	'Blue Tit'	LCla
	'Blue Veil' (d)	CLoc MJac SCoo
	'Blue Waves' (d)	CLoc CSBt EBak SVic
	'Blush o' Dawn' (d)	CLoc EBak SVic
	'Bobby Shaftoe' (d)	EBak
	'Bobby Wingrove'	EBak
	'Bobby's Girl'	EPts
	'Bobolink' (d)	EBak
	'Bob's Best' (d)	EPts
	boliviana Britton	see *F. sanctae-rosae*
	boliviana ambig.	CBcs IDee MHer
§	***boliviana*** Carrière	CLoc LCla
§	- var. ***alba*** ♀H2	CLoc EBak EPts LCla WFar
	- var. ***boliviana***	CRHN
	- var. ***luxurians*** 'Alba'	see *F. boliviana* Carrière var. *alba*
	- f. ***puberulenta*** Munz	see *F. boliviana* Carrière
	'Bon Accorde'	CLoc EBak EPts SLBF SVic
	'Bonnie Lass' (d)	EBak
I	'Boogie Woogie'	EPts LCla MJac SLBF
	'Borde Hill' (d)	EPts
	'Border Princess'	EBak
	'Border Queen' ♀H4	CLoc EBak EHDe EPts MJac SLBF SVic
	'Börnemann's Beste'	see *F.* 'Georg Börnemann'
	'Bouquet' (d)	SLBF
	'Bow Bells'	CLoc MJac
	'Boy Marc' (T) ♀H1c	LCla
	'Brandt's 500 Club'	CLoc
	'Breckland'	EBak
	'Breeder's Dream' (d)	EBak
	'Breevis Minimus'	SLBF
	'Brenda White'	CLoc EBak
	'Brian C. Morrison' (T)	LCla
	'Brian G. Soanes'	EBak
	'Brian Kimberley' (T)	LCla
	'Bridesmaid' (d)	EBak
	'Brilliant' ambig.	EHDe
	'Brilliant' Bull, 1865	CLoc EBak
	'Brookwood Belle' (d) ♀H3	EPts LCla MJac SLBF
	'Brutus' ♀H4	CLoc CRos EBak EHDe EHyd EPfP EPts LRHS NRHS SCoo SLBF SVic WFar
	'Bryan Breary' (E)	LCla
	'Buddha' (d)	EBak
	'Bugle Boy'	LCla
	'Buster' (d)	LCla
	'C.J. Howlett'	EBak
	'Caesar' (d)	EBak
	'Cambridge Louie'	EBak
	campos-portoi	EBee MGil WPGP
	'Candy Bells' (d)	CSBt
	canescens misapplied	see *F. ampliata*
	'Canny Bob'	MJac
	'Cara Mia' (d)	CLoc
	'Caradela' (d)	CLoc MJac
	'Cardinal'	CLoc
	'Cardinal Farges' (d)	CLoc SLBF SVic
	'Careless Whisper'	LCla SLBF
	'Carla Johnston' ♀H2	CLoc EPts MJac SVic
	'Carmel Blue'	CLoc SCob SVic
	'Carnoustie' (d)	EBak
	'Carol Grace' (d)	CLoc
	'Caroline'	CLoc EBak EPts SVic
	'Caroline's Joy'	MJac SCoo
	'Cascade'	CLoc EPts MJac SLBF
	'Cecil Glass'	EHDe
	'Cecile' (d)	CCCN EPts LCla MJac SLBF
	'Celebration' (d)	CLoc
	'Celia Smedley' ♀H3	CLoc CRos EBak EHDe EHyd EPts LCla LRHS MJac NRHS SLBF SVic WAvo
	'Centerpiece' (d)	EBak
	'Ceri'	CLoc WMal
	'Champagne Celebration'	CLoc
	'Champion'	XLum

'Chang' ♀H2	CLoc EBak LCla SLBF SVic
'Chantelle Garcia' (d)	EPts LCla MJac SLBF
'Chantry Park' (T)	LCla
'Chapel Rossan' (E)	SLBF
'Charisma'	SVic
'Charles Welch'	EPts
CHARLIE DIMMOCK ('Foncha'PBR) (d)	CLoc
'Charlie Gardiner'	EBak
'Charming'	CLoc CRos EHDe EHyd EPfP LRHS MAsh MJac NRHS SVic XLum
'Chatt's Delight'	SLBF
'Checkerboard' ♀H3	CLoc EBak EHDe EPts LCla MHer MJac SLBF SVic
'Chelsea Louise'	EPts
'Cherry Lee'	SLBF
'Chessboard'	CLoc
'Chillerton Beauty' ♀H4	CLoc CRos CTri EHDe EHyd ELan ELon EPts LCla LRHS MJac NLar NRHS SEND SLBF SVic WFar
'Chilli Red'	CRos EHyd EPfP EPts LRHS MAsh NRHS
'China Lantern'	CLoc SVic
'Chris Bright'	MJac
'Chris Tarrant' (d)	EPts
cinerea	LCla
'Cinnabarina' (E)	CLoc SVic
'Cinvenu'	LCla
'Citation'	EBak SVic
'City of Adelaide' (d)	CLoc
'Clair de Lune'	EBak SLBF
'Claudia' (d)	EPts LCla MJac SLBF
'Cliff's Hardy'	LCla SVic
'Cliff's Own'	SVic
'Cliff's Unique' (d)	EPts
'Clifton Beauty' (d)	MJac
'Clifton Charm'	EPts LCla MJac SVic
'Clifton Pride' **new**	MJac
'Clipper'	EHDe
'Cloth of Gold'	CLoc EBak EHDe MJac SLBF SVic
'Cloverdale Pearl'	EBak MAsh SPoG
'Coachman' ♀H4	CLoc EBak EHDe EPts LCla MBros SLBF
coccinea	CTsd SVic
'Codex' (d)	SLBF
× ***colensoi***	LCla
'Colette Kelly' **new**	SVic
'Collingwood' (d)	CLoc
I 'Comet' Tiret (d)	CLoc
'Connie' (d)	EBak SVic XLum
'Connor's Cascade'	SLBF
'Conspicua' ♀H4	LRHS SIvy SLBF SVic
'Constance' (d)	CLoc LCla MJac SLBF SVic
'Constance Comer'	MJac SVic
'Constellation' Schnabel, 1957 (d)	CLoc EBak
'Coquet Bell'	EBak
'Coral Baby' (E)	LCla SLBF
'Coralle' (T) ♀H1c	CCCN CLoc EBak EPts LCla MBros MJac SLBF
'Corallina' ♀H4	CLoc SEND SVic
* ***cordata*** B&SWJ 9095	WCru
- B&SWJ 10325	WCru
cordifolia misapplied	see *F. splendens*
'Core'ngrato' (d)	CLoc
'Cornelia Smith' (T)	LCla
'Cornish Blue'	CLoc
'Cornwall Calls' (d)	EBak EHDe
'Corsage' (d)	SVic
'Corsair' (d)	EBak
corymbiflora misapplied	see *F. boliviana* Carrière
'Costa Brava'	CLoc
'Cotta Bright Star'	LCla
'Cotta Carousel'	LCla
'Cotta Christmas Tree'	LCla SLBF
'Cottinghamii'	see *F.* × ***bacillaris*** 'Cottinghamii'
'Cotton Candy' (d)	CLoc SVic
'Countdown Carol' (d)	EPts
'Countess of Aberdeen'	EBak SLBF
'Countess of Maritza' (d)	CLoc
'Court Jester' (d)	CLoc
'Cover Girl' (d)	EPts
'Coxeen'	EBak
'Crackerjack'	CLoc
'Crescendo' (d)	CLoc
'Crinkley Bottom' (d)	EPts MJac SLBF
'Crosby Serendipity'	CLoc
'Crystal Blue'	EBak
'Cuddles and Kisses' (d) **new**	SLBF
'Cupid'	EBak
'Curly Q'	EBak
'Curtain Call' (d)	EBak
cylindracea misapplied	see *F.* × ***bacillaris***
'Dainty'	EBak
'Dainty Lady' (d)	EBak
'Daisy Bell'	CLoc EBak LCla MJac
'Dana Samantha'	EPts
'Dancing Bloom'	EPts
'Dancing Flame' (d) ♀H3	CLoc EBak EPts LCla MBros MJac SLBF
'Daniel Pfaller' (d)	MJac
'Danny Boy' (d)	CLoc EBak
'Dark Eyes' (d) ♀H4	CLoc EBak MJac SLBF
'Dark Secret' (d)	EBak
'Daryn John Woods'	LCla
'David' ♀H4	CLoc EHDe ELon EPts LCla LSRN MJac SLBF SPoG WAvo WLov
'David Alston' (d)	CLoc
'David Clifford'	EHDe
'David Lockyer' (d)	CLoc
'David Savage' (d)	LCla
'Dawn Fantasia' (v)	CLoc EPts
'Dawn Star' (d)	CLoc
'De Groot's Floriant'	LCla
'Debby' (d)	EBak
'Deborah Jane'	SLBF
'Deborah Street' (d)	CLoc
'DebRon's Black Cherry'	SLBF
'Dee Copley' (d)	EBak
'Deep Purple' (d)	CLoc EPts MCot MJac SCoo
'Delia Smith' (d)	EPts
'Delicate Blue'	SLBF
'Delicate Purple'	EPts SLBF WFar WMal
'Delphobe'	EPts
'Delta's Bride'	SLBF
'Delta's Groom'	LCla SLBF
'Delta's Sara'	CBcs CRos EHyd ELon EPfP EPts GBin LBuc LCro LOPS LRHS MAsh MBow MBros MJac MMrt MSCN NRHS SCob SLim SLon SPad SPoG SVic WFar WLov
§ ***denticulata*** ♀H2	CLoc CRos EBak EHDe EHyd EPts LCla LRHS MHer NRHS SLBF SVic
'Desperate Daniel'	EPts
'Devonshire Dumpling' (d) ♀H2	CLoc EBak EPts MJac
'Diablo' (d)	EBak
'Diamond Wedding'	SVic
'Diana Wright'	WAvo WLov

'Dipton Dainty' (d)	CLoc EBak SVic
'Display' ♀H4	CLoc CRos EBak EHDe EHyd EPfP EPts LCla LRHS MGos MJac NPer NRHS SCob SGol SLBF SPoG SVic
'Diva'	WCot
'Doc'	EPts SVic
'Docteur Topinard'	CLoc
'Doctor'	see *F.* 'The Doctor'
'Doctor Foster' ♀H4	CLoc CTri EBak EHDe SVic
'Doctor Olson' (d)	CLoc
'Doctor Robert'	EPts MJac
'Dodo'	LCla SLBF
§ 'Dollar Prinzessin' (d) ♀H4	CLoc CMac CRos EBak EHyd EPfP EPts EShb LCla LRHS MBros MGos MJac NPer NRHS SGol SLBF SLim SPlb SVic WFar
'Dominyana'	EBak EHDe LCla
'Dopy' (d)	EPts SVic
'Doray'	EPts
'Doreen Redfern'	CLoc MJac SVic
'Doris Joan'	SLBF
'Dorothea Flower'	CLoc EBak
'Dorothy'	EPts LCla SLBF
'Dorothy Ann'	LCla SLBF
'Dorothy Day' (d)	CLoc
'Dorothy Hanley' (d)	CCCN CLoc ELon EPts MJac SCob SLBF SVic
'Dorrian Brogdale' (T)	LCla
'Drake 400' (d)	CLoc
'Drame' (d)	EBak EHDe SVic
'Duchess of Albany'	CLoc EHDe
'Duchess of Cornwall' (d)	EPts
'Duke of Wellington' Haag, 1956 (d)	CLoc
'Dulcie Elizabeth' (d)	EBak MJac
'Dunrobin Bedder'	SLBF
'Dusky Rose' (d)	CLoc EBak MJac
'Dutch Mill'	CLoc EBak
'Dying Embers' ♀H4	CLoc MHer SDix SVen
'Earre Barré'	SLBF
'East Anglian'	CLoc
'Easter Belle'	CRos EHyd LRHS NRHS
'Ebb 'n' Flow'	EBak
'Ebbtide' (d)	CLoc
'Ed Largarde' (d)	EBak
'Eden Lady'	CLoc
'Eden Princess'	MJac
'Eden Rock' (d)	CLoc
'Edith' ambig.	EPts
'Edith' Brown (d)	LCla SLBF
'El Cid'	CLoc EBak SVic
'Elaine Ann'	EPts MJac
'Eleanor Leytham'	EBak
ELECTRIC LIGHTS ('Nufu1'PBR)	EPts
'Elfin Glade'	CLoc EBak SVic
'Elfriede Ott' (T) ♀H1c	CLoc EBak LCla
'Ellie's Charm'	SLBF
'Elma'	LCla MJac
'Elsa' (d)	SVic
'Emily Bright'	EHDe
'Emily Eve' (d)	EPts MJac SLBF
'Emma Payne'	SLBF
'Empress of Prussia' ♀H4	CLoc EBak EPts SLBF SVic
encliandra (E)	NWad
§ 'Enfant Prodigue' (d)	CLoc SDix SLBF XLum
'Eppsii'	SLBF
'Eric's Majestic' (d)	MJac
'Ernie'PBR	EPts SLBF
'Eruption' (T)	CLoc MJac
'Estelle Marie'	CLoc EBak
'Eternal Flame' (d)	EBak EPts
'Ethel May' (d)	MJac
'Eva Boerg' ♀H4	CCCN CLoc CTri EBak EPts MBros WKif
'Evensong'	CLoc EBak SVic
'Evita'PBR (Bella Series)	LCro LOPS
excorticata	CBcs CCCN CExl CTsd ESwi SPlb WBor WLov
'Fabian Franck' (T)	LCla
'Falklands' (d)	EPts SLBF
'Falling Stars'	CLoc
'Fancy Pants' (d)	CLoc SVic
'Fanfare'	LCla
'Felicity Kendal' (d)	SCoo
'Festival Lights' (E)	SLBF
'Ffion'	EPts
'Fiery Spider'	EBak
'Finn'	EPts
'Fiona'	CLoc EBak SVic
'Fire Mountain' (d)	CLoc
'Firecracker'	see *F.* 'John Ridding'
'Firelite' (d)	EBak
'First Success' (E)	LCla
'Flair' (d)	CLoc
'Flamenco Dancer' (California Dreamers Series) (d)	CLoc
'Flamingo Wings' (d)	EPts
'Flanders Field'	SLBF
'Flash' ♀H4	CLoc CRos CTri EHyd ELan EMor EPts LCla LRHS MJac MRav NRHS SLBF SPoG SVic
'Flashlight'	EWld LCla MAsh MJac SCoo
'Flat Jack o' Lancashire' (d)	SLBF
'Fleur de Picardie'	SLBF
'Flirtation Waltz' (d)	CLoc EBak MJac SVic
'Flocon de Neige'	SLBF
'Flogman'	EWld LCla
'Floral City' (d)	CLoc
'Florence Turner'	EBak
'Florentina' (d)	EBak SVic
'Florrie's Gem' (d)	SLBF
'Flying Cloud' (d)	CLoc EBak SVic
'Flying Scotsman' (d)	CLoc EBak EPts SCoo SVic
'Folk'	MHer
'Foolke'	EBak
'Forget-me-not'	CLoc SVic
'Fort Bragg' (d)	EBak
'Four Farthings' (d)	EPts
'Foxgrove Wood' ♀H4	EBak EPts SLBF SVic
'Frank Saunders'	LCla SLBF
'Frank Unsworth' (d)	EPts MJac
'Frankfurt 2006'	MJac
'Frankie Boy' **new**	SLBF
'Frankie's Magnificent Seven' (d)	EPts
'Frans Boers'	SLBF
'Franz von Zon'	LCla
'Frau Hilde Rademacher' (d)	EBak EPts SLBF SVic
'Fred's First' (d)	SVic
'Friendly Fire' (d)	CLoc
'Frosted Flame'	CLoc LCla MJac SLBF
'Frozen Tears'	EPts
'Frühling' (d)	EBak
'Fuchsiade '88'	CLoc
'Fuji-san'	ELon EPts
fulgens (T) ♀H2	LCla
* - 'Variegata' (T/v)	CLoc EPts LCla
'Fulpila'	LCla SLBF

	'Gala' (d)	EBak
	'Galadriel'	SLBF
	'Garden News' (d) $\mathbb{Y}^{H4}$	CBod CLoc CRos EHyd ELon EPfP EPts LCla LRHS MAsh MBow MBros MJac NBir NGBl NPer NRHS SCob SGol SLBF SPer SVic WFar
	'Gartenmeister Bonstedt' (T) $\mathbb{Y}^{H1c}$	CLoc EWld LCla
	'Gary Rhodes' (d)	EBak SCoo
	'Gay Fandango' (d)	CLoc
	'Gay Señorita'	EBak
	'Gay Spinner' (d)	CLoc
	'Gemma Fisher' (d)	EPts
	GENE ('Goetzgene'^{PBR}) (Shadowdancer Series)	SCoo
	'Général Monk' (d)	EBak EPts SGol
	'Genii' $\mathbb{Y}^{H4}$	Widely available
	'Geoffrey Smith' (d)	EPts
§	'Georg Börnemann' (T) $\mathbb{Y}^{H2}$	CLoc EBak MJac
	'George Barr'	CRos EHyd LRHS NRHS
§	'Gerharda's Aubergine'	CLoc
	'Gesneriana'	CLoc EBak
	'Giant Pink Enchanted' (d)	CLoc
	'Gilda' (d)	MJac
	'Gilt Edge' (v)	CLoc
	'Gina Bowman' (E)	EPts LCla SLBF
	GINGER ('Goetzginger'^{PBR}) (Shadowdancer Series)	SCoo
	'Gipsy Princess' (d)	CLoc
	'Gladiator' (d)	CMac EBak EHDe
	'Gladys Lorimer'	CRos EHyd EPfP EPts LRHS NRHS
	glazioviana $\mathbb{Y}^{H2}$	CSde EPts LCla MHer SLBF SMHy SVen
	'Glitters'	EBak
§	'Globosa'	CAgr
	'Glowing Embers'	EBak
	'Glowing Lilac' (d)	EPts
	'Gold Brocade'	ELan
	'Golden Anniversary' (d)	CLoc EBak
	'Golden Arrow' (T)	LCla
§	'Golden Border Queen'	CLoc EBak EHDe
	'Golden Dawn'	CLoc SVic
	'Golden Girl'	SLBF
	'Golden Herald'	SLBF
	'Golden la Campanella' (d/v)	CLoc
	'Golden Marinka' (v) $\mathbb{Y}^{H2}$	CLoc EBak EHDe MBros
	'Golden Swingtime' (d)	MJac
	'Golden Treasure' (v)	CLoc
	'Gordon's China Rose'	LCla
	'Governor Pat Brown' (d)	EBak
	'Grace Darling'	EBak
	gracilis	see *F. magellanica* var. *gracilis*
	'Graf Witte'	SVic
	'Grandad Fred' (d)	SLBF
	'Grandad Hobbs' (d)	LCla
	'Grandma Sinton' (d)	CLoc
	'Grandpa Jack' (d)	SLBF
	'Grayrigg'	ELon EPts EShb LCla LSRN SLBF SVic
	'Great Ouse' (d)	EPts
	'Great Scott' (d)	CLoc
	'Green 'n' Gold'	EBak EHDe
	'Greenpeace'	SLBF
	'Grumpy'	EPts SVic
	'Gruss aus dem Bodethal'	CLoc EBak EPts SLBF
	'Gunton Park' (T)	EHDe
	'Gustave Doré' (d)	EBak
	'H.G. Brown'	EBak SLBF
	'Hannah Louise' (d)	EPts
	'Hans Callaars'	LCla
	'Happy'	EPts MHer SVic
	'Happy Anniversary'	CLoc
	'Happy Fellow'	CLoc EBak
	'Happy Wedding Day' (d)	CLoc EPts MJac SCoo SVic
	'Hapsburgh'	EBak EHDe
	'Harbour Lites'	SLBF
	'Harlow Car'	EPts
	'Harmony' Niederholzer, 1946	EBak
	'Harriet Lye'	EHDe
	'Harry Gray' (d) $\mathbb{Y}^{H2}$	CLoc EBak EPts MJac
	'Harry Taylor' (d)	EPts
	'Harry's Sunshine'	SLBF
	hartwegii	LCla MHer
	'Harvey's Reward'	SLBF
	'Hathersage' (d)	EBak
	hatschbachii $\mathbb{Y}^{H2}$	EBee EHDe EHyd EPfP EShb EWes LCla LRHS MCot MHer SBrt SDix SLon SMHy SPlb SVen WFar WMal WPGP
	'Haute Cuisine' (d)	CLoc
	'Hawaiian Sunset' (d)	CLoc EPts SLBF
	'Hawkshead' $\mathbb{Y}^{H4}$	Widely available
	'Hayley Jay' (d)	SLBF
	'Heidi Ann' (d) $\mathbb{Y}^{H4}$	CLoc CRos EBak EHyd EPts LRHS MAsh MBros MRav NRHS SLBF SVic
§	'Heidi Weiss' (d)	CLoc
	'Heinrich Henkel'	see *F.* 'Andenken an Heinrich Henkel'
	'Helen Clare' (d)	CLoc
	'Helen Storer'	MJac
	'Hemsleyana'	see *F. microphylla* subsp. *hemsleyana*
	'Henning Becker' $\mathbb{Y}^{H3}$	ELan
	'Henri Poincaré'	EBak
	'Her Majesty's Crown' (T)	SLBF
	'Herald' $\mathbb{Y}^{H4}$	CRos EHyd LRHS MGos SLBF SVic
	'Herbé de Jacques'	see *F.* 'Mr West'
	'HeRi Trevally'	SLBF
	'Heritage' (d)	CLoc EBak
	'Herman de Graaff' (d)	SLBF
	'Hermiena'	CLoc EPts SLBF SVic
	'Herps Pierement'	SLBF
	'Herps Serang'	SLBF
	'Hessett Festival' (d)	EBak
	'Hi Di'	SLBF
	hidalgensis	see *F. microphylla* subsp. *hidalgensis*
	'Hidcote Beauty' $\mathbb{Y}^{H2}$	CLoc LCla SLBF
	'Highland Pipes'	LCla
	'Hindu Belle'	EBak
	'Hinnerike' (E)	LCla
	'Hiroshige' (T)	LCla
	'Hobson's Choice' (d)	SLBF
	'Holly's Beauty' (d)	CLoc EPts
	'Hot Coals'	EPts MJac SVic
	'Howlett's Hardy' $\mathbb{Y}^{H4}$	CLoc EBak SVic
	'Hula Girl' (d)	EBak MJac
	'Huntsman' (d)	CCCN
	'I Love You'	SLBF
	'Ian Storey'	CRos EHyd EPfP LRHS NRHS
	'Iceberg'	EBak
	'Icecap'	SVic
	'Iced Champagne'	CLoc EBak MJac
	'Ichiban' (d)	CLoc
	'Icicles Chandelier'	SLBF
	'Icy Pink' (d) **new**	LSou
	'Ida' (d)	EBak
	'Igloo Maid' (d)	CLoc EBak
	'Imogen Faye' (d)	LCla SLBF

	'Impudence'	CLoc EBak
	'Impulse' (d)	CLoc
	'Indian Maid' (d)	EBak
	'Insulinde' (T)	EPts LCla MHer MJac SLBF
	'Irene L. Peartree' (d)	LCla
	'Irene Sinton' (d)	MJac
	'Iris Amer' (d)	CLoc
	'Isn't She Lovely'	SLBF
	'Italiano' (d)	MJac
	'Jac Damen' **new**	SLBF
	'Jack Shahan' 🏆^{H2}	CCCN CLoc EBak EPts LCla MBow MJac
	'Jackpot' (d)	EBak
	'James Lye' (d)	EBak EHDe
	'James Travis' (E)	LCla
	'Janice Perry's Gold' (v)	MJac
	'Janie' (d)	CRos EHyd EPfP LBuc LRHS MAsh NRHS SVic
	'Jap Vantveer' (T)	LCla
	'Jasper's Formidable' (T)	SLBF
	'Jasper's Lightning' (T)	SLBF
	'Jean Frisby'	CLoc
	'Jean Shelton'	LCla
	'Jean Taylor'	EPts
	'Jean Webb' (v)	WCot
	'Jennifer' (d)	MJac
	'Jennifer Ann'	NRHS SLBF
	'Jenny May'	CLoc EPts LCla
	'Jess'	LCla SLBF
	'Jester' Holmes (d)	CLoc
	'Jet'	MJac
	'Jiddles' (E)	LCla
	'Jill Holloway' (T)	SLBF
	'Jim Dodge' (d)	EPts
	'Joan Cooper'	CLoc SLBF SVic
	'Joan Knight'	CLoc
	'Joan Margaret' (d)	MJac
	'Joan Morris'	SLBF
	'Joanna Lumley' (d)	EPts
	'Jo-Anne Fisher' (d)	EPts
	'Joanne Jackson'	MJac
	'Joe Kusber' (d)	EBak
	'John Bartlett'	CLoc
	'John Galea'	SLBF
	'John Hitchcock' (d)	SLBF
	'John Lockyer'	CLoc
	'John Maynard Scales' (T) 🏆^{H2}	LCla MJac
	'John Nicholass'	SLBF
§	'John Ridding'^{PBR} (T/v) 🏆^{H1c}	CLoc SPoG
	'Johnny Boy'	SLBF
	'Jon Oram'	CLoc
I	'Joy'	SLBF
	'Joy Patmore'	CLoc SLBF
	'Joyce Sinton'	CLoc
	'Jules Daloges' (d)	EBak
	'Julie Marie' (d)	MJac
	'June Marie Shaw'	MJac
	'Jungle'	LCla SLBF
	'Just Pat' **new**	MJac
	'Kaley Jackson'	MJac
	'Karen Isles' (E)	LCla SLBF
	'Karen Louise' (d)	CLoc
	'Kate Taylor' (d)	SLBF
	'Kath van Hanegem'	CLoc
	'Katie Rogers'	EPts
	'Katinka' (E)	LCla
	'Katjan'	EHDe GBin LCla SLBF WFar
	'Katrina Thompsen'	CLoc EPts SLBF
	'Ken Tudor'	MJac
	'Kenny Walkling' 🏆^{H2}	MJac SLBF
	'Kernan Robson' (d)	EBak
	'Keystone'	EBak
	'King's Ransom' (d)	CLoc EBak
	'Kit Oxtoby' (d)	MJac
	'Kiwi' (d)	EBak
	'Kobold'	SLBF
	'Kolding Perle'	SLBF
	'Kwintet'	EBak MJac
	'La Bianca'	EBak
	'La Campanella' (d) 🏆^{H2}	CCCN CLoc EBak EPts MBros MJac
	'La France' (d)	EBak
	'La Porte' (d)	CLoc
	'La Rosita' (d)	EBak
I	'La Traviata' Blackwell (d)	EBak
	'Lace Petticoats' (d)	EBak
	'Lady Boothby' 🏆^{H4}	Widely available
	'Lady Framlingham' (d)	EPts
	'Lady in Black' (d)	CBcs CRos LSou MCot SPoG WLov
	'Lady Isobel Barnett'	CLoc EBak MJac SLBF
	'Lady Ramsey'	EBak
	'Lady Rebecca' (d)	CLoc
	'Lady Thumb' (d) 🏆^{H3}	CDoC CLoc CMac CRos EBak EBee EHyd EPfP EPts LCro LOPS LRHS MAsh MGos MJac MSwo NLar NRHS SCoo SGol SLBF SLim SPer SPlb SPoG SVic WFar
	'Laing's Hybrid'	EBak
	'Lakeland Princess'	EBak
	'Lambada'	CLoc
	'Lancashire Lad' (d)	MJac
	'Lancelot'	EBak
	'Lapshead White'	CExl
	'Lassie' (d)	CLoc EBak
	'Last Chance' (E)	SLBF
	'Laura' ambig.	SVic
I	'Laura' (Dutch)	CLoc EPts LCla SLBF
	'Laura Cross' (E)	SLBF
	'Lavender Kate' (d)	EBak
	'Lechlade Bullet'	LCla
	'Lechlade Gorgon'	EHyd LCla LRHS NRHS SLBF
	'Lechlade Magician'	EPts LCla SEND SLBF WMal
	'Lechlade Potentate'	LCla
	'Lechlade Tinkerbell' (E)	LCla
	'Lechlade Violet' (T)	LCla
	'Len Bielby' (T)	LCla
	'Lena' (d) 🏆^{H2}	CLoc CMac CTri EBak EPts MJac SLBF SPlb SVic
	'Lena Dalton' (d)	CLoc EBak
	'Leonora'	CLoc SLBF SVic
	'Lesley' (T)	LCla
	'Lesley's Wonder'	MJac
	'Leslie Bowman' 🏆^{H2}	EHDe LCla SLBF
	'Lett's Delight' (d)	EPts
	'Letty Lye'	EBak EHDe
	'Leverhulme'	see *F.* 'Leverkusen'
§	'Leverkusen' (T)	CLoc EBak LCla MJac
	'Liebriez' (d) 🏆^{H4}	EBak SVic
	'Lilac Lustre' (d)	CLoc SVic
	'Lilac Mist'	SLBF
	'Lilac Queen' (d)	EBak
	'Lilian'	MJac
	'Lillian Annetts' (d) 🏆^{H2}	MJac SLBF
	'Lillibet' (d)	CLoc
	'Linda Goulding'	EBak
	'Linda Grace'	MJac
	'Linda Hinchliffe'	EPts MJac WFar
	'Lindisfarne' (d)	CLoc EBak MJac
	'Lisa' (d)	EPts

	Name	Suppliers
	'Little Beauty'	SVic
	'Little Boy Blue'	EPts
	'Little Brook Gem'	SLBF
	'Little Catbells' (E)	SLBF
	'Little Cracker'	CRos SPoG
	'Little Gene'	EBak
	'Little Jessica' (E)	LCla MJac NWad SLBF
	'Little Nan'	SLBF
	'Little Tony'	SLBF
	'Loeky'	CLoc SVic
	'Logan Garden'	see *F. magellanica* 'Logan Woods'
	'Lolita' (d)	EBak
	'London 2000'	CLoc EPts LCla MJac SLBF
	'London in Bloom'	LCla SLBF
	'Lonely Ballerina' (d)	CLoc
	'Long Distance' (T)	LCla
	'Long Wings'	LCla
	'Lord Byron'	CLoc
	'Lord Jim'	LCla
	'Lord Lonsdale'	EPts LCla
	'Lord Roberts'	CLoc SLBF
	'Lorna Swinbank'	SVic
	'Lottie Hobby' (E) $\mathbb{Y}^{H3}$	CLoc CMac CMea EHyd ELan EPts ITim LCla NWad SVic WCot
	'Louise Emershaw' (d)	EBak MJac
	'Louise Nicholls'	MJac
	'Loveliness'	CLoc EHDe SVic
	'Lovely Linda'	SLBF
	'Love's Reward' $\mathbb{Y}^{H2}$	CLoc MJac SLBF SVic
	loxensis misapplied	see *F.* 'Speciosa'
	'Loxhore Lullaby' (E)	LCla
	'Loxhore Minuet' (T)	LCla
	'Lucy Locket'	MJac
I	'Lycioides'	LCla
	lycioides misapplied	see *F.* 'Lycioides'
	'Lye's Elegance'	EHDe
	'Lye's Excelsior'	EHDe
	'Lye's Favourite'	EHDe
	'Lye's Own'	EHDe SLBF
	'Lye's Perfection'	EHDe
	'Lye's Unique' $\mathbb{Y}^{H3}$	CLoc EBak EHDe EPts LCla MJac SLBF SVic
	'Lyndon'	MJac
	'Lynette' (d)	CLoc
	'Lynne Patricia' (d)	EPts SLBF
	'Machu Picchu'	CLoc EPts LCla
	'Madame Butterfly' (d)	CLoc
	'Madame Cornélissen' (d) $\mathbb{Y}^{H4}$	CBod CLoc CMac CRos CSBt CTri EBak EHDe EHyd ELan EMor EPfP EPts LRHS MAsh NLar NRHS SCoo SEND SLBF SLim SVic WFar XLum
	magellanica $\mathbb{Y}^{H4}$	CBcs CRos EHyd LRHS MGil MMuc NLar NPer NRHS SPer SVic WCAu WFar WGwG WSpi
	- 'Alba'	see *F. magellanica* var. *molinae* 'Alba'
	- 'Alba Variegata' (v)	WFar
	- 'Arauco' **new**	SBrt
	- 'Floriade'	CCoa
	- 'Folius Aureus'	WFar
§	- var. ***gracilis*** $\mathbb{Y}^{H4}$	CAgr CLoc CTri EHyd EPfP LRHS NBro SVic
	- - 'Aurea' $\mathbb{Y}^{H4}$	CBcs CMac CRos CSde EHyd ELan ELon EPfP LCla LRHS MHer MRav NRHS SCoo SDix SLBF SPer SRms SVic WAvo XLum
	- - 'Purple Mountain'	CBod
	- - 'Variegata' (v) $\mathbb{Y}^{H4}$	CRos EBak EHyd EPfP LRHS MGos MRav SVic
§	- - 'Versicolor' (v) $\mathbb{Y}^{H4}$	Widely available
	- 'Lady Bacon'	CBcs CBod CRos EBee EHyd ELon EPts EShb EWes LRHS MCot MHer MMuc NLar NRHS SBrt SDys SEND SLBF SPoG WMal WPGP WSHC
§	- 'Logan Woods'	EBee ELon EPfP GKin SLBF SMad WPGP
	- var. ***molinae***	CLoc CRos CTri EBak EBee ELan EPfP EShb GBin GWyn LCla LRHS MBlu MNrw MSwo NBid NPer SCob SPer SPlb WFar
§	- - 'Alba' $\mathbb{Y}^{H4}$	CBod CCoa CDoC EHDe EPts NLar SGol WFar WGwG WSpi
I	- - 'Alba Aureovariegata' (v)	CBcs CMac WFar XLum
	- - 'Golden Sharpitor' (v)	CCCN WFar
	- - 'Mr Knight's Blush'	WSpi
§	- - 'Sharpitor' (v) $\mathbb{Y}^{H4}$	CCoa CDoC CSde EBak EBee ELan ELon EPfP LRHS NChi NPer SGol SPer SPoG WFar WKif WSHC WSMil
	- 'Mountain Gold'	CBod WFar
	- var. ***myrtifolia***	CTsd
	- 'Pumila'	CMea EWes MAsh MHer SMHy WAbe WFar WHal WPGP
§	- 'Thompsonii' $\mathbb{Y}^{H4}$	EHDe SMHy
	- 'Variegata Aurea' (v)	SGol WFar
	'Magic Flute'	CLoc MJac
	'Major Heaphy'	EBak
	'Mama Bleuss' (d)	EBak
	'Mandi Oxtoby' (T)	LCla
	'Mantilla' (T)	LCla MJac
	'Maori Maid' (d)	MJac
	'Marble Crepe' (T)	SLBF
	'Marcia'^{PBR} (Shadowdancer Series)	CLoc
	'Marcus Graham' (d)	CLoc EBak SLBF
	'Margaret' (d) $\mathbb{Y}^{H4}$	CLoc CTri EBak EPts SEND SLBF SVic WFar
	'Margaret Bird'	LCla
	'Margaret Brown' $\mathbb{Y}^{H4}$	CLoc CRos CTri EHyd LCla LRHS NRHS SLBF SVic
	'Margaret My Own'	EPts
	'Margaret Roe'	EBak MJac
	'Margaret Susan'	EBak
	'Margaret Viscountess Thurso'	SLBF
	'Margarite Dawson' (d)	SVic
	'Maria Landy'	MJac SLBF
	'Maria Mathilde' (d)	SLBF
	'Maria Shaw'	EPts
	'Marin Glow' $\mathbb{Y}^{H3}$	CLoc EBak SVic
	'Marinka' $\mathbb{Y}^{H2}$	CLoc EBak EPts LCla MBros MJac
	MARISKA ('Bf01') (Bella Series)	LCro LOPS
	'Marlies de Keijzer' (E)	EPts LCla NWad SLBF SVen
	'Martha Adcock'	SLBF
	'Martin's Inspiration'	LCla
	'Martin's Yellow Surprise' (T)	LCla SLBF
	'Marty' (d)	EBak
	'Mary' (T) $\mathbb{Y}^{H1c}$	CLoc EPts LCla SLBF WCot
	'Mary Lockyer' (d)	CLoc EBak
	'Mary Thorne'	EBak
	'Mauve Beauty' (d)	SLBF
	'Mauve Wisp' (d)	SVic
	'Mavis Enderby'	MJac SLBF
	'Max Cobi'	LCla MJac SLBF
I	'Maxima'	EPts LCla SLBF

	'Maxine's Smile'	SLBF
	'Meditation' (d)	CLoc
	'Melody Ann' (d)	EBak
	'Melting Moments' (d)	SCoo
	'Mercurius' ♀H4	XLum
	'Merel'	SLBF
	'Merlin'	LCla
	'Merry Mary' (d)	EBak
	'Mersty' (d)	SLBF
I	'Mexicali Rose' Machado	CLoc
	'Michael' (d/v)	EPts
	'Michael Wallis' (T)	SLBF
	michoacanensis misapplied	see *F. microphylla* subsp. *aprica*
	michoacanensis Sessé & Moç. (E) B&SWJ 9148	WCru
	'Micky Goult' ♀H2	CLoc EPts MJac SLBF
	'Microchip' (E)	LCla
	microphylla (E)	CAby CBcs CBod CElw CExl CLoc CTsd EBak EBee EHyd ELon GBin IDee LRHS MGil SDix SEdd SMHy SVic WAbe
	- B&SWJ 10331	WCru
§	- subsp. ***aprica*** (E)	LCla
	- - B&SWJ 9101	WCru
	- - 'Dolly's Dress' (E)	WCru
§	- subsp. ***hemsleyana*** (E)	CExl SVic
	- - B&SWJ 10478	WCru
	- - 'Silver Lining' (E)	CCCN CMil EShb MHer NCou NLar SDix SWvt WCot WCru WFar WNPC
§	- subsp. ***hidalgensis*** (E)	CBcs
	- 'Variegata' (E/v)	EWes
§	'Mieke Meursing' ♀H2	CLoc EBak MJac SVic
	'Miep Aalhuizen'	LCla
	'Millennium'	CLoc EBak EPts MJac SCoo SVic
	'Millfield Alpha'	EPts
	'Millfield Bravo'	EPts
	'Millfield Charlie'	EPts
	'Millfield Delta'	EPts
	'Millfield Echo'	EPts
	'Millfield Foxtrot' **new**	EPts
	'Ming'	CLoc
	'Miniature Jewels' (E)	SLBF
	minimiflora misapplied	see *F.* × *bacillaris*
	'Minipani'	SLBF
	'Minirose'	EPts SLBF
	'Minnesota' (d)	EBak
	'Miramere'	EPts
	'Mischief'	SVic
	'Miss California' (d)	CLoc EBak
	'Miss Lye'	EHDe
	'Miss Muffett' (d)	EPts
	'Miss Vallejo' (d)	EBak
	'Mission Bells'	CLoc EBak EPts SVic
	'Misty Mease'	MJac
	'Molesworth' (d)	MJac
	'Money Spinner'	CLoc
	'Mood Indigo' (d)	CLoc
	'Moonbeam' (d)	CLoc
	'Moonglow' (d)	MJac
	'Moonlight Sonata'	CLoc
	'More Applause' (d)	CLoc
	'Morning Light' (d)	CLoc
	'Morrells' (d)	EBak
	'Moth Blue' (d)	EBak
	'Mountain Mist' (d)	SVic
	'Mr A. Huggett'	CLoc EPts SLBF
	'Mr W. Rundle'	EBak
§	'Mr West' (v)	ELon MCot SCob WFar

	'Mrs B.' (E)	MJac
	'Mrs Churchill'	CLoc
	'Mrs Grant'	EHDe
	'Mrs Hobhouse' (d)	EHDe
	'Mrs J Bright'	EHDe
	'Mrs Lee Belton' (E)	LCla SLBF
	'Mrs Lovell Swisher' ♀H4	EBak LCla
	'Mrs Marshall'	SLBF
	'Mrs Popple' ♀H4	Widely available
	'Mrs W. Castle'	SVic
	'Mrs W.P. Wood' ♀H4	CBod CLoc CRos EHDe ELon LRHS MSCN SVic
	'Mrs W. Rundle'	CLoc SLBF
	'Muriel' (d)	CLoc
	'My Dad'	SLBF
	'My Fair Lady' (d)	EBak
	'My Grandchildren'	SLBF
	'My Little Cracker'	MJac
	'My Mum'	LCla SLBF
	'My Pat'	SLBF
	'My Sacha' **new**	SLBF
	'Nancy Lou' (d)	CLoc MJac SLBF SVic
	'Natasha Sinton' (d)	CCCN MJac
	'Nathan Rhys'	EPts
	'Neapolitan' (d)	SLBF
	'Neck'	LCla
	'Nell Gwyn'	CLoc
	'Nellie Nuttall' ♀H2	CLoc EBak EPts
	'Neopolitan' (E)	CLoc EHDe EPts SVic
	'Nephele'	EPts
	'Nice 'n' Easy' (d)	MJac
	'Nicki Fenwick-Raven' (E)	LCla
	'Nicki's Findling'	EPts LCla MJac
	'Nicola'	EBak
	'Nicola Jane' (d)	EBak EPts LCla MJac SHar SLBF SVic
	'Nicolette'	MJac
§	***nigricans*** B&SWJ 10664	WCru
	'Niula'	LCla
	'Nonchalance' (T)	LCla
	'Norman Welton'	SLBF
	'Normandy Bell'	EBak
	'Northern Jewel'	EPts SLBF
	'Northilda'	SVic
	'Northumbrian Pipes'	LCla
	'Northway'	CLoc MJac
	'Norvell Gillespie' (d)	EBak
	'Nuance'	LCla
	'O Sole Mio'	SVic
	'Obcylin' (E)	EPts LCla
	'Ocean Beach'	EPts
	'Oetnang' (d)	CTri SCoo
	'Oh Carol' (E)	LCla
	'Old Somerset' (v)	CCCN
	'Olga Storey'	CRos EHyd LRHS NRHS
	'Olive Smith'	EHDe EPts LCla MJac
	'Olympic Sunset'	SVic
	'Oosje' (E)	LCla
	'Opalescent' (d)	CLoc
	'Orange Crush'	CLoc EBak
	'Orange Crystal'	MJac SLBF SVic
	'Orange Drops'	CLoc EBak EPts
	'Orange Flare'	CLoc EBak SLBF
	'Orange King' (d)	CLoc
	'Orange Mirage'	CLoc
	'Orange Star' (E)	LCla SLBF
	'Orangeblossom'	SLBF
	'Orient Express' (T) ♀H1c	CLoc
	'Ornamental Pearl' (v)	CLoc SLBF
	'Other Fellow'	EBak EPts MJac SLBF

'Oulton Empress' (E)	LCla SLBF
'Oulton Fairy' (E)	SLBF
'Oulton Red Imp' (E)	LCla SLBF
'Oulton Travellers Rest' (E)	SLBF
'Our Carol'	SLBF
'Our Hilary'	SLBF
'Our Nan' (d)	MJac
'Our Spencer'	SLBF
'Our Ted' (T)	EBak EPts
'Overbecks'	see *F. magellanica* var. *molinae* 'Sharpitor'
'P.E. King' (d)	SLBF
'Pacific Queen' (d)	EBak
'Pacquesa' (d)	EBak
'Padre Pio' (d)	EBak
'Pam and Ted Love'	SLBF
'Pam Plack'	LCla SLBF
'Pamela Knights' (d)	EBak
'Pam's People'	LCla
'Panache' (d)	LCla
paniculata (T) 🏆^{H2}	CCCN CRHN EBak EHDe ELan EPts LCla MCot MHer SLBF WCot WCru
'Panique'	LCla
'Panylla Prince'	LCla
'Papa Bleuss' (d)	EBak
'Papoose' (d)	EBak SLBF SVic
'Party Frock'	CLoc EBak
parviflora misapplied	see *F.* × *bacillaris*
'Pat Meara'	CLoc EBak
'Pathétique' (d)	CLoc
'Patience' (d)	EBak SLBF
'Patio Princess' (d)	CLoc EPts SCob
'Patty Sue' (d)	EPts
'Paul Cambon' (d)	EBak
'Paula Jane' (d) 🏆^{H2}	MJac SLBF SVic
'Pauline Rawlins' (d)	CLoc
'Peachy' (California Dreamers Series) (d)	CLoc SCoo
'Peachy Keen' (d)	EBak
'Peacock' (d)	CLoc
'Pee Wee Rose'	EBak EHDe SVic
PEGGY ('Goetzpeg'^{PBR}) (Shadowdancer Series)	SCoo
'Peggy King'	EBak
'Peloria' (d)	CLoc EBak
'Peper Harow'	EBak
'Pepi' (d)	EBak
'Peppermint Candy' (d)	MJac
'Peppermint Stick' (d)	CLoc EBak
'Perky Pink' (d)	EBak EPts
'Perry Park'	MJac SVic
'Perry's Jumbo'	NPer
perscandens	CBcs CExl LCla
'Peter Meredith'	MJac
petiolaris	LCla
- B&SWJ 10675	WCru
'Phaidra' (T)	LCla
'Pharaoh'	CLoc
'Phénoménal' (d)	EBak
'Phryne' (d)	SVic
'Phyllis' (d) 🏆^{H4}	CLoc CRos EBak EHyd EPts LCla LRHS MJac NRHS SEND SLBF SVic
'Piet van der Sande'	LCla SLBF
'Pinch Me' (d)	EBak
'Pink Aurora'	CLoc
'Pink Ballet Girl' (d)	CLoc SVic
'Pink Bon Accord'	CLoc SVic
'Pink Cloud'	CLoc EBak

'Pink Cornet'	LCla
'Pink Darling'	CLoc EBak
'Pink Dessert'	EBak
'Pink Elephant' (d)	CLoc
'Pink Fandango' (d)	CLoc
'Pink Fantasia' 🏆^{H2}	CLoc EBak EPts LCla MJac SLBF SVic
'Pink Galore' (d) 🏆^{H2}	CLoc MJac SLBF
'Pink Goon' (d)	SLBF SVic
'Pink Haze'	SVic
'Pink Ice' (d)	MBros
'Pink la Campanella'	EBak
'Pink Marshmallow' (d) 🏆^{H4}	CLoc EBak MJac SLBF
'Pink Pearl' Bright (d)	EHDe
'Pink Profusion'	EBak
'Pink Quartet' (d)	CLoc EBak WCot
'Pink Rain'	MJac
'Pink Slippers'	CLoc
'Pink Spangles'	see *F.* 'Mieke Meursing'
'Pink Temptation'	CLoc
'Pinwheel' (d)	CLoc EBak
'Piper's Vale' (T)	MJac
'Pixie'	CLoc EBak EHDe MJac SEND SLBF SVic
'Playboy' (d)	SVic
'Playford'	EBak
'Plenty'	EBak SVic
'Popsie Girl' (v)	SLBF
'Port Arthur' (d)	EBak
'Postiljon'	EBak
'Powder Puff' Hodges (d)	CLoc
'Prelude' Blackwell	CLoc
'President'	EBak
'President Barrie Nash'	CLoc
'President George Bartlett' (d) 🏆^{H2}	CLoc EPts MJac SLBF
'President Joan Morris' (d)	SLBF
'President John Porter'	MJac SLBF
'President Leo Boullemier'	MJac
'President Margaret Slater'	CLoc
'President Moir' (d)	SLBF
'President Peter Holloway'	EPts LCla SLBF
'President Stanley Wilson' (d)	EBak EPts
'Preston'	CMac
'Preston Guild' 🏆^{H3}	CLoc EBak NPer SDys SRms SVic WFar
'Prince of Orange'	CLoc SVic
'Princess Dollar'	see *F.* 'Dollar Prinzessin'
'Princessita'	EBak
procumbens	CAby CBcs CBod CCCN CExl CLoc EBak EHDe ELon EPfP EPts IDee LCla MCot MHer SIvy SLBF WAbe
- 'Argentea'	see *F. procumbens* 'Wirral'
- grey-leaved	ESwi SBrt
- 'Variegata'	see *F. procumbens* 'Wirral'
§ - 'Wirral' (v)	CLoc CTsd EHDe EShb ESwi ITim
'Prodigy'	see *F.* 'Enfant Prodigue'
'Prosperity' (d) 🏆^{H3}	CLoc CRos EBak EHyd EPts LCla LRHS MAsh MJac NRHS SEND SLBF SPoG SVic
'Pumila'	CExl CMac ELan EPfP LRHS SDix SVic WSHC
'Purperklokje'	EBak
'Purple Emperor' (d)	CLoc

'Purple Heart' (d)	CLoc EBak
'Purple Lace'	SVic
'Purple Prince' (d) **new**	SVic
'Purple Rain'	EPts
'Pussy Cat' (T)	CLoc EBak
'Putney Pride'	EPts
'Put's Folly' Υ^{H2}	EBak MJac
putumayensis	EBak
'Quasar' (d)	CLoc EPts MBros MJac SLBF
'Queen Mary'	CLoc EBak EHDe
'Queen of Bath' (d)	SVic
'Queen of Mercia' (d)	MJac
'Queen Victoria' Smith (d)	EHDe
'Queen's Park' (d)	EBak
'Query'	SVic
'R.A.F.' (d)	CLoc EBak EPts
'Radings Gerda' (E)	LCla SLBF
'Radings Mia' (T)	SLBF
'Rambling Rose' (d)	CLoc
'Raspberry' (d)	CLoc EBak
'Reading Ruby'	EPts LCla MJac SLBF
'Reading Show' (d)	EPts SLBF
'Rebeka Sinton' (v)	CLoc EBak
'Red Jacket' (d)	EBak
'Red Shadows' (d)	CLoc EBak
'Red Spider'	CLoc EBak SCoo
'Red Wing'	CLoc
'Reflexa'	see *F.* × *bacillaris* 'Reflexa'
'Reg Gubler'	SLBF
'Regal'	CLoc
regia	WMal
- subsp. ***regia***	LCla XLum
- subsp. ***reitzii***	LCla XLum
- subsp. ***serrae***	WPGP
'Remember Carole Anne' (d)	SLBF
'Remembering Claire'	EPts
'Remembrance' (d)	EPts LCla SLBF
'Rene Schwab'	LCla
'Rhapsody' ambig.	SVic
'Riccartonii' Υ^{H6}	Widely available
'Riccartonii Variegated' (v)	EHDe
'Richard John' (v)	SVic
'Ridestar' (d)	CLoc
'Rijs 2001' (E)	SLBF
'Ringwood Market' (d)	EPts MJac SCoo SLBF
'Rivendell'	EPts
'Rocket Fire' (California Dreamers Series) (d)	SVic
'Roger de Cooker' (T)	CLoc EPts LCla MJac SLBF SVic
'Rohees New Millennium' (d)	SLBF
'Rolla' (d)	EBak
'Roman City' (d)	CLoc
'Romany Rose'	CLoc
'Ronald L. Lockerbie' (d)	CLoc
'Roos Breytenbach' (T)	LCla MJac
'Rosamunda' (d)	CLoc
'Rose Aylett' (d)	EBak
'Rose Bradwardine' (d)	EBak
'Rose Churchill' (d)	MJac
'Rose Fantasia' Υ^{H2}	CLoc EPts MJac SLBF
'Rose of Castile'	CLoc EBak EHDe EPts LCla MJac SLBF SVic
'Rose of Castile Improved' Υ^{H4}	LCla MJac SLBF
'Rose of Denmark'	CLoc EBak EHDe MJac SCoo SLBF
'Rose Winston' (d)	SCoo
rosea misapplied	see *F.* 'Globosa'
'Rosecroft Beauty' (d/v)	EBak EHDe
'Rosemarie Higham' (v)	MJac SCoo
'Rosemary Day'	CLoc
'Roswitha'	SAll
'Rosy Frills' (d)	MJac
'Rosy Morn' (d)	CLoc
'Rough Silk'	CLoc EBak
'Royal Academy' (d)	EPts
'Royal Mosaic' (California Dreamers Series) (d)	MJac
'Royal Purple' (d)	EBak
'Royal Velvet' (d) Υ^{H2}	CLoc CRos EBak EHyd EPts LRHS SLBF SVic
'Rubra Grandiflora'	LCla
'Ruby Tuesday' (d)	MJac
'Ruby Wedding' (d)	SLBF
'Rufus' Υ^{H4}	CLoc CMac EBak ELan EPts LCla MJac SLBF SVic
'Ruth'	SVic
'Ruth King' (d)	EBak
'Ryan'	SLBF
'S'Wonderful' (d)	CLoc EBak
'Sailor'	EPts
'Salmon Cascade'	EPts LCla MJac SLBF
'Sam Sheppard'	SLBF
'Samantha's Smile' (d)	SLBF
'San Mateo' (d)	EBak
§ ***sanctae-rosae***	LCla
'Sandboy'	EBak
'Santa Cruz' (d)	CMac SLBF SVic
'Santa Lucia' (d)	CLoc
'Santa Monica' (d)	EBak
'Sapphire' (d)	EBak
'Sappho Phaoon' (T)	EPts
'Sara Helen' (d)	CLoc EBak
'Sarah'^{PBR} (Bella Series)	LCro LOPS
'Sarah Brightman' (d)	CLoc
'Sarah Eliza' (d)	SCoo
'Sarah Jane' (d)	EBak
'Satellite'	CLoc EBak
'Saturnus' Υ^{H4}	EBak SEND SPoG
scabriuscula	LCla
'Scarcity'	EBak EHDe SVic
'Scarlet Jester'	EPts SLBF
'Schneeball' (d)	EBak
'Schneewitcher'	EPts
'Sealand Prince'	LCla SVic
'Seattle Blue' (T/d)	SLBF
'Sebastopol' (d)	CLoc
serratifolia Ruíz & Pav.	see *F. denticulata*
'Seventh Heaven' (d)	CLoc MJac SCoo
'Sharpitor'	see *F. magellanica* var. *molinae* 'Sharpitor'
'Shatzy B'	EPts SLBF
'Sheila Crooks' (d)	EBak
'Shelford'	CLoc EBak EPts MJac SCob SLBF SVic
'Shell Pink'	SVic
'She's a Beauty' (d)	MJac
'Shirley Halladay' (d)	LCla
'Shirley'^{PBR} (Shadowdancer Series)	SCoo
'Shirley Teece'	EPts
'Showfire'	EBak
'Shrimp Cocktail'	CLoc SGol WSMil
'Shuna Lindsay'	LCla
'Siberoet' (E)	SLBF
'Sid Garcia'	SLBF
'Sierra Blue' (d)	CLoc EBak
'Silver Surfer'	EPts LCla MJac SLBF
'Silverdale'	EPts

	'Simon J. Rowell'	LCla
	simplicicaulis	EBak EHDe
	'Sincerity' (d)	CLoc
	'Siobhan Evans' (d)	SLBF
	'Sir Alfred Ramsey'	EBak
	'Sir David Jason'	MJac
	'Sir Matt Busby' (d)	EPts MJac
	'Sister Ann Haley'	EPts
	'Sister Sister' (d)	SLBF
	'Skater's Waltz' (d)	CLoc
	'Sleepy'	EPts SVic
	'Sleigh Bells'	CLoc EBak SVic
	'Sneezy'	EPts SVic
	'Snow Burner' (California Dreamers Series) (d)	CLoc MBros
	'Snowbird' (d)	SLBF
§	'Snowcap' (d) ♀H4	CCCN CChe CLoc CRos EBak EHDe EHyd ELon EPfP EPts GKin LCla LRHS MGos MJac NPer NRHS SCob SCoo SGol SLBF SLim SPoG SVic WFar
	'Snowdrift' Colville (d)	CLoc
	'Snowdrift' Kennett (d)	EBak
	'Snowfire' (d)	CLoc
	'Snowflake' (E)	EPts WBor
	'Soila'PBR (Bella Series)	CLoc
	'Son of Thumb' ♀H4	CLoc CRos EHyd EPts LRHS MJac NRHS SGol SLBF SLim SPer SVic
	'Sonata' (d)	CLoc
	'Sophia'PBR (Bella Series)	LCro LOPS
	'Sophie Louise'	EPts MJac SLBF
	'Sophisticated Lady' (d)	EBak EPts
	'South Gate' (d)	CLoc EBak EPts MCot SVic
	'Space Shuttle'	CLoc LCla
	'Sparky' (T)	CLoc EHDe EPts LCla
	'Speciana'	EPts
§	'Speciosa'	EBak LCla
§	***splendens*** ♀H2	CCCN CLoc EBak LCla MCot NPer
	- B&SWJ 10469	WCru
	'Spring Bells' (d)	CRos EHyd LRHS NRHS
	'Squadron Leader' (d)	EBak EPts
	'Squirtie'	SLBF
	'Stanley Cash' (d)	CLoc
	'Star Wars'	CLoc EHDe EPts MJac
	'Stella Ann' (T)	EPts LCla
	'Straat Futami' (E)	EPts LCla
	'Straat Kobe' (T)	LCla
	'Straat La Plata'	LCla
	'Straat of Plenty'	LCla
	'Strawberry Delight' (d)	CLoc MJac
	'Strawberry Split'	CDoC
	'Strawberry Sundae' (d)	CLoc EBak
	'String of Pearls'	CLoc MJac SLBF SVic
	'Stuart Lockyer' (d)	CLoc
	'Sue'	SLBF
	'Suffolk Splendour' (d)	EPts
	'Sunray' (v)	CBcs CLoc CMac CRos EBak EHDe EHyd EPfP LBuc LRHS MAsh MGos NCou NRHS SCoo SLBF SLim SNig SPoG SVen WCot
	'Sunset'	CLoc
	'Susan Green'	EBak MJac
	'Susan Hampshire' **new**	SLBF
	'Susan McMaster'	CLoc
	'Susan Olcese' (d)	EBak
	'Susan Travis'	CLoc EBak SVic
	'Swanley Beauty'	EHDe
	'Swanley Gem' ♀H2	CLoc EBak SLBF SVic
	'Swanley Pendula'	CLoc
	'Swanley Yellow'	EBak
	'Sweet Sarah' (E)	EPts
	'Sweet Willow' **new**	EPts
I	'Sweetheart' van Wieringen	EBak
	'Swingtime' (d) ♀H2	CLoc EBak EPts LCla MBros MJac SLBF
	sylvatica misapplied	see *F. nigricans*
	'Sylvia Barker' ♀H2	LCla SLBF
	'Sylvia's Choice'	EBak
	'Symphony'	CLoc
	'Syreme' (d)	SLBF
	'T.I.S. Herentals'	SLBF
	'T.S.J.' (E)	LCla
	'Taco'	LCla
	'Taddle'	SLBF
	'Taffeta Bow' (d)	CLoc SLBF
	'Tamworth'	CLoc EBak MJac SVic
	'Tangerine'	CLoc SVic
	'Tanya Bridger' (d)	EBak
	'Tarra Valley'	EHDe LCla
	'Tausendschön' (d)	CLoc
	'Ted's Tribute'	SLBF
	'Temptation' Peterson	CLoc EBak
	'Tennessee Waltz' (d) ♀H2	CLoc EBak EPts SLBF SVic
	'Tess'	EPts
	tetradactyla misapplied	see *F.* × *bacillaris*
	'Texas Longhorn' (d)	CLoc EBak
	'Thalia' (T) ♀H1c	CCCN CLoc EBak EPts LCla LSRN MCot MHer MJac SCob SLBF SPlb SPoG
	'Thamar'	CLoc EPts SVic
	'That's It' (d)	SVic
	'The Aristocrat' (d)	CLoc EBak
§	'The Doctor'	CLoc EBak
	'The Jester' (d)	EBak
	'The Tarns'	EBak SVic
	'Thelma Copestake' **new**	MJac SLBF
	'Thomas' (d)	EPts
	'Thompsonii'	see *F. magellanica* 'Thompsonii'
	'Thornley's Hardy'	SVic
	'Three Cheers'	CLoc
	'Three Counties'	EBak
	'Thumbelina'	EHyd LRHS
	'Thunderbird' (d)	CLoc
	thymifolia (E)	CRos EHyd LRHS MHer SDys SEND SGro SMHy WKif
	- subsp. ***thymifolia*** (E)	CDoC SEle
	'Tia Clements' **new**	MJac
	'Tiara' (d)	EBak
	'Tillingbourne' (d)	SLBF
	'Time After Time'	CLoc MBros SLBF
	'Timlin Brened' (T)	EBak
	'Timothy Titus' (T) ♀H1c	EHDe LCla
	'Ting-a-ling'	CLoc EBak SVic
	'Tinker Bell' Hodges	EBak SVic
	'Tip Toes'	SLBF
	'Tjinegara'	LCla
	'Toby Bridger' (d)	CLoc EBak
	'Toby Foreman'	SLBF
	'Toby S' (d)	SLBF
	'Tolling Bell'	EBak
	'Tom Goedeman'	LCla
	'Tom Knights'	EBak
	'Tom Thumb' ♀H4	Widely available
	'Tom West' misapplied	see *F.* 'Mr West'
	'Tom West' ambig.	SNig
	'Tom West' Meillez (v) ♀H2	CChe CDoC CLoc CRos CSBt CWCL EBak EBee EHDe EHyd EPts LRHS MAsh MBros MHer MJac MRav MSCN NRHS SGol SLBF SLim WFar

'Ton Ten Hove'	LCla
'Tony Talbot'	MJac
'Tony's Treat' (d)	EPts
'Torch' (d)	CLoc EBak
'Torchlight'	EPts LCla
'Torvill and Dean' (d)	CLoc EPts MJac SLBF
'Tracid' (d)	SVic
'Trail Blazer' (d)	CLoc MJac
'Trailing Queen'	MJac
'Trase' (d)	EBak SVic
'Traudchen Bonstedt' (T) ♀H1c	CLoc LCla
'Traviata'	see *F.* 'La Traviata' Blackwell
'Treasure' (d)	EBak
'Tricolor'	see *F. magellanica* var. *gracilis* 'Versicolor'
'Trientje'	LCla SLBF
triphylla (T)	EBak MHer
'Trish's Triumph'	EPts
'Tristesse' (d)	CLoc EBak
'Tropicana' (d)	CLoc
'Troubador' Waltz (d)	CLoc
'Trudi Davro'	MBros SCoo
'Trudy'	EPts SVic
'Truly Treena' (d)	SLBF
'Trumpeter' Reiter (T)	CLoc EPts LCla MJac
'Tubular Bells' (T)	LCla
'Tuonela' (d)	CLoc
'Tutti-frutti' (d)	CLoc
'Twinkling Stars'	MJac
'Ullswater' (d)	EBak
'Uncle Charley' (d)	EBak
'University of Liverpool'	CLoc MJac
'Upward Look'	EBak
'Valerie Ann' (d)	EBak
'Valerie Bradley'	EPts
'Valerie Jane' new	SLBF
'Vanessa Jackson'	CLoc MJac SVic
'Vanessa Wright'	CRos EHyd LRHS NRHS
'Vanity Fair' (d)	EBak
'Variegated Procumbens'	see *F. procumbens* 'Wirral'
'Veenlust' (d)	EBak MJac
'Velvet Crush'	EPts SLBF
'Vendeta'	LCla
'Venus Victrix'	EBak EHDe
venusta	EBak EHDe LCla
'Vera Garcia'	EPts LCla MJac SLBF
'Versicolor'	see *F. magellanica* var. *gracilis* 'Versicolor'
'Vintage Dovercourt'	LCla
'Violet Bassett-Burr' (d)	CLoc EBak
'Violet Gem' (d)	CLoc
VIOLETTA ('Goetzviol') (Shadowdancer Series)	SCoo
'Viva Ireland'	EBak
'Vivien Colville'	CLoc SVic
'Voodoo' (d)	CLoc EBak EPts LCla MBros SCoo
'Vyvian Miller'	CRos
'Wagtails White Pixie'	EBak
'Wake the Harp'	SLBF
'Waldis Spezi'	LCla
'Walton Jewel'	EBak
'Walz Bella'	LCla
'Walz Freule'	MJac
'Walz Jubelteen' ♀H2	CLoc ELan ELon EPts LCla MJac SAdn SEle SLBF SVen SVic WCot WOld
'Walz Lucifer'	LCla SLBF
'Walz Panfluit'	LCla
'Walz Polka'	LCla
'Wapenveld 150'	LCla
'Wapenveld's Bloei'	EPts LCla SLBF
'Water Color'	SLBF
'Water Nymph'	CLoc MHer SLBF SVic
'Wattenpost'	SLBF
'Waveney Gem'	CLoc EBak LCla MJac SLBF
'Waveney Sunrise'	MJac
'Waveney Waltz'	EBak
'Welsh Dragon' (d)	CLoc EBak
'Wendy' Catt	see *F.* 'Snowcap'
'Wendy Bendy'	EPts MJac
'Wendy Jane Webster'	EPts
'Wendy's Beauty' (d)	CLoc EBak EPts MJac
'Westham'	LCla
'Westminster Chimes' (d)	CLoc
'Whaley Thorns' (d) new	MJac
'Wharfedale' ♀H4	CRos EHyd ELon EPts LRHS MJac NRHS SLBF SVic
'What's-it' (E)	SLBF
'Whirlaway' (d)	CLoc
'White Academy'	EPts
'White Ann'	see *F.* 'Heidi Weiss'
'White Clove'	SVic
'White Joy'	EBak
'White King' (d)	CLoc EBak
'White Pixie' ♀H4	EPts MJac SLBF SVic
'White Queen' ambig.	EHDe
'White Spider'	CLoc EBak
'Whiteknights Amethyst'	SVic
'Whiteknights Blush'	CExl EBee EPfP EWes LRHS
'Whiteknights Cheeky' (T)	EBak EPts SVic
'Whiteknights Pearl' ♀H4	ECha EPts LCla MMuc SDys SEND SGol SLBF SVic
'Whitton Starburst'	LCla
'Whoopee' (d)	EPts MJac SLBF
'Wicked Queen' (d)	SVic
'Widnes Wonder'	MJac SLBF
'Wigan Peer' (d)	EPts MJac
'Wight Magic' (d)	MJac
'Wilhelmina Schwab'	LCla
'Willow Tinsdale'	SGol
'Wilma van Druten'	LCla
'Wilson's Colours'	EPts LCla
'Wilson's Joy'	MJac
'Wilson's Pearls' (d)	SLBF
'Wilson's Sugar Pink'	EPts LCla MJac
'Windhapper'	LCla SLBF
'Wine and Roses' (d)	EBak
'Winifred Glass'	EHDe
'Winston Churchill' (d) ♀H2	CLoc EBak EPts MBros MJac SCob SCoo
'Winter's Tale'	SLBF
'Woodside' (d)	SVic
'Wyre Light' (E)	SLBF
'Yattendon Lady'	SLBF
'Yvonne Schwab'	LCla
'Zifi'	SLBF

Fumaria (*Papaveraceae*)

capreolata	WSFF
lutea	see *Corydalis lutea*

Furcraea (*Asparagaceae*)

bedinghausii	see *F. parmentieri*
§ ***foetida***	CCCN CPla WCot
§ - var. ***mediopicta*** (v)	CPla WSMil
- 'Variegata'	see *F. foetida* var. *mediopicta*
gigantea	see *F. foetida*
longaeva misapplied	see *F. parmentieri*

macdougalii	SPlb
§ ***parmentieri***	CBcs CTsd CCCN CDTJ CDoC CExl CSBt EShb GBin LEdu LRHS NCft NGKo SChr SIvy SPlb SVen WSMil
selloa var. ***marginata*** (v)	NCft SIvy

G

Gahnia (*Cyperaceae*)

sieberiana	SPlb

Gaillardia (*Asteraceae*)

aristata misapplied	see *G.* × *grandiflora*
aristata Pursch 'Maxima Aurea'	EHyd EPfP NBre SPhx
× ***grandiflora*** 'Amber Wheels'	ELan EPfP
- 'Arizona Apricot'	EHyd LRHS MBNS SCob
- 'Arizona Red Shades'	EAJP EHyd LRHS SCob WCav
- 'Arizona Sun'	EAJP EHyd LRHS MBros MNHC NLar SCob SVic WCav
- 'Bijou'	EBou SWvt
- 'Burgunder'	CSBt CSpe EAJP EHyd ELan EPfP LRHS MBow NGBl SGbt SPer SPhx SPoG SWvt
- 'Celebration'PBR	EHyd NLar
- 'Dazzler' ♀H5	CSBt EBee EHyd ELan EPfP LRHS SGbt SPer SPoG
§ - 'Fackelschein'	EAJP
- 'Fanfare'PBR	CWGN EHyd ELon LRHS NRHS SCoo
- 'Fanfare Blaze'	EHyd LRHS NRHS SCob WFar
- 'Frenzy'PBR (Commotion Series)	SPad
- (Gallo Series) GALLO DARK BICOLOR ('Kiegaldab'PBR)	CBod
- - GALLO PEACH ('Kiegalpea'PBR)	CBod NRHS
- GOBLIN	see *G.* × *grandiflora* 'Kobold'
§ - 'Kobold'	CBcs CMac CRos CSBt CTsd EBee EHyd ELan ELon EPfP GMaP LBuc LRHS NRHS SCob SGbt SHar SPer SPlb SPoG SWvt
- 'Mesa Red' (Mesa Series)	NLar
- Monarch Group	WFar
- 'Naomi Sunshine'	SHar
§ - 'Oranges and Lemons'PBR	SHar
- 'Red Sun'PBR	CWGN
- SAINT CLEMENTS	see *G.* 'Oranges and Lemons'
- (Sunburst Series) SUNBURST BURGUNDY PICOTEE ('Granretip')	LRHS
- - SUNBURST BURGUNDY	WFar
- (Sunset Dwarf Series) 'Sunset Cutie'	CRos LRHS NRHS SPoG
- - 'Sunset Flash'	CRos SPoG
- - 'Sunset Snappy'	CRos SPad SPoG
- - 'Sunset Sunrise'	CRos SPoG
- 'Tokajer'	EBee EHyd ELan EPfP LRHS NBre NRHS SPhx
- TORCHLIGHT	see *G.* 'Fackelschein'

Galactites (*Asteraceae*)

tomentosa	CPla EWTr SPhx
- white-flowered	CPla SPhx

Galanthus ✿ (*Amaryllidaceae*)

'Ailwyn' ♀H5	CAvo GEdr NDry
'Alison Hilary'	CAvo GEdr LEdu
× ***allenii***	EPot EPri GKev
alpinus var. ***bortkewitschianus***	CAvo
'Anne of Geierstein'	MHCG NDry WCot
'Ann's Millennium Giant'	CBro GEdr
'Armine'	CElw WCot
'Art Nouveau'	CElw
'Atkinsii' ♀H5	CAvo CBro CElw CMea CRos EHyd EMor EPot GAbr GEdr GKev LRHS MAsh MAvo MRav NBir NRHS SDir SDix WCot WFar WHoo WShi XEll
'Autumn Beauty'	CRos EHyd LRHS NRHS
'Autumn Belle' **new**	CRos
'Babraham Scented'	GBin GEdr
'Backhouse Spectacles'	GEdr
'Ballerina' (d)	GEdr MAsh NDry WCot
'Bankside'	CAvo
'Barbara's Double' (d)	CAvo EWes GEdr MAsh
'Basisgrüner' **new**	NDry
'Benhall Beauty'	CElw EWes GAbr GEdr MAsh
'Benton Magnet'	EPot
'Bertram Anderson' ♀H5	CAvo EPot GEdr MAsh WCot
'Bess'	CElw GEdr
'Betty Hansell' (d) **new**	CAvo
'Big Eyes'	CAvo
'Bill Bishop'	CBro CElw ECha GBin GEdr WCot
'Bitton' ambig.	GEdr NPol
'Blewbury'	ECha ITim LEdu
'Brenda Troyle'	CBro CElw CRos ECha EHyd EMor EPot EPri GAbr GBin GEdr GKev LRHS MAsh NPol NRHS WCot WFar
'Brigadier Mathias'	EPot
'Bungee'	GEdr
'By Gate'	GEdr
'Byfield Special'	CAvo EPot
byzantinus	see *G. plicatus* subsp. *byzantinus*
cabardensis	see *G. transcaucasicus*
'Caryl Baron'	CAvo
'Castle Plum' **new**	MAsh
'Castlegar'	CAvo
caucasicus misapplied	see *G. elwesii* var. *monostictus*
caucasicus (Bak.) Grossh. var. ***hiemalis*** Stern	see *G. elwesii* Hiemalis Group
caucasicus ambig.	NPol
'Charlotte'	LRHS
'Chequers'	GEdr MAsh
'Chthonic'	CAvo
'Cicely Hall'	GEdr NDry
cilicicus	GBin
'Cliff Curtis'	GEdr
'Compu.Ted' **new**	CAvo
corcyrensis spring-flowering	see *G. reginae-olgae* subsp. *vernalis*
- winter-flowering	see *G. reginae-olgae* subsp. *reginae-olgae* Winter-flowering Group
'Cordelia' (d)	CElw GAbr GEdr
'Corrin' **new**	GEdr
'Cowhouse Green'	CAvo GEdr MAsh NDry
'Crinkle Crankle' **new**	CAvo
'Curly'	CAvo CElw EWes GEdr
'Daglingworth'	EPri GEdr
'David Baker'	CAvo EPot GEdr
'Desdemona' (d)	EPot GEdr GMaP ITim WCot WFar
'Ding Dong'	GEdr MHCG

'Dionysus' (d) CExl ELon EMor EPot EWes GEdr GKev MAsh NBir NWad SDeJ WBrk WFar WShi XEll
'Dodo Norton' CAvo GEdr
'Dragonfly' CAvo
'Dryad Artemis' **new** NDry
'Dryad Gold Bullion' **new** NDry
'Dryad Gold Charm' **new** NDry
'Dryad Gold Medal' **new** NDry
'Dryad Gold Sovereign' **new** NDry
'Dryad Gold Star' **new** NDry
'Ecusson d'Or' CAvo
'Eliot Hodgkin' GEdr
§ ***elwesii*** ♀H5 CRos CTri EHyd ELan EMor EPot ERCP GWyn ILea LCro LRHS NBir NPol NRHS SDeJ SDir SEND SPer SRms WCot WFar WHoo WShi
- 'Abington Green' ELon EPot
- 'Beany' CAvo MAsh NDry
- 'Benjamin Britten' **new** GKev
- 'Bo Bette' GEdr
- 'Bubble' CAvo
- 'Byrkley' CAvo
- 'Cedric's Prolific' CElw ECha EMor GEdr NRya WBrk WFar
- 'Chantry Green Twins' **new** GEdr
- 'Daphne's Scissors' CElw GEdr
- 'David Shackleton' CAvo CElw GEdr MAsh
- 'Deer Slot' CAvo MAsh
- 'Early Twin' WCot
- 'Echoes' WCot
- (Edward Whittall Group) 'Two Eyes' GEdr
- 'Elmley Lovett' CElw
- var. ***elwesii*** 'Big Boy' GEdr MAvo NDry
- - 'Comet' ♀H5 CAvo CElw GEdr MAsh MAvo MNrw WFar
- - 'Fenstead End' CAvo GEdr
- - 'Fred's Giant' GMaP
- - 'John Tomlinson' GEdr
- - 'Kite' ELon GEdr MAsh
- - 'Maidwell L' CBro EPot
- - 'Paradise Giant' GEdr ITim
- - 'Sibbertoft Magnet' GEdr
- - 'Spring Greens' **new** GEdr
* - 'Flore Pleno' (d) NPol
- 'Godfrey Owen' ♀H5 CAvo CElw EPot GEdr MAsh NDry WBrk
- 'Green Brush' CAvo CBro EWes LRHS
- 'Grumpy' CAvo GEdr
- 'Helen Tomlinson' SHar
§ - Hiemalis Group CBro EPri GKev WCot XEll
- - 'Barnes' ♀H5 CAvo ECha GBin WCot
- - 'Hollis' **new** CAvo NDry
- 'Jack-in-the-Green' **new** CAvo
- 'Jessica' CAvo EPot GEdr
- 'Jonathan' CAvo MAsh
- 'Jubilee Green' CAvo
- 'Kencot Kali' **new** CAvo
- 'Kyre Park' GEdr MAsh
- late-flowering GEdr
- 'Long 'drop' GEdr MAsh
- 'Mandarin' CElw EWes
- 'Margaret Owen' **new** MNrw
- 'Marjorie Brown' CAvo CElw CFis ECha EPot GEdr
- 'Marlie Raphael' CAvo
- var. ***maximus*** see *G. elwesii* 'Yvonne Hay'
- 'Milkwood' see *G. elwesii* 'Mrs Macnamara'
- 'Miss Mowcher' WCot
§ - var. ***monostictus*** ♀H5 CBro CRos ECha EHyd GKev LRHS MAsh NRHS WBrk WFar WShi
- - 'B. Britten' LRHS
- - 'G. Handel' LRHS
- - 'Grayswood' GEdr
- - 'H. Purcell' EMor GEdr LRHS
- - 'Jimmy Platt' CAvo
- - 'Kryptonite' **new** CAvo
- - 'Miller's Late' CAvo
- - 'Mozart' LRHS
- - 'Rogers Rough' SDys
- - 'Smaragdsplitter' **new** CAvo
- - 'Warwickshire Gemini' MHCG
aff. ***elwesii*** var. ***monostictus*** WFar
- 'Moya's Green' **new** CAvo
- 'Mr Omer' WCot
- 'Mr Peggotty' WCot
§ - 'Mrs Macnamara' ♀H5 CAvo CElw ECha ELon EPri GEdr WBrk WFar
- 'Naughton' **new** CAvo
- November-flowering WCot
- 'Penelope Ann' ECha GEdr NRya
- 'Peter Gatehouse' ELon
§ - 'Ransom's Dwarf' GEdr
- 'Remember, Remember' GEdr MAsh
- 'Rosemary Burnham' **new** MAsh NDry
- 'Selborne Green Tips' NDry
- 'Sickle' MAsh
- 'Sir Edward Elgar' LRHS
I - 'Snowwhite' NDry
- 'The Bride' **new** NDry
- 'Three Leaves' CElw
- 'Washfield Colesbourne' see *G.* 'Washfield Colesbourne'
- 'Yashmak' CAvo MAsh
§ - 'Yvonne Hay' GEdr NDry
'Elworthy Bumble Bee' (d) **new** CElw
'Ermine House' (d) GEdr NDry
'Ermine Lace' CAvo
'Erway' GBin NDry
'Evenley Double' (d) **new** CAvo
'Falkland House' CElw EPot GEdr
'Fanny' CAvo
'Faringdon Double' (d) EPot EPri MAsh
'Feodora' **new** CAvo
'Fieldgate Forte' CAvo
'Fieldgate Prelude' GEdr NDry
'Fieldgate Superb' CAvo MAsh NDry
'Fly Fishing' CAvo GEdr NDry
'Forge Double' (d) GEdr
fosteri GEdr GKev NDry
fosteri × ***koenenianus*** **new** NDry
'Franz Josef' **new** CAvo
'Gabriel' CAvo EPot GEdr
'Galadriel' GEdr
'Galatea' CBro EMor EPri EWes GAbr ITim MAsh NRya SDys WBrk WFar
'George Elwes' CAvo GEdr
'Gill Gregory' GEdr
'Ginns' WBrk
'Glenchantress' **new** GEdr MAsh
'Gloria' CAvo
(Gold Group) 'Ronald Mackenzie' GEdr NDry
§ ***gracilis*** CBre CExl GEdr GKev NPol WCot
- 'Highdown' CElw
- Kew CElw
- 'Vic Horton' CElw GEdr NDry WThu

graecus misapplied	see *G. gracilis*
graecus Orph. ex Boiss.	see *G. elwesii*
'Gravity'	CAvo
'Grayling'	see *G. plicatus* 'Percy Picton'
'Green Comet'	CAvo
'Green Man'	GEdr WFar
'Green Necklace'	EWes GEdr
'Green Ribbon'	CAvo
'Greenfields'	CAvo GEdr WBrk
'Greenfinch' **new**	CAvo
green-tipped double (d)	GEdr
'Haconby Green' **new**	NDry
'Hans Guck in die Luft' **new**	NDry
'Headbourne'	ECha
'Heffalump' (d)	ELon EPri GEdr MAsh
'Hercule'	CAvo
'Hill Poë' (d)	CBro CElw EPot GBin GEdr ITim NDry WHoo
'Hippolyta' (d)	CBro CElw ECha EMor EPot GEdr GKev LEdu LRHS MAsh MAvo NPol WCot
'Hobson's Choice'	GEdr
'Homersfield'	CElw ELon EPri
'Honeysuckle Cottage'	CAvo
'Hörup' **new**	GEdr
× ***hybridus*** 'Merlin' 𝕐H5	CAvo CBro CElw EPri GEdr MAsh WCot WFar WHoo
- 'Robin Hood'	GEdr GKev
'Icicle'	CElw GEdr
§ ***ikariae*** Bak.	GEdr
- subsp. ***ikariae*** Butt's form	NPol
- Latifolius Group	see *G. platyphyllus*
- subsp. ***snogerupii***	see *G. ikariae* Bak.
'Imbolc'	GEdr
(Imperial Group) 'Shepton Merlin'	CElw NDry
'Ivy Cottage Corporal'	CAvo GEdr
'Jacquenetta' (d)	CBro CElw EWes GBin GEdr ITim LRHS MAsh
'Jade'	CAvo
'James Backhouse'	ECha EMor WShi
'Jennifer Hewitt' **new**	CElw
'John Gray' 𝕐H5	EPri EWes GBin GEdr GQue MAsh
'John Nash'	MAsh
'June Boardman'	CAvo
'Karneval' **new**	CAvo
'Kath Dryden' **new**	EPot
'Kersen'	CAvo
'Ketton'	CBro CElw GEdr NRya
'Kildare'	CAvo GEdr LEdu MAsh
'Kingston Double' (d)	GBin GEdr MAsh
'Kinn McIntosh'	MAsh WCot
'Lady Beatrix Stanley' (d) 𝕐H5	CAvo CBro CElw ECha EHyd EPot GEdr LRHS MAsh NWad WCot WFar
lagodechianus	CBro GEdr
'Lapwing'	EPot GEdr MAsh NDry
latifolius Rupr.	see *G. platyphyllus*
'Lavinia' (d)	CElw EWes GEdr WFar
'Limetree'	CElw EPri EWes GEdr ITim MAvo NPol WFar
'Little Ben'	CAvo CElw GEdr GMaP
'Little Dorrit'	CAvo GEdr
'Little John'	EPot GEdr WBrk
'Little Magnet'	CAvo
'Lord Lieutenant'	EPot GEdr MAsh
'Louise Ann Bromley'	CAvo
'Lucy' **new**	CAvo
lutescens	see *G. nivalis* Sandersii Group
'Lyn'	CBro EMor GEdr NBir
'Magnet' 𝕐H5	CAvo CBro CElw CMea CRos CWCL EHyd ELon EMor EPot GAbr GEdr GKev LEdu LRHS MAsh MNrw NBir NPol NRHS WBrk WCot WFar WHoo WShi XEll
aff. 'Magnet'	GMaP SDir WFar WHil
'Maidwell'	GEdr
'Matt Bishop' **new**	CAvo
'Megan' **new**	GEdr
'Melanie Broughton'	CAvo EPot EWes GEdr
'Midas' **new**	CAvo
'Midwinter'	CAvo
'Mighty Atom'	CBro GBin WBrk
'Miss Willmott' **new**	CAvo
'Moby Dick' **new**	EWes
'Moccas'	CElw
'Modern Art'	EPot GEdr MAsh MHCG
'Moortown'	CAvo GEdr
'Mordred' (d) **new**	CAvo
'Mothering Sunday' **new**	CAvo
'Mr Stinker' **new**	CAvo
'Mr Thompson'	EPot
'Mrs Thompson'	CElw ECha GEdr GKev MAsh MNrw
'Mrs Wrightson's Double' (d)	CElw GBin GEdr
'Muku' (d) **new**	NDry
'Natalie Garton'	CAvo EPot GEdr
'Neill Fraser'	EPri GEdr
'Nerissa' (d)	GEdr
nivalis 𝕐H5	Widely available
- 'Alan's Treat'	CAvo GEdr
- 'Alburgh Claw' **new**	CAvo
- 'Angelina' **new**	CAvo
- 'Anglesey Abbey'	CElw EWes GEdr NDry
- 'Ballynahinch'	GEdr ITim
- 'Bitton'	GBin GEdr
- 'Blonde Inge'	CAvo EPot GEdr MAsh
- 'Chedworth'	CAvo CElw GEdr WBrk
- 'Chilton Foliat'	CAvo
- 'Cornwood'	CAvo GEdr NDry
- 'Courteenhall' Wyatt	EPri NDry
- dwarf	ITim
- 'Egret' **new**	CAvo
- 'Elfin'	CAvo CElw EWes GEdr WCot
- Estonian Spirit Group **new**	NDry
- 'Flocon de Neige' **new**	CAvo
- 'Gloucester Old Spot'	GEdr
- 'Green Diamond'	CElw
- 'Green Tear' **new**	CAvo GEdr
- 'Greenish'	CAvo NDry
- subsp. ***imperati***	CExl WBrk
- 'Kullake' **new**	NDry
- 'Little Dancer' **new**	CAvo
- 'Llo 'n' Green' **new**	CAvo NDry
- 'Lutescens'	see *G. nivalis* Sandersii Group
- 'Margery Fish'	CAvo NDry
- 'Melvillei'	CAvo
- 'Oosterhouw' **new**	CAvo
- 'Pewsey Vale'	WBrk
- f. ***pleniflorus*** (d)	GKev MPri SPoG
- - 'Bagpuize Virginia' (d)	GEdr
- - 'Blewbury Tart' (d)	CAvo CBro CElw ELon EPri EWes GEdr WBrk WCot WFar WHoo
- - 'Boyd's Double' (d)	CAvo
- - 'Doncaster's Double Charmer' (d)	GBin NDry
- - 'Flore Pleno' (d) 𝕐H5	CArg CBro CExl CWCL EMor EPot ERCP GBin GWyn LCro LOPS LRHS

		MMuc NHpl NRya SDeJ SEND SPer SRms WBrk WCot WHoo WShi
	- - 'Lady Elphinstone' (d)	CBro ELon GEdr LRHS MAsh NPol NRya WCot
	- - 'Octopussy' (d)	GEdr
	- - 'Pusey Green Tips' (d)	CBro CElw EPot NPol WCot
	- - 'Walrus' (d)	CAvo CMea ELon GEdr GKev WBrk
	- Poculiformis Group	CElw
	- - 'Angelique'	CAvo NDry
	- - 'Francesca de Grammont' **new**	NDry
	- - 'Henry's White Lady'	GEdr
	- - 'Moreton Mill'	CAvo
	- cf. Poculiformis Group	CElw
	- 'Puck'	CAvo GEdr
	- 'Rosemary Mitchell'	MAvo
§	- Sandersii Group	GBin GEdr GMaP NDry WFar
	- - 'Lowick'	CAvo
	- - 'Norfolk Blonde'	GEdr
	- - 'Ray Cobb'	CAvo
§	- Scharlockii Group	CElw ELon WBrk
	- 'Sibbertoft White'	EPri WBrk
	- 'Tiny'	GEdr WFar
	- 'Tiny Tim'	EPot GEdr ITim MAsh WFar
	- 'Tippy Green'	CElw
	- 'Virescens'	NDry
	- 'Viridapice' ♀H5	CAvo CBro CElw CExl CWCL ECha EMor EPot ERCP GAbr GKev GMaP LRHS NBir NPol NWad SDeJ WCot WFar WHoo WShi
	- 'Warei'	CElw EPri GBin
	- 'White Cloud'	GKev
	- 'White Dream'	CElw GEdr
	aff. ***nivalis***	SDir
	'North Star' (d) **new**	CElw
	'One Drop or Two'	CAvo
	'Ophelia' (d)	CBro GEdr NPol WBrk WFar WHoo
	'Peardrop'	GEdr MAsh
	'Peg Sharples'	CAvo GEdr
	peshmenii	LEdu
	- 'Kastellorizo' **new**	NDry
	'Phantom'	CAvo
	'Philippe André Meyer'	CAvo
§	***platyphyllus***	CExl
	plicatus ♀H5	CBro CElw CRos EHyd EMor GKev LRHS MCot MWat NPol NRHS WBrk WCot WHoo WShi
	- from Coton Manor	MCot
	- 'Amy Doncaster'	CAvo MAsh
	- 'Amy Jade' **new**	EPot
	- 'Augustus' ♀H5	CBro CElw ELon EPot EWes GEdr MAsh WCot WHoo
	- 'Barbara Buchanan's Late' **new**	CElw
	- 'Baxendale's Late'	CAvo GEdr GKev MAsh
	- 'Beth Chatto'	EPot
	- 'Bolu Shades'	GKev
§	- subsp. ***byzantinus***	CBro MAsh MHCG WThu
	- - 'Conquest' **new**	CBro
	- - 'Patricia Ann' **new**	CElw
	- - 'Richard Blakeway-Phillips' **new**	NDry
	- - 'Ron Ginns'	CAvo
	- 'Clun Green Plicate' **new**	CElw
	- 'Colossus'	CBro CElw EWes MAsh WCot
	- 'Diggory' ♀H5	CAvo EPri GEdr MAsh MHCG NDry
	- 'Duckie'	GEdr WFar
	- 'E.A. Bowles' ♀H5	CAvo GEdr MAsh NDry
	- 'Florence Baker'	GEdr
	- 'Gerard Parker'	CAvo GEdr MAsh
	- 'Glenorma' **new**	GEdr
	- 'Gold Edge' **new**	EPot
I	- 'Grave Concern'	CAvo
	- 'Green Hayes'	CAvo
	- 'Green Teeth'	CElw GEdr
	- 'John Long'	EPot GEdr MAsh
	- 'Josie' **new**	GEdr
	- 'Lambrook Greensleeves'	CAvo
	- 'Madelaine'	CAvo CElw NDry
§	- 'Percy Picton'	CAvo EWes GEdr NDry WOld
	- 'Phil Cornish'	CAvo
	- 'Sally Pasmore'	CAvo
	- 'Sarah Dumont' **new**	CAvo
	- 'Seraph' **new**	CAvo
	- 'Sibbertoft Manor' **new**	CElw
	- 'Sophie North'	CElw EPot GEdr NDry NRya
	- 'The Pearl'	GEdr MAsh NDry
	- 'Three Ships' ♀H5	GBin GEdr NDry NHar
	- 'Trimmer'	CAvo GEdr NDry
	- 'Trinity' **new**	CAvo
	- 'Trym'	CElw EPri GEdr NDry NPol WFar
	- 'Trymlet'	CAvo EPot GEdr MAsh NDry
	- 'Walter Fish'	CAvo MAsh
	- 'Warham'	CBro CElw EPot GAbr ITim WCot
	- 'Wendy's Gold'	CBro EPot EPri EWes GEdr GKev LRHS MAsh NDry NRHS WBrk WFar
	- 'Woodtown'	IMou
	'Polar Bear'	CAvo CElw
	'Prestwood White'	MAsh
	'Pride o' the Mill'	GEdr
	'Primrose Warburg' ♀H5	CElw EPot EWes GEdr MAsh NDry WFar
	'Ransom's Dwarf'	see *G. elwesii* 'Ransom's Dwarf'
	reginae-olgae	GKev NDry
	- from Spetchley	MAsh
	- 'Blanc de Chine' **new**	NDry
	- subsp. ***reginae-olgae*** 'Cambridge'	NDry
	- - 'Eleni' **new**	NDry
	- - 'Sylvie' **new**	NDry
	- - 'Tilebarn Jamie'	NDry WCot
§	- - Winter-flowering Group	CBro
§	- subsp. ***vernalis***	LEdu WCot
	- - 'Christine' **new**	CElw
	- - 'Miss Behaving' **new**	CAvo
	'Reverend Hailstone'	CAvo GEdr
	'Richard Ayres' (d)	CElw CRos EHyd ELon EPri GEdr LRHS NDry NRHS
	rizehensis	CAvo CBro
	- Baytop 34474	CAvo GEdr MAsh
	'Rodmarton'	EPot EPri GEdr MAsh NDry
	'Rodmarton Regulus' **new**	GEdr
	'Ryton Ruth' (d) **new**	CAvo
	'S.Arnott' ♀H5	CAvo CBro CElw CExl CMea CRos EBee ECha EHyd EPot ERCP GAbr GBin GKev GMaP LCro LOPS LRHS NBir NPol NRHS NRya NSla SDeJ WBrk WCot WFar WHoo
	'Saint Anne's'	CAvo CElw GEdr MAsh
	'Saint Sylvestre' **new**	CAvo
	'Sally Wickenden' **new**	EPot
	'Scharlockii'	see *G. nivalis* Scharlockii Group
	'Seagull'	CElw GEdr MNrw
	'Sentinel'	CAvo CElw EPot GEdr
	'Shropshire Queen' **new**	GEdr
	'Silverwells'	GEdr
	'Sir Henry B-C' **new**	CAvo
	'Sir Herbert Maxwell'	GEdr

'Snow Angel' **new** CAvo
'Snow Fox' SDir
'South Hayes' ♀H5 CAvo EPot GEdr
'Spindlestone Surprise' ♀H5 GEdr ITim MAsh NDry
'Sprite' CAvo CElw MAsh
'St Pancras' CAvo
'Starling' CAvo
§ 'Straffan' ♀H5 CAvo CBro CElw EMor EPot EPri GEdr MAsh NPol WBrk WCot WFar
'Sutton Courtenay' GEdr
'The Apothecary' CElw
'The Linns' GEdr
'The O'Mahoney' see *G.* 'Straffan'
'The Wizard' CAvo
'Titania' (d) CElw ELon EPot GEdr WHoo
§ ***transcaucasicus*** GEdr
'Trotter's Merlin' CElw
'Trumps' ♀H5 CAvo GEdr NDry
'Trym Baby' **new** GEdr
'Trymming' GEdr
'Trympostor' CAvo GBin GEdr NDry
'Tryzm' CAvo
'Tubby Merlin' CElw MAsh
'Under Cherry Plum' CAvo
× ***valentinei*** 'Compton Court' CBro GEdr ITim
'Veronica Cross' **new** CAvo
'Vertigo' CAvo
Warburg No 1 **new** GBin
§ 'Washfield Colesbourne' CElw ECha
'Washfield Warham' CElw ECha EPri MAsh
'Wasp' CAvo EPot EPri GEdr MAsh NDry WCot
'Welsh Whiskers' CAvo
'Welshway' CAvo GEdr
'White Admiral' CAvo
'White Dreams' GEdr
'White Perfection' **new** MAsh
'White Swan' Ballard (d) CElw EWes GEdr ITim WBrk
'William Thomson' EWes MAsh
'Winifrede Mathias' CElw
woronowii ♀H5 CArg CBro CElw CTri EPot GBin ILea LCro LEdu LRHS MWat NBir SDeJ SDix WBrk WCot WFar WShi
- 'Elizabeth Harrison' GEdr MAsh

Galatella (*Asteraceae*)

§ ***linosyris*** CBod EBee EWes MAvo NLar SPer SPhx WFar WHer WOld XLum
- 'Goldilocks' see *G. linosyris*
§ ***sedifolia*** CBod ECtt EHyd ELon EPPr EWTr LEdu LRHS MAvo MWat NBid NRHS NSti SDix SEND SPoG WCot WOld
- subsp. ***dracunculoides*** RCB AM 5 WCot
§ - 'Jean Polignier' LPla
- 'Nana' CExl EBee MRav NBir NLar NWsh SPer WCAu WCot WFar WOld XLum
- 'Rosea' IMou

Galax (*Diapensiaceae*)

aphylla see *G. urceolata*
§ ***urceolata*** IBlr MNrw NHar WSHC

Galega (*Papilionaceae*)

bicolor NBir SRms
'Duchess of Bedford' ELon WCot
× ***hartlandii*** CExl
- 'Alba' ♀H7 ELon EWes GBin LRHS MArl MCot MRav SHar WCAu WCot WHoo WSHC XEll
- 'Lady Wilson' ♀H7 ECtt ELon EMor EPPr EWes GBin MArl MAvo MMrt MNrw SRms WCot WFar WKif
'Her Majesty' see *G.* 'His Majesty'
§ 'His Majesty' EBee ELon LEdu MAvo MCot MRav WCot
officinalis Widely available
- 'Alba' CBod CCBP ECtt ELan EMor EPfP GMaP LEdu MAvo MBel MBrN MHer MMuc SBut SEND SPer SRms WCAu WHrl WKif WSpi WTre
- COCONUT ICE ('Kelgal') (v) SPoG
orientalis EBee ECtt EWes LEdu MArl MAvo MCot MRav SBrt WPGP WSHC
- PAB 6771 WPGP

Galeobdolon see *Lamium*

Galeopsis (*Lamiaceae*)

tetrahit WSFF

Galium (*Rubiaceae*)

boreale IMou
cruciata see *Cruciata laevipes*
glaucum **new** SPhx
mollugo CHab
§ ***odoratum*** Widely available
verum CHab EBee EBou EMor ENfk GJos GPoy LCro LOPS MHer MMuc MNHC NAts NGrd NMir SEND SRms WFar WWild

Galtonia (*Asparagaceae*)

candicans ♀H4 Widely available
princeps CRos CSam ECha EHyd IMou LRHS NRHS WPGP
regalis CExl WPGP
viridiflora CAby CAvo CBro ECha ELan ERCP EShb GBin GKev MNrw SDeJ SDir WHil XLum

Galvezia (*Plantaginaceae*)

speciosa CCCN CSpe LRHS

Gamblea (*Araliaceae*)

ciliata B&SWJ 13907 **new** WCru
innovans WCru
pseudoevodiifolia B&SWJ 11707 WCru

Garcinia (*Clusiaceae*)

mangostana CCCN

Gardenia (*Rubiaceae*)

augusta see *G. jasminoides*
florida L. see *G. jasminoides*
grandiflora see *G. jasminoides*
§ ***jasminoides*** ♀H1c CBcs CCCN EBak SGsty
- 'Crown Jewel'PBR (d) CBcs CPla CRos EHyd EPfP LCro LOPS LRHS MAsh NRHS SPoG WCot
- 'Kleim's Hardy' Widely available
- PINWHEEL ('Piiga-I') **new** LCro LOPS

garlic see *Allium sativum*; also AGM Vegetables Section

garlic, elephant see *Allium ampeloprasum* 'Elephant'

Garrya ✿ (*Garryaceae*)

elliptica	CBcs CBod CDoC CMac CRos EBee EPfP LMil LRHS LSRN MAsh MGos MPri NOra NRHS SCob WAvo
- (f)	MSwo SGbt SWvt WAvo WSpi
- (m)	CAby CTri NLar SGol SLim WSpi
- 'James Roof' (m) ♀H4	CBcs CBrac CDoC CMac CRos CSBt CTsd EBee EHyd ELan ELon EPfP LCro LMil LOPS LRHS LSRN MAsh MGil MGos NOra NRHS SGbt SGol SLim SPer SPoG SRms SWvt WFar
× ***issaquahensis*** 'Glasnevin Wine' (m) ♀H4	CRos ELan EPfP IArd IMou LRHS MAsh MGos NRHS SCoo SPoG WSpi
- 'Pat Ballard' (m)	WSpi
× ***thuretii***	CBcs EBee MMuc NLar SGol WFar

Gasteria ✿ (*Asphodelaceae*)

batesiana ♀H2	SEND
bicolor	SPlb
var. ***liliputana*** ♀H1c	
carinata var. ***verrucosa***	EShb SEND SPlb SSim
'Dragon Skin' **new**	SPad
'Little Warty' ♀H2	SSim
nitida var. ***nitida*** variegated (v)	WCot
'Smokey'	EShb

× *Gaulnettya* see *Gaultheria*

Gaultheria ✿ (*Ericaceae*)

NJM 10.032	WPGP
antarctica	WThu
cuneata	CRos EHyd GEdr LRHS MAsh NRHS WThu
aff. ***dumicola*** NJM 10.032	WPGP
forrestii	CExl
- BWJ 7809	WCru
furiens	see *G. insana*
§ ***insana***	WPav
itoana	GEdr GKev
'John Saxton'	WAbe
miqueliana	GEdr NLar WThu
mucronata	CDoC EPfP GKev LRHS MAsh SCob WFar
- (m)	CBod CMac CSBt CTri EPfP MGos MMuc NWad SPer SRms WFar WPav
- 'Alba' (f)	WPav
- 'Bell's Seedling' (f/m) ♀H6	CBcs CBrac CDoC CRos CTri ELan EPfP LRHS MAsh MMuc NBir NLar SGbt SPer SPoG
- 'Cherry Ripe' (f)	MMuc WPav
- 'Crimsonia' (f) ♀H6	CBcs CMac EPfP SPer SRms
- 'Indian Lake'	NWad
- 'Lilacina' (f)	CMac MAsh
- 'Lilian' (f)	CSBt EPfP NWad
- MOTHER OF PEARL	see *G. mucronata* 'Parelmoer'
- 'Mulberry Wine' (f) ♀H6	CBcs CBod CBrac CSBt ELan MMuc NHol SGbt SPer
§ - 'Parelmoer' (f)	CSBt ELan SPer
- 'Pink Pearl' (f) ♀H6	SRms
- 'Rosea' (f)	WPav
§ - 'Signaal' (f)	CBcs CBod CRos ELan LRHS MAsh NLar NWad SPer
- SIGNAL	see *G. mucronata* 'Signaal'
§ - 'Sneeuwwitje' (f)	CBcs CBod ELan EPfP LRHS MAsh MMuc SPer
- SNOW WHITE	see *G. mucronata* 'Sneeuwwitje'
- 'Thymifolia' (m)	ELan EPfP
- white-berried (f)	SCob
- 'Wintertime' (f) ♀H6	CMac SRms
§ ***myrsinoides***	GKev WThu
nummularioides	NHar
'Pearls'	EPot NWad WThu
phillyreifolia	MGil
procumbens ♀H5	CAgr CBcs CDTJ CDoC CMac CRos EHyd ELan EPfP GBin GKev LRHS MAsh MBlu MGos NRHS SCob SLim SPer SPlb SPoG SRms SWvt WFar
- BIG BERRY ('Gaubi'[PBR]) **new**	CDoC LCro LOPS
- VERY BERRY ('Kieverber')	EShb NWad
prostrata	see *G. myrsinoides*
schultesii	WThu
shallon	CAgr CBrac EPfP MCoo NLar SCob SPer SRms SWvt WFar
sinensis	NHar
- lilac-berried	GEdr
tetramera	CExl
thymifolia	NWad
trichophylla	NHar
× ***wisleyensis***	CRos EHyd LRHS NRHS SLon SRms
- 'Pink Pixie'	CRos EHyd LRHS MAsh NRHS
- 'Ruby'	CMac
- 'Wisley Pearl'	SCoo SPer WFar
yunnanensis	CExl

Gaura (*Onagraceae*)

§ GAUDI PINK ('Florgaucompi'[PBR])	CRos EHyd EPfP LRHS NRHS
'Ice Cool Rosy'	EBee EWTr SHar
lindheimeri ♀H4	CAby CBar CBcs CCBP CMea CSBt CSpe EBee ECha EHyd ELan EPfP LCro LOPS LRHS MBow MCot MGos MHer NRHS SBut SDix SPer SPoG SWvt WCAu WHoo WOut XLum XSen
- Belleza Series	CWCL EHyd EPau EPfP LRHS NRHS
- - BELLEZA DARK PINK ('Kleau04263')	LRHS
- - BELLEZA WHITE ('Kleau04264')	LRHS
- 'Blaze'[PBR]	EHyd LRHS
- CHERRY BRANDY ('Gauchebra'[PBR])	CBod EBee ECtt ELan EPfP GWyn SWvt
- 'Chiffon'	SHar
- compact red	XSen
- 'Cool Breeze' **new**	SPhx
- 'Corrie's Gold' (v)	CAby CBod EAJP EBee ECha ECtt EHyd ELan EPfP LRHS MHer NRHS
- 'Crimson Butterflies'[PBR]	CWGN ECtt EHyd ELan EPfP
- FREEFOLK ROSY ('Harrfolk') (v)	CDor CRos EBee EHyd EPfP LCro LOPS LRHS LSou MSCN NRHS SHar
- 'Gambit Rose'	EAJP LSou
- 'Gambit White'	LSou
- GAUDI RED ('Florgaured')	CRos EHyd EPfP LRHS NRHS
- GAUDI ROSE ('Florgaucomro'[PBR])	CRos EHyd LRHS NRHS SCob
- (Geyser Series) GEYSER PINK ('Gaudros'[PBR])	EBee EPfP LSou
- - GEYSER WHITE ('Gaudwwhi'[PBR])	CBod EBee EPfP LSou

- 'Jo Adela' (v)	ECha EPfP
- KARALEE PETITE ('Gauka')	CWCL EPfP SEle
- KARALEE PETITE IMPROVED	see *G. lindheimeri* LILLIPOP PINK
- KARALEE WHITE ('Nugauwhite' PBR)	CBod CWCL EHyd ELan EPfP LRHS NLar NRHS SCoo SEdd SPoG
§ - LILLIPOP PINK ('Redgapi' PBR)	CAby CWCL EHyd EPfP LRHS MBrN NLar SPoG
- 'Little Janie'	CBod MHol
- 'My Melody' PBR (v)	CWCL
- 'Occitania' (v)	XLum
- PAPILLON ('Nugaupapil' PBR)	CRos EHyd LRHS NRHS SPoG
- 'Passionate Blush' PBR	CBcs CChe ECtt EHyd EPfP LRHS MGos NRHS SLon SPoG SRms
- 'Passionate Pink'	LRHS
- 'Passionate Rainbow' PBR (v)	CWCL EHyd EPfP LRHS NRHS SCob SRms
- 'Pink Dwarf'	EBee EPfP SAdn
- PINK FOUNTAIN ('Walgaupf')	EHyd LRHS NRHS
- 'Pink Gin'	SPoG
- ROSYJANE ('Harrosy' PBR)	Widely available
- RUBY RUBY ('Harruby' PBR)	CBcs SHar
- 'Siskiyou Pink'	CBar CBcs CBod CSBt CWCL EAJP EBee ECha ECtt EHyd ELan EPfP LCro LOPS LRHS MBel SAdn SCob SGbt SPer SWvt WCFE XLum
- SNOW FOUNTAIN ('Walsnofou')	CBod EHyd EPfP LRHS MNrw NRHS
- 'Sparkle White'	CBod EAJP EBee EHyd EPfP LRHS LSun WFar
- 'Summer Breeze'	CDor EAJP EHyd EPfP EWTr GPSL LRHS NGBl NRHS SPhx
- 'Summer Emotions'	LSou
- 'The Bride'	CBcs CBod CTri CWCL EBee EHyd ELan EPfP GQue LRHS LSRN MBel MNHC MRav MWat NRHS SAdn SEdd SGbt SWvt WCav
- 'Val's Pink'	WAvo
- 'Vanilla'	CKno LSou
I - 'Variegata' (v)	CWCL SRms
- 'Whirling Butterflies'	CKno CSpe CWCL ECtt ELan EPfP LBuc LCro LOPS LRHS SCob SPer SPhx SPoG SWvt WCAu
- 'Whiskers Deep Rose'	LSou MHol WFar
- 'White Dove'	EHyd LRHS
- 'White Heron'	MNrw
'Rosy Shimmers'	SHar
sinuata	CAby CFis SHar
STRATOSPHERE PINK PICOTEE	see *G.* GAUDI PINK

Gaylussacia (*Ericaceae*)

baccata (F)	CMac

Gazania (*Asteraceae*)

'Aztec' 🏆H2	CCCN
'Bicton Orange'	CCCN CSam ECtt SCoo SVen
'Big Kiss White Flame' (Kiss Series)	LBuc
'Big Kiss Yellow Flame' (Kiss Series)	LBuc
'Blackberry Ripple'	CCCN SCoo
'Christopher'	SCoo
'Christopher Lloyd'	CCCN WCav
'Cornish Pixie'	CCCN
'Cream Beauty'	MCot
Daybreak Series	MBros
- 'Daybreak Rose Stripe'	SCob
- 'Daybreak Red Stripe'	SCob
FROSTY KISS MIXED (Kiss Series)	SCob
Kiss Series **new**	MBros
krebsiana	CCCN
'Lemon Beauty'	ECtt
'Magic'	CCCN SCoo WCav
'Melbourne Sunshine'	CBor
NAHUI ('Suga119') (Sunbathers Series)	CCCN
'Orange Beauty'	ELan
rigens 'Variegata' (v) 🏆H2	CCCN ELan
RUMI ('Suga116') (Sunbathers Series)	CCCN
Sunbathers Series	CPla SCob
Sunburst Series **new**	LCro LOPS
SUNSET JANE LEMON SPOT ('Sugajale') (Sunbathers Series)	CCCN EHyd LRHS NRHS
SUNSET JANE ('Sugaja' PBR) (Sunbathers Series)	CCCN
Talent Series 🏆H3	LCro LOPS SEND
TIGER EYE ('Gazte') (v)	CCCN
TIGER STRIPES MIXED	MBros
TIKAL (Sunbathers Series) **new**	SCob
TOPTOKAI ('Suga407') (Sunbathers Series)	CCCN CRos EHyd LRHS NRHS
TOTONACA ('Suga212') (Sunbathers Series)	CCCN CPla EHyd LRHS NRHS

Geissorhiza (*Iridaceae*)

aspera	CPbh
corrugata	GKev
inflexa	WHil
radians	WHil
tulbaghensis	CPbh

Gelsemium (*Gelsemiaceae*)

rankinii	LRHS WCot
sempervirens 🏆H3	CBcs CCCN CRHN EBee EShb LRHS LSRN MGil SLim SPoG WCot

Genista (*Papilionaceae*)

aetnensis 🏆H5	EPfP EWes LRHS SArc SEND SPer SPtp SRms WLov WPGP WSpi
§ ***canariensis*** 🏆H3	CExl CSBt
cinerea	WCFE XSen
decumbens	see *Cytisus decumbens*
'Emerald Spreader'	see *G. pilosa* 'Yellow Spreader'
fragrans	see *G. canariensis*
hispanica	CBcs CBrac CDoC CSBt ELan EPfP MAsh MMuc NLar SCob SPer SRms SWvt WCFE
humifusa	see *G. pulchella*
lydia 🏆H5	CBcs CBod CBrac CDoC CMac CRos CSBt EBee EHyd ELan EPfP LRHS MAsh MGil MGos MMuc MPri MRav MSwo NHol NLar NRHS SCob SLim SPer SPoG SRms SSta SWvt WFar
pilosa	EPot MAsh
- 'Goldilocks'	LRHS MMuc
- 'Lemon Spreader'	see *G. pilosa* 'Yellow Spreader'
- var. ***minor***	NLar WAbe
- 'Procumbens' 🏆H5	CBrac GEdr

	- 'Vancouver Gold'	CMac ELan EPfP SPer SRms
§	- 'Yellow Spreader'	MAsh MSwo
§	'Porlock' 🏆H3	CBcs CDoC CExl CMac CRos CSBt CTri EHyd EPfP LRHS MAsh MMuc MRav NOra NRHS SEND SNig
§	***pulchella***	WAbe
	sagittalis	LRHS MMuc SBrt SPer WWFP
§	× ***spachiana*** 🏆H1c	CEnd CTri SPoG
	tinctoria	CCBP CHab GPoy MMuc NAts WHer WSFF XSen
§	- 'Flore Pleno' (d) 🏆H6	EBtc GEdr
	- 'Humifusa'	EPot GEdr
	- 'Moesiaca'	WAbe
	- 'Plena'	see *G. tinctoria* 'Flore Pleno'
	- 'Royal Gold' 🏆H6	MRav NLar NWad SPer SPlb
	umbellata	XSen
	villarsii	see *G. pulchella*

Genlisea (*Lentibulariaceae*)

	hispidula new	CHew

Gentiana ✿ (*Gentianaceae*)

§	***acaulis*** 🏆H5	CRos EHyd EPot GKev GMaP LRHS MAsh NGdn NHar NLar NRHS NSla SPlb SRms WAbe XEll
	- f. ***alba***	EPot
	- - 'Snowstorm'	GKev
	- 'Arctic Fanfare'	GEdr
	- B.A. selection	EPot
	- 'Belvedere'	EPot
	- 'Coelestina'	WThu
	- 'Holzmannii'	WAbe
	- 'Krumrey'	EPot GEdr GKev
	- 'Luna' PBR	NLar WIce
I	- 'Maxima Enzian'	EPot GEdr
	- 'Rannoch'	EPot GEdr GKev NLar
	- 'Stumpy'	GEdr
	- 'Trotter's Variety'	WAbe
	- 'Undulatifolia'	EPot
	- 'Velkokvensis'	EPot GEdr
	'Alex Duguid'	CRos EHyd GEdr LRHS NHar
	'Amethyst'	CRos EHyd GEdr LRHS WAbe
	angulosa misapplied	see *G. verna* 'Angulosa' hort.
	angulosa M.Bieb.	see *G. verna* subsp. *pontica*
	angustifolia	WAbe XEll
I	- 'Alba'	EPot
	- Frei hybrid	NSla
	'Ann's Special'	GEdr
	asclepiadea 🏆H5	CSpe EHyd ELan EMor GAbr GEdr GKev GMaP ITim LEdu LRHS MBel MNrw NBid NBir NHar NLar NRHS SPer SRms WBor WCAu WCFE WHoo WKif WSHC
	- 'Alba'	EBee EHyd EMor GEdr GKev GMaP LEdu LRHS NBid NRHS SPer SRms WCFE
	- dark blue-flowered	WPGP
	- 'Knightshayes'	EBee GKev LEdu
I	- 'Nana'	EBee GKev
	- 'Phyllis'	EBee GKev WHoo
	- 'Pink Cascade'	WHil
	- 'Pink Swallow'	GEdr
	- 'Rosea'	GEdr GKev
	- 'White Swallow'	GEdr
	- 'Whitethroat'	GKev
	'Balmoral' PBR	GMaP NHar
	'Barbara Lyle'	WAbe
	bavarica var. ***subacaulis***	SPlb
	× ***bernardii***	see *G.* × *stevenagensis* 'Bernardii'
	'Berrybank Dome'	CRos EHyd GMaP LRHS
	'Berrybank Sky'	CRos EHyd GAbr GEdr GMaP LRHS NHar SPer
	'Berrybank Snowflakes'	GMaP
	'Berrybank Star'	CRos GEdr LRHS
	bisetaea	SRms
	'Blauer Diamant'	GEdr
	'Blauer Kobold'	GEdr
	'Blauer Zwerg'	GEdr
	'Blue Flame'	GEdr
	'Blue Heaven'	GEdr
	'Blue Magic' PBR	LRHS NLar
	'Blue Sea'	CRos EHyd LRHS
	'Blue Silk' 🏆H5	CRos CSma EHyd EPfP GEdr LRHS NHar NRHS SPoG WAbe
	brachyphylla	WAbe
	'Braemar' PBR	GMaP NHar
*	***burrowthii***	GEdr
	cachemirica	ITim
	'Cairngorm'	CRos EHyd GEdr LRHS
	'Carmen'	GEdr
	× ***caroli***	WAbe
	clausa f. ***albiflora*** new	ITim
	clusii	EPot GKev
	'Compact Gem'	GEdr NHar WAbe
§	***cruciata***	ELan GEdr NLar
§	***dahurica***	GLog MMuc NGdn NLar
	'Dark Hedgehog'	GEdr
	David Sturrock's dark seedling	NHar
	decumbens	GKev
	depressa	EPot WAbe
	'Devonhall'	GEdr
	'Diana' PBR	LRHS NLar
	dinarica 'Colonel Stitt'	WThu
	- 'Frocheneite'	EPot
	'Dumpy'	GEdr
	'Elehn'	GEdr NHar
	'Elizabeth'	GEdr
	'Ettrick'	GEdr
	'Eugen's Allerbester' (d)	CRos CSma EHyd GEdr GKev GMaP LRHS NHar NHol NLar SPer WAbe WFar
	'Eugen's Bester'	NHar
	farreri	WAbe
	- Silken Star Group	WAbe
	'Faszination'	GEdr
	gelida	GKev
	'Gellerhard'	GEdr
	georgei	EPot
	'Gewahn'	GEdr
I	'Glamis Strain'	CRos EHyd GEdr LRHS NHar SPer
	'Glen Moy'	GEdr
	'Glendevon'	GEdr
§	***gracilipes***	GEdr GKev SPlb SRms
	grossheimii	GKev
	'Hamburg'	GEdr
	'Henry'	GEdr
	Inshriach hybrids	CRos EHyd LRHS
	'Inverleith'	GEdr LRHS NHol SPlb
	'Iona' PBR	NHar
	'Joan Ward'	CRos EHyd LRHS
	'John Aitken'	GEdr
	'Juwel'	GEdr
	'Kobold'	GEdr
	kochiana	see *G. acaulis*
	kurroo var. ***brevidens***	see *G. dahurica*
	lagodechiana	see *G. septemfida* var. *lagodechiana*
	ligustica	EPot
	'Little Diamond' PBR	LRHS NLar

	'Lucerna'	CRos EHyd GEdr GKev LRHS
	lutea	EMor GAbr GKev GPoy IMou NHar SRms WCAu
	× ***macaulayi***	CPla
	- 'Blue Bonnets'	GEdr
	- 'Elata'	NWad
	- 'Kidbrooke Seedling'	GEdr GKev LRHS WAbe
	- 'Kingfisher'	CPla CRos EHyd GEdr LRHS NBir WAbe
§	- 'Praecox'	EBou
	makinoi 'Marsha'PBR	LRHS NLar SPoG
	'Margaret'	GEdr
	'Maryfield'	GEdr
	'Melanie'	GEdr
	microdonta	EPot
	'Multiflora'	CRos EHyd LRHS
	'Mystic'PBR	NLar
§	***nubigena***	EPot
	'Oban'PBR	GMaP NHar
	occidentalis	EPot
	ornata	LRHS WAbe
	'Orva'	SPer
	paradoxa ♀H5	GKev NSla SBrt
	phlogifolia	see *G. cruciata*
	pneumonanthe	LRHS NLar SPlb
	przewalskii	see *G. nubigena*
	pumila subsp. ***delphinensis***	WAbe
	purdomii	see *G. gracilipes*
	robusta CC 7494	EBee GKev
	'Sapphire Blue'	GEdr
	saxosa	GKev GWyn ITim LRHS NBir NHpl NRHS NSla
	scabra	CRos LRHS
	- 'Little Pinkie'PBR	GEdr
	'Selektra'	GEdr
	septemfida ♀H5	CRos EBou EHyd EPot GAbr GKev LRHS MAsh NBir NHpl NRHS NSla SPlb SRms WHoo WIce WKif
	- 'Alba'	GKev
*	- var. ***kuznetzovii*** new	GKev
§	- var. ***lagodechiana*** ♀H5	GEdr GKev LRHS SRms WFar XLum
	'Serenity'	CRos CSma EHyd GEdr LRHS NHar WAbe
	'Shot Silk' ♀H5	CRos EHyd EPfP GAbr GEdr GMaP LRHS MGos NHol NHpl SPoG WAbe WIce
	'Silken Giant'	GEdr WAbe
	'Silken Glow'	WAbe
	'Silken Night'	GEdr WAbe
	'Silken Seas'	CSma GEdr NHar NWad WAbe
	'Silken Skies' ♀H5	GEdr WAbe
	'Silken Surprise'	WAbe
	sino-ornata ♀H5	CPla CSma EBou EPfP GAbr GKev GMaP LCro LSRN MAsh NHpl NRHS SEdd SRms WAbe WIce
	- SDR 5127	MGos
	- 'Alba'	CPla
	- 'Angel's Wings'	CRos GEdr LRHS
	- 'Bellatrix'	GEdr
	- 'Blautopf'	GEdr
	- 'Brin Form'	SRms
	- 'Downfield'	CRos EHyd GKev LRHS
	- 'Edith Sarah'	GEdr
	- 'Gorau Glas'	WAbe
	- 'Mary Lyle'	GEdr
	- 'Oha'	GEdr
	- 'Praecox'	see *G.* × *macaulayi* 'Praecox'
	- 'Purity'	CRos EHyd GEdr LRHS WAbe
	- 'Starlight'	GEdr NHar
	- 'Weisser Traum'	CRos EHyd GEdr LRHS NHar NHol NLar SPer
	- 'White Wings'	GEdr
	'Sir Rupert'	GEdr NHar
	'Sternschuppe'	GKev
	× ***stevenagensis***	EHyd LRHS
§	- 'Bernardii'	GEdr
	- dark-flowered	WAbe
	straminea	GKev
	'Strathmore' ♀H5	CRos CSma EHyd GAbr GEdr GKev GMaP LRHS NBir SPlb WAbe WIce
	'Surprise'	GEdr
	syringea	WAbe
	szechenyii	EPot
	subsp. ***stolonifera***	
	ternifolia 'Cangshan'	GEdr
	- 'Dali'	GEdr
	'The Caley'	CRos GEdr GMaP LRHS NHar
	tibetica	EMor GPoy WCAu XEll XLum
	- PAB 2357	LEdu WPGP
	Tough's form	GEdr
	triflora subsp. ***japonica***	NLar
	'Troon' new	GMaP
	veitchiorum	EPot WAbe
	verna	CRos CSma EDAr EHyd EPfP EWes GKev LCro LOPS LRHS LSRN NHpl NRHS NSla SPlb SPoG WAbe WHoo XEll
	- 'Alba'	GEdr NSla WAbe
§	- 'Angulosa' ♀H5	MAsh
§	- subsp. ***pontica***	WIce
	'Violette'	CRos EHyd GEdr LRHS NWad
	waltonii	EWes
	zekuensis	WCot

Geranium ✿ (*Geraniaceae*)

aconitifolium misapplied	see *G. palmatum*
aconitifolium L'Hér.	see *G. rivulare*
'Adam Moreland'	WOut
'Alan Mayes'	CBod CMac ECtt EHyd EPPr GBin GKin LRHS LSou NBPC NGdn NRHS WCra WFar WPnP
'Alan's Blue'	EBee
albanum	CElw EPPr GLog GPSL GWyn MMuc
albiflorum	EBee
'Allendale Gem' new	EBee
anemonifolium	see *G. palmatum*
'Ann Folkard' ♀H7	Widely available
'Ann Folkard' × ***psilostemon***	GWyn LSRN
'Anne Thomson' ♀H7	Widely available
'Ant Chilly'	EBee
× ***antipodeum*** 'Chocolate Candy'PBR	LBuc SPoG
- 'Pink Spice'PBR	CWGN GKin LBuc LRHS SPoG SRms
- 'Purple Passion'PBR	LBuc LRHS SPoG
- 'Stanhoe'	MHCG
- (*G. sessiliflorum* subsp. *novae-zelandiae* 'Nigricans' × *G. traversii* var. *elegans*)	SRms
argenteum	NSla XEll
aristatum	EBee EMor EPPr EWes MNrw MRav NBir SGbt SPhx WCru
armenum	see *G. psilostemon*
asphodeloides	CElw EHyd LRHS MNrw NBid NBir SGbt WBrk WFar
- subsp. ***sintenisii***	EPPr

- 'Starlight'	NBid
atlanticum Hook. f.	see *G. malviflorum*
'Azure Rush'	CBod CDoC CDor CRos CWGN CWld EBee ECtt EHyd EPfP EWTr GMaP ILea IPot LRHS MAvo MCot MHol NDov NRHS NSti SNig SPoG SRms WCAu WCra WFar WPnP
'Azurro'	EBee LRHS
'Baby Blue'	see *G. himalayense* 'Baby Blue'
'Bertie Crûg'	ECtt ELon EMor GWyn LLWG NBir NLar SRms SWvt
'Blue Boy'	NLar
'Blue Cloud' [H7]	Widely available
'Blue Pearl'	EPPr MAvo NBir NSti
§ BLUE SUNRISE ('Blogold'[PBR]) [H7]	Widely available
'Blue Thunder'	EPPr
'Blushing Turtle'[PBR]	CBod ELan EMor EPfP LBuc MAvo MHol NDov NLar SNig SPoG WCAu WCra WNPC
'Bob's Blunder'	CBod CRos ECtt GPSL LLWG LPot LRHS MBNS MBel MHol MNrw MSCN NBPC NCou SAko SEdd SPoG SRms SWvt WCot WCra WFar WHoo
bohemicum	WHer
- 'Orchid Blue'	SWvt
'Brookside' [H7]	Widely available
'Buckland Beauty'	CExl EBee EWes SGro
'Buxton's Blue'	see *G. wallichianum* 'Buxton's Variety'
caeruleatum	EBee NLar
canariense	see *G. reuteri*
candicans misapplied	see *G. lambertii*
§ × ***cantabrigiense***	CMac CRos EBee EBou ECtt EHyd LRHS MHer MNrw NBir NBro NLar NPer NRHS NSti SCob SRms WBor WBrk WCru
- 'Berggarten'	EBee EPPr GBin NLar SAko WBrk WCra
- 'Biokovo'	Widely available
- 'Cambridge'	CBod CRos EBee ECha ECtt ELan EPPr EPfP GAbr GKin LRHS MBow MCot MRav MSwo NRHS SCob SPer SPoG SRms SWvt WBrk WCra WFar WFib WPnP
- CRYSTAL ROSE ('Abpp')	EBee EHyd EPPr EPfP LRHS NRHS NSti WCot
- 'Hanne'	CDor EBee ECtt EPPr EWes WCra
- 'Harz'	CDor EPPr SAko WCra
- 'Hilary Rendall'	EBee ECtt EPPr WBrk
- 'Karmina'	CBod CDor EBee EHyd EPPr EPfP GBin GPSL LRHS NLar NRHS WBrk WCra WFar WHoo WPnP WSpi XEll XLum
- 'Rosalina'	EPPr
- 'Show Time'	EPPr
- 'St Ola'	CCBP CDor CRos EBee ECtt EHyd EPPr EPfP GMaP ILea LRHS MAsh MNrw MRav NBPC NBro NChi NGdn NRHS NSti SAko SCob WCot WCra WCru WFib WHoo WPnP WSpi WWtn
- 'Vorjura'	EBee EPPr SAko SMHy
- 'Westray'[PBR]	CDor CMac ECtt GJos GLog LCro LOPS LSou MBel MHol MMuc NGdn NLar NRya NSti SEND SRms SWvt WCra WFib WIce WPnP
'Chantilly'	CBod EBee ECtt EHyd EPPr EWTr LRHS MAvo NBir NChi WCru WFib WGwG
'Chipchase Castle'	NChi
christensenianum B&SWJ 8022	WCru
cinereum	NSla
- 'Apple Blossom'	see *G.* × *lindavicum* 'Apple Blossom'
- 'Elizabeth'	LSRN
- 'Sateene'[PBR]	CAby CBor CSma GMaP MSCN NLar SRms WCra
(Cinereum Group) 'Alice'[PBR]	CAby CBor CSma EBee LSRN NLar SRms WFar
- 'Ballerina' [H5]	Widely available
- 'Carol'	CAby CBor CSma CWGN ECtt EWes GKin LRHS LSRN MRav NLar NRHS SWvt WCra WFar WIce
I - 'Heather'	CBor CSma WFar
- 'Janette'	CBor NRHS
- JOLLY JEWEL CORAL ('Noortjjcor')	WCot
- JOLLY JEWEL HOT PINK ('Noortjjhpi')	LCro LOPS NSti WCra
- JOLLY JEWEL LILAC ('Noortlil'[PBR])	CWGN NSti WCot WCra
- JOLLY JEWEL NIGHT ('Noortnight'[PBR])	CWGN IPot MPnt MThu SEdd SHeu SNig WCAu WCot WCra
- JOLLY JEWEL PURPLE ('Noortpur'[PBR])	CWGN LCro LOPS NHar NSti SHeu WCot WHil
- JOLLY JEWEL RASPBERRY ('Noortjjrab')	CWGN IPot NHar WCot
- JOLLY JEWEL RED ('Noortimpred')	CMea MAvo MPnt NHar SHeu WCAu WCot WHil
- JOLLY JEWEL SALMON ('Noortsal'[PBR])	CBcs CKno CMil CWGN GAbr IPot LCro LOPS MBNS MCot MHol MSCN MThu NHar SEdd SHeu WCot WCra WTor
- JOLLY JEWEL SILVER ('Noortjjsil')	NHar WCot WCra
- JOLLY JEWEL VIOLET ('Noortvio')	WCot
- 'Lambrook Helen'	CAby CBor CExl CFis
- 'Laurence Flatman'	CAby CExl CSpe ECtt EHyd ELan EPfP EPri GMaP LRHS MAvo MCot MPnt NBid NChi NDov NQui NRHS NSla SPoG SRms WCra
- 'Lizabeth'[PBR]	CBor NLar WCot
- 'Melody'[PBR]	CAby CBor CSma CWCL NLar WCra
- 'Pandora'	CBor
- 'Penny Lane'[PBR]	CBor MHol
- 'Purple Pillow'	CBor CWGN ECtt ELan LSRN MHol NChi SAko SPer SRms SWvt WCra WFar
- ROTHBURY GEM ('Gerfos'[PBR]) [H5]	ECtt IPot MRav SWvt WCra
- 'Signal'	ECtt EPot MPnt WCra
- 'Sophie'[PBR]	CBor CSma EHyd LRHS LSRN NRHS
§ - 'Thumbling Hearts'	CBor CWGN EBee IPot LCro MHol NLar SAko WCot WCra WFar
- THUMPING HEART	see *G.* (Cinereum Group) 'Thumbling Hearts'
'Claridge Druce'	see *G.* × *oxonianum* 'Claridge Druce'
clarkei	SBut
§ - 'Kashmir White'	Widely available
- 'Mount Stewart'	CExl EBee EPfP WCru WPGP
- Purple-flowered Group	WCav

- - 'Kashmir Purple'	Widely available
- Raina 82.83	MNrw
clarum B&SWJ 10246	WCru
collinum	EPPr NBir WCru
'Color Carousel'	EBee GBin
'Coombland White'	CExl EBee ECtt EHyd LRHS LSun MAvo MBel MHol NRHS SEdd SPoG WCot WCra WFar WMal WSpi
'Copper Tiger'	LEdu
'Coquet Island'	EPPr
'Criss Canning'	EPPr
'Curly Girly'	EBee
'Cyril's Fancy'	EPPr
dalmaticum 𝕐H5	Widely available
- 'Album'	CRos EBee ECtt EHyd EPfP EPot LRHS MRav NRHS SRms WAbe WCra
- 'Bressingham Pink'	ECtt EPPr
- 'Bridal Bouquet'	CPBP ECtt NSla
- 'Stade's Hellrosa'	EPPr
dalmaticum* × *macrorrhizum	see *G.* × *cantabrigiense*
'Danny Boy' 𝕐H7	EBee
'Deep Purple'	EBee
delavayi misapplied	see *G. sinense*
'Deux Fleurs'	MAvo MNrw
'Devon Pride'	CElw EBee EPPr
'Dilys' 𝕐H7	CFis EBee ELan EPPr LPla MAvo MNrw MTis NBir NChi NDov NGdn NGrd NLar NSti WCra WCru WFar WHal WPnP WSpi
'Distant Hills'	EBee EPPr
'Diva'	EBee ELan EPPr
'Doctor Geert Lambrecht'	EBee
donianum	NSla
'Double Jewel'	see *G. pratense* 'Double Jewel'
DRAGON HEART ('Bremdra'PBR)	EBee ECtt ELan EPfP IPot LCro LOPS LPla LRHS LSRN MAvo MNrw MPnt NDov NLar NRHS NSti WBor WCAu WCra WFar WPnP WSpi
drakensbergense	WFar
DREAMLAND ('Bremdream'PBR)	CBod CDor CPou CWGN EBee ECtt EMor GMaP ILea LCro LOPS LPla LRHS MAvo MBNS MHol NLar SEdd WCAu WCot WCra
'Dusky Crûg'	CSam ECtt EHyd ELan ELon EMor EPfP MBel MHol MPie NHpl NLar NSti SDix SEdd SPoG SWvt WCot WCra WFar WSpi
'Dusky Rose'	CAby CCht CDor ECtt EMor GKev GWyn NLar SEdd SHar WFar
'Dylis'	WCAu
'Elizabeth Ross'	MAvo
'Elke'	Widely available
'Elworthy Eyecatcher'	CDor CElw LPla MNrw WMal WPGP
'Elworthy Tiger'	CElw EBee WCra
endressii 𝕐H7	CBod CBre CWCL ECha EMor EPfP GMaP LPot MBNS MCot MHer MMuc NBro NPer NPol SEND SPlb SRms SWvt WCra WFar XLum
- 'Album'	see *G.* 'Mary Mottram'
- 'Prestbury White'	see *G.* × *oxonianum* 'Prestbury Blush'
- 'Wargrave Pink'	see *G.* × *oxonianum* 'Wargrave Pink'
erianthum	GLog GMaP IMou NLar WCru
- 'Axeltree'	WCot
- 'Blues in the Night'	EBee
- 'Calm Sea'	WCru
- 'Neptune'	WCru
- 'Pale Blue Yonder'	EBee EWes
eriostemon Fischer	see *G. platyanthum*
'Eureka Blue'	CBod CPou CRos ECha ECtt EHyd GPSL LPla LRHS MAvo MHol MTis NLar NRHS NSti SEdd SPoG WCot WCra WPnP
'Expression'	see *G.* 'Tanya Rendall'
'Extravaganza'	EWes
'Farncombe Cerise Star'	CElw
§ ***farreri***	CBor CExl EHyd EPot LRHS NBir NRHS NSla
'Fay Anna'	CBct CBod CWGN EMor EPPr EPfP GBin GPSL MMrt MPnt SCob SPoG WCra WFar
'Finnish Pink'	NGrd
'Foundling'	CBct CPla
fremontii	EWld
gracile	CFis CRos EBee EHyd EPfP GMaP LRHS MNrw NBir NChi NRHS WBrk WCru
- 'Blanche'	EHyd EPPr LRHS MNrw
- 'Blush'	EPPr EWes
- 'Golden Gracile'	see *G.* 'Mrs Judith Bradshaw'
grandiflorum	see *G. himalayense*
'Grasmere'	ECtt
'Gwen Thompson'	WOut
gymnocaulon	CMac EBee EMor NLar WCru
gymnocaulon* × *platypetalum	EBee
'Harmony'	EBee EPPr
harveyi	EWes NChi SPhx WKif
§ ***hayatanum***	EHyd LRHS
- B&SWJ 164	NLar WCru WPnP
'Hexham Velvet' **new**	NLar
'Hilary'	WWtn
§ ***himalayense***	CBcs CPla CRos ECha EHyd ELan EPfP LRHS MBNS MMuc MRav NBir NBro NGrd NRHS SEND SPlb SRms WCra WFar XLum
- CC 1957 from Tibetan border	CExl EPPr
- ***alpinum***	see *G. himalayense* 'Gravetye'
§ - 'Baby Blue'	CElw CRos EBee ECtt EHyd ELon EPPr LRHS MAvo MNrw NGdn NLar NRHS NSti WBrk WCAu WCra WCru WFib WPnP
- 'Birch Double'	see *G. himalayense* 'Plenum'
- 'Derrick Cook'	CBod CElw CMea EBee ECha ECtt EPPr EPfP EWTr GAbr GBin MAvo MBel MNrw MTis NGrd NLar NSti SAko WBrk WCAu WCra WHal WHoo WPnP
- 'Devil's Blue'	EPPr MAvo WCAu
§ - 'Gravetye'	Widely available
- 'Irish Blue'	CDor CElw EBee EHyd EPPr GMaP LRHS NLar NPol NSti WCra WFib WPnP
- ***meeboldii***	see *G. himalayense*
- 'Pale Irish Blue'	EBee EPPr
§ - 'Plenum' (d)	Widely available
'Hola Guapa'	GBin IPot
ibericum misapplied	see *G.* × *magnificum*
ibericum ambig.	SRms
ibericum Cav.	CTri EHyd LRHS NBre NRHS
- 'Black and Blue'	EBee
- 'Blue Springs'	ECtt
- subsp. ***ibericum***	CMac WCra

- subsp. ***jubatum***	EPPr MNrw SGbt SRms
- - 'White Zigana'	ECtt LSRN MAvo NLar SRms WGwG WWtn
- subsp. ***jubatum* × *renardii***	SWvt
- var. ***platypetalum*** misapplied	see *G.* × *magnificum*
- var. ***platypetalum*** Boiss.	see *G. platypetalum* Fisch. & C.A.Mey.
§ - 'Ushguli Grijs'	EPPr IMou NLar WCot
ibericum* × *libani	EBee
incanum	CAby CCht CSpe EBee ELon EWes NBir NHpl SVen WCFE WSpi
- var. ***incanum***	SGro
'Ivan' 🏆^{H7}	CBod CElw EBee ECha ECtt EHyd EPPr LRHS MTis NChi NLar NRHS WCot WCra WCru WFib WWtn
'J.S. Matu Vu'	CSpe NDov SPoG WCAu WSpi
'Jean Armour'	CBod ECtt EHyd LRHS LSou MAvo NRHS SPoG WCra WFar WGwG
× ***johnsonii***	WFib
- 'Johnson's Blue'	Widely available
'Jolly Bee'	see *G.* ROZANNE
'Joy'	CBod CDor CRos EBee ECtt EHyd GWyn LRHS MAvo MBel MCot MRav NBPC NBir NDov NLar NRHS NSti NWad SEdd SGro SRms WCot WCra WFib WGwG WMal WPnP
§ 'Kanahitobanawa'	EBee MAvo
'Karen Wouters'	EPPr
'Kashmir Blue'	CExl CRos ECtt EHyd ELan EPfP GMaP LRHS NLar NRHS SWvt WCAu WCra WFar WKif WPnP
'Kashmir Pink'	Widely available
§ 'Khan'	CElw EPPr EWes LRHS MAvo NEoE NLar SDys SMHy WCru
'Kirsty'	EBee EWes NChi
kishtvariense	IMou MRav NSti WCru
koraiense	CFis WFar
- B&SWJ 797	WCru
- B&SWJ 878	CExl EBee WCru
koreanum misapplied	see *G. hayatanum*
koreanum ambig.	LRHS NLar
- B&SWJ 602	CExl WCru WHoo
krameri	IMou NLar
- B&SWJ 1142	CExl WCru
'Lakwijk Star'	CBod CFis ECtt EMor EPPr ILea LRHS NLar SPoG SRms WCra
§ ***lambertii***	NBir
'Larch Cottage Velvet'	MAvo
libani	CDor ELon EPPr MCot NBid NSti WBrk WCot WSHC
- RCB RL B-2	WCot
- 'Kew Gardens'	EPPr
'Light Dilys'	EBee EPPr LCro LOPS NDov STPC
'Lilac Ice'	CWGN EBee ECtt EHyd EPfP GMaP LCro LOPS LPla LRHS MNrw MPie NDov NLar NRHS SEdd SGbt WCra
§ × ***lindavicum*** 'Apple Blossom'	CMea EBee EPot LRHS MAsh NSla WFar
linearilobum subsp. ***transversale*** 'Foundling's Friend'	CCht CWGN MAvo
I - - 'Laciniatum'	WCot
§ 'Little David'	EPPr NLar WCra
'Little Devil'	see *G.* 'Little David'
'Little Gem'	CRos EBee EHyd GPSL LRHS MAvo NDov NRHS SGro WFar WHoo

lucidum	WOut WSFF
§ ***macrorrhizum***	CSBt ECrN GBin GJos GKev GKin GWyn LCro LEdu LOPS LSun MCot MRav MSCN MWat NBro SRms WCAu WFar WHil XLum
- 'Album'	CBre CMea CSpe ECha EHyd EPPr GMaP LRHS MBel MSpe MSwo NBid NBro NChi NRHS SAko WBrk WCAu WCot WCra WCru WFar WFib
- 'Bevan's Variety'	Widely available
- 'Bulgaria'	EPPr
- 'Cham Ce'	ECtt EPPr
- 'Czakor'	CDor CMac EBee ECtt EHyd ELan ELon EPPr EPfP LRHS MCot MRav MSpe NGdn NLar SAko SCob SRms SWvt WBrk WCot WCra WCru WFar WHoo XLum
I - 'De Bilt'	EPPr EWes
- 'Freundorf'	EPPr EWes GQue SAko
- 'Galgenveld'	WCra
- 'Glacier'	EPPr EWes
- 'Ingwersen's Variety' 🏆^{H7}	Widely available
- 'Lohfelden'	EPPr EWes WBrk WCru
- 'Montasch' **new**	NLar
- 'Mount Olympus'	see *G. macrorrhizum* 'White-Ness'
- 'Mytikas'	EPPr WBrk
- 'Olympos'	EPPr NLar
- 'Pastis'	SPoG
- 'Pindus'	CBod CWCL EBee EHyd EPPr EPed EWes GAbr LRHS NLar NRHS NSti SPtp WBrk WCru WFar
- 'Prionia'	EPPr NLar SAko WBrk
- 'Purpurrot'	WBrk
- 'Ridsko'	EPPr WBrk WCru
- ***roseum***	see *G. macrorrhizum*
- 'Rotblut'	EPPr WBrk
- 'Sandwijck'	EPPr MAvo WBrk
- 'Snow Sprite'	CMea CTsd EPPr GJos MHer NEoE NLar WBrk WHrl WPnP WWFP XLum
- 'Spessart'	CBar CBod CCBP CRos EBee EHyd ELan ELon EPPr EPfP GBin GMaP GQue LRHS MMuc NLar NRHS SCob SEND SGbt SPer SPhx SPoG SWvt WCav WCra WFar WFib WRHF XLum
- 'Variegatum' (v)	CFis EBee ELan GMaP LPot MBriF NBir SRms WCot WFar
- 'Velebit'	EPPr WCru XLum
§ - 'White-Ness' 🏆^{H7}	Widely available
macrostylum	CDor WCot
- 'Leonidas'	EPPr
- 'Talish'	EPPr
- 'Uln Oag Triag'	EPPr
maculatum	CFis EHyd LRHS MCot MMrt MNrw MRav NLar NRHS NSti WCru WHal
- from Kath Dryden	EPPr
- f. ***albiflorum***	CElw EBee EHyd ELan ELon EMor EPPr EWTr LRHS MBel MNrw MTis NChi NLar NSti SSut WBrk WCAu WCra WCru WFar WPnP
- 'Beth Chatto'	CBod CCBP CDor CElw CSam EBee ECha ECtt ELan ELon EPPr EPfP EWTr GMaP LEdu MBel MMuc MTis NBid NDov NLar SBut SPtp WAul WCAu WCra WFar WFib WPnP
- 'Elizabeth Ann'^{PBR} 🏆^{H7}	CSam CWGN EBee ECtt GBin LRHS LSou MBel MHol MNrw MTis NGdn

		NLar NSti NWad SDix SEdd WCot WCra WFar WFib WPnP
	- 'Espresso'	Widely available
	- 'Putnam County'	EBee EPPr
	- 'Shameface'	EBee EHyd EPPr LRHS NRHS
	- 'Silver Buttons'	EBee
	- 'Smoky Mountain'	EPPr
	- 'Spring Purple'	CElw EBee EPPr MAvo NChi NLar WFar
	- 'Sweetwater'	EPPr
	- 'Vickie Lynn'	CCBP EBee EMor EPPr MAvo MBel NDov NLar WCAu WCra
	maderense ♀H3	CAbb CBcs CBod CDoC CPbh CPla CSpe CTrC CTsd ECre EHyd ELan EWes GBin LCro LOPS LRHS NBir NPer NRHS SArc SDix SPhx SVen SWvt WFar WSMil
	- 'Guernsey White'	CCCN CPla CSpe CTrC SPhx WOut
§	× ***magnificum*** ♀H7	Widely available
I	- 'Anemoniflorum'	WCra
	- 'Blue Blood'	CBod EBee ECtt EHyd EPPr EPfP GAbr LRHS LSou MBNS MHol NBPC NGdn NSti SCob SEdd SRms SWvt WCot WCra WFar
	- 'Ernst Pagels'	CBod EMor MHol
	- 'Rosemoor'	CBod CElw CRos CWCL ECtt EHyd ELan EPPr EPfP LCro LOPS LRHS NLar NRHS SPer SPtp WFar WFib WHoo WSpi XLum
	- 'Vital'	XLum
	magniflorum	EBee EWes GKev NBid NGdn
	'Maître Hugo'	EBee NChi
§	***malviflorum***	CAby CDor CFis CPla ECha ELan EPPr NSti WCot WCru
	- from Spain	EWes
	- pink-flowered	EPPr WSHC
§	'Mary Mottram'	CElw MAvo
	'Mavis Simpson' ♀H6	Widely available
	'Maxwelton'	EBee
	'Melinda'	CDor EBee ECtt MMuc NMir NSti WCot WCra WFib
	'Memories'PBR	CBor CSma LSRN NLar SRms WCra
	'Menna Bach'	MAvo WFar
	microphyllum	see *G. potentilloides*
	'Midnight Star'	EBee EPPr EWes
	molle	WSFF
	× ***monacense***	CCBP EBee EHyd IMou LEdu LRHS NRHS WCru WFar WGwG WPnP WWtn
	- var. ***anglicum***	CDor EHyd EPPr EPfP LRHS NLar NRHS
	- 'Anne Stevens'	EBee
	- 'Claudine Dupont'	CDor CElw EPPr NWad WCot WFib
	- dark-flowered	WFar
	- 'Emma White'	EBee EPPr NChi NGrd
	- 'Jackie'	EBee EPPr NChi
	- var. ***monacense*** 'Breckland Fever'	EBee EPPr
§	- - 'Muldoon'	NBir WFar WPnP
	- 'Spotted in the Pass'	EBee
	'Mourning Widow'	see *G. phaeum* 'Lady in Mourning'
	'Mrs Jean Moss'	EBee EPPr EWes MAvo NChi
§	'Mrs Judith Bradshaw'	EMor EPPr
	napuligerum misapplied	see *G. farreri*
	'Natalie'	EBee EHyd EPPr LRHS LSRN MAvo NChi SWvt
	nepalense	SRms
	'Nicola'	CElw CRos EHyd EPPr EPfP LRHS MAvo NLar NRHS
	'Nimbus' ♀H7	Widely available
	nodosum	Widely available
	- 'Blueberry Ice'	CDor CElw MAvo
	- 'Clos de Coudray'	CSpe EBee EPPr EWTr GPSL ILea MAvo MBel NDov NLar NSti SHar WCAu WCra WFar WHil WPnP
	- 'Dark Heart'	MCot
	- dark-flowered	see *G. nodosum* 'Swish Purple'
	- 'Darkleaf'	EBee
	- 'Fielding's Folly' **new**	CElw CMea
	- 'Hexham Big Eye'	CDor CElw EBee EMor EWes LPla MAvo WBrk WFar
	- 'Hexham Face Paint'	EBee
	- 'Hexham Feathers'	CDor CElw
	- 'Hexham Freckles'	EBee EPPr
	- 'Hexham Lace'	CDor CElw EPPr
	- 'Hexham Whitethroat'	EBee
	- 'Julie's Velvet'	CElw LEdu SGro WHoo WPGP
	- pale-flowered	see *G. nodosum* 'Svelte Lilac'
	- 'Pascal'	EMor EPPr
	- 'Silverwood'	Widely available
	- 'Simon'	NLar WCra
§	- 'Svelte Lilac'	CBod CRos ECtt EHyd EMor EPPr EPfP LPla LRHS LSou NBro NHol NRHS NSti SPhx SPoG WBrk WCru WFar WFib WPnP
§	- 'Swish Purple'	EHyd EPPr LRHS NLar WCru
	- 'Tony's Talisman'	EBee EPPr MAvo
	- 'Whiteleaf'	CElw CFis CMac CMea EHyd EPPr GBin LRHS NChi NRHS SBut WCru WFar WHal WPnP
	- 'Wreighburn House White'	EBee EPPr MAvo
	'Nora Bremner'	EBee
	'Nunwood Purple'	EBee EPPr EWes MAvo
	'Old Rose'	EHyd LRHS NRHS WCru
	oreganum	EBee
§	***orientalitibeticum***	CExl CSpe EBee ECtt EHyd GKev LRHS MBow MCot MHer MMuc NBid NLar NRya SBrt SEND SMad WCot
	'Orion' ♀H7	Widely available
	'Orkney Blue'	CElw EPPr NChi WCru
	ORKNEY CHERRY ('Bremerry'PBR)	CMac EBee ECtt EMor GPSL LCro LOPS LRHS MBel SCob SEdd SHeu SRkn SRms WCra
	'Orkney Dawn'	MAvo WPnP
	'Orkney Flame'	EBee EPPr NChi
	'Orkney Pink'	EBou ECtt EHyd EPfP LRHS WCra
	'Out of the Blue'	WOut
	× ***oxonianum***	GQue
	- 'A.T. Johnson' ♀H7	CAby CBcs CBod CSde CTri CWCL EBee ECtt EHyd ELan EPPr EPfP EShb GKin GMaP LRHS MRav NBir NLar NRHS NSti SPer SPoG SRms SWvt WCra WCru WFar WSpi WWtn
	- 'Ankum's White'	EBee EPPr EWes
	- 'Beholder's Eye' ♀H7	CBod EPPr GWyn MMuc NLar WPnP
	- 'Breckland Sunset'	EBee EPPr NLar
	- 'Bregover Pearl'	CBre
	- 'Bressingham's Delight'	CRos EHyd LRHS NRHS
I	- 'Cally Seedling'	EWes
	- 'Cam Beauty'	WHoo
	- 'Chocolate Strawberry'	EBee EMor EPPr
§	- 'Claridge Druce'	CMac CTri ECha ELan EPfP GKin GMaP LPot LRHS MBow MRav MSwo NBir NGdn NGrd NLar NRHS SPer SRms WCra WFar WWtn XLum

	- 'Cream Chocolate'	EMor EPPr
	- 'David Rowlinson'	CDor EBee EPPr
	- 'Dawn Time'	CDor
	- 'Ella'	CWGN
	- 'Elworthy Misty'	CElw CFis EPPr
	- 'Frank Lawley'	NBid NChi WFar
§	- 'Fran's Star' (d)	WCru
	- 'Frilly Gilly'	EBee
	- 'Hexham Pink'	EBee EPPr EWes
	- 'Hexham White'	EBee EPPr
	- 'Hollywood'	ELan EPPr NLar NPer SAko SRms WCra WFar
	- 'Iced Green Tea'	EBee
	- 'Irene Hatwell'	EPPr
	- 'Julie Brennan'	EBee EHyd LRHS
	- 'Kate Moss'	EWes NSti
	- 'Katherine Adele'	CMea CSpe ECha ECtt EMor EPPr EPfP EShb EWes LRHS MAsh MMuc NLar NSti SBut SEND SRms WCAu WCra WFar WFib
§	- 'Kingston'	EPPr
	- 'Königshof'	EPPr EWes
	- 'Kurt's Variegated'	see *G.* × *oxonianum* 'Spring Fling'
	- 'Lace Time'	CBod CBre CRos ECtt EHyd EPPr EPfP GKin LRHS LSRN NRHS SPer SPoG SRms WCAu WCra WPnP WTyc
	- 'Lady Moore'	EMor EPfP
	- 'Lambrook Gillian'	CFis
	- 'Lasting Impression'	EPPr
	- 'Laura Skelton'	CElw EBee
	- 'Little John'	EPPr EWes
	- 'Maid Marion'	EWes
	- 'Maurice Moka'	EBee ECtt MSpe NLar
	- 'Miriam Rundle'	WCru
	- 'Miss Heidi' **new**	LCro LOPS
	- 'Music from Big Pink'	EBee EPPr EWes
	- 'Patricia Josephine'	WCAu
	- 'Phantom'	EBee EPPr
	- 'Phoebe Noble'	CBre CRos EBee EHyd EPPr LRHS MNrw NLar NRHS WCra WFib
	- 'Phoebe's Blush'	EPPr NChi
§	- 'Prestbury Blush'	CElw
	- 'Prestbury White'	see *G.* × *oxonianum* 'Prestbury Blush'
	- 'Raspberry Ice'	EBee EWes
	- 'Rebecca Moss'	CBod ECha ECtt EHyd ELan GAbr GPSL LRHS LSRN LSou NChi NRHS NSti SAko SBut WCru WFar WFib WOut
	- 'Red Sceptre'	EBee
	- 'Rose Clair'	CBod EHyd ELan LRHS NBir NLar NRHS WCAu WCra WCru
	- 'Rosenlicht'	EHyd EPPr GKin LRHS MRav WCra WCru XLum
	- 'Rothbury Sarah'	EBee EPPr
	- 'Sandy'	EBee EPPr
	- 'Something Special'	EBee EPPr
§	- 'Spring Fling' (v)	CDor ECtt EWes MSpe NWad WFar
	- 'Stillingfleet Keira'	EBee EPPr NSti
	- 'Summer Surprise'	EPPr EWes WCru
	- 'Susan'	EPPr EWes
	- 'Susie White'	EPPr WCru
	- 'Tess'	ECtt MHol WHoo
§	- f. ***thurstonianum***	CBod CMac ECtt EHyd EPPr EPfP EPri GAbr GBin LRHS MNrw MRav NBid NBir NBro NLar NRHS SBut SPoG SRms WBrk WCot WCru WFar WSHC WSpi XLum
	- - 'Breckland Brownie'	EBee EPPr EWes
	- - 'Crûg Star'	WCru
	- - 'David McClintock'	EBee EPPr WFar
	- - 'Robin's Ginger Nut'	EBee EWes
	- - 'Sherwood'	CSde EPPr GBee LPot MSpe NBro NSti WCra WFar
	- - 'Southcombe Double' (d)	ECtt ELan EPPr MHol SRms WCra WFar
§	- - 'Southcombe Star'	EBee EPPr GAbr NBro NGdn WCru
	- - 'Sue Cox' (d)	EPPr
	- - 'White Stripes'	EBee EMor EPPr
	- 'Trevor's White'	CDor EBee EHyd EPPr LRHS WCAu WCru
	- 'Tyne Salmon'	EBee
	- 'Wageningen' ♀H7	CBre EBee EHyd LRHS NGdn NLar NRHS SEND WCot WCru WGwG WHoo
	- 'Walter's Gift'	CBod ECtt EHyd EMor EPPr EPfP EPri EShb LRHS LSou MPie MRav NBPC NBir NBro NChi NLar NPer NRHS SAko SDix WCra WCru WFar WHoo WPnP WWtn
§	- 'Wargrave Pink'	Widely available
	- 'Waystrode'	EBee
	- 'Westacre White'	ECha EPPr EWes
	- 'Whiter Shade of Pale'	EBee
	- 'Winscombe'	EPfP NChi
	× ***oxonianum*** × ***sessiliflorum*** subsp. ***novae-zelandiae*** 'Nigricans'	EMor
§	***palmatum*** ♀H4	Widely available
	palustre	EBee EMor EPPr GLog MMuc MNrw NLar SBut WCot WCra
	- 'Money Peniche'	XEll
	'Pastel Clouds'	GWyn WFar
	PATRICIA ('Brempat') ♀H7	Widely available
	peloponnesiacum	EWes MNrw NLar NWad
	phaeum	Widely available
	- 'Acorn Bank'	EBee
	- 'Advendo'	EBee EPPr WCra
	- 'Album'	Widely available
	- 'Alec's Pink'	EBee NSti SHar WCAu WCra WPnP
	- 'All Saints'	EBee LEdu
	- 'Angelina'	EBee EMor EPPr
	- 'Ann Logan'	EBee
	- 'Aureum'	see *G. phaeum* 'Golden Spring'
	- 'Basket of Lavender'	EBee
	- 'Blauwvoet'	EPPr NChi
	- 'Blue Shadow'	EBee EPPr LEdu
	- 'Brown Sugar'	EBee
	- 'Calligrapher'	EPPr NChi
	- 'Chocolate Biscuit'	EBee EPPr
	- 'Chocolate Chip'	EPPr
	- 'Conny Broe' (v)	CDor EShb WSHC
	- 'Dark Angel'	EBee
	- 'Dark Dream'	EBee NGrd
	- 'David Bromley'	NChi WCru
	- 'David Martin'	EMor EPPr
	- 'Enid'	EPPr
	- 'Garage Door'	EBee
	- 'George Stone'	NChi NGrd
	- 'Golden Samobor'	CElw EPPr
§	- 'Golden Spring'	EBee EMor EPPr NChi NEoE NLar WFar
	- 'Green Ghost'	EBee EPPr
	- 'Hector's Lavender'	EBee
	- 'Hexham Halo' **new**	EBee
	- var. ***hungaricum***	EBee EPPr
	- 'James Haunch'	EPPr
	- 'Jenson's Purple'	EBee

	- 'Joan Grey'	MSpe
	- 'Joseph Green' (d) **new**	EBee
	- 'Judith's Blue'	EBee NChi
	- 'Klepper'	EBee EPPr GBin
§	- 'Lady in Mourning'	CExl EBee NChi SRms WCra WCru WFar
	- 'Lavender Pinwheel'	CBod CDor GPSL MSpe SPer WCot WCra
*	- 'Lilacina'	ECha
	- 'Lily Lovell'	Widely available
	- 'Lisa' (v)	CDor CElw ECha EPPr MAvo MBriF MNrw WCot WFar
	- 'Little Boy'	EPPr NEoE
	- var. ***lividum***	CBre GMaP MRav SRms WFar XLum
	- - 'Joan Baker'	CDor CFis CSam EBee MBriF MNrw NChi NGdn NSti SDys WCru WFar WFib
	- - 'Majus'	EBee EHyd ELan EMor EPPr EPfP LRHS NRHS WFar
	- 'Lustige Witwe' (v)	WCot
	- 'Marchant's Ghost'	SMHy
	- 'Margaret Wilson' (v)	CElw CWGN ECtt EShb EWes LEdu NBir NEoE NGdn NLar NSti WCot WFar WPnP WSHC
	- 'Mierhausen'	CElw EBee EPPr
	- 'Misty Samobor'	ECha
	- 'Mojito' (v)	ECha MAvo WCot
	- 'Moorland Dylan'	WFar WOut
	- 'Mottisfont Rose'	CDor CElw SGro
	- 'Mourning Widow'	see *G. phaeum* 'Lady in Mourning'
	- 'Mrs Charles Perrin'	CFis
	- 'Night Time'	EBee EPPr
	- 'Nightshade'	EBee EPPr
	- 'Our Pat' ♀H7	EBee EPPr NChi NGrd WCot
	- var. ***phaeum*** 'Langthorns Blue'	CRos EBee EHyd ELan EPPr EPfP LEdu LRHS MNrw NRHS SWvt WPGP
	- - 'Samobor'	Widely available
	- 'Phantom of the Opera' (v)	CElw EBee EMor EPPr
	- 'Pink Palava'	LEdu
I	- 'Ploeger de Bilt'	EBee
	- 'Purple Moon'	EPPr
	- 'Rachel's Rhapsody'	EBee EPPr
	- 'Raven'	CBod CDor EBee ECtt EMor EPPr LRHS MBel NChi NGrd NLar SCob SPer WCAu WCra WFar
	- 'Ray of Light'	EPPr
	- 'Rise Top Lilac'	EBee WPGP
	- 'Robin's Angel Eyes'	EBee ECha
	- 'Rose Air'	WFar
	- 'Rose Madder'	CCBP CDor CElw CMea LEdu MBriF MNrw NChi NLar SPhx WCru
	- 'Rothbury Ruby'	EBee EPPr
	- 'Sarah' **new**	WOut
	- 'Saturn'	EPPr
	- 'Séricourt'	MAvo WCot WFib
	- 'Shadowlight'	EBee ECtt EPPr NEoE NLar
	- 'Springtime' PBR	CDor EBee GPSL MSpe NBPC NGdn NLar WCAu WCra WFib
	- 'Stillingfleet Ghost'	EBee LEdu MBriF MNrw NChi NSti
	- 'Taff's Jester' (v)	NHol WCot
	- 'Tyne Mist'	EBee EPPr
§	- 'Variegatum' (v)	CBre CMac EBee ELan GMaP MSpe NBir WFar WHer
	- 'Vintage Dave'	WOut
	- 'Walküre'	EPPr EWes MBriF NChi NGrd NLar WCra
	'Philippe Vapelle'	Widely available
	'Pink Delight'	CElw MAvo SGro WMal
	'Pink Penny'	CAby CBct CBod CCht CDor CWCL ECtt EMor EPfP LSRN MNrw NLar NSti SCob SPoG SRms WCAu WCav WCra WFar WPnP
§	***platyanthum***	EPPr MNrw WCru WOut
	- 'Ankum'	EBee
	- var. ***reinii***	WCru
	- 'Russian Giant'	EPPr
	platypetalum misapplied	see *G. × magnificum*
	platypetalum Franch.	see *G. sinense*
§	***platypetalum*** Fisch. & C.A. Mey.	EHyd EPPr LRHS NBir NRHS WCru XLum
	- 'Dark Side of the Moon'	EBee EPPr
	- 'Genyell'	EBee EPPr NChi
	- 'Georgia Blue'	WCru
	- 'Turco'	EBee EPPr NLar WCAu WCra
§	***pogonanthum***	GLog NBir
	polyanthes	EWes NChi
§	***potentilloides***	NBir
	pratense	CBre CCBP CHab CMac CWld ELan EPPr GJos GMaP MBow MHer MNHC NAts NMir SBut SCob SPer SPlb SPoG SRms WCot WCra WFar WSFF XLum
	- 'Akaton'	NLar
	- 'Algera Double'	CBod ECtt EMor MHol NBPC SEdd WCAu WCot
	- 'Bittersweet'	EPPr
	- 'Black 'n' White'	CAby ELan SHeu
	- 'Blue Lagoon'	EPPr WCra
*	- 'Blue Skies'	WFar
	- 'Blue Sky Thinking'	EBee
	- 'Carrie's White'	EBee
	- 'Catforth Cadenza' (v)	MAvo
	- 'Cloud Nine' (d)	CBcs CWGN GBin MBel NSti WPnP WTyc
	- 'Cluden Sapphire'	EBee EPPr NHol NLar WCAu WCra WCru
	- 'Delft Blue'	CBod WWtn
	- 'Delft Blue Butterfly'	WCra
§	- 'Double Jewel' (d)	CWGN EBee EPfP MAsh MHol NBir NLar WFar
	- 'Else Lacey' (d)	CElw EBee MHol NSti WCot
	- 'Flore Pleno'	see *G. pratense* 'Plenum Violaceum'
	- 'Hexham Spook'	EBee
I	- 'Himalayanum'	NLar
	- 'Hocus Pocus'	CRos CWGN ECtt EHyd ELan LRHS MHol MNrw NBro NLar NRHS NSti SCob WCra WFar
	- 'Hoo House'	WHoo
	- 'Ilja'	EPPr MNrw
	- 'Janet's Special'	WHoo
	- 'Marshmallow'	EBee ECtt EMor EPPr LPla MBriF MHol NLar NSti SEdd SPoG WCAu WCot WCra WMal
	- 'Milou'	NLar WCra
	- 'Moondance' **new**	CBor
	- 'Mrs Kendall Clark' ♀H7	Widely available
	- 'Pink Splash'	WFar
	- 'Plenum Caeruleum' (d)	ECtt EPPr MRav NBid NChi WSHC
§	- 'Plenum Violaceum' (d) ♀H7	CBod CMiW CTri CWCL ECtt EHyd ELan EPPr GMaP LRHS MHol MNrw MRav NBir NChi NRHS NSti SGbt SRms SWvt WCAu WCra WCru WFar WPnP WSHC WTyc
	- 'Pope's Purple'	see *G. pratense* (Victor Reiter Group) BLACK BEAUTY
	- var. ***pratense***	CSam EHyd EPPr EWTr GMaP LRHS

	f. ***albiflorum***	MNrw NBid SBut SDix SGbt SPer WCra WFar WSpi
	- - - 'Galactic'	CMea ECtt GPSL LRHS MBriF MHol NBir NLar SEND SEdd SPoG WCot WCru WFib WPnP
	- - - 'Laura'PBR (d)	CExl EBee ECtt EPfP EWTr EWes LSRN MBel MHol NGdn NLar NSti WCra WFar
	- - - 'Plenum Album' (d)	CBod EBee ECtt ELan EMor EPPr EWes GWyn LRHS MNrw MRav NGdn NLar SGbt SRms SWvt WCot WFar WGwG WSpi
	- - - 'Silver Queen'	EBee ECtt EHyd EPPr GPSL LRHS LSou NBir NRHS SBut SPoG WGwG WPnP
	- 'Purple Ghost'	CAbb CBcs CSpe CWGN ECtt EHyd EMor GPSL LRHS LSou NEoE NLar NRHS NSti SCob SPoG WCra WFar
	- 'Rectum Album'	see *G. clarkei* 'Kashmir White'
	- 'Robin's Grey Beard'	EBee EPPr
§	- 'Rose Queen'	NBir SGbt WCru
	- 'Roseum'	see *G. pratense* 'Rose Queen'
	- 'Southease Celestial'	SMHy WGoo
	- 'Splish-splash'	see *G. pratense* 'Striatum'
	- 'Stanton Mill'	NBid
	- var. ***stewartianum***	MRav
	- - 'Elizabeth Yeo'	ECtt EHyd EPPr LRHS WCru
	- - 'Raina'	EPPr
§	- 'Striatum'	Widely available
	- variegated, white-flowered (v)	WCot
§	- (Victor Reiter Group) BLACK BEAUTY ('Nodbeauty'PBR)	CAby CExl CWGN EBee ECtt EMor EPfP EWes LBuc LRHS MGos MHol MPnt NHpl NLar SPoG SRkn WCra WFar WHoo WSpi
	- - 'Kaya'	CBod ECtt MAvo MHol NLar WCra
	- - 'Midnight Blues'	CWGN
	- - 'Midnight Clouds'	CWGN EBee EPfP LBuc WFar
	- - MIDNIGHT GHOST ('Midnightlyona'PBR)	EPfP MAsh
	- - 'Midnight Reiter'	CExl CWGN ELan EPfP GPSL GWyn LRHS MBel MHol NBro NChi NGdn NHpl NLar NQui SCob SDys SWvt WCAu WCra WFar WIce
	- - 'New Dimension'	NLar WFib
	- - 'Purple Heron'	NRHS
	- - 'Purple-haze'	GWyn NLar WFar WSHC
§	- - 'Victor Reiter'	CSpe EPPr LEdu NBir NChi NHpl WCot WCra
	- 'Wisley Blue'	EPPr WHal
	- 'Yorkshire Queen'	NGdn NSti WCru
	'Prelude'	CBre CDor CElw EBee ELon EPPr LPla NBir NEoE NLar SHar WCAu WFib WMal
	procurrens	CBre CTri GAbr WBrk WCru
§	***psilostemon*** ♀H7	Widely available
	- 'Bressingham Flair'	CBod CDor CTri ECtt EHyd LRHS MRav NBid NChi NLar SRms WCra WCru WFar
	- 'Catherine Deneuve'PBR	CBod CWGN EBee EPfP EWTr EWes GPSL ILea NLar NSti WCAu WCra
	- 'Coton Goliath'	EBee EPPr EWes MAvo
	- 'Jason Bloom'	CRos EHyd EPPr LRHS NRHS
	- 'Madelon'	MAvo NLar
	- 'Mount Venus'	IMou
	- 'Rosefinch'	EBee EPPr
	pulchrum	CDor EWes GWyn
	punctatum hort.	see *G.* × *monacense* var. *monacense* 'Muldoon'
	- 'Variegatum'	see *G. phaeum* 'Variegatum'
	'Purple Rain'	EBee EPPr NChi WCra
	pylzowianum	NBid NRya
	pyrenaicum	GAbr MBow NSti
	- f. ***albiflorum***	GAbr MNrw NBir SBut SPhx WBrk WCot WFar
	- 'Bill Wallis'	Widely available
	- 'Isparta'	EPPr LRHS MNrw SHar SPhx WBrk WGoo
	- 'Summer Sky'	SWvt
	- 'Summer Snow'	GPSL GWyn WFar
	'Rainbow'PBR	MBNS WCra
	Rambling Robin Group	CTsd ECre EWes
*	- 'Silver Shadow'	SPhx
	rectum	EPPr NBre NLar WCru
	- 'Album'	see *G. clarkei* 'Kashmir White'
	'Red Admiral'	Widely available
	'Red Propellers'	CElw
	reflexum	EHyd LRHS WCru
	- 'Katara Pass'	NChi
	refractoides	WCot
	refractum	CExl
	regelii	EPfP GWyn WCru
	renardii ♀H6	Widely available
	- 'Beldo'	MAvo
	- 'Tcschelda'	ECha ECtt NBir NLar SRms WCra WFar
	- 'Zetterlund'	CBod EBee EHyd EPfP EPri EWTr LRHS NQui NSti WFar
§	***reuteri***	CTrC SChr WCru
	'Richard Nutt'	EBee
	richardsonii	CBod CFis EBee EHyd LRHS MCot MNrw NBir NDov NRHS NWad SPoG WCra WCru WGwG
	- white-flowered	NChi
	× ***riversleaianum*** 'Russell Prichard' ♀H4	Widely available
§	***rivulare***	GLog NLar
	robertianum	ENfk EPPr SRms WSFF
§	- 'Album'	EPPr SHar SPhx SRms WHer
	- f. ***bernettii***	see *G. robertianum* 'Album'
	- 'Celtic White'	CBre EPPr MMuc SEND
	'Robin's Black Heart' <u>**new**</u>	EBee
	robustum	EPri GLog NBir NSti SBut SPlb WGoo WKif
	'Rosetta'PBR	CBod MSCN WCAu WCra
	'Rosie Crûg'	SWvt
	rosthornii	WCru
	'Rothbury Red'	EBee NChi WCra
§	ROZANNE ('Gerwat'PBR) ♀H7	Widely available
	rubescens	see *G. yeoi*
	rubifolium	WCru
	SABANI BLUE ('Bremigo'PBR)	CMac CWGN EBee ECtt EWes LCro LOPS MHol NLar NSti SEdd SMHy SPer WCot WCra WSHC
	'Salome'	CBcs CBod CDor EBee ECtt ELan GLog GWyn ILea MCot NBir NLar NSti SRms SWvt WCot WCra WGwG WKif
	'Sandrine'PBR	CBcs CBod CSpe CWCL CWGN IMou LRHS MBriF MHol MNrw NSti SPoG SRms WCot WCra WPnP
	sanguineum	Widely available
	- ALAN BLOOM ('Bloger'PBR)	EBee EHyd LRHS NLar NRHS WCra WFib
	- 'Album' ♀H7	Widely available
	- 'Alpenglow'	EBee ELon EPPr WBrk
	- 'Ankum's Pride' ♀H7	CDor CWld EAJP EHyd EPPr EPfP LRHS LSou MTis NChi NGdn NLar

		NRHS NSti SGro WBrk WCra WCru WFib WPnP XSen
	- 'Apfelblüte'	CCBP ELon EMor EPPr LSou MCot MTis NLar WCAu WCra
	- 'Aviemore' 🏆H7	CFis EPPr GBin NLar
	- 'Barnsley'	EPPr NBro
	- 'Belle of Herterton'	EPPr MAvo NChi NEoE WBrk WCru
	- 'Bloody Graham'	EHyd EPPr LRHS MAvo SPhx WBrk
	- 'Canon Miles'	ECtt EPPr IPot LSou NLar SRms WHoo
	- 'Catforth Carnival'	EPPr
	- 'Cedric Morris'	CElw ECha ELon EPPr MAvo NLar WBrk WCra WCru WPnP
	- 'Compactum'	EPPr WCra XLum
	- dark purple-flowered	SSut
	- dwarf	WAbe
	- 'Elsbeth'	CElw CRos EBee ECha ECtt EHyd ELan ELon EPPr EPfP EWes GBin LRHS LSou MSpe NGdn NLar NRHS NSti SPoG WBrk WCru WFar WFib WHal WPnP XLum XSen
	- 'Feu d'Automne'	EBee ELon EPPr NLar WBrk WCra
	- 'Fran's Star'	see *G.* × *oxonianum* 'Fran's Star'
	- 'Glenluce'	CBod CDor ECtt EHyd ELon EMor EPPr EPfP EShb LRHS MRav MSpe MTis NBPC NChi NDov NGrd NLar NRHS NWad SPoG SRms WBrk WCra WFar WHal WPnP
	- 'Hampshire Purple'	see *G. sanguineum* 'New Hampshire Purple'
	- 'Hannelore'	EBee
	- 'Holden'	ELon EPPr WBrk
	- 'Inverness'	EBee EPPr WCra XLum
	- 'Joanna'	CFis ELon EPPr MAvo WBrk
	- 'John Elsley'	EBee ECtt EHyd EPPr GPSL LRHS LSou NBro NGdn NRHS NSti WCra WPnP
	- 'John Innes'	EPPr
	- 'Jubilee Pink'	WCru
	- 'Kristin Jacob'	EPPr
	- var. ***lancastrense***	see *G. sanguineum* var. *striatum*
	- 'Leeds Variety'	see *G. sanguineum* 'Rod Leeds'
§	- 'Little Bead' 🏆H7	EPPr NHpl NWad WBrk XLum
	- 'Max Frei'	Widely available
	- 'Nanum'	see *G. sanguineum* 'Little Bead'
§	- 'New Hampshire Purple'	EBee ECtt EHyd ELon EPPr EWTr LRHS NBro NDov NLar SRms WBrk WCra WFib
	- 'Nyewood'	EBee ECtt EHyd EPPr LRHS NBPC SEND WBrk WCra WCru WFib
	- 'Pink Pouffe'	CBct CWGN EBee ECtt EHyd ELon GPSL LRHS NLar NRHS SCob SHeu WCra
	- 'Pink Summer'	EBee EWTr WCra
I	- 'Plenum' (d)	EPPr
	- 'Prado'	XLum
	- var. ***prostratum*** (Cav.) Pers.	see *G. sanguineum* var. *striatum*
	- 'Purple Flame'	see *G. sanguineum* 'New Hampshire Purple'
	- 'Red Robin'	EBee EPPr
§	- 'Rod Leeds'	EBee ELon
§	- 'Shepherd's Delight'	ECtt EPPr
	- 'Shepherd's Warning' misapplied	see *G. sanguineum* 'Shepherd's Delight'
	- 'Shepherd's Warning' 🏆H7	CMea CTri ECtt IPot MMuc MRav NBir NLar SEND WCru WFib WHoo WIce
	- 'Shooting Star'	EPPr IPot
	- 'South Nutfield'	CElw NChi
§	- var. ***striatum*** 🏆H7	Widely available
	- - deep pink-flowered	CSBt MSwo SWvt
	- - 'Mottisfont'	SGro
	- - 'Reginald Farrer'	WCru
	- - 'Splendens' 🏆H7	CRos EHyd EPPr LRHS NBid NChi NRHS SAko WCru
	- 'Vision Light Pink'	CBod EPPr WFar
	- 'Vision Violet'	CBod CSpe CTsd EBee EBou EMor MAvo NGrd SRms SWvt WBrk WCra WFar WPnP
	- 'Westacre Poppet'	EWes
	'Sanne'	CBod EPPr EWes LRHS LSou MHol SEdd STPC WCot WCra WFar WFib WPGP
	'Satin Velvet' **new**	CRos
	saxatile	EPPr GKev
	'Scapa Flow'	EPPr MAvo NChi WSHC
	schlechteri	EWes MMuc SEND WBrk WMal
	'Sea Pink'	EBou
	'Sea Spray'	CTri
	sessiliflorum	GAbr
	subsp. ***novaezelandiae***	
I	- - 'Nigricans'	ECha EPfP GAbr LPot SCob WFar
§	- - 'Porters Pass'	EWes NHpl SPlb WFar
	- - red-leaved	see *G. sessiliflorum* subsp. *novaezelandiae* 'Porters Pass'
	'Sheilah Hannay'	SHar
	shikokianum	GLog GWyn NLar WPnP
	- var. ***kaimontanum***	WCru
	- var. ***quelpaertense***	CFis EBee MAvo
	- - 'Crûg's Cloak'	WCru
	'Shocking Blue'	NLar NSti WFib
	'Shouting Star'	see *G.* 'Kanahitobanawa'
	'Simonside'	EBee EPPr
§	***sinense***	CExl EHyd LRHS LSou MCot XLum
	'Sirak' 🏆H7	Widely available
	soboliferum	CFis NBir NDov NLar SPer WCru WFar
	- Cally strain	EBee EPPr LPla WHoo
	- var. ***kiusianum***	CElw
	- 'Rothbury Star'	EBee
	- 'Starman'	MAsh NBPC NLar WCra WSHC
	'Solitaire'	EBee MAvo WCot
	'Southcombe Star'	see *G.* × *oxonianum* f. *thurstonianum* 'Southcombe Star'
	'Spinners'	CElw CMac EBee ECtt EHyd EPPr GMaP LRHS LSRN MAvo MRav NBid NBir NGdn NLar NRHS NSti SGro SPer WCra WCru WFar WFib WPnP
	stapfianum var. ***roseum***	see *G. orientalitibeticum*
	'Stephanie'	CCBP CElw EHyd EPPr EWes LPla LRHS LSRN MAvo MBNS MNrw MRav MSpe NChi NGdn NLar NRHS NSti WBor WCAu WCra WPnP WSHC
	'Storm Chaser'	EBee EMor LRHS NSti
	subcaulescens 🏆H4	CAby CBod CMea CWCL EBee EHyd ELan EPPr EPfP LRHS LSRN MCot NBid NLar NRHS NRya SBut SPhx SRms SWvt WAbe WCFE WFar WIce
	- 'Giuseppii' 🏆H5	CExl CRos ECtt EHyd ELon EPPr EPfP EPot GAbr LRHS MCot NBir NRHS SWvt WCra WSpi
	- 'Splendens' 🏆H5	CTri ECtt EHyd LRHS MHer NRHS NSla SRms WCra WFar
	'Sue Crûg'	EBee ECtt EHyd ELan LPla LRHS NChi NRHS WCra WCru

'Sue's Sister' WCru
'Summer Cloud' EPPr
SUMMER SKIES ('Gernic'PBR) (d) CDor CExl CMac CMiW CWCL EBee ECtt EHyd ELan EMor EPfP GAbr GKev LCro LOPS LRHS MHol MNrw MRav NBro NLar NSti SEdd SPer SWvt WCot WCra WSHC
suzukii B&SWJ 016 CExl
- NMWJ 14518 WCru
'Sweet Heidy'PBR CBod CDor EBee ECtt EPfP EWTr GPSL LPla MAsh MHol MNrw MPnt MSwo NLar NSti WBor WCAu WCra WFar WPnP
sylvaticum MBow NGdn NGrd NMir SBut WFar WShi
- f. ***albiflorum*** CBre NSti WCru
- - 'Cyril's Superb White' EBee EPPr
- 'Album' ♀H7 Widely available
- 'Amanda' EBee EPPr
- 'Amy Doncaster' CDor CElw CExl EBee ECtt EHyd ELan EPPr LRHS MRav NBir NLar NRHS NSti SPer WBor WCot WCra WCru WFar WFib WHoo WPnP
- 'Angulatum' CElw EPPr NChi
- 'Birch Lilac' CElw EBee EPPr EPri LRHS NLar WCra WFib
- 'Bridget Lion' WCra
- 'Coquetdale Lilac' CDor EBee EPPr
- 'Greek Fire' EBee EPPr MAvo
- 'Ice Blue' EPPr EWTr NChi WCAu
- 'Immaculée' EPPr MRav
- 'Jonah P' EBee
- 'Kanzlersgrund' CElw EPPr
- 'Lilac Eyes' EBee
- 'Lilac Time' EPPr
- 'Master Charles Wilson' EBee
- 'Master Niall Lawson' EBee WFar
- 'Mayflower' ♀H7 Widely available
- 'Miss Connie Wilson' EBee EPPr
- f. ***roseum*** NLar
- - 'Baker's Pink' EPPr MNrw MRav NBir WCAu WCru WFar
- 'Silva' MRav WCru
- subsp. ***sylvaticum*** var. ***wanneri*** WCru
§ 'Tanya Rendall'PBR ECtt ELan IPot NLar SRms WCot WCra WFar WFib WPnP
'Terre Franche' EPPr MAvo NLar SPhx WCAu WCra
§ ***thunbergii*** EWes WFar XLum
- 'Jester's Jacket' (v) CPla MNrw WFar
- pink-flowered EPPr
- white-flowered EPPr
thurstonianum see *G.* × *oxonianum* f. *thurstonianum*
'Tinpenny Mauve' MAvo
'Tiny Monster' Widely available
'Tod the Whippet' **new** NChi
transbaicalicum EPPr XLum
traversii var. ***elegans*** EHyd LRHS NRHS
tuberosum CDor CElw ECha IMou MBow MRav NBir NGdn NQui SPhx WCra WFar
- subsp. ***linearifolium*** EPPr
- 'Richard Hobbs' EPPr
- 'Rosie's Mauve' EPPr MAvo
'Ushguli Grijs' see *G. ibericum* Cav. 'Ushguli Grijs'
'Vectis' CElw
'Verguld Saffier' see *G.* BLUE SUNRISE
versicolor CMea EBee EPPr EPfP GAbr GPSL MHer NLar SRms WCAu WCra WFar WPnP XEll
- 'Kingston' see *G.* × *oxonianum* 'Kingston'
§ - 'Snow White' EPPr SEND WCru WFib
- 'White Lady' see *G. versicolor* 'Snow White'
'Victor Reiter' see *G. pratense* (Victor Reiter Group) 'Victor Reiter'
violareum see *Pelargonium* 'Splendide'
viscosissimum WFib
wallichianum CFis CPou EBee NBir NChi NSti
§ - 'Buxton's Variety' Widely available
- 'Chris' EWes
- 'Crystal Lake'PBR CWGN EBee ECtt EPfP IMou MBNS MHol MNrw NBir NDov NGdn NSti SCob SEdd WCAu WCra WFar WPnP
- HAVANA BLUES ('Noorthava'PBR) CBod CDor EBee ECha ECtt EPfP ILea IPot LCro LOPS LRHS MBel MHol NLar NSti SCob SDix SEdd WCot WCra WFar WHoo
- 'Pink Buxton' EWes NLar
- pink-flowered WCru
- 'Rise and Shine'PBR CWGN EBee ECtt ELan EWTr LCro LOPS MBriF MHol NSti SEdd SRms WCAu WCot WCra
- 'Rosetta' IMou
- 'Syabru' MNrw
- 'Sylvia's Surprise'PBR EBee ECtt EHyd IMou LRHS LSRN NRHS SCob WCAu WCra
'Wednesday's Child' WFar
'White Doves' NDov
wilfordii misapplied see *G. thunbergii*
Wisley hybrid see *G.* 'Khan'
wlassovianum Widely available
- 'Blue Star' MRav NEoE SBut WCra WFar
- from Crûg Farm **new** NLar
- 'Zeppelin' **new** NLar
§ ***yeoi*** CSpe NBir NSti WCru WOut
yesoense NSti
- var. ***nipponicum*** WCru
yoshinoi misapplied see *G. thunbergii*
yunnanense misapplied see *G. pogonanthum*

Gerbera (*Asteraceae*)

(Garvinea Series) GARVINEA LISA ('Garlisa') MHol
- GARVINEA RACHEL ('Garrachel'PBR) MHol
- GARVINEA SYLVANA ('Garsylvana'PBR) MHol
(Garvinea Sweet Series) GARVINEA SWEET DREAMS ('Gardreams'PBR) SPad
- GARVINEA SWEET GLOW ('Garglow'PBR) LRHS NRHS SPad
gossypina CPla

Gesneria (*Gesneriaceae*)

cardinalis see *Sinningia cardinalis*

Geum ✿ (*Rosaceae*)

'Abendsonne' CElw MAvo MNrw MRav MSpe NBPC NEoE
'Alabama Slammer' (Cocktails Series) Widely available
alpinum see *G. montanum*
'Apricot Beauty' CWCL
'Apricot Crush' MNrw
'Apricot Delight' NEoE NWad

'Apricot Pearl' (Censation Series) (d) **new**	CWGN ECtt EWTr MHol
'Bachelfe'	SBri
'Baked Beans'	NEoE
'Banana Daiquiri' (Cocktails Series)	CRos CWCL EBee ECtt ECul EHyd ELan EMor EPfP LRHS MBriF MHost MTis NRHS SCob SHeu SPalm WFar
'Beech House Apricot'	CDor CWCL ECtt EHyd EWes ILea LRHS MAvo MHost MNrw MRav NBro NEoE NHol NLar NWad WGrn XEll
'Beech's Double'	EWes MAvo
'Bell Bank'	Widely available
'Birkhead's Creamy Lemon'	EBee MHCG NBir SBri
'Blazing Sunset' (d)	CBod CMac CMea CRos CSpe EBee EHyd ELan ELon EMor EPfP GWyn ITim LRHS LSou MBel MHer MHol MNrw MRav NBir NGBl NGdn NRHS SCob SGbt SPoG SRkn SRms
'Blood Orange'	ECtt EHyd LRHS MAvo MBriF MCot MHost NEoE NRHS SPoG
'Borisii'	Widely available
'Bremner's Nectarine'	CElw EPPr MNrw NChi NEoE SHar
'Broomrigg Beauty'	NEoE
'Brown Sugar'	NEoE
bulgaricum	EBee MHost NBir NEoE NLar NRya WFar XLum
'Can-can' (d)	CDor CElw CMea MAvo WHoo
'Cantamos'	NEoE
capense	NBre NLar SPlb
'Centurion'	NEoE
chiloense 'Red Dragon'	CElw EMor GPSL SBut SWvt WHrl
'Chipchase'	CElw MAvo NChi NWad WHoo
coccineum ambig.	GKev
coccineum Sibth. & Sm.	GLog WHoo
- 'Ann'	ECtt EPri
- 'Cooky'	EHyd GPSL LPot LRHS MBriF MMuc NBro NGrd NLar NRHS SRms SWvt WFar
- 'Eos'	CSpe CWCL EBee ECtt ELon EMor EWes LEdu LRHS MBriF MHol MNrw MPnt MRav MSCN MSpe NBPC NGdn NLar SHeu SPoG SRms WGwG
- 'Koi'	EAJP EBee ELon EPfP EWTr GBin GEdr GPSL GWyn ILea ITim LEdu LSun MBros MHol MSCN NEoE NGrd SNig STPC WFar
- 'Queen of Orange'	CRos CSBt ECul MHost NEoE NGrd SRms WFar
- 'Tango'	CBod
- 'Werner Arends'	ECtt ELon GAbr LRHS MAvo MNrw MRav WCot WFar
'Copper Pennies'	CElw NEoE
'Coppertone'	CElw CWCL ELan EPri LPla LPot MHost MRav NBir NChi WCav XEll
'Coral Pearl' (Censation Series) (d) **new**	LCro LOPS
'Cosmopolitan' (Cocktails Series)	Widely available
'Cotton Candy'	MHost NEoE
'Country Rock' **new**	NEoE
'Country Rock Star'	WFar
'Cream Crackers'	NEoE WBrk
'Cumbrian Candy'	NEoE
'Cumbrian Cheddar'	NEoE
'Cumbrian Cherrypie'	NEoE WFar
'Cumbrian Cherrytart' **new**	NEoE
'Cumbrian Cream'	NEoE
'Custard Tart'	NEoE
'Dark and Stormy' (Cocktails Series)	MAvo
'Dawn'	NEoE SBri SMHy
'Deano's Delight'	NEoE
'Diamond White'	EWhm
'Diana'	ELon MNrw NLar
'Dingle Apricot'	ECtt GAbr MNrw MRav NBir
'Dolly North' (d)	CElw CWCL EBee EPPr EWhm GWyn MHol MHost MRav MSpe NBro NGdn SHar WCAu WHal XEll
'Double Sunrise' (d)	WFar
'East of Eden'	LPot NEoE
'Eden Apricot' **new**	NEoE
'Eden Rising'	NEoE
'Eden Valley Angel'	NChi NEoE WWtn
'Eden Valley Elf'	NEoE
'El Wano'	NEoE
'Elworthy Amber'	CElw
'Emory Quinn'	CFis EWes LRHS NEoE NSti WHrl
'Fancy Frills'	CElw ECtt MAvo WHoo
'Farmer John Cross'	CAby CElw EBee ECtt ELon EPPr EPri EShb GBin MBriF MTis NLar WFar WHal WWtn
'Feuermeer'	CElw NLar
'Fire Opal' (d) ♀H7	CElw CWCL EAJP GWyn MAvo MHost MNrw NBir
'Fire Storm'PBR	CBod CBre CMea CWGN EBee ECtt EHyd EPfP GAbr GBin LRHS LSun MNrw MPnt MSCN MTis NDov NGBl NLar SEdd SPad SPalm SPoG SRms WCot WFar WGrn WMal
'Fireball'	CBod CWCL ECtt EShb LRHS MArl MHost NLar
'Firefinch'	NEoE
'Flame'	NLar
'Flames of Passion'PBR	Widely available
'Flower of Darkness'	NEoE
'Georgenberg'	CRos ECtt EPfP EPri GMaP LRHS MBel MCot MHer MNrw NBir NGdn NHol NLar NRHS NWad SPer SRms SWvt WCAu WFar
'Gimlet' (Cocktails Series)	CWGN ECtt ELon EMor EShb GBin GPSL NLar WTyc XEll
'Golden Joy'	CDor CElw MAvo MNrw NEoE WHoo
'Goldfinch'	WFar
'Hannay's'	EBee MHCG MNrw MSpe NEoE SBri SHar SPtp
'Harvest Moon'	NEoE
'Hearts in Amber'	NEoE WFar
'Herterton Lemon'	CElw WCot
'Herterton Primrose'	CCBP CElw CWCL ECtt EPPr LLWG MHost MNrw NBPC NBid NSti SBri WBor WFar WHal WHoo
'Hilltop Beacon' (d)	CDor CElw EBee LPla MHCG NEoE NLar SGro WFar WGoo WHoo
* ***hybridum luteum***	NSti
× ***intermedium***	CBre GPSL NGdn NLar
- 'Diane'	NChi
- 'Hofrennydd'	NWad
'Jolly Roger'	EBee MHost NEoE NWad
'Karlskaer'	CBod CWCL ECtt EHyd EWes GQue LPla LRHS MBel MBow MHost MNrw NBPC NGdn NLar NRHS WFar WGwG WWtn

	'Lady Stratheden' (d) ♀H7	Widely available
	'Lemon Delight'	CDor CElw LEdu MAvo WMal
	'Lemon Drops'	Widely available
	'Limoncello'	SHeu
	'Lionel Cox'	CWCL ELan GAbr GMaP MBow MCot MHost MRav NBir NBro NChi NGdn NLar SGro SRms WFar
	'Lipstick Sunset'	NEoE
	'Lisanne'	CElw CSam CWCL EAJP EBee GBin GKev IPot MAvo MBel MHost MNrw MTis NDov NLar SHar SMHy SPtp WCAu WFar
	'Little Lottie'	NEoE
	'Little Twister'	NEoE
	'Maddy Prior'	NEoE
	magellanicum	CSpe EWes NBre NLar WMal
	'Magic Toybox'	NEoE
	'Mai Tai'PBR (Cocktails Series)	Widely available
	'Mandarin' (d)	SHar WMal
	'Mango'	NDov
	'Mango Lassi'	CElw ECtt EShb MSCN MTis NEoE NLar SHar WCAu WHoo
	'Marmalade'	ECtt EHyd EWhm GAbr LLWG LPla LRHS MNrw MRav NEoE NLar NRHS SHar SMHy SSut WFar WHrl WKif WOut
	'McClure's Magic'	NEoE
§	***montanum*** ♀H6	CRos EBee EHyd GLog LRHS MMuc NBir NRHS NRya NSla SRms XLum
	'Moonlight Serenade'	CBod CWCL EBee ECtt EHyd EMor LRHS MHost NEoE NRHS WWtn
	'Moorland Sorbet'	WFar
	'Mr Mojo' **new**	NEoE
	'Mrs J. Bradshaw' (d) ♀H7	Widely available
	'Mrs W. Moore'	CBre CElw CWCL EBee EShb GAbr MNrw MRav NBPC NBir NBro NChi NLar NQui
	'Nordek'	CElw ECha ECtt GAbr GQue LRHS MCot MNrw MRav NGdn SPoG WWtn
	'Norwell Lemon Lamp'	MNrw WMal
	'Onslow Cream'	LPla
	'Peach Daiquiri' (Cocktails Series) **new**	ECul
	'Peachy Proud'	NEoE
	'Pear Drops'	NEoE
	'Pink Fluffy' (Censation Series) **new**	IPot MHol
	'Pink Frills'	CBod CElw CWCL ECtt EPPr EPri EWTr EWes EWhm GAbr GBin GQue LEdu LLWG MAvo MHost MPnt MRav NBPC NLar SGbt SMHy SPtp WOut
	'Pink Petticoats'	MHol WHoo
	'Poco'	CRos CWCL EBee ECtt EHyd EPfP EWes EWhm GBin LRHS MAvo MHost MNrw MSpe NEoE NRHS
	'Prairie Dancer'	NEoE
	'Present'	ECtt NBre NChi
	'Primrose'	EWhm NBro NEoE NGdn NLar
	'Primrose Cottage'	EBee LRHS
	'Prince of Orange' (d)	CElw CRos EHyd GAbr LRHS MNrw MRav NBre NRHS SWvt WFar
	'Prinses Juliana'	Widely available
	'Proud's Pearl' **new**	WMal
*	***pseudococcineum***	EHyd LRHS
	pyrenaicum	GKev NBre
I	'Rearsby Hybrid'	CElw MRav SPlb

	'Red Wings' (d)	CElw CWCL EWTr GMaP GWyn ILea LRHS MBel MCot MHost MNrw MRav NBir SHar WGwG
	'Rijnstroom'	EPPr MNrw NBPC SHar WFar
	'Rise and Shine'	NEoE
	rivale	Widely available
	- from Switzerland	NWad
	- 'Album'	Widely available
	- 'Barbra Lawton'	LEdu NBPC SHar
	- 'Cream Drop'	LLWG MCot NChi SHar
	- 'Leonard's Variety'	Widely available
	- 'Marika'	EBee GBin
	- 'Marmalade'	CBre CElw CWCL IPot MBriF MPnt NBPC NChi WCav
	- 'Salmon Bells'	XEll
	- 'Snowflake'	CDor CElw MAvo MSpe NChi NEoE NLar
	'Roger's Ragamuffin'	NEoE
	'Roger's Rebellion'	NEoE WFar
	'Rubin'	EBee GBin NDov NSti SGro
	'Rusty Young'	CBod CWCL EBee ECtt EMor EWes GBee LRHS MBel MHost MNrw NEoE NRHS SGbt WWtn
	'Savanna Sunrise'	MNrw
	'Savanna Sunset'	EBee ECtt EHyd EWes LRHS MBel MHer MHost NEoE NRHS WHrl
	'Scarlet Tempest'	CRos CSpe CWCL CWGN EHyd EMor LBuc LCro LOPS LRHS MAvo MBel MHol MHost MMrt NRHS NSti SHar SMad SPoG WNPC WTor
	'Sea Breeze' (Cocktails Series)	SBri
	'Shannara' (d) **new**	CElw
	'Sigiswang'	ELon LEdu MNrw MRav WFar WMal
	'Snowdrop' **new**	MHost
	'Spanish Fly' (Cocktails Series)	LSou
	'Spellbound' **new**	NEoE
	'Spider Muffin'	NEoE
	'Stacey Proud' **new**	NEoE
	'Stacey's Sunrise'	CBod ECtt EHyd EMor EWes LRHS MBel MHCG MNrw NEoE NLar NRHS SPoG
	'Star of Bethlehem'	NEoE
	'Starker's Magnificum'	MAvo WCot
	'Stevie Nicks'	MBriF NEoE
	'Strawberries and Cream'	NEoE
	'Sundrud Star'	MHost NEoE
	'Sunkissed Lime'PBR	ECtt EMor LSou MHost MPnt NEoE
	'Sunrise' (d)	EHyd EMor LRHS MHol MSCN NRHS
	'Sweet Angel Dar'	NEoE
	'Sweet Stacey' **new**	MHost
	'Tangerine'	EPri MRav
	'Tango Dream'	LRHS
	'Tequila Sunrise' (Cocktails Series)	CBcs CBod CRos CWGN EBee ECtt EHyd ELan EMor EPfP ILea IPot LRHS MHol MHost MNrw MPnt MSCN MTis NDov NEoE NGdn NHpl NRHS SCob SPad SPalm WCAu
	'The Giant Peach' **new**	NEoE
	'Tinkerbell'	NEoE
	× ***tirolense***	EBee NBre
	'Toast of Cumbria'	NEoE
	'Toffee Apples'	NEoE
	'Tosai' **new**	NEoE
	'Totally Tangerine'PBR	Widely available
	triflorum	CBod CElw CSpe CWCL EMor EWes GEdr LEdu MHer MNrw NDov NGrd SHar SPhx

- SDR 8121	GKev
- var. ***campanulatum***	NEoE
- 'Peace Pipe'	MNrw
'Turbango'	NEoE
'Turbango Twister'	NEoE
'Turnpike Tales'	NEoE
'Turnpike Troubadour'	NEoE
'Tutti Frutti'	MAvo
'Two Tone Pearl' (Censation Series) (d) **new**	CWGN
urbanum	ENfk WHer
- 'Corinne Tremaine'	WHer
'Wet Kiss' (Cocktails Series)	NDov SHeu
'Wyn's Wish'	NEoE

Gevuina (*Proteaceae*)

avellana	WPGP

Gilia (*Polemoniaceae*)

achilleifolia	CSpe SPhx

Gillenia (*Rosaceae*)

stipulata	IPot LEdu LRHS MNrw SHar SPhx WPGP
trifoliata ♀H7	Widely available
- 'Pink Profusion'	CBod CKno CMiW CSpe CWCL EBee GBin IPot LPla MBel MHol MNHC MNrw NDov NLar SCob WCAu WCot WFar WGrn

Ginkgo ✿ (*Ginkgoaceae*)

biloba	Widely available
- B&SWJ 8753	WCru
- 'Anny's Dwarf'	MAsh MBlu NLar
- 'Autumn Gold' (m) ♀H6	CBcs CEnd CMCN ECrN ELan MBlu MGos MPkF SLim WMat
- 'Barabits' Fastigiata'	LRHS MBlu SMad
- 'Barabits' Nana'	MBlu
- 'Beijing Gold'	MBlu MPkF NLar SAko SMad WPGP XLot
- 'Blagon'	SGol
- 'Boleslaw Chrobry'	NLar
- 'Buddy' **new**	SLim
- 'California Sunset'	MBlu MMrt NLar SLim
- 'Chase Manhattan'	MPkF
- 'Chotek'	MBlu SMad
- 'Chris's Dwarf'	LRHS NLar
- 'David'	SLim
- 'Eastern Star' (f)	CAgr
- 'Everton Broom'	CMac CMen SLim SRms WHwl
- 'Fabulous Underwear' **new**	SLim
- 'Fairmount' (m)	MBlu NLar
- 'Fastigiata' (m)	CMCN EPfP LMaj MBlu SGsty SMad
- 'Fastigiata Blagon' **new**	CCVT LMaj
- 'Finger'	SLim
- 'Globosa'	MBlu
- 'Gnome'	LSRN MPkF
- 'Golden Dragon'	MBlu
- 'Golden Globe'	MPkF
- 'Gresham'	MPkF
- 'Horizontalis'	MBlu
- 'Jade Butterflies' ♀H6	MBlu MPkF NLar SLim
- 'Jehosaphat'	MBlu
- 'Jerry Vercade'	MPkF
- 'King of Dongting' (f)	CAgr MBlu SLim
- 'Lakeview' (m)	MPkF
- 'Landliebe'	MBlu
- 'Lil' Matthew' **new**	SLim
- 'Long March'	CAgr
- 'Magyar'	MBlu
- 'Mariken' ♀H6	CWGN ELan EPfP LMaj MGil MPkF SLim
- 'Mayfield' (m)	MBlu NLar SMad
- 'McFarland'	CAgr
- 'Menhir' PBR	CBcs EBee ELan EPfP ILea LRHS MMrt MPkF WCot WHwl
- 'Obelisk'	SGsty SLim
- Ohazuki Group (f)	CAgr
- Pendula Group	CEnd CMCN EBee MBlu MPkF SGol WMat
- 'Princeton Sentry' (m) ♀H6	ELan EPfP LRHS MBlu
- 'Robbie's Twist'	MPkF NLar SLim
- 'Saratoga' (m) ♀H6	CAgr CBcs CEnd CMCN EBee EPfP ESwi LRHS MBlu MPkF SAko SLim SRms WMat
- 'Shangri-La' (m)	MBlu
- 'Sinclair'	MPkF
- 'Survivor'	SMad
- 'Talon Variegated' (v) **new**	MBlu
- 'Thelma'	SLim
- 'Tit'	CEnd CMCN EPfP MBlu MPkF SLim
- 'Tremonia'	CMCN EPfP MBlu MPkF SAko
- 'Troll' ♀H6	LRHS MAsh MBlu MGil SCoo SLim SMad SPoG WHwl XLot
- 'Tubifolia'	CMCN ESwi MBlu MPkF NLar SLim SMad WPGP
- 'Umbrella'	SLim
- Variegata Group (v)	MPkF
- 'W.B.'	MPkF

ginseng see *Panax ginseng*

Gladiolus (*Iridaceae*)

'Adi'	WCot
'Ajax'	WPhe
'Akuta' (M/E)	CGrW
'Alba' (N)	LRHS WPhe
'Alice' (Min)	ERCP
'Amanda Mahy' (N)	GKev WMal WPhe
'Amsterdam' (G)	CGrW
angustus L.	CGrW
antakiensis	CPou
'Antica' (L)	WPhe
'Astarte' (L)	WPhe
'Atom' (S/P)	CAvo CBro CGrW GKev SDeJ WMal WPhe
aurantiacus	WCot
'Avalanche' (B)	SDeJ
'Azurro' (M) **new**	WPhe
'Bach' (L) **new**	WPhe
Barnard hybrids	CGrW
'Beautiful Angel'	CGrW
'Beauty Bride' (L)	CGrW
'Big Boss' (G)	CGrW
'Black Jack' (L)	SDeJ
'Black Surprise'	WPhe
'Blue Frost' (L)	SDeJ
'Blue Mountain'	WPhe
'Bocelli' (M) **new**	WPhe
'Bonfire' (G)	CGrW WPhe
'Boone'	GBin
'Brahms' (L) **new**	WPhe
byzantinus	see *G. communis* subsp. *byzantinus*
callianthus	see *G. murielae*
cardinalis	CPrp CSpe IBlr LEdu WCru
'Careless' (L) **new**	WPhe
carinatus	CGrW

carinatus* × *orchidiflorus	WCot
'Carine' (N)	GKev SDeJ WPhe
carmineus	CGrW WCot
carneus	CBro CGrW EPot SDeJ
- 'Georgina'	CGrW
'Carolina Primrose'	GBin
caucasicus	GKev
'Charm' (N/Tub)	EShb LEdu SDeJ WPhe
'Charming Beauty' (Tub)	GKev LRHS SDeJ WPhe
'Charming Lady' (Tub)	WPhe
'Chopin' (L) new	WPhe
citrinus	see *G. trichonemifolius*
'Claudia' (N)	CGrW
'Columbine' (P)	SDeJ
× ***colvillii*** 'Albus'	ERCP
- 'Galaxian'	GKev
communis	WCot
§ - subsp. ***byzantinus*** ♀H5	Widely available
'Coral Lace' (L)	SDeJ
'Côte d'Azur' (G)	SDeJ
crassifolius	CPbh
'Cream Perfection' (L)	CGrW SDeJ WPhe
'Creamy Yellow' (S)	CGrW
cruentus	CGrW WCot
§ ***dalenii***	CAby CExl CPbh CPou CSam IBlr LEdu SMad
- 'Apricot Delight' (v)	IBlr
- 'Boone'	WCot
- 'Citrone Spectrum' (v)	IBlr
§ - subsp. ***dalenii***	CBor CPbh CPrp IBlr WCot
- - 'Spinners'	EBee IBlr
- 'Guardsman' (v)	IBlr
'Dark Ruby' (*papilio* hybrid)	LEdu
'David Hills' (*papilio* hybrid)	CAvo CBro CDor CMea CPrp ECha SMHy WCot WSHC
'Delirium'	CGrW
'Dion' (M)	CGrW
ecklonii	CPbh
- spotted	SBrt
'Elvira' (N)	WMal WPhe
'Emerald Spring' (S)	WCot
'Espresso'[PBR] (S) new	ERCP
'Esta Bonita' (G)	CGrW WPhe
'Evergreen'	ERCP
'Extasy'[PBR] (L)	CGrW
'Far West' (L)	ERCP
'Farandole' (S)	SDeJ
'Fidelio' (L)	SDeJ
'Fiorentina' (L)	ERCP SDeJ
'Flame' new	WPhe
flanaganii	CAby CBor CBro CExl CPBP CPbh CSpe EBee EPot EPri GEdr GKev NHpl NSla SBrt WAbe WHil WMal WPav
'Flevo Bambino' (S)	EPri
'Flevo Cool' (S) new	CAvo
'Flevo Dancer' (S)	CGrW
'Flevo Laguna' (S)	CAvo
'Flevo Souvenir'[PBR] (L)	CGrW
'Flevo Spirit' (L)	CGrW
'Flevo Vito' (Min)	CAvo
floribundus subsp. ***fasciatus***	CGrW
'Fortarosa' (L)	WPhe
fourcadei	CGrW
'French Silk' (L)	CGrW
× ***gandavensis*** hort.	WCot
garnieri	see *G. dalenii* subsp. *dalenii*
geardii	WCot
'Gold Struck' (L)	CGrW
grandis	see *G. liliaceus*
'Green Star' (L)	CGrW LCro LOPS SDeJ WPhe
'Greyhound' (L) new	WPhe
gueinzii	CGrW
'Halley' (N)	GKev WPhe
'Hansnett'	WCot
'Happy Weekend' (L)	SDeJ
'Haydn' (L) new	WPhe
'Himalaya' (L) new	WPhe
'Holland Pearl' (B)	SDeJ
'Huron Silk' (L)	CGrW
huttonii	CGrW
huttonii* × *tristis	CPou
huttonii* × *tristis var. ***concolor***	WCot
'Ibadan'[PBR] (L)	CGrW
illyricus	CSam GKev SPlb
imbricatus	GKev MHer
'Imperialis'	IBlr
'Impressive' (N)	EMor GKev SDeJ WPhe
'Indian Summer'[PBR] (L)	ERCP WPhe
'Invitation'	SDeJ
§ ***italicus***	CGrW CMea GKev LRHS MHer
'Jacksonville Gold' (L)	SDeJ
'Jester' (L)	SDeJ
'Judy'[PBR] (M) new	WPhe
'Karaoke' (L) new	WPhe
'Kazimir' (L)	WPhe
'Lakeland'[PBR] (L) new	WPhe
'Las Vegas' (P)	CGrW WPhe
'Lemon Drop' (S)	CGrW
'Lennon' (L) new	WPhe
§ ***liliaceus***	CGrW
'Lucifer'[PBR] (L)	WPhe
'Mademoiselle de Paris'	CBro
'Magma' (L)	WPhe
'Mantovani' (L) new	WPhe
'Marina' (P)	WMal
'Matanzas' (M) new	WPhe
'Match Point' (L)	SDeJ
'Messina' (M) new	WPhe
'Mexico' (L)	SDeJ
miniatus	WCot
'Mirella' (N)	CAvo GKev WPhe
'Modena' (M) new	WPhe
'Mon Amour'[PBR] (L)	SDeJ WPhe
'Monsieur Piquet' (P)	EPri WCot
'Mount Everest' new	WPhe
§ ***murielae*** ♀H3	CAby CAvo CBod CBro CCBP CGrW CMea CRos EHyd ERCP EShb GBin GKev GWyn LCro LOPS LRHS MCot NRHS SCoo SDeJ SDir SPer SPlb SRms WCFE WHal WHil
'Mylena' (M) new	WPhe
natalensis	see *G. dalenii*
'Natan' (L)	WCot
'Nathalie' (N)	CAvo SDeJ WOut WPhe
'Nijmegen' (L) new	WPhe
'Nova Lux' (L)	SDeJ SDir
'Nymph' (N)	CAvo EMor GKev LCro LEdu LOPS MBow NBir SDeJ WPhe
'Oasis'[PBR] (G)	CGrW
ochroleucus	WHil
§ ***oppositiflorus***	CPbh CSpe EBee IBlr LEdu SPlb
- subsp. ***salmoneus***	see *G. oppositiflorus*
'Orangerie' (L) new	WPhe
orchidiflorus	CGrW
'Oscar' (G)	ERCP SDeJ
papilio	Widely available

§	- Purpureoauratus Group	CBro CSam SRms WSHC
	- yellow-flowered	CMea SMad
	'Passos'[PBR] (S)	ERCP
	'Peach Blossom' (N)	IBlr WCot
	'Penny Lane' (M) **new**	WPhe
	'Pescara' (M) **new**	WPhe
	'Peter Pears' (L)	ERCP SDeJ SDir
	'Phyllis M' (L)	CGrW
	Pilbeam hybrids	CGrW WCot
	'Pink Lady' (L)	SDeJ
	'Plum Tart' (L)	LCro LOPS SDeJ
	'Pop Art'	SDeJ
	'Prima Verde' (L) **new**	WPhe
	primulinus	see *G. dalenii*
	'Prins Claus' (N)	EShb GKev SDeJ SDir WPhe
	'Priscilla' (L)	SDeJ SDir
	'Purple Flora'	ERCP
	'Purple Mate'	LCro LOPS
	'Purple Prince' (M)	CGrW
	purple-striped **new**	WHil
	purpureoauratus	see *G. papilio* Purpureoauratus Group
	'Raspberry Sorbet' (S) **new**	WPhe
	recurvus	CGrW
	'Rigoletto' (L) **new**	WPhe
	'Robinetta' (*recurvus* hybrid) 🏆H3	GKev LCro LOPS LRHS MBow SDeJ WPhe
	'Rosalina' (L) **new**	WPhe
	'Rotary'[PBR] (L)	CGrW WPhe
	'Roussel' (L) **new**	WPhe
	'Ruby' (*papilio* hybrid)	Widely available
	'Ruth Ann'	CGrW
	'Salmon Star' (L) **new**	WPhe
	'San Siro'[PBR] (M) **new**	WPhe
	saundersii	LEdu
	segetum	see *G. italicus*
	'Slick Chick' (S)	CGrW
	'Sogno' (M) **new**	WPhe
	'Solveiga' (L/E)	CGrW
	'Sophie'[PBR] (L)	CGrW
	'Sourire' (S)	SDeJ
	'Spic and Span' (L)	SDeJ
	splendens	CGrW
	stefaniae	CGrW
	'Stiena' (L)	CGrW
	'Sugar Plum' **new**	ERCP
	'Terry' (G)	CGrW
	'Thalia'	WPhe
	'That's Love' (L)	SDeJ
	'The Bride'	CAvo CBro EBee GBin GWyn ITim LCro LOPS LSRN MPie SDeJ SDir WOut
	'Trader Horn' (G)	CGrW
§	***trichonemifolius***	CGrW GKev
	tristis	CAvo CBro CElw CGrW CMea CPou CSpe ELon MHer SMHy
	- var. ***concolor***	CGrW CPbh CPou CPrp WCot
	undulatus	CGrW WCot
	uysiae	CGrW
	vandermerwei	CGrW
	'Vasto' (M) **new**	WPhe
	'Venezia' (M) **new**	WPhe
	venustus	CGrW CPbh
	'Vesuvio' (L)	WPhe
	'Violetta' (M)	CGrW
	'Vivaldi' (L) **new**	WPhe
	'Volcano' (N)	WPhe
	'Wagner' **new**	WPhe
	watermeyeri	CPbh WHil
	'White Prosperity' (L)	ERCP LCro LOPS
	'Wine and Roses' (L)	SDir
	woodii	WCot
	'Yellow Star' (L) **new**	WPhe
	'Zamora' (L)	CGrW
	'Ziporra' (S)	EPri
	'Zizanie' (L)	SDeJ

Glandularia (*Verbenaceae*)

	'Abbeville' **new**	WMal
	(Aztec Series) AZTEC PEARL ('Balazpearl'[PBR])	SCoo
	- AZTEC RED ('Balazred')	SCoo
	- AZTEC SILVER MAGIC ('Balazsilma'[PBR]) 🏆H2	MBros MPri SCoo
	'Blue Prince'	CSpe
	'Boughton House'	SBut
	canadensis	CElw
	- 'Perfecta'	WCot
§	'Claret' 🏆H3	CBod CMac CRos CSpe EBee ECtt EHyd ELan EPfP LCro LOPS LRHS LSRN NRHS SBut SCoo SPhx SPoG
	corymbosa	CBod ECha LRHS SPer SPhx WHoo WSHC
	- 'Gravetye'	LPot
	'Edith Eddleman'	CMac CRos CWGN EHyd EPfP LRHS NRHS SPoG
	elegans	NDov
	ENDURASCAPE BLUE ('Balendlu') **new**	MPri
	ESTRELLA VOODOO RED STAR ('Wesverevoo'[PBR])	LSou
	'Hammerstein Pink'	EBee EHyd EPfP
	'Homestead Purple'	CMac CMea CRos EBee EHyd ELan EPfP EShb GBin LCro LOPS LRHS NRHS SDix SRkn SRms SWvt WOld
	'Jennys' Wine'	see *G.* 'Claret'
	'La France'	CRos ECha EHyd EPfP LRHS NRHS SMHy SPhx SPoG
	'Little Annie'	CBod MPnt WGrn
	'Lois' Ruby'	see *G.* 'Claret'
	'Merci' **new**	NDov
§	***peruviana***	CPBP EBou EHyd LRHS NRHS SRms XLum
	- ENDURASCAPE PINK BICOLOR ('Balendpibi') (Endurascape Series) 🏆H2	MPri
	'Pink Parfait'	EPfP
	platensis	ELan
§	Quartz Series 🏆H2	MBros MPri
	- 'Quartz Red Polka Dot'	EPfP
	SEABROOK'S LAVENDER ('Sealav'[PBR])	EHyd EPfP LRHS NRHS SCoo SHar SRkn SRms SWvt
	(Showboat Series) 'Showboat Magenta' **new**	LSou
	- 'Showboat Midnight' **new**	LSou
	- 'Showboat Salmon' **new**	LSou
	- 'Showboat White' **new**	LSou
§	'Sissinghurst' 🏆H3	CSam ECtt SDix SRms
	'Sparkle Purple Blues'	MPri
	'Strawberry Kiss'	EPfP SPoG
	'Tenerife'	see *G.* 'Sissinghurst'
	tenuisecta	CBod
	VECTURA LAVENDER (Vectura Series)	EHyd NRHS
	(Vepita Series) VEPITA BLUE VIOLET ('Invebluvio'[PBR])	MHol
	- VEPITA HOT PINK	MPri

Glaucidium (*Ranunculaceae*)

palmatum ♀H5	CExl EWld GEdr GKev NHpl NSla WCru WFar
- 'Album'	see *G. palmatum* var. *leucanthum*
§ - var. ***leucanthum***	GEdr GKev NHpl

Glaucium (*Papaveraceae*)

§ ***corniculatum***	CAby CRos CSpe EHyd EPfP LRHS NRHS SPhx
flavum	CSpe ECha LRHS MHer SPhx WHer XSen
- ***aurantiacum***	see *G. flavum* f. *fulvum*
§ - f. ***fulvum***	ECha MMuc MNrw SEND SPhx WHil
- orange-flowered	see *G. flavum* f. *fulvum*
- red-flowered	see *G. corniculatum*
grandiflorum	SPhx
phoenicium	see *G. corniculatum*

Glaucosciadium (*Apiaceae*)

cordifolium	WCot
- PAB 9003	LEdu
- from Hatay, Turkey	WCot

Glebionis (*Asteraceae*)

coronaria	MNHC SRms
§ ***segetum***	CHab LCro LOPS MBow

Glechoma (*Lamiaceae*)

hederacea	GPoy NMir WHer
§ - 'Variegata' (v)	EShb MPri SPer XLum

Gleditsia (*Caesalpiniaceae*)

caspia	LEdu SMad
- NJM 13.019	WPGP
japonica	ITim NLar
koraiensis	LEdu
- B&SWJ 12569	WCru
triacanthos	SPlb WTSh
- 'Calhoun'	CAgr
- 'Elegantissima' (v)	LMaj SPer
- 'Emerald Cascade'	CEnd
- f. ***inermis*** SPECTRUM ('Speczam')	MAsh
- - 'Sunburst'	Widely available
- 'Millwood'	CAgr
- 'Rubylace'	CCVT CEnd CMCN CMac ECrN ELan LMaj MAsh MBlu MGos MRav MSwo SGol SMad SPer WMat
- 'Skyline'	LMaj

Globba ✿ (*Zingiberaceae*)

racemosa var. ***hookeri*** HWJCM 471	ESwi WCru WSHC
radicalis	MHid WPGP

Globularia (*Plantaginaceae*)

bellidifolia	see *G. meridionalis*
cordifolia ♀H5	CSma EBou EHyd EPot GEdr GKev ITim LRHS NBir NHpl NRHS SHar SRms
- RCB UA 30	WCot
§ ***meridionalis***	CAby CBod EPot EWes
- 'Blue Bonnets'	GEdr
- 'Hort's Variety'	CTri NSla WAbe
nana	see *G. repens*
nudicaulis	CMea EPot GEdr GKev IMou SWvt
punctata	SRms WFar
pygmaea	see *G. meridionalis*
§ ***repens***	CPla GEdr WAbe
trichosantha	GEdr MMuc SRms XSen
valentina	GEdr GKev
vulgaris	ITim XSen

Gloriosa (*Colchicaceae*)

lutea	see *G. superba* 'Lutea'
§ ***modesta***	GKev
rothschildiana	see *G. superba* 'Rothschildiana'
superba ♀H1c	GKev SDeJ SDir
- 'Carsonii'	GKev SDeJ
- 'Greenii'	GKev SDeJ SDir
§ - 'Lutea'	GKev SDeJ
§ - 'Rothschildiana'	CBcs CDoC CGrW GKev LCro LOPS SDeJ SDir SRms
- 'Rothschildiana Salmon'	GKev SDir
- 'Sparkling Jip'	GKev
- 'Sparkling Striped'	GKev
- 'Tricolor'	GKev SDir

Gloxinella (*Gesneriaceae*)

lindeniana	WDib

Gloxinia (*Gesneriaceae*)

'Defiance'	SDeJ
nematanthodes 'Evita'	EShb WCot WFar
sylvatica	EShb
- 'Bolivian Sunset'	WDib

Glumicalyx (*Scrophulariaceae*)

flanaganii	CPbh SPlb
goseloides	CPbh

Glyceria (*Poaceae*)

aquatica variegata	see *G. maxima* var. *variegata*
maxima	MMuc NPer SEND SPlb
§ - var. ***variegata*** (v)	CWat ECha ECrN EHyd ELan EPfP EWat GMaP LLWG LRHS MMuc NBir NGdn NRHS SEND SRms SVic WMAq XLum
spectabilis 'Variegata'	see *G. maxima* var. *variegata*

Glycyrrhiza (*Papilionaceae*)

echinata	CAgr
§ ***glabra***	CAgr CBod CCCN CHby CLau CSpe EMor ENfk GPoy MHer MNHC SPlb SRms WJek
glandulifera	see *G. glabra*
uralensis	ELan EPPr SPhx
yunnanensis	CSpe LPla MHer SDix SMHy

Glyptostrobus (*Cupressaceae*)

pensilis	CExl IDee WPGP
- 'Wooly Mammoth' **new**	SMad

Gmelina (*Lamiaceae*)

hystrix	CCCN

Gnaphalium (*Asteraceae*)

'Fairy Gold'	see *Helichrysum thianschanicum* 'Goldkind'
trinerve	see *Anaphalis trinervis*

Godetia see *Clarkia*

Goeppertia (*Marantaceae*)

§ ***argyrophylla*** 'Exotica'	XBlo
§ ***crocata*** ♀H1a	CDoC
- 'Tassmania'	LCro LOPS
'Freddie' **new**	CDoC

§ ***louisae*** 'Maui Queen'	CDoC XBlo
§ ***majestica*** ♀H1a	XBlo
§ ***makoyana*** ♀H1a	CDoC XBlo
§ ***picturata*** 'Argentea' ♀H1a	XBlo
§ ***roseopicta*** ♀H1a	XBlo
- 'Rosastar'	XBlo
§ ***rufibarba*** ♀H1a	XBlo
- 'Wavestar'	CDoC
veitchiana 'Medaillon'	LCro LOPS XBlo
warscewiczii	CDoC
'Whitestar' **new**	LCro LOPS
§ ***zebrina*** ♀H1a	XBlo
'Zoizia'	XBlo

goji berry see *Lycium barbarum*, *L. chinense*

Gomphocarpus ✿ (*Apocynaceae*)

§ ***fruticosus***	SVen
§ ***physocarpus***	CBod

Gompholobium (*Papilionaceae*)

scabrum	SPlb

Gomphostigma (*Scrophulariaceae*)

virgatum	CBod CCCN CExl CFis CSpe EPPr EPfP GMaP LLWG MCot MHol MMuc SMad SPhx SPlb WCFE WCot WFar WSHC
- 'White Candy'	GBin LRHS MGil MPkF SVen

Gomphrena (*Amaranthaceae*)

globosa	CCCN
- 'Lizard Light' **new**	CCCN

Goniolimon (*Plumbaginaceae*)

collinum **new**	GEdr
- 'Sea Spray'	EDAr
incanum 'Blue Diamond'	GJos NHpl WCot
§ ***tataricum***	GJos MMuc
§ - var. ***angustifolium***	SEND SRms

Goodia (*Papilionaceae*)

lotifolia	CCCN

gooseberry see *Ribes uva-crispa*; also AGM Fruit Section

× *Gordlinia* (*Theaceae*)

grandiflora **new**	MPkF

Gordonia (*Theaceae*)

axillaris	see *Polyspora axillaris*

Gorgonidium (*Araceae*)

intermedium	WCot

Gossypium (*Malvaceae*)

herbaceum	XAbr

granadilla see *Passiflora quadrangularis*

granadilla, purple see *Passiflora edulis*

granadilla, sweet see *Passiflora ligularis*

grape see *Vitis*; also AGM Fruit Section

grapefruit see *Citrus* × *aurantium* Grapefruit Group

Graptopetalum (*Crassulaceae*)

filiferum	SPlb
§ ***paraguayense***	SVen
- subsp. ***bernalense*** **new**	NWad

Graptopetalum × *Echeveria* see × *Graptoveria*

Graptopetalum × *Sedum* see × *Graptosedum*

× *Graptosedum* (*Crassulaceae*)

'Darley Sunshine'	NWad
'Vera Higgins'	SSim

× *Graptoveria* (*Crassulaceae*)

'Ghostly'	WCot

Gratiola (*Plantaginaceae*)

officinalis	CBod EHyd LLWG LRHS MHer

Greenovia (*Crassulaceae*)

aizoon	SPlb
§ ***aurea***	SPlb
diplocycla 'Gigantea'	SPlb

Grevillea (*Proteaceae*)

* ***alba*** S	Ele
alpina	WPGP
banksii 'Canberra Hybrid'	see *G.* 'Canberra Gem'
- var. ***forsteri***	SPlb
'Bronze Rambler'	CCCN
§ 'Canberra Gem' ♀H4	Widely available
'Clearview David'	CBod CCCN CDoC LEdu LRHS LSRN MMuc SEdd SLim SVen WLov
crithmifolia	SPlb
'Cvd White' **new**	CCCN
'Desert Flame'	see *G. rosmarinifolia* 'Desert Flame'
'Ivanhoe'	CCCN
johnsonii	LRHS
juniperina	CBcs CCCN CExl CMac EPfP SEle SLim SVen
- f. ***sulphurea***	CCCN CExl CTsd EBee ELon MGil MMuc SEdd SEle SPer SPlb WLov WSHC
'Lady O' **new**	CCCN
lanigera 'Mount Tamboritha'	CBcs CCCN CDoC CExl CMac CPbh CSde CTsd EBee EPfP IDee LRHS SEdd SEle SPad SPoG WCot WFar
- prostrate	WAbe WGrn
lavandulacea 'Black Range'	WCot
- 'Penola'	CCCN
leucopteris	SPlb
'Murray Valley Queen'	WCot WPGP
'Olympic Flame'	CBcs CBrac CCCN CCht CDoC CExl CRos CSBt CTrC CTsd EBee EPfP LRHS MGos MMuc NOra SAko SCob SEdd SEle SIvy SPoG WBor WGrn
paniculata	SPlb
'Pink Lady'	CBcs CCCN ELon EPfP LRHS
'Poorinda Constance'	WCot
'Poorinda Queen'	CCCN
robusta ♀H2	SPlb
'Robyn Gordon'	CCCN
'Rondeau'	CCCN

	rosmarinifolia ♀H4	CBcs CCCN CExl CMac CSBt CTri ELan GKin SArc SEle SLim SLon SPer SPlb SSta WFar
§	- 'Desert Flame'	CBcs CExl
	- 'Jenkinsii'	CCCN CCht CDoC CExl CMac CSBt ELan EPfP SEle SIvy SLim
§	× ***semperflorens***	CCCN CRos CSde EBee EHyd LRHS SPlb
	'Spider Man'	CCCN
	tolminsis	see *G.* × *semperflorens*
	victoriae	CBcs CCCN CCht CDoC CJun CTsd EBee EPfP LRHS MHtn SAko SChF SEdd SEle WCot WPGP
	- subsp. ***victoriae***	CExl
	- yellow-flowered	LRHS
	williamsonii	CBcs CCht LRHS SIvy

Grewia (*Malvaceae*)

occidentalis	LRHS

Greyia (*Melianthaceae*)

sutherlandii	SPlb

Griffinia (*Amaryllidaceae*)

rochae	GKev

Grindelia (*Asteraceae*)

§	***camporum***	SPlb
	chiloensis	CPBP SMad
	integrifolia	XLum
	robusta	see *G. camporum*

Griselinia ✿ (*Griseliniaceae*)

littoralis ♀H5	Widely available
- 'Bantry Bay' (v)	CCCN CSde EBee EHyd ELan LRHS MAsh SPer SPoG SWvt WFar
- 'Brodick Gold'	CExl ELon GKin
- 'Dixon's Cream' (v)	CBcs CCCN CMac CRos CSBt EHyd EPfP LRHS MRav SGol SLon SRms SVen
- 'Green Favor'	EBee
- GREEN HORIZON ('Whenuapai' PBR)	CBod ELan IBal LRHS SCob SLim SPer SPoG
- 'Green Jewel' (v)	CBod CCCN NLar
- 'Variegata' (v) ♀H4	Widely available
ruscifolia	LEdu
scandens	CCCN SEND WCot

guava, common see *Psidium guajava*

guava, purple or strawberry see *Psidium littorale* var. *longipes*

Guichenotia (*Sterculiaceae*)

macrantha	SPlb

Gunnera ✿ (*Gunneraceae*)

cordifolia	LLWG
densiflora	GEdr
hamiltonii	ECha EPot LEdu NBir SRms XLum
killipiana B&SWJ 9009	WCru
magellanica	Widely available
- (f)	SRms
- 'Osorno'	EBee
manicata	Widely available
perpensa	CBcs CBen CCCN EBee ESwi IMou WCot WFar
prorepens	CBct CBod CExl CMac CPla EBee ECha ELan EPot ILea NWad SRms WFar
saint-johnii B&SWJ 14708 **new**	WCru

Guzmania (*Bromeliaceae*)

dissitiflora	NCft

Gymnocarpium ✿ (*Woodsiaceae*)

dryopteris ♀H5	CLAP EFer EShb GKev GMaP GWyn ISha WAbe WCot WFib WShi
- PAB 1757	LEdu
- PAB 8351	LEdu
- 'Plumosum' ♀H5	CBod CLAP CRos CWCL EHyd EMor LEdu LRHS MAsh NLar NRHS WFar WFib WHal
oyamense ♀H5	EShb SPlb
robertianum	EFer EWld

Gymnocladus (*Caesalpiniaceae*)

chinensis	WPGP
dioica	CBcs CLnd CMCN ELan EPfP LEdu MBlu SMad SPer WPGP WTSh

Gymnospermium (*Berberidaceae*)

§	***albertii***	GKev

Gynandriris see *Moraea*

Gynerium (*Poaceae*)

argenteum	see *Cortaderia selloana*

Gynostemma (*Cucurbitaceae*)

pentaphyllum	CAgr EBee LEdu SRms WJek
- B&SWJ 570	WCru

Gynura (*Asteraceae*)

§	***aurantiaca*** 'Purple Passion' ♀H1b	EShb
	sarmentosa misapplied	see *G. aurantiaca* 'Purple Passion'

Gypsophila (*Caryophyllaceae*)

	aretioides	EHyd EPot GKev LRHS NRHS NSla SPlb WAbe
§	- 'Caucasica'	CPBP
	- 'Compacta'	see *G. aretioides* 'Caucasica'
	cerastioides	CMea CTri EBou ECtt EDAr EHyd EMor EPfP EPot GAbr GWyn ITim LRHS MHol NGdn NHpl NLar NRHS NSla SPlb SRms SWvt WFar WHoo WIce XLum
	- 'Rosy Stripe'	GKev
	- silver variegated (v)	EMor MHol
	dubia	see *G. repens* 'Dubia'
	elegans	SVic
	fastigiata 'Silverstar'	CRos EHyd EPfP LRHS NRHS
	Festival Series (d)	CRos
	- 'Festival'	SGbt
	- 'Festival Pink Lady'	WFar
	gracilescens	see *G. tenuifolia*
	'Jolien' (v)	WIce
	muralis 'Garden Bride'	SWvt
	- 'Gypsy Deep Rose'	EHyd ELan EPfP LRHS NRHS
	- 'Gypsy Pink' (d)	SWvt
	NEW LOVE ('Dangypfirm' PBR)	WTyc
	pacifica	GQue
	paniculata	CBod MHol MRav SRms XLum
	- 'Bristol Fairy' (d)	CSBt ECha ELan EPfP GMaP LRHS NLar SCob SHar SPad SPoG SWvt WCAu WFar XLum
	- 'Compacta Plena' (d)	ECtt EPfP GMaP MRav NDov NGdn SGbt SRms

- double white-flowered (d)	XLum
- 'Flamingo' (d)	CBcs ECha EHyd LRHS NLar SCob SPer SWvt XLum
- 'Pacific Pink'	EBee
- 'Perfect Alba'	LRHS
- 'Perfekta'	CBcs SPer
- 'Pink Star' (d)	ECtt
§ - 'Schneeflocke' (d)	CBod CSpe EBou LBuc MHol SRms
- SNOWFLAKE	see *G. paniculata* 'Schneeflocke'
- SUMMER SPARKLES ('Esm Chispa'PBR)	CRos EHyd LRHS NRHS
- WHITE FIRE ('Dangypwhifa')	EBee
'Pink Festival' (Festival Series) (d)	CDor ECha ECtt EHyd EPfP LRHS NRHS SHar SPoG
repens ♀H5	ECtt GBin GJos MAsh SPlb SWvt WFar XLum XSen
- dark pink-flowered	CPBP
- 'Dorothy Teacher'	CMea CSma ECtt MAsh WFar
§ - 'Dubia'	EBou ECha EPot MAsh MHer NLar SRms WIce WSHC
- 'Filou Rose'	EBou EDAr GJos
- 'Filou White'	LBuc
- 'Fratensis'	WIce
- PINK BEAUTY	see *G. repens* 'Rosa Schönheit'
§ - 'Rosa Schönheit'	CMea ECha ECtt EPot NDov SPer WFar XLum
- 'Rosea'	CTri EBee EBou ECtt EDAr ELan EPfP GJos GMaP ITim MHol MMuc NGdn NHpl NSla SBut SEND SPer SPoG SRms SWvt WFar WHoo WIce XLum
- 'Ruby Gems' **new**	CBor WFar
- 'Silver Carpet' (v)	EBee ELan
- white-flowered	CMea NGdn SWvt WFar
§ 'Rosenschleier' (d) ♀H6	CBod CDor CMea EBee ECha ECtt ELan EPfP LCro LOPS MBel MRav NDov NGdn SGbt SPer SRms SWvt WCAu WHoo XLum
I 'Rosenschleier Variegata' (v)	EBee ELan EPfP
'Rosy Veil'	see *G.* 'Rosenschleier'
§ ***tenuifolia***	CPBP EPot GMaP ITim NHpl
VEIL OF ROSES	see *G.* 'Rosenschleier'
'White Festival'PBR (Festival Series) (d)	EHyd EPfP LRHS NRHS SHar SPoG WTor

H

Haberlea (*Gesneriaceae*)

ferdinandi-coburgii	GEdr
- 'Connie Davidson'	EBee GEdr GKev
rhodopensis ♀H5	ELan EPPr GEdr IMou NHar NHpl NSla SRms WAbe WCot WKif WThu XLum
- 'Virginalis'	CElw GEdr NSla WAbe WThu

Hablitzia (*Amaranthaceae*)

tamnoides	CAgr

Habranthus (*Amaryllidaceae*)

andersonii	see *H. tubispathus*
brachyandrus	SRms WCot
gracilifolius	WAbe
martinezii ♀H2	CPBP
§ ***robustus*** ♀H2	CBor CCCN CExl EPot EShb GKev
§ ***tubispathus*** ♀H2	CPla GKev SBrt WHil

Hacquetia (*Apiaceae*)

epipactis ♀H7	Widely available
- 'Harry Foley' (v)	NWad
§ - 'Thor' (v)	ECha EWes GBin GEdr MNrw NBir NGrd WAbe
- 'Variegata'	see *H. epipactis* 'Thor'

Haemanthus (*Amaryllidaceae*)

albiflos ♀H2	CPrp ELan EPri EShb GKev NGKo NSti SDir SRms
amarylloides	WCot
barkerae	WCot
carneus	WCot
coccineus ♀H2	EPri WCot
humilis	WCot
- subsp. ***hirsutus***	WCot
kalbreyeri	see *Scadoxus multiflorus* subsp. *multiflorus*
katherinae	see *Scadoxus multiflorus* subsp. *katherinae*
natalensis	see *Scadoxus puniceus*
nortieri	WCot
pubescens	WCot
sanguineus	WCot

Hagenia (*Rosaceae*)

abyssinica	WPGP

Hakea (*Proteaceae*)

baxteri	SPlb
§ ***drupacea***	CPbh
epiglottis	CTrC
laurina	CCCN CPbh SPlb
§ ***lissosperma***	CBcs EBee EPfP SPlb WPGP
nodosa	CCCN
oleifolia	CPbh
platysperma	SPlb
§ ***salicifolia***	CCCN SPlb
saligna	see *H. salicifolia*
sericea misapplied	see *H. lissosperma*
sericea Schrad. & J.C.Wendl. pink-flowered	SPlb
suaveolens	see *H. drupacea*
teretifolia	CTrC
victoriae	SPlb

Hakonechloa ✿ (*Poaceae*)

macra ♀H7	Widely available
§ - 'Alboaurea' (v) ♀H7	CBcs CExl CKno CRos CSde EHyd ELan EPfP LCro LOPS LRHS LSRN MGos MMuc NRHS SCob SRms WOld
- 'Albovariegata' (v)	CAbb CDoC CKno EBee EMor LCro LEdu LOPS LRHS MAvo SCob WAvo
§ - 'All Gold'	CBcs CBod CExl CKno EBee ECha ECtt ELan ELon EMor EPPr EShb EWes ITim LCro LEdu LRHS LSRN MGos NLar SDix SMad SPad SPoG WCot WPGP WPnP
- 'Aureola' ♀H7	Widely available
- 'Beni-kaze'	CBod CKno CMiW EBee ECtt ELan ELon IMou LPla MNrw NDov NLar SCob
- 'Fubuki' (v)	EBee
- 'Greenhills'	LPla
- 'Mediovariegata' (v)	EBee ECha
- 'Naomi' (v)	CMiW EBee ELan EMor SMea SPer WHwl

- 'Nicolas'	CBod CExl CMiW EBee ECtt ELan ELon EMor EPfP EWes GAbr LCro LEdu LOPS LPla LSRN NLar NSti SEle SPer WHwl WNPC
- 'Ogon'	see *H. macra* 'All Gold'
- 'Samurai' (v)	CKno EPPr EPfP WHwl
- 'Stripe It Rich' (v)	EBee ECtt EWes LPla
- SunFlare ('Habsfl007') new	CBct CBod CKno CMiW CWGN LCro LOPS MMrt WNPC
- 'Sunny Delight' (v)	EBee
- 'Variegata'	see *H. macra* 'Alboaurea'

Halenia (*Gentianaceae*)

elliptica	GKev

Halesia (*Styracaceae*)

§ ***carolina***	Widely available
- Monticola Group	CBcs CCVT CLnd CMCN CMac ELan EPfP LMaj LSRN MMuc NLar SWvt
I - - 'Variegata' (v)	EPfP MBlu NLar SSta
- 'Uconn Wedding Bells'	CJun MBlu WTSh
- Vestita Group ♀H5	CJun CTho EPfP EWTr MAsh MBlu MGil MGos MRav NLar SPer SSta
- - 'Rosea'	CJun EPfP MBlu NLar
diptera	MBlu
- Magniflora Group	CJun EPfP MBlu SSta
macgregorii	CMCN MBlu
tetraptera	see *H. carolina*

× *Halimiocistus* (*Cistaceae*)

algarvensis	see *Halimium ocymoides*
§ 'Ingwersenii' ♀H4	ELan EWes SPer SRms XLum
revolii misapplied	see × *H. sahucii*
§ ***sahucii*** ♀H4	CBcs CBod CDoC CRos CSBt CTri ECha ELan EPfP LRHS MAsh MBNS MPri MRav MSwo SPer SPoG SRms SWvt XLum
- Ice Dancer ('Ebhals'PBR) (v)	EBee MAsh SCob SPer SWvt WFar
'Susan'	see *Halimium* 'Susan'
§ ***wintonensis*** ♀H4	CBcs CBod CRos EHyd ELan EPfP LRHS MAsh MGil MMuc SLon SPer SRms
§ - 'Merrist Wood Cream' ♀H4	CBcs CBod CBrac CDoC CMac CRos CSBt CSde EBee ELan EPfP LRHS LSRN MAsh MGil MRav MSwo SCob SEle SLim SPer SPoG SRkn SWvt WFar WGrn WLov WSHC

Halimione (*Amaranthaceae*)

§ ***portulacoides***	CEls

Halimium (*Cistaceae*)

§ ***calycinum***	CBcs CBod CDoC CRos EHyd ELan EPfP LRHS MAsh MMuc NRHS SCob SCoo SLim SPer SPoG SWvt WCav
commutatum	see *H. calycinum*
halimifolium misapplied	see *H.* × *pauanum*
§ ***lasianthum***	CMac CSBt LRHS MRav SLim
- 'Concolor' ♀H4	LRHS MAsh MSwo SWvt
- subsp. ***formosum*** 'Sandling' ♀H4	CRos EHyd ELan EPfP LRHS MAsh MMuc SLon SPoG SRms
libanotis misapplied	see *H. calycinum*
§ ***ocymoides***	MGil MSwo WFar
§ × ***pauanum***	CRos EHyd LRHS MMuc NRHS
§ 'Susan' ♀H4	CBod CRos EBee EHyd ELan EPfP LRHS MMrt NRHS SCoo SLim SPer WAbe WLov
§ ***umbellatum***	EPfP
wintonense	see × *Halimiocistus wintonensis*

Halimodendron (*Papilionaceae*)

halodendron	CBcs MBlu SPer

Halleria (*Stilbaceae*)

lucida	CBcs CCCN EBee SEle SPlb SVen WKor

Haloragis (*Haloragaceae*)

erecta	SPlb SVen XLum
- 'Rubra'	WCot
- 'Wellington Bronze'	CBod CExl CPla CSpe EBee ELan EWld LEdu WHer XLum

Hamamelis ✿ (*Hamamelidaceae*)

'Amethyst'	CJun MBlu SGol
'Brevipetala'	CEnd CJun LMaj
'Danny'	CJun
'Dishi'	CJun
'Fire Blaze'	CJun MBlu NLar
× ***intermedia***	CJun MAsh
'Advent' ♀H5	
- 'Alexander'	NLar
- 'Allgold'	SCob
- 'Amanda'	NLar
- 'Andre'	WPGP
- 'Angelly' ♀H5	CJun MBlu NLar
- 'Anne' ♀H5	NLar WPGP
- 'Aphrodite' ♀H5	CBcs CJun CRos EHyd EPfP LRHS MAsh MBlu MGos MRav NLar NOra NRHS SPer
- 'Arnold Promise' ♀H5	Widely available
- 'Aurora' ♀H5	CJun EPfP MBlu NOra WPGP
- 'Barmstedt Gold' ♀H5	CJun CRos EHyd EPfP IArd LRHS LSRN MGos MRav NLar NOra NRHS SAko SPer SPoG SRms
- 'Bernstein'	CJun
- 'Birgit'	NLar
- 'Carmine Red'	CJun CMac
- 'Copper Beauty'	see *H.* × *intermedia* 'Jelena'
- 'Cyrille'	MMuc
- 'Diane' ♀H5	Widely available
§ - 'Feuerzauber'	CEnd CTri EBee EPfP LMaj MAsh NLar NOrn SMad SPer SWvt WFar
- Fire Cracker	see *H.* × *intermedia* 'Feuerzauber'
- 'Foxy Lady'	MAsh MBlu
- 'Frederic' ♀H5	CJun EPfP MAsh
- 'Gingerbread' ♀H5	CJun EPfP MAsh
- 'Glowing Embers'	CJun
- 'Harlow Carr'	NLar
- 'Harry' ♀H5	CJun LSRN MAsh NLar
- 'Heinrich Bruns'	CJun
§ - 'Jelena' ♀H5	Widely available
- 'John'	LSRN MAsh
- 'Limelight'	CJun MBlu MMuc
- 'Livia'	CJun CRos EHyd EPfP LRHS MAsh NLar NRHS SCoo WPGP
- Magic Fire	see *H.* × *intermedia* 'Feuerzauber'
- 'Moonlight'	CJun
- 'Nina'	EBee EPfP MAsh
- 'Old Copper'	NLar
- 'Orange Beauty'	CBcs CJun CRos EHyd LRHS MBlu MGos NLar NOrn NRHS SAko SCoo SGol SPer WPGP
- 'Orange Peel'	CJun EBee EPfP NLar
- 'Ostergold'	CJun
- 'Pallida' ♀H5	Widely available

- 'Primavera'	CBcs CJun
- 'Ripe Corn'	CJun
- 'Robert' ♀H5	CJun CRos EHyd EPfP LRHS LSRN NRHS
- 'Rubin' ♀H5	CBcs CJun CRos EHyd EPfP LRHS MGos NLar NRHS SCoo SPer
- 'Rubinstar'	CJun
- 'Ruby Glow'	CBcs CRos EHyd LRHS LSRN MAsh MGos NLar NRHS SCoo SPer SPoG SWvt
- 'Savill Starlight'	CJun
- 'Spanish Spider'	CJun MBlu MMuc NLar
- 'Strawberries and Cream'	CJun
- 'Sunburst'	CJun CRos EHyd LRHS MBlu MGos NLar SGol
- 'Twilight'	CJun NLar
- 'Vesna' ♀H5	CJun CMac EPfP MAsh MBlu SCoo
- 'Westerstede'	CJun LRHS LSRN MGos MMuc NHol NLar SCoo SEWo SGol SLim WFar
- 'Wiero'	CJun
- 'Zitronenjette'	CJun
japonica 'Pendula'	MBlu
- 'Zuccariniana'	NLar
mollis	Widely available
- 'Boskoop'	MMuc
- 'Coombe Wood'	CJun LRHS NOra
- 'Imperialis'	CJun MAsh
- 'Iwado'	CJun
- 'Jermyns Gold' ♀H5	CBcs CJun CRos EHyd EPfP LRHS MAsh NRHS
- 'Kort's Yellow'	CJun
- var. ***pallida***	SEWo SWvt
- 'Wisley Supreme' ♀H5	CJun ELan EPfP MGos SGol
'Rochester'	CJun
vernalis purple-flowered	MBlu
- 'Quasimodo'	MBlu
- 'Sandra'	CBcs CMCN EPfP MAsh MBlu MGos MRav NOra SLon
virginiana	CAgr CMCN GPoy IDee LMaj MMuc NLar
- 'Green Thumb' (v)	NLar
- 'Mohonk Red'	CJun
'Yamina'	NLar SGol

Hamelia (*Rubiaceae*)

patens	CCCN

Hanabusaya (*Campanulaceae*)

§ ***asiatica***	WFar

Haplocarpha (*Asteraceae*)

rueppellii	NHpl SRms

Haplopappus (*Asteraceae*)

coronopifolius	see *H. glutinosus*
§ ***glutinosus***	ECha ECtt EDAr EPot MMuc SPlb SRms
prunelloides var. ***mustersii*** F&W 9384	WCot

Hardenbergia (*Papilionaceae*)

comptoniana ♀H3	CExl
violacea ♀H3	CBod CCCN CRHN CSpe ELan MHer MMuc SEND SEdd SLim SPer WCot
- f. ***alba***	CBod SEND WLov
- - 'White Wanderer'	CCCN
- 'Happy Wanderer'	CCCN SIvy
- f. ***rosea***	CCCN

Harpephyllum (*Anacardiaceae*)

caffrum (F)	XBlo

Hasteola (*Asteraceae*)

§ ***suaveolens***	LEdu

Hastingsia (*Asparagaceae*)

alba	WSHC

Haworthia ✿ (*Asphodelaceae*)

attenuata	EShb
'Black Prince'	EShb SGro
coarctata ♀H2	SEND
fasciata	SEND
- 'Concolor'	CDoC SSim
glabrata var. ***concolor***	EShb
limifolia	EShb
- SPIDER WHITE ('Lock01'PBR)	EShb LCro LOPS
margaritifera	SSim
pumila ♀H2	SEND
retusa ♀H2 new	WOld
tesselata	see *H. venosa* subsp. *tesselata*
§ ***venosa*** subsp. ***tesselata*** ♀H2	SEND

hazelnut see *Corylus*; also AGM Fruit Section

Hebe ✿ (*Plantaginaceae*)

albicans ♀H4	CBcs CBrac CCoa CDoC CRos EHyd ELan EPfP GJos GKin LCro LOPS LRHS LSRN MAsh MGos MRav NRHS SCob SCoo SGbt SLim SPer SRms SWvt WCFE WSpi XLum
- prostrate	see *H. albicans* 'Snow Cover'
* - 'Snow Carpet'	CBrac LRHS
§ - 'Snow Cover'	EWes
- 'Snow Drift'	see *H. albicans* 'Snow Cover'
§ 'Alicia Amherst'	LRHS
'Amanda Cook' (v)	NPer
§ 'Amy'	ELon LRHS NPer SPer SWvt WCot
× ***andersonii***	CDoC
§ - 'Andersonii Variegata' (v)	LRHS SRms
- 'Argenteovariegata'	see *H.* × *andersonii* 'Andersonii Variegata'
'Andressa Paula'	LRHS
anomala misapplied	see *H.* 'Imposter'
§ ***armstrongii***	MMuc
'Autumn Glory'	CBrac CDoC CRos EHyd ELan EPfP LCro LOPS LPot LRHS LSRN MAsh MGos MRav MSwo NBir NRHS SCob SPer SPlb SPoG SWvt XLum
'Autumn Joy'	SWvt
azurea	see *H. venustula*
'Azurens'	see *H.* 'Maori Gem'
'Baby Boo' (v)	CDoC LRHS SCob SLon
'Baby Marie'	CDoC CRos CSBt EHyd ELan EPfP GJos GKin LBuc LRHS LSRN MAsh MSwo NPer NRHS SCoo SPoG SRms SWvt WFar
'Beverley Hills'PBR	CSBt EHyd LRHS
'Bicolor Wand'	CCCN CTsd LRHS
bishopiana	EPfP
'Black Beauty'	CRos EHyd EPfP LRHS MAsh NRHS SCob

	'Black Panther'	ELon
	'Blue Clouds' ♀H4	CBrac CRos EHyd EPfP LRHS MSwo NRHS NWad SPer WCFE WMal
	BLUE ELEGANCE ('Lowgeko'PBR) (Garden Beauty Series)	LRHS
§	'Blue Gem'	CCoa CDoC CMac
	BLUE ICE ('Lowapb') (Garden Beauty Series)	LRHS
	'Blue Shamrock'	SWvt
	BLUE STAR ('Vergeer 1'PBR)	CBod CDoC CRos EPfP GJos LBuc LRHS MAsh NRHS SLon SPoG SRms
	'Boscawenii'	WHer
	'Bouquet'PBR	LSou
§	'Bowles's Hybrid'	CBrac LRHS MRav MSwo SCob SEND SRms
	brachysiphon	CTri SEND SPer SRms SVen
	brevifolia	LRHS
	BRONZE GLOW ('Lowglo') (Garden Beauty Series)	CDoC LBuc LRHS
	'Bronzy Baby'PBR (v)	SPoG
	buchananii	NPer
§	- 'Fenwickii'	WHoo
	- 'Minor' ambig.	EPot GQue
	'Bullfinch'	LRHS
	'Burgundy Blush'	LBuc SPoG
	'Burning Heart' (v)	LBuc
	buxifolia	see *H. odora*
§	'Caledonia' ♀H4	CBcs CDoC CRos EHyd ELan EPfP LCro LOPS LRHS LSRN MAsh MGos NPer NRHS SCoo SLim SPoG SRms SWvt XLum
	'Carl Teschner'	see *H.* 'Youngii'
	'Carnea Variegata' (v)	CRos EHyd LRHS NRHS SPer SRms
	carnosula	SPer
	catarractae	see *Parabebe catarractae*
	'Celebration'PBR (v) **new**	SHar
	'Celine'	CCoa CRos EHyd EPfP LRHS NRHS
	'Champagne'	CBrac CDoC CRos EHyd ELan EPfP LCro LOPS LRHS LSRN MBlu NLar NRHS NWad SCoo SLim SRms XLum
	'Champagne Ice'	LBuc
	CHAMPION ('Champseiont'PBR)	CBod EBee GBin MSwo NLar SCoo
	'Charming White'	CChe CRos LRHS LSRN
	cheesemanii	WAbe
	'Christabel'	LRHS
	'Claret Crush'PBR	SPoG
	'Clear Skies'PBR	SRms
	'Cobb Valley' **new**	CRos
	'Conwy Knight'	SRms
	corstorphinensis	EBtc
	'County Park'	EWes GAbr
	'Cranleighensis'	LRHS
	cupressoides 'Boughton Dome'	ELan GAbr GEdr GJos MAsh MHer WAbe WCFE WHoo WOld
	'Dark Angel'	LBuc
	darwiniana misapplied	see *H. glaucophylla*
	decumbens	EWes GBin
	'Denise'	LRHS
	'Diamond'	LRHS LSRN SCob SLon SRms
	dieffenbachii	SVen
	diosmifolia	CBod CDoC CRos LRHS NRHS NWad
	- 'Wairua Beauty'	CDoC LRHS
	'Dorothy Peach'	see *H.* 'Watson's Pink'
	'E.B.Anderson'	see *H.* 'Caledonia'
	'Edington'	SPer WCFE
	'Ellie'	CBrac LRHS

	elliptica	CDoC
	- 'Variegata'	see *H.* 'Silver Queen'
	'Emerald Dome'	see *H.* 'Emerald Gem'
§	'Emerald Gem' ♀H4	CRos CTri EHyd ELan EPfP GJos GWyn LRHS LSRN MAsh MGos MHer MMuc MSwo NRHS SCob SPer SPlb SPoG WLov
	'Emerald Green'	see *H.* 'Emerald Gem'
§	'Eveline'	CRos CSBt CTri LRHS NBir
	'Evelyn'	SPer
	'Eversley Seedling'	see *H.* 'Bowles's Hybrid'
	'Eyecatcher'PBR (v)	LSou MAsh
	'Fairfieldii'	WAbe WAvo
	'First Light'PBR	CDoC LRHS LSou NLar SRms
	'Fragrant Jewel'	LRHS SEND
	× ***franciscana***	CBod NCou WSMil
	- 'Blue Gem' ambig.	CBrac CRos EHyd ELan LRHS MAsh MMuc MRav NBir NPer NRHS SCob SEND SPer SPlb SPoG SRms WSpi XLum
	- 'Foreness Pink'	SEND
	- 'Lavender Queen'	LRHS
	- lime variegated (v)	SEND
	- 'Purple Tips' misapplied	see *H. speciosa* 'Variegata'
	- 'Variegata'	see *H.* 'Silver Queen'
I	- 'White Gem'	SRms
	'Frozen Flame' (v)	ELan LBuc LRHS MAsh SPoG WMal
	(Garden Beauty Series)	CDoC CSBt LBuc LCro LOPS LRHS
	GARDEN BEAUTY BLUE ('Cliv'PBR)	LSou MAsh SRms WSpi
	- GARDEN BEAUTY PINK ('Lowink')	CDoC SRms
	- GARDEN BEAUTY PURPLE ('Nold'PBR)	CRos CSBt EHyd LBuc LCro LOPS LRHS LSou MAsh NRHS
	- GARDEN BEAUTY WHITE ('Lowhi')	LRHS
	(Garden Elegance Series) 'Garden Elegance Blush'	LRHS
	- 'Garden Elegance Rose'	LRHS
	'Gauntlettii'	see *H.* 'Eveline'
	'Gibby'	LRHS
§	***glaucophylla***	XLum
I	- 'Variegata' (v)	CRos EHyd LRHS NRHS SCoo SPer WKif
§	'Gloriosa'	SCob
	'Gold Beauty' (v)	SRms
	'Gold Pixie'	LBuc
	GOLDEN ANNIVERSARY ('Lowag'PBR)	LRHS
	'Golden Nugget'	LRHS
	'Goldrush'PBR (v)	SPoG
	gracillima	SEle
	'Gran's Favourite'	LSRN
	'Great Orme' ♀H4	CBrac CRos EHyd ELan EPfP GBin GLog LRHS LSRN MAsh MGos MRav MSwo NPer NRHS SCob SEND SPer SPlb SPoG SRms SWvt WCFE WOut WSFF
	'Green Globe'	see *H.* 'Emerald Gem'
	'Greensleeves'	CRos EHyd LRHS
	'Grethe'	CRos EHyd LRHS NRHS SCob SEND
	'Hadspen Pink'	CBrac CDoC LRHS
	'Hagley Park'	LRHS
	'Hanne'	CRos EHyd NRHS
§	'Hartii'	CBrac CRos LRHS MRav
	'Headfortii'	EBtc
	'Heartbreaker'PBR (v)	CDoC CRos EHyd ELan EPfP LBuc LCro LOPS LRHS MAsh MGos MPri NRHS SCob SCoo SLim SPoG SWvt

	'Helena' (Addenda Series) **new**	CDoC
	'High Voltage'[PBR]	GJos NEoE WTyc
	'Highdownensis'	LRHS
	'Hinderwell'	NPer
	hookeriana	see *Parahebe hookeriana*
	hulkeana	MGil MHer NLar WAbe WHoo WKif
§	'Imposter'	SRms
	'Inspiration'	EHyd LRHS NWad SCob SRms
	'James Stirling'	see *H. ochracea* 'James Stirling'
	'Jane Holden'	EHyd LRHS
	'Jewel of the Nile'[PBR] (v)	MMrt SCob SPoG
	'John Collier'	GAbr SEND
§	'Johny Day'	LRHS
	'Judy'	LRHS
	'Karna'	LPot SCob
	'Katrina' (v)	CDoC
	'Kirkii'	ELan EPfP MSwo NLar XLum
	'Knightshayes'	see *H.* 'Caledonia'
	'Lady Ann'[PBR] (v)	CRos EHyd EPfP LBuc LRHS MAsh NRHS SCob SPoG
	'Lady Ardilaun'	see *H.* 'Amy'
	laevis	see *H. venustula*
	laingii	EPot
	latifolia	see *H.* 'Blue Gem'
	'Lavender Spray'	see *H.* 'Hartii'
	LEOPARD ('Lowand') (Garden Beauty Series)	LRHS MPri
	'Lilac Fantasy'	LRHS
	'Lilac Wand'	CTsd
	'Linda'	SEND
	'Lindsayi'	LRHS
	'Lisa'	CRos EHyd NRHS
	'Liz'	LBuc LRHS SPoG
	'Louise'	SCob
	lyallii	see *Parahebe lyallii*
	lycopodioides 'Aurea'	see *H. armstrongii*
	'Lynash'	LRHS
	mackenii	see *H.* 'Emerald Gem'
	macrantha 𝕐H4	EHyd GBin GWyn LRHS SDix SRms
	'Magic Summer'[PBR]	LBuc LRHS MAsh NRHS SPoG
§	'Maori Gem'	MRav
	'Margery Fish'	see *H.* 'Primley Gem'
	'Margret' 𝕐H4	CBrac CDoC CRos CSBt EBee EHyd EPfP LPot LRHS LSRN MAsh MGos NRHS SCoo SLim SPer SPoG SRms
	'Maria'	SCob
	'Marie Antoinette'	CBod CRos LRHS
	'Marilyn Monroe'[PBR]	CBod LRHS LSou WTyc
	'Marjorie'	CMac CRos ELan EPfP GBin LRHS LSRN MSwo NLar NPer NRHS SCob SPer SPoG SRms SWvt WFar
	matthewsii 'Turkish Delight'[PBR]	NEoE
	MATTY BROWN ('Tull 303'[PBR])	LSou SPad
	'Mauve Queen'	LRHS
	'McKean'	see *H.* 'Emerald Gem'
	MIDNIGHT SKY ('Lowten'[PBR]) (Garden Beauty Series)	CDoC LBuc LCro LOPS LRHS MPri SCoo SPoG
	'Midsummer Beauty' 𝕐H4	CRos EHyd EPfP GBin LRHS LSRN MGos MRav NBir NRHS SCob SEND SPer SPlb SPoG SRms SWvt WOut WSFF XLum
	'Midsummer Ice' **new**	WOut
	'Midsummer Pink' **new**	WOut
	'Milmont Emerald'	see *H.* 'Emerald Gem'
§	'Mohawk'[PBR]	GJos LRHS MAsh NRHS SPoG WSpi
§	'Mrs Winder' 𝕐H4	CBrac CMac CRos EHyd ELan EPfP GJos GWyn LRHS LSRN MAsh MCot MGos MRav MSwo NLar NPer NRHS SCob SCoo SGbt SPer SPoG SWvt
	'Nantyderry'	CDoC LRHS MGil WOut
§	'Neil's Choice' 𝕐H4	CRos EHyd ELon LRHS
	'New Zealand'	GWyn XLum
	'Nicola's Blush' 𝕐H4	CDoC CMac CRos EBee EHyd ELon EPfP EShb GBin GWyn LRHS LSRN MCot MRav NBir NLar NRHS SCob SEND SPer SPoG SRms SWvt SavN WKif WMal
	ochracea	CRos EHyd EPfP LRHS NRHS
§	- 'James Stirling' 𝕐H4	CBcs CMac CRos CSBt ELan GJos LCro LOPS LRHS LSRN MAsh MGos MMuc MSwo NLar NWad SCob SCoo SPlb SPoG SWvt WSpi
	'Oddity'	LRHS
§	***odora***	CBod CCBP CCoa CSde ELan GAbr LRHS SEND WSpi XLum
I	- 'Nana'	MMuc
	- 'New Zealand Gold'	CRos EHyd EPfP GJos LRHS MAsh MMuc NRHS NWad
	- prostrate	SRms
	- 'Summer Frost'	CBrac CSde LRHS
	'Oratia Beauty' 𝕐H4	CDoC EHyd LRHS LSRN MMuc MRav SEND
	'Orphan Annie' (v)	CBrac CDoC LSRN NLar
	'Pacific Paradise'[PBR]	SPoG
	parviflora misapplied	see *H.* 'Bowles's Hybrid'
	- var. ***angustifolia***	see *H. stenophylla*
	- 'Holdsworth'	CBod LRHS
	'Pascal' 𝕐H4	CRos EHyd ELan EPfP LCro LOPS LRHS LSRN MAsh MGos NRHS SCoo SLim SLon SPer SPoG SRms SWvt WFar
	'Patti Dossett'	see *H. speciosa* 'Patti Dossett'
	pauciramosa	SRms
	'Pearl of Paradise'[PBR]	LBuc NRHS NWad SPoG
	perfoliata	see *Parahebe perfoliata*
	'Perry's Rubyleaf'	NPer
	'Petra's Pink'	CRos EHyd LRHS
	'Pewter Dome' 𝕐H4	EPfP LRHS MGos MRav SCob SDix SRms SWvt XLum
	pimeleoides	CBod
	- 'Glauca'	NPer
	- 'Quicksilver' 𝕐H4	CBrac CRos CSBt CTri EHyd ELan EPfP GJos LRHS LSRN MGil MGos MMuc MRav NBir NPer NRHS SCob SCoo SLim SPer SRms WAvo WSpi XLum
	pinguifolia	NLar SPlb
	- 'Pagei' 𝕐H5	Widely available
	- 'Sutherlandii'	CBcs CBrac CDoC CRos EHyd LRHS LSRN MAsh MGos NRHS SCob SCoo SWvt WFar XLum
	PINK CANDY ('Tulpink'[PBR])	WTyc
	'Pink Elephant' (v) 𝕐H4	CDoC LBuc LRHS SPoG
	'Pink Fantasy'	LRHS NWad SGbt
	'Pink Goddess'	CBrac CRos EHyd EPfP LRHS NRHS SEND
	'Pink Lady'[PBR]	ELan SPoG
	'Pink Paradise'[PBR]	CBod CRos ELan EPfP LRHS NRHS NWad SPoG SRms
	'Pink Payne'	see *H.* 'Eveline'
	'Pink Pearl'	see *H.* 'Gloriosa'
	'Pink Pixie'	LBuc LRHS MAsh SCoo SPoG SRms
	'Pink Wand'	CTsd
	poppelwellii	NLar
	'Porlock Purple'	see *Parahebe catarractae* 'Delight'

§ 'Primley Gem'	LRHS
I 'Prostrata'	CSBt
'Purple Emperor'	see *H.* 'Neil's Choice'
'Purple Paradise'PBR	LSou NLar SPoG
'Purple Pixie'	see *H.* 'Mohawk'
'Purple Princess'	CRos EHyd LRHS NRHS
'Purple Queen'	EHyd EShb LRHS MCot
PURPLE SHAMROCK ('Neprock'PBR) (v)	CDoC CRos EHyd EPfP GJos LRHS LSou MAsh NLar NRHS SCoo SLim SPer SPoG SRms SWvt
'Purple Tips' misapplied	see *H. speciosa* 'Variegata'
'Rachel'	LRHS LSRN
§ ***rakaiensis*** 🏆H4	Widely available
- 'Golden Dome'	see *H. rakaiensis*
ramosissima	EPot GAbr GBin
raoulii	SRms WAbe
RASPBERRY RIPPLE ('Tullyraspb'PBR)	NEoE
'Raven'	CBrac CDoC LRHS
recurva	CCoa CSam CSde CTri LPot LRHS MCot SRms
- 'Boughton Silver' 🏆H4	LRHS LSRN MMuc
'Red Edge' 🏆H4	Widely available
'Red Rum'	LRHS
'Red Ruth'	see *H.* 'Eveline'
RHUBARB AND CUSTARD ('Tull302')	LBuc LRHS MAsh MMrt SPoG WCot
rigidula	LRHS MMuc SEND
'Rosie'	LBuc LRHS LSRN NRHS SCoo SPer SWvt
'Royal Blue'	LRHS SCob
'Royal Purple'	see *H.* 'Alicia Amherst'
salicifolia	CMac CRos EHyd ELan EPfP GAbr IDee LRHS MMuc MRav NRHS NWad SEND SPlb SRms WFar WSpi XLum
- pale blue-flowered	SEND
'Sandra Joy'	CBrac LRHS LSRN
'Santa Monica'	LSou MHtn
'Sapphire' 🏆H4	CRos EHyd EPfP LRHS MAsh NRHS SCoo SRms SWvt
'Sarana'	LRHS LSRN
'Shiraz'	CRos EHyd LRHS
'Silver Dollar' (v)	CBcs CBod GBin LRHS LSou NRHS NWad SCob SPer SPoG SRms
§ 'Silver Queen' (v) 🏆H3	CBcs CBrac CCoa CDoC CRos CSBt EHyd ELan LCro LOPS LRHS MMuc NLar NPer NRHS SEND SPer SPoG SRms WOut
'Simon Délaux'	LRHS SEND SPer WOut
'Sparkling Sapphires'	LBuc LRHS SPoG
speciosa 'Johny Day'	see *H.* 'Johny Day'
- 'La Séduisante'	CTri LRHS SEND WSpi
§ - 'Patti Dossett'	CDoC LRHS
- 'Red Hugh'	SEND
§ - 'Variegata' (v)	CRos EHyd LRHS NPer NRHS SCob
'Spender's Seedling' misapplied	see *H. stenophylla*
'Spender's Seedling' ambig.	MCot MMuc MSCN
'Spender's Seedling' Hort.	LRHS MRav SEND SPoG SRms
'Spring Glory'	CRos EHyd EPfP LRHS NRHS
§ ***stenophylla***	EShb LRHS LSRN NLar SArc SDix SPer SPlb
stricta	LRHS SEND WOut
- var. ***egmontiana***	LRHS
- var. ***macroura***	CBrac
- var. ***stricta***	CDoC
subalpina	CSBt
'Summer Blue'	LRHS MBlu
'Sunset Boulevard'PBR	LSou
'Super Red'	CSBt
'Sweet Kim' (v)	CRos LBuc LRHS NRHS SPoG
tetrasticha	GRum
'Tiptop' (v) **new**	LSou
topiaria 🏆H4	CAgr CBod CDoC CMac CRos CSBt CSam EBou EPfP LRHS MBrN MMuc MRav MSwo NBir NLar NWad SCoo SEND SGbt SPer SPoG WRHF WSpi XLum
- 'Doctor Favier'	LRHS SRms
townsonii	LRHS
'Tricolor'	see *H. speciosa* 'Variegata'
'Trixie'	WSpi
'Trudi'	SCob
'Twisty'	LRHS
'Valentino'PBR	SCoo
'Veitchii'	see *H.* 'Alicia Amherst'
§ ***venustula***	LRHS MMuc
vernicosa 🏆H4	CCoa CDoC CRos EHyd EPfP LRHS MGos MHer NWad SCob SCoo SPer SPlb SPoG SWvt WAbe WSpi
'Violet Wand'	LRHS
'Vogue'	LRHS
'Waikiki'	see *H.* 'Mrs Winder'
§ 'Warley'	CBrac CDoC CRos EHyd LRHS NRHS WOut WSpi
'Warley Pink'	CRos LRHS
'Warleyensis'	see *H.* 'Warley'
§ 'Watson's Pink'	SPer WKif
'White Gem' (*brachysiphon* hybrid) 🏆H4	GWyn LRHS NPer SEND SPer
'White Heather'	CRos EHyd EPfP LRHS NRHS
'White Paradise'PBR	SPoG
'Wild Romance'	CDoC LBuc LRHS MAsh SPoG
'Willcoxii'	see *H. buchananii* 'Fenwickii'
'Wingletye' 🏆H4	CRos EHyd LRHS WAbe XLum
'Winter Glow'	LRHS
'Wiri Blush'	CBrac LRHS SWvt
'Wiri Charm'	CBcs CBrac CDoC CMac CRos CSBt EBee EHyd ELon EPfP LRHS MSwo NLar NRHS SEND SPer
'Wiri Cloud' 🏆H4	CBcs CDoC CMac CRos EHyd EPfP LRHS MMuc MSCN MSwo NRHS SCob SEND SRms
'Wiri Dawn' 🏆H4	CRos EHyd ELan EPfP LRHS NRHS SRms SWvt XLum
'Wiri Desire'	CRos LRHS
'Wiri Icing Sugar'	CBrac
'Wiri Image'	CBcs CRos CSBt EHyd LRHS MRav NRHS SEND
'Wiri Joy'	CRos EHyd EPfP LRHS NRHS
'Wiri Mist'	CBcs CRos EHyd ELan EPfP LRHS NRHS XLum
'Wiri Prince'	CRos LRHS SCob
'Wiri Splash'	CRos EHyd LRHS NRHS
'Wiri Vision'	CBrac CRos CSBt LRHS SEND
'Wiri Vogue'	LRHS
§ 'Youngii' 🏆H4	CBcs CDoC CRos CSBt CTri EHyd ELan EPfP GBin GJos LCro LOPS LRHS MGil MHer MMuc MRav NBir NRHS SCob SEND SPer SPlb SPoG SRms SWvt WCFE WHoo WMal WSpi

Hebenstretia (*Scrophulariaceae*)

dura	WAbe

Hechtia (*Bromeliaceae*)

sp.	WCot

Hedeoma (*Lamiaceae*)

	ciliolata	WAbe

Hedera ✿ (*Araliaceae*)

§	***algeriensis***	SArc WFib
	- 'Bellecour'	WFib XLum
§	- 'Gloire de Marengo' (v) 🏆^{H5}	CArg CBcs CDoC CMac CRos CTri EBee EHyd ELan EPfP GKin LRHS LSRN MAsh MGos MSwo NRHS SCob SDix SEND SGol SGsty SLim SPer SPoG SRms SWvt WFar WFib
	- 'Marginomaculata' (v)	CRos EHyd EPfP EShb LRHS MAsh SMad SPoG WFib
	- 'Montgomery'	CRos EHyd LRHS LSRN NRHS
	- 'Ravensholst' 🏆^{H5}	CMac EShb MRav SCob WFib
§	***azorica***	EShb WCot WFib
	- amber-fruited **new**	WCot
	- 'Pico'	EShb WFib
	- 'Saiga' **new**	WCot
	canariensis misapplied	see *H. algeriensis*
	- 'Variegata'	see *H. algeriensis* 'Gloire de Marengo'
	canariensis Willd.	SEND
	- var. ***azorica***	see *H. azorica*
	chinensis	see *H. nepalensis*
	- typica	see *H. nepalensis*
§	***colchica***	WFib
	- 'Batumi'	MBNS WFib
	- 'Dentata' 🏆^{H5}	CBod MRav SGol WFar WFib
	- 'Dentata Aurea'	see *H. colchica* 'Dentata Variegata'
§	- 'Dentata Variegata' (v) 🏆^{H5}	Widely available
	- 'My Heart'	see *H. colchica*
	- 'Paddy's Pride'	see *H. colchica* 'Sulphur Heart'
§	- 'Sulphur Heart' (v) 🏆^{H5}	CBcs CDoC CMac EBee ELan EPfP GKin LCro LOPS LSRN MAsh MGos MRav MSwo NHol NLar SCob SEND SEWo SGol SGsty SLim SPer SPlb SPoG SRms SWvt WFar WFib
	- 'Variegata'	see *H. colchica* 'Dentata Variegata'
	cristata	see *H. helix* 'Parsley Crested'
	helix	CCVT CMac CTri LCro LOPS SCob SWeb WSFF XLum
	- 'Adam' (v)	LSRN MHost WFib
	- 'Amber Waves'	MHost WFib
	- 'Anita'	GBin WFib
§	- 'Anna Marie' (v)	WFib
	- 'Arborescens'	EShb WGrn WSFF
	- 'Arborescens Variegata' (v)	EShb
	- 'Ardingly' (v)	WFib
	- 'Atropurpurea'	ELan GBin MMuc SEND WFib
	- (Aureovariegata Group) 'Chrysophylla' (v)	MSwo
	- 'Baltica'	WFib
	- 'Bettina' (v)	WCot
	- 'Bill Archer'	GBin WFib
	- 'Bird's Foot'	see *H. helix* 'Pedata'
	- 'Boskoop'	WFib
	- 'Bredon'	MRav
	- 'Brimstone' (v)	WFib
§	- 'Brokamp'	WFib
	- 'Buttercup' 🏆^{H5}	CMac CRos CTri ELan EPfP GQue LRHS LSRN MAsh MGos MMuc NBid NLar SCob SEND SPer SPoG SRms SWvt WCFE WFib
	- 'Caecilia' (v) 🏆^{H5}	EPfP MSwo SWvt WFib
	- 'Caenwoodiana'	see *H. helix* 'Pedata'
	- 'Caenwoodiana Aurea'	WFib
§	- 'Calico' (v)	WFib
	- 'Calypso'	WFib
	- 'Carolina Crinkle'	GBin
	- 'Cathedral Wall'	WFib
	- 'Cavendishii'	see *H. helix* Cavendishii Group
§	- Cavendishii Group (v)	SRms WFib
§	- 'Ceridwen' (v) 🏆^{H5}	SCob SPlb WFib
	- 'Cheeky'	WFib
	- 'Cheltenham Blizzard' (v)	CNat
	- 'Chester' (v)	WFib
	- 'Chicago'	MHost WFib
	- 'Chicago Variegated' (v)	WFib
§	- 'Classy Lassie' (v)	WFib
	- 'Clotted Cream' (v)	CDoC CRos LRHS MAsh WFib
	- 'Cockle Shell'	WFib
	- 'Colin'	GBin
§	- 'Congesta' 🏆^{H5}	CMac CTsd SRms WFib
	- 'Conglomerata'	ELan SRms WFib
	- 'Courage'	WFib
	- 'Crenata'	WFib
	- 'Crispa'	MRav
	- 'Cristata'	see *H. helix* 'Parsley Crested'
	- 'Curleylocks'	see *H. helix* 'Manda's Crested'
	- 'Curley-Q'	see *H. helix* 'Dragon Claw'
	- 'Curvaceous' (v)	WFib
	- 'Cyprus'	see *H. pastuchovii* subsp. *cypria*
	- 'Dealbata'	see *H. hibernica* 'Dealbata'
	- 'Deltoidea'	see *H. hibernica* 'Deltoidea'
	- 'Discolor'	see *H. helix* 'Minor Marmorata'
§	- 'Donerailensis'	MBlu NSla WFib
§	- 'Dragon Claw'	WFib
	- 'Duckfoot' 🏆^{H5}	EShb GBin WCot WFib
	- 'Dyinnii'	EPot GEdr NLar WAbe WCot
	- 'Eileen' (v)	WFib
§	- (Elegantissima Group) 'Marginata Elegantissima' (v)	SGsty
	- - 'Tricolor' (v)	CMac CTri EPfP LRHS SPoG WCFE WFib
	- 'Elfenbein' (v)	WCot WFib
	- 'Erecta'	EHyd EPPr GAbr IDee LRHS MBlu MHer NHol NWad SDix SPer SPlb WCFE WFib XLum
	- 'Ester' (v)	SCob
	- 'Eva' (v)	WFib
	- 'Fantasia' (v)	WFib
	- 'Feenfinger'	WFib
	- 'Filigran'	WFib
	- 'Flashback' (v)	WFib
	- 'Flavescens'	WFib
	- 'Fluffy Ruffles'	GKev WFib
	- 'Francis'	WFib
	- 'Frosty' (v)	WFib
	- 'Garland'	WFib
	- 'Gavotte'	WFib
	- 'Gilded Hawke'	WFib
	- 'Glache' (v)	MHost MRav WFib
	- 'Glacier' (v) 🏆^{H5}	CArg CBcs CMac CRos CTri EHyd ELan EPfP GKev LCro LOPS LRHS MAsh MGil MGos MMuc MRav MSwo NHol NRHS SCob SEND SPer SPoG SRms SWvt WFar WFib
	- 'Glymii'	ELan GBin MHost WFib
	- 'Gold Harald'	see *H. helix* 'Goldchild'
	- 'Gold Ripple'	see *H. helix* 'Golden Starlight'
§	- 'Goldchild' (v) 🏆^{H5}	CBcs CMac CRos EBee EHyd EPfP EShb LCro LOPS LRHS MAsh MGil MGos MMuc MRav MSwo NBir NHol NRHS SCob SLim SPer SPoG SWvt WFib

	- 'Golden Ann'	see *H. helix* 'Ceridwen'
	- 'Golden Arrow'	see *H. helix* 'Goldfinger'
§	- 'Golden Curl' (v)	CMac CRos EHyd EPfP LRHS WFib
	- 'Golden Ester'	see *H. helix* 'Ceridwen'
	- 'Golden Girl' (v)	WFib
§	- 'Golden Ingot' (v) ♀H5	CRos EHyd ELan LRHS WFib
	- 'Golden Jytte'	see *H. helix* 'Classy Lassie'
	- 'Golden Kolibri'	see *H. helix* 'Midas Touch'
§	- 'Golden Starlight' (v)	EShb GBin NLar SEND WFib
	- 'Goldfinch'	WFib
§	- 'Goldfinger'	CRos EHyd LRHS MAsh WFib
	- 'Goldheart'	see *H. helix* 'Oro di Bogliasco'
	- 'Goldstern' (v)	MRav WFib
	- 'Gracilis'	see *H. hibernica* 'Gracilis'
	- 'Green Finger'	see *H. helix* 'Très Coupé'
	- 'Green Man'	WFib
	- 'Green Ripple'	CBcs CRos CTri EHyd ELan EPfP LRHS MBlu MGos MHost MMuc MSwo MWht NRHS SCob SEND SPer SPlb SRms SWvt WFib
	- 'Halebob'	MHost WFib
	- 'Hamilton'	see *H. hibernica* 'Hamilton'
	- 'Harald' (v)	CTri WFib
	- 'Hazel' (v)	WFib
	- 'Heise' (v)	WFib
	- 'Heise Denmark' (v)	WFib
	- 'Helvig'	see *H. helix* 'White Knight'
	- 'Henriette'	WFib
	- 'Hispanica'	see *H. iberica*
	- 'Hite's Miniature'	see *H. helix* 'Merion Beauty'
	- 'Hullavington'	CNat
	- 'Humpty Dumpty'	CExl
	- 'Hunlaf's Winter Red' **new**	CNat
	- 'Ice Cream' (v)	LRHS WCot
	- 'Imp'	see *H. helix* 'Brokamp'
	- 'Ingrid' (v)	SRms
	- 'Ivalace'	EPPr EShb MSwo SCob SRms WFib XLum
	- 'Jake'	WFib
	- 'Jara' arboreal	WCot
	- 'Jasper'	WFib
	- 'Jersey Doris' (v)	WFib
	- 'Jerusalem'	see *H. helix* 'Calico'
	- 'Jubilee' (v)	WFar WFib
	- 'Kaleidoscope' (v)	WFib
	- 'Kevin'	WFib
	- 'Kolibri' (v)	SCob SRms WFib
	- 'Königer's Auslese'	WFib
	- 'Lalla Rookh'	MGil MRav WFib WRHF
	- 'Leo Swicegood'	WFib
	- 'Lightfinger'	WFib
	- 'Little Diamond' (v)	CMac CTri ELan SCob SLon SRms SWvt WFib
	- 'Little Luzii' (v)	WFib
§	- 'Lucida' **new**	SDix
	- 'Luzii' (v)	WFib
	- 'Maculata'	see *H. helix* 'Minor Marmorata'
§	- 'Manda's Crested' ♀H5	ELan NLar WFib
	- 'Maple Leaf' ♀H5	EShb WFib
	- 'Marginata Elegantissima'	see *H. helix* (Elegantissima Group) 'Marginata Elegantissima'
I	- 'Marmorata' Fibrex	WFib
	- 'Mathilde' (v)	EHyd WFib
	- 'Melanie'	ECha WCot WFib
	- 'Meon'	WFib
§	- 'Merion Beauty'	WFib
§	- 'Midas Touch' (v) ♀H5	CBod ELan WFib
	- 'Minikin' (v)	WCot
	- 'Minima' Hibberd	see *H. helix* 'Donerailensis'
	- 'Minima' M.Young	see *H. helix* 'Congesta'
§	- 'Minor Marmorata' (v)	XLum
	- 'Minty' (v)	WFib
	- 'Misty' (v)	WFib
	- 'Needlepoint'	XLum
	- 'Niagara Falls'	CRos LRHS
	- 'Nigra Aurea' (v)	WFib
	- 'Obovata'	WFib
	- 'Oro di Bogliasco' (v)	CArg CDoC CMac CRos CTri EBee EHyd EPfP LCro LOPS LRHS MMuc MRav MSwo NLar NRHS NWad SCob SEND SEWo SGsty SPer SPlb SRms SWvt WFar WFib
	- 'Ovata'	WFib
§	- 'Parsley Crested' ♀H5	CDoC ELan WFib
	- 'Patent Leather'	WFib
	- 'Pedata'	MHost MSwo SRms WFib
	- 'Perkeo'	WFib
	- 'Peter' (v)	WFib
	- 'Pink 'n' Curly'	WCot WFib
	- 'Pink 'n' Very Curly'	WCot
§	- 'Pittsburgh'	MHost WFib
	- 'Plume d'Or'	WFib
	- f. ***poetarum***	MBlu WCot WFib
	- - 'Poetica Arborea'	EShb
	- 'Poetica'	see *H. helix* 'Lucida'
	- 'Raleigh Delight' (v)	WCot
	- 'Ray's Supreme'	see *H. helix* 'Pittsburgh'
	- subsp. ***rhizomatifera***	see *H. helix* 'Rhizomatifera'
§	- 'Rhizomatifera'	WFib
	- 'Richard John'	see *H. helix* 'Golden Curl'
	- 'Ritterkreuz'	WFib
	- 'Romanze' (v)	WCot WFib
	- 'Russelliana'	WCFE WFib
	- 'Sagittifolia' ambig.	LRHS MAsh MBlu SPoG
	- 'Sagittifolia Variegata' (v)	WFib
	- 'Saint Agnes'	see *H. helix* 'Golden Ingot'
	- 'Sally'	WFib
	- 'Salt and Pepper'	see *H. helix* 'Minor Marmorata'
	- 'Schäfer Three' (v)	WFib
	- 'Seabreeze'	WFib
	- 'Shamrock' ♀H5	WFib
	- 'Shannon'	WFib
	- 'Silver Ferney' (v)	WFib
	- 'Silver King' (v)	MHost WFib
§	- 'Snow Cap' (v)	WFib
	- 'Spetchley'	see *H. hibernica* 'Spetchley'
	- 'Splashes' (v)	WFib
	- 'Sunrise'	WFib
	- 'Suzanne'	see *H. nepalensis* 'Suzanne'
	- 'Tanja'	WFib
	- 'Teardrop'	WFib
	- 'Telecurl'	WFib
	- 'Temptation' (v)	WFib
	- 'Teneriffe' (v)	WFib
	- 'Topazolite' (v)	WFib
§	- 'Très Coupé'	MMuc SArc SEND
	- 'Trinity'	WFib
	- 'Tripod'	MHost WFib
	- 'Triton'	WFib
	- 'Troll'	WFib
	- 'Ursula' (v)	MHost WFib
	- 'Very Merry'	WFib
	- 'Vitifolium'	see *H. hibernica* 'Vitifolia'
§	- 'White Knight' (v) ♀H5	WFib
	- 'White Mein Herz'	see *H. helix* 'Snow Cap'
	- 'White Ripple' (v)	MHost WFib
	- 'White Wonder'	LCro LOPS MHost SPoG
	- 'Williamsiana' (v)	WFib
	- 'Woerneri'	see *H.* × *soroksarensis* 'Woerneri'

	Name	Suppliers
	- 'Yellow Ripple'	see *H. helix* 'Golden Starlight'
	- 'Zebra' (v)	WFib
	hibernica	CBcs CCVT EPfP EWTr LBuc LRHS MRav MSwo NOrn SCob SEWo SGol SGsty SPer SWeb SWvt WFib
	- 'Angularis Aurea' ♀H5	WFib
	- 'Anna Marie'	see *H. helix* 'Anna Marie'
	- 'Betty Allen'	WFib
§	- 'Crûg Gold'	WCru
§	- 'Dealbata' (v)	CMac SRms WFib
§	- 'Deltoidea' ♀H5	MWht WCFE WFib
	- 'Digitata Crûg Gold'	see *H. hibernica* 'Crûg Gold'
	- 'Ebony'	see *H. hibernica* (Hibernica Group) 'Ebony'
	- 'Glengariff'	WFib
§	- 'Gracilis'	WFib
§	- 'Hamilton'	WFib
§	- (Hibernica Group) 'Ebony'	WFib
§	- - 'Rona' (v)	WFib
	- - 'Sulphurea' (v)	WFib
	- - 'Variegata' (v)	WFib
	- 'Lobata Major'	SRms
	- 'Palmata'	WFib
	- 'Rona'	see *H. hibernica* (Hibernica Group) 'Rona'
	- 'Sagittifolia'	CTri EPfP SCob
§	- 'Spetchley' ♀H5	CMac GKev MRav NLar NPer NWad WCot WFib WGrn
I	- 'Vitifolia'	WFib
§	***iberica***	WFib
	maderensis	WFib
	maroccana 'Morocco'	WFib
	- 'Spanish Canary'	WFib
§	***nepalensis***	WFib
	- KWJ 12345	WCru
	- 'Marbled Dragon'	WFib
§	- 'Suzanne'	WFib
	pastuchovii	EShb WFib
	- from Troödos, Cyprus	see *H. pastuchovii* subsp. *cypria*
	- 'Ann Ala' ♀H5	MBlu WAvo WCot WFib
§	- subsp. ***cypria***	WFib
	- 'Lagocetti'	see *H. pastuchovii* 'Lagodekhi'
§	- 'Lagodekhi'	WFib
§	***rhombea***	WCot WFib
	- 'Japonica'	see *H. rhombea*
	- 'Variegata' (v)	WFib
§	× ***soroksarensis*** 'Woerneri'	NLar WFib

Hedychium ✿ (*Zingiberaceae*)

	Name	Suppliers
	from Ziyadum, Myanmar **new**	WPGP
	'Anne Bishop'	SEND
	aurantiacum	CBcs CBct CCCN CDTJ CTsd GKev LEdu SPalm XLum
	aureum	LEdu WPGP
	brevicaule B&SWJ 7171	WCru
	'C.P. Raffill'	see *H.* × *moorei* 'Raffillii'
	chrysoleucum	CCCN
*	'Clarkei'	CCCN
	coccineum	CDTJ CTsd GKev MHid MNrw
	- B&SWJ 5238	WCru
	- from Mizoram, India	WPGP
	- var. ***angustifolium***	WPGP
	- 'Disney'	CDTJ
	- 'Hungphung Stripe'	LEdu WPGP
	- 'Khangkhui Tall Boy'	LEdu MHid WPGP
	- 'Khonoma Silver'	LEdu WPGP
	- 'Shillong Ghost'	LEdu WPGP
	coronarium ♀H1c	CAbb CAvo CBct CCCN CDTJ CExl CTsd GKev MHid SPer XBlo XLum
	- B&SWJ 3745	WCru
	- 'Gold Spot'	CCCN CTsd GKev
	- var. ***urophyllum***	see *H. flavum* Roxb.
	densiflorum	CAbb CCCN CDTJ CExl CTsd ECha GKev LCro LEdu LOPS MHid SDix SPalm SRms WCot WCru WPGP XLum
	- EN 562	CExl
	- LS&H 17393	CExl
	- 'Assam Orange'	CAvo CCCN CExl CPla CSam CTsd IDee IPot LEdu MHid MNrw SChr SDix SEND SPlb WCru WPGP WSMil
	- 'Sorung'	CDTJ CExl LEdu SChr WPGP
	- 'Stephen'	CAvo CBct CCCN CDTJ CExl EBee IPot LEdu LRHS MNrw SChr SPlb WPGP
	'Devon Cream'	CCCN CDTJ CExl CTsd LRHS SChr WSMil
	'Doctor Moy' (v)	CDTJ MHid NGKo
	'Elizabeth'	IPot
	ellipticum	CAbb CCCN CDTJ CTsd GKev SDir SPalm XLum
	- B&SWJ 8354	WCru
	- PAB 7867	LEdu WPGP
	'Filigree'	CExl
§	***flavescens***	CBct CCCN CDTJ CTsd EBee GKev LCro LOPS
	flavum misapplied	see *H. flavescens*
§	***flavum*** Roxb.	CAbb CBcs XLum
	- HWJ 604	WCru
	forrestii misapplied	see *H.* 'Helen Dillon'
	forrestii Diels	CTsd IDee SPlb
	- KWJ 12314	WCru
	gardnerianum ♀H2	CAbb CAby CDTJ CExl CTsd EBee GKev LCro LEdu LOPS LRHS MHid MNrw MSCN NGKo SArc SChr SDeJ SDir SPer SPlb WCru WSMil XLum
	- B&SWJ 12533	WCru
	- NJM 13.079 **new**	WPGP
	'Gold Flame'	EBee
	gomezianum	LEdu
	gracile	WCru
	greenii	CBcs CBct CCCN CDTJ CTsd EWld GKev IDee LEdu MNrw MPie SDir SPalm SPlb WBor WCru XLum
	- 'Mhui Fang'	WPGP
	griffithianum	CCCN CDTJ XLum
	- white-flowered	CCCN
§	'Helen Dillon'	CCCN CDTJ CExl ESwi LEdu SArc WCru WPGP
	'Keneggy'	SVen
	'Luna Moth'	WPGP
	luteum	CTsd
	maximum	CAby CDTJ SChr SMad WPGP
	- B&SWJ 8261A	WCru
	- HWJ 810	WCru
§	× ***moorei*** 'Raffillii'	WCru
	pink-flowered	WSMil
	'Samsheri'	CCCN SChr
	spicatum	CAbb CAvo CCCN CDTJ CExl CTsd GKev GPoy LEdu MNrw MRav SMHy WPGP
	- B&SWJ 7231	WCru
	- CC 1705	CExl
	- P. Bon. 57188	CExl WPGP
	- PAB 13.0718	LEdu
	- from Ciaojiang	SBrt

- from Salween Valley, China	CExl
- var. ***acuminatum***	CAby
- 'Himalayan Lipstick'	GKev
- 'Huani'	LEdu
- 'Liberty'	WCru
- 'Shirui Steps'	LEdu
- 'Singalila'	LEdu WCru WPGP
- 'Tresco'	IPot
- 'Troglodyte'	LEdu WPGP
'St Martin's'	CCCN
stenopetalum	MHid
- B&SWJ 7155	WCru
'Tai Pink Princess' (Tai Series)	CTsd
'Tara' ♀H4	CAvo CBct CCht CDTJ CExl CSam LEdu LRHS MNrw SArc SDix SMHy SMad SPad SPlb WCru WPGP WSMil
tengchongense 'Trum Trom'	WCru
- 'Y Tŷ' **new**	WCru
thyrsiforme	CDTJ CTsd GKev WCru XLum
villosum	CDTJ
- var. ***tenuiflorum***	MHid WPGP
- - KWJ 12305	WCru
wardii	CDTJ CExl CTsd ESwi LRHS MHid WCot WCru WPGP
yunnanense	LEdu SBrt SPlb WPGP
- B&SWJ 7900 **new**	ESwi
- B&SWJ 9717	WCru
- BWJ 7900	WCru
- L 633	CExl
- from Cally Gardens	MAvo WMal
- 'Lago' **new**	WCru

Hedysarum (*Papilionaceae*)

coronarium	CBod CSpe CWld ELan SPhx SPoG WKif WOut
multijugum	MBlu WSHC

Heimia (*Lythraceae*)

salicifolia	ECre IMou MGil SBrt WHil WPGP

Helenium (*Asteraceae*)

'Adios'	WFar
'Amber'	EBee ECtt MAvo MSpe MTis WFar
autumnale	CExl CSBt CTri EPfP LSRN MMuc MNHC NChi SWvt WFar XLum
- 'All Gold'	SWvt
- 'Bandera'	CBod ECtt NRHS
- 'Fuego'[PBR] (Mariachi Series)	CBod CMac CRos CWGN ECtt EHyd EMor LCro LOPS LRHS LSou MAvo MBel MHol MNrw MPri NRHS SCob SRms SWvt WCAu WHil WNPC WWtn
§ - Helena Series	CRos SWvt WFar
§ - - 'Helena Gold'	CBod EPfP NBre WBrk
- - 'Helena Rote Töne'	CBod CChe CRos CSpe EHyd EPfP GAbr LRHS LSun MHol NRHS WBor WBrk WHoo
- - 'Helena Yellow'	EHyd LRHS NRHS WCav
- 'Ranchera'[PBR] (Mariachi Series)	MBel NLar NRHS
- 'Salsa'[PBR] (Mariachi Series)	CBod CKno CMac CRos EHyd ELan ILea LCro LOPS LRHS LSou MAvo NRHS SPad SRms SWvt WNPC
- 'Short and Sassy'[PBR]	CKno EHyd EMor LSou MNrw MPri NLar NRHS SPoG SRms WHil WNPC
- 'Siesta'[PBR] (Mariachi Series)	CRos EHyd LRHS MNrw MPri NRHS SRms
- 'Sombrero'[PBR] (Mariachi Series)	CBod ECtt EHyd EMor LCro LOPS LRHS MPri NEoE SPoG WNPC WWtn
'Baudirektor Linne' ♀H7	EHyd ILea LRHS MTis WCAu WPGP
'Betty'	CBod ECtt LSou
'Biedermeier'	CWCL ECtt MNrw MSpe SAko
bigelovii	XLum
'Blütentisch' misapplied	see *H.* 'Riverton Beauty'
'Blütentisch' Foerster ♀H7	CMea EHyd GMaP LRHS MTis NLar NRHS
'Bressingham Gold'	EHyd LRHS MHCG MNrw WAvo WHrl
'Bruno'	CRos EHyd LRHS MArl NRHS SHar
'Butterpat' ♀H7	CDor CRos ECtt EHyd GMaP LRHS MArl MNrw MRav NRHS
'Can Can'	CBod CRos ECtt EHyd ELon EMor EPfP IPot LRHS MAvo MNrw MTis NGdn NRHS SPer SRms WCAu WFar WGoo
'Carmen' (UFO Series)	CBod MSpe
'Chelsey'	ECtt ELan EMor EPfP GQue LCro LOPS LPla LRHS LSRN MNrw MRav MSpe MTis NBPC NLar NSti SPoG SRms
'Chipperfield Orange'	CSam ECtt GMaP MArl NBPC NBir NGdn WOld
'Coppelia'	ECtt EHyd LRHS MHol MTis NBir NGdn WFar
COPPER SPRAY	see *H.* 'Kupfersprudel'
DARK BEAUTY	see *H.* 'Dunkle Pracht'
'Dauerbrenner'	MSpe MTis SHar
'Die Blonde'	SMHy
'Doktor Hartmann'	MSpe
'Double Trouble'[PBR]	CBod CCBP EBee ECtt EHyd EMor GBin LRHS MBNS MHol NGdn NHpl NRHS SGbt SPer SRms WCot WFar
§ 'Dunkle Pracht' ♀H7	EBee ECtt EWTr ILea LSRN MSpe NLar WFar WOld
'El Dorado'	CMea CRos CWCL EBee ECtt EHyd ELon EMor LEdu LRHS MAvo MSpe MTis NDov NRHS NSti SHar SRms WCot WFar
'Fata Morgana'	CBod ECtt EMor MAvo MSpe MTis NBre
'Festival'	ECtt
'Feuersiegel' ♀H7	CRos ECtt EHyd LRHS MSpe NRHS SAko WOld
'Fiesta'	ECtt MAvo MSpe MTis WFar
'Flamenco'	MSpe WFar
'Flammendes Käthchen'	CRos EBee ECtt EHyd LRHS NRHS SAko SHar
'Flammenrad'	EBee SAko
'Flammenspiel'	ECtt EHyd LRHS MNrw
flexuosum	SPhx
'Gartensonne' ♀H7	LPla MAvo WAvo
'Gay-go-round'	MAvo
'Gelbe Waltraut'	MAvo MSpe
'Gold Doubloons'	EBee
GOLD FOX	see *H.* 'Goldfuchs'
'Gold Intoxication'	see *H.* 'Goldrausch'
GOLDEN YOUTH	see *H.* 'Goldene Jugend'
§ 'Goldene Jugend'	ECtt ELon WCot
§ 'Goldfuchs'	WCot
§ 'Goldlackzwerg'	EHyd LRHS WMal
§ 'Goldrausch'	EBee ECtt EPfP GBin LSou MMrt MNrw MSpe MTis NGdn SAko WCAu WFar WOld
'Goldreif'	CMea

'Hartmut Rieger'	CSam
'Helena' misapplied	see *H. autumnale* 'Helena Gold'
'Herbstgold'	MSpe
hoopesii	see *Hymenoxys hoopesii*
'Hot Lava'	CWGN ECtt MNrw MSpe MTis
'Hot Luv'	WCot
'Indianersommer'	CDor CWCL ECtt GMaP GWyn ILea LRHS MNrw MSpe NLar SPhx SSut WCFE WGoo WSpi
'Jam Tarts'	WCot
'Julisamt'	LEdu
'July Sun'	NBir
'Kanaria'	CBod CDor CRos EBee ECtt EHyd EMor EPfP GBin GWyn ILea LPot LRHS MBel MRav MSpe MTis NLar NRHS NSti WHil
'Karneol' ♀H7	CRos EHyd EPfP LRHS NRHS
'Kleine Aprikose'	MTis
'Königstiger' ♀H7	CRos ECtt EHyd GBee GBin ILea LRHS LSou MAvo MHCG MNrw NRHS SAko WFar
'Kugelsonne'	CSam GBin ILea NBre NLar SAko WCAu
§ 'Kupfersprudel'	MAvo MTis SAko
'Kupferziegel'	MSpe
'Kupferzwerg'	CWCL EAJP ELan MSpe NBre SAko
'Lambada'	EBee SMHy
'Lemon Queen'	WSpi
'Little Orange'	WGoo
'Loysder Wieck'	CKno EBee ECtt EWTr MAvo MBel MSpe MTis NGdn WCAu
'Luc' ♀H5	ELon GBin MAvo MTis WCot
§ 'Mahagoni'	SHar
MAHOGANY	see *H.* 'Mahagoni'
'Mahogany'	see *H.* 'Goldlackzwerg'
MARDI GRAS ('Helbro')	CAby EBee ECtt EHyd EMor EPfP LRHS LSou MBel MCot MHol MSpe MTis NRHS SPoG SRms SWvt WCAu WNPC
'Margot'	MSpe MTis NBre
'Marion Nickig'	MAvo WFar
'Meranti'	CMea MAvo NDov SWvt WCot
'Moerheim Beauty' ♀H7	Widely available
'Monique' (UFO Series) **new**	CBod
'Moth'	MTis
'Oldenburg'	WCot
'Pat's Promise'	CMea SWvt
PIPSQUEAK ('Blopip')	CKno EMor LRHS NBre SRms
'Poncho'	MMrt SRms
'Potter's Wheel'	CBod EBee ECtt MSpe NLar SHar SRms
puberulum	CRos EHyd LRHS NBir NGrd NRHS
'Pumilum Magnificum'	EHyd ELan EPfP GQue LEdu MSpe NBPC NRHS SMad SPer WFar XLum
'Ragamuffin'	ECtt GQue MAvo MTis SWvt WCot
'Rauchtopas'	CAby GWyn ILea LCro LEdu LOPS LPla LSou MAvo MBel MSpe MTis NDov NLar SAko WGoo WPGP
RED AND GOLD	see *H.* 'Rotgold' Foerster
'Red Army'	CMea ECtt EHyd ELan ELon EMor GBee LEdu LRHS MAvo MSpe NGdn SRkn SRms SWvt
'Red Glory'	MTis
'Red Jewel'	CBod CRos EBee ECtt EHyd ELan ELon LRHS MAvo MBriF MHol MMuc MNrw MPie NGdn NLar NRHS SAko SCob SEdd WCAu WCFE WCot WHoo WKif WPGP
'Ring of Fire' ♀H7	SMHy
§ 'Riverton Beauty'	CSam ECha ECtt MNrw NChi SDix WCot WHoo
'Riverton Gem'	ECtt GBee GQue MHCG MSpe
'Rotgold' misapplied	see *H. autumnale* Helena Series
§ 'Rotgold' Foerster	ECtt SRms
'Rouge Foncé'	WCot WFar
'Rubinzwerg' ♀H7	Widely available
'Ruby Charm'	ECtt EPfP MHol MNrw WCot WFar
§ 'Ruby Thuesday'	Widely available
'Ruby Tuesday'	see *H.* 'Ruby Thuesday'
'Sahin's Early Flowerer' ♀H7	Widely available
'Septemberfuchs'	LEdu MCot MTis SAko SPhx
'Sonnenwunder'	CSam NBre
'Sophie zur Linden'	ECtt MTis WCot
'Sunshine Superman'	CMea
'The Bishop'	CRos EBee ECtt EHyd EMor EPfP LCro LOPS LRHS MRav NHol NRHS SCob SGbt SWvt WFar
'Tie Dye'	CBod EBee ECtt EPfP MAvo MHol NBPC NGdn SPoG WFar
'Tijuana Brass'	ECtt NLar
'Tip Top'	EHyd LRHS
'Vicky'	MHCG SHar
'Vivace'	ELon LEdu MSpe WCot WPGP
'Wagon Wheel'	ECtt WFar
'Waldhorn'	WPGP
'Waltraut' ♀H7	Widely available
'Wesergold' ♀H7	CRos EBee EHyd EMor EWTr LPla LRHS NDov NRHS NSti SPoG WCAu
'Wonnadonga'	MTis
'Wyndley'	CAby CBcs CDor CMea CRos ECtt EHyd ELan EMor EPfP EShb GMaP LPot LRHS MBel MHer MRav MTis NBir NGdn NLar NRHS SGbt SPer SRms WCAu WCav WFar WHoo
'Zimbelstern'	ECtt MAvo MCot MPie MSpe MTis NLar WCot WFar WPGP
'Zonnedam'	ECtt

Heliamphora (*Sarraceniaceae*)

nutans	SHmp

Helianthella (*Asteraceae*)

§ ***quinquenervis***	EBee EHyd EPfP LRHS NLar NRHS WFar

Helianthemum (*Cistaceae*)

'Albert's Brick'	NRush
'Alice Howorth'	NRush WIce
'Amabile Plenum' (d)	GAbr GBin NRush
'Amy Baring' ♀H5	CRos CTri ECtt EHyd LRHS NRHS NWad SRms WHoo
'Annabel' (d)	CRos ECtt EHyd GBin LRHS NRHS WFar
apenninum	EPPr LPla SBut SRms XSen
'Apricot'	CTri ECtt
'Apricot Blush'	WAbe
'Baby Buttercup'	CMea NRush
'Beech Park Red'	CSma CTri ECtt EPot ITim NRush WAbe WFar WHoo WIce WKif
'Ben Afflick'	CRos ECtt EHyd LRHS NRHS NRush NSla SRms
'Ben Alder'	ECtt GAbr
'Ben Dearg'	CMea ECtt SRms
'Ben Fhada'	Widely available
'Ben Heckla'	CRos ECtt EHyd GAbr LRHS NRHS SRms XLum

	'Ben Hope'	CRos CTri ECtt EHyd ELan EPfP LRHS NRHS SCob SRms WIce XLum XSen
§	'Ben Ledi'	CBcs ECtt ELan GAbr GJos GMaP MAsh MBros NHol SCob SEND SGbt SPoG SRms WAbe WFar WIce
	'Ben Lomond'	GAbr
	'Ben More'	CAvo CBcs CRos ECtt EHyd ELan EPfP GAbr GJos GMaP LRHS MAsh MBros MRav MSwo NBir NRHS NRush SCob SEND SPoG SRms WFar WHoo WIce
	'Ben Nevis'	CTri GAbr NRush SRms
	'Ben Vane'	CRos ECtt EHyd LRHS NRHS NRush SRms
	'Boughton Double Primrose' (d)	WAbe WFar
	'Broughty Sunset'	ECtt GAbr NRush
	'Bunbury'	ECtt ELon EPfP GJos NBir NRush SPoG SRms WFar
I	'Butter and Eggs'	SRms
	canum subsp. ***balcanicum***	WAbe
	'Captivation'	ECtt NHol NRush
	'Cerise Queen' (d)	CTri ECha ECtt EPfP GKev MHol MSwo NRush SEND SPer SRms WFar
	chamaecistus	see *H. nummularium*
	'Cheviot'	ECtt NBir WHoo XLum
	'Chocolate Blotch'	CRos EHyd LRHS NRHS NRush NWad SEND SRms
	'Coachman's Salmon Coral'	NRush
	'Cornish Cream'	ECtt GAbr NHol NRush SRms
	cupreum	GAbr GKev
	'David'	NHol
	'David Ritchie'	WHoo
	'Diana'	CMea ECtt EPot WIce
	'Elfenbeinglanz'	WFar
	'Etna'	NRush
	'Everton Ruby'	see *H.* 'Ben Ledi'
	'Fairy'	EHyd ELan EPfP NRush
§	'Fire Dragon' Υ^{H4}	CMea CRos EAJP ECtt EHyd ELan EPfP GAbr GMaP LRHS NBir NRHS NRush SGbt SRms WAbe XLum XSen
	'Fireball'	see *H.* 'Mrs C.W. Earle'
	'Georgeham'	CAvo CMea CSma EBou ECtt ELon GAbr NBir NHol NRush SPhx SRms WHoo XLum
§	'Golden Queen'	EBou ECtt EPfP MAsh MHol MSwo NRush SRms WFar
	'Hampstead Orange'	CTri
	'Hartswood Ruby'	CRos EHyd GMaP LRHS LSou NRHS NRush SAko SRms WFar
	'Henfield Brilliant' Υ^{H4}	CExl CPBP CRos CSpe ECha ECtt EHyd ELan ELon EPfP GAbr LRHS MHol MRav NBir NHol NRHS NSla SBut SPoG SRms WCav WCot WHil WHoo WSMil XLum
	'Highdown'	SRms
	'Highdown Apricot'	CRos ECtt EHyd ELon LRHS NRHS NRush SPoG SRms WRHF
	'Honeymoon'	ECtt NRush NWad
	'Jubilee' (d) Υ^{H4}	CBod CTri ECtt ELan GJos MAsh NBir NChi NHol SPoG SRms WCav WKif
	'Karen's Silver'	WAbe
	'Kathleen Druce' (d)	ECtt NWad
	'Kathleen Mary'	CMea WIce
	'Lawrenson's Pink'	CRos CSma ECtt EHyd GJos LRHS MHol NRHS SAko SRms WCAu WFar XSen
	'Lemon Queen'	ECtt NRush
	'Lucy Elizabeth'	ECtt
	lunulatum	CMea CRos EHyd LRHS NRHS NWad SRms WAbe
	'Mead Sunset'	CMea ECtt
§	'Mrs C.W. Earle' (d) Υ^{H4}	CTri ECtt EHyd ELan EPfP GKev LRHS MBow MBros NRHS NRush SRms
	'Mrs Clay'	see *H.* 'Fire Dragon'
	'Mrs Croft'	SRms
	'Mrs Hays'	ECtt
	'Mrs Lake'	NRush
	'Mrs Mold'	NRush
	'Mrs Moules'	SRms
	mutabile	SPlb SVic WFar
	'New Moon'	CSma NRush
§	***nummularium***	CBee ENfk GPoy GQue MBow MHer MNHC NAts NMir SRms WAbe WIce WSFF WWild
§	- subsp. ***tomentosum***	GAbr
	oelandicum	NSla NWad SRms WAbe
	- subsp. ***alpestre***	EBou
	- subsp. ***italicum***	ITim
	- subsp. ***piloselloides***	EPot WAbe
	'Old Gold'	ECtt SRms WAbe
	'Orange Phoenix' (d)	ECtt NRush NWad
	'Ovum Supreme'	NHol
	'Peach'	CTri
	'Pershore Orange'	NRush
	'Pink Angel' (d)	CPBP CSma NRush SRms WAbe WFar
	'Pink Glow'	GAbr
	'Praecox'	CMea CTri ECtt SRms WHoo
	'Prima Donna'	EHyd ELan EPfP
	'Prostrate Orange'	NRush SRms
	'Raspberry Ripple'	CRos CSma EBou ECtt EHyd ELan EPfP EPot LRHS NRHS NRush SPoG SRms
	'Razzle Dazzle' (v)	NRush SRms WHil
	'Red Dragon'	EPot NRush WAbe
	'Red Orient'	see *H.* 'Supreme'
	'Regenbogen' (d)	CPBP ECtt GAbr SEND
§	'Rhodanthe Carneum' Υ^{H4}	CMea CRos EAJP EBou ECha ECtt EHyd ELan EPfP EWTr GJos GMaP LRHS MMrt MRav MSwo NBir NRHS NRush SCob SEND SPer SPhx SPoG SRms WAbe WCav WKif
§	'Rosakönigin'	EBou ECtt GAbr NHol NRush SEND WAbe
	'Rose of Leeswood' (d)	CBod ECtt GJos SPoG SRms WHoo WKif XLum
	ROSE QUEEN	see *H.* 'Rosakönigin'
	'Roxburgh Gold'	NRush SRms
	'Ruth'	SEND
	'Saint John's College Yellow'	EHyd LRHS NRHS SRms
	'Salmon Queen'	CRos ECtt EHyd LRHS NRHS NRush SEND SRms
	'Shot Silk'	CSma ECtt EWes NRush SRms
	'Snow Queen'	see *H.* 'The Bride'
	'Sterntaler'	GAbr SAko SRms WFar
	'Strawberry Fields'	ECtt NSla
	'Sudbury Gem'	CRos CTri ECha ECtt EHyd LRHS NRHS NRush SRms
	'Sulphur Moon'	CRos EHyd LRHS NRHS SRms
	'Sunbeam'	ECtt NRush SRms
§	'Supreme'	ECtt ELan EPfP EWes MHol NRush SAko SRms

syriacum **new**	SPhx
'Tangerine'	ECtt
§ 'The Bride' 𝕐H4	Widely available
'Tigrinum Plenum' (d)	EWes
'Tomato Red'	ECtt NRush
tomentosum	see *H. nummularium* subsp. *tomentosum*
umbellatum	see *Halimium umbellatum*
'Voltaire'	ECtt NRush NWad
'Welsh Flame'	ECtt NHol WAbe
'Whenday'	CMea
'Wisley Pink'	see *H.* 'Rhodanthe Carneum'
'Wisley Primrose' 𝕐H4	Widely available
'Wisley Rose'	CRos EHyd LRHS NRHS
'Wisley White'	CTri ECha ECtt ELan GAbr SHar
'Wisley Yellow'	ECtt NRush WCav
'Yellow Queen'	see *H.* 'Golden Queen'

Helianthus (*Asteraceae*)

angustifolius	SDix
'Anne'	ELon NDov
annuus	SVic
- 'Claret' 𝕐H4	LCro LOPS
- 'Garden Statement' **new**	LCro LOPS
- 'Moonbright' **new**	SVic
- 'Ring of Fire' **new**	SVic
- 'Sonja' **new**	SVic
- 'Sunbright' 𝕐H4 **new**	SVic
- 'Sunrich Orange' (Sunrich Series) **new**	SVic
atrorubens	MRav NBro
'Bitter Chocolate'	LEdu WPGP
'Capenoch Star' 𝕐H5	ECtt EHyd GMaP LEdu LRHS MArl MRav MTis NBro NLar SDix SWvt WCAu
'Capenoch Supreme'	ECtt EHyd LRHS
'Carine'	ELon GBin LEdu MNrw MTis NLar SEdd WCot WFar WOld
debilis subsp. ***cucumerifolius*** **new**	SVic
- 'Vanilla Ice'	LCro LOPS
* ***decapetalus*** 'Kastle Kobena'	CDor
- MORNING SUN	see *H.* 'Morgensonne'
'Dorian Roxburgh'	ECha ECtt LPla MAvo WCot
× ***doronicoides***	GWyn
'Double Whammy' (d)	ECtt
'Flying Saucers'	CKno
giganteus	CMea SHar
- 'Sheila's Sunshine'	CElw CRos EBee EHyd EPPr EWes GBin ILea LPla LRHS MNrw NDov NRHS SAko SHar SMHy SPhx WFar WOld
'Gullick's Variety' 𝕐H5	CBre ECtt EMor NBro NChi NLar SPhx SWvt WFar WOld XLum
'Happy Days' 𝕐H5	CRos CSam ECtt EPfP EWes GBin LSou MAvo MHol MTis NGBl SPeP SRms WCot WFar WHoo WOld WRHF WTyc
'Hazel's Gold'	EHyd LRHS
× ***kellermanii***	EBee MAvo SPhx
§ × ***laetiflorus***	EPPr GPSL MMuc NLar
- 'Daniel Dewar'	MMuc
- var. ***rigidus***	see *H. pauciflorus*
§ 'Lemon Queen' 𝕐H4	Widely available
'Limelight'	see *H.* 'Lemon Queen'
'Loddon Gold' 𝕐H5	ECtt EHyd ELan EMor EPfP EShb LRHS MArl MBel MRav MTis NBir NRHS SMad SWvt WBor WCot WFar
§ ***maximiliani***	CBod ELan ELon EPPr MMuc SMad SPhx SPtp
microcephalus	CSam EBee ELon IMou MMuc NDov
- 'JS Straffe Prairie Gast'	MNrw WFar
'Miss Mellish' 𝕐H5	EBee ECtt LEdu LPla WBor WBrk WCot WFar WHoo
mollis	CBod CSam MMuc SBrt SPhx WFar
'Monarch' 𝕐H5	CMea CSam EBee EWhm GBee MBel MMuc MRav NLar SMad WCot WFar WHal WOld
§ 'Morgensonne'	MTis WBor WCot
× ***multiflorus*** 'Meteor'	EHyd LRHS NBre
'O Sole Mio'	SDix WCot WFar
occidentalis	EPPr SPhx
orgyalis	see *H. salicifolius*
§ ***pauciflorus***	EBee
quinquenervis	see *Helianthella quinquenervis*
'Razzmatazz'	SAko
rigidus misapplied	see *H.* × *laetiflorus*
rigidus (Cass.) Desf.	see *H. pauciflorus*
§ ***salicifolius***	CBod EBee ECtt EHyd ELan ELon GBin LEdu LRHS LSun MBel MBriF MCot MHol MMuc MPie NBir NRHS SAko SDix SEND SMad SPad SPoG SWvt WAul WCot WFar WPGP XLum
- 'Low Down'^{PBR}	SCob SWvt
- 'Table Mountain'^{PBR}	LRHS MBel SWvt WHil
- very fine-leaved	WCot
scaberrimus	see *H.* × *laetiflorus*
'Soleil d'Or'	ECtt SRms WFar WHal
strumosus	WCot
'Triomphe de Gand'	LEdu MTis NDov WFar
tuberosus	EBee GPoy
- 'Bleu Patate'	LEdu
- 'Drago'	LEdu
- 'Dwarf'	LEdu
- 'Fuseau'	LCro LOPS SVic
- 'Garnet'	LEdu
- 'Sakhalinski'	LEdu
- 'Sugarball'	LEdu

Helichrysum (*Asteraceae*)

adenocarpum	SPlb
alveolatum	see *H. splendidum*
amorginum 'Pink Bud'	MMuc
- RUBY CLUSTER ('Blorub'^{PBR})	CRos EHyd LBuc LRHS NRHS SCob
angustifolium	see *H. italicum* subsp. *italicum*
- from Crete	see *H. microphyllum* (Willd.) Cambess.
§ ***arwae***	WAbe
bellidioides	see *Anaphalioides bellidioides*
bellum	GBin
bracteatum	see *Xerochrysum bracteatum*
- 'King Fireball'	CSpe
'Coco'	see *Xerochrysum bracteatum* 'Coco'
coralloides	see *Ozothamnus coralloides*
'County Park Silver'	see *Ozothamnus* 'County Park Silver'
'Dargan Hill Monarch'	see *Xerochrysum bracteatum* 'Dargan Hill Monarch'
'Elmstead'	see *H. stoechas* 'White Barn'
frigidum	EPot WAbe
heldreichii	WMal
hookeri	see *Ozothamnus hookeri*
§ ***hypoleucum***	SDix

	'Icicles'	ELan GBin SEdd
	italicum	CBod CCBP EBou ECha ENfk GBin GMaP GPoy GQue GWyn MHer MMuc MNHC SArc SEND SPoG SRms SVen SVic WCav WHer XLum XSen
	- 'Dartington'	CBod ENfk GBin SRms
§	- subsp. ***italicum*** new	CTsd SEdi
	- 'Korma'PBR	CBod EHyd ELan EPfP EWTr EWhm GBin LRHS MAsh MHol NRHS SLon SRms
	- subsp. ***microphyllum***	see *H. microphyllum* (Willd.) Cambess.
§	- subsp. ***serotinum***	CBcs EPfP GPoy LCro LOPS LRHS MRav SLim SPer SRms SWvt
	lanatum	see *H. thianschanicum*
	ledifolium	see *Ozothamnus ledifolius*
	marginatum misapplied	see *H. milfordiae*
	microphyllum	see *Plecostachys serpyllifolia*
	microphyllum ambig.	MMuc SRms
§	***microphyllum*** (Willd.) Cambess.	CCBP ENfk MNHC SEND
§	***milfordiae*** ♀H4	ITim SPlb SRms WAbe
	orientale	EPot XSen
	pagophilum	GKev WAbe
	petiolare ♀H3	CSam EBak ECtt MCot SPer SPoG
	- 'Aureum'	see *H. petiolare* 'Limelight'
	- 'Goring Silver' ♀H3	SPoG
§	- 'Limelight' ♀H3	CSam ECtt MCot MPri SPer SPoG
	- 'Variegatum' (v) ♀H3	ECtt MCot SPoG
	populifolium misapplied	see *H. hypoleucum*
	rosmarinifolium	see *Ozothamnus rosmarinifolius*
§	'Schwefellicht'	EBee ECha EPfP MRav SPer WSHC
	selago	see *Ozothamnus selago*
	serotinum	see *H. italicum* subsp. *serotinum*
	serpyllifolium	see *Plecostachys serpyllifolia*
	sessilioides	EPot WAbe
§	***splendidum*** ♀H4	LRHS NBro SLon XSen
	stoechas	XSen
	- 'Silverball' new	CRos
§	- 'White Barn'	MAvo WCot WMal WRHF XLum
	SULPHUR LIGHT	see *H.* 'Schwefellicht'
§	***thianschanicum***	SRms XLum
	- GOLDEN BABY	see *H. thianschanicum* 'Goldkind'
§	- 'Goldkind'	NBir XLum
	- 'White Wonder'	EHyd LRHS NRHS SArc SEdd
	trilineatum misapplied	see *H. splendidum*
	tumidum	see *Ozothamnus selago* var. *tumidus*
	witbergense	GKev
	woodii	see *H. arwae*

Helicodiceros (*Araceae*)

§	***muscivorus***	NGKo WCot

Heliconia ✿ (*Heliconiaceae*)

	caribaea 'Burgundy'	see *H. caribaea* 'Purpurea'
§	- 'Purpurea'	XBlo
	'Golden Torch'	XBlo
	indica 'Spectabilis'	XBlo
	latispatha 'Orange Gyro'	XBlo
*	- 'Red Gyro'	XBlo
	metallica	XBlo
	psittacorum	CCCN
	rostrata	CCCN XBlo

Helictotrichon (*Poaceae*)

	planiculme new	EPPr
	pratense	CHab
§	***sempervirens*** ♀H5	Widely available

I	- 'Pendulum'	CBod GBin MSpe XSen
	- 'Saphirsprudel'	CBod EBee EHyd EPfP LRHS NRHS NSti WCot WPGP

Heliophila (*Brassicaceae*)

	coronopifolia	CSpe

Heliopsis (*Asteraceae*)

	GOLDEN PLUME	see *H. helianthoides* var. *scabra* 'Goldgefieder'
	helianthoides	CPla CRos EBee LRHS NBre WCav WFar
	- 'Limelight'	see *Helianthus* 'Lemon Queen'
	- LORAINE SUNSHINE ('Helhan'PBR) (v)	CWGN ECtt EMor MHol NWsh SPoG WCot WFar
	- var. ***scabra***	NHol
	- - 'Asahi'	CBod ECtt MSpe WHil
	- - BALLERINA	see *H. helianthoides* var. *scabra* 'Spitzentänzerin'
	- - 'Benzinggold' ♀H6	EHyd LRHS MRav
	- - 'Burning Hearts'	CWGN MCot NLar SRms
	- - GOLDEN PLUME	see *H. helianthoides* var. *scabra* 'Goldgefieder'
§	- - 'Goldgefieder' ♀H6	EBee MSpe NBre WFar
	- - 'Hohlspiegel'	EHyd GBin LPla LRHS
	- - 'Light of Loddon' ♀H6	EHyd LRHS
	- - 'Mars'	EBee WFar
	- - 'Patula'	EBee ECtt
	- - 'Prairie Sunset'PBR	CBod EBee ECtt SAko
§	- - 'Sommersonne'	CSBt ECtt EHyd ELan EMor EPfP LRHS NGBl NPer SPer SRms
§	- - 'Spitzentänzerin' ♀H6	EBee ECtt MSpe
	- - 'Summer Nights'	EBee ELan EPfP LCro LOPS MNrw NSti SBut SDix SPhx WFar
	- - SUMMER SUN	see *H. helianthoides* var. *scabra* 'Sommersonne'
	- - 'Sunburst' (v)	CRos EHyd LRHS NRHS
	- - 'Venus'	CBod EBee ECtt EHyd LRHS MAsh SRms
	- 'Summer Pink' (v)	CWGN EBee MHol SPoG WCot WFar WWtn
	- 'Sunstruck'	CBod ECtt
	- 'Tuscan Sun'PBR	EBee

Heliotropium ✿ (*Boraginaceae*)

§	***amplexicaule***	SDys
	anchusifolium	see *H. amplexicaule*
§	***arborescens***	ENfk EPfP EShb MCot
	- 'Chatsworth' ♀H1c	CAby CCCN ECre ECtt WABo
	- 'Dame Alice de Hales'	ECtt
	- 'Gatton Park'	ECtt
	- 'Lord Roberts'	ECtt WMal
	- MARINO BLUE ('Kleha07520'PBR) new	LSou MBros
	- 'Mary Fox'	ECtt
	- 'Mrs J.W. Lowther'	ECtt
	- pale lilac-flowered	CSam
	- 'Princess Marina' ♀H1c	LCro LOPS NLar WBor
	- 'Reva'	ECtt
	- 'White Lady'	CCCN CSpe ECtt
	- 'White Queen'	ECtt
	- 'Woodcote'	ECtt
	'Butterfly Kisses'	SPoG
	peruvianum	see *H. arborescens*

Helipterum see *Syncarpha*

	anthemoides	see *Rhodanthe anthemoides*

Helleborus ✿ (*Ranunculaceae*)

	abruzzicus	MAsh

- WM 0227	MPhe
abschasicus	see *H. orientalis* Lam. subsp. *abchasicus*
ANGEL GLOW ('Blt02'PBR)	CRos LRHS NRHS WHil
§ ***argutifolius*** 🏆H5	Widely available
- HGC SNOW FEVER ('Coseh 900'PBR) **new**	SCoo
- 'Red Riding Hood'	LRHS
- 'Silver Lace'	ELan EPfP GKev LRHS LSRN MHol NBir NLar SPoG
atrorubens misapplied	see *H. orientalis* Lam. subsp. *abchasicus* Early Purple Group
atrorubens ambig.	MAsh
atrorubens Waldst. & Kit.	MRav XEll
- WM 9028 from Slovenia	MPhe
- WM 9805 from Croatia	MPhe
- spotted	MPhe
× ***ballardiae***	EPfP GKev
- 'Candy Love'PBR	CRos EHyd EPfP LCro LOPS LRHS MHol NLar NRHS SCob
- HGC CAMELOT ('Coseh 940'PBR)	CRos ECtt EHyd EPfP LRHS NLar NRHS
- HGC CHAMPION ('Coseh 730'PBR)	EHyd LRHS
- HGC MAESTRO ('Coseh 890'PBR)	CRos EHyd EPfP LRHS NRHS
- HGC MERLIN ('Coseh 810'PBR)	CRos EShb LRHS NLar SCoo SPoG
- HGC SNOW DANCE ('Coseh 800'PBR)	CRos EHyd EPfP LRHS NRHS SPoG
bocconei WM 1332 from Sicily	MPhe
-WM 1334 from Calabria, Italy	MPhe
- WM 9719 from Italy	MPhe
- WM 9905 from Sicily	MPhe
colchicus	see *H. orientalis* Lam. subsp. *abchasicus*
corsicus	see *H. argutifolius*
- 'Marble' (v)	CSpe
croaticus WM 9810	MPhe
dumetorum	MAsh
- WM 1306 from Hungary	MPhe
- WM 1309 from Slovenia	MPhe
- WM 9209	MPhe
- WM 9627 from Croatia	MPhe
§ × ***ericsmithii***	CExl EPfP LRHS LSRN MAsh NLar WPGP WSpi
- 'Bob's Best'	CExl EPfP MHol SRms SWvt
- HGC JOKER ('Coseh 740'PBR)	EShb LRHS SPoG
- HGC MARLON CREAM ('Coseh 980'PBR)	LRHS NRHS
- HGC MONTE CRISTO ('Coseh 860'PBR)	CRos EHyd EPfP LRHS NRHS SCoo
- HGC SHOOTING STAR ('Coseh 790'PBR)	CRos ECre EHyd EPfP LRHS NLar NRHS
- 'HGC Silvermoon'PBR	LRHS NLar
- MOLLY'S WHITE ('Epbrd01'PBR)	CRos MPri
- 'Pink Beauty'PBR	CEnd EPfP MHtn NLar SEdd SLon SPoG WCot
- 'Pirouette'PBR	ECre EPfP EShb LCro LOPS LRHS MAsh NRHS
- 'Ruby Glow'	EHyd EPfP LRHS
- 'Snow Love'PBR	CRos EHyd EPfP LBuc LRHS NLar NRHS
- 'Winter Moonbeam'PBR	CBcs CEnd CRos ECtt EPfP LBuc LRHS LSRN LSou LSun MAsh MHol NRHS SEdd SLon SPoG SRms WCot
- 'Winter Sunshine'PBR	CRos EPfP LBuc LRHS NRHS SPoG SRms
foetidus 🏆H7	Widely available
- 'Chedglow'	CNat
- 'Chedglow Variegated' (v)	CNat
- 'Gold Bullion'	CAby CSpe MAsh SPoG
- 'Green Giant'	SEND
- 'Harvington Pewter'	EHyd LRHS NRHS
- 'Miss Jekyll'	MAsh
- 'Ruth'	MAsh
- Wester Flisk Group	CAby CBod CExl ECtt EPfP GWyn LEdu MAsh NHol NPer SEND SMad SPoG SPtp WAvo WPGP WSpi
Gold Collection	see *Helleborus* with names starting HGC
'Golden Sunrise' (Winter Jewels Series)	CBod
'Harvington Rebekah'PBR	CRos EHyd LRHS NRHS
HGC CINNAMON SNOW ('Coseh 700'PBR)	ECre EShb ESwi LRHS NLar NRHS SCoo
HGC ICE 'N' ROSES RED ('Coseh 4100') **new**	CRos
HGC ICE 'N' ROSES WHITE ('Coseh 4500') **new**	CRos
HGC MADAME LEMONNIER ('Lem 100'PBR)	CRos EHyd EPfP LRHS MPri NRHS
HGC PARADENIA ('Coseh 960'PBR) **new**	CRos
HGC PINK FROST ('Coseh 710'PBR)	CRos ECtt EHyd EPfP LRHS MPri NLar NRHS SPoG
× ***hybridus***	CBod CBro CMac CMea CSam ECha EHyd ELan EPfP GMaP ITim LCro LOPS LRHS MBel MCot MGos MRav NBid NRHS SCob SPer SRms WAvo WBrk WCAu WCot
- 'Amber Queen' (Queen Series)	EMor
- anemone-centred	EMor LEdu MNrw WFar
- - yellow **new**	CRos
- 'Apple Blossom'	WFar
- 'Apricot Blush' (Winter Jewels Series)	CWGN
- apricot-flowered	WFar
- 'Ashwood Blushing Bride'	MAsh
- 'Ashwood Elegance Pearl'	MAsh
- Ashwood Garden hybrids	ELan EMor EPfP MAsh MRav SRms
- - anemone-centred	MAsh
- - double-flowered (d)	MAsh
- 'Ashwood Lunar Neon'	MAsh
- 'Ashwood Neon Star'	MAsh
- Ballard's Group	EHyd LRHS WFar
- Barnhaven hybrids, anemone-centred	XBar
- - apricot	XBar
- - dark purple	XBar
- - double (d) **new**	XBar
- - green **new**	XBar
- - picotee	XBar
- - pink	XBar
- - red and green	XBar
- - slate	XBar
- - spotted	XBar
- - white	XBar
- - yellow	XBar
- BLACK BEAUTY ('Blck1'PBR)	WSpi
- black-flowered	GMaP WFar

- 'Blue Lady' (Lady Series)	CBar CBcs GKev LRHS MBNS NCou NGdn SPer
- 'Blue Metallic Lady' (Lady Series)	CBod CExl EHyd EPfP GAbr LRHS MBNS MHol NCou NGdn NRHS SPer WSpi WTor
- Bradfield hybrids	MCot
- - anemone-centred	MCot
- - double-flowered (d)	MCot
- - picotee	MCot
- 'Burgundy'	CBod MNHC
- 'Cherry Blossom' (Winter Jewels Series)	CWGN
- 'Cherry Frost'	MAsh
- 'Chocolate Truffle' **new**	CBor
- 'Cinderella'PBR (d)	LRHS SPoG
- 'Circe'	EBee
- 'Clare's Purple'	CBod EWTr
- 'Cosmos'	MBNS
- cream-flowered	WFar
- 'Dark as Night'	CBor WTyc
- dark picotee	WFar
- dark purple-flowered	WFar
- dark red-flowered	WFar
- dark-flowered	WFar
- deep red-flowered	MHol WFar
- double (d)	MNrw WFar
- - black-flowered (d)	CExl LEdu WFar
- - pink-flowered (d)	EMor WCAu WFar
- - white picotee (d)	CBod LRHS NRHS
- - yellow, cream-speckled (d)	CBod CRos EHyd LRHS NRHS
- - dark purple-flowered (d)	WFar
- - green-flowered (d)	CBod WFar
- - picotee (d)	WFar
- - purple-flowered (d)	CBod EMor GEdr MWat WFar
- - red-flowered (d)	CExl WFar
- - white-flowered (d)	CExl GEdr WCAu WFar
- - yellow-flowered (d)	CExl CWCL WFar
- 'Double Ellen Green' (d)	EWTr
- 'Double Ellen Picotee' (d)	CWGN LCro LOPS SEdd
- 'Double Ellen Pink' (d)	LCro LOPS
- 'Double Ellen Pink Spotted' (d) **new**	LCro LOPS
- 'Double Ellen Purple' (d)	LCro LOPS
- 'Double Ellen Red' (d)	LCro LOPS
- 'Double Ellen White' (d)	CWGN EPfP LCro LOPS SCob
- 'Double Ellen White Spotted' (d)	LCro LOPS SCob WCAu
- Double Ladies, mixed (d)	WCot
- 'Enchantment'	MAsh
- Farmyard anemone-centred	WFar
- - apricot	WFar
- - black	WFar
- - cream	WFar
- - - spotted	WFar
- - dark pink	WFar
- - double apricot (d)	WFar
- - - black (d)	WFar
- - - cream (d)	WFar
- - - - spotted (d)	WFar
- - - pink (d)	WFar
- - - - spotted (d)	WFar
- - - primrose (d)	WFar
- - - - spotted (d)	WFar
- - - red (d)	WFar
- - - slate-grey (d)	WFar
- - - white (d)	WFar
- - - - spotted (d)	WFar
- - green	WFar
- - - spotted	WFar
- - picotee	WFar
- - pink	WFar
- - - spotted	WFar
- - plum	WFar
- - primrose	WFar
- - - dark-eyed	WFar
- - - spotted	WFar
- - red	WFar
- - slate spotted	WFar
- - slate-grey	WFar
- - white	WFar
- - - dark-eyed	WFar
- - - splash	WFar
- - - spotted	WFar
- 'Farmyard Appleblossom'	WFar
- 'Farmyard Woodland'	WFar
- 'Gold Red Star'	WSpi
- 'Golden Lotus' (d)	CWGN
- 'Green Ripple'	WFar
- green-flowered	WFar
- Harvington apricot	CRos EHyd LCro LOPS LRHS NBir NLar NRHS SLon
- - double apricot (d)	CRos EHyd LRHS NRHS SHeu
- - - blush (d)	CRos EHyd LRHS NRHS
- - - cream speckled (d)	CRos EHyd LRHS NRHS SPoG
- - - dark purple (d)	CRos EHyd LRHS NRHS
- - - pink (d)	CRos EHyd LCro LOPS LRHS NRHS SHeu SLon SPoG
- - - - speckled (d)	CRos EHyd LCro LOPS LRHS NRHS SHeu
- - - purple (d)	CRos EHyd GAbr GBin LRHS NBir NLar NRHS SHeu SPoG
- - - - cascade (d)	CRos EHyd EPfP LRHS NRHS SHeu
- - - red (d)	CRos EHyd LCro LOPS LRHS NBir NLar NRHS SLon
- - - speckled (d)	SPoG
- - - white (d)	CRos EHyd LCro LOPS LRHS NBir NLar NRHS SHeu SLon SPoG
- - - - speckled (d) **new**	EHyd
- - - yellow (d)	CRos EHyd LRHS NBir NLar NRHS SHeu SLon
- - - - speckled (d)	CRos EHyd LRHS NRHS SHeu
- - - lime-green (d)	CRos EHyd LCro LOPS LRHS NRHS SHeu
- - dusky	CRos EHyd LRHS NRHS
- - picotee	CRos EHyd LRHS NBir NLar NRHS SHeu SLon SPoG
- - pink	CRos EHyd LRHS NLar NRHS SHeu SLon
- - - speckled	LCro LOPS NLar SHeu SLon SPoG
- - red	CRos EHyd LCro LOPS LRHS NLar NRHS SEdd SLon SPoG
- - speckled	CRos EHyd LRHS NRHS SHeu SLon
- - white	CRos EHyd LCro LOPS LRHS NLar NRHS SLon SPoG
- - - speckled	LCro LOPS SHeu SLon
- - yellow	CRos EHyd LRHS NLar NRHS SHeu SLon SPoG
- - - speckled	CRos EHyd EPfP LCro LOPS LRHS NLar NRHS SHeu SLon SPoG
- - lime	CRos EHyd LCro LOPS LRHS NRHS
- 'Harvington Black'	EHyd EPfP LRHS NRHS
- 'Harvington Blush Picotee'	LRHS SRms
- 'Harvington Chocolate'	EHyd LRHS
- 'Harvington Double Chocolate' (d)	CRos EHyd LCro LOPS LRHS NRHS SHeu
- 'Harvington Petticoat'	LRHS NRHS
- 'Harvington Shades of the Night'	CRos EHyd EPfP LCro LOPS LRHS NLar NRHS SHeu SLon SPoG
- 'Harvington Smokey Blues'	CRos LCro SEdd SHeu SLon

- 'Harvington Smokey Double' (d)	SHeu
- 'Harvington Special' **new**	CRos
- Hillier hybrids anemone-centred, spotted pink	EHyd LRHS
- - - yellow	CBod EMor LRHS
- - burgundy	EHyd LEdu LRHS
- - slate	EHyd LRHS
- - spotted, double yellow (d)	EHyd EPfP LRHS
- - - - pink (d)	EHyd EPfP LRHS
- - - pink	EHyd LRHS
- - - white	EHyd LRHS
- - - yellow	EHyd LRHS
- - white	EHyd LRHS
- - yellow, magenta eye	EHyd LRHS NRHS
- 'Kingston Cardinal'	LRHS MAsh
- Lady Series	EPau
- 'Lucy Black'	LRHS
- maroon-flowered	WFar
- mauve freckled, double (d)	WFar
- 'Mrs Betty Ranicar' (d)	CBro EPfP ILea SRms
- nearly black-flowered	WFar
- 'Onyx Odyssey'	CWGN
- pale pink-flowered	WFar
- 'Painted Bunting'	MPri
- 'Pamina'	SMHy
§ - Party Dress Group (d)	ELon GBin LSRN NLar WFar
- 'Peppermint Ice' (Winter Jewels Series) **new**	CBod
- 'Phoebe'	MPri
- Picotee Group	MPri NLar WFar WHoo
- pink freckled, double (d)	WFar
- 'Pink Lady' (Lady Series)	CBcs CBod CRos CSBt EHyd EPau EPfP GKev LRHS MWat NCou NGdn NRHS SPer
- 'Pink Lady Spotted' (Lady Series)	SCob
- pink-flowered	MBNS SDeJ WHoo
- pink-red-flowered	WFar
- plum-flowered	MMuc SEND
- 'Pluto'	WFar
- 'Pretty Ellen Pink'	GBin LCro LOPS
- 'Pretty Ellen Red'	LCro LOPS SCob
- 'Pretty Ellen White'	LCro LOPS
- 'Primrose Picotee'	WFar
- primrose-flowered	ELan MCot
- 'Purity'	MAsh
- purple-flowered	WFar
- Queen Series, dark red-flowered	GBin
- - double white-flowered (d)	GBin
- - - yellow-flowered (d)	GBin
- - picotee	GBin
- - pink-flowered	GBin
- - 'Queen of the Night'	CExl WSpi
- - white-flowered	GBin
- - yellow-flowered	GBin
- 'Red Lady' (Lady Series)	CBcs CBod CExl EHyd EPfP GAbr LRHS LSRN MBNS NHol NRHS SPer
- red-flowered	CBod LEdu WFar WHoo
- 'Rose Quartz' (Winter Jewels Series) **new**	CBod
- slaty blue-flowered	CBod LEdu SEND
- 'Smokey Blue'	CRos EHyd ELan LRHS NRHS
- smokey purple-flowered	LSRN SGbt
- SP Anja Oudolf ('Hlr 200') (Spring Promise Series)	CRos
- SP John Hopkins (Spring Promise Series)	CRos EHyd LRHS NRHS
- SP Lily ('Hlr 210') (Spring Promise Series) **new**	EPfP
- 'Speckled Draco'	CExl
§ - spotted	EPfP WCot WFar WHoo
- - cream	NBir WFar
- - double, pink (d)	CBod GEdr MWat WFar
- - - white (d)	CBod WFar
- - - yellow (d)	MWat WCot WFar
- - green	WFar
- - ivory	WFar
- - light purple	WFar
- - pink	EHyd LEdu LRHS MBNS NBir NRHS SCob SEND WFar WHoo
- - primrose	ELan SGbt WFar
- - white	EWTr MMuc MWat NBir SCob SEND WBor WCAu WFar
- - yellow	SCob WFar
- 'Stained Glass'	MAsh
- 'Tutu'PBR	EPfP LBuc LRHS NRHS SPeP SPoG SRms
- Washfield double-flowered (d)	CBod EMor EPau LEdu MBel SCob SPer SRkn WBor WHil
- 'White Lady' (Lady Series)	CBcs CBod CExl GAbr MBNS NCou SPer
- 'White Lady Spotted' (Lady Series)	CBar CBod EHyd ELon EPfP LRHS MHol NHol NRHS SPer WTor
- white-flowered	EPfP GMaP MWat WCFE WFar WHoo
- white-veined	WFar
- Wilgenbroek hybrids anemone-centred, red	SMad
- 'Yellow Lady' (Lady Series)	CBar CBcs CBod EHyd GKev LRHS MBNS MBel NRHS SPer WTor
- yellow-flowered	GMaP MCot SEND WFar WHoo
- Zodiac Group	CBod MBNS
§ 'Ivory Prince'PBR	CRos EHyd EPfP LRHS MAsh NRHS SPoG
liguricus	MAsh
- WM 0230	MPhe
lividus	CRos CSpe EHyd EPfP EWes GKev LRHS MBel NBir NRHS SDeJ SDir SRms
- subsp. ***corsicus***	see *H. argutifolius*
- 'Green Marble'	ELan
- 'Pink Marble'	ELan
- 'Purple Ear'	LRHS
- 'Purple Marble'	EPfP
- 'Purple Rose'	SRms
- 'Rose Green'	CSpe MHtn
- 'Silver and Rose'	CSpe
- 'White Marble'	LRHS MAsh
- white-flowered	GKev
lividus* × *niger	GKev
'Marshmallow'	WCot
'Moonshine'PBR	MHol NHol NLar SLon
multifidus	NBir
- WM 1316	MPhe
- subsp. ***hercegovinus***	XEll
- - WM 0020	MPhe
- - WM 0622	MPhe
- subsp. ***istriacus***	CBro MAsh
- - WM 9322	MPhe
- - WM 9324	MPhe
- subsp. ***multifidus***	MAsh
- - WM 9529	MPhe
- - WM 9833 from Croatia	MPhe
niger	Widely available
- Ashwood strain	MAsh
- Blackthorn Group	NLar
- 'Christmas Carol'	CRos EHyd EPfP LRHS NRHS

- double-flowered (d)	CDor
- Harvington hybrids	EHyd LRHS MAsh NRHS
- - double-flowered (d)	LCro LOPS SPoG
- 'HGC Jacob'PBR	LRHS LSRN NRHS SRms
- HGC JOEL ('Coseh 210'PBR)	CRos ECtt EHyd LRHS NLar NRHS
- HGC JONAS ('Coseh 220'PBR)	CRos ECtt EHyd EPfP LRHS NRHS SCoo
- 'HGC Josef Lemper'PBR	GKev LRHS LSRN NLar SRms
- 'HGC Joshua'PBR	EHyd LRHS
- HGC SNOW FRILLS ('Coseh 230'PBR)	ECtt EHyd LRHS NLar NRHS
- HGC WINTERGOLD ('Coseh 2010'PBR)	CRos ECtt EHyd EPfP EShb LRHS NRHS SCoo
- 'Ivory Prince'	see *H.* 'Ivory Prince'
- 'Mini Blanc'	CRos EHyd MPri NRHS
- 'Mont Blanc'	WCot
- pink-flowered	MAsh
- 'Potter's Wheel'	CRos EHyd EPfP LRHS NBir NRHS
- 'Praecox'	EHyd ELon EPfP EWes
- 'Snow Moon' **new**	CBor
- 'Wilgenbroek Select'	EPfP
× ***nigercors*** 'Emma'PBR	CEnd CRos ECtt EHyd EPfP LRHS MAvo MHol MPri NRHS SEdd SHar SPoG WCot
- 'HGC Green Corsican'	LRHS NRHS
- HGC ICE BREAKER FANCY ('Coseh 820'PBR)	EHyd EPfP LRHS NRHS
- HGC ICE BREAKER MAX ('Coseh 750'PBR)	EHyd EPfP LRHS NRHS
- HGC ICE BREAKER PICO ('Coseh 840')	ECre EPfP
- HGC ICE BREAKER PRELUDE ('Coseh 830'PBR)	LRHS NRHS
- 'Morning's Pride'PBR	EHyd LRHS
- 'Pink Beauty'	NLar
× ***nigristern***	see *H.* × *ericsmithii*
odorus	CBro EBee MPhe XEll XLum
- WM 0312 from Bosnia	MPhe
- WM 9415	MPhe
- WM 9728 from Hungary	MPhe
- subsp. ***cyclophyllus***	GKev MAsh MPhe
orientalis misapplied	see *H.* × *hybridus*
orientalis ambig.	CBar CTsd GKev MPri WHil XSen
orientalis Lam.	CBcs EHyd EWes LRHS MPhe MSwo NRHS XLum
§ - subsp. ***abchasicus*** (A. Braun) B. Mathew	CBro GKev MAsh WSpi
§ - - Early Purple Group	CTri MRav SRms
- subsp. ***guttatus*** misapplied	see *H.* × *hybridus* spotted
- subsp. ***guttatus*** (A. Braun & Sauer) B. Mathew	SRkn
- ***olympicus***	see *H. orientalis* Lam. subsp. *orientalis*
§ - subsp. ***orientalis***	GKev
purpurascens	CBro LCro LOPS MAsh MRav NBir XEll
- WM 0815 from Romania	MPhe
- WM 9211 from Hungary	MPhe
- WM 9412	MPhe
(Rodney Davey Marbled Group) ANNA'S RED ('Abcrd02'PBR)	CRos EBee ECtt EPfP GBin LCro LOPS LRHS MAsh MHol NRHS SPoG
- 'Dorothy's Dawn' (Frost Kiss Series)	SPoG
- PENNY'S PINK ('Abcrd01')	CBcs CMil CRos ECtt EHyd EPfP GBin LRHS LSRN LSun MAsh MHol MNrw SEdd SPoG WCot
- 'Sally's Shell' (Frost Kiss Series)	SPoG
× ***sahinii*** 'Winterbells'PBR	CRos EBee LCro LOPS LRHS LSou NRHS SPoG SRms
'Snow Crystal' **new**	LSou
'Snow White'	LBuc
(Spring Promise Series) SP CONNY ('Hlr 160'PBR)	CRos EHyd EPfP LRHS NRHS
- SP MARY LOU ('Hlr 150'PBR)	EHyd
- SP RACHEL	EHyd EPfP MPri
- SP SALLY	EPfP
- SP TIFFANY	EHyd
× ***sternii***	CBcs CBod CRos CTri EHyd ELan EMor EPfP GKev GMaP LCro LRHS MBel MNrw NLar NRHS SPoG WBrk
- Aberconwy strain	MAsh
- 'Ashwood Silver'	MAsh
- Ashwood strain	MAsh NLar
- Blackthorn Group	EHyd ELon EPfP LRHS SWvt
- 'Boughton Beauty'	CMea ELan WSpi
- pewter-flowered	CSpe
- 'Silver Dollar'	EBee EPfP GKev LRHS LSRN SPoG SRms
thibetanus	CBro CExl MAsh
torquatus	CBro MAsh MAvo MPhe XEll
- WM 0609 from Montenegro	MPhe
- WM 0617 from Serbia	MPhe
- WM 9106 from Montenegro	MPhe
- WM 9820 from Bosnia	MPhe
- 'Dido' (d)	CExl WFar
- double-flowered (d) WM 0621 from Montenegro	MPhe
- Party Dress Group	see *H.* × *hybridus* Party Dress Group
'Verboom Beauty'	CDoC CRos EHyd LCro LOPS LRHS NRHS
viridis	CRos LEdu LRHS MAsh SRms XEll XLum
- WM 0444 from Italy	MPhe
- WM 1303 from Slovenia	MPhe
- WM 9723 from Italy	MPhe
- subsp. ***occidentalis***	CBro MAsh
- - WM 1340 from Germany	MPhe
- - WM 1344 from Spain	MPhe
- - WM 9501 from Wales	MPhe
WALBERTON'S ROSEMARY ('Walhero'PBR) ♈H7	CRos EHyd EPfP LRHS MAsh NRHS SHar SPoG WSpi
'White Beauty'PBR	CMil EPfP NLar NRHS SPoG WCot

Helminthotheca (*Asteraceae*)

§ ***echioides***	WHer

Helonias (*Melanthiaceae*)

bullata	GKev

Heloniopsis (*Melanthiaceae*)

acutifolia B&SWJ 218	WCru
- B&SWJ 6817	WCru
- B&SWJ 6836	WCru
japonica	see *H. orientalis*
§ ***kawanoi***	IMou WCru
koreana B&SWJ 4173	WCru
leucantha B&SWJ 11148	WCru
§ ***orientalis***	GKev
- B&SWJ 6278	WCru
- B&SWJ 6327	WCru
- B&SWJ 6380 from Japan	WCru

- from Korea EPfP
- var. ***breviscapa*** EPfP GEdr LEdu SMad WCru
- - B&SWJ 5635 WCru
- - B&SWJ 5873 WCru
- - B&SWJ 5938 WCru
- - 'A-so' LEdu WCru
- 'Dark Single' GEdr
- var. ***flavida*** B&SWJ 11400 WCru
- - 'Snow White' GEdr
- variegated (v) WCru
- var. ***yakusimensis*** see *H. kawanoi*

tubiflora B&SWJ 822 WCot WCru
- 'Temple Blue' WCru

umbellata EBee EPfP WSHC
- B&SWJ 1839 WCru
- B&SWJ 3732 WCru
- B&SWJ 6836 WCru
- B&SWJ 6846 WCru
- B&SWJ 7117 WCru

Helwingia (*Helwingiaceae*)

chinensis CBcs CCCN CTsd ESwi EWTr EWld GBin LEdu MGil MHtn MPie NLar SBrt SEND SPoG WBor WLov WPGP
- broad-leaved EBee NLar SMad WPGP
- narrow-leaved ESwi

himalaica CExl ESwi SBrt

japonica EWld NLar
- broad-leaved WPGP

Helxine see *Soleirolia*

Hemerocallis ✿ (*Hemerocallidaceae*)

'A Bodacious Pattern' EStr
'A Groovy Kind of Love' EStr
'A Lady Named Hank' EStr
'Aabachee' CBgR EStr
'Aaron Brown' EStr
'Absolute Ripper' EStr
'Absolute Treasure' EStr
'Absolute Zero' SDay
'Addie Branch Smith' SDay
'Admiral' WNHG
'Adoration' SPer
'Aerial Display' EStr
'African Chant' ELan
'Ageless Beauty' ELon EStr SDir
'Agnes Elpers' WAul
'Ahoy Matey' EStr
'Ahoya' CBgR
'Airs and Graces' SDay
'Alabama Jubilee' WNHG
'Alabama Slammer' EStr
'Alan' CRos EHyd LRHS MRav NRHS
'Alan Adair' SDay
'Alaqua' WSMil
'Alayne Clare' **new** EStr
'Alec Allen' SDay
'Aleta Everett Adams' EStr
'Alexander the Great' WHrl
'Alien DNA' EStr
'Alien Fingerprint' EStr
'Aliens in the Garden' EStr
'All American Baby' EStr
'All American Chief' ♀H6 EStr SDay
'All American Plum' CWCL MSpe WAul WHrl
'All American Tiger' SDay
'All American Windmill' CBgR EStr
'All Fired Up' EStr SDay
'All the Magic' SDay
'Allegheny Skyline' EStr
'Allegiance' WNHG
'Alli Sheldon' ECha
'Alluring Peach' EStr
'Almond Puff' SDay
'Alpine Mist' SDay
'Alternate Universe' EStr
altissima EStr MNrw SDix SPhx XLum XSen
'Always Afternoon' ♀H6 CBgR CBod EPfP EStr MNrw SDay WCAu WHrl XSen
'Amadeus' EStr SCob
'Amazon Amethyst' WCAu
'Ambassador' CBgR
'Amber Classic' ELon
'American Revolution' CBgR CBod ELon EStr GBin LSun MBNS MHol NChi SDys SEdd SPoG WAul WCot WHrl WPnP WSMil WSpi XLum XSen
'America's Most Wanted' EStr SDay
'Amerstone Amethyst Jewel' EStr
'Amy Michelle' (d) EStr
'Amy's Rainbow' EStr
'Angel Artistry' SDay
'Angel in Oz' EStr
'Angel Rodgers' EStr
'Angels in America' **new** EStr
'Angelus Runaway' EStr
'Angelwalker' EStr
'Anna Rubinina' EStr
'Anna Warner' ELon MMuc SEND
'Annabelle's Ghost' CBgR
'Annie Golightly' SDay
'Annie Welch' EHyd ELon LRHS NBre
'Antique Lavender' WCAu
'Antique Rose' EStr
'Anzac' CBod CBro CTsd ECha ECtt EStr NGdn SWvt
'Apollo' XSen
'Apollodorus' SDay WNHG
'Apple Court Chablis' EStr
'Apple Court Damson' EStr
'Apple Court Ruby' ELon
'Apple Swirl' EStr
'Applique' EStr
'Après Moi' NLar
'Apricot Beauty' (d) WSpi
'Apricot Velvet' CBgR
'April Fools' EStr
'April in Paris' **new** SDay
'Aquamarine' SDay
'Aquarelle' EStr
'Arabian Magic' EStr
'Arctic Snow' ♀H6 CBgR CBod CBro CMac ECtt EHyd EMor EStr GJos LRHS MCot MNrw NRHS SDay SDir WAul
'Arles Sultry Eyes' **new** EStr
'Armed and Dangerous' EStr
'Arpeggio' EStr SDay
'Art Gallery Curly-Q' EStr
'Art Gallery Quilling' EStr
'Arthur Moore' SDay
'Artificial Evolution' EStr
'Ashee Dashee' **new** EStr
'Asheville Pink Lady' EStr
'Asheville White Winged Dove' EStr
'Ashton's Giggles' EStr
'Asian Artistry' WNHG
'Asterisk' ♀H6 EStr SDay

'Astolat'	EBee
'Aten'	CBgR SDay
'Atlanta Bouquet'	SDay
'Atlanta Cover Girl'	SDay
'Atlanta Fringe Benefit'	SDay
'Atlanta Full House'	SDay
'Atlas'	WGwG
'Augenstern'	EStr
'August Frost' ♀H6	EStr SDay
'August Morn'	CBgR
'Autumn Minaret'	EStr
'Autumn Red'	CBcs CBgR EStr GKin MHost MMuc MNrw NBir SCob SEND WCot
'Autumn Wood'	SDay
I 'Avant Garde' Moldovan	EStr
'Avant Garde' Russell	EStr WCAu
'Avon Crystal Rose'	WNHG
'Awakening Dream'	SDay
'Awash With Color'	EStr SDay
'Awesome Blossom'	EStr MBNS MNrw
'Awesome Candy'	EStr
'Aztec Beauty'	EStr
'Aztec Furnace'	EStr SDay
'Aztec Gold'	EStr
'Baby Betsy'	EStr
'Baby Blues'	SDay
'Baby Darling'	SDay
'Baby Red Eyes'	EStr WFar
'Bad Medicine'	EStr
'Baja'	WFar
'Bakabana'	CBod EHyd LRHS NRHS
'Bald Eagle'	EStr MNrw
'Bali Hai'	EStr SRms WHrl WSpi
'Bali Watercolor'	EStr
'Bama Bound'	EStr
'Bamboo Blackie'	CBgR XSen
'Banana Cream Beauty'	SDeJ WSpi
'Banana Man'	EStr
'Bandit Man'	EStr SDay
'Barbara Alsop'	EStr
'Barbara Mitchell'	EStr SDeJ WCAu WNHG XSen
'Barbary Corsair'	EStr SDay
'Baroni'	ECha
'Bas Relief'	EStr
'Batgirl'	EStr
'Battle Hymn'	WCAu
'Bayou Bride'	SDay
'Be Bop a Lula'	EStr
'Bea'	EStr
'Beautiful Design'	EStr
'Beautiful Edgings'	EStr SDay
'Beauty to Behold' ♀H6	SDay
'Becky Lynn'	ECtt EStr
'Bed of Nails'	EStr
'Bed of Roses'	EStr
'Bedarra Island'	SDay
'Before You Accuse Me'	EStr
'Beijing'	SDay
'Bela Lugosi'	CBgR CBod CMac EHyd ELon EPfP EStr GQue ILea LRHS LSRN LSun MBNS MNrw NBro NChi NQui NRHS SCob SDay SPer WHrl WNHG
'Believe It'	WNHG
'Bella Isabella'	EStr
'Belladonna Starfish' **new**	EStr
'Belly Button Slipknots'	EStr
'Beloved Deceiver'	SDay
'Ben Adams'	SDay
'Ben Bachman'	EStr
'Benchmark'	SDay
'Bengal Fire'	WNHG
'Berlin Oxblood'	WAul
'Berlin Red'	CAby CWCL ECha ELon GBee MNrw SDay SSut WFar
'Berlin Tallboy'	SDay WAul
'Berlin Yellow'	EStr
'Berliner Premiere'	EStr
'Bernard Thompson'	SDay
'Berry Blitz'	EStr
'Berry Patch'	EStr
'Berrylicious'	EStr
'Bertie Ferris'	EStr NLar SDay
'Beside Still Waters'	EStr
'Bess Ross'	XSen
'Best Seller'	CBod WCAu
'Bette Davis Eyes'	CBgR CWat EStr SDay
'Betts Allen'	EStr
'Betty Benz'	SDay
'Betty Jenkins'	EStr
'Bettylen'	EStr
'Beyond Riches'	EStr
'Beyond Thunder Dome'	EStr
'Bi-colored Blues'	EStr
'Big Apple'	EStr SDay
'Big Beautiful Babe'	EStr
'Big Bird'	EStr SDay
'Big Blue'	EStr SDay
'Big Honking Bahama Richie'	EStr
'Big Ogeeche'	EStr
'Big Red Wiggles' **new**	EStr
'Big Smile'	MBNS MNrw SDeJ
'Big Snowbird'	SDay
'Big Time Happy'	EHyd LRHS SCob SEdd SPoG STPC
'Big World'	CBgR
'Birthday Honours'	SDay
'Bitsy'	ELon WRHF
'Black Adder'	SDay
'Black Ambrosia'	EStr SDay
'Black Arrowhead'	CBod EStr WCAu
'Black Emanuelle'	CExl EMor LSun MNrw NLar
'Black Eye'	SDay WNHG
'Black Eyed Belle' **new**	WNHG
'Black Eyed Stella'	WSpi
'Black Eyed Susan'	CBod ECtt EStr
'Black Friday'	EStr
'Black Ice'	ELon SDay
'Black Knight'	NLar SRms
'Black Magic'	CBod CBro CTri ECtt EHyd ELan EPfP EStr GBin GKin GMaP LRHS LSRN MHer MRav NBir NGdn NRHS SPer WHrl WNHG
'Black Prince'	CBgR EShb MBNS NBre WAul
'Black Stockings'	EBee ELon EStr EWes MHol MNrw SCob SDeJ SDir
'Blackberries and Cream'	EStr
'Blackberry Candy'	CSam ECtt EHyd EStr GKin LRHS MNrw NHol NRHS NWad WCAu
'Blackberry Sherbert'	WFar
'Blackberry Sundae'	EStr
'Blacky'	EStr
'Blazing Cannons' **new**	EStr
'Blessed Again'	SDay
'Blessing'	EStr
'Blessing in Disguise'	EStr
'Blizzard Bay'	CBod EStr WFar
'Blizzard Blast'	EStr
'Blonde is Beautiful'	SDay
'Blood Spot'	SDay
'Blue Balloon'	EStr

'Blue Deva'	EStr
'Blue Sheen'	CBgR CMac CRos ECtt EStr GMaP WFar WRHF WSpi
'Blue Stardust'	EStr
'Blue Wrangler' **new**	EStr
'Blueberry Breakfast'	EStr WNHG
'Blueberry Candy'	ECtt EStr ILea
'Blueberry Cream'	CWCL MMrt MNrw
'Blueberry Frost'	CBgR
'Blueberry Sundae'	CWat
'Bluethroat'	EStr
'Blufftop Volunteer'	EStr
'Blushing Belle'	NBro
'Bob Faulkner'	EStr
'Bobby's Lavender Eyes'	EStr
'Bobo Anne'	EStr
'Bohemian Rhapsody'	EStr
'Boitzer Helicopter' **new**	EStr
'Bold Courtier'	CBgR
'Bonanza'	CBcs CBgR CBro CRos CTri ECha ECtt EHyd EMor EPfP EStr LEdu LLWG LPot LRHS MHost MRav NBir NBro NGdn NLar NRHS SCob SEND SPer SWvt WCAu WCot WFar
'Bone China'	WNHG
'Boney Maroney'	CBgR
'Bonfire Heart'	EStr
'Bonibrae Blue-eyed Baby'	EStr
'Bonibrae Heartbreaker' **new**	EStr
'Bonibrae Maggie Anne' **new**	EStr
'Bonibrae Smoke and Mirrors' **new**	EStr
'Bonnie Boy'	XLum XSen
'Booger'	SDay
'Booroobin Magic'	EStr
'Border Baby'	ECtt
'Border Lord'	EStr
'Border Music'	EStr
'Borgia Queen'	EStr
'Boss Hogg'	EStr
'Both Sides Now'	ECtt
'Boulderbrook Serenity'	SDay
'Bourbon Kings'	EHyd EMor SDeJ WHrl WWtn
'Bowl of Cream'	EStr
'Bowl of Roses'	EStr WCAu
'Brass Buckles'	see *H.* 'Puddin'
'Brazilian Orange'	XSen
'Breath of Blue Air'	EStr
'Breathing in Snowflakes' **new**	EStr
'Breathless Beauty'	WNHG
'Breathless Charm'	EStr
'Brenda Newbold'	EStr SDay
'Bridget'	ELan
'Bright and Morning Star'	EStr
'Bright Eyed and Bushy Tailed' **new**	EStr
'Bright Island'	XSen
'Bright Side'	CBgR
'Bright Spangles'	SDay WAul
'Brilliant Circle'	ECtt
'Broadway Last Mohican'	EStr
'Broadway Valentine'	XSen
'Brocaded Gown'	ELan SDay
'Brooklyn Twist'	EStr
'Brookwood Lee Causey'	EStr
'Brown Witch'	ELon
'Browns Ferry Royalty'	EStr WFar
'Bruce'	EStr
'Brutus'	WHrl
'Bubbling Brown Sugar'	EStr SDay
'Bubbly'	SDay
'Bucksport'	EStr
'Bud Producer'	CBgR
'Buddy's Wild and Wonderful'	EStr
'Buenos Aires'	XSen
'Buffys Doll'	SDay
'Bumble Bee'	CAby CBod ECtt EStr NBre SDay
'Burgundy Love'	EStr LLWG
'Burlesque'	SDay WCot
'Burning Daylight' ♀H6	CAby CBgR CRos EBee ECtt EHyd EPfP EStr GAbr LRHS MNrw MRav NRHS SCob SPer SRms WAul WCAu WCot WFar
'Burning Inheritance'	SDay
'Burnished Ruffles'	EStr
'Butterpat'	SDay
'Butterscotch'	WFar
'Butterscotch Ruffles'	SDay
'Buzz Bomb'	ECtt EHyd ELon EMor EStr GKin LRHS LSRN MCot NGdn NRHS SPer WFar
'By Myself'	XSen
'Byzantine Emperor'	EHyd LRHS NRHS
'Caballero'	EStr
'Cabbage Butterfly' **new**	EStr
'Cabbage Flower'	SDay XSen
'Cabriolet'	XSen
'Cajun Gambler'	EStr
'Calgary Stampede'	EStr
'Calico Jack'	EStr SPad
'Calico Spider'	EStr XSen
'Caliph's Robes'	SDay
'Call Girl'	SDay
'Calligraphy'	EStr
'Camden Ballerina'	SDay
'Camden Gold Dollar'	SDay
'Camelot Green'	WNHG
'Cameroons'	EStr SDay
'Campfire Embers'	EStr
'Canadian Border Patrol'	EStr MNrw NLar SCob SPer WHrl
'Canary Chaos'	EStr
'Canary Glow'	CTri WFar
'Canary Wings'	CBgR
'Candide'	SDay
'Candor'	SDay
'Candy Cane Dreams'	EStr
'Candy Gram'	EStr
'Can't Fault Ya'	EStr
'Cantique'	SDay
'Cape Breton'	EStr
'Cara Mia'	CBgR EHyd EStr LRHS NBir WFar
'Caramba'	CBgR
'Caramel Taffy'	WHrl
'Caribbean Frank League'	SDay
'Caribbean Purple Spires'	EStr
'Carlotta'	SDay
'Carmen Marie'	XSen
'Carmine Monarch'	EStr
'Carnal Emporium'	EStr
'Carolicolossal'	ELon SDay
'Carolina Cool Down'	EStr
'Carolina Cranberry'	ELan
'Carolina Dynamite'	EStr
'Carolina Lemon Squeezer'	EStr
'Caroline Taylor'	WHrl
'Carrick Wildon'	EBee MBros WFar

'Carrot'	SDay
'Cartwheels'	ECha EHyd EShb EStr GBee GKin GMaP LRHS MRav NBro NRHS SPer SRms SSut WCAu WFar
'Casino Gold'	SDay
'Catawampus'	EStr
'Catherine Neal'	EStr SDay
'Catherine Woodbery'	Widely available
'Cathy's Sunset'	CSam ECtt EHyd EWhm GKin LRHS LSRN MBNS NBro NGdn NRHS NWad
'Cause for Pause'	EStr
'Caviar'	SDay
'Cedar Waxwing'	MNrw
'Celebration of Angels'	EStr
'Cerulean Warbler'	EStr
'Chamonix'	XSen
'Chance Encounter'	EStr LRHS NHol
'Changing Latitudes'	WHrl
'Chantilly'	EStr
'Charles Johnston'	CBgR EPfP EStr MSpe SDay WSMil
'Charlie Pierce Memorial'	EStr
'Charm Alarm' **new**	EStr
'Checkerboard Curls'	EStr
'Cheerful Note'	WNHG
'Cheese and Wine'	EStr MHol
'Cherokee Star'	EStr
'Cherry Cheeks'	ECtt EHyd ELan ELon EStr LRHS MHol MNrw MRav NRHS WCAu WCot WFar WWtn
'Cherry Eyed Pumpkin' ♀H6	EStr SDay WCAu
'Cherry Grove Beach'	EStr
'Cherry Lace'	XSen
'Cherry Peacock'	EStr
'Cherry Stripes' **new**	EStr
'Cherry Tiger'	EStr
'Cherry Valentine'	ELon GWyn SPad
'Cherrystone'	EStr
'Chesapeake Crablegs'	EStr
'Chesières Lunar Moth'	CBgR ELon
'Chestnut Mountain'	SDay
'Chevron Spider'	EStr
'Chicago Apache'	EBee ELon EPfP EStr LLWG MBel NBir SCob SDay SPer WSpi
'Chicago Aztec'	ELon
'Chicago Blackout'	ECtt WAul WCot
'Chicago Cardinal'	EStr
'Chicago Cherry'	WNHG
'Chicago Fire'	EBee EPfP MNHC
'Chicago Firecracker'	XLum XSen
'Chicago Heirloom'	WCAu
'Chicago Jewel'	ELon NSti
'Chicago Knobby'	EBee EStr MNrw SDay
'Chicago Knockout'	EHyd ELan EPfP LRHS WAul
'Chicago Peach'	NBir WCAu
'Chicago Petticoats'	WFar
'Chicago Picotee Promise'	WNHG
'Chicago Picotee Queen'	WNHG
'Chicago Queen'	SDay WNHG
'Chicago Rainbow'	CBgR
'Chicago Royal Blue'	CTri
'Chicago Royal Crown'	CAby ECtt EHyd EMor LRHS
'Chicago Royal Robe'	CWCL ELon NBid SDay SPer SRms WCot WWtn
'Chicago Silver'	SDay WAul
'Chicago Star'	WNHG
'Chicago Sugarplum'	SDay
'Chicago Sunrise'	CBgR CBod CRos EHyd ELon GMaP LRHS MRav NGdn NRHS SDay SWvt WAvo WCot WNHG
'Chick Flick'	EStr
'Chick Magnet'	EStr
'Chicken Coop Madonna'	EStr
'Chief Sequoia'	EStr
'Child of Fortune'	SDay
'Children's Festival'	CMac CRos ECtt EStr GMaP LPot LRHS MRav NLar SWvt WFar
'China Bride'	EStr
'China Lake'	SDay
'Chinese Autumn'	EStr
'Chinese Cloisonne'	EStr
'Chinese Imp'	NLar SDay
'Chinese New Year'	EStr
'Chinese Temple Flower'	SDay
'Chocolate Candy'	CWGN EStr
'Chocolate Splash'	SDay
'Chokecherry Mountain'	EStr
'Chorus Line'	WNHG
'Christina's Pink Parasol'	EStr
'Christine Lynn'	WNHG
'Christmas Is'	CBgR CMac CPar CWGN EBee ECtt EHyd ELon EStr GBin GKin LPot LRHS NHol NRHS WAul WCot WHrl WNHG XSen
'Christmas Ornament'	EStr
'Christmas Wishes'	EStr
'Ciarra Vonnie'	SDay
'Cimarron Knight'	CBgR
'Cindy's Eye'	EStr WCot
'Cinnamon Stick'	EStr
'Cinnamon Sunrise'	EStr
citrina ♀H6	CBgR CExl CMac CRos EBee EStr IMou LRHS MBel MCot WCAu WCot WHoo WHrl XLum XSen
citrina × (× ***ochroleuca***)	WCot
'Civil Law'	SDay
'Civil Rights'	SDay
'Classic Caper'	WNHG
'Classic Edge'	SDay
'Claudine'	ELon
'Clearly a Thrill'	EStr
'Cleopatra'	ELon MSpe
'Clothed in Glory'	EStr WCot
'Clownfish'	EStr
'Cobraskin Necktie' **new**	EStr
'Cocktail Party'	EStr
'Colonel Jim Scheurich'	EStr
'Colonel Joe'	WNHG
'Colonel Mustard'	EStr
'Comanche Eyes'	SDay
'Coming Up Roses'	CAby CBod CPar CWld ELon
'Concorde Nelson'	SDay
'Condilla' (d) ♀H6	EStr SDay
'Conspicua'	CBgR SMHy
'Contessa'	CBro EHyd LRHS NRHS
'Conway Red Light'	EStr
'Cool It'	EStr LPot MPie MSpe NLar SCob SDeJ WHrl
'Cool Jazz'	EStr SDay
'Cooler Than Me'	EStr
'Copper Dawn'	EStr NChi
'Copper Windmill'	CBgR ELon EStr SDay WNHG
'Copperhead'	EStr
'Coral Majority'	EStr
'Coral Mist'	NBre
'Coral Sparkler'	WNHG
'Corky'	CAby CBro ECha EHyd ELan EMor EPfP GBin GMaP GWyn LRHS LSRN MBel MHost MNrw NGdn NLar SDix SPer SPhx SSut

	WAul WCAu WFar WSpi XLum XSen
'Cornwall'	EStr
'Cosmic Blast'	EStr
'Cosmic Hummingbird'	ECtt EHyd EStr LRHS NRHS
'Cosmik Debris' **new**	EStr
'Cosmopolitan'	ILea
'Country Club'	EBee GMaP
'Country Melody'	SDay
'Court Magician'	EStr SDay
'Court Troubadour'	ELon
'Coyote Moon'	EStr SDay
'Crackling Fire'	EStr
'Cranberry Baby'	ECtt EStr MTin WHoo WNHG
'Cranberry Coulis'	CWat
'Crawleycrow'	XSen
'Crayola Violet'	EStr
'Crazy Awesome'	EStr
'Crazy Ivan'	EStr
'Crazy Larry'	EStr
'Crazy Mr Jim'	EStr
'Crazy Pierre'	WHrl XSen
'Cream Drop'	ECtt EMor EPPr GMaP GQue LPot LRHS MBriF MCot MRav NBro NGdn NLar NRHS NSti SPer WAul WCot WFar WHrl
'Crimson Icon'	SDay
'Crimson Pirate'	CBgR CBod CBre CMac ELon EPfP EStr GBin GKev GLog GQue ILea LPot LRHS LSRN NBir NEoE NQui NRHS SCob SPer SPlb WCAu WFar WHrl WWtn XLum
'Crimson Wind'	EStr
'Cripple Creek'	EStr
'Croesus'	SRms
'Crooked Smile' **new**	EStr
'Crystal Cupid'	XSen
'Crystal Pinot'	ELon EStr
'Cumulus Sunset'	EStr
'Cupid's Gold'	SDay
'Curls'	CBgR SDay
'Curly Cinnamon Windmill' ♀H6	EStr SDay
'Curt's Gift'	EStr
'Custard Candy' ♀H6	CBod CWCL CWGN ECtt EHyd EPfP EStr GKin LRHS MBel MBriF MHost NHol NRHS WCAu WNHG
'Cute as can Be'	EStr
'Cyber Zone'	EStr
'Cyclone Twister'	EStr
'Cyclone Whirlaway' **new**	EStr
'Cynthia Lucius'	EStr
'Cynthia Mary'	ECtt GKin
'Cypriana'	XSen
'Czarina'	EStr
'Daddeeo Segrest'	EStr
'Daddy's Catfish Stew'	EStr
'Dad's Best White'	EStr
'Daily Dollar'	NGdn
'Dallas Spider Time'	SDay
'Dallas Star'	EStr SDay WHrl
'Dan Mahony'	EStr
'Dan Tau'	SDay
'Dance Ballerina Dance'	SDay
'Dance with Somebody'	EStr
'Dances with Giraffes'	EStr
'Dancing Crab'	CBgR
'Dancing Dreams'	EStr
'Dancing Elf'	EStr
'Dancing in the Rain'	EStr

'Dancing on Air' **new**	ECtt
'Dancing on Ice'	EStr
'Dancing Shiva'	SDay
'Dancing Summerbird'	ELon EStr SDay
'Dancing with Linda'	EStr
'Daring Deception'	ECtt EHyd ELon EPfP LLWG LRHS MNrw NRHS SDeJ
'Daring Dilemma'	EStr
'Daring Reflection'	MSpe SDay
'Darius'	WNHG
'Dark Angel'	NRHS
'Dark Magician'	EStr
'Dark Monkey'	EStr
'Darker Shade'	EStr
'Darrell'	SDay
'David Holman'	WNHG
'David Kirchhoff'	EStr SDay
'Davidson Update'	WNHG
'Davi's Dilemma' **new**	EStr
'Daylight'	WNHG
'De Colores'	EStr
'Debussy'	EStr
'Decatur Ballerina'	WNHG
'Decatur Captivation'	WNHG
'Decatur Dictator'	WNHG
'Decatur Festival' **new**	WNHG
'Decatur Imp'	SDay WHrl
'Decatur Jewel'	WNHG
'Decatur Piecrust'	EStr
'Decatur Rhythm'	WNHG
'Decatur Supreme'	WNHG
'Decatur Treasure Chest'	WNHG
'Decidedly Happy'	EStr
'Defuniak Peach Blossom' **new**	EStr
'Delicate Design'	SDay
'Deloris Gould'	SDay
'Demetrius'	CWat EStr
'Desdemona'	EStr XLum
'Desert Dreams'	WCot
'Desert Icicle'	EStr SDay
'Designer Gown'	EStr SDay
'Designer Jeans'	EStr SDay
'Designer Rhythm'	EStr
'Desirable Duchess'	EStr
'Desperate Housewife' **new**	EStr
'Destination Y'	XSen
'Destined to See'	CBcs CBro ECtt ELon EStr EWhm LPot MHol MNrw NBir NBro SPad SPer WAvo WCot WHrl
'Devon Cream'	SPer
'Devon Rugby'	SDay
'Devonshire'	SDay
'Diamond Dust'	ECtt LSRN NLar SPer WSpi
'Diana Grenfell'	CBgR
'Dick Kitchingman'	CBgR
'Digital Dynamics' **new**	EStr
'Dipped in Ink'	EStr
'Discarded Beauty'	EStr
'Disco Inferno' **new**	EStr
'Distant Galaxy'	EStr WCAu
'Diva Bride'	EStr
'Diva in Zebra' **new**	EStr
'Diva's Choice'	EStr MHol
'Divertissment'	CBgR ELon SDay WHrl
'Dizzy Miss Lizzy'	EStr
'Doc Holliday'	EStr
'Doctor Doom'	EStr
'Doctor Freckles Mr Hyde'	EStr
'Doctor McGregor's Garden'	EStr

'Doctor Strangelove'	EStr
'Dominic'	CBgR SDay WCot WFar
'Don Stevens'	WHrl
'Don's Wild Heather'	EStr
'Don't Leave Empty-handed'	EStr
'Dorethe Louise'	CBgR SDay
'Dorothy McDade'	MNrw
'Dot Paul'	ELan
'Double Action' (d)	SDay
'Double Charm' (d)	XSen
'Double Cream' (d)	WCot
'Double Cutie' (d)	EHyd EStr LRHS NLar NRHS SDay SRms
'Double Delicious' (d)	WCot
'Double Doubloon' (d)	XLum
'Double Dream' (d)	EStr WHrl
'Double Firecracker' (d)	EBee MBNS NBro NLar XSen
'Double Gardenia' (d)	EStr WNHG
'Double Glitter' (d)	XSen
'Double Honey' (d)	EStr
'Double Oh Seven' (d)	ELon
'Double Pompon' (d)	EStr
'Double Pop Art' (d)	XSen
'Double Red Royal' (d)	EPfP EStr XSen
'Double River Wye' (d)	CBgR ECtt EHyd EMor EShb EStr GBee LRHS MHer MNrw NGdn WAul WBrk WCot WFar WHoo WHrl
'Dowager Queen'	WNHG
'Dragon Fire Breath'	EStr
'Dragon Flight' **new**	LLWG
'Dragon King'	SDay
'Dragon Lore'	EPfP EStr
'Dragon Seeker'	EStr
'Dragon's Eye'	EHyd LRHS NRHS SDay WNHG
'Dragon's Orb'	SDay
'Dream Awhile' **new**	SDay
'Dream Baby'	NBre
'Dresden Doll'	SPer
'Driving Me Wild'	SDay
'Drooling Lizard'	EStr
'Drop Cloth'	EStr
'Duke of Durham'	EStr MSpe
'Duke of Earl'	CBgR
dumortieri	CAgr CBro EBee ECha ELan EWhm MCot MMuc MRav NBid NBir NSti SCob SEND SPer WCot WWtn XSen
- B&SWJ 1283	WCru
'Dumpy'	EStr
'Dune Buggy'	XSen
'Dune Needlepoint'	EStr WHrl
'Duplex' (d)	XSen
'Dutch Art'	SDay
'Dutch Artist' (d)	EStr
'Dutch Beauty'	WFar
'Dutch Gold'	MHCG MNrw
'Earl of Warwick'	CBgR
'Earlianna'	EStr
'Earnest Yearwood'	SDay
'Easter Star'	EStr
'Easy Ned'	ELon
'Eat Our Wake Pintaheads'	EStr
'Echo Echo'	EStr
'Ed Kirchhoff'	XLum
'Ed Murray'	EStr SDay WAul WCAu
'Edgar Brown'	SDay WCot
'Edge Ahead'	CMac ECtt EHyd GKin LRHS NHol NRHS SDay WCAu WHrl
'Edge of Darkness'	CWGN NLar NSti SDay WFar
'Edith Marie' **new**	EStr
'Edith Vaughan'	EStr
'Edna Spalding'	CRos EHyd LRHS NRHS SDay
'Eenie Allegro'	CBro ECtt SPer
'Eenie Fanfare'	EStr NBir
'Eenie Weenie'	CBro ECtt EHyd ELon EStr GKev NBro SRms WWtn
'Eenie Weenie Non-stop'	ECha EPPr
'Eggplant Escapade' ♀H6	CBgR ELon EStr SDay WHrl
'Egyptian Ibis'	WNHG
'Egyptian Queen'	CBgR
'Eight Miles High'	EStr
'Eighteen Karat'	EStr
'El Desperado'	CBgR CSam ECtt EHyd ELon EStr GQue ILea LRHS MBNS MHol MNrw NRHS WAvo WCAu WCot
'El Glorioso'	CWat EStr
'Elaine Farrant'	SDay
'Elaine Strutt'	MNrw SDay SWvt WCot WSpi
'Elegant Candy' ♀H6	CBgR CMac EPfP EStr WCAu
'Elegant Girls' **new**	EStr
'Eleonor'	WFar
'Elfin Illusion'	EStr
'Elizabeth Salter'	CWCL EStr NLar SDay
'Eloquent Silence'	SDay
'Elsie Stelter'	EStr
'Elva White Grow'	SDay
'Elven Elegance'	EStr
'Emerald Dew'	SDay
'Emerald Empress'	EStr
'Emerald Eye'	SDay
'Emerald Starburst'	EStr
'Emperor's Choice'	SDay
'Emperor's Dragon'	EStr SDay
'Enchanted Forest'	EStr WCAu
'Enchanter's Spell'	SDay
'Enchanting Blessing'	EStr SDay
'English Skies'	EStr
'Entrapment'	CBod ECtt EStr SDeJ WFar WSMil
'Entwined in the Vine'	EStr
'Envoyé Spécial'	XSen
'Erica Nichole Gonzales'	SDay
'Erin Prairie'	EStr
esculenta	SMad
'Eternity Road'	EStr
'Etruscan Tomb'	EStr
'Evelyn Claar'	CMac
'Evelyn Lela Stout'	SDay
'Evening Enchantment'	EStr SDay
'Ever So Ruffled'	EStr SDay
EVERYDAYLILY CREAM ('Ver00112'PBR) **new**	EStr
'Excellent'	EStr
'Exotic Love'	SDay
'Exotic Spider'	EStr
'Exotic Star'	EStr
'Exotic Treasure'	EStr
'Exploded Pumpkin'	EBee EStr
'Exploding Galaxy'	EStr
'Explosion in the Paint Factory'	EStr
'Eye of the Hurricane'	EStr
'Eye on a String'	EStr
'Eye on America'	EBee ELon EStr
'Eyes are Mosaics'	EStr
'Ezekiel'	XSen
'Fabergé'	SDay
'Facemaker' **new**	EStr
'Fairest Love'	MNrw
'Fairest of Them'	CBgR

'Fairy Charm'	SDay
'Fairy Summerbird'	SDay
'Fairy Tale Pink'	EStr SDay
'Fall Farewell'	WNHG
'Fall Guy'	SDay
'Fama'	EStr
'Fandango'	SPer
'Farmer's Daughter'	CBgR
'Father James Foster'	EStr
'Fellow'	EStr
'Femme Fatale'	SDay
'Femme Osage'	EStr SDay
'Feria'	XSen
'Fiestaville'	EStr
'Final Touch'	CBgR CBod EStr MSwo NBro
'Finders Keepers'	EBee EStr
'Fire and Fog'	EStr
'Fire Bird Suite'	EStr
'Fire Dance'	ELon
'Fire from Heaven'	WHrl
'Fire Tree'	CBgR ELon EStr
'Firestorm'	EStr
'First Formal'	SPer
'First Knight'	EStr SDay
'Flaming Firebird'	EStr
'Flaming Sword'	WBrk WRHF
'Flamingo Parade'	EStr
'Flash Mob' **new**	EStr
flava	see *H. lilioasphodelus*
'Fleeting Fancy'	SDay
'Flip Fiasco'	EStr
'Florentine Silk'	EStr
'Florida Sunshine' (d)	XSen
'Florissant Miss'	EStr
'Flower Basket' (d)	EStr
'Flower Pavilion'	SDay
'Floyd Cove'	SDay
'Fly Catcher'	CBgR SDay
'Flying Trapeze' **new**	EStr
'Fooled Me' ♀H6	ECtt EHyd EPfP EStr LRHS NRHS SDay
'Forbidden Desires'	EStr
'Forest Phantom'	EStr
'Forever Red'	EStr
'Forever Redeemed' **new**	SDay
forrestii	CExl GKev
'Forsooth'	CBgR
'Forsyth Ace of Hearts'	CBgR
'Forsyth Evening Glow'	EStr
'Forsyth White Buds'	EStr
'Fortress of Solitude'	EStr
'Forty Second Street'	EStr
'Fragrant Bouquet'	EStr
'Fragrant Pastel Cheers'	SDay
'Fragrant Reflections' **new**	EStr
'Fragrant Returns'	ECtt LEdu SPoG
'Frank Gladney'	XSen
'Frankly Scarlet'	EStr
'Frans Hals'	Widely available
'Fred Ham'	XSen
'Fred Manning'	EStr
'Free Wheelin''	EPfP EStr SCob
'French Connection'	SDay
'French Lingerie'	EStr
'French Pavilion'	SDay
'French Porcelain'	SDay
'Fresh Air'	MNrw
'Fried Green Tomatoes'	EStr
'Friends with Benefits'	EStr
'Frills and Furbelows'	SDay

'Frilly Bliss'	EStr
'Fritz Schroer'	CBgR
'Froggy' **new**	EStr
'Frosted Encore'	SDay
'Frosted Vintage Ruffles'	EBee EStr EWes MNrw WCAu
'Frozen Arrowhead' **new**	EStr
'Frozen Jade'	EBee EHyd LRHS NRHS SDay
'Full Grown'	EStr
'Fully Blessed'	EStr
fulva	CTri ELan GPSL LPot MMuc NBir SEND SRms WBrk WHrl XSen
- B&SWJ 8647	WCru
- 'Flore Pleno' (d)	CAvo CMac CTri CWld ECtt ELan GBin LPot MBriF MHer MRav NBir NBro NGdn NSti SMad SPer SRms WBrk WCAu WSMil XSen
- 'Green Kwanso' (d)	CBgR CExl ECha EHyd ITim LRHS NRHS WFar WPnP WWtn
- var. ***kwanso***	WWtn
- - B&SWJ 6328	WCru
- 'Kwanso' ambig. (d)	EHyd LRHS
- var. ***littorea***	CMac XLum XSen
- var. ***rosea***	LPla WCot XSen
§ - 'Variegated Kwanso' (d/v)	CBro ELon MRav NBir SMad WBor WCot WFar WHer WHoo WHrl
- yellow-variegated (v)	WCot
'Fun Fling'	EStr
'Funicular'	EStr
'Gadsden Light'	EStr SDay
'Gala Greetings'	XSen
'Galaxy Ranger'	EStr
'Gale Storm'	WNHG
'Galena Holiday'	EWes
'Galileo'	EStr
'Garden Butterfly' **new**	EStr
'Garden Crawler'	CBgR
'Garden Portrait'	SDay
'Garrett Allen'	EStr
'Gary Colby'	EStr
'Gay Octopus'	CBgR EStr MSpe WHrl
'Gay Rapture'	SPer
'Gemini'	SDay
'Gender Equality'	EStr
'Geneva Firetruck'	EStr
'Gentle Country Breeze'	SDay
'Gentle Rose'	EStr SDay
'Gentle Shepherd'	Widely available
'George Cunningham'	ECtt EHyd ELan LPot LRHS MRav NBir NRHS SDay WFar
'George David'	WHrl
'Georgette Belden'	ECtt EHyd GKin LRHS NHol SPeP
'Georgia Cream' (d)	NLar
'Gerda Brooker'	EStr
'Get All Excited'	ELon
'Ghost Pattern' **new**	EStr
'Giant Moon'	CBgR CRos ECtt EHyd ELan EStr LRHS NRHS SDay SRms
'Giddy Go Round'	SDay
'Ginger Twist'	EStr
'Girouette'	XSen
'Glacier Bay'	CBgR
'Glazed Heather Plum'	EStr
'Gleber's Top Cream'	EStr
'Gleeman Song'	CBgR
'Glendevon'	EStr
'Glittering Treasure'	XLum
'Glow Appeal'	EStr
'Glowing Heart'	SDay
'Go Seminoles'	EStr
'God's Handicraft'	EStr

'Going Bananas'^{PBR}	WCot
'Gold Elephant'	SDay
'Gold Fever' **new**	SDay
'Gold Imperial'	NBre
'Golden Bell'	NGdn
'Golden Chimes'	Widely available
'Golden Compass'	EStr
'Golden Firefly'	SDay
'Golden Ginkgo'	LPot SDay WAvo WNHG
'Golden Prize'	NGdn SDay WAvo WCot XSen
'Golden Scroll'	SDay
GOLDEN ZEBRA ('Malja'^{PBR}) (v)	CWGN EHyd ELan EPfP LRHS MRav NLar SRms
'Golliwog'	CBgR EStr
'Gorgeous Smile'	EStr
'Got Milk'	EStr
'Gothic Butterfly'	EStr
'Gothic Window'	SDay
'Graal'	XSen
'Grace and Favour'	SDay
'Graceful Eye'	SDay
'Graceland'	SDay WHrl
'Grand Masterpiece'	EStr NGdn SDay WFar
'Grand Palais'	SDay
'Granite City Towhead'	ELon
'Granny's Smokehouse'	EStr
'Grape Arbor'	WNHG
'Grape Harvest'	WNHG
'Grape Magic'	WCot
'Grape Velvet'	CSpe EStr ILea MHer NSti SRms WCAu WNHG WWtn
'Grapes of Wrath'	EStr
'Great Auntie Picklebottom'	EStr
'Green Arrow'	EStr
'Green Dolphin Street'	SDay
'Green Dragon'	SDay
'Green Eyes Wink'	MHol
'Green Flutter'	CBgR EStr GQue LSRN NBir NGdn NSti SPhx WAvo WSpi
'Green Fringe'	SDay
'Green Goddess'	XLum
'Green Icon'	EStr
'Green Lines'	EStr
'Green Mystique'	EBee EStr SDay
'Green Nautilus'	EStr
'Green Puff'	NBir
'Green Spider'	CBgR SDay
'Green Widow'	SDay
'Greenland'	EBee ECtt EHyd EStr GKev LRHS NRHS
'Greywoods Cowgirl Casanova'	EStr
'Greywoods Fashionista'	EStr
'Greywoods Fingers Malone'	EStr
'Greywoods Katz Kando'	EStr
'Greywoods Nautical Nellie'	EStr
'Groove-billed Ani'	EStr
'Groovy Green'	SDay
'Grumbly'	ELan WPnP
'Gryphon Hankow Legacy' **new**	EStr
'Gryphon Prague Gothic'	EStr
'Guardian Angel'	WCFE
'Gwen Leman'	EStr
'Gypsy Sweetheart'	WNHG
'Hail Mary'	SDay
'Halloween Green'	EStr
'Hall's Pink' **new**	CRos
'Hamlet'	SDay WNHG
'Happy Apache'	EStr
'Happy Medium'	EStr
'Happy Returns'	CBgR CRos CSBt CTri ECha EHyd ELan EPfP EStr GBin LCro LOPS LPot LRHS LSRN MBel MHost NGdn NHol NRHS SRms WCAu XLum
'Harbor Blue'	SDay
'Harrods'	EStr
'Harry Barras'	XLum
'Harvest Hue'	SDay
'Having Fun'	EStr
'Hawaiian Nights'	WNHG
'Hawk'	ELon SDay
'Hawkwoman'	EStr
'Hazel'	EStr
'Hazmatter's Ball'	EStr
'Heady Wine'	EStr SDay
'Heart Wishes'	EStr
'Heartless'	EStr
'Heart's Glee'	XSen
'Heavenly Angel Ice'	ELon EPfP
'Heavenly Beginnings'	EStr
'Heavenly Black Bird'	EStr
'Heavenly Curls'	EStr SDay
'Heavenly Fire and Ice'	EStr
'Heavenly Flight of Angels'	EStr
'Heavenly Pink Butterfly'	EStr
'Heavenly Pink Fang'	EStr
'Heavenly Thunderbird'	EStr
'Heavenly United We Stand'	EStr
'Heavenly Way Big'	EStr
'Heidi Eidelweiss'	CExl
'Heirloom Lace'	SDay WCAu
'Helen Sever'	EStr
'Helen Shooter'	EStr
'Helena Seabird'	EStr
'Helix'	EStr MBros SDay
'Helle Berlinerin'	SDay SEdd
'Hello Screamer'	EStr
'Helter Skelter'	SDay
'Heman'	EStr
'Henry D. Allnutt'	EStr
'Her Majesty's Wizard'	CBgR ELan ELon
'Here Lies Butch'	EStr
'Hermitage Newton'	SDay
'Hexagon'	EStr
'Hiding Place' **new**	EStr
'High Profile'	EStr
'High Tor'	ELon EStr SDay WHrl
'High Water Mark'	EStr
'Highland Lord' (d)	EStr SDay WCAu XSen
'Hold Your Horses'	SDay
'Holiday Delight'	EStr
'Holiday Mood'	ELan
'Holly Dancer' ♀H6	EStr
'Homeward Bound'	SDay
'Honeysuckle Rose'	EStr
'Honor Flight'	EStr
'Hooked on Romance'	EStr
'Hope Diamond'	SDay
'Hope Floats' **new**	EStr
'Hoping for Hugs'	EStr
'Hornby Castle'	CBro CRos EHyd LRHS NRHS
'Hot Chocolate'^{PBR}	EBee
'Hot Pink Fury'	EStr
'Hot Tamales and Red Hots'	EStr
'Hot Town'	ELan

'Hot Wheels'	CBgR
'Hot Wire'	SDay WNHG
'Houdini'	WCAu
'House Music'	XSen
'House of Orange'	EStr
'Humdinger'	EStr SDay WCot
'Hummingbird'	EStr
'Humungousaur'	EStr
'Hunker Down'	EStr
'Huntress'	EStr
'Hybridizer's Truffle'	EStr
'Hymn'	SDay
'Hyperion'	CBgR CMac CTri ECha ECtt ELon EShb EStr GKin LEdu MHol MMuc MRav NBid NGdn SDay SEND SPer SWvt WCot WWtn
'I Love to Tell the Story'	EStr
'Ice Carnival'	EStr NGdn NLar SCob SWvt WSpi
'Ice Castles'	CTri SDay
'Ice Cool'	SCob
'Icecap'	CBgR
'Icy Lemon'	EStr SDay
'Ida Duke Miles'	SDay
'Ida Mae Norris'	EStr
'Ida Wimberly Munson' **new**	SDay
'Ida's Magic'	EStr
'Identity Crisis' **new**	EStr
'Iditarod'	EStr
'Ikebana Star'	EStr
'Iktomi'	EStr
'Illini Jackpot'	SDay
'I'm a King Bee'	EStr
'Impromptu'	SDay
'In Depth' (d)	NBro NLar WCot WHrl
'In Her Shoes'	EStr
'In Search of Angels'	EStr
'In Strawberry Time'	WNHG
'Inca Puzzle'	SDay
'Inchon'	EStr
'Increased Complexity'	EStr
'Indian Paintbrush'	ELon NBir WNHG
'Indigo Moon'	XSen
'Indy Heart Stopper'	EStr
'Inner View'	ECtt EStr SDay
'Innocent Blush'	EStr
'Inspired Word'	SDay
'Instant Zéro'	XSen
'Iridescent Jewel'	SDay
'Irish Elf'	ELon GBin SDay SHar
'Irish Mixup' **new**	EStr
'Irish Veil'	EStr
'Iron Gate Glacier'	EBee EPPr EStr MBNS SDay XLum
'Irresistible You'	EStr
'Isaac'	EStr
'Isabelle Rose'	EStr SDay
'Isle of Dreams'	SDay
'Islesworth'	SDay
'Isolde'	CBgR EStr
'It's Soul Time'	EStr
'Itsy Bitsy Spider'	CBgR
'Itza Mirage'	EStr
'Ivelyn Brown'	EStr SDay
'Ivory Cloud' (d)	EStr
'Ivory Coast'	SDay
'J.T. Davis'	EStr
'James Marsh'	CBgR MNrw NSti WCAu WCot WFar WNHG
'Jane's Prism'	EStr
'Janice Brown'	CWCL ECtt EMor EStr GBee LRHS NHol NLar NRHS SDay WHrl

'Janie Wilson'	WNHG
'Jan's Twister'	EStr MNrw SDay WHrl
'Jason Salter'	EStr SDay WAul
'Jay Turman'	SDay
'Jealous Sky'	EStr
'Jean'	EStr SDay
'Jean Swann'	EStr
'Jedi Dot Pierce'	EStr SDay
'Jellyfish Jealousy' ♀H6	SDay
'Jenny Wren'	EPPr NBro WAul
'Jerry Hyatt'	EStr
'Jersey Breeze'	EStr
'Jerusalem'	SDay
'Jeu de Piste'	XSen
'Jeune Tom'	CBgR
'Jewel Case'	WNHG
'Jim McKinney'	EStr
'Joan Derifield'	EStr
'Joan Senior'	Widely available
'Job Creator'	EStr
'Jockey Club' (d)	ECtt WHrl
'Jogolor'	EStr
'John R. Pike'	EStr
'Johnny Come Lately'	EStr
'Jordan'	LSRN SWvt
'Jordan's Jazz'	EStr
'Josephine Marina'	EStr
'Journey's End'	SDay
'Jovial'	EStr SDay
'Joyful Participation'	EStr
'Juanita's Picotee Delight'	SDay
'Judge Roy Bean'	EStr SDay
'Judy Davidson'	WNHG
'Judy Farquhar'	EStr
'June Melody'	WNHG
'June Rose'	EStr
'Jungle Beauty'	CBgR SDay
'Just My Size'	EStr
'Just Whistle'	EStr
'Justin Brent'	XSen
'Justin George'	SDay
'Justin June'	WHrl
'Kaleidoscopic Intrigue'	EStr
'Kansas Kitten'	EStr
'Karen's Curls' ♀H6	SDay
'Kasia'	WHrl
'Kate Carpenter'	EStr SDay
'Kathleen Salter'	EStr SDay
'Katie Elizabeth Miller'	SDay
'Katisue Herrington'	EStr
'Kazuq'	SDay
'Kecia'	SDay
'Kempion'	CBgR
'Kermit's Scream'	EStr
'Key to my Heart'	CBgR
'Key West Sunset'	EStr
'Kharma Police'	EStr
'Kickin' Chicken'	EStr
'Killer' ♀H6	EStr
'Killer Purple'	EStr
'Kimberly Sue'	EStr
'King Crab' **new**	EStr
'King George'	EStr
'King Kahuna' (d)	EStr
'King of Anything'	EStr
'King's Gold'	EStr
'King's Throne'	WNHG
'Kirsten My Love'	EStr
'Kiss the Sky'	EStr
'Kissed by Moonlight'	EStr

'Knights in White Satin'	EStr
'Kokomo Queen'	EStr
'Kwanso Flore Pleno'	see *H. fulva* 'Green Kwanso'
'Kwanso Flore Pleno Variegata'	see *H. fulva* 'Variegated Kwanso'
'La Fenice'	EStr
'La Peche'	SDay
'Lacy Doily'	EStr WCAu WSMil
'Lacy Marionette'	ELon
'Lady Betty Fretz'	EBee EStr
'Lady Fingers'	CBgR
'Lady Inara'	EStr
'Lady Liz'	SDay WNHG
'Lady Mischief'	EStr SDay
'Lady Neva' ♀H6	CBgR ELon
'Lady Tiger'	WNHG
'Ladybug Hawk'	EStr
'Ladybug's Two Moons' (d)	EStr
'Ladykin'	ELon
'Lambada'	EStr
'Lamplighter's Circle'	EStr
'Land of Cotton'	XSen
'Land of Enchantment'	EStr
'Land's End'	EStr
'Lark Song'	EHyd LRHS NRHS WFar WHrl
'Larry's Candy Stripe Swizzle'	EStr
'Last Song'	EStr
'Late Report'	EStr
'Late Summer Rose'	WNHG
'Laughing Giraffe'	EStr WCot
'Laughton Tower'	SMHy
'Lauradell'	SDay
'Lauren Leah'	SDay
'Lava Burst'	EStr
'Lava Stream'	EStr
'Lavender Blue Baby'	EPfP EStr MHol
'Lavender Bonanza'	SDay
'Lavender Deal'	MNrw WNHG
'Lavender Handlebars'	SDay
'Lavender Memories'	EStr SDay WNHG
'Lavender Showstopper'	WCAu
'Lavender Spider'	CBgR
'Lavender Stardust'	SDay
'Lavender Tonic'	WNHG
'Lavender Tutu'	ECtt EStr MBros
'Layers of Gold' (d)	XSen
'Lazy Hazy Days'	EStr
'Leading Edge'	SDay
'Ledgewood's Frequent Flyer'	EStr
'Ledgewood's Irish Spirit'	EStr
'Ledgewood's Sunday Dessert'	EStr
'Lee Reinke'	EStr
'Leila Mantle'	CBgR
'Lemon Bells'	CWat ECha EHyd EPfP EStr GKev GKin GMaP LEdu LRHS NBro SHar WCAu WSpi
'Lemon Custard'	EStr
'Lemon Dessert'	ELon
'Lemon Madeline'	EStr
'Lemon Mint'	ELon
'Lemonora'	SDay
'Lenox'	SDay
'Leonard Bernstein'	EStr SDay
'Leprechaun's Curls'	EStr
'Let Loose'	EStr
'Let Love Rejoice'	EStr
'Lies and Lipstick'	EStr
'Life is a Highway'	EStr
'Life Unlimited'	EStr
'Light the Way'	GBin MHol SEdd SPoG WCot
'Light Years Away'	ELon MBNS MNrw
'Like a Gee Six'	EStr
'Lilac Lady'	EStr
§ ***lilioasphodelus***	Widely available
'Lillian's Good Intentions'	EStr
'Lilly Dache'	EStr
'Lilting Lady'	EStr
'Lilting Lavender'	ELon WCAu
'Lily Munster'	EStr
'Lime Frost' ♀H6	CBgR EStr
'Lime Painted Lady'	CBgR
'Limetree'	CBgR EStr
'Linda'	MRav
'Linda Sierra'	EStr
'Linda the Green Eyed Lady'	EStr
'Lip Smack'	EStr
'Litchfield Plantation'	EStr
'Little Anna Rosa'	ECtt EStr
'Little Audrey'	EStr
'Little Bee'	NBre
'Little Big Man'	SDay
'Little Bumble Bee'	WWtn
'Little Business'	SDay
'Little Cadet'	XLum
'Little Cranberry Cove'	GBin
'Little Dart'	ECha
'Little Deeke'	SDay WHrl
'Little Fantastic'	ELon SDay WWtn
'Little Fat Cat'	EStr
'Little Fellow'	EStr
'Little Girl'	ELon
'Little Grapette'	ELon EPfP EStr GQue LLWG NLar NSti SCob WAul
'Little Greenie'	SDay
'Little Gypsy Vagabond'	CBgR CWat EStr
'Little Heavenly Angel'	EStr
'Little Isaac'	EStr
'Little Kiki'	SDay
'Little Lassie'	CBgR
'Little Maggie'	SDay
'Little Men'	WCAu
'Little Miss Lucy'	EStr
'Little Miss Manners'	EStr NLar
'Little Missy'	CBgR EStr WHoo WNHG
'Little Monica'	SDay
'Little Music Maker' (d)	EStr
'Little Paul'	EStr
'Little Red Hen'	CSam EHyd GKin LRHS MSpe NBir NBro NGdn SDay WFar
'Little Show Stopper'	NBro NLar
'Little Showoff'	SDay
'Little Surfer Girl' **new**	EStr
'Little Swain'	SDay
'Little Sweet Talk'	ELon
'Little Swirling Shadows'	EStr
'Little Tawny'	ELon
'Little Toddler'	SDay
'Little Velma'	EStr
'Little Violet Lace'	SDay
'Little Wart'	CBgR SDay WHrl
'Little William'	EStr
'Little Wine Cup'	CMac CRos CSam ECtt ELon EStr GKin GMaP LPot LRHS MRav MSpe NBir NGdn NRHS SRms WAul
'Little Women'	SDay WHrl
'Little Zinger'	SDay
'Littlest Angel'	SDay

'Living in Amsterdam'	EBee EStr
'Lobo Lucy'	ELon EStr
'Loch Ness Monster'	EStr
'Lochinvar'	MRav
'Loco Bo'	EStr
'Lois Burns'	SDay
'Lonely Heart'	EStr
'Long John Silver'	ELon EStr
'Long Stocking'	EStr WCot
'Long Tall Sally'	EStr
'Longfields Beauty'	MSpe
'Longfields Cheese and Wine' **new**	EStr
'Longfields Dress Pink'	EStr
'Longfields × Factor'	EStr
'Longfields Glory'	EHyd LRHS NBre NRHS
'Longfields Maxim' (d)	EStr MHol SDeJ
'Longfields Pearl'	EStr
'Longfields Pride'	EStr SRms WBor
'Longfields Purple Eye'	NLar
'Longfields Think Pink'	EStr
'Longfields Twins'	MBNS WCot WFar
'Longfields Whoopy'	ELon EPfP MNrw SDir
longituba AIK 284	WCot
- B&SWJ 4576	WCru
'Look at Me'	ELan
'Look Lucky'	EStr
'Lost in the Toy Store'	EStr
'Lost in the Translation'	EStr
'Loth Lorien'	EBee EHyd LRHS NRHS
'Lots of Hoopla'	EStr
'Lotta Dotta'	EStr
'Lotus Land'	SDay
'Louis McHargue'	SDay
'Lourice Abdallah'	EStr
'Love Those Eyes'	EStr
'Lovely Margie'	EStr
'Lovely Rita'	EStr
'Loverboy'	EStr
'Loving Memories'	SDay
'Lowcountry Gem'	EStr
'Lucille Lennington'	WNHG
'Lullaby Baby'	ELan NLar WNHG
'Lunar Sea'	EStr
'Lupita Vindaz'	EStr
'Luscious Honeydew'	WNHG
'Lusty Lealand'	SDay
'Luxury Lace'	CAgr EBee ECtt EHyd ELan EStr GBin GKin LSRN MHost NBir NGdn NHol NWad SPer WFar WHrl WWtn XLum XSen
'Lydia Bechtold'	EStr SDay
'Lynn Hall'	EHyd NLar WSpi
'Mabel Fuller'	CBgR MRav SPer WHrl
'Mabel Nolen'	EStr
'Mable Lewis Nelson'	EStr
'Macbeth'	EStr MNrw SDir
'Mad Max'	EStr SDay
'Madeline Nettles Eyes'	EBee ELon EStr
'Madmoiselle Constanza'	SDay
'Maggie Fynboe'	CBgR
'Magic Amethyst'	CBgR
'Magic Carpet Ride'	EStr
'Magic Dancer'	CBod EStr
'Magic Lace'	EStr
'Magic of Oz'	EStr
'Magical Messenger'	EStr
'Magnificent Rainbow'	CBcs
'Mahogany Magic' ♀H6	ELon EStr
'Majestic Dark Eyes'	EStr
'Malachite Prism'	EStr
'Malaysian Monarch'	EStr SDay WNHG
'Malaysian Spice'	WNHG
'Maleny Canary'	EStr
'Maleny Chantilly Lace'	EStr
'Maleny Debutante'	EStr
'Maleny Kiwi Dazzler'	EStr
'Maleny Tiger'	SDay
'Mallard'	CAby CBgR ECtt EStr MRav NBir WCot
'Malmaison Plum'	EStr SDay
'Mama Sophia'	EStr
'Mama's Pajamas'	EStr
'Mambo Maid'	XSen
'Man on Fire'	WNHG
'Manchurian Apricot'	SDay
'Marble Faun'	SDay
'Margaret Perry'	MNrw NLar
'Margaret Seawright'	EStr
'Margo Reed Indeed'	EStr SDay WNHG
'Marietta Charmer'	SDay
'Marietta Delight'	EStr
'Marilyn Lee Bock'	EStr
'Marilyn Morss Johnson'	EStr
'Marion Vaughn'	CWld ECtt ELan EMor EPfP GKin GMaP MBel MRav NSti SDix SPer SWvt WCAu WCot WFar WHoo WSHC
'Mariska'	EStr SDay WNHG
'Marked by Lydia'	ELon
'Marshall McLuhan'	EStr
'Martina Verhaert'	CWGN EStr
'Mary Alice Stokes'	EStr
'Mary Ethel Anderson'	EStr
'Mary Todd'	EBee XSen
'Mary's Baby'	EStr
'Mary's Gold' ♀H6	SDay
'Masada'	WNHG
'Mask of Time'	EStr
'Mask of Zorro'	EStr
'Mata Hari'	SDay
'Matchless Fire'	EStr
'Maude's Valentine'	SDay
'Mauna Loa'	CSBt ELon EStr GQue LPot MNrw NLar SDeJ SWvt WAul WCot
'May May'	CBgR
'Mayan Poppy'	EStr
'Meadow Mist'	CBgR ELon
'Meadow Sprite'	WCot
'Meadowsweet'	EStr
'Mean Mister Mustard'	EStr
'Medieval Guild'	EStr
'Mema's Dingaling'	EStr
'MeMe's Guilty Pleasure'	EStr
'MeMe's Lovin' the Limelight'	EStr
'MeMe's Merlot' **new**	EStr
'MeMe's Pink Flamingo' **new**	EStr
'Memory Number One' **new**	EStr
'Merry Jo's Delight'	EStr
'Merry Moppet'	EStr
'Merry Witch'	EStr
'Metaphor'	ECtt SDay XSen
'Michael Poliga'	EStr
'Michael's Sword'	EStr
'Michele Coe'	ECtt GKin NBro NGdn SDay WCAu WFar WHrl
'Mico'	ELon

middendorffii	CMac EStr GKev GMaP NSti WHrl WSpi WThu
'Middle of Nowhere'	EStr
'Midnight Confession'	EStr
'Midnight Magic'	SDay
'Midnight Rambler'	SDay
'Midnight Rendezvous'	EStr
'Mikado'	CBgR CMac
'Mike Reed'	EStr
'Milady Greensleeves'	EStr SDay WHrl
'Milanese Mango'	EStr SDay
'Mildred Mitchell'	CBgR ELon EStr NLar
'Military School'	EStr
'Mimosa Umbrella'	EStr
'Ming Porcelain'	SDay WCAu WNHG
'Mini Pearl'	ECtt ELon EStr LRHS MPie NRHS SPer
'Mini Stella'	CBro ECtt WFar
'Minnie Wildfire'	EStr
minor	CBro EBee EHyd EPPr LRHS NRHS SPhx SRms XSen
– B&SWJ 8841	WCru
'Miracle Maid'	WNHG
'Miss Atomic Bomb'	EStr
'Miss Jessie'	EStr
'Miss North Carolina'	EStr
'Miss Piggy'	EStr
'Missenden'	CBgR MNrw
'Missouri Beauty'	SWvt
'Mister Lucky'	EStr
'Mojave Sunset'	EStr
'Mokan Butterfly'	SDay
'Moment of Truth'	NBre
'Monica Marie'	EStr SDay
'Mont Royal Demitasse'	ELon
'Moon Snow'	SDay
'Moonlight Masquerade'	CBgR ECtt ELon MMuc NLar SRms
'Moonlight Orchid'	WHrl
'Moonlit Caress'	CBgR EBee ECtt NBro SDay
'Moonlit Crystal'	EStr
'Moonlit Masquerade' ♀H6	CWGN EStr MBNS MNrw SDay SEND WHrl
'Moonlit Summerbird'	EStr
'Moontraveller'	WCot
'Morgen le Fay'	EStr
'Mormon Spider'	EStr
'Morning Face'	EStr
'Morning Sun'	WCot
'Morocco Red'	CBro ELan MHCG
'Morphin Time' **new**	EStr
'Morpho Butterfly'	EStr
'Moses' Fire'	ECtt EStr MHol NLar WFar
'Mossy Glade'	CBgR
'Mount Joy'	EStr
'Mountain Laurel'	ECtt EHyd EStr GKin LRHS MRav NRHS WFar WGwG
'Moussaka'	CWGN EStr WCAu WFar
'Move Over Moon'	EStr SDay
'Mrs Hugh Johnson'	CChe EShb LPot WHrl
* 'Mrs Lester'	SDay
'Muddy Creek Magic'	EStr
'Muffet's Little Friend'	WHrl
multiflora	XSen
'Multiple Multiplications'	EStr
'Muriel Rhem'	EStr
'Murphy's Law'	EStr
'Muscle Man'	EStr XSen
'My Belle'	SDay
'My Darling Clementine'	EStr SDay WNHG
'My Heart Belongs to Daddy'	EStr
'My Melinda'	SDay
'My Place or Yours'	EStr
'My Reggae Tiger'	EStr
'Mynelle's Starfish'	WHrl
'Mystical Rainbow'	SDay
'Nacogdoches Lady'	SWvt
'Nanuq'	ELon SDay
'Naomi Ruth'	EStr
'Nashville'	CBro ELan WHrl
'Nashville Lights'	CBgR EStr
'National Memento'	EStr
'Native Reflection'	EStr
'Natty Man' **new**	EStr
'Naughty Red'	EStr
'Navajo Jewel'	EStr
'Navajo Pony'	EStr
'Navajo Princess'	MNrw
'Neal Berrey'	EStr SDay
'Nefertiti'	CBgR ELon NBir WAul WCAu
'Neon Flamingo'	EStr
'Neon Sunshine'	EStr
'Neon Yellow'	EStr
'Neutron Star'	EStr
'Never Ending Fantasy'	EStr
'Never Get Away'	EStr
'New Wine'	WNHG
'New York Follies'	EStr
'Neyron Rose'	EHyd GKin LRHS NGdn NRHS WWtn XLum
'Night Beacon'	CBgR ECtt ELon EStr GKev GKin MNrw MPie NLar SCob SDay SDeJ WCAu WHrl
'Night Embers'	ECtt ELon EPfP NLar SDir WCAu
'Night Raider'	CBgR EStr SDay WNHG
'Night Whispers'	SPer
'Nile Crane'	CBgR ELon EStr MNrw SDay SPer WAul
'Nile Plum'	EStr SDay
'Nina Winegar'	EStr
'Ninja Storm'	EStr
'Nivia Guest'	SDay
'Nob Hill'	ELon EStr WHrl XLum
'Nona's Garnet Spider'	ELon
'Nordic Night'	CBgR EWes SDay
'North Wind Drifter'	EStr
'Norton Beauté'	WCot
'Norton Eyed Seedling'	WNHG
'Norton Orange'	EStr
'Not Forgotten'	WNHG
'Nothing is Easy'	EStr
'Notify Ground Crew'	EStr
'Nova'	ELon SDay
'Nowhere to Hide'	EStr
'Nuit Parisienne'	EStr
'Nuka'	XLum
'Nutmeg Elf'	CBgR
'Oakes Love'	MNrw
'Ocean Rain'	EStr SDay WNHG
'Ocean Spirit'	EStr
'Octopus Hugs'	EStr
'Oke-She-Moke-She-Pop'	EStr
'Old San Juan'	EStr
'Old Tangiers' ♀H6	EStr SDay WNHG
'Olive Bailey Langdon'	EStr SDay WCot
'Olive's Odd One'	EStr
'Oloroso'	CBgR
'Olympic Gold'	EStr XSen
'Olympic Showcase'	EStr
'Omomuki'	SDay
'On and On'	EStr GBin GQue MBros MNrw

'On Pointe'	EStr
'On Silken Thread'	SDay
'One Above You'	EStr
'One Fire'	XSen
'Oodles'	WHrl
'Open Hearth'	EStr WHrl
'Open my Eyes'	EStr
'Orange Dream'	SDay
'Orange Empire'	SDay
'Orange Exotica'	CBgR EStr
'Orange Nassau'	WCAu WFar
'Orange Prelude'	XSen
'Orange Velvet'	SDay
'Orangeman' misapplied	NGdn
'Orchid Candy'	EStr NBir
'Orchid Corsage'	ELon EStr
'Oriental Impressions'	EStr
'Oriental Ruby'	SDay
'Orphée'	XSen
'Osterized'	EStr
'Ostrich Plume'	EStr
'Ouachita Beauty'	CBgR ELon
'Our Kirsten'	EStr SDay
'Out of Balance'	EStr
'Outrageous'	CBgR EStr SDay WNHG
'Outrageous Ramona'	WNHG
'Oy Vey'	EStr
'Paige's Pinata'	EStr
'Painted Lady'	WNHG
'Painted Pink'	SDay
'Palace Pagoda'	WNHG
'Panda Bear'	EStr
'Pandora's Box'	CExl CTri CWat ECtt ELan EStr LLWG LRHS MMuc MNrw NBir NGdn NLar SDeJ SWvt WBor WFar
'Papa Goose'	EStr
'Paper Butterfly'	EStr SDay
'Papilion'	EStr
'Papoose'	XLum
'Paprika Flame'	EStr MHol
'Parade of Peacocks'	CBgR
'Paradise Bar and Grill'	EStr
'Paradise Lost'	EStr
'Pardon Me'	CBro CWld ECtt EHyd ELan ELon EStr GKin GMaP LRHS MPie NGdn NLar NRHS SDeJ SWvt WAul WBor WCAu WFar
'Parfait'	CBgR EStr WHrl WNHG
'Parrot Tattoo'	EStr
'Parson's Robe'	SDay
'Part-time Princess'	EStr
'Party Pants'	EStr
'Party Queen'	SDay
'Passion for Red'	SDay
'Passive Aggressive'	EStr
'Pastel Ballerina'	SDay
'Pat Mercer'	SDay XSen
'Patchwork Puzzle'	EStr
'Patricia Fay'	XSen
'Patrick Starfish'	EStr
'Patriotic Flavor'	EStr
'Pattern Breaker' **new**	EStr
'Patterns'	WNHG
'Patti Neyland'	EStr
'Paula Nettles'	EStr
'Paw Print'	EStr
'Pawn of Prophecy'	EStr
'Peach Jubilee'	EStr
'Peach Magnolia' (d)	EStr
'Peach Margarita' **new**	EStr
'Peach Whisper'	EStr SDay
'Peacock Maiden'	EStr WHrl XSen
'Pear Ornament'	SDay
'Pearl Anniversary'	EStr
'Pearl Jam'	SDay
'Pearl Lewis'	EStr SDay
'Peggy Jeffcoat'	EStr
'Penelope Vestey'	CBgR EStr NBir SDay
'Pennypurrs'	EStr
'Penny's Worth'	CRos LEdu LRHS WAul WCot WFar XLum
'Peppermint Ice'	EStr
'Persian Melon Plus'	WCAu
'Persian Ruby'	EStr SDay WNHG
'Petite Ballerina'	SDay
'Phill Warbasse' **new**	EStr
'Phyllis Cantini'	SDay
'Piano Man'	EStr WAul WNHG
'Piccadilly Princess'	EStr
'Pickin' and Grinnin''	EStr
'Piece of the Action'	EStr
'Pigment of Imagination'	EStr
'Pinhill Navajo Beauty'	EStr
'Pink Ambrosia'	ECtt EStr
'Pink Charm'	CMac CRos ECha ECtt EHyd EPPr GKin GMaP LRHS NBro NRHS
'Pink Circle'	SDay
'Pink Cotton Candy'	SDay
'Pink Damask' ♀H6	Widely available
'Pink Dazzler'	WNHG
'Pink Delight'	MPie
'Pink Dream'	CBgR NBir NBre
'Pink Flirt'	SDay
'Pink Lady'	MNrw MRav SRms
'Pink Monday'	SDay WNHG
'Pink Puff'	NBir NBre NLar
'Pink Spider'	SDay
'Pink Stripes'	EStr
'Pink Sundae'	WHrl
'Pink Thunderbird'	EStr
'Pink Whip Tips'	EStr
'Pink Windmill'	ELon
'Pinky Promise' **new**	EStr
'Pinocchio'	SMHy
'Pirate Treasure'	EStr
'Pirate's Patch'	SDay WCot
'Pixie Parasol'	WNHG WSpi
'Pixie Princess'	EStr
'Playing with Crayons' **new**	EStr
'Pleated Petticoats'	EStr
'Plum Beautiful'	EStr
'Plum Beauty'	NLar
'Plumas Lake' **new**	WNHG
'Poinsettia'	EStr
'Point of View'	EStr
'Pojo'	EStr
'Polar Vortex' **new**	EStr
'Polka Dot Bikini'	EStr
'Pony'	ELon
'Porcelain Pleasure'	SDay
'Possum in a Sack'	CBgR
'Post Time'	EStr
'Powerpuff Girls' **new**	EStr
'Prague Spring'	EStr WCAu WHrl WNHG
'Prairie Belle'	GKev NLar
'Prairie Blue Eyes'	EStr SDay SPlb WCot WHrl
'Prairie Charmer'	MMuc SEND WHrl
'Prankster'	EStr

'Precious d'Oro'	GQue SCob
'President Hadley'	SDay
'Pretty Face Nice Legs'	EStr
'Pretty Miss'	ECtt EMor EStr LRHS WGwG
'Preview Party'	WNHG
'Primal Scream' ♀H6	CAby EStr GAbr LSun MHol SDay SPoG WCot
'Primrose Mascotte'	NBir
'Prince of Midnight'	SDay
'Prince of Purple'	ELon
'Prince Poppycock'	EStr
'Prince Redbird'	SDay
'Princess Charming'	EStr
'Princeton Eye Glow'	SDay
'Princeton Silky'	ELon
'Printmaker'	EStr
'Prize Picotee Deluxe'	SDay
'Prize Picotee Elite'	SDay
'Protocol'	SDay
'Proud Mary'	SDay
'Ptarmigan'	CBgR EStr
'Pterodactyl Eye'	EStr SDay
§ 'Puddin'	SDay
'Pueblo Dancer'	EStr
'Pug Yarborough'	EStr SDay
'Pullin' Strings'	EStr
'Pumpkin Kid'	SDay
'Pumpkin Prince'	EStr
'Punxsutawney Phil'	EStr
'Puppet Show'	SDay
'Purple Avenger'	SDay
'Purple Bicolor'	WHrl
'Purple Flame'	CBod EStr
'Purple Oddity'	SDay
'Purple Passion's Promise' **new**	EStr
'Purple Penguin' **new**	EStr
'Purple Rain'	CWat MPie SDay SWvt
'Purple Waters'	MHost WPnP
'Purpleicious'	EStr NLar
'Pursuit of Excellence'	SDay
'Putting on the Ritz'	EStr
'Pygmy Plum'	SDay XSen
'Pyrotechnics'	EStr
'Quality of Mercy'	SDay
'Quartzitic Scintillation'	EStr
'Queen Charlotte'	EStr
'Queen Empress'	WNHG
'Queen Lily'	WNHG
'Queen of Green'	EStr
'Queen of May'	MNrw WCot
'Quick Results'	SDay
'Quiet Riot' **new**	EStr
'Quietly Awesome'	SDay
'Quilt Patch'	EStr
'Quinn Buck'	SDay
'Ra Hansen'	EStr
'Rachael My Love' (d)	XSen
'Radiant Greetings'	XSen
'Radiant Moonbeam' ♀H6	CBgR EStr
'Raging Bull'	EStr
'Raging Tiger'	SDay WHrl
'Rain Dance'	EStr
'Rainbow Candy'	CWGN
'Rainbow Gold'	XSen
'Rainbow Maker'	EStr
'Rajah'	CBgR CMac EHyd EStr NBro SPer WHrl
'Raspberry Candy'	CBro EStr MNrw SRms WHrl
'Raspberry Star'	EStr
'Raspberry Wine'	ECha
'Raspberry Winter'	EStr
'Razzle'	EStr
'Reach for the Heavens'	EStr
'Real Life Drama'	EStr
'Real Wind'	EStr
'Red Admiral'	EHyd LRHS
'Red Bull'	EStr
'Red Grace'	EStr
'Red Pennant'	SDay
'Red Precious' ♀H6	MNrw SMHy WCot
'Red Rain'	EStr WHrl XSen
'Red Ribbons'	ELon
'Red Rum'	CBgR EMor LSun MSwo NBro NRHS
'Red Suspenders'	ECtt EStr MBNS
'Red Tallboy'	EStr
'Red Twister'	ELon EStr
'Red Volunteer'	EStr SDay
'Redheaded Hussy'	EStr
'Regal Giant'	EStr
'Regency Dandy'	SDay XSen
'Regency Heights'	EStr
'Regency Masquerade'	SDay
'Renee'	MNrw
'Respighi'	EStr
'Return Trip'	ELon
'Rhubarb Wine'	EStr
'Rhythm of Love'	EStr
'Ribbonette'	EStr
'Rich Girls'	EStr
'Ricky Rose'	SDay XSen
'Riley Barron'	SDay
'Rise of the Phoenix'	EStr
'Rock Solid'	SDay
'Rocket Booster'	EStr
'Rocket City'	ELan EStr WNHG
'Roger Grounds'	CBgR
'Rolling Raven'	EStr
'Roman Toga'	CBgR SDay
'Romanian Rendevous'	EStr
* 'Romantic Rose'	MBNS NLar WHrl
'Romeo is Bleeding'	EStr
'Ron Azzanni'	EStr
'Root Beer'	GQue WCAu WHrl
'Rorschach Test'	EStr
'Rose'	SDay
'Rose Corsage'	SDir
'Rose Emily'	CBgR EStr SDay
'Rose F. Kennedy'	EStr
'Rose Tattoo'	EStr
'Roses in Snow'	EStr SDay
'Roswitha'	EStr
'Rosy Returns'	EPfP LRHS NLar WNHG
'Roy Likes Em Hot'	EStr
'Royal Braid'	NLar SPer WCot
'Royal Celebration'	WCot
'Royal Eventide'	XSen
'Royal Heritage'	EHyd EStr LRHS NRHS SDay
'Royal Parade'	SDay
'Royal Robe'	CTri
'Royal Saracen'	SDay
'Royal Thornbird'	CBgR
'Ruby Corsage'	EStr
'Ruby Sentinel'	SDay WNHG
'Ruby Spider' ♀H6	ELon EStr
'Ruby Storm'	EStr
'Ruffled Apricot'	LPot WNHG
'Ruffled Carousel'	WNHG
'Ruffled Dude'	EStr

'Ruffled Ivory'	SDay
'Ruffled Lemon Lace'	EStr
'Ruffled Magic'	SDay
'Ruffled Perfection'	EStr
'Rumble Seat Romance'	WNHG
'Running for the Border'	EStr
'Russian Easter'	EStr
'Russian Ragtime'	ELon EStr
'Russian Rhapsody' ♀H6	SDay
'Ruth Love'	WNHG
'Ruth Oliver'	EStr
'Sabie'	EStr
'Sabine Baur'	EStr MNrw WFar
'Sabra Salina'	EStr SDay WNHG
'Sacred Drummer'	SDay
'Saffron Glow'	SDay
'Sahara Sand Storm'	EStr
'Sahara Song'	EStr
'Sallie Brown'	EStr SDay
'Salmon Sheen'	SPer
'Sammy'	EStr SDay WHrl
'Sammy Russell'	Widely available
'Sandra Elizabeth'	SDay
'Sandy Beckman'	EStr
'Santa's Little Helper'	EStr
'Saratoga Belle'	EStr
'Sariah'	SDay
'Satin Glass'	CRos EHyd LRHS NRHS
'Satin Glow'	ECha
'Saved Soul' **new**	EStr
'Say Yes'	EStr
'Scarlet Flame'	ECha
'Scarlet Prince'	WNHG
'Scarlet Ribbons'	EStr
'Schnickel Fritz'	EBee
'School Girl'	EHyd LRHS NRHS
'Scorchio'	EStr
'Scorpio'	CBgR SDay WHrl
'Screamcicle' **new**	EStr
'Screaming Demon'	EStr WCot
'Sea Swept Dreams'	SDay
'Seal of Approval'	EBee EStr
'Seal the Deal'	EStr
'Sebastian'	SDay
'Seductive Fairy Tale'	EStr
'Seeing Stars'	SDay
'Selma Longlegs' ♀H6	EStr SDay
'Seminole Blood'	SDay
'Seminole Wind'	SDay
'Semiramide'	CBgR WNHG
'Serena Lady'	SDay
'Serena Sunburst' ♀H6	EHyd LRHS NRHS
'Serene Madonna'	ELan ILea
'Serenity Morgan'	CBgR
'Serge Rigaud'	WHrl
'Shadow Cabinet'	EStr
'Shadowed Pink'	WNHG
'Shady Lady'	SDay WNHG
'Shaggy Pumpkin'	EStr
'Shaman' Gates	SDay
'Shards of Kryptonite'	EStr
'Shark Attack'	EStr
'She Devil'	EStr
'Shelly Victoria'	SDay
'Sherry Lane Carr'	EStr SDay
'Sherwood Gladiator'	WNHG
'She's So Outrageous'	EStr
'Shimek September Morning'	EStr
'Shinto Etching'	EStr
'Shinto Shrine'	WNHG
'Shotgun'	EStr
'Shreddy'	EStr
'Shuffle the Deck'	EStr
'Sigudilla'	WNHG
'Silent Sentry'	EStr
'Silken Fairy'	CBgR
'Silken Touch'	CBgR EStr SDay
'Silly Wabbit' **new**	EStr
'Silly Whimsey'	EStr
'Siloam Amazing Grace'	SDay
'Siloam Angel Blush'	ECtt SDay
'Siloam Baby Talk'	ELon NBir SDay WAul WPnP
'Siloam Bo Peep'	SDay
'Siloam Button Box'	WHrl
'Siloam Bye Lo'	SDay
'Siloam Cinderella'	SDay
'Siloam David Kirchhoff'	XSen
'Siloam Doodlebug'	CBgR
'Siloam Double Classic' (d)	EStr SDay
'Siloam Dream Baby'	ELon
'Siloam Ethel Smith'	SDay
'Siloam Fairy Ruffles'	WNHG
'Siloam Fairy Tale'	SDay
'Siloam Flower Girl'	SDay
'Siloam French Doll'	NLar
'Siloam French Marble'	SDay
'Siloam Frosted Mint'	SDay
'Siloam Gold Coin'	SDay
'Siloam Helpmate'	WNHG
'Siloam John Yonski'	SDay
'Siloam June Bug'	CBgR ELan WCot
'Siloam Little Girl'	ECtt
'Siloam Mama'	SDay
'Siloam Merle Kent'	WAul
'Siloam New Toy'	EStr
'Siloam Nugget'	EStr
'Siloam Paul Watts'	EStr SDay
'Siloam Peewee'	ELon
'Siloam Pink Glow'	SDay
'Siloam Pocket Size'	SDay
'Siloam Red Toy'	EHyd LRHS NRHS SMHy
'Siloam Ribbon Candy'	SDay WNHG
'Siloam Ruffled Infant'	SDay
'Siloam Show Girl'	CWGN GKin
'Siloam Space Age'	WNHG
'Siloam Spizz'	EStr SDay
'Siloam Sugar Time'	ELon
'Siloam Tee Tiny'	WAul
'Siloam Tiny Mite'	SDay
'Siloam Tom Thumb'	CBgR
'Siloam Ury Winniford'	CBro CMac NLar WHoo
'Siloam Virginia Henson'	WWtn
'Silver Ice'	SDay
'Silver Lance'	EStr SDay WNHG
'Silver Sides'	EStr
'Silver Sword' **new**	EStr
'Silver Veil'	SDay
'Simmons Overture'	ECtt EStr MNrw
'Simple Twist of Fate' **new**	EStr
'Sinbad Sailor'	NLar
'Sings the Blues'	SDay
'Sink Into Your Eyes'	EStr WHrl
'Sir Blackstem'	ELon
'Sir Galahad'	EStr
'Sir Modred' ♀H6	EStr SDay WNHG
'Sissy Pants'	EStr
'Sister Grace'	SDay
'Sitting on a Rainbow'	EStr
'Skylight'	EStr

'Slapstick'	EStr SDay
'Sleepy'	ECha
'Sleepy Hollow'	EStr
'Slender Lady'	ELon XSen
'Slipping Into the Abyss'	EStr
'Smith Brothers'	ELon
'Smoke on the Water'	EStr
'Smoke Scream'	EStr
'Smoky Mountain Autumn'	WHrl
'Smooch Hollow'	CBgR EStr
'Smuggler's Gold'	ECtt EStr SDay
'Smurfette'	EStr
'Snaggle Tooth'	EStr
'Snowy Apparition'	ECtt EHyd EMor EStr GBin GKin LRHS NRHS NWad SWvt
'Snowy Eyes'	GKin WHrl
'So Cold' **new**	EStr
'So Excited'	SDay
'So Lovely'	XLum
'Soft Cashmere'	XLum
'Solid Geometry'	EStr
'Solid Scarlet'	EStr
'Solomon's Robes'	SDay
'Sombrero Way'	EHyd LRHS NRHS SDay
'Someone Special'	EStr SDay
'Somerset Fandango'	CBgR
'Song Sparrow'	CBro
'Sonic Duck' **new**	EStr
'Soraya Seline'	CBgR
'Sound of Color'	EStr
'South Carolina Peach'	EStr
'South Seas'	EStr
'Southern Cotton'	EStr
'Southern Wind' **new**	SDay
'Sovereign Queen'	WNHG
'Spacecoast Dream Catcher'	EStr
'Spacecoast Freaky Tiki'	EStr
'Spacecoast Irish Illumination'	EStr
'Spacecoast Scrambled'	NLar
'Spacecoast Starburst'	EStr WCot
'Spacecoast Sweet Eye'	EStr
'Spanish Fandango'	EStr
'Sparkling Dawn'	EStr
'Sparkling Orange'	SDay
'Spartan Warrior'	EStr
'Spider Breeder'	CBgR ELon EStr
'Spider Man' ♀H6	ELon EStr MSpe SDay WCAu XSen
'Spider Miracle'	MSpe SDay
'Spider Red'	CWGN EWTr
'Spider Web'	EStr
'Spin Master'	EStr
'Spindazzle'	CBgR SDay
'Spinne in Lachs'	EStr
'Spinneret'	EStr
'Spiral Nebula'	EStr
'Spirit Folk'	EStr
'Splatter'	EStr
'Splittin' Hairs'	EStr
'Spooner'	CBgR
'Spoons for Escargot'	EStr
'Spotted Fever'	EStr
'Spring Willow Song'	SDay
'Springfield Clan'	EStr
'Springmaid Beach'	EStr
'Spunky Monkey'	EStr
'Stack the Deck'	EStr
'Stafford' ♀H6	Widely available
'Staghorn Sumac'	GKin NHol WCAu
'Star of India'	EStr

'Star of Kryptonite'	EStr
'Star Poly'	EStr
'Stargate Portal'	EStr
'Starling'	EWes NChi WSpi WWtn
'Starman's Quest'	EStr
'Starstruck'	WNHG
'Startle'	ELon EStr MNrw WCot WHrl
'Steely Blue Eyes'	EStr
'Stella de Oro'	Widely available
'Stella in Purple'	EPfP
'Stella in Red'	CBod
'Stellar Masquerade' **new**	WNHG
'Stewart Mandel'	EStr
'Stoke Poges'	CBgR CBro EBee ELon EPPr EPfP EShb EStr GBin LPot MMuc WHrl WNHG
'Stop the Car' **new**	EStr
'Stop the Insanity'	EStr
'Stoplight'	CBgR EHyd ELon EStr LRHS SMHy WHrl
'Storm Damage'	EStr
'Storm of the Century'	CBod EStr
'Strasbourg'	CMac
'Strawberry Candy' ♀H6	CBgR CMac CSBt ECtt EHyd ELon EPfP EStr LRHS MPie NGdn NLar NRHS SDay SDir SPer WAul WCAu WHrl WNHG WSpi
'Strawberry Fields Forever'	EStr
'Strawberry Lemonade' **new**	EStr
I 'Streaker' B. Brown (v)	XSen
'Strider Spider'	EStr
'Strikingly Dramatic'	EStr
'String Bikini'	EStr
'Strutter's Ball'	EStr MCot NGdn SPer WAul WAvo WCAu WHrl
'Stupid in Love' **new**	EStr
'Stupidville USA'	EStr
'Stu's Old Pink Spider'	CBgR
'Suburban Golden Eagle'	EStr
'Sue Strickfaden'	EStr
'Sugar Cookie'	SDay
'Sugar Magnolia' **new**	EStr
'Summer Dragon'	EStr
'Summer Interlude'	WFar
'Summer Star'	EStr
'Summer Wine'	CBgR CBod CRos CSBt EBee ECtt ELon EPfP EWTr GMaP LRHS MBel MCot NBir NChi NHol NLar NRHS NSti SCob SPer SSut SWvt WBor WCAu WCot WHoo WHrl WSpi XLum
'Sun Dial' **new**	EStr
'Sun Scream'	EStr
'Sunday Gloves'	WNHG
'Sunday Morning'	SDay
'Sungold Candy'	EStr
'Sunset Lagoon'	EStr
'Sunshine on My Shoulders'	EStr
'Superlative'	EStr
'Supermodel'	EStr
'Svengali'	SDay
'Swallow Tail Kite'	SDay
'Swan Dance'	EStr SDay
'Sweet Country Luvin''	EStr
'Sweet Goldoni'	EStr
'Sweet Home Louisiana'	EStr
'Sweet Hot Chocolate'	LRHS MNrw
'Sweet Pea'	EStr

'Sweet Sugar Candy'	ECtt SDeJ
'Swirling Spider'	CBgR
'Symphony of Praise'	EStr
'Tachibana'	SDay
'Taj Mahal'	ELon GQue SDay
'Tangerine Twist'	EStr
'Tani'	SDay
'Taos'	EStr
'Tar and Feather'	EStr
'Tarantula'	ELon
'Taruga'	SDay
'Tasmania'	SPer
'Tattooed Lady'	SDay
'Tchao Pantin'	XSen
'Techny Peach Lace'	EStr
'Techny Spider'	EStr
'Teenie Girl'	EStr
'Tejas'	ELon SPer
'Témoin'	XSen
'Tennessee Afterglow' **new**	EStr
'Tequila and Lime'	CBod EStr SPeP
'Tet Set'	WNHG
'Tetraploid Siloam Red Toy'	SDay
'Tetraploid Stella de Oro'	SDay
'Tetrina's Daughter'	CBgR EPfP LRHS
'Texas Blue Eyes'	EStr WNHG
'Thank Your Lucky Stars'	EStr
'The Bird is the Word'	EStr
'The Blessing of Freedom'	EStr
'The Color of Wonderful'	EStr
'The Future of Desire' **new**	EStr
'The Ghosts of Boyfriends Past'	EStr
'The New Normal'	EStr
'The Senator' **new**	EStr
'The Ultimate Sacrifice'	EStr
'Thelma Douglas'	EStr
'Thelma Perry'	LEdu
'There's a Place' **new**	EStr
'Thermal Overload'	EStr
'Thin Man'	EStr SDay
'This World Aflame'	EStr
'Thomas Tew'	EStr
'Thorhalla'	EStr
'Thousand Voices'	EStr
'Thumbelina'	ECha XLum
§ ***thunbergii***	ECha XLum
'Thunder and Lightning'	EStr
'Thundercat' **new**	EStr
'Thundering Ovation'	CWGN
'Thy True Love'	SDay
'Tiger Blood'	EStr SDir
'Tiger Brother' **new**	LLWG
'Tigereye Spider'	EStr
'Tigerling'	EStr
'Tigger'	EStr GJos SDeJ SPad WCAu
'Tiki God'	EStr
'Till I Turn Purple'	EStr
'Timbercreek Ace'	EStr
'Time Lord'	SDay XSen
'Time of Angels'	EStr
'Time Together'	EStr
'Time Window'	EStr
'Tiny Temptress'	SDay
'Tip of the Iceberg'	EStr
'Tis Midnight'	WNHG
'Tixie'	EStr
'Tom Barnes'	EStr
'Tom Wise'	EStr
'Tone Poem'	WNHG
'Tonia Gay'	SDay
'Tooth'	EStr
'Toothpick'	WHrl
'Tootsie'	SDay
'Topguns Aztec Vision'	EStr
'Topguns Bandit's Bandana'	EStr
'Topguns Cactus Jack'	EStr
'Torpoint'	CBgR MRav
'Touch of Magic'	EStr
'Towhead'	MRav SDay WCot
'Toyland'	NBir NGdn NLar
'Trahlyta'	CBgR EStr SDay WHrl
'Tramps Like Us'	EStr
'Trance'	EStr
'Transatlantic Flutter' **new**	EStr
'Treasure Map'	EStr
'Treasure That I Seek'	EStr
'Triade'	EStr
'Tribute to Joe'	EStr
'Trickster'	EStr
'Tripped Out'	EStr
'Trog'	EStr
'Trond'	SDay
'Tropical Fusion'	EStr
'Tropical Hot Flash'	EStr
'Tropical Passion'	EStr
'True Gertrude Demarest'	WHrl
'Trump Card'	EStr
'Tune the Harp'	EStr
'Tupac Amaru'	EStr
'Turkish Tapestry'	CBgR
'Turkish Turban'	SDay
'Turn the Other Cheek'	EStr
'Turtle Island'	EStr
'Tuscawilla Blackout'	XSen
'Tuscawilla Princess'	EStr
'Tuscawilla Tigress'	EStr GKin MNrw SDay WAul WHrl
'Tutankhamun'	EStr SDay
'Tuxedo Junction' ♀H6	EStr
'Tuxedo Whiskers'	EStr
'Twenty Nine Flags over Conway' **new**	EStr
'Twilight Swan'	WNHG
'Twist of Lemon'	SDay
'Two Part Harmony'	WHrl
'Ultra Persuasion'	SDay
'Umbrella Parade'	EStr
'Uncle Lurch'	EStr
'Undefinable'	EStr
'Unlock Your Dreams'	EStr
'Up the Wazoo'	EStr
'Upper Class Peach'	EStr SDay
'Uptown Girl'	EStr
'Valiant'	WHrl
'Valley Sprite'	EStr
'Vanilla Fluff'	EStr
'Vanishing Mist'	EStr
'Varsity'	CExl EHyd LRHS NBir NRHS SPer
'Vectis Amy Hiscock' **new**	EStr
'Vectis Jean Merritt'	EStr
'Vectis Jean Peirce'	EStr
'Vectis Joan Morey' **new**	EStr
'Vectis Nora Malone' **new**	EStr
'Vegas Show Girl'	EStr
'Veins of Truth'	CBgR EStr WCAu
'Velvet Eyes'	EStr
'Velvet Shadows'	CBgR SDay
'Velvet Web'	EStr
'Vendetta'	WNHG
'Venusian Mirage'	EStr

'Vera Biaglow'	EStr SDay
'Vernal Tutone'	WNHG
'Very Berry Ice'	EStr
vespertina	see *H. thunbergii*
'Vesuvian'	SDay
'Veuve Joyeuse'	XSen
'Vi Simmons'	EStr
'Vicountess Byng'	WWtn
'Victoria Aden'	CBro
'Victoria Elizabeth Barnes'	WNHG
'Victorian Violet'	SDay
'Video'	SDay
'Vie en Rose'	EStr
'Viewpoint'	SDay
'Villa Vanilla'	WFar
'Vino di Notte'	EStr
'Vintage Bordeaux'	ELan SDay
'Vintage Burgundy'	CBgR WNHG
'Vintage Passion'	EStr
'Vintage Wine'	WNHG
'Violent Thunder'	EStr
'Violet Cuckoo'	EStr
'Violet Hour'	EStr SDay
'Violet Patch'	SDay
'Violet Stained Glass' **new**	WNHG
'Viracocha'	WNHG
'Virgin's Blush'	SPer
'Vohann'	SDay
'Volcanic Eruption' **new**	EStr
'Volcano Queen'	EPfP EStr WFar
'Voodoo Dancer'	EStr
'Waggle Dance' **new**	EStr
'Waiting in the Wings'	SDay
'Walking on Sunshine'	EStr WCot
'Walnut Hill'	EStr
'Walt Disney'	GKin
'Walter Kennedy'	EStr
'Wanda Evans'	EStr
'War Paint'	EStr SDay
'Warp Drive'	SDay
'Watch Tower'	CBgR
'Watchyl Dancing Spider'	EStr
'Water Witch'	CWat
'Watermelon Man'	CBgR
'Waxen Splendor'	EStr
'Wayne Johnson'	WNHG
'Wayside Green Imp'	MNrw
'Web Browser'	EStr
'Web Crawler'	EStr
'Webster's Aggie'	EStr
'Webster's Pastel Beauty'	EStr
'Webster's Pinched Peach'	EStr
'Webster's Pink Wonder'	EStr
'Wee Willie Winkie'	WNHG
'Welchkins'	WAul
'Wesley Lee Kirby'	EStr
'What a Day for a Daydream'	EStr
'When I Dream'	EStr
'When You Get to Asheville'	EStr
'Which Way Jim'	SDay
'Whichford'	CAby CBgR CBro CMea CRos CSam ECha ECtt EHyd ELan EPfP GKin LRHS NRHS SPhx SSut WGwG WHrl
'Whip City Fancy Free'	EStr
'Whirling Fury'	ELon
'White Coral'	EHyd LRHS LSRN NBro NRHS
'White Edged Madonna'	WHrl
'White Ensign'	SDay
'White Eyes Pink Dragon'	EStr
'White Magician'	EStr
'White Pansy'	SDay
'White Temptation'	EPfP EStr ILea LRHS LSun SDay WAul WHoo WNHG XSen
'White Zone'	SDay
'Whoopie'	SPad
'Wideyed'	XLum
'Wiggle Butt'	EStr
'Wigglesworth'	EStr
'Wild and Wonderful'	LSun SDay WFar
'Wild at Heart'	EStr
'Wild Horses'	EWes LRHS MNrw NLar SCob SMad WHrl
'Wild Mustang'	EStr
'Wild Planet'	EStr
'Wild Wookie'	SDay
'Wilson Spider'	EStr
'Wind Frills'	XSen
'Wind Song'	ELon SDay
'Wind Storm'	EStr
'Windham Blueberry Mojito' **new**	EStr
'Windmill Yellow'	SDay
'Window Dressing'	SDay
'Wineberry Candy'	EStr NLar
'Winged Migration'	EStr
'Winnie'	EStr
'Winsome Lady'	ECha ECtt GKin WHrl
'Winter Wolf'	EStr
'Winyah Eye'	EStr
'Wired'	EStr
'Wisest of Wizards'	WHrl
'Wishful Dreaming'	EStr
'Wishing Well'	WCot
'Wispy Rays'	EStr
'Witch Hazel'	WCAu WWtn
'Witch Hollow'	EStr
'Witch Stitchery'	EStr SDay
'Witches Brew'	CBgR
'Without Warning'	CBgR
'Womanizer'	EStr
'Wonder of it All'	EStr
'Wonders Never Cease' **new**	SDay
'Woodside Ruby'	WNHG
'Wounded Heart'	SDay
'Wyatt's Cameo'	SDay
'Wyoming Wildfire'	CBgR
'Xia Xiang'	SDay
'Xochimilco'	WNHG
'Ya Ya Girl'	EStr
'Yabba Dabba Doo'	EStr
'Yankee Pinstripes'	EStr
'Yazoo Elsie Hintson' **new**	EStr
'Yazoo Wild Violet'	EStr
'Yellow Angel'	ELon WCot
'Yellow Rain'	WCot
'Yellow Ribbon'	EStr
'Yellow Submarine'	EPfP
'Yes Man'	EStr
'Yesterday Memories'	SDay
'Yesterday, Today and Tomorrow'	SDay
yezoensis	EBtc
'You Angel You'	SDir
'You are Mine' **new**	EStr
'You Had Me at Woof' **new**	EStr
'Yum Yum Plum'	EStr SDay
'Yuma'	WNHG
'Zachary S. Hickey'	EStr

'Zagora' EStr WCAu
'Zampa' CBgR EStr SDay
'Zappa' SDay
'Zara' EStr SPer
'Zen Master' **new** WHrl
'Zenobia' EStr
'Zero Dark Thirty' EStr
'Zip Boom Bah' EStr
'Zuni Mountains' WNHG

Hemiboea (*Gesneriaceae*)

subcapitata SBrt WFar

Hemigraphis (*Acanthaceae*)

§ ***alternata*** XBlo
colorata see *H. alternata*
- 'Exotica' **new** XBlo
repanda **new** XBlo

Hemionitis (*Pteridaceae*)

arifolia SPlb

Hemipilia (*Orchidaceae*)

§ ***graminifolia*** GKev SDir
- white-flowered SDir

Hemiptelea (*Ulmaceae*)

davidii **new** SMad

Hepatica ✿ (*Ranunculaceae*)

acutiloba CWCL GEdr GKev MAsh NBir SDir WPnP XEll
- blue-flowered MAsh
- white-flowered MAsh NLar
acutiloba* × *nobilis MAsh SPer
acutiloba* × *nobilis 'Cremar' **new** MAsh
americana CWCL GEdr GKev MAsh NBir
- var. ***obtusa*** 'Ashwood Marble' MAsh
- - 'Rosea' CSpe
angulosa see *H. transsilvanica*
falconeri **new** MAsh
(Forest Series) 'Forest Pink' ELan GBin GKev XEll
- 'Forest Purple' ELan GKev LCro XEll
- 'Forest Red' ELan GBin GKev LCro WPnP XEll
- 'Forest White' ELan GBin GKev LCro WPnP XEll
ex 'Harold Bawden' **new** MAsh
henryi GEdr MAsh
insularis MAsh
maxima GEdr MAsh MBriF NDry
× ***media*** 'Ballardii' GEdr NDry
- 'Blaue Stunde' **new** GEdr
- Dryad Blush Group **new** NDry
- 'Harvington Beauty' GEdr MAsh NBir NDry WSHC
- 'Holzdorfe Silver' **new** GEdr
- 'Kim' GEdr NDry
- 'Millstream Merlin' GEdr NHpl
- 'Silberprinzessin' GEdr
§ ***nobilis*** ♀H6 Widely available
- 'Baby Rosa' **new** GEdr
- 'Bibo' EWld
- blue-flowered MAsh NSla SPlb WAbe
- 'Brockman' (d) GEdr
- 'Cobalt' GEdr NSla
- compact evergreen MAsh NDry
- 'Cremar' GEdr MAsh NDry
- dark-blue-flowered ITim NDry
- dwarf white-flowered NSla
- 'Edrom Pink' **new** GEdr
- 'Edrom White' **new** GEdr
- 'Elkofener Heidi' GEdr
- 'Flamingo' **new** GEdr
* - var. ***glabrata*** **new** MAsh
- - dwarf white-flowered **new** NDry
- var. ***glabrata* × *nobilis*** red-flowered **new** MAsh
- var. ***japonica*** EWes GEdr MAsh NBir NDry NSla
- - 'Aikawa' (5/d) GEdr
- - 'Akane' (1) GEdr
- - 'Akanezora' (6/d) GEdr
- - 'Akebono' (9/d) GEdr
- - 'Anjyu' (9/d) GEdr
- - 'Aozora' (1) GEdr
- - 'Asahi' (7/d) GEdr
- - 'Asahizuru' (6/d) GEdr
- - 'Benifusya' (1) GEdr
- - 'Benihagure' (9/d) GEdr
- - 'Benikanzan' (1) GEdr
- - 'Benikujyaku' (7/d) GEdr
- - 'Benioiran' (3) GEdr
- - 'Beniokesa' (9/d) GEdr
- - 'Benishinjyu' (6/d) GEdr
- - 'Benisuzume' (1) GEdr
- - 'Benitaiko' (9/d) GEdr
- - 'Bojyou' (5A/d) GEdr
- - 'Daishihou' (9/d) GEdr
- - 'Dewa' (9/d) GEdr
- - 'Ebisu-no-hana' (5A/d) GEdr
- - 'Echigobijin' (1) GEdr NDry
- - 'Fukujyu' (9/d) GEdr
- - 'Gosho-zakura' (5A/d) GEdr
- - 'Gyousei' (1) GEdr
- - 'Hakurin' (6/d) GEdr
- - 'Hakusetsu' (9/d) GEdr
- - 'Hanagoromo' (9/d) GEdr
- - 'Haruka' (2) GEdr
- - 'Harukaze' (5A/d) GEdr
- - 'Harumo-no-Gatari' (8/d) GEdr
- - 'Haruno-awajuki' (9/d) GEdr
- - 'Hatsune' (5/d) GEdr
- - 'Hidamari' (5/d) GEdr
- - 'Hohobeni' (9/d) GEdr
- - 'Hokutosei' (7/d) GEdr
- - 'Hoshizora' (2) GEdr
- - 'Hosyun' (1) GEdr
- - 'Isaribi' (1) GEdr NDry
- - 'Junissen' (6/d) GEdr
- - 'Kagura' (5A/d) GEdr
- - 'Kansashi' **new** NDry
- - 'Kasumino' (1) GEdr
- - 'Kiko' (9/d) GEdr
- - 'Kimon' (9/d) GEdr
- - 'Koshi-no-maboroshi' (7/d) GEdr
- - 'Kotobuki-hime' (5/d) GEdr
- - 'Kouen' (6/d) GEdr
- - 'Kougyoku' (9/d) GEdr
- - 'Kuetsu' (9/d) GEdr
- - 'Kurotaiyou' (d) GEdr
- - 'Kuukai' (8/d) GEdr
- - f. ***magna*** MAsh
- - - 'Murasaki-shikibu' (9/d) GEdr
- - 'Manazuru' (9/d) GEdr
- - 'Minamo' (5/d) GEdr
- - 'Miwaku' (1) GEdr
- - 'Miyoshino' (1) GEdr NDry

	- - 'Miyuki' (9/d)	GEdr
	- - 'Murasaki-sakama' (9/d)	GEdr
	- - 'Nanakubo' (1)	GEdr
	- - 'Notaniyama'	GEdr
	- - 'Noumurasaki' (1)	GEdr
	- - 'Oboryo' (1)	GEdr
	- - 'Odoriko' (9/d)	GEdr
	- - 'Okesabayashi'	GEdr
	- - 'Okina' (9/d)	GEdr
	- - 'Ō-murasaki' (1)	GEdr
	- - 'Orihime' (9/d)	GEdr NDry
	- - 'Reeka' (1)	GEdr
	- - 'Ryokurei' (5A/d)	GEdr
	- - 'Ryokusetsu' (9/d)	GEdr
	- - 'Ryokuun' (9/d)	GEdr NDry
	- - 'Sadobeni' (1)	GEdr
	- - 'Saichou' (7/d)	GEdr
	- - Sandan Group (7/d)	GEdr
	- - 'Satsuma' (5A/d)	GEdr
	- - 'Sawanemidori' (6/d)	GEdr
	- - 'Sayaka' (1)	GEdr
	- - 'Seikai' (5A/d)	GEdr
	- - 'Seizan' (9/d)	GEdr
	- - 'Senhime' (9/d)	GEdr
	- - 'Sen-nin' (6/d)	GEdr
	- - 'Sennin-buraku' (8/d)	GEdr
	- - 'Setsudu' (7/d)	GEdr
	- - 'Shikouden' (9/d)	GEdr
	- - 'Shikouryuu' (9/d)	GEdr
	- - 'Shio' (9/d)	GEdr
	- - 'Shirayuki' (9/d)	GEdr
	- - 'Shirin' (9/d)	GEdr
	- - 'Shiun' (9/d)	GEdr
	- - (Shiun Group) 'Shihou' (9/d)	GEdr
	- - 'Shoujyouno-homare' (9/d)	GEdr
	- - 'Sougetsu' (6/d)	GEdr NDry
	- - 'Souhou' (1)	GEdr
	- - 'Soushyunka' (9/d)	GEdr
	- - 'Subaru' (9/d)	GEdr
	- - 'Suien' (9/d)	GEdr
	- - 'Syouchikubai' (7/d)	GEdr
	- - 'Syunryuu' (9/d)	GEdr
	- - 'Taeka' (9/d)	GEdr
	- - 'Takase' (9/d)	GEdr
	- - 'Takumi' (9/d)	GEdr NDry
	- - 'Tamahime' (8/d)	GEdr
	- - 'Tamakujyaku' (6/d)	GEdr
	- - 'Tamamushi' (9/d)	GEdr
	- - 'Tamasaburou' (1)	GEdr
	- - 'Tenjinbai' (1)	GEdr NDry
	- - 'Tenjin-ume' (1)	GEdr
	- - 'Tennyonomai' (6A/d)	GEdr
	- - 'Toki' (9/d)	GEdr
	- - 'Tori-no-saezuri' **new**	NDry
	- - 'Touen' (9/d)	GEdr
	- - 'Touhou' (9/d)	GEdr
	- - 'Touryoku' (9/d)	GEdr
	- - 'Toyama-chiyo-iwai' (7/d)	GEdr
	- - 'Umezono' (1)	GEdr
	- - 'Unabara' (9/d)	GEdr
	- - 'Usugesyou' (9/d)	GEdr
	- - 'Utyuu' (1)	GEdr
	- - 'Wakakusa' (9/d)	GEdr
	- - 'Wakana' (1)	GEdr
	- - 'Yaegoromo' (6/d)	GEdr NDry
	- - 'Yahiko' (5/d)	GEdr
	- - 'Yahikomurasaki' (1)	GEdr

	- - 'Yamahibiki' (9/d)	GEdr
	- - 'Yellow Shades' **new**	GEdr
	- - 'Yukishino' (2)	GEdr
	- - 'Yumes' (7/d)	GEdr
	- - 'Yuunagi' (9/d)	GEdr
	- - 'Yuunami' (1)	GEdr
	- - 'Yuuzen' (5/d)	GEdr
	- - 'Yuzuru' (9/d)	GEdr
	- var. ***japonica*** × ***nobilis*** var. ***nobilis*** **new**	NDry
	- large, pale blue-flowered	NSla
	- 'Lilac Picotee'	NSla
	- var. ***obtusa*** **new**	MAsh
	- 'Oeland's Nacht' **new**	GEdr
	- patterned leaf	NSla
	- pink-flowered	MAsh
	- var. ***pubescens***	MAsh NSla
*	- var. ***pyrenaica***	LEdu MAsh NSla WAbe WThu
*	- - 'Apple Blossom'	GEdr NBir
	- - 'Harold Bawden' **new**	GEdr
*	- - 'Pyrenean Princess' **new**	MAsh
*	- - white-flowered	CSpe NBir
	- 'Pyrenean Marbles'	NBir
	- 'Rosa Elite' **new**	GEdr
	- var. ***rubra***	NSla
	- 'Rubra Plena' (d)	GEdr MAsh NDry NSla WPnP
	- 'Stained Glass'	EWld MAsh
	- 'Tabby'	NDry
	- violet-flowered	MAsh
	- 'White Sands'	ELan GBin GEdr
	- white-flowered	CWCL MAsh XEll
	- 'Woodside White' **new**	GBin
	'Noubeni'	GEdr
	× ***schlyteri***	NDry
	- Ashwood hybrids	MAsh
	- blue-flowered **new**	NDry
	- 'The Bride'	GEdr MAsh
§	***transsilvanica*** ♀H5	CBro CWCL GEdr MAsh MCot WCot WThu
	- 'Ada Scott'	GEdr
	- 'Blue Eyes'	CWCL GBin GEdr GKev
	- 'Blue Jewel'	CWCL EBee ELan GBin GEdr GKev MCot MHol WPnP
	- blue-flowered	MAsh
	- ex 'Blumenstadt Erfurt' **new**	MAsh
	- 'Buis'	ECha GEdr MAsh NLar
	- 'Connie Greenfield'	NSla
	- 'Donner Wolke' **new**	GEdr
	- 'Eisvogel'	GEdr NDry
	- 'Elison Spence' (d)	GEdr IBlr MCot
	- 'Fuchs' **new**	GEdr
	- ex 'Grethe' **new**	GEdr MAsh
	- 'Karpati Krönen'	GEdr
	- 'Lilacina'	GEdr MAsh NDry
	- 'Loddon Blue'	GEdr MAsh NDry
	- 'März' **new**	GEdr
	- pink-flowered	MAsh
	- 'Praecox'	GEdr
	- 'Sieben Bergen'	IBlr
	- 'Supernova'	GEdr MAsh
	- white-flowered	GEdr MAsh
	triloba	see *H. nobilis*
	aff. ***yamatutai***	MAsh

Heptacodium (*Caprifoliaceae*)

	jasminoides	see *H. miconioides*
§	***miconioides*** ♀H7	Widely available
	- TIANSHAN ('Minhep'PBR)	MPkF SGol WCot

Heptapleurum see *Schefflera*

Heracleum (*Apiaceae*)

dulce	EBee
sphondylium	WSFF
stevenii	MHol WCot
wallichii	WCru
B&SWJ 13931 **new**	

Herbertia (*Iridaceae*)

§ **lahue**	SBrt WAbe

Hereroa (*Aizoaceae*)

glenensis	CRos CSma EBou EDAr EHyd LRHS NRHS SPlb

Hermannia (*Malvaceae*)

erodioides	CPBP
flammea	SPlb
stricta	CPBP WAbe

Hermodactylus see *Iris*

Herniaria (*Caryophyllaceae*)

glabra	GPoy

Hertia (*Asteraceae*)

§ **cheirifolia**	CCCN CMea CSde EWes EWld NBir SEND WSHC XLum

Hesperaloe (*Asparagaceae*)

campanulata	WCot
engelmannii	WCot
'New Blue'	WCot
parviflora	LEdu SChr SPlb WSMil XSen
- creamy yellow-flowered	WCot
- 'Rubra'	MPkF

Hesperantha ✿ (*Iridaceae*)

§ **baurii**	CPbh GAbr GBin GKev NHpl WThu
coccinea	CBcs CMac CPla CPrp CTri CTsd EBee EPfP GBin GKev IBlr MBow MWts NChi NGdn NHol NLar SCob SDeJ SDir SGbt WFar WMAq XLum
- f. **alba**	CBro CExl CMea CPrp CTri CWCL EBee ECha EHyd ELan EPfP GKev ITim LRHS MCot MRav NBir NGdn NLar NRHS SDeJ SPeP SPer SPlb SRms SWvt WFar WPnP WSHC
- 'Anne'	NLar WFar
- 'Autumn's Dawn'	WFar
- 'Ballyrogan Giant'	CPrp ECtt IBlr WFar WHer WSHC
- 'Big Moma'	CPrp ELon WFar
- 'Cardinal'	NHol WFar
- 'Caroline'	CPrp WFar
- 'Cindy Towe'	CAbb CKno ELon EMor LSou SPoG WFar
- 'Elburton Glow'	WFar
- 'Eric's Early'	CPrp ELon WFar
- 'Fenland Daybreak'	Widely available
- 'Gigantea'	see *H. coccinea* 'Major'
- 'Good White'	CWCL NBir SMHy WFar
- 'Grandiflora'	see *H. coccinea* 'Major'
- 'Hilary Gould'	CMea CPrp ECtt MSpe WAvo WHal
- 'Ice Maiden'	CAbb EMor GWyn LSou NSti SPoG
- 'Jack Frost'	EBee WFar
- 'Jennifer' ♀H4	CBro CDor CElw CMac CPrp CRos CTri EBee ECha ECtt EHyd ELon EPfP GAbr LPot LRHS MCot MMuc MRav NLar NWad SRms SWvt WAvo WFar WPnP
- 'Maiden's Blush'	ECtt ELan LEdu LRHS MCot NLar SRms WFar
§ - 'Major' ♀H4	Widely available
- 'Marchants Seedling'	SMHy
- 'Marietta'	WFar
- 'Mollie Gould'	CAvo CBod CPrp ECtt EHyd EPfP LRHS MAvo MNrw MPie NBPC NHol NWad SCoo SGbt SRms WAvo WBrk WFar
- 'Mrs Hegarty'	CPrp CSam ECtt EHyd ELan ELon EMor EPfP GMaP GWyn MGos MHer NBid NBir NHol NLar NQui SDeJ SPer SPlb SPoG SRms SWvt WFar WPnP
- 'November Cheer'	CMac ECtt IBlr NBir NLar
- 'Oregon Sunset'	CAby CBcs CPla CPrp ECtt ELon EMor LLWG LSou SPad WFar WHil WHoo WKif
- 'Pallida'	CMil CPrp CSam ECtt NBir WFar
- 'Pink Marg'	CPrp ITim WFar
- 'Pink Princess'	see *H. coccinea* 'Wilfred H. Bryant'
- pink-flowered	MBel
- 'Professor Barnard'	CCCN EBee ECtt ELon EPfP EPri GWyn MBNS MNrw NBir NLar WFar WRHF
- 'Red Arrow'	EWes
- 'Red Dragon'	ECtt NHol WHoo
I - 'Rosea'	GKev MPie SDeJ WFar
- 'Ruth'	WFar
- 'Salmon Charm'	ECtt EHyd LRHS WFar
- 'Salmon's Leap'	WFar
- 'Salome'	CPrp ECtt WFar WMal
- 'Scarlet Queen'	WFar
- 'Simply Pink' **new**	SPad
- 'Snow Drift'	WFar
- 'Snow Maiden'	CElw CWCL EBee EShb EWTr LRHS WFar
- 'Strawberry'	CPrp WFar
§ - 'Sunrise' ♀H4	Widely available
- 'Sunset'	see *H. coccinea* 'Sunrise'
- 'Tambara'	CPou CPrp CSam ECtt WFar XLum
- 'Vibrant Scarlet'	WFar
- 'Viscountess Byng'	CTri CWCL EBee MNrw NBir
* - 'White Admiral'	WFar
§ - 'Wilfred H. Bryant' ♀H4	Widely available
- 'Zeal Salmon'	CBro CElw CPou CRos ECha ECtt GAbr NBir WFar
cucullata	CPbh
huttonii	EPPr GEdr ITim NBir WFar
mossii	see *H. baurii*
pauciflora	CPbh
vaginata	CPbh

Hesperis (*Brassicaceae*)

lutea	see *Sisymbrium luteum*
matronalis	Widely available
- **alba**	see *H. matronalis* var. *albiflora*
§ - var. **albiflora**	CCBP CLau CSpe ELan EPfP EWTr GMaP LCro LOPS LRHS MNHC NGdn NLar SBut SGro SPer SPhx WBrk WCFE WHil
- - 'Alba Plena' (d)	CRos EBee GWyn LRHS LSun MSCN NBir WCAu WCot
I - 'Variegata' (v)	CPla
nivea	LEdu
steveniana	SPhx

Hesperochiron (*Boraginaceae*)

californicus	SBrt

× *Hesperotropsis* see × *Cuprocyparis*

Heteromeles (*Rosaceae*)

arbutifolia	see *H. salicifolia*
§ ***salicifolia***	LEdu

Heteromorpha (*Apiaceae*)

arborescens	CExl SPlb SVen

Heteropolygonatum (*Asparagaceae*)

'Mikinori Ogisu'	EBee
roseolum	CAby EWld
urceolatum	WCru

Heteropterys (*Malpighiaceae*)

glabra new	WCru

Heterotheca (*Asteraceae*)

subaxillaris	WCot

Heuchera ✿ (*Saxifragaceae*)

'Alan Davidson'	MPnt
'Alison'	MPnt
'Amber Waves' PBR	CBod CExl ELan LRHS MPnt NBir SCob SWvt
§ ***americana***	MRav NBir SHeu SSut SWvt
- var. ***americana***	MPnt
- Dale's strain	GPSL MPnt NLar SHeu SPlb SWvt
- 'Harry Hay'	EPPr EPri EWld LEdu LPla MPnt SHeu WPGP WSHC
- 'Marvellous Marble'	EShb MPnt SHeu WOut
- 'Ring of Fire'	MPnt SHeu SRms SWvt
'Amethyst Myst'	EHyd EMor EPfP GKev LRHS LSRN MCot MPnt SCob SHeu SPer WSMil
'Apple Crisp' PBR	CBod EPfP LCro LOPS MPnt MTin SCob SHeu SWvt WNPC
'Apple Souffle'	MPnt SHeu
'Apricot'	CWGN MPnt WNPC
'Autumn Glow' (Seasonal Selection Series)	CRos EHyd LRHS MPnt NRHS SHeu WNPC
'Autumn Haze' PBR	MPnt SHeu
'Autumn Leaves' PBR	ECtt EHyd ELan LCro LOPS LRHS MAvo MPnt SEdd SHeu SPoG SWvt
'Baby's Breath'	MPnt
'Bardot'	MPnt
'Beaujolais' PBR	EHyd LRHS MNrw MPnt NBir SEdd SHeu WCot WNPC
'Beauty Colour'	ECha ELan EPfP GMaP LRHS LSRN MRav NGdn NRHS SHeu SWvt WSMil
'Belle Notte'	MPnt SHeu WNPC
'Berry Marmalade' PBR	EBee EPfP MAsh MPnt NDov SHeu SPer SWvt WNPC
'Berry Smoothie' PBR	CPla CRos CWGN EBee EHyd ELan EPfP LRHS LSRN LSou MBNS MGos MPnt NHol NLar NPer NRHS NSti SCob SHeu SPer SPoG SWvt
(Big Top Series) 'Big Top Bronze'	SHeu
- 'Big Top Burgundy'	SHeu
- 'Big Top Gold'	CWGN SHeu
'Bilberry' (Indian Summer Series)	MPnt SHeu
'Binoche' PBR	CRos EBee EHyd LRHS MPnt NRHS SCob SHeu WCot WNPC
'Birkin'	MPnt
'Black Cherry' (Heucheraholics Series)	SHeu
'Black Pearl' new	CWCL LCro LOPS MPnt SHeu WTor
'Black Sea'	ECtt EPfP GQue MPnt MSCN SEdd WCot WNPC
'Black Taffeta' PBR	CWGN EBee EPfP LBuc MPnt SHeu SPad WNPC
'Blackberry Crisp' PBR	EBee MPnt SHeu WNPC
'Blackberry Jam'	CRos ECha EHyd ELan ELon LPot LRHS LSou MAvo MPnt NBir NHol NRHS SHeu SWvt WFar
'Blackbird'	MPnt SHeu SWvt WFar WSpi
'Blackout'	MNrw MPnt NLar SHeu
'Blondie' PBR (Little Cutie Series)	CBcs CBod CWGN ECtt EHyd EPfP LRHS MPnt MSCN NLar NRHS SEdd SHeu SPad SPoG WCot WHoo WNPC
'Blondie in Lime' (Little Cutie Series)	CRos EHyd EPfP MPnt NLar NRHS SHeu WNPC
'Blood Red'	MPnt SHeu
'Blood Vein'	MPnt SHeu
'Blushing Down'	MPnt
'Bouquet'	MPnt SHeu
'Boysenberry' PBR (Indian Summer Series)	EBee MPnt SHeu
bracteata	MPnt XLum
'Bressingham Glow'	MPnt SHeu
Bressingham hybrids	CSBt NBir SRms SVic
'Bressingham Spire'	MPnt
'Bright and Breezy' (Seasonal Selection Series)	CBod CRos EHyd LRHS MPnt NRHS SHeu WNPC
'Bronze Beauty'	MPnt SHeu WBrk WCot
'Brown Sugar'	MPnt SHeu
'Brownfinch'	CElw LPla MPnt SBrt SHeu WCot
'Brownies'	MPnt SHeu WHrl WWtn
'Burgundy Frost'	MPnt SHeu WBrk
'Café Olé'	ECtt MPnt NLar SHeu WHer
'Cajun Fire' PBR	CWGN ELan MPnt SHeu
'Can-can' 🏆H6	CBod CPla CRos CTri EHyd ELan ELon EPfP GKev LRHS MNrw MPnt NBir NLar NRHS SCob SHeu SWvt WCAu WSpi
'Canyon Duet'	MPnt SHeu
'Cappuccino'	EBee EHyd ELan EPfP LRHS MPnt MRav SCob SHeu SWvt
'Caramel' PBR	CBod CMac CRos CWGN EBee ECtt EHyd ELan GMaP LCro LOPS LRHS MAsh MNrw NRHS NSti SCob SGbt SHeu SPer SPoG SWvt WAul WCot
'Carmen'	MPnt SHeu
'Carmencita' new	SHeu
(Carnival Series) CARNIVAL COCOMINT ('Balcarcint' PBR)	SHeu
- CARNIVAL COFFEE BEAN ('Balcarcean' PBR)	EHyd LRHS NRHS
- CARNIVAL LIMEADE ('Balcarmade' PBR)	CBod ELan SHeu
- CARNIVAL PEACH PARFAIT ('Balcarpait')	EHyd LRHS NRHS SHeu
- CARNIVAL PLUM CRAZY ('Balcarulm' PBR)	SHeu
- CARNIVAL ROSE GRANITA	SHeu
- CARNIVAL WATERMELON ('Balcarmelo')	MHol
'Cascade Dawn'	EBee MPnt NBir SWvt
'Cassis'	MPnt SEdd SHeu WCot WNPC
'Cézanne' (Master Painters Series)	MPnt SHeu

'Champagne Bubbles'	CWGN MPnt SHeu
CHAMPAGNE ('Tnheucha'PBR)	MPnt SHeu WNPC
CHARLES BLOOM ('Chablo')	EHyd LRHS MPnt SHeu
'Chatterbox'	MPnt SHeu
'Checkers'	see *H.* 'Quilter's Joy'
'Cherries Jubilee'PBR	EPfP GMaP MPnt SHeu
'Cherry Cola'PBR	CBcs CBod CPla CRos EBee EHyd ELan EPfP LRHS MAsh MAvo MCot MPnt MPri NLar NRHS SCob SEdd SHeu SPad SPoG SRkn WCot WFar WNPC WTor
'Chiqui'	MPnt SHeu
chlorantha	MPnt
'Chocolate Limes' **new**	MPnt WNPC
'Chocolate Ruffles'PBR	CBcs CRos ECha ELan EPfP EShb GMaP LRHS LSRN MCot MGos MHer MRav NBir NRHS SCob SLim SPer SPoG SRms SWvt WCav WFar WSpi
'Chocolate Veil'	MPnt
'Christa'	MPnt SHeu
'Cinnabar Silver'PBR	LSun MPnt NBir
'Circus'PBR	MPnt SHeu WNPC
'Citronelle'	CWGN ECtt EHyd EPfP LRHS MPnt NRHS SHeu SWvt WCot
'City Lights'	SHeu
'Coco'PBR (Little Cutie Series)	EBee EHyd EPfP LRHS MPnt NRHS SHeu WNPC
'Color Dream'PBR	MPnt SHeu
coral bells	see *H. sanguinea*
'Coral Bouquet'	MPnt SHeu
'Coral Cloud'	MPnt SHeu
'Coral Sea' **new**	WCot
'Coralberry'PBR (Indian Summer Series)	CRos MPnt SHeu
'Corallion'	MPnt
'Cranberry' (Indian Summer Series)	LSou MHol MPnt SHeu WNPC WTor
CRÈME BRÛLÉE ('Tnheu041') (Dolce Series)	CExl CRos EHyd ELan EPau EPfP LRHS MGos NBir NCou NLar NRHS SEdd SHeu SLim SPoG SWvt
'Crème Caramel'	CExl MPnt
'Creole Nights'PBR	MPnt SHeu
'Crimson Curls'	CBod EHyd ELan EPfP LBuc LRHS MPnt NRHS SHeu SRms SWvt WNPC
'Crispy Curly'	MPnt SHeu
cylindrica	EPfP GKev GWyn LRHS MPnt SHeu
- var. ***alpina***	GKev
- 'Cream'	MPnt
- 'Francis'	MPnt
- 'Greenfinch'	ELan GLog GMaP GWyn LRHS MPnt MRav NBir SHar SHeu SWvt XLum
- 'Hyperion'	EHyd LRHS MPnt SHeu
'Da Vinci' (Master Painters Series)	MPnt SHeu
'Damask'	EHyd LRHS MPnt SHeu
'Dark Beauty'PBR	CBod EMor LRHS NSti SCob SHeu WNPC
'Dark Secret'PBR	EBee MPnt SHeu
'Dark Storm' (Seasonal Selection Series)	CRos EHyd EPfP LRHS MPnt NRHS SHeu WNPC
'David'	MPnt SHeu WBrk
'Delta Dawn'PBR	CPla CWGN EBee LRHS MHol MPnt SHeu SPoG SWvt WNPC
'Dennis Davidson'	see *H.* 'Huntsman'
'Dew Drops' (v)	SHeu
'Dizzi Blonde' **new**	SHeu
'Earth Angel'	MPnt SHeu
EBONY AND IVORY ('E and I'PBR)	EBee EHyd EShb GMaP LRHS LSRN MPnt NBir NWad SRms SWvt WSpi
'Eden's Aurora'	MPnt
'Eden's Mystery'	NLar
'Electra'PBR	CMea MPnt NLar SHeu SWvt
'Electric Lime'	ELan MPnt NLar SHeu SPoG WNPC
'Elworthy Rusty'	CElw
'Emperor's Cloak'	GLog SHeu SWvt
'Emperor's Cloak' green-leaved	EWTr
'Encore'PBR	MPnt SHeu
'Fairy Dance'	MPnt
'Fantasia'	SHeu
'Fire Alarm'PBR	CWGN EHyd ELan EPfP LBuc LRHS MPnt NRHS SCob SHeu WNPC
'Fire Chief'PBR	CBod CRos CWGN EBee EHyd ELan EPfP LRHS LSou MAvo MPnt NBir NHol NLar NRHS SCob SHeu SPer SPoG SRkn SWvt
'Firebird'	EHyd LRHS MPnt
FIREFLY	see *H.* 'Leuchtkäfer'
'Fireworks'PBR ♀H6	MPnt MRav NLar SCob SHeu
'Fleur' (Fox Series)	MPnt WNPC
'Florist's Choice'	SHeu
(Forever Series) 'Forever Purple'	CBod CWGN EBee EHyd EPfP LBuc LRHS LSou MPnt NLar NRHS SHeu SPoG WNPC WTor
- 'Forever Red' **new**	MPnt SHeu
'French Quarter'	MPnt SHeu
'Frilly Lizzie' **new**	WNPC
'Frost' (Little Cutie Series)	CBod EPfP MPnt SHeu WNPC
'Frosted Violet'	see *H.* 'Frosted Violet Dream'
§ 'Frosted Violet Dream'PBR	EMor EPfP LSRN MPnt SHeu SWvt WNPC
'Galaxy'PBR	CWGN MPnt SHeu
'Gauguin' (Master Painters Series)	MPnt MSCN SEdd SHeu
'Georgia Peach'PBR	CPla CWGN EBee ELan EPfP MNrw MPnt NBir NLar SHeu SWvt WFar WNPC
'Georgia Plum'	CRos CWGN EBee EHyd ELan LRHS MPnt NRHS SHeu WNPC
'Ginger Ale'PBR	CRos CWGN EBee ECha EHyd ELan ELon EPfP EWes LRHS MHol MPnt NBir NHol NLar NRHS SHeu SPer SPoG SWvt
'Ginger Peach'PBR	ELan EPfP MPnt SCob SHeu WNPC
'Ginger Snap'PBR (Little Cutie Series)	MPnt SHeu WNPC
glabra	MPnt SHeu
glauca	see *H. americana*
'Glitter'PBR	CBod CWGN EBee EPfP LSou MPnt NDov SHeu SPoG WNPC
'Gloire d'Orléans'	MPnt XLum
'Gloriana'	EHyd LRHS
'Gojiberry' (Indian Summer Series)	EBee MPnt SHeu
'Gotham'PBR	MPnt SHeu WNPC
'Grape Soda'PBR (Soda Series)	CWGN LSou MHol MPnt SHeu WNPC
'Green Goddess' (Heucheraholics Series)	SHeu
'Green Ivory'	MPnt SHeu XLum
'Green Sashay'	MPnt SHeu
'Green Spice'	CBod CRos EBee ELan EPfP GBin LCro LOPS LRHS MPnt NBir NHol NRHS SCob SHar SHeu SPer SPoG SWvt WCav

	'Guacamole'	MPnt SHeu
	'Guardian Angel'	MPnt SHeu
	'Gypsy Dancer' PBR (Dancer Series)	MPnt SHeu
	'Hailstorm' (v)	MPnt
	hallii	MPnt SPlb
	'Happy Moon' **new**	WCot
	HARVEST BURGUNDY ('Balheubur')	EHyd LRHS MPnt SHeu
	HARVEST SILVER ('Balheusil')	EHyd EPfP LRHS MPnt SHeu
	'Havana' PBR	EHyd LRHS MPnt NRHS SHeu
	'Helen Dillon' (v)	GMaP MPnt NBir SHeu SWvt WSMil
	'Hercules' PBR	LRHS MPnt SHeu
	hispida	MPnt
	'Hocus Pocus'	SHeu
	'Hollywood' PBR	EBee EPfP MGos MPnt NBir NHol NLar SHeu SPoG
	'Hot Stuff'	SHeu
	'Huckleberry' (Indian Summer Series) **new**	SHeu WTor
§	'Huntsman'	EHyd LRHS MPnt MRav SHeu
	'Iron Maiden'	SHeu
	'Isabella' (Fox Series)	MPnt WNPC
	'Jade Gloss' PBR	EHyd EPfP LRHS MPnt SHeu SWvt WNPC
	'June Bride'	MPnt
	'Kadastra'	MPnt SHeu
	'Kassandra' PBR	EHyd LRHS MPnt NRHS SHeu SWvt
	KEY LIME PIE ('Tnheu042' PBR) (Dolce Series)	CBod CExl CWGN EHyd EPfP LRHS MGos NBir NHol NRHS SHeu SRms SWvt WFar
	'King Kong'	MPnt
	Kira Series	MPnt
	- 'Kira Purple Rain Forest'	SHeu
	'Lady in Red'	NBre
	'Lady Marmalade'	MPri
	'Lady Romney'	XLum
	'Lemon Chiffon' PBR	EHyd LRHS MPnt NRHS SHeu
§	'Leuchtkäfer'	CBod EBou EHyd EPfP EWTr GMaP GWyn MHer MMuc MPnt MRav NBir NMir SCob SHeu SPlb SRms XLum
	LICORICE ('Tnheu044' PBR) (Dolce Series)	CRos EHyd LRHS MBNS MGos MPnt NBir NLar NRHS SHeu SLim SPoG SWvt WFar
	'Lily the Pink'	SHeu
	'Lime Marmalade'	CBcs CBod CDoC CMea CRos CWGN EBee EHyd ELan EPfP LRHS LSou MAsh MBNS MGos MPie MPnt MPri NHol NLar NRHS NSti SHeu SPoG WFar
	'Lime Rickey' PBR	CWGN EHyd EPfP LRHS MGos MSCN NBir NGBl SCob SEdd SHeu SWvt WCot
	'Lime Ruffles' PBR	MPnt SHeu WNPC
	'Lipstick' PBR	CWGN EBee LRHS MPnt SHeu SWvt
	'Little Tinker'	MPnt SHeu
	'Lune Rousse'	MPnt SHeu
	'Madison Bride' (Fox Series)	MPnt WNPC
	'Magic Flute'	SHeu
	'Magic Wand' ♀H6	SHeu
	'Magma'	SHeu
	'Magnum'	CWGN MPnt SHeu WCot
	'Mahogany' PBR	EPfP LSou MPnt MPri NBir SHeu SLim SWvt WHoo
	'Malachite'	CRos EHyd EPfP LRHS MPnt NRHS SHeu
	'Mango'	MPnt SHeu
	'Marmalade' PBR	Widely available
	'Maroon Blush' PBR	SHeu
	'Mars'	CRos EHyd EPfP LRHS MPnt NRHS SHeu
	'Mary Rose'	MPnt SHeu
	maxima	MPnt SHeu
	'Mega Caramel'	MPnt SHeu
	'Mega Citronelle'	MPnt
	'Megan' (Heucheraholics Series) **new**	SHeu
	'Melting Fire'	CChe EHyd GPSL LRHS MPnt SHeu
	'Mercury'	SHeu
	'Metallic Shimmer' (Fox Series)	CBod MPnt WNPC
	'Metallica'	SHeu
	micans	see *H. rubescens*
	micrantha	MPnt SHeu SRms
	- var. ***diversifolia*** misapplied	see *H. villosa*
	- 'Martha's Compact'	MPnt
§	- 'Ruffles'	ECha MPnt SHeu
	'Midas Touch'	CWGN MPnt NLar
	'Midnight Bayou'	CPla ELan EPfP MPnt NLar NPer SHeu SWvt WNPC
	'Midnight Rose'	Widely available
	'Midnight Rose Select'	MPnt SHeu
	'Midnight Ruffles' PBR	LSun MPnt SHeu WFar WNPC
	'Milan' PBR	EHyd ELan LRHS MPnt NRHS SHeu WNPC
	'Mini Caramel'	MPnt
	'Mini Mouse'	MPnt SHeu
	'Mint Frost' PBR	ELan LRHS LSun MPnt NBir SHeu SWvt
	'Mint Julep' PBR	MPnt SHeu
	'Miracle' PBR	MPnt SHeu WNPC
	'Mocha' PBR	MNrw MPnt SHeu SWvt
	'Molly Bush' ♀H6	SHeu
	'Morello'	MPnt SHeu WNPC
	'Morning Mist'	WNPC
	'Mother of Pearl'	MPnt SHeu
	'Mulberry' (Indian Summer Series) **new**	SHeu WTor
	'Muscat'	MPnt SHeu
	'Mysteria' PBR	MPnt SHeu
	'Mystic Angel'	MPnt SHeu
	'Neptune'	MBel MPnt SHeu
	(Northern Exposure Series) NORTHERN EXPOSURE AMBER ('Tnheunea')	MPnt SHeu
	- NORTHERN EXPOSURE LIME ('Tnheunel')	MPnt SHeu
	- NORTHERN EXPOSURE RED ('Tnhheuner')	MPnt SHeu
	- NORTHERN EXPOSURE SILVER **new**	SHeu
	'Oakington Jewel'	MPnt
	'Obsidian' PBR	Widely available
	'Orange Dream'	MPnt SHeu
	'Orphée'	MPnt NChi
	'Paprika' PBR	CMea CRos CWGN EBee EHyd LRHS MBNS MPnt NRHS SCob SHeu WCot WFar WNPC
	'Paris' PBR	CBod CDoC CRos CWGN EHyd EPfP LRHS LSRN MAsh MGos MPnt NHol NRHS SHeu SPer SPoG STPC WNPC
	parishii NNS 93384	MPnt
	parvifolia var. ***nivalis***	MPnt
	- var. ***utahensis***	MPnt

'Pauline' (Fox Series)	CRos CWGN EHyd LBuc LRHS MPnt NRHS SHeu WNPC
'Peach Crisp'PBR	CWGN MPnt SHeu SRkn WNPC
'Peach Flambé'PBR	CBod CRos CWGN EHyd ELan EPfP LRHS MBNS MCot MGos MHer MPnt MPri NBir NLar NRHS SCob SEdd SHeu SLim SPoG SWvt WHer
'Peach Melba'	MPnt SHeu
'Peach Pie'	MPnt
'Peachy Keen'	SHeu
'Pear Crisp'PBR	MPnt SHeu WNPC
'Penelope'	MPnt SHeu WNPC
'Peppermint' (Little Cutie Series)	CBod EPfP MPnt MSCN SEdd SHeu WCot WNPC
'Peppermint Spice'PBR (21st Century Collection Series)	MPnt SHeu
'Persian Carpet'	LRHS MPnt NBir NRHS SHeu SWvt
(Petite Series) 'Petite Marbled Burgundy'	MPnt SHeu SWvt
- 'Petite Pearl Fairy'	MPnt SHeu SWvt
- 'Petite Pink Bouquet'	MPnt SHeu
'Pewter Moon'	ELan GMaP MPnt NBir SHeu WFar
'Pewter Veil'	MPnt SHeu
'Phoebe's Blush' (Fox Series)	LSou MHtn MPnt WNPC
'Picasso' (Master Painters Series)	MPnt SHeu WNPC
'Pilley Pink'	SHeu
'Pilley Pumpkin'	SHeu
pilosissima	XLum
'Pink Panther' (Heucheraholics Series)	SHeu
'Pink Pearls'PBR	CBod CWGN EHyd EPfP LRHS MPnt NRHS SEdd SHeu WCot WNPC
'Pinot Bianco'	MPnt SHeu
'Pinot Gris'PBR	CWGN MPnt SHeu WCot WNPC
'Pinot Noir'	MPnt SHeu WNPC
'Pistache'	LBuc MPnt SHeu WCot WNPC
§ 'Pluie de Feu'	EShb LRHS MPnt MRav SHeu XLum
'Plum Pudding'PBR	Widely available
'Plum Royale'PBR	EHyd ELan EPfP GKev LRHS MGos MPnt SHeu SWvt
'Pretty Perinne'PBR	MPnt SHeu
'Pretty Polly'	EHyd LRHS MPnt SHeu
'Prince'	EHyd ELan LRHS MPnt NRHS SHeu SWvt
'Prince of Orange'	SHeu
'Prince of Silver'	EHyd LRHS MPnt SHeu
pringlei	see *H. rubescens*
pubescens	MPnt SHeu XLum
- 'Alba'	MPnt
pulchella	CBod CPBP EBou EDAr GKev GLog MHer MPnt NLar SHeu SPlb SRms
'Purple Crinkle'	WNPC
'Purple Petticoats' ♀H6	CBcs CBod ELan LRHS MGos MPnt NLar SHeu SLim SPoG
'Quick Silver'	EHyd LRHS MPnt NBir NRHS SWvt
§ 'Quilter's Joy'	MPnt
'Rachel'	EHyd ELan EPfP GMaP LRHS LSRN MPnt MRav NDov NGdn NRHS SHeu SWvt XLum
RAIN OF FIRE	see *H.* 'Pluie de Feu'
'Raspberry' (Fox Series)	MPnt
'Raspberry Ice'PBR	MPnt SHeu
'Raspberry Regal' ♀H6	MPnt MRav NBir SHeu SWvt WCot WSHC
'Rave On'PBR	CWGN EBee ELan MPnt NHol NLar SHeu SPer SWvt
'Red Dress'	MPnt SHeu
'Red Lightning'PBR	CWGN MPnt SHeu
'Red Pearls'	MPnt SHeu
'Red Sea'	ECtt EHyd EPfP LRHS MPnt NRHS SHeu WCot WNPC
'Red Spangles'	EHyd LRHS MPnt NBir SHeu
'Regina' ♀H6	EHyd EPfP MPnt NRHS SHeu SWvt
'Renoir' (Master Painters Series)	CWGN MPnt SHeu
'Rex Lime' **new**	SPad
'Rhapsody'	EHyd LRHS
richardsonii	MPnt SHeu XLum
'Rickard'	MPnt
'Rio'PBR	CWGN LBuc MHtn MPnt NDov SHeu WNPC
'Robert'	MPnt
'Root Beer'PBR	EHyd EPfP LRHS MHol MPnt NRHS SHeu WNPC
ROSEMARY BLOOM ('Heuros')	EHyd LRHS SHeu
§ ***rubescens***	GKev NBro WThu
'Ruffles'	see *H. micrantha* 'Ruffles'
'Sanbrot'	MPnt
§ ***sanguinea***	CMac MMrt MPnt MRav NBir
- 'Alba'	EShb LPot MPnt SMHy
- 'Coral Petite'	EDAr EHyd LRHS NRHS SHeu
- 'Frosty'	EHyd LRHS NRHS
- 'Geisha's Fan'	MPnt SHeu SWvt
- 'Monet' (v)	MPnt SHeu
- var. ***pulchra***	EWld
- 'Ruby Bells'	EHyd LRHS LSRN MPnt NLar NRHS SHeu SRms
- 'Sioux Falls'	GPSL SHeu
- 'Snow Storm' (v)	ELan MPnt SHeu SRms
- 'Splendens'	MPnt XLum
- 'Taff's Joy' (v)	MPnt
- 'White Cloud' (v)	EPfP EWTr GQue MPnt MWat NBre SHeu SRms XLum
'Sashay' ♀H6	GBin MPnt SHeu WNPC
'Saturn'	MPnt SHeu SWvt
'Schneewittchen'	EShb MPnt MRav SHeu
'Scintillation' ♀H6	MPnt
'September Morn' (Seasonal Selection Series)	CRos EHyd EPfP LRHS MPnt NRHS SHeu WNPC
'Shanghai'PBR	CWGN EBee EHyd EPfP LRHS LSRN MAsh MPnt NRHS SHeu SWvt WFar WNPC
'Shenandoah Mountain'	MPnt
'Shere Variety'	EHyd LRHS MPnt
'Silver Celebration' (Fox Series)	CBod MPnt WNPC
'Silver Dollar'	CWGN EBee MPnt SHeu
'Silver Gilt'	SHeu
'Silver Gumdrop' (Dolce Series) **new**	MPnt SHeu
'Silver Heart'	EBee EHyd LRHS MPnt NRHS
'Silver Indiana'	MPnt SHeu
'Silver Light'PBR	MPnt SHeu
'Silver Lode'PBR	MPnt SHeu
'Silver Scrolls'PBR	CMac CRos EHyd EPfP GMaP LCro LOPS LRHS LSRN MBel MGos MPnt MRav NBir NRHS NSti SCob SEdd SLim SPoG SRkn SWvt WCot
'Silver Shadows'	MPnt SHeu
'Silver Streak'	see × *Heucherella* 'Silver Streak'
'Sioux Falls'	MPnt
'Slater's Pink' (Fox Series)	MPnt WNPC
'Sloeberry' (Indian Summer Series) **new**	SHeu

'Snow Angel'	CWGN MPnt NGBl SEdd SHeu SPoG WCot WNPC WRHF
'Snowfire' (v)	MPnt SHeu
'Southern Comfort'PBR	CWGN EBee LRHS MPnt NHol NLar NPer SHeu SLim SPoG SWvt
'Sparkler'	MPnt
'Sparkling Burgundy'	ELan MPnt SHeu SWvt
'Spellbound'PBR	CWGN EPfP MPnt SHeu SPoG SRkn WNPC
'Starry Night'	MPnt
'Steel City'	MPnt SHeu
'Stormy Seas'	EBee EHyd ELan EPfP EWTr LRHS MPnt MRav NBir NRHS SCob SHeu SWvt WCAu
'Strawberries and Cream' (v)	MPnt SHeu
'Strawberry Candy'PBR	CWGN MPnt NBir NLar SCob SHeu SLim WNPC WWtn
'Strawberry Swirl'	CElw ELan EPfP EWTr GMaP MPnt MRav NBir NDov SHeu SWvt WCAu WNPC
'Sugar Berry'PBR (Little Cutie Series)	EHyd EPfP LBuc LRHS LSun MPnt NRHS SEdd SHeu WCot WNPC
SUGAR FROSTING ('Pwheu0104'PBR)	CRos EHyd ELan EPau LRHS LSRN MCot MGos MPnt MPri NCou NHol NRHS SEdd SHeu SWvt
'Sugar Plum'PBR	CWGN EBee ELan EPfP LBuc LRHS LSRN MCot MPnt MPri SHeu WHoo WNPC
'Sunrise' (Seasonal Selection Series)	MPnt SHeu WNPC
'Sweet Berry'	MPnt
'Sweet Caroline' (Fox Series) **new**	MPnt WNPC
'Sweet Tart'PBR (Little Cutie Series)	CBod CRos EHyd EPfP LRHS MPnt NLar NRHS SHeu SPer SPoG WNPC
'Swirling Fantasy'PBR	MPnt SHeu WFar
'Tangerine Wave' (Fox Series)	MPnt SHeu WNPC
'Tara'	MPnt SHeu
'Tayberry' (Indian Summer Series) **new**	SHeu
'Thomas' (Fox Series)	CBod MPnt SHeu WNPC
'Tiramisu'PBR	CBod CWGN EHyd LRHS MPnt NBir SHeu SWvt WNPC
'Tokyo'PBR (City Series)	CWGN MPnt SHeu SPoG
'Topaz Jazz'	MPnt SHeu WNPC
'Tresahor White'	MPnt
'Van Gogh' (Master Painters Series)	MPnt SHeu
'Vanilla Spice'	MPnt SHeu
'Veil of Passion'	NBre
'Velvet Night'	MPnt NBir SHeu SPlb
'Venus'	CWGN EHyd LRHS MBel MHol MMuc MPnt NRHS NSti SHeu WCot WHoo
'Vesuvius'	MPnt SHeu
'Vienna'PBR (City Series)	MPnt SHeu WNPC
§ ***villosa***	CSam LEdu MPnt MRav WPGP XLum
- 'Autumn Bride'	MPnt SDix SHeu SMHy
- BRESSINGHAM BRONZE ('Absi'PBR)	EHyd LRHS MPnt SHeu
- 'Chantilly'	MPnt SHeu
- var. ***macrorhiza***	EShb MPnt NBre XLum
- 'Palace Purple'	Widely available
- 'Palace Purple Select'	CMac CTri LSun MBow MCot SLim SWvt WCAu WSpi
- 'Plumpower'PBR	SHeu
'Virginale'	MPnt
'Walnut' (Fox Series)	MPnt SHeu WNPC
'White Marble'	MPnt SHar SHeu
'White Spires'	EHyd LRHS MPnt SHeu
'White Swirls'	MPnt
'Wild Rose' (Primo Series) **new**	MPnt SHeu
'William How'	MPnt SHeu
'Winter Joy' (Seasonal Selection Series)	CRos EHyd LRHS MPnt NRHS SHeu WNPC
'Winter Red'	EHyd LRHS MPnt SHeu
'XXL'	MPnt SHeu
'Zabeliana'	MPnt SHeu
'Zipper'PBR	CWGN LBuc MPnt SHeu WNPC

Heuchera × *Tiarella* see × *Heucherella*

× *Heucherella* ✿ (*Saxifragaceae*)

'Alabama Sunrise'PBR	CBod CRos ELan EPfP EWhm LRHS MHol MPnt NLar NPer NRHS SHeu SPad SWvt WFar
alba 'Bridget Bloom'	EHyd ELan EPfP GMaP LPot LRHS MPnt MRav SHeu SPer SRms WCAu WFar XLum
§ - 'Rosalie'	LRHS MPnt MRav SHeu SPlb WSHC
'Art Deco'	LSou MPnt SHeu
'Art Nouveau'	LSou MPnt SHeu WNPC
'Autumn Cascade'PBR (Cascade Series)	MPnt SHeu
'Berry Fizz'	MPnt SHeu SWvt
'Birthday Cake'	MPnt SHeu
'Blue Ridge'	LSou MPnt WTor
'Brass Lantern'PBR	CBod CRos CSpe EMor EPfP LRHS LSou MAsh MBel MPnt MPri NHol NLar NRHS SCob SHeu SPer SRms SWvt WNPC
'Burnished Bronze'PBR	EPfP LRHS LSou MPnt NLar NWad SCob SHeu SWvt
'Buttered Rum'PBR	EBee MPnt SHeu WNPC
'Catching Fire' **new**	MPnt SHeu
'Chocolate Lace'PBR	MPnt SHeu
'Cinnamon Bear'	MPnt SHeu
'Citrus Shock'	EMor MPnt SHeu
'Copper Cascade'PBR (Cascade Series)	EMor LSou MPnt SHeu WNPC
'Cracked Ice'PBR	MHol MPnt SCob SHeu
'Dayglow Pink'PBR	CDor GMaP LSRN LSou MPnt NLar SHeu
'Fan Dancer'	MPnt SHeu
'Fire Frost'PBR	LSou MPnt SHeu
'Glacier Falls'PBR (Falls Series)	EMor SHeu WNPC
'Gold Cascade'PBR (Cascade Series)	EMor MPnt WNPC
GOLD STRIKE ('Hertn041')	EMor MBNS MPnt SHeu
'Golden Zebra'PBR	CWGN ELan LRHS MPnt NLar SHeu SWvt
'Great Smokies'	MPnt SHeu
'Gunsmoke'PBR	LSou MBel MPnt NWad SCob SHeu SWvt WFar WNPC
HAPPY HOUR LIME ('Tnherhhl')	MPnt SHeu WNPC
'Heart of Darkness'PBR	MPnt SHeu
'Honey Rose'PBR	EBee LSou MPnt SCob SHeu WNPC
'Hopscotch' (Fun and Games Series) **new**	SHeu
'Hot Spot'PBR	MPnt SHeu
'Infinity'PBR	LSou SHeu
'Kimono'PBR ♀H6	CBod CMac CRos EHyd ELan EMor EPfP GKev GMaP GWyn LRHS LSRN MBel MPnt NLar NRHS NSti NWad SCob SHeu

'Mojito'	MPnt SHeu WNPC
'Ninja'	see *Tiarella* 'Ninja'
'Onyx' **new**	SHeu WNPC
'Party Time'PBR	SHeu
PINK WHISPERS ('Hertn042')	LSou MPnt SHeu
'Plum Cascade'	MPnt SHeu SPer WNPC
'Quicksilver'	CBcs EPfP GMaP LSou MPnt SHeu SWvt
'Red Rover' (Fun and Games Series) **new**	MPnt SHeu
'Redstone Falls'PBR (Falls Series)	EBee MNrw MPnt MSCN NLar NWad SHeu SPoG SWvt WCot WNPC
'Ring of Fire'	SWvt
§ 'Silver Streak'	EHyd LRHS MPnt NRHS SHeu SWvt
'Solar Eclipse'	CBcs CRos EBee EHyd EMor LCro LOPS LRHS MAsh MPnt NLar NRHS NSti NWad SCob SHeu SPad SPer SPoG SWvt WFar WNPC
'Solar Power'PBR	CRos CWGN EBee EHyd EMor EPfP LRHS MPnt NLar NRHS NWad SHeu SWvt WFar WNPC
'Stoplight'PBR	CRos CWGN ECha EMor EPau EPfP GMaP MGos MPnt MRav NBir NDov NHol NSti SCob SHeu SPer SRkn SWvt WFar WNPC
'Summer Snowflake'	SHeu
'Sunrise Falls'PBR (Falls Series)	CBod EBee MNrw MPnt MSCN NWad SHeu SWvt WFar WNPC
'Sunspot'PBR (v)	EMor NBro SHeu SRms WHer
'Sweet Tea'PBR	Widely available
'Tapestry'PBR	CDor CRos EHyd ELan EMor EPfP GMaP LRHS MBNS MBel MHol MPnt NDov NHol NRHS NSti NWad SCob SHeu SPer SPoG SRkn SRms SWvt WFar WNPC
tiarelloides ♀H6	SRms
'Twilight'PBR	LSou MPnt SHeu WNPC
§ 'Viking Ship'	MPnt NBir SHeu
'Yellowstone Falls'PBR	EMor MPnt NCou NWad SHeu SWvt WNPC

Hexastylis see *Asarum*

Hibanobambusa see × *Phyllosasa*

Hibbertia (*Dilleniaceae*)

aspera	CAbb CBcs CCCN CRHN CTsd LRHS WCFE WCot WFar WKif WSHC
§ ***cuneiformis***	CCCN
pedunculata	WAbe
procumbens	ITim WAbe
§ ***scandens*** ♀H1c	CBcs CCCN CRHN EShb
'Spring Sunshine'	CBod SEle
tetrandra	see *H. cuneiformis*
volubilis	see *H. scandens*

Hibiscus (*Malvaceae*)

coccineus	EShb SPlb
- white-flowered	SBrt
'Cranberry Crush'PBR	CWGN ELan EWTr MNrw
'Eruption'	ELon
'Fireball'PBR	SPoG
hamabo	CCCN SGbt
huegelii	see *Alyogyne huegelii*
'Jazzberry Jam'PBR	ELan MNrw SPoG
'Kopper King'PBR	MBNS MNrw SPoG
moscheutos	EBee SBrt SVic XLum
- CAROUSEL JOLLY HEART ('Tahi56'PBR)	LCro LOPS
- CAROUSEL PINK CANDY ('Tahi12'PBR)	CWGN SPad
- CAROUSEL PINK PASSION ('Tahi16'PBR) **new**	LCro LOPS
- (Luna Series) 'Luna Red'	CCht
- - 'Luna Rose'	CCht
- - 'Luna White'	CCht
- 'Old Yella'PBR	ELan SPoG
- PLANET GRIOTTE ('Tangri'PBR) **new**	MPkF
- 'Royal Gems'PBR	ELan
'Newbiscus Pink'	CCCN
'Newbiscus Red'	CCCN
'Newbiscus White'	CCCN
paramutabilis	EWes
rosa-sinensis	CDoC EBak SPre
- 'Apple Blossom'	WFib
- 'Arcadian Spring'	WFib
§ - 'Bari' (Sunny Cities Series)	CCCN
- 'Blues Man'	WFib
§ - 'Bordeaux'PBR (Sunny Cities Series)	CCCN
- 'Byron Metts'	WFib
- 'Cajun Cocktail'	see *H. rosa-sinensis* 'Jambalaya'
- 'Candy Floss' (d)	WFib
- 'Carmen Keene'	WFib
- 'China Town'	WFib
- 'Cloud Nine'PBR	WFib
- 'Cockatoo'	WFib
- 'Cooperi' (v) ♀H1b	WFib
- 'Courier Mail'	WFib
- 'Dorothy Brady'	WFib
- 'Enid Lewis' (d)	WFib
- 'Fifth Dimension'	WFib
- 'Gabriel'	WFib
- 'Georgia Peach'	WFib
- 'Gwen Mary'	WFib
- 'Holly's Pride'	WFib
- 'Hot Bikini'	WFib
§ - 'Jambalaya'	WFib
- 'Jayella'	WFib
- 'June's Joy'	WFib
- 'Key West Thunderhead' (d)	WFib
- 'Lemon Chiffon'	WFib
- 'Linda Pear' (d)	WFib
- 'Madame Dupont'	WFib
- 'Me Oh My Oh'	WFib
- 'Mrs Andreasen' (d)	WFib
- 'Rhinestone'	WFib
- 'Roman Candle'	WFib
- 'Rose Flake'	WFib
- 'Rum Runner'	WFib
- 'Soft Shoulders'	WFib
- 'Spanish Lady'	WFib
- 'Sprinkle Rain'	WFib
- (Sunny Cities Series) 'Sunny Bary'	see *H. rosa-sinensis* 'Bari' (Sunny Cities Series)
- - 'Sunny Bordeaux'	see *H. rosa-sinensis* 'Bordeaux' (Sunny Cities Series)
- - SUNNY CANCUN ('Hican'PBR)	CCCN
- - SUNNY TORINO ('Hirio'PBR)	CCCN
- 'Susan Schlueter'	WFib
- 'Tahitian Christmas'	WFib
- 'Tahitian Desert Sands'	WFib
- 'Tarantella'	WFib

- 'The Path'	WFib
- 'Vermillion Queen'	WFib
- 'Weekend'	WFib
- 'White Swan'	WFib
ROSE MOON ('Walhirosmo'PBR)	CRos EHyd LBuc LRHS NRHS SPoG
sabdariffa	XAbr
schizopetalus 🏆H1b	WFib
sinosyriacus 'Lilac Queen'	CExl CRos EHyd EPfP LRHS WPGP
- 'Ruby Glow'	CExl EPfP LRHS LSRN WPGP
'Sunny Premiere'	CCCN
'Swazi Princess'	XBlo
syriacus	CCCN LMaj SChr SWeb SavN
§ - 'America Irene Scott'PBR	SPoG
- 'Aphrodite'	EHyd LRHS MAsh SSta
- 'Ardens' (d)	CEnd EBee SPoG WFar
§ - AZURRI BLUE SATIN ('Dvpazurri'PBR)	SSta
- 'Azzurri'	see *H. syriacus* AZURRI BLUE SATIN
- BLUE BIRD	see *H. syriacus* 'Oiseau Bleu'
- BLUE CHIFFON ('Notwood3'PBR) (d) 🏆H5	CRos CSBt EHyd ELan EPfP LCro LOPS LRHS NRHS SPoG
- 'Bredon Springs'	SSta
- CHINA CHIFFON ('Bricutts') (d)	EHyd LRHS MMuc SEND SGol SPer SPoG
- 'Diana' 🏆H5	CDoC CRos EHyd ELon EPfP LRHS LSRN MAsh NRHS SCob SCoo SLon SPer SSta
- 'Dorothy Crane'	CRos LRHS SSta
- 'Duc de Brabant' (d)	CCCN CSBt MBlu
- 'Elegantissimus'	see *H. syriacus* 'Lady Stanley'
- 'Gandini van Aart'PBR	LRHS SGol
- 'Hamabo' 🏆H5	CBod CBrac CRos CSBt CTri EBee EHyd ELan ELon EPfP LRHS LSRN MAsh MGos MMuc MPri NLar NRHS SCoo SEND SGol SLim SPer SPoG SWvt WFar
- 'Helene'	EHyd LRHS LSRN MBlu SSta
- 'Honghwarang'	SSta
- 'Jeanne d'Arc' (d)	SGol
§ - 'Lady Stanley' (d)	CBod CCCN CDoC CMac CSBt EHyd LRHS SCoo
- LAVENDER CHIFFON ('Notwoodone'PBR) (d) 🏆H5	CRos CSBt EHyd ELan EPfP EWes LCro LOPS LRHS LSRN MGos MMuc NRHS SCoo SEND SGol SPer SPoG
- MAGENTA CHIFFON ('Rwoods5'PBR)	CRos EHyd LCro LOPS NRHS SPoG
- 'Marina'	CBod CCCN CDoC EHyd ELon EPfP LRHS MBlu MRav SGol WFar
- 'Mathilde'	SSta
- 'Mauve Queen'	SSta
- 'Meehanii' misapplied	see *H. syriacus* 'Purpureus Variegatus'
- 'Meehanii' (v) 🏆H5	CEnd CRos EBee EPfP LRHS SCoo SPer SPoG SSta
- 'Melrose'	SSta
- 'Monstrosus'	EBee MGos NLar
§ - 'Oiseau Bleu' 🏆H5	Widely available
- PINK CHIFFON ('Jwnwood4'PBR) (d)	CRos EHyd ELan LCro LOPS LRHS NRHS
- PINK GIANT ('Flogi')	CMac EPfP LRHS SPer SSta
- PINKY SPOT ('Minspot'PBR)	LRHS MMrt
- PURPLE PILLAR ('Gandini Santiago'PBR)	LCro LOPS SGol SWeb
- PURPLE RUFFLES ('Sanchoyo') (d)	CDoC EPfP SPoG
§ - 'Purpureus Variegatus' (v)	CMac CRos EHyd LRHS
- 'Red Heart' 🏆H5	CBod CEnd CMac CRos CSBt CTri EHyd ELan EPfP LRHS MAsh MGos MMuc NRHS SCob SEND SGbt SLim SPer SPoG SRms SSta SWvt WCFE XSen
- ROSALBANE ('Minrosa')	SGol
- RUSSIAN VIOLET ('Floru')	CEnd CRos EPfP LRHS
- 'Shintaeyang'	EHyd LRHS
- 'Snowdrift'	SSta
I - 'Speciosus' (d)	SPoG WFar
- STARBURST CHIFFON ('Rwoods6') **new**	LCro LOPS LRHS
- SUGAR TIP	see *H. syriacus* 'America Irene Scott'
- SUP'HEART ('Minomb'PBR) **new**	EPfP SGsty
- 'Totus Albus'	SSta
- ULTRAMARINE ('Minultra'PBR)	CDoC EPfP LRHS MPri SGsty
- 'Variegatus'	see *H. syriacus* 'Purpureus Variegatus'
- WHITE CHIFFON ('Notwoodtwo'PBR) (d) 🏆H5	CRos CSBt EHyd ELan EPfP EWes LCro LOPS LRHS LSRN MAsh MGos MRav SCoo SPer SPoG
- 'William R. Smith' 🏆H5	CRos LRHS MSwo SSta
- 'Woodbridge' 🏆H5	Widely available
trionum	CSpe LRHS WKif
- 'Sunny Day'	ELan

hickory, shagbark see *Carya ovata*

Hieracium (*Asteraceae*)

aurantiacum	see *Pilosella aurantiaca*
brunneocroceum	see *Pilosella aurantiaca* subsp. *carpathicola*
laevigatum subsp. ***nivale***	MMuc
§ ***lanatum***	NBir NWad
maculatum Sm.	see *H. spilophaeum*
pilosella	see *Pilosella officinarum*
scullyi	EPPr WFar
§ ***spilophaeum***	MMuc NBid NPer NSti WOut
- 'Blue Leaf'	WCot
- 'Leopard'	GJos NDov
umbellatum	WOut
villosum	GJos WHer
waldsteinii	WMal
welwitschii	see *H. lanatum*

Hierochloe (*Poaceae*)

odorata	CBod EPPr GPoy LEdu XLum

Himalayacalamus (*Poaceae*)

asper	CDTJ XCre
§ ***falconeri***	SDix
§ - 'Damarapa'	EPfP
§ ***hookerianus***	CExl EPfP IMou XCre
- 'Himalaya Blue'	CDTJ

Himantoglossum (*Orchidaceae*)

robertianum	GKev

× *Hippeasprekelia* (*Amaryllidaceae*)

'Durga Pradhan'	WCot
'Red Beauty'	WCot
'Red Star'	CCCN

Hippeastrum ✿ (*Amaryllidaceae*)

× ***acramannii*** 🏆H2	CAvo WCot
'Amarantia' (d) **new**	GKev
'Baby Star' 🏆H2	GKev SDeJ

'Black Pearl'	LCro LOPS
(Butterfly Group) 'Exotic Star'PBR **new**	WPhe
- 'Santa Rosa' **new**	GKev
(Colibri Group) 'Balentino'PBR	GKev
- 'Rapido'	LCro LOPS
- 'Veneto'	GKev SDeJ
- 'Daphne' **new**	WPhe
(Diamond Group) 'Charisma' ♀H2	SDeJ WPhe
- 'Fairytale' ♀H2	LCro LOPS SDeJ
- 'Lemon Star' **new**	WPhe
- 'Picotee' ♀H2	GKev LCro LOPS SDeJ
- 'Red Fire'	GKev
- 'Très Chic' **new**	WPhe
(Double Diamond Group) 'Alfresco'PBR (d)	GKev SDeJ
- 'Alasca'PBR (d)	GKev
(Double Galaxy Group) 'Aphrodite' (d)	WPhe
- 'Blossom Peacock' (d)	WPhe
- CHERRY NYMPH ('Chernym'PBR) (d)	GKev WPhe
- 'Double Delicious' (d) **new**	WPhe
- 'Double Dream'PBR (d) **new**	GKev
- 'Double Record' (d)	SDeJ
- 'Elvas' (d)	WPhe
- 'Ice Queen' (d) **new**	WPhe
- 'Lady Jane' (d)	SDeJ
- 'Nymph' (d)	GKev WPhe
- 'Red Peacock' (d)	SDeJ
(Galaxy Group) 'Ambiance'	WPhe
- 'Apple Blossom' ♀H2	GKev LCro LOPS SDeJ WPhe
- 'Apricot Parfait'	GKev
- 'Barbados' **new**	WPhe
- 'Benfica'	WPhe
- 'Christmas Gift'	GKev LCro LOPS WPhe
- 'Clown' ♀H2	SDeJ WPhe
- 'Desire'	WPhe
- 'Flamenco Queen' ♀H2	WPhe
- 'Gervase'	WPhe
- 'Grand Diva'	GKev
- 'Hercules'	SDeJ
- 'Lagoon'PBR ♀H2	LCro LOPS
- 'Liberty'	SDeJ
- 'Limona'PBR	LCro LOPS
- 'Luna'	WPhe
- 'Minerva'	SDeJ WPhe
- 'Mont Blanc'	SDeJ
- 'Monte Carlo'PBR ♀H2 **new**	WPhe
- 'Orange Souvereign'	WPhe
- 'Park Red'	GKev
- 'Pink Surprise'	GKev WPhe
- 'Popov'PBR **new**	WPhe
- 'Purple Rain'	WPhe
- 'Red Lion' ♀H2	GKev LCro LOPS WPhe
- 'Red Pearl'PBR **new**	WPhe
- 'Rilona'	GKev SDeJ WPhe
- 'Royal Velvet' ♀H2	WPhe
- 'Showmaster'	WPhe
- 'Spartacus'PBR **new**	WPhe
- 'Susan'	SDeJ WPhe
- 'Tosca' **new**	WPhe
× ***johnsonii*** ♀H2	CExl WCot
papilio	GKev LCro LOPS MMrt SDeJ
puniceum	GKev
'Royal Red' **new**	LCro LOPS
'San Antonio Rose'	WCot
'Snow Queen'	LCro LOPS
(Sonatini Group) 'Eye Catcher' **new**	GKev
- 'Pink Rascal' **new**	GKev
- 'Red Rascal' **new**	GKev
- 'White Rascal' **new**	GKev
- 'Sonatini Valentino'	WCot
(Spider Group) 'Bogota'	GKev LCro LOPS
- 'Carmen' **new**	WPhe
- 'Emerald'	WCot
- 'Evergreen' ♀H2	LCro LOPS WPhe
- 'Rio Negro' **new**	GKev
- 'Sumatra'PBR	LCro LOPS
striatum	WCot
stylosum	WCot
'Toughie'	EBee
(Trumpet Group) 'Swan Lake'PBR	SDeJ
vittatum	GKev

Hippeastrum × Sprekelia

see × *Hippeasprekelia*

Hippocrepis (*Papilionaceae*)

§ ***comosa***	EDAr SPhx WAbe
§ ***emerus***	CBcs CCCN CExl CMac ELan EPfP IMou MAsh MGil MGos MMuc NOra SEND SVen WSpi

Hippophae (*Elaeagnaceae*)

rhamnoides	CArg CBcs CCVT CHab CLnd CMCN CMac CPla CSpe CTri ECrN ELan EPfP EPom LBuc LEdu LMaj MBlu MCoo MMuc SCob SEND SEWo SGol SPlb WKor WTSh XSen
- (m)	EPom
- 'Askola' (f/F)	CAgr
- 'Dorana' (f/F)	CAgr
- 'Frugna' (f/F)	CAgr NLar
- 'Hergo' (f/F)	CAgr MCoo
- 'Hikul' (m)	CAgr NLar
- 'Juliet' (f/F)	CAgr
- 'Leikora' (f/F) ♀H7	CAgr ELan EPfP MBlu MCoo SPer
- ORANGE ENERGY ('Habego'PBR) (f/F)	CAgr MCoo
- 'Pollmix' (m) ♀H7	CAgr ELan EPfP MBlu MCoo SPer
- 'Pollmix 3' (m)	MCoo
- 'Sirola' (f/F)	CAgr MCoo
salicifolia	CAgr WKor
- GWJ 9221	WCru
- 'Streetwise'	EHyd
sinensis LS&E 15724	WPGP

Hippuris (*Plantaginaceae*)

vulgaris	CBen CWat EWat LLWG NPer WMAq XLum

Hirpicium (*Asteraceae*)

armerioides	SPlb

Histiopteris (*Dennstaedtiaceae*)

incisa	WPGP

Hoheria ✿ (*Malvaceae*)

'Ace of Spades'	CAbb CBod CDoC CRos EHyd ELan ELon EPfP LRHS MGil NLar SEND SPer SWvt
§ ***angustifolia***	EBee EPfP IDee SVen WPGP

angustifolia* × *sexstylosa	WPGP
'Borde Hill'	CAbb CBcs CDoC CJun CMac CRos CTho CTrC EBee EHyd ELan ELon EPfP LRHS MAsh MGil SEND SPer SWvt WCFE WPGP WSpi
glabrata	CMac CTrC EPfP GBin IDee NBir
'Glory of Amlwch' 🏆H4	CAbb CAby CBcs CDoC CJun CTho ELan EPfP GGGa LRHS LSRN SChF SPer SPoG SWvt WKif WPGP WSpi
§ ***lyallii*** 🏆H4	CCCN CExl CTho LRHS LSRN SVen
microphylla	see *H. angustifolia*
populnea	CBcs CCCN CTsd
- 'Holbrook'	CSam
- 'Sunshine' (v)	CDoC EBee SPoG
sexstylosa	CAbb CBcs CTho CTri EPfP LRHS LSRN MGos SPer SPlb SVen SWvt WFar WSpi
- 'Crataegifolia'	EBee MGil NLar
- 'Pendula'	CMac
- 'Stardust' 🏆H4	Widely available
'Snow White'	LRHS SPoG WMat

Holarrhena (*Apocynaceae*)

pubescens 'Snowflake' **new**	CDoC

Holboellia (*Lardizabalaceae*)

FMWJ 13055 **new**	WCru
angustifolia	NLar WCru
- subsp. ***angustifolia***	LRHS WCru
- - H&M 1504	WPGP
- subsp. ***linearifolia*** BWJ 8004	WCru
- subsp. ***obtusa*** DJHC 506	WCru
brachyandra HWJ 1023	WCru WPGP
aff. ***chapaensis*** B&SWJ 7250	WCru
coriacea	CBcs CBod CCCN CRHN CRos EBee EHyd ELan EPfP IDee IMou LEdu LRHS MGil MRav NLar NQui SEND SIvy SMad SPer WCFE WCru
- B&SWJ 2818	WCru
aff. ***grandiflora*** FMWJ 13333 **new**	WCru
latifolia	CBcs CCCN CMac CRHN CRos CTri EBee EHyd ELan EPfP LEdu LRHS MGil NLar SAdn SArc SEle SNig SPer SPoG SWvt WBor WCFE WCru WPGP WSHC
- DJHC 98442	WCru
- HWJCM 008	WCru
- HWJK 2014	WCru
- subsp. ***chartacea*** dark-flowered HWJK 2213D	WCru
- - pale-flowered HWJK 2213C	WCru
- lanceolate-leaved	WPGP
- - HWJK 2419	WCru

Holcus (*Poaceae*)

lanatus	WSFF
mollis 'Albovariegatus' (v)	CWCL EBou ECha EPPr GMaP GWyn NBid NBro NPer NSti SPlb SRms XLum
- 'White Fog' (v)	CBod EBee EPPr MMuc NWad

Holmskioldia (*Lamiaceae*)

* ***lutea***	CCCN
sanguinea	CCCN

Holodiscus (*Rosaceae*)

discolor	CBcs CRos EBee EHyd ELan EPfP EWes LEdu LRHS MBlu MGil MMuc MRav NLar NQui NRHS SLon SPer SPlb WBor

Homalocladium (*Polygonaceae*)

§ ***platycladum***	EShb

Homeria (*Iridaceae*)

breyniana	see *Tulipa breyniana*
- var. ***aurantiaca***	see *Moraea collina*

Homoglossum see *Gladiolus*

Hordeum (*Poaceae*)

jubatum	CDor CKno CSpe CWCL EAJP EWes GBee LEdu MAsh NGdn NGrd SEdd SPhx
- 'Early Pink'	NDov
secalinum	CHab WWild

Horkelia (*Rosaceae*)

hendersonii **new**	GEdr

Horminum (*Lamiaceae*)

pyrenaicum	IMou MHol MMuc SBut SEND SRms
I - f. ***alboviolaceum***	EWhm SBrt SBut
- dark-flowered	SBrt WSHC

Hornungia (*Brassicaceae*)

alpina	GEdr NSla XLum

horseradish see *Armoracia rusticana*

Hosta ✿ (*Asparagaceae*)

AGSJ 302	WCot
'A Many-Splendored Thing'	IBal
'Abana' (v)	IBal
'Abba Dabba Do' (v)	CDor ECtt ELon EMic IBal MHost NSue SSien
'Abba Showtime'	IBal
'Abby' (v)	CBdn EMic IBal MHost NSue SSien WFar
'Abiqua Ariel'	EMic
'Abiqua Blue Crinkles'	IBal NBir
'Abiqua Blue Edger'	IBal MHost SSien
'Abiqua Blue Madonna'	IBal
'Abiqua Blushing Recluse'	SSien
'Abiqua Delight' (v)	EMic
'Abiqua Drinking Gourd' 🏆H7	CBdn CBod CDor ECtt ELon GBin GMaP IBal MHost NLar NSue SSien
'Abiqua Elephant Ears'	IBal
'Abiqua Ground Cover'	IBal
'Abiqua Moonbeam' (v)	EMic IBal NGdn SSien
'Abiqua Recluse'	EMic IBal
'Abiqua Trumpet'	CBdn EMic IBal LRHS NGdn NLar SSien
'Abraham Lincoln'	IBal
'Academy Flora'	IBal
'Academy Mavrodaphne'	EMic
'Ada Reed'	IBal
'Adorable'	CBdn IBal NSue SSien
aequinoctiiantha	EMic IBal SSien
'Afterglow' (v)	IBal SSien
'Aksarben'	EMic
'Alabama Gold'	EMic
'Alakazaam' (v)	EMic IBal NSue SSien WFar
'Alan Titchmarsh'	IBal MHost

albomarginata	see *H.* 'Paxton's Original' (*sieboldii*)
§ 'Albomarginata' (*fortunei*) (v)	CBcs CMac NBir NGdn SSien SWvt WFar
'Alex Summers'	EMic IBal SSien WFar
'All That Jazz' (v)	IBal
'Allan P. McConnell' (v)	EMic IBal LRHS MNrw NSue SSien WFar WHal
'Allegan Emperor' (v)	IBal SSien
'Allegan Fog' (v) ♀H7	EShb GEdr IBal LRHS NHpl NSue SSien
'Alligator Alley' (v)	EMic IBal
'Alligator Shoes' (v) ♀H7	EMic IBal
'Almost' **new**	IBal
'Alpine Aire'	EMic IBal
'Alpine Dream'	IBal
'Alternative'	IBal
'Alvatine Taylor' (v)	EMic IBal NGdn SSien
'Amalia'PBR (v)	IBal NSue SSien
'Amanuma'	EMic IBal NSue
'Amazing Grace' (v)	EMic IBal
'Amber Tiara'	EMic IBal MHost SSien
'American Dream' (v)	EMic IBal LRHS SSien
'American Gothic' (v)	IBal
'American Halo'	CBdn EMic IBal MHost NLar NSti SPalm SSien
'American Icon'	EMic IBal
'American Sweetheart'PBR	EMic IBal SSien
'Americana' (v)	IBal SSien
'Amethyst Gem'	IBal NSue
'Amos'	IBal SSien
'Amy Elizabeth' (v)	EMic IBal
'Andorian'	IBal NSue
'Andrew'	SSien
'Angel Feathers' (v)	IBal SSien
'Angelique' (v)	IBal
'Anglo Saxon' (v)	IBal
'Ani Machi' (v) ♀H7	NSue
'Ann Kulpa' (v)	CBdn EMic IBal MHost NGdn SSien
'Annabel Lee'	IBal
'Anne' (v)	IBal LSRN NSue SSien
'Ansly' (v)	IBal
'Antioch' (*fortunei*) (v)	EMic GLog IBal MRav NLar SSien
'Aoki' (*fortunei*)	EMic IBal
'Aphrodite' (*plantaginea*) (d)	EPfP EWTr SMad SSien
'Apple Candy' (v)	CBdn IBal NSue SSien
'Apple Green'	EMic GKev IBal
'Apple Pie'	IBal
'Appletini'	IBal NSue
'Aqua Velva'	IBal
'Arc de Triomphe'	ECtt EMic IBal MHost NLar SSien
'Arch Duke'	IBal SSien
'Arctic Blast'	EMic IBal
'Arctic Circle' (v)	EMic
'Argentea Variegata' (*undulata*)	see *H. undulata* var. *undulata*
'Aristocrat' (Tardiana Group) (v)	CBdn EMic EMor IBal NGdn SSien WFar
'Asian Pearl' (v)	IBal
'Aspen Gold' (*tokudama* hybrid)	EMic
'Astral Bliss'	IBal
'Athena' (v)	SSien
'Atlantis'PBR (v) ♀H7	EBee EMic EMor IBal NGdn NSue SSien
'Atom Smasher'	NSue
'Atomic Elvis'	CBdn IBal NSue
'August Beauty'	EMic IBal SSien
'August Moon'	CRos ECtt ELan ELon EMic EPed GBin GMaP IBal LPot LRHS MHost MMuc MRav NBir NChi NGdn NLar NRHS SCob SPer SPoG SRms SSien SWvt WCFE WFar WWtn XLum
'Aureafolia'	see *H.* 'Starker Yellow Leaf'
'Aureoalba' (*fortunei*)	see *H.* 'Spinners'
'Aureomaculata' (*fortunei*)	see *H. fortunei* var. *albopicta*
'Aureomarginata' ambig. (v)	EHyd LRHS SCoo SSien
'Aureomarginata' (*montana*) (v) ♀H7	CMac ELan EMic GMaP IBal MMuc NGdn NLar NSue WFar
'Aureomarginata' (*ventricosa*) (v) ♀H7	EMic IBal NBir NGdn WFar
'Aureostriata' (*tardiva*)	see *H.* 'Inaho'
'Austin Dickinson' (v)	ECtt EMic IBal LRHS SSien
'Autumn Frost' (Shadowland Series) (v)	EMic IBal NSue
'Avocado'	CBdn ELon EMic EWTr IBal NLar NSue SSien WFar
'Azure Snow'	IBal
'Azuretini'	IBal
'Babbiing Brook'	IBal NSue
'Baby Blue' (Tardiana Group)	EMic
'Baby Blue Eyes'	EMic IBal NSue
'Baby Booties' (v)	IBal NSue
'Baby Bunting' ♀H7	IBal MHost NBro NLar NSue
'Baby Doll' (v)	IBal
'Baby Kim'	EMic
'Backyard Monster' (v)	IBal
'Bailey's Cream' (v)	IBal
'Baja White'	IBal SSien
'Bali-Hai'	IBal
'Ballerina'	IBal LRHS NSue
'Bam Bam Blue'	IBal
'Banana Muffins'	IBal
'Band of Gold'	EMic IBal MHost
'Banyai's Dancing Girl'	EMic IBal
'Barbara Ann' (v) ♀H7	CBdn EBee EMic IBal ITim MHost NGdn SSien
'Barbara May'	IBal
'Barney Fife'	IBal
'Bashful' **new**	NSue
'Battle Star' (v)	IBal NSue SSien
'Beach Boy' (v)	CBdn IBal MHost MNrw NLar NSue
'Bea's Colossus'	IBal
'Beauty Little Blue'	IBal NSue
'Beauty Substance'	IBal SSien
'Beckoning'	EMic IBal MHost NSue
'Bedazzled' (v)	IBal
'Bedford Blue'	CBdn EMic IBal MHost
'Bedford Rise and Shine' (v)	EMic ESwi IBal LRHS MHost
'Bedford Wakey-Wakey'	IBal MHost
'Behemoth'	IBal NSue
'Bell Bottom Blues'	IBal
bella	see *H. crassifolia*
'Bells of Edinburgh'	IBal SSien
'Ben Vernooij' (v)	CBdn IBal SSien
'Bennie McRae'	IBal
'Best of Twenty'	IBal NSue
'Betcher's Blue'	EMic IBal
'Betsy King'	CMac MRav NLar
'Bette Davis Eyes'	IBal
'Betty'	IBal MHost NSue
'Beyond Glory' (v) **new**	EMic
'Biddy's Blue'	IBal
'Big Boy' (*montana*)	EWTr IBal LRHS
'Big Daddy' (*sieboldiana* hybrid) (v) ♀H7	Widely available
'Big John' (*sieboldiana*)	IBal NSue
'Big Mama'	EMic IBal MBNS MNrw NGdn NSue SSien

'Big Top'	IBal SSien
'Bigfoot'	IBal
'Biggie'	CBdn IBal
'Bill Brinka' (v)	IBal SSien
'Bill Dress's Blue'	EMic SSien
'Birchwood Blue Beauty'	IBal
'Birchwood Gem'	IBal
§ 'Birchwood Parky's Gold'	EBee ECtt EMic EPfP GMaP IBal MHost NGdn NHol NLar SSien
'Birchwood Ruffled Queen'	EMic SSien
'Bitsy Gold'	NSue
'Bitsy Green'	NSue
'Bix Blues'	IBal
'Black Beauty'	IBal
'Black Hills'	EMic IBal
'Blackfoot'	IBal
'Blackjack' (*sieboldiana*)	IBal SSien WFar
'Blarney Stone'	IBal SSien
'Blaue Venus'	IBal
'Blaugold'	CBdn
'Blaze of Glory'	IBal
'Blazing Saddles' (v)	CBdn EMic IBal SSien
'Blonde Elf'	EMic IBal MPnt NGdn NHol
'Blue Angel' misapplied	see *H. sieboldiana* var. *elegans*
'Blue Angel' (*sieboldiana*) 𝕐H7	Widely available
'Blue Arrow' 𝕐H7	IBal LRHS MHol NSue
'Blue Baron'	EMic IBal
'Blue Belle' (Tardiana Group)	EMic IBal MHost NEoE NGdn
'Blue Blush' (Tardiana Group)	EMic IBal MHost NGdn
'Blue Boy'	EMic SSien
'Blue Cadet'	CMac CRos EBee EMic EPed EShb GBin GQue LRHS MHost NBir NGdn NLar NRHS NSue NWad SSien WFar
'Blue Canoe'	IBal MHost
'Blue Cascade'	EMic IBal NSue
'Blue Chip'	EMic
'Blue Circle' PBR	IBal
'Blue Clown'	IBal
'Blue Cup' (*sieboldiana*)	MRav SRms
'Blue Danube' (Tardiana Group)	EMic IBal MHost
'Blue Diamond' (Tardiana Group)	EMic LRHS NSue WFar
'Blue Dimples' (Tardiana Group)	ECtt IBal MHost
'Blue Dolphin'	IBal SSien
'Blue Edger'	IBal MHost NBir SSien
'Blue Eyes'	EMic
'Blue Flame'	ECtt EMic IBal
'Blue Frost'	IBal
'Blue Haired Lady'	IBal
'Blue Hawaii'	CBdn IBal NSue SSien
'Blue Heart' (*sieboldiana*)	ECha EMic IBal
'Blue Ice' (Tardiana Group)	NSue SSien
'Blue Impression'	EMic
'Blue Ivory' (v)	EBee ECtt ELon EMor NSue SPad WWtn
'Blue Jay' (Tardiana Group)	EMic IBal
'Blue Lady'	EMic IBal
'Blue Magic' **new**	MHost
'Blue Mammoth' (*sieboldiana*)	CBdn EMic IBal NLar NSue SSien
'Blue Maui'	IBal
'Blue Monday'	EMic
'Blue Moon' (Tardiana Group)	EMic GKev IBal MHost NGdn NLar SSien

'Blue Mountains'	IBal
'Blue Mouse Ears' 𝕐H7	Widely available
'Blue River' (v)	EMic IBal
'Blue Seer' (*sieboldiana*)	EMic SSien
'Blue Shadows' (*tokudama*) (v)	ESwi NLar SSien WFar
'Blue Skies' (Tardiana Group)	IBal MHost
'Blue Sliver' **new**	SSien
'Blue Splendor' (Tardiana Group)	IBal
'Blue Umbrellas' (*sieboldiana* hybrid)	ECtt ELan EPfP GMaP IBal LRHS MHost NGdn NLar SSien
'Blue Vision'	ECtt IBal
'Blue Wedgwood' (Tardiana Group)	ELan EMic GQue IBal LRHS MHol MHost MWat NGdn SCob SSien
'Blue Wonder'	IBal
'Blue Wu'	EMic IBal
'Blueberry à la Mode'	IBal
'Blueberry Cobbler'	IBal MHost
'Blueberry Muffin'	CBdn EMic MHost NSue
'Blueberry Tart'	IBal
'Bluetooth'	IBal
'Bob Deane' (v)	EMic IBal SSien
'Bob Olson' (v)	ESwi IBal MHost SSien WFar
'Bobbie Sue' (v)	IBal SSien
'Bobcat'	IBal
'Bogie and Bacall' (v)	IBal
'Bold Edger' (v)	CBdn EMic IBal
'Bold Intrigue' (v)	IBal
'Bold Ribbons' (v)	EMic SSien
'Bolt out of the Blue'	EMic
'Bonanza'	EMic
'Bonfire' **new**	EMic
'Boracay'	IBal
'Border Bandit' (v)	EHyd IBal LRHS
'Border Favorite'	EMic
'Border Street' (v)	SSien
§ 'Borwick Beauty' (*sieboldiana*) (v)	ELon EMic IBal LSou NGdn SSien
'Bottom Line' (v)	IBal
'Bountiful'	EMic IBal NSue
'Boyz Toy'	EMic IBal NSue
'Brandywine'	IBal
'Brash and Sassy'	IBal
'Brave Amherst' (v)	IBal
'Brenda's Beauty' (v)	EMic IBal
'Bressingham Blue'	CRos ECtt ELon IBal LRHS MHost MRav NLar SPer SWvt WFar
'Bridal Falls' PBR (v)	CBdn IBal NSue SSien
'Bridal Veil'	EMic IBal
'Bridegroom'	EMic ESwi IBal SSien
'Bridgeville'	IBal
'Brigadier'	IBal
'Brigham Blue'	IBal
'Bright Glow' (Tardiana Group)	IBal
'Bright Lights' (*tokudama*) (v)	EMic NGdn SSien WFar
'Bright Star' (v)	IBal NSue SSien
'Brim Cup' (v)	CDor ECtt ELon EPfP EShb GAbr MBNS MNrw NBro NGdn SSien
'Broadband' (v)	IBal
'Broadway' (v)	IBal
'Bronx Bomber' (v)	IBal NSue
'Brooke'	EMic IBal
'Brother Ronald' (Tardiana Group)	EMic IBal LRHS MHost
'Brother Stefan'	CBdn EMic IBal MHost NSue SSien
'Brutus'	IBal

'Buckshaw Blue'	EMic IBal MHost NBir NEoE NGdn SSien WHrl
'Bulletproof'	IBal
'Bumblebee' **new**	SSien
'Bunchoko'	IBal
'Burke's Dwarf'	IBal
'Butter Rim' (*sieboldii*) (v)	IBal
'Buttered Popcorn' (v) **new**	SSien
'Cally Atom'	IBal MHost
'Cally Colossus'	IBal MHost
I 'Cally Strain' (*nigrescens*)	MHer
'Cally White' (*nigrescens*)	IBal MHost
'Calypso' (v)	EHyd EMic IBal LRHS MNrw NGdn NSue WFar
'Camelot' (Tardiana Group)	IBal LRHS MHost NGdn NSue
'Camouflage'	EMic IBal MHost
'Canadian Blue'	ECtt EMic IBal LPot LSou NLar NSue SPeP SSien WFar
'Candle Wax'	IBal MHost
'Candy Dish'	IBal NSue
'Candy Hearts'	CSam EMic IBal SSien
capitata B&SWJ 588	WCru
'Captain Kirk' (v) ♀H7	CBdn EHyd EMic ESwi IBal LRHS MHost NGdn NSue SSien WFar
'Captain's Adventure' (v)	EMic IBal LCro LOPS NSue SSien WFar
caput-avis	see *H. kikutii* var. *caput-avis*
'Carder Blue'	EMic IBal
'Carl' **new**	SSien
'Carnival' (v)	EHyd ELan EMic IBal LRHS NGdn NHpl SPoG SSien
'Carol' (*fortunei*) (v)	IBal MHost NGdn NLar NSue SSien
'Carolina Blue'	CBdn IBal
'Carolina Sunshine' (v)	SSien
'Carousel' (v)	EMic IBal SSien
'Carrie' (*sieboldii*) (v)	EMic NSue
'Cascades' (v)	EMic IBal NGdn SSien
'Cathedral Windows' (v) ♀H7	CLAP EMic IBal MHost NSue SSien
'Catherine'	ELon EMic IBal NLar NSue SSien WFar
'Cat's Eyes' (*venusta*) (v)	SSien
'Cavalcade' (v)	EMic
'Celebration' (v)	ELan EMic IBal
'Celestial'	IBal
'Celtic Dancer'	EMic IBal SSien
'Celtic Uplands'	EMic IBal
'Center of Attention'	EMic IBal NGdn SSien
'Centerfold'	NSue
'Cha Cha Cha'	IBal
'Chabo-unazuki' (*kikutii* var. *caput-avis*)	EMic
'Chain Lightning' (v)	EMic IBal NSue
'Challenger'	EMic
'Chameleon' (v)	EMic
'Champagne Toast' (v)	IBal NSue
'Change of Tradition' (*lancifolia*) (v)	EMic
'Chantilly Lace' (v)	EMic IBal
'Chariots of Fire' (v)	IBal
'Chartreuse Waves'	IBal
'Cheatin' Heart'	EMic IBal NSue WFar
'Chelsea Babe' (*fortunei*) (v)	IBal MHost SSien
'Cherish' ♀H7	NGdn NHpl WFar
'Cherokee' (v)	IBal
'Cherry Berry' (v)	CLAP CWGN ECtt EMor EShb GBin IBal LRHS MBNS MHol MHost MNrw NBro NEoE NGdn NLar NRHS NSue NWad SCob SPoG SSien WFar WWtn
'Cherry Flip' **new**	SSien

'Cherry Tart'	IBal NSue SSien
'Cherub' (v)	EMic IBal LRHS SSien
'Chesapeake Bay'	EMic IBal NSue
'Chesterland Gold'	IBal
'Chief Sitting Bull'	IBal
'Childhood Sweetheart' (v)	IBal NSue
'China Girl'	EMic IBal
'Chinese Sunrise' (v) ♀H7	CWCL EMic GBin GWyn IBal SRms SSien
'Chionea' (v)	EThi IBal
'Chiquita'	IBal
'Chi-town Classic' (v)	IBal
'Chodai Ginba'	IBal
§ 'Chōkō-nishiki' (*montana*) (v)	EHyd IBal LRHS NGdn NRHS SSien
'Choo Choo Train'	EMic SSien
'Chopsticks'	EMic SSien
'Christmas Candy'[PBR]	ECtt EMic IBal MHost NSue SSien
'Christmas Charm' (v)	IBal
'Christmas Cookies'	IBal SSien
'Christmas Island' **new**	NSue
'Christmas Pageant' (v)	EMic IBal
'Christmas Tree' (v) ♀H7	ECtt EHyd EMic EMor ESwi IBal LRHS MHost NGdn NLar NRHS NSue SSien
'Church Mouse'	CBdn EMic IBal NSue SSien
'Cinderella'	EMic IBal
'Cinnamon Sticks'	IBal NSue
'Citation' (v)	IBal
'City Lights'	ECtt EHyd EMic LRHS NRHS
'City Slicker' (v)	IBal
clausa	EMic
- var. ***normalis***	IBal NBir NGdn NLar
'Clear Fork River Valley'	EMic IBal SSien
'Clifford's Forest Fire'	ECtt EHyd EMic IBal LRHS NLar SSien WFar
'Clifford's Stingray' (v)	EMic IBal NSue SSien
'Climax' (v) ♀H7	EMic EPfP IBal SSien
'Cloudburst'	EMic IBal
'Clovelly'	IBal
'Clown's Collar' (v)	EMic IBal SSien
'Coal Miner'	IBal NSue SSien
'Coast to Coast' (Shadowland Series) **new**	SSien
'Coconut Custard'	EMic NSue
'Cody'	IBal NSue
'Cold Heart'	EMic IBal
'Collector's Banner'	IBal
'Collector's Choice'	IBal NSue
'Color à la Mode' (v)	IBal
'Color Festival' (v)	CBod CDor ELon EMic IBal NLar NSue SSien WFar
'Color Glory'	see *H.* 'Borwick Beauty'
'Colored Hulk' (v)	EMic IBal SSien
'Colossal'	EMic IBal
'Columbus Circle' (v)	EMic IBal
'Con Te Partiro' (v)	CBdn MHost NSue SSien WFar
'Confused Angel' (v)	IBal
'Cookie Crumbs' (v)	EMic IBal NSue
'Cool as a Cucumber' (v)	IBal NSue
'Coquette' (v)	EMic GAbr IBal
'Corkscrew'	NSue
'Corn Belt' (v)	EMic IBal
'Corn Muffins'	EMic
'Corona' (v)	EMic
'Corryvreckan'	IBal MHost
'Cotillion' (v)	CBdn EMic GEdr IBal NSue
'Count Your Blessings' (v)	EMic IBal
'Country Mouse' (v)	EMic GEdr IBal NHpl NSue SPoG SSien WFar WTor

'County Park'	EMic IBal MHost
'Cowrie' (v)	IBal
'Cracker Crumbs' (v) ♀H7	CBdn EMic GEdr IBal ITim LRHS MNrw NHpl NSla NSue SSien WAbe WCot WFar
'Craig's Temptation'	EHyd IBal LRHS NRHS NSue
'Cranberry Wine'	IBal
§ ***crassifolia***	EMic IBal LRHS XLum
'Cream Cheese' (v)	IBal
'Cream Delight' (*undulata*)	see *H. undulata* var. *undulata*
'Crepe Soul' (v)	IBal NSue
'Crepe Suzette' (v)	IBal SSien
'Crested Reef'	EMic SSien
'Crested Surf' (v)	EMic IBal
'Crinoline Petticoats'	IBal
§ ***crispula*** (v)	EHyd EMic IBal LRHS MCot MRav NChi NRHS
'Crocodile Socks' (v)	IBal
'Crown Prince' (v)	IBal NGdn
'Crown Royalty'	EMic IBal
§ 'Crowned Imperial' (*fortunei*) (v)	EMic IBal
'Crumples' (*sieboldiana*)	IBal MHost
'Crusader' (v) ♀H7	CBdn ELon EMic IBal LRHS WFar
'Crystal Dixie'	EMic GBin IBal NSue SSien WFar
'Cumulonimbus'	IBal MHost
'Cup of Grace'	IBal
'Curlew' (Tardiana Group)	EMic IBal MHost
'Curls'	EMic IBal
'Curly Fries'	CBdn IBal NSue SSien
'Curtain Call'	IBal
'Cutting Edge'	EMic IBal NSue
'Cuyahoga' (v)	IBal
'Dab a Green'	IBal
'Dance with Me' (v)	EMic IBal
'Dancing in the Rain' (v)	CWGN NBro WFar
'Dancing Mouse' (v)	CBdn IBal NSue WFar
'Dancing Queen'	IBal NSue SSien
'Dark Shadows'	EMic IBal NGdn NSti WFar
'Dark Star' (v)	EMic IBal MHost NGdn
'Dark Victory'	EMic
'Dartmoor Forest'	IBal MHost
'Dawn'	EMic IBal MHost NSue NWad
'Dawn's Early Light'	EMic IBal
'Dax'	IBal
'Daybreak' ♀H7	EMic IBal NBro
'Day's End' (v)	EMic IBal
'Deane's Dream'	EMic IBal MHost SSien
'Decorata'	EMic
decorata var. ***normalis***	EMic
'Deep Blue Sea' ♀H7	CAby EMic IBal NSue
'Deep Pockets'	IBal
'Dee's Golden Jewel'	CBdn EMic
'Déjà Blu' (v)	EMic IBal NSue
'Deliverance'	EMic IBal NSue
'Delta Dawn' (v)	EMic IBal NGdn
'Delta Desire'	IBal
'Derek Coxs' **new**	EMic
'Desert Mouse'[PBR] (v)	GEdr IBal NSue
'Designer Genes'	IBal SSien WFar
'Devil's Advocate'	IBal
'Devon Blue' (Tardiana Group)	EMic IBal LRHS MHost NSue
'Devon Cloud' **new**	MHost
'Devon Desire' (*montana*)	IBal MHost NLar
'Devon Discovery'	IBal MHost
'Devon Giant'	EMic MHost SSien
'Devon Gold'	EMic GAbr IBal MHost SSien
'Devon Green' ♀H7	Widely available
'Devon Hills'	MHost
'Devon Mist'	IBal MHost
'Devon Tor'	IBal MHost
'Dew Drop' (v)	EMic
'Dewed Steel'	IBal SSien
'Diamond Tiara' (v)	EMic IBal LRHS MHost NBir NGdn NSue SSien
'Diamonds are Forever' (v)	IBal
'Diana Remembered'	EMic EMor IBal MHost NGdn NSue SSien WFar
'Dick Ward'	EMic IBal
'Dilithium Crystal'	IBal NSue WFar
'Dillie Perkeo'	IBal
'Dilys'	EMic MNrw
'Dimple'	EMic
'Dinky Donna' (v)	EMic IBal NHpl NSue
'Dinner Jacket' (v)	EHyd EMor IBal LRHS MHost SSien
'Dino' (v)	IBal
'Dixie Chick' (v)	EMic IBal LRHS NHpl NSue SSien
'Dixie Chickadee' (v)	EMic NSue SSien
'Dixie Cups'	CBdn
'Dixieland Heat'	IBal
'Doctor Fu Manchu'	IBal
'Domaine de Courson'	EMic IBal MHost NSue WFar
'Don Stevens' (v)	IBal LRHS SSien
'Dorothy'	EMic
'Dorset Blue' (Tardiana Group)	EMic IBal LRHS MHost SSien
'Dorset Charm' (Tardiana Group)	EMic MHost
'Dorset Flair' (Tardiana Group)	EMic IBal MHost
'Double D Cup' **new**	SSien
'Doubled Up'	CBdn IBal
'Doubloons'	EMic
'Dracula' **new**	MHost
'Dragon Tails' ♀H7	CBdn EHyd EMic GEdr IBal LRHS NHpl NRHS NSue WFar
'Dragon Warrior' (v)	IBal
'Drake's Tail'	IBal NLar
'Dream Queen' (v)	CBdn ECtt EMic EMor EWTr IBal LRHS LSun MHost NLar SPad SPalm SSien
'Dream Weaver' (v) ♀H7	ELon IBal IPot LRHS MNrw NBro NGdn NSue SPoG SSien WFar
'Dress Blues'	CMac EMic IBal
'Drip Drop' (v) **new**	SSien
'Drummer Boy'	EMic IBal MHost
'Duchess' (*nakaiana*) (v)	EMic IBal
'Duke of Cornwall' (v)	IBal
'DuPage Delight' (*sieboldiana*) (v)	EMic IBal NGdn NLar
'Dust Devil' (*fortunei*) (v)	IBal SSien
'Dusty Waters'	IBal
'Dutch Flame' (v)	CBdn NSue
'Eagle's Nest' (v)	IBal
'Early Times'	CBdn IBal MHost
'Earth Angel'[PBR] (v) ♀H7	CBdn EMic IBal MHost NGdn NSue
'Ebony Towers'	EMic IBal
'Eclipse' (v) **new**	CRos
'Eco Mirror' **new**	IBal
'Edge of Night'	EMic IBal
'Edwin Bibby'	EMic MHost
'El Capitan' (v)	EHyd EMic IBal LRHS
'El Niño'[PBR] (Tardiana Group) (v) ♀H7	CBdn CDor CWGN EMic EPfP IBal LRHS MHost MNrw NBro NGdn NLar NSue SPoG SSien WFar
§ 'Elata'	EMic
'Elatior' (*nigrescens*)	IBal LRHS
'Elbridge Gerry' (v)	IBal
'Eldorado'	see *H.* 'Frances Williams'

'Eleanor Lachman' (v)	EMic IBal NSue
'Eleanor Roosevelt'	IBal
'Electrocution' (v)	IBal NSue SSien
'Elegans'	see *H. sieboldiana* var. *elegans*
'Elephant Burgers'	EMic
'Elisabeth'	EMic IBal LSRN
'Elizabeth Campbell' (*fortunei*) (v)	EMic IBal MHost SSien
'Elkheart Lake'	EMic IBal SSien
'Ellen'	EMic
'Ellerbroek' (*fortunei*) (v)	EMic
'Elsley Runner'	IBal NSue
'Elvis Lives'	EMic IBal LRHS NGdn NLar NSue SSien
'Embroidery' (v)	EMic
'Emerald Carpet'	IBal NSue
'Emerald Charger' (v)	IBal
'Emerald Crown'	EMic IBal
'Emerald Edger' **new**	EMic MHost
'Emerald Emperor'	IBal SSien
'Emerald Necklace' (v)	EMic IBal
'Emerald Paisley'	IBal
'Emerald Ruff Cut'	IBal
'Emerald Tiara' (v)	EHyd EMic IBal LRHS MHost NLar NSue SSien WFar
'Emeralds and Rubies'	EMic IBal NSue SSien
'Emily Dickinson' (v)	ECtt EMic IBal LRHS
'Emma' (v) **new**	SSien
'Empress Wu' PBR	Widely available
'Enchiladas' (v) **new**	SSien
'Encore'	IBal
'Enduring Beacon' **new**	NSue
'English Sunrise' (Tardiana Group)	IBal
'Enterprise' (v)	EMic IBal NGdn NSue SSien
'Eola Sapphire'	EMic IBal
'Eos'	IBal NLar
'Eric Smith' (Tardiana Group)	EMic IBal MHost SHar WFar
'Eric Smith Gold'	GKev
'Eric's Gold'	IBal MHost
'Erie Magic' (v)	EMic IBal SSien
'Eskimo Pie' (v)	WFar
'Essence of Summer'	EMic IBal
'Eternal Flame'	CBdn NSue SSien
'Everlasting Love' (v)	EMic IBal
'Excitation'	EMic IBal
'Exotic Presentation' (v)	EMic IBal
'Extasy' (v)	EMic IBal NGdn NSue WFar
'Eye Candy' (v)	IBal
'Eye Catcher'	EMic SSien
'Eye Declare' (v)	IBal
'Fair Maiden' (v)	NHpl
'Faith'	EMic SSien
'Faithful Heart' (v)	EMic IBal NSue
'Fall Dazzler' (v)	IBal SSien
'Fall Emerald'	EMic
'Fallen Angel'	EMic
'Fan Dance' (v)	IBal
'Fantabulous' (v)	IBal SSien
'Fantasy Island' (v)	CBdn IBal MHost NSue SSien WFar
'Fat Boy'	IBal
'Fat Cat' **new**	SSien
'Fatal Attraction'	IBal SSien
'Feather Boa'	CBdn EMic IBal LRHS NSue WFar
'Feng Shui'	IBal
'Fenman's Fascination'	EMic IBal
'Fiesta' (v)	IBal SSien
'Final Summation' (v)	EMic IBal NSue
'Final Victory' (v)	IBal

'Finlandia'	IBal
'Fire and Ice' (v) ♀H7	Widely available
'Fire Island' ♀H7	CBdn ECtt EHyd ELan ELon EMic EMor EPfP IBal LRHS MHost MNrw NLar NPoe NSue SPeP SSien WCot
'Fire Opal' (v)	IBal
'Firefly' (v)	IBal
'Fireplace' (v)	IBal
'Fireworks' (v) ♀H7	CBdn CBod ECtt EMor EPfP GEdr LBuc MBNS MHol MNrw NBro NCou NGdn SMad WCot
'Firn Line' (v)	CBdn IBal SSien
'First Blush' **new**	NSue
'First Frost' (v) ♀H7	CBdn CRos ECtt EHyd ELon EMic EMor EPfP IBal LRHS MHost MNrw NGdn NLar NRHS NSue SPoG SSien
'First Love' (*montana*)	CBdn EMic IBal NSue
'First Mate' (v)	IBal NSue SSien
'Five O'Clock Shadow' (v)	IBal
'Five O'Clock Somewhere' (v)	IBal
'Flamenco Mouse' **new**	NSue
'Flapjack' (v)	IBal
'Fleet Week'	EMic IBal
'Flemish Angel' (v)	IBal NSue SSien
'Flemish Design'	IBal
'Flemish Gold'	IBal
'Flemish Master' (v)	IBal SSien
'Flemish Sky'	EMic IBal NGdn NLar
'Flemish Steel'	IBal
'Floradora'	EMic IBal NSue
'Floratini'	NSue
'Flower Power'	CBdn
'Fluted Fountain'	EMic
'Fog Light'	IBal
'Fool's Gold' (*fortunei*)	EMic IBal
'Forbidden Fruit' PBR (v)	CBdn CBod ELan EMic EMor IBal MHost NSue SSien
'Forest Shadows'	EMic IBal
'Formal Attire' (*sieboldiana* hybrid) (v) ♀H7	EMic IBal LRHS
'Forncett Frances' (v)	IBal MHost
'Fortis'	see *H. undulata* var. *erromena*
fortunei	EMic GKev GWyn WFar
§ - var. ***albopicta*** (v)	CBcs CSam ECha ELan EMic EPfP GMaP GWyn LCro LPot LRHS MHost MRav NChi NLar NRHS SPer SRms SSien WBrk WFar WHoo
- - f. ***aurea***	CMac ECha EMic MHost MMuc NLar SRms SSien WFar WHal
- - - dwarf	EMic
§ - var. ***aureomarginata*** (v) ♀H7	CRos CSam CTri ECha ELan ELon EMic EPfP EShb GMaP IBal LRHS MHost MMuc NGdn NLar NRHS SCob SEND SPer SPlb SSien WFar
- var. ***gigantea***	see *H. montana*
- var. ***hyacinthina***	EMic EPfP IBal LRHS MRav NGdn NLar XLum
- - variegated	see *H.* 'Crowned Imperial'
- var. ***stenantha***	EMic
'Fountain'	CBdn
'Fountain of Youth' (*kikutii*)	IBal
'Fourteen Carats'	EMic IBal
'Fourth of July'	NSue
'Foxfire Palm Sunday' (v)	IBal
'Fragrant Blue'	CTsd EHyd ELan ELon IBal LBuc LRHS MHost NBro NGdn NHpl SPalm SPoG XLum

'Fragrant Blue Ribbons' (v)	EMic IBal
'Fragrant Bouquet' (v) ♀H7	ECtt ELan EMic IBal LRHS LSRN MHost NGdn NHol NLar NSue SSien WFar
'Fragrant Dream'	CBdn EHyd EMic IBal LRHS NLar NSue
'Fragrant Fire'	CBdn EMic IBal
'Fragrant Gold'	EMic
'Fragrant King'	IBal
'Fragrant Queen' PBR (v)	EMic IBal NSue SSien
'Fragrant Star'	EMic IBal MHost
'Fragrant Surprise' (v)	NSue
'Fran Godfrey'	EMic IBal MHost SSien
'Francee' (*fortunei*) (v) ♀H7	Widely available
§ 'Frances Williams' (*sieboldiana*) (v) ♀H7	Widely available
'Frances Williams Improved' (*sieboldiana*) (v)	EPfP
'Francheska' (v)	EMic IBal
'Frank Lloyd Wright'	IBal
'Free Jazz' (v)	IBal
'Fresh' (v)	EMic IBal
'Fried Bananas'	CBod EMic IBal ITim SSien WWtn
'Fried Green Tomatoes'	EMic IBal NLar
'Friends' (v)	EMic NSue SSien
'Fringe Benefit' (v)	EMic MHost SSien
'Frisian Pride'	EMic IBal NSue
'Frisian Waving Steel'	EMic IBal
'Frosted Dimples'	EMic IBal MHost
'Frosted Frolic' (v)	EMic IBal SSien WFar
'Frosted Jade' (v) ♀H7	EMic EPfP IBal LRHS MMuc NLar
'Frosted June'	EMic IBal
'Frosted Lollipop' (v)	IBal
'Frosted Mini Hearts'	IBal
'Frosted Mouse Ears' PBR	CBdn IBal NHpl NSue SSien
'Frozen Margarita'	CBdn EMic IBal NLar
'Fruit Punch'	EMic IBal MHost SSien
'Fujibotan' (v)	EMic IBal
'Fukurin-Fu' (*venusta*) (v)	GEdr
'Fulda'	EMic IBal
'Full Moon'	EMic
'Funky Monkey'	EMic IBal SSien
'Funny Frolic' (v)	IBal
'Funny Mouse' (v)	CBdn EMic IBal NHpl NSue SSien WFar
'Futura' (v)	IBal
'Gaiety' (v)	ECtt EHyd EMic IBal LRHS
'Gaijin' (v)	EMic IBal NSue
'Garden Party' (v)	IBal SSien
'Garnet Prince'	CBdn IBal
'Gay Blade' (v)	IBal LPla
'Gay Feather' (v)	SSien
'Gay Search' (v)	IBal MHost
'Geisha' (v)	IBal LRHS NEoE NGdn NSue
'Geisha Satin Ripples'	IBal
'Gemstone'	NSue
'Gene's Joy'	EMic
'Gentle Giant'	IBal
'Gentle Spirit' (v)	IBal
'George M. Dallas' (v)	IBal
'George Smith' (*sieboldiana*)	CBdn EMic IBal MHost SSien
'Georgia Sweetheart' (v)	IBal SSien
'Ghost Spirit' (v)	EBee IBal NSue SSien WFar
'Ghostmaster' (v)	IBal WFar
'Giantland Mouse Cheese'	IBal NSue
'Giantland Sunny Mouse Ears'	CBdn IBal NSue SSien
'Gig Harbor'	IBal
'Gigantea' (*sieboldiana*)	see *H.* 'Elata'
'Gilded Teacup' (v)	NSue
'Gilt by Association'	EMic IBal
'Gilt Edge' (*sieboldiana*) (v)	EMic
'Gin and Tonic' (v)	NSue
'Gingee'	EMic IBal SSien
'Ginko Craig' (v) ♀H7	CMac CRos ECha EHyd ELan EMic EPfP GKev GMaP IBal LRHS MRav NBir NGdn NLar NRHS NSti SPer SPoG SSien WFar
'Ginrei'	IBal
'Ginsu Knife' (v)	EMic IBal
'Glacial Towers' (v)	IBal SSien
'Glad Rags' (v)	IBal
'Glad Tidings'	IBal
'Glamour'	EMic IBal NSue SSien
'Glass Hearts'	EMic IBal
glauca	see *H. sieboldiana* var. *elegans*
'Glitter'	EMic IBal
'Glockenspiel'	EMic IBal MHost
I 'Gloriosa' (*fortunei*) (v)	IBal LRHS NSue
'Glory'	CBdn IBal
'Glory Hallelujah'	CBdn EMic IBal
'Goddess of Athena' (*decorata*) (v)	IBal
'Gold Bug' **new**	SSien
'Gold Drop' (*venusta* hybrid)	EMic IBal NHol NSue
'Gold Edger'	CDor CMac CRos EHyd ELan EMic EPfP EShb GMaP IBal LRHS MHost MRav NBir NGdn NLar NRHS NSti WFar
'Gold Edger Surprise' (v)	EMic
'Gold Flush' (*ventricosa*)	EMic
§ 'Gold Haze' (*fortunei*)	IBal MHost NBir SSien
'Gold Leaf' (*fortunei*)	IBal MHost
'Gold Pressed Latinum'	IBal
'Gold Regal'	EHyd EMic IBal LRHS WFar
'Gold Rush'	IBal MHost
'Gold Standard' (*fortunei*) (v) ♀H7	Widely available
'Goldbrook' (v)	EMic IBal MHost
'Goldbrook Galleon'	IBal
'Goldbrook Gayle' (v)	MHost
'Goldbrook Gaynor'	IBal MHost
'Goldbrook Genie'	CBdn IBal MHost
'Goldbrook Girl'	IBal MHost
'Goldbrook Glamour' (v)	IBal MHost SSien
'Goldbrook Gleam' (v)	IBal MHost
'Goldbrook Glimmer' (Tardiana Group) (v)	IBal LRHS MHost
'Goldbrook Glory'	EMic IBal MHost
'Goldbrook Gold'	IBal MHost
'Goldbrook Good Gracious' (v)	IBal
'Goldbrook Grace'	IBal MHost
'Goldbrook Gratis' (v)	IBal MHost
'Goldbrook Grayling'	ECtt EMic IBal LRHS MHost NRHS
'Goldbrook Grebe'	IBal MHost
'Goldbrook Greengage' (v)	IBal MHost
'Goldbrook Greenheart'	IBal
'Golden Age'	see *H.* 'Gold Haze'
'Golden Fountain'	EMic
'Golden Friendship'	SSien
'Golden Gate'	IBal
'Golden Goal'	IBal
'Golden Guernsey' (v)	EMic
'Golden Isle'	EMic IBal MHost
'Golden Meadows' PBR (*sieboldiana*)	CBdn CDor ECtt EMic IBal NGdn NSue SSien WFar
'Golden Medallion' (*tokudama*)	CRos ECtt EHyd EMic LRHS NGdn NRHS WFar

'Golden Nakaiana'	see *H.* 'Birchwood Parky's Gold'
'Golden' (*nakaiana*)	see *H.* 'Birchwood Parky's Gold'
'Golden Needles' (v)	IBal NSue
'Golden Oriole'	EMic LRHS MHost
'Golden Prayers' (*tokudama*)	ECtt ELan MRav NBir NBro NGdn NLar WFar WHal WSHC
'Golden Regal'	WFar
'Golden Scepter'	EMic IBal LRHS MHost SRms SSien WFar
'Golden Spades'	EMic NSue
'Golden Spider'	EMic MHost SSien
'Golden Sunburst' (*sieboldiana*)	ECtt NGdn NLar XLum
'Golden Sweetie'	EMic
'Golden Tiara' (v) 🏆H7	Widely available
'Golden Tusk'	IBal
'Golden Waffles'	ECtt EMic NSue SPeP
'Goldene Woge' **new**	SSien
'Goldpfeil'	MHost
'Goldsmith'	EMic MHost
'Gone Fishin'' (v)	IBal
'Gone with the Wind' (v)	IBal
'Goober'	IBal MHost
'Good as Gold'	CBdn EMic
'Goodness Gracious' (v)	IBal
'Gorgeous George'	IBal
'Gosan' (*tardiva*)	EMic
'Gosan Gold Midget'	EMic
'Gosan Leather Strap'	ESwi IBal
'Gosan Mina'	EMic
'Gosan Shining'	EMic
gracillima	IBal NRya NWad
'Granary Gold' (*fortunei*)	MHost
'Grand Canyon'	EMic SSien
'Grand Finale'	IBal
'Grand Marquee' (v)	EMic IBal NGdn NLar WFar
'Grand Master'	IBal
'Grand Prize' (v)	EMic IBal NSue SSien
'Grand Rapids'	EMic IBal
'Grand Slam'	IBal
'Grand Tiara' (v)	EHyd EMic IBal LRHS MHost NGdn NSue SSien
'Grand Total'	IBal
'Grant Park'	IBal
'Grape Fizz'	IBal
'Gray Cole' (*sieboldiana*)	EMic IBal ITim
'Great Arrival'	EMic IBal
'Great Escape' PBR (v)	CBdn EMic IBal SSien
'Great Expectations' (*sieboldiana*) (v)	CDor CMac CRos EHyd ELan EMic EPfP LRHS LSRN MBNS MHer MHost MNrw NBro NGdn NHpl NLar NRHS SCob SPoG SSien WFar WTyc
'Great Lakes Gold'	IBal
'Green Acres' (*montana*)	CBdn EMic IBal LEdu WFar
'Green Angel' (*sieboldiana*)	IBal
'Green Cheese'	IBal
'Green Dwarf'	WFar
'Green Eyes' (*sieboldii*) (v)	EMic IBal WFar
'Green Fountain' (*kikutii*)	EMic IBal
'Green Gold' (*fortunei*) (v)	EMic
'Green Lama'	EMic IBal
'Green Mouse Ears'	CBdn IBal NHpl NSue SSien WFar
'Green Piecrust'	EMic
'Green Platter'	EMic
'Green Sheen'	EMic
'Green Sleeve' **new**	EMic
'Green Velveteen'	IBal
'Green with Envy' (v) 🏆H7	EMic IBal MHost NSue NWad
'Greenie Weenie Bikini'	NSue
'Greensleeves' (v)	IBal
'Grey Ghost'	EMic
'Grey Glacier' (v)	IBal
'Grey Goose' (Tardiana Group)	EMic MHost
'Groo Bloo'	IBal
'Ground Master' (v)	CMac ECtt EHyd ELan EPfP GMaP LRHS MRav NBro NGdn NLar NSti WFar
'Ground Sulphur'	EMic NSue SSien
'Grover Cleveland'	IBal
'Grünherz'	IBal
'Grunspecht' (Tardiana Group)	IBal
'Guacamole' (v) 🏆H7	CAby CBcs CBdn CDor CRos ECha ECtt EHyd ELon EMic EMor EPfP EWTr GBin IBal LRHS MHost NGdn NLar NRHS SCob SPoG SSien WFar
'Guardian Angel' (*sieboldiana*) 🏆H7	EMic IBal NSue SSien
'Gum Drop'	EMic
'Gun Metal Blue'	IBal
'Gunther's Prize' (v)	IBal
'Gunther's Rim' (v)	IBal
'Gypsy Rose' 🏆H7	CBdn EMic EShb IBal LRHS NGdn NLar NSue SSien WFar
'Hacksaw'	EMic IBal SSien
'Hadspen Blue' (Tardiana Group) 🏆H7	CSBt CWCL EBee ELan EMic EPfP GMaP IBal LRHS MBrN MGos MHost MRav NBir NBro NGdn NHol NLar NSti SCob SPer SPoG SSien WSpi
'Hadspen Hawk' (Tardiana Group)	IBal
'Hadspen Heron' (Tardiana Group)	EMic IBal NWad XLum
'Hadspen Honey'	EHyd LRHS
'Hadspen Nymphaea'	IBal
'Hadspen Rainbow'	EMic IBal
'Hadspen Samphire'	EMic IBal NBir NBro
'Hadspen White' (*fortunei*)	EMic IBal NLar
'Haku-chu-han' (*sieboldii*) (v)	EMic NHpl
'Hakujima' (*sieboldii*)	IBal NSue
'Hakumuo' (v)	IBal SSien
§ 'Halcyon' (Tardiana Group) 🏆H7	Widely available
'Half and Half'	CBdn EMic IBal NSue SSien
'Hampshire County' (v)	EMic IBal SSien
'Hands Up' PBR (v)	CBdn EMic EPfP IBal MHost NSue SSien
'Hanky Panky' (v)	CBdn IBal NGdn NSti NSue SSien WFar
'Hannibal Hamlin' (v)	IBal
'Happily Ever After' (v)	IBal
'Happiness' (Tardiana Group)	EMic IBal MHost MRav SSien
'Happy Camper' (v)	IBal
'Happy Dayz' (v)	IBal SSien
'Happy Hearts'	EMic MHost
'Happy Valley' (v)	IBal NSue
'Harmony' (Tardiana Group)	EMic MHost
'Harpoon' (v)	EMic
'Harriette Ward'	IBal
'Harry van de Laar'	EMic IBal SSien
'Harry van Trier'	EMic GWyn MHost
'Hart's Tongue'	IBal
'Harvest Delight'	EMic
'Harvest Glow'	IBal

'Hawkeye' (v)	IBal
'Hazel'	EMic IBal
'Heart and Soul' (v)	EMic IBal NSue
'Heart Broken'	IBal
'Heart of Chan'	IBal
'Heart Throb'	EMic
'Heartbeat' (v)	NSue SSien
'Heartleaf'	EMic
'Heart's Content' (v)	IBal
'Heartsong' (v)	CBdn EMic IBal LRHS
'Heat Wave'PBR (v)	EMic IBal SSien
'Heavenly Beginnings' (v)	IBal
'Heavenly Tiara' (v)	NSue SSien
'Heavy Duty'	IBal SSien
'Heideturm'	IBal
'Helen Doriot' (*sieboldiana*)	EMic IBal
'Helen Field Fischer' (*fortunei*)	IBal NLar
helonioides f. ***albopicta*** misapplied	see *H. rohdeifolia*
'Herifu' (v)	EMic
'Hertha' (v)	EMic
'Hida-no-hana' (*montana*) (v)	IBal
'Hidden Cove' (v)	IBal NSue SSien
'Hidden Treasure' (v)	IBal
'Hideout' (v)	IBal NSue
'High Kicker'	IBal
'High Noon'	SSien
'High Society' (v)	EPfP IBal MNrw NHpl NSue SSien
'High Tide'	IBal
'Hi-ho Silver' (v)	EMic IBal NSue SSien
'Hilda Wassman' (v)	IBal
'Hillbilly Blues' (v)	NSue
'Hippodrome' (v)	EMic IBal
'Hirao Elite'	EMic IBal
'Hirao Majesty'	IBal
'Hirao Supreme'	EMic IBal
'His Honor' (v)	EMic IBal
'Holar Purple Flash' **new**	IBal
'Hollywood Lights' (v)	EMic EPfP IBal NGdn NSue
'Holstein'	see *H.* 'Halcyon'
'Holy Molé' (v)	EMic IBal
'Holy Mouse Ears'PBR	CBdn IBal NSue SSien
'Honey Moon'	EMic IBal SSien
'Honeybells'	CBcs CMac EBee ECha EHyd ELan EMic EPfP GBin IBal LEdu LRHS MCot MHost MRav NBid NGdn NSti SPer WCAu WFar XLum
'Honeysong' (v)	CBdn EMic IBal SSien
'Hoosier Dome'	EMic
'Hoosier Harmony' (v)	EMic
'Hope' (v)	EMic NLar
'Hot Air Balloon'	IBal SSien
'Hotcakes'	EMic IBal
'Hudson Bay' (Shadowland Series) (v)	EMic IBal
'Humpback Whale'	IBal NSue SSien
'Hush Puppie'	EMic IBal MHost MNrw NHpl NSue SSien WFar
'Hyacintha Variegata' (*fortunei*) (v)	CMac
'Hydon Gleam'	EMic IBal MHost NSue
'Hydon Sunset'	CNor CRos EBee ECtt EHyd EMic GEdr IBal LRHS MHost MNrw NBir NLar NRHS NRya NSti NSue SSien WHal
hypoleuca	IBal
'Hyuga-urajiro' (v)	EMic IBal NSue SSien WFar
'Ice Cream' (*cathayana*) (v)	IBal LRHS NGdn
'Ice Cube' (v)	IBal SSien
'Ice Prancer'	EMic IBal
'Iced Lemon' (v)	EMic GEdr IBal MHost NHpl NSue SSien WFar
'Illicit Affair'	ECtt EMic IBal NHpl NSue SSien
'Imp' (v)	EMic IBal
§ 'Inaho'	LRHS NSue
'Inca Gold'	IBal NSue
'Incoming'	IBal
'Independence' (v)	EBee EMic IBal LRHS MHost NBro NSue SPoG SSien WFar
'Independence Day' (v)	EMic
'Inniswood' (v)	CDor CWCL ECtt EMic IBal MBNS NBro NGdn NLar NSti SSien WFar
'Invincible'	CDor ECtt EMic EMor IBal MHost NBid NGdn NLar SSien WFar
'Invincible Spirit'	IBal
'Iona' (*fortunei*)	EMic IBal MHost SSien
'Irische See' (Tardiana Group)	IBal
'Irish Eyes' (v)	EMic IBal SSien
'Irish Luck'	EMic IBal NSue
'Iron Gate Special' (v)	EMic
'Iron Sky'	IBal
'Island Charm' (v) ♀H7	EBee EHyd IBal LBuc LRHS NHpl NLar NSue SCob SSien WFar
'Itty Gold'	IBal
'Ivory Coast' (v)	ECtt EHyd EMic EMor IBal LRHS MHol NRHS SSien
'Ivory Necklace' (v)	IBal SSien
'Ivory Queen' (v)	EMic IBal NSue SSien
'Iwa Yara Moto'	IBal
'Jack of Diamonds'	IBal SSien
'Jade Beauty'	CBdn EMic
'Jade Cascade'	EMic GBin IBal NBir NLar WFar WHal
'Jade Scepter' (*nakaiana*)	EMic MHost
'Jane Ward' (v) **new**	SSien
'Janet Day' (v)	EMic
'Janet' (*fortunei*) (v)	EMic NGdn SSien
'Janet's Green Sox'	EMic
'Jason and Katie' (v)	EMic IBal
'Jaws'	IBal NSue
'Jaz'	IBal SSien
'Jennifer' (v)	IBal
'Jerry Landwehr'	EMic IBal
'Jewel of the Nile' (v)	IBal
'Jimmy Crack Corn'	EMic IBal NGdn
'Jingle Bells'	IBal
'John Wargo'	IBal
'Johnny Angel'	EMic
'Joker' (*fortunei*) (v)	CBdn
'Jolly Green Giant' (*sieboldiana* hybrid)	EMic
'Joseph'	EMic IBal MHost
'Josephine' (v)	SSien
'Joshua's Banner' (v) **new**	SSien
'Journeyman'	EMic IBal MHost
'Journey's End' (v)	EMic IBal
'Joyce Trott' (v)	SSien
'Joyful' (v)	IBal
'Jubilee' (v)	EMic IBal
'Judy Rocco'	IBal
'Juha' (v)	EMic
'Jules'	IBal
'Julia' (v)	EMic IBal NSue
'Julie Morss'	EMic GMaP IBal MHost SSien
'June'PBR (Tardiana Group) (v) ♀H7	Widely available
'June Fever'PBR (Tardiana Group)	ELon EMic ESwi IBal NBro NGdn NLar NSue SPoG SSien WFar

'June Moon' (v)	SSien
'June Spirit' (v)	IBal NSue
'Jurassic Park'	IBal LLWG LRHS MNrw NLar NSue SSien
'Just So' (v)	EMic IBal SSien
'Justine' PBR	EMic IBal NSue SSien
'Kabitan'	see *H. sieboldii* var. *sieboldii* f. *kabitan*
'Kabuki'	IBal
'Kalamazoo' (v)	CBdn EMic IBal SSien
'Kaleidochrome' (v)	IBal
'Karin'	EMic IBal
'Katherine Lewis' (Tardiana Group) (v)	EMic IBal LRHS LSRN MHost NHol SSien
'Kath's Gold'	EMic
'Katie Q' (v)	EMic IBal SSien
'Katsuragawa-beni' (v)	EMic IBal SSien
'Kayak'	IBal
'Kelly'	CBdn EMic
'Kelsey'	EMic IBal
'Kenzie' (v)	EMic IBal
'Key Lime Pie'	EMic IBal MHost SSien
'Key West'	NSue SSien
'Kifukurin' (*kikutii*)	see *H.* 'Kifukurin-hyuga'
§ 'Kifukurin-hyuga' (v)	IBal
'Kifukurin-kiyosumi'	IBal
'Kifukurin-ko-mame' (*gracillima*) (v)	EMic NSue
'Kifukurin-otome' (*venusta*) (v)	EMic NSue
'Kifukurin-ubatake' (*pulchella*) (v)	EMic IBal
kikutii	CBdn EMic IBal IMou LRHS
§ - var. ***caput-avis***	EMic
§ - var. ***yakusimensis***	EMic GEdr IBal SMad
'Ki-nakafu-otome' (*venusta*)	IBal
'Kinbotan' (*venusta*) (v)	EMic GEdr SSien
'Kinbuchi Tachi' (*rectifolia*) (v)	IBal
'King James'	CBdn IBal
'King Michael' **new**	CBdn
'King of Spades'	IBal
'King Tut'	EMic
'Kingfisher' (Tardiana Group)	LRHS MHost
'Kingsize'	IBal NSue SArc SSien
§ 'Kirishima'	EMic NHpl NSue NWad
'Kisuji'	see *H.* 'Mediopicta'
'Kitty Cat'	IBal MHost WFar
'Kiwi Black Magic'	IBal
'Kiwi Blue Baby'	EMic IBal
'Kiwi Blue Ruffles'	IBal
'Kiwi Blue Sky'	IBal
'Kiwi Canoe'	IBal
'Kiwi Cream Edge' (v)	EMic
'Kiwi Forest'	IBal
'Kiwi Full Monty' (v)	CBdn CDor EMic IBal NSue SSien WFar
'Kiwi Gold Rush'	CBdn SSien
'Kiwi Hippo'	IBal NSue
'Kiwi Jordan'	IBal
'Kiwi Kaniere Gold'	IBal
'Kiwi Minnie Gold'	IBal ITim
'Kiwi Parasol'	IBal
'Kiwi Skyscraper'	CBdn IBal
'Kiwi Spearmint'	ECtt EMic WFar
'Kiwi Sunshine'	CBdn IBal
kiyosumiensis	IBal
'Klopping Variegated' (v)	EMic
'Knight's Journey'	IBal
'Knockout' (v)	MBNS MRav NBro NGdn NLar
'Kogarashi Nakafu' **new**	NSue
'Komodo Dragon'	EMic IBal SSien
'Konkubine'	EMic
'Korean Snow'	IBal
'Koriyama' (*sieboldiana*) (v)	EMic
'Krossa Cream Edge' (*sieboldii*) (v)	IBal
'Krossa Regal' ♀H7	Widely available
'La Donna'	IBal
'Lacy Belle' (v)	CBdn CDor CSBt EBee EHyd EMic EPfP IBal LRHS NBro NEoE NGdn NSue SSien
'Lady Godiva'	IBal
'Lady Guineverre'	EMic IBal SSien
'Lady Helen'	EMic
'Lady in Red'	IBal
'Lady Isobel Barnett' (v) ♀H7	IBal
laevigata	IBal
'Lake Hitchcock' (v) **new**	IBal
'Lake Superior'	IBal
'Lake Tekapo' (v)	IBal
'Lakeside Accolade'	IBal
'Lakeside Alex Andra' (v)	IBal
'Lakeside April Snow' (v)	EMic IBal NGdn SSien
'Lakeside Baby Face' (v)	EMic IBal NHpl NSue SSien WFar
'Lakeside Banana Bay' (v)	IBal NGdn SSien
'Lakeside Beach Bum'	IBal
'Lakeside Beach Captain' (v)	EMic SSien
'Lakeside Black Satin'	WFar
'Lakeside Blue Cherub'	EMic IBal
'Lakeside Breaking News' (v)	EMic IBal
'Lakeside Butter Ball'	IBal
'Lakeside Cha Cha' (v)	CBdn EMic IBal WFar
'Lakeside Cindy Cee' (v)	IBal
'Lakeside Circle O' (v)	IBal
'Lakeside Coal Miner'	NGdn NLar SSien
'Lakeside Color Blue'	IBal
'Lakeside Contender'	IBal SSien
'Lakeside Cupcake' (v)	EMic IBal MHost NGdn NSue
'Lakeside Cupid's Cup' (v)	IBal
'Lakeside Dimpled Darling' (v)	NSue
'Lakeside Dividing Line' (v)	IBal
'Lakeside Doodad' (v)	IBal NSue
'Lakeside Down Sized' (v)	CBdn EMic IBal MNrw NSue SSien WFar
'Lakeside Dragonfly' (v)	ECtt ELon EMic EPfP EShb IBal MNrw NGdn NLar NSue WFar
'Lakeside Elfin Fire'	NSue
'Lakeside Fancy Pants' (v)	CBdn IBal
'Lakeside Feather Light' (v)	IBal
'Lakeside Foaming Sea'	IBal
'Lakeside Full Tide'	IBal
'Lakeside Hazy Morn' (v)	IBal
'Lakeside Hoola Hoop' (v)	IBal
'Lakeside Iron Man'	IBal
'Lakeside Jazzy Jane' (v)	IBal
'Lakeside Kaleidoscope'	CBdn EMic IBal NGdn
'Lakeside Keepsake' (v)	IBal
'Lakeside Khum Kaw'	IBal
'Lakeside Legal Tender'	IBal
'Lakeside Lime Time'	IBal
'Lakeside Little Gem'	IBal NSue
'Lakeside Little Tuft' (v)	CBdn EMic IBal NLar NSue SSien
'Lakeside Lollipop'	EMic IBal SSien
'Lakeside Looking Glass'	EMic
'Lakeside Love Affaire'	IBal NSue WFar
'Lakeside Maestro'	IBal NLar
'Lakeside Maverick'	IBal SSien

'Lakeside Meadow Ice' (v)	IBal SSien
'Lakeside Meter Maid' (v)	IBal NSue
'Lakeside Midnight Miss'	IBal
'Lakeside Miss Muffett' (v)	EMic IBal NSue
'Lakeside Missy Little' (v)	IBal
'Lakeside Neat Petite'	IBal NSue
'Lakeside Ninita' (v)	ECtt EHyd EMic IBal LRHS NRHS NSue
'Lakeside Old Smokey'	IBal
'Lakeside Paisley Print' (v)	CBdn ECtt EMic EPfP IBal MHol MNrw NSue SSien WFar
'Lakeside Party Dress'	GEdr
'Lakeside Pebbles'	IBal
'Lakeside Premier'	EMic IBal
'Lakeside Prophecy'	IBal
'Lakeside Prophecy Fulfilled' (v)	IBal
'Lakeside Rhapsody' (v)	EMic IBal SSien
'Lakeside Ring Master' (v)	IBal
'Lakeside Ripples'	IBal
'Lakeside Rocky Top' (v)	IBal WFar
'Lakeside Roy El' (v)	IBal SSien
'Lakeside Sapphire Pleats'	EMic
'Lakeside Sassy Sally'	IBal
'Lakeside Scamp' (v)	CBdn EMic EMor GEdr IBal MHost NSue SSien
'Lakeside Shadows' (v)	IBal
'Lakeside Shoremaster' (v)	CBdn IBal
'Lakeside Slick Chick' (v)	IBal
'Lakeside Sophistication' (v)	IBal
'Lakeside Sparkle Plenty' (v)	IBal
'Lakeside Spellbinder' (v)	CLAP IBal LRHS
'Lakeside Spruce Goose' (v)	CBdn EMic IBal NSue
'Lakeside Storm Watch'	EMic IBal NSue SSien
'Lakeside Swan Pon' (v)	IBal
'Lakeside Symphony' (v)	EMic
'Lakeside Tee Ki' (v)	IBal
'Lakeside Whizzit' (v)	IBal NSue
'Lakeside Zesty Zeno' (v)	IBal
'Lakeside Zinger' (v)	EMic IBal NSue SSien
lancifolia	CMac EBee ELan EMic GMaP IBal MHost MRav NGdn NSti SPer SRms SSien WKif WSHC WThu
'Last Dance' (v)	IBal
'Last Train Home' **new**	SSien
'Laura Lanier'	EMic IBal
'Laura Z'	IBal
'Lavender Doll'	IBal
'Leading Lady' 🏆H7	IBal
'Leather Sheen'	EMic
'Leatherneck'	IBal
'Lederhosen'	EMic
'Lemon Delight'	EHyd EMic ESwi IBal LRHS MHost NRHS NSue SSien WFar
'Lemon Frost'	EMic IBal
'Lemon Lime'	ECtt EMic EWld IBal LRHS MHost MNrw NEoE NRHS NSue SSien WAbe WCot
'Lemon Meringue'	NSue
'Lemonade'	GBin IBal
'Lemontini' **new**	MHost NSue
'Leola Fraim' (v)	CBdn IBal LRHS MHost
'Let Me Entertain You'	EMic
'Leviathan'	EMic
'Lewis and Clark'	IBal
'Libby'	EMic IBal MHost NSue
'Liberty'^{PBR} (v) 🏆H7	CBdn CBod CDor CWGN EMic EMor EPfP IBal MHost NBro NGdn NLar NSue SAko SPer SSien
'Light of Zetar'	IBal
'Li'l Abner' (v)	IBal
* ***lilacina***	WFar
'Lily Blue Eyes'	EMic MHost SSien
'Lime Fizz'	EMic IBal MHost NHpl NSue SSien WFar
'Lime Regal' **new**	MHost
'Lime Shag' (*sieboldii* f. *spathulata*)	IBal MHost NSue SSien WFar
'Limetini' **new**	MHost
'Limey Lisa'	EMic IBal NSue
'Linda Sue' (v)	IBal
'Lionheart' (v)	EMic IBal NSue
'Little Aurora' (*tokudama* hybrid)	EMic IBal WFar
'Little Bit'	EMic IBal MHost NSue
'Little Black Scape'	EMic IBal LSRN NGdn NLar NWad SSien
'Little Blue' (*ventricosa*)	EMic
'Little Bo Beep' (v)	IBal WFar
'Little Boy'	IBal
'Little Caesar' (v)	IBal LRHS NGdn NSue SSien WFar
'Little Devil'	EMic NSue SSien
'Little Doll' (v)	IBal
'Little Jay' (v)	NSue
'Little Maddie'	EMic NSue
'Little Miss Magic'	IBal NSue
'Little Miss Muffett'	NSue
'Little Miss Sunshine'	IBal NSue
'Little Prayer'	WFar
'Little Red Joy'	EMic IBal MHost NSue
'Little Red Rooster'	EMic GEdr IBal MHost NGdn NHpl NLar NSue SSien WFar
'Little Star Struck'	NSue
'Little Stiffy'	IBal
'Little Sunspot' (v)	EMic NSue
'Little Treasure' (v)	EMic IBal NSue SSien WFar
'Little White Lines' (v)	EBee EHyd EMic GKev IBal LRHS MHost NRHS NSue SSien
'Little Willie' (v)	NSue
'Little Wonder' (v) 🏆H7	EMic NSue SSien
'Living Water'	EMic
'Lizard Lick'	EMic IBal NSue
'Lollapalooza' (v)	CBdn IBal
'London Fog' (v)	GBin GEdr IBal
'Lonesome Dove' (v)	SSien
'Long Fellow' (v)	IBal
longipes	SSien
- B&SWJ 10806	WCru
- f. ***hypoglauca*** **new**	SSien
longissima var. ***brevifolia***	NSue
'Lost World'	EMic IBal
'Lothar the Giant'	IBal
'Love Pat' 🏆H7	ECtt EMic EPfP IBal LSRN MRav NGdn NLar NSue NWad
'Love Song'	IBal SSien
'Loyalist'^{PBR} (v)	IBal LRHS NGdn NLar SPoG SSien WFar
'Lucky Mouse'^{PBR} (v)	CBdn EMic IBal NSue SSien
'Lucy Vitols' (v)	EMic ESwi IBal
'Lullabye'	EMic
'Luna Moth'	CBdn CBod ECtt IBal NSue
'Lunar Eclipse' (v)	EMic
'Lunar Orbit' (v)	SSien
'Machete'	IBal
'Mack the Knife'	EMic IBal NLar WFar
'Maekawa'	IBal
'Magic Fire'^{PBR} (v)	ECtt EMic EPfP IBal NLar NSue SSien
'Magic Island'	IBal MHol MHost NSue SSien
'Magica'	IBal

'Majesty'	EMic IBal MNrw NGdn SSien
'Major Tom'	IBal
'Majordomo'	EMic
'Malabar' (v)	EMic IBal
'Mama Mia' (v)	EHyd EMic EMor EPfP IBal LRHS LSou MBNS NBro NGdn NHol NWad SSien WFar
'Mango Salsa'	IBal
'Mango Smoothie' **new**	SSien
'Mango Tango' (v)	IBal SSien
'Maple Leaf' (*sieboldiana*) (v)	EMic
'Maraschino Cherry'	EMic IBal LPla NGdn
'Mardi Gras' (v)	EMic IBal
'Marge' (*sieboldiana* hybrid)	EMic
'Margie's Angel' (v)	NSue
'Margin of Error' (v)	IBal
'Marginata Alba' misapplied	see *H.* 'Albomarginata' (*fortunei*), *H. rispula*
'Marilyn'	EMic IBal NSue
'Marilyn Monroe'	EMic IBal MHost NSue SSien
'Marmalade on Toast'	EMic MHost
'Marquis' (*nakaiana* hybrid)	IBal
'Marrakech'	EMic IBal LRHS NSue
'Marshmallow Sky' (v) **new**	SSien
'Mary Joe'	EMic
'Mary Marie Ann' (*fortunei*) (v)	EMic IBal
'Masquerade' (v)	EMic MHost SMHy WFar WHal WThu
'Maui Buttercups'	EMic NSue
'May'	EMic IBal
'Maya' (*fortunei*) (v)	EMic IBal
'Medieval Age' (v)	IBal
§ 'Mediopicta' (*sieboldii*)	EMic IBal
'Mediovariegata' (*undulata*)	see *H. undulata* var. *undulata*
'Medusa' (v)	NGdn NSue
'Memories of Dorothy'	EMic IBal MHost
'Mesa Fringe' (*montana*)	EMic NLar
'Mid Afternoon'	IBal
'Midas Touch'	NLar
'Middle Ridge'	EMic
'Midnight at the Oasis' (v)	EMic IBal NSue SSien
'Midnight Ride'	IBal SSien
'Midwest Magic' (v)	EMic IBal MHost NLar
'Mighty Mite'	IBal
'Mighty Mouse' (v)	IBal
'Mikawa-no-yuki'	IBal
'Mike Shadrack' (v)	EMic IBal SSien
'Miki'	IBal
'Mildred Seaver' (v)	CBdn EMic IBal LRHS
'Milkmaid' (v) **new**	NSue
'Millennium'	CBdn ECtt EMic IBal
'Ming Jade'	EMic
'Mini Skirt'	IBal NSue SSien
I 'Minima Aurea'	IBal
'Minnesota Wild' (v)	IBal
'Minnie Bell' (v)	IBal
'Minnie Klopping'	EMic
minor misapplied f. ***alba***	see *H. sieboldii* var. *alba*
§ ***minor*** Maekawa	GBin GEdr ITim NWad WFar XLum
- B&SWJ 1209 from Korea	WCru
- B&SWJ 8775 from Korea	WCru
- B&SWJ 11103 from Japan	WCru
- from Japan	EMic
- from Korea	IBal
'Minor' (*ventricosa*)	see *H. minor* Maekawa
'Mint Julep' (v)	IBal
'Minuet' (v)	IBal
'Minuta' (*venusta*)	MHost
'Minuteman' (*fortunei*) (v) ♀H7	CBcs CBdn CDor ECtt EHyd ELon EMic EPfP IBal LRHS MBNS MHost MMuc NGdn NHpl NLar SEND SSien WFar
'Minutini'	NSue
'Miracle Lemony'	IBal
'Miss Linda Smith'	EMic IBal MHost
'Miss Ruby'	EMic IBal SSien
'Miss Saigon' (v)	IBal
'Miss Susie'	IBal
'Miss Tokyo' (v)	EMic IBal SSien
'Mississippi Delta'	EMic
'Mister Watson'	EMic IBal
'Misty Waters' (*sieboldiana*)	EMic
'Misweave' (v)	IBal
'Moerheim' (*fortunei*) (v)	EMic IBal LRHS MHost WFar WHal
'Mohegan'	EMic
'Mohrchen'	EMic
'Moi Marleen'	EMic
'Mojito'	EMic
'Monster Ears'	IBal NSue
montana	EMic WFar
- B&SWJ 4796	WCru
- B&SWJ 5585	LEdu WCru
- f. ***macrophylla***	IBal NSue
aff. ***montana***	SSien WFar
'Moody Blues' (Tardiana Group)	CBdn EMic
'Moon Dance' (v)	IBal
'Moon Lily'	EMic SSien
'Moon River' (v)	EMic IBal
'Moon Split' (v)	EMic EPfP IBal NGdn SSien
'Moon Waves'	IBal
'Moonbeam'	EMic EShb
'Moongate Flying Saucer'	EMic
'Moonlight' (*fortunei*) (v)	EMic GMaP IBal LRHS
'Moonlight Sonata'	CBdn EMic IBal SSien
'Moonstruck'^{PBR} (v)	ECtt EMic IBal NSue SSien
'Morning Light'	ECtt EMor EPfP IBal MBNS MHost NBro NGdn NLar SRkn SSien WFar
'Morning Star' (v)	EMic IBal LCro LOPS NSue SSien WFar
'Moscow Blue'	EMic
'Moulin Rouge'	IBal NSue
'Mount Everest'	EMic IBal SSien
'Mount Fuji' (*montana*)	IBal
'Mount Kirishima' (*sieboldii*)	see *H.* 'Kirishima'
'Mount Tom' (v)	IBal SSien
'Mountain Green' **new**	SSien
'Mountain Snow' (*montana*) (v)	EHyd EMic LRHS SSien
'Mourning Dove' (v)	EMic IBal SSien
'Mr Big'	IBal NGdn WCot
'Mr Blue'	IBal NSue
'Mrs Minky'	EHyd EMic LRHS MHost
'Muffie' (v)	EMic
'Munchkin' (*sieboldii*)	MHost WFar
'My Child Insook' (v)	SSien
'My Claire' (v)	IBal SSien
'My Cup of Tea'	IBal SSien
'My Marianne' (v) **new**	SSien
'My Precious' (v)	IBal NSue
'Mystic Mouse'	IBal
'Mystic Star'	IBal NSue
nakaiana	EMic GWyn
'Nakaimo'	IBal NLar
'Nana' (*ventricosa*)	see *H. minor* Maekawa
§ 'Nancy Lindsay' (*fortunei*)	CBdn CDor EMic IBal MHost NGdn NLar

'Nancy Minks'	EMic IBal
'Neat and Tidy'	IBal
'Neat Splash' (v)	CWCL NBir SSien
'Neat Splash Rim' (v)	SSien
'Needlepoint' **new**	IBal
'Neelix'	IBal
'Nemesis' (v)	IBal
'Neptune'	EMic IBal SSien
'Nesmith's Giant'	EMic
'Niagara Falls' 🏆H7	CBdn EMic IBal NGdn NSue SSien
'Nicola'	CBdn EMic IBal MHost NSue
'Nifty Fifty' (v) **new**	SSien
'Night before Christmas' (v) 🏆H7	EMic EWTr IBal LRHS MBNS MHost MNrw NBro NGdn NHol NLar SPalm SSien WHoo
'Night Life'	EMic IBal
nigrescens	EMic IBal LRHS NChi
'Niko' (v)	IBal
'Nippers'	EMic IBal NSue
'None Lovelier' (v)	EMic IBal
'North Hills' (*fortunei*) (v)	EMic IBal NBir NGdn SWvt WFar
'Northern Exposure' (*sieboldiana*) (v)	EMic IBal NGdn NLar SPoG SSien WFar
'Northern Halo' (*sieboldiana*) (v)	CDor
'Norwalk Chartreuse'	IBal
'Number Nine' **new**	IBal
'Nutty Professor' (v)	IBal
'Oberon'	NSue
'Obscura Marginata' (*fortunei*)	see *H. fortunei* var. *aureomarginata*
'Ocean Isle' (v)	IBal
'October Sky'	CBdn EMic IBal SSien
'Oder'	EMic IBal
'Ogon-tachi' (*rectifolia*) (v)	EMic IBal
'Ogon Tsushima' **new**	SSien
'Ogon-chirifu-hime'	EMic IBal
'Ogon-hime-tokudama'	IBal
'Ogon-koba'	IBal
'Oh Cindy' (v)	EMic IBal
'O'Harra'	CBdn EMic NSue
'Old Faithful'	EMic IBal LRHS
'Old Glory'[PBR] (v)	ECtt EMic IBal SSien
'Olga's Shiny Leaf'	EMic
'Olive Bailey Langdon' (*sieboldiana*) (v)	CDor EMic IBal
'Olive Branch' (v)	EMic IBal SSien
'Olympic Edger'	EMic IBal
'Olympic Glacier' (v)	EMic IBal SSien
'Olympic Gold Medal'	EMic IBal
'Olympic Silver Medal'	EMic IBal
'Olympic Sunrise' (v)	EMic IBal SSien
'Olympic Twilight'	CBdn EMic IBal
'On Stage'	see *H.* 'Chōkō-nishiki'
'On the Border' (v)	IBal
'On the Marc' **new**	SSien
'One Iota' (v)	IBal
'One Last Dance' (v) **new**	SSien
'One Man's Treasure' 🏆H7	EMic IBal LSou MBel MHost NGdn SSien
'Ooh La La' (v)	IBal NSue
'Ophir'	EMic SSien
'Ops' (v)	EMic IBal NSue SSien
'Orange Crush' (v)	IBal
'Orange Marmalade' (v) 🏆H7	CAbb CBcs CBdn CBod CRos CWGN ECtt EHyd ELan EMic EMor EPfP IBal LCro LOPS LRHS MBNS MHol MHost MNrw MPnt NGdn NLar NRHS NSue SCob SPoG WFar
'Orange Star'[PBR] (v)	IBal NSue SSien
'Oriana' (*fortunei*)	EMic MHost SSien
'Orion's Belt' (v)	IBal MHost
'Osprey' (Tardiana Group)	MHost
'Over the Waves'	IBal MHost NSue
'Oxheart'	EMic IBal
'Oze' (v)	SSien
pachyscapa	CBdn
'Pacific Blue Edger'	EMic MHost SPalm WAul WFar
'Painted Lady' (*sieboldii*) (v)	GKev
'Pamela Lee' (v)	IBal NGdn SSien
'Pandora's Box' (v)	EMic GEdr NHar NHpl NSue WCot WFar WTor
'Papa' (v)	IBal
'Paradigm' (v)	CBdn EMic IBal LRHS MHost NGdn NLar SSien
'Paradise Backstage' (v)	EMic IBal
'Paradise Beach'	EMic IBal WFar
'Paradise Blue Sky'	IBal
'Paradise Expectations' (*sieboldiana*) (v)	EMic IBal SSien
'Paradise Glory'	CBdn EMic IBal
'Paradise Gold Line' (*ventricosa*) (v)	IBal
'Paradise Island'[PBR] (*sieboldiana*) (v)	CBdn ECtt EMic EPfP IBal NGdn NSue WFar
'Paradise Joyce'[PBR]	EMic EMor IBal LRHS NSue
'Paradise Ocean'	CBdn EMic IBal SSien
'Paradise on Fire' (v)	EMic IBal NSue SSien
'Paradise Parade' (v)	EMic IBal
'Paradise Passion' (v)	IBal
'Paradise Power'[PBR]	EMic SSien
'Paradise Puppet' (*venusta*) 🏆H7	EBee EMic IBal MHost NSue NWad SSien
'Paradise Red Delight' (*pycnophylla*)	EMic IBal MHost SSien
'Paradise Sandstorm'	IBal SSien
'Paradise Standard' (d)	EMic IBal
'Paradise Sunset'	CBdn EMic IBal MHost NHpl NSue SSien WFar
'Paradise Sunshine'	EMic IBal
'Paradise Surprise' (v)	IBal SSien
'Paradise Tritone' (v)	EMic IBal
'Parasol' (v) **new**	IBal
'Parky's Prize' (v)	CBdn IBal MHost SSien
'Party Popper' (v)	MHost NSue
'Pastures Green'	IBal MHost
'Pastures New'	EMic MHost
'Pathfinder' (v)	EMic IBal SSien WFar
'Patricia'	EMic
'Patrician' (v)	IBal MHost
'Patriot' (v) 🏆H7	Widely available
'Patriot's Fire' (v)	EHyd IBal LRHS NRHS SSien
'Patriot's Green Pride'	IBal
'Paul Revere' (v)	CBdn
'Paul's Glory' (v) 🏆H7	CBdn CDor EMic EPfP GLog GMaP IBal LRHS MHost NBir NGdn NSue SCob SPoG SSien WFar
§ 'Paxton's Original' (*sieboldii*) (v)	SSien
'Peace' (v)	CBdn EMic IBal LRHS MHost
'Peacock Strut'	IBal
'Peanut'	IBal NSue SSien
'Pearl Lake'	EMic IBal NBir NGdn NHol NLar
'Peedee Absinth'	EMic
'Peedee Elfin Bells' (*ventricosa*)	IBal
'Pelham Blue Tump'	EMic MHost SSien
'Peppermint Ice' (v)	EMic IBal NGdn SSien

'Percy'	EMic SSien
'Permanent Wave'	IBal
'Perry's True Blue'	CBdn EMic IBal
'Peter Pan'	EMic IBal SSien
'Pete's Dark Satellite'	EMic IBal NSue
'Pete's Passion' (v) **new**	CBdn
'Pewterware'	EMic IBal
'Phantom'	CBdn IBal
'Philadelphia'	EMic IBal
'Phoenix'	EMic IBal NLar
'Photo Finish' (v)	IBal SSien
'Phyllis Campbell' (*fortunei*)	see *H.* 'Sharmon'
'Picta' (*fortunei*)	see *H. fortunei* var. *albopicta*
'Piecrust Power'	IBal
'Piedmont Gold'	EHyd EMic IBal LRHS SSien
'Pilgrim' (v)	CDor EHyd EMic IBal LRHS MHost MMuc NBro NGdn NHpl NRHS SEND SSien WFar
'Pineapple Poll'	EMic MHost WFar WHoo
'Pineapple Upside Down Cake' (v)	EMic IBal NBro NLar NSue SSien
'Pinky'	IBal
'Pin-up' (v)	IBal NSue
'Pistache' (v)	IBal NSue
'Pixie Vamp' (v)	EMic IBal SSien
'Pizzazz' (v)	EMic IBal LRHS MHost NGdn NHol NLar SSien WFar
plantaginea	LEdu LRHS SSien WFar WSpi WWtn
- var. ***grandiflora***	see *H. plantaginea* var. *japonica*
§ - var. ***japonica*** 🏆H7	CAby EBee ECha LRHS MNrw MRav SMHy SMad SPhx WCFE WFar WSpi
'Platinum Tiara' (v)	EMic IBal NBir NSue SSien
'Playmate' (v)	CBdn IBal
'Plug Nickel'	EMic IBal MHost NSue SSien
'Pocketful of Sunshine' (v)	IBal NSue SSien
'Poker'	IBal
'Polar Moon' (v)	IBal
'Pole Cat' (v)	IBal
'Pooh Bear' (v)	EMic NSue SSien
'Popcorn'	CBdn IBal NSue SSien
'Popo' 🏆H7	EMic IBal MHost NHpl NSue SSien
'Porter' (*venusta*)	EMic IBal
'Pot of Gold'	EMic
'Potomac Pride'	EHyd EMic LRHS MHost NRHS
'Powder Blue' (v)	IBal
'Powder Keg' (v)	IBal
'Prairie Moon'	NSue
'Prairie Sky'	ECtt EMic EMor IBal NGdn NLar SSien WFar
'Prairie Sunset' (v)	NSue
'Prairie's Edge' (v) **new**	SSien
'Praying Hands' (v) 🏆H7	Widely available
'Precious Metal'	IBal
'Prestige and Promise' (v)	IBal
'Pretty Flamingo'	EMic MHost
'Prima Donna'	CBdn EMic
'Prince of Wales'	CRos EHyd EMic IBal LPla LRHS MHost NRHS SPoG SSien
'Private Dancer'	IBal
'Prom Queen' (v)	EMic IBal
'Proud Dragon' (v)	IBal
'Proud Sentry'	EMic IBal SSien
'Punk Rock'	IBal
'Punky' (v)	EMic IBal SSien
'Purbeck Mist' **new**	MHost SSien
'Purbeck Ridge' (Tardiana Group) **new**	MHost
'Purple and Gold'	EMic SSien
'Purple Boots'	EMic IBal MHost SSien
'Purple Bouquet' **new**	MHost
'Purple Dwarf'	EMic IBal NLar NSue WCru WHal
'Purple Glory'	CBdn EMic MHost
'Purple Haze'	EMic IBal NGdn WFar
'Purple Heart'	CAby CBcs ECtt EMor EPfP EWTr IBal LCro LOPS LPla LRHS NEoE NHpl NSti NSue NWad SPalm SSien WNPC
'Purple Passion'	EMic IBal NSue
'Purple Profusion'	EMic IBal
'Purple Python'	IBal MHost
'Quarter Note' (v)	IBal
'Queen Josephine' (v)	CBdn CRos ECtt EMic EMor EPfP IBal LRHS MBNS MHost NGdn NHpl SSien WFar
'Queen of Islip' (*sieboldiana*) (v)	SSien
'Queen of the Seas'	CBdn EMic ESwi IBal NSue
'Quill'	EMic NSue
'Quilting Bee'	EMic IBal NSue
'Radiant Edger' (v)	EHyd EMic IBal LRHS MHost NHol NRHS NSue
'Rain Dancer'	EMic IBal SSien
'Rain Forest'	EMic IBal
'Rainbow's End' (v)	EBee ECtt EPfP IBal NLar NSue SSien
'Rainforest Sunrise' (v)	CBod ELon EMic IBal LSou NGdn NSue SSien WFar
'Randy Rachel' (v)	LRHS
'Rare Breed' (v)	IBal
'Rascal' (v)	EMic IBal
'Raspberries and Cream' (v)	IBal
'Raspberry Sorbet'	EHyd EMic IBal LRHS MHost NRHS
'Raspberry Sundae' (v)	CBdn CMil CWGN ECtt EMor IBal MHol MMrt NGdn NHpl NSue NWad SPalm SPoG SSien WNPC
'Raucous Ruffles' **new**	EMic
'Rebel Heart' (v)	IBal
'Red Alert' (v)	IBal
'Red Cadet'	EMic ESwi IBal MHost NSue SSien WFar
'Red Dog'	EMic NSue
'Red Dragon'	EMic IBal SSien
'Red Hot Flash' (v)	EMic IBal SSien
'Red Hot Poker'	IBal
'Red Neck Heaven' (*kikutii* var. *caput-avis*)	IBal
'Red October'	ECtt EHyd EMic EPfP GAbr GQue IBal LEdu LRHS LSou MBNS MHol MHost NGdn NHpl NLar SSien WCAu WFar
'Red Salamander'	CBdn EMic ESwi IBal
'Red Sox'	IBal
'Red Stepper'	EMic IBal SSien WFar
'Red Stilts'	IBal
'Red Tubes' (*venusta*)	IBal
'Regal Rhubarb'	EMic IBal
'Regal Splendor' (v) 🏆H7	CBdn CDor ECtt EHyd ELan ELon EMic IBal LCro LOPS LRHS MHost NBro NGdn NRHS NSue SCob SPoG SSien WFar WHoo
'Regal Supreme' (v)	IBal NSue
'Regal Tot'	NSue
'Regalia'	NSue
'Reginald Kaye'	EMic
'Rembrandt Blue'	EMic IBal
'Remember Me' PBR 🏆H7	CWCL ELan IBal LSRN MBNS MPnt NHol NSue SSien WFar

	'Reptilian'	EMic IBal
	'Resonance' (v)	IBal NGdn NLar
	'Restless Sea'	CBod EMic NGdn NSue
	'Reverend Mac'	IBal MHost
	'Reversed' (*sieboldiana*) (v)	CAby EMic EMor IBal LRHS NBro NGdn WFar WHal
	'Revolution'[PBR] (v) ♀[H7]	GKev IBal LSRN MHost NBro NGdn NLar NSue SSien WFar
	'Rhapsody' (*fortunei*) (v)	EMic IBal
	'Rhein' (*tardiana*)	EMic IBal
	'Rhinestone Cowboy' (v)	IBal
	'Rhino Hide' (v)	CBdn IBal MHost NSue SSien
	'Rhythm and Blues'	CBdn IBal NSue
	'Rich Uncle'	IBal
	'Richland Gold' (*fortunei*)	EMic MHost
	'Rim Rock'	EMic IBal
	'Ringtail'	EMic IBal NSue
	'Ripple Effect' (v)	CBdn EMic IBal MHost NSue SSien
	'Rippled Honey'	EMic IBal MHost NEoE SSien
	'Rippling Waves'	EMic
	'Riptide'	EMic NGdn
	'Risa'	IBal
	'Risky Business'[PBR] (v)	CWGN EMic IBal NLar NSue SSien
	'Robert Frost' (v)	EMic IBal
	'Robin Hood'	IBal NSue
	'Robin of Loxley'	EMic IBal
	'Robusta' (*fortunei*)	see *H. sieboldiana* var. *elegans*
	'Robyn's Choice' (v)	IBal MHost
	'Rock and Roll'	EMic IBal SSien
	'Rock Island Line' (v)	EMic IBal NSue NWad WFar
	'Rock Princess'	IBal
	'Rocket's Red Glare'	IBal
§	***rohdeifolia*** (v) B&SWJ 10862	WCru
	- f. ***albopicta***	ELan
	'Roller Coaster Ride'	IBal
	'Ron Damant'	IBal MHost
	'Rootin'-Tootin'' (v)	IBal
	'Roseann Walter' (v)	EMic IBal
	'Rosedale Knox'	IBal
	'Rosedale Lost Dutchman'	IBal
	'Rosedale Melody of Summer' (v)	IBal
	'Rosedale Misty Magic' (v)	IBal
	'Rosedale Richie Valens'	IBal
	'Rosemoor'	EHyd IBal LRHS MHost NSue
	'Rossing's Pride' **new**	SSien
	'Roxsanne'	EMic MHost
	'Roy Klehm' (v)	EMic IBal
	'Royal Charm'	IBal
	'Royal Charmer' (v)	CBdn IBal
	'Royal Flush' (v)	IBal
	'Royal Golden Jubilee'	EMic IBal MHost
§	'Royal Standard' ♀[H7]	CBdn CMac CRos ECha ELan EMic EPfP EShb EWTr GMaP LEdu LRHS MGos MHost MMuc MRav NBid NGdn NLar SCob SEND SPer SRms SWvt WCAu WFar XLum
	'Royal Tapestry' (v)	IBal
	'Royal Tiara' (*nakaiana*) (v)	IBal
	'Royalty'	IBal NSue
	'Rubies and Ruffles' (v)	IBal
	'Ruffed Up' **new**	EMic
	'Ruffled Mouse Ears'	IBal NSue
	'Rufus Rider'	IBal
	rupifraga	IBal
	'Rusty Bee'	IBal MHost
	'Ryan's Big One'	IBal
§	'Sagae' (v) ♀[H7]	EHyd EMic EWhm IBal LRHS MHost MNrw NGdn NRHS SSien WAul WFar
	'Saint Elmo's Fire' (v)	EMic GBin IBal LRHS
	'Saint Fiacre'	EMic
	'Saint John'	IBal
	'Saint Paul'	IBal MNrw NSue
	'Saishu-jima' (*sieboldii* f. *spathulata*)	EMic GEdr ITim NSue WCru
	'Saishu-yahato-sito' (v)	IBal MHost NSue
	'Salute' (Tardiana Group)	EMic SSien
	'Samurai' (*sieboldiana*) (v)	MRav NBir NBro NGdn NLar SSien
	'Sandhill Crane' (v)	LSou
	'Sarah Kennedy' (v)	IBal MHost
	'Sara's Sensation' (v)	IBal NSue
	'Satisfaction' (v) ♀[H7]	EMic IBal
	'Savannah'	IBal
	'Sazanami' (*crispula*)	see *H. crispula*
	'Scallion Pancakes'	EMic
	'Scarlet Ribbons' (v)	EMic IBal
	'School Mouse' (v) **new**	NSue
	'Schwan'	GBin
	'Sea Current'	IBal
	'Sea Dream' (v)	CBdn EMic LRHS NGdn
	'Sea Fire'	IBal
	'Sea Gulf Stream'	EMic NSue
	'Sea Lotus Leaf'	EMic NLar
	'Sea Monster'	IBal
	'Sea Nymph'	EMic
	'Sea Thunder' (v)	EMic EMor IBal LRHS SSien
	'Sea Yellow Sunrise'	EMic IBal SSien
	'Searing Flame' (v)	IBal
	'Second Wind' (*fortunei*) (v)	EMic MHost SSien
	'Secret Ambition'[PBR] (v)	IBal
	'Secret Love'	EMic IBal
	'Secret Treasure'[PBR] (v)	IBal NSue
	'Seducer' (v)	EMic IBal SSien
	'See Saw' (*undulata*)	EMic IBal
	'Semperaurea' (*sieboldiana*)	IBal
	'September Sun' (v)	EMic IBal LRHS SSien
	'Serena' (Tardiana Group)	IBal
	'Serendipity'	CBdn EMic IBal
	'Shade Beauty' (v)	EMic IBal
	'Shade Fanfare' (v)	CDor CRos ECtt EHyd ELan ELon EMic EPfP GQue IBal LRHS MBNS MRav NBir NGdn NLar NRHS NSti SSien WFar
	'Shade Finale' (v)	IBal
	'Shade Master'	EMic
	'Shade Parade' (v)	EMic IBal
	'Shady Affair'	EMic
§	'Sharmon' (*fortunei*) (v)	ELon EMic MBNS MHost NLar SSien
	'Sharp Dressed Man'	IBal
	'Shazaam'	IBal
	'Sheila West'	EMic MHost
	'Shelleys' (v)	IBal
	'Sherborne Profusion' (Tardiana Group)	EMic IBal MHost SSien
	'Sherborne Songbird' (Tardiana Group)	IBal MHost
	'Sherborne Swallow' (Tardiana Group)	EMic IBal MHost SSien
	'Sherborne Swan' (Tardiana Group)	IBal MHost
	'Sherborne Swift' (Tardiana Group)	CBdn EMic ESwi IBal LRHS MHost MWat NRHS SSien
	'Shere Khan' (v)	EMic IBal
	'Shimmy Shake'	EMic SSien
	'Shining Tot' ♀[H7]	IBal
	'Shiny Penny' (v)	EMic IBal NSue
	'Shiny Sonata'	IBal
	'Shirley Levy'	IBal

	'Showboat' (v)	EMic LRHS
	sieboldiana	CAgr CMac CSBt ECha ELan EMic GMaP MRav MSwo NChi SCob SPlb SRms XLum
§	- var. ***elegans*** 🏆^{H7}	Widely available
	- var. ***mira***	EMic
§	- var. ***sieboldiana***	NGdn SSien
	sieboldiana* × *venusta	NGdn
	sieboldii	MRav
§	- var. ***alba***	IBal
§	- var. ***sieboldii*** f. ***kabitan*** (v)	EMic IBal NGdn NSue SSien
	- - f. ***shiro-kabitan*** (v)	EMic LRHS
	- f. ***spathulata***	EMic
	'Silberpfeil'	EMic NSue
	'Silk Road' (v)	IBal
	'Silver Bay' 🏆^{H7}	EMic SSien
	'Silver Crown'	see *H.* 'Albomarginata'
	'Silver Halo' (v)	EMic
	'Silver Lance' (v)	EMic IBal
	'Silver Lode' (v)	IBal
	'Silver Mine'	NSue
	'Silver Moon'	EMic IBal
	'Silver Serenity'	IBal
	'Silver Shadow' (v)	IBal NBir NGdn NLar NWad
	'Silver Spray' (v)	IBal
	'Silver Star' (v)	IBal
	'Silver Threads and Gold Needles' (v)	IBal NHpl NSue SSien
	'Silverado' (v)	IBal
	'Silvery Slugproof' (Tardiana Group)	IBal LRHS MHost
	'Simply Sharon' (v)	IBal
	'Singin' the Blues'	IBal
	'Singing in the Rain' (v)	IBal NSue
	'Sitting Pretty' (v)	IBal
	'Sizzle'	IBal NSue SSien
	'Sky Dancer'	ECtt EMic IBal NSue
	'Sleeping Beauty'	CWGN ECtt EMic IBal NGdn NSue SSien
	'Sleeping Star'^{PBR} (v)	IBal NSue SSien
	'Slick Willie'	EMic
	'Slim and Trim'	EMic IBal NHpl NSue
	'Small Parts'	ECtt EMic IBal NSue SSien
	'Small Sum'	IBal
	'Smash Hit' (v)	IBal NSue
	'Smiley Face'	NSue
	'Smiling Mouse' (v)	IBal NSue
	'Smoke Signals'	IBal
	'Snake Eyes' (v)	CBdn ELon EMic IBal MBel NSue
	'Snow Boy' (v)	EMic IBal NSue
	'Snow Bunting' (v) **new**	MHost
	'Snow Cap' (v)	CDor ECtt EMic EMor IBal NEoE NGdn NLar SPoG WFar
	'Snow Crust' (v)	EMic SSien
	'Snow Flakes' (*sieboldii*)	CMac NBro NEoE NGdn NLar SCob
	'Snow Mouse' (v)	IBal NHpl NSue SSien WFar
	'Snowden' 🏆^{H7}	ECha EMic EWTr GMaP IBal LRHS MHost NBir NGdn NRHS SPhx SSien WCru
	'Snowy Lake' (v)	IBal SSien
	'So Sweet' (v)	CRos EBee ECtt EHyd ELan ELon EMic EMor EPfP GEdr GLog LRHS LSun MHost MSwo NBro NGdn NHol NRHS SSien WFar
	'Something Blue'	EMic IBal
	'Something Else'	EMic
	'Southern Gold'	EMic
	'Space Odyssey'	IBal NSue SSien
	'Sparkler' (v)	IBal NSue

	'Sparkling Burgundy'	EMic LRHS
	'Sparky' (v)	IBal
	'Spartacus' (v)	EMic IBal MHost NSue SSien
	'Spartan Arrow'	NSue
	'Spartan Glory' (v)	IBal SSien
	'Special Blend' (v)	IBal
	'Special Gift'	EMic IBal MHost SSien
	'Spellbound' (v)	CBdn IBal
	'Spilt Milk' (*tokudama*) (v) 🏆^{H7}	EMic IBal SSien WHoo
	'Spinach Souffle' (v)	IBal
§	'Spinners' (*fortunei*) (v)	ECha EMic IBal MHost
	'Spock's Ears'	IBal
	'Sporting Green' **new**	SMHy
	'Spring Break' (v)	EMic
	'Spring Fling'	EMic IBal
	'Spring Love'	IBal
	'Spritzer' (v)	CBdn EMic MNrw NSue SSien
	'Squash Casserole'	IBal NSue
	'Stained Glass' (v) 🏆^{H7}	CBcs CBdn CDor ECtt EHyd ELon EMic EMor EPfP IBal LRHS MHost NGdn NSue SSien WFar
	'Stand by Me' (v)	CBdn EMic IBal MHost NSue
	'Stand Corrected' (v)	IBal SSien
	'Star Kissed'	IBal
	'Star Light Star Bright'	EMic IBal
	'Star Wars'	NSue
	'Starburst' stable (v)	IBal
	'Stardust'	IBal
	'Stargate'	IBal
§	'Starker Yellow Leaf'	EMic
	'Starship' (v)	EMic IBal
	'Steffi' (v)	IBal
	'Step Sister'	EMic IBal
	'Stepping Out' (v)	EMic IBal
	'Stetson' (v)	EMic IBal
	'Stiletto' (v)	ELon EMic GBin GEdr GKev IBal LRHS MBNS MHost MNrw NBro NEoE NGdn NHpl NLar NSue SPalm SPoG SSien SWvt WFar WSHC
	'Stimulation'	IBal
	'Sting' (v)	CBdn LCro LOPS
	'Stirfry'	EMic SSien
	'Stone's Valentine'	EMic
	'Strawberry Surprise' (v)	EMic IBal
	'Strawberry Yoghurt'	NSue
	'Striker' (v)	IBal NSue
	'Striptease' (*fortunei*) (v) 🏆^{H7}	CMac EMic EPfP GLog IBal LRHS MBNS MNrw NGdn NHol NLar NSue SSien WFar
	'Stuck in Time'	CBdn IBal SSien
	'Subcrocea'	SSien
	'Sugar and Cream' (v)	CBdn EMic IBal LRHS MWat NGdn
	'Sugar and Spice' (v)	CBod ELon EMic EPfP IBal MHost SSien
	'Sugar Babe' (v)	EMic
	'Sugar Daddy'	EMic IBal MHost SSien
	'Sugar Mama' (v) **new**	SSien
	'Sugar Plum' **new**	IBal
	'Sulphur Glory' **new**	SSien
	'Sultana' (v)	EMic IBal SSien
	'Sum and Substance' 🏆^{H7}	Widely available
	'Sum and Subtle' (v)	EMic IBal
	'Sum Cup-o-Joe' (v)	EMic
	'Sum it Up' (v)	EMic
	'Sum of All' (v)	EMic NSue
	'Summer Breeze' (v)	EMic IBal NGdn NSue
	'Summer Dress'	GBin NSue
	'Summer Fragrance'	EBee ECtt EMic GBin IBal LRHS

'Summer Gold'	EMic
'Summer Lovin'' (v)	IBal
'Summer Music' (v) ♀H7	CWCL EMic IBal SSien
'Summer Serenade' (v)	EMic NGdn NSue SSien
'Summer Squall'	IBal
'Sumsational'	EMic IBal
'Sun Catcher'	EMic
'Sun Mouse'	IBal NSue SSien
'Sun Power'	EBee EHyd ELon EMic LRHS MBNS NBro NLar SSien
'Sun Worshipper'	IBal
'Sundance' (v)	IBal
'Sunlight Child'	EMic IBal NSue
'Sunny Delight'	CBdn
'Sunny Disposition'	SSien
'Sunny Smiles' (v)	EMic
'Sunnybrook' (v)	SSien
'Sunset Grooves' (v)	CBdn EMic IBal
'Sunshine Glory'	EMic IBal
'Super Bowl'	IBal
'Super Nova' (v)	EMic IBal SSien
'Super Sagae'	CDor IBal MHost SSien WFar
'Surfer Girl'	NSue
'Surprised by Joy' (v)	CBdn IBal MHost NHpl NSue SSien
'Susy'	IBal
'Sutter's Mill'	IBal
'Suzuki Thumbnail'	EMic
'Swamp Thing' (v)	IBal
'Sweet Bo Beep'	EMic IBal LRHS
'Sweet Bouquet'	EMic
'Sweet Home Chicago' (v)	EHyd EMic IBal LRHS SSien
'Sweet Innocence' (v)	EMic IBal
'Sweet Marjorie'	IBal
'Sweet Susan'	CRos EHyd LRHS LSRN MBNS NRHS SPer SSien SWvt
'Sweet Tater Pie'	EMic IBal
'Sweetheart'	EMic
'Sweetie' (v)	EMic IBal LRHS
'Sweetness'	IBal
'Swirling Hearts'	IBal NSue
'Swizzle Sticks'	EMic
'T. Rex'	CBod CDor ELon EMic EMor IBal NSue SSien WFar
takudama	see *H. sieboldiana* var. *sieboldiana*
'Tall Boy'	GBin IBal NBir
'Tamborine' (v)	CBdn EMic EMor IBal LRHS
'Tango'	EMic IBal
'Tappen Zee' (v)	EMic IBal SSien
Tardiana Group	GWyn NGdn
tardiflora	CExl IBal LRHS
tardiva	EMic NLar
'Tattle Tails'	CBdn EMic IBal NHpl NSue SSien
'Tattoo'PBR (v)	CWGN EMic LSRN MBNS NLar SSien
'Tea at Bettys' ♀H7	CBdn EMic IBal MHost NSue SSien
'Teacher's Pride'	IBal MHost NSue
'Tears of Joy'	NSue WFar
'Teaspoon'	EMic IBal MHost NHpl NSue SSien
'Teatime' (v)	EMic IBal NSue
'Teeny-weeny Bikini' (v)	NSue SSien WFar
'Templar Gold'	IBal SSien
'Temple Bells'	IBal
'Temptation'	EMic IBal
'Tequila Sunrise'	IBal
'Terpsichore'	EMic
'Terry Wogan'	IBal MHost
'The King' (v)	IBal NSue
'The Leading Edge' (v)	IBal
'The Queen' (v)	IBal

'The Razor's Edge'	IBal WFar
'The Right One' (v)	IBal
'The Shining'	IBal
'The Twister'	EMic
'Theo's Blue'	CBdn EMic IBal
'Theo's Red'	IBal
'Thomas Hogg'	see *H. undulata* var. *albomarginata*
'Thumb Nail'	EMic IBal NSue NWad SMHy
'Thumbelina'	EHyd IBal LRHS NGdn NRHS NSue SSien
'Thunderbolt'PBR (*sieboldiana*)	ECtt IBal MBNS MHol NGdn NLar SSien WFar
tibae	IBal
'Tick Tock' (v)	ECtt EMic IBal NSue SSien
'Tickle Me Pink'	EMic IBal NSue WFar
'Tidewater'	IBal
'Tilt-a-Whirl'	IBal
'Time Tunnel' (*sieboldiana*) (v)	EMic IBal
'Timeless Beauty' (v)	IBal MHost NSue SSien WFar
'Tiny Tears'	GAbr NSue SSien
'Titanic'PBR	EMic IBal NSue
'Titanium'	IBal NSue
'Toasted Waffles'	WFar
tokudama	EMic IBal LRHS NBir NGdn WFar XLum
§ - f. ***aureo-nebulosa*** (v)	EMic IBal MHost NGdn SRms SSien
- f. ***flavocircinalis*** (v) ♀H7	CBod ELon EMic EPfP GMaP IBal MHost NBro SSien WFar WHoo
'Tokyo Smog' (v)	NSue
'Toledo'	IBal
'Tom Schmid' (v)	CBdn EMic IBal MHost MWat NSue SSien
'Tom Thumb'	EMic IBal NSue SSien
'Tongue Twister'	IBal
'Tootie Mae'	CBdn
'Topaz'	IBal
'Torchlight' (v) ♀H7	CBdn IBal LRHS NSue
tortifrons	EMic IBal SSien
'Tortilla Chip'	EMic IBal WFar
'Tot Tot'	EMic IBal NSue
'Totally Twisted'	EMic IBal NSue
'Touch of Class'PBR (v) ♀H7	CBdn CDor EBee ECtt EMor GBin IBal MHost NGdn NHol NSue SSien WFar WTyc
'Touchstone' (v)	EMic SWvt
'Toy Soldier'	EMic IBal NGdn NLar NSue SSien
'Trail's End'	EMic
'Tranquility' (v)	EMic
'Tremors'	EMic IBal
'Trixi' (v)	IBal
'Tropical Dancer'	IBal
'Tropical Storm' (v)	IBal NSue SSien
'True Blue'	ECtt EMic
'Tsugaru Komachi'	EMic
'Tsugaru Komachi Kifukurin' (v)	IBal
'Tugaux' (v) **new**	IBal
'Turnabout' (v)	IBal
'Turning Point'	IBal LRHS
'Twiggie'	EMic MHost
'Twilight' (*fortunei*) (v)	CAby ECtt EHyd EMic EMor EShb IBal LRHS MBNS MHol MHost NGdn NLar NRHS NSue SSien SWvt WFar
'Twilight Time'	CBdn IBal LRHS
'Twinkle Toes'	EMic IBal NSue
'Twist of Green' **new**	MHost
'Twist of Lime' (v)	EHyd EMic IBal LRHS MHost NGdn NRHS NSue SSien WCot

'Twitter'	IBal
'Tycoon' (v) **new**	SSien
'UFO'	EMic IBal NSue WFar
'Ultramarine'	IBal
'Ultraviolet Light'	IBal SSien
'Ulysses S. Grant'	IBal
'Unchained Melody'	IBal
undulata (v)	WFar
§ - var. ***albomarginata*** (v)	CMac CSam EHyd EMic EPfP GMaP LRHS LSRN MHost MRav NBid NBir NGdn NLar NRHS SCob SPer SRms SWvt WFar XLum
§ - var. ***erromena***	CRos EHyd GMaP LRHS NRHS XLum
§ - var. ***undulata*** (v) ♀H7	EHyd EMic GMaP IBal LRHS MCot MRav NGdn NLar NRHS SPer
- var. ***univittata*** (v)	ECha EMic GKev NBir NEoE SRms WFar
'Unforgettable'	EMic IBal SSien
'Unruly Child' **new**	IBal
'Upper Crust' (v)	IBal
'Uprising' (v)	IBal SSien
'Urajiro' (*hypoleuca*)	IBal
'Urajiro-hachijo' (*longipes* var. *latifolia*)	IBal
'Valentine Lace'	EMic IBal
'Valley's Blue Curaçao'	IBal
'Valley's Cathedral'	IBal
'Valley's Chute the Chute'	EMic IBal MHost SSien
'Valley's Glacier' (v)	IBal WFar
'Valley's Lemon Squash' **new**	IBal
'Valley's Paparazzi' (v)	IBal
'Valley's Sushi' (v) **new**	IBal SSien
'Valley's Vanilla Sticks'	EMic IBal MHost SSien
'Van Wade' (v)	EMic IBal MHost
'Vanilla Cream' (*cathayana*)	EHyd EMic IBal LRHS NRHS NSue WFar
'Variegata' (*gracillima*)	see *H.* 'Vera Verde'
'Variegata' (*tokudama*)	see *H. tokudama* f. *aureo-nebulosa*
'Variegata' (*undulata*)	see *H. undulata* var. *undulata*
'Variegata' (*ventricosa*)	see *H.* 'Aureomarginata' (*ventricosa*)
'Variegated' (*fluctuans*)	see *H.* 'Sagae'
'Velvet Moon' (v)	ECtt EMic IBal SSien
'Venetian Skies' (v) **new**	IBal
ventricosa ♀H7	CBdn CMac EMic IBal WFar XLum
- BWJ 8160 from Sichuan	WCru
'Venus' (d)	CAby ECtt ITim LEdu MHol NGdn WCot WFar
'Venus Star'	EMic MHost
venusta ♀H7	CRos EBee EHyd EMic EWld GBin GEdr IBal LRHS MHost MRav NBid NBir NRHS NRya NSue SSien WFar
- B&SWJ 4389	WCru
- dwarf	IBal
- ***yakusimensis***	see *H. kikutii* var. *yakusimensis*
§ 'Vera Verde' (v)	NBir NSue
'Verdi Valentine'	EMic IBal
'Verkade's One'	IBal
'Verkade's Two' **new**	NSue
'Vermont Frost' (v)	IBal NSue
'Verna Jean' (v)	ECtt EHyd EMic IBal LRHS NRHS NSue
'Veronica Lake' (v)	ECtt EHyd EMic IBal LRHS MHost NRHS NSue SSien WHal
'Vibrant Hope' **new**	SSien
'Victor'	IBal
'Victory' ♀H7	EHyd IBal LRHS MHost NRHS NSue SSien
'Viking Ship'	IBal SSien

'Vilmoriniana'	EMic
'Vim and Vigor'	EMic IBal
'Vina'	IBal
'Virginia Reel' (v)	IBal NSue
'Viridis Marginata'	see *H. sieboldii* var. *sieboldii* f. *kabitan*
'Volcano Island'[PBR] (v)	CBdn EMic IBal NSue SSien
'Vulcan' (v)	EMic IBal SSien
'Wagtail' (Tardiana Group)	IBal MHost SSien
'Wahoo' (*tokudama*) (v)	IBal
'War Paint' ♀H7	CBdn IBal ITim NSue SSien WFar
'Warwick Comet' (v)	EMic IBal NSue SSien
'Warwick Curtsey' (v)	EMic IBal
'Warwick Delight' (v)	NSue
'Warwick Edge' (v)	EMic IBal SSien
'Warwick Essence'	EMic IBal
'Warwick Sheen'	IBal
'Watermark' (v)	EMic
'Waukon Glass'	CBdn EMic IBal
'Waukon the Moon' **new**	CBdn
'Waukon Thin Ice'	EMic IBal
'Waukon Water'	EMic IBal
'Waving Winds' (v)	EMic IBal
'Waving Wuffles'	EMic
'Wayne' (v)	EMic
'Wayside Blue'	EMic
'Wayside Perfection'	see *H.* 'Royal Standard'
'Weihenstephan' (*sieboldii*)	EMic IBal
'Well Shaked' (v)	IBal
'Weser'	IBal
'Wheaton Blue'	EMic LRHS
'Wheaton Thunder' (v)	EMic
'Wheee!' (Shadowland Series)	ESwi IBal NSue SSien
'Whirligig' (v)	EMic
'Whirling Dervish' (v)	IBal
'Whirlwind' (*fortunei*) (v) ♀H7	CBdn EBee ELan EMic EPfP IBal LRHS MHost MNrw MRav NBro NGdn NLar NSue SPoG SPtp SSien WAul WCAu WFar
'Whirlwind Tour' (v)	IBal
'Whiskey Sour'	IBal
'White Bikini' (v)	CBdn IBal NSue SSien
'White Ceiling'	IBal
'White Christmas' (*fortunei*) (v)	NGdn SSien
'White Christmas' (*undulata*) (v)	SSien
'White Dove' (v)	IBal NSue
'White Edger'	EMic
'White Elephant' (v)	IBal
'White Fairy' (*plantaginea*) (d)	EMic
'White Feather' (*undulata*)	CRos CWGN EHyd ELan EPfP LCro LOPS LRHS LSou MNrw NBir NEoE NGdn NLar SMad SPoG SSien WFar
'White Gold'	EMic SSien
'White Jewel' (v)	IBal
'White Knight'	IBal
'White On' (*montana*)	EMic
'White Triumphator' (*rectifolia*)	IBal
'White Trumpets'	EMic
'Wide Brim' (v) ♀H7	Widely available
'William Lachman' (v)	IBal NLar
'Wily Willy'	IBal SSien
'Wind River Gold'	EMic
'Windsor Gold'	see *H.* 'Nancy Lindsay'
'Winfield Blue'	EMic IBal NBir
'Winfield Gold'	EMic MHost

'Winfield Mist' (v) — IBal
'Winsome' (v) — EMor IBal LRHS NSue SSien
'Winter Snow' (v) — CBdn CDor EMic IBal LRHS NSue SPalm SSien WFar
'Winter Warrior' (v) — EMic IBal SSien
'Wishing Well' **new** — SSien
'Wogon' (*sieboldii*) — EMic GKev GMaP ITim NSue
'Wogon's Boy' — EMic LRHS
'Wolverine' (v) 🏆H7 — CBod EBee ECtt EHyd EMic GBin LRHS MBNS NGdn NSue SPad SSien SWvt WFar
'Wonderful' **new** — NSue
'Woodland Elf' (v) — IBal NSue
'Woolly Mammoth' (v) — IBal
'Woop Woop' (v) — IBal NSue
'World Cup' — IBal
'Worldly Treasure' — IBal
'Wrinkles and Crinkles' — EMic
'Wylde Green Cream' — IBal NGdn SSien
'Xanadu' (v) — IBal
'X-ray' (v) — NSue SSien
'Yakushima-mizu' (*gracillima*) — EMic IBal NSue
'Yankee Blue' — IBal NSue
'Yellow Boa' — EMic IBal NSue
'Yellow Edge' (*fortunei*) — see *H. fortunei* var. *aureomarginata*
'Yellow Edge' (*sieboldiana*) — see *H.* 'Frances Williams'
'Yellow Polka Dot Bikini' (v) — CBdn EMic EPfP IBal NSue SSien
'Yellow River' (v) — EBee EHyd EMic IBal LRHS MHost NGdn NSue SSien WFar
'Yellow Splash' (v) — CBdn EMic LRHS
'Yellow Splash Rim' (v) — EMic SSien
'Yellow Waves' — SSien
'Yesterday's Memories' (v) — EMic IBal SSien
'Yin' (v) — EMic IBal SSien
yingeri — WPGP WSHC
- B&SWJ 546 — LEdu WCru
'Yucca Ducka Do' (v) — EMic IBal
'Zager Blue' — EMic
'Zager Green' — EMic
'Zager White Edge' (*fortunei*) (v) — CBdn EMic IBal SSien
'Zebra Stripes' (v) — IBal
'Zion's Hope' — EMic
'Zitronenfalter' — IBal
'Zodiac' (*fortunei*) (v) — IBal
'Zorro' — IBal
'Zounds' — EBee ECtt EHyd EMic EPfP EShb IBal LRHS MRav NGdn NLar SRms SSien WFar

Hottonia (*Primulaceae*)

palustris — LCro LLWG LOPS NPer

Houstonia (*Rubiaceae*)

caerulea L. — EBou SPlb
- var. ***alba*** — EWes SPlb
- 'Millard's Variety' — WIce
michauxii 'Fred Mullard' — EWes

Houttuynia (*Saururaceae*)

cordata — CAgr CMac GKev GPoy LEdu LLWG LPot NSti SDix WFar WWtn XLum
§ - 'Boo-Boo' (v) — CMac WSMil
§ - 'Chameleon' (v) — Widely available
- 'Fantasy' (v) — LLWG
- 'Flame' (v) — CPla LLWG MHol WFar WSMil
- 'Flore Pleno' (d) — CBen CMac CPla CWat ECha EPfP EWld LCro LLWG LOPS MRav MSCN NBir NPer SPer SPlb SRms XLum
- 'Joker's Gold' — ECtt ELan EMor EPPr EPfP WFar
- 'Pied Piper' (v) — ELan NBir SPtp
- 'Terry Clarke' — see *H. cordata* 'Boo-Boo'
- 'Tricolor' — see *H. cordata* 'Chameleon'
- Variegata Group (v) — LLWG LPot NBro

Hovea (*Papilionaceae*)

celsii — see *H. elliptica*
§ ***elliptica*** — SPlb
montana — SPlb

Hovenia (*Rhamnaceae*)

dulcis — CAgr CBcs EBee EPfP LEdu MBlu NLar SEND WKor
- B&SWJ 11024 — WCru
- NJM 11.003 — WPGP

Howea (*Arecaceae*)

§ ***belmoreana*** 🏆H1b — XBlo
§ ***forsteriana*** 🏆H1a — CCCN LCro LOPS SArc SPlb XBlo

Hoya (*Apocynaceae*)

§ ***australis*** — EShb
bella — see *H. lanceolata* subsp. *bella*
carnosa 🏆H2 — CRHN EBak EOHP WWFP
- 'Compacta Regalis' (v) — NPer
- 'Krinkle 8' — NPer
- 'Tricolor' (v) — CCCN CDoC NPer
- 'Variegata' (v) — EShb
* ***compacta*** 'Tricolor' — NPer
darwinii misapplied — see *H. australis*
gracilis — CCCN EShb
lacunosa — CCCN
§ ***lanceolata*** — CCCN CDoC EShb
subsp. ***bella*** 🏆H1c
linearis — CDoC EShb
tsiangiana **new** — EShb

Humata (*Davalliaceae*)

tyermannii — CCCN CDoC CMen EShb LEdu SBrt SPlb WCot WFib
- 'Bunny' — CCCN LCro LOPS
- 'Selcka' — CMen

Humea see *Calomeria*

elegans — see *Calomeria amaranthoides*

Humulus ✿ (*Cannabaceae*)

japonicus 'Variegatus' (v) — SGol
lupulus — CBcs CDoC EPfP GPoy MBow NLar NMir SRms WHer WSpi
- 'Aureus' 🏆H6 — Widely available
- 'Aureus' (f) — CRHN GKev MGil SPoG WCot
* - ***compactus*** — GPoy
- 'Fuggle' — CAgr GPoy
- 'Golden Tassels' (f) — CBod CRos ECrN EHyd ELon LRHS MGil MGos MMuc MNHC NLar SEND SGol SNig SPer SPoG SRms WBor WFar
- 'Magnum' (f) **new** — LCro LOPS
- 'Northern Brewer' (f) — EBee
- 'Prima Donna' — CAgr CMac LEdu MCoo MGil MMuc NLar SPer SPoG SWvt
- 'Taff's Variegated' (v) — EWes
- 'Wye Challenger' — CAgr GPoy MHer
- 'Wye Northdown' — CAgr

Hunnemannia (*Papaveraceae*)

fumariifolia	CSpe

Huodendron (*Styracaceae*)

biaristatum	IArd

Hutchinsia see *Hornungia*

Hyacinthella (*Asparagaceae*)

glabrescens	WCot
leucophaea	WCot

Hyacinthoides (*Asparagaceae*)

aristidis	WCot
'Bakkum Blue'	GKev WHil
ciliolata	CBro GKev SGro WAbe WCot
§ ***hispanica***	NBir SEND WCot
- 'Alba'	EHyd LRHS NRHS
- subsp. ***algeriensis***	WCot
- 'Dainty Maid'	WCot
- 'Excelsior'	GKev
- 'Miss World'	GKev WCot
- 'Queen of the Pinks'	WCot
- 'Rose'	SEND
- 'White City'	WCot
§ ***italica*** 🏆H6	GKev WCot WShi
lingulata	NDry WAbe WCot
mauritanica	GKev
§ ***non-scripta***	CArg CAvo CHab CRos CTri EHyd ELan EPot GKev ILea LCro LEdu LOPS LRHS MBow MCot MMuc MPri MWat NBir NRHS SDeJ SDir SEND SPer SRms SVic WHer WShi XLum
- 'Alba'	CAvo LRHS MMuc NBir SDir SEND SRms WHil
- 'Backkum's Blue'	SDir
- 'Bracteata'	CNat WCot
- 'Chedglow Weeping'	CNat
- cleistogamous	CNat
- double-flowered, blue (d)	WCot
- double-flowered, pink (d)	WCot
- double-flowered, white (d)	WCot
- long-bracteate, white-flowered	WCot
- 'Rosea'	ILea
- 'Wavertree'	GKev WCot
reverchonii	WCot

Hyacinthus ✿ (*Asparagaceae*)

amethystinus	see *Brimeura amethystina*
azureus	see *Muscari azureum*
comosus 'Plumosus'	see *Muscari comosum* 'Plumosum'
orientalis 'Aiolos'	ECul SDeJ SDir
- var. ***albulus*** 'Roman Blue'	CAvo GKev
- - 'Roman White'	CAvo GKev
- 'Anastasia'	CAvo
- 'Anna Liza'	SDeJ
- 'Anna Marie' 🏆H4	GKev SDeJ
- 'Apricot Passion'	ERCP GKev SDeJ
- 'Blue Eyes'	SDeJ
- 'Blue Festival' 🏆H4	GKev SDeJ SDir
- 'Blue Giant'	SDeJ
- 'Blue Jacket' 🏆H4	ECul GKev SDeJ
- 'Blue Magic'	SDeJ
- 'Blue Pearl' PBR	GKev LCro LOPS SDeJ
- 'Blue Star'	SDeJ SDir
- 'Blue Tango'	ERCP
- 'Carnegie'	CArg CAvo ERCP GKev LCro LOPS SDeJ
- 'Chestnut Flower' (d)	SDeJ SDir
- 'China Pink'	CRos EHyd GKev LRHS NRHS SDeJ
- 'City of Haarlem' 🏆H4	CArg CRos EHyd GKev LCro LOPS LRHS NRHS SDeJ
- 'Crystal Palace' (d)	SDeJ
- 'Dark Dimension'	ERCP SDir
- 'Delft Blue' 🏆H4	CArg CAvo CRos EHyd GKev LCro LOPS LRHS NRHS SDeJ SPer WShi
- 'Distinction'	SDir
- 'Eros'	SDeJ
§ - 'Fairly' PBR 🏆H4	SDir WHil
- FAIRY WHITE	see *H. orientalis* 'Fairly'
- 'Fondant'	CArg CRos EHyd LCro LOPS LRHS NRHS SDeJ
- 'General Köhler' (d)	SDeJ
- 'Gipsy Queen' 🏆H4	CAvo GKev SDeJ SDir WCot
- 'Hollyhock' (d) 🏆H4	SDeJ SDir
- 'Jan Bos' 🏆H4	CArg CRos EHyd GKev LCro LOPS LRHS NRHS SDeJ
- 'Lady Derby'	SDeJ
- 'Madame Sophie' (d)	SDeJ
- 'Miss Saigon' 🏆H4	CAvo ECul ERCP SDeJ
- multi-flowered	ERCP SDeJ
- 'Odysseus'	SDeJ
- 'Paul Hermann' 🏆H4	GKev SDeJ
- 'Peter Stuyvesant'	ERCP LCro LOPS SDeJ SDir
- 'Pink Festival' 🏆H4	GKev SDeJ
- 'Pink Pearl'	CAvo CRos EHyd GKev LCro LOPS LRHS NRHS SDeJ
- 'Purple Sensation' PBR	GKev LCro LOPS SDeJ
- 'Purple Star'	LCro LOPS
- 'Red Magic'	SDeJ
- 'Rosette' (d)	SDeJ
- 'Royal Navy' (d) 🏆H4	ERCP SDeJ
- 'Sky Jacket'	GKev LCro LOPS
- 'Snow Crystal' (d)	ERCP
- 'Splendid Cornelia'	ERCP SDeJ
- 'White Festival' 🏆H4	GKev SDeJ
- 'White Pearl'	CAvo CRos EHyd GKev LCro LOPS LRHS NRHS SDeJ SPer
- 'Woodstock'	CAvo ERCP GKev LCro LOPS SDeJ SDir SPer WHil
- 'Yellowstone'	SDeJ

Hydrangea ✿ (*Hydrangeaceae*)

angustipetala	see *H. scandens* subsp. *chinensis* f. *angustipetala*
anomala subsp. ***anomala*** BWJ 8052 from China	WCru
- - HWJK 2065 from Nepal	WCru
§ - - 'Winter Glow'	EBee ESwi MRav SGol WCru WFar
- subsp. ***glabra*** B&SWJ 6804	WCru
- - 'Crûg Coral'	SMad SPoG WCru
§ - subsp. ***petiolaris*** 🏆H5	Widely available
- - B&SWJ 5996 from Yakushima	WCru
- - B&SWJ 6337	WCru
- - from Yakushima	WLov
§ - - var. ***cordifolia***	CBcs NBro NLar
- - - B&SWJ 6081	WCru
- - - B&SWJ 11487	WCru
§ - - - 'Brookside Littleleaf'	IDee NBro NLar WFar
- - dwarf	see *H. anomala* subsp. *petiolaris* var. *cordifolia*
- - 'Early Light' (v)	SGbt
- - var. ***megaphylla*** B&SWJ 4400	WCru

- - - B&SWJ 8497	WCru
* - - var. ***minor*** B&SWJ 5991	WCru
- - 'Mirranda' (v)	CBcs CRHN ELan MGos MNHC NBro NLar NOra SGol SPer SPoG SRms SWvt
§ - - var. ***ovalifolia***	CRHN ESwi LRHS SEdd
- - - B&SWJ 8799	WCru
- - - B&SWJ 8846	WCru
- - 'Silver Lining'^{PBR}	CBcs CRos CWGN EBee EHyd EPfP LCro LOPS LRHS NRHS SGsty SMad SPoG SRms
- - 'Summer Snow' (v)	CRos EHyd LRHS NRHS SPoG
- - var. ***tiliifolia***	see *H. anomala* subsp. *petiolaris* var. *ovalifolia*
- - 'Yakushima'	WCru
- subsp. ***quelpartensis***	see *H. anomala* subsp. *petiolaris* var. *ovalifolia*
- 'Winter Surprise'	see *H. anomala* subsp. *anomala* 'Winter Glow'
§ ***arborescens***	CExl MRav WPGP
- 'Annabelle' 🏆H6	Widely available
- 'Bounty'	MAsh MBlu SGol WLov
§ - subsp. ***discolor***	GBin LEdu
- - 'Sterilis'	SHyH WLov WPGP
- 'Eco Pink Puff'	SEdd WPGP
- 'Emerald Lace'	CMil IArd MBlu SEdd SGol WLov
- 'Grandiflora'	CBcs NBro WPGP
- 'Hayes Starburst'^{PBR}	CDoC CMil CRos EBee EHyd ELan EPfP LEdu LRHS MAsh MMrt SGol SHyH SPoG SWvt WPGP
- 'Hills of Snow'	NLar
- INCREDIBALL ('Abetwo'^{PBR})	CBcs CDoC CRos EHyd ELan EPfP LCro LRHS LSRN MAsh MBlu NLar NRHS SCob SGol SLon SPoG WHwl
- INCREDIBALL BLUSH ('Ncha4')	LCro LOPS LRHS
§ - INVINCIBELLE SPIRIT ('Ncha1'^{PBR})	CAby CBcs CDoC CRos ECre ECul EHyd ELan ELon EPfP LCro LOPS LRHS LSRN MAsh MBlu MThu NLar NRHS SCob SGol SGsty SHyH SLon SMad SPer SPoG SWvt WSpi
- 'Invincible Spirit'	see *H. arborescens* INVINCIBELLE SPIRIT
- LIME RICKEY ('Smnhalr')	LCro LOPS LRHS NLar SGol
- 'Magical Pinkerbell'	LRHS NLar
- 'Picadilly'	NLar
- 'Pink Annabelle'	see *H. arborescens* INVINCIBELLE SPIRIT
- 'Pink Pincushion'	NBro NLar WFar
- 'Puffed Green'	NLar
- subsp. ***radiata***	CRos EHyd LRHS MRav SGol WFar WPGP
- - 'Samantha'	EBee EPfP LRHS SPoG WLov WPGP
- RUBY ANNABELLE ('Ncha3')	LCro LOPS
- 'Ryan Gainey'	LEdu WSpi
- 'Sheep Cloud'	MBlu
- 'Vasterival'	NLar
- 'Visitation'	CTsd
- WHITE DOME ('Dardom'^{PBR})	NBro
aspera	CMac SHyH SLon SSta WCru WKif WPGP
- HWJCM 452	WCru
- from Gongshan, China	CExl CMil WPGP
- 'Anthony Bullivant' 🏆H5	EPfP IArd IDee LRHS MAsh NLar SGol SHyH SWvt WKif WLov
- 'Bellevue'	IArd WPGP
- 'Dark Chocolate'	CRos
- Farrell form	EPfP WPGP
- HOT CHOCOLATE ('Hpopr012')	CDoC CMil CTsd ELan EPfP MBlu MGos MRav SCob SGol SHyH SPoG
- Kawakamii Group	CExl CSpe ESwi LRHS NLar SGol SHyH SWvt WCru WPGP
- - B&SWJ 3456	WCru
- - B&SWJ 3527	WCru
- - B&SWJ 6702	WCru
- - B&SWJ 6714	WCru
- - B&SWJ 6827	WCru
- - B&SWJ 6996	WCru
- - B&SWJ 7101	WCru
- - 'August Abundance'	WCru
- - 'Formosa'	WCru
- - 'Maurice Mason'	CExl
- - 'September Splendour'	WCru
- Kawakamii Group × ***involucrata***	EPfP WPGP WSpi
- 'Koki'	WPGP
- 'Macrophylla' 🏆H5	ELan EPfP GKin MGil MGos MRav NLar SHyH SPer SWvt WCru WPGP WSpi
- 'Mauvette'	CMil CRos EHyd EPfP GKin LRHS MBlu NBro NLar SGol SHyH SPer WCru
- 'Peter Chappell' 🏆H5	CExl CMac CMil LRHS NLar SHyH WLov WPGP
§ - subsp. ***robusta***	CExl LRHS WPGP WSpi
- - B&SWJ 13999	WCru
- - GWJ 9430	WCru
- - KR 10735	WPGP
- - WWJ 11888	WCru
- 'Rocklon'	ESwi NLar SGol
- 'Rosthornii'	see *H. aspera* subsp. ***robusta***
- 'Sam MacDonald'	CExl CRos EHyd EPfP LRHS NLar WPGP WSpi
- 'Sapa'	EPfP WPGP
§ - subsp. ***sargentiana***	Widely available
- - 'La Fosse'	WPGP
- - large-leaved	CExl WCru
- 'Spinners'	NLar
- subsp. ***strigosa***	CExl CMil CRos CSde EHyd EPfP LRHS SMad SWvt WCru WPGP
- - B&SWJ 8201	WCru
- - KWJ 12151 from northern Vietnam	WCru
- - from Gong Shan, China	CExl
- - 'Elegant Sound Pavilion' **new**	WPGP
- - 'Gongshan'	WPGP
- 'Taiwan Pink'	NLar SGol
- 'The Ditch'	ESwi NLar
- 'Titania' **new**	WPGP
§ - Villosa Group	Widely available
- - 'Trelissick'	WPGP
- - 'Velvet and Lace' 🏆H5	EPfP LRHS MGos NLar WPGP
asterolasia B&SWJ 10481	WCru
§ 'Blue Deckle' (L)	CMac MAsh MGos MRav NBro NLar SDys SGol SHyH WBor WLov
cinerea	see *H. arborescens* subsp. *discolor*
davidii B&SWJ 8307	WCru
- B&SWJ 11692	WCru
- B&SWJ 11717	WCru
- f. ***purpurascens*** KWJ 12233B	WCru
'Dharuma'	GKin LRHS SGol
EARLY SENSATION ('Bulk'^{PBR})	CBcs CCVT CDoC CRos EHyd EPfP EShb GBin GKin LRHS MSwo NRHS SGol SHyH SPoG WFar WGrn WPGP

'Garden House Glory'	CExl CMil SAko WPGP
glabrifolia	see *H. scandens* subsp. *chinensis*
glandulosa B&SWJ 4031	WCru
'Glyn Church'	EPfP SAko SChF WPGP
aff. ***gracilis*** B&SWJ 3942	WCru
§ ***heteromalla***	CMCN LEdu NBro WPGP
- B&SWJ 2142 from India	WCru
- B&SWJ 2602 from Sikkim	WCru
- BWJ 7657 from China	WCru
- GWJ 9337 from Sikkim	WCru
- HWJ 526 from Vietnam	WCru
- HWJ 938 from Vietnam	WCru
- HWJCM 180	WCru
- HWJK 2127 from Nepal	WCru
- KR 9913 from India	WPGP
- Bretschneideri Group	EBee EPfP GKin SHyH WCru
- 'Fan Si Pan'	WCru
- 'Jermyns Lace' **new**	NLar
- 'June Pink'	NLar
- 'Long White'	NLar
- 'Morrey's Form'	NLar WCru
- 'Nepal Beauty'	EBee EPfP ESwi NLar SGol WPGP
- 'Snow in June'	GGGa
- 'Snowcap'	IArd LRHS NLar SHyH
- f. ***xanthoneura*** NJM 11.009	WPGP
- - 'Wilsonii'	WCru WKif
- 'Yalung Ridge'	WCru
aff. ***heteromalla***	SGol WSpi
'Hidcote Pink'	see *H. macrophylla* 'Juno'
hirta	MBlu
- B&SWJ 5000	WCru
- B&SWJ 11022	WCru
indochinensis	CExl
- B&SWJ 8307	WCru
- WWJ 11609	WCru
* - f. ***purpurascens***	MGil
integerrima	see *H. serratifolia*
integrifolia	WPGP
- B&SWJ 022	WCru
- B&SWJ 6967	NLar WCru
involucrata	CSde EPfP LRHS MMrt SBrt SGol WSpi
- B&SWJ 4790	WCru
- B&SWJ 11578	WCru
- dwarf	CExl WCru
- 'Hortensis' (d)	CMil NLar SMad WCru WKif WPGP WSpi
- var. ***idzuensis***	WCru
- 'Mihara-kokonoe'	CMil SGol WPGP
- 'Multiplex'	ESwi MBlu WCru
- 'Oshima'	WPGP
- 'Plena' (d)	EPfP LRHS NLar WLov WPGP WSpi
- 'Plenissima' (d)	WCru
- 'Sterilis'	CMil EPfP WCru
- 'Tokada Yama'	CMil IArd IDee NLar
- 'Viridescens' ♀H4	CBcs LRHS NLar SHyH WCru WPGP
- 'Yohraku-tama' ♀H4	EPfP NLar SGol WPGP
- 'Yokudanka' (d)	CMil IArd IDee NLar WPGP
- 'Yoraku' (d)	WCru
kawagoeana	WCru
var. ***grosseserrata*** B&SWJ 11500	
- - B&SWJ 11511	WCru
lobbii	see *H. scandens* subsp. *chinensis*
longifolia CWJ 12413	WCru
longipes	CExl WCru
- var. ***fulvescens*** B&SWJ 8188	WCru

- var. ***longipes***	CExl
- - NJM 11.084 **new**	WPGP
luteovenosa	WCru
- B&SWJ 5647	WCru
- B&SWJ 5929	WCru
- B&SWJ 6220	WCru
- B&SWJ 6317	WCru
macrophylla 'AB Green Shadow'^{PBR} (H)	MMrt SGol
- 'Adria' (H)	NLar SGol
- 'Aduarda'	see *H. macrophylla* 'Mousmée'
- 'All Summer Beauty' (H)	CBod CSBt ELan ELon GBin GGGa MAsh MNHC SHyH
- ALPEN GLOW	see *H. macrophylla* 'Alpenglühen'
§ - 'Alpenglühen' (H)	CBcs CExl CSBt LRHS SHyH SLim
- 'Altona' (H) ♀H5	CBcs CBrac CCVT CRos EHyd EPfP IArd LCro LOPS LRHS MAsh MGos MRav NBir NLar SHyH SPer SRms
- 'Amethyst' (H/d)	LRHS
- 'Ami Pasquier' (H)	CBcs CDoC CMac CRos CSBt CSde CTri EHyd ELan EPfP LRHS LSRN MNHC MRav MSwo SAko SCob SCoo SHyH SLim SPoG SRms SWvt WLov
- 'Amor' (H)	SCob SGol
- 'Angélique' (Rendez-vous Series) (H) **new**	MAsh
* - 'Aureomarginata' (v)	WCot
- 'Ave Maria' (H)	GGGa MAsh
§ - 'Ayesha' (H)	Widely available
- 'Bachstelze' (Teller Series) (L)	MAsh WLov WPGP
- 'Bavaria'^{PBR} (H)	GKin SGol WFar
- 'Beauté Vendômoise' (L)	CMil LRHS NLar SHyH
- 'Bela'^{PBR} (H)	LRHS MAsh
- 'Benelux' (H)	CBcs
- 'Bergfink' (Teller Series) (L)	NLar
- BERLIN ('Rabe'^{PBR}) (City-line Series) (H)	MAsh SGol
- 'Bicolor'	see *H. macrophylla* 'Harlequin'
- Black Steel Series (H)	LRHS NRHS
- - 'Black Steel Zambia' (H)	ELan LCro LOPS SGol WCot
- - 'Black Steel Zaza' (H)	EPfP
- - 'Black Steel Zebra' (H)	ELan SGol
- 'Black Trombone' (H)	SGol
- BLACKBERRY PIE ('Makz') (Flair & Flavours Series) (L)	CRos EHyd SPoG
§ - 'Blanc Bleu' (L)	EPfP LRHS LSRN SLim WFar
§ - 'Blauer Prinz' (H)	SHyH SRms
§ - 'Bläuling' (Teller Series) (L) ♀H5	CBod CDoC GKin LRHS LSRN MAsh SGbt SGol SLim
§ - 'Blaumeise' (Teller Series) (L) ♀H5	CDoC CSBt EBee ELon EShb GGGa LRHS MAsh MGil MGos MRav NLar SCob SCoo SDix SGol SGsty SHyH SLim SLon SPoG SWvt WFar WLov WPGP
- 'Blue Bonnet' (H)	EPfP LRHS LSRN MRav SCob SHyH SPer
- BLUE BUTTERFLY	see *H. macrophylla* 'Bläuling'
- BLUE PRINCE	see *H. macrophylla* 'Blauer Prinz'
- BLUE SKY	see *H. macrophylla* 'Blaumeise'
- BLUE TIT	see *H. macrophylla* 'Blaumeise'
- 'Blue Wave'	see *H. macrophylla* 'Mariesii Perfecta'
- BLUEBIRD	see *H. macrophylla* 'Bläuling'
- 'Bluebird' misapplied	see *H. serrata* 'Bluebird'
§ - 'Blushing Bride' (H)	LCro LOPS
- 'Bodensee' (H)	CCVT CMac MAsh SGsty WFar WSpi

	- 'Bottstein' (H)	CCVT
	- 'Bouquet Rose' (H)	ECtt MMuc NLar SEND SHyH
	- 'Brestenburg' (H)	MAsh
	- 'Brügg' (H)	LRHS MAsh SAko SGol SHyH SLim SPer
	- CAIPIRINHA ('H212907'PBR) (H)	SGol
	- 'Cameroun' (H)	MAsh SGol
	- 'Camilla'PBR (H)	SGol WFar
	- 'Camino' (L)	EPfP SGol
	- CARDINAL	see *H. macrophylla* 'Kardinal' (Teller Series)
§	- 'Cardinal Red' (H)	CRos ECre EHyd EPfP LRHS NRHS WFar
	- 'Charm' (H) **new**	SGol
	- CHIQUE ('Hbachi'PBR) (H)	LRHS NRHS
	- 'Choco Chic' (L)	SGol
	- 'Choco Pur' (Rendez-vous Series) (H) **new**	MAsh
	- CLARISSA ('Hba 208901'PBR) (H)	LRHS
	- 'Cocktail' (H)	SGol
	- 'Coco' (Beautensia Series) (H)	LRHS NRHS
	- 'Coco Blanc' (H/d)	SGol
	- COLOR FANTASY (H)	MBrN
	- 'Cordata'	see *H. arborescens*
	- 'Cotton Candy Two' (L)	CMil CRos EPfP LRHS MMrt NRHS SNig
	- 'Dark Angel' (L)	ELan LCro LOPS LRHS MGil NRHS SGol
	- 'Dark Angel Purple' (Black Diamonds Series) (L)	LCro LOPS
	- DEEP PURPLE DANCE ('Schrolla02'PBR) (Music Collection) (H)	MGos
	- 'Deutschland' (H)	CTri
	- 'Doctor Jean Varnier' (L)	EMil EPfP
	- 'Dolce Chic' (Rembrandt Series) (H) **new**	SGol
	- DOLCE FARFALLE ('Dolfarf'PBR) (H)	WCot
	- DOLCE GIPSY ('Dolgip'PBR) (L)	EPfP LRHS MGos
	- DOLCE KISS ('Dolkis'PBR) (L)	EPfP LRHS MGos SGol
	- 'Domotoi'	see *H. macrophylla* 'Setsuka-yae'
	- 'Doppio Bianco'	see *H. macrophylla* 'Wedding Gown'
	- 'Doppio Rosa' (L/d) **new**	LCro LOPS
	- 'Doris' (H)	SCob SGol SHyH
	- DRAGONFLY	see *H. macrophylla* 'Libelle'
	- EARLY BLUE ('Hba 202911'PBR) (H)	CDoC EHyd LRHS MAsh SCob SGol SPoG
§	- 'Early Sensation' (Forever & Ever Series) (H)	CMac GKin MHol
§	- 'Eisvogel' (L)	SHyH
	- 'Eldorado' (H)	CBod MGil SHyH SNig WLov WSpi
	- 'Elégance' (L)	MAsh SGol
	- 'Elegant Rosa' (Rembrandt Series) (H) **new**	SGol
	- ENDLESS SUMMER ('Bailmer') (H)	ELan SEWo SGsty
	- ENDLESS SUMMER BLUSHING BRIDE	see *H. macrophylla* 'Blushing Bride'
§	- 'Enziandom' (H)	CBcs CExl CSBt MAsh SGol
	- 'Etoile Violette' (L)	CDoC LRHS SGol
	- 'Eugen Hahn'	SGsty
	- 'Europa' (H) ♀H5	CBcs CBrac CDoC CExl NLar SHyH
	- EXPRESSION ('Youmesix') (H/d)	SGol
	- 'Fanfare'PBR (H)	SGol
§	- 'Fasan' (Teller Series) (L)	MAsh NBro SGol WFar
	- FIRELIGHT	see *H. macrophylla* 'Leuchtfeuer'
	- FIREWORKS	see *H. macrophylla* 'Hanabi'
	- FIREWORKS BLUE	see *H. macrophylla* 'Jōgasaki'
	- FIREWORKS PINK	see *H. macrophylla* 'Jōgasaki'
	- FIREWORKS WHITE	see *H. macrophylla* 'Hanabi'
	- FIRST WHITE ('Hba 202903'PBR) (H) **new**	MAsh
	- (Forever and Ever Series) FOREVER & EVER	see *H. macrophylla* 'Early Sensation'
	- - FOREVER & EVER DOUBLE PINK ('Rie 09') (H/d) **new**	SGol
	- - FOREVER & EVER PEPPERMINT ('Rie 13'PBR) (H)	CBod CSBt SGol SNig
	- - FOREVER & EVER TOGETHER ('Rie 05') (H/d)	CRos CSBt EHyd LRHS SGol SPoG
	- 'Forever Pink' (H)	GGGa MAsh NLar SGol
	- FOREVER ('Youmeone'PBR) (H/d)	CBod CSBt EPfP
§	- 'Frau Fujiyo' (Lady Series) (H)	CExl
§	- 'Frau Katsuko' (Lady Series) (H)	SPer
§	- 'Frau Mariko' (Lady Series) (H)	MRav SGol
§	- 'Frau Taiko' (Lady Series) (H)	SPer
	- 'French Cancan' (Rendez-vous Series) (L)	SGol
	- 'Frillibet' (H)	MRav NLar
	- FRISBEE ('H211903'PBR) (L)	ELan SGol
	- 'Ganku Bo Chokens' (H)	WCot
	- 'Gartenbaudirektor Kühnert' (H)	SHyH
§	- 'Générale Vicomtesse de Vibraye' (H) ♀H5	CBcs CBod CChe CDoC CEnd CRos CSde CTri EBee EHyd ELan ELon EPfP GBin LRHS MAsh MGil NBir NRHS SHyH SLim SNig SPer SPoG WBor WFar
	- GENTIAN DOME	see *H. macrophylla* 'Enziandom'
	- 'Geoffrey Chadbund'	see *H. macrophylla* 'Möwe'
	- 'Gerda Steiniger' (H)	SHyH
	- 'Gertrud Glahn' (H)	SHyH
	- 'Gimpel' (Teller Series) (L)	MAsh
§	- GLAM ROCK ('Horwack'PBR) (H)	CBcs CBod CDoC LCro LOPS MPkF SGol
	- 'Glowing Embers' (H)	IArd
	- GOLDRUSH ('Nehyosh') (L/v)	NHol SRms WCot
	- 'Gräfin Cosel' (H)	SGol
§	- 'Grant's Choice' (L)	NBro
	- GREAT STAR	see *H. macrophylla* 'Blanc Bleu'
	- 'Green Lips' (H) **new**	SGol
	- 'Grünes Gewölbe' (H)	SGol
	- 'Hamburg' (H)	CBcs CTri ECtt EPfP LRHS SDix SHyH SLim WFar
§	- 'Hanabi' (L/d) ♀H5	CBcs MBlu MGil NLar SGol SHyH WSpi
§	- 'Harlequin' (H)	CMac
	- 'Hatfield Rose' (H)	SHyH
	- 'Hatsu-shime' (L)	CMil NLar
	- 'Heinrich Seidel' (H)	CBcs CTri SHyH

- 'Hercule Poirot' (H) SGol
- 'Holehird Purple' (H) MAsh
- 'Hopcorn'PBR (H) SGol
- HOT RED ('Hba 206901'PBR) (H) CDoC CRos EHyd LRHS MAsh NRHS
- 'Hot Red Violet' (H) LCro LOPS SPoG
- (Hovaria Series) 'Hobella'PBR (L) CBcs SGol WFar
- - 'Hobergine'PBR (H) SGol
- - 'Holibel'PBR (H) SGol
- - 'Homigo'PBR (H) SGol
- - 'Hopaline'PBR (H) WPGP
- 'Inspire'PBR (H) SGol
- 'Izu-no-hana' (L/d) CAbb CBcs CMil ELan EPfP GBin MBlu MGil NLar SGol SHyH SPoG WBor WSpi
- 'James Grant' see *H. macrophylla* 'Grant's Choice'
- JIP ('H213910') (H) SGol
- 'Jofloma' (H) NLar
§ - 'Jōgasaki' (L/d) CBcs CExl CSde LRHS MAsh MBlu NLar SDys SHyH WPGP
- 'Jomari' (Fireworks Series) (L/d) SGol
- 'Joseph Banks' (H) CBcs CTri EWld SHyH
- 'Julisa' (H) **new** MPkF
§ - 'Juno' (L) SGol SHyH
- KANMARA SPLENDOUR IN CHAMPAGNE (H) **new** CRos
- KANMARA SPLENDOUR IN LILAC (H) **new** CRos
- KANMARA SPLENDOUR IN STRONG PINK (H) **new** CRos
- KANMARA SPLENDOUR IN WHITE (H) **new** CRos
- 'Kardinal' see *H. macrophylla* 'Cardinal Red' (H)
§ - 'Kardinal' (Teller Series) (L) ♀H5 MAsh SGol SHyH SPoG WLov
- 'Kardinal Violet' (L) LCro LOPS
- 'King George' (H) CBar CBcs CBod CBrac CDoC CRos CSBt EBee ECtt EHyd ELon EPfP LRHS MGil MGos MMuc NHol NRHS SAdn SAko SGol SHyH SLim SNig SPer SPoG SWvt WFar
- KINGFISHER see *H. macrophylla* 'Eisvogel'
§ - 'Klaveren' (L) ♀H5 CMil MAsh NBro SHyH
- 'Kluis Superba' (H) CTri SHyH
- 'Koria'PBR (L) CRos EMil LRHS NRHS SGol SPoG
§ - 'Kumico' (H) MAsh SCob SGol
- 'L.A. Dreamin' (H) SGol
- 'La France' (H) CBod CRos CTri EHyd LRHS MGil MNHC SHyH SLim SNig SPoG
- 'La Marne' (H) LRHS
- 'La Vie en Rose' (H) SCob SGol
- 'Lady Fujiyo' see *H. macrophylla* 'Frau Fujiyo'
- 'Lady in Red' (L) CMil CRos EHyd EPfP LRHS NRHS SPoG
- LADY KATSUKO see *H. macrophylla* 'Frau Katsuko'
- 'Lady Mariko' see *H. macrophylla* 'Frau Mariko'
- 'Lady Oshie' (Teller Series) (L) SGol
- 'Lady Taiko Blue' see *H. macrophylla* 'Frau Taiko'
- 'Lady Taiko Pink' see *H. macrophylla* 'Frau Taiko'
- 'Lanarth White' (L) ♀H5 Widely available
- 'Lemon Wave' (L/v) NLar
§ - 'Leuchtfeuer' (H) CRos ELon LRHS MGil SGol SHyH WLov
§ - 'Libelle' (Teller Series) (L) ♀H5 CBcs CMac CRos EHyd ELan ELon EPfP EShb LMil LPot LRHS MGos MMuc MRav NBir NLar NRHS SCob SEND SGol SGsty SHyH SLim SPer SPoG
- 'Lilacina' see *H. macrophylla* 'Mariesii Lilacina'
- LITTLE LIME see *H. paniculata* LITTLE LIME
- 'Love You Kiss'PBR (Hovaria Series) (L) ♀H5 CBcs CDoC CRos LRHS NLar NRHS SCoo SGol SPoG WCot
- LOVE ('Youme H1917'PBR) (H/d) CRos EPfP LOPS SGol SPer SPoG
- 'Lutin'PBR (L) CDoC
§ - 'Maculata' (L/v) WGwG
- 'Madame A. Riverain' (H) EPfP NLar SHyH
- 'Madame Emile Mouillère' (H) ♀H5 Widely available
- 'Madame Plumecocq' (H) LRHS
- (Magical Series) MAGICAL AMETHYST ('Hokomathyst'PBR) (H) CBcs CDoC SGol
- - MAGICAL CLEOPATRA ('Hortmaclepa') (H) SGol
- - MAGICAL CORAL ('Hokomac'PBR) (H) CBcs SGol
- - MAGICAL CRYSTAL ('Ankong'PBR) (H) SGol
- - MAGICAL GREENFIRE ('Qufu') (H) SGol
- - MAGICAL HARMONY ('Hortmahar'PBR) (H) NLar
- - MAGICAL JADE ('Hortmaja'PBR) (H) EPfP MBlu WCot
- - MAGICAL NOBLESSE ('Hokomano'PBR) (H) CBcs SGol
- - MAGICAL OCEAN ('Hortmoc'PBR) (H) NLar
- - MAGICAL REVOLUTION ('Hokomarevo') (H) CBcs CDoC SGol
- - MAGICAL RUBY RED ('Kolmaru'PBR) (H) SGol
- - MAGICAL RUBY TUESDAY (H) SGol
- - MAGICAL WINGS ('Hortmawin'PBR) (H) MBlu
- 'Maréchal Foch' (H) CTri NLar
- 'Mariesii' (L) CBod CTri ELan GBin LRHS MGil MSwo NLar SCob SHyH SPer
§ - 'Mariesii Grandiflora' (L) CMac CRos EHyd EPfP LRHS MMuc NBro SCob SGol SHyH SPer SRms WFar
§ - 'Mariesii Lilacina' (L) ♀H5 MMuc SEND SHyH SPer WFar WSpi
§ - 'Mariesii Perfecta' (L) Widely available
- 'Masja' (H) CBar CBcs CCVT ELon GKin IArd MAsh MGos MMuc MRav MSwo NBro NLar SAko SGol SHyH SLim WBor
- 'Mathilde Gütges' (H) CCVT SCob SGsty
- 'Max Löbner' (H) SHyH
- 'Merveille' (H) NBro
- 'Merveille Sanguine' (H) Widely available
- 'Messalina' (L) MAsh SHyH
- 'Mini Penny'PBR (H) SGol
- MINTY ICE ('Es11'PBR) (Flair & Flavours Series) (H) SGol
- 'Mirai'PBR (H) CBcs EPfP ESwi LRHS NRHS SEdd WCot WPGP
- 'Miss Belgium' (H) CMac CTri GKin
- 'Moritzburg' (H) **new** CBcs
§ - 'Mousmée' (L) SHyH
- 'Mousseline' (H) LRHS MAsh

§ - 'Möwe' (Teller Series) (L) ♕^{H5} CBcs CBod CExl CMil ECtt ELon EPfP GBin MAsh MGil MMuc NLar SCob SCoo SDix SEND SEdd SGol SHyH SLim SPer SRms WLov WSpi
- MRS KUMICO see *H. macrophylla* 'Kumico'
- 'Mrs W.J. Hepburn' (H) CSBt SPer
§ - 'Nachtigall' (Teller Series) (L) ♕^{H5} EPfP MAsh SHyH WLov WPGP
- 'Nadeshiko-gaku' (L) SHyH
- 'Nanping'^{PBR} (Sturdy Series) (L) SPoG
- 'Niedersachsen' (H) CTri MRav SHyH
- NIGHTINGALE see *H. macrophylla* 'Nachtigall'
- 'Nigra' (H) CAby CBcs CBod CExl CMac CRos EHyd ELan ELon EPfP GBin LRHS MGil MGos MMuc MNHC MRav NBro NLar NRHS SAdn SDix SEND SHyH SLim SPer WGrn WGwG
- 'Nikko Blue' (H) CBcs EBee GKin NLar SHyH
- var. ***normalis*** (L) CExl
- 'Oregon Pride' (H) GGGa MAsh WFar
- 'Otaksa' (H) CMil NLar
- 'Papagei' (Teller Series) (L) SPer
- 'Pfau' (Teller Series) (L) ♕^{H5} ELon MAsh MGil SHyH WSpi
- PHEASANT see *H. macrophylla* 'Fasan'
- 'Pia' (H) CExl CMac CMil EHyd EShb ESwi GBin LRHS MRav SMad SPer SRms WLov WSpi
- PIGEON see *H. macrophylla* 'Taube'
- 'Pink Lollipop' (Flair & Flavours Series) (H) SGol
- 'Pirate's Gold' (v) WFar
- PRINCESS DIANA ('H213') (H) **new** SGol
- 'Prinses Beatrix' (H) SHyH
- 'Quadricolor' (L/v) ♕^{H5} CDow CExl CMac CMil CTsd MGos MHol MRav SAdn SDix SHyH SPlb SRms WCot
- 'Queen Elizabeth' (H) GKin
- 'R.F. Felton' (H) CBcs SHyH
- 'Radiant' (H) SRms
- 'Rathen' (H) SGol
- 'Red Ace' (H) **new** SCob
- 'Red Angel' (Black Diamonds Series) (H) LRHS NRHS SGol
- 'Red Baron' see *H. macrophylla* 'Schöne Bautznerin'
- 'Red Beauty'^{PBR} (H) EHyd LRHS SGol
- 'Red Red' (H) MAsh
- REDBREAST see *H. macrophylla* 'Rotkehlchen'
- 'Regula' (H) SHyH
- 'Renate Steiniger' (H) CBod CBrac EBee MRav SGol SHyH SLim WAvo WSpi
- ROMANCE ('Youmenine'^{PBR}) (H/d) CRos EHyd LRHS MAsh NRHS SCob SGol SPoG WCot
- 'Rosita' (H) CBrac MAsh NBir SGol SGsty WAvo
- 'Rosso Glory' (Rembrandt Series) (H) **new** SGol
- 'Rotdrossel' (Teller Series) (L) GBin
§ - 'Rotkehlchen' (Teller Series) (L) NLar SGol SHyH SLim SPlb SWvt
- 'Rotschwanz' (Teller Series) (L) ♕^{H5} CDoC CMil GBin LRHS MAsh NLar SCob SHyH WBor WLov WPGP
- 'Rouge Baiser' (H) SGol
- 'Royal Red' (H) LRHS SGol
- 'Sabrina' (H) CBcs CBod CChe CDoC CRos EHyd LRHS MAsh NRHS SCob SGol SHyH SRkn WFar
- 'Saint Claire' (H) CBcs
- 'Salsa' (H) CBrac CDoC CRos EHyd LRHS MAsh MMrt NRHS SCob SGol SHyH
- 'Sandra' (Dutch Ladies Series) (L) CBcs CRos WFar
- 'Saskia' (Dutch Ladies Series) (H) SCob SGol
- SCHLOSS WACKERBARTH see *H. macrophylla* GLAM ROCK
- 'Schneeball' (H) CCVT MAsh SGol WLov
§ - 'Schöne Bautznerin' (H) CCVT CDoC LRHS MAsh SHyH SLim WFar WLov WSpi
- 'Sea Foam' (L) NLar
- 'Selina' (Dutch Ladies Series) (L) CBcs EHyd EPfP LRHS LSRN SCoo SGol WLov
- 'Selma'^{PBR} (Dutch Ladies Series) (L) CBcs EPfP SGol
- 'Sensation' (H) **new** CBcs
§ - 'Setsuka-yae' (L/d) SGol
- 'Shakira' (H) SGol
- 'Shamrock' (L) SHyH
- 'Sheila' (Dutch Ladies Series) (L) CBcs EPfP EShb LCro LOPS LSRN
- 'Shin-ozaki' (H) NLar
- 'Shooting Star'^{PBR} (L) LRHS
- 'Sibilla' (H) SGol SHyH SPlb WFar
- SISTER THERESE see *H. macrophylla* 'Soeur Thérèse'
- 'Sita' (L) SHyH
§ - 'Soeur Thérèse' (H) CBar CBcs CSBt EPfP MAsh MMuc NLar SGol SGsty SWvt WGwG
- 'Spike'^{PBR} (H) LRHS NRHS
- STAR GAZER ('Kompeito'^{PBR}) (Double Delight Series) (L/d) MPkF SGol
- STRAWBERRIES 'N' CREAM ('Mak2') (L) CRos EPfP SPoG
- subsp. ***stylosa*** WCru WFar WPGP
- - MF 942115 WPGP
* - 'Sunset' (L) CBcs
- 'Sweet Fantasy' (Hovaria Series) (H) ELan EPfP SGol
- 'Tandem' (H) **new** MAsh
§ - 'Taube' (Teller Series) (L) CBcs CExl ELan MAsh SGol SHyH SLim SWvt
- 'Teller Pink' see *H. macrophylla* 'Taube'
- 'Teller Red' see *H. macrophylla* 'Rotkehlchen'
- Teller Series (L) CDoC
- Teller variegated see *H. macrophylla* 'Tricolor'
- Teller Weiss see *H. macrophylla* 'Libelle'
- TIFFANY ('H211902'^{PBR}) (Flair & Flavours Series) (L) SGol
§ - 'Tivoli'^{PBR} (H) EHyd LCro LOPS LRHS NRHS SGol WFar
- TIVOLI BLUE see *H. macrophylla* 'Tivoli'
- TIVOLI PINK see *H. macrophylla* 'Tivoli'
- 'Tokyo Delight' (L) ♕^{H5} CExl CMac ESwi LRHS MAsh SDys SHyH
- 'Tovelit' (H) SGol
§ - 'Tricolor' (L/v) CBcs CTri ELan EShb LRHS MGos NLar SHyH SLon SPer WAvo WFar
- 'Variegata' see *H. macrophylla* 'Maculata'
- 'Veitchii' (L) ♕^{H5} CBcs CExl CMil CRos CSBt ECre EHyd EPfP LRHS MGos MRav MSwo SDix SHyH SPer
- 'Vibrant Verde' (Rembrandt Series) (H) **new** SGol
- 'Vicomte de Vibraye' see *H. macrophylla* 'Générale Vicomtesse de Vibraye'

- 'Warabe'	see *H. serrata* 'Warabe'
§ - 'Wedding Gown'[PBR] (L/d)	MPkF SGol
- 'Weisse Königin' (H)	SHyH
- 'Westfalen' (H) 🏆H5	CMac SDix
- 'White King'[PBR] (H)	SGol
- 'White Spirit' (L)	SGol
- 'White Wave'	see *H. macrophylla* 'Mariesii Grandiflora'
- 'Wudu'[PBR] (H)	SGol
- 'Xian'[PBR] (Sturdy Series) (H)	SGol
- 'Yola' (H)	NBro WFar
- YOU & ME TOGETHER ('Youmefive'[PBR]) (H/d)	LCro LOPS MAsh
- 'Zebra'[PBR] (H)	ELan LCro LOPS MHol WCot
- 'Zhuni Hito' (L)	NLar
- 'Zorro'[PBR] (L) 🏆H5	CBcs CBod CDoC CRos CTsd CWGN EHyd ELan EPfP ESwi GGGa LRHS LSun MAsh MGos NCou NRHS SCoo SHyH SLim SLon SPer SPoG WCot
- 'Zurichsee'	SHyH
aff. ***mangshanensis*** BWJ 8120	WCru
MISS SAORI ('H20-2') (H/d)	CBcs CBod CRos CWGN EMil LCro LOPS LRHS MPkF NRHS SPoG
paniculata	CDoC CMCN SavN
- B&SWJ 3556 from Taiwan	WCru WFar
- B&SWJ 5413 from Japan	WCru
- B&SWJ 8894 from Japan	WCru
- ANGEL'S BLUSH	see *H. paniculata* 'Ruby'
- BABY LACE ('Piihp-1')	SGol
- 'Big Ben' 🏆H5	CRos EHyd EPfP GGGa LRHS NRHS SGol
- BOBO ('Ilvobo'[PBR])	CDoC CRos ECul EHyd EPfP LRHS MGos MPkF NRHS SCob SGol
- 'Bombshell'[PBR]	EBee EMil LCro LOPS NLar NRHS SCob SGol SHyH
- 'Brussels Lace'	EPfP GWyn LSRN MRav NLar NRHS SGol SHyH SLon SSta WLov
- 'Burgundy Lace'	MBlu NLar
- CANDLELIGHT ('Hpopr013'[PBR])	MMrt SGol
- CONFETTI ('Vlasveld 02'[PBR])	LCro LOPS SGol SNig
- DART'S LITTLE DOT ('Darlido'[PBR])	GBin LSRN NLar WFar WPGP
- DIAMANT ROUGE ('Rendia'[PBR])	CCVT ECul ELan LCro LOPS LRHS MPkF NRHS SCob SGol
- DIAMANTINO ('Ren101'[PBR])	SGol
- 'Dolly'	CRos EHyd EPfP LRHS LSRN SGol SPoG
- 'Everest'	CBod CCVT CRos EHyd EPfP LRHS MMrt NLar NRHS SPoG
- FIRE LIGHT ('Smhpfl') **new**	LCro LOPS
- 'Floribunda'	CRos EHyd ELan EPfP LRHS NRHS WFar
- FRAISE MELBA ('Renba')	MPkF SGol
- 'Grandiflora'	Widely available
- 'Great Escape'	NLar
- GREAT STAR	see *H. paniculata* 'Le Vasterival'
- 'Greenspire'	CRos EHyd EPfP LRHS MBlu MRav NRHS SHyH WFar
- 'Harry's Souvenir'	NLar
- 'Kyushu'	CBcs CMac CRos CSBt CSpe CTho ELan EPfP EWhm GWyn LRHS LSRN MAsh MGos MMuc MSwo NLar NRHS SCob SDix SGol SHyH SLim SNig SPer SRkn SWvt WFar WPGP
- 'Last Post'	NRHS
§ - 'Le Vasterival'[PBR]	EMil SCob WSpi
- 'Levana'[PBR]	CMil SGol SHyH WFar
- 'Limelight'[PBR] 🏆H5	Widely available
§ - LITTLE LIME ('Jane'[PBR])	CBcs CCVT CDoC CWGN EMil EPfP LCro LOPS LRHS LSRN MAsh MMrt NLar NOra NRHS SCob SGol SGsty SPoG
- LITTLE QUICK FIRE ('Smhplqf'[PBR])	LCro LOPS SEdd SGol
- (Magical Series) MAGICAL CANDLE ('Bokraflame'[PBR])	CDoC ELan EPfP NRHS SGol
- - MAGICAL FIRE ('Bokraplume'[PBR])	LRHS MPkF NLar NRHS SGol
- - MAGICAL FLAME ('Bokratorch'[PBR])	ELan EPau
- - MAGICAL HIMALAYA ('Kolmahima'[PBR])	MGos SGol
- - MAGICAL MONT BLANC ('Kolmamon'[PBR])	EBee
- - MAGICAL MOONLIGHT ('Kolmagimo'[PBR])	SGol
- - MAGICAL STARLIGHT	see *H. paniculata* PERLE D'AUTOMNE
- - MAGICAL SUMMER ('Bokrathirteen')	SGol
- - MAGICAL VESUVIO ('Kolmavesu'[PBR])	EBee MGos SGol
- 'Mathilde'	NLar SGol
- MEGA MINDY ('Ilvomindy'[PBR])	CBcs SGol
- 'Mega Pearl'	LSRN NLar
- 'Melody'	NLar
- 'Mount Aso'	NBro SGol
- 'October Bride'	CEnd NLar WPGP
- 'Papillon'	WPGP
- 'Pee Wee'	NLar
§ - PERLE D'AUTOMNE ('Degustar')	SGol
- 'Phantom' 🏆H5	Widely available
- 'Pink Beauty'[PBR] (H)	LSRN
- PINK DIAMOND ('Interhydia') 🏆H5	CBcs CBod CDoC CMCN CRos CSBt EBee EHyd ELan EPfP GBin GKin LEdu LRHS LSRN MAsh MGos MMuc MRav NBro NLar NRHS SDix SGol SHyH WCru WFar WLov WPGP
- 'Pink Lady'	NBro SHyH
- PINKY-WINKY ('Dvppinky'[PBR]) 🏆H5	CDoC CRos CWGN EHyd EPfP ESwi GKin IArd LBuc LCro LOPS LRHS MBlu MGos MPkF NLar NRHS SCob SCoo SGol SHyH SLim SPoG SSta WFar
- 'Polar Bear'[PBR] **new**	LEdu NLar
- POLAR BEAR ('Wrhpbb2')	CWGN EBee SCob SGol SHyH
- POLESTAR ('Breg14') **new**	NLar
- 'Praecox'	MRav WCru
- PRIM'WHITE ('Dolprim')	LRHS MBlu NLar
- 'Rosy Morn'	CRos EHyd LRHS
§ - 'Ruby'	CBcs LSRN NLar SGol
- 'Silver Dollar' 🏆H5	CDoC CRos EHyd EPfP GBin IArd LCro LOPS LRHS LSRN MAsh NRHS SCob SEdd SGol SHyH SWvt WFar WSpi
- 'Sparkling'	SGol
- 'Starlight' **new**	MPkF
- 'Starlight Fantasy'	see *H. paniculata* PERLE D'AUTOMNE

	- SUNDAE FRAISE ('Rensun'[PBR])	CBod CCVT CChe CDoC CRos CWGN EBee EHyd EPfP EShb GGGa LRHS MAsh MGos MPkF NRHS SCob SEdd SGol WGrn
	- 'Tardiva'	CBcs CBod CTho EBee EPfP GKin LCro LOPS MGos NBro SDix SGol SHyH SPer SRms SWvt WFar WLov WPGP
	- 'Tender Rose'	NLar
	- 'Unique'	CBcs CBod CCVT CRos CTho EHyd ELan EPfP LRHS LSRN MAsh MRav MSwo NBro NLar NRHS SCoo SGol SHyH SPer SSta WAvo WCru WFar WKif WLov WPGP
	- VANILLE FRAISE ('Renhy'[PBR])	Widely available
	- 'White Goliath'	NLar
	- 'White Lace'	NLar
	- 'White Lady'	CBcs LRHS NRHS SGol
	- 'White Moth'	GGGa LRHS NBro NLar SAdn SHyH
	- 'Wim's Red'[PBR]	CBcs CBod ECul ELan EPfP EShb ESwi LCro LOPS MMrt MPkF MThu NLar NOra SCob SGol SSta WSpi
	- 'Yuan-Yang'	WCru
	peruviana var. ***oerstedii*** B&SWJ 10750	WCru
	peruviana × ***seemannii***	CEnd GKin IArd SSta
	peruviana × ***serratifolia***	CRHN
	petiolaris	see *H. anomala* subsp. *petiolaris*
	'Preziosa' 🏆[H4]	Widely available
	quercifolia	Widely available
	- 'Alice'	CDoC CMac EBee EHyd ELan EPfP ESwi LRHS LSRN MAsh NLar SGol SHyH WPGP
	- 'Alison'	SGol
I	- 'Amethyst' Dirr	CJun NLar SGol
	- 'Applause'	CRos EBee EHyd ELan EPfP LRHS NLar SGol WPGP
	- 'Back Porch'	NLar SGol
	- 'Burgundy'	CBcs CJun CMil EBee EPfP ESwi IArd LRHS MBlu NLar SGol WPGP WSpi
	- 'Flore Pleno'	see *H. quercifolia* SNOWFLAKE
	- 'Harmony'	CMil CRos EBee EHyd ELan EPfP ESwi IDee LRHS MGos NLar NRHS SHyH SSta WLov WPGP
	- ICE CRYSTAL ('Hqopr010'[PBR])	CDoC CTsd EBee ELan EPfP ESwi LRHS MMrt NLar SGol SMad WAvo WPGP WSpi
	- 'Lady Anne'	WPGP
	- 'Little Honey'[PBR]	SGol
	- LITTLE HONEY ('Brihon')	LRHS MAsh NLar SGol WPGP
	- 'Munchkin'	LRHS SGol
	- 'Pee Wee'	CBcs CDoC CRos EBee EHyd ELan EPfP LRHS MAsh MPkF SAko SGol SHyH SLon SPoG SSta SWvt WLov WPGP
	- 'Queen of Hearts'	ESwi
	- 'Ruby Slippers'	CDoC ESwi LRHS MThu NLar SEdd SGol
	- 'Sike's Dwarf'	ELan MPkF MRav NLar SGol WCFE WLov
	- SNOW QUEEN ('Flemygea') 🏆[H5]	Widely available
	- 'Snowdrift'	CJun
§	- SNOWFLAKE ('Brido') (d) 🏆[H5]	CBcs CDoC CEnd CMac CRos CSde CWGN ELan EPfP LCro LOPS LRHS MAsh MGos MPkF MRav NLar NRHS SGol SHyH SLon SPer SPoG WLov WPGP WSpi

	- 'Tennessee Clone'	CJun EBee LRHS NLar
	'Renatea'	CSBt
	sargentiana	see *H. aspera* subsp. *sargentiana*
	scandens	NBro
	- B&SWJ 5448	WCru
	- B&SWJ 5481	WCru
	- B&SWJ 5496	WCru
	- B&SWJ 5523	WCru
	- B&SWJ 5602	WCru
	- B&SWJ 5725	WCru
	- B&SWJ 5893	WCru
	- B&SWJ 6159	WCru
	- B&SWJ 6317	WCru
§	- subsp. ***chinensis***	CExl
	- - B&SWJ 1488	WCru
	- - B&SWJ 3214	WCru
	- - B&SWJ 3410 from Taiwan	WCru
	- - B&SWJ 3420	WCru
	- - B&SWJ 3423 from Taiwan	WCru
	- - B&SWJ 3487 from Taiwan	WCru
	- - B&SWJ 3869	WCru
	- - BWJ 8000 from Sichuan	WCru
	- - BWJ 8035	WCru
§	- - f. ***angustipetala***	WPGP
	- - - B&SWJ 3454	WCru
	- - - B&SWJ 3553	WCru
	- - - B&SWJ 3667	WCru
	- - - B&SWJ 3733	WCru
	- - - B&SWJ 3814	WCru
	- - - B&SWJ 6038 from Yakushima	WCru
	- - - B&SWJ 6041 from Yakushima	WCru
	- - - B&SWJ 6056 from Yakushima	WCru
	- - - B&SWJ 6787	WCru
	- - - B&SWJ 6802	WCru
	- - - B&SWJ 7121	WCru
	- - - B&SWJ 7128	WCru
§	- - - 'Golden Crane'	EPfP WCru WFar WPGP
	- - - 'Monlongshou'	see *H. scandens* subsp. *chinensis* f. *angustipetala* 'Golden Crane'
	- - 'Big White'	EBee WPGP
	- - f. ***formosana***	CMil SBrt
	- - - B&SWJ 1488	WCru
	- - - B&SWJ 7058	NLar
	- - - B&SWJ 7097	NLar WCru
	- - f. ***macrosepala*** B&SWJ 3423	ESwi WCru
	- - - B&SWJ 3476	WCru
	- - - CWJ 12441	WCru
	- - f. ***obovatifolia*** B&SWJ 3487b	WCru
	- - - B&SWJ 3683	WCru
	- - - B&SWJ 3869 from the Philippines	WCru
	- - - B&SWJ 7121	WCru
	- subsp. ***liukiuensis***	WCru
	- - B&SWJ 6022	WCru
	- - B&SWJ 11471	WCru
	- 'Splash' (v)	CMil
	seemannii	Widely available
	- 'Roger Grounds' (v)	WCot
	aff. ***seemannii***	CBod GKin WHwl WSpi
	SEMIOLA ('Inovalaur'[PBR])	CBcs CRos EBee EHyd EPfP LRHS NRHS SGol SLim
	serrata	CExl CTri WKif
	- B&SWJ 6184	WCru
	- B&SWJ 6241	WCru
	- PAB 4757	LEdu

	- 'Acuminata'	see *H. serrata* 'Bluebird'
	- 'Aigaku' (L)	CExl CMil
	- 'Akabe-yama'	NBro NLar
	- 'Aka-tsanayama'	LRHS
	- 'Akishino-temari'	EBee WPGP
	- Amacha Group	SGol
	- - 'Amagi-amacha' (L)	CMil NBro NLar
	- - 'Ō-amacha' (L)	CMil WPGP
	- 'Amagyana' (L)	CExl
	- subsp. ***angustata***	WCru
	- 'Ao-yama'	WPGP
	- AVELROZ ('Dolmyf'PBR)	EPfP SGol
	- 'Belladonna'	LRHS NBro
	- 'Belle Deckle'	see *H.* 'Blue Deckle'
	- 'Beni-gaku' (L)	CExl CRos ECre EHyd LRHS MAsh NBro NLar NRHS SGol SHyH
	- 'Beni-temari'	LRHS NBro
	- 'Beni-yama' (L) ♀H4	CMil
	- 'Blue Billow' (L)	NBro NLar
	- BLUEBERRY CHEESECAKE	see *H. serrata* TUFF STUFF
§	- 'Bluebird' (L) ♀H4	Widely available
I	- 'Boothii' (L)	CMac
	- 'Cap Sizun'	SChF SGol WPGP
	- 'Chiba Cherry-lips'	ESwi WCru
	- 'Chiri-san Sue' (d)	WCru
	- COTTON CANDY	see *H. serrata* TUFF STUFF
	- 'Crûg Bicolor' (L)	WCru
	- 'Crûg Caerulean'	WCru
	- 'Crûg Cobalt' (L)	ESwi GGGa WCru
	- 'Crûg Sō Cool' (L)	ESwi WCru
	- 'Diadem' (L) ♀H4	CAbb CBod CExl CMil ELon EPfP LRHS NBro SEdd
	- 'Forget Me Not'	LRHS NBro
	- 'Fuji Snowstorm' (v)	CMil
	- 'Fuji Waterfall'	see *H. serrata* 'Fuji-no-taki'
	- 'Fuji-no-shirayuki' (L/d)	LRHS
§	- 'Fuji-no-taki' (L/d) ♀H4	CMil WPGP
	- 'Gaka'	LRHS
	- 'Golden Showers' (L)	NBro
	- 'Golden Sunlight'PBR (L)	SGol SWvt
	- 'Grayswood' (L) ♀H4	CBcs CBod CDoC CExl CMac CRos CSBt EHyd ELan EPfP LRHS MAsh MGil MRav NBro NRHS SCob SDix SEdd SGol SHyH SLim SPer WKif WLov WPGP
	- 'Hagoromo' **new**	CMil
	- 'Hakucho' (L/d)	CMil NBro WPGP
	- 'Hallasan' misapplied	see *H. serrata* 'Maiko', 'Spreading Beauty'
	- 'Hallasan' R. & J. de Belder (L)	CMil WPGP
	- 'Hime-benigaku' (L)	CMil MAsh MBlu SEdd WFar
	- 'Hoshi-kuzu' **new**	CMil
	- 'Impératrice Eugénie' (L)	LRHS NLar
	- 'Intermedia' (L)	CExl NBro
	- 'Kiyosumi' (L) ♀H5	CBcs CBrac CEnd CExl CMil EBee ECre ELon EPfP LRHS NBir NLar SBrt SHyH WBor WCru WLov WPGP
	- 'Klaveren'	see *H. macrophylla* 'Klaveren'
	- 'Koreana' (L)	SAko SGol
	- 'Kurenai' (L)	CMil EBee NBro NLar WFar WPGP
	- 'Kurohime' (L)	CDoC EBee NBro WFar WPGP
	- 'Macrosepala' (L)	WPGP
§	- 'Maiko' (L)	IArd
	- 'Midori' (L)	CExl
	- 'Mikamba'	see *H. serrata* 'Mikanba-gaku'
§	- 'Mikanba-gaku' (L)	SGol
	- 'Mikata Yae'	CMil WPGP
	- 'Miranda' (L) ♀H4	CExl CMil CRos EHyd EPfP LRHS MAsh NBro NLar SDys SGol SHyH WFar
	- 'Miyama-yae-murasaki' (L/d) ♀H4	CExl CMil SGol SRms WPGP
	- 'Momo-beni-yama'	CMil NBro
	- 'Mont Aso'	CMil IArd NLar SEdd
	- 'Niji' (L)	WPGP
	- 'Odoriko-amacha'	CMil EBee LRHS SChF WPGP
	- 'Otsu-hime'	NLar
	- 'Pretty Maiden'	see *H. serrata* 'Shichidanka'
§	- 'Prolifera' (L/d)	CMil
	- 'Pulchella'	see *H. serrata* 'Prolifera'
	- 'Ramis Pictis' (L)	CBcs NBro NLar SHyH
	- 'Rosalba' (L) ♀H4	CExl ECre NBro
	- 'Santiago'PBR (L)	EPfP SGol WPGP
	- 'Sekka'	SEdd WPGP
§	- 'Shichidanka' (L/d)	EPfP LRHS NBro SHyH
	- 'Shichidanka-nishiki' (L/d/v)	CExl
	- 'Shinonome' (L/d)	CExl CMil
	- 'Shirahuzi' (L/d)	SGol
	- 'Shirofuji' (L/d) ♀H4	CMil
	- 'Shiro-gaku' (L)	CMil MAsh NBro NLar
	- 'Shiro-maiko'	SEdd WPGP
	- 'Shirotae' (L/d)	CExl LRHS SGol
	- 'Shōjō' ♀H4	CMil EBee NBro SGol WPGP
	- subsp. ***sinensis***	GKev
§	- 'Spreading Beauty' (L)	WPGP
	- 'Suzukayama-yama'	WPGP
*	- var. ***thunbergii*** 'Plena' (L/d)	WCru
	- 'Tiara' (L) ♀H4	CAbb CExl CMil CRos EBee EHyd EPfP GGGa LRHS LSRN MAsh NBir NBro NLar NRHS SDix SDys SEdd SGol SHyH SLim SPoG WPGP
§	- TUFF STUFF ('Mak 20'PBR) (L)	CRos EPfP LRHS NRHS SGol SPoG SReu
	- 'Veerle' (L)	NBro NLar SGol
§	- 'Warabe'	CMil SGol
	- 'Yae-no-amacha' (L/d)	CBcs CExl CMil NBro NLar
	- subsp. ***yezoensis***	CMil NLar SGol
	- - 'Hime-gaku'	CMil
§	***serratifolia***	CBcs CExl IArd IDee SSta WPGP
	- HCM 98056	WCru
	sikokiana B&SWJ 11174	WCru
	- B&SWJ 5035	WCru
	- B&SWJ 5855	WCru
	- B&SWJ 11381	WCru
	'Silver Slipper'	see *H. macrophylla* 'Ayesha'
	steyermarkii B&SWJ 10501	WCru
	tiliifolia	see *H. anomala* subsp. *petiolaris* var. *ovalifolia*
	villosa	see *H. aspera* Villosa Group
	xanthoneura	see *H. heteromalla*
	aff. ***zhewanensis*** MF 93117	WCru

Hydrastis (*Ranunculaceae*)

canadensis	EMor GPoy LEdu

Hydrocharis (*Hydrocharitaceae*)

morsus-ranae	CBen CHab CWat EWat LLWG MWts NPer WPnP

Hydrocleys (*Alismataceae*)

nymphoides	XBlo

Hydrocotyle (*Araliaceae*)

asiatica	see *Centella asiatica*

leucocephala **new**	XBlo
sibthorpioides 'Crystal Confetti' (v)	LLWG WHil
vulgaris	CWat EWat

Hydrophyllum (*Boraginaceae*)

canadense	IMou
virginianum	LEdu WHal WPGP

Hygrophila (*Acanthaceae*)

corymbosa 'Stricta' **new**	XBlo

Hylomecon (*Papaveraceae*)

hylomeconoides	EWld WCru
§ ***japonica***	CAby CMiW CRos EBee EHyd ELan EPot EWld GEdr GKev GLog IMou LEdu LRHS MAvo NBir NHar NHpl NQui NRHS NRya WCot WPGP

Hylotelephium (*Crassulaceae*)

§ 'Abbey Dore'	CBod EBee ECtt ELan ELon EPfP LRHS MTis NBir SPhx WCAu
AMBER ('Florseamb')	WCot
§ ***anacampseros***	GQue MHer MMuc NDov NWad SEND XLum
'Aquarel'	GBin GWyn
'Autumn Charm'	see *H.* (Herbstfreude Group) 'Lajos'
§ 'Bertram Anderson' ♀H7	Widely available
'Birthday Party' (Birthday Party Series)	SPoG
'Blade Runner'	LRHS
'Blue Pearl'PBR (SunSparkler Series)	CSpe EBee LCro LOPS LRHS MPnt MSCN SPoG WHil
§ 'Carl' ♀H7	Widely available
§ ***cauticola*** ♀H5	EPot MAsh MMuc MRav NWad SRms WIce XLum
- 'Coca-Cola'	CMac CWGN EBou ECtt EHyd EMor EPfP GBin GWyn LRHS MAsh MAvo MCot MRav NBir NDov NHpl NRHS NWad SEdd SPhx SPoG SSim SWvt WFar WHoo
- 'Lidakense' ♀H5	CMea CSpe CTri ECha ECtt EPot MAsh MHer NHol NLar NWad SPlb XLum XSen
- 'Robustum'	see *H.* 'Ruby Glow'
'Chocolate Cherry'	SHeu
'Chocolate Drop'PBR	CWGN NLar SHeu SRms
'Class Act'PBR	CRos ECtt EHyd LRHS MNrw NDov NLar NRHS SPoG SRms
'Cloud Walker'PBR	ECtt MNrw SPoG WFar
'Crazy Ruffles'	WCot
cyaneum 'Sakhalin'	CRos EHyd LRHS NRHS
'Dark Jack'	ECtt GQue MTis NGdn WCot
'Dazzleberry'PBR (SunSparkler Series)	EPfP LCro LOPS
§ ***erythrostictum***	GBin XLum
- B&SWJ 11384	WCru
- 'Frosty Morn' (v)	Widely available
§ - 'Mediovariegatum' (v)	CDor ELan LPot LRHS MHer MNrw SWvt WFar XLum
§ ***ewersii***	ECtt MAsh MMuc NBro NLar SPhx SPlb
- CC 5288	GKev
- var. ***homophyllum*** 'Rosenteppich'	CDoC EHyd EPPr EPfP GWyn LRHS NBir NRHS SPoG SRms SWvt WAvo
'Firecracker'PBR (SunSparkler Series)	LOPS LSou MHol MPnt MSCN WNPC
'Frosted Fire'	CBod MAsh SRms WFar
'Green Expectations'	MRav NBre
§ Herbstfreude Group	EHyd LPot LRHS NWsh SGbt WCav WMal
- 'Autumn Fire'	EBee MAsh
- 'Elsie's Gold' (v)	EBee ECtt EPfP LRHS MAvo MNrw SRms WHil
§ - 'Herbstfreude' ♀H7	Widely available
- 'Jaws'PBR	CKno EBee ECtt LSou NLar WCot WFar XLum
§ - 'Lajos' (v)	MAsh WCot WFar WHil
- 'Mini Joy'	ELon LRHS MHol MNrw
'Ice Ruffles' (v)	MCot SPoG WFar
'José Aubergine'PBR	CBod CKno EBee ECtt EHyd EPfP EWTr IPot LCro LOPS LRHS MAsh MBel MRav MTis NDov NHol NLar NRHS NSti SCob SHeu SPoG SRms WCAu WPGP
§ 'Joyce Henderson'	CDor CElw EHyd ELan EPfP GBin LRHS MCot MRav MTis NChi NLar SPer SRms WAvo WBrk WCot WOld XSen
'Lac d'Oô'	GBin
'Lime Zinger'PBR (SunSparkler Series)	CRos LCro LOPS LSou SEdd WNPC
I 'Marchants Best Red' ♀H7	LRHS MNrw MRav SPhx WCot WMal
§ 'Matrona' ♀H7	Widely available
§ 'Mr Goodbud'PBR ♀H7	CAby CBct ECtt GPSL LRHS LSun MAsh MAvo MHol MNrw NBir NLar NRHS SAko SCob SHeu SPoG SRms WCAu WCot WSpi WTor
'Munstead Purple'	MCot
§ 'Munstead Red'	CBod CDor CRos EBee ECha ECtt EHyd EPfP LRHS MNHC MNrw MRav MTis NLar NRHS SCob SPer SPhx SRms WCAu WFar WKif WMal
§ 'Oriental Dancer' **new**	MThu
'Pinky'	EBee
§ ***pluricaule***	EHyd EPot LRHS NBro NHol NRHS NWad SPlb SRms WCav WHoo
'Pool Party'PBR (Party Hardy Series)	CRos EHyd EPfP LRHS NLar NRHS SRms
§ ***populifolium***	ECha IMou MHer MMuc NLar WMal XLum
§ 'Red Cauli' ♀H7	Widely available
'Red Rum'	GWyn
'Red Setter'	SAko SPhx WMal WPGP
§ 'Ruby Glow' ♀H5	CRos CSBt CTri EBee ECha ECtt EHyd ELan EPfP EWTr GMaP GWyn LCro LOPS LRHS MAvo MCot MHer MRav MSwo NBid NDov NGdn NRHS SPer SPhx SWvt WBrk WSpi XLum
'Ruby Port'	CSpe
§ ***sieboldii***	NDov
- 'Dragon'	MHCG
- 'Mediovariegatum' (v) ♀H4	MHer MRav SPlb XLum
§ ***spectabile*** ♀H7	CBod CTri EHyd ELan EPfP GJos LRHS MCot MHer MRav NGdn NRHS SGbt SPlb SRms WBor WBrk WFar WSFF
- BLACK BEAUTY ('Florseblab')	ECtt MNrw NLar
- Brilliant Group	CBar CRos SCob SRms WCAu
- - 'Brilliant' ♀H7	CBcs CBod CSBt CTri ECha ECtt EHyd ELan EPfP LCro LOPS LRHS MAvo MGos MRav NGdn NLar NWsh SCob SPer SPoG SWvt WFar WSpi

- - 'Carmen'	NBir XLum
- - 'Hot Stuff'	CAby CRos ECtt EHyd ELan EPau EPfP LRHS LSRN NCou NRHS SPoG SRms WCot
- - 'Lisa'	GWyn NLar
- - 'Meteor'	MRav NLar
- - 'Neon'	EHyd EPfP LRHS MAsh
- - 'Pink Fairy'	MNrw
- - 'Rosenteller'	NBre WBrk
§ - - 'Septemberglut'	CRos EHyd LRHS NBre NRHS WSpi XLum
- - 'Steven Ward'	EWes
- 'Crystal Pink'PBR	MNrw NLar
- 'Humile'	XLum
- 'Iceberg'	CBod EBee ECha ECtt EHyd EPfP GBin LPot LRHS MCot MGos MRav NGdn NLar NRHS SPhx SWvt WCAu WFar WSFF WSpi XLum XSen
- 'Nordlicht'	GWyn
- 'Pink Chablis' (v)	WCot
- SEPTEMBER GLOW	see *H. spectabile* (Brilliant Group) 'Septemberglut'
- 'Stardust'	CRos CTri EBee EHyd EPfP GBin GKev GMaP LCro LRHS LSou MBNS MTis NBPC NRHS SCob SPer SRms WBrk WFar XLum
- 'Variegatum'	see *H. erythrostictum* 'Mediovariegatum'
- WALBERTON'S PIZAZZ	EHyd EPfP LRHS NRHS SPoG
§ 'Stewed Rhubarb Mountain'	CKno EBee ECha ECtt EHyd ELan EPfP EWTr LRHS MBNS MRav NLar NRHS SGbt WCAu
'Sunset Cloud'	EWes LPla LPot MRav
§ ***tatarinowii***	WCot
§ ***telephium***	NBir SIvy SRms WSFF XLum
§ - Atropurpureum Group	MRav NLar SWvt
- - 'African Pearl'	GWyn
- - 'Arthur Branch'	EHyd GWyn LRHS NChi
- - 'Bon Bon'	EPfP MTis NLar SPoG
- - 'Bressingham Purple'	CRos EBee EHyd LRHS NRHS
- - 'Chocolate'	GPSL NLar
- - 'Dark Knight'	CRos EHyd EPfP GPSL LRHS NRHS
- - 'El Cid'	EWes
- - 'Karfunkelstein' ♀H7	CKno EBee ECha ECtt EHyd GLog LCro LOPS LPot LRHS MAvo MHol MTis MWat NBir NDov SPhx WCot XLum
- - 'Lynda et Rodney'	EWes
- - 'Lynda Windsor'	ECtt EPfP NLar SWvt
- - 'Möhrchen'	GMaP MRav NGdn NLar SPhx
- - 'Picolette'	EBee ECtt EHyd EPfP LRHS MNrw NGdn NRHS SPoG SRms WCot
- - 'Postman's Pride'PBR	CWGN ECtt EPfP GWyn NGdn
§ - - 'Purple Emperor' ♀H7	Widely available
- - 'Purple Moon'	SPhx
- - 'Ringmore Ruby'	EBee MNrw SPhx WCot WPGP
- - 'Xenox'PBR ♀H7	CBct CBod CWGN EBee ECtt EHyd EPfP EShb GBin IPot LRHS MAsh MAvo MCot MNrw NLar NRHS NWad SPoG SRms WAvo WCAu
- 'Cherry Truffle'PBR	SHeu
- 'Desert Black'PBR **new**	LSou
- Emperor's Waves Group	CPla ELan MNHC NGdn NWad
§ - subsp. ***fabaria***	ECtt MRav NWsh WCot
- - var. ***borderei***	CElw LPla SGro SPhx
- 'Jennifer'	CAby EBee ECtt GQue MAvo MBel MHol SGro WCAu WCot WHoo WRHF
- 'Marina'PBR **new**	NDov
- subsp. ***maximum*** 'Atropurpureum'	see *H. telephium* Atropurpureum Group
- - 'Gooseberry Fool'	CMea EBee ECtt ELan EPfP GMaP LRHS LSou MAvo MBriF NEoE SPhx SRms WCAu
- 'Moonlight Serenade'PBR	EBee ECtt EHyd EPfP LRHS SRms
- 'Orange Xenox'PBR	EPfP LPla
- 'Raspberry Truffle'	EPfP LRHS SHeu
§ - subsp. ***ruprechtii***	CDor ECha ECtt EHyd EPfP GMaP LRHS MCot MRav NLar NRHS SPer SPhx WWtn
- - 'Citrus Twist'	ECtt LRHS MRav WMal
- - 'Hab Gray'	CAby CSpe EBee ECtt EWes EWld LRHS NLar SGro SRms
- - 'Pink Dome'	ECha LPla
- 'Strawberries and Cream'	CMac EBee ECha ECtt EHyd ELan ELon EPfP EShb GMaP LCro LRHS MBNS MBel MMuc MRav NGdn NLar NRHS SGbt SPer WHil
- 'Sunkissed'PBR	ECtt LPla NLar WHil
- 'Touchdown Flame'PBR	SHeu
- 'Touchdown Teak'PBR	CKno EBee EHyd EPfP IPot LEdu MAsh NRHS SCob SHeu WTor
- 'Twinkling Star'PBR	MNrw
- YELLOW MATRONA ('Eline'PBR)	LCro LOPS MAsh MSCN WHil
- 'Yellow Xenox'PBR	ECtt EHyd LRHS NLar
'Thundercloud'PBR	EPfP GJos MTin NLar NWad SCob SRms
'Thunderhead'PBR	NLar SHeu
'Tropical Night' (Censation Series) **new**	CBod
§ ***ussuriense***	EPfP GBin GPSL NBir
- 'Chuwangsan'	EWld WCru
'Veluwse Wakel'	ECtt GBin GWyn
§ 'Vera Jameson' ♀H5	CRos EAJP ECha ECtt EHyd ELan EPfP EShb GKev LRHS LSRN MBel MCot MRav MWat NBir NHol NRHS NWsh SPer SRms SWvt WHoo WKif WSMil WSpi WWtn
§ ***viviparum***	NLar
- B&SWJ 8662	WCru
WALBERTON'S PINK WHISPER	EHyd EPfP LRHS NRHS SPoG
'Washfield Purple'	see *H. telephium* (Atropurpureum Group) 'Purple Emperor'

Hymenanthera see *Melicytus*

Hymenocallis (*Amaryllidaceae*)

× ***festalis***	see *Ismene* × *deflexa*
harrisiana	CCCN GKev SDeJ
longipetala	see *Ismene longipetala*
'Sulphur Queen'	see *Ismene* 'Sulphur Queen'

Hymenolepis (*Asteraceae*)

parviflora	see *Athanasia parviflora*

Hymenosporum (*Pittosporaceae*)

flavum	EShb

Hymenoxys (*Asteraceae*)

grandiflora	see *Tetraneuris grandiflora*
§ ***hoopesii***	CMac CRos EHyd EMor GMaP GWyn LPot LRHS NBir NGrd NLar NRHS SPer SRms WFar XLum

Hyoscyamus (*Solanaceae*)

niger	GPoy WSFF XAbr

Hypericum ✿ (*Hypericaceae*)

	Name	Suppliers
	CC 4131	CExl
	CC 4544	CExl
	aegypticum	CPBP CTri EPot MHer SBrt SPlb WAbe WThu
	androsaemum	CBod ECha ELan GAbr MHer MMuc MSwo NPer SCob SEND WFar WOut
§	- 'Albury Purple'	ELan EShb XLum
	- 'Autumn Blaze'	CBcs
	- 'Excellent Flair'	NLar
§	- f. ***variegatum*** 'Mrs Gladis Brabazon' (v)	CMac EShb NBir WCot
	'Archibald'	EWes NWad
	athoum	WThu
	balearicum	MMuc SBrt WAbe WIce XSen
	bellum	SPtp
	buckleyi	WAbe
	calycinum	CBod CBrac CMac CTri ELan EPfP LBuc MGos MRav SCob SEND SPer SRms SWvt WFar XLum
	- 'Brigadoon' 🏆H5	MAsh SGol
	- CARNIVAL ('Crowthyp') (v)	LSou NEoE
	- 'Senior'	CBod
	cerastioides	CSma CTri EDAr EWes GJos MMuc NGdn SRms WAbe
	coris	EWes SRms
	cuneatum	see *H. pallens*
	× ***cyathiflorum*** 'Gold Cup'	CMac EHyd LRHS MAsh
	× ***dummeri*** 'Peter Dummer'	NLar WSpi
	'Eastleigh Gold'	CMac
	elodes	CWat LLWG
	'Fancy Pants'	LEdu WPGP
	forrestii 🏆H5	MMuc SEND
	fragile misapplied	see *H. olympicum* f. *minus*
	GOLDEN BEACON ('Wilhyp'PBR) 🏆H5	CEnd CSpe EHyd ESwi LRHS MAsh MHer MMuc MNrw NBir NWad SEND WCot
	grandiflorum	see *H. kouytchense*
	grandifolium	EDAr
	henryi L 753	SRms
	- subsp. ***hancockii*** NJM 10.092	WPGP
	'Hidcote'	see *H.* × *hidcoteense* 'Hidcote'
§	× ***hidcoteense*** 'Hidcote' 🏆H5	Widely available
	- 'Hidcote Variegated' (v)	MAsh SLim SRms
	hirsutum	CHab NMir
	× ***inodorum*** 'Albury Purple'	see *H. androsaemum* 'Albury Purple'
	- 'Autumn Surprise'PBR	NWad
	- 'Dream'	NLar
	- 'Elstead'	EPfP MRav NLar NWad WSpi
	- MAGICAL CHERRY ('Kolmcherrip'PBR)	ELan EPfP SCob
	- MAGICAL GRACE ('Kolmagrace'PBR)	CBod LSou SCob SPad
	- MAGICAL LIGHTNING ('Kolmligh'PBR)	CBod LSou MMrt NEoE NLar
	- MAGICAL LIMELIGHT ('Kolmalimeli'PBR)	ELan
	- MAGICAL PUMPKIN ('Kolmapuki'PBR)	CBod LSou NEoE SCob
	- MAGICAL SUNSHINE ('Kolmasun'PBR)	NEoE SCob SPer
	- MAGICAL UNIVERSE ('Kolmuni'PBR)	CBod LSou NEoE NLar
	- MAGICAL WHITE ('Kolmawhi'PBR)	CBod ELan EPfP LSou MMrt NEoE SPoG
	- 'Rheingold'	MAsh NLar
	- 'Ysella'	MRav
	kalmianum	IDee SBrt
	kamtschaticum	XLum
	kazdaghense	EWes
§	***kouytchense*** 🏆H5	CRos EHyd EPfP EWes GBin LRHS MAsh MMuc MRav SEND SPoG SWvt WKif WSpi
	lancasteri	CRos EHyd EPfP ESwi LRHS MAsh SPoG SPtp
	leschenaultii misapplied	see *H.* 'Rowallane'
	'Little Misstery'	CDoC CRos EBee EHyd EMil EPfP LBuc LRHS MAsh NEoE NRHS SCob SPoG
	maclarenii	EWes
	MAGICAL BEAUTY ('Kolmbeau'PBR)	CBod ELon EPfP MMrt NEoE NLar SGbt SPer SPoG
	MAGICAL RED FLAME ('Kolmaref'PBR)	CBod EPfP
	MAGICAL RED ('Kolmred')	EPfP NEoE NLar SPoG
	MIRACLE ATTRACTION ('Alldiablo'PBR)	CDoC CRos LRHS SRms
	MIRACLE BLIZZ ('Allblizz')	CRos EHyd LRHS NRHS
	MIRACLE BLOSSOM ('Allblossom'PBR)	CRos EHyd LRHS NRHS
	MIRACLE FANTASY ('Hymirfan')	NLar
	MIRACLE MARVEL ('Allmarvel'PBR) **new**	CDoC
	MIRACLE SUMMER ('Hymirsum')	EPfP NEoE NLar
	MIRACLE WONDER ('Hymirwon')	CRos LRHS
	× ***moserianum*** 🏆H5	CMac CRos EHyd EPfP EWes LRHS NPer SCob SLon SPer SRms WFar
	- 'Daybreak'	CRos EHyd LRHS MAsh NEoE SGol SPoG
§	- 'Tricolor' (v)	CBcs CBod CBrac CMac CRos CSBt CTri EBee ECrN EHyd ELan ELon EPfP LCro LOPS LRHS MAsh MGos MRav MSwo NRHS SCob SGol SLim SPer SPlb SPoG SWvt WFar WSMil
	- 'Variegatum'	see *H.* × *moserianum* 'Tricolor'
	'Mr Bojangles'	SCob
	'Mrs Brabazon'	see *H. androsaemum* f. *variegatum* 'Mrs Gladis Brabazon'
	oblongifolium	CExl
	olympicum 🏆H4	CBod CRos CTri ECha EHyd ELan GJos LRHS MAsh NRHS SEND SPer SRms SWvt WIce XLum XSen
	- 'Grandiflorum'	see *H. olympicum* f. *uniflorum*
§	- f. ***minus***	CSma CTri ECtt GRum MAsh NGdn NHpl SPlb SRms WHrl
§	- - 'Sulphureum'	CChe CRos EHyd ELon EWes GMaP LRHS NBir NRHS SHar SPer SRms SWvt WCFE WFar
	- - 'Variegatum' (v)	EWes NBir SWvt
§	- f. ***uniflorum***	EBou MMuc NBro WIce
	- - 'Citrinum' 🏆H5	CBod CMea CSpe ECha ECtt EPfP LSun MHol MMuc MRav NLar SEND SMad SPad WAbe WCot WHoo WKif WRHF XSen
	orientale	EWes GLog
§	***pallens***	WAbe
	patulum	SPtp
	- var. ***henryi*** Rehder & hort.	see *H. pseudohenryi*

perforatum	CCBP CHab CHby ENfk EPfP GJos GPoy IRos MGil MHer MNHC NGrd NLar NMir SEND SRms WHer WSFF XAbr
- 'Topaz'	GJos
polyphyllum misapplied	see *H. olympicum* f. *minus*
- 'Citrinum'	see *H. olympicum* f. *minus* 'Sulphureum'
- 'Grandiflorum'	see *H. olympicum* f. *uniflorum*
§ ***pseudohenryi***	MMrt SPtp
quadrangulum L.	see *H. tetrapterum*
reptans misapplied	see *H. olympicum* f. *minus*
reptans Hook.f. & Thomson ex Dyer	EWes NWad
revolutum PAB 3861	LEdu WPGP
§ 'Rowallane' ♀H4	CTri LRHS NLar SDix SPoG SWvt
subsessile	CExl
'Sungold'	see *H. kouytchense*
'Sweet Lion'	CMac
§ ***tetrapterum***	MMuc
trichocaulon	EWes ITim
uralum	CPla SPtp
- HWJ 520	WCru
- NJM 10.097	WPGP

Hypocalyptus (*Papilionaceae*)

sophoroides	SPlb

Hypochaeris (*Asteraceae*)

radicata	CHab NMir

Hypocyrta see *Nematanthus*

Hypoestes (*Acanthaceae*)

aristata	CExl EShb SVen

Hypolepis (*Dennstaedtiaceae*)

millefolium	CRos EBee LEdu LRHS SPlb WCot

Hypoxis (*Hypoxidaceae*)

hirsuta	CBor CCCN GKev
krebsii	CBor
longifolia	MAsh
parvula	CAby CBor XLum
§ - var. ***albiflora*** 'Hebron Farm Biscuit'	CCCN EWes GEdr NWad WAbe WFar
villosa	GKev

Hypoxis × *Rhodohypoxis* see × *Rhodoxis*

H. parvula* × *Rhodohypoxis baurii	see × *Rhodoxis hybrida*

Hypsela (*Campanulaceae*)

longiflora	see *H. reniformis*
§ ***reniformis***	CBor EBou ITim LLWG MAsh MSCN NHpl

Hyssopus ✿ (*Lamiaceae*)

officinalis	CBod CCBP CHby CLau CTsd ECha ELan ENfk EPfP GMaP GPoy LCro LOPS MHer MNHC MPri MRav NBir NGrd SCob SEND SEdi SPer SPlb SPoG SRms SVic WSHC XAbr XLum
- f. ***albus***	ECha ENfk EPfP GPoy MHer MNHC SPlb SRms WHer XLum XSen
- subsp. ***aristatus***	CBod EBou ELon ENfk EPfP GPoy IMou LCro LOPS MHer MNHC SPoG WHoo XLum XSen
- subsp. ***officinalis***	XSen
- 'Roseus'	CBod EBou ECha ENfk EPfP GPoy MHer MHol MNHC SPer SPoG WHer XLum XSen
- f. ***ruber***	CLau
- white-flowered	CBod SEdi

Hystrix (*Poaceae*)

patula	CBod EMor EPPr EShb MNrw SPlb XLum

I

Iberis (*Brassicaceae*)

ABSOLUTELY AMETHYST ('Ib2401')	ELan EWTr GBin SPoG WFar WIce
amara	SVic
candolleana	see *I. violacea* Candolleana Group
commutata	see *I. sempervirens*
gibraltarica	SRms
- 'Betty Swainson' ♀H4	CElw CSpe ELan EWld SPhx
- 'Lavish'PBR	MHol
jordanii	see *I. violacea*
'Masterpiece'PBR	CDoC EHyd ELan EPfP LRHS LSou NPer NRHS SPoG WFar
'Pink Ice'	EHyd ELan EPfP LRHS NRHS SCob WFar WIce WTor
pruitii	see *I. violacea*
saxatilis	CRos EHyd ITim LRHS NRHS SRms WThu
semperflorens	WAvo WBrk WCFE
§ ***sempervirens***	CMea CTri EBou ELan EPfP MAsh MCot MMuc NBro SAdn SBut SCob SEND SHar SRms WCFE XSen
- 'Appen-Etz'	CRos EHyd EPfP GMaP LRHS NRHS NWad SRms WFar
- 'Fischbeck'	SRms
- 'Golden Candy'	CBod CSma CTri ECtt MHer NHpl SPoG SRms WFar WIce XSen
- 'Little Gem'	see *I. sempervirens* 'Weisser Zwerg'
- 'Pygmaea'	WHil
- SCHNEEFLOCKE	see *I. sempervirens* 'Snowflake'
- 'Snow Cushion'	EPfP WRHF
§ - 'Snowflake' ♀H5	CCBP EBou EPfP EPot GKev GMaP LCro LOPS MHer SCob SPer SPoG SRms SWvt WBrk WIce XLum
§ - 'Weisser Zwerg'	CMea EBou ECha ELan GMaP MHer MRav SRms WHoo WThu
- 'Whiteout' new	CBod
'Snowball'	MHol SRms
umbellata	ECrN
- DWARF FAIRY MIX (Fairy Series) new	LCro LOPS
§ ***violacea***	NSla SPlb WAbe
§ - Candolleana Group	GEdr

Ichthyoselmis (*Papaveraceae*)

§ ***macrantha***	EPot IMou LEdu NLar WCru WFar WSHC

Idesia (*Salicaceae*)

polycarpa	CBcs EBee EPfP SChF WKor WPGP
- CWJ 12837	WCru

Ilex ✿ (*Aquifoliaceae*)

× ***altaclerensis*** 'Balearica' (f)	CJun

	Name	Suppliers
§	– 'Belgica Aurea' (f/v) ♀H6	CBcs CJun CTho EPfP MSwo NHol NLar WAvo
	– 'Camelliifolia' (f) ♀H6	CBcs CJun CTho MBlu SGol SPer WSpi
	– 'Camelliifolia Variegata' (f/v)	CMac
	– 'Golden King' (f/v) ♀H6	Widely available
	– 'Hodginsii' (m)	CTri
	– 'Howick' (f/v)	CJun
	– 'Lawsoniana' (f/v) ♀H6	CBod CBrac CCVT CJun CMac CRos CSBt CTri EHyd EPfP EShb LRHS MAsh MBlu MMuc NHol NRHS SCob SEND SGol SLim SLon SPer SPoG SRms WAvo WFar
	– 'Purple Shaft' (f)	CJun CMCN MRav
	– 'Ripley Gold' (f/v)	CBrac CJun CMac CRos LRHS MAsh MRav NOra WAvo
	– 'Silver Sentinel'	see *I.* × *altaclerensis* 'Belgica Aurea'
	– 'W.J. Bean' (f)	CJun
	– 'Wilsonii' (f)	NLar
	aquifolium ♀H6	Widely available
	– 'Alaska' (f)	CBrac CCCN CCVT CJun CLnd CMCN CRos EHyd EPfP ILea LBuc LMaj LRHS MAsh NLar NOra NRHS SCob SGol SGsty SWvt SavN WAvo WFar WMat WMou
	– 'Amber' (f) ♀H6	CJun CTho NLar
	– 'Ammerland' (f)	CJun
	– 'Angustifolia' (f)	CJun EHyd WCFE
	– 'Angustifolia' (m or f)	CRos EPfP LRHS SPoG
§	– 'Argentea Marginata' (f/v) ♀H6	Widely available
§	– 'Argentea Marginata Pendula' (f/v)	CMac CRos CTri ELan EPfP LRHS MAsh NOra SGsty SRms WFar
	– 'Argentea Pendula'	see *I. aquifolium* 'Argentea Marginata Pendula'
	– 'Argentea Variegata'	see *I. aquifolium* 'Argentea Marginata'
	– 'Atlas' (m)	CBcs LBuc SWvt
	– 'Aurea Marginata' (f/v)	CMac EPfP LMaj MGos NOra SCob SEWo WAvo WCFE WFar WMat
	– 'Aurea Marginata Pendula' (f/v)	WLov
	– 'Aurea Regina'	see *I. aquifolium* 'Golden Queen'
	– 'Aurifodina' (f)	CJun WAvo
	– 'Bacciflava' (f)	CBcs CDoC CJun CMac CTho CTri ELan ELon EPfP IArd MBlu MGos MRav NLar SPer SRms SWvt WCFE WFar
	– 'Bowland' (f/v)	NOra
	– 'Chris Whittle'	NOra
	– 'Crassifolia' (f)	EBee
	– 'Crispa' (m)	CBod
	– 'Elegantissima' (m/v)	CBrac CJun
	– 'Fastigiata Sartori'	NLar
	– 'Ferox' (m)	CJun CRos EHyd ELan EPfP LRHS
	– 'Ferox Argentea' (m/v) ♀H6	Widely available
	– 'Ferox Aurea' (m/v)	CBrac CJun ELon MAsh NOra
§	– 'Flavescens' (f)	MBlu
	– 'Frogmore Silver' (m/v)	CJun
	– 'Glanzzwerg'	SAko
	– 'Gold Flash' (f/v)	CJun LRHS NLar
	– 'Golden Milkboy' (m/v)	CBrac CJun CMac MAsh SGol WAvo WCot WLov
§	– 'Golden Queen' (m/v) ♀H6	NBir SRms
	– 'Golden Tears' (f/v)	CJun
	– 'Golden van Tol' (f/v)	CBcs CJun CLnd CSBt CTri EBee ELan ELon EPfP EShb LRHS MAsh MBlu MGos MSwo NLar NOra SCoo SGol SPer SRms WFar
	– 'Green Minaret'	SAko
	– 'Handsworth New Silver' (f/v) ♀H6	Widely available
	– 'Harpune' (f)	CJun IArd SAko
	– 'Hastata' (m)	IArd IDee
	– HECKENZWERG ('Hachzwerg'PBR)	SAko
	– 'Heterophylla Aureomarginata' (m/v) **new**	CDoC
	– 'Ingramii' (m/v)	CJun LRHS
	– 'J.C. van Tol' (f) ♀H6	Widely available
	– 'Latispina' (f)	CJun
	– 'Lichtenthalii' (f)	CJun IArd
	– 'Madame Briot' (f/v) ♀H6	CBod CDoC CJun CMac CRos CTri EBee EHyd ELan EPfP LBuc LRHS MAsh MPri MRav MSwo NHol NRHS SCob SEND SGol SPer SPoG SRms SWvt WFar
	– 'Monstrosa' (m)	CJun
	– moonlight holly	see *I. aquifolium* 'Flavescens'
	– 'Myrtifolia' (f)	CBod SWvt WPav
	– 'Myrtifolia' (m)	CDow CJun CMac ELan EPfP NLar WPav
	– 'Myrtifolia Aurea' (m/v)	SWvt
	– 'Myrtifolia Aurea Maculata' (m/v)	CBod CDoC CJun CRos CTri EHyd ELan LRHS MAsh MRav NOra SPoG SWvt WCot WLov
	– 'Northern Lights' (v)	EPfP MSwo SGsty
	– 'Pendula' (f)	MRav
	– 'Pyramidalis' (f) ♀H6	CBcs CJun CMac CRos CTri ELan LRHS MAsh MGos NLar NOra SCob SGol SRms WFar
	– 'Pyramidalis Aureomarginata' (f/v)	NLar NOra
	– 'Pyramidalis Fructu Luteo' (f) ♀H6	MAsh
	– 'Recurva' (m)	CJun CMac
	– 'Rubricaulis Aurea' (f/v)	CJun NLar
	– 'Scotica' (f)	CJun
	– 'Silver King'	see *I. aquifolium* 'Silver Queen'
	– 'Silver Lining' (f/v)	CJun
	– 'Silver Milkboy' (f/v)	EPfP MBlu WFar
	– 'Silver Milkmaid' (f/v)	CJun CRos EHyd LRHS MAsh MMuc NOra NRHS SLim SWvt
§	– 'Silver Queen' (m/v) ♀H6	CBar CBcs CCVT CDoC CEnd CRos ECrN EPfP LCro LOPS LRHS MAsh MGos MPri MRav MSwo NBir NHol NLar NOra SAko SGbt SLim SLon SPer SPoG SWvt WMat
	– 'Silver Sentinel'	see *I.* × *altaclerensis* 'Belgica Aurea'
	– 'Silver van Tol' (f/v)	CBod CDoC CJun CLnd EBee ELan EPfP EShb MAsh MRav NLar NOra NPer WFar
	– 'Somerset Cream' (f/v)	CJun CTri
*	– 'Variegata' (v)	SArc SWeb
	– 'Victoria' (m)	CJun
§	– 'Watereriana' (m/v)	NOra
	– 'Waterer's Gold'	see *I. aquifolium* 'Watereriana'
	– 'White Cream' (m/v)	SAko
	– 'Zig Zag' (f)	CJun
	× ***aquipernyi*** DRAGON LADY ('Meschick') (f) ♀H6	CBod CDoC CTho IArd LMaj LRHS NLar
	– 'San Jose' (f)	CJun
	× ***attenuata***	WFar
	– 'Sunny Foster' (f/v)	CBcs CMCN LRHS NOra SAko WFar
	× ***beanii***	CJun

§ ***bioritsensis***	CMCN
cassine L.	CMCN
chapaensis HWJ 946	WCru
'Clusterberry' (f)	CJun
colchica	CMCN IArd
cornuta	EPfP ESwi LMaj
- B&SWJ 8756	WCru
- 'Anicet Delcambre' (f)	CJun
- 'Burfordii' (f)	NLar
§ - 'Dazzler' (f)	CJun
- 'Ira S. Nelson' (f)	CJun IArd SAko
- 'Mercury' (f)	CJun
- 'O. Spring' (f/v)	CJun CMac WSpi
crenata	CDoC CMCN CTri ECrN EPfP LCro LOPS MGos NHol SArc SCob SPer SWeb WFar
* - 'Akagi'	WFar
- 'Aureovariegata'	see *I. crenata* 'Variegata'
- 'Blondie' PBR (f)	SWeb
- 'Carolina Upright' (m)	EBee SEWo
- 'Convexa' (f) ♀H6	CJun CRos CTho EHyd EPfP LMaj LRHS MAsh MRav NRHS SGsty SReu SWeb
- 'Convexed Gold' (f/v)	EPfP NLar NOra NWad SPoG WFar
- DARK GREEN ('Icoprins11' PBR)	CDoC CLnd ELan EPfP LBuc LCro LOPS LRHS LSRN SCob SGsty SVic SWeb
- 'Dwarf Pagoda' (f)	SAko
- 'Eden's Paradise' PBR **new**	SGsty
- Fastigiata Group	CRos LRHS SCob WFar
- - 'Fastigiata' (f) ♀H6	CRos EHyd EPfP LRHS LSRN MAsh MGos NLar SPer SPoG
- - 'Sky Pencil' (f)	CMCN
* - 'Glory Gem' (f)	CBcs LSRN
- 'Golden Gem' (f/v) ♀H6	CBor CJun CMac CRos CTho CTri EBee ELan EPfP LRHS MAsh MGos MSwo NLar NRHS NWad SAko SGol SPer SPoG SWvt WFar
- 'Green Hedger' ♀H6	CLnd EPfP MGos SGsty
- 'Green Lustre' (f)	LSRN
- 'Hetzii' (f)	CBod
- 'Kinme' (f)	SGsty SWeb
- 'Luteovariegata'	see *I. crenata* 'Variegata'
- LUXUS GLOBE ('Annys5' PBR) (m) **new**	NLar
- 'Mariesii' (f)	CMac EBee MBlu
I - 'Pyramidalis' (f)	CMac MRav
§ - 'Shiro-fukurin' (f/v)	CJun CMCN CRos EHyd ELan EPfP LRHS NRHS SLon SPoG
- 'Snowflake'	see *I. crenata* 'Shiro-fukurin'
- 'Stokes' (m)	CBod CDoC MSwo NLar NWad
§ - 'Variegata' (v)	CMCN CMac CRos EHyd EPfP LRHS NLar NRHS
cyrtura (f)	WPGP
- (m)	WPGP
'Dazzler'	see *I. cornuta* 'Dazzler'
dimorphophylla 'Somerset Pixie' (f)	CJun
dipyrena	SAko
'Doctor Kassab' (f)	CMCN
'Elegance' (f)	MBlu WFar
excelsa	CMCN
fargesii	IArd
- subsp. ***fargesii*** var. ***fargesii***	WPGP
aff. ***gagnepainiana*** FMWJ 13168	WCru
glabra	CJun
- f. ***leucocarpa*** 'Snow White' (f)	CJun
'Good Taste' (f)	CJun WFar
'Hohman' (f)	CJun
'Indian Chief' (f)	CJun WAvo
× ***koehneana***	CCVT MMuc SDix SEND
- 'Chestnut Leaf' (f) ♀H5	CBcs CBod CCVT CDoC CJun CLnd CMCN CTho ELan EWTr LRHS MRav NLar SSta WFar WGrn
laevigata	CMCN
latifolia	CJun IArd NLar
'Leonardo'	EBee
* 'Little Diamond'	LSRN
'Mary Nell' (f)	CJun IArd
§ × ***meserveae*** 'Anny's Dwarf' (m)	LRHS
- BLUE ANGEL ('Conang') (f)	CBrac CCCN CDoC CMac CSBt CTho EBee ELan EPfP LRHS MRav NLar NOra NRHS SPer SPoG SRms WAvo WFar
- BLUE MAID ('Mesid') (f)	CCCN CDoC LOPS LRHS MGos NLar NRHS SWeb
- BLUE PRINCE ('Conablu') (m) ♀H7	CBcs CCCN CDoC CMCN CMac CRos ELan LBuc LRHS MBlu MMuc NHol NLar NOra SCob SLim SPer WFar
- BLUE PRINCESS ('Conapri') (f) ♀H7	CBcs CBod CBrac CCVT CMCN CMac ELan EPfP GBin LBuc MBlu MGos MRav NLar SCob SCoo SLim SPer WFar
- CASTLE SPIRE ('Hachfee' PBR) (f)	CLnd SEWo SWeb WFar
- CASTLE WALL ('Hecken Star' PBR) (m)	LRHS NLar SEWo WFar
- GENTLE	see *I.* × *meserveae* 'Anny's Dwarf' (m)
- GOLDEN GIRL ('Mesgolg') (f)	SGsty
- 'Goliath' (f)	WFar
- 'Heckenpracht' PBR (m)	WFar
- LITTLE RASCAL ('Mondo') (m)	CRos EPfP LRHS MGos MPkF
- 'Little Sensation'	LRHS MBlu SPoG
myrtifolia	CDoC MAsh MRav NHol
'Nellie R. Stevens' (f)	CCVT CJun CLnd CRos CTho EBee ECrN ELan EPfP ILea LMaj MPri NLar SEWo SGsty SWeb WAvo WMat
opaca	CMCN
pedunculosa	MBlu NLar
perado subsp. ***azorica***	WPGP
- - B&SWJ 12526	WCru
- subsp. ***platyphylla***	CMCN EBee MBlu SArc
pernyi	CJun CMCN MAsh
- var. ***veitchii***	see *I. bioritsensis*
rotunda	LEdu
rugosa	CMCN
'September Gem' (f)	CJun CMCN
serrata	CMac CMen
- 'Koshobai' (f)	CMen
- 'Leucocarpa' (f)	CMac
sikkimensis **new**	LEdu
spinigera	CBcs
sugerokii var. ***longipedunculata*** B&SWJ 10856	WCru
'Tanager' (f)	CJun
triflora var. ***kanehirae***	NLar
verticillata	CMCN EBee LRHS WFar
- (f)	CBcs EPfP MMrt NLar
- (m)	EPfP MMrt NLar
- f. ***chrysocarpa*** (f)	NLar
- 'Compacta'	see *I. verticillata* 'Nana'

- 'Maryland Beauty' (f) CJun NLar
§ - 'Nana' (f) CJun
- 'Red Sprite' see *I. verticillata* 'Nana'
- 'Southern Gentleman' (m) CJun MBlu
- 'Sunset'PBR (f) CJun
- 'Winter Gold' (f) CJun MBlu
- 'Winter Red' (f) CJun CMCN MBlu
vomitoria CMCN EBtc
× ***wandoensis*** WFar
'Washington' (f) IArd WFar
'William Cowgill' (f) CJun
yunnanensis EBee IArd IDee

Iliamna see *Sphaeralcea*

Illicium (*Schisandraceae*)

anisatum CBcs CCCN CExl EPfP LEdu SSta WLov WPGP
- B&SWJ 8411 WCru
floridanum CBcs CCCN SBrt SSta WLov
- 'Halley's Comet' CExl NLar
aff. ***griffithii*** WWJ 11911 WCru
- WWJ 11971 WCru
- WWJ 11974 WCru
henryi CExl EBee EPfP LRHS NLar WPGP
aff. ***henryi*** CBcs
jiadifengpi NLar
lanceolatum CExl
- KWJ 12245 WCru
macranthum B&SWJ 11809 WCru
majus WWJ 11919 WCru
aff. ***majus*** WCru
- WWJ 12017 WCru
merrillianum HWJ 1015 WCru
mexicanum CExl
oligandrum CBcs CExl NLar WPGP
philippinense CWJ 12466 WCru
simonsii CExl MBlu WPGP
- BWJ 8024 WCru
tashiroi CWJ 12468 WCru
'Woodland Ruby' WPGP

Ilysanthes see *Lindernia*

Impatiens (*Balsaminaceae*)

CC 4980 CExl
P1961 EPPr ESwi
from China, Darrell Probst collection WFar
apiculata WFar
arguta CExl CSam EBee EWld SBrt WBor WFar WPGP
- 'Alba' CExl CSpe MPie MSCN WFar
- big blue-flowered ESwi
- 'Big Boy' **new** SEdd
- big form CSpe WFar
auricoma × ***bicaudata*** MPie WDib
balansae **new** CDTJ
bicaudata CSpe SPlb
(Celebrette Series) CELEBRETTE FROST ('Balcebfro'PBR) (NG) **new** LSou
- CELEBRETTE GRAPE CRUSH IMPROVED ('Balcebgushi') (NG) **new** LSou
- CELEBRETTE ORCHID STAR IMPROVED ('Balceborcari') (NG) **new** LSou
congolensis CCCN
DIVINE LAVENDER ('Pas425593') (Divine Series) (NG) **new** MBros
ernstii CExl
flanaganae CDTJ ESwi SBrt WFar WPGP
gomphophylla CDTJ WFar
hawkeri Divine Series MBros
hochstetteri **new** WFar
insignis EBee EWld
keilii WDib
kilimanjari subsp. ***kilimanjari*** CDTJ CSpe ECre MPie
kilimanjari × ***pseudoviola*** CSpe ECre MPie WDib WFar
- -, dark pink-flowered **new** WFar
- -, pale pink-flowered ECre WFar
langbianensis HWJ 1054 WCru WFar
macrophylla B&SWJ 10157 WCru
mengtszeana PB 02-519 WFar
- trailing **new** WFar
namchabarwensis CCCN
niamniamensis ♀H1b EBak EShb NCft WDib
- 'Congo Cockatoo' CDTJ NPer SRms
- 'Golden Cockatoo' (v) CDTJ EBak EShb
noli-tangere WSFF
omeiana CCCN CDTJ CPla CSpe EBee ELan EPPr ESwi EWld GEdr GWyn ILea LEdu MNrw MSCN NLar SPtp WCru WFar WPGP
- DJHC 98492 WCru WFar WMal
- 'High Voltage' WFar
- 'Ice Storm' CDTJ EBee EPPr ESwi EWld GEdr IPot LEdu MPie NBro NLar WCot WCru WFar WPGP
- long-leaved **new** WFar
- 'Pink Nerves' EBee ESwi LEdu MPie WFar
- 'Red Leaf' EPPr ESwi
- 'Sango' CPla CSpe EWld LEdu SEdd WFar WMal
- variegated (v) GEdr
oxyanthera 'Milo' SBrt WFar
parasitica WDib
pritzelii **new** CDTJ
- 'Sichuan Gold' CDTJ EBee EPPr ESwi WFar
puberula WFar
- HWJK 2063 EBee ESwi EWld SBrt WCru WPGP
qingchengshanica 'Emei Dawn' CExl EBee EPPr ESwi WCru WFar WPGP
repens ♀H1b MPie WDib
rothii ESwi WCot WPGP
rupestris CDTJ
scabrida CSpe
§ 'Secret Love' CCCN CDoC
sodenii ♀H1c CDTJ CSpe EShb ESwi SBrt WDib WFar
- 'Flash' **new** WFar
- white-flowered **new** WFar
- -, red eye **new** WFar
stenantha EBee ESwi GEdr SBrt WFar
(SunPatiens Series) SUNPATIENS COMPACT ELECTRIC ORANGE ('Sakimp025'PBR) (NG) ♀H1b **new** MBros
- SUNPATIENS SPREADING VARIEGATED SALMON ('Sakimp005') (NG/v) ♀H1b MBros

- SunPatiens Spreading Variegated White ('Sakimp018'PBR) (NG/v) ♀H1b — MBros
- SunPatiens Vigorous Blush Pink ('Sakimp023'PBR) (NG) new — MBros
- SunPatiens Vigorous Lavender ('Sakimp006') (NG) new — MBros
- SunPatiens Vigorous Magenta ('Misato Fg3') (NG) new — MBros
- SunPatiens Vigorous Orange ('Misato Fg2') (NG) new — MBros
- SunPatiens Vigorous White Improved ('Sakimp010'PBR) (NG) new — MBros

tinctoria — CAbb CAby CDTJ CExl CSpe ESwi EWld IPot SBrt SDix
tuberosa — WDib
uniflora — SBrt WBor
Velvetea — see *I.* 'Secret Love'
walleriana DeZire Series — MBros MPri
- - 'DeZire Red' new — MBros
- - 'DeZire White' new — MBros
- 'Salsa Red' (Fiesta Series) (d) — SCob
- (Xtreme Series) 'Xtreme Pink' new — MBros
- - 'Xtreme Red' new — MBros
- - 'Xtreme White' new — MBros

Imperata (*Poaceae*)

cylindrica — CMen XLum
- 'Red Baron' — see *I. cylindrica* 'Rubra'
§ - 'Rubra' — Widely available

Incarvillea (*Bignoniaceae*)

arguta — XLum
- from Tajikistan — WPGP
beresowskii new — GKev
brevipes — see *I. mairei*
compacta — GKev
- BWJ 7620 — WCru
delavayi — CAby CBcs CBod CRos CSBt CTsd ECha EDAr EHyd ELan EPfP GKev LRHS MGos MSCN NBir NRHS SDeJ SRms SVen SWvt WAvo WFar XLum
- 'Alba' — see *I. delavayi* 'Snowtop'
- 'Bees' Pink' — CPla EPfP LPla LRHS
- dark pink-flowered — SBrt
§ - 'Snowtop' — CAby CBcs CBod CTsd EBee EDAr EHyd ELan EPfP EWld GBin LRHS MHol NBir SDeJ SWvt WBor WCot WFar WHil
cf. ***delavayi*** — MHol
forrestii — GKev
grandiflora — EBee GKev
himalayensis 'Frank Ludlow' — GKev
lutea — EBee GKev
§ ***mairei*** — CRos EBee EHyd GKev GWyn LRHS NRHS SRms
- var. ***mairei*** f. ***multifoliata*** — see *I. zhongdianensis*
olgae — ELan GKev
'Snowdrop' — EMor
§ ***zhongdianensis*** — CFis EBee EDAr GEdr GKev SBrt
- BWJ 7692 — WCru
- BWJ 7978 — WCru

Indigofera (*Papilionaceae*)

NJM 9166 new — WPGP
§ ***amblyantha*** — CBcs CCCN CExl CRos EHyd EPfP EWTr GKev LRHS MAsh MBlu NLar NRHS SEND SPlb WCFE WSHC WSpi
aff. ***amblyantha*** — MMrt
balfouriana Craib BWJ 7851 — WCru
cassioides — WCru
§ 'Claret Cascade' ♀H5 — WSHC
dielsiana — CCCN CRos EHyd ELan EPfP LRHS WSpi
'Dosua' — MMuc SEND
gerardiana — see *I. heterantha*
hancockii — CExl EPfP SChF WPGP WSHC
hebepetala — EPfP SBrt WPGP WSHC
§ ***heterantha*** ♀H5 — Widely available
heterophylla — CCCN
himachalensis — EBee
- H&M 1818 — WPGP
himalayensis — CExl EBee MGil
- Yu 10941 — CExl WPGP
- 'Silk Road' — CCCN CRos EBee EHyd ELan EPfP GKev LRHS MBlu MGil MGos MNHC MSCN NLar NRHS SPoG SPtp WSpi
§ ***howellii*** — CExl SChF WCru WPGP
kirilowii — CCCN CRos EHyd ELan EPfP GKev LRHS MBlu NLar WPGP WSHC WSpi
- var. ***alba*** — EPfP LRHS WSHC
§ ***pendula*** — CCCN CExl CMac CRos CSde CWGN EBee EHyd ELan EPfP LRHS MGil SMad SPoG WCFE WKif WPGP WSHC WSpi
- B&SWJ 7741 — WCru
potaninii misapplied — see *I. howellii*, *I. howellii* 'Reginald Cory', *I. amblyantha*, *I.* 'Claret Cascade', *I. pendula*
potaninii ambig. — CBcs CExl CMac MMrt WHer
pseudotinctoria — CCCN SRms
aff. ***pseudotinctoria*** — CCCN
subverticillata — LRHS WSHC
szechuensis — LRHS MGil WSpi
tinctoria — CCCN MGil

Indocalamus (*Poaceae*)

latifolius — MMuc MWht
- 'Hopei' — XCre
longiauritus — XCre
solidus — see *Bonia solida*
§ ***tessellatus*** ♀H5 — CAbb CBcs ELon MWht NGdn SMad XCre
- f. ***hamadae*** — CBdn MWht XCre

Inula (*Asteraceae*)

acaulis — WCot
dysenterica — see *Pulicaria dysenterica*
ensifolia — CBcs EHyd ELan EMor EPfP LRHS MBel MSCN WCav WHoo XLum
- 'Gold Star' — EBee MRav NBid NBir WAvo WCot WFar
glandulosa — see *I. orientalis*
helenium — CBod CCBP CHab CHby EBou EMor ENfk GPoy ILea LCro LEdu LOPS MHer MNHC NBid NBir

	NGrd NLar SRms WGwG WHer XAbr
hirta	XLum
hookeri	CChe CMea CSam ECha ELan EShb GBin GMaP GWyn ILea LEdu LLWG MBel MHol MMuc MSpe NBid NChi NDov NPer NSti SAdn SDix SEND WBrk WCAu WCav WOld WWtn
- GWJ 9033	WCru
macrocephala misapplied	see *I. royleana*
magnifica	Widely available
- 'Sonnenstrahl' 🏆H6	EPPr LEdu NLar SPhx
oculus-christi	EBee EWes WCot
§ ***orientalis***	CRos EHyd EPfP ILea LRHS NGBl NLar NRHS SPad SPer SRms XLum
racemosa	EBee EHyd EPPr EWes GBin GQue LRHS MNrw NRHS SPlb SRms WBor
- 'Sonnenspeer'	CBod NBid NLar
§ ***royleana***	MNrw MRav

Inulanthera (*Asteraceae*)

calva	IMou WCot WFar

Iochroma (*Solanaceae*)

§ ***australe*** 🏆H3	CBcs CCCN CDow CExl CSpe EBee ELan EMdy LSRN MGil NGKo NSti SEND SIvy SPlb SPoG SPtp SVen WCot WPGP
§ - 'Andean Snow'	CCCN CSpe EShb MGil NGKo WHil WPGP
- white-flowered	see *I. australe* 'Andean Snow'
cyaneum	CCCN CDow ECre SPlb SVen
§ - purple-flowered	CCCN NGKo
fuchsioides **new**	NGKo
gesnerioides 'Coccineum'	CCCN
§ ***grandiflorum***	CCCN SEND
violaceum hort.	see *I. cyaneum* purple-flowered
warscewiczii	see *I. grandiflorum*

Ipheion (*Alliaceae*)

'Alberto Castillo' 🏆H5	CAby CAvo CBro CMea EHyd ELan ELon EPot ERCP EShb EWes LCro LOPS LRHS MNrw NBir NHpl NRHS SDeJ SDys SPhx SRms WAul WCot WFar WHil WHoo WMal WPGP WWFP
'Alice'	WCot
'Diana'	WCot
'Jessie'	CAby CBro CMea CPrp EBee ECha EHyd EPot ERCP EWes GKev LRHS NHpl NRHS SDeJ WBrk WHoo WRHF WTor WTyc
'Judy'	WCot
'Rolf Fiedler' 🏆H4	CAby CAvo CBro CPrp CTri EBee EHyd ELan EPot ERCP EWes GKev LRHS NRHS NRya SDeJ SRms WAul WFar WHil
sellowianum	CAby WCot
'Tessa'PBR	EBee ECha EHyd ERCP EWes LRHS NHpl
§ ***uniflorum***	CBro CTri ECha ITim SEND SRms WBrk WCav WCot WTyc XLum
- f. ***album***	CBro CPrp EBee ECha EHyd EWes LEdu LRHS NRHS WBrk WCot WHil WMal
- 'Charlotte Bishop'	CAvo CBro CPrp CRos EBee ECha EHyd ELon ERCP EWes LRHS MNrw MPie NBir NHpl NRHS NRya SDeJ SRms WAul WBrk WCav WCot WHil WHoo WMal WTyc
- 'Froyle Mill' 🏆H5	CAvo CBro CPrp EHyd ELon EPot ERCP EWes LRHS MNrw NHpl NRHS SDeJ SRms WCot WHoo
- 'Hoo House' **new**	WHoo WMal
- 'Miss Hannah' **new**	WMal
- subsp. ***tandiliense***	EPPr
- 'Wisley Blue' 🏆H5	CBod CBro CExl CPrp CRos CTri CWCL ECha EHyd ELan ELon EPot ERCP GKev LRHS MBros MRav NRHS NRya SDeJ SPoG SRms WCot WHoo
- 'Wisley Star'	GKev

Ipomoea (*Convolvulaceae*)

acuminata	see *I. indica*
alba	CBre CCCN EShb
batatas	CCCN
- 'Beauregard' **new**	SVic
- 'Bonita'	LRHS
- (Bright Ideas Series) BRIGHT IDEAS BLACK	EShb
- - BRIGHT IDEAS LIME ('Fripalligr')	EShb
- 'O'Henry' **new**	SVic
- (Sweet Caroline Series) 'Sweet Caroline Sweetheart Light Green'PBR	ESwi
- - 'Sweet Caroline Sweetheart Purple'PBR	ESwi
'Black Tone'	MBros
cairica	WCot
carnea	CCCN
coccinea var. ***hederifolia***	see *I. hederifolia*
§ ***hederifolia***	CCCN
× ***imperialis*** 'Sunrise Serenade'	CCCN
§ ***indica*** 🏆H1c	CCCN CRHN ECre EShb SPer
learii	see *I. indica*
lindheimeri	SMad
§ ***lobata*** 🏆H1c	CSpe LCro LOPS MGil
mauritiana	CCCN
'Milky Way'	CCCN
muellerii	CCCN
× ***multifida***	CSpe
purpurea 'Kniola's Black Night'	CSpe
quamoclit	CSpe
SOLAR POWER BLACK ('Balsolablack') **new**	MPri
SOLAR POWER LIME ('Balsolalime') **new**	MPri
tricolor 'Heavenly Blue' 🏆H1c	LCro LOPS
tuberosa	see *Merremia tuberosa*
versicolor	see *I. lobata*

Iris ✿ (*Iridaceae*)

AGSJ	EPPr
KR 3739	GEdr
'Abbey Chant' (IB)	XSen
'About Town' (TB)	WCAu
'Absolute Treasure' (TB)	WCAu
'Action Front' (TB)	CRos ECtt EHyd EIri EPfP EShb GBin LRHS MCot MGos NRHS SDeJ WGwG

'Actress' (TB)	CRos ECtt EHyd EPfP LRHS LSRN MCot MGos NRHS WGwG
acutiloba* × *afghanica new	GKev
'Adobe Rose' (TB)	SIri XSen
'Adventuress' (TB)	XSen
'Afternoon in Rio' (TB)	WCAu
'Agatha Christie' (IB)	WCAu
'Agnes James' (CH)	CBro MAvo
'Ahwahnee Princess' (SDB)	ELon
'Aichi-no-kagayaki' (SpH)	WCot XLum
'Al Segno' (TB) new	GKev
albicans ♀H5	CBro EPot GKev LEdu
'Alcazar' (TB)	LSRN
'Alida' (Reticulata)	EHyd EPot ERCP GKev LCro LOPS LRHS NBir NRHS SDeJ WBor WBrk XEll
'Alien Mist' (TB)	EIri
'Alizes' (TB) ♀H7	LRHS WViv XSen
'Ally Oops' (SpH)	LLWG
'Amadora' (TB)	EIri
'Amber Queen' (DB)	ECtt EHyd ELan LRHS NBir SCob SDeJ SPer
'Amethyst Flame' (TB)	SRms
'Amherst Blue' (IB)	EIri
'Amherst Caper' (SDB)	EIri
'Amherst Glacier' (IB)	WCAu
'Amphora' (SDB)	CBro
'Andalou' (TB) ♀H7	CWCL WViv XSen
anglica	see *I. latifolia*
'Ann Chowning' (La)	LCro MWts SDir WPnP
'Ann Dasch' (Sib)	WAul
'Annabel Jane' (TB)	ELon WCAu
'Anne Elizabeth' (SDB)	CBro
'Annemarie Troeger' (Sib) ♀H7	ELon
'Annick' (Sib)	EBee EHyd LRHS MMrt XSen
'Aphrodisiac' (TB)	XSen
aphylla	GBin SBrt WAbe
'Apollo' (Dut)	CAvo
'Appointer' (SpH)	NChi WWtn
'Apricorange' (TB)	SRms WCot
'Apricot Drops' (MTB) ♀H7	WCAu
'Apricot Frosty' (BB)	XSen
'Apricot Silk' (IB)	NLar NQui WCot
'Aquamarine' (IB)	MHol
'Archie Owen' (Spuria)	WCAu
'Arctic Night' (IB)	WCAu
'Around Midnight' (TB)	EHyd LRHS
'Arpège' (TB)	GWyn LCro LOPS XSen
'Arrows' (La)	LLWG
'Art Deco' (TB)	SIri XSen
'As de Coeur' (TB)	XSen
'Ask Alma' (IB)	SIri XSen
'Atlantic Crossing' (Sib)	WAul
attica	CBro CMea CPBP GEdr GKev WThu
- blue-flowered	GKev
- lemon-flowered	EPPr GKev WAbe WThu
- violet-flowered new	GKev
§ ***aucheri*** ♀H4	EPot GKev XSen
- indigo-flowered	GKev
'Audition' (La) new	LLWG
'Aunty Ruth' (CH)	MAvo
'Aurélie' (TB)	WViv
'Austrian Sky' (SDB)	CAby CMac ECtt EHyd ELon EPfP LRHS SDeJ WAul WCot
'Autumn Circle' new	WCAu
'Autumn Echo' (TB)	XSen
'Autumn Encore' (TB)	SRms
'Autumn Princess' (Dut)	CAvo SDeJ
'Autumn Riesling' (TB)	WCAu
'Autumn Tryst' (TB)	WCAu
'Avalon Sunset' (TB)	EIri
'Az Ap' (IB)	ELon WCAu
babadagica	GEdr WAbe
'Babbling Brook' (TB)	GWyn XSen
'Baby Bengal' (BB)	XSen
'Baby Blessed' (SDB)	CBro WCAu
'Baby Sister' (Sib)	EHyd ELon GBin LRHS LSRN NBro WFar
'Badlands' (TB)	WCAu
'Baie Rose' (IB)	SIri
'Bal Masqué' (TB)	WViv XSen
'Ballerina Pink' (BB)	WCAu
'Ballyhoo' (TB)	XSen
'Baltic Star' (TB)	WCAu
'Banbury Beauty' (CH) ♀H4	MAvo NLar
'Banbury Gem' (CH)	MAvo NLar WMal
'Banbury Melody' (CH)	MAvo
'Banbury Ruffles' (SDB)	LRHS NLar WCAu
'Bangles' (MTB) ♀H7	WCAu
'Banish Misfortune' (Sib)	EPri LLWG WAul WGob
'Barbara May' (TB)	WCAu
'Barbara My Love' (TB)	WCAu
barbatula	SBrt
- BWJ 7663	WCru
'Barcoo' (La)	LLWG
'Batik' (BB)	WCot XSen
'Beauty Becomes Her' (TB) new	WCAu
BEAUTY SUPER MIX (Dut)	GKev
'Bedtime Story' (IB)	XSen
'Before the Storm' (TB)	ELan ELon LRHS MNHC SEdd WCAu XSen
'Bel Azur' (IB)	LRHS
'Belgian Princess' (TB)	WCAu
'Belise' (Spuria) ♀H7	WCot
'Belle de Nuit' (TB)	WViv
'Benbow' (TB)	WMil
'Benton Ankaret' (TB)	EMal
'Benton Apollo' (TB)	ECha EMal LRHS WMal
'Benton Argent' (TB)	ECha
'Benton Arundel' (TB)	EMal LRHS
'Benton Bluejohn' (TB)	EMal LRHS
'Benton Caramel' (TB)	ECha ECtt EMal EPfP LRHS MBriF NRHS
'Benton Cordelia' (TB)	ECtt EMal LRHS MBriF MCot WMal
'Benton Daphne' (TB)	EMal LRHS
'Benton Dierdre' (TB)	ECha ECtt ELan ELon EMal EPfP LRHS MBriF NRHS SRms
'Benton Duff' (TB)	ECha NRHS
'Benton Evora' (TB)	ECha EMal LRHS
'Benton Farewell' (TB)	ECha LRHS
'Benton Judith' (TB)	ECha WMal
'Benton Lorna' (TB)	ECha ECtt EMal GBin LRHS MBriF NRHS
'Benton Menace' (TB)	ECha EMal LRHS
'Benton Nigel' (TB)	ECha ECtt ELan EMal LRHS MBriF WGwG WMal
'Benton Nutkin' (TB)	EMal LRHS
'Benton Old Madrid' new	EMal
'Benton Olive' (TB)	ECha EMal LRHS NRHS
'Benton Opal' (TB)	ECha EMal LRHS
'Benton Pearl' (TB)	ECha EMal LRHS
'Benton Primrose' (TB)	ECha EMal LRHS NRHS
'Benton Sheila' (TB)	ECha ELan ELon
'Benton Susan' (TB)	ECha ECtt EMal LRHS MBriF MCot NRHS WGwG

'Berkeley Gold' (TB)	CRos CSBt ECtt ELan EWes LRHS NRHS SCob SDeJ SPer WGwG
'Berlin Bluebird' (Sib)	SMHy
'Berlin Purple Wine' (Sib)	EPri WGob
'Berlin Ruffles' (Sib) 🏆H7	EWes WAul
'Berlin Sky' (Sib)	EWes
'Berlin Tiger' (SpH) 🏆H7	EPPr EWTr LLWG MSCN NLar SDix SMHy
'Best Bet' (TB)	MNHC WCAu
'Bethany Claire' (TB)	WCAu
'Better Believe It' (La) **new**	LLWG
'Better Together' (TB) **new**	WCAu
'Betty Cooper' (Spuria)	WCAu
'Betty Simon' (TB)	XSen
'Beverly Sills' (TB)	CRos CWld ECtt EHyd EIri EPfP IPot LCro LRHS MHer MRav NRHS SDeJ XSen
'Bewilderbeast' (TB)	XSen
'Bianco' (TB)	GWyn WCAu WHil
bicapitata	CPBP
'Bickley Cape' (Sib)	GBin
'Big Blue' (Sib)	WFar
'Big Heart' (Sib)	EIri
'Big Squeeze' (TB)	SIri
biglumis	see *I. lactea*
biliottii	CBro
'Bishop's Robe' (TB)	LCro LOPS LRHS
'Black as Night' (TB)	XSen
'Black Aura'	NWad
'Black Dragon' (TB)	CSpe GWyn XSen
'Black Flag' (TB)	XSen
'Black Gamecock' (La)	CWCL ECtt EWTr IPot LCro LLWG LOPS MHer MNrw MSCN MWts NLar WCAu WFar WMAq WPnP WWtn
'Black is Back' (TB)	WCAu
'Black Joker' (Sib) **new**	LLWG MHol
'Black Knight' (TB)	LRHS MRav NLar NQui SCob WKif WSpi
'Black Suited' (TB)	SIri
'Black Swan' (TB)	CAby CBor CMac ECha ECtt EHyd ELan EPfP EShb LCro LOPS LRHS LSRN MCot NQui NRHS SCob SEdd SPer SPoG SRms WCot XSen
'Black Tie Affair' (TB)	CBod CWld ECtt EHyd ELan EPfP IPot LRHS MAsh MCot NRHS XSen
'Black Watch' (IB)	GWyn LCro LOPS
'Blackbeard' (BB) 🏆H7	WCAu
'Blackbeard's Ghost' (AB)	WCAu
'Blackberry Tease' (TB)	WCAu
'Blackcurrant' (IB)	WCAu
'Blatant' (TB)	XSen
'Blaue Milchstrasse' (Sib)	GBin GWyn MMrt
'Blaues Schweben' (Sib)	GBin
'Blazing Light' (TB)	XSen
'Blenheim Royal' (TB)	XSen
bloudowii	WAbe
'Blue Admiral' (TB)	GBin
'Blue Bird' (Sib)	ECtt MBros SPoG WFar WGob
'Blue Burgee' (Sib)	ECha
I 'Blue Butterfly' (Sib)	EBee EPfP NGdn
'Blue Celeste' (Sib)	GKev
'Blue Denim' (SDB)	CRos ECtt ELon EPfP GMaP MHol MRav NBir NLar SCob WCot
'Blue Eyed Blond' (IB)	MBriF
'Blue Hendred' (SDB)	NBir
'Blue Hill' (Reticulata)	GKev
'Blue King' (Dut) **new**	EHyd SCob
'Blue King' (Sib)	CBod CDor ELan EPfP GMaP ILea LRHS LSun MRav NBro NGdn SPer
'Blue Mere' (Sib)	MCot
'Blue Moon' (Sib)	ELon IMou WFar
'Blue Mountain Mist' (La)	LLWG
'Blue my Mind' (TB) **new**	WCAu
'Blue Note' (Reticulata)	EHyd EPot ERCP LRHS NRHS SPer
'Blue Note Blues' (TB)	WCAu
'Blue Pearl' (TB) **new**	WRHF
'Blue Pigmy' (SDB)	CAby CBod CWat CWld ECtt EHyd EPfP LRHS MRav MTin NLar SDeJ SPer
'Blue Reverie' (Sib)	ELon
'Blue Rhythm' (TB)	EHyd ELan ELon EPfP EWTr GBin GMaP GPSL LRHS MCot MRav NRHS SCoo SDeJ SPer
'Blue Sapphire' (Dut)	MHol
'Blue Shimmer' (TB)	CMac EBee ECha ECtt ELan EPfP EShb LRHS LSRN MCot MWat NRHS SDeJ SPer SRms WGwG
'Blue Splash' (IB)	WCAu
'Blue Staccato' (TB)	WCAu XSen
'Blue Suede Shoes' (TB)	LSRN XSen
'Blue Trill' (TB)	WCAu
'Bockingford' (MTB)	SIri
'Bold Encounter' (TB)	WCAu
'Bold Pretender' (La)	CBod ECtt ELon EPfP MBros MHol NLar WHil
'Bold Print' (IB)	CAby CBod CRos ECtt EHyd ELon GMaP IPot LRHS LSRN MCot MGos MHer MWat NRHS SPoG WCAu WLov
'Boo' (SDB)	CPBP WCAu XSen
'Border Town' (Spuria)	WCAu
'Bottled Sunshine' (IB)	LRHS
'Bound for Glory' (La)	LLWG
'Bournemouth Ball Gown' (Sib)	WAul
'Bournemouth Beauty' (Sib) 🏆H7	WAul
'Bouzy Bouzy' (TB)	XSen
'Bracknell' (Sib)	WAul
bracteata	EBee SPhx
'Braithwaite' (TB)	CAby CRos CWGN EHyd ELan EPfP EShb LRHS NRHS SCob SDeJ SPer SRms WGwG
'Brannigan' (SDB)	NBir NSti
'Brasilia' (TB)	NBir
'Brassie' (SDB)	CBro XSen
'Breakers' (TB) 🏆H7	WCAu
'Brenchley' (IB)	SIri
'Bride's Halo' (TB)	LSRN XSen
'Bright White' (MDB)	CBro
'Bright Yellow' (DB)	MRav
'Brighteyes' (IB)	SRms
'Brindisi' (TB)	XSen
'Brise de Mer' (TB)	XSen
'Bristo Magic' (TB)	XSen
'Bristol Gem' (TB)	XSen
'Broadleigh Angela' (CH)	CBro
'Broadleigh Carolyn' (CH) 🏆H5	CElw WSHC
'Broadleigh Lavinia' (CH)	CBro
'Broadleigh Nancy' (CH)	CBro MAvo
'Broadleigh Peacock' (CH)	CElw MAvo NLar WSHC
'Broadleigh Penny' (CH)	NLar
'Broadleigh Rose' (CH)	CBro CElw EPri MAvo MBrN WSHC
'Bronzaire' (IB)	EIri WCAu WGwG
'Bronze Beauty' (Dut)	ERCP
'Bronze Beauty' (TB)	SDeJ
'Bronze Beauty' van Tubergen (*boogiana* hybrid)	NBir SDeJ

	'Brother Carl' (TB)	XSen
	'Bruno' (TB)	LSRN NLar WMil
	bucharica misapplied	see *I. orchioides* Carrière
	bucharica ambig.	CAvo GKev LSun MBow MNrw NHpl SDeJ XSen
§	***bucharica*** Foster ♀H5	CBro EPot WHil
*	- 'Top Gold' (J)	GKev
	'Buckwheat' (TB)	SIri
	'Buisson de Roses' (TB)	XSen
	bulleyana	CBro GKev SRms
	- BWJ 7912	WCru
	- black-flowered	CExl GKev
	- - SDR 1792	EBee
	'Bumblebee Deelite' (MTB) ♀H7	CBor WCAu WMal
	'Bundle of Joy' (Sib)	ECtt WGob
	'Bundle of Love' (BB)	WCAu
	'Burgermeister' (TB)	XSen
	'Burgundy Party' (TB)	XSen
	'Burnt Toffee' (TB)	SIri XSen
	'Butter and Sugar' (Sib) ♀H7	Widely available
	'Buttermere' (TB)	SRms
	'Butterscotch Kiss' (TB)	CMac EHyd ELan ELon EPfP GMaP LRHS MGos MRav NBir NLar NRHS SDeJ SPer WHoo WLov
	'Bye Bye Blues' (TB)	XSen
	'Cabaret Royale' (TB)	XSen
	'Caesar' (Sib)	SRms
	'Caesar's Brother' (Sib)	EHyd ELan GWyn LCro LOPS LRHS MGos NHol NLar NRHS SHar SPer WBrk WFar WHoo WWtn
	'Cajun Rhythm' (TB)	XSen
	'Caliente' (TB)	MRav WCAu XSen
	'California Style' (IB)	XSen
§	Californian hybrids	CElw CMac CPBP NBir WCot
	'Calm Stream' (TB)	WCAu
	'Calypso Mood' (TB)	XSen
	'Cambridge' (Sib) ♀H7	CAvo CRos EHyd EIri EPfP IMou LRHS NRHS WAul WFar WWtn
	'Camelot Rose' (TB)	XSen
	'Cameo Blush' (BB)	XSen
	'Cameo Wine' (TB)	MNrw XSen
	canadensis	see *I. hookeri*
	'Canadian Streaker' (TB/v)	WCot
	'Candy Rock' (IB)	WCAu
	'Cannington Ochre' (SDB)	CBro
	'Canonbury Belle' (Sib)	WAul
	'Cantab' (Reticulata)	EHyd GKev LRHS NBir NRHS SDeJ
	'Canterbury' (TB) **new**	CRos
	'Cape Cod Boys' (Sib) **new**	WGob
	'Captive Sun' (SDB)	ECtt EHyd EPfP LRHS MAsh SIri WTor
	'Caramel' (TB)	XSen
	'Cardinal' (TB)	WMil
	'Care to Dance' (TB)	WCAu
	'Careless Sally' (Sib)	WAul
	'Carfax' (TB)	WMil
	'Caribbean Dream' (TB)	NLar XSen
	'Carnaby' (TB)	CBod CWld EHyd ELon EPfP EShb LRHS MRav NRHS SDeJ WGwG XSen
	'Carnival Time' (TB)	CBod CMac CRos CWGN CWld ECtt EHyd EPfP LRHS MBriF MCot MHer NRHS SPer WLov XSen
	'Carolina' (Reticulata)	CRos EHyd LRHS NRHS
	'Carolina Gold' (TB)	XSen
	'Carriage Trade' (TB)	LRHS
	'Cartouche' (BB)	SIri
	'Casbah' (TB)	XSen
	'Cascade Springs' (TB)	XSen

	'Cascade Sprite' (SDB)	SRms
	'Casque d'Or' (TB) **new**	LCro LOPS
	'Catalyst' (TB)	XSen
	'Cat's Eye' (SDB)	SIri
	'Catwalk Idol' (La)	LLWG
	caucasica	CMac
*	'Cedric Morris'	EWes
	'Cee Cee' (TB)	XSen
	'Celebration Song' (TB)	SIri WCAu XSen
	'Celestial Glory' (TB)	XSen
	'Cerdagne' (TB)	XSen
	chamaeiris	see *I. lutescens* subsp. *lutescens*
	'Champagne Elegance' (TB)	EIri EPfP NBir XSen
	'Champagne Encore' (IB)	ELon
	'Champagne Frost' (TB)	XSen
	'Champagne Waltz' (TB)	SIri XSen
	'Change of Pace' (TB)	XSen
	'Chanted' (SDB)	XSen
	'Chantilly' (TB)	ELan LRHS MRav NBir NGdn NLar NRHS SPer
	'Chapeau' (TB)	WCAu
	'Charlotte's Tutu' (La)	LLWG
	'Charmaine' (TB)	XSen
	'Charming Billy' (Sib) **new**	ECtt MHol NLar
	'Chartreuse Bounty' (Sib)	ECtt ELan EMor EPri EWes GMaP MHol MMrt NLar NSti WFar
	'Chasing Rainbows' (TB)	WCAu
	'Cheap Frills' (TB)	WCAu
	'Cher' (TB)	LSRN
	'Cherished One' (La)	LLWG
	'Cherry Blossom Song' (TB)	SIri
	'Cherry Garden' (SDB)	CBro CPBP CWat CWld ECtt EHyd ELan ELon EPfP EShb EWes GMaP LRHS MBNS MRav MTin NBir NGdn NLar SCob SDeJ WAul WCot WGwG
	'Cherub's Smile' (TB)	XSen
	'Chicken Little' (MDB)	CBro
I	'Chieftain' (SDB)	MRav
	'Childhood Sweetheart' (La)	LLWG
	'Chilled Wine' (Sib)	ELan ELon LRHS
	'China Dragon' (TB)	XSen
	'Chinese Coral' (TB)	XSen
	'Chinese Treasure' (TB)	XSen
	'Chou Bleu' (TB)	SIri
	'Christine Mullins' (Sib)	WBor
	'Christmas Angel' (TB)	NLar
	Chrysofor Group	CAby
	chrysographes ♀H6	CBcs CBod CBro CDor CTsd CWCL EHyd EPfP EPri EWhm GJos GKev LCro LOPS LRHS MHer MRav NRHS SDir SPeP SPoG WFar WPnP XSen
	- BWJ 7930	WCru
I	- 'Black Beauty'	CTsd
	- 'Black Gold'	EPri MHol NLar
I	- 'Black Knight'	CExl EHyd EPfP GBin LRHS MCot NChi NLar SMad
I	- 'Black Velvet'	GEdr WSpi
	- black-flowered	CAby CExl EBee ELan GAbr GKev GKin LCro LOPS LRHS MAvo MNrw NGdn NHpl NLar NRHS SCob SPer WCru WFar WGwG WPGP WPnP WSHC WSpi WWtn
	- 'Bob's Fancy'	SDeJ
	- dark-flowered	GKev WFar
	- hybrid	WFar
	- 'Inshriach'	IMou
	- 'Kew Black'	CExl GKev LEdu NBir

– 'Mandarin Purple'	GQue SPer
– yellow-flowered	WFar
chrysographes* × *forrestii	NBir
'Château d'Auvers-sur-Oise' (TB)	SIri WViv
'Ciel et Mer' (TB)	WViv
'Cimarron Strip' (TB)	EPfP WCot XSen
'Cinque Terre' (TB)	WCAu
'Circle of Light' (TB)	WCAu
'Circus Stripes' (TB)	XSen
'Citoyen' (TB)	XSen
'Claire' (Reticulata)	NBir
'Clairette' (Reticulata)	CRos EHyd EPot GKev LRHS NRHS SDeJ
'Clarence' (TB)	XSen
clarkei B&SWJ 2122	WCru
– CC 2751	CExl
– SDR 3819	GKev
'Class Ring' (TB)	WCAu
'Classic Look' (TB)	SIri
'Clear Blue Sky' (SDB) **new**	WCAu
'Clee Hills' (Sib)	WAul
'Cleedownton' (Sib)	WAul
'Clematis' (TB)	WMil
'Cleo' (TB)	NSti
'Cleve Dodge' (Sib)	EPri WGob XLum
'Cliffs of Dover' (TB)	EIri LCro LOPS MCot SCob SRms
'Cloudcap' (TB)	SRms
'Clownerie' (TB)	WViv
'Clyde Redmond' (La) ♀H5	WMal
'Coal Face' (TB)	WCAu
'Coal Seams' (TB)	WCAu
'Coalignition' (TB)	WCAu
'Codicil' (TB)	EIri XSen
colchica	LEdu
'Colette Thurillet' (TB)	WViv XSen
'Colin's Pale Blue' (Sib)	SMHy
'Collingwood Ingram'	WThu
'Color Glory' (TB)	SIri
'Color Me Blue' (TB)	WCAu
'Color Splash' (TB)	XSen
'Color Strokes' (TB)	WCAu
'Colorific' (La)	WGob
'Colortart' (TB)	XSen
'Coming Up Roses' (TB)	XSen
'Con Fuoco' (TB)	XSen
'Concertina' (IB)	WCAu
'Concoction' (IB)	GKev
'Concord Crush' (Sib)	MHol WGob WPnP WTor WTyc WWtn
confusa ♀H4	ESwi MBriF SArc SMad SPlb XSen
§ – 'Martyn Rix'	CAbb CBct CMac CPou CWCL ELon EPfP ESwi IMou LRHS MBriF MPie SBrt SEND SRms WGwG
'Conjuration' (TB)	SIri WCAu
'Constant Wattez' (IB)	NLar
'Contrast in Styles' (Sib)	ECtt EPri MNrw MSCN NQui SDir WFar WGob WWtn
'Cool Change' (TB) **new**	WCAu
'Copatonic' (TB)	WCAu
'Copper Classic' (TB)	ELon LSRN WCAu
'Coquet Waters' (Sib)	NBid WAul
'Coraband' (TB) **new**	NLar
'Coral Sunset' (TB)	XSen
'Cordoba' (TB)	WCAu XSen
'Coronation Anthem' (Sib)	EPri WAul
'Côte d'Azur' (Sib) **new**	CBor
'Côte d'Or' (TB)	XSen
'Country Charm' (TB)	WCAu
'Country Kisses' (TB)	WCAu
'County Town Red' (TB)	SIri
'Cracklin' Burgundy' (TB)	XSen
'Crackling Caldera' (TB)	MMrt WCot
'Cranapple' (BB) ♀H7	EIri WCAu
'Cranberry Ice' (TB)	ELon XSen
'Cranberry Sauce' (TB)	SIri
'Cranbrook' (IB) ♀H7	SIri
'Crathie' (TB)	ECha EHyd EMal LRHS
'Cream Beauty' (Dut)	GKev LCro LOPS SDeJ
cretensis	see *I. unguicularis* subsp. *cretensis*
'Crinoline' (TB)	XSen
cristata	GEdr GKev NHpl SGro SMad
– 'Abbey's Violet'	EBee
– 'Alba'	CPBP SGro WAbe WThu
§ – 'Captain Collingwood'	WAbe
crocea ♀H6	GBin SPtp
'Croftway Lemon' (TB)	ELon
'Crowned Heads' (TB)	WCAu XSen
'Crushed Ice' (La)	LLWG
'Crystal Gazer' (TB)	WCAu
'Cumulus' (TB)	SIri
cuniculiformis	WCot
'Cup Race' (TB)	XSen
'Curlew' (IB)	WCAu
'Cute or What' (SDB) **new**	SIri
'Cyanea' (DB)	GKev
'Cyclamint' (La)	LLWG
cycloglossa	GKev
'Daedalus' (Rc)	GKev
'Daemon Imp' (MTB)	WCAu
'Dainty Lace' (La)	LLWG
'Dale Dennis' (DB)	XSen
'Dame de Coeur' (TB)	SIri
'Dance Ballerina Dance' (Sib)	CBod CWCL EBee EPfP EPri GWyn MRav NLar WFar WGob
'Dance for Joy' (TB)	XSen
'Dance the Night Away' (TB)	WCAu
'Dancer's Veil' (TB)	CMac EBee ECtt EHyd ELon EPfP LRHS MRav NRHS SPer
'Dancing Nanou' (Sib)	ECtt
danfordiae	CRos EHyd EPot GKev LCro LOPS LRHS NHpl NRHS SDeJ
'Daphne' (TB)	WMil
'Dardanus' (Rc)	EPot ERCP GKev SDeJ WCot
'Dark Circle' (Sib)	EBee WFar
'Dark Desire' (Sib)	MRav
'Darkness' (IB)	SIri
'Darkside' (TB)	XSen
'Dating a Royal' (TB) **new**	WCAu
'Daughter of Stars' (TB)	ELon
'Dawn Waltz' (Sib)	CBre WFar WGob
'Dazzling Gold' (TB)	XSen
'Dear Currier' (Sib)	WAul
'Dear Delight' (Sib)	CBod ELon MNrw NLar WFar
'Death by Chocolate' (SDB)	SIri
'Decadence' (TB)	WCAu
§ ***decora***	SBrt WAbe
'Deep Black' (TB)	CRos CWGN EBee ELan EPfP GMaP LRHS LSRN MBNS MBriF MCot MRav MWat NLar NRHS NWad SDeJ SPer SPoG WGwG
'Deepening Shadows' (CH)	MAvo
'Deft Touch' (TB)	XSen
delavayi ♀H6	EWes GMaP
– SDR 50	CExl GKev
– 'Didcot'	CRos EHyd LRHS NRHS
'Delirium' (IB)	WCAu
'Delta Blues' (TB)	SIri
'Delta Butterfly' (La)	WMAq

	'Demon' (SDB)	NBPC XSen
	'Demure Illini' (Sib)	MNrw
	'Derwentwater' (TB)	SRms WCAu
	'Desert Echo' (TB)	XSen
	'Dewful' (Sib)	WFar
	'Diabolique' (TB) 𝕐H7	XSen
	'Discovered Treasure' (TB)	WCAu
	'Discovery'^{PBR} (Dut)	SDeJ
	'Disguise' (TB)	WCAu
	'Distant Music' (La)	LLWG
	'Ditzy' (SDB)	SIri
	'Dividing Line' (MTB)	WCAu
	'Dixie Darling' (TB)	XSen
	'Dixie Pixie' (SDB)	WCAu
	'Dolce' (SpH)	WCAu
§	***domestica***	CBro CPla EHyd GKev LRHS SMad SPlb SRms WSHC
	- 'Freckle Face'	CWCL MHol
	'Dominion' (TB)	WMil
	'Dotted Swiss' (TB)	XSen
	'Double Byte' (SDB)	XSen
	'Double Espoir' (TB)	XSen
	'Double Lament' (SDB)	CBro
	'Double Standards' (Sib)	EPri NLar SDir WFar WGob
	'Double Vision' (TB)	XSen
	'Douce Reverie' (TB)	WViv
	douglasiana	GKev
	'Dover Beach' (TB)	SIri
	'Dover Castle' (BB) 𝕐H7	SIri
	'Downtown Brown' (TB)	WCAu
	'Draco' (TB)	ECtt EPfP IPot XSen
	'Dream Indigo' (IB)	XSen
	'Dreaming Green' (Sib)	EBee
	'Dreaming Orange' (Sib)	ECtt EPri SDir
	'Dreaming Spires' (Sib)	GBin
	'Dreaming Yellow' (Sib)	CAby CAvo CBar CBre CSam ECha EHyd EPfP EPri EWhm GBin GKin LRHS MRav NGdn NRHS SPer WAul WCAu WGob WGwG WWtn
	'Duke of Bedford' (TB)	WMil
	'Dunkler Wein' (Sib)	EWes
	'Dunlin' (MDB)	CBro NBir
	'Dural White Butterfly' (La)	EPfP
	'Dusky Challenger' (TB)	CBod EBee ECtt IPot LCro LOPS SRms WCAu XSen
	'Dusky Evening' (TB)	XSen
	'Dutch Chocolate' (TB)	EWes LCro LOPS XSen
	'Dynamite' (TB)	XSen
	'Dyonisos' (TB)	SIri
	'Eagle's Flight' (TB)	XSen
	'Earl of Essex' (TB)	XSen
	'Early Light' (TB) 𝕐H7	EIri
	'Easter' (SDB)	SIri
	'Eastman Winds' (La)	LLWG
	'Easy' (MTB)	EIri
	'Échassier' (TB) **new**	SIri
	'Echo de France' (TB)	SRms XSen
	'Edge of Winter' (TB)	XSen
	'Edith Wolford' (TB)	GWyn MMrt SCob XSen
	'Edna Grace' (La)	LLWG
	'Ed's Blue' (DB)	ELan
	'Edward' (Reticulata)	SDeJ
	'Edward of Windsor' (TB)	ELan GMaP LRHS NLar
	'Ego' (Sib)	ECha ELon EPfP EPri WFar
	'Eileen Louise' (TB) 𝕐H7	WCAu
	'Eleanor's Pride' (TB)	SRms
	elegantissima	see *I. iberica* subsp. *elegantissima*
	'Elizabeth Poldark' (TB)	XSen
	'Ellesmere' (Sib)	WAul
	'Elsie Petty' (IB)	SIri
	'Elvinhall'	CBro
	'Emperor' (Sib)	CWat NSti
	'Empress of India' (TB)	EWTr
	'Endless Love' (TB)	EIri
	'English Charm' (TB)	XSen
	'English Cottage' (TB)	ELon GBin LSRN MHer NLar SRms WCAu XSen
	'Ennerdale' (TB)	SRms
	'Enriched' (MTB) 𝕐H7	WCAu
§	***ensata***	CBcs CBro CRos CTri ELan EPfP EWTr LRHS LSun MMuc MNrw NLar NRHS SCob SPlb SRms WPnP WWtn
	- 'Activity'	ELon WFar
	- 'Alba'	ECha MMuc WCFE
	- 'Angel Mountain'	IPot LLWG MBNS WFar WGob
	- 'Angelic Choir'	LLWG
	- 'Asian Warrior'	WFar
	- 'August Emperor'	MBel
	- 'Azuma-kagami'	MNrw
	- 'Azure'	SDir WFar
I	- 'Blue King'	NHol
	- 'Blue Mandarin' **new**	ECtt
	- 'Blue Spritz'	LLWG
	- 'Carnival Prince'	WFar
	- 'Cascade Crest'	WFar
	- 'Celestial Emperor'	LLWG
	- 'Center of Interest'	NBir
*	- 'Charm'	EHyd LRHS
	- 'Christina's Gown'	WFar WGob
	- 'Crepe Paper'	WFar
	- 'Cry of Rejoice'	ECtt
	- 'Crystal Halo' 𝕐H6	EBee MNHC WWtn
I	- 'Darling'	EPfP WFar
	- 'Dirigo Editor'	LLWG
	- 'Dirigo Maiden's Blush' **new**	LLWG
	- 'Dramatic Moment'	WFar WSpi
I	- 'Dresden China'	WFar
	- 'Eden's Blush'	EBee
	- 'Eden's Paintbrush'	EShb SPer
	- 'Eileen's Dream' **new**	ECtt LLWG
	- 'Electric Rays'	ELon LLWG SDir WFar
I	- 'Emotion'	CMac WFar
I	- 'Fortune'	CBod GBin MSCN SDir WWtn
	- 'Freckled Geisha'	CBrac CMac EBee ECtt ELon EPfP IPot NBir NQui SRms WFar
	- 'Frilled Enchantment' 𝕐H6	IPot WFar
	- 'Galatea Marx'	CBod CExl WFar
	- 'Gipsy'	CMac LRHS
	- 'Gold Bound'	ECtt ELon SDir WGob
	- 'Good Omen'	ECtt WGob
	- 'Gracieuse'	CMiW CRos CTsd LRHS NLar
	- 'Greywoods Catrina'	WFar WGob
	- 'Gusto'	CMac ELon EPfP MNrw SRms WFar
	- 'Harlequinesque'	ECtt IPot SMad WFar WGob
	- 'Harpswell Chantey'	IPot
	- 'Hercule'	CExl NBir WFar
	- Higo white	SPer
	- 'Hoshi-akari'	WFar
	- 'Ike-no-sazanami'	LLWG
	- 'Imperial Velvet'	WFar
	- 'Indigo Delight'	LLWG
*	- 'Innocence'	NLar SRms WFar
	- 'Iso-no-nami'	WFar
	- 'Japanese Plum' **new**	LLWG
	- 'Jocasta'	EPfP WFar
	- 'Jodlesong'	WFar

	– 'Kalamazoo'	WFar
	– 'Katy Mendez' ♀H6	IPot
	– 'Kogesho'	NLar
	– 'Koh Dom'	SPer
	– 'Kongo-san'	NLar WFar
	– 'Kuma-funjin'	CExl
	– 'Kumo-no-obi'	CExl CFis EHyd GBin LRHS MCot NHol WFar WWtn
	– 'Lady in Waiting'	CBod ECtt EPfP NLar SDir WGob WOld WTyc WWtn
	– 'Laughing Lion'	ECtt WFar
	– 'Light at Dawn'	MBel
	– 'Lilac Blotch'	SPer
	– 'Ling'	CRos
	– 'Loyalty'	CExl LRHS WFar
	– 'Momogasumi'	ECtt LLWG MNrw NQui WHil
§	– 'Moonlight Waves'	CExl CMac CRos EBee EHyd ELan EPfP GBin GKin GMaP IPot LRHS MCot MHer MRav NGdn NHol NRHS SRms WFar WGob WSpi WWtn
	– 'Murasame' ♀H6	EShb
	– 'Neptune's Trident' **new**	LLWG
	– 'Oase'	ECtt
	– 'Ocean Mist'	ECtt
	– 'Oku-banri'	CExl WFar
	– 'Oriental Eyes'	NGdn
	– pale mauve-flowered	NBir
	– 'Pin Stripe'	WFar
	– 'Pink Frost'	CFis EBee EPfP MHer WFar
	– 'Pleasant Earlybird'	WFar
	– 'Pleasant Journey'	ECtt
	– 'Prairie Frost'	NLar
	– 'Pure Emotion'	LLWG
	– 'Purple Parasol'	ECtt LLWG
	– purple-flowered	SPer
	– 'Queen's Tiara'	ECtt ELon EWTr IPot WBor WGob WTyc
	– 'Rakka-no-utage'	NLar
	– 'Red Tessa' **new**	LLWG
	– 'Rivulets of Wine'	LLWG
	– Rodionenko hybrids **new**	WMal
§	– 'Rose Queen' ♀H6	CExl CMac CRos CSam CTsd ECha EHyd ELan EPfP GBin GKin GMaP LRHS MCot MRav NBir NGdn NHol NRHS SPer SRms WFar XLum
	– 'Rowden King'	NChi
	– 'Rowden Mikado'	NChi
I	– 'Royal Banner'	ECtt LRHS WFar
	– 'Royal Crown'	XLum
I	– 'Ruby King'	LRHS
	– 'Ruffled Dimity'	IPot
I	– 'Sensation'	CWCL ECtt GBin NLar SRms WWtn
	– 'Snowy Hills'	XLum
	– 'Sorcerer's Triumph'	WFar
	– 'Splish Splash'	GKev
	– var. ***spontanea*** B&SWJ 1103	WCru
	– – B&SWJ 8699	WCru
	– 'Stippled Ripples'	IPot
	– 'Sugar Dome'	LLWG
	– 'Taketori-hime' (v)	XLum
	– 'Topas'	EBee WFar
	– 'Umi-kaze'	NLar
	– 'Variegata' (v) ♀H6	CBct CMac CRos EBee ECha EHyd EIri ELon EPfP GBin GMaP LRHS MHer MHol MMuc NLar NRHS NSti SEND SMad SPoG SRms WFar WMal WPnP WWtn
	– 'Velvety Queen'	ECtt
	– 'Wave Action'	EWTr IPot
I	– 'White Ladies'	CSBt LRHS SPeP WCAu WSpi
	– 'Wine Ruffles'	LSRN
	– 'Yako-no-tama'	WFar
	– 'Yedo-yeman'	IMou WFar
	'Epicenter' (TB)	XSen
	'Eramosa Skies' (SDB)	WCAu
	'Eric the Red' (Sib)	ELon
	'Erste Sahne' (Sib)	GBin
	'Eternal Bliss' (TB)	SIri
	'Evadne' (TB)	WMal WMil
	'Evening Drama' (TB)	SIri
	'Evening Gown' (TB)	XSen
	'Ever After' (TB)	XSen
	'Ever Again' (Sib)	ELon
	'Everything Plus' (TB)	XSen
	'Ewen' (Sib)	CPou GKin GLog GMaP NGdn WAul WCot
	'Exotic Isle' (TB)	EPPr XSen
	'Experiment' (SDB)	EIri
	'Extra' (BB)	CPBP
	'Extra Dazzle' (La)	LLWG
	'Eye Catcher' (Reticulata)	EPot ERCP GKev XEll
	'Eye Magic' (IB)	XSen
	'Eye of Tiger'	see *I.* 'Tigereye'
	'Eyebright' (SDB) ♀H7	CBro
	'Fabiola' (Reticulata)	EHyd EPot ERCP LRHS NRHS SDeJ
	'Fabuleux' (TB)	SIri
	'Face of an Angel' (TB)	WCAu
	'Fall Fiesta' (TB)	XSen
	'Fanciful Whimsy' (IB)	WCAu
	'Fancy Brass' (TB)	SIri
	'Fanfaron' (TB)	XSen
	'Farleigh Damson' (SDB)	SIri
	'Fashion Holiday' (IB)	SIri
	'Fashion Lady' (MDB)	CBro
	'Fathom' (IB)	WCAu
	'Faubourg-St John' (La)	LLWG
	'Feather and Fan' (La)	LLWG
	'Feminine Charm' (TB)	MRav
	'Feu du Ciel' (TB) ♀H7	XSen
	'Few Are Chosen' (La)	LLWG
	'Fiesta Time' (TB)	XSen
	'Film Festival' (TB)	ECtt EPfP
	'Finalist' (TB)	XSen
	'Finola' (Reticulata)	ERCP GKev
	'Firebreather' (TB)	EPfP MHol
	'Firebug' (IB)	XSen
	'Firecracker' (TB)	MRav
	'First Interstate' (TB)	XSen
	'First Romance' (SDB)	LSRN
	'Five Star Admiral' (TB)	XSen
	'Flaming Dragon' (TB)	XSen
	'Flaming Victory' (TB)	XSen
	flavescens	XSen
	'Fleece of White' (BB)	WCAu
	'Flibbertigibbet' (SDB)	SIri
	'Flight of Butterflies' (Sib) ♀H7	Widely available
	'Flirting Again' (SDB) ♀H7	SIri
	'Floorshow' (TB)	XSen
§	'Florentina' (IB/TB) ♀H6	CBro CHby GPoy LRHS MHer MNHC MRav NBid NBir SAko SEND SRms WCAu XAbr XSen
	'Florentine Silk' (TB)	WCAu
	'Flumadiddle' (IB)	CBro
	'Flûte Enchantée' (TB)	XSen
	'Focus' (TB)	XSen
	foetidissima ♀H6	Widely available

	– 'Aurea'	WCot
	– ***chinensis***	see *I. foetidissima* var. *citrina*
§	– var. ***citrina***	CBre EPri EWld GAbr GKev LEdu NLar WGwG WOut
	– 'Fructu Albo'	WCot
	– var. ***lutescens***	NSti
	– 'Variegata' (v) ♀H6	CBct NBir NPer WTor
	'Fogbound' (TB)	WCAu
	'Foggy Dew' (TB)	EHyd EPfP LRHS NRHS SDeJ
	'Fond Kiss' (Sib)	WGob
	'Fondation Van Gogh' (TB)	XSen
	'Foolish Fancy' (TB)	SIri
	'Footloose' (TB)	XSen
	'Forecasting Rain' (SDB)	SIri
	'Foreign Legion' (TB)	WCAu
	'Forest Light' (SDB)	CBro
	'Forever Blue' (SDB)	WCAu
	'Forever Gold' (TB)	XSen
*	'Forever Trevor' (CH)	MAvo
	formosana B&SWJ 3076	WCru
	'Forrest Hills' (TB)	EHyd EPfP LRHS
	forrestii ♀H6	CAby CBro CExl CMac EPfP GAbr GKev GLog LRHS NBir SPtp WOut
	'Fort Apache' (TB)	EWes
	'Fortunata' (TB)	XSen
	'Fortunate Son' (TB)	WCAu
	'Fourfold Blue' (SpH)	GBin
	'Fourfold Lavender' (Sib)	EWes NLar
	'Framboise' (TB)	XSen
	'Francina' (TB)	WMil
	'Frank Elder' (Reticulata)	EHyd EPot ERCP LRHS NRHS SDeJ WAbe
	'French Can Can' (TB)	GWyn SIri
	'Fresno Calypso' (TB)	WCAu XSen
	'Friends' Song' (La)	LLWG
	'Frigiya' (Spuria)	GBin
	'Frimousee' (TB)	WViv
	'Frison-roche' (TB)	WViv
	'From this Moment' (La)	LLWG
	'Frontier Marshall' (TB)	XSen
	'Frost and Flame' (TB)	CAby EBee ECtt EHyd ELan GBin LCro LRHS MAsh MRav NBir NLar NRHS SDeJ SPoG WGwG
	'Frosted Angel' (SDB)	CBro
	'Frosted Velvet' (MTB)	WCAu
	'Frosty Jewels' (TB)	XSen
	'Fruit Cocktail' (IB)	XSen
	fulva ♀H5	EBee EPri EWat EWhm MMrt NBir NSti SBrt WCAu WCot
	– 'Marvell Gold' (La)	EWat
	× ***fulvala*** ♀H5	EWes NBir NSti
	– 'Violacea'	EHyd LRHS
	'Furnaceman' (SDB)	CBro
	'Futuriste' (TB)	SIri WViv
	'Gallant Moment' (TB)	SIri XSen
	'Galway' (IB)	SIri XSen
	'Garnet Storm Dancer' (La)	LLWG
	'Gelbe Mantel' (Sino-Sib)	NBir
	'George' (Reticulata) ♀H7	CAby CAvo EHyd EMor EPot ERCP GKev LRHS NRHS SDeJ WBor WBrk XEll
	'George Smith' (TB)	ECtt EPfP
	'Gerald Darby'	see *I.* × *robusta* 'Gerald Darby'
§	***germanica***	MMuc SEND WCot WGwG
	– var. ***florentina***	see *I.* 'Florentina'
§	– 'Nepalensis'	WCAu
	– 'The King'	see *I. germanica* 'Nepalensis'
	'Ghost Train' (TB)	SIri
	'Ginger Twist' (Sib) **new**	WGob
	'Gingerbread Man' (SDB)	CBro CMea EWld GEdr MBrN SWvt WCAu
	'Ginny's Choice' (La) **new**	LLWG
	'Girly Girl' (TB)	WCAu
	'Glacier Gold' (TB)	XSen
	'Glad Rags' (TB)	XSen
	'Gladys Austin' (TB)	XSen
	'Glenthorn' (TB)	SIri
	'Gnu' (TB)	XSen
	'Godfrey Owen' (TB)	WCAu
	'Godinton' (TB) **new**	SIri
	'Going Home' (TB) ♀H7	SIri
	'Going My Way' (TB)	SIri XSen
	'Gold Burst' (TB)	XSen
	'Gold Country' (TB)	XSen
	'Gold Galore' (TB)	SIri
	'Golden Alps' (TB)	SRms
	'Golden Beauty' (SpH)	GKev SDeJ
	'Golden Child' (SDB)	XSen
	'Golden Edge' (Sib)	CBod ECtt ELon GBin GQue LLWG NLar WFar WGob
	'Golden Encore' (TB)	WCAu
	'Golden Fireworks' (La)	LLWG
	'Golden Immortal' (TB)	WOld
	'Golden Zebra' (TB)	CBod LCro LOPS MBros MHol
	'Good Show' (TB)	XSen
	'Good Vibrations' (TB)	XSen
	'Goodbye Heart' (TB)	LSRN
	'Gordon' (Reticulata)	CAvo EHyd ERCP GKev LRHS NRHS
	gormanii	see *I. tenax*
	'Gossip' (SDB)	CBro
	'Goudhurst' (SDB)	SIri
	'Grace Sturtevant' (TB)	WMil
	gracilipes	SBrt
	– 'Alba'	EPot GEdr
	graeberiana	EPot GKev SDeJ
	graminea ♀H6	CBro CFis CMac EIri ELan EPri GKev NBir NChi NSti WCot XEll
	– var. ***pseudocyperus***	GBin
	graminifolia	see *I. kerneriana*
	'Granada Gold' (TB)	SRms XSen
	'Grand Amiral' (TB)	WViv
	'Grand Canari' (TB) **new**	WMal
	'Grand Waltz' (TB)	XSen
	'Grandis' (Sib)	GBin
	'Grapelet' (MDB)	CPBP
	'Green Ice' (TB)	LRHS MRav
	'Green Spot' (SDB) ♀H7	CBod CBro ECha ECtt EHyd LRHS MBriF MRav NBir NLar NRHS SDeJ SPer WAul
	'Greensand Way' (TB) **new**	SIri
	'Grenade' (TB)	SIri WViv
	grey-flowered (Sib)	ELon
	'Grosser Wein' (Sib)	GBin
	'Gull's Wing' (Sib)	EPfP LLWG LRHS MBel MHol NLar NSti SPoG WGob WPnP WTyc
	'Gurkha's Dance' (SDB)	SIri
	'Gypsy Beauty' (Dut)	CAvo ELan GKev LCro LOPS MNrw SDeJ
	'Gypsy Jewels' (TB)	XSen
	'Gypsy Lord' (TB) **new**	WCAu
	'Gypsy Romance' (TB) ♀H7	EIri SIri
	'Gypsy Tart' (SDB)	SIri
	'Habit' (TB)	WCAu
	'Hail Mary' (La)	LLWG
	halophila	see *I. spuria* subsp. *halophila*
	'Happenstance' (TB)	WCAu
	'Happiness' (Reticulata) **new**	GKev
	'Happy Mood' (IB)	EIri

'Harbor Blue' (TB)	CRos CTsd NLar WCAu
'Harmony' (IB)	EHyd
'Harmony' (Reticulata)	CAby CAvo EHyd EPot GKev LCro LOPS LRHS NBir NRHS SDeJ SPhx WBrk
'Harpswell Happiness' (Sib) ♀H7	EBee ELon EPfP EPri GBin ILea SDir WAul WGob
'Harpswell Haze' (Sib)	ECha
'Harpswell Velvet' (Sib)	GBin
'Harriette Halloway' (TB)	CWGN EHyd EPfP EShb LRHS LSRN NLar SHar WCot
'Harvest Home' (BB) new	SIri
'Harvest King' (TB)	XSen
'Harvest of Memories' (TB)	GWyn SPoG
'Haut les Voiles' (TB)	WViv
'Haute Couture' (TB)	XSen
'Haviland' (TB)	XSen
'Headcorn' (MTB) ♀H7	SIri
'Headline Banner' (BB)	WCAu
'Heather Carpet' (SDB)	WCAu
'Heather Stream' (La)	ELon
'Heavenly Blue' (Sib)	SPer
'Helen Astor' (Sib)	CDor MRav
'Helen Proctor' (IB)	WCot XSen
'Helene C.' (TB)	WViv XSen
'Hello Darkness' (TB) ♀H7	WCAu WCot XSen
'Hell's Fire' (TB)	ELan ELon
'Hemstitched' (TB)	MHol
henryi new	GKev
'Her Royal Highness' (TB)	LCro LOPS
'Here Be Dragons' (Sib)	WGob
'Here Comes The Night' (TB)	WCAu
'Here Comes The Sun' (TB)	WCAu
'Hester Prynne' (TB)	WMil
'Heure Bleue' (TB)	WViv
'Hey True Blue' (TB)	WCAu
'High Blue Sky' (TB)	WCAu
'Highland Mist' (La)	LLWG
'Hildegarde' (Dut)	SDeJ
'Hippolyta' (Rc)	GKev
'His Royal Highness' (TB)	WCAu
histrio	EPot
- subsp. ***aintabensis***	GKev
histrioides 'Halkis'	EHyd EPot ERCP GKev LRHS NRHS SDeJ
- 'Lady Beatrix Stanley'	CAvo CRos EHyd EPot ERCP GKev LRHS MNrw MWat NBir NRHS SDeJ WBrk WHoo
'Hoar Edge' (Sib)	EPri NChi WAul
'Hocus Pocus' (SDB)	CWGN CWld ECtt EHyd EPfP LRHS NRHS WAul
'Hohe Warte' (Sib) ♀H7	GBin WAul
'Holden Clough' (SpH) ♀H7	CExl CPla EBee ELan EPPr EPfP GBin LEdu MBriF MMuc MNrw MRav NBir NChi NGdn NSti NWad WBrk WFar WSHC
'Holden's Child' (SpH)	CWat LLWG
'Holidaze' (IB) ♀H7	EIri
× ***hollandica***	EShb
'Hollywood Ending' (La) new	LLWG
'Holy Night' (TB)	SRms
'Honey Glazed' (IB)	ELon
'Honey Stars' (La)	LLWG
'Honeyplic' (IB) ♀H7	SIri
'Honington' (SDB)	WCAu
'Honky Tonk Blues' (TB)	LSRN
hoogiana ♀H5	GKev MBow

I	- 'Amphion'	GKev
I	- 'Antiope'	GKev
	- 'Purpurea'	GKev
§	***hookeri***	CFis CSma CTsd GKev GMaP MHol NHpl NSla SPtp SRms WAbe WIce
	'Hopelessly Devoted' (La)	LLWG
	'Hortensia Rose' (TB)	SIri WViv
	'Hot and Spicy' (La)	LLWG
	'Hot Spiced Wine' (TB)	SIri
	'How Audacious' (Sib) new	ECtt
	'Hubbard' (Sib)	EPri LLWG MNrw SPoG WFar WGob
	'Huckleberry Fudge' (TB)	XSen
	'Humors of Whiskey' (Sib) new	WGob
	hyrcana	GKev WCot
	'I Repeat' (TB)	XSen
§	***iberica*** subsp. ***elegantissima***	GKev
	'Ice Capades' (TB) new	WCAu
	'Ila Crawford' (Spuria) ♀H7	XSen
	'Illini Charm' (Sib)	WFar
	illyrica	see *I. pallida*
	'I'm Back' (TB)	WCAu
	'Immortality' (TB)	CBod CRos CWGN EPfP GKev GWyn LRHS MHol SCob SRms STPC WCAu XSen
	'Imperative' (IB)	SIri
	'Imperator' (TB)	ELan
	'Imperial Opal' (Sib)	ECtt NGdn WFar WGob
I	'Imperial Velvet' (Sib)	ELon WFar
	'Imprimis' (TB)	WCAu XSen
	'In Full Sail' (Sib)	WGob
	'In Love' (TB)	XSen
	'In Town' (TB)	XSen
	'Indian Chief' (TB)	CWCL ELan EPfP LCro LOPS MCot MHer MRav
	'Indigo Princess' (TB)	XSen
	'Ink Patterns' (TB)	WCAu
	'Inn-Keeper' (La)	LLWG
	innominata	CPla EHyd GKev LRHS NBir NBro NRHS NSla SRms WAbe
	- yellow-flowered	NRya
	'Inspired' (TB)	WCAu
	'Interpol' (TB)	XSen
	'Intrepid' (TB)	WViv
	'Invicta Celebration' (BB)	SIri
	'Invicta Daybreak' (IB)	SIri
	'Invicta Gold' (SDB)	SIri
	'Invicta Reprieve' (IB)	SIri
	'Invicta Sapphire' (TB)	SIri
	'Irisades' (TB)	SIri WViv
	'Isabelle' (Sib)	LSRN XSen
	'Island Sunset' (TB)	SIri
	'Isobel Rose' (TB)	SIri
	'Italian Ice' (TB)	EIri
	'Italian Velvet' (TB)	WCAu
	'It's Amazing' (IB)	WCAu
	'J.S. Dijt' (Reticulata)	CAvo EHyd EPot ERCP GKev LCro LOPS LRHS MGos NRHS SDeJ
	'Jack Attack' (La)	WWtn
	'Jac-y-do' (Sib)	EWes
	'Jamie Roo' (TB)	SIri
	'Jane Phillips' (TB) ♀H7	Widely available
	japonica ♀H4	CExl CTsd EWTr NLar NPer SPlb WCot WFar XLum XSen
	- B&SWJ 8921	WCru
	- 'Bourne Graceful'	CExl
	- 'Ledger'	CAby CExl CMac ECha MRav SEND SIvy SMad WWFP

	- 'Monty'	WWFP
	- 'Rudolph Spring'	WSHC
§	- 'Variegata' (v) 🏆H4	CAby CBcs CBct CBro ECha ELan ESwi NPer NSti SArc WAvo WBrk WFar WOut WWFP XSen
	'Java Bleue' (TB)	SIri
	'Jazz Festival' (TB)	SIri WCAu XSen
	'Jazz Hot' (La)	LLWG
	'Jazzed Up' (TB)	XSen
	'Jeanne Price' (TB)	LSRN
	'Jerry Murphy' (Sib) **new**	ECtt
	'Jesse's Song' (TB)	XSen
	'Jewel Baby' (SDB)	CBro
	'Jiansada' (SDB)	CBro
	'Jigsaw' (TB)	XSen
	'Joanna' (TB)	LSRN NLar
	'John' (IB)	LSRN
	'Joie de Vivre' (La)	LLWG
	'Joyce' (Reticulata)	CRos EHyd GKev LRHS NRHS SDeJ
	'Joyful Skies' (TB)	WCAu
	'Jubilant Spirit' (Spuria)	EWes
	'June Prom' (IB)	EHyd ELan EPfP LRHS NRHS
	'June Rose' (IB)	ELan
	'Jungle Shadows' (BB)	ELon MRav NBir
	'Jurassic Park' (TB)	WCAu XSen
	'Just Imagine' (La)	LLWG
	'Just Jennifer' (BB)	WCAu
	'Kabluey' (Sib)	EBee ECtt MWts WFar WGob
	'Kaboom' (Sib)	MHol WFar
	kaempferi	see *I. ensata*
	'Katharine Hodgkin' (Reticulata) 🏆H7	CAby CAvo CRos EBee ECha EHyd EMor EPot ERCP GAbr GKev LCro LOPS LRHS MNrw MRav NBir NHpl NLar NRHS SDeJ WBrk WCot WFar WHoo
	'Katherine's Gold' (Reticulata)	EPot ERCP GKev WBrk
	kemaonensis PAB 8473	LEdu
	'Kent Arrival' (Sib)	SIri
	'Kent Compote' (IB)	SIri
	'Kent Pride' (TB)	CAby CBod CSBt ECha ECtt ELan EPfP GBin LCro LOPS LRHS MCot MRav NBir NLar NRHS SCob SEdd SIvy SPer SPoG SRms WHoo
	'Kent Skylark' (IB)	SIri
	Kenta No Se129 (Sib)	EPri
	'Kentish Icon' (SDB)	SIri
	'Kentish Lad' (IB)	SIri
	'Kentucky Derby' (TB)	XSen
§	***kerneriana*** 🏆H5	CBro GKev NBir
	'Kęstutis Genys' (Sib)	WAul
	'KhoJa' **new**	GKev
	'Kingfisher' (Sib)	WAul
	'Kinshikou' (SpH) **new**	LLWG
	'Kita-no-seiza' (Sib)	ECtt EWTr LLWG NGdn WBrk WFar
	'Kiwi Slices' (SDB)	CWat
	'Knick Knack' (MDB)	CBro CPBP ECtt EHyd ELan ELon EPfP GMaP LRHS MRav MTin NRHS SDeJ SPoG
	korolkowii	GKev
	'La Meije' (TB)	SIri WViv
	'La Senda' (Spuria)	WCot
	'Lace Legacy' (TB)	LSRN
	'Laced Cotton' (TB)	XSen
§	***lactea***	SBrt SMHy XEll XSen
	- CC 7174	GKev
	lacustris	CPBP WAbe WCot
	- 'Captain Collingwood'	see *I. cristata* 'Captain Collingwood'
	'Lacy Snowflake' (TB)	LRHS
	'Lady Byng' (TB)	WMil
	'Lady Friend' (TB)	WCAu XSen
	'Lady in Red' (SDB)	WCAu
	'Lady Mohr' (AB)	WMal
	'Lady of the Night' (BB)	WCAu
	'Lady Vanessa' (Sib)	CPou EBee ELon MRav NSti WGob
	laevigata	CRos CWat EPfP EWat ITim MRav NBro NPer SRms WFar WMAq WShi
	- var. ***alba***	LLWG SRms
	- 'Atropurpurea'	LLWG
	- blue-flowered	LLWG
	- 'Colchesterensis'	CWat EWat NGdn NPer WMAq
I	- 'Dorothy'	NGdn
	- 'Dorothy Robinson'	EPfP MRav
*	- 'Elgar'	WMAq
	- 'Liam Johns'	LLWG
	- 'Midnight'	see *I. laevigata* 'Weymouth Midnight'
	- 'Monstrosa'	EWat
	- 'Richard Greaney'	EWat LLWG
	- 'Rose Queen'	see *I. ensata* 'Rose Queen'
	- 'Rowden Starlight'	LLWG
	- 'Royal Cartwheel'	LLWG
I	- 'Snowdrift'	CWat EWat LLWG NBir NGdn NLar NPer WCAu WFar WMAq
	- 'Variegata' (v) 🏆H6	CBen CWat ECha ELon EPfP EWat LLWG MWts NBro NGdn NPer SCob WMAq WPnP WWtn
	- 'Weymouth'	see *I. laevigata* 'Weymouth Blue'
§	- 'Weymouth Blue'	EWat LLWG
§	- 'Weymouth Midnight'	LLWG
	- 'Weymouth Purity'	EWat
	laevigata* × *versicolor **new**	WCAu
	laevigata* × *versicolor Tamberg hybrid	LLWG
§	'Lake Niklas' (Sib)	ELon MHol
	'Langport Storm' (IB)	EHyd ELon EPfP LRHS MBriF MRav NRHS SDeJ WHoo
	'Langport Wren' (IB) 🏆H7	CAby CBro CWld ECtt EHyd ELon EPfP EPri EShb GPSL LRHS MBel NBir NGdn NRHS WAul
	'Langthorns Pink' (Sib)	ELan MRav WAul
§	***latifolia***	WShi
	- ***alba***	WCot
	- 'Duchess of York'	EBee
	- 'Isabella'	GKev SDeJ
	- 'King of the Blues'	CAvo EBee GKev SDeJ SDix
	- 'Mansfield'	MNrw
	- 'Montblanc'	CAvo GKev SDeJ
	- 'Queen of the Blues'	SDeJ
	'Laura Louise' (La)	LLWG WGob
	'Laurenbuhl' (Sib)	CExl
	'Lavender Bounty' (Sib)	GBin
	'Lavender Light' (Sib)	WAul
	lazica 🏆H5	CBct CBod CBro CMac EIri EPPr EPfP EPot EPri GKev IBlr LRHS MMrt MPie MRav NBir NChi NSti SEND SPer SPlb SRms WAul WGwG WHil
	- 'Joy Bishop'	CJun
*	- 'Richard Nutt'	CJun ELon WCot WSHC
	- 'Turkish Blue'	CJun IBlr
	'Lemon Flare' (SDB)	MRav SRms
	'Lemon Ice' (TB)	ECha EHyd GBin LRHS SDeJ SPer WLov
	'Lemon Pop' (IB)	WCAu
	'Lemon Puff' (MDB)	CBro
	'Lemon Veil' (Sib)	MNrw SDir WGob

	'Lena' (SDB)	CBro
	'Lenora Pearl' (BB)	XSen
	'Leo Hewitt' (Sib)	ELon
	leptophylla	GKev
	'Let's Elope' (IB)	WCAu
	'Licorice Stick' (TB)	XSen
	'Light Beam' (TB)	XSen
	'Lilli-white' (SDB)	CAby CWat EHyd ELon EPfP LRHS MRav NRHS SPoG WCAu
	'Lilting' (TB)	XSen
	'Limbo' (SpH)	LLWG
	'Lime Fizz' (TB)	XSen
	'Limeheart' (Sib)	CPou
	'Limelight' (TB)	SRms
	lineata	GKev
	'Lion King' (Dut) ♀H6	GAbr LCro LOPS MNrw
	'Little Black Belt' (SDB)	LRHS
	'Little Blackfoot' (SDB)	WCot
	'Little Episode' (SDB)	CBro ELon
	'Little Nutkin' (La)	LLWG
	'Little Rosy Wings' (SDB)	CBro CPBP
	'Little Shadow' (IB)	CWGN MRav SRms
	'Little Tilgates' (CH)	WCot WMal WSHC
	'Little Twinkle Star' (Sib)	MHer WFar
	'Local Color' (TB)	SIri XSen
	'Lodore' (TB)	SRms
	longipetala	EPPr NBir
	'Loop the Loop' (TB)	CMac CRos SPoG SRms
	'Loose Valley' (MTB) ♀H7	SIri
	'Lord Warden' (TB)	ECtt EHyd EPfP LRHS WGwG
	'Lost in Love' (TB)	WCAu
	'Lottie Lou' (TB)	SIri
	'Lotus Land' (TB)	WCAu
	Louisiana hybrids	ELan
	'Louvois' (TB)	NLar
	'Love the Sun' (TB)	XSen
	'Lovely Again' (TB)	GKev MRav WCAu
	'Lovely Señorita' (TB)	WCAu
	'Love's Tune' (IB)	ECtt EHyd EPfP LRHS NRHS WTor
	'Loyalist' (TB)	SIri
	'Lucky Devil' (Spuria) ♀H7	WCAu
	'Lullingstone Castle' (Kent Castles Series) (IB)	SIri
	'Lumarco' (TB)	WViv
	'Lumière d'Automne' (TB)	XSen
	'Lurline' (TB)	WMil
	lutescens ♀H7	EPot GKev MHid WAbe
§	- subsp. ***lutescens***	XSen
	- subsp. ***subbiflora***	EPot
	'Ma Mie' (IB)	WViv
	'Mabel Coday' (Sib)	EBee EPri
	'Mad Magenta' (Sib)	GBin
	'Madeira Belle' (TB)	CWld ECtt EHyd EPfP LRHS NRHS WAul WGwG
	'Magic Man' (TB)	XSen
	'Magical Encounter' (TB)	SIri
	magnifica 'Alba'	GKev
	'Mahogany Lord' (Spuria) **new**	WCAu
	'Maid of Orange' (BB)	WCAu
	'Majestic' (TB)	WMil
	'Majestic Overtures' (Sib)	LLWG
	'Making Eyes' (SDB)	ELon
	'Man's Best Friend' (IB)	SIri
	'Marden Beech' (IB)	SIri
	'Marden Meadow' (MTB)	SIri
	'Margot Holmes' (Cal-Sib)	WFar
	'Margrave' (TB)	XSen
	'Marilyn Holmes' (Sib)	GLog GQue WCot
	'Mariposa Autumn' (TB)	SIri WOld

	'Marjorie' (TB)	SRms
	'Marmalade Skies' (BB)	WCAu
	'Mars Landing' (Reticulata)	EPot ERCP GKev
	'Marsh Marigold' (TB)	WMil
	'Martyn Rix'	see *I. confusa* 'Martyn Rix'
	'Mary Frances' (TB)	XSen
	'Mary McIlroy' (SDB) ♀H7	CBro
	'Marybill' (TB)	SIri
	'Master Touch' (TB)	ELon WLov XSen
	'Matinata' (TB)	ELan XSen
	'Maui Moonlight' (IB) ♀H7	NLar WCAu
	'Meadow Court' (SDB)	CBro GEdr
	'Media Luz' (Spuria)	WCAu
	'Medici Prince' (TB)	WCAu
	'Medway Valley' (MTB) ♀H7	SIri
	mellita	see *I. suaveolens*
	'Melon Honey' (SDB)	ELon WCAu
§	'Melton Red Flare' (Sib)	CWld EHyd EMor GBin LRHS MBNS MSpe NRHS WAvo
	'Memphis Memory' (Sib)	EBee ELan ELon MHol NLar SPer WFar WGob
	'Mer du Sud' (TB) ♀H7	CAby ECtt EIri EPfP LCro LRHS MCot SCob WCot WViv XSen
*	'Merebrook Blue Lagoon' (La)	WMAq
	'Merebrook Jemma J' (La)	WMAq
	'Merebrook Purpla' (La)	WMAq
	'Merebrook Rum 'n' Raisin' (La)	WMAq
*	'Merebrook Rusty Red' (La)	WMAq
	'Merebrook Sunnyside Up' (La)	WMAq
	'Merebrook Symphony' (La)	WMAq
	mesopotamica	see *I. germanica*
	'Miami Beach' (TB)	WCAu
	'Midhurst White' (TB)	SIri
I	'Midnight Blue' (MDB)	CBro
	'Midnight Caller' (TB)	XSen
	'Midnight Tryst' **new**	WCAu
	'Mighty Mouse' (MDB)	ELon
	milesii ♀H3	CExl EPri GBin GKev NBir SBrt WSHC
	'Millennium Sunrise' (TB)	WCAu
	'Mini-Agnes' (SDB)	CBro
	'Minidragon' (SDB)	SIri
	'Miss Apple' (Sib) **new**	CBod WGob
	'Mission Ridge' (TB)	MHol
	'Missouri Autumn' (Spuria) **new**	WCAu
	missouriensis	CMac EPPr GKev
	Monspur Group	WCot
	'Moon Silk' (Sib)	CBro EAJP ECtt ELon EPri EWes MBel SCob WCot WFar WGob
	'Moonlight Masquerade' **new**	WCAu
	'Moonlight Waves'	see *I. ensata* 'Moonlight Waves'
	'Moonlit Water' (TB)	WCAu
	'Morwell' (TB)	WMil
	'Mount Everest'PBR (TB)	GKev SDeJ
	'Mountain Lake' (Sib)	EHyd EPfP EShb GBin LRHS MPie NRHS WFar WGob WSpi
	'Mr Peacock' (Sib) **new**	WGob
	'Mrs Rowe' (Sib)	CPou EIri ELon EPri MRav WAul WCAu WFar
	'Mrs Tait' (Spuria)	NChi
	'Mrs Valerie West' (TB)	WMil
	'Muggles' (SDB)	SIri
	'Music' (SDB)	SIri

	'My Cher' (SDB) **new**	WCAu
	'My Cher of Happiness' (BB) **new**	WCAu
	'My First Kiss' (Sib)	WAul
	'My Love' (Sib)	IMou WAul
	'My Seedling' (MDB)	CBro
	'Myra' (SDB)	XSen
	'Mysterieux' (TB)	SIri
	'Mystic' (TB)	WMil
	'Mystic Beauty' (Dut)	SDeJ
	'Mythology' (TB)	SIri
	'Nada' (SpH)	WCot
	'Nancy Hardy' (MDB)	CBro
	'Naples' (TB)	SIri
	'Natascha' (Reticulata)	EPot GKev SDeJ
	'Natasha' (MTB)	EMor
	'Natchez Trace' (TB)	EPri LCro LOPS LRHS XSen
	'Navajo Jewel' (TB)	XSen
	'Navy Brass' (Sib)	EPri WAul
	'Needlecraft' (TB)	XSen
*	'Nel Jupe' (TB)	LRHS NLar
	nepalensis	see *I. decora*
	'New Centurion' (TB)	XSen
	'New Face' (TB)	WCAu
	'New Idea' (MTB)	CBro WCAu
	'New Leaf' (TB)	WCAu
	'Nibelungen' (TB)	CBro ELan XSen
	'Nickel' (IB) **new**	WCAu
	'Night Breeze' (Sib)	EPri
	'Night Edition' (TB)	XSen
	'Night Game' (TB)	XSen
	'Night Owl' (TB)	ELon MHer WLov
	'Nightfall' (TB)	NLar
	'Ninja Turtles' (SDB) **new**	SIri
	'Noctambule' (TB) 🏆H7	SIri WViv
§	× ***norrisii***	EHyd LRHS NRHS
	'North Downs' (BB)	SIri
	'North Star' (TB)	GKev
	'Northern Jewel' (IB)	SIri
	'Northumberland Piper' (TB)	SIri
	'Now and Forever' (La)	LLWG
	'Oblivion' (IB)	WCAu
	'Ochre Doll' (SDB)	CBro
	ochroleuca	see *I. orientalis* Mill.
	'October Sun' (TB)	ELan
	'Oh Happy Day' (La)	LLWG
	'Oh Jamaica' (TB)	XSen
	'Oktoberfest' (TB)	XSen
	'Ola Kalá' (TB)	CBod CRos EHyd GMaP LRHS MGos NLar NRHS SPer XSen
	'Old Black Magic' (TB)	XSen
	'Old Flame' (TB)	XSen
	'Olympiad' (TB)	XSen
	'Olympic Challenge' (TB)	MRav
	'Ominous Stranger' (TB)	MMrt
	'Once Again' (TB)	XSen
	'One Desire' (TB)	XSen
	'Open Sky' (SDB)	LRHS XSen
	'Orageux' (IB)	SIri WMal
	'Orange Caper' (SDB)	CMac ECtt EHyd LRHS MRav MTin NRHS SCob WCot
§	'Orange Chariot' (TB)	MBros
	'Orange Glow' (TB)	GKev
	'Orange Harvest' (TB)	XSen
	'Orange Tiger' (SDB)	CBod
	orchioides misapplied	see *I. bucharica* Foster
§	***orchioides*** Carrière	CAby ELan
	'Oriental Beauty' (TB)	SDeJ
	orientalis ambig.	ELan EWes MNrw
§	***orientalis*** Mill. 🏆H6	GBin GKev MMuc SEND WCot WCru XSen
	'Orinoco Flow' (BB) 🏆H7	WCAu
	'Orville Fay' (Sib)	GWyn WBor WCot
	'Osborne's Grey' (Sib)	WAul
	'Ottawa' (Sib)	CPou CWat EHyd LRHS MMuc WFar
	'Oulo' (TB)	XSen
	'Our Marcus' (TB)	SIri
	'Our Sassy' (La)	LLWG
	'Out of the Dark' (TB)	WCAu
	'Outset' (Sib)	ELon
	'Overjoyed' (TB)	XSen
	'Owyhee Desert' (TB)	WCAu
	Pacific Coast hybrids	see *I.* Californian hybrids
	'Pacific Panorama' (TB)	XSen
	'Pagan Pink' (TB)	XSen
I	'Pageant' (Sib)	WCot WFar
	'Pageant' (TB)	WFar
	'Paint It Black' (TB)	XSen
	'Painted Lady' (Reticulata)	EPot ERCP GKev LCro LOPS WBrk WRHF
	'Painted Woman' (Sib) **new**	CBod LLWG
	'Pale Shades' (IB)	CBro
§	***pallida***	CBod CBro CMac CPla GMaP MRav SEND SRms XSen
§	- 'Argentea Variegata' (TB/v)	Widely available
	- 'Aurea'	see *I. pallida* 'Variegata' Hort.
	- 'Aurea Variegata'	see *I. pallida* 'Variegata' Hort.
	- subsp. ***cengialtii***	GKev
	- var. ***dalmatica***	see *I. pallida* subsp. *pallida*
§	- subsp. ***pallida***	CExl ECha EHyd ELan EPfP LRHS MHid NRHS SCob SHar SPer
	- 'Variegata' misapplied	see *I. pallida* 'Argentea Variegata'
§	- 'Variegata' Hort. (v) 🏆H7	CBcs CBct CBro CMac CWat ECha ELan EPfP LRHS MAsh MHol MPie MRav NRHS SDix SPer SPlb SPoG SRms SWvt WBrk XSen
	'Palm Springs' (IB)	EHyd EPot LRHS SDeJ
	'Palm Springs' (Reticulata)	NRHS SDeJ
	'Pamplemousse' (IB)	SIri
	'Pansy Purple' (Sib)	LRHS MNrw WHil
	'Panther' (SDB)	WCAu
	'Papillon' (Sib)	CTri ECtt EHyd ELan ELon EPri EWes GWyn LRHS NBir NGdn NRHS NSti SCob SDeJ SPer WAul WFar WWtn
	'Paprika Fono's' (TB)	WCAu
	'Paprikash' (Sib) **new**	LLWG
	paradoxa	GKev
	'Paris Lights' (TB)	XSen
	'Parisian Dawn' (TB)	WCAu
	'Parisien' (TB)	EIri
	'Parting Glances' (IB)	WCAu
	'Party Dress' (TB)	CMac EBee ECtt EHyd ELan EShb LRHS MRav NBir NLar NRHS NWad SCob SPoG SRms WGwG
	'Party's Over' (TB)	WCAu
	'Pastel Accent' (La)	LLWG
	'Patina' (TB)	EIri LRHS
	'Patterdale' (TB)	NBir
	'Pauline' (Reticulata)	CAvo EPot ERCP GKev LRHS NRHS SPhx
	'Pauline' (TB)	EHyd
	'Pause' (SDB)	WCAu
	'Peaceful Waters' (TB)	XSen
	'Peach Eyes' (SDB)	CBro
	'Peach Picotee' (TB)	XSen
	'Peaches in Wine' (La)	LLWG
	'Peachy Face' (IB)	XSen

'Pearl Queen' (Sib) MCot
'Pearly Dawn' (TB) ECtt
* 'Pêche Melba' (TB) XSen
'Pelion Hills' LRHS
'Pennywhistle' (Sib) new NLar
'Percheron' (Sib) EPri MNrw
'Perfect Interlude' (TB) EIri XSen
'Perfect Vision' (Sib) ♀H7 MHCG
'Performer' (MTB) EIri
'Perry's Blue' (Sib) CBcs CMac CRos CSBt EBee EHyd EPfP EPri GKin GMaP LCro LOPS LRHS LSun MBel MGos MHol MRav NBir NGdn NPer NRHS SPer SRms WFar WWtn
I 'Perry's Favourite' (Sib) WAul
'Perry's Pigmy' (Sib) ELon
'Persian Berry' (TB) XSen
'Persimmon' misapplied see *I.* 'Tycoon'
'Persimmon' ambig. (Sib) CAby CRos ECtt EHyd EShb GKin GQue LRHS MHer NRHS WFar WGwG WWtn
'Peter Hewitt' (Sib) ♀H7 EPri MAvo WAul
'Peter's Heir' (La) new LLWG
'Petit Tigre' (IB) SIri
'Petite Charm' (IB) new WCAu
'Petite Polka' (SDB) NLar
'Petticoat Shuffle' (TB) new WCAu
'Phyllis Bliss' (TB) WMil
'Pigeon' (SDB) XSen
'Pinewood Amethyst' (CH) MAvo
'Pinewood Charmer' (CH) CElw
'Pinewood Sunshine' (CH) MAvo
'Pink Attraction' (TB) XSen
'Pink Bubbles' (BB) XSen
'Pink Charm' (TB) ECtt EHyd ELan EPfP LRHS NRHS SDeJ SPlb SPoG
'Pink Confetti' (TB) XSen
'Pink Haze' (Sib) CDor
'Pink Horizon' (TB) XSen
'Pink Kitten' (IB) WGwG XSen
'Pink Lavender' (TB) ELon SRms
'Pink Parfait' (Sib) MBNS MHol NGdn WFar WGob WTor WWtn
'Pink Swan' (TB) XSen
'Pink Taffeta' (TB) XSen
'Pioneer' (TB) WMil
'Pipes of Pan' (TB) MRav
'Pirate Ahoy' (TB) new WCAu
'Pirate Prince' (Sib) NPer
'Pirate's Quest' (TB) CWld ECtt MHer XSen
'Piroska' (TB) XSen
'Pixie' (DB) EHyd GKev
'Pixie' (Reticulata) ♀H7 CAvo CMea ELan EPot ERCP LRHS SDeJ SPhx XEll
'Pleasures of May' (Sib) EBee ELon WGob
'Plickadee' (SDB) CBro
'Plissée' (Sib) ♀H7 GBin GWyn
'Plum Lucky' (SDB) SIri
'Poesie' (TB) WViv
'Pogo' (SDB) CMac CRos CWld ECtt EHyd LRHS MRav MTin NBir NRHS SDeJ SRms
'Polar Ice' (Reticulata) new WBrk
'Polar Ice' (TB) EPot ERCP GKev
'Poodle Parade' (TB) new WCAu
'Pop Culture' (IB) new WCAu
'Post Master' (La) LLWG
'Potpourri Rose' (La) LLWG
'Pounsley Purple' (Sib) CPou EPri
'Power Point' (TB) WCAu
'Presence' (TB) SIri
PRETTY IN BLUE (mixed) (Dut) SDeJ
'Pretty Reward' (MTB) new WCAu
'Primrose Cream' (Sib) WCot
'Prince Indigo' (TB) MRav
'Prince of Tuscany' (DB) CBor
'Princess Bride' (BB) ♀H7 WCAu
'Princess Leia' (La) LLWG
'Princess Osra' (TB) WMil
'Princesse Caroline de Monaco' (TB) WViv
prismatica GKev MHid
'Private Eye' (TB) WCAu
'Professor Blaauw' (Dut) ♀H5 CAvo CWCL
'Prosper Laugier' (IB) WLov
'Proud Tradition' (TB) SIri XSen
'Provençal' (TB) ELon WCAu XSen
'Prussian Blue' (Sib) ♀H7 GBin SMHy
pseudacorus Widely available
- B&SWJ 5018 from Japan WCru
- 'Alba' NGdn SRms
- var. ***bastardii*** CBen CWat ECha ELon EPfP LCro LLWG LOPS NPer SLon SPer WBrk WFar WPnP WWtn XLum
- 'Clotted Cream' GLog
- 'Come in Spinner' LLWG
- cream-flowered NBir
- 'Crème de la Crème' ELon EPfP LLWG NLar NSti NWad WFar
- 'Dragonfly Dance' LLWG
- 'Flore Pleno' (d) CBen NLar NPer SRms WBrk WCot WFar WPnP WWtn
I - 'Golden Fleece' SPer
- 'Golden Queen' EWat LLWG
- 'Ivory' LLWG
- 'Kelis Choice' LLWG
- 'Krill' EPPr LLWG
- 'Mandchurica' XBlo
- 'Mini Mart' LLWG
- 'Roy Davidson' ♀H7 CBre CBro LLWG MWts NLar WCot WFar WHil WWtn
- 'Spartacus' EBee
- 'Sulphur Queen' GBin LLWG NLar WCot
- 'Sun Cascade' GBin
- 'Tiger Brother' CBro LLWG WBrk
- 'Turnipseed' WCot
- 'Variegata' (v) ♀H7 Widely available
pumila CPla CRos EHyd EPot ITim LRHS MCot NRHS NSla
- f. ***atroviolacea*** WAbe
* - 'Gelber Mantel' NBir WFar
- 'Violacea' (DB) SRms
- yellow-flowered GKev WAbe
'Pure As Gold' (TB) CWCL WCot XSen
'Purple Gem' (Reticulata) CAby EHyd LRHS NRHS
PURPLE LAVENDER MIXED (Dut) GKev
'Purple Mere' (Sib) MHCG
'Purple Sensation' (Dut) SDeJ
'Pussycat Pink' (SDB) WCAu
'Quark' (SDB) CBro
'Quechee' (TB) CWld EHyd EPPr EPfP GMaP GPSL IPot LBuc LRHS MBriF MCot MRav NLar NRHS NWad SCob SDeJ SPer WGwG
'Queen Adelaide' (La) new LLWG
'Queen Jeanne' (La) LLWG
'Queen of Angels' (TB) WCAu
'Queen of Hearts' (TB) XSen

'Queen of the Mist' (TB) **new**	WCAu
'Queen's Circle' (TB) ♀^{H7}	WCAu
'Rabbit's Foot' (SDB)	SIri
'Radiant Apogee' (TB)	EIri
'Radiant Burst' (IB)	SIri
RAINBOW GRAND MIXTURE	SDeJ
'Rainbow Rim' (SDB)	WCAu
'Rajah' (TB)	CAby CBod CRos EHyd ELan GMaP LRHS LSRN MHer MNrw MRav NRHS SCob SDeJ SPoG WAul
'Rancho Rose' (TB)	XSen
'Rare Edition' (IB)	NBir XSen
'Rare Quality' (TB)	XSen
'Rare Treat' (TB)	XSen
'Raspberry Acres' (IB)	MRav
'Raspberry Blush' (IB) ♀^{H7}	CBod CWld ECtt EHyd EIri EPfP GBin LRHS MCot MRav NBir NRHS SDeJ WAul WGwG WTor XSen
'Raspberry Tiger' (SDB)	WCAu
'Razoo' (SDB)	CPBP
'Re La Blanche' (TB)	SIri
'Recurring Delight' (TB)	WCAu
'Red Echo' (La)	LLWG
'Red Ember' (Dut)	CAvo ERCP GKev LCro LOPS MMrt MNrw MPie WRHF
'Red Enigma' (TB) **new**	SIri
'Red Flare' (TB)	WFar
'Red Heart' (SDB)	ELon MRav XSen
'Red Orchid' (IB)	ELan LRHS SRms
'Red Revival' (TB)	MRav WCAu
'Red Rum' (TB)	EWes
'Red Velvet Elvis' (La) **new**	LLWG
'Red Zinger' (IB)	CMac LRHS
'Redelta' (TB)	XSen
'Reflets Safran' (TB)	SIri XSen
'Regal Surprise' (SpH) ♀^{H7}	EWat LLWG SBrt WWtn
'Regality' (Sib)	EBee MHer MMuc
'Regards' (SDB)	CBro XSen
'Regency Buck' (Sib)	WFar
§ ***reichenbachii***	CPBP GKev WAbe
'Rendez-Vous' (Dut)	SDeJ
'Renee Fleming' (La) **new**	LLWG
'Repartee' (TB)	XSen
reticulata	ELan GKev SDeJ
- var. ***bakeriana***	XEll
'Reuthe's Bronze' (CH) **new**	SReu
'Rhapsody' (Reticulata)	EHyd EPot GKev LRHS NRHS SDeJ
'Rhinelander' (TB) **new**	SIri
'Rigamarole' (Sib)	MWts WFar WGob
'Rikugi-sakura' (Sib)	ELon EPri NLar SHar WCot WGob
'Rimfire' (TB)	ELan
'Ringo' (TB)	LSRN MRav
'Rio Rojo' (TB)	WCAu
'Rising Moon' (TB)	SIri
'Riverbuds' (SDB)	SIri
'Riveting' (SDB) **new**	WCAu
'Roanoke's Choice' (Sib)	CBro CElw ELon EWes MNrw SDir WFar
'Roaring Jelly' (Sib)	EPri EWes NLar WCot WGob
'Robe d'Été' (TB)	WViv
§ × ***robusta*** 'Dark Aura' ♀^{H7}	LLWG LRHS MWts SIri WCot
§ - 'Gerald Darby'	CAby CBct CBod CRos CWat EHyd ELan EPPr EPfP EWhm LLWG LRHS MBow MCot MHer MHol MNHC MNrw NGdn NLar NRHS NSti SDix SPeP WBrk WCAu WFar WOut WPnP WSpi
- 'Mountain Brook'	LLWG
- 'Purple Fan'	LLWG
'Rochester Castle' (Kent Castles Series) (IB)	SIri
§ 'Rocket' (TB)	ECtt EHyd GMaP LBuc LRHS MRav NBir NRHS SDeJ SPer
'Romantic Evening' (TB)	EIri WCAu XSen
'Romney Marsh' (IB)	SIri
'Romola' (TB)	WMil
'Roryu' (SpH)	LLWG
'Rosalie Figge' (TB)	CMac MHol WCot
'Rosé' (TB)	LSRN
'Rose Queen'	see *I. ensata* 'Rose Queen'
'Rosebud Melody' (Sib)	GBin GWyn
'Roseplic' (TB)	LRHS
'Rosselline' (Sib)	MAvo WAul
'Rosy Bows' (Sib)	WCAu WFar
'Roucoulade' (TB)	SIri
'Rouge Gorge' (TB)	SIri WViv
'Roussette' (IB)	SIri
'Rowden Aurelius' (Sib)	WAul
I 'Royal Blue' (Sib)	EBee ECha
'Royal Crusader' (TB)	XSen
'Roy's Repeater' (SpH)	LLWG
'Ruby Chimes' (IB)	WCAu
'Ruby Contrast' (TB)	WCAu
'Ruby Eruption' (SDB)	EIri
'Ruby Wine' (Sib)	EPri
rudskyi	see *I. variegata*
'Ruffled Velvet' (Sib) ♀^{H7}	CBcs CDor CElw ECtt ELan EPfP EPri GBin GLog GMaP ILea IMou LRHS MCot MHol MRav NChi NLar SCob SPer WAul WCAu WFar WWtn
'Ruffles and Flourishes' (Sib)	LLWG
'Ruffles Plus' (Sib)	EPri WGob
'Rumor Has It' (TB) **new**	WCAu
'Rusty Beauty' (Dut)	SDeJ
ruthenica	WHil
- var. ***nana***	CExl GEdr GKev
'Sable' (TB)	CRos EHyd ELan EPfP GMaP LRHS MRav NLar NRHS SCob SDeJ SHar SPer WAul WGwG
'Saint Crispin' (TB)	CRos ECtt EHyd EPfP GMaP LRHS MRav NRHS SPer SPoG WGwG
'Salamander Crossing' (Sib) ♀^{H7}	WAul
'Salonique' (TB)	NLar
'Saltwood' (SDB)	CBro
'Saltwood Castle' (Kent Castles Series) (IB)	SIri
'Sam Carne' (TB)	WCAu
× ***sambucina***	XSen
'Sandling Sunset' (TB)	SIri
§ ***sanguinea*** 'Snow Queen'	CAvo CBcs ELan EPfP EPri EWTr GBin GKev GWyn IMou LRHS MMuc NBid NLar NQui NRHS NSti WAul WCot WFar WWtn
'Sapphire Beauty' (Dut)	GKev SDeJ
'Sapphire Gem' (SDB)	LSRN
'Sapphire Hills' (TB)	LRHS XSen
'Savoir Faire' (Sib)	ECha
'Scent Sational' (Reticulata)	EPot GKev SPhx
'Scented Wonder' (TB)	WCAu
schachtii	CPBP EPot
- purple-flowered	WAbe
'Scheherazade' (J) **new**	GKev
'Scramble' (Sib)	WCot WFar WOld

	'Scribe' (MDB)	CBro NBir
	'Sea Breeze' (Reticulata)	EPot ERCP GKev
	'Sea Fret' (SDB)	CBro
	'Sea of Joy' (TB)	XSen
	'Sea Power' (TB)	SIri
	'Sea Shadows' (Sib)	EPri NBir
	'Season Ticket' (IB)	XSen
	'Second Look' (TB)	GKev XSen
	'Second Wind' (TB)	WCAu
	'Secret Melody' (TB)	XSen
	'Senlac' (TB)	ELan NLar WMil
	serbica	see *I. reichenbachii*
	'Serene Moment' (TB)	SIri
	setosa 🏆^{H7}	CMac CTri CWCL EAJP EHyd EPPr GBin GKev LRHS MNrw NHpl NRHS WFar WOld
	- ***alba***	NLar
	- var. ***arctica***	GKev LEdu
I	- 'Baby Blue'	EHyd EPfP LRHS MBNS NRHS
	- subsp. ***canadensis***	see *I. hookeri*
	- dark violet-flowered	EPri
	- var. ***nana***	see *I. hookeri*
	'Shaker's Prayer' (Sib) 🏆^{H7}	GBin MNrw SDir WGob
	'Share the Spirit' (TB)	WCAu
	'Sharp Dressed Man' (TB)	WCAu
	'Sharrie Carrie' (TB)	SIri
	'Sheila Ann Germaney' (Reticulata)	CRos EHyd EPot ERCP GKev LRHS NRHS WBrk
	'Sherbet Lemon' (IB) 🏆^{H7}	WCAu
	'Shirley Chandler' (IB) 🏆^{H7}	SIri
	'Shirley Pope' (Sib) 🏆^{H7}	EWes GBin GWyn LRHS NSti WFar WPnP WSpi
	'Shirley's Choice' (Sib)	EPri SIri
	'Shiryukyo' (SpH) **new**	WMal
	'Short Distance' (IB)	SIri
	'Showdown' (Sib)	CRos ECtt EHyd GMaP LRHS NRHS
	'Shrawley' (Sib)	WAul
	shrevei	see *I. virginica* var. *shrevei*
	'Shurton Inn' (TB)	SRms WCAu
	sibirica	CAvo CCBP CTri CTsd GAbr GBin GKev MCot MHid MMuc NChi SCob SPlb WBrk WCFE WFar WGwG WHer WShi
	- PAB 6119	LEdu
	- 'Niklas Sea'	see *I.* 'Lake Niklas'
	- 'Redflare'	see *I.* 'Melton Red Flare'
	- 'Snow Queen'	see *I. sanguinea* 'Snow Queen'
	'Sibirica Alba' (Sib)	ECha EPfP EPri SRms WBrk WFar
	sichuanensis	CExl SPlb
	'Side Effects' (TB)	WCAu
	'Sierra Grande' (TB)	SIri XSen
	'Sierra Nevada' (Spuria)	XSen
	'Sign of Leo' (TB)	XSen
	'Silver Edge' (Sib) 🏆^{H7}	Widely available
	'Silverado' (TB)	GBin LRHS WCAu
	'Silvery Beauty' (Dut) 🏆^{H6}	CAvo ELan GKev LCro LOPS MPie NBir SDeJ
	'Silvery Princess' (Dut)	SDeJ
	'Simply Coral' (TB) **new**	WCAu
	'Simply Irresistible' (La) **new**	LLWG
	sindjarensis	see *I. aucheri*
	'Sinfonietta' (La)	LLWG WCot
	'Sing to Me' (TB)	WCAu
	'Sinister Desire' (IB)	SIri
	sintenisii 🏆^{H6}	CPBP GKev SBrt WAbe XSen
	'Siva Siva' (TB)	MRav
	'Sixtine C' (TB)	SIri
	'Skating Party' (TB)	XSen
	'Skiers' Delight' (TB)	LRHS
	'Sky Beauty' (Dut)	SDeJ
	'Sky Hooks' (TB)	XSen
	'Sky Wings' (Sib)	CSam ECha MArl WFar
	'Skydancer' (SDB)	WCAu
	'Skylark's Song' (TB)	EIri
	'Small Sky' (SDB)	CBro
	'Smart' (SDB)	WCAu
	'Smart Girl' (TB)	EIri
	'Smash' (MTB)	WCAu
	'Smiling Faces' (TB)	WCAu
	'Smitten Kitten' (IB)	LSRN
	'Smooth Orange'	see *I.* 'Orange Chariot'
	'Snow Prince' (Sib)	EPri
	'Snow Tracery' (TB)	ECtt EHyd EPfP LRHS NRHS
	'Snowcrest' (Sib)	EHyd GBin LRHS MRav NRHS WAul WHoo WWtn
	'Snowy Owl' (TB)	WCAu
	'Snugglebug' (SDB)	WCAu
	'Social Event' (TB)	XSen
	'Soft Blue' (Sib) 🏆^{H7}	ELon EPri WAul
	'Solid Mahogany' (TB)	MRav
	'Song of Norway' (TB)	EIri XSen
	songarica	MHid
	sophenensis	EPot GKev
	'Sorbonne' (TB)	WCAu
	'Sordid Lives' (TB)	WCAu
	'Southcombe White' (Sib)	SMHy
	'Sparkling Rose' (Sib)	Widely available
	'Speckled Hen' (La)	LLWG
I	'Speckles' (Sib)	EPPr
	'Spellbreaker' (TB)	ELon SIri
	'Spice Lord' (TB)	WCAu
	'Spiced Custard' (TB)	EIri
	'Spicy Cajun' (La)	WHil
	'Spindazzle' (Sib) **new**	ECtt
	'Spinning Wheel' (TB)	SIri
	'Spirit of Memphis' (TB)	XSen
	'Splashacata' (TB)	XSen
	'Spot On' (Reticulata)	EPot GKev
	'Spree' (SDB)	WCAu
	'Spring Blush' (MTB) 🏆^{H7}	SIri
	'Spring Kiss' (TB)	SIri
	'Spring Madness' (TB)	WCAu
	'Spring Time' (Reticulata)	SDeJ
	spuria	CMac CPou
§	- subsp. ***halophila***	GKev
	- subsp. ***notha*** CC 725	WCot
	- subsp. ***ochroleuca***	see *I. orientalis* Mill.
	'St Louis Blues' (TB)	XSen
	'Stairway to Heaven' (TB)	WCAu
	'Stapleford' (SDB)	CBro
	'Staplehurst' (MTB) 🏆^{H7}	SIri
	'Star Cluster' (Sib)	WFar
	'Star in the Night' (TB)	WCAu
	'Star Shine' (TB)	WCAu
	'Starship' (TB)	XSen
	'Starwoman' (IB) 🏆^{H7}	WCAu
	'Staten Island' (TB)	SRms WCAu
	'Stella Polaris' (TB)	ELon
	'Stellar Lights' (TB)	EIri WCAu
	'Stephen Wilcox' (Sib)	EPri WAul
	'Stepping Out' (TB) 🏆^{H7}	CMac CRos ECtt EHyd EPfP GBin LRHS NRHS SCob SDeJ WTor
	'Steve' (Sib)	CPar EWes MSpe
	'Steve Varner' (Sib)	EPri
	'Stitch in Time' (TB)	EIri
	stolonifera	GKev
	- 'Augustus'	GKev
	- 'Claudius' **new**	GKev

	'Stop the Music' (TB)	XSen
	'Storrington' (TB)	ECha ECtt EMal LRHS
	'Strathmore' (TB)	ECha EMal LRHS
	'Strut your Stuff' (TB)	WCAu
	'Study In Black' (TB)	XSen
	'Stylish Socialite' (La)	LLWG
	stylosa	see *I. unguicularis*
§	***suaveolens***	CPou GEdr NHpl NWad
	- var. ***flavescens***	see *I. suaveolens* yellow-flowered
§	- purple-flowered	GEdr GKev SGro WAbe
	- var. ***violacea***	see *I. suaveolens* purple-flowered
§	- yellow-flowered	GKev WAbe
	'Succès Fou' (TB)	SIri WViv
	'Sugar' (IB)	NSti WCAu
	'Sugar Magnolia' (TB)	SIri
	'Sugarmouse' (BB)	SIri
	'Sultan's Palace' (TB)	EBee ECtt EPfP IPot LCro LRHS MCot NLar WHoo WSpi XSen
	'Summer Holidays' (TB)	XSen
	'Summer Revels' (Sib)	EPri EWes MAvo
	'Summer Sky' (Sib)	LEdu MHCG MSCN WAul WCot
	'Sunadokei' (SpH)	LLWG
	'Sunlit Shores' (La)	LLWG
	'Sunny Disposition' (TB)	XSen
	'Sunnyside Up' (TB)	GKev
	'Sunset Sky' (TB)	CWGN
	'Sunshine' (Reticulata)	EPot ERCP SDeJ
	'Sunshine' (TB)	GKev
	'Superstition' (TB) ♀H7	CBod CWGN EIri ELan EWes LCro LOPS LRHS MRav WCAu XSen
	'Supreme Sultan' (TB)	SCob WCAu XSen
I	'Surprise' (Dut)	MNrw
	'Susan Bliss' (TB)	ELan EPfP WMal WMil
	'Sutton Valence' (Sib)	SIri
	'Swank' (Sib)	WAul
	'Swazi Princess' (TB)	ELon SEdd SRms
	'Sweet Lavender' (TB)	WMil
	'Sweet Musette' (TB)	SRms WCAu
	'Sweet Surrender' (Sib)	EPri
	'Sweeter than Wine' (TB)	MRav
	'Swingtown' (TB)	WCAu
	'Swirling Waters' (La)	LLWG
	'Swiss Majesty' (TB)	WCAu
	'Swizzle' (IB)	XSen
	'Sybil' (TB)	GBin
	'Sylvan' (TB)	XSen
	'Symphony' (Dut)	NBir SDeJ
	'Syncopation' (TB)	ELon XSen
	'Syrian Hills' (TB)	WCAu
	'Tact' (IB)	SIri
	'Taking Chances' (TB) **new**	WCAu
	'Tan Tingo' (IB)	XSen
	'Tangerine Sky' (TB)	LRHS MBriF
	'Tantara' (SDB)	XSen
	'Tantrum' (IB)	XSen
	'Tanz Nochmal' (Sib)	GBin
	'Tarn Hows' (TB)	SRms
	'Taubenblau' (Sib)	SAko
	'Teal Velvet' (Sib)	ECha ELon EPfP EPri EWes GLog LRHS MCot SCob WFar WGob
	'Tealwood' (Sib)	GBin
	'Teapot Tempest' (BB)	WCAu
	'Teasaucer Hill' (MTB) ♀H7	SIri
	tectorum	GKev LRHS SChr WCot WMal XLum XSen
	- BWJ 8191	WCru
	- from Yunnan **new**	MHid
	- 'Alba'	GKev WThu XSen
	- 'Cruella'	GWyn MSCN
	- 'Variegata' misapplied	see *I. japonica* 'Variegata'
	- 'Variegata' (v)	ECrN SRms
	'Tell Fibs' (SDB)	CBro
	'Teller of Tales' (La)	LLWG
	'Temper Tantrum' (Sib)	CBrac LRHS
	'Temple Gold' (TB)	NPer
	'Temple Meads' (IB)	WCAu
	'Tempting Fate' (TB)	SIri
§	***tenax***	EHyd LRHS
	'Tenebrae' (TB)	WMil
	'Tenterden' (BB)	SIri
	'Teven' (La) **new**	LLWG
	'Teverlae' (Sib)	CRos EBee EHyd LRHS NRHS
	'That's Red' (MTB)	EIri
	'The Citadel' (TB)	ELon
	'The Rocket'	see *I.* 'Rocket'
	'Theseus' (AB)	GKev
	'Third Charm' (SDB)	CBro
	'Third World' (SDB)	CBro
	'Thornbird' (TB) ♀H7	EIri SRms WCAu
	'Three Part Harmony' (TB) **new**	WCAu
	'Three Quarters' (Sib)	ELon NChi
	'Thriller' (TB)	WCAu XSen
	'Thunder Echo' (TB)	SIri
	'Thundering Ovation' (TB)	WCAu
	'Tickety Boo' (SDB)	ECtt MBros NBPC
§	'Tigereye' (Dut)	ERCP GAbr GBin GKev LCro LOPS MNrw SDeJ
	tigridia	CExl
	'Time Zone' (TB)	WCAu
	'Tinkerbell' (SDB)	CBod CPBP EBee ECtt EHyd GMaP LRHS NBir NRHS SDeJ WTor
	'Titan's Glory' (TB) ♀H7	CMac CWld ECtt LEdu LRHS MPie MRav SRms WCot WHoo
	'Tollong'	ILea IMou
	'Tom Tit' (TB)	WMil
	'Tomato Bisque' (La)	LLWG
	'Top Flight' (TB)	EHyd ELan LRHS SRms
	'Topaz Jewel' (TB)	MHol
	'Torero' (TB)	SIri
	'Total Eclipse' (TB)	SRms
	'Totally Cool' (SDB)	LSRN
	'Touch of Mahogany' (TB)	WCAu
	'Trim the Velvet' (Sib)	WAul
	'Triple Whammy' (TB)	XSen
	'Tristram' (TB)	WMil
	'Tropic Night' (Sib)	CRos CSam CTri EBee ECtt EHyd EIri ELan EPfP EPri GBin GKin LCro LOPS LRHS MBel MRav MWts NRHS NRya NSti SCob SSut WAul WAvo WBrk WFar WGob WWtn
	tuberosa	CAvo CBro CFis CTri ECha ELan ERCP LPot MHer SDeJ WShi
	- MS 76	WCot
	- MS 964	WCot
	- PB	GKev WCot
	'Tumble Bug' (Sib)	ECtt WGob
	'Tumultueux' (TB)	WViv
	'Tuxedo' (TB)	XSen
§	'Tycoon' (Sib)	EHyd EShb GBin LCro LOPS LRHS NChi SPer
	'Ultimate' (SDB)	WCAu
	'Unbuttoned Zippers' (Sib) **new**	NLar
	'Uncorked' (Sib) **new**	ECtt LLWG
	'Undercurrent' (TB)	WCAu
§	***unguicularis***	Widely available
	- from Karpathos, Greece	GKev
	- 'Abington Purple'	CJun EIri

	– 'Alba'	CAvo CExl XEll XSen
	– subsp. ***angustifolia***	WSHC
§	– subsp. ***cretensis***	GKev
	– – white-flowered	WSHC
	– 'Diana Clare'	CJun
	– 'Marondera'	CBct CJun
	– 'Mary Barnard' ♀H5	CAvo CBro CJun CPou EHyd LRHS MHer WHoo
	– 'Peloponnese Snow'	CJun GEdr SBrt
§	– 'Walter Butt'	CAvo CJun EBee XEll
	'Valda' (Sib)	ELon
	'Vamp' (IB)	GBin XSen
	'Vanilla Mist' (La)	LLWG
	'Vanilla Skies' (TB)	WCAu
	'Vanity' (TB)	XSen
	'Vanity's Child' (TB)	WCAu XSen
§	***variegata*** ♀H7	CMea EBee GBin SCob XSen
	– from Podyjí, Moravia	SBrt
	'Velvet Purple'	XBlo
	'Venus Vortex' (La) **new**	LLWG
	versicolor	CBen CSpe GBin GKev GMaP GPoy MMuc MNHC MWts SEND SPlb SRms WFar WMAq WPnP WShi
	– 'Algonquin'	LLWG
	– 'Bellerive Harmony'	LLWG
	– 'Between the Lines'	LLWG
	– 'Candystriper'	LLWG
	– 'China West Lake'	LLWG
	– 'Claret Cup'	CPou ILea SHar
	– 'Kermesina'	CWat ECha ELan LCro LLWG LOPS MMuc MWts NPer NSti SRms WFar WMAq WPnP
	– 'Mint Fresh'	LLWG
	– 'Mysterious Monique'	CWat LLWG MWts
	– purple-flowered	EWat
	– 'Raspberry Slurp' **new**	LLWG
	– 'Rowden Allegro'	LLWG
	– 'Rowden Aria'	LLWG
	– 'Rowden Cadenza'	EWat LLWG
	– 'Rowden Calypso'	LLWG
	– 'Rowden Cantata'	LLWG
	– 'Rowden Concerto'	LLWG
	– 'Rowden Electro'	LLWG
	– 'Rowden Lyric'	LLWG
	– 'Rowden Melody'	LLWG
	– 'Rowden Pastorale'	LLWG
	– 'Rowden Sonata'	LLWG
	– 'Rowden Waltz'	LLWG
	'Vi Luihn' (Sib)	ECha ELon SAko WFar
	'Vibrations' (TB)	WCAu
	'Victoria Falls' (TB)	MHol
	'Victorian Secret' (Sib)	EBee ELon
	'Viel Schnee' (Sib)	ELon
	'Vin Nouveau' (TB)	XSen
	'Violet Beauty' (Reticulata)	EHyd LRHS NRHS
	'Violet Turner' (TB)	MHol
	virginica	LLWG
	– 'De Luxe'	see *I.* × *robusta* 'Dark Aura'
	– 'Lavender Lustre'	LLWG
	– 'Orchid Purple'	LLWG
	– 'Pale Lavender'	LLWG
	– 'Pink Perfection'	LLWG
§	– var. ***shrevei***	LLWG
	– 'Slightly Daft'	LLWG
	'Vitality' (IB)	ELon
	'Voilà' (IB)	CMea
	'Volts' (SDB)	XSen
	'Voyage' (SDB)	XSen
	'Wabash' (TB)	XSen
	'Waihi Wedding' (La)	LLWG
	'Walmer Castle' (Kent Castles Series) (IB)	SIri
	'Walter Butt'	see *I. unguicularis* 'Walter Butt'
	'War Chief' (TB)	EPfP MBriF MRav WCAu
	'War Sails' (TB)	SIri WCAu
	wattii	CExl WGwG
	– KWJ 12172	WCru
	'Wealden Butterfly' (Sib) ♀H7	SIri WAul
	'Wealden Carousel' (Sib)	SIri WAul
	'Wealden Mystery' (Sib)	EPri SIri WAul
	'Wealden Skies' (Sib)	SIri WAul
	'Wealden Spires' (Sib)	WAul
	'Wealden Summer' (Sib)	WAul
	'Wearing Rubies' (TB)	WCAu
	'Webelos' (SDB)	MRav
	'Wedding Vow' (TB)	EIri
	'Wedgwood' (Dut)	GBin
*	'Wedgwood Blue' (Sino-Sib)	GBin
	'Weisse Etagen' (Sib)	ELon
	'Welcome Return' (Sib)	LLWG LRHS MMuc SDir WGob
	'Welfenfürstin' (Sib)	GBin SAko
	'Welfenprinz' (Sib) ♀H7	SMHy WAul
	'Westwell' (SDB)	GEdr
	'Westwood' (IB)	SIri
	'What Again' (SDB)	XSen
	'What It's Worth' (TB) **new**	WCAu
	'What's New Pussycat' (BB) **new**	WCAu
	'White Amber' (Sib)	ECtt
	'White Caucasus' (Reticulata)	EPot ERCP WBrk XEll
	'White City' (TB)	CRos EHyd EPfP GMaP LRHS MRav MWat NPer NRHS SDeJ SPer SRms
	'White Knight' (TB)	EBee EPfP WSpi
	'White Reprise' (TB)	XSen
I	'White Swan' (Sib)	EPri
	'White Swirl' (Sib)	CAby CBar CBro CTri CWld EBee ECha ECtt ELon EPfP GBin GLog GWyn LCro LRHS MRav MSpe NBro NLar NRHS NSti SCob SPer SRms WFar WGob WPnP
	'White Triangles' (Sib)	ELon
	'White Umbrella' (La)	ECtt LLWG MBros
	'White van Vliet' (Dut)	SDeJ
	'White-Wave' (TB)	XBlo
	'Wild' (BB) **new**	WCAu
	'Wild Wings' (TB)	LRHS MCot SGbt
	wilsonii ♀H7	CExl GKev NRya WGob
	'Windjammer Seas' (TB)	WAul
	'Wine Wings' (Sib)	WGob
	'Winemaster' (TB)	SIri
	winogradowii ♀H7	EHyd EPot ERCP GKev LRHS NRHS WAbe XEll
	'Winter Olympics' (TB)	CBod CRos ECtt EHyd ELan EPfP LRHS MRav NRHS SPer WGwG
	'Winterfest' (TB) **new**	WCAu
	'Wintry Sky' (TB)	WCAu
	'Wishful Thinking' (TB)	SIri
	'Wizard's Return' (SDB)	SIri
	'Wondrous' (TB)	CAby ECtt EPfP
	'Word of Warning' (La)	LLWG
	'Wrangler' (IB)	SIri
	xiphioides	see *I. latifolia*
	xiphium var. ***lusitanica***	GKev
	'Yankee Consul' (Sib)	EPri
	'Yaquina Blue' (TB)	WCAu
	'Yarai' (SpH)	LLWG
	'Yasha' (SpH)	LLWG
	'Yellowtail' (Sib)	CBod

'Yeoman' (TB)	WMil
'Yukiyanagi' (SpH)	LLWG
'Zakopane' (Sib)	EWes WAul
'Zantha' (TB)	XSen
'Zero' (SDB)	SIri
'Zinger' (BB)	WSpi
'Zweites Hundert' (Sib)	WFar WKif

Isatis (*Brassicaceae*)

glauca	SPhx
tinctoria	CBod CHab CHby ENfk GJos GPoy MHer MNHC SRms WSFF WTre XSen
- subsp. ***athoa***	WCot

Ismene (*Amaryllidaceae*)

'Advance'	GKev
§ × ***deflexa*** ♀H1c	CCCN EShb GKev LCro LOPS SDeJ
§ - 'Zwanenburg'	CGrW GKev
§ ***longipetala***	GKev
§ 'Sulphur Queen' ♀H1c	CBor CGrW GKev SDeJ

Isodon (*Lamiaceae*)

calycinus	SPlb
effusus	MNrw WPGP
excisus	EBee EWld LPla WPGP
longitubus	EWld GEdr LEdu
- B&SWJ 11027	WCru
rubescens	IMou SMad

Isolepis (*Cyperaceae*)

§ ***cernua***	CBen CWat EWat LCro LLWG LOPS LRHS MWts SCoo WCot WMAq
nodosa (Rottb.) R. Br.	see *Ficinia nodosa*

Isoloma see *Kohleria*

Isomeris see *Cleome*

Isoplexis see *Digitalis*

Isopogon (*Proteaceae*)

anemonifolius	CCCN SPlb
anethifolius	SPlb
formosus	MPkF

Isopyrum (*Ranunculaceae*)

biternatum	LEdu
hallii	EBee
nipponicum	WPGP
thalictroides	EBee EPot IMou LEdu NRya WCot

Isotoma (*Campanulaceae*)

§ ***axillaris***	CSpe NPer SCoo SPer
- 'Fairy Carpet'	CBod LLWG NCou NHpl SRms
fluviatilis	NLar

Itea (*Iteaceae*)

chinensis	CExl
ilicifolia ♀H5	Widely available
* - 'Rubrifolia'	ELan SLon
virginica	CBcs CMCN LRHS MMrt MRav SLon
§ - 'Henry's Garnet' ♀H5	CAby CDoC CEnd CMCN CMac EBee ECrN EHyd EPfP EShb EWhm GBin LEdu LRHS MGil MGos NLar SCob SEle SGol SMad SPad SPer SPoG SRms SWvt WLov WPGP
- LITTLE HENRY ('Sprich'PBR)	CBcs CMac CSBt EBee EPfP ILea LSRN NLar
- 'Long Spire'	NLar
- 'Merlot'	CBod ELon MBlu NLar SGol SIvy
- 'Sarah Eve'	CMCN NLar
- 'Saturnalia'	NLar
- Swarthmore form	see *I. virginica* 'Henry's Garnet'
yunnanensis	CBcs CExl MBlu NLar

Itoa (*Salicaceae*)

orientalis var. ***glabrescens***	CMCN

Ixeris (*Asteraceae*)

stolonifera	XLum

Ixia (*Iridaceae*)

'Blue Bird'	SDeJ
'Castor'	CAvo
'Giant'	EShb GKev SDeJ WHil
'Hogarth'	GKev
'Jesse'	SDeJ WHil
latifolia	CPbh
'Mabel'	CAvo CWCL GKev WHil
'Marquette'	GKev
paniculata 'Eos'	GKev
polystachya	CPbh GKev
'Rose Emperor'	GKev SDeJ
scillaris	CPbh
'Spotlight'	CAvo EShb GKev
thomasiae	WCot
'Venus'	CWCL EShb GKev SDeJ
viridiflora	SPlb WHil
'Yellow Emperor'	GKev SDeJ WHil

Ixiolirion (*Ixioliriaceae*)

pallasii	see *I. tataricum*
§ ***tataricum***	EBee GKev SDeJ

J

Jaborosa (*Solanaceae*)

integrifolia	CExl EBee LEdu SVen XLum

Jacaranda (*Bignoniaceae*)

acutifolia misapplied	see *J. mimosifolia*
§ ***mimosifolia*** ♀H1c	CCCN CPla CTsd EShb SPlb

Jacobaea (*Asteraceae*)

candida	WCot
§ ***maritima***	SCob SEND
- 'Ramparts'	ECre
- 'Silver Dust' ♀H4	MBros

Jacobinia see *Justicia*

Jamesbrittenia (*Scrophulariaceae*)

§ ***microphylla***	CPBP

Jamesia (*Hydrangeaceae*)

americana	CMCN GEdr NLar SBrt WCru

Jasione (*Campanulaceae*)

§ ***heldreichii***	NBir SRms
jankae	see *J. heldreichii*
§ ***laevis***	EHyd EPfP GAbr SRms
§ - 'Blaulicht'	CBor CRos ECha EHyd EPfP LRHS NRHS SPlb WFar
- BLUE LIGHT	see *J. laevis* 'Blaulicht'

montana	MNHC SRms WWild
perennis	see *J. laevis*

Jasminum ✿ (*Oleaceae*)

CC 4728	CExl
CW&T 6374	CMCN
affine	see *J. officinale* f. *affine*
angulare 🏆H2	CExl CRHN EShb WFib
azoricum 🏆H2	CBcs CCCN CRHN CTsd EPfP EShb SEND SPalm SPre WFib
beesianum	Widely available
bignoniaceum	WSHC
blinii	see *J. polyanthum*
dispermum	CRHN NLar
farreri	see *J. humile* f. *farreri*
fruticans	CMac EBee ELon GAbr LRHS SBrt SEND WCru WGob
- RCB UA 22	WCot
giraldii misapplied	see *J. humile* f. *farreri*
grandiflorum misapplied	see *J. officinale* f. *affine*
grandiflorum L. 'De Grasse' 🏆H2	CRHN EShb WFib
humile	CExl MGil NLar SEND SPtp WKif WOut
§ - f. ***farreri*** Farrer 867	WPGP
- var. ***glabrum***	see *J. humile* f. *wallichianum*
- 'Pershore Purple'	WAvo
§ - 'Revolutum' 🏆H5	CBcs CMac CRHN CRos CSBt CWCL EBee EHyd ELan EPfP EShb LRHS MGos MRav NLar SEND SGbt SLon SNig SPer SPoG SRms SWvt WSHC
§ - f. ***wallichianum*** B&SWJ 2559	WCru
- - PAB 2534	LEdu
- - PAB 9962	LEdu
humile × ***parkeri***	SEle
§ ***mesnyi*** 🏆H3	CBcs CCCN CExl CMac CRHN CTri EBak EPfP EShb LRHS SEND SGol SGro SPer SVen WSHC
multiflorum	CCCN
multipartitum	CCCN EShb
§ ***nudiflorum*** 🏆H5	Widely available
- 'Argenteum'	see *J. nudiflorum* 'Mystique'
- 'Aureum'	CMac CRos ELan LRHS MAsh MRav NLar NOra SPer SPoG SRms
§ - 'Mystique' (v)	CRos EHyd ELan LRHS MRav NRHS SLon
odoratissimum	WFib
officinale	Widely available
§ - f. ***affine***	CBcs CCCN CRHN CRos CTri CWCL EHyd ELan EPfP LRHS MAsh MRav NRHS SCoo SDix SLim SRms
§ - 'Argenteovariegatum' (v) 🏆H5	CMac CRos CTsd CWGN ELan EPfP LRHS LSRN MAsh MGos MHer MMuc MRav SEND SMad SPer SPoG SWvt WCFE WLov WSHC
- 'Aureovariegatum'	see *J. officinale* 'Aureum'
§ - 'Aureum' (v)	CBcs CBod CMac CRos CTsd CWCL ELan EPfP LRHS MAsh MHer MPri SCoo SLim SLon SRms
- 'Clotted Cream'	see *J. officinale* 'Devon Cream'
- 'Crûg's Collection'	WCru
§ - 'Devon Cream' PBR	Widely available
- Fiona Sunrise ('Frojas' PBR) 🏆H5	Widely available
- 'Grandiflorum'	see *J. officinale* f. *affine*
- 'Inverleith' 🏆H5	CCCN CRos CWCL EBee ECtt ECul ELan EPfP EWTr LRHS MAsh MBNS MGil MGos MRav NOra NRHS SCoo SLim SMad SNig SPad SPer SPoG WGrn
- Sunbeam ('Lobeam')	CDoC CRos EBee EHyd LRHS NRHS SNig
- 'Variegatum'	see *J. officinale* 'Argenteovariegatum'
parkeri	CBcs CCCN CMac CRos CTri EBee EHyd ELon GMaP LRHS MGil NLar SEle WThu XEll
- 'Bychan'	WAbe
§ ***polyanthum*** 🏆H2	CBcs CExl CRHN CSBt CSde CTri EBak ELan EPfP EShb ETho LCro LOPS SEND SLim SPer SPre SRms SWeb
- dark red-leaved	CCCN CExl EBee EPfP
primulinum	see *J. mesnyi*
reevesii hort.	see *J. humile* 'Revolutum'
sambac 🏆H2	CCCN CRHN ELan SPre WFib
- 'Grand Duke of Tuscany' (d)	CCCN SPre
- 'Maid of Orleans' (d)	CCCN EShb SPre
sieboldianum	see *J. nudiflorum*
§ ***simplicifolium*** subsp. ***suavissimum***	CRHN
stenalobium	WCot WFib
× ***stephanense***	Widely available
- 'Variegatum' (v) new	CWld
suavissimum	see *J. simplicifolium* subsp. *suavissimum*

Jatropha (*Euphorbiaceae*)

cinerea	SPlb
integerrima	CCCN
multifida	CDoC SPlb
podagrica 🏆H1b	CDoC SPad

Jeffersonia (*Berberidaceae*)

diphylla	CRos EBee EHyd EPPr EPot EPri EWld GBin GKev LEdu LRHS MBel MNrw NBir NChi NRHS WCru WFar WPGP WPnP WThu XEll
dubia	CAby CRos EHyd EPot EWes EWld GBin GKev LEdu LRHS MNrw NBir NChi NRHS SBrt WAbe WCot WPGP WThu XEll
- 'Sunago-fu' (v)	GEdr

jostaberry see *Ribes* × *nidigrolaria*

Jovellana (*Calceolariaceae*)

punctata	CBcs CCCN CExl CTsd EBee IArd IMou SPlb WLov
sinclairii	CExl CTsd
violacea 🏆H3	CAbb CBcs CCCN CExl CMac CPla CRos CTrC CTsd EBee EHyd EPfP IDee IMou LRHS MGil SEdd SEle SVen WPGP WPav

Jovibarba ✿ (*Crassulaceae*)

§ ***allionii***	CBod CMea CTri EBou EDAr EPot MHer MSCN NHpl SRms SSim WCav WFar WHal WHoo
- 'Oki'	CRos EHyd LRHS NRHS SRms
allionii × ***hirta***	SDys SPlb
§ ***arenaria***	GAbr NMen XLum
* ***echiniformis***	XLum
'Emerald Spring'	GFgr
§ ***heuffelii***	CRos EHyd LRHS NHpl NRHS WFar XLum

	- 'Achisia' **new**	NMen
	- 'Adagdak' **new**	NMen
	- 'Agaffa' **new**	NMen
	- 'Aiolos'	NHol
	- 'Aldicia' **new**	NMen
	- 'Alena' **new**	NMen
	- 'Almkroon'	NHol NWad
	- 'Ambassadeur' **new**	NMen
	- 'Angel Wings'	SRms WHoo
	- 'Ardysia' **new**	NMen
	- 'Arnia' **new**	NMen
	- 'Askja' **new**	NMen
	- 'Atoll' **new**	NMen
	- 'Atria' **new**	NMen
	- 'Bandana'	NMen
	- 'Barbel' **new**	NMen
	- 'Baripper' **new**	NMen
	- 'Beacon' **new**	NMen
	- 'Beacon Hill'	NMen
	- 'Belcore'	NMen XLum
	- 'Bermuda'	NMen
	- 'Biapho' **new**	NMen
	- 'Bibiana' **new**	NMen
	- 'Big Brother' **new**	NMen
	- 'Big Red'	NHol NWad
	- 'Bolero'	NMen
	- 'Bora'	NWad
	- 'Brandaris'	SDys
	- 'Brocade'	MSCN NHol NMen NWad
	- 'Bronze Ingot'	NMen
	- 'Bulgarien'	NMen
	- 'Burgharis' **new**	NMen
	- 'Cauvery' **new**	NMen
	- 'Centaurus' **new**	NMen
	- 'Charell' **new**	NMen
§	- 'Cherry Glow'	NMen
	- 'Chocoleto'	NMen
	- 'Cimmanon' **new**	NMen
	- 'Comanchero' **new**	NMen
I	- 'Compacta'	NMen
	- 'Copper King'	NMen
	- 'Corbierie' **new**	NMen
	- 'Coutanche' **new**	NMen
	- 'Cover Girl'	NMen
	- 'Crill' **new**	NMen
	- 'Deciso'	NMen
	- 'Dream' **new**	NMen
	- 'Drechter Gem' **new**	NMen
	- 'Dynosia' **new**	NMen
	- 'Elmo's Fire'	NMen
*	- 'Emerald and Ruby'	WFar
	- 'Enicia' **new**	NMen
	- 'Eos Moment'	NMen
	- 'Ernest' **new**	NMen
	- 'Etysia' **new**	NMen
	- 'Fan Joy'	NMen
	- 'Fandango'	NMen
	- 'Geronimo'	NHol NMen
	- 'Ghaysia' **new**	NMen
	- 'Giuseppi Spiny'	NMen SPlb
	- var. ***glabra***	WHoo
	- - from Anaba Kanak, Bulgaria	NHol
	- - from Treska Gorge, Macedonia	SRms
§	- - 'Cameo'	NMen
	- 'Gladiator'	NMen
	- 'Gold Rand'	NHol NWad
*	- 'Golden Touch'	WFar
	- 'Grand Slam'	NMen
	- 'Green Land'	NMen
	- 'Greenstone'	NHol NMen NWad
	- 'Harmony'	NHol
	- 'Henry Correvon'	NMen
	- var. ***heuffelii***	NMen
	- 'Heulin' **new**	NMen
	- 'Hot Bikini' **new**	NMen
	- 'Hot Chocolate' **new**	NMen
	- 'Hot Lips'	NMen
	- 'Idylle'	NMen
	- 'Ikaros'	NHol
	- 'Inferno'	NMen NWad
	- 'Ithaca'	NHol NWad
	- 'Iuno'	NHol
	- 'Jackpot' **new**	NMen
	- 'Jade'	NMen
I	- 'Jovi King'	NMen
	- 'June's Choice' **new**	NMen
	- 'King Sunny'	NMen
	- 'Konrada' **new**	NMen
	- var. ***kopaonikensis***	NMen NWad
	- 'Lorelei'	NMen
	- 'Lucky Bell'	NMen
	- 'Machon' **new**	NMen
	- 'Madera' **new**	NMen
	- 'Major' **new**	NMen
	- 'Mary Ann'	NMen
	- 'Miller's Violet'	NMen
	- 'Mink'	NMen
	- 'Minuta'	NMen
	- 'Misty' **new**	NMen
	- 'Mystique'	NMen WHoo
	- 'Nannette'	NMen
	- 'Olivia' **new**	NMen
	- 'Orion'	NMen XLum
	- var. ***patens***	NMen
	- 'Penponds' **new**	NMen
	- 'Pink Skies'	NMen
	- 'Pink Star'	NMen
	- 'Prisma'	NMen
	- 'Pronker' **new**	NMen
	- 'Purple Haze'	XLum
	- 'Purple Heide'	NMen
	- 'Quennevalis' **new**	NMen
	- 'Red Rose'	NMen
	- 'Red Start' **new**	NMen
	- 'Rhapsody' **new**	NMen
	- 'Samares' **new**	NMen
	- 'Sarabande' **new**	NMen
	- 'Serenade'	NMen SRms
	- 'Silex'	NMen
	- 'Springael's Choice'	NMen
	- 'Summer King' **new**	NMen
*	- 'Sun and Silver Edge'	WFar
	- 'Sungold'	NHol NWad
	- 'Suntan'	NWad
	- 'Superduper' **new**	NMen
	- 'Sylvan Memory'	NMen
	- 'Tancredi'	NMen
	- 'Torrid Zone'	MBrN NMen
	- 'Trinity' **new**	NMen
	- 'Troon' **new**	NMen
	- 'Try Me' **new**	NMen
	- 'Tuxedo'	NHpl NMen
	- 'Violet'	NMen SDys
	- 'Yuppy Alone' **new**	NMen
§	***hirta***	EDAr GAbr GKev WFar XLum
	- from Wintergraben, Austria	SPlb SRms
	- 'Belansky Tatra'	NMen SRms

- subsp. ***glabrescens*** from High Tatra, Slovakia/Poland — XLum
- - from Smeryouka, southern Carpathians — NMen
- var. ***neilreichii*** — CRos EHyd LRHS NRHS SRms
- 'Purpurea' — XLum

§ ***sobolifera*** — EDAr GKev SPlb WHal XLum
- 'Green Globe' — CRos EHyd LRHS NRHS SDys
- 'Miss Lorraine' — XLum

Jubaea (*Arecaceae*)

§ ***chilensis*** 𝒱H2 — CPHo SArc SPalm SPlb
spectabilis — see *J. chilensis*

Juglans ✿ (*Juglandaceae*)

§ ***ailanthifolia*** — CMCN IDee
- B&SWJ 11026 — WCru
- var. ***cordiformis*** 'Brock' (F) — CAgr
- - 'Campbell Cw3' (F) — CAgr
- - 'Fodermaier' seedling (F) — CAgr
- - 'Imshu' (F) — CAgr
- - 'Rhodes' (F) — CAgr
- - 'Simcoe' (F) — CAgr

ailanthifolia × ***cinerea*** — see *J.* × *bixbyi*
§ × ***bixbyi*** — CAgr
cinerea (F) — LMaj
- 'Beckwith' (F) — CAgr
- 'Booth' (F) — CAgr
- 'Booth' seedling (F) — CAgr
- 'Chamberlin' (F) — CAgr
- 'Craxezy' (F) — CAgr
- 'Kenworthy' seedling (F) — CAgr
- 'Myjoy' (F) — CAgr

mandshurica (F) — CBcs CMCN
- B&SWJ 12550 from Korea — WCru
- BWJ 8097 from China — WCru
- RWJ 9905 from Taiwan — WCru

nigra (F) 𝒱H6 — CBcs CCVT CHab CLnd CMCN CMac CSBt CTho EBee ECrN ELan EPfP LCro LMaj LOPS MAsh MGos MMuc NOra NOrn SCob SEND SGbt SGol SPer WMat WTSh
- 'Bicentennial' (F) — CAgr
- 'Emma Kay' (F) — CAgr
- 'Laciniata' — EPfP MBlu
- 'Potsdam' (F) — CAgr
- 'Thomas' (F) — CAgr
- 'Weschke' (F) — CAgr

regia (F) — Widely available
- 'Axel' (F) — CAgr WMat
- 'Broadview' (F) — CAgr CArg CEnd CMac CTho ELan EPom LBuc LCro LOPS LRHS MBlu MGos MWat NOra SCoo SEWo SKee SPoG SSFT SVic WMat
- 'Buccaneer' (F) — CAgr CArg CMac CTho ELan EPom MWat NOra SKee WMat
- 'Chandler' (F) — CAgr
- 'Corne du Périgord' (F) — CAgr
- 'Excelsior of Taynton' (F) — WMat
- 'Ferjean' (F) — CAgr
- 'Fernette'[PBR] (F) — CAgr NOra WMat
- 'Fernor' (F) — CAgr WMat
- 'Franquette' (F) 𝒱H6 — CAgr NOra WMat
- 'Hansen' (F) — CAgr
- 'Hartley' (F) — CAgr
- 'Laciniata' 𝒱H6 — CMCN
- 'Lara' (F) 𝒱H6 — NOra WMat
- 'Mayette' (F) — CAgr
- 'Meylannaise' (F) — CAgr
- 'Mini Multiflora 14' (F) — CAgr
- number 16 (F) — WMat
- 'Parisienne' (F) — CAgr SGol
- 'Plovdivski' (F) — WMat
- 'Proslavski' (F) — WMat
- 'Purpurea' — CMCN MBlu
- 'Rita' (F) — LBuc
- 'Ronde de Montignac' (F) — CAgr
- 'Sychrov' (F) — WMat

sieboldiana — see *J. ailanthifolia*
sigillata — LEdu

jujube see *Ziziphus jujuba*

Juncus (*Juncaceae*)

articulatus — LLWG XLum
bulbosus — CNat
§ ***decipiens*** 'Curly-wurly' — CDoC CRos EHyd EPfP LRHS NRHS NWad WBrk
- 'Spiralis' — see *J. decipiens* 'Curly-wurly'

effusus — CBen LRHS NPer WMAq XLum
- 'Carman's Japanese' — NSti
- 'Gold Strike' (v) — LLWG
- § f. ***spiralis*** — CBen CRos CSpe CWat EHyd EPfP GQue LCro LOPS LPot LRHS MAsh NBir NRHS SCob SPlb SVic WCot WMAq XLum

ensifolius — CWat EWat EWes LLWG MMrt MWts NPer NSti WMAq
inflexus — CBen CWat LLWG WSMil XLum
- 'Afro' — NBro NWsh SPlb WSMil

pallidus — EPPr
patens 'Carman's Gray' — CKno CWCL EHyd GQue LRHS MMuc
- 'Elk Blue' — CKno

subnodulosus — LLWG
'Swarm of Hedgehogs' — NWsh

Junellia (*Verbenaceae*)

azorelloides — WAbe
congesta — WAbe
§ ***micrantha*** — WAbe
odonnellii — WAbe
§ ***succulentifolia*** — WAbe
thymifolia — CPBP

Juniperus ✿ (*Cupressaceae*)

chinensis — CMen
- 'Aurea' 𝒱H6 — CBcs SEND
- § 'Blaauw' 𝒱H6 — CMac CMen LRHS SLim XLot
- 'Blue Alps' 𝒱H6 — LRHS MGos MMuc SCoo SEND SLim XLot
- 'Echiniformis' — CKen
- 'Expansa Aureospicata' (v) — CMac EPfP SEND SPoG SRms
- § 'Expansa Variegata' (v) — SLim
- 'Itoigawa' — CMen
- § 'Kaizuka' 𝒱H6 — SLim
- 'Kaizuka Variegata' — see *J. chinensis* 'Variegated Kaizuka'
- 'Kuriwao Gold' — see *J.* × *pfitzeriana* 'Kuriwao Gold'
- § 'Parsonsii' — WCFE
- 'Plumosa' — SLim
- 'Plumosa Aurea' 𝒱H6 — LRHS
- 'Plumosa Aureovariegata' (v) — CKen
- 'Pyramidalis' 𝒱H6 — CBrac EPfP MAsh SCob SCoo
- 'San José' — CMen
- § var. ***sargentii*** — CMen
- 'Shimpaku' — CKen CMen
- 'Stricta' — CSBt LRHS NOrn SLim XLot
- 'Sulphur Spray' — see *J.* × *pfitzeriana* 'Sulphur Spray'

	- 'Torulosa'	see *J. chinensis* 'Kaizuka'
§	- 'Variegated Kaizuka' (v)	SLim
	- 'Wilson's Weeping'	NLar
	communis	CHab GPoy SCob SPre WKor WTSh
	- 'Arnold'	NLar
	- 'Arnold Sentinel'	CKen
	- 'Barton'	NLar NWad
	- 'Barton Gem'	NWad
	- 'Brien'	CKen
	- 'Brynhyfryd Gold'	CKen SLim
	- 'Compressa' ♀H7	CBcs CKen CMac CSBt CTri EPfP GEdr LBee LRHS MAsh MGos NHol SCob SLim SPer SPoG WIce XLot
	- 'Corielagan'	CKen
	- 'Cracovia'	CKen
	- var. ***depressa***	GPoy SEND
	- 'Depressa Aurea'	CBrac CKen CSBt LBee
	- 'Depressed Star'	SPoG
	- 'Effusa'	CKen
	- 'Gold Cone'	CBrac CKen ELan EPfP LBee MAsh MGos SLim SPoG
	- 'Goldschatz'	CKen EPfP LRHS SLim SPoG
	- 'Green Carpet' ♀H7	CKen ELan EPfP GKin LBuc LRHS MAsh MGos NLar SCoo SLim SPoG SVic WCFE XLot
	- 'Greenmantle'	LRHS
	- 'Haverbeck'	CKen
	- 'Hibernica' ♀H7	CBrac CSBt ELan EPfP EWTr LRHS MGos SCob SLim SPer SPoG
	- 'Hibernica Aurea'	CMac
	- 'Hornibrookii'	SRms
I	- 'Horstmann's Pendula'	NLar
	- 'Kenwith Castle'	CKen
	- 'Meyer'	CMac
	- 'Pyramidalis'	SPlb
	- 'Repanda' ♀H7	CBcs CBrac CMac CSBt EPfP LRHS MGos NLar SCob SCoo SGol SLim SPer SPoG WFar XLot
	- 'Sentinel'	LRHS SLim WCFE
	- 'Sieben Steinhauser'	CKen
	- 'Silver Mist'	CKen
	- 'Spotty Spreader' (v)	SLim
	- Suecica Group	XLot
	- - 'Suecica Nana' <u>**new**</u>	SLim
	- 'Zeal'	CKen
	conferta	see *J. rigida* subsp. *conferta*
	- var. ***maritima***	see *J. taxifolia*
	davurica 'Expansa'	see *J. chinensis* 'Parsonsii'
	- 'Expansa Albopicta'	see *J. chinensis* 'Expansa Variegata'
	- 'Expansa Variegata'	see *J. chinensis* 'Expansa Variegata'
	× ***gracilis*** 'Blaauw'	see *J. chinensis* 'Blaauw'
	'Grey Owl' ♀H7	CBrac ELan LRHS MMuc SCob SEND SGol SGsty SLim SRms XLot
	horizontalis	SGsty
§	- 'Andorra Compact'	XLot
I	- 'Andorra Variegata' (v)	CKen SCoo
	- 'Bar Harbor'	CMac
§	- 'Blue Chip'	CKen ELan EPfP LBee MGos SCob SCoo SGsty SLim SPoG XLot
	- 'Blue Moon'	see *J. horizontalis* 'Blue Chip'
	- 'Blue Rug'	see *J. horizontalis* 'Wiltonii'
	- 'Glacier'	LRHS
	- 'Glauca'	CBrac SCob SGsty
	- 'Golden Carpet' ♀H7	ELan LBuc LCro LOPS LRHS NLar SLim XLot
	- 'Grey Pearl'	CKen
	- 'Hughes'	LBee MRav
	- ICEE BLUE ('Monber') ♀H7	CKen ELan EPfP LRHS NLar SPoG
	- 'Limeglow' ♀H7	CBrac ELan EPfP MGos NLar SCoo SPoG XLot
	- 'Mother Lode'	CKen
	- 'Neumann'	CKen
	- 'Pancake'	NLar SLim
	- 'Plumosa Compacta'	see *J. horizontalis* 'Andorra Compact'
	- 'Prince of Wales'	MAsh XLot
	- 'Turquoise Spreader'	CSBt
	- 'Villa Marie'	CKen SPoG
§	- 'Wiltonii'	SLim XLot
	- 'Yukon Belle'	CKen
	× ***media***	see *J.* × *pfitzeriana*
	oxycedrus	XSen
§	× ***pfitzeriana***	CMac SCob SGol WFar
	- 'Arctic'	NLar
	- 'Blaauw'	see *J. chinensis* 'Blaauw'
	- 'Blue and Gold' (v)	CKen SPoG
	- 'Blue Cloud'	see *J. virginiana* 'Blue Cloud'
§	- 'Carbery Gold' ♀H6	CBcs CBrac CMac CSBt EPfP GKin LRHS MAsh MGos NOrn SCoo SLim SPoG
	- 'Gold Coast'	CBrac CKen CSBt LBee MGos NOra SGol XLot
	- GOLD SOVEREIGN ('Blound')	LBee NOra
	- 'Gold Star'	LRHS
*	- 'Golden Joy'	SLim
	- 'King of Spring'	SLim
§	- 'Kuriwao Gold'	GKin SEND
	- 'Mint Julep'	CBrac CSBt EPfP LRHS SCob SCoo SGol SGsty SLim XLot
	- 'Old Gold' ♀H6	EPfP GKin LBee LCro LOPS LRHS MGos MMuc SCob SCoo SEND SGol SGsty SPer SPlb SVic WCFE WFar XLot
	- 'Old Gold Carbery'	see *J.* × *pfitzeriana* 'Carbery Gold'
	- 'Pfitzeriana Aurea'	CBrac CMac LRHS SCob SGol
§	- 'Sulphur Spray' ♀H6	LRHS MMuc SCob SEND SLim WCFE
	phoenicea	XSen
	- subsp. ***turbinata***	XSen
§	***pingii*** 'Glassell'	NLar
	- 'Hulsdonk Yellow'PBR	LRHS SLim SPoG
§	- var. ***wilsonii***	CKen
	procumbens 'Kishiogima'	LRHS
	- 'Nana' ♀H7	CKen CMac EPfP LBee LRHS MAsh MGos NHol NLar SCoo SLim SPoG SavN XLot
	recurva	IDee
	- 'Castlewellan'	MGil NLar WFar
	- var. ***coxii***	CMac MBlu NHol NLar SRms
§	- 'Densa'	CKen
	- 'Nana'	see *J. recurva* 'Densa'
	rigida	CMen
§	- subsp. ***conferta***	CMac SEND
	- - 'All Gold' ♀H6	LRHS SLim SPoG
*	- - 'Blue Ice'	CKen
	- - 'Blue Pacific'	CKen LRHS SGsty SPoG SWeb
	- - 'Blue Tosho'	NLar
	- - 'Schlager' ♀H6	SLim XLot
	- - 'Silver Mist'	CKen
	sabina	XLot
	- 'Skandia'	CKen
	- 'Tamariscifolia'	CBcs GKin LBee LRHS MAsh MGos NOrn SArc SCob SEND SGol SGsty SLim SPer SPoG WCFE XLot
	sargentii	see *J. chinensis* var. *sargentii*
	scopulorum 'Blue Arrow' ♀H6	Widely available
	- 'Blue Banff'	CKen

	- 'Skyrocket'	CBcs CCVT CMac CSBt ECrN EPfP LMaj MGos MRav SCob SGol SPad SRms SWeb WCFE
	- 'Springbank'	WCFE
	- 'Wichita Blue'	CCVT EPfP
§	***squamata***	SavN
	- 'Blue Carpet' 🏆H7	CBcs CKen CMac CSBt EPfP LBuc LRHS MAsh MGos NHol NLar NOra NOrn SCob SEND SGol SGsty SLim SPer SPoG WCFE WFar XLot
	- 'Blue Star' 🏆H7	CBod CBrac CKen CMac CSBt ELan EPfP LBee LCro LOPS LRHS MAsh MGos NHol NLar SCob SLim SPer SPoG WCFE WFar XLot
	- 'Blue Star Variegated'	see *J. squamata* 'Golden Flame'
	- 'Blue Swede'	see *J. squamata* 'Hunnetorp'
	- 'Dream Joy'	CBod CKen NLar
	- var. ***fargesii***	see *J. squamata*
	- 'Filborna'	LBee NLar
	- 'Floreant'	SLim SPoG
	- 'Glassell'	see *J. pingii* 'Glassell'
§	- 'Golden Flame' (v)	CKen
	- 'Holger' 🏆H7	CMac EPfP LBee LRHS MAsh MGos NHol NLar SCoo SLim SPoG WFar XLot
§	- 'Hunnetorp'	LRHS WFar XLot
	- 'Meyeri'	XLot
	- 'Tropical Blue'	SPoG
	- 'Wilsonii'	see *J. pingii* var. *wilsonii*
§	***taxifolia***	CSBt
	thurifera	XSen
§	***virginiana*** 'Blue Cloud'	SLim
	- 'Frosty Morn'	CKen
	- 'Golden Spring'	CKen
	- SILVER SPREADER ('Mona')	CKen
	- 'Sulphur Spray'	see *J.* × *pfitzeriana* 'Sulphur Spray'

Jussiaea see *Ludwigia*

Justicia (*Acanthaceae*)

	americana	LLWG SBrt
	aurea	EShb SPlb
§	***brandegeeana*** 🏆H1b	CCCN CTsd EShb
	- 'Lutea'	see *J. brandegeeana* 'Yellow Queen'
	- variegated (v)	EShb
§	- 'Yellow Queen'	EShb
	- yellow-flowered	EShb
§	***carnea***	EMdy EShb WFar
	- 'Alba'	CCCN
	- dark-leaved	EShb
	- 'Radiant'	SMad
	guttata	see *J. brandegeeana*
	'Penrhosiensis'	EShb
	pohliana	see *J. carnea*
	rizzinii 🏆H1b	CBcs CCCN SEle WLov
	spicigera	CCCN EShb
	suberecta	see *Dicliptera sericea*

K

Kadsura (*Schisandraceae*)

coccinea B&SWJ 11793	WCru
- FMWJ 13489	WCru
heteroclita FMWJ 13385	WCru
- WWJ 11947	WCru
japonica	CBcs
- B&SWJ 1027	WCru
- B&SWJ 4463 from Korea	WCru
- B&SWJ 11109 from Japan	WCru
- B&SWJ 14672	ESwi WCru
- from Japan	WSHC
- 'Fukurin' (v)	IDee NLar
- 'Variegata' (v)	CCCN CRos EBee EHyd EPfP LRHS
- white fruit	NLar
aff. ***japonica*** NMWJ 14550	WCru

Kaempferia ✿ (*Zingiberaceae*)

pulchra	CDTJ
rotunda	CCCN SDir

Kageneckia (*Rosaceae*)

oblonga	SPlb

Kalanchoe (*Crassulaceae*)

	beauverdii new	EShb
	beharensis 🏆H1b	CCCN CDTJ CDoC ELan EShb WCot
	- 'Fang' 🏆H1b	CDTJ ELan EShb WCot
	- 'Rusty'	CDTJ CSpe
	daigremontiana	EShb
§	***delagoensis***	CCCN CDoC EShb
	'Dorothy' new	EShb
	fedtschenkoi 'Variegata' (v)	EShb WCot
	hildebrandtii	EShb
	humilis	CDoC EShb WCot
	× ***kewensis*** new	EShb
	laciniata	EShb
	laetivirens	SSim
	luciae 🏆H1b new	CDoC
	manginii 🏆H1b	EShb
	'Oak Leaf'	EShb
	orgyalis	EShb WCot
	pinnata	EShb
	'Prebella'	EShb
	pumila 🏆H1b	CDoC EShb SGro
	scandens 'Kalahari Survivor'	EShb
	serrata	EShb
	sexangularis	EShb
	'Tessa' 🏆H1b	WCot
	thyrsiflora	CDoC EShb
	- 'Bronze Sculpture'	CAbb CBct MCot SSim
	- RED LIPS ('Ubilips') new	LCro LOPS
	- 'Variegata' (v)	EShb
	tomentosa 🏆H1b	CDoC EShb WCot XAbr
	tubiflora	see *K. delagoensis*

kale, curly see AGM Vegetables Section

Kalimeris (*Asteraceae*)

	altaica	EMor EPPr
§	***incisa***	CFis CMea MMuc
	- 'Alba'	CKno ECha ELon GMaP NLar WCAu WFar
	- 'Blue Star'	CAby CBod CKno ECha ECtt ELon GMaP GQue MNrw MSpe NLar SIvy SPad WCAu WFar WSHC
	- 'Charlotte'	EWes GBee LPla MNrw NBre NDov NHol SAko SDix SPoG WFar WGoo
	- 'Edo Murasaki'	SBrt
	- 'Jürgen Wever' new	LPla
	- 'Madiva'	CAby CSam EBee ELon GBee IMou LPla NDov SAko WGoo

	- 'Nana Blue'	EBee NDov SPoG
	integrifolia	MMuc
	- 'Daisy Mae'	NDov
	'Mon Jardin'	EBee WCot
§	***mongolica***	ECha EPPr LEdu MMuc SAko SBut WFar WGoo WSHC
	- 'Antonia'	EBee ECha IMou LPla NDov WCot
§	***pinnatifida***	EHyd LRHS
	- 'Hortensis'	EBee MNrw
§	***yomena*** 'Shogun' (v)	CBod CMac ECha ECtt EHyd EMil EMor EPfP LEdu LRHS MBel MHtn MNrw MPie NSti SDix SPer SPoG SRms WFar XLum
	- 'Variegata'	see *K. yomena* 'Shogun'

Kalmia ✿ (*Ericaceae*)

	angustifolia ♀H5	GKev MGil WSpi
	- var. ***angustifolia*** f. ***candida***	LRHS
	- f. ***rubra*** ♀H5	CBcs CCCN CDoC CRos EBee EHyd ELan EPfP LRHS MAsh NLar SCob SPer WFar WSpi
I	- 'Rubra Nana'	CMac
§	***buxifolia*** ♀H4	NLar
	- subsp. ***hugeri***	GRum
§	- 'Maryfield'	WAbe
	latifolia	CBcs EPfP LRHS SPer SWvt
	- 'Alpine Pink'	WSpi
	- 'Bay State'	LRHS
	- 'Bullseye'	MAsh SAko SPoG
	- 'Carousel'	CBcs CCCN MAsh
	- 'Clementine Churchill'	CMac
	- 'Freckles' ♀H6	CMac SCob SPoG
	- 'Galaxy'	LRHS SAko
	- 'Ginkona'	LRHS MAsh SAko
	- 'Kaleidoscope'	MAsh
	- 'Minuet'	CBcs CCCN CRos EHyd LRHS MAsh MGil SPoG SWvt
	- 'Mitternacht'	GGGa MAsh
	- f. ***myrtifolia***	EHyd LRHS
	- - 'Elf'	CRos EHyd LRHS MAsh
	- 'Nipmuck'	CMac
	- 'Olympic Fire' ♀H6	CBcs CRos EHyd ELan GGGa LRHS MGil SAko SWvt WSpi WTSh
	- 'Olympic Wedding'	SPoG
	- 'Ostbo Red'	CBcs CMac EHyd LRHS MAsh MMuc SCob SPoG SWvt
	- 'Peppermint'	GGGa LRHS
	- 'Pink Charm' ♀H6	CMac SAko
	- 'Pinwheel'	LRHS MAsh MGil SAko SPoG
	- 'Snowdrift'	LRHS
§	***microphylla***	WAbe
	polifolia	CBcs CCCN CDoC LCro LOPS LRHS MGil NLar SPer SavN WThu
	- 'Alba'	see *K. polifolia* f. *leucantha*
	- 'Glauca'	see *K. microphylla*
§	- f. ***leucantha***	LRHS WAbe
	- 'Newfoundland'	CBcs

Kalmiopsis (*Ericaceae*)

	leachiana 'Glendoick'	LRHS

Kalmiopsis × *Phyllodoce* see × *Phylliopsis*

Kalmiopsis × *Rhodothamnus* see × *Kalmiothamnus*

× *Kalmiothamnus* (*Ericaceae*)

	'Haytor'	ITim
	'Sindelberg'	ITim

Kalopanax ✿ (*Araliaceae*)

	pictus	see *K. septemlobus*
§	***septemlobus***	CBcs EPfP MMuc NLar SEND
	- var. ***magnificus*** B&SWJ 10900	WCru
	- f. ***maximowiczii***	EPfP MBlu NLar

Keiskea (*Lamiaceae*)

	japonica	GEdr
	- pink-flowered	SBrt

Kelseya (*Rosaceae*)

	uniflora	WAbe

Kennedia (*Papilionaceae*)

	coccinea	CCCN SPhx WHil
	macrophylla	CRHN
	nigricans	CCCN
	prostrata	SPhx
	rubicunda	CCCN CRHN WHil

Kentia (*Arecaceae*)

	belmoreana	see *Howea belmoreana*
	forsteriana	see *Howea forsteriana*

Kentranthus see *Centranthus*

Kerria (*Rosaceae*)

	japonica misapplied single	see *K. japonica* 'Simplex'
	japonica (L.) DC.	CBod CTho SGbt
	- (d)	see *K. japonica* 'Pleniflora'
	- 'Albescens'	NLar WCot
	- 'Golden Guinea' ♀H5	CBod CBrac CExl CMac CRos ELan EPfP LCro LOPS LRHS MAsh MGos MRav NRHS SCoo SPer SPoG SRms SWvt WFar
	- 'Honshu'	IArd
§	- 'Picta' (v)	CMac CTho EBee MGos MRav MSwo SGol SLim SLon SRms WAvo WFar WLov
§	- 'Pleniflora' (d) ♀H5	Widely available
§	- 'Simplex'	CExl CMac EShb SRms WAvo
	- 'Variegata'	see *K. japonica* 'Picta'

Khadia (*Aizoaceae*)

	acutipetala	CCCN

Kiggelaria (*Flacourtiaceae*)

	africana	SVen

Kirengeshoma (*Hydrangeaceae*)

	palmata	Widely available
	- 'Black Style'	EBee
	- dwarf	WCot
	- Koreana Group ♀H7	Widely available

Kitagawia (*Apiaceae*)

§	***litoralis***	EBee

Kitaibela (*Malvaceae*)

	vitifolia	CExl CSpe ILea NBid NSti SEND SPlb WAvo WFar WHer WOut

Kitchingia see *Kalanchoe*

kiwi fruit see *Actinidia deliciosa*

Klasea (*Asteraceae*)

§	***bulgarica***	EPPr MPie NDov SDix SHar SPhx WGoo

§ ***coronata***	LPla
coronata subsp. ***insularis*** B&SWJ 8698	WCru
§ ***lycopifolia***	WCot WMal
§ ***radiata*** subsp. ***gmelinii***	EBee EHyd EMor EPPr LRHS NRHS

Kleinia (*Asteraceae*)

articulata	see *Curio articulata*
fulgens **new**	ECre
§ ***grantii***	EShb SGro WCot
neriifolia	EShb
repens	see *Curio repens*

Knautia (*Caprifoliaceae*)

§ ***arvensis***	CBod CCBP CElw CHab CWld EBee EHyd ELan EPfP LCro LOPS MBow MHer MNHC NAts NLar NMir SPer SPhx SRms WCAu WHer WOut WSFF WWild
- white-flowered	SPhx
dipsacifolia	LPla SBut SHar
drymeia **new**	WOut
'Jardin d'en Face'	LRHS WCav
§ ***macedonica***	Widely available
- 'Crimson Cushion'	CSpe ECtt
- 'Mars Midget'	CBod CExl CRos CSpe EBee EHyd ELan ELon EMor EPed EPfP GMaP LRHS MBel MGos MHol NBPC NLar NRHS SCob SPhx SPoG SWvt WCAu WFar WHoo WSHC
- Melton pastels	CBod CChe CDor CExl CRos EBee EHyd ELan EPPr EPfP GJos GMaP LRHS MGos NLar NPer NRHS SCob SPhx SPoG SRkn SRms SWvt WCAu WCav WFar
- pink-flowered	SRms
- 'Red Baron'	CChe
- 'Red Knight'	CBod CDor CRos EBee EHyd EPfP GWyn LRHS MBNS NLar NRHS WSMil
- tall, pale-flowered	SPhx
- 'Thunder and Lightning'PBR (v)	CBct CBod CDoC CDor CRos CWGN EBee ECtt EHyd EMor EPfP EWes ILea LBuc LRHS LSou MHol MNrw MRav NLar NRHS SCob SEdd SPer SPoG SRms WCAu WCot WKif
sarajevensis	MAvo

Knightia (*Proteaceae*)

excelsa	CBcs

Kniphofia ✿ (*Asphodelaceae*)

'Ada'	ELon
albescens	SPlb
'Alcazar'	CBcs CTsd ECtt ELon EMor EPfP EWhm LCro LOPS MAvo MBel MHer SCob SPer SWvt WCAu WCFE WFar WSpi
'Amazing Fun' **new**	CRos CWGN
'Ample Dwarf'	ECtt WCot
'Amsterdam'	GBin MWat
angustifolia	SPlb
'Apricot'	EHyd LRHS WCot
'Apricot Souffle'	EPri WCot
'Atlanta'	EHyd LRHS
'Barton Fever' ♀H6	WCot
baurii	CExl SPlb
'Bees' Jubilee'	MAvo NChi
'Bees' Lemon'	Widely available
§ 'Bees' Sunset' ♀H5	CAvo CPrp CRos CSam EBee ECha ECtt EHyd EPfP LRHS MBel MMuc NLar NRHS SEND SPoG SWvt WSHC
'Bees' Yellow'	SGro
'Blacksmith's Delight'	MAvo
'Border Ballet'	EHyd LBuc LRHS NBir NGdn NLar NRHS XLum
brachystachya	SBrt SPlb
'Bressingham Comet'	CRos EBee ECtt EHyd ELon GKev LRHS NBir NRHS SRms
BRESSINGHAM SUNBEAM ('Bresun')	CRos EBee ECtt EHyd LRHS NBir NRHS
'Bressingham Yellow'	ECtt
'Brimstone' Bloom ♀H5	CDor CPrp CRos ECtt EMor EPfP EPri LEdu LRHS MMuc NBir NRHS SCob SEND SWvt WFar
bruceae	SPlb SVen
'Buttercup' ♀H5	CAvo LSRN
'Butterfly'	EBee
'C.M. Prichard' misapplied	see *K. rooperi*
'C.M. Prichard' Prichard	WCot
'Candlelight'	EBee ECtt EPri WSHC
caulescens	Widely available
- LEG 053	GKev
- 'Coral Breakers'	CExl CPrp ECtt EHyd ELon GMaP LRHS MHol NBPC SEND WCot
- early-flowering	WSpi
- 'John May'	CAby CBod EBee ECtt ESwi LEdu MAvo MHer SEdd SWvt WCot
- short	ECha
- 'Tiny Girl'	ECtt
'Champagne'	WCot
'Chichi'	MAvo WCot
'Christmas Cheer'	EBee
citrina	CSpe CTsd GKev GLog MBrN NGBl WCot XLum
'Cobra'	CDor CRos EBee ECtt EHyd GMaP LRHS NRHS WAul WCot
'Coral Flame' ♀H5	CRos EHyd LRHS NRHS
'Coral Sceptre'	WCot
'Creamsicle'PBR (Popsicle Series)	ECtt WCot
'Dingaan'	EBee ECtt MNrw MTis NBir NLar WCot
'Dorset Sentry'	CAby CBod ECtt EHyd ELon EMor EPfP LRHS MBNS MBel MGos MNrw NBPC NBir NLar WCot WFar
'Drummore Apricot'	CBod CKno CPrp CRos ECha ECtt ELan ELon EPfP LRHS LSRN MPie MSpe NBir NRHS NWsh WCot WFar WGwG
'Early Buttercup'	NBPC WFar
'Elvira'PBR	CRos ECtt EHyd EMor LRHS NRHS SAko SPoG WCot
EMBER GLOW ('Tneg'PBR) (Glow Series)	CAbb EBee ECtt LCro LOPS
ensifolia	ECtt NGdn SVen XLum
'Ernest Mitchell'	WCot
Express hybrids	XLum
'Feuerkerze'	SAko
'Fiery Fred' ♀H6	CPrp CRos EBee ECtt EHyd ELon EPfP EWhm GBee LRHS MMuc MPie MSpe NRHS NWsh SGbt WAul WCot WHoo WSpi
'Fire Brand' **new**	WCot
FIRE GLOW ('Tnfg'PBR) (Glow Series)	GPSL NLar

	'First Sunrise'[PBR]	ECtt LRHS
	'Flamenco'	CRos EHyd ELon LRHS MBros NGdn NRHS SCob SRms SVic WFar WLov
	'Florence Bedecked'	WCot
	fluviatilis	GKev
	foliosa Hochst.	LEdu
	'Frances Victoria'	WCot
	galpinii misapplied	see *K. triangularis* subsp. *triangularis*
	galpinii Baker ♀H4	EMor MMuc
	'Gelbe Flamme'	SAko
	'Gilt Bronze'	WCot
	'Gladness'	MAvo NBir WCot
	'Goldelse'	CRos EBee EHyd LRHS NBir NRHS
	'Goldfinch'	CSam
	gracilis	LEdu
	'Green and Cream'	MHCG
	'Green Jade'	CAby CBcs CExl EBee ECha ECtt EHyd ELan EMor EWTr LEdu LRHS MCot MNrw MRav NBPC NBir NGBl NLar NRHS SCob SEND SGbt SPer SRms STPC WCAu WCot WFar
	'Green Jewel'	LRHS
	'H.E. Beale'	WCot
	'Happy Halloween' **new**	CRos MAvo
	'Hen and Chickens'	ECtt MAvo NBPC WCot WFar
	hirsuta	EHyd LRHS SRms WSHC
	- 'Fire Dance'	CTsd EBou EHyd LRHS LSun NLar WFar
	'Ice Queen'	CAby CAvo CBcs CDor EBee ECha ECtt ELon EPPr EPri MAvo MCot MHer MNrw MRav MTis NChi NLar SCob SEND SEdd SPeP SRms SWvt WABo WCAu WCot WFar
	ichopensis	LEdu SVen WPGP
	'Incandesce' ♀H5	CBod EMor EPPr EWhm MBNS MNrw NBPC SPoG WCot WMal
	'Innocence' ♀H4	CRos EBee EHyd EPfP LRHS NRHS
	'Jane Henry'	LEdu
	'Jenny Bloom'	CPrp CRos ECtt ELan EPfP EWTr GMaP LEdu LRHS MRav MSpe NLar NRHS NSti SEND SRms WAul WCot WFar
	'Jess's Delight'	WCot
	'John Benary'	CPrp CRos ECtt EHyd GLog GMaP LRHS MBel MSpe NBir NLar NRHS SEND SRms WCAu WCot WGwG WKif
	'Jonathan' ♀H5	WCot
	laxiflora	EPri WPGP
	'Lemon Popsicle'[PBR] (Popsicle Series)	CAbb CBct CBod CRos CWCL CWGN EHyd ELan EMor LRHS MPri NRHS SCob SRms WABo WFar WNPC
	'Light of the World'	see *K. triangularis* subsp. *triangularis* 'Light of the World'
	'Limelight'	CPar ECtt WCAu
	linearifolia	CExl EBee SPlb WCot WPGP XLum
	'Little Elf'	CDor MAvo XLum
	'Little Maid'	CBcs CBod CRos CSBt CWCL ECha ECtt EHyd ELan EMor EPfP EPri EShb GMaP LRHS MHer MRav MTis NBPC NBir NLar NRHS SCob SPer SRms SWvt WCAu WCot WFar
	'Lord Roberts'	MAvo MRav WCot
	'Luna'	WCot
	macowanii	see *K. triangularis* subsp. *triangularis*
	'Mango Popsicle'[PBR] (Popsicle Series)	CAbb CBod CMac CRos CTsd EBee ECtt EHyd ELan EMor EPfP EWTr LRHS LSou MNrw MPnt MPri NBPC NLar NRHS NSti SCob SPoG SRms WCot WFar WHoo
	'Mermaiden'	ECtt MAvo MMuc MNrw SEND WCot
	'Minister Verschuur'	CRos EBee ECtt EHyd LRHS NRHS
	'Modesta'	WSHC
	'Molten Lava'	EBee
	'Moonstone' ♀H5	CSam EBee ECtt ELon EMor EPPr GBin LSun MNrw MTis NBPC NLar NSti SEND SEdd SPoG WCot WRHF WSpi
	'Mount Etna'	WAvo
	multiflora 'November Glory'	WCot WFar WMal
	'Nancy's Red'	Widely available
	nelsonii Mast.	see *K. triangularis* subsp. *triangularis*
	'New Sensation'	WCot
	'No Rhyme nor Reason'	WCot
§	'Nobilis' ♀H5	CAby CBod CExl CRos ECha ECtt ELan ELon EMor EPfP GAbr GMaP LRHS LSRN MAvo MHol MMuc MNrw NBPC NGdn SArc SDix SEND SPer SRms SWvt WCAu WCot WMal
	northiae ♀H4	CCht CExl CPla EBee ELan EPfP EPri EWes MAvo MNrw NLar SArc SEND SEdd SPad SPlb SWvt WABo WCot WCru WPGP WSpi XLum
	'Old Court Seedling'	EBee WCot WFar
	'Orange Fackel'	SAko
	'Orange Vanilla Popsicle'[PBR] (Popsicle Series)	CBct CRos CSBt ECtt EHyd EMor EWTr IPot LLWG LRHS MPnt MPri MThu NLar NRHS SCob SEdd SPad SPoG WFar WNPC WTyc
§	'Painted Lady'	CDor CSam CSde CTri EBee ECtt GMaP MHol MNrw NLar SEND SWvt WCot
	'Papaya Popsicle'[PBR] (Popsicle Series)	CBct CRos CWGN EBee ECtt EHyd ELan ELon EMor LLWG LRHS LSou MAvo MNrw MThu NLar NRHS SCob SEdd SPoG SRms WABo WFar WSpi
	parviflora	XLum
	pauciflora	CPbh WCot WMal
	'Penny Rockets' ♀H6	CRos EHyd EPPr LRHS NRHS
	'Percy's Pride'	Widely available
	'Pfitzeri'	SRms
	'Pineapple Popsicle'[PBR] (Popsicle Series)	CTsd CWGN ECtt ELon EMor LSou MPnt NEoE NLar SRms WNPC
	POCO ORANGE ('Tnknipo'[PBR]) **new**	NLar
	'Primrose Upward' ♀H6	WCot
I	'Primulina' Bloom	EHyd LRHS NRHS
	'Prince Igor' misapplied	see *K.* 'Nobilis'
	'Prince Igor' Prichard	ECtt NBir
	'Red Rocket'[PBR]	LRHS MNrw NLar WCot
	'Redhot Popsicle'[PBR] (Popsicle Series)	CTsd CWGN EHyd EMor EPfP LRHS MAvo MHol MNrw MPnt NBPC SPoG WCot WNPC
	'Rich Echoes' ♀H5	CBod CWGN ECtt ELon EMor EPPr ESwi EWhm LEdu MHol MNrw MTis NLar WCot WMal
	ritualis	CExl
§	***rooperi*** ♀H5	Widely available
	'Royal Castle'	CExl CRos CTsd EHyd EPfP GMaP LRHS NBir NGdn NRHS SCob SEND SRms WFar XLum

'Royal Standard' ♀H5	CBcs CBod CRos EBee ECtt EHyd ELan ELon EMor EPfP GMaP LCro LOPS LRHS NLar NRHS SCob SPer SPoG SWvt WCAu WFar WGwG WSpi
rufa Baker	LEdu WPGP
- 'Rasta' **new**	CBcs
'Safranvogel' ♀H5	EBee ECtt NBPC WCot
'Samuel's Sensation' misapplied	see *K.* 'Painted Lady'
'Samuel's Sensation' Samuel ♀H5	EBee ECtt EHyd EPPr LRHS NLar NRHS SWvt WCot
sarmentosa	CExl SPlb SVen WCot
'Saturn'	MAvo
'Scorched Corn'	EMor LEdu MAvo
'Sherbet Lemon'	MNrw WCot
'Shining Sceptre' misapplied	see *K.* 'Bees' Sunset'
'Slush Puppy'	CBod
'Springtime'	WCot
'Star of Baden-Baden'	MAvo MMuc NBir SEND WCot
Stark's early perpetual-flowering hybrids	XLum
'Strawberries and Cream'	CPrp EBee ECha ECtt ELon EWld NLar SGbt SWvt
stricta	XLum
'Sunningdale Yellow' ♀H5	ECha ECtt GMaP MAvo SMHy SRms WHoo WSpi
'Sweet Corn'	CBod EMor
'Tawny King' ♀H5	Widely available
'Tetbury Torch'PBR	CBod CExl CWGN EBee ECtt EHyd EMor LRHS MAvo MCot NRHS SEND SPtp SWvt WAul WCAu
thomsonii	CExl NGdn
- 'Kichocheo'	LEdu MAvo WCot
- var. ***snowdenii*** misapplied	see *K. thomsonii* var. *thomsonii*
- var. ***snowdenii*** ambig.	CExl WPGP XLum
§ - var. ***thomsonii***	LEdu SMHy WABo WSHC
- - 'Stern's Trip' ♀H4	EBee
'Timothy' ♀H5	Widely available
'Toffee Nosed' ♀H5	Widely available
'Torchbearer'	WCot
triangularis	EMor EPfP GKev WFar XLum
§ - subsp. ***triangularis***	CRos EHyd EPfP LRHS NRHS SPer SRms SVen XLum
§ - - 'Light of the World'	ECtt EHyd GAbr LRHS NBPC NBir NLar SWvt WCot WFar
'Tuckii' misapplied	SRms
typhoides	NBir SPlb
tysonii	SPlb XLum
uvaria	EBee EHyd GKev LCro LOPS LRHS NBir NRHS SCob SRms WABo WCAu WCot XLum XSen
'Vanilla'	LRHS MMuc NLar SEND
'Vesta'	CRos EHyd LRHS NRHS
'Vincent Lepage'	NLar
'Walter Reuthe' **new**	SReu
'Wol's Red Seedling'	CAvo CSam ECtt ELon GBee MCot MNrw NBPC SEND WCot WGwG
'Wrexham Buttercup' ♀H6	CDor CSam EBee ECtt ELan EMor EWTr EWhm GMaP LSRN MCot MHol MNrw MSpe MTis NBPC NLar SCob SEND WCot WFar WHal WSpi
'Yellow Cheer'	WCot WMal
'Yellow Hammer' Slieve Donard	CSam ECha ELon MMuc SEND

Knowltonia (*Ranunculaceae*)

filia	CExl

Koeleria (*Poaceae*)

cristata misapplied	see *K. macrantha*
glauca	CBod CRos ECha EHyd EPfP EShb GMaP LRHS MBNS NGdn NRHS NWsh SCob SPlb SWvt WFar XCre
§ ***macrantha***	EPPr

Koelreuteria (*Sapindaceae*)

bipinnata	IDee LRHS
elegans subsp. ***formosana***	CMCN
paniculata	CBee CCVT CLnd CMCN CMac CTri EBee ECrN ELan EPfP ILea LEdu LMaj MGos MMuc NOrn SCob SEND SGol SGsty SPlb WFar WTSh
- 'Coral Sun'PBR ♀H5	CExl EBee ELan EPfP LRHS MBlu MGos NOra NOrn WCot WMat
- 'Fastigiata'	EBee ELan EPfP MBlu SCoo
- 'Rosseels'	NLar
- 'September'	EPfP MBlu

Kohleria (*Gesneriaceae*)

'Ampallang'	WDib
'An's Nagging Macaws'	WDib
'Brazil Gem'	WDib
'Bristol's Evil Storm'	WDib
'Cybele'	WDib
'Dark Velvet'	WDib
eriantha ♀H1c	WDib
'Flashdance'	WDib
'Hcy's Jardin de Monet'	WDib
'Heartland's Blackberry Butterfly'	WDib
hirsuta	WDib
'Jester' ♀H1b	WDib
'Lilla Gubben'	WDib
'Manchu'	WDib
'Marquis de Sade'	WDib
'Queen Victoria'	WDib
I ***sciadotydaea***	WDib
'Silver Feather'	WDib
§ 'Sunrise'	WDib
'Sunshine'	see *K.* 'Sunrise'
'Texas Rainbow'	WDib
warszewiczii ♀H1b	WDib
'Yf's Emma'	WDib
'Yf's Josse'	WDib

kohlrabi see AGM Vegetables Section

Kolkwitzia (*Caprifoliaceae*)

amabilis	CExl CSBt CTri ELan EPfP GBin SavN SGol SPlb SRms WCFE WSHC
- DREAM CATCHER ('Maradco')	CMac MAsh MRav NEoE NLar NOra SGol WSpi
- 'Pink Cloud' misapplied	see *K. amabilis* 'Rosea'
- 'Pink Cloud' ♀H6	Widely available
§ - 'Rosea' **new**	CBrac

Kosteletzkya (*Malvaceae*)

virginica	MHol

kumquat see *Citrus japonica*

Kunzea (*Myrtaceae*)

ambigua	CTsd EBee SPlb
- pink-flowered	SEle
'Badja Carpet'	SEle

	baxteri	CPbh
	ericifolia	SPlb
§	***ericoides***	CTsd GPoy
	parvifolia	SPlb
	pauciflora	SPlb

L

Lablab (*Papilionaceae*)

§	***purpureus***	CLau
	- 'Ruby Moon'	CSpe MGil XAbr

+ *Laburnocytisus* (*Papilionaceae*)

	'Adamii'	CMac EBee ELan EPfP ESwi LSRN MGil MGos NLar NOrn SPer

Laburnum ✿ (*Papilionaceae*)

	alpinum	SPlb SavN
§	- 'Pendulum'	CCVT ELan LCro LSRN MAsh MGos MRav NOrn SGol SPer SPoG
§	***anagyroides***	MMuc SEND SRms WMou
	- 'Erect'	SPoG WMat
	- 'Yellow Rocket' **new**	WMat
	'Famous Walk'	see *L.* × *watereri* 'Vossii'
	'Pendula'	see *L. alpinum* 'Pendulum'
	vulgare	see *L. anagyroides*
§	× ***watereri*** 'Vossii' 🏆H6	Widely available
*	- 'Vossii Pendulum'	CCVT

Lachenalia ✿ (*Asparagaceae*)

§	***aloides***	CGrW CPbh SDeJ
	- var. ***aurea***	see *L. flava*
	- var. ***luteola***	see *L. flava*
	- var. ***quadricolor***	see *L. quadricolor*
	bifolia	see *L. bulbifera*
§	***bulbifera*** 🏆H2	GKev WCot
	- 'George' 🏆H2	WCot
	contaminata 🏆H2	CGrW CPbh
	ensifolia	WCot
§	***flava*** 🏆H2	CAby CPbh SGro WCot
	kliprandensis	GKev
	liliiflora	CGrW
§	***longituba*** 🏆H2	CPBP
	'Nelsonii'	SGro WCot
	obscura	WCot
	orthopetala	WCot
I	'Pearsonii'	SPlb
	pendula	see *L. bulbifera*
	pustulata blue-flowered	CGrW
§	***pygmaea***	CPBP
§	***quadricolor*** 🏆H2	CGrW CTsd WCot
	'Romaud' (African Beauty Series)	SDeJ
	'Romelia' (African Beauty Series)	WCot
	'Rosabeth' (African Beauty Series)	WCot
	rubida	WCot
	'Rupert' (African Beauty Series) 🏆H2	SDeJ WCot
	tricolor	see *L. aloides*
	unicolor	WCot
	zeyheri	WCot

Lactuca (*Asteraceae*)

	alpina	see *Cicerbita alpina*
	perennis	EPPr WHer

Lagarostrobos ✿ (*Podocarpaceae*)

§	***franklinii***	CBcs IDee WPGP

Lagenaria (*Cucurbitaceae*)

	siceraria 'Speckled Swan'	SVic

Lagerstroemia (*Lythraceae*)

	indica 🏆H3	CBod CCCN EPfP ILea MGil SCob SEND SEle SPlb SVen WFar
	- B&SWJ 12660	WCru
	- BERRY DAZZLE ('Gamad VI')	LCro LOPS
	- BRAISE D'ÉTÉ ('Indybra'PBR) (Indya Charms Series) **new**	ILea
	- 'Cedar Lane Red'	see *L. indica* 'Cedar Red'
§	- 'Cedar Red'	WPGP
	- 'Red Imperator'	CBcs
	- RHAPSODY IN PINK ('Whit VIII')	CBcs ELan LRHS
	- 'Rosea'	CBcs LRHS SEND
	- (With Love Series) WITH LOVE BABE ('Milaperi'PBR)	SPoG
	- - WITH LOVE CHERIE ('Cov')	SPoG
	- - WITH LOVE VIRGIN ('Milabla'PBR)	LCro LOPS
	STRAWBERRY DAZZLE ('Piilag-II')	LRHS
	subcostata CWJ 12352	WCru
	'Tuscarora'	WPGP
	'Tuskegee'	WPGP

Lagotis (*Plantaginaceae*)

	glauca	GEdr
	takedana	GEdr

Lagunaria (*Malvaceae*)

	patersonii	LRHS

Lagurus (*Poaceae*)

	ovatus	SAdn SPhx

Lamiastrum see *Lamium*

Lamium (*Lamiaceae*)

	album	CHab
	- 'Friday' (v)	NBir
	armenum	WAbe
	- subsp. ***sintenisii***	WAbe
§	***galeobdolon***	CTri CWld EShb NAts SPhx SRms WHer WWtn XSen
§	- 'Florentinum' (v)	CMac ECha GQue MMuc MRav SCob WCAu WFar WSFF
	- 'Hermann's Pride'	CBod CRos EHyd ELan EPfP GMaP LRHS NBir NDov NMir NRHS SCob SPer SPoG SRms SWvt WAul XLum
	- 'Kirkcudbright Dwarf'	EPPr EWes GBin WFar XLum
§	- 'Silberteppich'	ECha MRav XLum
	- 'Silver Angel'	XLum
	- SILVER CARPET	see *L. galeobdolon* 'Silberteppich'
	- 'Variegatum'	see *L. galeobdolon* 'Florentinum'
	garganicum subsp. ***garganicum***	EWes
	- subsp. ***pictum***	see *L. garganicum* subsp. *striatum*
	- subsp. ***reniforme***	see *L. garganicum* subsp. *striatum*
§	- subsp. ***striatum***	CDor WAbe
	LAMI DARK PURPLE (Lami Series)	EHyd LRHS NRHS

luteum	see *L. galeobdolon*
maculatum	GWyn MMuc SRms WCot WWtn
- 'Album'	EPfP SHar SPer SRms WWtn
- 'Anne Greenaway' (v)	EWes LPot SCob
§ - 'Aureum'	ECtt SWvt WFar XLum
- 'Beacon Silver'	CMac EBee ECha ECtt EHyd ELan EMor EPfP EShb GWyn LCro LOPS LPot LRHS MGos MMuc NBir NRHS SCob SPer SPlb SPoG SRms SWvt WFar XLum
- 'Brightstone Pearl'	ELon EWes EWld SHar
- 'Cannon's Gold'	ECtt SWvt
- 'Chequers' ambig.	EBee
- 'Chequers Board'	GAbr
- 'Dingle Candy'	MHCG
- 'Forncett Lustre'	EWes
- 'Ghost'	ECtt ELon EPPr EPfP LBuc LRHS NLar SCob SRms
- 'Gold Leaf'	see *L. maculatum* 'Aureum'
- GOLDEN ANNIVERSARY ('Dellam'PBR) (v)	EHyd ELan GJos LRHS LSRN NBro NRHS SWvt
- 'Golden Nuggets'	see *L. maculatum* 'Aureum'
- 'Golden Wedding'	SRms
- 'James Boyd Parselle'	WCot
- LAMI MEGA PURPLE (Lami Series)	EBee
- 'Margery Fish'	SRms
- 'Orchid Frost'	EBee ELon GQue
- PINK CHABLIS ('Checkin'PBR)	ELon MHol MRav NCou NLar SPer
- 'Pink Nancy'	SWvt
- 'Pink Pearls'	CSBt NLar SHar
- 'Pink Pewter'	CBod CRos EBee ECha ECtt EHyd ELan EMor EPfP EShb GMaP GWyn LRHS NRHS SCob SHar SPer SPlb SPoG SRms WWtn
- 'Purple Dragon'	SPoG
- 'Red Nancy'	CRos EHyd ELan EMor EPfP LRHS NLar NRHS SCob SWvt XLum
§ - 'Roseum'	EBee ELan EPfP GWyn MCot MRav SPer XLum
- 'Shell Pink'	see *L. maculatum* 'Roseum'
- 'Silver Shield'	EWes
- 'White Nancy'	CBod CRos CSBt EBee ECha ECtt EHyd ELan EMor EPfP EWTr GJos GMaP GWyn LPot LRHS LSRN MBel MBros MCot MRav NBir NGrd NRHS SCob SPer SPoG SRms SWvt WCAu
- 'Wootton Pink'	MHCG NBir SWvt
'Marshmallow'	ELon
orvala	Widely available
- 'Album'	CDor CExl CMiW EBee EMor EPPr GBin LEdu LPla LRHS MAvo MBel MBriF NBir NLar SEND WCAu WHer
- 'Silva'	CExl EPPr EPfP LEdu LRHS WCot WMal
purpureum	GJos WSFF
sandrasicum	CPBP WAbe

Lampranthus (*Aizoaceae*)

sp.	CDoC
aberdeenensis	see *Delosperma aberdeenense*
apricot-flowered	CRos EHyd LRHS NRHS
aurantiacus	CBcs
blandus	CBcs CCCN
'Blousey Pink'	SVen
§ ***brownii***	CBcs CCCN CRos EHyd ELan EPfP LRHS NRHS SPlb
coccineus	CPla
deltoides	see *Oscularia deltoides*
edulis	see *Carpobrotus edulis*
'Exposure'	CCCN SSim
glaucus	SEND
multiradiatus	SEND
oscularis	see *Oscularia deltoides*
'Pink'	CPla ELan SPlb SSim
purple-flowered	CBod SPlb WABo
roseus	CCCN CRos CSma EHyd LRHS NRHS
'Salmon Pink'	SPlb
'Shanklin'	SPlb SVen
spectabilis	CBcs CCCN CTri GLet SSut
- orange-flowered	CBod SSim WFar
- purple-flowered	CPla ELon SPlb SSim
- 'Tresco Apricot'	CCCN
- 'Tresco Brilliant'	CBod CCCN ELon MBros SSim WABo
- 'Tresco Fire'	CCCN CExl CSma ELon SPlb SRms SVen
- 'Tresco Orange'	CCCN CPla
- 'Tresco Peach'	CCCN
- 'Tresco Purple'	ELan
- 'Tresco Red'	CCCN CPla ELon SEND SEdd SSim
- white-flowered	SPlb SSim SVen WFar
- yellow-flowered	CPla SSim SVen WFar
stipulaceus	SPlb
'Tresco Pearl'	CPla WCav
'Ventnor Red' **new**	SChr SEdd

Lamprocapnos (*Papaveraceae*)

§ ***spectabilis*** ♀H6	Widely available
- 'Alba' ♀H6	Widely available
- 'Gold Heart'PBR	CAby CBcs CWCL EBee ECha ECtt EMor EPfP GLet LRHS LSou MGos MHol MRav MSCN NBid NHpl NLar NRHS NSti SCob SPeP SPoG WCot WFar WHil WSpi
- 'Valentine' ♀H6	Widely available
- 'White Gold' **new**	GLet SPad
- 'White Heart'	WHil

Lamprothyrsus (*Poaceae*)

hieronymi	CBod CSam CSde
- RCB RA K2-2	CAby CCht CKno EBee ELon MAvo MHol WCot WPGP WRHF

Lancea (*Phrymaceae*)

tibetica	CPBP GEdr

Lantana ✿ (*Verbenaceae*)

'Calippo Tutti Frutti'	CPla LSou
camara	ELan EShb SEle
- (Lucky Series) LUCKY PEACH ('Balucpea')	SPoG
- - LUCKY PURE GOLD ('Balucpure'PBR)	SPoG
- - LUCKY RED FLAME ('Balandimfla')	SPoG
- - LUCKY SUNRISE ROSE ('Balandrise'PBR)	SPoG
- - LUCKY WHITE ('Balucwite'PBR)	SPoG
- orange-flowered	CCCN
- pink-flowered	CCCN ELan
- red-flowered	CCCN
- white-flowered	CCCN
'Chapel Hill Gold'PBR	EMdy
'Dallas Red'	EHyd ELan EMdy LRHS NRHS

'Miss Huff'	ELan EMdy EPfP
§ ***montevidensis***	CSam EShb
* - ***alba***	EShb
'Pink Caprice'	ELan EPfP
'Radiation'	ELan
sellowiana	see *L. montevidensis*
'Sunny Side Up'PBR	EMdy

Lapageria ✿ (*Philesiaceae*)

rosea ♀H3	CCCN CExl CRHN CTsd SAdn SChF SWvt WPav
- var. ***albiflora*** ♀H3	CRHN SChF
- - 'Hugletts Blush'	SChF
- 'Beatrix Anderson'	CRHN
- 'Flesh Pink'	CExl CRHN
- 'Pink Panther'	CRHN WPav

Lapeirousia (*Iridaceae*)

cruenta	see *Freesia laxa*
laxa	see *Freesia laxa*

Lapsana (*Asteraceae*)

communis 'Inky'	CNat

Lardizabala (*Lardizabalaceae*)

biternata	see *L. funaria*
§ ***funaria***	WCru WPav

Larix ✿ (*Pinaceae*)

decidua	CCVT CMen ECrN ELan EPfP EWTr MGos MMuc SCob SEND SPlb WTSh
- 'Corley'	CKen
- 'Horstmann Recurved'	NLar SLim
- 'Krejci'	NLar
- 'Little Bogle'	CKen LRHS MBlu NLar SLim SMad
- 'Lucek'	NLar SLim
- 'Oberförster Karsten'	CKen
- 'Pendula'	CMen
- 'Puli' ♀H7	LRHS MAsh MBlu NHol NLar NOra SPer SPoG WMat
× ***eurolepis***	see *L.* × *marschlinsii*
gmelinii var. ***gmelinii***	CMen
- 'Tharandt'	CKen
§ ***kaempferi***	CCVT CMen ELan EPfP LBuc LMaj LRHS SCob SCoo SEWo WTSh
- 'Bambino'	CKen SLim
- 'Bingman'	CKen
- 'Blue Ball'	CKen NLar
- 'Blue Dwarf' ♀H7	EPfP LRHS MAsh SLim
- 'Blue Rabbit'	CKen
- 'Blue Rabbit Weeping'	SLim
- 'Cruwys Morchard'	CKen
- 'Diana'	CKen CMen LRHS MAsh NHol NLar NOrn SLim
- 'Elizabeth Rehder'	CKen
- 'Grant Haddow'	CKen
- 'Grey Pearl'	CKen LRHS MAsh SLim
- 'Hobbit'	CKen
- 'Jakobsen'	LRHS NLar
- 'Jakobsen's Pyramid'	CMen MAsh NOrn WMat
- 'Lobby Dosser'	CMen
I - 'Nana'	CKen CMen NHol
I - 'Nana Prostrata'	CKen
- 'Pendula'	EPfP SPer SPoG
- 'Pulii'	SLim
- 'Stiff Weeper' ♀H7	LRHS NLar NOrn SLim
- 'Varley'	CKen
- 'Wehlen'	CKen
- 'Wolterdingen'	CKen LRHS NLar
laricina 'Arethusa Bog'	CKen
- 'Bear Swamp'	CKen
- 'Bingman'	CKen
- 'Blue Sparkler'	NLar
- 'Greg Williams' **new**	CKen
- 'Hartwig Pine'	CKen
- 'Iron Red'	NLar
- 'Michigan Tower'	NLar
- 'Newport Beauty'	CKen
- 'Stubby'	CKen
leptolepis	see *L. kaempferi*
§ × ***marschlinsii***	MMuc
- 'Domino'	CKen CMen
- 'Gail'	CKen
- 'Julie'	CKen

Laser (*Apiaceae*)

trilobum	MAvo SPhx
- PAB 3382	LEdu WPGP

Laserpitium (*Apiaceae*)

gallicum	GPSL SPhx
halleri	SPhx
latifolium	EBee SPhx
§ ***siler***	CSpe IMou IPot MAvo MNrw NDov SPhx SPlb WHil WSHC WSpi

Lasiagrostis see *Stipa*

Lasiospermum (*Asteraceae*)

bipinnatum	SPlb

Lathraea (*Orobanchaceae*)

clandestina	CAvo

Lathyrus ✿ (*Papilionaceae*)

§ ***articulatus***	CSpe
§ ***aureus***	CBor CDor CSpe EBee EPPr EWld GEdr MCot MHer MNrw NBid NBir SBrt SPhx WAul WCAu WFar WHal WSHC
chilensis	GWyn WPav WSHC
cirrhosus	WSHC
clymenum articulatus	see *L. articulatus*
cyaneus misapplied	see *L. vernus*
davidii	EPPr LEdu SBrt WBor WCot WPav
fremontii hort.	see *L. laxiflorus*
gmelinii	SBrt
grandiflorus ♀H6	CCBP CMea NChi NHpl SBrt SMHy WCot
× ***hammettii*** 'Erewhon'	SPhx
inermis	see *L. laxiflorus*
japonicus	CEls EBee
- subsp. ***maritimus***	SPhx WCot
laevigatus	SBrt
latifolius ♀H7	CAgr CRHN CSde EPPr EPfP GQue MHol NPer SCob SRms SVic WBrk WCot WFar WHer XLum
§ - 'Albus' ♀H7	CTri SHar SRms WFar WKif XLum
- PINK PEARL	see *L. latifolius* 'Rosa Perle'
- 'Red Pearl'	CBcs CBod CRos CTsd CWGN EBee EHyd ELan EPfP GAbr LBuc LRHS LSRN MHer NLar NRHS SEND SPer SPlb SPoG SRms SWvt WFar
§ - 'Rosa Perle' ♀H7	CBcs CBod CRos CTri EBee ECha EHyd ELan EPfP LCro LOPS LRHS LSRN MRav NBir NLar NPer NRHS SPer SPoG SWvt WBor WFar XLum

	– 'Rose Queen'	GJos
	– WEISSE PERLE	see *L. latifolius* 'White Pearl'
	– 'White Pearl' misapplied	see *L. latifolius* 'Albus'
§	– 'White Pearl' ♀H7	Widely available
§	***laxiflorus***	CBor MCot WOut WSHC
	linifolius	EBee NLar SBrt
	montanus	GPoy
	nervosus	MCot SRms WMal
	niger	CFis CSpe EBee EWld LEdu MCot MHer MMrt SBut SHar
	nissolia	WSFF
	odoratus	XAbr
	– 'Albutt Blue' **new**	CSpe
	– 'Anniversary'	MCot
	– 'Beaujolais'	LCro LOPS SPhx
	– 'Beth Chatto'	MCot
	– 'Betty Maiden'	MCot
	– 'Blue Medley'	MCot
	– 'Blue Velvet'	CSpe
	– 'Bobby's Girl' ♀H3	LCro LOPS
	– 'Bristol' ♀H3 **new**	CSpe
	– 'Burnished Bronze'	MCot
	– 'Cathy' ♀H3	EPfP
	– 'Charlie's Angel' ♀H3	LCro LOPS MCot
	– 'Cupani'	LCro LOPS MNHC SPhx
	– 'Daphne'	LCro LOPS
	– 'Dark Passion'	MCot
	– 'Dawn'	MCot
	– 'Ethel Grace'	MCot
	– 'Evening Glow' ♀H3	MCot
	– 'Flora Norton'	CSpe
	– 'George Priestley'	MCot
I	– 'Gwendoline' ♀H3	LCro LOPS
	– 'Henry Eckford' **new**	SPhx
	– 'High Scent' ♀H3	LCro LOPS
	– 'Honey Pink'	MCot
	– 'Honeymoon'	MCot
	– 'Jilly' ♀H3	LCro LOPS MCot
	– 'Just Julia' ♀H3 **new**	CSpe
	– 'Karen Louise'	LCro LOPS
	– 'King Edward VII' ♀H3	LCro LOPS
	– 'Marion'	MCot
	– 'Marti Caine'	MCot
	– 'Matucana' ♀H3	CSpe ELan LCro LOPS SPhx
	– 'Midnight'	LCro LOPS
	– 'Milly'	MCot
	– 'Misty Mountain'	MCot
	– 'Mollie Rilstone'	LCro LOPS MCot
	– 'Mrs Bernard Jones' ♀H3	LCro LOPS MCot
	– 'Mrs Collier'	CSpe SPhx
	– 'Old Spice' **new**	SVic
	– 'Oxford Blue'	LCro LOPS
	– 'Painted Lady'	LCro LOPS SPhx
	– 'Pluto'	LCro LOPS
	– 'Promise'	MCot
	– 'Restormel'	MCot
	– 'Richard and Judy'	MCot
	– 'Royal Wedding'	LCro LOPS
	– SPENCER MIXED	LCro LOPS SVic
	– 'Wedding Day' ♀H3	MCot
	– 'White Frills'	LCro LOPS
	palustris	EBee LLWG MMuc SPhx SPlb
	pratensis	CHab EBee NMir SPhx WSFF
	pubescens	CRHN EBee
	roseus	EBee WSHC
	rotundifolius ♀H6	GLog SMHy SPhx WSHC
	– 'Tillyperone' ♀H7	EBee SPhx WSHC
	sativus	CSpe MCot SPhx
	subandinus	SPlb
	sylvestris	EBee NAts WBrk
	tingitanus	CSpe
	transsylvanicus	SBrt SPhx
	tuberosus	EBee LEdu WCot WSHC
	'Tubro'	EBee
	venetus	EBee EWes MNrw SPhx WSHC
§	***vernus*** ♀H6	Widely available
	– 'Albiflorus'	MNrw XEll
	– 'Alboroseus' ♀H6	CDor ELan EMor EPPr EPfP GBin ILea MAvo MNrw NBPC NBir NChi NLar SPhx SPoG SWvt WCAu WCot WFar WHoo WOut
	– var. ***albus***	CMea MNrw NChi SRms WCot
	– ***aurantiacus***	see *L. aureus*
	– 'Caeruleus'	WHoo
*	– 'Cyaneus'	CDor WCot
	– 'Dama Emily'	SHar
I	– 'Filifolius'	CSpe
	– 'Flaccidus'	CAby MAvo MNrw WCot WMal
*	– 'Gracilis'	EBee LEdu NLar SHar
	– 'Little Elf'	SHar
	– 'Madelaine'	WCot
I	– 'Pendulus'	SHar
	– purple-flowered	CRos EHyd LRHS MMuc NRHS SEND
	– 'Rainbow'	CRos EHyd EPfP LRHS NRHS
	– 'Rosenelfe'	GJos LEdu LSou MHer SAdn SPhx WCot WHal WHil
	– f. ***roseus***	CRos ECha EHyd LRHS MMuc MRav NBir NRHS SEND SRms WBrk WCot
	– 'Spring Melody'	EBee MRav SHar WCot
	– 'Subtle Hints'	SHar WCot

Latua (*Solanaceae*)

	pubiflora	WPav

Laurelia (*Atherospermataceae*)

§	***sempervirens***	WPGP
	serrata	see *L. sempervirens*

Laureliopsis (*Atherospermataceae*)

	philippiana	CBcs CMCN EBee IDee NLar WPGP

Laurentia see *Isotoma*

Laurus (*Lauraceae*)

§	***azorica***	CBcs
	canariensis	see *L. azorica*
	nobilis ♀H4	Widely available
	– f. ***angustifolia*** ♀H4	CJun CMac LRHS MBlu MHer MMuc MRav NLar SArc SEND SPoG WAvo
	– 'Aurea' ♀H4	CBcs CMac ELan ELon EPfP MHer MMuc NLar SEND SLon SPer SPoG SWvt
	– clipped pyramid	LSRN
	– 'Crispa'	MRav
	– variegated (v)	CMac SRms

Lavandula ✿ (*Lamiaceae*)

	'After Midnight'	see *L.* 'Avonview'
	'Alba'	see *L. angustifolia* 'Alba', *L.* × *intermedia* 'Alba'
	'Alba' ambig.	SPer
§	***angustifolia***	CBee CCBP CCVT CRos EBee ECul EHyd ENfk EPfP GPoy GWyn LCro LOPS LRHS LSRN MGos MHer MHol MPri NGdn NPer NRHS SCob SDow SEdi SLim SPlb SPoG XLum XSen

- 'Alba' misapplied	see *L. angustifolia* 'Blue Mountain White'
§ - 'Alba'	ELan EPfP GPoy MHer MSwo SCob SEdi SLon SPlb SVen SVic WAvo WGwG WJek WLov WSpi XSen
- 'Alba Nana'	see *L. angustifolia* 'Nana Alba'
- 'Arctic Snow'	CBcs CRos EHyd ENor EPfP LCro LOPS LRHS MAsh MHer MSwo NGdn NRHS SDow SFai SGol SPoG SRms WLav WSpi XSen
- AROMATICO BLUE ('Lablusa'[PBR])	CRos EHyd LRHS NRHS
- AROMATICO FORTE BLUE ('Laa20001')	CRos EHyd LRHS NRHS SPoG
- AROMATICO SILVER ('Lasila')	EHyd LRHS
- 'Ashdown Forest'	EBee ELan ENfk EWhm MNHC SAdn SDow SFai SPer SRms SSut WLav WSpi XSen
- 'Backhouse Purple'	SDow
- 'Beechwood Blue' ♀H5	SDow WLav
- 'Betty's Blue'	SDow
- BLUE CUSHION ('Schola'[PBR])	ELan LCro LOPS MAsh SFai SPoG SRms WLav
- BLUE ICE ('Dow3'[PBR])	ENor NLar SAko SDow SFai SGol WLav XSen
- 'Blue Lance'	MHol
§ - 'Blue Mountain White'	WLav XSen
- 'Blue Rider'	LRHS NRHS WLav
- BLUE SCENT ('Syngablusc')	LRHS
§ - 'Bowles's Early'	WGwG
- 'Bowles's Grey'	see *L. angustifolia* 'Bowles's Early'
- 'Bowles's Variety'	see *L. angustifolia* 'Bowles's Early'
- 'Cedar Blue'	ELan EWhm MHer MHol SDow SRms WLav
- 'Coconut Ice'	ELan WLav WSpi XSen
- 'Compacta'	SDow WLav
- 'Contrast' **new**	GBin
- 'De Lagrasse' **new**	XAbr
- 'Dursley White'	WLav
- 'Dwarf Blue'	CBod LSRN MHed SRms WFar XSen
- ELIZABETH ('Fair 16'[PBR])	ENor LSRN SDow SFai SPoG WLav XSen
- (Ellagance Series) 'Ellagance Ice'	LSou SRms
- - 'Ellagance Pink'[PBR]	MBros
- - 'Ellagance Purple'	CRos LRHS LSou MBros SRms XSen
- - 'Ellagance Sky'	LSou MBros MHol SRms
- 'Essence Purple'	CBod
- 'Felice'[PBR]	LRHS
- 'Folgate' ♀H5	CBod ECtt EWhm MHer MNHC NGdn SDow SEdi SRms WHoo WLav WSpi
- 'Forever Blue' **new**	MHol SFai
- GARDEN BEAUTY ('Lowmar'[PBR]) (v)	MAsh XSen
- GRANNY'S BOUQUET ('Lavang38')	GWyn WSpi XSen
- HAVANA ('Arbelpaso'[PBR])	EBee LRHS MAsh MHol SPoG XSen
§ - 'Hidcote' ♀H5	Widely available
- 'Hidcote Pink'	CBrac EWhm MHer MNHC MRav NGdn SCob SDow SEdi SPer SRms
- 'Hidcote Superior'	NGdn
- 'Imperial Gem' ♀H5	Widely available
- 'Jean Davis'	see *L. angustifolia* 'Rosea'
- 'Lady'	NPer WSpi
- 'Lady Ann'	SDow WLav
- 'Lavenite Magic Blue Chip' **new**	NLar
- 'Lavenite Petite'[PBR]	EHyd ENor LRHS LSRN SFai WLav WSpi XSen
- LITTLE LADY ('Batlad') ♀H5	CMea ECtt ENor LCro LOPS LRHS LSRN MAsh MHed MNHC MSwo NLar NRHS SAko SCob SFai SGol SPoG SRms SWvt WCav WHoo WLav WSpi XSen
- LITTLE LOTTIE ('Clarmo') ♀H5	EWhm MHer SDow SEdi WLav WRHF XSen
- 'Loddon Blue'	CRos EHyd ENor EPfP EWhm LRHS MAsh NRHS SDow SFai SRms WLav WSpi XSen
§ - 'Loddon Pink'	CRos EHyd ELan ENor EPfP EWhm GMaP LRHS MAsh MMuc MRav NGdn NRHS SEND SEdi SFai SRms WAvo WLav WLov XSen
- 'Lullaby Blue'	SDow
- 'Maillette'	NGdn SDow SRms WLav
- 'Melissa'	MHol XSen
- MELISSA LILAC ('Dow4'[PBR])	CBcs CRos CSBt EHyd ENfk ENor LCro LOPS LRHS LSRN MAsh MGos MHer MHol MNHC NRHS SCob SDow SFai SRkn SRms WLav XSen
- 'Middachten'	EHyd XSen
- 'Miss Dawnderry'	SDow
- 'Miss Donnington'	see *L. angustifolia* 'Bowles's Early'
- 'Miss Katherine'[PBR] ♀H5	ECtt ENor EPfP LRHS MAsh MHed NLar SDow SPoG WLav XSen
- MISS MUFFET ('Scholmis') ♀H5	SDow SRms WLav XSen
- 'Munstead'	Widely available
§ - 'Nana Alba' ♀H5	CMea CRos EHyd ELan ENfk EPfP EWhm GMaP GPoy LRHS MAsh MHer SEdi SPer SRms SWvt WSpi XSen
- 'Nana Atropurpurea'	SDow XSen
- 'Nikita'	XSen
- 'No 9'	SDow
- 'Pacific Blue'	SDow XSen
- 'Peter Pan'	ECtt ELan GBin MAsh MHer MNHC SCob SDow WLav XSen
- PLATINUM BLONDE ('Momparler'[PBR])	CNor CRos EHyd ENor LRHS LSou MAsh NRHS SCob SPoG XSen
- 'Princess Blue'	ENor LRHS SEdi WLav
- 'Princess Rose' **new**	XAbr
- 'Purity'	SDow
- 'Purple Treasure'	SDow
§ - 'Rosea'	CRos CSBt EAJP ECha EHyd ELan ENfk EPfP GPoy LCro LOPS LRHS MAsh MHer MNHC MRav NBir SCob SDow SFai SGol SPer SPlb SPoG SRms SWvt WLav XSen
- 'Royal Blue'	LRHS
- 'Royal Purple'	EWes NGdn SDow SSut SWvt WLav WRHF XSen
- 'Royal Velvet'	SDow
- 'Saint Jean'	SDow
- 'Siesta'	GBin XSen
- 'Silver Blue'	XSen
- 'Silver Mist'	CBod CMea SRms WHer XSen
- 'Sophie'	XSen
- 'Thumbelina Leigh'[PBR]	ENor MAsh SFai SRms WSpi XSen
- 'Twickel Purple'	CBar CBcs CRos CWld EBee EHyd ELan EPfP LRHS LSRN MAsh MHed MHol MNHC NRHS SCob SDow SEdi SFai SGbt SPer SRms SWvt WLav WSpi XSen
- 'Walberton's Silver Edge'	see *L. × intermedia* WALBERTON'S SILVER EDGE

	aristibracteata	MHer WLav
§	'Avonview'	MHer WLav
	'Ballerina' ♀H4	SDow
§	'Bee Brilliant'[PBR]	ENfk EWhm WLav
§	'Bee Cool'[PBR]	ENfk WLav
§	'Bee Happy'	ENfk EWhm NBir WLav
§	'Bee Pretty'	ENfk EWhm
	'Blue Star'	EPfP EWhm MNHC WGwG
	'Bouquet of Roses'	CRos EHyd LRHS NRHS
	buchii var. ***buchii***	SDow SVen WLav
	'Bulls Cross'	WLav
	canariensis	MHer SDow SVen WLav
	× ***chaytoriae*** 'Bridehead Blue'	SDow
	- 'Gorgeous'	SDow
	- 'Joan Head'	XSen
	- 'Molton Silver'	XSen
	- 'Richard Gray' ♀H4	LRHS LSRN MHed MHer MNHC SDow SRms WAvo WLav XSen
§	- 'Sawyers' ♀H4	CBod CBrac CRos EHyd EPfP EShb GMaP LRHS LSRN MAsh MHed MHer MNHC MRav NBir NPer NRHS SDow SEND SGol SPer SPhx SPoG SRms WMal XSen
	- 'Silver Sands'	CBcs EBee ELan EPfP MCot SFai SPoG XSen
	× ***christiana***	EHyd ENor LRHS MHol SDow SFai SVen WLav
	'Cornard Blue'	see *L.* × *chaytoriae* 'Sawyers'
	dentata	CBrac ENfk SEND SRms WJek XAbr XSen
§	- var. ***candicans***	MHer SDow SRms WLav
	- var. ***dentata*** 'Dusky Maiden'	SDow WLav
	- - 'Ploughman's Blue'	SVen WGwG
	- - f. ***rosea***	SDow
	- - 'Royal Crown' ♀H3	WLav
	- silver-leaved	see *L. dentata* var. *candicans*
	'Devonshire Compact'	CSBt MHol SRms
	'Fathead'	CBcs CBod CBrac CChe CRos EHyd ELan EPfP LRHS LSRN MAsh MGos MHer MNHC NBir NGdn NLar SCob SCoo SDow SFai SGol SPoG WAvo WLav
	'Flaming Purple'	SDow
	× ***ginginsii*** 'Goodwin Creek Grey' ♀H4	MHer SDow SGol SRms WLav
	'Hazel'	CRos EHyd EPfP LRHS NRHS
	'Helmsdale'[PBR]	CBcs CEnd CRos CSBt ELan ENor EPfP GMaP LRHS LSRN MAsh NLar SCoo SFai SGol SLim SPer
	heterophylla misapplied	see *L.* × *heterophylla* Viv. Gaston Allard Group
§	× ***heterophylla*** Viv. Gaston Allard Group	WLav
	- - 'African Pride'	SVen
	- - 'Meerlo'	MHol SFai
	'Hidcote Blue'	see *L. angustifolia* 'Hidcote'
	× ***intermedia*** 'Abrialii'	SDow
§	- 'Alba' ♀H5	CMea MHed MHer MNHC SEND SEdi SGbt SPer SVen XSen
	- 'Anniversary Bouquet'	SDow SFai
	- 'Arabian Night'	see *L.* × *intermedia* 'Impress Purple', 'Sussex'
	- 'Arabian Night' ambig.	SRms
§	- Dutch Group	CBod CSBt EHyd ENfk EPfP LRHS MAsh MNHC MRav MSwo SArc SCob SCoo SFai SLim SPer SRms SVic XSen

	- 'Edelweiss'	CBcs CBod CRos CSBt EAJP ECul EHyd ENfk EPfP EWhm LRHS MAsh MNHC MRav NLar NRHS SDow SEdi SFai SGol SPer SPoG SRms SWvt WGwG WLav WSpi XSen
§	- 'Enigma'	CBar
	- 'Fragrant Memories'	SDow SRms WLav XSen
	- 'Fred Boutin'	WSpi
	- GOLDBURG ('Burgoldeen') (v)	SGol
	- 'Grappenhall' misapplied	see *L.* × *intermedia* 'Enigma', 'Pale Pretender'
	- 'Grappenhall' ambig.	EWhm MNHC WSpi XSen
	- 'Grey Hedge'	SRms WLav
	- 'Gros Bleu'	SDow SFai WLav
	- 'Grosso'	Widely available
	- (Heavenly Series) HEAVENLY ANGEL ('Dowphangel'[PBR])	ENor SAko SDow XSen
	- - HEAVENLY NIGHT ('Dowphnight'[PBR])	LSRN SDow XSen
	- - HEAVENLY SCENT ('Dowphscent')	ENor SDow XSen
	- 'Hidcote Giant' ♀H5	CRos EHyd EPfP LRHS NPer NRHS SDow WKif WLav WSpi XSen
§	- 'Impress Purple'	SDow WAvo WLav XSen
	- 'Lullingstone Castle'	ENfk EWhm SIvy SRms SSut WAvo WLav
	- 'Old English' misapplied	see *L.* × *intermedia* 'Seal'
	- 'Old English'	CBod CBrac CLau ENfk SDow SRms SWeb
	- Old English Group	MMuc MNHC SEND WHoo WLav XSen
	- OLYMPIA ('Downoly'[PBR])	MHol NLar SAko SDow SPoG XSen
§	- 'Pale Pretender'	CSBt GQue MHer MSwo SPer SRms
	- PHENOMENAL ('Niko'[PBR])	ENor LCro LOPS LSRN NDov NLar SFai WNPC XSen
	- 'Provence'	NLar SDow SFai SRms XSen
§	- 'Seal'	ENfk GMaP MNHC SDow SRms
§	- 'Sussex' ♀H5	CBod CFis CRos EHyd EPfP LRHS NRHS SDow WLav
	- 'Twickel Purple'	ELan EWes SGol
§	- WALBERTON'S SILVER EDGE ('Walvera') (v)	CRos EHyd ELan EPfP LBuc LRHS MGos NRHS SCoo SDow SRms
	'Jamboree'	WLav
	'Jean Davis'	see *L. angustifolia* 'Rosea'
	lanata ♀H3	ECha SRms WLav XSen
§	***latifolia***	XAbr XSen
	'Loddon Pink'	see *L. angustifolia* 'Loddon Pink'
	'Madrid Blue'	see *L.* 'Bee Happy'
	'Madrid Pink'	see *L.* 'Bee Pretty'
	'Madrid Purple'	see *L.* 'Bee Brilliant'
	'Madrid White'	see *L.* 'Bee Cool'
	minutolii	SDow
	multifida	MHer WLav
	- 'Spanish Eyes'	MBros
	officinalis	see *L. angustifolia*
	PASSIONNÉ ('Lavsts 08'[PBR]) ♀H4	WLav
	pedunculata	EBee ENor XSen
	- subsp. ***lusitanica***	CRos EHyd EPfP LRHS NRHS SPoG
	- - LUSI PINK ('Wijs02'[PBR])	CRos ENfk SFai
	- - 'Lusi Purple'	CRos EHyd LRHS NRHS SFai SPoG
§	- subsp. ***pedunculata***	CAby CBar CBrac CRos ECha EHyd ELan EPau EPfP LCro LOPS LRHS LSRN MAsh MBow MGos MNHC MSwo NGdn NRHS SCob SDow SFai SGbt SGol SPer SRms WAvo WSpi
	- - 'James Compton' ♀H3	CRos ECha EHyd LRHS MAsh NGdn
	- subsp. ***sampaiana*** 'Purple Emperor'	CRos EHyd EPfP LRHS NRHS WLav

pinnata	ENfk ENor MHol SDow
'Pretty Polly' 🏆H4	CBcs CRos EHyd ELan EPfP LRHS MAsh NLar SDow SFai SRkn WLav XSen
'Pukehou'	CRos EHyd EPfP LRHS NRHS SCoo WLav
'Purple Ribbon'	LRHS
'Regal Splendour'PBR	CRos CSBt EHyd ELan ENor EPfP LRHS LSRN MAsh MGos MHer MPri NRHS SCoo SDow SFai SGol SLim SPoG SRms WLav
ROCKY ROAD ('Fair09'PBR)	CSBt ENor SFai WLav
'Rosea'	see *L. angustifolia* 'Rosea'
rotundifolia	SDow
'Silver Edge'	see *L.* × *intermedia* WALBERTON'S SILVER EDGE
'Silver Line'	CRos EHyd LRHS NRHS
SILVER SANDS ('Fair 14'PBR)	ENfk
'Somerset Mist'	WLav
spica nom. rejic.	see *L. angustifolia*, *L. latifolia*
- 'Hidcote Purple'	see *L. angustifolia* 'Hidcote'
stoechas	CBcs CBod CRos CSBt ECha EHyd ELan EPfP GMaP GPoy LRHS LSRN MGil MNHC MSwo NRHS SCob SDow SPer SPlb SWeb SWvt WCav
- var. ***albiflora***	see *L. stoechas* subsp. *stoechas* f. *leucantha*
- 'Anouk'PBR	EBee ELan EPfP LRHS SPoG
- 'Antibes' (Provençal Series)	SRms
- 'Arles' (Provençal Series)	CPla
- 'Bandera'	MBros
- (Bella Series) BELLA LAVENDER ('Bellav')	CRos EHyd LRHS NRHS
- - BELLA ROSE ('Belros')	CRos EHyd EPfP LRHS NRHS
- 'Blueberry Ruffles'PBR (Ruffles Series)	ELan
- 'Boysenberry Ruffles'PBR (Ruffles Series)	ELan ENfk XSen
- 'Dark Royalty'PBR	ELan SCob
- JAVELIN BLUE ('Jin Bulle') (Javelin Series)	CRos EHyd LRHS NRHS
- LAVENDER LACE ('Colace')	WLav
- LITTLE BEE DEEP PURPLE ('Florvendula Deep Purple') (Little Bee Series)	EHyd LRHS
- 'Mulberry Ruffles'PBR (Ruffles Series)	ELan SCob
- 'Night of Passion'	SDow
- 'Papillon'	see *L. pedunculata* subsp. *pedunculata*
- subsp. ***pedunculata***	see *L. pedunculata* subsp. *pedunculata*
- 'Purley'	SRms
- Ruffles Series	ENfk
- 'Silver Anouk'PBR	EPfP LRHS
- 'Spring-break Princess'	CRos EHyd LRHS NRHS
§ - subsp. ***stoechas*** f. ***leucantha***	EPfP MSwo SDow
- - - 'Snowman'	CBcs CRos CSBt EHyd EPfP LRHS MAsh MHer NLar NRHS SCob SCoo SFai SPoG SWvt
- - LILAC WINGS ('Prolil'PBR)	CRos EHyd ENor EPfP LRHS NRHS SCoo SDow SFai WLav
- - 'Provençal'	CRos EHyd LRHS NRHS SCoo
- - 'Purple Wings'	CRos EHyd ELan EPfP LRHS MAsh MGos SLim
- - f. ***rosea***	ENor
- - - 'Kew Red'	CBrac CTri ENfk GQue LRHS MGos MHer SFai SRms SWvt WLav
- 'Sugarberry Ruffles'PBR (Ruffles Series)	ENfk
- 'Victory'	CRos EHyd LRHS NRHS SPoG
- 'With Love'PBR	SDow
SUPERBLUE ('Balavurlu') **new**	LSou
TIARA ('Fair 10'PBR)	CRos CSBt EHyd ENfk ENor LRHS MGos NEoE NLar NRHS SCob SCoo SFai SPad SPoG SRms WLav
'Van Gogh'	SDow
vera misapplied	see *L.* × *intermedia* Dutch Group
vera DC.	see *L. angustifolia*
viridis	CRos EHyd ELan EPfP LRHS MHer NPer NRHS SDow SRms WJek WLav
'Whero Iti'	SDow
'Willow Vale' 🏆H3	CRos EHyd ENor EPfP EWhm LRHS MAsh MHer NRHS SDow SWvt WAvo WJek

Lavatera (*Malvaceae*)

arborea	CPla SChr SEND WHer
- 'Rosea'	see *L.* × *clementii* 'Rosea'
- 'Variegata' (v)	CPla ELan MAvo NPer SEND WCot
bicolor	see *L. maritima*
BLUE BIRD ('Renlav') **new**	CRos MNrw
cachemiriana	NPer
CHAMALLOW ('Inovera'PBR)	CRos LRHS LSRN
× ***clementii*** 'Barnsley'	Widely available
- 'Barnsley Baby'	CBod CRos EBee EHyd ELan EPfP LBuc LRHS MAsh MTin NGdn NLar NPer SChF SCob SEle SGbt SPer SPoG SRkn SWvt WFar WNPC
- 'Blushing Bride'	CRos EPfP LRHS MGos NLar SCob SPer SWvt
- 'Bredon Springs' 🏆H5	CBod CBrac CRos CSBt EBee ECha EHyd ELon EPfP LRHS LSRN MAsh MGos MMuc MSwo NGdn NRHS SCob SEND SGbt SGol SLim SPer SWvt WAvo XLum
- 'Burgundy Wine' 🏆H5	CBcs CBod CBrac CDoC CMac CRos EBee EHyd ELan EPfP LRHS MAsh MGos MNHC MPri MSwo NBir NLar NPer NRHS SGbt SGol SLim SLon SPer SPoG SWvt WAvo WFar WMal
- 'Candy Floss' 🏆H5	CBrac LRHS NBir NLar NPer SGol
- 'Eye Catcher'	CBod CBrac LRHS MSwo NLar SPer
- 'Kew Rose'	MMuc MSwo NLar NPer SEND SLim SRms XLum
- 'Lavender Lady'	NPer SEND
- 'Lisanne'	EHyd LRHS MMuc MSwo SGol
- 'Mary Hope' 🏆H5	CDoC CRos EBee EHyd EPfP EWld LRHS MAsh NRHS SEle SWvt
- MEMORIES ('Stelav')	LRHS
- 'Pavlova'	CExl
§ - 'Pink Frills'	SWvt WCot WFar
- RED RUM ('Rigrum'PBR) 🏆H5	CDoC CMac CRos CSBt EBee EHyd EPfP LBuc LRHS LSRN MAsh MGos MHol MPri NLar NRHS SCob SEND SLim SPoG SWvt WFar
§ - 'Rosea' 🏆H5	CBcs CBod CBrac CDoC CMac CRos EBee EHyd EPfP LCro LOPS LRHS LSRN MAsh MGos MPri NBir NHol NRHS SCob SGbt SGol SLon SPer SPoG SWvt
- RUBY STAR ('Jostar'PBR)	CRos EBee EHyd LRHS NRHS
- 'Songbird'	NRHS SEle SPad
§ - 'Wembdon Variegated' (v)	NPer

'Frederique'	CMac CRos LRHS SWvt WKif
'Grey Beauty'	LRHS
'Magenta Magic'PBR	MHol SPoG
§ ***maritima*** ♀H3	CBod CDoC CExl CMac CRos CSde ELan EPfP LRHS MNHC SEND SEle SRkn SRms SWvt WCFE WCot WFar WKif WOut WSMil
- 'Princesse de Lignes'	XLum
olbia	SDix SPlb SRms WFar
- 'Lilac Lady'	CBod ECha ECrN ELan EWTr MGos MMuc SGol WFar WKif
'Peppermint Ice'	see *L. thuringiaca* 'Ice Cool'
phoenicea new	WMal
'Pink Frills'	see *L.* × *clementii* 'Pink Frills'
'Rosea'	see *L.* × *clementii* 'Rosea'
tauricensis	MAvo
thuringiaca	LPla
- 'First Light'	SPhx
§ - 'Ice Cool'	SCob SWvt WKif
trimestris 'Silver Cup' ♀H3 new	LCro LOPS
'Variegata'	see *L.* × *clementii* 'Wembdon Variegated'
'White Satin'PBR	NHol NLar

Lawsonia (*Lythraceae*)

inermis	WSFF

Ledebouria (*Asparagaceae*)

adlamii	see *L. cooperi*
concolor misapplied	see *L. socialis*
§ ***cooperi***	CBor EAJP EHyd ELan EPri EShb GKev LEdu LRHS MPie SBrt WBor WPGP XLum
'Gary Hammer'	SBrt
ovalifolia	NWad
§ ***socialis***	EShb LEdu MCot MPie SGro SIvy WCot WFar WOld
- green-leaved	EShb
violacea	see *L. socialis*

Ledum see *Rhododendron*

leek see AGM Vegetables Section

Leibnitzia (*Asteraceae*)

anandria	EPPr

Leiophyllum see *Kalmia*

Lembotropis see *Cytisus*

Lemna (*Araceae*)

gibba	NPer
minor	CWat NPer
polyrrhiza	see *Spirodela polyrrhiza*
trisulca	CWat EWat NPer

lemon see *Citrus* × *limon*

lemon balm see *Melissa officinalis*

lemon grass see *Cymbopogon citratus*

lemon, rough see *Citrus* × *taitensis*

lemon verbena see *Aloysia citrodora*

lemonquat see *Citrus* × *taitensis* × *Citrus* × *limon*

Leonotis (*Lamiaceae*)

leonurus	CBcs CCCN CDTJ CSam ECre EMdy EShb EWes LRHS SMad SPlb XLum
- var. ***albiflora***	CCCN EShb
nepetifolia	CCCN
var. ***nepetifolia*** 'Staircase'	
§ ***ocymifolia***	CCCN CExl

Leontice (*Berberidaceae*)

albertii	see *Gymnospermium albertii*

Leontochir see *Bomarea*

Leontodon (*Asteraceae*)

hispidus	CHab NMir
§ ***rigens***	ELan GEdr MMuc NBid NBir SDix WFar
- B&SWJ 12527	WCru WSHC
- 'Girandole'	see *L. rigens*

Leontopodium (*Asteraceae*)

alpinum	see *L. nivale* subsp. *alpinum*
coreanum	GKev
discolor	WAbe
himalayanum	GKev
kurilense	GKev
nanum	GKev SPlb
§ ***nivale*** subsp. ***alpinum***	CPla CTri EBou ELan EPfP GKev ITim MAsh MBel NHpl NSla SPlb SPoG SRms XLum
- - BLOSSOM OF SNOW ('Berghman') new	SPad
- - 'Everest'	EDAr
- - 'Matterhorn'	GEdr GMaP NLar
- - 'Mignon'	EPfP EWes GMaP WAbe
§ ***ochroleucum*** var. ***campestre***	NLar XLum
palibinianum	see *L. ochroleucum* var. *campestre*
pusillum	SPlb WAbe
souliei	NSla XLum
stracheyi	GKev

Leonurus (*Lamiaceae*)

cardiaca	CBee CBod CCBP GPoy MHer MNHC NGrd SPhx SRms
- 'Grobbebol'	EPPr WCot WHer
sibiricus L.	SPhx
turkestanicus	EBee

Leopoldia (*Asparagaceae*)

sp.	CPla
caucasica	GKev
comosa	see *Muscari comosum*
cycladica	GKev
subsp. ***subsessilis*** new	
tenuiflora	see *Muscari tenuiflorum*
weissii	GKev

Lepechinia (*Lamiaceae*)

bella	SDys
chamaedryoides	CExl
hastata	CSpe LRHS SPlb WJek WOut
salviae	WFar WHer

Lepidium (*Brassicaceae*)

campestre	CHab
latifolium	ENfk LEdu

Leptinella (*Asteraceae*)

atrata subsp. ***luteola***	ELan
'County Park'	EDAr
dendyi	ECtt ELan EWes GEdr MHer NSla WIce
dioica	GBin
- 'Minima'	WFar
hispida	see *Cotula hispida* (DC.) Harv.
§ ***pectinata***	ITim
§ ***potentillina***	CTri ECha GQue MBNS NBro NLar SRms XLum
§ ***pusilla***	MPkF
§ ***pyrethrifolia***	EDAr
reptans	see *L. scariosa*
§ ***scariosa***	GAbr
§ ***squalida***	ECha GBin MBel NSti
* - 'Minima'	WFar
§ - 'Platt's Black'	CBcs EBee EBou ECha ECtt EDAr EWes GAbr GBin GKev GQue GWyn LLWG MBel MHer MPkF NHpl NLar SDix SPtp SWvt WCav WFar WGwG XLum
traillii	NBro

Leptodermis (*Rubiaceae*)

oblonga 'Summer Stars'	LRHS

Leptopus (*Euphorbiaceae*)

§ ***chinensis***	EWTr WCot

Leptospermum ✿ (*Myrtaceae*)

citratum	see *L. petersonii*
'Copper Sheen'	CBcs CTrC
'County Park Blush'	ELon
cunninghamii	see *L. myrtifolium*
'Electric Red' (Galaxy Series)	CAbb CBod CCht CTsd EPfP LRHS MGil SEle
ericoides	see *Kunzea ericoides*
flavescens misapplied	see *L. glaucescens*
flavescens Sm.	see *L. polygalifolium*
§ ***glaucescens***	SPlb
§ ***grandiflorum***	CBcs CTrC ELan EPfP SVen
grandifolium	LRHS
'Havering Hardy'	SEle
humifusum	see *L. rupestre*
juniperinum	SPlb
'Karo Pearl Star'	CBcs CBod CTrC MGil MPkF WLov
'Karo Spectrobay'	CBcs MGil
laevigatum	SVen
§ ***lanigerum***	CExl CTri CTsd EPfP SPlb SPtp SVen
- 'Cunninghamii'	see *L. myrtifolium*
liversidgei	SPlb
§ ***myrtifolium***	CMac CTrC CTsd EWes
namadgiensis new	IDee
nitidum	SPlb
§ ***petersonii***	GPoy XAbr
phylicoides	see *Kunzea ericoides*
'Pink Cascade'	CBcs CMac CTri SEle
§ ***polygalifolium***	SPlb
prostratum	see *L. rupestre*
pubescens	see *L. lanigerum*
'Red Cascade'	SWvt
rodwayanum	see *L. grandiflorum*
rotundifolium	CBcs CCht SPlb
- from Jervis Bay	EBee
§ ***rupestre***	CTrC CTri SPlb SVen WKif
scoparium	CBee CTrC GPoy SPlb SVen WJek WKor XAbr
- 'Adrianne'	CRos EHyd EPfP LRHS NRHS
- 'Appleblossom' ♀H4	CBcs CCht CDoC CEnd CTrC EPfP SAko SEle SGol
- 'Autumn Glory'	WLov
- 'Blossom' (d)	CBcs CMac
- 'Burgundy Queen' (d)	CBcs CCCN CMac CTrC
- 'Chapmanii'	CCCN WPGP
- 'Coral Candy'	CBcs CBod CCCN CEnd MGil MPkF SGbt WFar
- 'Crimson Glory' (d)	CSBt
- 'Elizabeth Jane'	MMuc WFar
- 'Gaiety Girl' (d)	CSBt
- 'Jubilee' (d)	CBcs CCCN CMac
- 'Leonard Wilson' (d)	CTri
- 'Martini'	CAbb CBcs CCCN CDoC CMac CRos CSBt EHyd EPfP LRHS MGil MMuc MPkF NRHS SGol SIvy SPoG WLov
- (Nanum Group) 'Huia'	SCob
- - 'Kea'	CBcs MHer
- - 'Kiwi' ♀H4	CAbb CBcs CBrac CCCN CRos CSBt CTsd EBee EHyd ELan EPfP LRHS MAsh MMuc SEle SIvy SLim SLon SPoG WFar
- - 'Nanum'	CCCN
- - 'Pipit'	ITim
- - 'Tui'	CMac CSBt CTrC
- 'Nichollsii' ♀H4	CBcs SVen
- 'Nichollsii Nanum' ♀H4	ITim WAbe WThu
- 'Pink Damask'	SWvt
- var. ***prostratum*** misapplied	see *L. rupestre*
- 'Red Damask' (d) ♀H4	Widely available
- 'Red Ensign'	SPoG
- 'Red Falls'	CExl
- 'Ruby Glow' (d)	LSRN
* - 'Ruby Wedding'	CRos EHyd ELan EPfP LRHS LSRN MAsh SLon SPoG
- 'Snow Flurry'	CBcs CRos EHyd EPfP LRHS NRHS SGol SVen WFar
- 'Sunraysia'	CTsd
- 'Winter Cheer' (d)	CBcs CTrC EHyd EPfP LRHS SGol
- 'Wiri Donna'	CSde
- 'Wiri Joan' (d)	CBcs
- 'Wiri Kerry' (d)	MPkF
- 'Wiri Linda'	CBcs CMac
'Silver Sheen' ♀H3	CAbb CBcs CCCN CDoC CEnd CRos CSde CTrC ELan EPfP LRHS MAsh NLar SEdd SPer SPoG SVen WPGP

Lespedeza (*Papilionaceae*)

bicolor	CAgr CCCN LRHS MMuc WCFE WFar WSHC
- 'Yakushima'	NLar
buergeri	EHyd LRHS MMrt NLar SHar WSHC
capitata	EBee
japonica	SPlb
thunbergii ♀H5	CBcs CDoC CRos CSde EBee EHyd ELan EPfP LRHS MAsh MBlu MGil NRHS SLon SMad SPer SPoG SSta WCFE WHil WPGP WSHC
- subsp. ***formosa***	EBee MGil
- 'Gibraltar'	EBee WPGP
- 'Summer Beauty'	CBcs
- subsp. ***thunbergii*** 'Albiflora'	ELan LRHS WPGP
- - 'Edo-shibori'	EBee ELan NLar SPer WHil WPGP WSHC

- - 'White Fountain'	CRos EHyd EPfP LRHS MAsh NRHS SPoG WSHC
tiliifolia	see *Desmodium elegans*

Lesquerella (*Brassicaceae*)

arctica	WCFE
- var. ***purshii***	GKev

lettuce see AGM Vegetables Section

Leucadendron (*Proteaceae*)

argenteum	CCCN CPbh CTrC SPlb
'Bell's Supreme'	CTrC
'Burgundy Sunset'	CBcs CCCN MPkF
conicum	CPbh
'Cream Delight'	CCCN
daphnoides	SPlb
'Deacon Red'	MPkF
discolor	SPlb
eucalyptifolium	CPbh SPlb
galpinii	CPbh
gandogeri	CPbh
'Highlights'	CCCN
'Inca Gold' ♀H1c	CBcs CPbh
'Jack Harre'	LRHS MPkF
'Jester' (v)	CCCN CPbh
'Jubilee Crown'	MPkF
laureolum	CCCN CPbh
'Maui Sunset'	CTrC
modestum 'Strawberry Fair'	CCCN
'Mrs Stanley'	CTrC
'Pisa'	MPkF
'Red Dwarf'	CPbh
'Safari Magic'	CCCN
'Safari Sunset' ♀H3	CBcs CCCN CPbh CTrC CTsd IDee MPkF
salicifolium	SPlb
salignum	CCCN CPbh
- 'Fireglow'	CTrC LRHS MPkF
sessile	CPbh
strobilinum	CPbh
'Sundance'	MPkF
tinctum	CPbh

Leucaena (*Mimosaceae*)

leucocephala	SPlb

Leucanthemella (*Asteraceae*)

§ ***serotina*** ♀H7	Widely available
- 'Herbststern'	IMou NLar

Leucanthemopsis (*Asteraceae*)

§ ***alpina***	NSla
hosmariensis	see *Rhodanthemum hosmariense*

Leucanthemum ✿ (*Asteraceae*)

'Angel'	ELon MBros NCou NLar
atlanticum	see *Rhodanthemum atlanticum*
catananche	see *Rhodanthemum catananche*
hosmariense	see *Rhodanthemum hosmariense*
mawii	see *Rhodanthemum gayanum*
maximum misapplied	see *L.* × *superbum*
§ ***maximum*** (Ramond) DC.	NBro NPer
- uliginosum	see *Leucanthemella serotina*
nipponicum	see *Nipponanthemum nipponicum*
'Osiris Neige'	ECtt XLum
'Real Charmer'PBR	CRos EHyd LRHS LSou MAsh MHol NEoE NRHS SPeP SRms SWvt
'Sante'	EBee EHyd ELan EMor EPfP LRHS MHol NRHS
'Sunshine Peach'	EBee EBou EHyd LRHS
§ × ***superbum***	CMac MBow MMuc SEND WBrk
- 'Aglaia' (d)	Widely available
- 'Alaska'	CBod CExl CRos EBee EHyd ELan GAbr GBin LRHS LSun MCot NLar NRHS SPer SWvt WRHF XLum
- 'Amelia'	CRos EBee EHyd LRHS NBre NLar NRHS
- 'Anita Allen' (d)	ECtt WCot
- 'Antwerp Star'	NBre NLar WBrk
- 'Banana Cream'	CBcs CBod CRos CWGN EBee ECtt EHyd IPot LCro LEdu LRHS MAsh MBriF MBros MHol MSCN NHol NLar NRHS SCob SEle SPoG STPC WCav WFar WHoo WTor
- 'Barbara Bush' (v/d)	SWvt
§ - 'Beauté Nivelloise'	CElw ECtt EHyd EPfP GWyn IPot LRHS LSou MBel MMrt NBir SRms WFar WSpi WTor
- 'Becky'	CElw CMac CRos EBee ECha EHyd ELan ELon EWTr GBin GWyn ILea IPot LRHS LSRN MBel NEoE NLar NRHS WCAu WSpi
- 'Belgian Lace' **new**	NLar
- 'Bishopstone'	EBee ECtt ELan LEdu MSpe
- 'Bridal Bouquet'PBR	CRos ECtt EHyd LRHS NRHS
- 'Brightside'	EHyd ELan ELon EMor LRHS LSun NRHS SBut WFar
- BROADWAY LIGHTS ('Leumayel'PBR)	CRos EBee EHyd EMor EPfP EWes GBin LPot LRHS MAsh MBel MRav NBir NRHS SCob SRms WAvo WCAu WFar WGrn WHil WSpi WTor
- 'Christine Hagemann'	CElw EBee ECtt EWTr EWes ILea MNrw MRav SHar WBrk WCFE
- 'Cloud Cumulus' **new**	CBod WHil
- 'Cobham Gold' (d)	CWCL NBre
- 'Crazy Daisy'	CBod CChe CTri EAJP ECtt EHyd EMor EPfP GWyn LRHS NRHS SWvt WFar
- 'Droitwich Beauty'	ECtt MAvo WAvo WCav WHoo
- 'Dwarf Snow Lady'	NBre
- 'Edgebrook Giant'	WBrk WHil
- 'Eisstern'	EBee LEdu SHar
- 'Elworthy Sparkler'	CElw MAvo WBrk
- 'Engelina'PBR	CBod EBee ECul EPfP MBriF NBir WCAu
- 'Esther Read' (d)	EBee ECtt EHyd ELan EPau EPfP GBin LRHS LSRN NBPC NBro NChi NLar NRHS SRms SWvt WBrk WCot WFar
§ - 'Everest'	SRms
- 'Exhibition'	EHyd LRHS NRHS
- 'Fiona Coghill' (d)	CBod CElw CWGN ECtt EHyd EPfP GBin LRHS MNrw MSCN MSpe NBPC NBir NGdn NLar NRHS WCot WHoo
- 'Flore Pleno' (d)	MMuc SEND SPlb
- FREAK! ('Leuz0001'PBR)	CBcs CRos EHyd EPfP LRHS LSou NRHS SWvt
- 'Goldfinch'PBR	CBod CMea CWCL CWGN ECtt EMor ILea LRHS MHol MPri NHpl NLar NWsh SCob SPoG SRms WCot WHil WRHF
- 'Goldrausch'PBR	EBee ECtt EHyd ELan EPfP LEdu LRHS MRav NBPC NBir NGdn NHol SCob SGbt SRms SWvt WFar
- 'Gruppenstolz'	SAko
- 'H. Seibert'	MArl
- 'Highland White Dream'PBR	EHyd LRHS

- 'Horace Read' (d)	CDor CElw CMea ECtt NBir NHol SWvt
- 'Ice Star'	EBee EHyd LRHS NBPC NRHS
- 'Jennifer Read'	NLar
§ - 'John Murray' (d)	NBir NWsh WFar
- 'King's Crown' **new**	CBod
- 'Lacrosse'	CRos EBee EHyd ELon EPfP LRHS NLar NRHS SCob WFar
- 'Laspider'	EBee EHyd GBee LRHS NRHS
- 'Little Miss Muffet'	CSBt CWGN ECtt EHyd LEdu LRHS MBNS NRHS
- 'Little Princess'	see *L.* × *superbum* 'Silberprinzesschen'
- 'Macaroon'PBR **new**	CBod
- 'Manhattan'	CDor EBee EWes GBin SEdd
- 'Marion Bilsland'	MSpe NChi WBrk
- 'Mount Everest'	see *L.* × *superbum* 'Everest'
- 'Old Court'	see *L.* × *superbum* 'Beauté Nivelloise'
- 'Paladin'PBR	ECtt
- 'Phyllis Smith'	CBod CRos EBee ECtt ELan ELon GWyn LSRN MAvo MHer MPie MRav MSpe NBPC NGdn SMad WBrk WCAu WCot WFar
- 'Polaris'	CRos EBee LRHS NBre NRHS XLum
- 'Rags and Tatters'	ECtt EWes
- 'Real Dream'PBR	CRos EBee EHyd ELan EMor IPot LRHS MTis NEoE NRHS SCob SWvt WFar WNPC
- 'Real Galaxy'PBR	CRos EHyd ELan EPfP LBuc LRHS MTis NEoE NRHS SPoG
- 'Real Glory'	CRos ECtt EHyd ELan ILea LRHS LSou MHol MTis NEoE NHpl NRHS SCob SWvt WCAu WFar WNPC
- 'Real Neat'	CAby CRos EBee ECtt EHyd ELan EMor LRHS LSou MAsh MHol MTis NEoE NHpl NRHS SCob SHar STPC WNPC
- 'Shaggy'	see *L.* × *superbum* 'Beauté Nivelloise'
- 'Shapcott Gossamer'	CAby CBod CPou ECtt EMor MTis NGBl SEdd SPoG SRms WBrk WCot
- 'Shapcott Ruffles'	CBod EBee ECtt EMor MTis SEdd WBrk WCot
- 'Shapcott Summer Clouds'	CBod CDor CKno EBee ECtt GAbr GMaP MHol MSCN MTis SEdd SPoG WBrk WCot
§ - 'Silberprinzesschen'	CSBt EBou EHyd EMor EPfP GMaP GWyn LRHS NRHS SPlb SRms XLum
- 'Silver Spoon'	EHyd
- 'Snehurka'	EHyd LRHS WCot WFar WHoo
- 'Snow Lady'	EAJP EHyd EPfP GWyn LPot LRHS NPer SRms WFar
- 'Snow Queen'	GWyn
- 'Snowbound'	EHyd NEoE NRHS
- 'Snowcap'	CRos ECha EHyd EPfP LCro LOPS LRHS MBel MRav MTin NRHS SPer SWvt WCAu WGwG
- 'Snowdrift'	CRos LRHS MWat NBre NLar NRHS WBrk WCot WFar
§ - 'Sonnenschein'	CAby CBod CDor CRos EBee ECha ECtt ELan EPfP GMaP GQue LRHS LSRN MArl MBel MHol MRav NBPC NBir NGdn NRHS NWsh SPer SRms WCAu
- 'Starburst' (d)	CRos EHyd ELan LRHS NRHS SRms WFar
- 'Stina'	EBee IPot XLum
- 'Summer Snowball'	see *L.* × *superbum* 'John Murray'
- 'Sunny Side Up'PBR	CBod CWCL EBee ECtt EHyd EWes LRHS LSou NLar NRHS SCob WAul WFar
- SUNSHINE	see *L.* × *superbum* 'Sonnenschein'
- 'T.E. Killin' (d) ♀H4	CBod CRos EBee ECha ECtt EHyd ELan EPau EPfP GMaP LCro LRHS MRav MWat NRHS WCAu WFar WHoo
- 'Victorian Secret'PBR	EBee ECtt EHyd GAbr LBuc LRHS LSou MNrw NEoE NRHS SMad WCot WHil WTor
- WHITE MOUNTAIN ('Gfleuwhmtn'PBR)	EHyd LRHS NRHS
- 'Wirral Pride'	CRos EPfP WBrk
- 'Wirral Supreme' (d) ♀H5	CBcs CRos CSBt EBee EHyd ELan EPfP GJos GMaP ILea LCro LOPS LRHS MNrw MRav NBir NLar NRHS SCob SRms SWvt WCAu WFar WSpi
'Tizi-n-Test'	see *Rhodanthemum catananche* 'Tizi-n-Test'
§ ***vulgare***	Widely available
- 'Filigran'	CRos EHyd LRHS NRHS WFar
- 'Lollipop'	GWyn
§ - 'Maikönigin'	CRos EHyd GWyn LRHS NRHS SCob XLum
- MAY QUEEN	see *L. vulgare* 'Maikönigin'
- 'Sunny'	CBre
'White Knight'	EHyd LRHS NRHS SCob

Leucocoryne (*Alliaceae*)

'Andes' ♀H3	CCCN GKev SDeJ
'Dione'	GKev SDeJ
'Double Fantasy'	GKev
ixioides 'Blue Ocean'	GKev SDeJ
'Spotlight'	GKev
'White Dream'	SDeJ

Leucogenes (*Asteraceae*)

grandiceps	EPot WAbe
leontopodium	EPot NSla WAbe
tarahaoa	EPot WAbe

Leucogenes × *Raoulia* see × *Leucoraoulia*

Leucojum ✿ (*Amaryllidaceae*)

aestivum	CAby CBcs CDor CTri EAJP EBee GKev ILea LRHS MCot MMuc NBir NChi NHol NRHS SDeJ SEND SRms WCFE WCot WFar WHil WShi
- 'Gravetye Giant' ♀H7	Widely available
- var. ***pulchellum***	CElw
autumnale	see *Acis autumnalis*
roseum	see *Acis rosea*
tingitanum	see *Acis tingitana*
trichophyllum	see *Acis trichophylla*
valentinum	see *Acis valentina*
vernum ♀H5	CAvo CBor CBro CExl CRos CWCL EBee EHyd ELan EPfP EPot GKev LCro LOPS LRHS MNrw NBir NHol NHpl NPol NRHS NRya SDeJ SPhx SRms WCot WHer WPnP WShi
- var. ***carpathicum***	EPri
- var. ***vagneri***	ECha SDys WSHC
- var. ***vernum*** 'Green Lantern' **new**	CElw

Leucophyta (*Asteraceae*)

§ ***brownii***	CCht CDoC WSMil
- 'Silver Sand'	MCot

Leucopogon (*Ericaceae*)

§ ***colensoi***	MGil WThu
ericoides	GKev
§ ***fraseri***	WThu

× *Leucoraoulia* (*Asteraceae*)

§ ***loganii***	WAbe

Leucosceptrum (*Lamiaceae*)

canum	CExl SBrt
- GWJ 9424	WCru
japonicum B&SWJ 10804	WCru
- B&SWJ 10981	WCru
stellipilum	IMou
var. ***formosanum***	
- - B&SWJ 1926	WCru
- - RWJ 9907	SBrt WCru
- var. ***tosaense*** B&SWJ 8892	WCru

Leucospermum (*Proteaceae*)

(Carnival Series) 'Carnival Copper'	CBcs CCCN
- 'Carnival Red'	CCCN
cordifolium	CCCN CPbh
glabrum	SPlb
'Scarlet Ribbon'	CCCN
'Succession'	CCCN
'Tango'	CPbh
'Vulkano'	CCCN

Leucostegia (*Davalliaceae*)

immersa PAB 7836	LEdu WPGP

Leucothoe (*Ericaceae*)

axillaris	MAsh
- 'Curly Red'[PBR]	CDoC CMac CRos EBee ELan EPfP LRHS MAsh MGos NLar NRHS SCob SGol SLim SLon SPoG SWvt SavN WFar
- 'Royal Red'	SavN
- 'Tricolor' (v) **new**	SavN
- TWISTING RED ('Opstal20'[PBR])	MBlu
CARINELLA ('Zebekot')	CRos EPfP LRHS NLar NRHS SPoG
davisiae	NLar
§ ***fontanesiana***	CMac
- 'Makijaz'[PBR] (v)	CBod EPfP NLar SPoG
- 'Rainbow' (v)	CBcs CBod CBrac CDoC CMac CRos EBee EHyd EPfP LRHS MGos NLar SCob SGbt SGol SLim SPer SPoG SRms SSta SWvt WFar
- 'Rollissonii' 🏆H6	MRav SRms
- WHITEWATER ('Howw'[PBR]) (v)	CMac LCro LOPS MPkF NLar
keiskei BURNING LOVE ('Opstal50'[PBR])	NLar
- HALLOWEEN ('Opstal16'[PBR])	EBee
- 'Royal Ruby'	MAsh MGos MPkF NLar SGbt SGol SNig SPoG SavN WFar
LOVITA ('Zebonard')	MRav NLar SCoo
RED LIPS ('Lipsbolwi'[PBR])	EPfP SCob
SCARLETTA ('Zeblid') 🏆H6	CBcs CBod CBrac CDoC CMac CRos CSBt CTri EHyd EPfP LCro LOPS LRHS MAsh MGos MRav NHol NLar NOra NRHS NWad SCob SGbt SGol SLim SPad SPer SPoG SWvt WFar
walteri	see *L. fontanesiana*
- 'Hokus Pokus' (v) **new**	SPad

Leuzea (*Asteraceae*)

centaureoides	see *Rhaponticum centaureoides*
rhaponticoides	see *Rhaponticum exaltatum*

Levisticum (*Apiaceae*)

officinale	CAgr CBod CCBP CHby CLau EBou EMor ENfk EPfP EWhm GAbr GPoy GQue LEdu MBow MHer MMuc MNHC MPri NGrd SDix SEND SEdi SPlb SRms SVic WHer WJek XAbr

Lewisia ✿ (*Portulacaceae*)

'Archangel'	EPot NRya
Ashwood Carousel hybrids	CPBP CTri MAsh NHar
- orange shades **new**	NHpl
- pink shades **new**	NHpl
- yellow shades **new**	NHpl
Birch strain	CBcs ELan
brachycalyx 🏆H4	EWes
Brynhyfryd hybrids pink-flowered	GKev
- white-flowered	GKev
- yellow-flowered	GKev
cantelovii	MAsh
columbiana	MAsh NHpl
- 'Alba'	EPot GKev NSla
- 'Rosea'	MAsh
- subsp. ***rupicola***	NSla
- subsp. ***wallowensis***	MAsh NSla
cotyledon 🏆H4	CRos CWCL EHyd GKev GMaP ITim LCro LOPS LRHS NHpl NRHS NSla SSim WIce
- f. ***alba***	CWCL
- 'Ashwood Ruby'	MAsh
- Ashwood strain	CRos EPfP EWes LRHS MAsh NHpl SRms WOld
- 'Brannan Bar'	MAsh
- 'Bright Eyes'	GKev
- double-flowered (d)	GKev
- ELISE MIXED	CBod MHol
- var. ***heckneri***	MAsh
- hybrid	GKev NRya SPoG
- 'John's Special'	MAsh
- magenta-flowered	CWCL
- orange-flowered	CWCL
§ - 'Regenbogen'	LRHS MHer MHol
- rose-pink-flowered	CWCL
- salmon-flowered	CWCL
- Sunset Group 🏆H4	ELon EPfP NHpl NLar
- 'White Splendour'	MAsh
'George Henley'	CPBP EPot EWes MAsh NRya WAbe
leeana	MAsh
(Little Series) 'Little Mango'	EDAr NHar NRya NSla SSim
- 'Little Peach'	CPBP CWCL ECtt EDAr EPot MAsh MCot NHpl NRya NSla SSim
- 'Little Plum'	CMea ECtt EDAr EHyd GEdr ITim LRHS MAsh MCot NHpl NLar NRya NSla SSim WHoo WThu
- 'Little Raspberry'	EDAr NSla
- 'Little Snowberry' **new**	EDAr
- LITTLE TUTTI FRUTTI (mix)	CSma
§ ***nevadensis***	CRos EBou EHyd EPot LRHS NRHS NRya WThu
I - 'Alba'	GKev NHpl

- ***bernardina***	see *L. nevadensis*
- 'Rosea'	NHpl NRya NSla
oppositifolia	MAsh
- 'Richeyi'	EPot
'Pinkie'	CPBP NHpl
pygmaea	CRos EBou EHyd EWes GKev LRHS MAsh MHer NBir NRHS NRya NSla SPlb XLum
- carmine-flowered	GKev
Rainbow mixture	see *L. cotyledon* 'Regenbogen'
rediviva	EPot GKev ITim MAsh NHpl NSla
- dark pink-flowered	GKev
- white-flowered	GKev
'Trevosia'	MAsh
tweedyi 𝕐H4	CRos EHyd EPot GKev LRHS MAsh NHar NHpl NRHS SPlb WAbe
- 'Alba'	WAbe
- 'Elliott's Variety'	MAsh
- 'Rosea'	CRos EHyd EPot LRHS MAsh NHar NRHS WAbe

Leycesteria (*Caprifoliaceae*)

crocothyrsos	CBcs EBee ILea NLar NWad SPoG WFar
formosa	Widely available
- from Longstock	SLon
- 'Gold Leaf'	CBod CMac CPla GAbr MGil MHer SPad WBor WFar
- GOLDEN LANTERNS ('Notbruce'^{PBR}) 𝕐H4	CAby CBcs CBod CDoC CRos CSBt EBee EHyd ELan EPfP LBuc LRHS LSRN MAsh MGos MMrt MMuc MSwo NLar NRHS SCob SCoo SPer SPoG SRms SWvt WFar
- 'Lydia'	LRHS
- 'Purple Rain'	CDoC CRos EBee EHyd EPfP EWes LRHS MAsh MGos NLar NRHS SGsty

Leymus (*Poaceae*)

from the Falkland Islands	ELon EPPr
§ ***arenarius***	CAby CBod CElw CKno EBee ECha ELan EShb GBin GMaP LRHS MMuc NBid NBro SCob SDix SEND SEdd SGbt SGol SPlb SRms WABo WFar WSMil XCre XLum XSen
- 'Blue Dune'	EBee SEdd
cinereus	WCot
hispidus	see *Elymus hispidus*

Lhotzkya see *Calytrix*

Liatris (*Asteraceae*)

aspera	SPhx
cylindracea	SPhx
elegans	GKev SPlb
ligulistylis	SPhx
microcephala	SPhx
mucronata	NLar
pycnostachya	CSpe SAko SRms
scariosa	SPhx
- 'Alba'	CBcs LSun SAko SPhx
§ ***spicata***	Widely available
- 'Alba'	CMac CSBt EAJP ECha ELan EMor EPfP GBin GKev LSRN MPri MSCN NLar SCob SPer SPlb WWtn XLum
- ***callilepis***	see *L. spicata*
- 'Floristan Violett'	CBod CMea CRos CTri EBee EHyd EPfP GMaP LRHS MHer MHol MSpe MWat NLar NRHS SCob SCoo SGbt SPlb SPoG SWvt WFar WGwG XLum
- 'Floristan Weiss'	CBod CExl CRos CTri EHyd EPPr EPfP ERCP GMaP LRHS MBel MHer MRav NLar NRHS SDeJ SGbt SPoG SRms STPC SWvt WFar WGwG
- GOBLIN	see *L. spicata* 'Kobold'
§ - 'Kobold'	CBod CMac CRos EBee EBou EHyd ELan EMor EPfP GBin LCro LRHS LSun MBel MBow MRav NBir NLar NRHS SCob SGbt SMad SPad SRms SWvt WCAu WFar WWtn XLum
squarrosa	SPhx

Libanotis see *Seseli*

montana	see *Seseli libanotis*

Libertia ✿ (*Iridaceae*)

'Amazing Grace'	EBee
breunioides	see *L. cranwelliae*
§ ***chilensis*** 𝕐H3	Widely available
- Elegans Group	CExl EBee WCru
§ - Formosa Group	CBcs CBod CBro CCBP CExl CTri EBee EHyd ELan LRHS MMuc NChi NRHS NSti SArc SCob SRms SWvt WHer
- Procera Group	CAby CSpe CTsd EBee EPfP GBin GLog LEdu LRHS SPlb WPGP WSHC
§ ***cranwelliae***	CExl WPGP
formosa	see *L. chilensis* Formosa Group
grandiflora misapplied	see *L. chilensis*
grandiflora ambig.	CBod CCht CDoC CTsd GAbr GBin GKev LSun MAvo MBow MMrt MSCN SCob SEdd SIvy WCAu WSHC WSMil
grandiflora (R. Br.) Sweet	CAby EHyd SDix SVen
'Grasshopper'	CAby CBod GBin
ixioides	CBcs ECha ILea LEdu LRHS MMuc SPtp WPGP WSHC
- 'Goldfinger' (v)	CBcs CBct CBor CExl CKno CMac EBee EHyd ELan EMor EPfP LEdu LLWG LRHS MHol MPkF NHol NRHS SCob SEdd SLon SPoG SWvt WCot WFar WGrn WHer
- 'Highlander'	LRHS MHol
- 'Taupo Blaze'	CBct CBor CMac ELan ELon EPfP GBin LRHS MRav SCob SEdd SIvy SLon SPoG
- 'Taupo Sunset'^{PBR}	CBcs CBct CCCN CExl EPfP LRHS MBNS MPkF NSti SWvt
- 'Tricolor'	CSde ECha GEdr GKev MRav
'Nelson Dwarf'	EBee ESwi
paniculata	CExl EBee
peregrinans	CAbb CExl CKno CSpe EBee ECha EHyd ELan EPri GKev ILea LEdu LRHS MMuc MRav NBir NRHS SCob SEND SEdd SIvy SPer SPtp SRkn SWvt WLov WPGP
- 'Gold Leaf'	CBcs CCCN CTri CTsd EBee ELan EPfP LRHS SMad SWvt WFar
- 'Gold Stripe'	CPla SWvt
pulchella misapplied	EHyd LRHS NRHS
pulchella ambig. blue-flowered	GKev
sessiliflora	CExl NBir
- 'Ballyrogan Blue'	EBee GKev WMal
- 'Caerulescens'	CBcs CBod CCCN CCht CExl CMac CPla CSde EPfP LRHS NBir NGBl SIvy SMad SPer SPtp WFar

'Sunset Strain'	CBod CPla EMor LRHS MHtn WFar
tricocca misapplied	see *L. umbellata*
§ ***umbellata*** HCM 98.089	WPGP

Libocedrus (*Cupressaceae*)

chilensis	see *Austrocedrus chilensis*
decurrens	see *Calocedrus decurrens*
plumosa	CBrP

Libonia see *Justicia*

Ligularia (*Asteraceae*)

amplexicaulis	GKev
aff. ***atkinsonii*** WJC 13663	WCru
'BBQ Banana'	CBod EPfP WWtn
'Bottle Rocket'PBR	CBor NLar
'Britt Marie Crawford'PBR ♀H6	Widely available
clivorum	see *L. dentata*
§ ***dentata***	CPla ECtt GAbr NBro SRms
- 'Dark Beauty'	MBNS
- 'Desdemona'	Widely available
- 'Franz Feldweber'	ELon
- 'Midnight Lady'	CTsd EHyd ELan EMor GPSL GWyn MHol NLar
- 'Orange Princess'	NPer
- 'Osiris Café Dark'PBR	SCob
- 'Osiris Fantaisie' (v)	CDor CExl EBee ECtt EPfP EWes GWyn MAvo MHol MNrw NLar NSti SPoG WCot WFar WPnP
- 'Othello'	CBod CRos ECtt EHyd EPfP LRHS NBid NGdn NLar NRHS NWad SCob SRms SWvt WCAu
- 'Pandora' **new**	ECtt SPad
- 'Sommergold'	ECha WFar
- 'Twilight'	CBct CBod ECtt MBNS
§ ***fischeri***	ECha
- B&SWJ 2570	WCru
- B&SWJ 4381	WCru
- B&SWJ 4478	WCru
- B&SWJ 5653	WCru
- B&SWJ 8802	WCru
- var. ***megalorhiza*** 'Cheju Charmer'	ELon WCru
'Garden Confetti'	ECtt
'Gold Torch'	ECtt NLar
§ 'Gregynog Gold' ♀H6	ECha ECtt EHyd GBee GMaP LRHS MRav NBro NLar NRHS
× ***hessei***	EHyd GMaP LRHS MMuc WWtn
hodgsonii	EPPr MRav
- B&SWJ 10855	WCru
intermedia B&SWJ 606a	WSHC
japonica	CDor ECha EHyd LEdu LRHS NLar WWtn
- B&SWJ 2883	WCru
- 'Rising Sun'	CExl NLar WCot WCru
'Laternchen'PBR	ECtt NLar SAko
'Little Rocket'PBR	CBct CBod CExl EBee ECtt EPfP MBNS MWts NBro NGdn NLar NRHS SPoG WFar
'Osiris Café Noir'	ECtt NLar SMad WFar
'Osiris Pistache' (v)	EBee ECtt
× ***palmatiloba***	see *L.* × *yoshizoeana* 'Palmatiloba'
§ ***przewalskii***	Widely available
- SSSE 176	WCot
- 'Dragon Wings'	GBin MAsh MHol NEoE NLar SCob
- 'Dragon's Breath'	ECtt GBin MAsh MHol SCob
sibirica	CSam MMuc NLar
- B&SWJ 4383	WCru
- B&SWJ 5841	WCru
- var. ***speciosa***	see *L. fischeri*
smithii	see *Senecio smithii*
speciosa	see *L. fischeri*
stenocephala	EBee EMor NBro NLar WWtn XLum
'Sungold'	CMac CRos CSam ECtt EHyd LRHS NGdn NRHS
tangutica	see *Sinacalia tangutica*
'The Rocket' ♀H6	Widely available
tussilaginea	see *Farfugium japonicum*
- 'Aureo-maculata'	see *Farfugium japonicum* 'Aureomaculatum'
veitchiana	CBod CSam WWtn
vorobievii	CElw NLar
'Weihenstephan'	EHyd LRHS
wilsoniana	EHyd GAbr LRHS MMuc MRav NRHS SEND WFar WWtn
- B&SWJ 14195	WCru
§ × ***yoshizoeana*** 'Palmatiloba'	CRos EHyd ELan EWTr EWes LRHS MRav NRHS SHar SPhx WFar WWtn
'Zepter' ♀H6	CBod CRos ECtt EHyd ELan EPfP EShb GBee GQue LRHS MMuc NHol NLar NRHS NWad WCot WWtn

Ligusticum (*Apiaceae*)

hultenii	WCot
lucidum	EPfP LEdu MAvo MBel SPhx SPtp WBor WCot WPGP
- subsp. ***lucidum***	CSpe
mutellina	LPla
porteri	EBee
§ ***scoticum***	CBod CPla EBee ELan ELon EMor EShb EWes GLog GPSL GPoy GQue LEdu LRHS MAvo MBel MHer NAts SBut SDix SPhx SPtp SRms WFar WJek WOut WPGP
- variegated (v)	LEdu WCot

Ligustrum ✿ (*Oleaceae*)

B&L 12261	EBee WPGP
chenaultii	see *L. compactum*
§ ***compactum***	NLar
§ ***delavayanum***	CBod ELan EShb GKev MNHC NLar SCob SGol SGsty SWeb WCFE WPGP
- B&L 12083	CExl
ibota	EBtc NLar
- MUSLI ('Muster'PBR) (v)	LRHS SPoG WCot
ionandrum	see *L. delavayanum*
japonicum	CLnd EBar ECrN EHyd LMaj LRHS LSRN SCob SEND SGol SGsty SPer SWeb
- B&SWJ 14604	WCru
- 'Coriaceum'	see *L. japonicum* 'Rotundifolium'
- GREEN CENTURY ('Melgreen'PBR)	LRHS WMat
- 'Korea Dwarf'	NLar
§ - 'Rotundifolium'	CBcs CBod CDoC CExl CRos EBee EHyd ELan EPfP GBin LRHS MAsh MRav NLar SPer SPoG SPtp WCFE WCot WFar
§ - 'Silver Star' (v)	NLar SGol
§ - 'Texanum'	CDoC ECrN EPfP LMaj LRHS SArc SavN WCFE
- 'Texanum Argenteum'	see *L. japonicum* 'Silver Star'
- 'Variegatum' (v)	SGol SWeb
lucidum ♀H5	CCVT CSBt CSde CTri ELan IDee MRav SArc SCob SEND SGol SPer SWvt WFar

- Guiz 296	CExl
- 'Curly Wurly'	CRos EHyd LRHS NRHS
- 'Excelsum Superbum' (v) 🏆H5	CCVT CLnd CMac CRos EBar ECrN EHyd ELan EPfP LMaj LRHS LSRN MGos SGol SGsty SPoG SWeb WCot
- 'Golden Wax'	CJun MRav
- 'Tricolor' (v) 🏆H5	CRos EHyd ELan EPfP LRHS MAsh MGos NLar SPer SWvt
obtusifolium var. ***regelianum***	MMuc NLar
ovalifolium	Widely available
§ - 'Argenteum' (v)	CBcs CBod CCVT CMac CTri ECrN ELan EShb MMuc MRav SCob SEND SGol SLim SPer SPoG SWvt WFar
- 'Aureomarginatum'	see *L. ovalifolium* 'Aureum'
§ - 'Aureum' (v) 🏆H5	Widely available
- 'Lemon and Lime' (v)	CBod EBee ELan LSRN MAsh MThu SCoo SRms SWvt WCot
- 'Variegatum'	see *L. ovalifolium* 'Argenteum'
- 'Vicaryi'	ELan EPfP GBin MGos NEoE NWad SDix SGol SPer WFar
quihoui	CRos CTri EBee EHyd ELan EPfP IDee LRHS MBlu NLar SDix SEND SLon SPer SPoG
sinense	CMCN MRav
- 'Multiflorum'	WFar
- var. ***myrianthum***	SPtp
- 'Sunshine'	CRos EHyd LRHS NRHS SPoG
- 'Variegatum' (v)	MRav SPer
strongylophyllum	CExl
texanum	see *L. japonicum* 'Texanum'
tschonoskii	MBlu NLar
undulatum 'Lemon Lime and Clippers'	CRos EHyd EShb LRHS NLar NRHS SDix SPoG
vulgare	CArg CCVT CHab CMac CTri ECrN ELan EPfP LBuc MMuc MSwo SCob SEND SEWo SGsty SWvt WMat WMou WSFF WTSh
- 'Lodense'	EBtc

Lilaeopsis (*Apiaceae*)

brasiliensis new	XBlo

Lilium ✿ (*Liliaceae*)

'Abbeville's Pride' (Ia/b)	SDeJ
'Acapulco' (VII-/d)	SDeJ
§ 'Acoustic' (Colour Carpet Series) (VIIa/b-c)	EHyd LRHS
'Adonis' (Ic/d)	GEdr
African Queen Group (VI-/a) 🏆H6	ERCP LCro LOPS SCoo SDir SRms
- 'African Queen' (VIb-c/a)	SDeJ
'Altari' (VIIIa-b/b)	SDeJ
'Anastasia' (VIIIb-c/b-d)	GKev LCro LOPS SDeJ SDir
'Annemarie's Dream' (Ia/c)	SDeJ SDir
APOLLO (Ia/b)	see *L.* 'Blizzard'
'Apricot Fudge'PBR (VIIIa/b)	GKev SDir
'Arabian Knight' (IIc/d)	CBcs GKev IPot MAvo SDeJ SDir WFar
'Arena' (VIIa/b)	SCoo
Asiatic hybrids (I)	EHyd
auratum (IXb/c)	GKev
- 'Gold Band'	see *L. auratum* var. *platyphyllum*
§ - var. ***platyphyllum*** (IXb/c)	SDeJ
- - B&SWJ 4824	WCru
- - B&SWJ 5041	WCru
- var. ***virginale*** (IXb/c)	SDeJ
Backhouse hybrids	see *L.* × *dalhansonii* Backhouse Group
'Baferrari' (VIIa/b)	SDeJ
'Bamako' (VIIa-b/b)	SDeJ
'Barbara North' (Ic/d)	GEdr
'Barbaresco' (VIIa-b/b)	SCoo
'Beijing Moon' (VIb-c/a)	GKev SDeJ SDir
'Belgrado'PBR (VIIa/b-c)	SDeJ
'Belladonna'PBR (VIIIb-a/b)	SDeJ
'Belle Epoque' (VIIb/b-c)	SDeJ
'Bergamo' (VIIb/b)	SCoo SDeJ
'Beverly Dreams' (VIIIa/a)	GKev
'Beverly Hills'PBR (VIIIa-b/b)	SDeJ
'Black Beauty' (VIIIb-c/d)	CCBP GBin GKev LCro LOPS NHpl SDeJ SDir
§ 'Blizzard' (Ia/b)	NBir SCob SDeJ
'Blushing Joy' (Ia/b) new	CRos
'Boogie Woogie' (VIIIa-b/b)	SDeJ
'Bracelet' (VIIIa-b/b)	SDeJ
'Brasil'PBR (Ia/b)	GKev
BRASILIA ('Zora') (VIIa/b-c)	SDeJ SDir
'Bright Joy' (Ia/c) new	CRos
BRIGHT PIXIE ('Ceb Bright') (Ia/b)	SDeJ
'Broken Heart' (VIIb-a/c)	SDeJ
brownii (IXb-c/a)	GKev
bulbiferum var. ***croceum*** (IXa/b)	XEll
'Butter Pixie'PBR (Ia/b)	NBir SCob SDeJ
§ ***canadense*** (IXc/a)	GEdr WCot WCru XEll
- var. ***flavum***	see *L. canadense*
'Cancun' (Ia/b-c)	SDeJ
candidum (IXb/a)	CAvo CBcs CTri ECha ELan EPot ERCP GKev ILea LCro LOPS LSun MWat SCob SDeJ SDir SRms WSpi
'Candy Blossom' (Ia/b)	SDeJ
'Casa Blanca' (VIIb/b-c) 🏆H6	CAvo CBro GKev LCro LOPS NBir SCoo SDeJ SDir
'Castellani' (VIIa/b) new	ILea
'Cecil' (VIIIa/b)	SDeJ
cernuum (IXc/d)	SDeJ
* - 'Album'	SDeJ
'Chill Out' (VIIa/b)	LCro LOPS
§ 'Chocolate Canary' (Ic/-)	SDeJ
Citronella Group (Ic/d)	NHpl SDeJ
'Classic Joy' (Ia/b) new	CRos
'Claude Shride' (IIc/d)	CAvo CBro EPot GEdr GKev ILea IPot LRHS NHpl SDeJ WPnP
'Cocktail Twins' (Ia/b)	SDeJ
'Cogoleto'PBR (VIIIa-b/b) new	SDir
'Coldplay' (Colour Carpet Series) (VIIa-b/b-c)	EHyd LBuc LRHS NRHS
columbianum (IXc/d) B&SWJ 9564	WCru
'Con Amore' (VIIb/b)	SCoo
'Conca d'Or'PBR (VIIIb/b)	SDeJ
concolor (IXa/c)	GKev
'Corsage' (Ib/b-c)	GKev
'Creation' (VIa/b)	SDeJ
'Crimson Pixie' (Ia/b)	LCro LOPS NRHS SDeJ
'Curly Sue' (VIIa-b/b) new	LCro LOPS
× ***dalhansonii*** (IIc/d)	CAby ERCP SDeJ
§ - Backhouse Group (IIc/d)	WFar
- 'Guinea Gold' (II)	GKev SDir
- 'Mrs R.O. Backhouse' (IIc/d)	GEdr SDeJ
- 'Sutton Court' (IIc/c)	GEdr
- Terrace City Group (IIc/d)	GKev SDeJ
'Dark Romance' (Romance Series) (VIIb/b)	CRos EHyd LRHS NRHS
dauricum f. ***rebunense*** (IXa/b)	CBor

	davidii (IXc/d)	CExl NHpl SDeJ WCru
§	- var. ***willmottiae*** (IXc/d)	WCru
	DAZZLER ('Maru') (Colour Carpet Series) (VIIa/b)	LBuc LRHS
	'Debby' (VIIIa-b/b-c)	GKev SDeJ
	'Dimension' (Ia/b-c)	LCro LOPS
	'Disco' (Ia)	SDeJ
	distichum (IXb-c/d) B&SWJ 4465	WCru
	- B&SWJ 794	WCru
	'Dizzy' (VIIa-b/b-c)	CBod SDeJ
	duchartrei (IXc/d)	CAby CExl WCru
	'Electric Yellow'	see *L.* 'Yellow Electric'
	'Elgrado' (Ia/b)	GKev SDeJ
	'Elodie'PBR (Ia/b)	SDeJ SDir
	'Elusive' (VIIIb/b-d)	GKev SDeJ SDir
	'Enchantment' (Ia/b)	SDeJ
	'Eros' (Ic/d)	GEdr
	'Eurydike' (Ic/d)	GEdr
	'Expression' (VII)	SDeJ
	fargesii (IXc/d)	CExl
	'Fata Morgana' (Ia/b) ♀H6	SCoo SDeJ SDir
	'Fifty Fifty' (VIIIa/b-c)	GKev
	'Fire King' (Ib/d)	SCoo SDeJ SRms
	'Fopapo' (Ia-b/c)	SDeJ
	'Forever Marjon' (Ib-a/b-c)	GKev
	'Forever Susan' (Ia/b)	GKev SDeJ
	formosanum (IXb/a)	MCot
	- short, from high altitude RWJ 10005 (IXb/a)	WCru
	- var. ***formosanum*** B&SWJ 1589 (IXb/a)	WCru
	- var. ***pricei*** (IXb/a)	EBou EDAr EHyd ELan EWTr GBin GEdr LEdu LRHS MHer MTin NRHS SRms WIce
	- - 'Snow Queen' (Vb/a)	EShb SDeJ
	'Foxtrot' (Ia/b)	SDeJ
	'Friso' (VIIIb/b)	GKev SDeJ
	'Fusion' (IVb-c/b-c)	NHpl SDir
	'Garden Party' (VIIb/b) ♀H6	CBod GKev SDeJ SDir
	'Gironde' (Ia/b)	SDeJ
	GLIMMER	see *L.* 'Acoustic'
	'Gold Band' (VII)	SDeJ
	'Gold Class' (VIIIb-a/b-c)	SDeJ
	Golden Splendor Group (VIb-c/a) ♀H6	GKev SCoo SDeJ SDir
	'Golden Stargazer' (VIIa-b/b)	CBod
	'Golden Stone' (VIIIa-b/b)	SDeJ
	'Grand Cru' (Ia/b)	SDeJ
	'Hannah North' (Ic/d)	GEdr
	hansonii (IXb-c/d)	CWCL ECha GBin GKev NHpl SDeJ WPnP
	- B&SWJ 4309	WCru
	- B&SWJ 4756 from Aomori, Japan	WCru
	- B&SWJ 8506	WCru
	- B&SWJ 8528	WCru
	'Happy Kiss' (Ia/b-c)	GKev
	henryi (IXc/d) ♀H6	CAvo EBee GKev SDeJ SDir WCru
	'Hit Parade' (VII)	SDeJ
	'Honeymoon' (VIIIa-b/b)	SDeJ
	humboldtii (IXc/d)	CWCL EBee
	'Ice Pixie' (Ia/b)	SDeJ
	'Inuvik' (Ia/b)	GKev SDeJ
	'Island Joy' (Ia/b-c) **new**	CRos
	'Ivory Pixie' (Ia/b)	SDeJ
	'João Pessoa' (Ia/b-c)	SDeJ
	'Jo's Choice' (VIa-b/a)	SDeJ
	'Josephine' (VIIa/b)	SDeJ SDir
	'Joy'	see *L.* 'Le Rêve'
	'Karen North' (Ic/d)	GEdr
§	***kelleyanum*** (IXc/d)	CWCL EBee
	'King Pete' (Ib/b-c)	SDeJ
	'Kingdom'PBR (VIIIa/b-c)	SDeJ
	'Kushi Maya'PBR (VIIIc/b-c)	GKev IPot SDeJ SDir
	'Lady Alice' (VI-/d)	GKev SDeJ SDir
	'Lake Tulare' (IVc/c-d)	GEdr
§	***lancifolium*** (IXc/d)	EPot GBin XAbr XLum
	- B&SWJ 4352	WCru
	- var. ***flaviflorum*** (IXc/d)	SDeJ
	- 'Flore Pleno' (IXc/d)	EHyd EPPr GKev GQue LRHS MHer NBir SDeJ WCot WCru WHil XLum
	- var. ***fortunei*** (IXc/d)	EPPr SDix
	- - B&SWJ 539	WCru
	- pink-flowered	SDeJ
	- 'Splendens' (IXc/d)	GKev NBid SDeJ SDir WCot
	'Landini'PBR (Ia/b)	CAby SDeJ
	'Lankon' (VIIIc/a)	CAby
	lankongense (IXc/d)	CBor CWCL EPot GBin GGGa GKev SDir WCru
	- BWJ 7554	WCru
	- BWJ 7691	WCru
	'Late Morning' (VIIIb-c)	SDeJ
	'Latvia' (Ia/b)	SDeJ
	'Lazy Lady'	see *L.* 'Chocolate Canary'
§	'Le Rêve' (VIIa-b/b)	SDeJ
	leichtlinii (IXc/d)	CAvo CCBP EPot GBin IMou NHpl SDeJ
	'Lemon Pixie' (Ia/b)	NRHS SCob
	leucanthum var. ***centifolium*** (IXb-c/a)	WCru
	- - BWJ 8130	WCru
	'Levi'PBR (Ia/c)	SDeJ
	lijiangense (IXc/d)	GEdr XEll
I	'Linda' (Ia/b)	SDeJ
	'Little John' (VIIa-b/b)	SDeJ
	'Little Kiss' (Ia/d)	SDeJ
	LOLLYPOP ('Holebibi') (Ia/b)	SCoo SDeJ
	'Londrina' (Ia/b)	SDeJ
	longiflorum (IXb/a)	EBee SCoo SDir XLum
	- B&SWJ 11376	WCru
	- 'Foliis Variegatis' (Vb/a/v)	MAvo
	- 'Rose' (V)	SDeJ
	- 'White Heaven'PBR (Vb/a)	LCro LOPS
	'Lovely Girl' (VII-/b)	SDeJ
	'Luxor' (Ia/b)	CTsd NBir
	'Luzia' (VIIa-b/c)	CRos EHyd LRHS NRHS
	mackliniae (IXc/a) ♀H5	CAby CWCL EWes GGGa GKev ITim NBir WHal WPGP
	- PAB 9327	LEdu WPGP
	- PAB 9668	LEdu WPGP
	- from Nagaland, India	GGGa
	- deep pink-flowered	GGGa
	'Magic Star'PBR (VIIa-b/b)	CBod SDeJ
	'Magny Cours' (VIIa/b) **new**	CRos
	'Manitoba Morning' (IIc/c)	GKev ILea MAvo NHpl SDeJ SDir
	'Mapira' (VIIIb/b)	GKev SDeJ
	'Marco Polo' ambig.	SCoo SDeJ
	'Marie North' (Ic/d)	GEdr
	'Maroon King' (IIc/d)	CBcs WFar
	martagon (IXc/d) ♀H6	CBro CWCL ECha ELan EMor EPot ERCP GKev GPoy LCro LOPS LRHS NBir NChi NGrd NHpl SDeJ SRms WCAu WPnP WShi WSpi
	- var. ***albiflorum*** (IXc/d)	SDeJ

- var. ***album*** (IXc/d)	CBro CSpe CWCL ELan EMor EPot GBin GKev LRHS MCot NBir NChi NRHS SDeJ SRms WShi
- var. ***cattaniae*** (IXc/d)	GEdr
- 'Fairy Morning' (IIc/c)	GKev WFar
- 'Slate's Morning' (IIc/c)	CAvo
'Mascara' (Ia-b/b)	GKev
medeoloides (IXc/d) B&SWJ 4184	WCru
- B&SWJ 4363	WCru
'Miss Feya' (VIIIb/c)	CAby GKev SDeJ SDir
'Miss France' (VIIb/b-c)	SDeJ
I 'Miss Lily' (VIIIb/b-c)	SDeJ
'Miss Lucy'^{PBR} (VIIa-b/b-c)	SDeJ
'Miss Peculiar' (VIII b-c/a) **new**	GKev
MISS RIO	see *L.* 'Rio'
'Mister Job' (VIIIa/c)	SDeJ
'Mona Lisa' (VIIb/b-c)	LRHS NGdn SCob SDeJ
monadelphum (IXc/d)	SDeJ XEll
- pale-flowered	GKev
'Moneymaker' (VIIIa/b) **new**	CBod
'Mont Blanc' (Ia/b-c)	SCob SDeJ
'Montezuma'^{PBR} (VIIa-b/b)	SDeJ
'Montreux' (Ia/b-c)	SDeJ
'Mount Cook' (VIIa/b)	GKev SDeJ SDir
'Muscadet' (VIIa-b/b)	GKev LCro LOPS SDeJ SDir
'My Wedding' (VIIb-a/c) **new**	CBod
'Navona' (Ia/b)	GKev SDeJ
nepalense (IXc/a)	CAby CBcs CBro CExl CWCL EPot ERCP GBin GKev LCro LOPS MCot SDeJ SDir WCru WPnP WTyc XLum
- B&SWJ 2985	WCru
'Netty's Pride' (Ia/b-c)	CAvo SDeJ SDir
'New Wave' (Ia/b)	SDeJ
'Night Flyer' (Ib-c/b-c)	GKev SDeJ
'Nightrider' (VIIIa/b) **new**	GKev
'Nove Cento' (Ia/b)	SDeJ
'Orange County' (Ia/b)	SDeJ
'Orange Electric' (Ia/b)	SDeJ SDir
'Orange' (FantAsiatic Series) (I) **new**	CBod
'Orange Marmalade' (IIb/c-d)	GKev NHpl SDeJ SDir WPnP
'Orange Pixie' (Ia/b)	NRHS SCob SCoo
'Orange Planet' (VIa/a)	SDeJ
'Orange Twinkle' (Ib-c/b)	SDeJ
'Orania'^{PBR} (VIIIb/b)	SDeJ
* Oriental Superb Group	NGdn
oxypetalum var. ***insigne*** (IXb-c/b)	EBee GBin NHpl SDir
'Pan' (Ic/d)	GEdr
pardalinum (IXc/d) 🏆^{H6}	CWCL EBee SBrt WCot WCru
- var. ***giganteum*** (IXc/d)	MNrw
- subsp. ***pardalinum*** (IXc/d)	SDeJ
§ - subsp. ***vollmeri*** (IXc/d)	GKev WCru
§ - subsp. ***wigginsii*** (IXc/d)	WCru
× ***parkmanii*** 'Rosy Dimple' (VIIa/b)	SDeJ
'Passion Moon' (VIIb-c/a)	GKev SDeJ SDir
'Patricia's Pride' (Ia-b/b-c)	SDeJ SDir
'Peach Butterflies' (Ic/d)	SDeJ
'Peach Dwarf' (Ia/b-c)	SDeJ
'Peach Pixie' (Ia/b)	NBir SCob SCoo
'Pearl Jennifer' (Ib-a/c)	SDeJ
'Pearl Jessica' (Ib-c/b-c)	SDeJ SDir
'Pearl Justien' (Ia-b/c)	SDeJ
'Pearl Loraine' (Ib-c/b-c)	GKev SDeJ SDir
'Pearl Melanie' (Ib/c)	SDeJ SDir
'Pearl Sonja' (Ib/b)	SDeJ
'Pearl Stacey' (Ib-c/c)	GKev SDeJ
'Peggy North' (Ic/d)	GEdr
'Pepard Gold' (IIc/d)	GEdr GKev
philippinense (IXa-b/a)	GKev SDir WPGP
'Pieton' (Ia/b-c)	SDeJ
'Pimento' (VIIa/b)	SDeJ
'Pink' (FantAsiatic Series) (I) **new**	CBod
'Pink Flavour' (Ic/c)	SDeJ
'Pink Giant' (Ic/-) **new**	GKev
'Pink Morning' (IIc/c)	GKev IPot NHpl SDir
Pink Perfection Group (VIb/a) 🏆^{H6}	ERCP EShb GKev LCro LOPS SCoo SDeJ SDir
'Pink Pixie'^{PBR} (Ia/b)	NBir NRHS SDeJ
'Pink Zsar' (VIIa/b) **new**	CRos
poilanei misapplied	see *L. primulinum*
'Polar Star' (VIIa-b/b)	SDeJ
pomponium (IXc/d)	CBor
§ ***primulinum*** (IXc/a) HWJ 681	WCru
- WWJ 11679	WCru
- var. ***ochraceum*** (IXc/a)	WCru
- aff. var. ***ochraceum*** (IXc/a) KWJ 12064	WCru
'Proud Bride' (VIIa/b)	SDeJ
'Prunotto'^{PBR} (Iab/b)	GKev SDeJ
§ ***pumilum*** (IXc/d)	EPot GKev SDeJ SDir
'Purple Eye' (Ia-b/b)	GKev SDeJ
'Purple Prince' (VIIIa-b/a-b)	SDeJ
pyrenaicum (IXc/d)	GKev WShi XEll
'Red Carpet' (Ia/b)	NBir SCob SDeJ
'Red County' (Ia/c-b)	SDeJ
'Red Electric' (Ia/b)	SDeJ
'Red' (FantAsiatic Series) (I) **new**	CBod
'Red Flavour' (Ic/b-c)	SDeJ
'Red Hot' (VIIIc-d/b)	SDeJ
'Red Life' (Ib-a/c)	NHpl
'Red Twinkle'	SDeJ
'Red Velvet' (Ic/d)	CAvo GKev SDeJ SDir
regale (IXb/a) 🏆^{H6}	CAvo CBro ECha ELan EMor ERCP EShb EWTr GKev LCro LOPS LRHS MCot SCob SDeJ SDir SPer SRms
- 'Album' (IXb/a)	CAvo ERCP GKev IMou LCro LOPS LRHS SCoo SDeJ SDir
'Reinesse' (Ia/b)	NRHS SDeJ
§ 'Rio' (VIIb/b-c)	SCoo
RIO NEGRO ('Corvara'^{PBR}) (VIIa-b/b-c)	SDeJ
'Robert Griesbach' (VIIIc/b-c)	SDir
'Robert Swanson' (VIIIb-c/b)	GKev SDeJ
'Robina' (VIIIa-b/b-c)	WCot WWFP
ROSELILY CAROLINA ('DL044040'^{PBR}) (VIIa-b)	SDir
ROSELILY ELENA ('DL04581'^{PBR}) (VIIa-b)	MSCN
ROSELILY ISABELLA ('DL044033'^{PBR}) (VIIa-b/-) **new**	SDir
ROSELILY NATALIA ('DL04544'^{PBR}) (VIIa-b/-)	SDir
'Rosella's Dream' (Ia/b)	GKev SDeJ
'Rosemary North' (Ic/d)	GEdr
'Rosselini' (VIIIa-b/b)	SDeJ

rosthornii (IXc/d)	CExl WCru
rubellum (IXb/a)	GEdr
'Russian Morning' (IIc/c)	GKev
sachalinense (IXa/b) RBS 0235	EPPr
'Salinas' (VIIa/b)	SDeJ
'Salmon Flavour' (Ic/b-c)	SDir
'Salmon Tiger'	SDeJ
'Salmon Twinkle' (Ib-c/c)	SDeJ
'Satisfaction' (VIIIa-b/-)	SDeJ
'Scarlet Delight' (VIIb-c/c-d)	SDeJ SDir
'Scheherazade' (VIIIc/d)	GKev SDeJ SDir
'Set Point' (VIIb/b)	SDeJ
shastense	see *L. kelleyanum*
'Showwinner' (VIIa/b-c)	CRos EHyd LRHS NRHS
'Smoky Mountain' (VIIIc/d)	SDeJ
'Souvenir'[PBR] (VIIa-b/b)	SDeJ
'Sparkling Joy' (I) **new**	CRos
speciosum (IXb-c/d) B&SWJ 4847	WCru
- B&SWJ 4924	WCru
- var. ***album*** (IXb-c/d)	GKev NBir NHpl SDeJ WFar
- 'Ida Uchida' (IX)	SDir
- var. ***rubrum*** (IXb-c/d)	CAvo ECha LCro LOPS NBir SDeJ SRms
§ - - 'Uchida' (IXb-c/d)	CExl GKev SDeJ
'Sphinx' (Ia/d)	WCot
'Spring Pink' (Ia/-)	CAvo GKev SDeJ SDir
'Stainless Steel' (Ia/b)	GKev SDeJ
'Star Gazer' (VIIa/c)	CRos EHyd GKev LCro LOPS LRHS NRHS SCoo SDeJ SDir
'Starfighter' (VIIa-b/c)	SDeJ
'Sun Ray' (Ia/b)	SCob
'Sunny Morning' (IIc/d)	GKev MAvo
superbum (IXc/d)	GKev WCru WPGP
'Sweet Desire'[PBR] (VIIIa-b/b) **new**	SDir
'Sweet Lord' (Ia/b)	SDeJ
'Sweet Surrender' (Ib-c/c-d)	SDeJ SDir
'Tailor Made' (Ia/b)	SDeJ
taliense (IXc/d)	WCru
'Tarragona'[PBR] (VIIIb/b)	SDeJ
tenuifolium	see *L. pumilum*
'Tiber' (VIIa-b/b) **new**	ILea
Tiger Babies Group (VIIIb-c/c-d)	SDeJ
'Tigermoon' **new**	CBod
'Tigerwoods' (VIIa/c)	LCro LOPS
tigrinum	see *L. lancifolium*
'Tiny Dino'[PBR] (Ia-b/b)	MAsh
'Tiny Ghost'[PBR] (Ia-b/b-c)	MAsh SCob
'Tiny Invader'[PBR] (Ia-b/b-c)	MAsh
'Tiny Nanny'[PBR] (Ia-b/b-c)	MAsh SCob
'Tiny Skyline'[PBR] (Ia-b/b)	MAsh
'Tom Pouce' (VIIa/b)	SDeJ
'Toronto' (Ia-b/b)	SDeJ
'Toscane' (Ia/b-c)	SDeJ
TRIUMPHATOR ('Zanlophator'[PBR]) (VIIIb/a-b)	GKev MCot SDeJ
tsingtauense (IXa/c)	SDeJ
- B&SWJ 519	WCru
- B&SWJ 4263	WCru
- B&SWJ 4698	WCru
'Uchida Kanoka'	see *L. speciosum* var. *rubrum* 'Uchida'
'Urandi' (VIIIc/b)	SDeJ
'Val Di Sole'[PBR] (Ia/b)	SDeJ
'Venezuela' (VIIa-b/b-c)	SDeJ SDir
'Visaversa' (VIIIa-b/b)	SDeJ
'Vivaldi' (Ia/b)	SDeJ
vollmeri	see *L. pardalinum* subsp. *vollmeri*
wallichianum (IXb/a)	GKev SDeJ XLum
wardii (IXc/d)	CExl EBee
washingtonianum (IXb/a)	EBee
'Whistler' (Ia/c)	SDeJ
'White' (FantAsiatic Series) (I) **new**	CBod
'White Paradise' (V)	SCoo
'White Pixels' (Ia/b)	SDeJ
'White Planet' (VIa/a)	GKev
'White Present' (Vb/a)	SDeJ
'White Twinkle' (Ia-b/b)	SDeJ
wigginsii	see *L. pardalinum* subsp. *wigginsii*
willmottiae	see *L. davidii* var. *willmottiae*
'Wine Electric' (Ia/c)	SDeJ
xanthellum var. ***luteum*** (IXb-c/d)	WCru
'Yellow Bruse' (I c/c)	SDeJ
'Yellow Cocotte' (Ia/c)	SDir
'Yellow County' (Ia/b-c)	SDeJ
§ 'Yellow Electric' (Ia/b-c)	SDeJ
'Yellow Eye' (Ia/b)	SDeJ
'Yellow' (FantAsiatic Series) (I) **new**	CBod
'Yellow Power' (VIII a-b/b) **new**	GKev
'Yeti' (Ia/b)	SDeJ

lime see *Citrus × aurantiifolia*

lime, Philippine see *Citrus × microcarpa*

limequat see *Citrus × floridana*

Limnanthes (*Limnanthaceae*)

douglasii ♀H5	LCro LOPS MNHC MPri NBir
- subsp. ***rosea***	CSpe

Limnobium (*Hydrocharitaceae*)

spongia **new**	LLWG

Limonium (*Plumbaginaceae*)

bellidifolium	CFis CMea EBou EDAr SWvt
binervosum	NAts
cosyrense	CMea MHer
dumosum	see *Goniolimon tataricum* var. *angustifolium*
gmelinii	SPlb
* - subsp. ***hungaricum***	SBut XLum
latifolium	see *L. platyphyllum*
minutum	CPla
perezii	GJos
§ ***platyphyllum***	CBod CMea EPfP GMaP LRHS LSun MHer MMuc SCob SEND SEdd SGbt SPer SRms SSut WCAu WCot
- 'Blue Cloud'	SRms
- 'Robert Butler'	ECtt GPSL MRav WCot
- 'Violetta'	CBod CTri EBee ECtt EHyd ELan EPfP GBin LRHS MBel MPie NRHS SEdd SPer SPoG WAul WHoo
§ ***sinuatum***	MPri SVic
- Fortress Series	CWCL
tataricum	see *Goniolimon tataricum*
vulgare	LRHS WHer XSen

Linaria (*Plantaginaceae*)

aeruginea	CMea CPBP SBut
- 'Lindeza Violet'	CSpe

- 'Neon Lights'	CSpe EDAr SPoG WFar
- subsp. ***nevadensis*** 'Gemstones'	SGro
alpina	CSpe NRya NSla SRms
anticaria 'Antique Silver'	CExl MMrt MRav WHil
cymbalaria	see *Cymbalaria muralis*
§ ***dalmatica***	CBod EPPr MMuc MPie NBid NGBl NSti SPhx WCot WFar
dalmatica × ***purpurea***	WCot
'Dial Park'	CBod CBre EBee ECtt LSou MHol SPad WBrk WCot WMal WRHF
× ***dominii*** 'Carnforth'	SBut
'Florence Lily Sophia Brown'	WCot WFar
genistifolia	WCot
- W&B BGB-6	WCot WFar
- subsp. ***dalmatica***	see *L. dalmatica*
hepaticifolia	see *Cymbalaria hepaticifolia*
'Lemon Cream' **new**	WCot
* ***lobata alba***	SPlb
* 'Lucy's Pink'	ECha
maroccana Fairy Bouquet Group ♀H6 **new**	LCro LOPS
origanifolia	see *Chaenorhinum origanifolium*
pallida	see *Cymbalaria pallida*
'Peachy'	CBod CBre CDor CSpe ECha ECtt GBin LSou MHol MTis SBut SEdd SMHy SPad SPoG WBrk WCot WFar WRHF WWFP
'Phillant Ruby' **new**	WMal
pilosa	see *Cymbalaria pilosa*
'Pink Kisses'	CBod ECtt LSou MHol MPie MSCN SPad SPoG WBrk WCot WFar WMal WRHF
purpurea	CBod CDor CTri ELan EMor EPfP MBow MHer MNHC NBro NPer NPol SEND SPhx SRms WCot WFar WSFF
- 'Alba'	see *L. purpurea* 'Springside White'
- 'Brown's White Strain'	CBre EPPr WCot
- 'Canon Staid'	CNat
- 'Canon Went'	Widely available
- 'Evensong' **new**	CSpe
- 'Freefolk Piccolo'	SHar
- pink-flowered	CSpe LEdu
- 'Poached Egg'	CMea MAvo WGoo WMal
- 'Radcliffe Innocence'	see *L. purpurea* 'Springside White'
§ - 'Springside White'	CBod CDor CSpe EWTr GJos LRHS NBir NGdn SGro SPhx WFar
repens	WCot WHer
× ***sepium***	WCot
triornithophora	ELan GJos SPlb WKif WWFP
- 'Rosea'	CSpe WMal
vulgaris	CHab CWld EBou EMor EPfP MBow MHer MMuc MNHC NAts NGrd NMir SRms WHer WWild
- f. ***peloria***	CPBP EPPr

Lindelofia (*Boraginaceae*)

anchusoides (Lindl.) Lehm.	NBid

Lindera (*Lauraceae*)

aggregata	CBcs WPGP
angustifolia	NLar
- FMWJ 13156	WCru
assamica B&SWJ 13984 **new**	WCru
benzoin	CBcs CMCN EPfP LRHS MBlu NLar
erythrocarpa B&SWJ 6271	WCru
- B&SWJ 8730	WCru
metcalfiana var. ***dictyophylla*** KWJ 12312	WCru
neesiana B&SWJ 13984 **new**	WCru
obtusiloba ♀H5	CBcs MBlu WLov WPGP
- B&SWJ 8723	WCru
- B&SWJ 11054	WCru
- B&SWJ 12555 from Korea	WCru
praecox	NLar
- B&SWJ 10802	WCru
- B&SWJ 10953 from north Japan	WCru
- B&SWJ 11125 from south Japan	WCru
reflexa	NLar
sericea B&SWJ 11123	WCru
- B&SWJ 11141	WCru
- var. ***lancea***	NLar
- - B&SWJ 11071	WCru
- - B&SWJ 11118	WCru
tonkinensis FMWJ 13123	WCru
triloba B&SWJ 5570	WCru
- B&SWJ 11121	WCru
- B&SWJ 11466	WCru
umbellata B&SWJ 10881	WCru
- var. ***membranacea*** B&SWJ 6227	WCru
- - B&SWJ 10837	WCru

Lindernia (*Linderniaceae*)

grandiflora	CBod LLWG WTor

Linnaea (*Caprifoliaceae*)

borealis	CExl EPot GRum ITim NSla WAbe XEll
- subsp. ***americana***	NWad

Linum (*Linaceae*)

alpinum	SBut
arboreum ♀H4	GKev NBir
flavum	XSen
- 'Compactum'	CBor CFis CMea EBou NSla SRms
'Gemmell's Hybrid' ♀H4	EWes WAbe WThu
grandiflorum ♀H4	LCro LOPS
- 'Bright Eyes'	CSpe
- 'Rubrum'	CSpe
hypericifolium	SPhx
narbonense	CSpe LRHS SPhx
- 'Heavenly Blue'	LSun
§ ***perenne***	CBod EBou ECha ELan ENfk EPfP GKev MHer MNHC SPer SPoG WJek XAbr
- 'Album'	EBee ECha ELan EPfP SBut
- subsp. ***alpinum*** 'Alice Blue'	WAbe
§ - 'Blau Saphir'	MBel NHol SBut
- BLUE SAPPHIRE	see *L. perenne* 'Blau Saphir'
- 'Himmelszelt'	LSun
- 'Nanum' **new**	NSla
- 'Nanum Sapphire'	see *L. perenne* 'Blau Saphir'
rigidum	CPla
rubrum	SPhx
sibiricum	see *L. perenne*
uninerve	WAbe

Lippia (*Verbenaceae*)

canescens	see *Phyla nodiflora* var. *canescens*
chamaedrifolia	see *Glandularia peruviana*
citriodora	see *Aloysia citrodora*

	Name	Suppliers
	dulcis	ENfk MNHC SRms WFar WJek
	nodiflora	see *Phyla nodiflora*
	repens	see *Phyla nodiflora*

Liquidambar ✿ (*Hamamelidaceae*)

	Name	Suppliers
	acalycina	CBcs EBee ELan EPfP NOra SCoo SGol SLim SSta WHwl WLov WMat WPGP
	- 'Burgundy Flush' 🏆^{H5}	CJun NLar SSta
	- 'Spinners'	CBcs CRos EHyd ELan EPfP LMil LRHS SMad WPGP
	formosana	CMCN CMac IArd IMou SGol SReu SSta WPGP
	- 'Afterglow'	CJun NLar
	- 'Ellen'	CJun NLar
	- Monticola Group	CJun SLim SSta
	orientalis	CJun CLnd CMCN EPfP IDee SReu SSta WPGP
	styraciflua	Widely available
	- 'Andrew Hewson'	CJun CLnd CRos EBee EHyd EPfP LRHS MBlu NRHS SSta
	- 'Anja'	CJun MBlu SSta
	- 'Anneke'	CJun SSta
	- 'Aurea'	see *L. styraciflua* 'Variegata' Overeynder
	- 'Aurea Variegata'	see *L. styraciflua* 'Variegata' Overeynder
	- 'Aurora'	CJun
	- 'Burgundy'	CJun MBlu SSta
I	- 'Corky'	LRHS SSta WMat
	- 'Emerald Sentinel'	CJun SSta
	- 'Festeri'	CEnd SSta
	- 'Festival'	CLnd MBlu SGol
	- 'Frosty' (v)	CJun SSta
	- 'Globe'	see *L. styraciflua* 'Gum Ball'
	- 'Golden Sun'PBR	LSRN NLar
	- 'Golden Treasure' (v)	CJun CLnd CMCN LSRN MGos SGol SSta
	- 'Goldmember'	CJun SSta
	- 'Granary Sunset'	SSta
§	- 'Gum Ball'	CCVT CEnd CMCN EBee ELon EPfP EWes NLar NOra SLim SPoG SSta SWvt WLov
	- 'Jennifer Carol'	SSta
	- 'Kia'	CEnd CJun
	- 'Lane Roberts' 🏆^{H6}	CCVT CLnd CMCN CMac CSBt CTho ELan EPfP IArd LMaj LRHS LSRN MAsh MBlu MGos NLar NOra NOrn SCoo SGbt SGsty SPer SPoG SSta SWvt WCFE WHwl WLov WMat
	- 'Lynn'	SSta
	- 'Manon' (v)	CJun
	- 'Midwest Sunset'	CJun MBlu NLar
	- 'Moonbeam' (v)	CJun SLim SSta
	- 'Moraine'	CJun
	- 'Naree'	SSta WHwl
	- 'Nina'	SSta
	- 'Oconee'	CEnd SSta WHwl
	- 'Paarl' (v)	CLnd SGol
	- 'Palo Alto' 🏆^{H6}	CEnd EBee EPfP MBlu SCoo SLim SSta WHwl WLov WMat WMou WPGP
	- 'Parasol'	CEnd CJun CLnd SSta
	- 'Pasquali Fastigiata' **new**	CRos ELan
	- 'Pendula'	CJun MBlu SSta WMou
	- 'Penwood' 🏆^{H6}	CJun NLar SSta
	- 'Red Sunset'	SSta
	- 'Rotundiloba'	CJun CMCN EPfP LRHS MBlu SGsty SSta WLov WPGP
	- 'Savill Torch'	CJun SSta
	- 'Schock's Gold'	CJun NLar SSta
§	- 'Silver King' (v)	CJun CLnd CMCN CMac EBee LRHS MGos NLar NOrn SCoo SGol SLim SPer SSta
	- 'Simone'	SGol SSta
	- 'Slender Silhouette' 🏆^{H6}	Widely available
	- 'Stared'	CEnd CJun CLnd EBee EPfP MBlu MGos NOra SCoo SLim SSta WLov WMat WMou
	- 'Teresa' **new**	EBee
	- 'Thea'	CJun CRos EBee EHyd ELan EPfP LMil LRHS MBlu NRHS SReu SSta
	- 'Variegata' misapplied	see *L. styraciflua* 'Silver King'
§	- 'Variegata' Overeynder (v)	CJun CMac EBee ELan SLim SSta
	- 'White Star' (v)	CJun
	- 'Woorby Rose'	CJun
	- 'Worplesdon' 🏆^{H6}	Widely available

Liriodendron (*Magnoliaceae*)

	Name	Suppliers
	chinense 🏆^{H6}	CBcs CLnd CMCN EBee EPfP MBlu SGol WPGP
	× ***sinoamericanum*** 'Chapel Hill'	MBlu NLar
	- 'Doc Deforce's Delight'	MBlu NLar
	tulipifera 🏆^{H6}	Widely available
	- 'Aureomarginatum' (v) 🏆^{H6}	CBcs CCVT CEnd CMCN CMac CTho ECrN ELan EPfP EWTr LMaj MAsh MBlu MGos MSwo NOrn SGol SMad SPer SPoG SSta WMat WMou
	- 'Fastigiatum'	CEnd CLnd CMCN CTho EBee ECrN ELan EPfP LMaj MAsh MBlu MGos NLar NOrn SGol SPer
	- 'Glen Gold'	CEnd MBlu NLar
	- 'Purgatory'	MBlu
	- 'Roodhaan'	MBlu NLar
	- 'Rotundiloba'	MBlu
	- 'Snow Bird' (v)	EBee MAsh SPoG WMat

Liriope ✿ (*Asparagaceae*)

	Name	Suppliers
	'Big Blue'	see *L. muscari* 'Big Blue'
	exiliflora 'Ariaka-janshige' (v)	EHyd LRHS NRHS
	- SILVERY SUNPROOF misapplied	see *L. spicata* 'Gin-ryu', *L. muscari* 'Variegata'
	graminifolia misapplied	see *L. muscari*
	hyacinthifolia	see *Reineckea carnea*
	'Majestic'	MHer WHoo
	minor	CMac
§	***muscari*** 🏆^{H5}	Widely available
	- 'Alba'	see *L. muscari* 'Monroe White'
	- AMETHYST ('Liptp')	CBod EBee NRHS WNPC
§	- 'Big Blue'	Widely available
	- 'Big Pink'	CBod
	- 'Christmas Tree'	WHoo
	- 'Gold-banded' (v)	CBct EBee EHyd EPfP GWyn LCro LOPS LRHS SCob WFar
	- 'Goldfinger'	CExl EBee SMad
	- 'Ingwersen'	CExl CKno EBee ELon EPPr EPfP NRHS SCob XLum
	- ISABELLA ('Lirf')	EBee EPPr
	- 'John Burch' (v)	CBct CExl ELon SCob WGob WSMil
	- 'Kindi Pink' **new**	ELan
	- 'Lilac Wonder'	EHyd EMor EPPr LRHS
	- 'Moneymaker'	EPPr EPfP LCro LOPS MNrw SCob SPoG XEll
§	- 'Monroe White'	CBct CBod CExl CMac EBee ELan EPfP EShb LCro LOPS MCot MRav NBid NLar SCob SMad SPer SWvt

- 'Okina' (v)	CAby CBod CPla EBee ELon LCro LOPS MBNS MBel MNrw NGBl NLar NSti SEdd SMad SPer SPoG WBrk WCot WMal
- 'Pee Dee Ingot'	CBod SPoG
- 'Royal Purple'	CBct EBee ECtt EHyd ELon EPfP LCro LOPS LRHS MAsh NLar NRHS SCob SPer WHoo
- 'Silver Ribbon'	CBro EPfP LSRN MGos WSMil
- 'Super Blue'	NLar
§ - 'Variegata' (v)	CExl CPla CRos EBee EHyd ELan EWes LCro LEdu LOPS LRHS NBir NRHS SCob SPer SPoG SWvt
- 'Webster Wideleaf'	EBee WCot
platyphylla	see *L. muscari*
spicata	CBod EBee WFar XLum
- 'Alba'	MRav
§ - 'Gin-ryu' (v)	CBct CExl ELan EPfP EShb EWes MAvo MCot MRav NSti SCob SGol SPer XLum
- 'Silver Dragon'	see *L. spicata* 'Gin-ryu'

Litchi (*Sapindaceae*)

chinensis	CCCN

Lithocarpus ✿ (*Fagaceae*)

densiflorus var. ***echinoides***	CMCN
edulis	CExl SArc
fenestratus NJM 13.074 **new**	WPGP

Lithodora (*Boraginaceae*)

§ ***diffusa***	SGol
- 'Alba'	CWCL SPer SPoG
- 'Compacta'	CSma WAbe
§ - 'Grace Ward' ♀H5	ECtt ELan EPfP MHol MMuc NRHS SGbt WIce
§ - 'Heavenly Blue' ♀H5	Widely available
- 'Pete's Favourite'	NWad
- 'Picos'	CMea NLar NSla WAbe WThu
- 'Star' PBR	CBod CWCL EHyd ELan GKev LLWG LRHS MHol NHpl NLar NRHS SCoo SEdd SPer SPoG SWvt WFar WIce
- 'White Star'	WIce
× ***intermedia***	see *Moltkia* × *intermedia*
§ ***oleifolia*** ♀H4	EHyd LRHS NBir NRHS
rosmarinifolia	CRos EBee EHyd LRHS NRHS WCFE
zahnii	EHyd GKev LRHS NRHS SVen
- 'Azure-ness'	CPBP SChF SGro WAbe

Lithophragma (*Saxifragaceae*)

parviflorum	CMiW

Lithops ✿ (*Aizoaceae*)

sp.	CDoC
hallii ♀H2	SSim

Lithospermum (*Boraginaceae*)

diffusum	see *Lithodora diffusa*
doerfleri	see *Moltkia doerfleri*
'Grace Ward'	see *Lithodora diffusa* 'Grace Ward'
'Heavenly Blue'	see *Lithodora diffusa* 'Heavenly Blue'
officinale	GPoy NMir XAbr
oleifolium	see *Lithodora oleifolia*
purpureocaeruleum	see *Buglossoides purpurocaerulea*

Lithraea (*Anacardiaceae*)

caustica	WPav

Litsea (*Lauraceae*)

NJM 13.047	WPGP
glauca	see *Neolitsea sericea*
japonica	CMCN SVen

Littonia (*Colchicaceae*)

modesta	see *Gloriosa modesta*

Livistona (*Arecaceae*)

chinensis ♀H2	CPHo SPalm XBlo
decora	SPalm
rotundifolia	CDoC

Llagunoa (*Sapindaceae*)

glandulosa	WPav

Loasa (*Loasaceae*)

triphylla var. ***volcanica***	EWes WSHC

Lobelia ✿ (*Campanulaceae*)

angulata	see *Pratia angulata*
'Bordervale'	WBor
bridgesii	CDTJ CExl EBee ECtt EWes EWld LEdu LRHS SPad SPlb WKif WPav
§ ***cardinalis*** ♀H3	CMac ELon EWld GMaP LCro LOPS NGBl NLar NPer SPlb SRms SWvt WFar WMAq WSMil
- 'Bee's Flame'	CNor CRos CWGN ECtt EHyd LRHS MArl MRav MSpe NGdn NRHS SRkn WOut WWtn
- 'Black Truffle'	see *L. cardinalis* 'Chocolate Truffle'
§ - 'Chocolate Truffle' PBR	EBee ECtt GBin LSou SPad SRms
§ - 'Elmfeuer'	CWCL ECtt NLar SPlb SPoG SWvt XLum
§ - 'Queen Victoria' ♀H3	Widely available
- 'Russian Princess' misapplied	CRos EHyd EPfP LLWG LRHS MAsh MHol NGdn NRHS SPoG SRkn SWvt WFar WMal
chinensis	LLWG
'Cinnabar Deep Red'	see *L.* × *speciosa* 'Fan Tiefrot'
'Cinnabar Rose'	see *L.* × *speciosa* 'Fan Zinnoberrosa'
COMPLIMENT BLUE	see *L.* × *speciosa* 'Kompliment Blau'
COMPLIMENT DEEP RED	see *L.* × *speciosa* 'Kompliment Tiefrot'
COMPLIMENT PURPLE	see *L.* × *speciosa* 'Kompliment Purpur'
COMPLIMENT SCARLET	see *L.* × *speciosa* 'Kompliment Scharlach'
'Compton Pink'	CBcs CBod CNor ECtt ELan EMor EShb EWTr EWes IPot LBuc LCro LOPS LRHS NBPC NGBl NRHS NSti WFar WOut WWtn
Elizabeth Strangman selection	NDov
erinus BIG BLUE ('Weslobigblue' PBR)	CPla
- 'Cambridge Blue' ♀H2	MBros
- Cascade Series ♀H2	LCro LOPS
- 'Crystal Palace' ♀H2	CPla MBros MPri
- (Fountain Series) 'Fountain Blue'	MBros MPri
- - 'Fountain Rose'	MBros
- - 'Fountain White'	MBros MPri
- 'Mrs Clibran' ♀H2 **new**	LCro LOPS
- Riviera Series	MPri
- 'Sapphire'	LCro LOPS MBros MPri
- 'String of Pearls' ♀H2	MBros
- WATERFALL BLUE ICE (Waterfall Series)	LSou MPri

- 'White Lady'	MBros
excelsa	CSpe SBrt SEND WPav
FAN DEEP RED	see *L.* × *speciosa* 'Fan Tiefrot'
FAN DEEP ROSE	see *L.* × *speciosa* 'Fan Orchidrosa'
FAN SALMON	see *L.* × *speciosa* 'Fan Lachs'
'Flamingo'	see *L.* × *speciosa* 'Pink Flamingo'
fulgens	see *L. cardinalis*
- SAINT ELMO'S FIRE	see *L. cardinalis* 'Elmfeuer'
× ***gerardii***	see *L.* × *speciosa*
giberroa	CDTJ
'Gladys Lindley'	LRHS
'Grape Knee-Hi'	ECtt EHyd LRHS NRHS
'Hadspen Purple'	see *L.* × *speciosa* 'Hadspen Purple'
inflata	GPoy
laxiflora	CFis SAdn WFar
- var. ***angustifolia***	CDTJ CPbh CPla CWCL EWld SBrt SEdd SMHy SRms SVen WCot
linnaeoides	SPlb
§ ***montana***	EWld WMal
- B&SWJ 8220	ESwi WCru
pedunculata	see *Pratia pedunculata*
polyphylla	WPav
'Queen Victoria'	see *L. cardinalis* 'Queen Victoria'
sessilifolia	CExl NLar
- B&SWJ 8875	WCru
siphilitica	CBcs CExl CMac CRos CSpe EHyd ELan EMor EPfP ILea LEdu LRHS MHer MMuc NBPC NGdn NRHS NSti SBrt SGbt SPer SPlb SRms SWvt WCav WFar WHoo WMal WWtn XLum
- f. ***albiflora***	EBee ECtt LEdu WHoo WOut
- - 'Alba'	EMor EPfP SGro SRms SWvt WFar
- 'Rosea'	MNrw
'Sombre Purple'	EBee
§ × ***speciosa***	SVic WFar XLum
- 'Butterfly Blue'	CNor ELan SGbt
- 'Cranberry Crush'	ECtt EHyd LRHS NRHS
- CRIMSON PRINCESS ('Gencrim'PBR) (Princess Series)	CAbb LSou SPoG
- 'Dark Crusader'	EBee ECtt EHyd EPfP LRHS MPie MSpe NDov NRHS SGbt WOut
- Fan Series	MRav
- - 'Fan Blau'	EHyd ELan EMor EPfP LRHS MCot MHol NLar SCob WFar
- - 'Fan Burgundy'	EHyd ELan EMor EPfP LRHS MCot MHer MHol NGdn NLar
§ - - 'Fan Lachs'	CBod EHyd EMor EPfP LRHS MHer MHol NLar SCob WFar WOut
§ - - 'Fan Orchidrosa' 🏆H5	EHyd EPfP LRHS
- - 'Fan Scharlach' 🏆H5	EHyd EPfP LRHS NLar NRHS SPoG SWvt WFar
§ - - 'Fan Tiefrot' 🏆H5	SRms SWvt
§ - - 'Fan Zinnoberrosa' 🏆H5	SRms SWvt
§ - 'Hadspen Purple'PBR	Widely available
- 'Kimbridge Beet'	CMac EBee LRHS
- Kompliment Series	WFar
§ - - 'Kompliment Blau'	SWvt WFar
* - - 'Kompliment Pale Pink'	WFar
§ - - 'Kompliment Purpur'	MMuc SWvt
§ - - 'Kompliment Scharlach' 🏆H5	CWat EHyd EPfP MNrw NPer NRHS SWvt
§ - - 'Kompliment Tiefrot'	EHyd EPfP LRHS MMuc MNrw SWvt
- 'Monet Moment'	CRos CWCL EBee ECtt EHyd ELon EWes ILea LRHS NLar NRHS SWvt
- 'Pauline'	ECtt
- 'Pink Elephant' 🏆H5	ECtt EHyd ELan EMor NRHS SGbt
§ - 'Pink Flamingo'	ELan EPfP LRHS
- ROSE PRINCESS ('Genross'PBR) (Princess Series)	EMor EWTr SPoG
- 'Ruby Slippers'	CMac EBee ELan EPfP
- 'Russian Princess' purple-flowered	ECtt ELan ELon MBel MHer MPie MSpe NDov NGBl NHol SCob SGbt WFar WKif WSMil WWtn
- SCARLET PRINCESS ('Genlet'PBR) (Princess Series)	CAbb
- 'Sparkling Burgundy'	LRHS
- 'Sparkling Ruby'	CAby CBod EBee EMor EPfP EWTr LBuc MCot NDov NRHS SWvt WWtn
- 'Starship Deep Rose'	CBod CRos EHyd MHol NRHS
- 'Starship Scarlet'	CRos EHyd LRHS MBros MHol NRHS SCob
- 'Tania'	Widely available
§ - 'Vedrariensis'	CMac CSpe ECtt EPfP LRHS MBel MMuc MNrw NGBl SRms SWvt WCFE WCav WFar WHoo XLum
'Tania's Sister'	EBee IPot MHol WCot WFar
treadwellii	see *Pratia angulata* 'Treadwellii'
tupa	Widely available
- JCA 12527	IBlr
- Archibald's form	CExl WPGP
valida	SWvt
- 'True Blue'	SWvt
vedrariensis	see *L.* × *speciosa* 'Vedrariensis'
wollastonii	SPlb

Lobostemon (*Boraginaceae*)

belliformis	CPbh

Lobularia (*Brassicaceae*)

maritima GOLF BRIGHT MIXED (Golf Series) **new**	LCro LOPS
- 'Snow Crystals'	MPri
- 'Violet Queen' 🏆H3 **new**	LCro LOPS
PRINCESS IN PURPLE	MHol
SNOW PRINCESS ('Inlbusnopr'PBR)	CPla MHol

loganberry see *Rubus* × *loganobaccus*; also AGM Fruit Section

Loiseleuria see *Kalmia*

Lomandra (*Asparagaceae*)

hystrix	SPlb
longifolia	LEdu SPlb
- PLATINUM BEAUTY ('Roma13') (v)	CBod SPeP SPoG
- TANIKA ('Lm300'PBR)	GBin XCre

Lomaria see *Blechnum*

Lomatia (*Proteaceae*)

dentata	MGil MRav
ferruginea	CBcs CCCN CDTJ CDoC CExl CSde EBee EPfP LRHS MGil MPkF SArc SChF SPoG WCru WPGP
fraseri	CCCN CDoC CRos EBee EHyd EPfP LRHS NLar SPoG WPGP
hirsuta	MGil
longifolia	see *L. myricoides*
§ ***myricoides***	CBcs CCCN CDoC CExl EBee EHyd EPfP LRHS NLar SLon SPer SPoG
tinctoria	CBcs CExl CPbh EPfP IDee LRHS MPkF

Lomatium (*Apiaceae*)

grayi	SPhx

Lomatogonium (*Gentianaceae*)

perenne	GKev

Lonicera ✿ (*Caprifoliaceae*)

sp.	CMen
KR 10106	WPGP
KR 10608	CRHN
§ ***acuminata***	CMCN EBee
- B&SWJ 3480	WCru
- B&SWJ 6743	CRHN WCru
- B&SWJ 6815	WCru
- var. ***acuminata***	WCot
albertii	EPfP MBNS NLar
alseuosmoides	CBcs CRHN EBee EPfP LEdu LRHS MMuc NLar SEND SLon SPoG WCru WPGP WSHC WSpi
× ***americana*** misapplied	see *L.* × *italica*
americana ambig.	ETho
§ ***americana*** (Mill.) K. Koch	CBcs EPfP LEdu MSwo NLar SEND SLim SRms WBor
§ × ***brownii*** 'Dropmore Scarlet'	Widely available
- 'Fuchsioides' misapplied	see *L.* × *brownii* 'Dropmore Scarlet'
caerulea	CRos EPom IDee LRHS MRav SEdi SPre SRms SVic WBor WKor WLov
- var. ***altaica***	LEdu
- 'Atut'	NLar
- 'Duet'	NLar
- var. ***edulis***	CAgr EPfP LBuc LEdu MCoo MMuc NLar WMat
- var. ***kamtschatica***	EPom IDee LCro LOPS NLar WPGP
- - 'Balalaika' (F)	CAgr MCoo
- - 'Borealis' (F)	CAgr
- - 'Eisbar' (F)	CAgr
- - 'Erin' (F)	LEdu
- - 'Fialka'PBR (F)	NLar
- - 'Honey Bee' (F)	CAgr
- - 'Indigo Gem' (F)	CAgr
- - 'Kalinka' (F)	CAgr
- - 'Larisa' (F)	LEdu WPGP
- - 'Maistar' (F)	XAbr
- - 'Maries' (F)	LEdu WFar WPGP
- - 'Morena'PBR (F)	EBee EPom
- - 'Rebecca' (F)	LEdu WPGP
- - 'Ruth' (F)	LEdu WPGP
- - 'Sinoglaska' (F)	NLar
- - 'Vicky' (F)	LEdu WFar WPGP
- - 'Wojtek' (F)	NLar SPre
- 'Kirke'	NLar
* - var. ***longifolia***	NLar
§ ***caprifolium***	CRHN CRos ECrN EHyd EPfP LRHS NLar SPer WCot
- 'Anna Fletcher'	CRHN WCFE
- 'Cornish Cream'	SGol
- f. ***pauciflora***	see *L.* × *italica*
'Celestial'PBR	CRos EPfP LCro LOPS LRHS
chaetocarpa	CEnd WSHC
ciliosa	CRHN WCFE
'Clavey's Dwarf'	EPPr
crassifolia	CBcs EWld GEdr IDee IMou NLar SBrt WPGP
- 'Little Honey'	MBNS MMrt MRav NLar SPoG
deflexicalyx	CMCN NLar
'Early Cream'	see *L. caprifolium*
'Elegant'	see *L. ligustrina* 'Elegant'
elisae	CBcs CMac CRos EPfP EWTr GBin IMou LRHS MMuc NLar NRHS SEle SMad SPoG SSta WCot WHwl WLov
etrusca	MRav
- 'Donald Waterer'	CRHN CRos EPfP LRHS LSRN NLar WFar
- 'Michael Rosse'	ELan IArd LRHS MBNS NLar SNig WLov
- 'Superba' ♀H5	CRHN CRos EBee ELan EPfP LEdu LRHS NLar SEND SLim WSHC
'Fire Cracker'	NLar SLon
flexuosa	see *L. japonica* var. *repens*
fragrantissima	Widely available
giraldii misapplied	see *L. acuminata*
giraldii Rehder	CRHN EBee WSHC
glabrata	SCoo
- B&SWJ 2150	WCru
- 'Damchin La' **new**	WPGP
'Golden Trumpet'	CWGN EPfP LSRN
grata	see *L.* × *americana* (Mill.) K. Koch
× ***heckrottii***	CRHN CSBt NLar
§ - 'American Beauty'	EBee
- 'Gold Flame' misapplied	see *L.* × *heckrottii* 'American Beauty'
- 'Gold Flame' ambig.	GKin LSRN NLar SCob
- 'Gold Flame' hort. ♀H5	CArg CMac CRos EBee EHyd ELan EPfP ETho LBuc LCro LOPS LRHS MAsh MMuc NRHS SEND SLim SNig SPer SPoG SRms SWvt WFar WLov WSHC
§ ***henryi***	CArg CBcs CDoC CMac CRHN CRos EBee EHyd EPfP GKin LRHS LSRN MAsh MGos MMuc MSwo NRHS SCob SEND SLim SNig SPer SPlb SRms WCFE WFar WSHC
- B&SWJ 8109	WCru
- NJM 11.033	WPGP
- 'Copper Beauty'PBR	Widely available
- var. ***subcoriacea***	see *L. henryi*
hildebrandiana ♀H2	CCCN CExl CRHN WPGP
hirsuta	EBee SBrt
hispidula	SBrt
'Honey Baby'PBR	ELon EPfP LCro LOPS NHol NWad WHwl
implexa	CMCN CRHN
insularis	see *L. morrowii*
involucrata	CExl CMCN EBee EPfP MBNS MBlu MMuc SEND WCFE
- var. ***ledebourii***	CBcs CRos EHyd ELan EPPr EPfP LRHS MGil NLar
- - 'Vian'	NLar
§ × ***italica***	CRHN CRos CTri EBee LRHS MBNS MSwo NPer SCob SCoo SPer
§ - HARLEQUIN ('Sherlite') (v)	CMac EPfP LRHS SPlb SRms SWvt
japonica	CMen WFar XSen
§ - 'Aureoreticulata' (v) ♀H5	CMac ELan EPfP EShb LRHS MRav NPer SGol SRms WFar WLov
- 'Cream Cascade'	MSwo NLar SCoo SGol
- 'Dart's Acumen'	CRHN
- 'Dart's World'	CArg CRos CSBt EBee EHyd LRHS NLar NRHS WLov
- 'Halliana'	Widely available
- 'Hall's Prolific' ♀H5	CDoC CRos CSBt EBee EHyd ELan EPfP LBuc LCro LOPS LRHS LSRN MAsh MBlu MGos MHer MRav MSwo NOra NRHS SCob SGol SLim SNig SPad SPoG SWvt WFar
§ - 'Horwood Gem' (v)	CDoC ECtt NLar SCoo SLim

- 'Maskerade' (v)	NLar
- 'Mint Crisp'PBR (v)	CBod CDoC CMac CPla CRos CSBt CWGN EBee ECrN ECtt ELan EPfP EShb LRHS LSRN LSou MGos NLar SGol SLon SNig SPad SPer SPoG SRms SWvt
- 'Peter Adams'	see *L. japonica* 'Horwood Gem'
- 'Princess Kate'	ELan NLar SRms
- 'Red World'	WLov
§ - var. ***repens*** 🏆H5	CMac CRos CSBt CTri ECtt EHyd ELan EPfP EShb LRHS MRav MSwo NLar NRHS SCoo SGol SLim SLon SNig SPad SPer SPoG SRms WFar
- 'Variegata'	see *L. japonica* 'Aureoreticulata'
korolkowii	EPPr MBNS MMuc NBir NLar WAvo WCFE WCot
- 'Blue Velvet'	CAgr MCoo NLar
- 'Mayberry Farm'	MCoo
- var. ***zabelii*** misapplied	see *L. tatarica* 'Zabelii'
lanceolata BWJ 7935	WCru
§ ***ligustrina*** 'Elegant'	LBuc SArc
- 'Lemon Beauty' (v)	CBcs CBod CMac EBee EHyd EShb LSRN MAsh MBNS MGos NLar NWad SCob SGbt SGol SPer SRms SWvt WAvo WFar WLov
§ - var. ***pileata***	CBcs CBrac CCVT CMac CRos CSBt CTri ECrN EHyd ELan EPfP EShb EWTr GQue LBuc MGos MSwo NPer SBrt SCob SGol SPer SRms WAvo WCFE WCot WFar WLov
- - 'Moss Green'	EShb
§ - var. ***yunnanensis***	CArg CBar CBcs CBrac CCVT CDoC CMac CMen CSBt CTri ECrN ELan SEND SEWo SGbt SGol SGsty SPer WMat WTSh XSen
- - EDMÉE GOLD ('Briloni')	MAsh WCot
- - 'Ernest Wilson'	EPPr
- - 'Fertilis'	CBrac
- - 'Golden Glow'PBR	NEoE
- - 'Lemon Queen'	MMuc MSwo
- - 'Maigrün'	CBar CBcs CCVT EBee EHyd ELan EShb GBin MSwo NEoE SCob SPer SWvt WFar
- - 'Red Tips'	EShb NLar SCoo SRms
- - 'Silver Beauty' (v)	CMac ECrN MGos MSwo SPer SPlb SPoG SRms SWvt WFar
- - 'Silver Lining' (v)	WCFE
- - 'Tidy Tips'	CBcs CBod CDoC MTin NEoE SCob
- - 'Twiggy' (v)	CSBt EDAr MAsh NHol NLar NWad SCob WAvo WFar WLov
maackii	CMCN CRos EHyd EPPr EPfP LRHS MRav NLar NRHS WCFE
macrantha B&SWJ 11687	WCru
- WWJ 11606	WCru
'Mandarin' 🏆H5	CBcs CRHN LCro LOPS LRHS MBlu NLar SCoo SGol SWvt WLov WSHC
maximowiczii var. ***sachalinensis***	NLar
§ ***morrowii***	SBrt
- 'Ullung do'	CMCN
myrtillus	NLar SBrt
nitida	see *L. ligustrina* var. *yunnanensis*
- 'Lime Twist' **new**	CBod
- MAYGREEN	see *L. ligustrina* var. *yunnanensis* 'Maigrün'
periclymenum	CCVT CTri CWld GPoy MHer MRav SCob SPlb WSFF XSen
- 'Belgica' misapplied	see *L.* × *italica*
- 'Belgica'	Widely available
- 'Belgica Select'	SNig
- CAPRILIA IMPERIAL ('Inov86'PBR)	LCro LOPS
- CHIC ET CHOC ('Inov205'PBR)	LRHS SPoG WCot
§ - 'Chojnów'PBR	ETho LBuc LRHS
- 'Florida'	see *L. periclymenum* 'Serotina'
- FRAGRANT CLOUD	see *L. periclymenum* 'Chojnów'
- 'Graham Thomas' 🏆H6	Widely available
- 'Harlequin'	see *L.* × *italica* HARLEQUIN
- 'Heaven Scent'	CDoC ETho LBuc LCro LOPS LSRN NLar WFar
- 'Honeybush'	CJun CWGN MAsh MGos NHol NWad SLim WFar WNPC
- 'Munster'	WSHC
- 'Purple Queen'	CChe
- 'Red Gables'	CBod CDoC CRHN ELon LSRN MBNS NLar SCoo SEND SWvt WCot WKif WLov
- 'Rhubarb and Custard'	CDoC LCro LOPS NOra WHwl WNPC
- 'Scentsation'PBR	CMac CRos CSBt CWGN EBee EHyd ELan EPfP GBin LCro LOPS LRHS MAsh NLar NRHS SCoo SLon SPoG WHwl WNPC
- 'Serotina' 🏆H6	Widely available
- 'Strawberries and Cream'	CDoC LCro LOPS NOra WHwl WNPC
- 'Sweet Sue'	CDoC CRHN CRos CTsd EBee EHyd ELan ELon EPfP LRHS LSRN MAsh MGos MSwo NLar NRHS SCoo SNig SPoG SWvt WFar
- 'Winchester'	SRms
pileata	see *L. ligustrina* var. *pileata*
pilosa Maxim.	see *L. strophiophora*
pilosa (Kunth) Willd. ex Kunth	CRHN EWld
- F&M 207	WPGP
prolifera	CRHN NLar
× ***purpusii***	CMac CRHN CTri EBee ECrN LMaj MBNS SCob SRms WCFE WFar
- 'Spring Romance'	CMac
- 'Winter Beauty' 🏆H6	Widely available
quinquelocularis	CMCN
ramosissima	NLar
reticulata 'Silver'	NLar
saccata	EPfP
sempervirens	CBcs CRHN CSBt IDee MRav
- 'Blanche Sandman' **new**	EShb
- 'Cedar Lane'	CRHN CRos EHyd LRHS SBrt
- 'Dropmore Scarlet'	see *L.* × *brownii* 'Dropmore Scarlet'
- 'Leo'	CWGN
- f. ***sulphurea***	CMCN WSHC
- - 'John Clayton'	CRos EHyd EPfP LRHS
setifera 'Daphnis'	CJun EPfP WPGP
similis var. ***delavayi*** 🏆H5	CRHN CWGN EHyd ELan EPfP ETho LRHS MAsh MRav NLar SDix SEND SRms SWvt WCot WCru WSHC
'Simonet'	CWCL EBee NLar
'Spring Purple'	NLar
standishii	CTri WFar
- var. ***lancifolia*** 'Budapest'	CRos EHyd ELan ELon EPfP LRHS MAsh MBlu MRav NLar SRms WFar
§ ***strophiophora***	WAvo
subaequalis	WHwl
- Og 93.329	CExl WPGP WSHC
syringantha	CBcs CRHN CTho EBee ECrN ELan EPfP MMuc MNrw MRav NLar NWad SBut SDix SEND SPer WCFE WFar WSHC

tatarica	CMCN MRav
- 'Alba'	ELan
- 'Arnold Red'	ELan EPfP MBlu NLar SEND
- 'Hack's Red'	CMCN EBee ELan EPfP EWTr LEdu LRHS NLar SCoo SPer SVen SWvt WBor WGrn
§ - 'Zabelii'	ELan MNrw
× ***tellmanniana*** ♀H5	CArg CBcs CBrac CExl CMac CRHN CRos CWCL EBee ECtt EHyd ELan EPfP LCro LOPS LRHS LSRN MAsh MBlu MGos MSwo NLar NRHS SCob SLim SNig SPer SPoG SRms
- 'Joan Sayers'	SCoo WCFE
- 'Pharaoh's Trumpet'	SLon
thibetica	MBlu
tomentella B&SWJ 2654	WCru
tragophylla ♀H5	ELan IMou MBNS MRav NLar NOra SCoo SLim SWvt
- 'Maurice Foster'	CBcs CRHN EBee EWTr LEdu NLar WLov WSpi
trichosantha var. ***deflexicalyx*** new	WHil
× ***xylosteoides***	NLar
xylosteum	EPPr MMuc NLar SGsty
yunnanensis var. ***yunnanensis*** 'Baggesen's Gold' ♀H5	Widely available

Lophomyrtus ✿ (*Myrtaceae*)

§ ***bullata*** ♀H2	CDTJ SPer
- 'Matai Bay'	LRHS
× ***ralphii*** 'Black Pearl'	CDoC CMac CRos EHyd EShb LRHS SCoo SEle SGbt SLim WFar
- 'Gloriosa' (v)	CCCN CTrC
- 'Kathryn'	CBcs CCoa CDoC CSde CTrC LRHS NLar
- 'Krinkly'	SVen
- 'Little Star' (v)	CBcs CCht CSde CTrC EHyd LRHS SEle
- Logan's form (v)	CBcs LRHS MGil NLar NRHS WAvo
- 'Magic Dragon'PBR (v)	CBod CRos EHyd ELan LCro LOPS LRHS MPkF NRHS SEle SGbt SPoG WFar
- 'Multicolor' (v)	CBcs CCoa CDoC EBee EPfP LRHS MRav SVen
- 'Pixie'	CBcs CBod CCoa CDoC CSde CTrC LRHS MAsh SEle SIvy SPoG SVen
- 'Purpurea'	CTrC
- 'Red Dragon'	CBcs CMac CRos EHyd LRHS MAsh MGos NOra NRHS SIvy WFar
- 'Wild Cherry'	LRHS

Lophosoria ✿ (*Dicksoniaceae*)

quadripinnata	CBdn CDTJ

Lophospermum (*Plantaginaceae*)

'Cream Delight'	CCCN
§ ***erubescens*** ♀H2	CRHN SGro
- 'Bridal Bouquet'	CPla
- white-flowered new	EShb SGro
LOFOS WINE RED ('Sun-asaro') (Lofos Series)	EShb
§ 'Magic Dragon'	CPla SEND SLim SPlb
§ 'Red Dragon'	CCCN SGro
§ ***scandens***	CCCN
- 'Joan Loraine' new	SGro

loquat see *Eriobotrya japonica*

Loropetalum (*Hamamelidaceae*)

chinense	SEle
- BLACK PEARL	see *L. chinense* var. *rubrum* 'Pearl'
- CAROLINA MOONLIGHT ('Nci 002') new	SEle
§ - 'Chang Nian Hong'	CDoC LCro LOPS LRHS SEle
- EVER RED	see *L. chinense* 'Chang Nian Hong'
- HOT SPICE	SEle
- 'Ming Dynasty'	MAsh SEle SSta WFar
- var. ***rubrum***	CExl SGsty
- - 'Blush'	CBcs SEle SGol SIvy
- - 'Daybreak's Flame'	CBcs CWld MGil SEle SGol SIvy
- - 'Fire Dance'	Widely available
§ - - 'Pearl'PBR	SGsty WCot
- 'Tang Dynasty'	CBct CDoC EBee WFar

Lotus (*Papilionaceae*)

berthelotii	CCCN CDTJ ECtt EShb LPot MCot
- deep red-flowered ♀H2	SWvt
berthelotii × ***maculatus*** ♀H2	CCCN MCot MSCN
corniculatus	CHab CWld EBou GJos LCro LOPS MBow MCoo MHer MMuc MNHC NAts NGrd NMir SEND SPhx SRms WSFF WWild
- 'Plenus' (d)	GRum
creticus	SPhx
hirsutus ♀H4	CBod CExl ECha ELan EPfP LPot MAsh MCot MRav NSti SAdn SEND SLon SPer SPhx SPlb SPoG SWvt WIce XLum XSen
- 'Brimstone' (v)	MRav SIvy SPer SPoG SWvt
* - var. ***italica***	LSun
- LITTLE BOY BLUE ('Lisbob'PBR)	CRos CSBt EHyd EPfP LRHS NRHS
- 'Lois'	LRHS SIvy SNig SPoG WAvo
jacobaeus	MCot
maritimus	XLum
mearnsii	SPlb
pedunculatus	CHab MCoo NAts NMir SPhx WSFF
pentaphyllus	XSen
tetragonolobus	SPhx SVic WSFF

lovage see *Levisticum officinale*

Loxostigma (*Gesneriaceae*)

kurzii GWJ 9342	WCru

Ludwigia (*Onagraceae*)

inclinata var. ***verticillata*** 'Cuba' new	XBlo
natans	XBlo
palustris	LLWG

Luetkea (*Rosaceae*)

pectinata	GEdr

Luma ✿ (*Myrtaceae*)

§ ***apiculata*** ♀H4	Widely available
§ - 'Glanleam Gold' (v)	Widely available
- 'Nana'	LEdu WJek
- 'Penlee'	WJek
- 'Rainbow's Gold' (v)	EShb
- 'Saint Hilary' (v)	CTrC EPfP WJek WPav
- 'Variegata' (v)	CTri WFar
§ ***chequen***	CBcs CBod CCoa CSde EShb LEdu NLar WJek WPGP WPav

Lunaria (Brassicaceae)

§ ***annua***	GJos LCro LOPS MNHC WCot WSFF
- var. ***albiflora*** ♀H6	LCro LOPS NBir SEND WCot
I - - 'Alba Variegata' (v) ♀H6	CSpe WBrk
- 'Chedglow'	CNat CSpe GBin LEdu LRHS MAvo SGro WCot
- 'Corfu Blue' ♀H6	CSpe EWes GBin SPtp WCot
- 'Cynthia'	CNat
- 'Munstead Purple' ♀H6	CSpe
- 'Nettleton'	CNat
- 'Pattern Pod' **new**	CNat
- purple-leaved	CMea
- 'Ruth'	LEdu
- 'The Optimist'	CNat
- 'Variegata' (v)	CSpe GJos NBir WCot
biennis	see *L. annua*
rediviva ♀H7	CSpe ECha EHyd EMor EPPr GAbr GBin GMaP LEdu LRHS MAvo MBel MHer MMuc NBid NChi NPer NSti SBrt SEND SPtp WCAu WCot WFar WPGP
- 'Partway White' (v)	CMil MAvo WCot

Lunathyrium (Woodsiaceae)

pycnosorum	ISha

Lupinus ✿ (Papilionaceae)

angustifolius	SPhx
arboreus ♀H4	CBcs CRos CSBt CTri CWCL EHyd ELan EPfP LRHS MCoo MGil MHer MNHC MNrw MRav NBir NLar NRHS SCob SEle SIvy SPer SPlb SPoG SRms SVic WFar
- 'Barton-on-Sea'	CBod CDoC CWld ELon SPad
- blue and white-flowered	WFar
- 'Blue Boy'	ELan LRHS SWvt
- blue-flowered	CBcs CBod CRos CWCL CWld EHyd LRHS NLar NRHS SPer SPlb SPoG SRms SWvt WFar WOut
- 'Chelsea Blue'	CRos EHyd EPfP LRHS NRHS
- 'Lavender Spires'	LCro LOPS
- prostrate	WAvo
- 'Snow Queen'	CDoC CPla CWCL SPer SPoG SWvt
- 'Sulphur Yellow'	SWvt
- white-flowered	CBcs CBod CSpe CWld ELan GMaP LEdu MMrt SPlb
- yellow and blue-flowered	NBir SRkn WFar
- yellow-flowered	CBod CDoC CWld ELan SPhx SWvt
arcticus	EBee
'Beefeater'	CRos CWCL EHyd ELan EPfP EWes GBee LBuc LRHS LSou MHol MPri NLar NRHS SPoG
'Blacksmith' **new**	CBcs ECtt EPfP LSou
'Blossom'PBR	CRos CWCL CWGN EHyd EPfP EWes LRHS LSRN LSou MPri NRHS SPoG
caespitosus	see *L. lepidus* var. *utahensis*
(Camelot Series) 'Camelot Blue'	EPfP
- 'Camelot White'	ECul
- 'Camelot Yellow'	ECul
'Cashmere Cream'	CWCL CWGN EBee LRHS MPri NRHS
'Chameleon'	LRHS NRHS
chamissonis	CCCN CSpe CWCL EBee EHyd EWes LRHS NRHS SBut SPer WKif
'Chandelier' (Band of Nobles Series)	CAby CBcs CBod CSBt CTri ELan ELon EPfP GAbr GMaP GQue LCro LOPS MAsh MCot MSCN MWat NBir NGBl NHol NLar SCob SGbt SNig SPer SPhx SPoG SWvt WCAu WFar
'Desert Sun'PBR	CRos CWCL EHyd EPfP LRHS LSou MPri NLar NRHS SPoG
'Dwarf Lulu'	see *L.* 'Lulu'
Gallery Series	CBod CSBt MBros SCob SCoo SPlb WFar
- 'Gallery Blue'	CRos EAJP ECtt ECul EHyd ELan EPfP EWhm LBuc LCro LOPS LRHS LSRN MBros MHol MPri NLar NRHS SCoo SPoG WFar
- 'Gallery Pink'	CRos EAJP EHyd ELan EPfP EWhm LCro LOPS LRHS MHol MPri NLar NRHS SCoo SPoG SRms WFar
- 'Gallery Red'	CRos EAJP ECtt EHyd ELan EPfP EWhm GPSL LCro LOPS LRHS MBros MHol MPri NLar NRHS SCob SCoo SPoG WFar
- 'Gallery Rose'	EWhm LSRN NRHS SPoG WFar
- 'Gallery White'	CRos EAJP ECul EHyd ELan EPfP EWhm LCro LOPS LRHS MBros MHol MPri NLar NRHS SCoo SPoG WFar
- 'Gallery Yellow'	CRos EAJP ECtt EHyd ELan EPfP EWhm LCro LOPS LRHS MBros MHol MPri NLar NRHS SCob SPoG WFar
'Gladiator'PBR	CRos CWCL ECtt EHyd EPfP EWes LRHS LSou MHol MMrt NLar NRHS SCob SPoG
hartwegii **new**	SPhx
'Heathcliffe Blue'	WOut
'Judy Harper'	ECtt GBee LRHS
'Jupiter'	LRHS MPri NLar
'King Canute'	CRos CWCL CWGN EHyd EPfP LRHS MMrt MPri NLar NRHS
latifolius subsp. ***parishii***	EBee
lepidus	CPbh
§ - var. ***utahensis***	SPlb
§ 'Lulu'	EPfP LRHS SGbt SPoG SWvt
'Magic Lantern'	CRos CWCL EHyd EPfP LRHS LSou MHol MMrt NRHS SPoG
'Manhattan Lights'PBR	CBcs CChe CRos CWCL CWGN EPfP EWes LRHS LSou MHol MPri NLar NRHS SCob SPoG
'Masterpiece'PBR	CBcs CDoC CRos CWCL EHyd EPfP EWes GBin LCro LOPS LRHS LSRN LSou MPri NLar NRHS SPoG WCAu
Minarette Group	CRos EHyd EPfP LRHS MNrw NRHS SRms
montanus	SPhx
mutabilis	SPhx
'My Castle' (Band of Nobles Series)	CBcs CBod CRos CSBt CTri ECtt EHyd ELan EPfP GAbr GMaP GQue LRHS LSRN MAsh MBow MGos MWat NGBl NLar NRHS SCob SGbt SNig SPer SPoG SWvt WFar
'Noble Maiden' (Band of Nobles Series)	Widely available
nootkatensis	GLog
'Pam Ayres'	ECtt GBee GBin LRHS
perennis	CBod
'Persian Slipper'PBR	CBcs CChe CRos CWCL CWGN ECtt EHyd EPfP EWes LBuc LRHS LSRN LSou MPri NLar NRHS SCob SPoG WCAu
'Polar Princess'	CWCL CWGN ECtt EHyd EPfP EWes GBee LRHS LSou MHol MMrt MPri NRHS SCob SPoG

'Purple Swirl'	EHyd EPfP LRHS MPri NRHS
'Rachel de Thame'	CChe CRos CWCL CWGN EBee EHyd EPfP EWes LRHS LSou MHol MPri NLar NRHS SPoG
'Red Rum'PBR	CWCL CWGN EHyd LBuc LRHS LSRN MPri NLar NRHS SCob SPoG
§ × ***regalis*** Russell Group	CPla CSBt EPfP MHer SCob SPlb SRms SVic SWvt WFar
'Rote Flamme'	ELon EWes WOut
Russell hybrids	see *L.* × *regalis* Russell Group
'Saffron'PBR	CRos EHyd LBuc LRHS MPri NRHS
'Salmon Star'PBR	CRos CWCL CWGN EHyd LRHS LSou NLar NRHS SCob
sericeus	SPhx
'Silver Fleece'	CCCN CWld EHyd LRHS WFar
'Tequila Flame'PBR	CRos CWCL LBuc LRHS LSou MPri NLar NRHS SCob SPoG
'Terracotta'	CWCL LRHS MPri NRHS SPoG
texensis	CSpe SMHy SPhx WSHC
'The Chatelaine' (Band of Nobles Series)	Widely available
'The Governor' (Band of Nobles Series)	Widely available
'The Page' (Band of Nobles Series)	CAby CBcs CRos EHyd ELan ELon EPfP GBin GMaP LCro LOPS LRHS LSRN LSun MAsh MNHC MSCN NLar NRHS SNig SPer SPoG SWvt WBor WFar
'Thundercloud'	EBee
'Towering Inferno'	CRos CWCL ECtt EHyd EPfP EWes LBuc LRHS LSou MPri NLar NRHS SPoG
varius subsp. ***orientalis***	SPhx
Woodfield hybrids	LRHS

Luzula (*Juncaceae*)

alpinopilosa	EPPr
× ***borreri*** 'Botany Bay' (v)	EHyd GBin LRHS
'Engel'	EPPr EWes
forsteri	IMou
luzuloides 'Schneehäschen'	NWsh WSHC
maxima	see *L. sylvatica*
nivalis	GAbr
nivea	Widely available
pedemontana	EBee
pilosa 'Grünfink'	EBee
- 'Igel'	CBod CKno EShb LEdu NBid WSpi
§ ***sylvatica***	EBee ELan EPPr GBin GQue LRHS MBow MMuc MNHC MRav NBro NLar NMir NPol NRHS SCob SEND SPer WPnP WShi XLum
- from Tatra Mountains, Slovakia	EPPr
- 'A. Rutherford'	see *L. sylvatica* 'Taggart's Cream'
- 'Aurea'	CAby CDoC CKno CRos EBee ECha EHyd EPPr EPfP GWyn LRHS MMuc MRav NRHS NSti NWsh SEND WCot WFar WGrn
- 'Aureomarginata'	see *L. sylvatica* 'Marginata'
I - 'Auslese'	EPPr
- 'Bromel'	EPPr
- 'Hohe Tatra' ♀H7	CBod CSpe EPPr EWes GBin GMaP GQue LEdu MBNS NGdn SCob SPer SPoG
§ - 'Marginata' (v) ♀H7	CKno CPla EBee ECha ELan EMor EPPr GBin GMaP LRHS MAvo MBNS MMuc MRav NBid NGdn NLar NSti SArc SCob SEND WCot WFar WHoo WPnP
- 'Mariusz'	EPPr
* - f. ***nova***	EPPr
- 'Onderbos'	EBee
- 'Solar Flair'	CBod CKno EBee GBin NRHS
- 'Starmaker'	CBod
§ - 'Taggart's Cream' (v)	CRos EBee EHyd EPPr LRHS NHol NRHS NWad WFar
- 'Tauernpass'	EPPr LRHS SPhx
- 'Thierry's Cream' (v)	CAby EBee EMor EPPr MBNS MHol SPoG WBrk WCot WFar
- 'Wäldler'	EBee
- 'Wintergold'	EPPr
ulophylla	GEdr SPlb

Luzuriaga (*Luzuriagaceae*)

polyphylla HCM 98202	WCru
radicans	CCCN CRHN CTsd GEdr WCru WPav WSHC
- RH 0602	ESwi WCru

Lychnis (*Caryophyllaceae*)

alpina	EDAr NGdn WFar WIce XLum
- 'Rosea'	MBel NBir
- 'Snow Flurry'	GKev
§ × ***arkwrightii***	ECha LRHS NRHS
- 'Orange Zwerg'	SGbt
- 'Vesuvius'	CBcs CMac EBee MBel NBPC SCob SPer SRms
chalcedonica ♀H7	Widely available
- var. ***albiflora***	EMor EPPr EPfP NBro NLar WCAu WHrl
- 'Carnea'	EHyd EPPr EPfP EShb LRHS NBPC NGdn SPhx WCAu
- 'Dusky Salmon'	WHrl
- 'Flore Pleno' (d)	EShb WCot
- 'Pinkie'	MMuc NLar NWad
- 'Rauhreif'	NLar SPhx WHer
- 'Rosea'	CBod EMor EPfP NBir WHrl
* - 'Salmonea'	EMor EPPr GPSL NBir SRms
- salmon-pink-flowered	MBow
cognata B&SWJ 4234	ESwi WCru
§ ***coronaria*** ♀H7	Widely available
- MESE 356	MAvo SPhx
- 'Abbotswood Rose'	see *L.* × *walkeri* 'Abbotswood Rose'
- 'Alba' ♀H7	Widely available
- 'Angel's Blush'	GQue LSun NBPC NBir NGrd NLar SBut SRkn
- Atrosanguinea Group	CBod CBre CDoC CRos EHyd EPfP GMaP LRHS MBel MHol MRav MWat NGdn NRHS NSti NWad SCob SGbt SPer WTor
- 'Blood Red'	CSpe GPSL LEdu LRHS WBrk
- 'Cerise'	CCBP MArl NBir
- dark red-flowered	MAvo
- GARDENERS' WORLD ('Blych') (d)	CBod CSpe EBee ECha ECtt EHyd ELan EMor EWes LRHS LSou MAsh MBNS MBel MHol NBPC NRHS NSti SPer SRkn WBrk WCot WSMil
- Oculata Group	CSpe EBee ELan EMor EPPr EPfP LEdu LPot SPlb WFar WKif
§ ***coronata*** var. ***sieboldii***	SBrt SPhx
dioica	see *Silene dioica*
flos-cuculi	Widely available
- var. ***albiflora***	CBre CSam EMor NLar WHer
- JENNY ('Lychjen'PBR) (d)	CDor CRos EBee ECtt EHyd ELan EMor EPfP LEdu LRHS LSRN MBNS MBel MHol MNrw MSCN NDov NRHS NSti SCob SRkn WCAu WCot
- 'Little Robin'	EBou LLWG

	- 'Nana'	CPBP GAbr GJos MHol NGdn NLar WGwG
	- 'Petit Henri' **new**	WTor
	- 'Petite Jenny' (d)	CRos EBee ECtt EHyd EMor GWyn LRHS LSou MBNS MSCN NDov NRHS SCob SPoG SRms WCAu WCot
	- 'White Robin'	Widely available
	flos-jovis ♀H6	CCBP ECha EHyd GJos LRHS NBir NRHS SPhx SRms XLum
	- 'Hort's Variety'	EBee EHyd LRHS NBir NRHS
	- 'Minor'	see *L. flos-jovis* 'Nana'
§	- 'Nana'	CPla GAbr SGro
	- 'Peggy'	EBee EBou EHyd EMor EPfP LRHS NBre NGdn NLar SBut
	× ***haageana***	SRms
	'Hill Grounds'	CElw EBee ECha ECtt ELon WCot WGoo WSHC
	kiusiana	GEdr
	miqueliana	EBee
	'Molten Lava'	CBod EHyd EPfP LRHS NRHS SRms
I	***sieboldii*** 'Plena' (d) **new**	WFar
§	***viscaria***	CWld ECha EMor GJos GPSL
	- 'Alba'	ECha NBre XLum
	- ***alpina***	see *L. viscaria*
§	- subsp. ***atropurpurea***	EHyd ELan EPPr EWes GJos LRHS MMuc MPie SHar SPhx SRms
	- 'Feuer'	EWes NGBl
	- 'Firebird'	EWes
	- 'Plena' (d)	NBPC NBir SRkn
	- 'Schnee'	GJos NGBl NLar
	- 'Splendens'	EMor MBel NGrd SCob SMad WCav WFar XLum
	- 'Splendens Plena' (d) ♀H5	CCBP WSMil XLum
§	× ***walkeri*** 'Abbotswood Rose' ♀H7	MAvo
	wilfordii	NWad
§	***yunnanensis***	NSti SPhx WBrk
	- ***alba***	see *L. yunnanensis*

Lycianthes (*Solanaceae*)

§	***rantonnetii*** ♀H3	CBcs CCCN ELan EShb SEND SIvy SPoG WAvo WKif

Lycium (*Solanaceae*)

	afrum	SVen
	barbarum	CAgr CBcs CCCN CLau CSBt ECrN EPom IDee LCro LEdu LOPS MAsh MCoo MGil MHtn NLar SEND SEdi SPre SVic SWvt WKor WLov XAbr
	- 'Big Lifeberry'	CAgr LEdu
	- 'Number 1 Lifeberry'	CAgr
	- 'Sweet Lifeberry'	CAgr LEdu
	chinense	MGil NQui

Lycopodium (*Lycopodiaceae*)

	clavatum	GPoy

Lycopsis see *Anchusa*

Lycopus (*Lamiaceae*)

	europaeus	CHab EBee GPoy MMuc NAts WSFF

Lycoris (*Amaryllidaceae*)

	aurea	GKev SDeJ WHil
	radiata	CCCN GKev SDeJ WHil

Lygeum (*Poaceae*)

	spartum	XSen

Lygodium (*Lygodiaceae*)

	japonicum	WFib

Lygos see *Retama*

Lyonothamnus (*Rosaceae*)

	floribundus subsp. ***aspleniifolius***	CCCN CExl EBee SArc WPGP

Lysichiton (*Araceae*)

	camtschatcensis ♀H7	CAby CBen CWat ECha GBin LCro LLWG LOPS LRHS NLar NPer SWvt WPnP WShi XLum
	× ***hortensis***	ECha

Lysiloma (*Mimosaceae*)

	watsonii	SPlb

Lysimachia (*Primulaceae*)

	albescens	CExl XLum
§	***atropurpurea***	CBod CSpe EAJP EBee EHyd ELan LRHS NLar SPer WHil
	- 'Beaujolais'	CChe CExl CRos CWld LCro LEdu LOPS LRHS LSun MGos MHol MWat NGBl NRHS SBut SPeP SPoG WHil
	- 'Geronimo'	CSpe
	barystachys ♀H6	LEdu MArl MBel MRav SHar WCot WFar XLum
	- PAB 8755	LEdu
	- 'Huntingbrook'	LEdu MAvo SEdd WPGP WWtn
	CANDELA ('Innlyscand')	CAby CBod CSpe ECtt EHyd GPSL GWyn LRHS LSou MHer MHol MMuc NBir NCou NGBl NRHS SGbt SPoG WCot WTor WWtn
	candida	WCot
	christinae 'Zixin' **new**	LEdu WPGP
	ciliata	CMac ECha EHyd GMaP LRHS MNrw NBir NGdn NLar
§	- 'Firecracker' ♀H6	Widely available
	- 'Purpurea'	see *L. ciliata* 'Firecracker'
	clethroides ♀H6	Widely available
	- 'Geisha' (v)	EBee WCot
	- 'Lady Jane'	CPla CRos MAvo MNrw SRms
	- 'Leigong Storm'	WPGP
§	***congestiflora***	NPer
	- 'Midnight Sun' PBR	CCCN ECtt
	- 'Outback Sunset' PBR (v)	ECtt MBros
	- 'Persian Carpet'	WCot
	- 'Persian Chocolate'	WCot WFar WMal
	ephemerum ♀H6	Widely available
	fordiana Og 454 **new**	SPtp
	fortunei	WFar XEll XLum
	japonica var. ***minutissima***	GRum ITim
	lichiangensis	EHyd GKev GPSL IMou LRHS NBir
	lyssii	see *L. congestiflora*
	minoricensis	GKev WSpi XLum
	nemorum	CWld IMou NAts
	- 'Lola Playle' PBR	WCot
	- 'Pale Star'	CBre
	nummularia	CSBt CWat EPfP GPoy MBow NAts NBir WBrk
	- 'Aurea' ♀H5	CMac CSBt EBou ECha ECtt EPfP GAbr GQue LCro LOPS LPot MBros MHer MMuc MPri MRav NBid NBir NBro NLar NMir SCob SEND SPer SPoG SRms SWvt WWtn XLum
	paridiformis var. ***paridiformis***	LEdu

- - NJM 11.067	WPGP
- var. ***stenophylla***	CDTJ CExl GBin SPtp WMal
punctata misapplied	see *L. verticillaris*
punctata L.	CBod CSBt EBou ECha EPfP GAbr GMaP MHer MMuc MRav NBro NMir NPer SCob SPer SPlb SRms WBrk WCAu WFar WMAq
§ - 'Alexander' (v)	Widely available
- 'Gaulthier Brousse'	EBee MHCG WCot
- GOLDEN ALEXANDER ('Walgoldalex'PBR) (v)	CChe LBuc LRHS MBNS MBros NHol NLar
- 'Golden Glory' (v)	WCot
- 'Hometown Hero'	EBee NLar
- 'Ivy Maclean' (v)	SWvt
- 'Variegata'	see *L. punctata* 'Alexander'
- ***verticillata***	see *L. verticillaris*
'Purpurea'	see *L. atropurpurea*
SNOW CANDLES ('L9902')	EBee EWes MNrw SIvy WFar
thyrsiflora	CWat EBee NPer WCot WMAq
§ ***verticillaris***	CTri WCot
vulgaris	CHab EWat LLWG
- subsp. ***davurica***	WCot
- - B&SWJ 8632	WCru

Lysionotus (*Gesneriaceae*)

gamosepalus B&SWJ 7241	WCru
kwangsiensis HWJ 625	WCru
pauciflorus	IArd
- B&SWJ 303	WCru
- B&SWJ 335	WCru
- HWJ 643 from Vietnam	WCru
- HWJ 811 from Vietnam	WCru
- dwarf B&SWJ 189	WCru
- 'Lady Lavender'	EBee WFar
serratus HWJK 2426	WCru

Lythrum (*Lythraceae*)

anceps	NBre NLar
'Rose Dream'	NWad
salicaria	CBee CBen CCBP CHab CWat CWld EBou ENfk GJos LLWG MBow MCot MHer MMuc MNHC MWts NAts NBro NGrd SEND SPlb SRms WBrk WHer WPnP WSFF WShi WWtn XLum
- 'Augenweide'	XLum
- 'Blush' ♀H7	Widely available
§ - 'Feuerkerze' ♀H7	CAby CBod CMea CRos CSam CWld EBee ECtt ELan ELon EPed EPfP EShb GBin LRHS MArl MBel MRav MSpe NBir NHol NRHS NSti SCob SGbt SPer WFar WHrl WWtn
- FIRECANDLE	see *L. salicaria* 'Feuerkerze'
- 'JS Pink Tails' **new**	IPot NLar
- 'Lady Sackville'	EBee ECtt ECul ELon EMor EPed GMaP IPot LSou MCot MTis NLar WSHC
- 'Little Robert'	ECtt ECul WFar
- 'Morden Pink'	CTri EBee EHyd ELan ELon MMuc NLar NRHS SCob SEND WFar XLum
- 'Prichard's Variety'	ELon
- 'Red Beauty'	LSun
- 'Robert'	Widely available
- 'Robin'	CBod CRos ECtt EHyd EMor LRHS MAsh MHol MPri NDov NLar NRHS SGbt SWvt
- 'Rose'	NBir SWvt
- 'Stichflamme'	ELon
- 'Swirl'	CMea ECtt EHyd ELan ELon EMor EPfP ILea LEdu LLWG MTis NDov NLar NRHS NSti SHar WHoo
- 'The Beacon'	CPla EBee ELon EMor NLar SRms
- 'Zigeunerblut'	ECtt ELon MRav NLar WCAu XLum
virgatum	SMHy SPhx WCFE WOut WSHC
- 'Dropmore Purple'	Widely available
- 'Helene'	IMou NDov SDix
- pale-flowered	NDov
- 'Rose Queen'	IPot MRav
- 'Rosy Gem'	EBee EMor EPfP GJos GMaP LRHS NBPC NBro NRHS SCob SDix SRms SWvt WFar
- 'The Rocket'	CBod CTri EHyd EPfP EShb LRHS MPie MRav NBro NDov NRHS SWvt WFar WPnP

M

Maackia (*Papilionaceae*)

amurensis	CBcs CMCN EPfP GBin LMaj NLar
hupehensis	MBlu NLar

Macadamia (*Proteaceae*)

integrifolia (F)	SVic XBlo

mace, English see *Achillea ageratum*

Macfadyena (*Bignoniaceae*)

unguis-cati	see *Dolichandra unguis-cati*

Machaerina (*Cyperaceae*)

rubiginosa	LLWG

Machilus see *Persea*

Mackaya (*Acanthaceae*)

§ ***bella*** ♀H1b	EShb

Macleaya (*Papaveraceae*)

cordata misapplied	see *M.* × *kewensis*
§ ***cordata*** (Willd.) R. Br. ♀H6	CRos EBee EMor LRHS LSun MHol NBir NRHS SPer SPlb SRms WCAu XLum
- NJM 11.002	WPGP
§ × ***kewensis***	CBod GKev SCob SPoG
- 'Flamingo' ♀H6	EBee EBou ECha ECtt EHyd GWyn LRHS MBNS SMad SPer SWvt WCot WSMil
§ ***microcarpa***	GQue MHol WSMil
- 'Kelway's Coral Plume' ♀H6	CBcs CMac EBee ECtt EHyd ELan EPfP GAbr GMaP LCro LOPS LRHS LSRN MRav NBid NBro NLar SCob SDix SPeP SPer SPoG SWvt WBor WSMil
- 'Spetchley Ruby'	EBee ECha GBin LRHS MRav NLar SPhx WCot XLum

Maclura (*Moraceae*)

pomifera	CBcs CMCN IDee MBlu SBrt SEND SPlb
- 'Cannonball'	CDoC SAko
- 'Naughty Boy'	NLar
- 'Pretty Woman'	NLar

tricuspidata B&SWJ 12755	WCru
- 'Parthenos' (F)	CAgr
- seedless (F)	CAgr

Macrodiervilla see *Weigela*

Macropiper (*Piperaceae*)

§ ***excelsum***	GPoy

Macrothelypteris (*Thelypteridaceae*)

torresiana	CBdn WPGP

Macrozamia (*Zamiaceae*)

communis	CBrP
lucida	CBrP
moorei	CBrP

Maddenia (*Rosaceae*)

hypoleuca	IDee MBlu NLar

Maesa (*Primulaceae*)

japonica CWJ 12371	WCru

Magnolia ✿ (*Magnoliaceae*)

acuminata	CBcs CMCN LMaj
- 'Blue Opal'	CBcs CJun LRHS NLar XLot
* - 'Kinju'	CEnd CJun
- 'Koban Dori'	CBcs CJun
- 'Patriot'	CMCN
- 'Patriot' × (× ***brooklynensis*** 'Yellow Bird')	MAsh
- 'Seiju'	CJun NLar
§ - var. ***subcordata***	CBcs
- - 'Miss Honeybee'	CJun
- - 'Mister Yellowjacket'	CJun
'Advance'	CBcs CDoC CJun NLar
'Albatross'	CBcs CEnd CJun WPGP
'Alex'	CJun LMil LRHS
'Alixeed'	CJun
'Amber'	CJun
'Ambrosia'	CJun
'Angelica'	CJun
'Anilou'	CJun
'Anna'	CJun
'Anticipation'	CBcs CEnd CJun WPGP
'Aphrodite' **new**	NLar
'Apollo'	CBcs CDoC CJun LSRN WPGP
'Apricot Brandy'	NLar
'Archangel'	CJun
ashei	see *M. macrophylla* subsp. *ashei*
'Asian Artistry'	CDoC CJun LRHS
'Athene' ♀H5	CBcs CDoC CEnd CJun LMil NLar SAko WPGP XLot
'Atlas'	CDoC CEnd CJun WPGP XLot
'Aurora'	CJun
'Avocet'	LRHS
'Banana Split'	LMil LRHS MAsh XLot
'Barbara Nell' **new**	XLot
'Betty'	CBcs CMac ELon LRHS LSRN MBlu MGos MMuc NLar SLim SSta SWeb
'Big Dude'	CBcs CEnd CJun EPfP IDee NLar SLim WMat XLot
'Binette'	CJun
biondii	IMou MBlu NLar
'Black Beauty'	CBcs CJun LRHS XLot
'Black Swan'	WPGP
BLACK TULIP ('Jurmag1'PBR)	CBcs CDoC CRos CTho ELan EPfP GGGa LCro LMil LOPS LRHS LSRN MAsh MGos NLar NOrn SCoo SLon SPoG WHwl WMat WPGP XLot
'Blackbird'	LRHS
'Blushing Belle'	CJun
'Brenda'	CJun
'Brixton Belle'	CBcs WPGP
× ***brooklynensis*** 'Evamaria'	CTho XLot
- 'Golden Joy'	CJun
- 'Hattie Carthan'	CBcs CJun LRHS NLar
- 'Woodsman'	CBcs NLar NOra WMat XLot
- 'Yellow Bird'	CBcs CCVT CDoC CEnd CJun CMCN CMac EBee EPfP LMil LRHS LSRN MAsh MBlu MGos MPri MThu NLar NOrn SCob SLim SPoG SWeb WHwl WMat
BURGUNDY STAR ('Jurmag4')	CBcs LCro LOPS SPer SWeb
'Butterbowl'	CJun
'Butterflies'	CBcs CCCN CDoC CJun CRos CTho CTsd EHyd ELan EPfP LRHS LSRN MBlu MGos NLar NOra NRHS SCob SGol SLim SPer SRms SSta WFar WMat WSpi
'Caerhays Belle' ♀H5	CBcs CDoC CJun LMil LRHS NLar SAko SPoG WHwl WPGP
'Caerhays Surprise' ♀H5	CBcs CEnd CJun WPGP XLot
campbellii	CMCN CTsd EPfP LRHS WHwl
- Alba Group	WPGP
- - 'Chyverton'	WPGP
- - 'Ethel Hillier'	CBcs
- - 'Sir Harold Hillier'	CJun WPGP
- - 'Strybing White'	WPGP
- 'Ambrose Congreve'	WPGP
- 'Betty Jessel'	CBcs CJun IDee WPGP
- 'Darjeeling' ♀H4	CBcs CJun LRHS SReu WPGP
- 'Lionel de Rothschild'	WPGP
- subsp. ***mollicomata***	LRHS WHwl
- - 'Lanarth'	CBcs WPGP
- - 'Peter Borlase'	WPGP
- - 'Werrington'	CBcs
- 'Queen Caroline'	LRHS WPGP
- (Raffillii Group) 'Charles Raffill'	CDoC EPfP LMil LRHS SPoG WHwl
- - 'Kew's Surprise'	CBcs WPGP
- 'Sidbury'	CBcs CTho
campbellii × ***sprengeri***	WPGP
'Candy Cane'	CJun
'Carlos'	CBcs CJun NLar XLot
cathcartii	WPGP
- B&SWJ 11802	WCru
- HWJ 874	WCru
caveana	LEdu
- NJM 13.037	WPGP
- NJM 13.044	EBee WPGP
'Cecil Nice'	CBcs CJun
CHAMELEON	see *M.* 'Chang Hua'
§ 'Chang Hua'	CJun NLar XLot
changhungtana × ***insignis***	WPGP
'Charles Coates'	CJun EPfP NLar WPGP
'Charming Lady'	CJun
chevalieri B&SWJ 11802	WCru
- DJHV 06037	WCru
- HWJ 621	WCru
CHINA TOWN ('Jing Ning')	CJun XLot
'Columnar Pink'	CDoC NLar WHwl
'Coral Lake'	CJun LMil LRHS
cordata	see *M. acuminata* var. *subcordata*
'Cornish Chough'	WPGP

	crassifolia hort.	see *M. fansipanensis*
	'Crescendo'	CJun
	'Crystal Chalice'	CJun
	'Cup Cake'	CJun
	'Curlew'	WPGP
	cylindrica misapplied	see *M.* 'Pegasus'
	cylindrica ambig.	CBcs CMCN SPtp
	cylindrica E.H.Wilson	WPGP
	- 'Bjuv'	CJun
	'Daphne' ♀H6	CBcs CDoC CEnd CJun EPfP EWTr LMil LRHS LSRN MAsh NLar SLim SPoG SReu WMat WPGP
	'Darrell Dean'	CJun
	'David Clulow' ♀H5	CBcs CDoC CJun LMaj SSta WPGP
	dawsoniana	CBcs CMCN IDee IMou WSpi
	- 'Barbara Cook'	CJun
	- 'Chyverton Red'	CBcs WPGP
	- 'Ruby Rose'	CJun
	- 'Valley Splendour'	CJun
	'Daybreak' ♀H6	CBcs CJun CTho ELan LMil LRHS MBlu MRav NLar NOra SGol SSta WMat WPGP XLot
	'Deborah'	CJun
	delavayi	CBrP CJun CMCN CTho EPfP LRHS SArc SEND WPGP
	'Delia Williams'	CBcs WPGP
§	***denudata*** ♀H6	CBcs CMCN CTho ELan EPfP LMil MBlu SSta
	- 'Double Diamond'	CJun
	- FESTIROSE ('Minfor')	LRHS
	- 'Forrest's Pink'	CBcs LMaj LRHS XLot
	- FRAGRANT CLOUD ('Dan Xin')	CJun
	- 'Gere'	CBcs CJun
	- 'Ghost Ship'	CJun
	- YELLOW RIVER ('Fei Huang')	CDoC CEnd CJun LMaj NLar NOra SCob SPoG WMat XLot
	doltsopa	CAby CBcs CCCN CExl EPfP IMou LRHS SSta WPGP
	- B&SWJ 13996	WCru
	- NJM 12.028	WPGP
	- NJM 12.047	WPGP
	'Early Rose'	CJun
	'Elegance'	CJun
	'Elisa Odenwald'	LMil LRHS
	'Elizabeth' ♀H6	CBcs CDoC CJun CMCN CRos CTho EHyd EPfP LMil LRHS LSRN MAsh MBlu MGos MPri NLar NOrn NRHS SGsty SPer SPoG SRms SWvt WHwl WMat XLot
	'Emma Cook'	CJun
§	***ernestii***	SBrt WPGP
	'Eskimo'	CJun EPfP WMat
	'F.J. Williams'	CBcs WPGP
	'Fairy'	MThu
	FAIRY BLUSH ('Micjur01'PBR)	CBcs CDoC LCro LOPS MGos WHwl
	FAIRY CREAM ('Micjur02'PBR)	CBcs CCCN LCro LOPS LRHS WHwl
	FAIRY MAGNOLIA WHITE ('Micjur05'PBR)	CBcs CCCN LCro LOPS SPoG WHwl
§	***fansipanensis*** FMWJ 13054	WCru
	- FMWJ 13163	WCru
	'Felicity'	CJun
	FELIX JURY ('Jurmag2'PBR)	CBcs ELan EPfP LRHS
	figo	CBcs CCCN CDoC CExl CRos CTsd EBee EHyd ELan EPfP EShb LRHS MGil NRHS SSta WPGP
	'Fireglow'	CJun
	'Flamingo'	CJun NLar XLot
	floribunda	SReu
	- FMWJ 13384 from Tonkin, Vietnam	WCru
	- NJM 09.179	WPGP
	- WWJ 11874	WCru
	- WWJ 11982 from Tonkin, Vietnam	WCru
	- WWJ 11996	WCru
	- WWJ 12003	WCru
	- WWJ 12011	WCru
	- 'Fansipan Furry'	WCru
	- 'Furry Uok'	WPGP
	× ***foggii*** 'Jack Fogg'	XLot
	fordiana	CExl
	'Foster's Late White' **new**	WPGP
§	***foveolata*** B&SWJ 11749	WCru
	- DJHV 06105	WCru
	- WWJ 11900	WCru
	- WWJ 11929	WCru
	- WWJ 11955	WCru
	'Frank Gladney'	CJun
	'Frank's Masterpiece'	CJun XLot
	fraseri	CBcs CMCN
	'Galaxy' ♀H6	CBcs CBrac CDoC CEnd CJun CMac ELon EPfP IArd IDee LMaj LMil LRHS MAsh MGos MMuc MPri NLar NOrn SAko SLim SSta SavN WMat WMou
	'Genie'PBR	CBcs CCVT CDoC CRos EHyd LMaj LMil LRHS NLar NRHS SCob SWeb WMat WPGP XLot
	'George Henry Kern' ♀H6	CBcs CBrac CLnd CTho EHyd EPfP LRHS MGos MMuc MPri NLar SEND
	'Ghislaine'	WPGP
	'Gladys Carlson'	CJun
	globosa	CExl CRos EHyd LEdu LRHS NRHS WPGP
	'Gold Crown'	CJun
	'Gold Star' ♀H6	CBcs CEnd CJun CRos CTho EHyd LMil LRHS MGos MPri NLar NOra NRHS SPoG SSta WMat WPGP XLot
	'Golden Endeavour'	CJun
	'Golden Gala'	CJun
	'Golden Gift'	CJun LMil LRHS MAsh WPGP
	'Golden Pond'	CJun LRHS
	'Golden Rain'	CJun
	'Golden Sun'	CJun
	'Goldfinch'	CJun
I	× ***gotoburgensis*** Chollipo clone	WPGP
	grandiflora	CBcs CMCN CSBt CTsd EBee EPfP ESwi LCro LEdu LOPS LSRN MGos MMuc MPri MRav NLar NOrn SArc SEND SEWo SWeb WTSh
	- ALTA ('Tmgh'PBR)	LMaj LRHS
	- 'Blanchard'	CBcs CJun LRHS NLar
	- 'Bracken's Brown Beauty'	CRos EHyd LMil LRHS NRHS
	- 'Charles Dickens'	SVen
	- 'Edith Bogue'	LRHS NLar SSta
	- 'Exmouth'	CBcs CDoC CEnd CMCN CMac CRos CSBt CTho CTri EHyd ELan EPfP LMil LRHS LSRN MAsh MBlu MGos NLar NRHS SCob SPer SPoG SRms SSta SWvt
	- 'Ferruginea'	CBcs CBod CJun EPfP SGol WLov
	- 'Flore Pleno' (d)	SGol
	- 'Foothills' **new**	CMCN
	- 'François Treyve'	CDoC EPfP LRHS LSRN NLar WHwl

	– 'Galissonnière'	CBcs CCVT CDoC CRos EHyd EPfP LMaj LRHS MGos MPri SCob SGol SGsty SWvt WHwl
I	– 'Galissonnière Nana'	WHwl
	– 'Goliath'	CBcs ELan EPfP LMaj LRHS MPri SEWo SGsty SPer SSta
	– 'Harold Poole'	CJun
	– 'Kay Parris' ♀H5	CBcs CJun CRos EHyd EPfP LMil LRHS MAsh NRHS SPoG
	– 'Little Gem'	CBcs CBod CCCN CDoC CJun ELan ELon EPfP IDee LCro LMaj LOPS LRHS LSRN SGol SPer SPoG SSta WFar
	– 'Mainstreet'	CJun LRHS
	– 'Monlia'	CJun
	– 'November Fox'	LRHS
	– 'Pistoiese' **new**	SGsty
	– 'Purpan' **new**	NLar
	– 'Russet'	CJun
	– 'Saint Mary'	CJun
	– 'Samuel Sommer'	CJun SLim
	– 'Symmes Select'	CJun
	– 'Treyvei'	CJun
	– 'Victoria' ♀H5	CJun CRos CTho CTri EHyd ELan ELon EPfP LMil LRHS LSRN MAsh MBlu MGos NLar NRHS SPer SSta
	'Green Bee'	CBcs CJun
	'Hawk'	CBcs EBee WPGP
	'Heaven Scent' ♀H5	Widely available
	'Helen Fogg'	CJun
	heptapeta	see *M. denudata*
	'Honey Belle'	CJun
	'Honey Flower'	CJun
	'Honey Liz'	LRHS
	HONEY TULIP ('Jurmag5')	CBcs NLar SPer SWeb
§	'Hong Yun'	CJun
	'Hot Flash'	CBcs CJun
	'Hot Lips'	CJun SLim
	hypoleuca	see *M. obovata* Thunb.
	'Ian's Red'	CBcs CDoC CJun LMaj LMil LRHS WMat WPGP XLot
§	***insignis***	CBcs CExl EBee LEdu LRHS WPGP
	– B&SWJ 11810	WCru
	– NJM 12.040	WPGP
	– WWJ 11854	WCru
	insignis* × *yuyuanensis	WPGP
	'Iolanthe'	CBcs CDoC CEnd CJun CMCN EPfP LRHS MAsh MGos NOrn WMat WPGP
	'Iufer'	CJun
	'J.C.Williams'	CBcs CJun SSta WPGP
	'Jane'	CJun CMac CRos EHyd EPfP LMil LRHS MAsh MGos NOrn NRHS
	'Jersey Belle'	CBcs CJun
	'Joe McDaniel'	CBcs CJun IArd NLar SAko XLot
	'John Bond'	SSta
	'John Congreve'	CJun WPGP
	'Joli Pompom'	CBcs CJun LMil LRHS SSta WMat XLot
	'Judy Zuk'	CBcs CJun LRHS
	× ***kewensis*** 'Wada's Memory'	see *M. salicifolia* 'Wada's Memory'
	'Kim Kunso'	SSta
	kobus	CBcs CCCN CCVT CLnd CMCN CTho CTsd EPfP EWTr GKin LMaj MBlu NLar SEWo SPer WMou
	– B&SWJ 12751	WCru
	– 'Esveld Select'	CJun
	– 'Janaki Ammal'	CJun SAko

§	– 'Norman Gould'	CJun CMCN EPfP
	– 'Octopus'	CJun
	– pink-flowered	CBcs CJun
	– 'White Elegance'	CJun
	– 'Wisley Star'	CJun SSta
	kwangtungensis	WPGP
	laevifolia	CDoC CExl CJun CMCN CTho IMou LRHS MGil WPGP
	– 'Dali Velvet'	CExl
	– 'Gail's Favourite'	CRos EHyd EPfP LMil LRHS MAsh NRHS
	– 'Mini Mouse'	CRos EHyd EPfP LMil LRHS MAsh NRHS
	– 'Summer Snowflake' **new**	NLar
	– 'Willow Leaf'	NLar
	'Laura Saylor'	CJun
	'Leda'	CBcs CJun LMil SSta WPGP XLot
	'Legacy'	CJun WPGP
	'Lemon Star'	CBcs LRHS
	'Lennarth Jonsson'	CJun
	liliiflora 'Darkest Purple'	CJun MPri
§	– 'Nigra' ♀H6	Widely available
	– 'Raven'	LMil LRHS WPGP
*	'Limelight'	CBcs CJun EPfP NLar NOra WMat WPGP XLot
	× ***loebneri*** 'Ballerina'	CBcs
	– 'Donna' ♀H6	CBcs CDoC CJun EPfP LMil LRHS SSta
	– 'Encore'	CJun
	– 'Green Mist'	CJun CRos EHyd LRHS NRHS
	– 'Leonard Messel' ♀H6	Widely available
	– 'Lesley Jane'	CJun
	– 'Mag's Pirouette' ♀H6	CAby CBcs CJun EPfP LMil LRHS SAko SPoG SSta
	– 'Merrill' ♀H6	CBcs CDoC CJun CLnd CMCN CMac CRos CTho EHyd ELan EPfP LMaj LMil LRHS MAsh MGos MMuc MRav NLar NOrn NRHS SGol SGsty SPer SSta
	– 'Neil McEacharn'	CJun
	– 'Pink Cloud'	CJun
	– 'Powder Puff'	CJun
	– 'Raspberry Fun'	CBcs CJun NLar
	– 'Snowdrift'	CJun LMaj SLim
	– 'Spring Snow'	CJun
	– 'Star Bright'	CJun
	– 'White Stardust'	CJun
	– 'Wildcat' ♀H6	CBcs CJun NLar SLim SSta XLot
	– 'Willow Wood'	CJun
	'Lois' ♀H6	CBcs CEnd CJun CRos EHyd EPfP GGGa LMil LRHS NLar NRHS SSta WPGP
	lotungensis	WPGP
	'Lotus'	CBcs CJun WPGP XLot
	'Lucy Carlson'	CJun
	'Luscious'	CJun
	macrophylla	CBcs CBrP CMCN CMac EPfP IDee LRHS MBlu MPkF NLar SMad WPGP
§	– subsp. ***ashei***	CBcs CMCN WPGP
	– subsp. ***ashei*** × ***sieboldii*** **new**	CJun
	– subsp. ***ashei*** × ***macrophylla*** subsp. ***dealbata***	WPGP
	– subsp. ***ashei*** × ***virginiana***	CJun WPGP
	macrophylla* × *sieboldii	CJun
	'Malin'	CJun
	'Manchu Fan'	CBcs CDoC CJun EPfP IArd LMil LRHS LSRN SChF SLim WMat WPGP

§	'March til Frost'	CBcs CDoC CJun LMil LRHS WPGP
	'Margaret Helen'	CBcs CJun WPGP
	'Marj Gossler'	CJun
	'Marjorie Congreve'	WPGP
	'Mark Jury'	CBcs
	martinii	CBcs
	'Mary Nell'	CJun
	'Maryland'	CJun GGGa NLar
	maudiae	CBcs CExl NLar
	'Maxine Merrill'	CBcs CJun
	'May to Frost'	see *M.* 'March Til Frost'
	'Milky Way' ♀H5	CBcs CJun EPfP MGos WPGP
	'Mister Yellowjacket'	CJun
	'Moondance'	CJun
	'Nimbus'	CJun CRos EHyd LRHS NRHS WPGP
	nitida	CExl
	obovata Diels	see *M. officinalis*
§	***obovata*** Thunb.	CBcs CMCN EPfP IDee NLar WPGP
	- B&SWJ 10821	WCru
	- B&SWJ 12626	WCru
	- pink-flowered	WPGP
	obovata* × *sargentiana var. ***robusta***	WPGP
§	***officinalis***	CBcs NLar
	- var. ***biloba***	CBcs CMCN GKev MBlu NLar WPGP
	'Old Port'	CBcs
	'Olivia'	CJun EBee WPGP
	'Paul Cook'	CBcs CDoC CEnd
	'Peaches 'n' Cream'	CBcs CJun
	'Peachy'	CBcs CJun LMil LRHS WMat
§	'Pegasus' ♀H6	CBcs CEnd CJun LMil LRHS SSta
	'Peppermint Stick'	NLar WMat
	'Peter Smithers'	CJun
	'Petit Chicon'	CBcs EBee
	'Phelan Bright'	CBcs CJun SAko WPGP
	'Phillip Tregunna'	CBcs LMil WPGP
	'Phil's Masterpiece'	CJun
	'Pickard's Sundew'	see *M.* × *soulangeana* 'Sundew'
	'Piet van Veen'	CJun
	'Pink Beauty' **new**	XLot
	'Pink Delight'	CJun XLot
	'Pink Goblet'	CRos EHyd LRHS NRHS
	'Pink Surprise'	CJun
	'Pinkie'	CJun
	'Porcelain Dove'	CBcs CJun LMil LRHS WPGP
	'Premier Cru'	LRHS
	'Princess Margaret'	CBcs CDoC CJun LMil WMat
	'Pristine'	EPfP LMil LRHS
	× ***proctoriana***	CBcs CRos EBee EHyd LMil LRHS MBlu MMuc NRHS WPGP
	- 'Robert's Dream'	CJun CRos EHyd LRHS MAsh NRHS SSta
	- 'Slavin's No 44'	CJun
	- 'Slavin's Snowy'	CTsd
	'Purple Breeze'	CJun LRHS MBlu NLar SAko SLim
	'Purple Globe'	CEnd CJun
	'Purple Platter'	CBcs
	'Purple Sensation'	CBcs CJun SLim WPGP
	'Purple Star'	WPGP XLot
	'Raspberry Ice'	CMac CRos EHyd EPfP LRHS MAsh NRHS SRms
	'Raspberry Swirl'	SSta
	'Rebecca's Perfume'	CBcs CJun LRHS NLar WMat
	'Red as Red'	CBcs CDoC CJun SLim XLot
	'Red Baron'	CJun
	'Red Lion'	CBcs CJun LRHS
	'Ricki'	CJun CMac LSRN MBlu
	'Roseanne'	CJun
	rostrata	CExl WPGP
	'Rouged Alabaster'	CBcs
	'Royal Crown'	CBcs EPfP IArd LRHS
	'Ruby'	CBcs CJun
	'Ruth'	CBcs
	salicifolia	CBcs CMCN MMuc WSpi
	- var. ***concolor***	CJun
	- 'Garden House Upright'	EBee
	- 'Jermyns'	CJun
	- 'Louisa Fete'	CJun LMaj
	- 'Miss Jack'	CMCN
*	- 'Rosea'	CJun
	- upright	WPGP
	- 'Van Veen'	CJun WPGP
§	- 'Wada's Memory' ♀H6	CExl CJun CMCN EHyd ELan EPfP LMaj LMil LRHS MAsh MBlu MMuc MPri SPer SSta WFar WMat
	- 'Windsor Beauty'	CJun SSta
	'Sangreal' **new**	NLar
	sapaensis FMWJ 13315	WCru
	- FMWJ 13330	WCru
	- HWJ 533	WCru
	- NJM 09.168	WPGP
	'Sara Koe'	CJun WMat
	sargentiana	CBcs SSta
	- 'Broadleas'	CJun
	- var. ***robusta***	CBcs CMCN EPfP MMuc
	- - ***alba***	SavN
	- - 'Blood Moon'	CBcs CJun EBee WPGP
	- - 'Multipetal'	WPGP
	'Satisfaction'	CBcs ELon NLar XLot
	'Sayonara' ♀H6	CBcs CDoC CJun EPfP LMaj LMil LRHS WMat
	'Scented Gem'	SSta
	'Schmetterling'	see *M.* × *soulangeana* 'Pickard's Schmetterling'
	'Sentinel'	WMat XLot
	'Serene'	CBcs CEnd CJun EPfP IArd LMil LRHS XLot
	SHIRAZZ ('Vulden')	CBcs CDoC EPfP IArd LMil LRHS NLar SLim SPoG WPGP
	sieboldii	Widely available
	- B&SWJ 4127	WCru
	- 'Colossus' ♀H6	CBcs CJun EBee MBlu SAko WPGP
	- 'Genesis'	CJun NLar
	- 'Genesis' × ***tripetala***	CJun
	- 'Genesis' × ***virginiana***	CJun
	- 'Michiko Renge' (d)	CJun
	- 'Min Pyong-gal'	CJun
	- 'Pride of Norway'	CBcs CJun EBee
	- subsp. ***sieboldii*** B&SWJ 12553 from Korea	WCru
	- subsp. ***sinensis***	CBcs CJun CMCN CTho ELan EPfP WPGP
I	- - 'Grandiflora'	CJun WPGP
	- 'White Flounces' (d)	CJun NLar
	'Sir Harold Hillier'	CBcs WPGP
	'Snow Goose'	CJun
	'Solar Flair'	CBcs CJun NLar
	× ***soulangeana***	Widely available
	- 'Alba Superba'	CBcs CDoC CTsd EPfP LCro LMil LOPS LRHS MBlu MMuc MRav NLar SLim SPer SPoG SavN WFar WSpi
	- 'Alexandrina'	CBcs CLnd EPfP MBlu
	- 'André Leroy'	EPfP LRHS
	- 'Beugnon'	IArd

- 'Big Pink'	XLot
- 'Brozzonii' ♀H6	CDoC CMac EPfP LMil LRHS SSta
- 'Cleopatra'PBR	CBcs NLar XLot
- 'Fukuju'	CJun
- 'Just Jean'	CJun
- 'Lennei'	CBcs CBrac CMCN CMac CRos CSBt CTho EHyd EPfP IArd LRHS MGos MRav NOrn NRHS SCob SPer SPoG SRms WFar WLov
- 'Lennei Alba'	CMCN ELan IArd MBlu NLar NOra WFar WMat WSpi
- 'Nigra'	see *M. liliiflora* 'Nigra'
- 'Pickard's Opal'	CMCN
§ - 'Pickard's Schmetterling' ♀H6	CBcs EPfP LMil MAsh
- 'Pickard's Snow Queen'	CBcs CJun
- 'Pickard's Sundew'	see *M. × soulangeana* 'Sundew'
- 'Picture'	CBcs NOrn
- 'Purpliana'	MPri
- RED LUCKY	see *M.* 'Hong Yun'
- 'Rubra' misapplied	see *M. × soulangeana* 'Rustica Rubra'
§ - 'Rustica Rubra'	CBcs CBod CMCN CRos CTri EHyd EPfP LMil LRHS LSRN MAsh NLar NRHS SGol SRms SavN
- 'San José'	CJun LMil LRHS MAsh WFar
- 'Speciosa'	SSta SavN
§ - 'Sundew'	EPfP NLar
- 'Superba'	CMac LRHS
- 'Verbanica'	EPfP LMil LRHS MAsh
'Spectrum' ♀H6	CBcs CEnd CJun EPfP IArd IDee IMou LMaj LMil LRHS MBlu MGos MMuc SSta
sprengeri from Guizhou, China	WPGP
- var. ***diva***	CBcs CEnd CExl LMil WPGP XLot
- - 'Burncoose' ♀H6	CBcs
- - 'Copeland Court' ♀H6	CJun LMil LRHS WPGP
- - 'Dark Diva'	CJun
- - 'Diva'	LRHS WPGP
- - 'Eric Savill' ♀H6	CJun WPGP
- - 'Lanhydrock'	CBcs CDoC CJun WPGP
- - 'Marwood Spring'	CBcs CJun LMil WPGP
- - 'Westonbirt'	WPGP
'Spring Rite'	CJun
'Star Wars' ♀H5	CBcs CCVT CDoC CEnd CExl CJun CMac CRos CTho CTsd EHyd ELan EPfP GGGa LMil LRHS MAsh MGos NOra NOrn NRHS SEWo SPoG SSta WHwl WMat WPGP XLot
'Stellar Acclaim'	CBcs CJun LMil
stellata	Widely available
- 'Centennial' ♀H6	CJun LMil
- 'Chrysanthemumiflora'	CJun
- 'Dawn'	CJun
- 'Jane Platt' ♀H6	CBcs CJun CRos EHyd ELan EPfP LMil LRHS MGos NLar NRHS SSta WPGP
- f. ***keiskei***	CBcs CEnd CJun MGos NHol SLim
- 'Kikuzaki'	CJun
- 'King Rose'	CBcs CJun CTsd EPfP SPer
- 'Massey'	CJun
- 'Norman Gould'	see *M. kobus* 'Norman Gould'
- 'Rosea'	CBod CJun CLnd CMCN ELan ELon EPfP LMaj LMil MGos MPri MRav MSwo NLar NOrn SCob SWeb WFar
- 'Rosea Massey'	CJun
- 'Royal Star' ♀H6	CAby CBcs CBrac CCVT CDoC CEnd CJun CLnd CMCN CRos CTho CTri ELon EPfP ILea LMil LRHS MBlu MGos MRav NLar NRHS SCob SGol SPer SSta WFar WMou
- 'Scented Silver'	CJun CRos LMil LRHS
- 'Shi-banchi Rosea'	CJun
- 'Water Lily'	CBcs CDoC CJun CMac CMCN CRos CTho EHyd ELan ELon EPfP LMil LRHS LSRN MAsh MBlu MGos NRHS SCob SPer SPoG SSta WPGP
- 'Wisley Stardust'	LRHS
'Summer Solstice'	CBcs CJun EBee EPfP LMil LRHS SSta WPGP
'Summer Sonnet' **new**	WPGP
'Sun Ray'	CJun
'Sunburst'	CBcs CJun SRms
'Sundance'	CBcs CJun MBlu
'Sunrise'	CBcs LRHS SAko
'Sunsation'	CBcs CJun ELan LRHS NLar SLim
'Sunset Swirl'	CBcs CJun
'Sunspire'	CJun
'Suntown'	CJun
'Susan' ♀H6	Widely available
'Susanna van Veen'	CBcs CDoC CEnd CJun LMil WPGP
'Swedish Star'	CJun
'Sweet Merlot'	CBcs CJun
'Sweet Valentine'	CBcs CJun NLar WPGP
'Sweetheart' ♀H5	CBcs CJun
'Sybille'	CMCN SLim WPGP
'Theodora'	CBcs LMil LRHS SSta XLot
× ***thompsoniana***	CBcs CMCN
- 'Olmenhof'	IArd
'Thousand Butterflies'	CJun
'Tikitere' **new**	XLot
'Tina Durio'	CBcs CDoC LRHS NLar WMat
'Todd Gresham'	CJun
'Tranquility'	CBcs CJun
tripetala	CBcs CExl CMCN ELan EPfP LMaj MBlu NLar SSta
- 'Bloomfield'	CJun
'Ultimate Yellow'	CJun NLar
× ***veitchii***	CBcs
- 'Columbus'	CJun LRHS WPGP
- 'Isca'	CBcs
- 'Peter Veitch'	CTho
virginiana	CBcs CJun CMCN LMaj
- var. ***australis*** 'Green Shadow'	SGol
§ - 'Jim Wilson'	CJun EPfP MBlu
- MOONGLOW	see *M. virginiana* 'Jim Wilson'
'Vulcan'	CBcs CDoC CEnd CJun ELan EPfP LRHS NLar NOrn
× ***watsonii***	see *M. × wieseneri*
'Wedding Vows'	CJun
'White Mystery'	CJun XLot
§ × ***wieseneri***	CBcs CJun CMCN EBee EPfP LRHS MBlu NLar SPer WPGP
- 'Aashild Kalleberg'	CBcs CJun WPGP XLot
- 'William Watson'	SSta
wilsonii ♀H6	CBcs CCVT CDoC CExl CJun CMCN CRos CTho CTri EHyd ELan EPfP IArd IDee LRHS MBlu MGos MMuc MNrw SEND SSta WGob WPGP
- 'Gwen Baker'	CEnd CJun
'Yaeko'	XLot
'Yellow Fever'	CBcs CJun WPGP
'Yellow Garland'	CJun
'Yellow Lantern' ♀H6	CBcs CEnd CJun CRos EHyd ELan EPfP GGGa LMaj LMil LRHS LSRN MAsh MBlu NLar NRHS SPoG SSta WPGP XLot

'Yellow Sea'	CJun LRHS
Yuchelia No. 1	CBcs WPGP
yunnanensis	CCCN CTsd ELon MPkF
zenii	CBcs CMCN IArd IDee IMou
- 'Pink Parchment'	CJun

× *Mahoberberis* (*Berberidaceae*)

aquisargentii	CBcs CMac CRos EBee EHyd EMil EPfP LRHS MMuc MRav NLar SEND WFar
'Dart's Desire'	NLar
miethkeana	SRms
§ ***neubertii***	NLar

Mahonia ✿ (*Berberidaceae*)

§ ***aquifolium***	CAgr CBcs CBrac ECrN GPoy MGos MMuc MRav SCob SEND SGbt SGol SPer SPlb SWvt
- 'Apollo' ♀H5	CBcs CDoC CMac CRos CTho EBee EHyd ELan EPfP LCro LOPS LRHS LSRN MAsh MBlu MGos MRav NLar SCob SCoo SPoG SRms SWvt WFar
- 'Atropurpurea'	CMac CSBt CTsd ELan EPfP MRav NLar SPer
- 'Fascicularis'	see *M.* × *wagneri* 'Pinnacle'
- 'Moseri'	NLar SPer WLov
- 'Smaragd'	CMac CRos ELan EPfP LRHS LSRN MBlu MGos MRav NLar SCob
- 'Versicolor'	MBlu
'Arthur Menzies'	CRos EHyd LRHS NRHS
§ ***bealei***	CBcs CBod CBrac CDoC CRos CSBt CTho EHyd ELan ELon EPfP LRHS MAsh MGos MRav MSwo NLar NPer SCob SCoo SGol SLim SWvt
BLACKFOOT ('Bokrafoot'PBR)	CRos EHyd ELan EPfP LRHS MAsh SLon
bodinieri	WPGP
- Og 93.033	WPGP
chochoco	CExl
confusa* × *gracilipes	WSpi
§ ***duclouxiana***	SPtp
- KR 7692	WPGP
'Esme' **new**	WPGP
eurybracteata	CExl LRHS WCru WPGP
- subsp. ***ganpinensis***	SEND WPGP
- - 'Soft Caress'	CBcs CBod CDoC CMCN CRos EBee EHyd ELan EPfP EWTr LCro LOPS LRHS MGos MRav NLar NRHS SCob SCoo SGol SPad SPoG SWvt SavN WSMil
- 'Minganpi'PBR	LSRN
- 'Narihira' **new**	SGsty
- 'Sweet Winter'	CDoC EBee IDee LRHS MAsh MMrt SPer SWvt
eutriphylla misapplied	see *M. trifolia*
fargesii	see *M. sheridaniana*
fortunei	CBcs
- 'Curlyque'	WPGP
gracilipes	CExl CMCN EBee EPfP ESwi EWes IMou MBlu NLar SMad WAvo WCru WPGP
gracilis	EBee
haematocarpa	EBee WPGP
hartwegii	WPGP
huiliensis	see *M. sheridaniana*
japonica ♀H5	CBar CBcs CDoC CMac CRos CTri EBee ECrN EHyd EPfP LRHS MAsh MGos MMuc MRav MSwo NHol NLar NRHS SCob SEND SGbt SPer SPoG SRms SSta WCFE
- 'Gold Dust'	MBlu
lanceolata	WPGP
leschenaultii B&SWJ 9535	WCru
× ***lindsayae***	IMou WPGP
- 'Cantab' ♀H4	EBee EPfP WPGP
lomariifolia	see *M. oiwakensis* subsp. *lomariifolia*
longibracteata	GKin
mairei	see *M. duclouxiana*
× ***media*** 'Buckland' ♀H5	CBcs CMac CRos CTho EPfP SRms WLov
- 'Charity'	Widely available
- 'Lionel Fortescue' ♀H5	CBcs CBod CMac CRos CSBt CTho EBee EHyd EPfP GKin LRHS MAsh NRHS SPer SWvt
- 'Winter Sun' ♀H5	Widely available
moranensis	CExl EBee
- T 292	WPGP
napaulensis	NLar
- 'Maharajah'	IArd IMou NLar
nervosa	CMac EPfP MBlu WCru WPGP
- B&SWJ 9562	WCru
- B&SWJ 13580	WCru
neubertii	see × *Mahoberberis neubertii*
nevinii	SBrt
nitens	EBee WCru WPGP
- 'Cabaret'PBR ♀H4	CBcs CRos EBee EHyd EPfP LCro LOPS LRHS LSRN MAsh MBlu MGos NRHS SCob SPoG SSta SWvt WSpi
oiwakensis	NLar WPGP
- B&SWJ 371	WCru
- B&SWJ 3660	LEdu WCru
- PBR 371 from Hong Kong	WCru
§ - subsp. ***lomariifolia*** ♀H4	CExl CRos EPfP IMou LRHS SArc SPtp
pallida	CExl SPtp WPGP
'Pan's Peculiar'	EBee WPGP
pinnata misapplied	see *M.* × *wagneri* 'Pinnacle'
pinnata (Lag.) Fedde 'Ken S. Howard'	NLar WPGP
- 'Maurice Foster'	NLar
- subsp. ***insularis*** 'Schnilemoon'	WPGP
repens	NLar WKor WSpi
- 'Rotundifolia'	SPlb
× ***savilliana***	EBee NLar WPGP
§ ***sheridaniana*** Og 93033	WPGP
- Og 93056	WPGP
SIOUX ('Bokrasio'PBR)	CRos EHyd LRHS MAsh NRHS SPoG
§ ***trifolia***	IArd IMou LRHS
- EKB 4618	EBee WPGP
trifoliolata	SMad
volcania B&SWJ 10400	WCru
× ***wagneri***	SWvt
- 'Hastings' Elegant'	NLar
§ - 'Pinnacle' ♀H5	CRos EHyd ELan EPfP LRHS MAsh MBlu NLar SPoG SWvt WFar
- 'Sunset'	MBlu NLar
- 'Undulata'	MBlu NLar SPer
- 'Vicaryi'	NLar

Maianthemum (*Asparagaceae*)

amoenum B&SWJ 10390	WCru
atropurpureum	WCru
bicolor	LEdu
bifolium	CAvo CBct GLog GMaP LEdu MAvo MBel MNrw NBro SRms WCru WShi WThu XLum
- from Yakushima, Japan	GRum

§ - subsp. ***kamtschaticum***	CAvo EMor EPPr LEdu MAvo NLar NRya WCot WPGP
- - B&SWJ 4360	WCru
- - CD&R 2300	WCru
- - var. ***pumilum***	EBee LEdu WCru
canadense	EAJP EBee EPPr EPot LEdu MNrw NBid SIvy WCru
chasmanthum	see *M. bifolium* subsp. *kamtschaticum*
comaltepecense B&SWJ 10215	WCru
dilatatum	see *M. bifolium* subsp. *kamtschaticum*
flexuosum	EWld LEdu
- B&SWJ 9069	WCru
- B&SWJ 9079	WCru
- B&SWJ 9150	WCru
aff. ***flexuosum*** B&SWJ 9026	WCru WFar
- B&SWJ 9055	WCru
formosanum B&SWJ 349	EPPr WCru WFar
forrestii	WCru
fuscum	WCot WCru WPnP
- var. ***cordatum***	WCru
- 'Shirui Giant'	WPGP
- 'Tangkhul Giant'	LEdu
gigas B&SWJ 10470	WCru
henryi	GKev LEdu WCru WPGP
- BWJ 7616	WCru WFar
japonicum	LEdu
- B&SWJ 1179	WCru
- B&SWJ 4714	WCru
- B&SWJ 7306	WCru
oleraceum	CBct CExl GEdr GKev LEdu SDir WFar WHil WPnP
- B&SWJ 2148	WCru
paniculatum	LEdu SHar
- B&SWJ 9137	WCru
- B&SWJ 9140	WCru
- purple-flowered B&SWJ 9139	WCru
pendent, B&SWJ 10305 from Guatemala	WCru
purpureum	LEdu
- G-W&P 150	EPPr
racemosum 🏆H6	Widely available
- subsp. ***amplexicaule***	ILea
- - 'Emily Moody'	CBct CExl EPPr EPfP IPot SChF WCot WPGP
- 'Major'	EHyd LRHS
aff. ***salvinii***	CBct
- B&SWJ 9000	WCru
- B&SWJ 9030 **new**	ESwi
- B&SWJ 9088	WCru
- B&SWJ 10402	WCru
scilloideum B&SWJ 10407	WCru
* - var. ***roseum*** B&SWJ 10335	CBct WCru
stellatum	CBct CSam EBee ECha EHyd EMor EPPr EPfP GQue ILea IMou LEdu LRHS NChi NLar NRHS WCru WFar WKor WPnP XLum
szechuanicum	WCru
tatsienense	CBct CExl GEdr GKev LEdu WCru

Maihuenia (*Cactaceae*)

poeppigii	SPlb
- F&W 9670	WCot
- JCA 2.575.600	WCot

Maihueniopsis (*Cactaceae*)

darwinii	SPlb

Mallotus (*Euphorbiaceae*)

japonicus B&SWJ 14613	WCru
- B&SWJ 14679	WCru

Malotigena (*Aizoaceae*)

§ ***frantiskae-niederlovae***	CCCN CSma EBou EPot GEdr NHpl SSim WHal WIce XLum
- 'Album'	see *M. frantiskae-niederlovae* 'White Nugget'
- 'Gold Nugget' 🏆H4	EHyd LRHS NRHS
§ - 'White Nugget'	CCCN CSma EPot EWes GEdr LRHS NHpl NRHS SSim WIce

Malus ✿ (*Rosaceae*)

§ 'Adirondack' 🏆H6	CLnd CSBt ELan EPfP LBuc LCro LOPS LRHS MMuc MPri NLar NOra SCoo SPoG WJas WMat WMou
'Admiration'	see *M.* 'Adirondack'
× ***adstringens*** 'Almey'	ECrN
- 'Hopa'	CAgr CLnd
- 'Simcoe'	EBee
'Aldenhamensis'	see *M.* × *purpurea* 'Aldenhamensis'
'Allow Super' (D)	WMat
'Appletini' (D) **new**	LCro LOPS
baccata	CLnd CMCN CTho GKev NOra SCoo SEND SPlb
- 'Braendkjaer' **new**	CLnd
- var. ***mandshurica***	CTho
- 'Street Parade'	LMaj
'Barbara'	WMat
§ ***bhutanica***	CLnd
- 'Mandarin'	SCoo
brevipes	CLnd LRHS SCoo
- 'Wedding Bouquet' 🏆H6	EBee EPfP LCro LSRN MAsh NLar NOra SPer WMat
'Butterball' 🏆H6	CLnd CSBt CTho EBee EPfP EPom LMaj LRHS NOra SCoo SEdi SLim SPer SPoG SRms SVic WJas WMat WMou WWct
'Candymint Sargent'	NOra SLim SPoG
'Cave Hill'	CLnd
'Cheal's Scarlet'	CHab
* 'Cheal's Weeping'	CLnd CMac SEdi SRms WMou
COCCINELLA ('Courtarou')	LMaj SGol SMad
'Comtesse de Paris' 🏆H6	CLnd EBee EPfP EWTr LRHS MAsh MBlu NLar NOra NOrn WMat
CORALBURST ('Coralcole')	LCro LOPS MAsh NOra SPoG WMat
coronaria	SPtp
- var. ***dasycalyx*** 'Charlottae' (d)	CCVT CLnd EWTr SPer
- 'Elk River'	NOra SCoo WMat
'Cowichan'	CLnd ECrN SSFr
'Crimson Brilliant'	CLnd
'Crittenden'	EPfP
'Dartmouth'	CHab CLnd CSBt CTri
'Directeur Moerlands'	CArg CCVT CLnd CSBt ECrN EPfP LMaj LRHS NOra SCoo SEND SPer SWvt WMat
domestica 'Acklam Russet' (D)	CHab SKee
- 'Acme' (D)	ECrN
- 'Adams's Pearmain' (D)	CArg CHab CLnd CTho CTri ECrN NOra SKee WMat WWct
§ - 'Alexander' (C)	SKee
- 'Alfriston' (C)	CAgr CHab SKee WMat
§ - 'Alkmene' (D) 🏆H6	CAgr ECrN NOra SKee
- 'All Doer' (C/D/Cider)	SEdi
- 'Allen's Everlasting' (D)	SKee

- 'Allington Pippin' (D)	CArg CHab CSBt CTri ECrN MGos NOra SKee WMat
- AMBASSY ('Dalil'[PBR]) (D)	SEdi SSFr
- 'American Mother'	see *M. domestica* 'Mother'
- 'Ananas Reinette' (D)	CHab SKee
- 'Annie Elizabeth' (C)	CAgr CArg CHab ECrN IArd MGos NLar NOra SKee SSFr SVic WJas WMat WWct
- 'Apache' (F)	SSFr
- 'Api' (D)	LSRN MPri NOra SKee WMat
- 'Api Noir' (D)	SKee
- 'Ard Cairn Russet' (D)	ECrN IArd SKee
- 'Aromatic Russet' (D)	SKee
- 'Arthur Turner' (C) ♀H6	CArg CCVT CHab CLnd CTri ECrN EPom LBuc MWat NOra SKee SSFr WJas WMat
- 'Arthur W. Barnes' (C)	SKee
- 'Ashmead's Kernel' (D) ♀H6	CAgr CArg CHab CLnd CRos CSBt CTho CTri EBee ECrN EPfP EPom LBuc LRHS MRav MWat NOra SEdi SKee SLim SLon SSFT SSFr SVic WJas WMat WWct
- 'Ashton Bitter' (Cider)	CHab CTri
- 'Ashton Brown Jersey' (Cider)	CArg
- 'Askham Pippin' (F)	MCoo
- 'Autumn Pearmain' (D)	SKee
- 'Baker's Delicious' (D)	ECrN NOra SKee SSFr WMat
- (Ballerina Series) 'Ballerina Bolero' (D)	WMat
- - 'Ballerina Polka' (D)	WMat
- - 'Ballerina Samba' (D)	CArg LCro NLar WMat
- 'Ballyfatten' (C)	IArd
- 'Ballyvaughan Seedling' (D)	IArd
- 'Balsam'	see *M. domestica* 'Green Balsam'
- 'Banana Pippin' (F)	CEnd
- 'Banns' (D)	ECrN
- 'Bardsey' (D)	CAgr CArg CHab EPom NOra SKee WGwG WMat
- 'Barnack Beauty' (D)	CHab NOra SKee
- 'Barnack Orange' (D)	SKee
- 'Baron Ward' (C)	CHab
- 'Baumann's Reinette' (D)	SKee
- 'Beauty of Bath' (D)	CAgr CArg CCVT CHab CLnd CTho CTri ECrN ELan EPom LBuc MRav MWat NOra SEdi SKee SPer SSFr WJas WMat WWct
- 'Beauty of Blackmoor' (D) **new**	CLnd
- 'Beauty of Hants' (C/D)	CLnd ECrN
- 'Beauty of Kent' (C)	SKee
- 'Beeley Pippin' (D)	SKee
- 'Belfleur Krasnyi' (D)	SKee
- 'Bell Apple' (Cider/C)	CTho
- 'Belle de Boskoop' (C/D) ♀H6	CAgr CHab ECrN MCoo NOra SKee
- 'Bembridge Beauty' (F)	CHab
- 'Ben's Red' (D)	CAgr CDoC CEnd CTho CTsd SKee WMat
- 'Bess Pool' (D)	CHab
- 'Bewley Down Pippin'	see *M. domestica* 'Crimson King' (Cider/C)
- 'Bismarck' (C)	SKee
- 'Black Dabinett' (Cider)	CArg CEnd CTho WMat
- 'Blenheim Orange' (C/D) ♀H6	Widely available
- 'Blood of the Boyne' (D)	IArd
- 'Bloody Ploughman' (D)	CArg CHab CLnd ECrN MAsh NOra SKee SLon WMat
- 'Blue Moon' (D)	LRHS
- BOLERO	see *M. domestica* 'Tuscan'
- 'Bonum' (D/C)	WMat
- 'Bountiful' (C)	CAgr CArg CLnd CMac CSBt CTri ECrN EPom LRHS LSRN MAsh MRav NLar NOra SKee SSFT SSFr WMat WWct
- 'Braddick's Nonpareil' (D)	SKee
- 'Braeburn' (D)	CAgr CArg CLnd CSBt ECrN EPom LBuc LEdu LRHS MWat NOra SEND SEWo SEdi SKee SPer SSFr WJas WMat
- 'Braeburn Hillwell' (D)	EPom NOra
- 'Braintree Seedling' (D)	ECrN
- 'Bramley 20' (C)	CSBt LCro LOPS SGbt WMat
- 'Bramley's Seedling' (C) ♀H6	Widely available
- 'Bramley's Seedling' clone 20 (F)	CLnd CSBt CTsd EBee LBuc LSRN MAsh MNHC MWat NLar NOra SCoo SKee SLim SPoG WWct
- 'Bramshott Rectory' (D/C)	CLnd
- 'Bread Fruit' (C/D)	CEnd CTsd
- 'Bright Future' (D)	CArg EPom NOra WMat WWct
- 'Brith Mawr' (C)	WGwG
- 'Broadholme Beauty' (C)	CArg EPom NOra WMat
- 'Brown Crofton' (D)	IArd
- 'Brownlee's Russet' (D)	CAgr CHab CTri MCoo NOra SKee SSFr WMat
- 'Brown's Apple' (Cider)	CAgr CArg CHab CTri NOra WMat
- 'Burrowhill Early' (Cider)	WMat
- 'Bushey Grove' (C)	SKee
- 'Calville Blanc d'Hiver' (D)	NOra SKee
- 'Cambusnethan Pippin' (D)	SKee
- 'Camelot' (Cider/C)	SEdi
§ - 'Captain Broad' (Cider/D)	CDoC CEnd CTho CTsd
- 'Captain Kidd' (D)	EPom NOra
- 'Captain Tom' (C/D)	WMat
- 'Carlisle Codlin' (C)	NLar NOra WMat
- 'Carswell's Honeydew' (D)	SKee
- 'Carswell's Orange' (D)	SKee
- 'Catherine' (C)	SKee
- 'Catshead' (C)	CAgr CArg CDoC CHab CTri ECrN NOra SKee WMat WWct
- 'Cellini' (C)	NOra SKee
- 'Cevaal' (D)	WWct
- 'Channel Beauty' (D)	WGwG
- 'Charles Ross' (C/D) ♀H6	CAgr CArg CCVT CHab CLnd CMac CSBt CTho CTri ECrN EPom IArd LBuc LRHS LSRN MAsh MCoo MRav NOra SCob SKee SLim SPer SSFT SSFr WJas WMat WWct
- 'Cheddar Cross' (D)	CAgr CCVT CTri ECrN
- 'Chelmsford Wonder' (C)	ECrN SKee
- 'Chisel Jersey' (Cider)	CAgr CTri NOra SKee
- 'Chivers Delight' (D)	CAgr CArg CLnd EBee ECrN EPom LBuc LRHS MCoo NOra SKee SSFr
- 'Christmas Pearmain' (D)	CAgr CArg CLnd ECrN SKee SSFr WMat
- 'Christmas Pippin'[PBR] (D) ♀H6	CArg CRos CTri EBee EPom LBuc LCro LRHS MCoo MPri NLar NOra NRHS SGbt WMat
- 'Cider Lady's Finger' (Cider)	SKee
- 'Cissy' (D)	WGwG
- 'Claygate Pearmain' (D)	CAgr CHab CTri ECrN MCoo NOra SKee SVic WMat
- 'Cleeve' (D)	SKee
- 'Clopton Red' (D)	ECrN

- 'Cobra' (F) — CAgr CArg MCoo MPri NOra SKee SPoG SSFr WJas WMat
- 'Cockle Pippin' (D) — CAgr SKee
- 'Cockpit' (C) — CHab
- 'Coeur de Boeuf' (C/D) — SKee
- 'Coleman's Seedling' (Cider) — CTho
- 'Collogett Pippin' (C/Cider) — CDoC CEnd CTho CTsd
- 'Core Blimey' (D) — EPom LRHS
- 'Cornish Aromatic' (D) — CAgr CArg CDoC CTho CTri CTsd NOra SKee WMat
- 'Cornish Gilliflower' (D) — CAgr CDoC CEnd CHab CTho CTsd ECrN MCoo NOra SKee WMat
- 'Cornish Honeypin' (D) — CDoC CEnd CTsd SKee SSFr
- 'Cornish Longstem' (D) — CAgr CEnd
- 'Cornish Mother' (D) — CEnd CTho
- 'Cornish Pine' (D) — CDoC CEnd CTsd SKee
- 'Cornish Queen' (C/D) **new** — CTsd
- 'Coronation' (D) — CHab
- 'Costard' (C) — CHab SKee
- 'Coul Blush' (D) — GBin SKee WMat
- 'Court of Wick' (D) — CAgr CArg CHab CTho ECrN NOra SKee SVic WMat
- 'Court Pendu Plat' (D) — CAgr CArg CHab GQue LEdu MAsh MWat NOra SKee SSFT WJas WMat WWct
- 'Court Royal' (Cider) — SKee
- 'Cox Cymraeg' (D) — WGwG
- 'Cox's Orange Pippin' (D) — Widely available
- 'Cox's Rouge de Flandres' (D) — SKee
- 'Cox's Selfing' (D) — CMac CSBt CTri EBee EPfP LBuc LRHS MAsh MGos MNHC NLar SKee SPer SPoG WJas WMat WWct
- 'Crawley Beauty' (C) — CAgr CArg CHab SKee SSFT WMat
- 'Crawley Reinette' (D) — CHab
- 'Crimson Beauty of Bath' (D) — CAgr
- 'Crimson Bramley' (C) — IArd SKee
- § 'Crimson King' (Cider/C) — CAgr
- 'Crimson King' (D) — CAgr CHab CTri
- 'Crimson Peasgood' (C) — ECrN
- 'Crimson Victoria' (Cider) — CTho
- § 'Cripps Pink'^{PBR} (D) — SSFr
- CRISPIN — see *M. domestica* 'Mutsu'
- 'Croen Mochyn' (D) — WGwG
- § 'Crowngold' (D) — EPom
- 'Dabinett' (Cider) — CAgr CArg CHab CMac CTho CTri EPom LBuc NOra SKee WMat WWct
- 'D'Arcy Spice' (D) — CAgr ECrN EPfP GQue MCoo MWat NOra SKee WMat WWct
- 'Decio' (D) — SKee
- 'Devonshire Buckland' (C) — CEnd CTho
- 'Devonshire Quarrenden' (D) — CAgr CHab CTho NOra SKee SVic WMat
- 'Diamond' (D) — WGwG
- 'Discovery' (D) ♀H6 — Widely available
- 'Doctor Harvey' (C) — ECrN SKee
- 'Doctor Hogg' (C) — CLnd
- 'Doctor Kidd's Orange Red' — see *M. domestica* 'Kidd's Orange Red'
- 'Doddin' (D) — WWct
- 'Domino' (C) — MCoo
- 'Don's Delight' (C) — CTho WMat
- 'Downton Pippin' (D) — CHab SKee
- 'Duchess of Oldenburg' (C) — NOra SKee
- 'Duchess's Favourite' (D) — SKee
- 'Duck's Bill' (D) — SKee
- 'Dufflin' (Cider) — CTsd
- 'Duke of Cornwall' (C) — CTho
- 'Duke of Devonshire' (D) — CSBt CTri
- 'Dumeller's Seedling' — see *M. domestica* 'Dummellor's Seedling'
- § 'Dummellor's Seedling' (C) ♀H6 — CHab MCoo NOra SKee
- 'Dunkerton Late Sweet' (Cider) — CArg CCVT CHab SEdi WMat
- § 'Dutch Mignonne' (D) — SKee
- 'Eady's Magnum' (C) — SKee
- 'Early Blenheim' (D/C) — CEnd
- 'Early Bower' (D) — CEnd
- 'Early Julyan' (C) — GBin
- 'Early Victoria' — see *M. domestica* 'Emneth Early'
- EARLY WINDSOR — see *M. domestica* 'Alkmene'
- 'Early Worcester' — see *M. domestica* 'Tydeman's Early Worcester'
- 'Easter Orange' (D) — CLnd
- 'Eccleston Pippin' (D) — SKee
- 'Ecklinville' (C) — SKee
- 'Eden' (D) — WMat
- 'Edith Hopwood' (D) — ECrN
- 'Edward VII' (C) ♀H6 — CHab NOra SKee WMat WWct
- 'Egremont Russet' (D) ♀H6 — Widely available
- 'Ellis' Bitter' (Cider) — SKee SVic
- 'Ellison's Orange' (D) ♀H6 — CAgr CArg CHab CLnd CMac CSBt CTri ECrN EPfP EPom LBuc LRHS MMuc MWat NOra SEND SEdi SGbt SKee SLon SPer SRms SSFr SVic SWeb WJas WMat WWct
- 'Elstar' (D) ♀H6 — CCVT CLnd ECrN EPom NOra SEdi SKee
- 'Elton Beauty' (D) — SKee
- § 'Emneth Early' (C) ♀H6 — CAgr CArg CHab ECrN NOra SEdi WJas WMat WWct
- 'Emperor Alexander' — see *M. domestica* 'Alexander'
- 'Empire' (D) — NOra SKee
- 'English Codlin' (C) — CTho CTri
- 'Epicure' — see *M. domestica* 'Laxton's Epicure'
- 'Eros' (D) — ECrN
- 'Esopus Spitzenburg' (D) — SKee
- 'Excelsior' (C) — ECrN
- 'Exeter Cross' (D) — CSBt ECrN
- 'Exquisite' (D) — SRms SWeb
- 'Eynsham Dumpling' (C) — MWat
- 'Fair Maid of Devon' (Cider) — CAgr CArg CEnd WMat
- 'Falstaff' (D) — CAgr CTri ECrN EPfP EPom LSRN MGos NOra SCoo SEdi SKee SPer SSFr
- 'Fameuse' (D) — NOra SKee
- 'Farmer's Glory' (D) — CAgr CTho WMat
- 'Fearn's Pippin' (D) — SKee
- 'Feuillemorte' (D) — SKee
- 'Fiesta' (D) ♀H6 — Widely available
- 'Fillbarrel' (Cider) — CHab
- 'Fillingham Pippin' (C) — CHab
- 'Firedance' (D) — LRHS
- 'First and Last' (D) — NOra WMat
- 'Flamenco' — see *M. domestica* 'Obelisk'
- § 'Flower of Kent' (C) — CHab EPom MAsh NOra SKee SSFr WMat
- 'Flower of the Town' (D) — CHab SKee
- 'Forfar' — see *M. domestica* 'Dutch Mignonne'
- 'Forge' (D) — CAgr CHab SKee
- 'Fortune' — see *M. domestica* 'Laxton's Fortune'

	Cultivar	Suppliers
	- 'Foxwhelp' (Cider)	CArg CHab SKee
	- 'Francis' (D)	SKee
	- 'Frederick' (Cider)	CArg WMat
	- 'Freyberg' (D)	NOra SKee
	- 'Fuji' (D)	LMaj NOra SGsty SKee
	- 'Gala' (D)	CSBt CTri EBee EPom NOra SCoo SEdi SGbt SKee SSFr WMat
	- 'Galaxy'PBR (D)	NOra SEdi
	- 'Galloway Pippin' (C)	GBin NLar NOra SKee WMat
	- 'Garden Fountain' (D)	LRHS
	- 'Gascoyne's Scarlet' (C/D)	SKee
	- 'Gavin' (D)	CAgr
	- 'Genet Moyle' (C/Cider)	CTri MCoo WMat
	- 'George Carpenter' (D)	CTri SKee
	- 'George Cave' (D)	ECrN IArd MCoo NOra SEdi SKee SSFr WJas
	- 'George Neal' (C)	CAgr
	- 'Gibbon's Russet' (D)	IArd
	- 'Gladstone' (D)	CAgr NOra SKee WMat WWct
	- 'Glansevin' (D)	WGwG
§	- 'Glass Apple' (C/D)	CEnd
	- 'Gloster '69' (D)	CLnd
	- 'Gloucester Royal' (D)	SKee
	- 'Golden Ball' (Cider)	CTho
	- 'Golden Bittersweet' (D)	CAgr CTho WMat
	- 'Golden Delicious' (D)	CArg CCVT CMac ECrN ELan EPom LBuc LMaj LRHS MPri NOra SEWo SEdi SGsty SKee SSFr SVic WMat
	- 'Golden Harvey' (D)	CAgr SKee
	- 'Golden Jubilee' (F)	CEnd
	- 'Golden Knob' (D)	CTri SKee
	- 'Golden Noble' (C) ♀H6	CAgr CTri ECrN IArd MCoo NOra SKee
	- 'Golden Nugget' (D)	CAgr
	- 'Golden Pearmain' (D)	LMaj
	- 'Golden Pippin' (C)	CAgr NOra SKee WMat
	- 'Golden Reinette' (D)	SKee
	- 'Golden Russet' (D)	CAgr ECrN NOra SKee
	- 'Golden Spire' (C)	CHab MCoo NOra SKee
	- 'Grandpa Ailes' (D)	CTho
	- 'Grandpa Buxton' (C)	CHab
	- 'Granny Smith' (D)	CBcs ECrN LMaj LSRN NOra SEdi SGbt SGsty SKee SPer SVic WMat
	- 'Gravenstein' (D)	CHab NOra SEdi SKee
§	- 'Green Balsam' (D)	CHab CTri
	- 'Green Roland' (C/D)	ECrN
	- 'Greenfinch' (D)	LRHS
	- 'Greensleeves'PBR (D) ♀H6	CAgr CArg CMac CTri ECrN ELan EPfP EPom MAsh MGos MMuc NLar NOra SEND SEdi SKee SLim SPer SSFT SSFr WJas WMat WWct
	- 'Greenup's Pippin' (D)	CHab
	- 'Grenadier' (C) ♀H6	CAgr CArg CHab CLnd CTri ECrN EPom MGos MMuc NLar NOra SEND SEdi SKee SLon SPer SSFT SSFr WJas WMat
	- 'Groninger Kroon' (D)	CLnd
	- 'Guillevic' (Cider)	CHab
	- 'Gwell Na Mil' (D)	WGwG
	- 'Halstow Natural' (Cider)	CAgr
	- 'Hambledon Deux Ans' (C)	CLnd SKee
	- 'Hangy Down' (Cider)	CArg WMat
	- 'Hanwell Souring' (C)	SKee
	- 'Harling Hero' (D)	ECrN
§	- 'Harry Master's Jersey' (Cider)	CAgr CArg CTho CTri EPom NOra SKee WMat WWct
	- 'Harry Master's Red Streak' (Cider) **new**	SEdi

	Cultivar	Suppliers
	- 'Harry Pring' (D)	SKee
	- 'Harvey' (C)	SKee
	- 'Hawthornden' (C)	CHab SKee
	- 'Herefordshire Redstreak' (Cider)	CAgr CArg EPom LBuc NOra WMat
	- 'Herefordshire Russet'PBR (D)	CArg EBee EPom LBuc LRHS MAsh MCoo NLar NOra NRHS SKee SPer SSFr WJas WMat WWct
	- 'Herring's Pippin' (C/D)	CTri
	- 'Hoary Morning' (C)	CTho ECrN
	- 'Hocking's Green' (C/D)	CAgr CEnd CTsd
	- 'Hollow Core' (C)	CAgr
	- 'Holstein' (D)	LMaj NOra SEdi SKee
	- 'Honey Pippin' (D)	ECrN
§	- 'Honeygold' (D)	CEnd
	- 'Horneburger Pfannkuchen' (C)	SKee
	- 'Horsham Russet' (D)	SKee
	- 'Howgate Wonder' (C) ♀H6	CAgr CArg CCVT CHab CLnd CSBt CTri ECrN EPfP EPom LBuc LRHS MMuc MWat NOra SEdi SKee SPer SSFr SVic WJas WMat WWct
	- 'Hubbard's Pearmain' (D)	SKee
	- 'Hunter's Majestic' (D/C)	ECrN
	- 'Idared' (D)	ECrN NOra SEdi SKee SSFr SVic WMat
	- 'Improved Keswick' (C/D)	CEnd
	- 'Improved Lambrook Pippin' (Cider)	CArg CTri
	- 'Ingrid Marie' (D)	SKee SSFr
	- 'Irish Peach' (D)	CAgr CArg CHab CTri ECrN IArd MCoo NOra SKee SSFr WMat
	- 'Isaac Newton's Tree'	see *M. domestica* 'Flower of Kent'
	- 'Isle of Wight Pippin' (D)	CLnd
	- 'Jackson's'	see *M. domestica* 'Crimson King' (Cider/C)
	- 'James Grieve' (D) ♀H6	Widely available
	- JAZZ ('Scifresh'PBR) (D)	SSFr
	- 'Jersey Beauty' (C/D)	CLnd
	- 'Jester' (D)	ECrN SSFr
	- 'Joaneting' (D)	CAgr CHab
	- 'John Broad'	see *M. domestica* 'Captain Broad'
	- 'John Standish' (D)	CAgr CTri SKee
	- 'John Toucher's'	see *M. domestica* 'Crimson King' (Cider/C)
	- 'Johnny Andrews' (Cider)	CAgr
	- 'Johnny Voun' (D)	CEnd CTsd
	- 'Jonagold' (D) ♀H6	CArg CLnd CTri ECrN ELan EPom IArd NLar NOra SEdi SGsty SKee SPer SSFr WWct
	- 'Jonagold Crowngold'	see *M. domestica* 'Crowngold'
§	- 'Jonagored' (D)	NOra SEdi WMat
	- 'Jonathan' (D)	NOra SKee
	- 'Julie's Late Golden' (F)	CTri
	- 'Jumbo' (C/D)	MAsh MCoo NOra SKee WJas WMat
	- 'Jupiter'PBR (D) ♀H6	CAgr CArg CSBt CTri ECrN EPfP LSRN MRav NLar NOra SEdi SKee SLon SSFr WJas WMat
	- 'Kandil Sinap' (D)	SKee
	- 'Karmijn de Sonnaville' (D)	NOra SKee
§	- 'Katja' (D)	CAgr CArg CCVT CLnd CMac CTri EBee EPfP EPom GQue IArd LBuc MAsh MRav NLar NOra SCoo SEWo SEdi SKee SPer SRms SSFr WJas WMat WWct
	- KATY	see *M. domestica* 'Katja'
	- 'Kenneth' (D)	WGwG
	- 'Kent' (D) ♀H6	ECrN
	- 'Kentish Fillbasket' (C)	SKee

- 'Kerry Pippin' (D) — IArd SKee
- 'Keswick Codlin' (C) — CArg CHab EBee ECrN LRHS MCoo NLar NOra SKee SSFr WJas WMat
- § 'Kidd's Orange Red' (D) 🏆H6 — CAgr CArg CLnd CMac CRos CTri ECrN EPfP EPom LBuc LRHS MWat NOra SKee SLon SSFr WMat WWct
- 'King Byerd' (C/D) — CDoC CEnd
- 'King George V' (D) — CLnd
- § 'King of the Pippins' (D) 🏆H6 — CArg CHab CLnd CTri ECrN EPom LBuc MCoo NOra SGsty SKee SVic
- 'King's Acre Bountiful' (C) — SKee
- 'King's Acre Pippin' (D) — NOra WMat
- 'Kingston Bitter' (Cider) — CTho
- 'Kingston Black' (Cider/C) — CAgr CArg CEnd CHab CMac CTho CTri EPom LBuc MGos NOra SKee WMat
- 'Knobby Russet' (D) — SKee SSFr
- 'Lady Henniker' (C) — CEnd CHab ECrN SKee
- 'Lady Hollendale' (D) — SKee
- 'Lady Lambourne' (C/D) — CHab SKee
- 'Lady of the Wemyss' (C) — GBin
- 'Lady Sudeley' (D) — CEnd CHab SKee
- 'Lady's Finger' (C/D) — CDoC CEnd
- 'Lady's Finger of Lancaster' (C/D) — CHab
- 'Lady's Finger of Offaly' (D) — IArd
- 'Landsberger Reinette' (D) — SKee
- 'Lane's Prince Albert' (C) 🏆H6 — CAgr CArg CHab CLnd CSBt CTri ECrN EPfP LRHS MGos MRav MWat NOra SCoo SEdi SSFr SVic SWeb WMat
- § 'Laxton's Epicure' (D) 🏆H6 — CAgr CHab CTri ECrN SKee
- § 'Laxton's Fortune' (D) 🏆H6 — CArg CHab CMac CSBt CTri ECrN IArd LRHS NOra SEdi SKee SSFr WJas WMat WWct
- 'Laxton's Pearmain' (D) — MCoo
- § 'Laxton's Superb' (D) — CArg CBcs CCVT CHab CLnd CMac CSBt CTri EBee ECrN EPom GKin LBuc MCoo MPri NOra SEWo SEdi SKee SPer SRms SSFr SVic SWeb WJas WMat WWct
- 'Lemon Pippin' (C) — ECrN ELan NOra SKee
- 'Lewis's Incomparable' (C) — SKee
- 'Limelight' (D) 🏆H6 — CArg EBee MAsh MCoo NLar NOra SCoo SKee SSFT SSFr WMat
- 'Link Wonder' (D) — CEnd
- 'Little Pax' (D) — EPom MCoo MWat NLar NOra
- 'Llwyd Hanner Goch' (D) — WGwG
- 'London Pippin' (C) — CAgr
- 'Longkeeper' (D) — CAgr CEnd
- 'Lord Derby' (C) — CAgr CArg CHab CLnd CMac CTho ECrN EPom LRHS MRav NLar NOra SEND SEdi SKee SPer SSFT SVic WMat WWct
- 'Lord Grosvenor' (C) — SKee
- 'Lord Hindlip' (D) — CHab NOra WMat WWct
- 'Lord Lambourne' (D) 🏆H6 — CAgr CArg CHab CLnd CMac CSBt CTri ECrN ELan EPom LSRN MAsh MCoo MGos MWat NLar NOra SEdi SKee SLon SPer SSFr WJas WMat WWct
- 'Lord of the Isles' (Cider) — CAgr
- 'Lord Stradbroke' (C) — ECrN SKee
- 'Lord Suffield' (C) — CTri ECrN SKee
- 'Lough Tree of Wexford' (D) — IArd
- 'Lucombe's Pine' (D) — CAgr CDoC CEnd ECrN SVic
- 'Lynn's Pippin' (D) — ECrN
- 'Machen' (D) — WGwG
- 'Madresfield Court' (D) — WWct
- 'Maggie Sinclair' (D) — GBin
- 'Major' (Cider) — CAgr WMat
- 'Maldon Wonder' (D) — ECrN
- 'Maltster' (D) — MCoo
- 'Manaccan Primrose' (C/D) — CDoC CEnd CTsd
- 'Mannington's Pearmain' (D) — WMat
- 'Marged Nicolas' (D) — WGwG
- 'Markham Pippin' (D) — MCoo
- 'Maxton' (D) — ECrN
- 'May Queen' (D) — WWct
- 'Maypole' (D) — SEdi
- 'McIntosh' (D) — NOra SKee
- 'Médaille d'Or' (Cider) — CArg SKee WMat
- 'Megabite' (C/D) **new** — EPom
- 'Melba' (D) — SKee
- 'Melrose' (D) — ECrN
- 'Meridian' PBR (D) — CAgr ECrN MCoo NOra SEdi SSFr WMat
- 'Merton Beauty' (D) — SKee
- 'Merton Worcester' (D) — ECrN SKee
- 'Michelin' (Cider) — CAgr CArg CTri MGos NOra SKee WMat WWct
- MIEL D'OR — see *M. domestica* 'Honeygold'
- 'Miller's Seedling' (D) — NOra SKee
- 'Millicent Barnes' (D) — SKee
- 'Mollie's Delicious' (D) — SKee
- 'Monarch' (C) — CAgr CTri ECrN EPom SKee SSFr
- 'Monmouthshire Green' (D) — WGwG
- 'Montfort' (D) — ECrN
- 'Morgan's Sweet' (C/Cider) — CArg CEnd CHab CTri NOra WMat
- § 'Mother' (D) 🏆H6 — CAgr CEnd CLnd CTri ECrN SKee SSFr
- § 'Mutsu' (C/D) — CArg CLnd CTri ECrN MRav NOra SEdi SKee SPer SSFr WMat
- 'Mylor Pike' (D) — CEnd
- 'Nancy Jackson' (C) — CHab
- 'Nanny' (D) — CLnd
- 'Nant Gwrtheyrn' (D) — WGwG
- 'Newton Wonder' (C) — CAgr CArg CHab CSBt CTho CTri ECrN EPom LRHS MCoo MGos NOra SEdi SKee SRms SSFr WJas WMat WWct
- 'Nine Square' (D) — CTho
- 'Nolan Pippin' (D) — ECrN
- 'Nonpareil' (D) — SKee
- 'Norfolk Beauty' (C) — ECrN SKee
- 'Norfolk Beefing' (C) — CArg CHab NOra SKee WMat
- 'Norfolk Royal' (D) — CLnd ECrN NOra
- 'Norfolk Royal Russet' (D) — NOra SKee WMat
- 'Norfolk Summer Broadend' (C) — ECrN
- 'Northern Greening' (C) — SKee
- § 'Northwood' (Cider) — CTho WMat
- 'Nutmeg Pippin' (D) — ECrN
- NUVAR CHEERFULL GOLD (D) — SKee
- NUVAR FRECKLES (D) — SKee
- NUVAR GOLDEN HILLS (D) — SKee
- 'Oaken Pin' (D) — CEnd CTho
- § 'Obelisk' PBR (D) — CArg NLar NOra SKee WMat
- 'Old Somerset Russet' (D) — CTho
- 'Opalescent' (D) — CEnd
- 'Orleans Reinette' (D) — CAgr CArg CTri ECrN EPom LBuc MWat NOra SKee SSFr WJas WMat WWct
- 'Oslin' (D) — GBin SKee WMat

- 'Otava'PBR (C/D)	SKee
- 'Oxford Conquest' (D)	MWat
- 'Paignton Marigold' (Cider)	CTho
- PARADICE GOLD (D) **new**	CRos EPom
- 'Payhembury' (C/Cider)	CAgr
- 'Pear Apple' (D)	CAgr CEnd
- 'Pearl' (D)	NOra WMat
- 'Peasgood's Nonsuch' (C) ♀H6	CAgr CArg CHab ECrN EPom IArd LSRN MAsh NOra SKee SLon WMat
- 'Pendragon' (D)	CEnd CTho
- 'Peter Lock' (C/D)	CAgr CEnd
- 'Pethyre' (Cider)	CCVT
- 'Pig Aderyn' (C)	CHab WGwG
- 'Pig y Colomen' (C)	WGwG
- 'Pig's Nose Pippin' (D)	CEnd
- 'Pig's Nose Pippin' Type III (D)	CAgr
- 'Pig's Snout' (Cider/C/D)	CEnd
- 'Pine Apple Russet' (C/D)	CAgr
- 'Pine Apple Russet of Devon' (D)	CEnd
- PINK LADY	see *M. domestica* 'Cripps Pink'
- 'Pinova'PBR (D)	CAgr EPom SSFr
- 'Pitmaston Pine Apple' (D)	CArg CHab CLnd CTho CTri ECrN MCoo MWat NOra SKee SLon SSFr WMat WWct
- 'Pixie' (D) ♀H6	CSBt EPom LRHS MPri MWat NOra SKee SLon WWct
- 'Plum Vite' (D)	CAgr CTri
- 'Plymouth Cross' (D)	SKee
- 'Plympton Pippin' (C)	CEnd CTho CTri
- POLKA ('Trajan') (D)	NOra
- 'Pomeroy of Somerset' (D)	CHab CTri
- 'Ponsford' (C)	CAgr CTho WMat
- 'Port Wine'	see *M. domestica* 'Harry Master's Jersey'
- 'Porter's Perfection' (Cider)	CTri NOra
- 'Princesse' (F)	ECrN SKee
- 'Queen' (C)	CAgr ECrN SKee
- 'Queen Cox' (D)	CLnd CTri ECrN EPom LSRN NOra SEdi SKee SSFr SWvt WMat WTSh
- 'Queens' (D)	CEnd
- 'Rajka'PBR (D)	GQue NOra SKee WWct
- 'Red Alkmene'	see *M. domestica* 'Red Windsor'
- 'Red Astrachan' (D)	SKee
- 'Red Belle de Boskoop' (D)	CAgr
- 'Red Bramley' (C)	ECrN
- 'Red Delicious'	see *M. domestica* 'Starking'
- 'Red Devil' (D)	CAgr CLnd CMac CSBt CTri EBee ECrN EPom LBuc LRHS MPri MRav NLar NOra NRHS SCoo SEWo SKee SLim SLon SSFT SSFr WJas WMat WWct
- 'Red Ellison' (D)	CTri ECrN
- 'Red Falstaff'PBR (D) ♀H6	CAgr CArg CCVT CMac CTri ECrN EPfP GKin LBuc LRHS LSRN MAsh MCoo NLar NOra NRHS SGbt SKee SLim SLon SPoG SSFT WMat WWct
- 'Red Gravenstein' (D)	SEdi
- 'Red James Grieve' (D)	SKee
- 'Red Jonagold'	see *M. domestica* 'Jonagored'
- 'Red Miller's seedling' (D)	ECrN
- 'Red Pixie' (D)	CArg GQue MCoo WMat
- 'Red Rattler' (D)	CTri
- 'Red Roller' (D)	CTsd
§ - 'Red Windsor' (D)	CArg CLnd CMac CRos CTri EPom LBuc LCro LOPS LRHS MAsh NLar NOra SCoo SKee SLim SPoG SSFr WJas WMat
- 'Redsleeves' (D)	CAgr CLnd ECrN NOra
- 'Reine des Reinettes'	see *M. domestica* 'King of the Pippins'
- 'Resi'PBR (C/D)	WWct
- 'Reverend W. Wilks' (C)	CAgr CArg CHab CLnd CSBt CTri EBee ECrN EPom NOra SEdi SKee SSFr WJas WMat WWct
- 'Ribston Pippin' (D) ♀H6	CArg CTho CTri ECrN MCoo MRav MWat NOra SKee SLon SSFr WJas WMat WWct
- 'Rival' (D)	CAgr
- 'Rivers' Nonsuch' (D)	CHab
- 'Rosemary Russet' (D) ♀H6	CAgr CArg CHab CTho ELan MCoo NOra SKee SLon SSFr WMat WWct
- 'Rosette' (D)	CArg EPfP EPom LRHS MAsh MWat NLar NOra WMat
- 'Ross Nonpareil' (D)	CAgr IArd NOra SKee WMat
- 'Rosy Blenheim' (D)	ECrN
- 'Rough Pippin' (D)	CEnd
- 'Roundway Magnum Bonum' (C/D)	CAgr CLnd CTho
- 'Royal Gala' (D)	CMac ECrN EPom LBuc MRav SLon
- 'Royal Russet' (C)	CAgr CEnd ECrN
- 'Royal Somerset' (C/Cider)	CTho CTri WMat
- RUBINETTE ('Rafzubin') (D)	ECrN NOra SKee
- RUBINETTE ROSSO ('Rafzubex'PBR) (D)	NOra WMat
- 'Rubinola'PBR (D)	SKee WWct
- 'Ruby' Seabrook (D) **new**	SKee
- 'Ruby' Thorrington (D)	ECrN
- 'Saint Ailred' (D)	SKee
- 'Saint Albans Pippin' (D)	SKee
- 'Saint Cecilia' (D)	CHab WGwG
§ - 'Saint Edmund's Pippin' (D) ♀H6	CHab CTho ECrN ELan EPfP MCoo NOra SKee SSFr
- 'Saint Edmund's Russet'	see *M. domestica* 'Saint Edmund's Pippin'
- 'Saint Everard' (D)	SKee
- 'Saltcote Pippin' (D)	WMat
- 'Sam Young' (D)	CAgr SKee
- 'Samba' (C/D)	LOPS
- 'Sandlin Duchess' (D)	NOra WMat
- 'Sandringham' (C)	ECrN
- 'Sanspareil' (D)	CAgr
- 'Santana'PBR (D) ♀H6	NOra WMat
- 'Saturn' (D)	CAgr CArg CCVT CTri NOra SKee SSFr WMat WWct
- 'Saw Pits' (D)	CAgr CEnd
- 'Scarlet Crofton' (D)	IArd
- 'Scarlet Nonpareil' (D)	SKee
- 'Scotch Bridget' (C)	CArg CHab EBee GQue NBid NOra SKee WMat WWct
- 'Scotch Dumpling' (C)	GBin GKin GQue LRHS MCoo NOra SKee WMat
- 'Scrumptious'PBR (D) ♀H6	Widely available
- 'Sheep's Nose' (C)	CHab IArd
- 'Shenandoah' (C)	SKee
- 'Sidney Strake' (C)	CAgr CEnd
- 'Sir Isaac Newton's'	see *M. domestica* 'Flower of Kent'
- 'Sir John Thornycroft' (D)	CLnd
- 'Sisson's Worksop Newtown' (D)	MCoo
- 'Slack Ma Girdle' (Cider)	CArg NOra SKee WMat
- 'Smart's Prince Arthur' (C)	CHab
- 'Snell's Glass Apple'	see *M. domestica* 'Glass Apple'

- 'Somerset Lasting' (C)	CTri
- 'Somerset Redstreak' (Cider)	CAgr CArg CHab CTri NOra WMat
- 'Sops in Wine' (Cider/D)	CArg CDoC NOra SKee SVic WMat
- 'Sour Bay' (Cider)	CAgr
- 'Spartan' (D)	CArg CCVT CLnd CMac CSBt CTri EBee ECrN ELan EPom GKin LRHS MAsh MCoo MGos MRav MWat NOra SEdi SKee SPer SSFT SSFr SVic WJas WMat WWct
- 'Spencer' (D)	CTri ECrN SKee
- 'Spotted Dick' (Cider)	CTho
- 'Stanway Seedling' (C)	ECrN
- 'Star of Devon' (D)	CEnd SKee
§ - 'Starking' (D)	ECrN LMaj NOra SKee
- 'Stark's Earliest' (D)	SVic
- 'Stembridge Cluster' (Cider)	CTri
- 'Steyne Seedling' (D)	CLnd
- 'Stirling Castle' (C)	CAgr NOra SKee WMat
- 'Stoke Red' (Cider)	CArg NOra WMat
- 'Striped Beefing' (C)	ECrN
- 'Sturmer Pippin' (D)	CSBt CTri EBee ECrN MWat NOra SKee SWeb WWct
- 'Summer Golden Pippin' (D)	SKee
- 'Summerred' (D)	ECrN
- 'Sunburn' (D)	ECrN
- 'Sunrise'PBR (D)	NOra SKee
- 'Sunset' (D) ♀H6	CAgr CArg CCVT CHab CLnd CMac CSBt CTri ECrN EPfP EPom GKin LBuc LRHS LSRN MRav NOra SCoo SEdi SKee SLim SLon SPer SSFT SSFr SVic WJas WMat WWct
- 'Suntan' (D)	ECrN MWat NOra SKee
- 'Superb'	see *M. domestica* 'Laxton's Superb'
- 'Sure Crop' (D)	SKee
- SURPRIZE (D) **new**	EPom NOra
- 'Sussex Mother' (C/D)	CHab SKee
- 'Sweet Alford' (Cider)	CArg CTho WMat WWct
- 'Sweet Bay' (Cider)	CAgr
- 'Sweet Coppin' (Cider)	CArg CTri WMat
- 'Sweet Lilibet'	see *M. domestica* 'Red Windsor'
- 'Sweet Pethyre' (C)	SEdi
- 'Sweet Society' (D)	NOra SKee WJas WMat
- 'Tamar Beauty' (D)	CEnd
- 'Tan Harvey' (Cider)	CEnd
- 'Taunton Cross' (D)	CAgr CArg WMat
- 'Taylor's' (Cider)	CAgr
- 'Ten Commandments' (Cider/D)	SKee WWct
- 'The Rattler' (Cider)	CEnd
- 'Thomas Jeffrey' (D)	GBin
- TICKLED PINK ('Baya Marisa') (C/D)	CArg EPom LBuc LRHS MWat NLar NOra SPer WMat
- 'Tidicombe Seedling' (D)	CTho WMat
- 'Tinsley Quince' (D)	WMat
- 'Tom Putt' (C)	CAgr CArg CCVT CHab CLnd CSBt CTho CTri LBuc NOra SKee WJas WMat WWct
- 'Tommy Knight' (D)	CAgr CEnd
- 'Topaz'PBR (D) ♀H6	SKee
- 'Totnes Apple' (D)	CTho
- 'Tower of Glamis' (C)	CHab SKee
- 'Tregonna King' (C/D)	CDoC CTho CTsd
- 'Tremlett's Bitter' (Cider)	CAgr CArg CHab CTsd NOra SKee SVic WMat
- 'Trwyn Mochyn' (C)	WGwG
§ - 'Tuscan' (D)	SKee
§ - 'Tydeman's Early Worcester' (D)	CAgr CHab CLnd ECrN SEdi SKee SRms SSFr WWct
- 'Tydeman's Late Orange' (D)	CArg CHab CTri ECrN MCoo NOra SKee WMat
- 'Tyler's Kernel' (C)	SKee
- 'Upton Pyne' (C/D)	CTho
- 'Veitch's Perfection' (C/D)	WMat
- 'Venus Pippin' (C/D)	CEnd
- 'Vileberie' (Cider)	CTri
- 'Violette' (C)	SKee
- 'Vista-bella' (D)	ECrN SEdi
- 'Wagener' (D)	CLnd SKee
- 'Warner's King' (C) ♀H6	CTri NOra SKee
- 'Wealthy' (D)	SKee
- 'Wellington' (C)	see *M. domestica* 'Dummellor's Seedling'
- 'Wellington' (Cider)	CAgr
- 'Werrington Wonder' (D)	CEnd
- 'West View Seedling' (D)	ECrN
- 'White Melrose' (C)	NOra WMat
- 'White Transparent' (C/D)	SKee
- 'Whitpot Sweet' (Cider)	CEnd
- 'William Crump' (D)	CHab CTho ECrN NOra SKee WMat WWct
- 'Windsor Early' (D)	SSFr
- 'Winston' (D) ♀H6	CAgr CCVT CMac CTri ECrN MCoo SKee SRms SVic SWeb WWct
- 'Winter Banana' (D)	CArg CHab ECrN NOra SKee SVic WMat
- 'Winter Gem' (D)	CAgr CArg CCVT CLnd ECrN EPom LBuc NOra SKee SSFr WJas WMat
- 'Winter Peach' (D/C)	CAgr ECrN
- 'Winter Pearmain' (D)	SKee
- 'Winter Red' (F)	CEnd
- 'Withington Welter' (C/D) **new**	SKee
- 'Woodbine'	see *M. domestica* 'Northwood'
- 'Woodford' (C)	ECrN
- 'Woolbrook Pippin' (D)	CAgr CEnd CTho WMat
- 'Woolbrook Russet' (C)	CEnd ECrN
- 'Worcester Pearmain' (D) ♀H6	Widely available
- 'Wormsley Pippin' (D)	ECrN
- 'Wyken Pippin' (D)	ECrN SKee WWct
- 'Yarlington Mill' (Cider)	CAgr CArg CHab CTri NOra SKee SVic WMat WWct
- 'Yellow Ingestrie' (D)	CArg CHab CLnd MAsh MCoo NOra SKee WMat WWct
- 'Yorkshire Aromatic' (C)	SKee
- 'Yorkshire Greening' (C)	CHab NOra SKee
- 'Zabergäu Renette' (D)	NOra SKee
'Donald Wyman'	CLnd EPfP LMaj MAsh NLar NOra SCoo WMat
§ 'Echtermeyer'	CTri
'Evelyn'	CBcs CLnd NOra WMat
§ 'Evereste' ♀H6	Widely available
florentina	CTho EBee
- 'Rosemoor'	CLnd
× ***floribunda*** ♀H6	CEnd CLnd CMac CSBt EBee ELan EWTr LBuc LMaj LRHS MGos MMuc MPri MRav MSwo NLar NOra NOrn SCob SEND SEdi SGbt SGol SPer SPoG SRms WMat WMou
fusca	CLnd
'Gardener's Gold'	CEnd CLnd CTho SRms
× ***gloriosa*** 'Oekonomierat Echtermeyer'	see *M.* 'Echtermeyer'
'Golden Gem'	CLnd GQue MAsh NLar NOra NOrn SEWo SKee WMat
'Golden Hornet'	see *M.* × *zumi* 'Golden Hornet'

	'Gorgeous'	Widely available
	'Harry Baker'	CCVT CDoC CEnd CLnd CMac CSBt ECrN EMil EPfP EPom EWTr LSRN MBlu MRav NOra SCoo SLim SPer SPoG WJas WMat WMou WWct
	× ***hartwigii***	CLnd
	'Hillieri'	see *M.* × *scheideckeri* 'Hillieri'
	'Honeycrisp'PBR	NOra WMat
	hupehensis ♀H6	CAby CBcs CEnd CLnd CMCN CSBt CTho CTri EPfP EWTr GKev IMou LRHS MBlu MGos MRav NLar NOra NOrn SCob SDix SPer SPtp WMat WMou WTSh
	'Hyde Hall Spire'	SCoo
	'Hyslop'	CLnd
	'Indian Magic'	CLnd EBee EPfP EWTr LRHS MAsh NLar NOra SPer WHCr WMat WMou
	'Indian Summer'	CLnd
	JELLY KING ('Mattfru') ♀H6	CDoC CLnd EBee ECrN EPfP EPom LBuc LCro LOPS LRHS LSRN MAsh MPri NLar NOra SEWo SGbt SPer SPoG WHCr WMat WMou
	'John Downie' (C)	Widely available
	'Kaido'	see *M.* × *micromalus*
	'Lady Northcliffe'	CLnd
	'Laura' ♀H6	CLnd EBee EPfP EPom LCro LOPS LRHS LSRN MAsh MPri NLar NOra SCoo SKee SLim SLon SPer SPoG WJas WMat WMou
	'Louisa'	EBee EPfP LSRN NOra SCoo SGbt SGol SLim WMat
	× ***magdeburgensis***	CCVT CLnd CSBt
	'Mariri Red' (D)	WMat
	'Mary Potter'	CLnd
§	× ***micromalus***	CLnd
	× ***moerlandsii***	CLnd
	- 'Liset'	CEnd CLnd ECrN MRav NOra SCob SCoo SEdi WFar
§	- 'Profusion'	CBcs CTri ECrN ELan EPfP LCro LOPS MGos MPri MRav MSwo NOra NRHS SEND SGol SPer SRms SWvt WJas WMou WSpi
	'Mokum'	CLnd LMaj LSRN
	'Molten Lava'	CLnd MAsh
	'Montreal Beauty'	CLnd EPom WJas
	niedzwetzkyana	CLnd CTho
	NUVAR CARNIVAL	SKee
	NUVAR MARBLE	EBee NOra NOrn SKee WMat
	PERPETU	see *M.* 'Evereste'
	'Peter's Red'	CLnd LMaj
	'Pink Mushroom'	ECrN
	'Pink Perfection'	CEnd EPfP EWTr LCro LOPS MAsh MPri NLar NOra SGbt SPoG WMat
	'Pond Red'	CLnd
	'Prairifire'	CLnd LRHS MAsh MPri NOra SCoo SLim SLon SPoG WMat
	prattii	CLnd CTho EBee GLog WLov
	- 'Pourpre Noir'	CLnd
	'Princeton Cardinal' ♀H6	CLnd CMac EPfP SCoo SLim SPoG
	'Professor Sprenger'	see *M.* × *zumi* 'Professor Sprenger'
	'Profusion'	see *M.* × *moerlandsii* 'Profusion'
	prunifolia	MBlu
	- var. ***rinkii***	CLnd
	'Purple Prince'	CLnd
§	× ***purpurea*** 'Aldenhamensis'	CLnd
	- 'Eleyi'	CLnd EPfP LMaj SEdi
	- 'Lemoinei'	CLnd
	- 'Neville Copeman'	CCVT CLnd EPom SEdi SSFr WJas
	- 'Pendula'	see *M.* 'Echtermeyer'
	'R.J. Fulcher'	CTho
	'Ralph Shay'	CLnd
	'Red Barron'	CLnd
	'Red Glow'	CLnd ECrN WJas
	'Red Jade'	see *M.* × *scheideckeri* 'Red Jade'
	'Red Jewel'	CLnd
§	'Red Jonaprince'PBR	WMat
	RED OBELISK ('Dvp Obel')	CCVT CLnd LBuc LMaj NOra NOrn SCoo SPoG WLov WMat
	'Red Peacock'	CLnd
	'Red Prince'	see *M.* 'Red Jonaprince'
	'Roberts Crab'	EWTr
§	× ***robusta***	CLnd LSRN SLon SRms
	- 'Dolgo'	CLnd CSBt EPfP EPom LCro MBlu NLar NOra SCoo SKee SPoG WMat
	- 'Red Sentinel' ♀H6	Widely available
	- 'Red Siberian'	SPer
	- 'Yellow Siberian'	CLnd
	'Rosehip'	CEnd CLnd EBee LBuc LCro LOPS MPri NLar NOra NOrn WMat WMou
	'Royal Beauty'	CLnd EPfP EWTr LMaj LRHS MAsh MBlu MGos MPri MSwo NOra NOrn SCoo SEdi SLon SPer WMat
	'Royalty'	CBcs CLnd CSBt EBee ECrN ELan LBuc LCro LMaj LOPS LRHS MGos MMuc MRav MSwo NOra NOrn SCob SEND SEWo SEdi SGol SGsty SPer WJas WMat
	'Rudolph'	CCVT CLnd EBar EBee ECrN LBuc LMaj LSRN MAsh MGos MPri NOra NOrn SCob SCoo SEWo SEdi SLim SPer SPoG WJas WMat
	'Ruth Ann'	CLnd
	sargentii	CLnd EWTr GKev NOra
	- 'Candy Mint'	MAsh WHCr WMat
	- 'Tina'	CLnd MAsh NOra SPoG WMat
	'Satin Cloud'	CLnd
§	× ***scheideckeri*** 'Hillieri'	CLnd MBlu NOra
§	- 'Red Jade'	CLnd CTri ELan EWTr MGos MRav MSwo NOrn SEdi SPer SRms WJas
	Siberian crab	see *M.* × *robusta*
	sieboldii	see *M. toringo*
	sieversii	CLnd
	sikkimensis B&SWJ 2431	WCru
	'Silver Drift'	CLnd
	'Simon'	WMat
	'Snowcloud'	CLnd MAsh NOrn SLim
	'Snowdrift'	CLnd
	'Street Parade'	CLnd
	× ***sublobata***	CLnd
	'Suffolk Pink'	ECrN
	SUGAR TYME ('Sutyzam')	CLnd
	'Sun Rival' ♀H6	CCVT CEnd CLnd CMac EBee ELan EPfP EPom LRHS LSRN MAsh MBlu MPri MRav NOra NOrn SCoo SEWo SEdi SLim SPer SPoG SRms WJas WMat WMou
	sylvestris	CArg CBrac CCVT CHab CLnd ECrN EPfP LBuc LMaj MMuc MRav SCob SEND SEWo SEdi SPer SPre WKor WMou WTSh
§	***toringo***	CLnd ECrN EPfP LMaj NOra
I	- var. ***arborescens***	CLnd CTho
	- 'Aros'PBR **new**	LBuc LCro LOPS NOra WMat
	- 'Browers'	LMaj
	- 'Scarlett' ♀H6	CCVT CEnd CLnd EBee ELan EPfP EWTr IArd LMaj LRHS LSRN MAsh

	NLar NOra SCoo SEWo SLim SPer SPoG WMat WMou
- 'Wintergold'	MMuc
- 'Wooster'	CLnd
toringoides	see *M. bhutanica*
transitoria ♀H6	CEnd CLnd CMac CTho ELan EPfP EWTr GKin MAsh MBlu MRav NLar NOra SCoo SLau SPer WMat WMou WPGP
- 'Roundabarrow Ruby' **new**	EBee WPGP
- 'Thornhayes Tansy'	CTho NOra SLim SPoG WMat
trilobata	CTho EBee ELan EPfP LMaj MBlu MGos MMuc SCoo SEND
- 'Guardsman'	CLnd CMac EBee EPfP MPri WMat
tschonoskii	CLnd CMCN CMac CTri ELan LMaj MBlu MGos MMuc NOrn SCob SEND SEdi SPer SRms SWvt WJas WMou WTSh
- 'Belmonte'	MBlu
'Van Eseltine'	CAgr CMac CSBt EPfP LMaj MMuc SEdi SPer WJas
'Veitch's Scarlet'	CHab CLnd CSBt
VELVET PILLAR ('Velvetcole')	SPer
WEEPING CANDIED APPLE ('Weepcanzam')	CLnd
'White Angel'	CLnd
'White Star'	CCVT CLnd CSBt EBee ECrN EWTr NOra SEWo SLon WMat
'Winter Gold'	LMaj SEdi SGol
'Wisley Crab'	CLnd SEdi SKee SLon SRms
yunnanensis	EPfP WPav
× ***zumi***	GLog
- var. ***calocarpa***	CLnd CTho
§ - 'Golden Hornet'	Widely available
§ - 'Professor Sprenger'	CLnd EPfP LMaj NOra SCoo

Malva (*Malvaceae*)

alcea	CAgr
- var. ***fastigiata***	CMac CRos EPPr LRHS SPer SRms WOut
- 'Royal Flush'	NRHS
bicolor	see *Lavatera maritima*
crispa	see *M. verticillata*
'Gibbortello'	NBPC
moschata	CAgr CBcs CBod EBee ECha ELan ENfk EPfP GPoy GQue MBow MHer MMuc MNHC NAts NLar NMir SPer SPlb SRms WFar WHer WOut WWild
§ - f. ***alba*** ♀H5	Widely available
- 'Appleblossom'	WOut
- 'Romney Marsh'	see *Althaea officinalis* 'Romney Marsh'
- 'Rosea'	CRos EHyd EPfP GMaP LRHS NPer NRHS SPoG SWvt
- 'Snow White'	see *M. moschata* f. *alba*
- 'White Perfection'	WFar
pusilla	CCCN
sylvestris	CBod MBow SRms
- 'Blue Fountain'[PBR]	EBee LRHS SRms
- 'Brave Heart'	SWvt WOut
- MARINA ('Dema'[PBR])	NLar
- var. ***mauritiana***	LCro LOPS NLar NPer WOut
- - 'Bíbor Fehlö'	CSpe
- - 'Primley Blue'	CBod EBee ELan EMor EPfP GMaP ILea LRHS MRav NLar NPer WSpi
- - 'Zebrina'	EPfP MBow NGBl NPer SAko SBut SWvt
- 'Perry's Blue'	NPer
§ ***verticillata***	CLau

Malvastrum (*Malvaceae*)

× ***hypomadarum***	see *Anisodontea* × *hypomadara* (Sprague) D.M. Bates

mandarin see *Citrus reticulata* Mandarin Group

mandarin, Cleopatra see *Citrus reticulata*

Mandevilla ✿ (*Apocynaceae*)

§ × ***amabilis***	CCCN
- 'Alice du Pont' ♀H1c	CBcs CCCN ELan EMdy EShb SPre
× ***amoena***	see *M.* × *amabilis*
'Audrey'[PBR] (Vogue Series)	CBcs CWGN LSou SPoG
boliviensis ♀H1c	CCCN CRHN
(Diamantina Series) DIAMANTINA OPALE CITRINE ('Lancalifornia')	EMdy
- DIAMANTINA OPALE FUCHSIA FLAMMÉ ('Lanmissouri') **new**	LCro LOPS
- DIAMANTINA OPALE GRENAT ('Lanutah')	EMdy
'Ginger' (Vogue Series)	CBcs CWGN LSou SPoG
§ ***laxa*** ♀H2	CBcs CCCN CRHN CSam CSpe ECre ELan EMdy EShb LRHS SBrt SVen WSHC
(Rio Series) RIO DEEP RED ('Fisrix Dered'[PBR])	CCCN
- RIO PINK ('Fisrix Pinka'[PBR])	CCCN
- RIO WHITE ('Fisrix Whit'[PBR])	EMdy
'Ruby' (Vogue Series)	CWGN
sanderi	CCCN EShb SPre
- 'Pink of Hint'	EMdy
- 'Rosea'	CCCN
splendens ♀H1c	CCCN EMdy
suaveolens	see *M. laxa*
Sundaville Series	CCCN
- SUNDAVILLE CREAM PINK ('Sunparapibra'[PBR])	EMdy
- SUNDAVILLE DARK RED ('Sunparabeni'[PBR])	EMdy
- SUNDAVILLE GRAND RED ('Sunpara15'[PBR])	EMdy
- IMPROVED WHITE 16 ('Sunparamakuho')	EMdy
- SUNDAVILLE PEARL ('Patmandewi')	EMdy
- SUNDAVILLE PINK ('Sunmandecripi'[PBR])	EMdy
- SUNDAVILLE PRETTY ROSE ('Sunparaprero'[PBR])	EMdy
- SUNDAVILLE RED ('Sunmandecrim'[PBR])	EMdy
- SUNDAVILLE ROSE STAR ('Sunpararosta'[PBR])	EMdy

Mandragora (*Solanaceae*)

autumnalis	GEdr SBrt SPhx WSFF
caulescens	GEdr
§ ***officinarum***	GEdr GPoy SPhx XAbr

Manettia (*Rubiaceae*)

cordifolia	SBrt
inflata	see *M. luteorubra*
§ ***luteorubra***	CCCN

Manfreda see *Agave*

× *Mangave* see *Agave*

Mangifera (*Anacardiaceae*)

indica (F) — CCCN SPre SVic

Manglietia see *Magnolia*

yunnanensis — see *Magnolia insignis*

mango see *Mangifera indica*

Manihot (*Euphorbiaceae*)

carthaginensis — SPlb

Mantisia (*Zingiberaceae*)

saltatoria PAB 4208 — LEdu WPGP

Maranta (*Marantaceae*)

leuconeura var. ***erythroneura*** ♀H1a — XBlo
- var. ***kerchoveana*** ♀H1a — XBlo

Margyricarpus (*Rosaceae*)

§ ***pinnatus*** — EWld WPav
setosus — see *M. pinnatus*

Mariscus see *Cyperus*

marjoram, pot see *Origanum onites*

marjoram, sweet see *Origanum majorana*

marjoram, wild, or oregano see *Origanum vulgare*

marrow see AGM Vegetables Section

Marrubium (*Lamiaceae*)

§ ***bourgaei*** var. ***bourgaei*** 'All Hallows Green' — ECha ECtt EHyd LRHS SRms
candidissimum — see *M. incanum*
* ***cylleneum*** 'Velvetissimum' — WCot XSen
§ ***incanum*** — SEND XSen
libanoticum — NSti
supinum — EBou ECha ELan LRHS SEND SGro
vulgare — CBod CCBP EBee ENfk GJos GPoy MHer MNHC SRms WJek

Marsdenia (*Apocynaceae*)

oreophila — CBcs CRHN LRHS SLon SPoG WPGP WSHC

Marshallia (*Asteraceae*)

grandiflora — EBee

Marsilea (*Marsileaceae*)

mutica — EWat LLWG
* ***schelpiana*** — XBlo

Massonia (*Asparagaceae*)

depressa ♀H2 — SChF WCot
echinata — SChF WCot
longipes **new** — WCot
pseudoechinata **new** — WCot
pustulata ♀H2 — SChF WCot
- purple-leaved **new** — WCot
thunbergiana **new** — WCot

Mathiasella (*Apiaceae*)

bupleuroides 'Green Dream' — CAby CAvo CBcs CBod CBre CSpe EBee ELan EPfP EWld GBin GMaP ILea LCro LEdu LOPS LRHS MBel MHol MNrw MPnt NSti SCob SDix SEdd SPoG WCAu WCot WHil

Matricaria (*Asteraceae*)

chamomilla — see *M. recutita*
maritima — see *Tripleurospermum maritimum*
parthenium — see *Tanacetum parthenium*
§ ***recutita*** — GPoy MNHC XAbr
tchihatchewii — XLum XSen

Matteuccia ✿ (*Onocleaceae*)

orientalis ♀H5 — CAby CBdn CDTJ CLAP CRos CWCL ECha EFer EHyd EMor GMaP IBal LEdu LLWG LRHS MMuc MPie NBid NBro NLar NRHS SCob SEND SPad WHwl WPGP WPnP XLum
pensylvanica — EHyd LRHS NRHS
struthiopteris ♀H5 — Widely available
* - 'Depauperata' — CLAP
- 'Jumbo' — CBdn CCCN CRos EHyd ISha LRHS NRHS WPGP
- 'The King' — WCot

Matthiola (*Brassicaceae*)

fruticulosa 'Alba' — EPfP WPGP
- subsp. ***perennis*** — NSti WHal
incana — CEls LRHS SVic WKif
- 'Alba' — CWld EBee ECha ELan LRHS MHol SEND SPad SPhx WBrk WCot WRHF
- Cinderella Series, mixed ♀H4 **new** — LCro LOPS
- dwarf, mixed **new** — MBros
- 'Low' — WCot
- purple-flowered — SEND
- VINTAGE MIXED — MPri
scapifera — CPBP WAbe
sinuata — CEls WABo
white-flowered perennial — CSpe NPer

Maurandya (*Plantaginaceae*)

antirrhiniflora — CPla
§ ***barclayana*** — CSpe IDee
erubescens — see *Lophospermum erubescens*
lophantha — see *Lophospermum scandens*
lophospermum — see *Lophospermum scandens*
'Magic Dragon' — see *Lophospermum* 'Magic Dragon'
'Red Dragon' — see *Lophospermum* 'Red Dragon'
§ ***scandens*** — CPla

Maytenus (*Celastraceae*)

boaria — CMCN MGos SAko SArc SEND
disticha (Hook.f.) Urb. — LEdu
magellanica — WPGP

Mazus (*Phrymaceae*)

reptans — CBod EBou ECtt ELan GEdr NLar NPer NQui WFar WIce XLum
- B&SWJ — CExl
- 'Albus' — CBod ECtt LLWG NLar SPlb WFar WIce
- 'Blue' — LLWG

Mecardonia (*Plantaginaceae*)

'Goldflake' — CCCN

Meconopsis ✿ (*Papaveraceae*)

§ ***baileyi*** ♀H5	CBcs CBod CTri EBee EHyd GGGa GKev ITim LCro LOPS LRHS NBir NChi SCob WFar WSFF
* - var. ***alba***	CPla CTsd EBee EHyd GGGa GKev IMou LRHS NLar NRHS
- 'Hensol Violet'	CBod CPla CTsd EBee EWes GGGa GKev NRHS
- violet-flowered Ballyrogan form	ITim
	GEdr GKev
× ***beamishii***	GKev
betonicifolia misapplied	see *M. baileyi*
'Biggar Park' **new**	GEdr
cambrica	see *Papaver cambricum*
chelidoniifolia	see *Cathcartia chelidoniifolia*
'Clydeside Early Treasure' **new**	GEdr
× ***cookei***	EBee GKev NHpl
- 'Old Rose'	GGGa GKev GMaP
'Edrom'	GEdr
Fertile Blue Group	ITim MBel
- 'Blue Ice'	see *M.* (Fertile Blue Group) 'Lingholm'
- 'Harry Bush'	GEdr
- 'Lingholm'	Widely available
- 'Louise'	GEdr GMaP
- 'Mop-head' ♀H5	GEdr GKev GMaP
§ George Sherriff Group	EBee MArl NBir
- 'Ascreavie'	GEdr GKev GMaP
- 'Barney's Blue'	GEdr GKev GMaP
- 'Dalemain' ♀H5	GEdr GMaP
- 'Branklyn' ambig.	CExl GEdr
- 'Burgundy'	GWyn
- 'Huntfield'	GEdr GGGa GKev GMaP
- 'Jimmy Bayne'	GEdr GMaP
- 'Susan's Reward' ♀H5	GEdr GMaP
grandis misapplied	see *M.* George Sherriff Group
grandis ambig.	ITim
- GS 600	see *M.* George Sherriff Group
'Himal Sky' **new**	GEdr
(Infertile Blue Group) 'Bobby Masterton' ♀H5	GEdr GKev GMaP
- 'Bryan Conway'	GEdr
- 'Crarae'	GEdr GGGa GKev GMaP
- 'Crewdson Hybrid'	GEdr GKev GMaP
- 'Cruickshank'	GKev
- 'Dawyck'	see *M.* (Infertile Blue Group) 'Slieve Donard'
- 'Maggie Sharp'	GEdr
- 'Mrs Jebb' ♀H5	GEdr GGGa GMaP
- 'P.C. Abildgaard' ♀H5	GEdr GGGa GKev GMaP
§ - 'Slieve Donard' ♀H5	CRos EHyd GEdr GGGa GKev GMaP LRHS NRHS
integrifolia	CCCN GEdr
'Inverewe' ♀H5	GEdr GMaP
'Keillour' ♀H5	GEdr GMaP
'Keillour Violet'	GKev
'Kilbryde Castle White' **new**	GEdr
'Marit' ♀H5	GEdr GKev GMaP
'Mervyn Kessell'	GEdr GKev
'Mildred'	GEdr GKev GMaP
napaulensis misapplied	EBee GAbr GKev ITim
- red-flowered	CPla
nudicaulis	see *Papaver nudicaule*
paniculata	EBee GGGa GKev GMaP
prattii	CPla
'Pride of Angus'	GEdr
pseudointegrifolia	GGGa
punicea	GGGa GKev NHpl
- 'Sichuan Silk'	NHpl
quintuplinervia ♀H5	CPla GKev GRum NHpl NSla
racemosa	EWld
× ***sheldonii*** misapplied (fertile)	see *M.* Fertile Blue Group
× ***sheldonii*** misapplied (sterile)	see *M.* Infertile Blue Group
× ***sheldonii*** ambig.	CBcs EPfP GAbr LRHS NBir NLar NPer NRHS
staintonii red-flowered CC 3964 **new**	NWad
'Stewart Annand'	GEdr GKev GMaP
'Strathspey'	GEdr GMaP NHpl
sulphurea	GGGa GKev
superba	GGGa GKev
villosa	see *Cathcartia villosa*
wallichii Hook.	GGGa
'Willie Duncan'	GEdr GMaP
wilsonii subsp. ***orientalis***	CPla

Medeola (*Asparagaceae*)

virginiana	EBee

Medicago (*Papilionaceae*)

arborea	SEND SPlb
lupulina	CHab NGrd SPhx
sativa	NGrd SVic WHer WSFF
- 'Lucerne'	CWld

Medinilla (*Melastomataceae*)

magnifica ♀H1a	CCCN CDoC
- 'Bella'PBR (Florinilla Series) **new**	CDoC

medlar see *Mespilus germanica*; also AGM Fruit Section

Meehania (*Lamiaceae*)

cordata	EBee
urticifolia	GEdr WPnP
- B&SWJ 1210	WCru
- 'Japanblau'	IMou

Megaskepasma (*Acanthaceae*)

erythrochlamys	SVen

Melaleuca (*Myrtaceae*)

acuminata	SPlb
alternifolia	CCCN CTsd EShb GPoy MHer NWad SPlb SVen XAbr
armillaris	CCCN CTsd SEND SPlb
cuticularis	SPlb
decussata	CSde SPlb
§ ***diosmatifolia***	CExl
diosmifolia	CPbh
ericifolia	CTri CTsd SEND SPlb
erubescens	see *M. diosmatifolia*
fulgens	SPlb
gibbosa	CExl SEND SVen
hypericifolia	CExl SPlb SVen
linariifolia	CCCN SPlb
nesophila	SPlb
pungens	SPlb
pustulata	SVen
squamea	SEND SPlb
squarrosa	CExl EBee SPlb SVen
thymifolia	SPlb
trichophylla	SPlb
wilsonii	IDee

Melampodium (*Asteraceae*)

§ ***montanum*** AZTEC GOLD ('Starbini'PBR)	MBros MPri
- 'Gold Queen' **new**	LSou MPri
- 'Sunbini'PBR	CCCN LSou

Melandrium see *Vaccaria*

rubrum	see *Silene dioica*

Melanoselinum (*Apiaceae*)

§ ***decipiens***	CAbb CBod CSpe GBin IMou LEdu LRHS MHer MNrw NBPC SDix SHar SPhx WOut WPGP

Melanoseris (*Asteraceae*)

taliensis BWJ 7891	WCru

Melanthium (*Melanthiaceae*)

virginicum	MNrw

Melasphaerula (*Iridaceae*)

graminea	see *M. ramosa*
§ ***ramosa***	CBor

Melia (*Meliaceae*)

§ ***azedarach***	CBcs CCCN SBrt SPlb
- B&SWJ 14625	WCru
- var. ***japonica***	see *M. azedarach*

Melianthus (*Melianthaceae*)

comosus	CDTJ CPla EPri ESwi EWes NLar SCoo SPlb WPGP
major 🏆H3	Widely available
villosus	EBee EWes SPad SPlb WPGP

Melica (*Poaceae*)

altissima 'Alba'	EHyd LCro LRHS SWvt
- 'Atropurpurea'	CBod CCBP ECha EHyd LRHS MNrw SEND SPlb SPoG XCre
ciliata	CBod EAJP EBee ELon EPPr XLum XSen
- subsp. ***taurica***	SPhx
cupani	EPPr
nutans	CWCL EPPr EShb GMaP GQue MAsh NWsh SPhx WCot
persica	EPPr
transsilvanica 'Red Spire'	XLum
uniflora	EAJP IMou NWsh SPhx
- f. ***albida***	CKno ECha EHyd GQue LRHS MAvo MRav SPhx WCot WSHC
- 'Variegata' (v)	CBre ECha EShb LPla MAvo SMHy WCot

Melicytus (*Violaceae*)

alpinus	WThu
crassifolius	EBee
obovatus	NLar

Melilotus (*Papilionaceae*)

albus	SPhx
officinalis	CHab WHer

Melinis (*Poaceae*)

nerviglumis	CBod

Meliosma (*Sabiaceae*)

dilleniifolia WJC 13819	WCru
- subsp. ***cuneifolia***	CBcs CExl EBee SBrt WPGP
- subsp. ***tenuis***	CBcs CExl
myriantha var. ***discolor*** MF 97132	WCru
pinnata var. ***oldhamii***	CExl
simplicifolia subsp. ***pungens***	CExl
veitchiorum	CBcs CExl NLar SBrt

Melissa ✿ (*Lamiaceae*)

officinalis	Widely available
- 'All Gold'	CBre CLau ECha ENfk GQue NBid SPer SPoG SRms WFar WJek
- subsp. ***altissima***	MNHC
§ - 'Aurea' (v)	CBod CExl CLau CTsd EBou ELan EMor GPoy MHer MMuc MNHC MRav NBid NBir NBro NGrd SEND SPer SPoG SRms WFar
- 'Citronella' **new**	MGil
* - 'Compacta'	GPoy LEdu
- 'Lemona'	CAgr SPhx
- 'Lime Balm'	LEdu NPol
- 'Variegata' misapplied	see *M. officinalis* 'Aurea'

Melittis (*Lamiaceae*)

melissophyllum	CAby CMea EHyd IMou LEdu LRHS MHol MNrw MPie MPnt MRav SGro SHar WCAu WCot
- subsp. ***albida***	EBee EMor ILea LEdu LRHS WCAu WCot WHil WTor
- pink-flowered	LEdu WCot
- 'Royal Velvet Distinction'PBR	CBod CRos EBee EHyd ELan EMor EPfP GEdr ILea LLWG LRHS MHol MRav MSCN NBPC NDov NGBl NHpl NRHS SHar SPoG WCot WHil WTyc

Melliodendron (*Styracaceae*)

xylocarpum	CExl EBee SAko WPGP

melon see AGM Vegetables Section

Melothria (*Cucurbitaceae*)

scabra	LRHS SVic

Menispermum (*Menispermaceae*)

canadense	CTri GPoy
dauricum	NLar

Mentha ✿ (*Lamiaceae*)

angustifolia Corb.	see *M.* × *villosa*
angustifolia Host	see *M. arvensis*
aquatica	CBen CBod CHab CWat GPoy MHer MWts NAts NMir NPer NPol SPlb SRms SVic WHer WMAq WPnP WSFF XLum
§ ***arvensis***	MHer
- 'Banana'	CBod EMor ENfk LEdu MHer MNHC SEdi SRms SVic WFar WJek
- 'Lemon'	EMor LEdu
- var. ***piperascens***	CBod LEdu MHer SRms WJek
§ - - 'Sayakaze'	CLau
- 'Thai'	ENfk SRms
asiatica	MHer
'Berries and Cream'	CCBP CLau ENfk LCro LEdu LOPS MHer MNHC SRms
'Blackcurrant' **new**	MHer
Bowles's mint	see *M.* × *villosa* var. *alopecuroides* Bowles's mint
cervina	CBen CWat LEdu LLWG MHer MWts SRms WJek XLum
* - ***alba***	ENfk MHer MWts WJek WMAq

I	'Chocolate Peppermint'	CLau ENfk EWhm LEdu NBir NLar SPhx
	citrata	see *M.* × *piperita* f. *citrata*
	cordifolia	see *M.* × *villosa*
	corsica	see *M. requienii*
	crispa L. (1753)	see *M. spicata* var. *crispa*
	'Eau de Cologne'	see *M.* × *piperita* f. *citrata*
	eucalyptus mint	MHer
	× ***gentilis***	see *M.* × *gracilis*
§	× ***gracilis***	CBod CLau ENfk EWhm GAbr GJos MBow MPri NGrd NLar NSti SEdi SRms SVic WFar
	- 'Aurea'	see *M.* × *gracilis* 'Variegata'
§	- 'Variegata' (v)	CCBP ECha EMor GPoy LEdu MHer MNHC MPri SPlb WHer WJek XLum
*	'Hillary's Sweet Lemon'	ECul ENfk MHer SRms
	'Jessica's Sweet Pear'	ENfk
	'Julia's Sweet Citrus'	MHer
	lavender mint	GPoy LEdu MHer MNHC SRms
§	***longifolia***	ENfk LEdu MBow MMuc SEND SPlb SRms
	- Buddleia Mint Group	CCBP ENfk GAbr LEdu MHer MRav NSti WJek WWFP XLum
	- - variegated (v)	CBod LEdu WJek
	- 'Lake Van'	LEdu
	- subsp. ***schimperi***	LEdu MHer SRms WJek
	- silver-leaved	GAbr LEdu MHer MNHC SEND SRms SVic WFar WJek
*	- 'Variegata' (v)	GAbr SRms
	Nile Valley mint	CLau LEdu SRms
	'Orange Fresh' **new**	CBod
	× ***piperata*** f. ***citrata*** 'Kumin'	LEdu
	× ***piperita***	CHby ECha EMor GJos GPoy GQue LCro LOPS MBow MHer MNHC MPri NGrd NPol SPlb SVic WFar XAbr
	- 'After Eight'	ECul ENfk
	- 'Black Mitcham'	CLau SPhx WFar WJek XAbr
	- black peppermint	CAgr CBod CHby CLau ENfk EPfP LEdu MMuc MNHC NBir NLar SEND SRms SVic
§	- f. ***citrata***	CBod CHby CLau CTri ECha EMor ENfk GAbr GMaP GPoy GQue LEdu MBow MHer MNHC MPri MRav NBir NLar NPer SEdi SPlb SRms SVic WGwG WJek
	- - 'Basil'	CBod CLau CTsd ECul EMor GJos GLog LCro LEdu LOPS MHer MNHC MRav SEdi SRms SVic WFar WJek
	- - 'Bergamot'	SRms
	- - 'Chocolate'	CBod CCBP ECul EHyd EMor ENfk EPfP EWhm GJos LCro LEdu LOPS LRHS MBros MHer MNHC NGrd NPer NRHS SEdi SPlb SRms SVic WFar WGwG WJek XLum
	- - 'Grapefruit'	CBod EWhm LCro LOPS MHer MNHC NWad SRms SVic
	- - 'Lime'	CLau EMor ENfk EWhm LEdu MBow MHer MNHC SEdi SPlb SRms SVic WFar WJek
	- - 'Orange'	CLau EMor ENfk GJos LEdu MHer MMuc MNHC NGrd NPer SEdi SRms WJek
	- - 'Swiss Ricola'	CLau MHer WJek
	- 'Crispa'	NPol
	- 'Logee's' (v)	WFar
§	- 'Multimentha'	SRms
	- 'Strawberry'	ENfk GJos LCro LOPS MBros SVic WFar
	- 'Swiss'	CBod ENfk GJos LCro LOPS NGrd NLar SRms WHer
	pulegium	CBen CBod CCBP CHby ENfk EWhm GJos GPoy GQue LLWG MHer MNHC SPlb SRms SVic WHer WSFF XAbr
	- 'Cunningham Mint'	WJek
	- 'Upright'	CBod ENfk GPoy MHer SRms WJek
§	***requienii***	CBod CCBP EBou ENfk GAbr GPoy LCro LEdu LLWG LOPS MHer MNHC NBir NWad SDix SPlb SPtp SRms SVic WGwG WJek WNPC XEll
	rotundifolia misapplied	see *M. suaveolens*
	rotundifolia (L.) Huds.	see *M.* × *villosa*
	rubra var. ***raripila***	see *M.* × *smithiana*
	sachalinensis	SVic
	'Sayakaze'	see *M. arvensis* var. *piperascens* 'Sayakaze'
§	× ***smithiana***	CCBP CLau EMor GPoy LCro LEdu LOPS MHer MNHC MRav NBir NGrd SRms SVic WFar WJek
§	***spicata***	CAgr CBod CCBP CTri CTsd ENfk GJos GPoy GQue LCro LOPS MBow MBros MCot MHer MMuc MNHC MPri NPol SCob SEND SPhx SPlb SRms SVic WFar WHer XAbr XLum
	- Algerian fruity	LEdu
	- 'Cretan'	LEdu
*	- var. ***crispa***	ECha EMor ENfk LEdu MHer MMuc SPlb SRms SVic WFar WGwG WJek
	- - 'Moroccan'	CCBP CLau EBou ECul EMor ENfk EWhm GAbr GJos GLog GPoy LCro LEdu LOPS MBow MHer MNHC MPri NGrd NLar SEdi SRms SVic XAbr
	- 'Crispula'	XLum
	- 'Erdbeere'	WFar
	- 'Guernsey'	CLau SRms
	- 'Kentucky Colonel'	LEdu
	- 'Mexican'	CLau
	- 'Newbourne'	CLau SRms
	- 'Nile Valley'	LEdu WJek
	- 'Russian'	CAgr LEdu MHer SVic WFar
	- 'Spanish'	ECul NGrd NLar SRms
	- 'Spanish Furry'	MHer
	- 'Tashkent'	CHby CLau EHyd ENfk EWhm LCro LEdu LOPS LRHS MHer MNHC NGrd NRHS SRms WFar WGwG WHer WJek
I	'Strawberry Mint'	CCBP CLau ECul EWhm LEdu MHer MNHC SEdi SRms WFar
§	***suaveolens***	CAgr CBod CCBP CHby EBou ENfk GJos GMaP GPoy GQue LCro LOPS MBow MBros MHer MNHC NGrd SPlb SRms SVic WFar WSFF
*	- 'Grapefruit'	CAgr CLau ECul EMor GJos LEdu SVic WFar
*	- 'Pineapple'	CBod CLau EBou ECul ENfk EWhm GLog MBow SVic WFar WJek
	- subsp. ***timija***	LEdu MHer SRms WJek
	- 'Variegata' (v)	CCBP CTri ECha EMor GJos GMaP GPoy GQue LEdu MCot MHer MMuc MNHC MPri MRav NSti SPlb SRms SVic WHer XLum
	'Sweet Pear'	MHer SRms

	sylvestris L.	see *M. longifolia*
I	'Tangerine Mint'	LEdu
	Thüringer minze	see *M.* × *piperita* 'Multimentha'
§	× ***villosa***	MMuc SEND
	- var. ***alopecuroides***	EMor
§	- - Bowles's mint	CBre CLau GPoy LCro LEdu LOPS MHer MNHC NBir NLar NSti SRms WFar WHer WJek
	- 'Jack Green'	CLau
	viridis	see *M. spicata*

Menyanthes (*Menyanthaceae*)

	trifoliata	CBen CWat EWat GPoy LLWG MWts NPer WHal WMAq WSFF WWtn XLum

Menziesia see *Rhododendron*

	alba	see *Daboecia cantabrica* f. *alba*
	ciliicalyx lasiophylla	see *Rhododendron multiflorum* var. *purpureum*
	polifolia	see *Daboecia cantabrica* 'Polifolia'

Mercurialis (*Euphorbiaceae*)

	perennis	GPoy WHer WSFF WShi

Merendera (*Colchicaceae*)

§	***montana***	EPot
	- 'Norman Barratt'	WCot
	pyrenaica	see *M. montana*
	sobolifera	WCot

Merremia (*Convolvulaceae*)

§	***tuberosa***	MGil

Merrilliopanax (*Araliaceae*)

	alpinus B&SWJ 13906	WCru
	- B&SWJ 13939	WCru
	membranifolius **new**	LEdu

Mertensia (*Boraginaceae*)

	lanceolata	EBee
§	***maritima***	CEls CLau CSpe CWCL EBee EHyd EWes GKev GPoy GRum LRHS NBir SPlb SRms WHoo XAbr
	- subsp. ***asiatica***	see *M. maritima*
	pterocarpa	see *M. sibirica*
	pulmonarioides	see *M. virginica*
§	***sibirica***	SBrt SPlb SPtp
§	***virginica*** ♀H4	CMiW CWCL EBee ECtt ELan EPfP EPot LCro LEdu LOPS LRHS MHol MNrw MPie NBir NLar NSti SPhx SRms WFar
	viridis	SPlb

Merwilla (*Asparagaceae*)

§	***plumbea***	WCot

Merxmuellera (*Poaceae*)

	cincta	see *Capeochloa cincta*

Mesembryanthemum (*Aizoaceae*)

	brownii	see *Lampranthus brownii*
	crystallinum	GPoy MPri

Mespilus ✿ (*Rosaceae*)

	'Flanders Giant' (F)	LRHS WMat
	germanica (F)	CHab CLnd CMCN CTri ECrN LMaj MGil NLar SLon SReu WFar
	- 'Brabant Giant' (F)	IArd
	- 'Bredase Reus' (F)	ELan SKee
	- 'Dutch' (F)	SKee
	- 'Iranian' (F)	SKee
	- 'Large Russian' (F)	CAgr
	- 'Macrocarpa' (F)	SKee
	- 'Nottingham' (F) ♀H6	Widely available
	- 'Royal' (F)	CAgr LRHS MCoo NOra SCoo SKee WMat
	- 'Westerveld' (F)	CLnd EPom SKee

Metapanax ✿ (*Araliaceae*)

	davidii	SPtp WPGP
	delavayi	SPtp WPGP

Metaplexis (*Apocynaceae*)

	japonica	SBrt

Metasequoia ✿ (*Cupressaceae*)

	glyptostroboides	Widely available
	- 'All Bronze'	NLar
	- AMBER GLOW ('Wah-08ag') **new**	CBcs
	- 'Chubby'PBR	EPfP
	- 'Emerald Feathers'	SLim
	- 'Fastigiata'	see *M. glyptostroboides* 'National'
	- GOLD RUSH ('Golden Oji') ♀H7	CBcs CCVT CKen CMac CMen CTri ELan EPfP IArd LRHS LSRN MAsh MBlu MGos NLar NOra NOrn NPoe SAko SCob SCoo SGol SLim SMad SPer SPoG SWvt WFar WHwl WMat
	- 'Golden Dawn'	NLar
	- 'Hamlet's Broom'	SLim
	- 'Little Creamy'	NLar
	- 'Little Giant'	MBlu
	- 'Matthaei'	MBlu SLim SMad
	- 'McCracken's White' (v)	NLar
	- 'Miss Grace'	NLar SLim
§	- 'National'	MBlu
	- 'Schirrmann's Nordlicht'	SLim
	- 'Sheridan Spire'	CEnd MBlu
	- 'Waasland'	MBlu SLim
	- 'White Spot' (v)	MBlu

Metrosideros (*Myrtaceae*)

	sp.	CPla
	carminea	CCCN CTsd
§	***excelsa***	CTrC ECre ESwi
	- 'Parnell'	CBcs CCCN
	- 'Vibrance'	CCCN
	kermadecensis 'Twisty' (v)	CBcs
	- 'Variegata' (v)	CBcs
	lucida	see *M. umbellata*
	robusta	CBcs CCCN SPlb
	- ***aureovariegata*** (v)	CCCN EShb
§	'Springfire'	CCCN
	× ***subtomentosa*** 'Mistral'	IDee MPkF
	'Thomasii'	see *M.* 'Springfire'
	tomentosa	see *M. excelsa*
§	***umbellata***	CBcs CCCN EBee
	- 'Gold Nugget'	CBcs CCCN MPkF SSta
	- MOONLIGHT ('Lowmoo')	CBcs CCCN SEle SIvy SLim

Meum (*Apiaceae*)

	athamanticum	CSpe EBee EMor EPPr GPoy IMou LEdu LRHS MHol MRav SPhx SPtp WJek WOld WSHC

Michauxia (*Campanulaceae*)

	campanuloides	CSpe GJos
	tchihatchewii	CDTJ NGBl

Michelia see *Magnolia*

fulgens	see *Magnolia foveolata*
wilsonii	see *Magnolia ernestii*

Microbiota (*Cupressaceae*)

decussata 🏆H7	CBcs CMac CSBt LBee LRHS MGos NHol SLim WFar WPav XLot
- 'Gold Spot' (v)	WFar
- 'Jakobsen'	CKen
- 'Trompenburg'	CKen

Microcachrys ✿ (*Podocarpaceae*)

tetragona	IDee WThu

Microglossa (*Asteraceae*)

albescens	see *Aster albescens*

Microlepia (*Dennstaedtiaceae*)

strigosa	CBdn CCCN CLAP CRos EBee EHyd EShb ISha LEdu LRHS NRHS WPGP
- 'MacFaddeniae'	CBdn CLAP CRos EBee EHyd ISha LEdu LRHS NRHS WPGP

Micromeria (*Lamiaceae*)

sp.	SRms
corsica	see *Clinopodium corsicum*
fruticosa	WJek
juliana	EBee XLum
rupestris	see *M. thymifolia*
§ ***thymifolia***	SPlb

Microseris (*Asteraceae*)

ringens hort.	see *Leontodon rigens*

Microsorum (*Polypodiaceae*)

§ ***diversifolium***	CDoC EShb LEdu SIvy SPlb WPGP
musifolium 'Crocodyllus' PBR	EShb

Microtropis (*Celastraceae*)

petelotii HWJ 719	WCru

Milium (*Poaceae*)

effusum 'Aureum' 🏆H7	Widely available
- 'Yaffle' (v)	CBod CBre CKno EBee EPPr EShb

Millettia (*Papilionaceae*)

murasaki-natsu-fuji	see *Callerya reticulata*
pachycarpa	CMen
reticulata	see *Callerya reticulata*

Mimetes (*Proteaceae*)

chrysanthus	SPlb
cucullatus	CPbh
- 'Crackerjack Red'	CCCN

Mimosa (*Mimosaceae*)

pudica 🏆H1b	CCCN CDTJ CDoC EShb ESwi

Mimulus (*Phrymaceae*)

'Andean Nymph'	see *M. naiandinus*
§ ***aurantiacus*** 🏆H2	CMac CSpe EBak ECtt EShb MGil NPer SPlb SPoG SRms WFar WMal
- 'Primrose'	MGil
cardinalis 🏆H4	EBee ELan EPfP EWes GKev NBir WBor
- gold-flowered	EBee
- 'Red Dragon'	CBod
cardinalis × ***lewisii***	EWes
cupreus 'Red Emperor' **new**	LCro LOPS
'Eleanor'	ECtt EShb
glutinosus	see *M. aurantiacus*
- ***atrosanguineus***	see *M. puniceus*
- ***luteus***	see *M. aurantiacus*
§ ***guttatus***	LCro LOPS MBow NPer WMAq
'Highland Orange'	EPfP GWyn MAsh SPlb SPoG WIce
'Highland Pink'	EPfP GWyn MAsh NHpl SPlb SPoG
'Highland Red' 🏆H4	EBou EPfP GKev GWyn MAsh NHpl SPlb SPoG WIce
'Highland Yellow'	GWyn NHpl SPlb SPoG WIce
hose-in-hose (d)	NPer
langsdorffii	see *M. guttatus*
lewisii 🏆H3	EWes MNrw SRms
'Lothian Fire'	CWat
luteus	CWat GAbr LLWG NPer WBrk XLum
- 'Variegatus' ambig. (v)	NPer
Magic Series	SVic
§ ***naiandinus*** 🏆H4	EWes GKev SPlb
'Orange Glow'	LLWG
§ 'Orkney Gold' (d)	ECtt
'Popacatapetl'	CSpe WMal
primuloides	EWes SPlb
§ ***puniceus***	SChF SRkn WFar WMal
RED EMPEROR	see *M.* 'Roter Kaiser'
ringens	CBen CWat LLWG NBir NPer SPlb SRms WMAq
§ 'Roter Kaiser'	ELan
yellow hose-in-hose	see *M.* 'Orkney Gold'

Mina see *Ipomoea*

mint, apple see *Mentha suaveolens*

mint, basil see *Mentha* × *gracilis*

mint, Bowles's see *Mentha* × *villosa* var. *alopecuroides*

mint, curly see *Mentha spicata* var. *crispa*

mint, eau-de-Cologne see *Mentha* × *piperita* f. *citrata*

mint, ginger see *Mentha* × *gracilis*

mint, horse or long-leaved see *Mentha longifolia*

mint (pennyroyal) see *Mentha pulegium*

mint (peppermint) see *Mentha* × *piperita*

mint, round-leaved see *Mentha suaveolens*

mint (spearmint) see *Mentha spicata*

Minuartia (*Caryophyllaceae*)

parnassica	see *M. stellata*
§ ***stellata***	EPot GKev
verna subsp. ***caespitosa***	CTri
- - 'Aurea'	see *Sagina subulata* var. *glabrata* 'Aurea'

Mirabilis (*Nyctaginaceae*)

dichotoma	EShb
jalapa	CExl EPfP GKev SDeJ SRms WHil XAbr

	- 'Buttermilk'	CCCN
	longiflora	EShb SBrt WHil
	multiflora	EBee WHil

Miscanthus (*Poaceae*)

	capensis	SPlb
	chejuensis B&SWJ 8803	WCru
	flavidus	ESwi SRms XLum
	floridulus misapplied	see *M.* × *giganteus*
	floridulus ambig.	MMuc MNrw SEdd SPlb XLum
§	× ***giganteus***	CKno ELon EPPr MAsh MNrw MWht NWsh SCob SDix SDys SVic WABo WCot XCre XLum
	- 'Aksel Olsen'	SAko
	- 'Gilt Edge' (v)	CKno EPPr NWsh
	- 'Gotemba' (v)	ELon EPPr EWes
	- 'Jubilar' (v)	MWht
	- 'Meidl'	SAko
	lutarioriparius **new**	WPGP
	nepalensis	Widely available
	- NJM 09.141	WPGP
	- 'Shikola'	WCru
	oligostachyus	IMou
§	- 'Afrika'	CMea EBee EPPr GBin IMou MNrw WPGP
I	- 'Nanus Variegatus' (v)	ELon LEdu SAko WCot
	'Purpurascens'	CBod CKno ECha EHyd ELan EPPr EPfP LPot LRHS LSRN MAsh MNrw NRHS SCob SPer XCre XLum
	sacchariflorus misapplied	see *M.* × *giganteus*
	sacchariflorus ambig.	CBcs CKno EBee EBou ECha EHyd ELan EPfP LRHS MBrN NGdn NRHS SEdd SPer XCre
	sacchariflorus (Maxim.) Hack.	LEdu WSpi
	- 'Robustus'	SPeP
	sinensis	CTri WFar XSen
	- 'Abundance'	CKno CRos EHyd EPPr EPfP LRHS MAsh NRHS
	- 'Adagio' ♀H6	Widely available
	- 'Afrika'	see *M. oligostachyus* 'Afrika'
	- 'Aldebaran'	EPPr IMou MNrw
	- ALLIGATOR ('Lottum'PBR) **new**	CKno
	- 'Andante'	CKno EBee
	- 'Arabesque'	EPPr XLum
	- 'Augustfeder'	EPPr MAvo SMea XLum
	- 'Autumn Light'	EPPr SMea XLum
	- 'Barney Campbell'	NWsh
	- 'Blütenwunder'	EBee EPPr NWsh SMea XLum
	- 'Bogenlampe'	GBin
	- 'China' ♀H6	CKno CPar CRos EBee EHyd ELon EPPr EPed EPfP EShb EWes IPot LEdu LRHS MAsh MAvo MNrw NRHS NWsh SDys SRms XCre
	- 'Cindy'	CKno
	- var. ***condensatus***	XCre
	- - NJM 11.021	WPGP
	- - 'Cabaret' (v)	CBod CKno EBee EHyd EPPr EPfP EShb GMaP ILea LEdu LRHS LSRN MNrw NRHS NSti NWsh SMad SPoG WCot WFar WHal WPGP WSpi XCre XLum XSen
	- - 'Central Park'	see *M. sinensis* var. *condensatus* 'Cosmo Revert'
§	- - 'Cosmo Revert'	EPPr NWsh WPGP
	- - 'Cosmopolitan' (v) ♀H6	Widely available
	- - 'Emerald Giant'	see *M. sinensis* var. *condensatus* 'Cosmo Revert'

	- - 'Laigong'	LEdu
	- 'Cute One' **new**	CBct
	- 'David'	ELon EPPr LEdu MBNS XLum
	- 'Digestif' **new**	EBee
	- 'Dixieland' (v)	CKno ELan ELon EMor EPPr EWes IMou LEdu NLar
	- 'Dreadlocks'	CKno EBee EPPr GBin MAvo MNrw
	- 'Dresdner Rotgold'	SAko
	- 'Dronning Ingrid'	CKno EPPr IMou MNrw SMea XLum
	- EARLY HYBRIDS	EBou
	- 'Elfin'	CKno EPPr
	- 'Emmanuel Lepage'	CKno EPPr LPla MAvo NWsh XLum
	- 'Etincelle'	CKno EPPr EWes ILea WSMil
	- 'Federriese'	EBee GBin
	- 'Ferner Osten' ♀H6	Widely available
	- 'Feuergold'	SAko
	- 'Flamingo' ♀H6	Widely available
	- 'Flammenmeer'	EPPr SAko
	- 'Gearmella'	EBee EPPr
	- 'Gewitterwolke' ♀H6	EWes NWsh SMHy XLum
	- 'Ghana' ♀H6	CSpe EBee ECha ELon EMor EPPr GBin IMou LEdu LPla MAvo MNrw SDys SEdd SMHy SMad SPoG SRms SSut XCre XLum
	- 'Giraffe'	CDTJ CKno EWes LEdu XCre XLum
	- 'Gnome'	CKno EHyd EPPr EShb IMou LRHS MAsh MTin NRHS SRms
	- 'Gold Bar'PBR (v)	CBod CChe CRos CWGN ECha EHyd ELan ELon EPfP LLWG LRHS LSRN MAsh MBNS NGdn NLar NRHS NWad SCob SEle SPad SPeP SPer SPoG WGrn
	- 'Gold Breeze'PBR	CDoC EHyd LRHS NRHS
	- 'Gold und Silber' ♀H6	XLum
	- 'Goldfeder' (v)	EWes XLum
	- 'Goldglanz' **new**	EBee
	- 'Goliath'	CKno ELan ELon EPPr GBin GLog LEdu MBNS WFar XCre XLum
	- 'Gracillimus'	Widely available
	- 'Graziella'	CBod CEnd CKno CSam EHyd EPPr EPfP GBin GWyn LRHS MAsh NGdn NRHS SPer SRms WFar WHoo WSMil XCre XSen
	- 'Grosse Fontäne' ♀H6	ELon EPPr GBin LEdu LRHS LSRN NWsh SCob SEdd SMHy WCot XLum
	- 'Gutenberg Gold'	XLum
	- 'Haiku'	CKno EBee EPPr LEdu XLum
	- 'Helga Reich'	EWes
	- 'Hercules'	EPPr MAvo XLum
	- 'Hermann Müssel'	CRos EBee EHyd EPPr EWes IMou LEdu LRHS NRHS SMHy SMea XCre XLum
§	- 'Hinjo' (v)	ECha ECtt EHyd ELon EPPr GBin LRHS MAsh NGdn NRHS NWsh WCot
	- 'Ibiza'	CKno
I	- 'Jubilaris' (v)	ELon EPPr
	- 'Juli'	EHyd EPPr LRHS WSpi XCre
	- 'Kaskade' ♀H6	CBod CKno CPar EHyd EPPr GBin LEdu LRHS MMuc NDov NLar NRHS NWsh
	- 'Kirk Alexander' (v)	EPPr
	- 'Kleine Fontäne' ♀H6	Widely available
	- 'Kleine Silberspinne' ♀H6	Widely available
	- 'Korea'	EBee EPPr
	- 'Krater'	EBee EHyd EPPr ILea LRHS MBrN NRHS NWsh SDys SMea XCre XLum

- 'Kupferberg'	SMea XLum
- 'Kupferzwerg'	EBee EPPr
§ - 'Little Kitten'	EPPr EPed LEdu SCob SMad SMea SRms XLum
- 'Little Miss' **new**	CKno CRos SPad
- LITTLE NICKY	see *M. sinensis* 'Hinjo'
- 'Little Zebra'^{PBR} (v)	CDoC EBee EPfP GMaP LSRN MGos MPnt NWsh SEdd SEle SMad SRms
- 'Malepartus'	Widely available
- 'Memory'	EPPr MAvo
- 'Morning Light' (v) 🏆^{H6}	Widely available
- 'Mrs Higgins' **new**	NWsh
- 'München' **new**	EBee
- 'Navajo'	CBct CKno
- 'Nippon'	CRos EHyd EPPr EPfP GBin LEdu LRHS MAsh NGdn NRHS NWsh SCob SDys SPer WSpi XCre XLum
- 'Nishidake'	EPPr XCre XLum
- 'November Sunset'	EPPr XLum
- 'Overdam'	ECtt NGdn
- 'Poseidon'	EPPr MAvo SDys SMad XCre XLum
- 'Positano'	EBee EPPr XCre XLum
- 'Professor Richard Hansen'	CKno EBee EPPr EWes SMHy SMea XLum
- 'Purple Fall'	CKno CPar CSpe ECha EHyd EWes GBin GMaP IPot LEdu LRHS MAvo MNrw SMad STPC
- 'Pünktchen' (v)	ECha EHyd ELon EPPr GBin LRHS SMHy SRms XCre XLum
- 'Red Chief'	CMiW CRos EHyd EPPr EPfP EWes IMou LPla LRHS MAvo MHtn NDov NLar NRHS SCob SMad WTor
- RED CLOUD ('Emphis01')	LCro LOPS
- 'Red Meister'	CKno EHyd EPfP LRHS NRHS
- 'Red Wine'	GBin MNrw
- 'Roland'	CKno EPPr SMad XLum
- 'Rosi'	EPPr GBin MAsh MAvo
- 'Roterpfeil'	EPPr
- 'Rotfeder'	EPPr
- 'Rotfuchs'	EBee MAvo XCre XLum
- 'Rotsilber'	CBod CKno ECha EHyd EMor EPPr GMaP IArd LEdu LRHS MAsh MMuc NRHS NWsh SRms WHoo WOld WPGP XLum
- 'Russia'	NWsh
- 'Samurai'	EPPr GMaP MAvo MNrw SCob
- 'Sarabande' 🏆^{H6}	EPPr SMHy SMea WSpi XCre
- 'Septemberrot' 🏆^{H6}	EPPr MMuc SEND
- 'Serim'	EPPr
§ - 'Silberfeder' 🏆^{H6}	Widely available
- 'Silberpfeil' (v)	NWsh
- 'Silberspinne'	EBee ELon EPPr GBin ILea SCob SMHy SMea SPlb XLum
- 'Silberturm'	EPPr XCre XLum
- SILVER FEATHER	see *M. sinensis* 'Silberfeder'
- 'Silver Sceptre'	MAvo SMHy
- 'Silver Stripe'	EPPr MAvo
- 'Sioux'	ECtt EHyd EPPr EPfP EShb GBin GQue LRHS MBNS NRHS SPer
- 'Sirene'	EPPr MBNS MMuc NBir
- 'Spätgrün'	EPPr
- 'Starlight'	CKno MAsh
- 'Strictus' (v) 🏆^{H6}	Widely available
- 'Super Stripe' (v)	EPPr IMou
- 'Taiwan'	EBee EPPr
- 'Tiger Cub' (v)	EPPr EWes
- 'Undine' 🏆^{H6}	CMea ECha EPPr EPfP MBel MBrN MMuc NWsh XCre XLum
- 'Vanilla Sky' **new**	EBee
- 'Variegatus' (v)	CBod ECha ECtt EHyd ELan ELon EPPr EPfP GMaP LRHS LSRN LSun MMuc MRav NGdn NRHS NSti SDix SPer SPoG SRms WCot WSMil WSpi XCre XLum
- 'Verneigung'	GBin
- 'Vorläufer'	EBee EPPr GBin XCre
- 'Westacre Wine'	EPPr EWes
- 'Wetterfahne'	EPPr LEdu
§ - 'Yaku-jima'	CBod CSam ECha ECtt EHyd ELan EPPr LRHS MMuc MWht NRHS SMea XCre
- 'Yakushima Dwarf'	CEnd CExl CRos EHyd ELan ELon EPPr EPed EPfP LRHS MCot NGdn NRHS NSti NWsh SCob SDys SRms SSut WCot WHoo WOld XCre XLum
- 'Zebrinus' (v) 🏆^{H6}	Widely available
- 'Zwergelefant'	EBee MAvo SMHy XLum
tinctorius 'Nanus Variegatus' misapplied	see *M. oligostachyus* 'Nanus Variegatus'
transmorrisonensis	CKno EHyd ELan EPPr LEdu LPla LRHS MAvo NDov NRHS NWsh WCot WPGP XCre
yakushimensis	see *M. sinensis* 'Little Kitten', *M. sinensis* 'Yaku-jima'

Mitchella (*Rubiaceae*)

repens	CBcs CBod EBee EPot GEdr IMou LEdu MNrw WCru
undulata B&SWJ 10928	WCru
* - f. ***quelpartensis*** B&SWJ 4402	WCru

Mitella (*Saxifragaceae*)

acerina B&SWJ 11029	EWld WCru
breweri	CBod CMac ECha EWld GLog IMou MAvo MBriF MPnt MRav NSti WBor WFar WPnP
caulescens	ECha NBro
diphylla	MHer
formosana B&SWJ 125	WCru
furusei var. ***subramosa*** B&SWJ 11097	WCru
× ***inami***	IMou
- B&SWJ 11122	WCru
japonica B&SWJ 4971	WCru
kiusiana B&SWJ 5888	WCru
makinoi	EWld
- B&SWJ 4992	CExl WCru
pauciflora B&SWJ 6361	WCru
stylosa B&SWJ 5669	WCru
yoshinagae	WFar
- B&SWJ 4893	CExl EPPr WCru

Mitraria (*Gesneriaceae*)

coccinea	CCCN CExl CMac CPbh CRHN CTsd GBin GEdr GKev MBlu NLar SLon SPer SPlb WPav
- Clark's form	LRHS NLar SIvy
- 'Lago Puyehue'	CAbb CBcs CCCN CDoC CExl CRos CSpe EBee EPfP LRHS MAsh MGil SIvy SPlb SVen SWvt WPav WSHC WThu
- 'Lake Caburgua'	CAby CCCN ELon EWld NLar WPav

Modiolastrum (*Malvaceae*)

lateritium	CRHN CSpe CTri EBee ELan EPPr EPri LRHS MAvo NBir SIvy SPhx SPoG SRms WAvo WHal WSHC XLum

Moehringia (*Caryophyllaceae*)

muscosa	WCot

Molinia ✿ (*Poaceae*)

altissima	see *M. caerulea* subsp. *arundinacea*
caerulea	CKno CPla EHyd EPPr LRHS MAsh MBlu NRHS
§ - subsp. ***arundinacea***	CFis CKno CSpe CWCL ECha EPPr SSut XLum
- - 'Automne Bronze'	EPPr
- - 'Autumn Charm'	CKno
- - 'Bergfreund'	CKno CSam EPPr GBin MAvo SMHy
- - 'Black Arrows'	MAvo NDov
- - 'Breeze'	CKno NDov
- - 'Cordoba'	CBod EBee ECha ELan EMor EPPr GBin GQue MAvo NDov SMHy WFar XLum
- - 'Fontäne'	CSam EPPr GQue MAsh MAvo SMea SPhx
- - 'Golden Chimes' **new**	EPPr
- - 'JS Mostenveld' (v)	EPPr GBin SMad
- - 'JS Witches Broom'	EPPr GBin
- - 'JS Yellow Pipe'	EPPr GBin
- - 'Karl Foerster'	Widely available
- - 'Les Ponts de Cé'	EBee ECha EPPr
- - 'Liebreiz'	EPPr
- - 'Skyracer'	CBod CKno CRos CSde EBee EHyd ELan ELon EMor EPPr GBin GLog GMaP GQue LEdu LRHS MAvo MNrw NRHS SEdd SMHy SPhx WCot WGrn WPGP WPnP
- - 'Staefa'	EPPr
- - 'Sunbeam'	EPPr
- - 'Tears of Joy'	EBee EPPr
- - 'Transparent'	Widely available
- - 'Welcome Stranger' **new**	NWsh
- - 'Windsaule'	CKno EPPr IMou MAvo NDov
- - 'Windspiel' ♀H7	CAby CBod CKno CSam CSde CWCL EAJP EBee EBou ECha EHyd ELon EMor EPPr EPed EShb GBin GQue LRHS MAvo MNrw NDov NRHS NWsh SDix SPer SPoG WCAu WCot XLum
- - 'Zuneigung'	CSam ECha EHyd EPPr LRHS MAvo
- subsp. ***caerulea***	EPPr
- - 'Carmarthen' (v)	EHyd ELon EPPr LRHS
- - 'Claerwen' (v)	ECha ELon EPPr MAvo SPhx
- - 'Coneyhill Gold' (v)	EPPr
- - 'Dark Defender'	EPPr LEdu MAvo NDov SPhx
- - 'Dauerstrahl'	CKno EPPr EPed GQue LEdu MAsh MNrw NBid NDov SEdd
- - 'Edith Dudszus'	CAby CBod CKno CMea CSam EAJP EBou ECha EHyd ELan ELon EMor EPPr EPed EPfP GBin GQue LRHS MBel MBrN NDov NGdn NHol NRHS SCob SPer WGrn WPnP XCre
- - 'Heidebraut'	CBod CMea CSam EHyd ELon EMor EPPr EPed EPfP GBin GMaP GQue LCro LOPS LRHS MBel MRav NDov NRHS SAko SCob SEdd SPhx WCot XCre
- - 'Heidezwerg'	CKno EBee ELon EMor EPPr GBin
- - 'Igel'	CKno EBee EPPr GBin
- - 'Moorflamme'	CSam ELon MAvo NDov
- - 'Moorhexe' ♀H7	CAby CBod CMea EBee ECha EHyd ELon EMor EPed EPfP EShb GBin GMaP GQue GWyn LRHS MAvo NBid NDov NGdn NHol NRHS NSti NWsh SCob SSut WCAu WCot WFar WHoo
- - 'Overdam'	CKno EBee EPPr MNrw NDov
- - 'Poul Petersen'	CKno EBee EMor EPPr GBin MBel NDov SCob SPhx
- - 'Rotschopf'	EBee
- - 'Strahlenquelle'	CAby CBod CFis CSam EHyd EPPr EPed EWhm GBin GQue LRHS NDov NHol NRHS NWsh WCAu
- - 'Variegata' (v) ♀H7	Widely available
- 'Showers of Gold'	SPhx
- 'Torch'PBR **new**	CKno
- 'Winterfreude'	EPPr
litoralis	see *M. caerulea* subsp. *arundinacea*

Molopospermum (*Apiaceae*)

peloponnesiacum	CSpe EBee ELan EMor EPPr GBin LEdu LRHS MMrt SBrt SMHy SPhx SPtp WCru WOut WPGP WSHC

Moltkia (*Boraginaceae*)

§ ***doerfleri***	CPla NBir NChi SBrt WSHC
§ × ***intermedia*** ♀H4	CMea CRos EHyd LRHS NRHS WAbe
petraea	CRos EHyd LRHS NRHS SBut

Moluccella (*Lamiaceae*)

laevis	CSpe LCro LOPS SPhx SVic

Monanthes (*Crassulaceae*)

laxiflora	WCot
pallens	WCot

Monarda ✿ (*Lamiaceae*)

'Adam'	GBee GQue LSRN MRav NGrd NLar WMon WSHC
'André Eve' **new**	NDov
'Aquarius'	CBod CWCL EAJP EHyd GQue LRHS NLar NRHS WCAu WFar WMon XLum
austromontana	see *M. citriodora* subsp. *austromontana*
'Baby Spice'	WMon
§ 'Balance'	CFis EBee ECtt EHyd LRHS MMrt MPie MRav NGdn NRHS WMon WSHC XLum
'Beauty of Cobham' ♀H4	Widely available
(Bee-You Series) 'Bee-Free'	CWGN NLar SHeu WMon
- 'Bee-Happy'	CWGN NLar SHeu
- 'Bee-Lieve'	NLar SHeu WMon
- 'Bee-True'	CWGN SHeu
'Bergamo'	CSpe LCro LOPS MHol
§ 'Blaustrumpf'	CElw ECtt EHyd EPfP EWes GQue LRHS NGrd NLar SPer WFar WMon WSHC XLum
BLUE STOCKING	see *M.* 'Blaustrumpf'
BOWMAN	see *M.* 'Sagittarius'
bradburyana	EBee LPla LRHS MMuc SAko SBrt SPhx
- 'Grey Summit' **new**	NDov
- 'Maramek'	IPot NLar WMon
- 'Ozark'	ECha NDov SAko
- Schm. 2004-0076	WMon
'Cambridge Scarlet'	Widely available
'Camilla'	WGoo WMon
'Capricorn'	WMon XLum
'Cherokee'	WMon
citriodora	GJos GPoy NSti SRms SVic
§ - subsp. ***austromontana***	NBir

'Comanche'	EWes NLar WMon
'Croftway Pink'	CBcs CBod CRos CSBt CWCL CWld ECha ECtt EHyd ELan EPfP GMaP LCro LOPS LRHS MAvo MTis NLar NRHS SCob SPer SWvt WBor WCAu WFar WMon WSHC XLum
I 'Dark Ponticum'	WMon
didyma	CBod CLau EBou ENfk EPfP MNHC NBro SRms SVic WFar XAbr
- 'Alba'	WMon
- BALMY LILAC ('Balbalmac'PBR)	CBod EHyd LRHS MHol NRHS SCob SPoG
- BALMY PINK ('Balbalmink'PBR)	CBod LSou SPoG WHil
- BALMY PURPLE ('Balbalmurp'PBR)	EHyd LRHS LSou MHol NRHS SCob SPoG WFar WHil
- BALMY ROSE ('Balbalmose'PBR)	LSou SCob SNig WHil
- 'Coral Reef'	EHyd LRHS WFar WMon
- 'Cranberry Lace'PBR	CRos EBee ECtt EHyd EPfP LRHS MBel MHol NRHS SPoG WCAu
- 'Pardon My Pink'	CBod EBee NLar SPad WMon
- 'Pardon My Purple'	EPfP NLar SPoG WHil WMon
- 'Pink Lace'PBR	CRos ECtt EHyd EPfP LRHS LSou LSun MBros MHol MNrw NDov NHol NLar NRHS NSti SCob SPoG WCAu WFar WHil WMon
- 'Pocahontas White Blush' **new**	WHil
- 'Sugar Lace'PBR	LBuc
'Earl Grey'	CBod ECtt NChi SCoo SEdi WFar WMon
'Elsie's Lavender'	EBee EHyd EPfP GMaP LRHS NDov NLar NRHS WFar WMon WSHC
'Elworthy'	CElw WWFP
'Eugens Kirschrot'	WMon
'Eugens Purpursamt'	WMon
'Feckenham Danielle' **new**	WMal
'Feckenham Delight' **new**	WMal WMon
§ 'Feuerschopf'	EBee
'Fireball'PBR	CBcs CBod CRos CWCL EAJP EBee ECtt EHyd EPfP EShb LCro LOPS LRHS LSRN LSou MBel MHer MHol MTis NDov NHol NLar NRHS SPoG SRkn WBor WCAu WFar WHil WMon
FIRECROWN	see *M.* 'Feuerschopf'
§ 'Fishes'	CExl CMac EBee ECtt ELan EWes GQue LEdu LRHS MRav NDov NGdn SGbt SWvt WFar WMon
fistulosa	CBod CFis CHby CMac EBou MBow MMuc MNHC NDov SRms XAbr XLum
- 'Humdinger'	EBee WMon
- var. ***menthifolia*** 'Mohikaner'	EBee NDov SAko WGoo WMon
- - 'Pummel' **new**	NDov WMon
- 'Wahpe Washtemna'	NDov
'Gardenview Scarlet' ♀H4	Widely available
GEMINI	see *M.* 'Twins'
'Gewitterwolke'	CSam ECtt MNrw NDov WMon
'Hartswood Wine'	EWes LEdu WFar WMon WPGP
'Häuptling'	WMon
'Heidelerche'	WFar WMon
'Huckleberry'	GBin NDov WMon
'Jacob Cline'	CDor CMea CRos EAJP ECtt EHyd EWes GBin GWyn IMou IPot LEdu LPla LRHS MBel MNrw MPie NBre NLar NRHS SGbt SHar SPhx SRms WBor WCAu WFar WMon WPGP XLum
'Kardinal'	GBin LRHS MTis NDov NLar WMon XLum
'Lederstrumpf'	EBee WMon
LIBRA	see *M.* 'Balance'
'Loddon Crown'	ECtt LPla MBNS MHer NHol NLar SHar WCAu WFar WMon WSHC
'Mahogany'	CBod CRos EBee ECtt EHyd ELan EMor EPfP GMaP IPot LRHS LSou MCot NRHS NSti SPer SPhx SPoG WFar WMon XLum
'Marshall's Delight' ♀H4	CRos EBee ECtt EHyd EPfP EWes GQue LEdu LRHS LSou MNrw MRav NDov NRHS SWvt WCAu WFar WMon
'Melissa'	CRos EBee EHyd EPfP LRHS NBre NLar NRHS WMon WSHC
menthifolia	SRms
'Mohawk'	CBod CWld ECtt EHyd EPfP GQue LRHS MPie MRav NDov NGdn NGrd SGbt WCAu WMon XLum
'Neon'	LRHS NDov SPhx WMon
'On Parade'	CBod CSam CWCL CWld ECtt EHyd ELon GBee GPSL LEdu LPla LRHS MMrt MTis NDov NGdn NRHS WAul WMon
'Othello'	EHyd LRHS NDov NRHS WGoo WMon
'Ou Charm'	EBee EWes NLar WFar WMon
Panorama Series	SPlb
- 'Panorama Red Shades'	CCBP EPfP WCFE WFar WMon
'Pawnee'	GBin WGoo WMon
PETITE DELIGHT ('Acpetdel')	EWTr LSou WMon XLum
'Petite Wonder'	EBee WFar WMon
'Pink Supreme'PBR	CBod ECtt EHyd ELan EPfP LRHS MBel MTis NLar SCoo WFar WHil WMon WTor
'Pink Tourmaline'	WMon
PISCES	see *M.* 'Fishes'
'Poyntzfield Pink'	GPoy LEdu LPla
PRAIRIE NIGHT	see *M.* 'Prärienacht'
§ 'Prärienacht'	Widely available
punctata	MNHC
- 'Bee Bop'	LCro LOPS
'Purple Ann'	XLum
'Purple Lace'PBR	CRos EHyd LRHS NRHS WFar WMon
'Purple Tower'	EWes
'Raspberry Wine'	CBod CDor CRos EBee ECtt EHyd EMor EPPr EPfP EWes LEdu LRHS LSou MTis NRHS WFar WMon WPGP
'Rebecca'	NDov WMon
'Remie'	WMon
'Ruby Glow'	CRos CSam EHyd GWyn LRHS NRHS WMon
§ 'Sagittarius'	EBee EHyd LRHS MAvo NGdn NRHS NSti SPoG WFar WMon
'Saxon Purple'	EBee LPla MBel NDov WMon XLum
§ 'Schneewittchen'	CAby CBod CWCL EBee ECha ECtt ELan EPfP LRHS MRav MTis NDov NHol NLar SCob SCoo SGbt SPer SPoG SRms SWvt WCAu WFar WMon XLum
'Scorpion'	CRos EBee ECtt EHyd ELan EPfP GBin GQue LCro LOPS LRHS MRav NBir NGdn NLar NRHS NSti SGbt SPoG SWvt WCAu WMon XLum

	'Shelley'	ECha WMon
	'Snow Maiden'	see *M.* 'Schneewittchen'
	'Snow Queen'	EBee ECtt EHyd EShb LRHS MPie
	SNOW WHITE	see *M.* 'Schneewittchen'
	'Squaw' ♀H4	Widely available
	'Talud' ♀H4	IPot MNrw NDov WMon
	'Tante Polly'	WMon
§	'Twins'	NLar SWvt WFar WMon WSHC
	'Vintage Wine'	CElw NDov WMon
	'Violacea'	NHol WFar WMon
	'Violet Queen' ♀H4	CBod CRos CWCL CWld EBee ECtt EHyd ELan EWes GQue LEdu LRHS MAvo MBel MCot MPie MSpe NEoE NRHS SCoo SPhx WCAu WCot WFar WMon WPGP
	'Violette'	EBee WFar WMon
	'Westacre Purple'	ECha EPPr EWes

Monardella (*Lamiaceae*)

	macrantha	CPBP
	odoratissima	GEdr MHer SPhx

Monochoria (*Pontederiaceae*)

§	***hastata***	LLWG

Monstera (*Araceae*)

	deliciosa (F) ♀H1b	CDoC LCro LOPS XBlo
	obliqua 'Monkey Mask' **new**	LCro LOPS

Montbretia see *Crocosmia*, *Tritonia*

Montia (*Portulacaceae*)

	perfoliata	see *Claytonia perfoliata*
	sibirica	see *Claytonia sibirica*

Moraea (*Iridaceae*)

	alticola	SPlb
§	***aristata***	WHil
	bipartita	WCot
§	***collina***	GKev
	comptonii	WHil
	glaucopsis	see *M. aristata*
	huttonii	CBor CCCN CFis CPbh CSpe CTsd EPri GAbr GKev NWad SBrt SMad WKif WSHC
	iridioides	see *Dietes iridioides*
	longifolia (Jacq.) Pers.	MHol
	mediterranea	GKev
	ochroleuca	CBor GKev
	polystachya	CGrW
	sisyrinchium	GKev NWad SDeJ
	spathacea	see *M. spathulata*
§	***spathulata***	CExl GKev WCot
	vegeta	SBrt

Morella (*Myricaceae*)

	californica	CAgr
	pensylvanica	CAgr NLar

Moricandia (*Brassicaceae*)

	moricandioides	WCot

Morina (*Caprifoliaceae*)

*	***afghanica***	NWad
	betonicoides	GKev
	bulleyana	see *M. nepatensis* var. *delavayi*
	longifolia	Widely available
§	***nepatensis*** var. ***delavayi***	GKev
	persica	EWes NWad
	polyphylla	GPoy

Morinda (*Rubiaceae*)

	umbellata WWJ 11688	WCru

Morisia (*Brassicaceae*)

	hypogaea	see *M. monanthos*
§	***monanthos***	GEdr LRHS WCav WIce
	- 'Fred Hemingway'	ELan LRHS NSla WAbe

Morus ✿ (*Moraceae*)

§	***alba***	CBcs CCVT CHab CLnd CMCN ECrN ELan EPfP LBuc LMaj MRav SPer SPre SVic WFar WLov WMou WTSh
	- 'Issai' (F)	MGos
	- 'Laciniata'	EBee ELan
	- 'Macrophylla'	CMCN MBlu
	- 'Pakistan' (F)	CAgr SPoG
	- 'Paradise' (F)	CAgr
	- 'Pendula'	CEnd CMCN CMac ELan MBlu NOra SCoo SPoG SWeb SWvt WMat
	- 'Platanifolia'	MBlu SCob
	- var. ***tatarica***	CAgr LEdu NLar
	'Black Tabor' (F)	CAgr
	'Capsrum' (F)	CAgr
	'Carman' (F)	CAgr NLar NOra
	cathayana	EBee WPGP
	'Illinois Everbearing' (F)	CAgr
	'Italian' (F)	CAgr
	'Ivory' (F)	CAgr
	kagayamae	see *M. alba*
	latifolia 'Spirata'	NLar
	macroura	LCro LOPS WSpi
	nigra (F)	Widely available
§	- 'Chelsea' (F) ♀H6	CEnd CSBt CTho CTri EPfP EPom LRHS MGos NLar NOra SCoo SEWo SKee SLim SPer SPoG SSFT WMat
	- 'Izvor' (F)	CAgr
	- 'Jerusalem' (F) ♀H6	NOra WMat
	- 'King James'	see *M. nigra* 'Chelsea'
	- 'Large Black' (F)	EPom
	- 'Repsime' (F)	CAgr
	- 'Sham Dudu' (F)	CAgr
	rubra	EBtc
	'Wellington' (F)	CCVT CEnd CLnd EBee LRHS LSRN NOra SSFT WMat

Mosla (*Lamiaceae*)

	dianthera	MAvo

Muehlenbeckia ✿ (*Polygonaceae*)

	astonii	EBee WPGP
	axillaris misapplied	see *M. complexa*
§	***axillaris*** (Hook. f.) Endl.	CBcs CTri EBee EShb GBin MGil XLum
§	***complexa***	CBcs CBod CMac CSpe CTrC CTri EBee ELon EPfP EShb LCro LOPS LRHS MBlu MGil MSCN NQui SAdn SArc SCob SEND SIvy SLim SLon SPer SPoG SWvt WCFE WPGP XLum
	- (f)	CDoC
	- 'Nana'	see *M. axillaris* (Hook. f.) Endl.
	- 'Spotlight'PBR (v)	EShb
	- 'Texture Big Leaf'	WPGP
	- var. ***trilobata***	CTrC EShb ESwi SSta WBor XLum

	platyclados	see *Homalocladium platycladum*
	volcanica	WCru
	B&SWJ 14913 **new**	

Muhlenbergia (*Poaceae*)

	capillaris	CBcs CBod CSpe EBee LSRN MBNS MMrt SDix SMad WSpi XCre
	dumosa	CKno WCot WPGP
	emersleyi	XCre
	lindheimeri	CKno EBee SDix WCot XCre
	mexicana	SRms
	rigens	CKno WSpi XCre XLum

Mukdenia (*Saxifragaceae*)

	acanthifolia	LEdu WPGP
	rossii	CAby CPla ECha ELon GBin LEdu LPla MBel MNrw NBid NLar SBut SIvy WFar WOld WPGP XLum
	- 'Crimson Fans'	see *M. rossii* 'Karasuba'
	- dwarf	MNrw
§	- 'Karasuba'	Widely available
	- 'Shishiba'	GEdr LEdu

× *Mukgenia* (*Saxifragaceae*)

§	'Flame'	CAby CBct EBee EMor GEdr IBal LEdu LSou MHol MPnt NHar SPad SPoG
	NOVA	see × *M.* 'Flame'

mulberry see *Morus*

Murraya (*Rutaceae*)

	exotica	see *M. paniculata*
	koenigii	see *Bergera koenigii*
§	***paniculata***	EShb

Musa ✿ (*Musaceae*)

§	***acuminata*** 'Dwarf Cavendish' (AAA Group) (F) ♀H1b	CAbb CBod CCht CDoC ELan SPlb XBlo
	- 'Williams' (AAA Group) (F)	XBlo
	- 'Zebrina' ♀H1b	CDTJ EHyd LRHS XBlo
	basjoo ♀H2	CAbb CBcs CBod CCht CDoC CSBt CTsd ELan EPfP LCro LEdu LOPS MGos MMuc SArc SChr SEND SGsty SMad SPalm SPer SPlb SPoG WLov WSMil
I	- 'Rubra'	CCCN
	'Cavendish Super Dwarf'	CDoC XBlo
	cavendishii	see *M. acuminata* 'Dwarf Cavendish'
§	***coccinea*** ♀H1b	XBlo
	ensete	see *Ensete ventricosum*
	hookeri	see *M. sikkimensis*
	lasiocarpa ♀H2	CDTJ LCro LOPS MGos MPkF SPalm SPlb
	nana misapplied	see *M. acuminata* 'Dwarf Cavendish'
	ornata ♀H1b	CCCN XBlo
	× ***paradisiaca*** 'Ney Poovan' (AB Group) (F)	CCCN
§	***sikkimensis*** ♀H2	CDTJ CTsd SGsty SPlb XBlo
	- 'Red Tiger'	CCCN CDTJ SPalm
	uranoscopus misapplied	see *M. coccinea*
	velutina ♀H1b	CCCN CTsd

Muscari ✿ (*Asparagaceae*)

	adilii	GKev
	ambrosiacum	see *M. muscarimi*
	anatolicum	WCot
	- giant	GKev
	armeniacum ♀H6	CArg CRos CTri ECul GKev GWyn LCro LOPS LRHS NRHS SEND SPer SRms WCot WShi
	- PAB 6748	LEdu
	- 'Alida'	GKev
	- 'Artist'	GKev SDeJ
	- 'Atlantic'	CRos EHyd GKev LRHS NRHS
	- 'Blue Spike' (d)	GKev NBir SDeJ WBrk
	- 'Cantab'	SDeJ XLum
	- 'Carola'	GKev
	- 'Christmas Pearl' ♀H6	GKev
	- 'Cupido'	GKev
	- 'Dark Eyes'	EMor GKev SDeJ
	- 'Early Giant'	SDeJ
	- 'Fantasy Creation'	GKev SDeJ
	- 'Gül'	WCot
	- 'Lady Blu'	LRHS
	- 'Peppermint'	CRos EHyd GKev LRHS NRHS SDeJ SPhx
	- 'Saffier' ♀H6	WCot
	- 'Siberian Tiger'	CDoC CRos ECul EHyd EPot ERCP LRHS MWat NHpl NRHS WTor
	- 'Touch of Snow'	GKev LCro LOPS LRHS SPhx
	- 'Valerie Finnis'	CAby CAvo EPfP EPot ERCP EWTr GKev LRHS MWat NLar SDeJ SMad WBrk WCot
	aucheri ♀H6	GKev NRya
*	- var. ***bicolor***	WCot
	- 'Blue Magic'	CAvo ECul EPot ERCP GKev LRHS SDeJ
	- 'Ocean Magic'	CAvo GKev LCro LOPS MBriF NHpl NLar
	- 'White Magic'	CAvo EMor ERCP GKev LCro LOPS LRHS NHpl SDeJ WBrk WFar
§	***azureum*** ♀H6	CAvo ELan ERCP GKev GMaP LRHS NBir NLar SPhx WCot WFar
	- 'Album'	SPhx WCot
	- 'Bling Bling'	ERCP GKev LRHS SDeJ WCot
	'Baby's Breath'	see *M.* 'Jenny Robinson'
	'Big Smile'	CRos EHyd EPfP GKev LRHS NRHS WCot
	'Blue Eyes'	WCot
	botryoides	GKev WCot
	- 'Album'	CAvo CTri EPfP GKev LCro LOPS SDeJ SRms WCot WShi
	bourgaei	GKev
	caucasicum	WCot
	chalusicum	see *M. pseudomuscari*
	coeleste	GKev WCot
	commutatum	GKev
	- white-flowered	GKev
§	***comosum***	CBro ERCP WCot WFar
	- 'Monstrosum'	see *M. comosum* 'Plumosum'
§	- 'Plumosum'	SDeJ
	inconstrictum	GKev
	'Ivor's Pink'	WCot
§	'Jenny Robinson' ♀H5	CAvo ECul LRHS SDys SMad WCot
	'Joyce Spirit'	ECul ERCP GKev LRHS
	kerkis **new**	GKev
	latifolium ♀H6	CAby CDoC CRos EHyd ERCP GKev LCro LOPS LRHS MWat NLar NRHS SDeJ WBor WCot
*	- 'Blue Angels'	NBir
	- 'Grape Ice' **new**	GKev
	macbeathianum	WCot
§	***macrocarpum***	ECha GKev WShi
	- 'Golden Fragrance' PBR	CAvo CBro CExl EPot ERCP GKev MNrw SDeJ
	'Memory of Gary Fisher'	WCot

	mirum	WCot
	'Morgenhimmel'	GKev
	moschatum	see *M. muscarimi*
	'Mount Hood'	EMor ERCP GKev SDeJ SPhx
	'Mountain Lady'	GKev
§	***muscarimi***	CAvo GKev SDeJ WCot
	- var. ***flavum***	see *M. macrocarpum*
§	***neglectum***	GKev NLar SEND WCot WShi
	pallens	GKev
	paradoxum	see *Bellevalia paradoxa*
	parviflorum	GKev WCot
	'Pink Sunrise'	EMor EPot ERCP EWTr GKev LRHS NHpl SDeJ WCot
§	***pseudomuscari*** ♀H5	GKev WCot
	pulchellum subsp. ***clepsydroides***	GKev
	- subsp. ***pulchellum***	GKev
	racemosum	see *M. neglectum*
	'Rosy Sunrise'	GKev WCot
	'Sky Blue'	WCot
	'Superstar'	GKev
§	***tenuiflorum***	WCot
	aff. ***tenuiflorum*** JCA 0.691.251	WCot
	'Venus'	GBin GKev WCot
	verticillaris	GKev
	'White Beauty'	SPhx WCot
	'Winter Amethyst'	WCot

Muscarimia (*Asparagaceae*)

ambrosiacum	see *Muscari muscarimi*
macrocarpum	see *Muscari macrocarpum*

Musella see *Musa*

Mussaenda (*Rubiaceae*)

'Tropic Snow'	CCCN

Mutisia (*Asteraceae*)

oligodon	GKev
retrorsa	GKev

Myoporum (*Scrophulariaceae*)

	acuminatum	see *M. tenuifolium*
	laetum	CExl IDee SPlb SVen
§	***tenuifolium***	SPlb SVen

Myosotidium (*Boraginaceae*)

§	***hortensia***	CAbb CAby CBcs CBct CExl CPla CSpe CTsd ELan EWes EWld GAbr GBin GKev IBal ITim LRHS NRHS SChF SEdd SIvy
	nobile	see *M. hortensia*

Myosotis (*Boraginaceae*)

	arvensis	MBow
	australis	WCot
	dissitiflora 'Elegantissima' (v)	CNat
	'Malmesbury'	CNat
	MY OH MY ('Myomark'PBR)	CBod
	palustris	see *M. scorpioides*
	pulvinaris	SPlb
	rakiura	EWes
§	***scorpioides***	CHab CWCL CWat LCro LLWG LOPS MMuc MWts NAts NMir SCoo SPlb SRms WBrk WMAq WPnP XLum
	- 'Alba'	LLWG MWts
	- 'Ice Pearl'	ECha
	- MAYTIME ('Blaqua') (v)	NBir
	- 'Mermaid'	CBen CWat ECha EWat LLWG SRms
	- 'Pinkie'	LLWG
	- 'Snowflakes'	CWat EWat
	sylvatica	LCro LOPS MMuc NMir WWild
	- 'Bluesylva' (Sylva Series) ♀H6	LRHS SPhx
	- 'Indigo' **new**	ELan
	- 'Ultramarine' ♀H6	LCro LOPS
	'Sylvia Blue' **new**	LCro LOPS

Myrceugenia (*Myrtaceae*)

ovata var. ***nannophylla*** **new**	WPGP

Myrica (*Myricaceae*)

gale	CAgr GPoy NLar WSpi

Myricaria (*Tamaricaceae*)

germanica	NLar

Myriophyllum (*Haloragaceae*)

propinquum	LLWG
spicatum	EWat MWts WMAq
verticillatum	CWat SCoo

Myrmecodia (*Rubiaceae*)

beccarii 'Adventure' **new**	SPad

Myrrhis (*Apiaceae*)

odorata	Widely available
- 'Forncett Chevron'	LEdu SPhx

Myrsine (*Primulaceae*)

africana	EShb MHer
australis	SVen
divaricata	GBin SVen
nummularia	WThu
salicina **new**	CTsd

Myrteola (*Myrtaceae*)

§	***nummularia***	GAbr GRum ITim WPav WThu

Myrtus ✿ (*Myrtaceae*)

	apiculata misapplied	see *Luma apiculata*
	bullata	see *Lophomyrtus bullata*
	chequen	see *Luma chequen*
	communis ♀H4	Widely available
	- 'Flore Pleno' (d)	MHer
	- 'Jekka's All Gold'	WJek
	- 'Jenny Reitenbach'	see *M. communis* subsp. *tarentina*
	- 'Merion'	WJek
	- 'Microphylla'	see *M. communis* subsp. *tarentina*
	- 'Nana'	see *M. communis* subsp. *tarentina*
	- 'Pyewood Park'	SRms WJek
§	- subsp. ***tarentina*** ♀H4	Widely available
	- - 'Compacta'	LRHS SCoo SLon
	- - 'Microphylla Variegata' (v)	EShb MNHC SPer SRms WJek
I	- - 'Variegata' (v)	CBod EPfP
	- 'Tricolor'	see *M. communis* 'Variegata'
§	- 'Variegata' (v)	CBod CMac CRos CSBt CTri EBee EHyd ELan ENfk EPfP EShb LEdu LRHS MGil MHer MSwo NLar NRHS SCob SGbt SGol SLon SPer SPoG WAvo WFar WJek
	'Glanleam Gold'	see *Luma apiculata* 'Glanleam Gold'
	lechleriana	see *Amomyrtus luma*
	luma	see *Luma apiculata*

	nummularia	see *Myrteola nummularia*
*	***paraguayensis***	EBee
	ugni	see *Ugni molinae*

N

× *Nananopsis* (*Aizoaceae*)

hybrid (*Aloinopsis spathulata* × *Nananthus transvaalensis*)	CPBP

Nandina (*Berberidaceae*)

	domestica	Widely available
	- B&SWJ 4923	WCru
	- B&SWJ 11113	WCru
	- BLUSH PINK ('Aka'PBR)	CDoC CMac LRHS LSRN MAsh MThu SPoG SWvt
	- 'Filamentosa'	EPfP LRHS MPkF NLar SGol
	- 'Fire Power'	Widely available
	- FLIRT ('Murasaki'PBR)	MAsh SGol
	- 'Gulf Stream'	CBrac CRos EHyd ELan EPfP LBuc LRHS LSRN MAsh MGos MPkF NLar NRHS SGsty SMad SavN
	- 'Harbour Dwarf'	CEnd LRHS WFar
	- var. ***leucocarpa***	NLar
	- MAGICAL LEMON AND LIME ('Lemlin'PBR)	CBcs ELan LCro LOPS LRHS MPkF SGol SavN WHwl
	- 'Nana'	see *N. domestica* 'Pygmaea'
	- OBSESSED	see *N. domestica* 'Seika'
	- PLUM PASSION ('Monum')	EHyd EPfP LRHS MAsh MGos SavN
§	- 'Pygmaea'	CMen ELon SGol
	- 'Red Dragon'	MPkF
	- 'Richmond' 🏆H5	CBcs CBrac CDoC CRos EBee EHyd ELan EMil EPfP LRHS MAsh MGos MPri NLar NRHS SCob SPer SPoG SWvt WCFE WFar WHwl
§	- 'Seika'PBR	CBod CDoC CMac CRos CSpe CWGN EBee EHyd EPfP LCro LOPS LRHS MAsh MGos MPkF MThu NLar NRHS SCob SGol SGsty SMad SPad SPoG SWvt SavN WCot WHwl
	- SIENNA SUNRISE ('Monfar')	CBod ELan LRHS SGol
	- 'Sunset'PBR	CAbb CBod EBee LSRN NLar SCob SMad SPad
	- 'Tuscan Flame'	LRHS
	- 'Twilight'PBR (v)	CBod CWGN EPfP SWvt
	- 'Wood's Dwarf'	CBcs MPkF NLar WFar

Nannorrhops (*Arecaceae*)

	arabica	see *N. ritchieana*
§	***ritchieana***	SPlb
	- blue-leaved	SPlb

Napaea (*Malvaceae*)

dioica	LEdu SPhx WCot WPGP

Narcissus ✿ (*Amaryllidaceae*)

'Abba' (4) 🏆H6	CFen CQua
'Abbey Road' (5)	CQua
'Aberfoyle' (2) 🏆H6	CQua
'Abstract' (11a)	CQua
'Accent' (2)	CQua
'Achduart' (3)	CQua
'Achentoul' (4)	CQua
'Achnasheen' (3)	CQua
'Acropolis' (4)	CQua GKev SDeJ
'Actaea' (9) 🏆H6	CBro CFen CQua GBin GCro LCro LOPS SDeJ SPer
'Acumen' (2)	CQua
'Admiration' (8)	CQua
'Ad-Rem' (2)	CFen
'Adversane' (3)	CQua
'Advocat' (3)	CQua
'Aflame' (3)	CFen
'After All' (3)	CFen
'Ahwahnee' (2)	CQua
'Ainley' (2)	CQua
'Aintree' (3)	CQua
'Aircastle' (3)	CQua
'Albatross' (3)	CQua GCro WShi
'Albus Plenus Odoratus'	see *N. poeticus* 'Plenus' ambig.
'Alex Jones' (2)	CQua
alpestris (13) **new**	NDry
'Altruist' (3)	CQua ERCP SDeJ
'Altun Ha' (2)	CQua GKev
'Amabilis' (3)	CQua
'Amadeus Mozart' (2)	CQua
'Amazing Grace' (2)	CQua
'Amber Castle' (2)	CQua
'Ambergate' (2)	CQua GKev SDeJ WPhe
'American Dream' (1)	CQua
'American Goldfinch' (7)	CQua
'American Heritage' (1)	CQua
'Amstel' (4)	CQua
'Andrew's Choice' (7) 🏆H6	CQua
'Androcles' (4)	WPhe
'Andy Blanchard' (5) **new**	NDry
'Angel' (3)	CQua
'Angel Face' (3)	CQua
'Angel's Breath' (5) 🏆H6	CAvo EPot
Angel's tears	see *N. triandrus* subsp. *triandrus* var. *triandrus*
'Angel's Whisper' (5)	CQua GKev WShi
'Angel's Wings' (2)	CQua
'Angkor' (4)	CQua
'An-gof' (7)	CQua
'Annequin' (3)	CQua
'Apollo Gold' (10)	NHpl
'Apotheose' (4)	CFen SDeJ
'Apricot' (1)	GCro
'Apricot Whirl' (11a)	CQua LRHS
'April Tears' (5)	WShi
'Ara' (6)	CQua GKev
'Aranjuez' (2)	CFen GCro
'Arctic Gem' (3)	CQua
'Arctic Gold' (1) 🏆H6	CQua
'Ard Righ' (1)	GCro
'Areley Kings' (2)	CQua
'Argent' (4)	CQua GCro
'Argosy' (1)	CQua
'Ariel'PBR (8)	GKev
'Arish Mell' (5)	CQua
'Ark Royal' (1)	CFen
'Arkle' (1) 🏆H6	CQua SDeJ
'Arleston' (2)	CQua
'Armada' (2)	CFen CQua
'Armidale' (3)	CQua
'Armoury' (4)	CQua
'Arndilly' (2)	CQua
'Arpege' (2)	CQua
'Arthurian' (1)	CQua
'Articol' (11a)	CQua
'Arwenack' (11a)	CQua
'Ascot' (4)	SDeJ
'Ashmore' (2)	CQua
'Ashton Wold' (2)	CQua

	'Aspasia' (8)	GKev
§	***assoanus*** (13)	EPot GKev WCot WShi
	'Astropink' (11a)	CQua
§	***asturiensis*** (13)	GKev NDry SEND WShi
	- giant	see *N. asturiensis* 'Wavertree'
§	- 'Wavertree' (1)	CQua NDry
	asturiensis* × *cyclamineus	NDry
	Asturiet Group (2) **new**	NDry
	'Audubon' (2)	CQua GKev SDeJ
	'Auntie Eileen' (2)	CQua
	'Ava Grace' (2) **new**	CQua
	'Avalanche' (8) ♀H4	CFen CQua ELan GKev LCro LOPS SDeJ
	'Avalanche of Gold' (8)	CQua
	'Avalon' (2)	CQua ERCP GKev SDeJ WPhe
	'Baby Boomer' (7)	CQua ERCP GKev WPhe
	'Baby Moon' (7)	CFen CQua EPot GKev SDeJ SDir
	'Back Flash' (2)	CQua
	'Badbury Rings' (3) ♀H6	CQua
	'Badgeworth' (3) **new**	CQua
	'Bahama Beach' (7) **new**	CQua
	'Bala' (4)	CQua
	'Balalaika' (2)	CQua
	'Balanced Equation' (11a) **new**	CQua
	'Baldock' (4)	CQua
	'Ballyrobert' (1)	CQua
	BALMACARA BEAUTY (2)	GCro
	'Balvenie' (2)	CQua
	'Banana Daiquiri' (11a) **new**	WPhe
	'Bandesara' (3)	CQua
	'Bandit' (2)	CQua
	'Banker' (2)	CQua
	'Banstead Village' (2)	CQua
	'Bantam' (2) ♀H6	CBro CQua SDeJ
	'Barbara Hunt' (7)	CQua
	'Barbara's Passion' (1) **new**	CQua
	'Barbary Gold' (2)	CQua
	'Barn Dance' (3)	CQua
	'Barnham' (1)	CQua
	'Barnsdale Wood' (2)	CQua
	'Barrett Browning' (3)	GKev MBros SDeJ
	'Barrii' (3)	CQua
	'Bath's Flame' (3)	CAvo CQua GCro GKev WShi
	'Bear's Gold' (4)	CQua
	'Beaulieu' (1)	CQua
	'Beautiful Dream' (3)	CQua
	'Beautiful Eyes' (7)	GKev
	'Beauvallon' (4)	SDeJ
	'Bebop' (7)	CBro
	'Bedruthan' (2)	CQua
	'Beersheba' (1)	CQua
	'Belcanto' (11a)	CQua SDeJ
	'Belisana' (2)	SDeJ
	'Belize' (2) **new**	CQua
	'Bell Rock' (1) ♀H6	CQua
	'Bell Song' (7)	CBro CFen CQua SDeJ WShi
	'Bella Estrella' (11a)	ERCP
	'Berceuse' (2)	CQua
	'Bere Ferrers' (4)	CQua
	'Bernardino' (2)	CQua GCro
	'Beryl' (6)	CQua WShi
	'Best Friend' (3)	CQua
	'Best Seller' (1)	CArg
	'Bethal' (3)	CQua
	'Bethan-Sîan' (2)	CQua
	'Biffo' (4)	CQua
	BIGGAR BOUNTIFUL (2)	GCro

	'Bilbo' (6)	CBro
	'Billy Graham' (2)	CQua
	'Binkie' (2)	CQua
	'Biondina' (1) **new**	NDry
	'Bionic' (2) **new**	CQua
	'Birchwood' (3)	CQua
	'Birma' (3)	SDeJ
	'Bittern' (12)	CBro CQua GKev SDeJ
	'Black Prince' (9) **new**	CQua
	'Blackstone' (2)	CQua
	'Blarney' (3)	CQua
	'Blisland' (9)	CQua
	'Blossom Lady' (4)	CQua
	'Blue Danube' (1)	CQua
	'Bluntington' (3) **new**	CQua
	'Blushing Lady' (7)	GKev
	'Blushing Maiden' (4)	CQua
	'Bob Spotts' (2)	CQua
	'Bobbysoxer' (7)	CBro CQua LEdu
	'Bobolink' (2)	CQua
	'Boconnoc' (2)	CQua
	'Bodelva' (2)	CQua
	'Bolton' (7)	GCro
	'Bombay' (2)	CFen
	'Bonython' (1)	GCro
	'Bosbigal' (11a)	CQua
	'Boscastle' (7)	CQua
	'Boscoppa' (11a)	CQua
	'Boslowick' (11a) ♀H6	CQua
	'Bosmeor' (2)	CQua
	'Bossa Nova' (3)	CQua
	'Bossiney' (11a)	CQua
	'Brackenhurst' (2)	SDeJ
	'Brahms' (2)	CFen
	'Bravoure' (1) ♀H6	CQua GBin SDeJ SDir SPhx
	'Breezand Tristar' (11a) ♀H6	CBro
	'Brentswood' (8)	CQua
	'Bridal Crown' (4) ♀H6	CDoC CFen GKev LCro LOPS LRHS SDeJ
	'Brideshead' (2)	CFen
	'Bright Flame' (2)	CQua
	'Bright Spangles' (8)	CQua
	'Bright Spot' (8)	CQua
	BRIGHTERWELL (2/3)	GCro
	'Brilliancy' (3)	CQua
	'Broadway Star' (11b)	SDeJ
	'Brodick' (3)	CQua
	'Brooke Ager' (2) ♀H6	CBro CQua
	'Broomhill' (2) ♀H6	CQua
	'Broughshane' (1)	CQua
	broussonetii (13)	EPot GKev
	- from Morocco	WPGP
	'Brunswick' (2)	CFen GCro SDeJ
	'Bryanston' (2) ♀H6	CQua
	'Buckshead' (4)	CQua
	'Budock Water' (2)	CQua
	'Bugle Major' (2)	CQua
	bulbocodium (13) ♀H4	CBro CWCL EHyd GKev LCro LOPS LRHS NRHS SRms WCot
§	- subsp. ***bulbocodium*** (13)	CBro
§	- - var. ***citrinus*** (13)	CRos EHyd LRHS NRHS
	- - var. ***conspicuus*** (13)	CBro CQua CWld ERCP GKev NHpl SDeJ SDix WCot WShi XLum
*	- - var. ***filifolius*** (13)	CBro
§	- - var. ***graellsii*** (13)	NSla
	- - var. ***nivalis*** (13)	EPot GKev NDry
§	- Golden Bells Group (10)	CAby CQua CRos CWCL EHyd EPot GBin LRHS NHol NRHS SDeJ
	- subsp. ***obesus*** (13)	GKev NDry WCot

	- - JW 90-13	GKev
§	- - 'Diamond Ring' (10)	CQua CRos EHyd EPot GKev LRHS MNrw NRHS
	- - 'Lee Martin' (10) **new**	NDry
	- subsp. ***praecox*** (13)	CRos EHyd LRHS NRHS
	- - var. ***paucinervis*** (13)	GKev
	- - - Rrw84.18 **new**	NDry
	- subsp. ***tananicus***	see *N. cantabricus* subsp. *tananicus*
	- subsp. ***vulgaris***	see *N. bulbocodium* subsp. *bulbocodium*
	'Bunting' (7) ♀H6	CQua
	'Burntwood' (4) **new**	CQua
	'Burravoe' (1)	CQua
	'Busbie' (12) **new**	NDry
	'Bute Park' (4)	CQua
	'Butter and Eggs' (4)	CAvo GKev
	'C.J. Backhouse' (2)	GCro
	'Cadgwith' (2)	CQua
	'Cairngorm' (2)	SDeJ WPhe
	'Cairntoul' (3)	CQua
	'Calamansack' (2)	CQua
	calcicola (13)	NDry
	'Calgary' (4)	CQua GKev MBriF WCot
	'Callisto' (10) **new**	NDry
	'Camaraderie' (2)	CQua
	'Camden' (1)	CQua
	'Camelot' (2) ♀H6	CFen CQua SDeJ
	'Cameo Angel' (2)	CQua
	'Cameo Baron' (2)	CQua
	'Cameo Frills' (2)	CQua
	'Cameo Gem' (1)	CQua
	'Cameo Joy' (2) **new**	CQua
	'Cameo King' (2)	CQua
	'Cameo Magic' (4) **new**	CQua
	'Cameo Marie' (3)	CQua
	'Cameo Mist' (2) **new**	CQua
	'Camilla Duchess of Cornwall' (2)	CFen
	'Campernelli' (7)	CQua
	'Campernelli Plenus'	see *N.* 'Double Campernelle'
	'Campion' (9)	CQua
	'Canaliculatus' (8)	CArg CFen CQua CTri EHyd ERCP GBin GKev LCro LOPS LRHS SDeJ SPer
	canaliculatus Gussone	see *N. tazetta* subsp. *lacticolor*
	canariensis (13)	CQua
	'Canary' (7)	CQua
	'Canarybird' (8)	CQua
	'Canasta' (11a)	CQua
	'Candlepower' (1)	CQua NDry
	'Canoodle' (2) **new**	CQua
	'Cantabile' (9) ♀H6	CQua
	cantabricus (13)	CQua ERCP LCro LOPS NDry
	- subsp. ***cantabricus*** (13)	EPot GKev
	- - var. ***eu-albidus*** (13)	NDry
	- - var. ***foliosus*** (13) ♀H4	GKev NDry
I	- subsp. ***monophyllus*** var. ***laciniatus*** (13)	NDry
§	- subsp. ***tananicus*** (13)	GKev
	cantabricus* × *romieuxii (13)	NDry
	cantabricus* × *romieuxii subsp. ***albidus*** var. ***zaianicus*** f. ***lutescens*** (13)	NDry
	'Canterbury' (5)	CQua
	'Capability Brown' (9) **new**	CQua
	'Capax Plenus'	see *N.* 'Eystettensis'
	'Cape Cornwall' (2)	CQua

'Cape Point' (2)	CQua
'Capisco' (3)	CQua
'Capitol Hill' (2) **new**	NCft
'Capree Elizabeth' (2)	GKev
'Carbineer' (2)	CQua GCro SDeJ
'Cardiff' (2)	CFen
'Cargreen' (9)	CQua
'Carib Gipsy' (2) ♀H6	CQua
'Carlton' (2) ♀H6	CArg CFen GKev LCro LOPS SDeJ
'Carn Brea' (3)	CQua
'Carnkief' (2)	CQua
'Carole Lombard' (3)	CQua
'Carwinion' (2)	CQua
'Casiah' (2)	CQua
'Cassandra' (9)	GCro
'Cassata' (11a)	GKev NBir SDeJ
'Casterbridge' (2)	CQua
'Castle Rings' (4)	CQua
'Castlerock' (2)	CFen
'Cavalli King' (4)	CQua
'Caye Chapel' (3)	CQua
× ***cazorlanus*** (13)	NDry
'Cedar Hills' (3)	CQua
'Cedric Morris' (1)	ECha WCot WSHC
'Celestial Fire' (2)	CQua
'Celtic Gold' (2)	CQua
'Centenary Gold' (2)	CQua
'Changing Colors' (11a)	GKev SDeJ
'Chanterelle' (11a)	GKev SDeJ
'Charity May' (6)	CQua
'Charleston' (2)	CQua
'Charlie Connor' (1)	CQua
'Chaste' (1)	CQua
'Chat' (7)	CQua
'Cheeky Chappie' (6) **new**	NDry
'Cheep' (1) **new**	NDry
'Cheer Leader' (3)	CQua
'Cheerfulness' (4) ♀H6	CArg CFen CQua ELan GKev LCro LOPS MBros NPer NRHS SDeJ WPhe
'Cheetah' (1)	CQua
'Chelsea China' (2) **new**	CQua
'Chelsea Girl' (2)	CQua
'Chemeketa' (2)	GKev
'Chérie' (7)	CQua
'Cherish' (2)	CQua
'Cherry Ice' (2)	CQua
'Cherry Spot' (3) **new**	CQua
'Cherrygardens' (2)	CQua
'Chesapeake Bay' (1)	CQua
'Chesterton' (9) ♀H6	CQua
'Chickadee' (6)	CQua
'Chicken Hill' (1)	CQua
'Chief Inspector' (1)	CQua
'Chiffon' (2)	CFen
'Children's Promise' (2) **new**	CFen
'Chiloquin' (1)	CQua
'Chinita' (8)	CQua
'Chipper' (5)	CQua
'Chirp' (1) **new**	NDry
'Chit Chat' (7) ♀H6	SDeJ SPlb
'Chitter' (2) **new**	NDry
'Chobe River' (1)	CQua
'Chortle' (3)	CQua
'Chorus Line' (8)	CQua
'Christelle' (4) **new**	CQua
'Chromacolor' (2) ♀H6	GKev WPhe
'Churchfield Bells' (5)	CQua
'Churston Ferrers' (4)	CQua
'Cisticola' (3)	CQua

citrinus	see *N. bulbocodium* subsp. *bulbocodium* var. *citrinus*
'Citron' (3)	CQua
'Citronita' (3)	CQua
'Clare' (7)	CQua
'Classic Gold' (10) ♀H6	CQua
'Claverley' (2)	CQua
'Cloth of Gold' (8)	CQua
'Cloud Nine' (2)	CBro CQua
'Clouded Yellow' (2)	CQua
'Clovelly Ayr' (9)	CQua
'Codlins and Cream'	see *N.* 'Sulphur Phoenix'
'Coker's Frome' (9)	CQua
'Colin's Joy' (2)	CQua
'Colley Gate' (3)	CQua
'Colorama' (11a)	CQua
'Colville' (9)	CQua
'Come to Good' (2)	CQua
'Compressus'	see *N.* × *intermedius* 'Compressus'
'Conestoga' (2)	CQua
'Conowingo' (11a)	CQua
'Conspicuus' Barr (3)	GCro WShi
'Content' (1)	GCro
'Coo' (12) **new**	NDry
'Cool Crystal' (3)	CQua
'Cool Evening' (11a)	CQua
'Cool Shades' (2)	CQua
'Corbiere' (1)	CQua
'Corbridge' (2)	CQua
'Corby Candle' (2)	CQua
'Corky's Song' (2)	CQua
'Cornet' (6)	CQua
'Cornish Chuckles' (12) ♀H6	CFen CQua
'Cornish Gold' (1)	LCro LOPS
'Cornish King' (1)	GKev WPhe
'Cornish Pride' (2)	CFen
'Cornish Vanguard' (2) ♀H6	CFen CQua
'Corofin' (3)	CQua
'Coromandel' (2)	CQua
'Corozal' (3)	CQua
'Cotinga' (6)	CBro CQua SDeJ
'Cottrell' (1) **new**	CQua
'Countdown' (2)	CQua
'Court Martial' (2)	CFen
'Crackington' (4) ♀H6	CQua
'Cragford' (8)	SDeJ
'Craig Stiel' (2)	CQua
'Craigton Chorister' (13) **new**	NDry
'Craigton Clumper' (13) **new**	NDry
'Creag Dubh' (2)	CQua
Crème Fraîche Group (2) **new**	NDry
'Crenver' (3)	CQua
'Crill' (7)	CQua
'Crimson Chalice' (3)	CQua
'Cristobal' (1)	CQua
'Croesus' (2)	CQua
'Crofty' (6)	CQua
'Croila' (2)	CQua
'Crowndale' (4)	CQua
'Crugmeer' (11a)	CQua
'Crystal Star' (2)	CQua
cuatrecasasii (13)	NDry
- var. ***segimonensis*** (13)	GKev
'Cudden Point' (2)	CQua
'Cul Beag' (3)	CQua
'Culmination' (2)	CQua
'Cultured Pearl' (2)	CQua
'Cum Laude' (11a)	ERCP SDeJ
'Curlew' (7) ♀H6	CQua LCro LOPS SDeJ WShi
'Curly' (2)	SDeJ
'Cuscarne' (8)	CQua
cyclamineus (13) ♀H6	CAvo CBor CBro CExl CRos CWCL EHyd EPot GKev LEdu LRHS NDry NRHS SRms
'Cynosure' (2)	GCro
cypri (13)	CQua
'Cyros' (1)	CQua
'Dailmanach' (2)	CQua
'Dalcharn' (2)	LRHS
'Dallas' (3)	CFen CQua
'Dalmeny' (2)	CQua
'Damson' (2)	CQua GCro
'Dan du Plessis' (8)	CFen CQua
'Danehill' (1) **new**	CQua
'Danger Zone' (2) **new**	CQua
'Daphnis' (10) **new**	NDry
'Dateline' (3)	CQua
'Dave's Favorite' (2) **new**	CQua
'David Mills' (2)	CQua
'Dawn Brooker' (2)	CQua
'Dawn Cloud' (2)	CQua
'Dawn Duel' (12) **new**	NDry
'Dawn Sky' (2)	CQua
'Daydream' (2)	CQua
'Daymark' (8)	CQua
'Daymer Bay' (1)	CFen
'Dayton Lake' (2)	CQua
'De Lacey' (11a)	CQua
'Dean' (2)	CQua
'Dear Love' (11a)	CQua
'Dear Me' (2) **new**	CQua
'Debutante' (2)	CQua
'December Bride' (11a)	CQua
'Del Rey' (1)	CQua
'Dell Chapel' (3)	CQua
'Delnashaugh' (4)	CFen CQua ERCP GKev NHol SDeJ
'Delos' (3)	CQua
'Delta' (11a)	CQua
'Delta Flight' (6)	CQua
'Demand' (2)	CQua
'Demmo' (2)	CQua
'Denali' (1)	CQua
'Derek Tangye' (2)	CQua
'Derringer' (7)	CAvo GKev
'Descant' (1)	CQua
'Desdemona' (2) ♀H6	CQua SDeJ
'Desert Bells' (7)	CQua
'Desert Orchid' (2)	CQua
'Desert Storm' (2) **new**	CQua
'Diamond Ring'	see *N. bulbocodium* subsp. *obesus* 'Diamond Ring'
'Dick Wellband' (2)	GCro
'Dick Wilden' (4)	SDeJ
'Dickcissel' (7) ♀H6	CQua ERCP GKev
'Dimple' (9)	CQua
'Dispatch Box' (1) ♀H6	CQua
'Disquiet' (1)	CQua
'Diversity' (11a)	CQua
'Doctor Hugh' (3) ♀H6	CQua
'Doctor Jazz' (2)	CQua
'Doctor Who' (4)	CQua
'Dolcoath' (2)	CQua
'Don Stead' (10) **new**	NDry
'Doombar' (1)	CQua
'Dorchester' (4)	CQua
'Dorothy Yorke' (2)	GCro
§ 'Double Campernelle' (4)	CQua GKev SDeJ WShi

	'Double Fashion' (4)	GKev SDeJ
	double pheasant eye	see *N. poeticus* 'Plenus' ambig.
	double Roman	see *N.* 'Romanus'
	'Double White' (4)	CQua
	'Doublet' (4)	CQua
	'Dove Wings' (6)	CQua
	'Dover Boy' (11a)	CQua
	'Downing College' (2)	CQua
	'Downlands' (3)	CQua
	'Dragon Run' (2)	CQua
	'Drama Queen' (11a)	CQua
	'Dream Castle' (3)	CQua
	'Dream Catcher' (2)	CQua
	'Dreamlight' (3)	CQua GKev
	dubius (13)	EPot GKev
	'Duchess of Westminster' (2)	GCro
	'Duke of Windsor' (2)	CFen
	'Dunadry Inn' (4)	CQua
	'Dunkeld' (2)	CQua GCro
	'Dunkery' (4)	CQua
	'Dunley Hall' (3)	CQua
	'Dunskey' (3)	CQua
	'Dunstan's Fire' (1)	CQua
	'Dutch Lemon Drops' (5) ♀H6	CQua EPot
	'Dutch Master' (1) ♀H6	CFen LCro LOPS SDeJ SDir
	'Early Bride' (2)	CFen CQua
	'Early Flame' (2)	CFen
	'Early Sensation' (1)	EHyd LRHS NRHS
	'Early Splendour' (8)	CQua
	'Earthlight' (3)	CQua
	'Eastbrook Sunrise' (1) **new**	CQua
	'Easter Moon' (2)	CQua
	'Eastern Dawn' (2)	CFen CQua SDeJ
	'Eastern Promise' (2)	CQua
	'Eaton Song' (12) ♀H6	CQua GKev
	'Ebony' (1)	CQua
	'Eddy Canzony' (2)	CFen
	'Eden Gold' (2)	CFen
	'Edge Grove' (2)	CQua
	'Editor' (2)	CQua
	'Edna Earl' (3)	SDeJ
	'Edward Buxton' (3)	CFen CQua
	'Egard' (11a)	CQua
	'Egmont King' (2)	CQua
	'Egmont Star' (2) **new**	CQua
	'Eira Hibbert' (3)	CQua
	'El Camino' (6) **new**	CQua
	'Eland' (7)	CQua
	'Elegance' (2)	CQua
	'Elf' (2)	CQua
	'Elfin Gold' (6)	CQua
	'Elite' (8)	GKev
	'Elizabeth Ann' (6)	CQua
	'Elka' (1) ♀H6	CAvo CBro CQua CWld ECha EPot ERCP GKev SPhx WShi
	'Ellen' (2)	CArg
	'Elphin' (4)	CQua
	'Elusive' (3) **new**	CQua
	'Elven Lady' (2)	CQua
	'Elvira' (8)	CQua WShi
	'Emerald Green' (2) **new**	SDir
	'Emerald Pink' (3)	CQua
	'Emily' (2)	CQua
	'Emperor' (1)	GCro
	'Empire' (2)	GCro
	'Empress' (1)	GCro
	'Empress of Ireland' (1)	CQua
	'Englander' (6)	EPot
	'Epona' (3)	CQua
	'Erin' (3)	CQua
	'Erlicheer' (4)	CQua GKev LCro LOPS SDeJ
	'Estrella' (3)	CQua
	'Estremadura' (2)	CQua
§	***eugeniae*** (13)	GKev WCot
	'Euryalus' (1)	CQua
	'Evangeline' (3)	GCro
	'Eve Robertson' (2)	CQua
	'Evelyn Roberts' (11a)	CQua
	'Evesham' (3)	CQua
	'Exotic Beauty' (4)	CQua
	'Exotic Mystery' (11a)	GKev
	'Extravaganza' (4)	SDeJ
§	'Eystettensis' (4)	IBlr NDry WFar
	'Fair Head' (9)	CQua
	'Fair Prospect' (2)	CQua
	'Fairgreen' (3)	CFen
	'Fairlawns' (3)	CQua
	'Fairmile' (3)	CQua
	'Fairy Chimes' (5)	CQua EPot
	'Fairy Island' (3)	CQua
I	'Faith' (1)	SDeJ
	'Falaise' (4)	CQua
	'Falconet' (8) ♀H6	CQua GKev SDeJ
	'Falmouth Bay' (3)	CQua
	'Falstaff' (2)	CQua
	'Far Country' (2)	CQua
I	'Fashion' (11b)	CQua
	'Fastidious' (2)	CQua
	'Fat Rascal' (12) **new**	NDry
	'February Gold' (6) ♀H6	CArg CAvo CBro CQua CRos CTri EHyd ELan EPot ERCP GKev LCro LOPS LRHS NBir NRHS SDeJ SRms WHil WPhe WShi
	'February Silver' (1)	CBro CQua EPot ERCP GKev SDeJ
	'Feeling Lucky' (2)	CQua
	'Felindre' (9)	EPot
	'Feock' (3)	CQua
	'Ferial Wendy' (2)	CFen
	fernandesii (13)	EPot ITim WCot
	- from Spain	ITim
	- var. ***cordubensis*** (13)	CAvo CBro CQua EPot GKev ITim NDry
	'Ferndown' (3)	CQua
	'Fertile Crescent' (7)	CQua
	'Feu de Joie' (4)	GCro
	'Ffitch's Ffolly' (2)	CQua
	'Fiery Maiden' (2)	CFen CQua
	'Filoli' (1)	CQua
	'Filskit' (2)	CQua
	'Finchcocks' (2)	CQua
	'Fine Gold' (1)	CQua
	'Fine Romance' (2)	CQua
	'Finland' (2)	CFen
	FINTRY BEAUTY (2)	GCro
	'Fiona MacKillop' (2)	CQua
	'Fire-Blade' (2)	CQua
	'Firebrand' (3)	CQua WShi
	'Firehills' (2)	CQua
	'Firetail' (3)	CQua GCro
	'First Born' (6)	CQua
	'First Hope' (6)	CFen
	'Five Ashes' (2) **new**	CQua
	'Flambards Village' (4)	CQua
	'Fletching' (1)	CQua
	'Fling' (6) **new**	NDry
	'Flirt' (6)	CQua
	'Flora Brava' (2) **new**	CQua
	'Flower Drift' (4)	SDeJ
	'Flying High' (3)	CQua

'Foff's Way' (1)	CQua
'Folkestone Girl' (11a)	CQua
'Foresight' (1)	CQua
'Fortissimo' (2)	GKev SDeJ
'Fortune' (2)	CArg CQua SDeJ
'Fowey' (3)	CFen
'Foxhunter' (2)	CQua
'Fragrant Breeze' (2)	SDeJ
'Fragrant Rose' (2)	CQua GKev
'Frances Delight' (11a)	CQua
'Frank Miles' (2)	CQua GCro
'Freedom Rings' (2)	CQua
'Freedom Stars' (11a) 🏆H6	GKev
'Fresco' (11a)	CQua
'Fresh Field' (2)	CQua
'Fresh Lime' (1)	CQua
'Frigid' (3)	CQua
Fringella Group (6) **new**	NDry
'Frostkist' (6)	CBro CQua
'Fruit Cup' (7)	SDeJ
'Full House' (4)	SDeJ
'Fulwell' (4)	CQua
'Furbelow' (4)	CQua
'Gabriella Rose' (4)	CQua
gaditanus (13)	CBro
gaditanus* × *rupicola subsp. ***watieri*** (13)	GKev
Galantoquilla Group (12) **new**	NDry
'Gale Force' (6) **new**	NDry
'Gallipoli Dawn' (2) **new**	CQua
'Gamebird' (1)	CQua
'Ganilly' (2)	CFen
'Garden Opera' (7) 🏆H6	CFen
'Garden Princess' (2)	CQua
'Gay Kybo' (4) 🏆H6	CQua
'Gay Song' (4)	CQua
'Gay Swain' (4) **new**	CQua
'Gay Time' (4)	CFen SDeJ
gayi (13)	CQua WShi
'Gee Tee' (2) **new**	CQua
'Geevor' (4)	CQua
'Gellymill' (2)	CQua
'Gemini Girl' (2)	CQua
'Gentle Giant' (2)	SDeJ
'George Leak' (2)	CFen
'Georgia Moon' (2)	CFen
'Georgie Girl' (6)	CQua
'Georgie May' (2)	CQua
'Geranium' (8) 🏆H6	CBro CFen CQua ERCP GKev LCro LOPS LRHS NRHS SDeJ WShi
'Gigantic Star' (2)	SDeJ
'Gillan' (11a)	CQua
'Gilly Drummond' (1) **new**	CQua
'Gin and Lime' (1)	CQua
'Gipsy Moon' (2)	CQua
'Gipsy Queen' (1)	CBro EPot GKev NDry WCot WFar WShi
'Gipsy Vale' (1) **new**	NDry
'Giselle' (10) **new**	NDry
'Glapthorne' (2)	CQua
'Glasnevin' (2)	CQua
'Glasney' (3)	CQua
'Glen Cassley' (3)	CQua
'Glen Clova' (2)	CQua
'Glendurgan' (2)	CQua
'Glenfarclas' (1)	CQua
'Glenside' (2)	CQua
'Glissando' (2)	CQua
'Gloaming Hill' (1) **new**	CQua
'Gloria Townsin' (4)	CQua
'Gloriana Fair' (2) **new**	CQua
'Gloriosus' (8)	CQua
'Glorious' (8)	CQua
'Glory of Lisse' (9)	WShi
'Glover's Reef' (1)	CQua
'Glowing Phoenix' (4)	CQua
'Glowing Red' (4)	CQua
'Goblet' (1)	SDeJ
'Golant' (2)	CQua
'Gold Bond' (2)	CQua
'Gold Charm' (2)	CQua
'Gold Convention' (2) 🏆H6	CQua
'Gold Ingot' (2) 🏆H6	CQua
'Gold Medallion' (1)	CQua
'Gold Sails' (2) **new**	CQua
'Gold Top' (2)	CQua
'Golden Amber' (2)	CQua
'Golden Anniversary' (2)	CFen CQua
'Golden Aura' (2) 🏆H6	CQua
'Golden Bear' (4)	CQua
'Golden Bells'	see *N. bulbocodium* Golden Bells Group
'Golden Cheer' (2)	CFen CQua
'Golden Cycle' (6)	CQua
'Golden Dawn' (8) 🏆H4	CFen CQua SDeJ
'Golden Ducat' (4)	CArg CFen NBir SDeJ
'Golden Echo' (7)	CQua SDeJ WPhe
'Golden Flute' (2)	CQua
'Golden Harvest' (1)	NPer
'Golden Incense' (7)	CQua
'Golden Jewel' (2) 🏆H6	CQua
'Golden Joy' (2)	CQua
'Golden Lion' (1)	CFen
'Golden Mary' (3)	GCro
'Golden Orbit' (4)	CQua
'Golden Perfection' (7)	CQua
'Golden Phoenix' (4)	CQua WShi
'Golden Sheen' (2)	CQua
'Golden Spur' (1)	CQua GCro
'Golden Torch' (2)	CQua
'Golden Trumpet' (1) **new**	CQua
'Golden Twins' (7)	CQua
'Golden Vale' (1)	CQua
'Golden Years' (6) **new**	CQua
'Goldfinger' (1) 🏆H6	CQua SDeJ
'Goldhanger' (2)	CQua
'Golitha Falls' (2)	CQua
'Good Fella' (2)	CQua
'Good Measure' (2)	CQua
'Good Success' (11a)	CQua
'Goonbell' (2)	CQua
'Goose Green' (3)	GKev
'Gorran' (3)	CQua
'Gossamer' (3)	GBin
'Gossmoor' (4)	CQua
graellsii	see *N. bulbocodium* subsp. *bulbocodium* var. *graellsii*
'Grand Monarque'	see *N. tazetta* subsp. *lacticolor* 'Grand Monarque'
'Grand Primo' (8)	LCro LOPS
'Grand Primo Citronière' (8)	CQua
'Grand Prospect' (2)	CQua
'Grand Soleil d'Or' (8)	CQua GKev LCro LOPS SDeJ SDir
'Great Expectations' (2)	CQua
'Greatwood' (1)	CQua
'Green Eyed Lady' (3)	GKev SPhx XEll
'Green Eyes' (1) **new**	SPer
'Green Howard' (3)	CQua
'Green Island' (2)	CFen GKev SDeJ

	Name	Suppliers
	'Green Lawns' (9)	CQua
	'Green Pearl' (3)	SPhx XEll
	'Greenodd' (3)	CQua
	'Grenoble' (2)	CQua
	'Gresham' (4)	CQua
	'Gribben Head' (4)	CQua
	'Guiding Spirit' (4)	CQua
	'Gulliver' (3)	CQua GCro
	'Gunwalloe' (11a)	CQua
	'Gwawr' (2)	CQua
	'Gwendoline Rae' (3)	CQua
	'Gwenllian' (3)	CQua
	'Gwennap' (1)	CQua
	'Gwinear' (2)	CQua
	'Gylly Glow' (6) **new**	CQua
	'Hacienda' (1)	CQua
	'Half Moon Caye' (2)	CQua
	'Halley's Comet' (3)	CQua
	'Halloon' (3)	CQua
	'Hampton Court' (2)	CQua
	'Hannah Jesse' (7)	CQua
	'Happy Fellow' (2)	CQua
	'Happy Valley' (2)	CQua
	'Harmony Bells' (5)	CQua
	'Harpers Ferry' (1)	CQua
	HARTLAND'S IRVING (1)	GCro
	'Hartlebury' (3)	CQua
	'Harvard' (2)	CQua
*	'Hat' (10)	EPot
	'Havelock' (2)	GCro
	'Hawera' (5) ♀H6	CArg CAvo CBro CFen CQua CTri EPot ERCP GKev GQue LCro LOPS LRHS SDeJ WShi
	'Heamoor' (4) ♀H6	CQua GKev
	hedraeanthus (13)	EPot NDry
	- subsp. ***luteolentus*** (13) **new**	NDry
	'Helene' (10) **new**	NDry
	'Helford Dawn' (2)	CQua
	'Helford Sunset' (2)	CQua
	'Helios' (2)	CQua
	hellenicus	see *N. poeticus* var. *hellenicus*
	henriquesii	see *N. jonquilla* var. *henriquesii*
	'Henry Irving' (1)	CQua GCro
	'Hero' (1)	CQua
	'Hesla' (7)	CQua
	'Heslington' (3)	CQua
	'Hexameter' (9)	CQua
	'High Life' (2)	CFen
	'High Society' (2) ♀H6	CQua LCro LOPS SDeJ
	'Highfield Beauty' (8) ♀H6	CQua
	'Highgrove' (1)	CQua
	'Highlite' (2)	CQua
	'Hilda's Pink' (2)	CQua
	'Hillstar' (7) ♀H6	CQua GKev SDeJ
	'Hindenburg' (1)	CQua
	hispanicus var. ***propinquus*** (13)	GKev
	'Holland's Glory' (4)	GCro
	'Holly Berry' (2)	CFen
	'Hollywood' (2)	CFen
	'Holme Fen' (2)	CQua
	'Home Fires' (2)	CFen CQua
	'Honeybird' (1)	CQua
	'Honeybourne' (2)	CQua
	'Hoopoe' (8) ♀H6	CQua
	'Horace' (9)	CQua GCro
	'Horn of Plenty' (5)	GKev SPhx WPhe
	'Hors d'Oeuvre' (1)	CBro
	'Hospodar' (2)	CQua GCro

	Name	Suppliers
	'Hot Gossip' (2)	CFen CQua
	HOWICK BEAUTY (2)	GCro
	HOWICK'S HALF NELSON (2)	GCro
	'Hugh Town' (8)	CQua SEND
	'Hugus' (7)	CQua
	'Hummingbird' (6)	EPot
	'Hungarian Rhapsody' (11a) ♀H6 **new**	WPhe
	'Hunting Caye' (2)	CQua
	'Huntley Down' (1)	CQua
	'Huon Pride' (4) **new**	CQua
	'Ice Dancer' (2)	CQua
	'Ice Diamond' (4)	CQua
	'Ice Follies' (2) ♀H6	CArg CFen CQua GBin LCro LOPS LRHS NBir SDeJ
	'Ice King' (4)	CWld GKev MBros NBir SDeJ
	'Ice Wings' (5) ♀H6	CFen CQua EPot GKev SDeJ SPhx WShi
	'Immaculate' (2)	CQua
	'Impeccable' (2)	CQua
	'Inara' (4)	CQua
	'Inbal'PBR (8)	GKev
	'Inca' (6)	CQua
	'Inchbonnie' (2)	CQua
	× ***incomparabilis*** (13)	MMuc SEND
§	× ***incurvicervicus*** (13) **new**	NDry
	'Indian Maid' (7) ♀H6	CQua
	'Indian Ruler' (2)	CFen
	'Indora' (4)	CQua
	'Inglescombe' (4)	GCro
	'Innovator' (4)	CQua
	'Insulinde' (4)	CQua
	'Interim' (2)	CFen CQua SDeJ
	× ***intermedius*** (13)	CBro CQua GKev
§	- 'Compressus' (8)	CBro CQua NPoe
	'Intrigue' (7) ♀H6	CQua
	'Invercassley' (3)	CQua
	'Inverpolly' (2)	CQua
	'Ipi Tombi' (2)	GKev
	'Ireland's Eye' (9)	CQua
	'Irene Copeland' (4)	CQua GCro GKev
	'Irish Cream' (3)	CQua
	'Irish Fire' (2)	CQua
	'Irish Light' (2)	CQua
	'Irish Linen' (3)	CQua
	'Irish Luck' (1)	CArg
	'Irish Minstrel' (2) ♀H6	CFen CQua
	'Irish Wedding' (2)	CQua
	'Isambard' (4)	CQua
	'Isenhurst' (2) **new**	CQua
	'Island Pride' (8)	CQua
	'Isobel Salt' (8) **new**	CQua
	'Itzim' (6) ♀H6	CBro CQua GKev SDeJ
	'Jabberwocky' (11a)	CQua
	'Jack Snipe' (6) ♀H6	CBro CQua ELan EPot ERCP GKev LCro LOPS LRHS MWat NHol SDeJ SEND WCot WShi XEll
	'Jack Wood' (11a)	CQua
	'Jacob Maurer' (6)	CQua
	'Jamage' (8)	CQua
	'Jambo' (2)	CQua
	'Jamboree' (2)	CQua
	'Janelle' (3)	CQua
	'Jantje' (11a)	CQua
	'Jazz' (11b) **new**	CQua
	'Jeanne Bicknell' (4)	CQua
	'Jeannie Tangye' (2)	CQua
	'Jenna' (3) **new**	CQua
	'Jenny' (6) ♀H6	CBro CQua EMor EPot ERCP GKev LCro LOPS NBir SDeJ SPhx WShi

'Jenny Out' (7) 🏆H6	CFen
'Jersey Lace' (2)	CQua GKev WPhe
'Jersey Roundabout' (4)	CQua
'Jersey Star' (4)	CQua
'Jersey Torch' (4)	CQua
'Jessie Jane' (8) **new**	CQua
'Jetfire' (6) 🏆H6	CArg CQua CRos CWld EHyd EPot ERCP GKev LCro LOPS LRHS NHol NRHS SDeJ SPer WShi
'Jim Lad' (2)	NDry
'Jimmy Noone' (1)	CQua
'Jim's Gold' (2)	CQua
'Johanna' (5)	CBro
'John Daniel' (4)	CQua
'John Evelyn' (2)	CQua GCro
'John Lanyon' (3)	CQua
'John's Delight' (3)	CQua
'Joke Fulmer' (2)	CFen
jonquilla (13)	CBro CQua EPot GKev WShi
§ - var. ***henriquesii*** (13)	CQua EPot GKev
'Joy Bishop'	see *N. romieuxii* 'Joy Bishop'
'Juanita' (2)	CFen LCro LOPS NPer SDeJ
'Julia Jane'	see *N. romieuxii* 'Julia Jane'
'Jumblie' (12) 🏆H6	CBro CQua CRos EHyd EPot LRHS NRHS SDeJ
'Jumbo Gold' (1)	CTri
'Jump Start' (1) **new**	CQua
juncifolius Req. ex Lag.	see *N. assoanus*
'June Allyson' (2)	CFen
'June Christy' (2) **new**	CQua
'June Lake' (2)	CQua
'Kabani' (9)	CQua
'Kamms' (1)	CQua
'Kamura' (2)	CQua
'Kapiti Talisman' (8) **new**	CQua
'Karamudli' (1)	CQua
'Kate Davies' (2)	CQua
'Katherine Jenkins' (7) 🏆H6	CQua
'Kathy's Clown' (6)	CQua
'Katie Heath' (5)	ERCP SDeJ SDir WBrk WPhe
'Katrina Rea' (6)	CQua
'Kaydee' (6) 🏆H6	CQua EMor GKev SDeJ SDir WShi
'Kea' (6)	CQua
'Keats' (4)	CQua
'Kebaya' (2)	CQua
'Kedron' (7)	ERCP GKev SDeJ
'Kelly Bray' (1)	CQua
'Ken Sunshine Johnson' (2)	CQua
'Kerryteuila' (8) **new**	CQua
'Kidling' (7)	CQua
'Killara' (8)	CQua
'Killearnan' (9)	CQua
'Killigrew' (2)	CQua
'Killivose' (3)	CQua
'Kilndown' (2) **new**	CQua
'Kilworth' (2)	CQua
'Kimmeridge' (3)	CQua
'King Alfred' (1)	CArg CQua LCro LOPS SDeJ SPer
'Kingham' (1)	CQua
'Kinglet' (7)	CQua
'King's Grove' (1)	CQua
'Kings Pipe' (2)	CQua
'Kingscourt' (1)	CQua
'Kingsleigh' (1)	CQua
'Kingsmill Lake' (2)	CQua
'Kissproof' (2)	SDeJ
'Kit Hill' (7)	CQua
'Kitten' (6)	CQua
'Kiwi Magic' (4)	CQua
'Kiwi Ruler' (3) **new**	CQua
'Kiwi Sunset' (4)	CQua
'Knight of Saint John' (2)	CFen
'Knightsbridge' (1)	CQua
'Knocklayde' (3)	CQua
'Kokopelli' (7) 🏆H6	CBro CQua GKev SDeJ
'Kuantan' (3)	CQua
'La Belle' (7)	SDeJ
'La Fiancée' (8) **new**	CQua
'La Riante' (3)	CQua
'Lady Be Good' (2)	CQua
'Lady Godiva' (3)	GCro
'Lady Hilaria' (2)	CQua
'Lady Margaret Boscawen' (2)	CQua GCro
'Lady Marina Cowdray' (1)	CFen
'Lady Moore' (3)	GCro
'Lady Sainsbury' (2)	CFen
'Lady Serena' (9)	CQua
'Ladymeads' (2) **new**	CQua
'Lake Alabaster' (2)	CQua
'Lake District' (2)	CQua
'Lakeland Fair' (2) **new**	CQua
'Lalique' (3)	CQua
'Lamanva' (2)	CQua
'Lanarth' (7)	CQua GCro
'Lancaster' (3)	CFen CQua GKev
'Landewednack Lady' (4)	CQua
'Lara Lovely' (1) **new**	NDry
'Larkwhistle' (6)	GKev SDeJ
'Las Vegas' (1)	GKev SDeJ
'Latchley Meadows' (2)	CQua
'Latvian Freedom' (2)	GKev
'Laura Webb' (4)	CQua
'Laurens Koster' (8)	CQua
'Lavender Lass' (6)	CQua
'Lavender Mist' (2)	CQua
'Leedsii' (3)	CQua
'Lemon Beauty' (11b)	CQua SDeJ
'Lemon Brook' (2)	CQua
'Lemon Drizzle' (2)	CQua
'Lemon Drops' (5)	CQua EPot ERCP GKev SDeJ SPhx WShi
'Lemon Haze' (2)	CQua
'Lemon Silk' (6)	CBro CQua ELan
'Lemon Spice' (3) **new**	CQua
'Lemonade' (3)	CQua
'Lennymore' (2)	CQua
'Letsee' (2) **new**	CQua
'Lezant' (3)	CQua
'Liberty Bells' (5)	CQua GQue
'Liebeslied' (3)	CQua
'Lieke' (7)	EPot ERCP GKev LCro LOPS SDeJ
'Lilac Mist' (2)	CQua
'Limbo' (2)	CQua
'Limey Lass' (10) **new**	NDry
'Lincolnshire Lady' (3)	CQua
'Lindsay Joy' (2)	CQua
'Lingerie' (4) 🏆H6	CQua
'L'Innocence' (8) **new**	CQua
'Little Beauty' (1)	CQua
'Little Dancer' (1)	CBro CQua
'Little Jewel' (3)	CQua
'Little Meg' (7)	CQua
'Little Oliver' (7)	SDeJ
'Little Racer' (6) **new**	NDry
'Little Rusky' (7)	CBro CQua
'Little Sentry' (7)	CAvo CBro CQua
'Little Soldier' (10)	CQua EPot
'Little Spell' (1)	NDry
'Little Tweet' (6) **new**	NDry

'Little Tyke' (2)	CQua
'Little Witch' (6)	CQua SDeJ WShi
'Littlefield' (7)	CQua
'Liverpool Festival' (2)	CQua
'Living Colour' (3)	CQua
'Lizard Beacon' (2)	CQua
'Lobularis'	see *N. lobularis* (Haw.) Schult. & Schult. f.
lobularis misapplied	see *N. nanus*
§ ***lobularis*** (Haw.) Schult. & Schult. f. (13)	CAby CAvo CBro CQua CRos CTri CWld EHyd EPot ERCP GKev LCro LOPS LRHS MWat NRHS SDeJ SPer
'Loch Assynt' (3)	CQua
'Loch Brora' (2)	CQua
'Loch Coire' (3)	CQua
'Loch Fada' (2)	CQua
'Loch Fyne' (2)	GCro
'Loch Hope' (2)	CQua
'Loch Leven' (2)	CQua
'Loch Loyal' (2)	CQua
'Loch Lundie' (2)	CQua
'Loch Maberry' (2)	CQua
'Loch Naver' (2)	CQua
'Loch Owskeich' (2)	CFen
'Logan Rock' (7)	CQua
'Lord Kitchener' (2) **new**	GCro
'Lordship' (1)	CQua
'Lorikeet' (1)	CQua
'Lough Gowna' (1)	CQua
'Louise de Coligny' (2)	ERCP
'Loveday' (2)	CFen
'Lowin' (1)	CFen
'Lubaantun' (1)	CQua
'Lucie Nottingham' (4)	CQua
'Lucifer' (2)	CQua GCro WShi
'Ludo' (1) **new**	NDry
'Lundy Light' (2)	CQua
'Lynher' (2)	CQua
'Lyric' (9)	CQua
'Lysander' (2)	CQua
'Machan' (2) **new**	CQua
'Madam Speaker' (4)	CQua
'Madame Plemp' (1)	GCro
'Madison' (4)	CQua GKev
MAGGIE MAYBE (2)	GCro
'Magic Moment' (3)	CQua
'Magician' (2)	CQua
'Magnificence' (1)	CFen CQua GCro
'Maker's Mark' (1)	CQua
'Mallee' (11a) ♀H6	CQua
'Malpas' (3)	CQua
'Malvern City' (1)	CFen
'Manaccan' (1)	CQua
'Mangaweka' (6)	CQua
'Manly' (4) ♀H6	CQua ERCP SDeJ
'March Sunshine' (6)	CQua
'Margaret Herbert' (7)	CQua
'Marguerite Patten' (8) **new**	CQua
'Marie Curie Diamond' (7) ♀H6	CFen CQua
'Marieke' (1)	SDeJ
'Marilyn Anne' (2)	CQua
'Marjorie Hine' (2)	CQua
'Marjorie Treveal' (4)	CQua
'Market Merry' (3)	GCro
'Marlborough' (2)	CQua
'Marshfire' (2)	CQua
'Martha Washington' (8)	CQua
'Martinette' (8)	CAvo CFen CQua GKev SDeJ
marvieri	see *N. rupicola* subsp. *marvieri*
'Mary Bohannon' (2)	SDeJ
'Mary Copeland' (4)	CQua
'Mary Jose' (2) **new**	CQua
'Mary Kate' (2)	CQua
'Mary Moore' (2)	CQua
'Mary Rosina' (4)	CQua
'Mary Veronica' (3)	CQua
'Masked Light' (2)	CFen
'Matador' (8)	CFen CQua
'Mawla' (1)	CQua
'Max' (11a)	CQua
'Maximus Superbus' (1)	CQua
'Maya Dynasty' (2)	CQua
'Mayor's Choice' (11a)	CQua
'Maywood' (11a)	CQua
'Mazzard' (4)	CQua
× ***medioluteus*** (13)	CBro CQua GCro
'Medway Gold' (7)	CQua
'Mega' (9) **new**	CQua
'Meldrum' (1)	CQua
'Melen' (2)	CFen
'Memento' (1)	CQua
Memorina Group (2) **new**	NDry
'Mên-an-Tol' (2)	CQua
'Menehay' (11a) ♀H6	CQua
'Merlin' (3) ♀H6	CFen CQua SDeJ SDir
'Merrymeet' (4)	CQua
'Mersing' (3)	CQua
'Merthan' (9)	CQua
'Midas Touch' (1)	CQua
'Midget'	see *N. nanus* 'Midget'
MIDTOWN AEROLITE (2)	GCro
MIDTOWN ALFIE (1)	GCro
MIDTOWN AMBER (2)	GCro
MIDTOWN BRIGADIER (2)	GCro
MIDTOWN LAURIE (1)	GCro
MIDTOWN NOBLE (1)	GCro
'Mike Pollock' (8)	CFen CQua
'Milan' (9)	CQua
'Millennium Gold' (1)	CQua
'Millennium Sunrise' (2)	CQua
'Millennium Sunset' (2)	CQua
'Milly's Magic' (2)	CQua
Minicycla Group (6)	NDry
minimus misapplied	see *N. asturiensis*
'Minnie Hume' (3)	GCro
'Minnow' (8) ♀H6	CArg CAvo CBro CFen CQua CRos EHyd ELan EPot ERCP GKev LCro LOPS LRHS MWat NBir NRHS SDeJ SPer
'Minnowlet' (11a)	CQua
minor (13) ♀H5	CQua ECha EPot GKev WFar WShi
- 'Douglasbank' (1)	ITim NDry
- 'Little Gem' (1) ♀H6	CBro CQua CTri GKev SDeJ SDir
- var. ***pumilus*** 'Plenus'	see *N.* 'Rip van Winkle'
- Ulster form (13)	IBlr
'Mint Julep' (3) ♀H6	GKev SDeJ SPhx
'Mirar' (2)	CQua
'Mirror Lake' (2) **new**	CQua
'Misquote' (1)	CQua
'Miss Diddles' (7)	CQua
'Miss Mabel' (6) **new**	CQua
'Miss Muffit' (1)	CQua
'Mission Bells' (5) ♀H6	CQua
'Mission Impossible' (11a)	CQua
'Mist of Avalon' (4)	CQua
'Mistress Mine' (2) **new**	CQua
'Misty Glen' (2) ♀H6	CQua GKev SDeJ SPhx
'Mite' (6) ♀H6	CAvo CBro CQua EPot NDry NHpl WShi

	'Mitimoto' (10)	NDry
	'Mitzy' (6)	NDry
	'Modern Art' (2)	CQua SDeJ
	'Modulation' (2)	GKev SDeJ
	'Mondragon' (11a)	GKev
	'Mongleath' (2)	CQua
	'Monks Wood' (1)	CQua
	'Monksilver' (3)	CQua
	'Montego' (3)	CQua
	'Monterrico' (4)	CFen
	'Moon Ranger' (3)	CQua
	'Moon Shadow' (3)	CQua
	'Moonlight Sensation' (5) **new**	GKev
	'Morab' (1)	CQua
	'Moralee' (4)	CQua
	'More and More' (7)	CAvo CBro CWCL EPot GKev NHpl SDir
	'Mortie' (6) **new**	NDry
	moschatus (13) ♀H6	CAvo CBro CQua EPot GKev WShi
	'Mother Duck' (6)	GKev
	'Motmot' (8)	CQua
	'Mount Fuji' (2)	CQua
	'Mount Hood' (1) ♀H6	CArg GKev NBir SDeJ SDir
	'Mountain Poet' (9)	CQua
	'Mousehole' (3)	CQua
	'Mowser' (7)	CQua
	'Mrs Langtry' (2)	CQua GCro GKev WShi
	'Mrs R.O. Backhouse' (2)	CQua WShi
	'Mulatto' (1)	GCro
	'Mullion' (3)	CQua
	'Mulroy Bay' (1)	CQua
	'Murlough' (9)	CQua
	'Muscadet' (2)	CFen
	'My Story' (4) ♀H6	SDeJ SDir WPhe
	'My Sunshine' (2)	CQua
	'My Sweetheart' (3)	CQua
	'My Word' (2)	CFen
	'Mystic' ambig. (3)	CQua
	'Namraj' (2)	CQua
	'Nancegollan' (7)	CQua
	'Nangiles' (4)	CQua
	'Nanpee' (7)	CQua
	'Nanpusker' (2)	CFen
	'Nansidwell' (2)	CQua
	'Nanstallon' (1)	CQua
§	***nanus*** (13)	CQua CWCL EMor
§	- 'Midget' (1)	CBro CQua EPot ERCP NHpl WShi
	'Nare Celebration' (2)	CFen
	'Neahkahnie' (1)	CQua
	'Nelly' ambig.	CQua
	× ***neocarpetanus*** var. ***romanensis*** (13) **new**	NDry
	'Nessa' (7)	CQua
	nevadensis (13)	NDry
	'New Hope' (3)	CQua
	'New Life' (3)	CQua
	'New Penny' (3)	CQua
	'New World' (2)	CQua
	'New-Baby' (7)	CQua ERCP GKev MMrt SDeJ SDir
	'Newcomer' (3)	CQua
	'Nickelodeon' (8)	CQua
	'Night Life' (2) **new**	CQua
	'Night Music' (4)	CQua
	'Nightcap' (1)	CQua
	'Nightflight' (1)	CQua
	'Niphetos' (2)	GCro
	'Nirvana' (7)	CQua
	'Niveth' (5)	CAvo CFen CQua GCro
	'No Worries' (3) **new**	CQua
§	***nobilis*** (13)	CQua EPot GKev NDry
	'Nonchalant' (3)	CQua
	'Norma Jean' (2)	CQua
	'North Rim' (2)	CQua
	'Notre Dame' (2) ♀H6	CQua
	'Nuage' (2)	CFen
	'Nudger' (6) **new**	NDry
	Nylon Group (10)	EPot EPri GKev
	'Nynja' (2)	CQua
	'Oadby' (1)	CQua
	'Obdam' (4)	GBin SDeJ
	'Obsession' (2)	CQua
	obsoletus (13)	GKev WCot
	obvallaris (13) ♀H6	CAvo CBro CFen CQua EPot ERCP GCro GKev LCro MWat SDeJ WBrk WShi
	'Ocarino' (4)	CFen
	'Odd Job' (12)	CQua
	× ***odorus*** (13)	CQua WShi
	- 'Plenus' (4)	CQua ERCP WPhe
	old pheasant's eye	see *N. poeticus* var. *recurvus*
	Old World Group (2) **new**	NDry
	'Oliver Carne' (4) **new**	CQua
	'Ombersley' (1)	CQua
	'Omri' (8)	GKev
	'Orange Comet' (6) **new**	CQua
	'Orange Phoenix' (4)	CQua GCro WShi
	'Orange Progress' (2)	SDeJ
	'Orange Queen' (3)	GKev
	'Orange Supreme' (2)	CQua
	'Orangery' (11a)	GKev SDeJ
	'Oregon Cedar' (2) **new**	CQua
	'Orkney' (2)	CQua
	'Ornatus' (9)	CQua GCro GKev WShi
	'Oryx' (7) ♀H6	CQua
	'Otaki Lights' (1) **new**	CQua
	'Ouma' (1)	CQua
	'Oundle' (2) **new**	CQua
	'Oxford Gold' (10) ♀H6	CAvo CQua MNrw
	'Ozan' (2) **new**	CQua
	pachybolbus (13)	CQua
	'Pacific Coast' (8) ♀H6	CQua LCro LOPS
	'Pacific Mist' (11a)	CQua
	'Pacific Rim' (2)	CQua
	'Pacific Waves' (3)	CQua
	'Paean' (1) **new**	CQua
	'Painted Desert' (3)	CQua
	'Palette' (11a)	GKev
	pallidiflorus (13)	ECha
	'Palmares' (11a)	CQua SDeJ
	'Pamela Hubble' (2)	CQua
	'Pamela Joan' (2)	CQua
	'Pampaluna' (11a)	CQua
	'Panache' (1)	CQua
	panizzianus (13)	CQua
	'Paper White'	see *N. papyraceus*
	'Paper White Grandiflorus' (8)	CQua NRHS SDeJ SPer
	'Papillon Blanc' (11b)	ERCP GKev
	'Papua' (4)	CFen CQua
§	***papyraceus*** (13)	CQua GKev
	- subsp. ***polyanthos*** (13)	GKev
	- 'Ziva' (8)	CAvo ELan GKev LCro LOPS SDeJ SPhx
	'Parcpat' (7)	CQua
	'Parisienne' (11a)	GKev SDeJ
	'Park Springs' (3)	CQua
	'Parkdene' (2)	CQua
	'Passionale' (2) ♀H6	CQua GKev NBir

	'Pastiche' (2)	CQua
	'Pat Redman' (3)	CQua
	'Patois' (9)	CBro CQua
	'Patrick Hacket' (1) ♀H6	CFen
	'Paujen Gold' (7) **new**	CQua
	'Pawating' (4) **new**	CQua
	'Pay Day' (1)	CQua
	'Peach Prince' (4)	CQua
	'Pearl Wedding' (3)	CQua
	'Pearlshell' (11a)	CQua
	'Peeping Jenny' (6)	ERCP SDeJ
	'Peeping Tom' (6) ♀H6	CBro CQua ERCP GKev LRHS SDeJ SRms
	'Peggy Irene' (3) **new**	CQua
	'Pemboa' (1)	CQua
	'Pencrebar' (4)	CQua EPot GKev NHol SDeJ WShi
	'Pend Oreille' (3)	CQua
	'Penjerrick' (9)	CQua
	'Penkivel' (2) ♀H6	CQua
	'Pennine Way' (1)	CQua
	'Penny Perowne' (7)	CQua
	'Pennyfield' (2)	CQua
	'Penpol' (7)	CFen CQua
	'Penril' (6)	CQua
	'Penselwood' (2)	CQua
	'Penstraze' (7)	CQua
	'Pentewan' (2)	GCro
	'Pentire' (11a)	CQua
	'Penvale' (7)	CQua
	'Pequenita' (7)	NDry
	'Percuil' (6)	CQua
	'Perdredda' (3)	CQua
	'Perfect Peace' (2)	CQua
	'Peridot' (2)	GKev
	'Peripheral Pink' (2)	CQua
	'Perpetuation' (7)	CQua
	'Personable' (2)	CQua
	'Peter Chown' (11a)	CQua
	'Petit Four' (4)	LRHS SDeJ
	'Petrel' (5)	CQua ERCP GKev SDeJ WShi
	'Phantom' (11a)	CQua
	'Philomath' (7) **new**	CQua
	'Phil's Gift' (1)	CQua
	'Phoenician' (2)	CQua
	'Pickwick' (2) **new**	CQua
	'Picoblanco' (2)	CBro CQua
	'Pimpernel' (2) ♀H6 **new**	GKev WPhe
	'Pinafore' (2)	WFar
	PINEAPPLE PLEMP (1)	GCro
	'Pink Angel' (7)	CQua
	'Pink Champagne' (4)	CQua
	'Pink Charm' (2)	CQua GKev NBir SDeJ WPhe
	'Pink Chimes' (5) **new**	CQua
	'Pink China' (2)	CQua
	'Pink Formal' (11a)	CQua
	'Pink Gilt' (2)	CQua
	'Pink Glacier' (11a)	CQua
	'Pink Ice' (2)	CQua
	'Pink Pageant' (4)	CQua
	'Pink Paradise' (4)	CQua
	'Pink Parasol' (1)	SDeJ
	'Pink Pride' (2)	CArg
	'Pink Silk' (1)	CQua SDeJ
	'Pink Smiles' (2)	CFen CQua
	'Pink Surprise' (2)	CQua
	'Pink Tango' (11a)	CQua
	'Pinza' (2) ♀H6	CQua SDeJ
	'Pipe Major' (2)	CQua
	'Pipers Barn' (7)	CQua
	'Piper's Gold' (1)	CQua
	'Pipestone' (2)	CQua
	'Pipit' (7)	CAvo CBro CFen CQua EPot ERCP GBin LRHS NBir SDeJ WPhe WShi
	'Pismo Beach' (2)	CQua
	'Pistachio' (1) ♀H6	GKev
	'Pitchroy' (2)	CQua
	'Pitt's Diamond' (3)	CQua
	'Pixie's Sister' (7) ♀H6	CQua
	'Pledge' (1)	CQua
	'Plymouth Hoe' (1)	CQua
§	***poeticus*** var. ***hellenicus*** (13)	CBro CQua GCro
	- old pheasant's eye	see *N. poeticus* var. *recurvus*
	- var. ***physaloides*** (13)	CQua GKev
	- 'Plenus' misapplied	see *N. poeticus* 'Spalding Double White', *N.* 'Tamar Double White'
§	- 'Plenus' ambig. (4)	CBro CQua ERCP GKev SDeJ WShi
§	- var. ***recurvus*** (13) ♀H6	CAvo CBro CFen CQua ELan ERCP GKev LCro LOPS MBros NBir NPoe SDeJ SDir SEND SPer SPhx WPhe WShi
§	- 'Spalding Double White' (4)	CQua GCro
	- white-flowered (13)	SDeJ
	'Poet's Way' (9)	CQua
	'Pol Crocan' (2)	CQua
	'Pol Voulin' (2)	CQua
	'Polar Ice' (3)	CFen CQua GKev SDeJ
	'Polgoon' (2)	CFen
	'Polgooth' (2)	CQua
	'Polindra' (2)	GCro
	'Polly's Pearl' (8)	CQua
	'Polmenor' (2)	CQua
	'Polnesk' (7)	GCro
	'Polonaise' (2)	CQua
	'Polruan' (7)	CQua
	'Polyphant' (2)	CQua
	'Pomona' (3)	GCro
	'Pooka' (3)	CQua
	POOLEWE PINTUCK (2)	GCro
	'Poppy's Choice' (4)	CQua
	'Port Noo' (3)	CQua
	'Porthchapel' (7)	CQua
	'Portloe Bay' (3)	CQua
	'Portrush' (3)	CQua
	'Posai' (2) **new**	CQua
	'Postulate' (2) **new**	CQua
	'Praecox' (9)	CBro
	'Prairie Fire' (3)	CQua
	'Preamble' (1)	CQua
I	'Precocious' (2) ♀H6	CQua GKev SDeJ
	'Presidential Pink' (2)	CQua
	'Pretty in Yellow' (11a)	SDeJ
	'Pride of Cornwall' (8)	CQua
	'Primegold' (2)	CFen
	'Primrose Beauty' (4)	CFen CQua
	'Princeps' (1)	CQua GCro
	'Princess Alexandra' (6)	CFen
	'Princess Diana' (6)	CFen
	'Princess Zaide' (3)	GKev
	'Printal' (11a)	SDeJ
	'Prism' (2)	CQua
	'Probus' (1)	CQua
	'Professor Einstein' (2)	CQua SDeJ
	'Prologue' (1)	CQua
	'Prom Dance' (11a) ♀H6	CQua
	'Proska' (2)	CQua
	'Prototype' (6)	LRHS
	pseudonarcissus (13)	CArg CHab CQua CWld LCro LOPS MMuc NPoe WBrk WHer WShi

- JMH 7821	GKev
- subsp. ***eugeniae***	see *N. eugeniae*
- subsp. ***nobilis***	see *N. nobilis*
- var. ***porrigens*** (13)	GCro
- subsp. ***pseudonarcissus*** (13) 🏆H6	MBow
- - double-flowered (4)	CQua
'Ptolemy' (1)	CFen GCro
'Pueblo' (7)	CQua GKev LRHS SDeJ
'Pukenui' (4)	CQua
pumilus ambig. (13)	CQua SDeJ
'Punchline' (7) 🏆H6	CQua
'Punk' (1) **new**	NDry
'Puppet' (5)	CQua GKev SDeJ
'Purbeck' (3) 🏆H6	CQua
'Quail' (7) 🏆H6	CFen CQua GKev SDeJ
'Quasar' (2) 🏆H6	CQua
Queen Anne's double daffodil	see *N.* 'Eystettensis'
'Queen Bess' (2) **new**	CQua
'Queen of Spain' (5)	CQua
'Queen of the North' (3)	CQua GCro WShi
'Queensland' (2)	CFen
'Quetta' (3)	GCro
'Quick Step' (7)	CQua
'Radiant Gem' (8)	CQua
radiiflorus (13)	EPot
- var. ***poetarum*** (13)	CQua GCro
- var. ***radiiflorus*** (13)	GCro
- var. ***stellaris*** (13)	GCro
'Radjel' (4)	CQua
'Raffles' (4) **new**	CQua
'Rager' (4) **new**	CQua
'Rainbow' (2) 🏆H6	CQua
'Rainbow of Colors' (11a) **new**	LCro LOPS
'Raj' (2)	CQua
'Rame Head' (1)	CQua
'Rameses' (2)	CQua
'Raoul Wallenberg' (2)	GKev SDeJ
'Rapture' (6) 🏆H6	CQua ERCP GKev SPhx
'Rashee' (1)	CQua
'Raspberry Ring' (2)	CQua WPhe
'Rathowen Gold' (1)	CQua
'Ravenhill' (3)	CQua
'Rebekah' (4)	CQua
'Red Beacon' (3)	GCro
'Red Coat' (2)	CQua
'Red Devon' (2)	CArg CFen LCro LOPS LRHS SDeJ
'Red Ember' (3)	CQua
'Red Era' (3)	CQua
'Red Mantle' (2)	CQua
'Red Marvel' (3)	CFen
'Red Reed' (1)	CQua
'Red Rim' (9)	GCro
'Refrain' (2)	CQua
'Regal Bliss' (2)	CQua
'Reggae' (6) 🏆H6	LRHS SDeJ
'Rembrandt' (1)	CFen CQua
'Rendezvous Caye' (2)	CQua
'Renovator' (1)	CQua
'Replete' (4)	CQua CWld GKev SDeJ
requienii	see *N. assoanus*
'Resolute' (2)	GCro
'Reverse Image' (11a)	CQua
rifanus	see *N. romieuxii* subsp. *romieuxii* var. *rifanus*
'Rijnveld's Early Sensation' (1) 🏆H6	CAvo CBro CFen CQua ECha ERCP LCro LOPS SDeJ
'Rikki' (7)	CBro
'Rimmon' (3)	CQua
'Rimski' (2)	CQua
'Ring Fence' (3)	CQua
'Ringing Bells' (5)	CQua
'Ringleader' (2)	CQua
§ 'Rip van Winkle' (4)	CAby CBro CFen CQua CRos EHyd EPot ERCP GKev LRHS NHol NHpl NRHS SDeJ SPer WBrk WShi
'Rippling Waters' (5)	CQua GKev
'Rival' (6)	CQua
'River Queen' (2)	CQua
'Roberta' (1)	CFen
'Rockall' (3)	CQua
'Roger' (6)	CQua
'Rogue' (2)	CBro
§ 'Romanus' (4)	CQua
'Romeo' (8) **new**	CQua
romieuxii (13) 🏆H4	CRos EHyd EPri LRHS NDry NRHS WCot
- JCA 805	EPot
- SF 370	WCot WMal
- subsp. ***albidus*** (13)	EPot GKev
- - SF 110	NDry WCot
- - var. ***zaianicus*** M168 (13) **new**	NDry
- - - SB&L 82 from Morocco	WCot
§ - 'Joy Bishop' (10)	EPot NDry WCot
§ - 'Julia Jane' (10)	CAvo CQua ERCP GKev LCro LOPS SDir WCot
- 'Mrs McGee' (10) **new**	NDry
* - subsp. ***pallidus*** (13) SB&L 237	WCot
§ - subsp. ***romieuxii*** var. ***rifanus*** (13) B 8929	WCot
'Rongoiti Gem' (4)	CQua
'Rosannor Gold' (11a)	CQua
'Rose Lake' (2) **new**	CQua
'Rose of May' (4)	CQua WShi
'Rose Royale' (2)	CQua
'Rose Villa' (2)	CQua
'Rosemary Pearson' (2)	CQua
'Rosemerryn' (2)	CQua
'Rosemoor Gold' (7) 🏆H6	CFen CQua
'Rosemullion' (4)	CQua
'Rosevine' (3)	CQua
'Roulette' (2)	GKev SDeJ
'Round Oak' (1)	CQua
'Royal Armour' (1)	CFen
'Royal Connection' (8)	CQua
'Royal Marine' (2)	CQua
'Royal Princess' (3)	CQua GKev
'Royal Regiment' (2)	CQua
'Rubilina' (2) **new**	NDry
'Ruby Red' (2)	CQua
'Rubythroat' (2)	CQua
'Ruddynosey' (1) **new**	CQua
'Rugulosus' (7)	CQua
rupicola (13)	CBro CQua GKev NDry NSla WCot
§ - subsp. ***marvieri*** (13)	NDry
§ - subsp. ***watieri*** (13)	CBro CQua ERCP GKev NDry SDir
'Rushlake Green' (2) **new**	CQua
'Rustom Pasha' (2)	CQua GCro
'Saberwing' (5)	CQua
'Sabine Hay' (3)	CQua EPot GKev
'Sabrosa' (7) 🏆H6	CBro CQua CWCL GKev LCro LOPS WShi
'Sacajawea' (2)	CFen
'Sagana' (9)	CQua
'Sailboat' (7) 🏆H6	CAvo CBro CQua CWCL GKev LCro LOPS SDeJ SPer SPhx WBrk
'Saint Agnes' (8)	CQua

'Saint Budock' (1) CQua
'Saint Day' (5) CQua
'Saint Keverne' (2) ♀H6 CFen CQua SDeJ
'Saint Keyne' (8) CQua
'Saint Olaf' (3) GCro
'Saint Patrick's Day' (2) CFen CQua GBin SDeJ
'Saint Peter' (4) CFen CQua
'Saint Petroc' (9) CQua
'Saint Piran' (7) CQua
'Salakee' (2) CQua
'Salcey Forest' (1) CQua
'Salome' (2) ♀H6 CQua CWld LCro LOPS MBros NBir NPer SDeJ
'Salute' (2) CQua
'Sandra's Diamond' (3) CQua
'Sandycove' (2) CQua
'Sargeant's Caye' (1) CQua
'Satchmo' (1) CQua
'Saturn' (3) CQua
'Saxby' (11a) CQua
'Saxonbury' (2) **new** CQua
'Scarlet Chord' (2) CQua
'Scarlet Elegance' (2) CQua
'Scarlet Gem' (8) SDeJ
'Scarlett O'Hara' (2) CFen
'Scilly White' (8) CFen CQua WShi
'Scorrier' (2) CQua
'Scrum Half' (1) **new** NDry
'Scrumpy' (2) CQua
'Sea Dream' (3) CQua
'Sea Green' (9) CQua
'Sea Princess' (3) SDeJ
'Seagrave' (4) **new** CQua
'Seagull' (3) CQua
'Sealing Wax' (2) CFen CQua SPer
'Segovia' (3) ♀H6 CAvo CBro CQua EHyd ELan ERCP GKev LRHS NRHS SDeJ SPhx
'Sempre Avanti' (2) CArg SDeJ
'Sentinel' (2) GKev SDeJ
'Seraglio' (3) CQua
'Serena Lodge' (4) ♀H6 CQua
'Sharnden' (1) CQua
'Sharon's Champagne' (3) **new** CQua
'Shauna Rose' (8) **new** CQua
'Shepherd's Hey' (7) CQua SDeJ
'Sherborne' (4) ♀H6 CQua
'Sherpa' (1) CQua
'Shining Light' (2) CQua
'Shockwave' (2) CQua
'Shrike' (11a) ♀H6 **new** CQua
'Shurdington' (3) **new** CQua
'Shykowski' (4) **new** CQua
'Sidley' (3) CQua
'Sidney Torch' (2) CFen
'Sidora' (1) **new** NDry
'Silk Cut' (2) CQua
'Silver Chimes' (8) CAvo CBro CFen CQua GKev LCro LOPS NBir SDeJ
'Silver Kiwi' (2) CQua
'Silver Moon' (2) CFen
'Silver Smiles' (7) SPhx
'Silver Surf' (2) CQua
'Silversmith' (2) CQua
'Silverwood' (3) CQua
'Sinopel' (3) SDeJ
'Sir Samuel' (2) CQua
'Sir Watkin' (2) CQua GCro
'Sir Winston Churchill' (4) ♀H6 CAvo CQua LCro LOPS LRHS SDeJ SPer
'Sirius' (2) GCro
'Sissy' (6) CQua
'Skerry' (2) CQua
'Skilliwidden' (2) ♀H6 CQua
'Skookum' (3) CQua
'Sleek' (6) **new** NDry
'Slim Whitman' (2) GKev
'Small Fry' (1) CQua
'Small Talk' (1) ♀H6 CQua
'Smiling Twin' (11a) CQua SDeJ
'Smokey Bear' (4) CQua
'Smooth Sails' (3) CQua
'Snipe' (6) CQua WShi
'Snook' (6) NDry
'Snow Baby' (1) CBro CQua ERCP GKev ITim
'Snowball' (4) GKev
'Snowcrest' (3) CQua
'So Sweet' (3) CQua
'Solar Tan' (3) CQua
'Soleil d'Or' (8) CQua
'Solferique' (2) CQua
'Solveig's Song' (12) EPot
'Sonata' (9) CQua
'Songket' (2) CQua
'Sophie Girl' (2) GKev
'Soprano' (2) CQua
'Sorbet' (11b) CQua SDeJ
'Sorcerer' (3) CQua
'Southease' (2) CQua
'Southern Gem' (2) CQua GCro
'Spaniards Inn' (4) CQua
'Sparkling Tarts' (8) CQua
'Special Envoy' (2) CQua
'Speedie' (6) **new** NDry
'Spellbinder' (1) CQua SDeJ
'Spencer Tracy' (2) CFen
'Spirit of Rame' (3) CQua
'Split Vote' (11a) CQua
'Spoirot' (10) ♀H6 CQua ERCP GBin GKev MNrw MPie NHpl SDeJ
'Sportsman' (2) CQua
'Spring Dawn' (2) LCro LOPS
'Spring Morn' (2) CQua
'Spun Honey' (4) CQua
'Squinney' (12) **new** NDry
'Stadium' (2) CFen
'Stainless' (2) SDir SPhx WPhe
'Standard Value' (1) CFen
'Stann Creek' (1) CQua
'Stanway' (3) CQua
'Star Glow' (2) CQua
'Starfire' (7) CQua
'Starlight Sensation' (5) SPhx
'Starlit' (1) **new** NDry
'State Express' (2) CQua
'Stella' (2) GCro
'Stella Corscadden' (6) **new** LToo
'Step Child' (6) CQua
'Step Forward' (7) CQua
'Steren' (7) CQua
'Stilton' (9) CQua
'Stint' (5) ♀H6 CQua GKev SDeJ SDir SPhx
'Stoke Charity' (2) CQua
'Stoke Doyle' (2) CQua
'Stratosphere' (7) ♀H6 CQua SDeJ
'Strines' (2) ♀H6 CQua
'Suave' (3) GKev SDeJ
'Suda' (2) GCro
'Sugar and Spice' (3) CQua

	'Sugar Cups' (8)	CQua
	'Sugar Loaf' (4)	CQua
	'Sugar Rose' (6)	CQua
	'Suisgill' (4)	CQua
§	'Sulphur Phoenix' (4)	CQua GCro WShi
	SULPHUR STAR (2)	GCro
	'Sumo Jewel' (6)	CQua
	'Sun Bronze' (2) **new**	CQua
	'Sun Disc' (7) ♀H6	CBro CFen CQua CTri GKev LCro LOPS MBros SDeJ WPhe WShi
	'Sundial' (7)	CBro
	'Sunny Girlfriend' (11a)	SDeJ WPhe
	'Sunnyside Up' (11a) ♀H6	SDeJ
	'Sunrise' (3)	CQua
	'Sunstroke' (2)	CQua
	'Suntory' (3)	CQua
	'Surfside' (6) ♀H6	CQua GKev SDeJ SPhx
	'Suzy' (7)	CFen CQua SDeJ
	'Swallow' (6)	CQua SDeJ
	'Swan of Avon' (1)	CQua
	'Swedish Sea' (2) **new**	CQua
	'Sweet Blanche' (7)	CQua
	'Sweet Georgia' (2) **new**	CQua
	'Sweet Lorraine' (2)	CQua
	'Sweet Memory' (2)	CQua
	'Sweet Pepper' (7)	CQua
	'Sweet Pomponette' (4)	CWld SDeJ
	'Sweet Sue' (3)	CQua
	'Sweetness' (7) ♀H6	CAvo CFen CQua GCro LCro LOPS SDeJ WShi
	'Swift Arrow' (6) ♀H6	CQua
	'Swing Wing' (6)	CQua
	'Swoop' (6)	SDeJ
	'Sydling' (5)	CQua
	'Taffeta' (10)	EPri
	'Tahiti' (4) ♀H6	CFen CQua ELan LCro LOPS SDeJ
	× ***taitii*** (13)	GKev WShi
	'Talgarth' (2)	CQua
§	'Tamar Double White' (4)	CBro CQua
	'Tamar Fire' (4) ♀H6	CQua
	'Tamar Lad' (2)	CQua
	'Tamar Lass' (3)	CQua
	'Tamar Snow' (2)	CQua
	'Tamara' (2)	CArg CFen
	'Tangent' (2)	CQua
	'Tao' (3)	CQua
	'Tasgem' (4)	CQua
	'Taslass' (4)	CQua
	tazetta (13)	CQua GKev
§	- subsp. ***lacticolor*** (13)	CQua ERCP GKev SDeJ SDir
§	- - 'Grand Monarque' (8)	CQua
	- subsp. ***ochroleucus*** (13)	CQua
*	- var. ***odoratus*** (13)	CQua WShi
	- subsp. ***tazetta*** (13)	CQua
	'Teal' (1)	CQua
	'Tehidy' (3)	CQua
§	'Telamonius Plenus' (4)	CQua GBin GCro GKev SEND WShi
	× ***tenuior*** (13)	GKev
	'Terminator' (2)	CQua
	'Terracotta' (2)	CQua
	'Terwegen' (4)	CFen
	'Tête Bouclé'^{PBR} (4)	CQua GKev SDir WPhe
	'Tête Rosette'	LCro
	'Tête-à-tête' (12) ♀H6	CArg CAvo CBro CFen CQua CRos CWCL EHyd EMor EPot ERCP GAbr GKev GQue LCro LOPS LRHS MBros NHpl NRHS SDeJ SDir SPer WBrk WPhe
	'Tethys' (10) **new**	NDry
	'Texas' (4)	GCro
I	'Thalia' (5)	CArg CAvo CBro CQua ELan ERCP LCro LOPS MBriF NBir NHol SDeJ SPer SPhx WShi
	'The Alliance' (6) ♀H6	CQua
	'The Caley' (2)	CQua
	'The Grange' (1)	CQua
	'The Little Gentleman' (6)	CQua
	'Themisto' (10) **new**	NDry
	'Thomas Kinkade' (2)	CQua
	'Three Oaks' (1)	CQua
	'Thriplow Gold' (1) **new**	CQua
	'Tibet' (2)	CFen
	'Tickled Pinkeen' (2) **new**	WPhe
	'Tidebrook' (3) **new**	CQua
	'Tideford' (2)	CQua
	'Tiercel' (1)	CQua
	'Tiffany Jade' (3)	CQua
	'Timolin' (3)	CQua
	'Tinhay' (7)	CQua
	'Tino Pai' (9) **new**	CQua
	'Tintagel Lady' (4) **new**	CQua
	'Tiny Bubbles' (12)	CBro CQua GKev
	'Tiritomba' (11a)	CQua
	'Tittle-tattle' (7)	CFen CQua
	'Tiwi' (2) **new**	CQua
	'Toby' (2)	SDeJ
	'Toby the First' (6)	CQua
	'Top Hit' (11a)	CQua
	'Topolino' (1) ♀H6	CAvo CBro CFen CQua CRos EHyd EPot ERCP GKev LCro LOPS LRHS NRHS
	'Topsy Turvy' (4)	CQua
	'Toreador' ambig. (3)	CFen
	'Torianne' (2) ♀H6	CQua
	TOROSAY ELEGANCE (2)	GCro
	'Torridon' (2)	CQua
	'Toto' (12) ♀H6	CAvo CBro CQua ERCP GKev LCro LOPS MBriF SDeJ SDir SPhx
	'Transmitter' (4)	CQua
	'Trebah' (2) ♀H6	CQua
	'Treble Two' (7)	CQua
	'Trecara' (3)	CQua
	'Tregarrick' (2)	CQua
	'Treglisson' (2)	CFen
	'Trelawney Gold' (2)	CFen CQua
	'Trelissick' (7)	CQua
	'Tremelling' (2)	CFen
	'Tremough Dale' (11a)	CQua
	'Trena' (6) ♀H6	CQua ERCP GKev SDeJ
	'Trenwith' (1)	CQua
	'Trepolo' (11b)	SDeJ
	'Tresamble' (5)	CBro CQua GCro GKev LCro LOPS NBir SDeJ
	'Tresserve' (1)	GCro
	'Treviddo' (2)	CQua
	'Trevithian' (7)	CQua GCro GKev SDeJ
	triandrus var. ***albus***	see *N. triandrus* subsp. *triandrus* var. *triandrus*
	- subsp. ***triandrus*** (13)	NDry
§	- - var. ***triandrus*** (13)	CBor GBin
	'Tricollet' (11a)	SDeJ
	'Trigonometry' (11a) ♀H6	CQua
	'Tripartite' (11a) ♀H6	CFen CQua GKev SDeJ
	'Triple Crown' (3) ♀H6	CQua
	'Tristar' (11a) **new**	CQua
	'Tristram' (2)	CQua
	'Tropic Isle' (4)	CQua
	'Trousseau' (1)	CFen CQua
	'Tru' (3)	CQua
	'Truculent' (3)	CQua

'Trumpet Voluntary' (1) **new**	NDry
'Trumpet Warrior' (1) 🏆H6	CQua
'Tryst' (2)	CQua
'Tudor Minstrel' (2)	CQua
'Tuesday's Child' (5) 🏆H6	CQua
'Tunis' (2)	GCro
'Turncoat' (6)	CQua
'Twicer' (2)	CQua
'Twin Cam' (12) **new**	NDry
'Twink' (4)	CQua GCro
'Twinkling Yellow' (7) 🏆H6	CBro CQua GKev
'Tyrone Gold' (1) 🏆H6	CQua
× ***ubriquensis*** hort.	see *N.* × *incurvicervicus*
'Ulster Bank' (3)	CQua
'Ultimus' (2)	CQua
'Uncle Duncan' (1)	CQua
'Unique' (4) 🏆H6	GKev SDeJ
'Unsurpassable' (1)	CFen CQua GCro
'Upalong' (12)	CQua
'Upshot' (3)	CQua
'Utiku' (6)	CQua
'Val d'Incles' (3)	CQua
'Valdrome' (11a)	CQua
'Valinor' (2)	CQua
'Van Sion'	see *N.* 'Telamonius Plenus'
'Vanilla Peach' (11a)	GKev LRHS SDeJ WPhe
'Vantage' (2)	CQua
'Vanya Noeletta' (2) **new**	CQua
'Vaticaan' (1)	SDeJ
'Verdin' (7)	CQua
'Verger' (3)	SDeJ
'Vernal Prince' (3) 🏆H6	CQua
'Verona' (3) 🏆H6	CQua
'Vers Libre' (9)	CQua
'Viking' (1) 🏆H6	CQua
'Vineland' (6)	CQua
'Violetta' (2)	CQua
'Vitrina' (5) **new**	NDry
'Voltage' (2)	CQua
'Vulcan' (2)	CQua
'W.P. Milner' (1)	CAvo CBro CQua EMor ERCP GKev LCro LOPS MWat SDeJ SEND SPhx WShi
'Walden Pond' (3)	CQua
'Waldorf Astoria' (4)	CQua
'Walton' (7)	CQua
'War Dance' (3)	CQua
'Warbler' (6) 🏆H6	CQua GKev SDeJ
'Warleggan' (2)	CFen
'Watership Down' (2)	CQua
'Watersmeet' (4)	CQua
watieri	see *N. rupicola* subsp. *watieri*
'Wave' (4)	CQua SDeJ
'Wavertree'	see *N. asturiensis* 'Wavertree'
'Waxwing' (5)	CQua
'Wee Bee' (1)	CQua
'Wee Dote' (1) **new**	NDry
'Welcome' (2)	CFen CQua
'Welsh Rugby Union' (1)	CQua
'Welsh Warrior' (1)	CQua
'Wendron' (1)	CFen
'Westward' (4)	CQua WPhe
'Wheal Coates' (7) 🏆H6	CQua
'Wheal Jane' (2)	CQua
'Wheal Kitty' (7)	CQua
'Whetstone' (1)	CQua
'Whipcord' (7) 🏆H6	CQua
'Whippet' (6) **new**	NDry
'White Emperor' (1)	GCro
'White Empress' (1)	CQua
'White Lady' (3)	CAvo CQua GCro GKev WShi
'White Lion' (4) 🏆H6	CFen SDeJ SDir
'White Marvel' (4)	CQua GKev SDeJ
'White Medal' (4)	GKev SDeJ
'White Nile' (2)	CQua GCro
'White Petticoat' (10) **new**	NHpl
'White Plume' (2)	CQua
'White Tea' (2)	CQua
'White Tie' (3)	CQua
'Whitewell' (2)	GCro
'Wicklow Hills' (3)	CQua
'Widgeon' (2)	CQua
'Wild Carnival' (2) **new**	WPhe
willkommii (13)	CBro CQua EPot EPri GKev
'Wimbledon County Girl' (2) 🏆H6	CQua
'Windy City' (2) **new**	CQua
'Winholm Jenni' (3)	CQua
'Winifred van Graven' (3)	CFen CQua
'Winter Sun' (8)	GKev LRHS
'Winter Waltz' (6)	CQua GKev
'Wisley' (6) 🏆H6	ERCP MWat
'Witch Doctor' (3)	CQua
WOODCROFT BEAUTY (2)	GCro
WOODCROFT GOLD (2)	GCro
'Woodland Prince' (3)	CQua
'Woodland Star' (3)	CQua
'Woodley Vale' (2)	CQua
'Woodstar' (5)	CQua EPot
'Woolaroo' (4) **new**	CQua
'Woolsthorpe' (2)	CQua
'World Class' (5)	CQua
'Wychbold' (3) **new**	CQua
'Xit' (3)	CBro CQua EPot
'Xunantunich' (2)	CQua
'Yellow Cheerfulness' (4) 🏆H6	CArg CQua ELan GKev LCro LOPS NRHS SDeJ WPhe
'Yellow Triumphator' (1)	CFen
'Yellow Xit' (3)	CQua
'York Minster' (1)	CQua
'Young American' (1)	CQua
'Young Blood' (2)	CQua
'Your Grace' (2)	CQua
'Zeekie' (2) **new**	NDry
'Zekiah' (1)	CQua
'Zion Canyon' (2)	CQua
'Zoë's Pink' (3)	CQua
'Zonk' (11a) **new**	CQua

Nardostachys (*Caprifoliaceae*)

grandiflora	see *N. jatamansi* 'Grandiflora'
§ ***jatamansi*** 'Grandiflora'	GPoy

Nassauvia (*Asteraceae*)

darwinii	WAbe
digitata	SPlb
gaudichaudii	SPlb WAbe
lagascae	WAbe

Nassella (*Poaceae*)

cernua	EPPr
tenuissima	see *Stipa tenuissima*
trichotoma	LPla WHal
- 'Palomino'	EHyd LRHS

Nasturtium (*Brassicaceae*)

officinale	MWts SVic WMAq

Natal plum see *Carissa macrocarpa*

nectarine see *Prunus persica* var. *nectarina*

Nectaroscordum (*Alliaceae*)

§ ***siculum***	CArg CAvo CBod CBre CBro CPla CSpe CTri EAJP ERCP GKev LCro LEdu LOPS LRHS MBel NBir NChi NSti SCob SDeJ SDir SDix SPer SPoG WBor
§ - subsp. ***bulgaricum***	CAby CRos EBee ECha EHyd EPot EWhm LRHS MNrw NRHS SPhx WBrk WCot WHil WPnP XEll XLum
- subsp. ***bulgaricum*** × ***tripedale***	GKev

Neillia (*Rosaceae*)

affinis	CBod CExl CRos EBee EHyd EPfP EWTr IDee LRHS MGil NBid NLar SLon SPad SPoG SWvt WLov
longiracemosa	see *N. thibetica*
rubiflora	CPla
sinensis	NLar
§ ***thibetica***	Widely available
thyrsiflora	EBee
- PAB 3267	LEdu
- var. ***tunkinensis*** HWJ 505	WCru

Nelumbo (*Nelumbonaceae*)

lutea	XBlo
nucifera	XBlo
'Pink 'n' Yellow'	EWat

Nematanthus (*Gesneriaceae*)

'Apres'	WDib
'Black Magic'	WDib
'Christmas Holly'	WDib
'Freckles'	WDib
§ ***gregarius*** ♀H1b	WDib
§ - 'Golden West' (v)	WDib
- 'Variegatus'	see *N. gregarius* 'Golden West'
'Lemon and Lime'	WDib
radicans	see *N. gregarius*
'Tropicana' ♀H1b	WDib

Nemesia (*Scrophulariaceae*)

§ AMELIE ('Fleurame'PBR)	LBuc MPri SPoG
(Aroma Series) AROMA BANANA SPLIT **new**	MPri
- AROMA PLUMS AND CUSTARD	MPri SCob
- AROMA RHUBARB AND CUSTARD	LSou MBros MPri SCob
'Belcombe Blue'	CSpe
BERRIE WHITE ('Fleurow'PBR)	LSou
BERRIES AND CREAM ('Fleurbac'PBR)	ECtt LBuc LSou MCot SPoG
BLUE LAGOON ('Pengoon'PBR) (Maritana Series)	MCot SCoo
'Bordeaux'	SPoG
caerulea 'Joan Wilder' (clonal)	WAvo
CANDY GIRL ('Pencand') (Maritana Series)	SCoo
§ ***denticulata*** ♀H3	LRHS MHer SCoo
- 'Confetti'	see *N. denticulata*
'Easter Bonnet' (French Connection Series)	LSou MPri SCob SPoG
'Fleurie Blue'	LBuc SPoG
FRAMBOISE ('Fleurfram'PBR)	LBuc MPri
HONEY GIRL ('Penhon') (Maritana Series)	SCoo
'Innocence' ♀H3	SCoo
(Karoo Series) KAROO BLUE ('Innkablue'PBR)	SCoo
- KAROO DARK BLUE ('Innemkadab'PBR)	MCot
- KAROO SOFT BLUE ('Innkarsofb'PBR)	MCot
'Lyric Copper' (Lyric Series) **new**	LSou
MARITANA SKY LAGOON ('Pensky') (Maritana Series)	SCoo
'Mirabelle'	LBuc MPri SPoG
MYRTILLE ('Fleurmyr'PBR)	LBuc SPoG
NESIA BANANA SWIRL (Nesia Series)	MPri
OPAL INNOCENCE	see *N.* AMELIE
RASPBERRIES AND CREAM ('Fleurrac')	LBuc SPoG
'Sugar Almond'	CMac
'Sundrops'	MBros MPri
(Sunsatia Series) SUNSATIA BANANA ('Intraibana')	SPoG
- SUNSATIA BLACKBERRY ('Inuppink'PBR)	SCoo
- SUNSATIA CRANBERRY ('Intraired'PBR)	SCoo
- SUNSATIA LEMON ('Intraigold'PBR)	SCoo
- SUNSATIA PEACH ('Inupcream')	CWCL SCoo
(Sunsatia Plus Series) SUNSATIA PLUS CHERRY ON ICE	CPla CWCL LSou SPoG
- SUNSATIA PLUS LYCHEE **new**	CRos
- SUNSATIA PLUS POMELO ('Innemsunpo'PBR)	CRos
sylvatica	CSpe
TRIOMIO ALEGRIA **new**	CWCL
TRIOMIO POETRY **new**	CWCL
TRIOMIO TUTTI FRUTTI **new**	CWCL
'Vanilla Lady'	ECtt
'Wisley Vanilla'	CRos EHyd LBuc LRHS LSou MBros MPri NRHS SCob SPoG

Nemophila (*Boraginaceae*)

menziesii 'Penny Black'	CSpe SPer

Neodypsis (*Arecaceae*)

decaryi	see *Dypsis decaryi*

Neohenricia (*Aizoaceae*)

sibbettii ♀H2	CPBP

Neolepisorus (*Polypodiaceae*)

lancifolius	CExl

Neolitsea (*Lauraceae*)

glauca	see *N. sericea*
polycarpa B&SWJ 11705	WCru
- KWJ 12309	WCru
§ ***sericea***	CBcs CCCN EBee NLar WPGP
- B&SWJ 12738	WCru
- CWJ 12800	WCru
- yellow-fruited CWJ 12830	WCru

Neomarica (*Iridaceae*)

caerulea	WCot

Neopanax ✿ (*Araliaceae*)

§	***arboreus***	CAbb CDTJ CTrC CTsd EBee LEdu
	colensoi	CTsd
§	***laetus*** ♀H3	CTrC CTsd WPGP

Neoregelia ✿ (*Bromeliaceae*)

	'Atlantis'	NCft
	carolinae (Meyendorffii Group) 'Meyendorffii'	XBlo
	'Fireball' ♀H1b	NCft
	'Hojo Rojo'	XBlo
	lilliputiana	NCft
	'Luca'	SPlb
	'Marconfos'	XBlo
	'Narciss'	NCft
	pauciflora	NCft
I	***paulinae*** 'Paulinae'	NCft
I	***schultesiana***	NCft
I	- 'Variegata' (v)	NCft

Neoshirakia (*Euphorbiaceae*)

	japonica	MBlu WPGP
	- B&SWJ 8744	WCru

Nepenthes ✿ (*Nepenthaceae*)

	sp.	SRms
	alata × ***ventricosa*** ♀H1a	SHmp
	'Bloody Mary' PBR	LCro LOPS SHmp
	bongso	SHmp
	burbidgeae × ***robcantleyi***	SHmp
	× ***burkei*** × ***hamata***	SHmp
	× ***burkei*** × ***singalana***	SHmp
	(***copelandii*** × ***truncata***) × ***spathulata***	SHmp
	densiflora	SHmp
	diatas	SHmp
	dubia × ***singalana***	SHmp
	dubia × ***spathulata***	SHmp
	fusca	SHmp
	fusca × ***maxima***	SHmp
	glabrata × ***spathulata***	SHmp
	× ***hookeriana*** ♀H1a	SHmp
	jacquelineae × ***spectabilis***	SHmp
	'Linda' PBR	SHmp
	'Louisa'	SHmp
	macfarlanei	SHmp
	maxima × (× ***mixta***)	SHmp
	maxima × ***talangensis***	SHmp
	mira × ***spathulata***	SHmp
	ovata	SHmp
	ovata × ***ventricosa***	SHmp
	petiolata × ***veitchii***	SHmp
	platychila × ***spathulata***	SHmp
	ramispina	SHmp
	'Rebecca Soper' ♀H1a	SHmp
	robcantleyi	SHmp
	robcantleyi × ***spathulata***	SHmp
	robcantleyi × ***talangensis***	SHmp
	sanguinea	SHmp
	sibuyanensis	SHmp
	singalana	SHmp
	spectabilis	SHmp
	talangensis	SHmp
	talangensis × ***veitchii***	SHmp
	truncata highland form	SHmp
	- 'King of Spades' × ***truncata*** 'Queen of Hearts'	SHmp
	ventricosa	SHmp

Nepeta ✿ (*Lamiaceae*)

	badachschanica new	LEdu
	'Blue Beauty'	see *N. sibirica* 'Souvenir d'André Chaudron'
	'Blue Dragon'	CBod CCBP CKno CMea CNor ECtt EHyd EPed GBin GPSL GQue GWyn LRHS LSou MAvo MPie MSpe MTis NLar NRHS SPad SPoG SRms WCot WFar WHoo
*	***buddlejifolium***	NLar
*	- 'Gold Splash'	NLar
	camphorata	WSpi
	cataria	CBee CBod CCBP CLau CTsd EBou ENfk GJos GPoy LCro LOPS MHer MNHC NBro NGrd SRms SVic WSpi XAbr
§	- 'Citriodora'	CBod CLau ENfk NGrd SPhx SRms SVic
	'Chettle Blue'	CDor MAvo
	citriodora Dum.	see *N. cataria* 'Citriodora'
	clarkei	CBod GMaP MRav MTis WSpi
	curviflora	SHar SPhx SPtp
	'Dropmore'	EBee EHyd GWyn LPla LRHS MTis NLar NRHS WSpi
	'Early Bird'	WCAu WHil
§	× ***faassenii*** ♀H7	Widely available
	- 'Alba'	EBee ECtt EHyd ELan EPfP EWhm LPot LRHS NLar SRms WSpi
	- 'Blauknirps'	EBee NLar
	- 'Blue Wonder'	CRos EBee EHyd ELan EPfP LRHS LSou MHol MTis NDov NLar NRHS WCAu WFar WSpi
	- 'Crystal Cloud'	CBod CKno CRos ECtt EHyd LRHS MBriF NRHS SHar WCAu
	- 'Gletschereis'	EBee NLar WCAu
	- JUNIOR WALKER ('Novanepjun' PBR)	CBod CRos EBee EHyd EPfP GMaP LCro LOPS LRHS LSRN MAsh MBel MMrt NDov NLar NRHS SCob SWvt WCot XSen
	- 'Kit Cat'	CRos EBee ECtt EHyd EPfP GBin GWyn LRHS LSRN MAsh MBel MHol MTis NRHS SCob SEdd SWvt WAvo WCAu XSen
	- 'Purrsian Blue' PBR	CRos MHol MTis NCou SGbt SPoG WCav
	- 'Senior'	XLum
	glechoma 'Variegata'	see *Glechoma hederacea* 'Variegata'
	govaniana	Widely available
	grandiflora	CDor MRav NBre
	- 'Blue Danube'	EBee GBin GWyn MTis SDix XLum
	- 'Blue Elf'	NDov
	- 'Bramdean' ♀H6	CCBP CDor CMea CRos CSde EBee ECtt EHyd EPfP EWes GBin GWyn LRHS MCot MRav MTis NRHS SPhx SRms WCAu WCot XLum
	- 'Dawn to Dusk'	Widely available
	- 'Pool Bank'	EBee ECtt EWes MTis NLar XLum
	- 'Summer Magic' PBR	CRos EBee EHyd EMor EPfP LRHS LSou MBel MHol NLar NRHS SCob SEdd SHar SPoG SRkn SWvt WCAu WFar WNPC WTor
	- 'Wild Cat'	MAvo MTis WCAu
	- 'Zinser's Giant'	EBee SAko
	hederacea 'Variegata'	see *Glechoma hederacea* 'Variegata'
	'Hill Grounds'	CBod CKno ECha LSun MAvo MHol WCot WRHF
	italica	LRHS SPhx

'Joanna Reed'	GBin MAvo NLar WSpi
kubanica	CSpe EBee EHyd EWTr IMou LRHS MBel MRav NLar NRHS SDix SPhx SPtp WCot WSHC
'Lamendi'	NDov
latifolia 'Super Cat'	EPfP
§ 'Leeds Castle'	CBod CSam EBee ECtt EHyd EPed EPfP LRHS MTis NGdn NRHS NSti SHar SPer SPoG WAvo WCAu WHal
'Limelight'	MHer NLar
longipes hort.	see *N.* 'Leeds Castle'
macrantha	see *N. sibirica*
manchuriensis 'Manchu Blue'	EBee
'Maurice'	LPla
mussinii misapplied	see *N.* × *faassenii*
mussinii Spreng.	see *N. racemosa*
NEPTUNE ('Bokratune') **new**	LCro LOPS WTor
nervosa	CDor CSpe ECha ELan EPfP NBro NLar NSti SHar SPer
- 'Blue Carpet'	CSpe
- 'Blue Moon'	CBod CFis EBee EHyd EPfP EWes GJos LRHS MBNS MHol MMrt MPie MPnt NBPC NDov NLar NQui NRHS SRms WFar WHil WSpi
- 'Forncett Select'	CSam MRav NBre
- 'Pink Cat'	CBod CRos EHyd EPfP GJos LRHS NLar NRHS WFar
- 'Schneehäschen'	SAko WSpi
§ ***nuda***	ECha EWes LPla MAvo MRav SBut SHar SMHy WGoo
- 'Accent'	EBee
- 'Alba' **new**	SBut
- subsp. ***albiflora***	ECha
- 'Anne's Choice'	MAvo
* - 'Grandiflora'	NBre
- 'Lake Sevan'	LEdu
- 'Purple Cat'	EBee EPfP MAvo
- 'Romany Dusk'	ECha LEdu LPla SWvt
- 'Snow Cat'	SPhx
pannonica	see *N. nuda*
parnassica	EMor EPPr GLog GQue MAvo MBel MCot MHol MMuc MTis
phyllochlamys	CPBP
'Pink Candy'	SPhx SRms
'Poseidon'	MAvo
§ ***prattii***	NLar SEND
'Purple Haze'PBR	CBod ECtt EHyd ELan EPfP LSou MHol NRHS
§ ***racemosa*** ♀H7	CHby CMac CRos EBou EHyd EPfP EWhm GJos GWyn LRHS MCot MNHC
- RCBAM 3	WCot
- 'Alba'	CBod CDor SBut XLum
- 'Amelia'	CBod CElw EBee EPfP LPla MAvo MBriF MHer WAvo WCAu WGoo WTor
- 'Felix'	CRos WFar
- 'Grog'	CBod EWTr GBin GWyn LRHS MTis NLar SBut SEdd SPoG
- 'Little Titch'	CBod EBee ECha ECtt EHyd EPfP GWyn LRHS LSRN MAsh MCot MTin NBPC NGdn NLar SCob WHoo
- 'Senior'	CBod MHol
- 'Snowflake'	CBcs CBod CMea CNor CRos ECtt EHyd ELan EPfP EShb GMaP GQue GWyn LRHS MBel MBriF MTis NBir NLar NRHS SCob SGbt SPer SPoG SWvt WAvo WCAu WSpi WTor
- 'Superba'	NBre XSen
- 'Toria'	IMou MAvo MTis NDov
- 'Walker's Low' ♀H7	Widely available
'Rae Crug'	ECtt EWes
* ***recta*** **new**	WCAu
reichenbachiana	see *N. racemosa*
§ ***sibirica***	CCBP ECha EHyd ELan EPfP LRHS MMuc NBid NBro NRHS SRkn WCAu WCot XLum
§ - 'Souvenir d'André Chaudron' ♀H6	CAby CDor CRos CSam CWCL EBee ELan EPfP GMaP GWyn LRHS MBel MCot MHer MRav MTis NLar NRHS SCob SPer SPoG WCAu WHil WSpi
'Six Hills Giant'	Widely available
'Six Hills Gold' (v)	CDor EBee LBuc MAsh NBPC WCAu WCot WFar WSpi
stenantha **new**	WCot
stewartiana	EAJP MRav
subsessilis	CAby CBod CRos ECtt EHyd ELan EMor EPfP GLog GMaP LRHS LSou MBel MCot MRav MSpe NBid NBir NGdn NLar NRHS NSti SPhx SPoG SRms WCAu WCru
- 'Blue Dreams'	CBod EMor GQue GWyn MHol NLar SBut SHar SPhx SRkn WSpi XLum
- 'Candy Cat'	MCot MTis NBre NLar
- 'Cool Cat'	EBee EPfP LSRN NBre
- NIMBUS ('Yanim')	MHol MPnt
- 'Pink Dreams'	CBod EBee EHyd ELan EMor EPfP GWyn LRHS MHer SHar XLum
- pink-flowered	ECha SPhx
- 'Sweet Dreams'	EHyd EMor EPfP EShb LRHS MRav MTis NBPC NLar NRHS XLum
- 'Washfield'	MTis NLar SAko
transcaucasica	SDix
- 'Blue Infinity'	GMaP NGrd WFar
tuberosa	CDor CPla CTsd ECha EMor EPPr XSen
'Veluws Blauwtje'	ECha NLar WSpi
'Veluwse Wakel'	IMou
'Weinheim Big Blue'	MAvo
'Weinheim Summer Blues'	ECha
* ***yunnanensis***	EBee EPPr SPhx WPGP

Nephrolepis (*Lomariopsidaceae*)

cordifolia	CBdn
duffii	EShb
exaltata ♀H1b	LCro LOPS
- 'Bostoniensis'	EShb
- 'Marisa' **new**	EShb
- 'Smithii'	EShb
- 'Verona'	WCot
obliterata 'Emerald Queen' **new**	CBdn

Nerine ✿ (*Amaryllidaceae*)

'Afterglow'	LRHS WCot
'Alexandra'	WCot
alta	see *N. undulata* Alta Group
angustifolia	SPtp WAbe
'Aurora'	WCot
'Baghdad'	SChr WCot
'Belladonna'	CWCL WCot
'Bennett-Poë'	WCot
'Berlioz'	WCot
'Blanchefleur'	WCot

bowdenii ♀H5	Widely available
- 'Alba' misapplied	see *N. bowdenii* 'Pallida'
- 'Alba' ambig.	CPrp EBee ELan EPot ERCP SCoo SMHy
- 'Alba'	CAby CBro CWCL ECha EMor EPri GBin GKev IBal LRHS MNrw NHoy SDeJ SDir WCot WFar
- 'Albivetta'	ELon EPri GKev IBal MNrw NHoy
- 'Blanca Perla'	CAvo ELan EPri EShb GKev MAvo MNrw NHoy WCot
- 'Castlewellan'	IBlr
- 'Codora'	see *N.* 'Codora'
- 'Edelweiss'	CAvo GKev NHoy
- 'Ella K'	EPfP EPot EPri IBal LCro LOPS MNrw NHoy SPer WFar
- 'Eric Smith'	WCot
- 'Gletsjer'	NHoy WCot
- Irish clone	WCot
- 'Isabel'	CAby CAvo CBro CMac CWCL ECha ELan EPot EPri ERCP EShb EWes GKev IBal LSou NHoy NWad SDeJ WBor WCot WHoo
- 'Kathleen Pollock'	WCot
- 'Linda Vista'	WCot
- 'Lipstick'	NHoy
- 'Marjorie'	EHyd EMal LRHS NRHS
- 'Mark Fenwick'	CBro WCot
- 'Marney Rogerson'	CBro SMHy WCot
§ - 'Mollie Cowie' (v)	IBlr WCot WCru
- 'Mount Stewart'	IBlr WCot
- 'Nikita'	EPri ERCP GKev IBal LRHS MNrw NHoy NWad SDeJ WCot
- 'Ostara'	CBod ELan EPot EPri GKev IBal LCro LOPS LRHS MNrw NHoy NWad WCot WFar
§ - 'Pallida'	LRHS
- 'Patricia'	EPot EPri GKev IBal LRHS MNrw NHoy
- 'Pink Frostwork'	EPri
- 'Pink Surprise'	EPri MAvo WCot WMal
- 'Pink Waveline'	SMHy
§ - 'Quinton Wells'	CAby WCot WMal
- 'Quinton Wells' pale yellow-leaved **new**	WCot
- 'Richard Blakeway-Phillips'	WCot WHil
- 'Robert Smith'	WCot
- 'Rowie'	EPri LRHS
- 'Sheila Owen'	WCot WMal
- 'Stam 63'	CWCL EPot ERCP GKev IBal LRHS NWad WCot WHil
- 'Stefanie'	CAby EBee ELan EMor EPri EShb EWTr GKev IBal NHoy SDeJ
- Ted Allen No 2	WCot
- 'Tess Allen' **new**	WCot
- 'Variegata'	see *N. bowdenii* 'Mollie Cowie'
- 'Vesta K'	EPot EPri GKev IBal LRHS NHoy
- 'Wellsii'	see *N. bowdenii* 'Quinton Wells'
bowdenii × ***sarniensis***	WFar
'Canasta'	WCot
'Caryatid'	WCot WFar
'Catkin'	WCot
'Clent Charm'	WCot
§ 'Codora'	CCCN EPfP SPer WCot WFar
'Corlette'	WCot
'Countess of Mulgrave'	WCot
'Cranfield'	WCot
crispa	see *N. undulata* Crispa Group
'Cynthia Chance'	WCot
'Diana Oliver'	WCot
'Doris Vos'	WCot
Elegance Series	GKev LRHS NHoy WCot WHil
- 'Elegance Red'	CBro ELan
'Elspeth'	WCot
'Exbury Red'	WCot
'Falaise'	WCot
filamentosa misapplied	see *N. filifolia* Baker
filamentosa ambig.	CBro
§ ***filifolia*** Baker	CPBP WAbe
'Firelight'	WCot
flexuosa	see *N. undulata* Flexuosa Group
gaberonensis	WAbe
'Giraffe'	WCot
'Glacier'	EBee LRHS MNrw
gracilis	WCot
'Harlequin'	WCot
'Helena'	WCot
'Hera'	CBro ELon
'Hertha Berg'	WCot
* ***hirsuta***	WCot
humilis ♀H2	CBro
- from Bredasdorp, South Africa	WCot
- Breachiae Group	CPBP
'Iman'	WCot
'Isobel'	CSpe LEdu LRHS SDir WFar XEll
'Janet'	WCot
'Jenny Wren'	SChr WCot
'Judith' **new**	SChr
'King Leopold'	WCot WFar
'King of the Belgians'	LRHS
'Kinn McIntosh'	EPri WCot
krigei	WCot XEll
'Kyle'	WCot
'Lady Cynthia Colville'	WCot
'Lady Downe'	WCot
'Lady Eleanor Keane'	WCot
'Lady Havelock-Allen'	WCot
'Lady Llewellyn'	WCot
'Lady St Aldwyn'	WCot
'Lambourne'	WCot
laticoma	WCot
'Lawlord'	WCot
'Leila Hughes'	WCot
'Long Island Beauty'	WCot
'Lucinda'	WCot
'Lyndhurst Salmon'	WCot
'Malvern'	WCot
'Maria'	WCot
masoniorum ♀H2	EPot SGro WAbe
'Meadowbankii'	WCot
'Miss E. Cator'	WCot
'Miss Florence Brown'	WCot
'Miss Frances Clarke'	WCot
'Mr John'	CBro CWCL EBee ELan EPri ERCP EShb GKev LRHS LSou NHoy SDir WCot WHil XEll
'Mrs Cooper'	WCot
'Mrs Dent Brocklehurst'	WCot
'Natasha'	WCot
'Nena'	WCot
'Oberon'	WCot
'Ophelia'	WCot
'Owslebury'	WCot
'Pamela'	LRHS
'Pink Triumph'	CBcs CMac CTsd CWCL EBee EHyd ELan EPot ERCP EShb GKev IBal LRHS NHoy NRHS NWad SDeJ SPer WCot WHoo
'Plymouth'	SChr

	pudica pink-flowered	WCot
	'Quivotina'	WCot
	'Red Pimpernel'	NHoy
	'Red Surprise' **new**	SDir
	'Regina'	WCot
	'Rembrandt'	WCot
	'Rose Princess'	WCot
	'Rushmere Star'	SChr WCot
	'Ruth'	WCot WFar
	sarniensis	CBro CWCL ECha EPot EPri EShb GKev LRHS SDeJ SDir WCot WFar
*	- 'Alba'	NHoy
*	- 'Borde Hill White'	WCot
	- var. ***corusca*** 'Major'	SChr WCot
	- var. ***curvifolia***	CBro
	- - f. ***fothergillii***	WCot
	- 'Hanley Castle'	WCot
	- 'Lydia'	NHoy
	- 'Mother of Pearl'	WCot
	- 'Mottistone'	WCot
	- red-flowered	NHoy
	- rose-pink-flowered	NHoy
	- 'Salmon Star'	LRHS
	- var. ***sarniensis***	CBor
	'Snowflake'	WCot
	'Stephanie'	CCCN ELon EShb LEdu LRHS MAvo MNrw WCot WHoo
	'Susan Norris'	WCot
	'Tweedledee'	WCot
	undulata	CAby CCCN CWCL ECha EPri GKev IBal MPie NHoy SDeJ SDir SPer WMal
§	- Alta Group	WCot
§	- Crispa Group	CBod EPfP WFar
§	- Flexuosa Group	MRav
	- - 'Alba' ♀H3	CAby CAvo CBro ECha EPri GKev MRav WCot WMal
	× ***versicolor*** 'Mansellii'	CBro
	'Vestal'	SDir
	'Vicky'	WCot
	'Winter Sun'	LRHS SRms
	'Zeal Giant' ♀H3	CAvo CBro EPri WCot WFar
	'Zeal Grilse'	WCot
	'Zeal Purple Stripe'	WCot
	'Zennor'	WCot

Nerium (*Apocynaceae*)

§	***odoratum*** 'Miss Agnes Campbell'	SEND
	oleander misapplied	see *N. oleander* 'Soeur Agnès'
	oleander L.	CAbb CDoC CTri EBak ELan EShb SEND SPer SPlb SPoG
	- from Morocco	WPGP
	- 'Agnes Campbell'	see *N. odoratum* 'Miss Agnes Campbell'
	- 'Album'	CTri EShb LRHS SEND
	- 'Album Plenum' (d)	XSen
	- 'Alsace'	SEND
*	- 'Atlas'	XSen
*	- 'Barcelona'	SEND
	- 'Cavalaire' (d)	XSen
*	- 'Claudia'	SEND
	- 'Commandant Barthélemy' (d)	XSen
	- double apricot (d)	SEND
	- 'Flavescens Plenum' (d)	EShb XSen
	- 'Hardy Red'	XSen
*	- 'Harriet Newding'	XSen
	- 'Italia'	XSen
	- 'Madame Allen' (d)	EShb
	- 'Magaly'	SEND
	- 'Margaritha'	SEND XSen
	- 'Minouche'	SEND
	- subsp. ***oleander***	SEdd
	- 'Petite Red'	XSen
	- 'Professeur Granel' (d)	EShb
	- 'Provence' (d)	XSen
	- 'Red Beauty'	XSen
	- red-flowered	SPad
	- 'Roseum Plenum' (d)	CRHN SEND
§	- 'Soeur Agnès'	XSen
	- 'Soleil Levant'	ELan XSen
	- 'Splendens Giganteum' (d)	EShb
	- 'Tito Poggi'	XSen
	- 'Variegatum' (v) ♀H2	ELan EShb
	- 'Villa Romaine'	XSen
	- white-flowered	ELan

Neviusia (*Rosaceae*)

	alabamensis	NLar

Nicandra (*Solanaceae*)

	physalodes	CHby ELan ENfk NBir SEle WSFF XAbr
	- ***alba***	CSpe
	- 'Splash of Cream' (v)	CCCN MNHC
	- 'Violacea'	CSpe GLog SRms SWvt

Nicotiana ✿ (*Solanaceae*)

	alata	CSpe LCro LOPS WSFF
	- 'Grandiflora'	CBre LCro LOPS
	glauca	CCCN CDTJ EWld NGKo SPlb
	knightiana	CDTJ CSpe
	langsdorffii ♀H2	CSpe LCro LOPS SPhx
	- 'Hot Chocolate'	CSpe
	'Lime Green' ♀H2	CSpe LCro LOPS
	mutabilis	CBre CCBP CSpe LCro LOPS SDys SGro SPhx
	- 'Marshmallow'	CBod
	rustica	CSpe SPhx
	× ***sanderae***	GJos
	- Avalon Series **new**	MBros
	- Cuba Series	MPri
	- 'Perfume Deep Purple' (Perfume Series)	CSpe SPhx
	solanifolia	SPlb
	suaveolens	SPhx
	sylvestris ♀H2	CBod CDTJ CSpe ELan GJos LCro LOPS MMuc MPri SEND SPhx SPoG SWvt WHil
	tabacum	XAbr
	'Tinkerbell'	CSpe

Nidularium (*Bromeliaceae*)

	billbergioides	NCft
	innocentii	XBlo

Nierembergia (*Solanaceae*)

§	***repens***	NLar WCot XLum
	rivularis	see *N. repens*

Nigella (*Ranunculaceae*)

	damascena 'Albion Green Pod'	LCro
	- 'Miss Jekyll' ♀H3	LCro LOPS LRHS MNHC SPhx
	- 'Miss Jekyll Alba' ♀H3	CSpe LCro LOPS
	- 'Oxford Blue'	LCro LOPS
	- Persian Jewels Group	SVic
	hispanica L.	SPhx

papillosa 'African Bride'	CSpe MNHC SPhx
- 'Delft Blue'	LCro SPhx
- 'Midnight'	CSpe SPhx
sativa	XAbr

Niphidium (*Polypodiaceae*)

crassifolium	EShb WCot

Nipponanthemum (*Asteraceae*)

§ ***nipponicum***	CBod EBee ELon GBin GWyn IMou LRHS MMuc NLar NSti SAko SPoG SRms XLum
- 'Hama-giku'	NWad

Noccaea see *Thlaspi*

Nolina (*Asparagaceae*)

lindheimeriana	WCot
microcarpa	XSen
nelsonii	CCht CDoC SArc SPlb XSen
parviflora	XSen
texana	WCot

Nomocharis (*Liliaceae*)

aperta	CExl CWCL EPot GGGa GKev NHpl WCru
mairei	see *N. pardanthina*
meleagrina	GEdr NHpl
§ ***pardanthina***	EBee NHpl
- f. ***punctulata***	GGGa
saluenensis	GGGa

Nonea (*Boraginaceae*)

lutea	EPPr MMrt NSti WHal

Nothochelone see *Penstemon*

Nothofagus ✿ (*Nothofagaceae*)

§ ***alpina***	SCob WPav
antarctica	CBcs CMCN CTho EBee ELan EPfP EWTr GKin LMaj MBlu MGos MMuc NOra NOrn SAko SReu WMat
betuloides	GBin IArd SAko SPlb SReu WPGP
cunninghamii	CBcs CBrP IArd IDee SAko SPlb SReu
dombeyi ♀H5	CBcs EPfP IArd IDee MBlu SArc SReu WPGP WSpi
fusca	SAko WPGP
menziesii	SReu WPGP
moorei	WPGP
nervosa	see *N. alpina*
nitida	CBcs
obliqua	GAbr WMou WPav
procera Oerst.	see *N. alpina*

Notholaena see *Cheilanthes*

Notholirion (*Liliaceae*)

bulbuliferum	EBee GBin
campanulatum	EBee GKev
macrophyllum	EBee GBin
thomsonianum	CBor GKev

Nothoscordum (*Alliaceae*)

bivalve	IMou
dialystemon	EPot NHpl WAbe
montevidense	WCot
neriniflorum	see *Allium neriniflorum*
ostenii	WCot

Nothotsuga (*Pinaceae*)

longibracteata	SPtp

Nuphar (*Nymphaeaceae*)

japonica	LLWG
lutea	CBen CHab LCro LLWG LOPS
- subsp. ***advena***	LLWG
pumila	LLWG

Nuytsia (*Loranthaceae*)

floribunda	SPlb

Nylandtia (*Polygalaceae*)

spinosa	SPlb

Nymphaea ✿ (*Nymphaeaceae*)

alba (H)	CBen CHab CWat LCro LOPS MWts NBir SVic WCAu WMAq
'Alba Plenissima' (H)	EWat
'Albatros' misapplied	see *N.* 'Hermine'
§ 'Albatros' Latour-Marliac (H)	CWat LLWG NPer WMAq XBlo
'Albatross'	see *N.* 'Albatros' Latour-Marliac, *N.* 'Hermine'
* 'Albida'	LLWG WMAq XBlo
'Almost Black' (H)	CBen EWat LCro LLWG LOPS
'Amabilis' (H)	CBen EWat WMAq
'Andreaa Berthold' (H) new	LLWG
'Andreana' (H)	EWat LLWG
'Angelique' (H)	LLWG
'Anna Epple' (H)	LLWG
'Arc-en-ciel' (H)	EWat LLWG WMAq
'Atropurpurea' (H)	CBen EWat LLWG NPer WMAq
'Attorney Elrod' (H)	LLWG
'Attraction' (H)	CBen EWat LLWG MWts NPer SVic WMAq XBlo XLum
'Aurora' (H)	CBen LCro LLWG LOPS MWts SVic WMAq
'Barbara Davies' (H)	EWat LLWG
'Barbara Dobbins' (H)	CBen EWat LCro LLWG LOPS
'Bateau' (H)	LLWG
'Bernice Ikins' (H)	LLWG
'Betsy Sakata' (H)	EWat LLWG
'Black Cherry' (H)	LLWG
'Black Princess' (H)	CBen EWat LLWG
'Blushing Bride' (H) new	LLWG
'Bua Rapee' (H)	LLWG
'Burgundy Princess' (H)	CWat EWat LLWG NPer
candida (H)	CBen MWts NPer WMAq
'Candidissima' (H)	CBen
§ ***capensis*** (T/D)	XBlo
'Carolina Sunset' (H)	EWat LLWG
'Caroliniana Nivea' (H)	CBen
'Caroliniana Perfecta' (H)	CBen
'Celebration' (H)	EWat LLWG
'Charlene Strawn' (H)	CWat EWat LLWG WMAq
'Charles de Meurville' (H)	CBen LCro LLWG LOPS NPer SVic WMAq
'Chompoo Pairat' (H)	LLWG
'Chrysantha' (H)	LLWG
'Château le Rouge' (H)	CBen LLWG
'Chubby' (H)	LLWG
'Citrus Twist' (H)	LLWG
'Cliff Tiffany' (H)	CBen LLWG
'Clyde Ikins' (H)	EWat LLWG XBlo
'Colonel A.J. Welch' (H)	CBen NPer WMAq
'Colorado' (H)	CBen EWat LLWG NPer
colorata	see *N. capensis*
'Colossea' (H)	CBen CWat NPer
'Comanche' (H)	CBen EWat LLWG NPer WMAq

	'Concordia' (H) **new**	LLWG
	'Conqueror' (H)	CBen CWat LLWG NPer SVic
	'Cranberry Cup' **new**	LLWG
	'Crazy Pom Pom' (H)	LLWG
	'Curly Purple' (H) **new**	LLWG
	'Cynthia Ann' (H)	LLWG
§	'Darwin' (H)	CBen CWat LLWG MWts NPer SLon WMAq
	'David' (H)	CBen EWat LLWG
	'Debbie June' (H)	LLWG
	'Denver' (H)	EWat LLWG
	'Dwarf Beauty' (H) **new**	LLWG
	'Ellisiana' (H)	LLWG NPer
	'Erhard Van Oldehoff' (H) **new**	LLWG
	'Escarboucle' (H) ♀H5	CBen CWat EWat LLWG NPer SVic WMAq XBlo
§	'Fabiola' (H)	NPer WMAq
	'Fiesta' (H)	CBen
	'Fire Cracker' (H)	LLWG
	'Fire Crest' (H)	CBen LLWG NPer SVic WMAq
	'Flore de Cologne' (H) **new**	LLWG
	'Florida Sunset' (H)	EWat
	'Frezzby' (H) **new**	LLWG
	'Fritz Junge' (H)	CBen
	'Froebelii' (H)	CBen CWat EWat LLWG NPer WMAq
	'Fuchsia Pom-pom' (H)	LLWG
	'Galatée' (H)	CBen
	'Georgia Peach' (H)	LLWG
	'Gladstoniana' (H) ♀H5	CBen MWts NPer WMAq
	'Gloire du Temple-sur-Lot' (H)	CBen EWat LLWG NPer WMAq
	'Gloriosa' (H)	CBen LLWG NPer
	'Gold Medal' (H)	CBen EWat LLWG
	'Golden Goblet' (H) **new**	LLWG
	'Golden Star' (H) **new**	LLWG
	'Gonnère' (H) ♀H5	CBen CWat EWat LLWG MWts NPer SLon WMAq
	'Graziella' (H)	WMAq
	'Guava Chiffron' (H) **new**	LLWG
	'Gypsy' (H)	EWat LLWG
	'Hal Miller' (H)	LLWG
	'Hassell' (H)	LLWG
	'Hawaiian Gold' **new**	LLWG
	'Hazorea Dagan White' (H)	EWat LLWG
	'Heart Beat' (H) **new**	LLWG
	'Helen Fowler' (H)	WMAq
	'Helen Hariot' (H)	LLWG
	× ***helvola***	see *N.* 'Pygmaea Helvola'
§	'Hermine' (H)	CBen NPer WMAq
	'Hidden Violet' (H)	LLWG
§	'Highlight' (H)	EWat LLWG
	'Hilite'	see *N.* 'Highlight'
	'Hollandia' misapplied	see *N.* 'Darwin'
	'Indiana' (H)	CBen LLWG NPer WMAq
	'Inner Light' (H)	EWat LLWG
	'Irene Heritage' (H)	CBen
	'J.C.N. Forestier' (H)	CBen
	'James Brydon' (H) ♀H5	CBen CWat EWat LLWG MWts NPer SLon SVic WMAq
	'Jean de Lamarsalle' (H)	LLWG
§	'Joanne Pring' (H)	CBen
	'Joey Tomocik' (H)	CBen CWat EWat LLWG WMAq
	'Kiss the Sky' (H) **new**	LLWG
	'Lactea' (H)	CBen LLWG
	'Laura Strawn' (H)	EWat
	'Laydekeri Fulgens' (H)	CBen EWat LLWG MWts WMAq
	'Laydekeri Lilacea' (H)	CBen LLWG WMAq
	'Laydekeri Rosea' misapplied	see *N.* 'Laydekeri Rosea Prolifera'
§	'Laydekeri Rosea Prolifera' (H)	CBen EWat
	'Lemon Cup' (H) **new**	LLWG
	'Lemon Meringue' (H)	LLWG
	'Lemon Mist' (H)	LLWG
	'Lily Pons' (H)	CBen EWat LLWG
	'Liou' (H)	CBen LLWG
	'Little Champion' (H)	LLWG
	'Little Sue' (H)	EWat LLWG
	'Lucida' (H)	LLWG WMAq
	'Lucky Red' (H)	LLWG
	'Madame Bory Latour-Marliac' (H)	CBen
	'Madame Wilfon Gonnère' (H)	CBen CWat EWat LLWG MWts NPer SVic WMAq
	'Manee Red' (H) **new**	LLWG
	'Manee Siam' (H)	LLWG
	'Mangkala Ubol' (H)	CBen
	'Marliacea Albida' (H)	CBen CWat EWat LCro LLWG LOPS MWts NPer WMAq XBlo XLum
	'Marliacea Carnea' (H)	CBen LCro LOPS MWts NPer WMAq
§	'Marliacea Chromatella' (H) ♀H5	CBen CWat EWat MWts SVic WMAq XBlo XLum
	'Marliacea Rosea' (H)	CBen WMAq XBlo XLum
	'Martha' (H)	EWat
	'Mary' (H)	EWat LLWG
	'Masaniello' (H)	CBen WMAq
	'Maurice Laydeker' (H)	LLWG
	'Maxima'	see *N.* 'Odorata Maxima'
	'Mayla' (H)	CBen EWat LLWG NPer
§	'Météor' (H)	CBen EWat WMAq
	mexicana (H)	LLWG
	'Miss Siam' (H)	LLWG
	'Moon Dance' (H)	LLWG
	'Moorei' (H)	CBen MWts WMAq
	'Mrs Richmond' misapplied	see *N.* 'Fabiola'
	'Mrs Richmond' Latour-Marliac (H)	CBen XBlo
	'Munkala Ubon' (H)	LLWG
	'Murillo' (H)	EWat
	'Myra' (H) **new**	LLWG
	'Neptune' (H)	LLWG
	'Newchapel Beauty'	WMAq
	'Newton' (H)	CWat LLWG WMAq
	'Nigel' (H)	EWat LLWG
	'Norma Gedye' (H)	CBen CWat WMAq
§	***odorata*** (H)	CBen LLWG WMAq
§	- var. ***minor*** (H)	CBen EWat WMAq
	- 'Pumila'	see *N. odorata* var. *minor*
	- subsp. ***tuberosa*** (H)	CBen
	'Odorata Alba'	see *N. odorata*
	'Odorata Juliana' (H)	CBen
§	'Odorata Maxima' (H)	WMAq
	'Odorata Sulphurea' (H)	LLWG
	'Odorata Sulphurea Grandiflora' (H)	LLWG XBlo
	'Odorata William B. Shaw'	see *N.* 'W.B. Shaw'
	'Ori Flame' (H) **new**	LLWG
	'Ori Oruba' (H) **new**	LLWG
	'Pam Bennett' (H)	CBen
	'Panama Pacific' (T/D)	XBlo
	'Patio Joe' (H)	EWat LLWG
	'Paul Hariot' (H)	EWat LLWG NPer WMAq
	'Peace Lily' (H)	EWat LLWG
	'Peach Glow' (H)	EWat LLWG
	'Peach Sunrise' (H) **new**	LLWG
	'Peaches and Cream' (H)	EWat LLWG
	'Perry's Baby Red' (H)	CBen CWat EWat LLWG MWts NPer WMAq

'Perry's Deepest Red' (H)	LLWG
'Perry's Double White' (H)	EWat LLWG NPer
'Perry's Double Yellow' (H)	LLWG
'Perry's Dwarf Red' (H)	LLWG
'Perry's Fire Opal' (H)	EWat LLWG NPer
'Perry's Orange Sunset' (H)	LLWG
'Perry's Pink' (H)	WMAq
'Perry's Red Glow' (H)	LLWG
'Perry's Red Star' (H)	EWat
'Perry's White Star' (H)	LLWG
'Perry's Yellow Sensation'	see *N.* 'Yellow Sensation'
'Peter Slocum' (H)	CBen
'Phoebus' (H)	CBen
'Pia Stella Berthold' (H) **new**	LLWG
'Picciola' (H)	LLWG
'Pink Beauty' (H)	LLWG
'Pink Dawn' (H) **new**	LLWG
'Pink Grapefruit' (H)	LLWG XBlo
'Pink Lemonade' (H)	LLWG
'Pink Opal' (H)	EWat LLWG
'Pink Peony' (H)	EWat
'Pink Pom-pom' (H)	LLWG
'Pink Pumpkin' (H)	EWat LLWG
'Pink Ribbon' (H)	LLWG
'Pink Sensation' (H)	CBen EWat LLWG NPer SLon WMAq
'Pink Sparkle' (H)	EWat LLWG
'Pink Starlet' (H)	EWat
'Pink Sunrise' (H)	EWat LLWG
'Pink Tulip' (H)	LLWG
'Pinwaree' (H)	LLWG
'Pöstlingberg' (H)	LLWG
'Prakeisap' (H)	LLWG
'Princess Elizabeth' (H)	LLWG
'Purple Fantasy' (H)	LLWG
'Pygmaea Alba'	see *N. tetragona*
§ 'Pygmaea Helvola' (H) ♀H5	CBen CWat EWat LCro LLWG LOPS MWts NPer SLon SVic WMAq
'Pygmaea Rubis' (H)	WMAq
'Pygmaea Rubra' (H)	CBen CWat EWat LCro LLWG LOPS MWts NPer SVic WMAq
'Queen of the Whites' (H)	LLWG
'Radiant Red' (H)	LLWG
'Rattana Ubol' (H) **new**	LLWG
'Ray Davies' (H)	CBen LLWG
'Razzberry' (H)	LLWG
'Red Paradise' (H)	LLWG
'Red Queen' (H)	LLWG
'Red Spider' (H)	CWat EWat LLWG NPer SVic
'Reflected Flame' (H)	EWat LLWG
'Rembrandt' misapplied	see *N.* 'Météor'
'René Gérard' (H)	CBen LLWG MWts NPer WMAq
'Rosanna Supreme' (H)	LLWG
'Rose Arey' (H)	CBen EWat LCro LOPS NPer SVic WMAq
'Rose Magnolia' (H)	CWat
'Rosennymphe' (H)	CBen NPer WMAq
'Rosy Morn' (H)	CBen LLWG
'Ruby Star' (H) **new**	LLWG
'Savanlamp' (H)	LLWG
'Seignoureti' (H)	LLWG
'Shady Lady' (H)	LLWG
'Siam Angel' (H)	LLWG
'Siam Beauty' (H) **new**	LLWG
'Siam Jasmine' (H)	LLWG
'Siam Purple 1' (H)	LLWG
'Siam Purple 2' (H)	LLWG
'Siam Sunset' (H)	LLWG
'Sioux' (H)	CBen LLWG NPer SVic WMAq XBlo
'Sirius' (H)	CBen LLWG
'Snow Princess' (H)	EWat
'Snowflake' (H)	LLWG
'Solfatare' (H)	EWat LLWG
'Splendida' (H)	WMAq
'Starbright' (H)	EWat LLWG
'Steven Strawn' (H)	LLWG
'Strawberry Milkshake' (H) **new**	LLWG
'Sunfire' (H) **new**	LLWG
'Sunny Pink' (H)	CBen EWat LLWG
'Sunrise' (H) **new**	LCro LOPS
'Superba' (H)	CBen
'Sweet Pea' (H)	LLWG
'Tangerine Pink' (H) **new**	LLWG
'Tan-khwan' (H)	LLWG
§ ***tetragona*** (H)	CWat EWat LCro LLWG LOPS NPer WMAq
- 'Alba'	see *N. tetragona*
- 'Johann Pring'	see *N.* 'Joanne Pring'
'Texas Dawn' (H)	CBen CWat LLWG SLon WMAq XBlo
'Thomas O'Brian' (H)	LLWG
'Thongsup' (H)	LLWG
'Tony's Starlike' **new**	LLWG
'Tuberosa Flavescens'	see *N.* 'Marliacea Chromatella'
'Tuberosa Richardsonii' (H)	CBen NPer
'Turtle Island Tropic Star' (H × T) **new**	LLWG
'Turtle Island Violicious' (H × T) **new**	LLWG
'Venusta' (H)	EWat
'Vésuve' (H)	LLWG
'Virginalis' (H)	CBen LLWG NPer WMAq
'Virginia' (H)	LLWG
§ 'W.B. Shaw' (H)	CBen NPer WMAq
'Walter Pagels' (H)	EWat LLWG MWts WMAq
'Wanvisa' (H)	CBen LCro LLWG LOPS
'Weymouth Red' (H)	CBen
'White Star' (H)	LLWG
'White Sultan' (H)	CWat LCro LLWG LOPS
'William Falconer' (H)	CBen LLWG NPer
'Wow' (H)	LLWG
'Yellow Princess' (H)	EWat
'Yellow Queen' (H)	LLWG
§ 'Yellow Sensation' (H)	CBen
'Yellow Watermelon' (H)	LLWG
'Yul Ling' (H)	EWat LLWG
'Ziyu' (H)	EWat

Nymphoides (*Menyanthaceae*)

indica	XBlo
peltata	CBen CBod CHab CWat EWat LCro LLWG LOPS NPer SVic WMAq WPnP XLum

Nyssa ✿ (*Nyssaceae*)

aquatica	CBcs IDee MBlu SMad SSta
leptophylla	EBee NLar WPGP
shweliensis FMWJ 13122	WCru
sinensis	CBcs CLnd CMCN CRos EHyd ELan EPfP IDee LRHS MAsh MBlu MPkF NLar SPer WFar
- 'Inferno'	CRos CTho NLar SPoG WMat
- 'Jim Russell' ♀H5	EBee LRHS WPGP
- 'Volcano' **new**	CRos
sylvatica	CBcs CCVT CLnd CMCN CMac CTho EBee ECrN ELan ELon EPfP GQue IArd IDee LMaj MAsh MBlu MGos NLar NOrn SCob SEWo

	SGol SPer SSta SWvt WFar WHwl WMat WTSh
- 'Autumn Cascades'	CJun CRos EHyd EPfP LRHS MAsh MBlu SSta
- var. ***biflora***	CMCN SSta
- Bulk's form	SSta
- 'Haymen's Red'	see *N. sylvatica* RED RAGE
- 'Isabel Grace'	CRos EHyd EPfP LRHS MAsh
- 'Jermyns Flame'	CRos EHyd EPfP LRHS MAsh NLar
- JOLLY ('Yiping') (v)	MPkF
- 'Lakeside Weeper'	CRos ELan LRHS
- 'Miss Scarlet' (f)	NLar SSta WPGP
§ - RED RAGE ('Haymanred')	ELan EPfP LRHS MAsh MPkF
- 'Sheffield Park'	MAsh SLim
- 'Wildfire'	LRHS NLar SGol
- 'Windsor'	CRos EHyd EPfP LRHS MAsh NLar
- 'Wisley Bonfire' (m) ♀H6	CBcs CJun CRos EBee EHyd ELan EPfP LMil LRHS MAsh NLar NRHS SPoG SSta WMat WPGP

O

Oakesiella see *Uvularia*

Ochagavia (*Bromeliaceae*)

carnea	NCft
elegans	WCot
§ ***litoralis***	SArc SMad
* ***rosea***	SPlb

Ochna (*Ochnaceae*)

serrulata	CCCN

Ocimum (*Lamiaceae*)

'African Blue'	CBod CSpe ENfk EWhm GPoy LCro LOPS MHer MHol SPoG SRms
§ × ***africanum***	ENfk MNHC
- 'Lesbos' **new**	MHer
- 'Lime'	ENfk MNHC
§ - 'Perpetuo'PBR (v)	ENfk
- PESTO PERPETUO	see *O. × africanum* 'Perpetuo'
- 'Siam Queen'	MHer SRms
basilicum	EWhm GPoy LCro LOPS MPri SRms
- 'Anise'	see *O. basilicum* 'Horapha'
- 'Ararat'	SRms
- 'Aristotle'	SRms
- 'Aroma 2' ♀H1c **new**	LCro LOPS
- 'Blue Spice' **new**	SEdi
I - 'British Basil'	MBros SRms
- ***camphorata***	see *O. kilimandscharicum*
- 'Christmas'	SEdi SRms
- 'Cinnamon'	ENfk MNHC SEdi SRms WJek
- 'Crimson King'PBR	SRms
- 'Dark Opal'	ENfk SEdi SRms
- 'Genovese'	CLau MHer MNHC SEdi
- 'Glycyrrhiza'	see *O. basilicum* 'Horapha'
- 'Green Globe'	SRms
- 'Green Ruffles'	SRms
- 'Holy'	see *O. tenuiflorum*
- 'Holy Tulsi'	see *O. tenuiflorum*
§ - 'Horapha'	CLau ENfk LCro LOPS MNHC SEdi WJek XAbr
* - 'Horapha Nanum'	ENfk SRms
- large-leaved **new**	XAbr
- 'Lemonade' ♀H1c	SRms
- lettuce leaf **new**	SEdi
- 'Magic Mountain'	SPoG
- 'Magic White'	SPoG
- 'Medinette'	CLau
- 'Mrs Burns' Lemon' ♀H1c	EKin MCtn SRms WJek
- 'Napoletano'	ENfk LCro LOPS SRms
- 'Pluto' ♀H1c	LCro LOPS
- 'Puck'	SRms
- var. ***purpurascens*** 'Purple Ruffles'	EHyd ENfk LCro LOPS LRHS SRms
- - 'Red Rubin'	LRHS MHer NRHS SRms WJek
- var. ***purpurascens*** × ***kilimandscharicum***	CSpe GPoy WJek
- 'Sweet Genovese'	SVic
- 'Thai'	see *O. basilicum* 'Horapha'
× ***citriodorum***	see *O. × africanum*
gratissimum	SEdi
§ ***kilimandscharicum***	CLau GPoy
minimum	ENfk LCro LOPS MHer MNHC SRms
sanctum	see *O. tenuiflorum*
'Spice'	ENfk
§ ***tenuiflorum***	GPoy MNHC SPre SVic WJek XAbr

Odontonema (*Acanthaceae*)

schomburgkianum	CCCN
tubaeforme	CCCN

Oemleria (*Rosaceae*)

cerasiformis	CBcs CJun CTri ELan ELon EPfP EWes LEdu LRHS MGil MMuc WCot WGwG WSHC

Oenanthe (*Apiaceae*)

fistulosa	LLWG
javanica	LEdu
- 'Flamingo' (v)	CBod CWat ELan EWat LEdu LLWG MWts SRms WMAq XLum
pimpinelloides	CHab SPhx

Oenothera ✿ (*Onagraceae*)

§ ***acaulis***	CSpe EBee GKev MNrw WCot
§ - 'Aurea'	XLum
- 'Lutea'	see *O. acaulis* 'Aurea'
'Apricot Delight'	SGbt
§ ***biennis***	CFis EBou ELan ENfk GAbr GJos GPoy LCro LOPS MBow MHer MNHC NBro SPhx SRms WBrk WHer WSFF
'Blood Orange'	CPla GEdr
childsii	see *O. speciosa*
cinaeus	see *O. fruticosa* subsp. *glauca*
'Crown Imperial'	CChe CMac MArl NHol SHar SLon
§ ***elata*** subsp. ***hookeri***	EWes NBre
erythrosepala	see *O. glazioviana*
'Finlay's Fancy'	WCru
§ ***fruticosa***	NLar SPlb
- 'African Sun'	ECtt MMrt
- 'Camel' (v)	XLum
- FIREWORKS	see *O. fruticosa* 'Fyrverkeri'
§ - 'Fyrverkeri'	CBcs CMea CRos ECtt EHyd GMaP GWyn ILea LEdu LRHS MRav NBPC NRHS SCob SMad SPer SWvt WCAu XLum
§ - subsp. ***glauca***	CElw CFis ILea MHer SRms
- - 'Erica Robin' (v)	CChe CDor ECtt EHyd GBin LPla LRHS MNrw MRav NGdn SCob SMad SWvt WCav WCot WHoo
- - 'Longest Day'	MBrN
- - SOLSTICE	see *O. fruticosa* subsp. *glauca* 'Sonnenwende'

§ - - 'Sonnenwende'	CBre CElw EHyd ILea IMou LRHS MMrt NEoE NLar XLum
- HIGHLIGHT	see *O. fruticosa* 'Hoheslicht'
§ - 'Hoheslicht'	EBee NLar
- 'Lady Brookeborough'	MRav
- 'Michelle Ploeger'	NBre
- 'Yellow River'	CElw EBee
- 'Youngii'	MMuc SEND
'Give-me-Sunshine'	SLon
glabra Miller	see *O. biennis*
§ ***glazioviana***	NBir
hookeri	see *O. elata* subsp. *hookeri*
kunthiana	EBou ECha
- 'Glowing Magenta'	SPoG
lamarckiana	see *O. glazioviana*
'Lemon Sunset'	EAJP EWTr
linearis	see *O. fruticosa*
§ ***macrocarpa*** 🏆^{H5}	CBod CHab CSBt EBee EBou ECha EHyd ELan EPfP EShb LRHS MBel MHer MMuc SEND SPer SPhx SPlb SPoG SRms SVic SWvt WCAu WMal XLum XSen
- subsp. ***fremontii*** 'Silver Wings'	ELan SPhx
- subsp. ***incana***	CSpe SPhx WHoo
missouriensis	see *O. macrocarpa*
oakesiana	SPhx
odorata misapplied	see *O. stricta*
odorata Hook. & Arn.	see *O. biennis*
odorata Jacquin	XLum
- cream-flowered	CSpe
organensis	EBee MNrw
pallida	CFis
- 'Innocence'	LCro
§ ***perennis***	MPie SRms WThu XLum
pilosella	IMou
- 'Yella Fella'	ELan NWad
pumila	see *O. perennis*
rosea	XLum
§ ***speciosa***	MMuc SEND SRms XLum
* - 'Alba'	EBee SCob
- var. ***childsii***	see *O. speciosa*
- 'Pink Petticoats'	ECha LSun NPer SBut
- 'Rosea'	SPlb
- 'Siskiyou'	CAby CBcs CBod CFis CMea ECtt EHyd ELan EPfP ILea LEdu LRHS MAvo MHol MNrw NRHS SCob SCoo SMad SPer SPoG SSut WGwG WMal XLum
- TWILIGHT ('Turner01'^{PBR}) (v)	CAbb EBee ECtt EHyd ELan EPfP ILea LRHS LSou NEoE NHol NLar WNPC
§ ***stricta***	CMea MNrw
- 'Sulphurea'	CDor CMea EAJP EHyd ELan EPfP LCro LRHS NPer SPhx WMal
'Summer Sun'	CBod EHyd LRHS NRHS SGbt SPer WCAu
'Sunny Delight'	ECtt MHol
taraxacifolia	see *O. acaulis*
tetragona	see *O. fruticosa* subsp. *glauca*
- var. ***fraseri***	see *O. fruticosa* subsp. *glauca*
versicolor 'Sunset Boulevard'	CSpe EHyd LRHS SPer XLum

Olea (Oleaceae)

europaea (F)	Widely available
- 'El Greco' (F)	CBcs
- 'Fastigiata'	LRHS MPri
- 'Leccino' (F)	LMaj SWeb

Olearia ✿ (Asteraceae)

algida	GBin
arborescens 'Moondance' (v)	CBcs CBod CSBt EBee LRHS
argophylla	CExl
avicenniifolia	CMac CTrC
§ ***cheesemanii***	CExl CTrC NLar SPer SVen
- compact	LRHS
erubescens	CTrC LRHS
erubescens × ***ilicifolia***	SVen
fragrantissima	GBin
gunniana	see *O. phlogopappa*
× ***haastii***	CBar CBcs CBod CBrac CCCN CDoC CMCN CMac CRos CSBt CSde CTrC CTri EBee ELan EPfP GKin LCro LOPS LRHS MGos MRav MSwo NLar SCob SGol SPer SRms SWvt WFar
- FAIRLIE FRAGRANT ('Hutfair') **new**	GBin
- 'McKenzie'	ELon
§ 'Henry Travers'	CCCN CExl SVen
ilicifolia	EPfP LRHS WPGP
insignis	see *Pachystegia insignis*
lacunosa	IDee WPGP
macrodonta 🏆^{H4}	Widely available
- 'Major'	CCCN CTrC EBee SCob
- 'Minor'	CCCN CDoC CMac CTrC EBee ELan ELon EPfP SPlb SRms WPGP WSpi
§ × ***matthewsii***	CCoa SPer
× ***mollis*** misapplied	see *O.* × *matthewsii*
× ***mollis*** (Kirk) Cockayne	CMac CSde EHyd LRHS WKif
- 'Zennorensis' 🏆^{H4}	CBcs CCCN CTsd EBee ELan SDix WKif
myrsinoides	CSde
nummularifolia	CBcs CCCN CDoC CTrC CTri ELan EPfP GBin LRHS NLar SPer SVen SWvt WKif
× ***oleifolia*** 'Waikariensis'	CCCN CExl CRos EHyd LRHS SEND SLon WCFE
paniculata	CBod CCCN CCoa CDoC CRos CSde CTri EHyd EPfP LRHS MMuc SEND SRms SVen
§ ***phlogopappa***	CTri SVen
- 'Comber's Blue'	CBcs CCCN CRos EHyd ELan EPfP LRHS MMuc MNHC SAko SNig SPer WLov
§ - 'Comber's Pink'	CBcs CCCN CExl CRos ELan EPfP LRHS MAsh MMuc NPer SAko SEle SPer SPoG
- 'Rosea'	see *O. phlogopappa* 'Comber's Pink'
I - var. ***subrepanda*** (DC.) J.H.Willis	CTrC GBin
ramulosa	CCCN CExl CSde
- 'Blue Stars'	CMac LRHS SRms
rani misapplied	see *O. cheesemanii*
× ***scilloniensis*** misapplied	see *O. stellulata* DC.
× ***scilloniensis*** ambig.	CBcs CBod CCoa CDoC CRos CTrC EWld LRHS MAsh SPoG WKif
× ***scilloniensis*** Dorrien-Smith 🏆^{H4}	CCCN MMuc
- 'Master Michael' 🏆^{H4}	CCCN CCht CRos CTri EHyd ELon EPfP EWld LRHS NLar SEdd SNig SPer SPoG
semidentata misapplied	see *O.* 'Henry Travers'
solandri	CBod CCCN CCoa CMac CSde CTrC EPPr LRHS NLar SDix SEND

	- 'Aurea'	CBcs
	'Stardust'	LRHS SPlb SVen
	stellulata misapplied	see *O. phlogopappa*
§	***stellulata*** DC.	CExl CMac CSBt EPfP MAsh
	- 'Michael's Pride'	CExl
	traversii	CBcs CBod CCCN CCht CCoa CDoC CRos CSBt CSde CTrC CTsd EHyd EPfP LRHS SArc SEND SRms WHer
	- 'Compacta'	CCCN CTrC
	- dwarf	CBod EBee
	- 'Tweedledee' (v)	SEND
	- 'Tweedledum' (v)	CBod CCCN CCoa CSde WRHF
	virgata	CCCN IDee NLar
	- var. ***laxiflora***	WHer
	- var. ***lineata***	CCht CCoa CSde MMuc NLar SEND WHer
	- - 'Dartonii'	CBcs CBod CRos GBin LRHS NLar SPlb SSta SVen

Oligoneuron see *Solidago*

Oligostachyum (*Poaceae*)

	lubricum	see *Semiarundinaria lubrica*
§	***oedogonatum***	MWht

olive see *Olea europaea*

Olsynium (*Iridaceae*)

	biflorum	GEdr
§	***douglasii*** ♀H5	CBor CBro CMea EBee ELon EPot GAbr GEdr ITim NHar NHpl NRya NSla
	- 'Album'	CBor EBee ELon EPot EWes MNrw NHar NRya NSla WFar
	- var. ***inflatum***	EWes
§	***junceum***	CBor CSpe SPlb WKif
	trinerve B&SWJ 10459	WCru

Omphalodes ✿ (*Boraginaceae*)

	'Blue Eyes'	MHol NLar SEdd WCot WMal
	cappadocica ♀H5	CMac EPfP EPot EWld MRav NBro NPer NSla SRms WBrk WMal
	- 'Alba'	SPoG
	- 'Cherry Ingram' ♀H5	Widely available
	- 'Lilac Mist'	EBee SRms SWvt WMal
	- 'Starry Eyes'	Widely available
§	***linifolia*** ♀H3	CSpe ELan GWyn LCro LOPS MCot SPhx
	- ***alba***	see *O. linifolia*
	luciliae	GKev
	nitida	CSpe EWes EWld GWyn IMou MMuc MNrw NQui SHar WMal
	verna	CBod CMiW CRos CTri EBee ECha ELan EPPr EPfP GAbr GEdr GJos GMaP GWyn LRHS MCot MHer MNrw NChi NLar NRHS SCob SPer SPlb SPoG WBor WCAu WFar
	- 'Alba'	CBre CMac EBee ECha ELan EMor EPPr EPfP GAbr GBin GMaP MBel MBriF MCot MNrw NBid NChi NGdn NLar SCob SPer SRms SWvt WBor WBrk WGwG WMal WPnP
	- 'Elfenauge'	EBee EPPr GMaP IMou NBir NLar WCot
I	- 'Grandiflora'	WCot

Omphalogramma (*Primulaceae*)

	delavayi	EPot GEdr

Oncostema see *Scilla*

onion see *Allium cepa*; also AGM Vegetables Section

Onixotis (*Colchicaceae*)

	stricta	see *Wurmbea stricta*

Onobrychis (*Papilionaceae*)

	montana	SPhx
	viciifolia	NGrd SPhx

Onoclea ✿ (*Onocleaceae*)

	sensibilis ♀H6	Widely available
	- copper-leaved	CJun EBee EPfP EWes WPGP
*	- var. ***minima*** new	LEdu
	- 'Rotstiel'	EBee

Ononis (*Papilionaceae*)

	natrix	SPhx
	repens	NAts
	spinosa	CDor IMou MHer WSpi

Onopordum (*Asteraceae*)

	acanthium	CDor CRos ECha EHyd ELan ENfk EPfP GAbr GPoy LRHS MWat NGBl NRHS SCob SHar SPhx SPtp WOut WSpi
	arabicum	see *O. nervosum*
	cyprium	SPhx
	illyricum	SPhx
§	***nervosum*** ♀H7	CSpe SEND

Onosma (*Boraginaceae*)

	alborosea	EBee ECha ECre ELan IMou SEND WKif
	echioides	GJos
	nana	EDAr EPot WAbe

Onychium ✿ (*Pteridaceae*)

	contiguum	LEdu WCot
	japonicum	CBdn CExl CLAP CRos EBee EFer EHyd ISha LEdu LRHS MRav NRHS SPlb WAbe WCot
	- 'Dali'	CLAP

Ophiopogon ✿ (*Asparagaceae*)

	BWJ 8244 from Vietnam	WCru
	NJM 11.018 new	WPGP
	'Black Dragon'	see *O. planiscapus* 'Nigrescens'
	bodinieri	EShb EWes LEdu
	- B&L 12505	EBee EPPr
	caulescens B&SWJ 8230	WCru
	- B&SWJ 11813	WCru
	aff. ***caulescens*** B&SWJ 11287	WCru
	- HWJ 590	WCru
	chingii	EBee EPPr EPfP EWes IMou LEdu WCot
*	- 'Crispum'	EBee
	clavatus KWJ 12267	WCru
	formosanus B&SWJ 3659	ESwi WCru
	'Gin-ryu'	see *Liriope spicata* 'Gin-ryu'
	graminifolius	see *Liriope muscari*
	'Hosoba Kokuryu'	EShb LRHS MAsh MPie NEoE WOut
	intermedius	CSpe EPPr EShb ESwi WCot
	- GWJ 9387	WCru
§	- 'Argenteomarginatus' (v)	EWes
	- 'Variegatus'	see *O. intermedius* 'Argenteomarginatus'

§ ***jaburan***	CMac EBee EMor LEdu
- 'Variegatus'	see *O. jaburan* 'Vittatus'
§ - 'Vittatus' (v)	EWes LEdu WCot
japonicus	CMac EBee EShb LEdu LRHS SCob SGol XLum
- B&SWJ 1871	WCru
- 'Albus'	EPri
- 'Compactus'	WPGP
- 'Gyoku-Ryu'	EBee
- 'Kigimafukiduma'	CExl CMac MRav NGdn SGol
- 'Kyoto'	EPPr ESwi
- 'Lengteng Giant'	LEdu
- 'Minor'	CKno EBee ELon EPPr GMaP LRHS NLar NWsh SCob WPGP XLum
- 'Nanus Variegatus' (v)	EBee
- 'Nippon'	EPPr LPot NGdn
- 'Silver Dragon' (v)	EPPr WCFE
- 'Tama-ryu'	WAbe
* - 'Variegatus' (v)	CDTJ CMac LEdu SRms
aff. ***latifolius*** KWJ 12031	WCru
longifolius FMWJ 13278 **new**	WCru
malcolmsonii B&SWJ 7271	WCru
megalanthus FMWJ 13118 **new**	WCru
parviflorus GWJ 9387	WCru
- HWJK 2093	WCru
planiscapus	CCBP CExl CKno CSpe ECha EPPr NBro NWsh SPtp
* - 'Albovariegatus' (v)	WFar
- 'Black Beard'	CKno EMor GWyn LRHS MAsh NRHS SCob SHar SPoG WFar
- 'Black Needle'	EBee
- 'Black Smaragd'	EBee
- f. ***leucanthus***	CDor EPPr WCot
- 'Little Tabby' (v)	CMil EBee EShb ESwi MAsh WCot WGrn WHal WHoo WSHC
§ - 'Nigrescens' ♀H5	Widely available
scaber B&SWJ 1842	ESwi WCru
- B&SWJ 3655	WCru
'Spring Gold'	EShb ESwi

Oplopanax (*Araliaceae*)

horridus B&SWJ 9551	WCru
japonicus	WCru

Opopanax (*Apiaceae*)

chironium	SPhx
- PAB 845	LEdu WPGP
- PAB 872	WPGP

Opuntia (*Cactaceae*)

angustata	see *O. phaeacantha*
camanchica	see *O. phaeacantha*
compressa	see *O. humifusa*
elata	SChr
§ ***engelmannii***	SChr
erinacea var. ***utahensis***	see *O. polyacantha* var. *erinacea*
§ ***ficus-indica***	SPlb WKor
fragilis	SPlb XSen
§ ***humifusa***	CDTJ SChr WKor XLum XSen
* - subsp. ***littoica*** **new**	SPlb
joconostle	see *O. ficus-indica*
lindheimeri	see *O. engelmannii*
linguiformis	see *O. engelmannii*
monacantha	SEND
§ ***phaeacantha***	SChr
- NNS 99-264	WCot
- var. ***major*** NNS 95-285	WCot
pollardii	see *O. humifusa*
polyacantha	SChr SPlb
- 'Carmin'	XSen
§ - var. ***erinacea***	SChr WCot
salmiana	SEND
spinosior	see *Cylindropuntia spinosior*
tardospina	see *O. engelmannii*

orange, sour or Seville see *Citrus* × *aurantium* Sour Orange Group

orange, sweet see *Citrus* × *aurantium* Sweet Orange Group

Orbea (*Apocynaceae*)

§ ***variegata*** ♀H2	CBen EShb WSMil

Orbexilum (*Papilionaceae*)

pedunculatum var. ***psoralioides***	SBrt SPhx

Orchis (*Orchidaceae*)

elata	see *Dactylorhiza elata*
foliosa	see *Dactylorhiza foliosa*
fuchsii	see *Dactylorhiza fuchsii*
maculata	see *Dactylorhiza maculata*
maderensis	see *Dactylorhiza foliosa*
majalis	see *Dactylorhiza majalis*
§ ***mascula***	WHer

oregano see *Origanum vulgare*

Oreocharis (*Gesneriaceae*)

aurea B&SWJ 11718	WCru

Oreopanax ✿ (*Araliaceae*)

cecropifolius B&SWJ 14761 **new**	WCru
dactylifolius	WCot
floribundus	see *O. incisus*
hypargyreus B&SWJ 14870 **new**	WCru
§ ***incisus*** B&SWJ 10669	WCru
mutisianus B&SWJ 14912 **new**	WCru
sectifolius B&SWJ 14805	WCru
xalapensis B&SWJ 10444	WCru

Oreopteris ✿ (*Thelypteridaceae*)

§ ***limbosperma***	EFer

Origanum ✿ (*Lamiaceae*)

from Kalamata, Greece	SEND
acutidens	XSen
amanum ♀H4	CPBP EWes NBir NSla WAbe
- var. ***album***	WAbe
'Amethyst Falls'	CWCL IPot XSen
'Barbara Tingey'	ELan EPot EWes SRms WAbe WCFE
'Bellissimo' **new**	IPot
'Bristol Cross'	ECtt EPPr EPot MHer SBut WFar WGoo XSen
'Buckland'	ECtt EPot WSHC
caespitosum	see *O. vulgare* 'Nanum'
creticum	see *O. vulgare* subsp. *hirtum*
dictamnus	EPot GPoy MHer WAbe WJek WOld XEll
'Dingle Fairy'	EBee ECtt EPot EWes GJos MCot MHer NBir SGro SWvt WSpi XSen
'Emma Stanley'	EPot WAbe WMal

	'Frank Tingey'	ELan
	'French'	CLau SRms WJek
	'Golden Narrow'	EHyd LRHS
	heracleoticum L.	see *O. vulgare* subsp. *hirtum*
	'Hot and Spicy'	CBod CLau ECrN EMor ENfk EWhm SRms WFar WJek XSen
	'Jekka's Beauty'	WJek
	'Kent Beauty' ♀H4	Widely available
	laevigatum ♀H6	EWhm MHer NBro NPer WCot WKif WSHC XSen
I	- 'Aromaticum'	IMou
	- 'Dingle'	NLar
	- 'Herrenhausen' ♀H6	Widely available
	- 'Hopleys' ♀H6	Widely available
	- 'Purple Charm'	EDAr SRms
	libanoticum	SPhx
	majorana	CHab ENfk GQue MHer MNHC SRms SVic WJek
I	- 'Aureum'	GKev
	- Italian	SEdi
	- PAGODA BELLS ('Lizbell'PBR)	IPot
	- var. ***tenuifolium***	WJek
	× ***majoricum*** new	WJek
	'Norton Gold'	CBre ECha ECtt MHer NPer
	'Nymphenburg'	XSen
	onites	CBod CCBP CHby CLau CTsd EBou EMor ENfk GQue LEdu MHer MNHC SPlb SRms
	- 'Limelight'	NWad
	'Rosenkuppel' ♀H7	CAby CBar CBod CDor CMea EBee ECha ECtt ELan EPPr GQue LCro LOPS LRHS MHer NDov NLar SCob SPer SPhx SPlb SRms SWvt WCAu XSen
	'Rotkugel'	ELon WCFE
	rotundifolium ♀H4	CMea ELan IMou LEdu MHer NBir WMal
	- hybrid	CMea
	scabrum subsp. ***pulchrum*** 'Newleaze'	SGro
	syriacum	WJek
	vulgare	Widely available
	- 'Acorn Bank'	CBod EBou ECtt ENfk EWes LEdu MHer MNHC NLar SPoG SRms WFar WHer WJek
	- 'Aureum' ♀H6	Widely available
	- 'Aureum Crispum'	CBod ECha ENfk GBin GQue GWyn NBid SRms WFar
	- 'Compactum'	CBod CCBP CLau CMea EBee EBou ECha ECtt EMor ENfk EWhm GBin GPoy LEdu MHer MNHC NBir NPol NRHS NSla SPlb SRms WJek XLum
	- 'Corinne Tremaine' (v)	WHer
	- 'Country Cream' (v)	Widely available
	- 'Curly Gold'	CLau CTsd
§	- 'Gold Tip' (v)	CBod CMea EBou EMor ENfk EWhm GJos MCot MHer MHol MNHC SCob SPlb SRms WFar WHer
	- 'Golden Shine'	EWes EWhm SEdi
	- 'Greensleeves' new	WFar
§	- subsp. ***hirtum***	CHby EMor GPoy LCro LOPS SPlb XAbr XSen
	- - 'Greek'	CBod CCBP CLau ECul EMor ENfk EWhm MHer MNHC SEdi SRms SVic WJek
§	- 'Nanum'	SRms WJek
	- 'Pink Mist'	MNrw NWad SRms WHoo
	- 'Pink Thumbles' new	ECha
	- 'Polyphant' (v)	SRms
	- 'Thumble's Variety'	CBod CMea CRos EBee ECha ECtt EHyd EPfP LRHS MHer MRav NRHS NWad SRms SWvt WCFE WFar XLum XSen
	- 'Tomintoul'	GPoy
	- 'Variegatum'	see *O. vulgare* 'Gold Tip'
	- 'Waddow Delight' new	NWad
	- 'White Charm'	EBee NWad SEdi
	'Z'Attar'	MNHC

Orixa (*Rutaceae*)

	japonica	CExl EBee NLar WPGP
	- 'Variegata' (v)	NLar

Orlaya (*Apiaceae*)

	grandiflora ♀H7	CAvo CBre CMiW CPla CSpe EPfP IPot LCro LEdu LOPS LRHS MAvo MCot SBut SPhx WHal WTor

Ornithogalum (*Asparagaceae*)

	arabicum	CBro CCCN EShb GKev IMou SDeJ SRms
	arcuatum	WCot
	atticum	GKev
	balansae	see *O. oligophyllum*
	caudatum	see *O. longibracteatum*
	collinum	GKev
	creticum	GKev
	cuspidatum	GKev
I	***dictaeum*** new	GKev
	dubium ♀H2	SDeJ
	- hybrids	GKev
	fimbriatum	GKev
	lanceolatum	GKev WCot
§	***longibracteatum***	NGKo SChr WHer
	magnum	CBro CWCL EBee ERCP GBin MCot MNrw SDeJ WCot XEll
	- 'Saguramo'	GKev
	'Mount Fuji'	GKev
	'Namib Gold'	SDeJ
	narbonense	GKev WCot
	nutans ♀H5	CAby CAvo CMea CWCL EAJP EBee EHyd ELan EPot GKev LRHS MMuc MNrw NBir SDeJ SEND SPer SPhx WFar WShi
§	***oligophyllum***	EPot GKev MNrw SDeJ
	ponticum	WCot
	- 'Sochi'	ERCP MBow XEll
	pyramidale	GKev SMHy
	pyrenaicum	CAvo CSpe ECha EPPr GKev WCot WShi XEll
	reverchonii	EBee ERCP GKev WShi
	saundersiae	GKev NGKo
	sintenisii	GKev
	thyrsoides ♀H2	CCCN GKev LCro LOPS LRHS SDeJ
	umbellatum	CAvo CHab CRos CTri EHyd ELan GKev GPoy LRHS MBow MCot MMuc MNrw NRHS SDeJ SEND SRms WShi

Orontium (*Araceae*)

	aquaticum	CWat EWat LCro LLWG LOPS NPer SEND WMAq

Orostachys (*Crassulaceae*)

	boehmeri	WCot
	furusei	WFar WHal
	iwarenge	CBod SPlb SSim
§	***spinosa***	CRos EDAr EHyd EWes LRHS NRHS SPlb WAbe WFar

Orthophytum (*Bromeliaceae*)

gurkenii	WCot

Orthrosanthus (*Iridaceae*)

chimboracensis JCA 13743	CPou EBee
laxus	CAbb CBod CPla CWCL NBir SMad WCAu
multiflorus	CBor CPbh CSde EBee EPri
polystachyus	CAby CTsd LPla MHer WSHC

Orychophragmus (*Brassicaceae*)

violaceus	CCCN

Oryzopsis (*Poaceae*)

lessoniana	see *Anemanthele lessoniana*
miliacea	CSpe EPPr MAvo NSti SDix SEND WCot WPGP
paradoxa	EPPr

Osbeckia (*Melastomataceae*)

stellata NJM 13.058	WPGP

Oscularia (*Aizoaceae*)

§ ***deltoides*** ♀H2	CCCN EShb SVen WFar WOld

Osmanthus (*Oleaceae*)

armatus	CBcs CJun CMac EPfP LRHS NLar SEND SGol
× ***burkwoodii*** ♀H5	Widely available
§ ***decorus***	CBcs CBrac CMac CTri EBee EPfP MGos MRav NLar SBrt SGol SPer WPav
- 'Angustifolius'	NLar
delavayi ♀H5	Widely available
- 'Frank Knight'	EPfP LRHS MAsh
- 'George Gardner'	CMac SRms
- 'Heaven Scent'	SPoG
- 'Latifolius'	CExl CJun CRos EHyd LRHS MAsh SLon SWvt
forrestii	see *O. yunnanensis*
× ***fortunei***	CBcs CCVT CExl CRos EBee EHyd EPfP LMaj LRHS
fragrans	SLon SWeb SWvt WCFE WPGP
§ ***heterophyllus***	CBcs CDoC CMac EBee ELan EPfP LMaj MGos MRav NLar SArc SCob SGol SPer SRms SSta SWeb WCFE
§ - all gold	EBee ELan EMil EPfP LRHS SPer SPoG
- 'Argenteomarginatus'	see *O. heterophyllus* 'Variegatus'
§ - 'Aureomarginatus' (v)	CBcs ELon SLon SRms WCFE
- 'Aureus' misapplied	see *O. heterophyllus* all gold
- 'Aureus' Rehder	see *O. heterophyllus* 'Aureomarginatus'
§ - 'Goshiki' (v) ♀H5	Widely available
- 'Gulftide'	CRos EHyd EPfP LRHS MAsh MGos NLar NRHS
- 'Kembu' (v)	NLar
- 'Myrtifolius'	CMac NLar
- 'Ōgon'	NLar
- 'Purple Shaft' ♀H5	CRos EHyd ELan EPfP LRHS MAsh NRHS
- 'Purpureus'	CAby CBcs CBod CMac CTsd EBee ELon EShb EWTr MGos MRav MSwo NLar SCoo SEND SGol SLon SNig SPer
- 'Rotundifolius'	CMac NLar SMad
- 'Sasaba'	NLar
- TRICOLOR	see *O. heterophyllus* 'Goshiki'
§ - 'Variegatus' (v) ♀H5	CBcs CBrac CDoC CMac CRos CSBt ECrN EHyd ELan EPfP LRHS LSRN MAsh MGil MGos MRav MSwo NLar SCob SEND SGbt SGol SLim SPer SPoG SRms SVen WSHC
ilicifolius	see *O. heterophyllus*
serrulatus	EPfP LRHS NLar WPGP
suavis	NLar
§ ***yunnanensis*** ♀H5	CBcs CMCN EBee EPfP LSRN MBlu MRav NLar SArc WPGP

× *Osmarea* see *Osmanthus*

Osmaronia see *Oemleria*

Osmorhiza (*Apiaceae*)

aristata B&SWJ 1607	WCru
claytonii **new**	SPhx

Osmunda ✿ (*Osmundaceae*)

sp.	CCCN
asiatica	EBee WCru
cinnamomea ♀H6	CBdn CBod CCCN CLAP CRos CWCL EBee EFer EHyd ELan EMor EWes ISha LEdu LRHS MMuc NBro NLar NRHS SPlb
claytoniana	CBdn CLAP CRos EBee EFer EHyd IBal ISha LRHS MAsh NBro NLar NRHS WCot XLum
japonica	CLAP EBee EMor ISha NBro
regalis ♀H6	Widely available
- from southern USA	CLAP
- 'Cristata' ♀H6	EHyd LRHS NBid NRHS SWvt WFib
- 'Purpurascens'	CAby CBod CRos CSpe CWCL ECtt EFer EHyd ELan EMor EPfP IBal LEdu LLWG LRHS MAsh MAvo MGos MRav NBid NBir NBro NHol NLar NRHS WFar WFib WPGP WPnP XLum
- var. ***spectabilis***	CCCN CLAP CRos EHyd ISha LRHS MAsh NRHS
- 'Undulata'	WFib

Osteomeles (*Rosaceae*)

subrotunda	WPGP

Osteomeles × *Pyracantha* see × *Pyracomeles*

Osteospermum (*Asteraceae*)

3D Series	SPoG
- 3D BERRY WHITE ('Kleoe11185') **new**	MPri
- 3D PURPLE ('Kleoe12198'PBR) **new**	MBros
- 3D VIOLET ICE ('Kleoe14223')	MBros MPri
'African Queen'	see *O.* 'Nairobi Purple'
AKILA GRAND CANYON MIXED (Akila Series) **new**	MBros
BANANA SYMPHONY ('Sekiin47') (Symphony Series)	CCCN
barberae misapplied	see *O. jucundum*
barberae (Harv.) Norl. 'Compactum'	WFar
BLUE EYED BEAUTY ('Balostlueye'PBR)	LCro LOPS MBros MPri
'Blue Streak'	CCCN CMac
'Buttermilk' ♀H3	CCCN ELan

'Cannington John'	CCCN
'Cannington Joyce'	CCCN
'Cannington Roy'	CBcs CCCN CEnd CMac CSma EBee ECtt ELan ELon EPfP GBee LRHS NRHS WFar WMal
caulescens misapplied	see *O.* 'White Pim'
ecklonis	CBcs CCCN CDTJ CTri NBro NGdn
- var. ***prostratum***	see *O.* 'White Pim'
Flowerpower Double Series (d)	LBuc
- FLOWERPOWER ICE WHITE ('Kleoe06123'PBR) **new**	LCro LOPS
'Giles Gilbey' (v)	CCCN
'Gweek Variegated' (v)	CCCN
'Helen Dimond'	LRHS
'Hopleys' 🏆H3	SEND
'Iced Gem'	LRHS
'In the Pink'	LCro LOPS
'Irish'	ECtt ELon EPPr EPot WIce WMal
§ ***jucundum*** 🏆H3	CCht CMea CTri ECha EHyd EPPr EPfP GAbr LCro LOPS LRHS LSRN NBir NPer NRHS SPlb SRms WIce WThu
- 'Blackthorn Seedling' 🏆H3	CBor CCCN CMea CWGN ECha SPtp
- var. ***compactum***	CBod CMac CPBP CPrp CRos CTsd EHyd ELan ELon EPfP GBee GLog GMaP LRHS LSRN MHol MPri NPer NRHS SIvy SPer SPtp SWvt WABo WFar WHil WHoo
- 'Elliott's Form'	WHoo
- 'Nanum'	EDAr
'Keia' (Springstar Series)	CCCN
§ 'Lady Leitrim' 🏆H3	Widely available
'Lisa Traxler'	SVen
MILK SYMPHONY ('Seiremi') (Symphony Series)	CCCN
§ 'Nairobi Purple'	CBcs CBod CCCN CCht CDoC EBee ECtt EHyd ELan EPfP EShb LRHS MHol MPri NRHS SSut SWvt WABo WFar WHil
NASINGA CREAM ('Aknam'PBR) (Cape Daisy Series)	CCCN
ORANGE SYMPHONY ('Seimora'PBR) (Symphony Series)	CCCN MBNS
'Pale Face'	see *O.* 'Lady Leitrim'
'Peggyi'	see *O.* 'Nairobi Purple'
'Pink Gem'	MHer WFar
'Pink Whirls' 🏆H3	CCCN
'Port Wine'	see *O.* 'Nairobi Purple'
(Serenity Series) SERENITY BLUSHING BEAUTY ('Balostush') **new**	MBros
- 'Serenity Bronze'	WBor
- SERENITY RED ('Balsered') **new**	MBros WBor
'Silver Sparkler' (v) 🏆H3	CCCN CDTJ MHer SVen
'Snow Pixie'	CWGN EBee ECtt ELan LCro LOPS LRHS MPri SPoG SWvt WHil WIce
SONJA	see *O.* 'Sunny Sonja'
'Sparkler'	CCCN
'Stardust'	CRos ECtt EHyd LRHS NPer NRHS SCoo
(Sunny Series) 'Sunny Bronze'	CSpe
- 'Sunny Carlos'PBR	SPoG
- 'Sunny Cherry'	SPoG
- 'Sunny Mary'PBR	LCro LOPS SPoG
§ - 'Sunny Sonja'PBR	SPoG
- 'Sunny Victoria'PBR	SPoG
- 'Sunny Xena'PBR	SPoG
I 'Superbum'	MHol WFar
'Tauranga'	see *O.* 'Whirlygig'
'Tresco Peggy'	see *O.* 'Nairobi Purple'
'Tresco Pink'	CCCN
'Tresco Purple'	see *O.* 'Nairobi Purple'
'Upright Purple' **new**	CDoC
VOLTAGE YELLOW ('Balvoyelo') (Voltage Series)	MBros
'Weetwood' 🏆H3	CCCN CEnd CMea ECtt ELan EPPr EPot GLog LRHS MCot MHer SPoG SWvt WFar WMal
'Westwood White'	EDAr
§ 'Whirlygig' 🏆H3	CCCN
§ 'White Pim' 🏆H3	CDTJ CPrp NPer SEND
'Wine Purple'	see *O.* 'Nairobi Purple'
'Zaurak' (Springstar Series)	CCCN
'Zulu' (Cape Daisy Series)	CCCN

Ostrowskia (*Campanulaceae*)

magnifica	EPot GKev

Ostrya (*Betulaceae*)

carpinifolia	CBcs CCVT CMCN ELan EPfP LMaj MBlu MMuc NLar NOra NOrn SCob SEND SGol SWvt WMat WTSh
japonica	CMCN
virginiana	SBrt

Otacanthus (*Plantaginaceae*)

caeruleus 'Atlantis' **new**	CDoC

Otholobium (*Papilionaceae*)

glandulosum	EBee

Othonna (*Asteraceae*)

cheirifolia	see *Hertia cheirifolia*
coronopifolia	SVen

Othonnopsis see *Hertia*

Ourisia (*Plantaginaceae*)

× ***bitternensis*** 'Cliftonville Canary'	WAbe
- 'Cliftonville Crimson'	WAbe
- 'Cliftonville Old Rose'	WAbe
- 'Cliftonville Pink'	WAbe
- 'Cliftonville Roset'	WAbe
caespitosa	GAbr WAbe
- var. ***gracilis***	MHol
coccinea	EBee EWes EWld GBin GKev GQue NBir NHpl WHal
'Loch Ewe'	CExl EBee EWld GKev
macrophylla	GKev
microphylla	WAbe
- f. ***alba***	WAbe
- 'Hollowcliffe'	WAbe
polyantha 'Cliftonville Scarlet'	CPBP WAbe
'Snowflake' 🏆H4	GAbr IMou NHpl

Ovidia (*Thymelaeaceae*)

andina	MGil

Oxalis (*Oxalidaceae*)

acetosella	GPoy MHer MMuc NQui WHer WShi
- var. ***rosea***	IMou

	- var. ***subpurpurascens***	WCot
	adenophylla Y^{H4}	CExl CMiW CRos EHyd ELan ELon EPfP GBin GKev GMaP LRHS NHol NHpl NLar NRHS SDeJ SPoG SRms WBrk WCav
	adenophylla* × *enneaphylla	see *O.* 'Matthew Forrest'
	'Anne Christie'	CPBP NSla
	arenaria F&W 10584	WCot
§	***articulata***	ELan NPer SEND WCav WSHC XLum
	- 'Alba'	ELan WCot XLum
	- f. ***crassipes*** 'Alba'	WCot
	- 'Festival'	GKev
	- 'Jill' **new**	CMea
§	- subsp. ***rubra***	GKev SDeJ
	'Autumn Pink' **new**	GKev
	bowiei	WCot
	- 'Amarantha'	GKev
*	- ***purpurea***	CBor
	brasiliensis	CBor GKev
	'Clemence Knight' **new**	CPBP
	'Dark Eye'	EPot
	dentata 'Pot of Gold'	GKev
	deppei	see *O. tetraphylla*
§	***depressa***	EPot EWes GKev NBir NSla SDeJ SGro
	'Double Trouble' (d)	CBor
	enneaphylla Y^{H4}	CElw CRos EHyd ELon GBin GEdr GMaP LRHS NRHS NRya SGro
	- F&W 2715	CPBP
	- 'Alba'	CElw CPBP NRya NSla
	- subsp. ***ibari***	EPPr GEdr NRya NSla
	- 'Minutifolia'	GEdr GQue NRya
*	- 'Minutifolia Rosea'	CPBP
	- 'Rosea'	CBor EPot GKev ITim NLar NRya NSla SGro
	- 'Sheffield Swan'	CPBP GEdr NSla WAbe
	- 'Ute'	EPPr GEdr NRya
	'Fanny'	GKev
	flava	SChr
	- white-flowered	EPot GKev
	floribunda misapplied	see *O. articulata*
	gracilis	EPot GKev
	griffithii double-flowered (d)	CMiW
	- 'Pink Charm'	GEdr
	- 'Snowflake'	CMiW GEdr
	'Gwen McBride'	CPBP GEdr WAbe
	hedysaroides misapplied	see *O. spiralis* subsp. *vulcanicola*
	hedysaroides Kunth	CCCN
	'Hemswell Knight'	CPBP EPPr
	hirta	SGro
	- 'Gothenburg'	EPri EShb GKev ITim
	inops	see *O. depressa*
	'Ione Hecker' Y^{H4}	CBor CMiW EPot GKev ITim NHpl NLar NRya WAbe WOld
	'Irish Mist' (v)	GKev
	'Jay'	NSla
*	***karroica***	NHpl WCot
§	***laciniata***	CPBP
	- hybrid	GEdr
	lactea double-flowered	see *O. magellanica* 'Nelson'
	lasiandra	CCCN GKev
§	***latifolia***	GKev
	magellanica	GAbr IMou SPlb
	- 'Flore Pleno'	see *O. magellanica* 'Nelson'
§	- 'Nelson' (d)	GBin NBir NPer
	magnifica	GKev
	massoniana Y^{H2}	ECha WAbe WCot
§	'Matthew Forrest'	CPBP WCot
§	***megalorrhiza***	GKev NWad SChr
	melanosticta	EPot GEdr SDeJ WCot
§	- 'Ken Aslet' Y^{H3}	GKev ITim NHpl SDeJ
	obtusa	EPot
	- apricot-flowered	SDeJ
	oregana	CMac ELon EWld SPhx WCot WCru
	- 'Bob Haszeldine'	GEdr
	- 'Klamath Ruby'	WSHC
	- f. ***smalliana***	EWld GEdr IMou MNrw NLar WCot WCru
	- white-flowered	WCot
	perdicaria	CRos EHyd EPot EWes LRHS NRHS WAbe WIce
	- 'Citrino'	WAbe WCot
	'Pink Pillow'	CBod
	polyphylla var. ***heptaphylla***	GEdr
*	***purpurea*** 'Alba' **new**	GKev
	- 'Garnet' **new**	GKev
	- 'Ken Aslet'	see *O. melanosticta* 'Ken Aslet'
	regnellii	see *O. triangularis* subsp. *papilionacea*
	rosea misapplied	see *O. articulata* subsp. *rubra*
	Slack Top hybrids	NSla
	'Slack's Peacock' **new**	NSla
	'Snipe'	NSla
§	***spiralis*** subsp. ***vulcanicola***	CCCN
	- - 'Sunset Velvet'	WCot
	squamata	CPla SPlb
	squamoso-radicosa	see *O. laciniata*
	succulenta Barnéoud	see *O. megalorrhiza*
	succulenta ambig.	CSpe
	'Sunny'	GKev
§	***tetraphylla***	CExl GKev NPer
	- 'Iron Cross'	GKev LCro LOPS NLar SDeJ SPlb WHil
	'Tina'	CPBP XEll
	triangularis	CCCN CExl MHer NPer WBrk
	- 'Birgit'	GKev SDeJ
	- BURGUNDY WINE ('JR Oxburwi') (Xalis Series)	CWGN NPer
	- 'Mijke'	GKev
§	- subsp. ***papilionacea*** Y^{H3}	GKev
	- - 'Atropurpurea'	CSpe SDeJ
	- subsp. ***triangularis***	GKev MAvo MBow
	tuberosa	CLau EPfP GPoy LEdu SPoG WKor
	- 'Polar Bere'	LEdu
	- scarlet-flowered, white-eye	LEdu
	'Ute'	CPBP NSla
	valdiviensis	CPla NWad
	versicolor Y^{H3}	CBor EPot GEdr GKev ITim NBir SDeJ WHil XEll
	- 'Golden Cape'	CBor EPot GKev
	vespertilionis Zucc.	see *O. latifolia*
I	'Waverley Hybrid'	GKev

Oxycoccus see *Vaccinium*

Oxydendrum ✿ (*Ericaceae*)

	arboreum	CBcs CEnd CMCN CRos EBee EHyd EPfP IArd LRHS MAsh MBlu MGil MMuc SCob SPer SPoG SSta

Oxypetalum (*Apocynaceae*)

	caeruleum	see *Tweedia coerulea*

Oxyria (*Polygonaceae*)

digyna	CAgr

Oxytropis (*Papilionaceae*)

campestris var. ***gracilis***	GKev WSHC
podocarpa	SPlb
purpurea	CBor SPlb
shokanbetsuensis	CPla

Ozothamnus (*Asteraceae*)

§ ***coralloides***	EPot WAbe
§ 'County Park Silver'	GEdr GKev WAbe
§ ***hookeri***	CBct CDoC EBee SVen WCFE WPGP
§ ***ledifolius***	CBcs CCoa CDoC ELan EPfP LRHS SPer
§ ***rosmarinifolius***	CBcs CDoC CRos EHyd ELan EPfP GBin LRHS MAsh MSwo SPer SVen
- 'Silver Jubilee'	CBcs CCht CRos CSBt ECre ELan EPfP LRHS MAsh MMuc MRav MSwo NRHS SLon SPer SPlb
§ ***selago***	ELan EPot WCot
- 'Major'	SPlb
§ - var. ***tumidus***	EBee ITim WThu
'Threave Seedling'	CCht CDoC CRos EBee EHyd ELan LRHS MAsh SPer

P

Pachyphragma (*Brassicaceae*)

§ ***macrophyllum***	ECha ELon EWTr EWld IBlr IMou LEdu MMuc MRav NLar NSti SDix WCAu WCot WCru WPGP WPnP WSHC

Pachyphytum (*Crassulaceae*)

bracteosum	CDoC

Pachypodium (*Apocynaceae*)

lamerei 🏆H1a	SPlb

Pachysandra (*Buxaceae*)

axillaris	WCot
- BWJ 8032	WCru
- 'Crûg's Cover'	ESwi EWld SMad WCru
- var. ***stylosa***	MRav
procumbens	EBee GKev IMou MNrw NLar WCot
- 'Angola' (v)	WCot
terminalis	Widely available
- 'Green Carpet'	CBcs CChe CDoC CExl CRos CSBt EBee EHyd ELan EPfP GMaP LRHS LSRN MAsh MGos MSwo NHol NLar NRHS SCob SGol SLim SPer SPoG SWvt XLum
- 'Green Sheen' 🏆H5	CBod CRos ECha EHyd ELan EPPr EPfP GWyn LRHS NRHS SCob WCAu
- 'Silver Edge' (v)	EBee
- 'Variegata' (v) 🏆H5	Widely available

Pachystachys (*Acanthaceae*)

lutea 🏆H1b	CCCN

Pachystegia (*Asteraceae*)

§ ***insignis***	CAby CTsd LRHS MPkF

× *Pachyveria* (*Crassulaceae*)

scheideckeri new	CDoC

Paederia (*Rubiaceae*)

scandens new	SBrt

Paederota (*Plantaginaceae*)

§ ***bonarota***	GEdr GKev WAbe
lutea	GEdr GKev WCot

Paeonia ✿ (*Paeoniaceae*)

'Alexander Woollcott'	GBin
anomala	EPot GKev ILea MPhe NLar
arietina	see *P. mascula* subsp. *arietina*
'Armani'	EBee EPfP LRHS
'Athena'	EHyd GBin LRHS WCAu
'Avant Garde'	WCAu
'Bai Xue Ta' (S)	NTPC
'Ballarena de Saval' new	ILea
banatica	see *P. officinalis* subsp. *banatica*
§ 'Bartzella' (d) 🏆H6	CRos EHyd ELan ELon EPfP GBin ILea LCro LOPS LPla LRHS MNrw NLar NRHS SEdd SPeP SPoG WCAu WCot
'Berry Garcia'	GBin
'Blaze'	EHyd GMaP ILea LRHS NLar NRHS WCAu WCot
'Border Charm'	GBin ILea SDir
'Bridal Icing'	GBin WCAu
'Bride's Dream'	GBin
'Buckeye Belle' (d)	EBee ELan EPfP EWTr GBin GMaP ILea LCro LOPS LRHS LSRN MBel NLar SCob SMad SPoG WCAu WCot
'Burma Midnight'	GBin WKif
'Callie's Memory'	ELon GBin ILea WCAu
cambessedesii 🏆H3	CAby CBro CRos CSpe EHyd EPot GEdr GKev LRHS NBir NRHS NSla WAbe WKif
cambessedesii* × *mlokosewitschii	CRos EHyd LRHS NRHS
'Canary Brilliant' PBR	GBin
'Cardinal's Robe'	GBin
'Carol'	ILea LSRN
caucasica	see *P. mascula* subsp. *mascula*
× ***chamaeleon***	LPla
'Chocolate Soldier'	GBin WCAu
'Christmas Velvet' (d)	GBin WCAu
'Claire de Lune'	GBin GKev GMaP ILea IPot LRHS MGil WCAu WCot WKif WTor
'Claudia'	GBin
'Color Magnet'	GBin WCAu
'Command Performance'	GBin ILea IPot WCAu
'Convoy' (d)	GBin
'Copper Kettle' (d)	ELan GBin ILea
'Cora Louise'	ELan ELon ILea LRHS MBros MHol WCAu WHil
'Coral Charm' 🏆H6	EPfP GBin GMaP ILea LCro LOPS LRHS LSRN MHol MMrt MPri NLar SDeJ SPeP WCAu WCot WHoo XSen
'Coral Fay'	GBin
'Coral 'n' Gold'	MPri WCAu
'Coral Sunset'	EWTr GBin ILea LCro LOPS MPri NLar SCob SDeJ SMad SPer WCot WHil WTyc
'Coral Supreme'	GBin
corallina	see *P. mascula* subsp. *mascula*
'Court Jester'	ELan ILea

'Cytherea'	GBin LRHS WCAu
'Dancing Butterflies'	see *P. lactiflora* 'Zi Yu Nu'
daurica misapplied	see *P. mascula* subsp. *triternata*
daurica Andrews subsp. ***coriifolia*** RCB UA 12	WCot
'Dearest' new	GBin
decora	see *P. peregrina*
delavayi (S)	CPla CRos CTho CTsd EHyd ELan EPfP GKev GMaP LCro LRHS MAsh MGil MGos NBir SCob SDix SPer SPoG SRms WCot
- BWJ 7775	WCru
- from China (S)	MPhe
- var. ***angustiloba*** f. ***alba*** (S)	CExl
§ - - f. ***angustiloba*** (S)	CBcs GKev MMuc SEND
§ - - f. ***trollioides*** (S)	CExl SPtp
- var. ***atropurpurea***	see *P. delavayi* var. *delavayi* f. *delavayi*
§ - var. ***delavayi*** f. ***delavayi*** (S)	CPla
§ - - f. ***lutea*** (S)	CCVT CDoC CJun CRos CTho EHyd EPfP GAbr GKev GLog GMaP LEdu LRHS MAsh MGos NBir SCob SIvy SLon SNig SPoG SRms WHoo
- var. ***lutea***	see *P. delavayi* var. *delavayi* f. *lutea*
- 'Mrs Sarson' (S)	SPtp
- Potaninii Group	see *P. delavayi* var. *angustiloba* f. *angustiloba*
- 'Tapestry' (S)	CSpe
- Trollioides Group	see *P. delavayi* var. *angustiloba* f. *trollioides*
delavayi* × *suffruticosa	LSRN
'Diana Parks'	ILea NLar
'Early Daybreak'	GBin
'Early Scout'	CBod GBin LRHS
'Early Windflower'	GBin ILea WCAu
'Eden's Perfume'	EPfP LRHS NLar SPer
'Eliza Lundy' (d)	GBin WCAu
'Ellen Cowley'	WCAu
emodi	CAvo CMiW CPla GKev ILea LRHS MCot WCot
'Etched Salmon'	GBin WCAu
'Fairy Princess'	GBin
§ × ***festiva*** 'Alba Plena' (d)	CPou EHyd EPfP GMaP ILea LRHS MBel MRav NLar NRHS SCob SPer SWvt WFar
- 'Rosea Plena' (d) ♀H6	CRos ECtt ELan EPfP GMaP LRHS SCob SWvt WCot WFar
§ - 'Rubra Plena' (d) ♀H6	CPou CTri EBee ECtt ELan EPfP GMaP ILea LRHS LSun MBel MHol MRav NGdn NLar SCob SPer SRms SWvt WBor WCAu WCot
'Firelight'	GBin
'First Arrival'	GBin ILea MHol WCAu
'First Dutch Yellow'	see *P.* 'Garden Treasure'
'Flame'	CRos EHyd EPfP EWTr GMaP ILea LRHS MNrw NRHS NSti SDeJ SMad SPeP WCAu WCot
§ Gansu Group (S)	MPhe NTPC
- 'Bai Bi Lan Xia' (S)	MPhe
- 'Bai Zhang Bing' (S)	NTPC
- 'Bing Shan Xue Lian' (S)	MPhe
- 'Bing Xin Zi' (S)	NTPC
- 'Dan Feng Ling Kong' (S)	NTPC
- 'Er Long Nao Hai' (S)	MPhe
- 'Fen Guan Yu Zhu' (S)	NTPC
- 'Fen He' (S)	MPhe NTPC
- 'Fen Jin Yu' (S)	NTPC
- 'Gan Lan Yu' (S)	NTPC
- 'Han Hai Bing Xin' (S)	MPhe
- 'Hei Fa Nü Lang' (S)	MPhe
- 'Hei Feng Die' (S)	MPhe
- 'Hei Xuan Feng' (S)	MPhe NTPC
- 'Hei Yuan Shuai' (S)	MPhe
- 'Hui He' (S)	MPhe
- 'Jiao Rong' (S)	MPhe
- 'Lan He' (S)	MPhe
- 'Lan He Qi Ming' (S)	NTPC
- 'Lan Tian Meng' (S)	MPhe
- 'Lan Yu San Cai' (S)	NTPC
- 'Long Yu Er Qiao' (S) new	NTPC
- 'Long Yuan Hong' (S)	MPhe
- 'Mo Hai Yin Bo' (S)	MPhe
- 'Ren Mian Tao Hua' (S)	NTPC
- 'Ri Yue Tong Hui' (S)	MPhe
- 'San Hua Nu' (S)	MPhe
- 'Shu Sheng Peng Mo' (S)	MPhe
- 'Tie Mian Wu Si' (S)	MPhe
- 'Tong Xin Tong De' (S)	MPhe
- 'Wu Kong Xiu Xing' (S)	NTPC
- 'Xiao Xue' (S)	MPhe
- 'Xiong Mao' (S)	MPhe
- 'Xue Hai Bing Xin' (S)	MPhe NTPC
- 'Xue Lian' (S)	NTPC
- 'Xue Yuan Yu Hui' (S)	NTPC
- 'Ye Guang Bei' (S)	MPhe NTPC
- 'Yi Du Chun Qiu' (S)	NTPC
- 'Yin Yang Shan' (S)	MPhe
- 'Yu Ban Xiu Qiu' (S)	MPhe
- 'Yu Lu Lian Dan' (S)	MPhe
- 'Yuan Yang Pu' (S)	MPhe
- 'Zi Ban Bai' (S)	NTPC
- 'Zi Die Ying Feng' (S)	MPhe NTPC
- 'Zi Yan' (S)	NTPC
- 'Zong Ban Bai' (S)	MPhe NTPC
Gansu Mudan Group	see *P.* Gansu Group
'Garden Peace'	GBin WCAu
§ 'Garden Treasure'	EHyd EPfP GBin LRHS NRHS SDeJ SPoG WCAu
'Golden Dream'	see *P.* 'Bartzella'
'Hei Hua Kui'	see *P. suffruticosa* 'Hei Hua Kui'
'Hélène Martin' new	GBin
'Henry Bockstoce' (d)	GMaP ILea MGil NLar WCAu
'Hillary'	GBin ILea NLar WCAu
'Hoki'	EHyd LRHS NRHS
'Hong Bao Shi' (S)	NTPC
'Honor'	WCAu
'Huo Lian Jin Dan' (S)	NTPC
'Illini Warrior'	GBin ILea WCAu
japonica ambig.	GEdr
'Jin Ge' (S)	NTPC
'Joanna Marlene'	GBin ILea WCAu
'Joseph Rock'	see *P. rockii*
'Julia Rose'	CRos EHyd GBin ILea LRHS NRHS SMad SPoG WCAu
'Kinkaku'	see *P.* × *lemoinei* 'Souvenir de Maxime Cornu'
'La Donna' (d)	GBin
lactiflora 'Abalone Pearl'	GBin
- 'Adolphe Rousseau'	ILea LCro LOPS LRHS WCAu
- 'Agida'	CRos CWld ECtt EHyd LRHS MRav NRHS WGwG
- 'Albert Crousse'	CBcs MRav NBir WCAu
- 'Alertie'	CRos GBin LRHS
- 'Alice Harding'	WCAu
- 'Allan Rogers'	GBin

- 'Amabilis'	ILea WHil
- 'Amalia Olson'	GBin
- 'Angel Cheeks'	GBin IPot LCro LOPS WCAu
- 'Ann Cousins'	MGil WCAu
- 'Antwerpen'	CRos EHyd LRHS NRHS
- 'Argentine'	WCAu
- 'Auguste Dessert'	WCAu
§ - 'Augustin d'Hour'	ILea NLar SHar
- 'Aureole'	MRav
- 'Avalanche'	CRos EPfP ILea LRHS NLar NRHS
- 'Ballerina'	MRav
- 'Barbara'	WCAu
- 'Baroness Schröder'	CWld GBin MGil WCAu
- 'Barrington Belle'	EHyd EPfP LRHS MBros NRHS WFar WHoo
- 'Bess Bockstoce'	WCAu
- 'Big Ben'	CRos ILea LRHS NLar
- 'Black Beauty'	CRos EBee EHyd GBin IPot LRHS NRHS SCob SDeJ WTor
- 'Blush Queen'	CWld GBin WCAu
- 'Border Gem'	CRos CSam EHyd LRHS MRav NRHS WCAu
- 'Bouchela'	NSti
- 'Boule de Neige'	ILea
- 'Bouquet Perfect'	EHyd LRHS NRHS WCAu
- 'Bowl of Beauty' ♀H6	Widely available
- 'Bowl of Cream'	GBin ILea LRHS SCob SWvt WCAu
- 'Bridal Gown'	WCAu
- 'Bunker Hill'	CRos ECtt EHyd ILea LRHS NRHS SPer SWvt
- 'Candy Stripe'	GBin
- 'Catharina Fontijn'	CBod EHyd EWTr GBin ILea LRHS NRHS WCAu
- 'Charles Burgess'	EPfP ILea WCAu
- 'Charlie's White'	GBin ILea LRHS NLar SDeJ SPer WCAu
- 'Charm'	WCAu
- 'Cheddar Charm'	CWld
- 'Cheddar Gold'	WCAu
- 'Cherry Hill'	GBin SMad WCAu
- 'Chiffon Parfait'	EWTr
- 'Claire Dubois'	EBee EHyd LRHS NRHS
- 'Class Act'	GBin
- 'Cora Stubbs'	GBin LRHS SPer WCAu
- 'Cornelia Shaylor'	WCAu
- 'Couronne d'Or'	ILea WCAu
- 'Cringley White'	SRms
- 'Dawn Pink'	EPfP
- 'Daystar'	MRav
- 'Dinner Plate'	GBin MGil SHar WCAu
- 'Do Tell'	EPfP ILea MMrt NLar SPer WCAu
- 'Doctor Alexander Fleming'	CBod EBee EHyd EPfP GBin ILea LRHS MBNS MGil MHol MNrw MWat NBir NRHS SDeJ SNig SWvt WCAu WFar
- 'Doreen'	EBee EHyd EPfP GBin LRHS NRHS SHar WCAu
- 'Drumline'	SDeJ
- 'Duchesse de Nemours' ♀H6	Widely available
- 'Edulis Superba'	CRos CWld EHyd GBin ILea LEdu LRHS MBNS MRav NPer NRHS WCAu
- 'Elaine'	MRav
- 'Elsa Sass'	GBin ILea WCAu
- 'Emma Klehm'	GBin LSRN WCAu
- 'Evelyn Tibbets'	GBin
- 'Fairy's Petticoat'	WCAu
- 'Félix Crousse' ♀H6	CBcs CBod CTri CWld ELan EPfP GBin GMaP ILea LRHS LSRN MBNS MPri MRav NBir NLar SDeJ SPer WCAu WFar XSen
- 'Felix Supreme'	GBin
- 'Festiva Maxima' ♀H6	CSBt CTri EBee EHyd ELan EPfP GBin ILea LCro LOPS LRHS LSun MGil MPri NBir NLar NRHS SCob SPer SPoG SRkn SRms SWvt WCAu WFar WHoo WKif
- 'Florence Ellis'	WCAu
- 'Florence Nicholls'	ELan EPfP ILea WCAu
- 'Foxtrot'	GBin
- 'François Ortegat'	CRos EPfP
- 'Garden Lace'	SDeJ WCAu
- 'Gardenia'	CRos EHyd ELan EPfP EWTr GBin LRHS NRHS SDeJ WCot WKif
- 'Gay Paree'	ILea MGil MRav WCAu
- 'Gayborder June'	WCAu
- 'Général Joffre'	MRav
- 'Général MacMahon'	see *P. lactiflora* 'Augustin d'Hour'
- 'Germaine Bigot'	MRav WCAu
- 'Gilbert Barthelot'	WCAu
- 'Golden Frolic' **new**	WCAu
- 'Goldilocks'	WCAu
- 'Goldmine'	SPeP
- 'Great Lady'	GBin
- 'Great Sport'	MRav
- 'Green Halo'	GBin WCot
- 'Hari-ai-nin'	ILea
- 'Helen Hayes'	WCAu
- 'Hermione'	GBin
- 'High Adventure' **new**	GBin
- 'Honey Gold'	GBin ILea IPot LRHS MMrt SPoG WCAu WSpi
- 'Hot Chocolate'	WCAu
- 'Immaculée'	CBod EHyd GBin ILea LCro LOPS LRHS MRav SCob SPer SPoG WKif
- 'Inspecteur Lavergne'	CRos EBee ECtt EHyd EPfP ILea LRHS NGdn NRHS SPer WCAu WCot
- 'Instituteur Doriat'	LRHS WCAu
- 'Jacorma'	ILea LRHS NLar
- 'Jadwigha'	ILea
- 'Jan van Leeuwen'	EPfP GBin GMaP LCro LOPS LRHS SEdd WCAu WCot WKif WTor
- 'Joker'	GBin WCAu
- 'Jubilee' **new**	CRos
- 'Judith Eileen'	WCAu
- 'Kansas'	CWCL EBee EHyd ELan EPfP ILea LRHS MHol MPri NBir NGdn NLar NRHS SCob SPeP SPoG WCAu WCot WFar
- 'Karen Gray'	GBin
- 'Karl Rosenfield'	CBcs CBod CRos CSBt EBee EHyd EPfP GBin ILea LCro LOPS LRHS LSRN LSun MGil MNrw MPri MRav NLar NRHS SCob SPer SPoG SRms SWvt WFar WHoo XSen
- 'Kelway's Glorious'	CRos EHyd EPfP EWTr LRHS MBNS MHol MRav NLar NRHS WCAu WGwG WHoo WKif
- 'Kelway's Majestic'	MRav
- KIEV	EHyd NRHS
§ - 'Koningin Wilhelmina'	EPfP MNrw
- 'Krinkled White'	CBod CRos EHyd EPfP GBin GKev GMaP ILea LRHS MPri MRav NLar NRHS SDeJ SPeP SPoG WCAu WKif
- 'Lady Alexandra Duff' ♀H6	EWTr GBin ILea LRHS MRav NBir NGdn SWvt WCAu WKif

- 'Lady Anna'	ILea
- 'Lady Orchid'	EPfP
- 'Largo'	WCAu
- 'Laura Dessert' ♀H6	GBin ILea LCro LOPS LRHS WCAu WKif
- 'L'Éclatante'	LRHS
- 'Lemon Queen'	GKev
- 'Little Medicineman'	EHyd
- LONDON	EHyd LRHS NRHS
- 'Lord Kitchener'	CRos CSam CWld ECtt EHyd EPfP GBin LRHS MWat NRHS WGwG
- 'Lotus Queen'	ECtt
- 'Love's Touch'	GBin
- 'Lowell Thomas'	GBin WCAu
- 'Madame Calot'	EHyd LRHS NRHS WCAu
- 'Madame Claude Tain'	WCot
- 'Madame Edouard Doriat'	WCAu
- 'Madame Emile Debatène'	EBee MBNS MHol WCAu WFar
- 'Madame Gaudichau'	WCot
- MADRID	EHyd LRHS NRHS
- 'Margaret Truman'	WCAu
- 'Marie Crousse'	WCAu
- 'Marie Lemoine'	GBin GKev ILea LRHS WCAu WCot
- 'Mischief'	MRav
- 'Miss America' ♀H6	EPfP GBin NLar WCAu WKif
- 'Miss Eckhart'	WCAu
- 'Mister Ed'	WCAu
- 'Monsieur Jules Elie' ♀H6	EBee ELan EPfP GBin ILea LCro LOPS LRHS MHol NGdn NLar SPer WCAu
- 'Monsieur Martin Cahuzac'	ILea LRHS
- 'Moon of Nippon'	ILea WCAu
- 'Moon River'	CBcs EPfP GBin NLar WCAu
- 'Morning Kiss'	EPfP
- 'Mother's Choice'	GBin LCro LOPS LSRN NGdn NLar WCAu WCot
- 'Mr G.F. Hemerik'	GBin WBor WCAu WCot
- 'Mrs Edward Harding'	WCAu
- 'Mrs Livingston Farrand'	GBin
- 'Myrtle Gentry'	WCAu
- 'Nancy Nora'	SPer WCAu
- 'Neon'	LRHS
- 'Nice Gal'	GBin WCAu
- 'Nick Shaylor'	WCAu
- 'Nippon Beauty'	ILea LRHS NLar SCob SDeJ WCAu WCot WFar WTor
- 'Noémie Demay'	LRHS
- 'Nymphe'	MRav NLar SDeJ WCAu
- 'Paul M. Wild'	ELan ILea NLar WCAu
* - 'Pecher'	CBod EHyd EPfP LRHS NLar NPer NRHS SDeJ
- 'Peter Brand'	CRos ECtt ELan GBin ILea IPot LSRN NLar
- 'Petite Elegance'	WCAu
- 'Petite Porcelain'	WCAu
- 'Philippe Rivoire'	WCAu
- 'Philomèle'	WCAu
- 'Pietertje Vriend Wagenaar'	GBin
- 'Pillow Talk'	EBee ELan ILea NLar SPoG WCAu
- 'Pink Cameo'	WCot WFar
- 'Pink Dawn' Kelways **new**	WCAu
- 'Pink Delight'	GBin
- 'Pink Giant'	WCAu
- 'Pink Parfait'	ILea LRHS NLar SCob SPer WCAu
- 'Pink Princess'	GBin
- 'President Franklin D. Roosevelt'	CRos ECtt EHyd LRHS NRHS
- 'Président Poincaré'	MRav
- 'President Taft'	see *P. lactiflora* 'Reine Hortense'
- 'Primevère'	ECtt EWTr LRHS NBir NLar SPer WFar
§ - 'Purple Spider'	EBee LRHS MHol
- 'Queen Wilhelmina'	see *P. lactiflora* 'Koningin Wilhelmina'
- 'Raspberry Sundae'	EHyd ELan EPfP EWTr ILea LRHS MRav NLar NRHS SPer SPoG WCAu WCot
- 'Red Queen'	GBin
- RED SARAH BERNHARDT	EPfP GBin ILea SDeJ SPer
- 'Red Spider'	see *P. lactiflora* 'Purple Spider'
§ - 'Reine Hortense'	ECtt LRHS MRav
- 'Renato'	EHyd LRHS MHol
- 'Riches and Fame'	LRHS
- ROME	EHyd LRHS NRHS
- 'Ruth Clay'	EWTr
- 'Santa Fe'	EHyd EPfP LRHS NRHS
- 'Sarah Bernhardt' ♀H6	Widely available
- 'Sea Shell'	GMaP ILea WCAu
- 'Sebastiaan Maas'	ILea
- 'Serene Pastel'	WCAu
- 'Shawnee Chief'	GBin
- 'Shirley Temple'	CRos EBee EHyd ELan EPfP GBin ILea LCro LOPS LRHS MBNS MGos MHol MPri MRav NBir NGdn NRHS SCob SDeJ SPoG WCAu WCot WFar
- 'Silver Rose'	GBin
- 'Sir Ernest Shackleton'	MRav
- 'Soft Salmon Joy'	GBin
- 'Solange'	ILea LRHS
- 'Sorbet'	EBee EPfP LRHS MHol NBir NLar NPer SDeJ SMad WCAu WFar
- 'Surugu'	WCAu
- 'Sweet Sixteen'	WCAu
- 'Sword Dance'	CRos EHyd EPfP ILea LRHS MMrt NRHS SDeJ WCAu WSpi
- 'The Fawn'	GBin ILea WCAu
- 'The Nymph'	LRHS NBir
- 'Tom Eckhardt'	SPer WCAu
- 'Top Brass'	ECtt ILea MRav SDeJ WCAu
- 'Unique'	ELan
- 'Victoire de la Marne'	ILea
- 'Vogue'	CRos EHyd EPfP LRHS MRav NRHS SWvt WCAu
- 'Westerner'	WCAu
- 'White Angel'	SPer
- 'White Cap'	ILea IPot NLar WCAu
- 'White Sands'	GBin
- 'White Wings'	CBcs CRos CTri ECtt EHyd ELan EPfP EWTr GMaP ILea LRHS NLar NRHS NSti SMad SPeP SPer SWvt WCAu WCot
- 'Whitleyi Major' ♀H6	WCot
- 'Wilbur Wright'	WCAu
- 'Wine Red'	GBin
- 'Władysława'	CBod LRHS NLar SPer WCot
§ - 'Zi Yu Nu'	LSRN NRHS SMad
- 'Zuzu'	GBin
× ***lagodechiana***	GKev LEdu
'Late Windflower'	GKev LPla WCAu
'Lavender Baby' **new**	GBin
× ***lemoinei*** (S)	WHal
- 'High Noon' (S) ♀H5	CRos EBee LRHS MPhe
§ - 'Souvenir de Maxime Cornu' (S)	EBee EHyd LRHS NRHS
'Lemon Chiffon'	EWTr GBin WCAu WCot
'Lemon Dream' PBR	ELan GBin ILea WCAu
lobata 'Fire King'	see *P. peregrina*

	'Lollipop' (d)	ELan GBin ILea
	'Love Affair'	WCAu
	'Lovely Rose'	WCAu
	ludlowii (S)	Widely available
	ludlowii × ***suffruticosa*** 'Hakuojisi' (S)	EHyd LRHS
	lutea	see *P. delavayi* var. *delavayi* f. *lutea*
	'Magenta Gem'	GBin
	'Magical Mystery Tour'	GBin
	'Mahogany'	GBin
	'Mai Fleuri'	WCAu
	mairei	CExl GGGa SPtp WMal
	'Many Happy Returns'	GBin ILea WCAu
	mascula	CBro GEdr GKev GLog IMou NBir WCot
§	- subsp. ***arietina*** W&B BG A-4	WCot
	- 'Immaculata'	MHol
§	- subsp. ***mascula***	GKev
§	- subsp. ***russoi***	ITim LPla
	- - 'Reverchoni'	EPot
§	- subsp. ***triternata***	EPot GKev WCot
	'Merry Mayshine'	GBin GKev
	'Mikuhino-akebono'	SDeJ
	mlokosewitschii ♀H6	CBro CExl CMea CPBP CRos ECha EHyd GEdr GKev ILea LEdu LRHS MBel MNrw NBir NRHS SDix SLon SWvt WAbe WCAu WCot WHoo WKif WSpi
	- hybrids	GKev
	mollis	see *P. officinalis* subsp. *villosa*
	'Moonrise'	GBin MMrt WCAu
	'Morning Lilac'	GBin ILea WCAu
	'My Love'	GBin WCAu
	'Norwegian Blush'	GBin ILea WCAu
	obovata	CPla GKev SPtp
	- var. ***alba*** ♀H5	CExl GEdr GKev WSHC WSpi
	- var. ***willmottiae***	CExl GKev
	officinalis	GKev MCot WCot
	- WM 9821 from Slovenia	MPhe
	- from NW Croatia	LEdu
	- 'Alba Plena'	see *P.* × *festiva* 'Alba Plena'
	- 'Anemoniflora Rosea' ♀H6	EHyd EPfP ILea LRHS NRHS SMad SPer SWvt WCAu
§	- subsp. ***banatica***	GKev MPhe
	- 'James Crawford Weguelin'	WCot
	- 'Rosea Plena'	see *P.* × *festiva* 'Rosea Plena'
	- 'Rubra Plena'	see *P.* × *festiva* 'Rubra Plena'
§	- subsp. ***villosa***	LRHS SEND WCAu
	'Old Faithful'	GBin
	'Old Rose Dandy'	ELan GBin ILea NLar
	'Oriental Gold'	WHil
	ostii (S)	CExl
	papaveracea	see *P. suffruticosa*
	'Paris'	EHyd LRHS
	'Pastel Splendor'	CRos EHyd ELan GBin ILea LRHS NRHS WCAu
	'Patio Moscow Deep' (Patio Series) **new**	CRos
	'Paula Fay'	CBod EPfP GMaP ILea IMou MGil MRav NLar SDeJ WCAu WCot
	'Pehrson's Violet Frisbee' **new**	GBin
§	***peregrina***	CBro CSpe GEdr GKev LEdu MPhe WCAu
	- 'Fire King'	WCAu
§	- 'Otto Froebel' ♀H6	NLar WCAu WCot WKif
	- 'Rosabella'	CRos EHyd LRHS NRHS
	- 'Sunshine'	see *P. peregrina* 'Otto Froebel'
	'Pink Ardour'	GBin

	'Pink Double Dandy' (d) **new**	GBin
	'Pink Hawaiian Coral'	GBin ILea NLar WCot WTor
	potaninii	see *P. delavayi* var. *angustiloba* f. *angustiloba*
	'Prairie Charm'	CRos EPfP ILea MMrt
	'Prairie Moon'	GBin
	'Purple Sensation'	GBin
	'Raggedy Ann'	GBin
	'Raspberry Charm'	SDir
	'Red Charm'	EPfP GBin ILea LRHS SPer WCAu WFar WHil WKif WSpi WTor
	'Red Grace' (d)	GBin
	'Red Magic'	EPfP WFar WSpi
§	***rockii*** (S)	CSpe MPhe SPtp WSpi
	- from Tianshui, Gansu	MPhe
	- from Wenshian, Gansu	MPhe
	- hybrid	see *P.* Gansu Group
	romanica	see *P. peregrina*
	'Roselette'	GBin LRHS WCAu
	'Roy Pehrson's Best Yellow'	GBin
	russoi	see *P. mascula* subsp. *russoi*
	'Scarlet Heaven'	ELan GBin ILea MMrt MNrw WCAu
	'Scarlet O'Hara'	SPer WCAu WCot
	'Scrumdidleumptious' (d)	GBin
	'Sequestered Sunshine'	ILea NLar WCAu
	'Serebrenyi Velvet' **new**	GBin
	'Shimano-fuji' (S)	CRos LRHS WCAu
	'Simply Red'	GBin
	'Singing in the Rain'	ILea NLar
	× ***smouthii***	EHyd GEdr LRHS NRHS
	'Sonoma Amethyst' **new**	ELan
	'Sonoma Apricot' **new**	WCAu
	'Sonoma Kaleidoscope'	GBin ILea
	'Soshi'	LRHS SHar
	'Starlight'	LCro LOPS LRHS WCAu WCot WTor
	sterniana	CExl
§	***suffruticosa*** (S)	CDoC MGil MGos
	- BIRD OF RIMPO	see *P. suffruticosa* 'Rimpo'
	- BLACK FLOWER CHIEF	see *P. suffruticosa* 'Hei Hua Kui'
	- CHARMING AGE	see *P. suffruticosa* 'Howki'
	- dark lavender-flowered (S) **new**	ILea
	- dark pink-flowered (S) **new**	ILea
	- dark red-flowered (S) **new**	ILea
	- 'Dou Lu' (S)	NTPC
	- DOUBLE CHERRY	see *P. suffruticosa* 'Yae-zakura'
	- ETERNAL CAMELLIAS	see *P. suffruticosa* 'Yachiyo-tsubaki'
	- FLIGHT OF CRANES	see *P. suffruticosa* 'Renkaku'
	- FLORAL RIVALRY	see *P. suffruticosa* 'Hana-kisoi'
	- 'Gekkyu-den' (S)	LRHS
	- 'Guan Shi Mo Yu' (S)	CRos
	- 'Hai Huang' (S)	NTPC
§	- 'Hakuo-jisi' (S/d)	LRHS
	- 'Hakushin' (S)	LRHS
§	- 'Hana-daijin' (S)	LRHS
§	- 'Hana-kisoi' (S)	EBee EHyd LRHS NRHS
	- 'Hei Hai Sa Jin' (S)	NTPC
§	- 'Hei Hua Kui' (S)	NTPC
§	- 'Howki' (S)	LRHS
	- 'Iso-no-nami' (S)	LRHS
	- 'Jin Jiang Hong' (S)	NTPC
	- 'Joseph Rock'	see *P. rockii*
§	- 'Kamada-fuji' (S)	LRHS
§	- 'Kaow' (S)	EHyd LRHS NRHS
	- KING OF FLOWERS	see *P. suffruticosa* 'Kaow'
	- KING OF WHITE LIONS	see *P. suffruticosa* 'Hakuo-jisi'

	- 'Kinkaku'	see *P.* × *lemoinei* 'Souvenir de Maxime Cornu'
	- 'Koshino-yuki' (S)	LRHS
	- 'Lan Bao Shi' (S)	NTPC
	- light pink-flowered (S) **new**	ILea
	- light red-flowered (S) **new**	ILea
	- MAGNIFICENT FLOWER	see *P. suffruticosa* 'Hana-daijin'
	- 'Ofuji-nishiki' (S) **new**	CRos
	- purple-flowered (S) **new**	ILea
§	- 'Renkaku' (S)	LRHS
§	- 'Rimpo' (S)	WSpi
	- 'Rou Fu Rong' (S)	WSpi
	- 'Shimadaijin' (S)	EHyd LRHS NRHS WCAu
	- 'Shimane-chōjuraku' (S)	LRHS
	- 'Shin Shima Kagayaki' (S)	LRHS
	- 'Shin-fusōtsukasa' (S)	LRHS
§	- 'Taiyo' (S)	EBee EHyd LRHS NRHS
	- THE SUN	see *P. suffruticosa* 'Taiyo'
	- white-flowered (S) **new**	ILea
	- WISTERIA AT KAMADA	see *P. suffruticosa* 'Kamada-fuji'
	- 'Wu Long Peng Sheng' (S)	WSpi
§	- 'Yachiyo-tsubaki' (S)	LRHS
§	- 'Yae-zakura' (S)	LRHS
	- 'Yatsu-kazishi' (S)	EBee
	- yellow-flowered (S)	ILea
	- 'Yin Hong Qiao Dui' (S)	NTPC
	- 'Yoshinogawa' (S)	LRHS
	- 'Zhao Fen' (S)	NPer NTPC SRms
	'Sugar 'n' Spice'	GBin
	'Summer Glow' (d)	WCAu
	'Sunny Girl'	WCAu
	'Sunshine'	see *P. peregrina* 'Otto Froebel'
	tenuifolia	CBro CJun CPla CSpe EPot EWTr EWes EWld GEdr GKev MAvo MBel NSti SMad WCAu WSpi
	- 'Plena' (d)	CRos
	tenuifolia* × *veitchii* var. *woodwardii	CJun
	'Unique' **new**	ILea
	veitchii	GBin GKev GMaP ILea NBid NLar WCAu WCot WPGP WSpi
	- var. ***woodwardii***	CExl CJun GAbr GKev LPla NWad WCot WHoo WThu
	'Viking Full Moon'	ILea
	'Watermelon Wine'	ILea WCAu
	'White Charm' **new**	GBin
	'White Emperor'	ELan GBin ILea WCAu
	'White Towers'	EPfP WFar
	'Whopper'	GBin
	wittmanniana	GEdr
	- PAB 3673	LEdu
	- 'Rosea'	WCAu
	'Yankee Doodle Dandy' (d)	WCAu
	'Yellow Crown'	MHol SCob SDir WCAu

Paesia (*Dennstaedtiaceae*)

	scaberula	LEdu NBir WCot WPGP

pak choi see AGM Vegetables Section

Pallenis (*Asteraceae*)

§	***maritima***	CCCN

Pamianthe (*Amaryllidaceae*)

	peruviana	WMal

Panax (*Araliaceae*)

	ginseng	GPoy
	japonicus	WCru
	- BWJ 7932	WCru

Pancratium (*Amaryllidaceae*)

	illyricum	XEll
	maritimum	GKev SDeJ WCot

Pandorea (*Bignoniaceae*)

	jasminoides 🏆H1c	CCCN CDoC CPla CRHN CTri EBak EShb
	- 'Alba'	CRHN EShb
§	- 'Charisma' (v)	CBcs CCCN ECre EPfP EShb SEND WAvo
	- 'Lady Di'	CCCN
	- 'Rosea'	CCCN WAvo
	- 'Rosea Superba' 🏆H1c	CBcs CRHN SEND WLov
	- 'Variegata'	see *P. jasminoides* 'Charisma'
	lindleyana	see *Clytostoma calystegioides*
	pandorana	CRHN MGil SLim WAvo
	- 'Golden Showers'	CBcs CCCN CRHN MRav WLov
	- 'Snowbells'	IArd IMou

Panicum (*Poaceae*)

	amarum	CBod EPPr
	- var. ***amarulum***	CKno
	- 'Dewey Blue'	SMHy
	bulbosum	EBee EPPr
	clandestinum	EHyd EPPr EShb EWes LRHS MMuc
	'Frosted Explosion'	CSpe LRHS
	miliaceum	EHyd LRHS
	- 'Violaceum'	SPhx
	virgatum	CKno EPPr MAsh XLum
	- 'Black and Blue' **new**	MNrw
	- 'Black and Light' **new**	MNrw
	- 'Blue Tower'	CKno EHyd ELon EPPr LRHS SMea XLum
	- 'Cardinal'	CKno EMor EPPr MNrw WFar WHoo
	- 'Carthage' **new**	EPPr
	- 'Cheyenne Sky'	EBee EPPr
	- 'Cloud Nine' 🏆H5	CKno EBee EPPr EPed LRHS MAvo SMea WHal XCre
	- 'Dallas Blues'	CBod CKno EAJP EBee ECha EHyd ELan ELon EMor EPPr EPed EShb EWes LRHS MAvo MSpe NLar NRHS NWsh SCob SGbt SMHy SPeP SPer SPoG WFar XCre XLum
	- 'Emerald Chief'	CBod EHyd LRHS
	- 'Farbende Auslese'	EPPr MAvo
	- 'Hänse Herms'	CBod CKno EHyd ELon EMor EPPr EPed LRHS NLar NRHS SMea WFar
	- 'Heavy Metal'	Widely available
	- 'Heiliger Hain'	EHyd ELon EPPr LRHS NRHS WCot WFar
	- 'Külsen Moor'	EBee IPot WCot
I	- 'Kupferhirse'	CMea EPPr MAvo WFar
	- 'Kurt Bluemel'	EBee EPPr
	- 'Nican'	EBee EPPr MAvo
	- 'Northwind'	CKno CRos CSde EBee EHyd ELon EPPr EPfP GBin LRHS MAvo NRHS SCob SEdd SMHy SMad SMea SPeP SRms WFar XCre
	- 'Prairie Fire'	ECtt
	- 'Prairie Sky'	CBod CKno CRos EBee EHyd ELon EPPr EPed EWTr EWhm GMaP LEdu LRHS MAsh MAvo MMuc NBro NLar NRHS NWsh SCob SEdd SGbt SMHy SMea SRms XCre
	- PURPLE BREEZE ('Joz276'PBR) **new**	LCro LOPS
	- 'Purple Haze'	EHyd EPPr LRHS

	- 'Red Cloud'	CKno ELon MAvo
	- 'Rehbraun'	CBod CSde EBee EHyd ELan EMor EPPr EPfP LCro LOPS LRHS LSRN NRHS SCob SRms WCAu WSMil XCre XLum
	- 'Rotstrahlbusch'	CBod CKno EBee ELan EMor EPPr GMaP LSun MAvo SPer SRms WCot XCre XLum
	- 'Rubrum'	EPfP MAvo SRms
	- 'Sangria'PBR	CSpe LEdu SPoG
	- 'Shenandoah' ♀H5	Widely available
	- 'Squaw'	Widely available
	- 'Straight Cloud'	EPPr WFar
	- 'Strictum'	EPPr EWes GQue SCob SMHy SPer SPhx
I	- 'Strictum Compactum'	CBod
	- 'Thundercloud'	CKno
	- 'Warrior'	CBod CKno CRos CTri ECtt EHyd ELan ELon EMor EPPr EPed EPfP EWhm LRHS MAsh MAvo NLar NRHS NWsh SCob SEdd SPer WFar XCre
	- 'Wood's Variegated' (v)	WCot

Papaver (*Papaveraceae*)

	alboroseum	EHyd LRHS NRHS
	alpinum	CSpe EBou EHyd GQue LRHS MAsh NRHS
	atlanticum	EBou NBro SPlb
	- 'Flore Pleno' (d)	CSpe GAbr NBro
	bracteatum	see *P. orientale* var. *bracteatum*
§	***cambricum***	CCCN CExl CMac CTri EBee EHyd ELan EPfP LEdu MMuc NAts NRHS SPer WBrk WCot WFar WHer
	- var. ***aurantiacum***	WCot
	- double-flowered, orange (d)	NBir
§	- 'Frances Perry'	CSpe GKev WBor
	carmeli	SPhx
	'Cherry Glow' **new**	SPhx
	commutatum ♀H5	CSpe LCro LEdu LOPS SPhx
	- 'Ladybird' ♀H5	GAbr SPoG SVic
	dubium	CSpe GPoy LRHS SPhx
	- subsp. ***lecoqii*** 'Albiflorum'	CSpe LRHS SDix SPhx
	glaucum	CSpe LRHS SPhx
	guerlekense W&B BG-K-5	WCot
	'Heartbeat' (Super Poppy Series)	CBod EPfP LRHS MHol NBPC SEdd WCot WFar
	heldreichii	see *P. pilosum* subsp. *spicatum*
	lateritium	CPou SRms
	'Lauffeuer'	CSam
	'Matador'PBR ♀H6	EHyd LRHS NRHS
	'Medallion' (Super Poppy Series)	LRHS
	miyabeanum	CSpe EHyd LRHS NRHS
	'Moondance'	CRos EHyd LRHS NRHS SVic
§	***nudicaule***	LCro LOPS SVic
	- Champagne Bubbles Group	CSBt EAJP EHyd LRHS NRHS WFar
	- DELUXE MIXED **new**	CSpe
	- Garden Gnome Group	see *P. nudicaule* Gartenzwerg Group
§	- Gartenzwerg Group ♀H7	EHyd EPfP LRHS NRHS SPoG SWvt
	- 'Kelmscott Giant'	SVic
	- orange-flowered	LRHS
	- 'Pacino'	EAJP LRHS
	- Spring Fever Series **new**	CBod
	(Oriental Group) 'Aglaja' ♀H7	CBcs CDor ECtt IPot NGdn NLar SEdd SPad SPhx WCAu WCot WSpi
	- 'Allegro'	CSBt EHyd GMaP LSun NGdn SCob SPlb SPoG SVic SWvt WFar
	- 'Baby Kiss'PBR	WFar
	- 'Beauty of Livermere'	CBod CDor CSam CWCL EAJP ECha EHyd ELan EShb ILea LCro LOPS LRHS LSun MBel MNHC MPri NGdn NLar SGbt SPer SPoG SRms WCAu WFar
	- 'Beauty of Livermere' clonal	WCot
	- 'Beauty Queen'	CDor NGdn
	- 'Bolero'	CElw ECtt EPri NLar
	- 'Bonfire Red'	SCob
	- 'Brilliant'	CTsd EHyd NGdn NRHS WFar
	- 'Brooklyn' (New York Series)	ECtt LRHS
	- 'Burning Heart'	CWGN ECtt EPri
	- 'Carneum'	EHyd LRHS NRHS SPoG SRms
	- 'Cedar Hill'	EPri
	- 'Cedric Morris' ♀H7	ECha
	- 'Central Park' (New York Series)	EHyd LRHS WFar
	- 'Charming' red-flowered	EHyd
	- 'Clochard'	ECtt
	- 'Curlilocks'	EHyd NLar SRms SWvt WFar
	- 'Double Pleasure' (d)	ECtt
	- Double Red Shades (d)	NGdn
	- 'Doubloon' (d)	WFar
	- 'Dwarf Allegro'	MPri
	- 'Dwarf Allegro Vivace'	EHyd
	- 'Fancy Feathers'PBR	ECtt
	- 'Fiesta'	ELon
	- 'Flamenco'	WFar
	- 'Forncett Summer'	MHol NLar SEdd SPoG WCAu WCot
	- 'Frosty' (v)	SHar
	- 'Garden Glory'	ECtt LSRN
	- 'Glowing Embers'	ECtt
	- 'Goliath'	ELan NBro SRms WFar
	- HAREMSTRAUM (mixed)	WFar
	- 'Harlem' (New York Series)	CBcs CBod CElw CRos EHyd EPfP LRHS MNrw NLar STPC
	- 'Harvest Moon' (d)	EHyd NPer NRHS
	- 'Indian Chief'	EPri NPer SCob WFar
	- 'Inferno'PBR	ECtt
	- 'John III' ♀H7	SPhx
	- 'Karine' ♀H7	EHyd EPPr SCob
	- 'King Kong'	CBod ECtt LSun MBNS NLar WCot WFar
	- 'Kleine Tänzerin'	SEND WFar
	- 'Ladybird'	EHyd
	- 'Louvre' (Parisienne Series)	WFar
	- 'Mandarin'PBR	MHol SEdd
	- 'Manhattan' (New York Series)	CElw CSam ECtt EHyd EPfP ILea MNrw NRHS NSti SGbt WFar
	- 'Marlene'	LRHS WCAu
	- 'May Queen' (d)	ECtt EWes WCot WFar
	- 'Miss Piggy'PBR	ECtt SGbt WFar
	- 'Mrs Perry'	CRos EHyd NPer SGbt SRms WBrk WFar
	- 'Orange Glow'	CBod NBPC
	- 'Papillon'PBR	CBcs EHyd NRHS
	- 'Patty's Plum'	Widely available
	- 'Perry's White'	CBcs EBee ECtt EHyd LRHS NChi SCob SRkn SWvt WCAu WSpi
	- 'Picotée'	ECtt ELan NLar SCob SWvt WFar
	- 'Pink Ruffles'PBR	ECtt EHyd SGbt WFar
	- 'Pinnacle'	WFar
	- 'Pizzicato'	CBod CRos EHyd ELan NPer WFar WHil WRTC
	- 'Place Pigalle' (Parisienne Series)	CBod ECtt NBPC
	- 'Plum Pudding'	EHyd

- 'Prince of Orange' SWvt
- 'Prinz Eugen' WFar
- 'Prinzessin Victoria Louise' CDor CRos EHyd ELan EPfP GMaP MNHC MPri NGdn NLar NRHS SPoG SRms WBrk
- 'Queen Alexandra' CDor EHyd EPfP MBel
- 'Raspberry Brûlée' EHyd LRHS NRHS
- 'Raspberry Queen' CDor ECtt EHyd LRHS NChi NLar
- 'Rembrandt' WCot
- 'Royal Chocolate Distinction' ECtt ELan EPfP NBPC WFar
- 'Royal Wedding' CBcs CBod CDor CMac CRos CTri CTsd EAJP EBee EHyd ELan EPfP EShb LCro LOPS LSun MGos MPri NLar NRHS SCob SEND SEdd SGbt SRms WCot WFar WSpi
- 'Ruffled Patty' PBR CBod ECtt ELan EPfP MSCN NLar SEdd SGbt SPad WCot
- 'Salmon Glow' (d) WFar
- scarlet-flowered SEND
- 'Scarlett O'Hara' PBR (d) ECtt WFar
- 'Snow Goose' CBod CDor CSam CWGN ECtt EHyd EPfP ILea IPot LSun NBPC NLar NRHS SCob SEdd SPoG WCot WKif
- 'Staten Island' (New York Series) MAvo MNrw
- 'Tiffany' ECtt
- 'Türkenlouis' CBod EAJP ECtt EHyd NQui SPoG WBrk WCAu WFar
- 'Turkish Delight' EHyd NBir SWvt WCAu
- 'Walking Fire' MNrw
- 'Watermelon' SCob SPoG
- 'White Ruffles' PBR EPfP MSCN SGbt

orientale CBcs CTsd EPfP SRms SVic
§ - var. ***bracteatum*** NBir
- 'Guardsman' see *P.* (Oriental Group) 'Beauty of Livermere' clonal
- 'Mrs Marrow's Plum' see *P.* (Oriental Group) 'Patty's Plum'
- PRINCESS VICTORIA LOUISE see *P.* (Oriental Group) 'Prinzessin Victoria Louise'

pavoninum SPhx
§ ***pilosum*** subsp. ***spicatum*** CSpe ECha NBir SPhx WCot
radicatum CPla
rhoeas CHab LCro LOPS MBow MNHC SPhx SVic
- 'Bridal Silk' LCro
- 'Bridal White' LOPS SPhx
- Mother of Pearl Group CSpe LRHS SPhx
- 'Paradise' **new** CSpe

rupifragum CBod ECha MMuc SPhx WCot
- 'Double Tangerine Gem' see *P. rupifragum* 'Flore Pleno'
§ - 'Flore Pleno' (d) CDor CSpe EPPr GBin SVic WBrk
- 'Tangerine Dream' GPSL

'Shasta' (Super Poppy Series) CBod LRHS WFar
somniferum CLau ENfk GPoy SVic
- var. ***album*** XAbr
- 'Blackcurrant Fizz' (d) LCro LOPS SPhx
- 'Boudoir Babe' (d) CSpe
- 'Double Shiraz' (d) LRHS SPhx
- 'Drama Queen' **new** CSpe
- 'Lauren's Grape' CSpe LCro LOPS LRHS SPhx
- 'Lilac Pompom' (d) LCro LOPS
- (Paeoniiflorum Group) 'Black Beauty' (d) CSpe LRHS SDeJ SPhx SVic
- - 'Black Paeony' (d) LCro LOPS LRHS SPhx
- - 'Schwarzer Drachen' (d) LRHS
- 'Persian White' CSpe SPhx
- 'Rye Beaner' **new** SVic
- single black-flowered CSpe
- - white-flowered CSpe
- 'White Cloud' (d) CSpe

thianschanicum SPhx
triniifolium MMuc SPhx WCot

papaya (pawpaw) see *Carica papaya*

Parabenzoin see *Lindera*

Parachampionella see *Strobilanthes*

Paradisea (*Asparagaceae*)

liliastrum misapplied see *P. lusitanica*
liliastrum (L.) Bertol. ♀H5 EBee EPri LRHS NBid NChi
§ ***lusitanica*** CAvo CNor CSam CSpe EBee ECtt EPot EPri GBin GKev LEdu MCot MHol SIvy SPhx WCot WPGP XEll

Parahebe (*Plantaginaceae*)

× ***bidwillii*** GJos SRms
- 'Kea' ECtt

§ ***catarractae*** CExl EHyd ELan EPfP EWld ITim LRHS MSCN NBir NRHS SRms WKif
- 'Avalanche' PBR CWGN EHyd EPfP GMaP LRHS MAsh MSCN NRHS SGbt SPoG WNPC
- 'Baby Blue' EHyd LRHS NRHS
- blue-flowered GJos SGbt SPer

§ - 'Delight' ♀H4 CExl EHyd EWes GMaP GQue LRHS MHer NPer NRHS SCob WLov
- subsp. ***diffusa*** NPer
- 'Miss Willmott' ECtt SPer SPlb
- 'Porlock' CBod CDoC EAJP EBee EPfP GKev GWyn NSla SBut SDix SRms SWvt WCav WHoo
- 'Porlock Purple' see *P. catarractae* 'Delight'
- 'Rosea' SRms WTyc
- white-flowered GAbr SRms
- 'Whittallii' GBin

densifolia see *Chionohebe densifolia*
§ ***formosa*** SPlb SVen
'Greencourt' see *P. catarractae* 'Delight'
§ ***hookeriana*** GKev
'Jean' GBin
'Kenty Pink' MMuc
linifolia 'Blue Skies' ECtt EPot GBin
§ ***lyallii*** CPla CTri EBee ELan EPfP GMaP MHer MMuc MRav MSwo NQui SPlb SRms WKif
- 'Julie-Anne' ♀H4 LRHS
- 'Snowcap' EBee LRHS MRav SPlb SRms

'Mervyn' CNor CTri
§ ***perfoliata*** CCBP CDor CExl CMea CSde EBee ECha ECre GMaP LEdu LRHS MAsh MCot MNrw MRav SBrt SBut SDix SEND SPer SRms WWFP XLum
'Snow Clouds' CBar CBod CMea CSpe EBee ECtt EHyd ELan EPfP GKev LRHS MMuc NEoE NHpl NRHS SBut SDix SEdd SGro SPad WCav WFar WHoo WTor

Parajubaea (*Arecaceae*)

torallyi SPalm

Parakmeria see *Magnolia*

Paranomus (*Proteaceae*)

	reflexus	SPlb

Paraquilegia (*Ranunculaceae*)

	adoxoides	see *Semiaquilegia adoxoides*
§	***anemonoides***	CExl GKev WAbe
	grandiflora	see *P. anemonoides*

Parasenecio (*Asteraceae*)

	delphiniifolius B&SWJ 5789	WCru
	- B&SWJ 10885	WCru
	- B&SWJ 11189	WCru WSHC
	- B&SWJ 11415	WCru
	farfarifolius	WCru
	- var. ***acerinus*** B&SWJ 11549	WCru
	- - B&SWJ 11554	WCru
	- var. ***bulbifer***	WCru
	hastatus var. ***farfarifolius***	see *P. maximowiczianus*
§	***maximowiczianus*** B&SWJ 11468	WCru
	mortonii GWJ 9419	WCru
	- HWJK 2214	WCru
	tebakoensis B&SWJ 11167	WCru
	- B&SWJ 11536	WCru

Paraserianthes (*Mimosaceae*)

	distachya	see *P. lophantha*
§	***lophantha*** ♀H2	CExl CTsd EBak EShb SPlb

Parastyrax (*Styracaceae*)

	BWJ 15185 from Northern Vietnam **new**	WCru

Parasyringa see *Ligustrum*

Parathelypteris (*Thelypteridaceae*)

	beddomei	LEdu WCot WPGP

× *Pardancanda* see *Iris*

Pardanthopsis see *Iris*

Parietaria (*Urticaceae*)

	judaica	GPoy WHer WSFF

Paris ✿ (*Melanthiaceae*)

	chinensis	WCru
	- B&SWJ 265 from Taiwan	WCru
	forrestii	WCru
	incompleta	ESwi GEdr LEdu MAvo WCru
	japonica	GEdr
	lancifolia B&SWJ 3044 from Taiwan	WCru
	polyphylla	CMiW CSpe ECha EPot GKev MNrw NBid NHpl NLar SDir SDix SPalm WCru WPnP
	- B&SWJ 2125	WCru
	- HWJCM 475	WCru
	- var. ***alba***	GEdr
	- var. ***polyphylla***	GKev
	- var. ***stenophylla***	WCru
*	- var. ***yunnanensis*** f. ***alba***	MAvo
	quadrifolia	CSpe CWCL EBee EMor EPfP GEdr GKev GPoy LEdu MNrw NGrd NLar SPhx WCru WFar WHer WPnP WShi
	tetraphylla	GEdr WCru
	thibetica	EBee GKev WCru
	- var. ***thibetica***	SDir
	verticillata	WCru

Parkinsonia (*Caesalpiniaceae*)

	aculeata	CBcs SPlb

Parnassia (*Celastraceae*)

	foliosa	NHar
	gansuensis	NHar
	- SDR 5128	EBee GKev
	nubicola	GKev
	palustris	GKev WHer
	- var. ***yakushimensis***	NHar

Parochetus (*Papilionaceae*)

	communis ambig.	CExl MSCN NPer
	- subsp. ***africanus*** ♀H2	WHil
*	- 'Blue Gem'	CCCN

Parolinia (*Brassicaceae*)

	ornata	WCot

Paronychia (*Caryophyllaceae*)

§	***capitata***	CTri SRms
	kapela	SPlb XSen
§	- subsp. ***serpyllifolia***	XLum
	- - 'Binsted Gold' (v)	XLum
	nivea	see *P. capitata*
	serpyllifolia	see *P. kapela* subsp. *serpyllifolia*

Parrotia ✿ (*Hamamelidaceae*)

	persica	Widely available
	- PAB 13.046	LEdu
	- 'Bella'	CJun EBee MBlu WMou
	- 'Biltmore'	CJun NLar SSta
	- 'Burgundy'	CJun EPfP NLar
	- 'Cobhay Upright'	CJun
	- fastigiate	CJun
	- 'Felicie'	CJun EPfP IArd NLar
	- 'Het Plantsoen'	NLar
	- 'Horizontalis'	CJun
	- 'Jodrell Bank'	CJun MBlu NLar
	- 'Pendula'	CJun CMCN EPfP MBlu SSta
	- 'Persian Carpet'	NLar
	- PERSIAN SPIRE ('Jlpn01'PBR)	CBcs LCro LOPS SMad
	- 'Summer Bronze'	CJun CRos EHyd LRHS MAsh
	- 'Vanessa' ♀H6	CBcs CCVT CJun CLnd CMCN CRos CTho EHyd EPfP EWes IArd LMaj LRHS LSRN MAsh MBlu MPkF NLar NRHS SCob SGol SReu SSta WMou
	subaequalis	CBcs CJun NLar WPGP

Parrotia × *Sycopsis* see × *Sycoparrotia*

Parrotiopsis (*Hamamelidaceae*)

	jacquemontiana	CBcs CJun GBin MBlu NLar

parsley see *Petroselinum crispum*; also AGM Vegetables Section

parsnip see AGM Vegetables Section

Parsonsia (*Apocynaceae*)

	heterophylla	CTsd

Parthenium (*Asteraceae*)

	integrifolium	EMor GPoy IMou LRHS SPhx WCot

Parthenocissus (*Vitaceae*)

§	***henryana*** ♀H5	Widely available
	- 'Malene'	EShb
	himalayana 'Purpurea'	see *P. himalayana* var. *rubrifolia*
§	- var. ***rubrifolia***	CBcs CMac ELan GBin MAsh MRav SLim SLon SPtp WCru
	inserta misapplied	see *P. quinquefolia*
	inserta ambig.	CMac NLar
	laetevirens	NLar
§	***quinquefolia***	Widely available
	- var. ***engelmannii***	CBcs EBee EShb LBuc SEND WCFE
	- 'Guy's Garnet'	WCru
	- RED WALL ('Troki')	CRos EHyd LRHS NRHS
	- STAR SHOWERS ('Monham') (v)	EBee EPfP NLar
	- 'Yellow Wall'PBR	CRos EHyd LRHS NRHS
	semicordata B&SWJ 6551	WCru
	striata	see *Cissus striata*
	thomsonii	see *Cayratia thomsonii*
§	***tricuspidata***	CCVT CMCN EPfP MAsh MGos SArc SGol SPer
	- 'Beverley Brook'	CRHN ELon LSRN NLar SNig SPer SRms
	- 'Crûg Compact'	WCru
	- 'Fenway Park'	EBee ELan LRHS MRav NLar
	- 'Green Spring'	CBcs ELan IArd MGos NLar
	- 'Lowii'	CDoC CMac EHyd ELan EPfP LRHS MBlu MRav NLar SLon SNig SPoG
	- 'Robusta'	EBee
§	- 'Veitchii' ♀H5	Widely available

Pasithea (*Hemerocallidaceae*)

	caerulea	CBod EPri MHol SMHy WCot WPGP

Paspalum (*Poaceae*)

	glaucifolium	MNrw
	quadrifarium RCB RA S-5	WCot

Passiflora ✿ (*Passifloraceae*)

	actinia	CCCN CRHN SPlb
	'Adularia'	CCCN
	alata (F) ♀H1c	CCCN
	× ***alatocaerulea***	see *P.* × *belotii*
	× ***allardii***	CCCN
	ambigua	CCCN
§	'Amethyst' ♀H3	CBcs CCCN CRHN CRos CSBt LSRN MAsh SEdd SPoG
	amethystina misapplied	see *P.* 'Amethyst'
§	***amethystina*** Mikan	CRos ECre EHyd LRHS NRHS
	'Anastasia'	CCCN
	'Andy'	CCCN
	'Anemona'	CCCN
	'Angelo Blu'	CCCN
	'Annika'	CCCN
	antioquiensis misapplied	see *P.* × *exoniensis*
	antioquiensis ambig.	CBcs CCCN
	antioquiensis H. Karst. × ***parritae*** new	CRHN
	'Ariane'	CCCN
	× ***atropurpurea***	CCCN
§	***aurantia***	CCCN
	banksii	see *P. aurantia*
§	× ***belotii***	CCCN
	- 'Impératrice Eugénie'	see *P.* × *belotii*
	- 'Perfume Passion'PBR	CCCN
	'Betty Myles Young'	CCCN CRHN ECre ELan EPfP
	'Blue Bird'	CCCN
	'Blue Bouquet'	CCCN
	'Blue Crown'	CCCN
	'Blue Moon'	CCCN
	'Blue Stripper'	CCCN
	'Blue Velvet'	CCCN
	bogatensis B&SWJ 14951	WCru
	'Byron Beauty'	CCCN
	'Byte'	CCCN
§	***caerulea*** ♀H4	Widely available
	- 'Chinensis'	CCCN
	- 'Clear Sky'PBR	CBod CCCN ELan EPfP NLar SEdd SRms
	- 'Constance Eliott' ♀H4	CAgr CBcs CBod CBrac CCCN CMac CRHN CRos EBee EHyd ELan EPfP LCro LOPS LRHS MAsh MGos NLar NRHS SCob SNig SPer SWvt
	- 'Pierre Pomié'	CCCN
I	- 'Rubra'	CBod CCCN CDoC CSBt SLim
	- WHITE LIGHTNING ('Yanpas'PBR)	CCCN CRos EHyd ELan EPfP EShb LRHS NRHS SLim SPoG SWvt
	× ***caeruleoracemosa***	see *P.* × *violacea*
	× ***caponii***	CCCN
	- 'John Innes'	CCCN
	'Celine'	CCCN
	chinensis	see *P. caerulea*
	citrifolia	CCCN
	citrina	CCCN
*	***classica*** × ***coccinea***	CCCN EShb
	× ***colvillii***	CCCN
	'Coordination'	CCCN
§	***coriacea***	CCCN
	'Crimson Tears'	CCCN
	cuatrecasasii B&SWJ 14834	WCru
§	'Damsel's Delight'	CCCN CRos CWGN EBee ECre EHyd ELan LRHS NRHS
	'Daylight'	CCCN
	'Debby'	CCCN
	× ***decaisneana*** (F)	CCCN
	'Divertido'	CCCN
	EDEN ('Hil Pas Eden') ♀H3	CCCN SRkn
	edulis (F)	CBcs CCCN CPla SPre SVic
	- 'Byte' (F)	CCCN
§	- f. ***edulis*** (F)	CCCN
	- f. ***flavicarpa*** (F)	CCCN
	- 'Norfolk' (F)	CCCN
	- 'Parati' (F)	CCCN
	'Elizabeth' (F)	CCCN
	'Empress Eugenie'	see *P.* × *belotii*
	'Evatoria'	CCCN
§	× ***exoniensis*** ♀H2	CCCN CRHN CSBt ECre
	'Fairylights'	CCCN
	'Fantasma'	CCCN
	'Fata Confetto'	CCCN
	'Fledermouse'	CCCN
	'Flying V'	CCCN
	gracilens new	CRHN
	'Grand Duchess'	CCCN
	gritensis	CCCN
	'Guglielmo Betto'	CCCN
	'Heidi'	CCCN
	'Hetty Nicolaas'	CCCN
	'Hildegard'	CCCN
	incarnata (F)	CCCN GPoy SPlb
	'Incense' (F) ♀H2	CCCN SPlb
	'Inspiration'	CCCN
	'Jara'	CCCN
	'Jelly Joker'	CCCN
	'Justine Lyons'	CCCN MMrt
	karwinskii	CCCN

	× ***kewensis***	CCCN
	'Lady Margaret'	CCCN
	'Lambiekins'	CCCN
§	***ligularis*** (F)	CCCN SVic
	'Lilac Lady'	see *P.* × *violacea* 'Tresederi'
	'Livie'	CCCN
	lowei	see *P. ligularis*
	lutea	CCCN
	'Luzmarina'	CCCN
	'Manapany'	CCCN
	manicata (F)	CCCN
	- B&SWJ 14284	WCru
	- B&SWJ 14868	WCru
	'Maria'	CCCN
	'Marijke'	CCCN
	'Mary Jane'	CCCN
I	***matthewsii*** 'Alba'	CRHN
	'Mavis Mastics'	see *P.* × *violacea* 'Tresederi'
	mayana	see *P. caerulea*
	membranacea (F)	CCCN
	'Michael'	CCCN
	'Minai'	CCCN
	'Mini Lamb'	CCCN
	mixta (F)	CCCN
	- B&SWJ 14832	WCru
	- clone 2	CCCN
	- red-flowered	CCCN
	aff. ***mixta*** B&SWJ 14302	WCru
	mollissima misapplied	see *P. tarminiana*
	mollissima ambig. (F)	CBcs CCCN EShb SPlb
	mollissima (Kunth) L.H. Bailey (F) ♀^{H2}	CRHN
	- B&SWJ 14876	WCru
	'Monika Fischer'	CCCN
	mucronata	CCCN
	murucuja	CCCN
	'New Incense'	CCCN
	'Nightshift'	CCCN
	obtusifolia	see *P. coriacea*
	onychina	see *P. amethystina* Mikan
	'Panda'	CCCN
	'Party Animal'	CCCN ECre SEdd
	'Pink Festival'	CCCN
	'Pink Nightmare'	CCCN
	'Pink Passion'^{PBR}	CCCN
	'Pinky'	CCCN
	× ***piresiae***	CCCN
	'Poppet'	CCCN
	'Precioso'	CCCN
	'Pura Vida'	CCCN
	'Purple Companion'	CCCN
	'Purple Haze'	CCCN CDoC CRos CTsd EHyd ELan LCro LOPS LRHS NLar NRHS WFar
	'Purple Passion'	see *P. edulis* f. *edulis*
	'Purple Pendulum'	CCCN
	'Purple Rain'	CCCN
	quadrangularis (F) ♀^{H1a}	CCCN
	quinquangularis	CCCN
	racemosa ♀^{H1a}	CCCN
	- 'Blushing Bride' new	CCCN
	- 'Buzios'	CCCN
	- 'Diva' new	CCCN
	- pink-flowered	CCCN
	'Red Inca'	CCCN
	reitzii	CCCN
	riparia	CCCN
	semiciliosa B&SWJ 14824	WCru
	sexocellata	see *P. coriacea*
	'Silly Cow'	see *P.* 'Damsel's Delight'
	'Silvie'	CCCN
	'Simply Red'	CCCN
	'Snow Queen'	CBod CCCN CWGN ELan EPfP
	'Star of Kingston'	CCCN
	'Star of Surbiton'	CCCN ELan LRHS
	'Sunburst'	CCCN
	'Surprise'	CCCN
§	***tarminiana*** (F)	CCCN CRHN CSBt
	- B&SWJ 14960	WCru
	- white-flowered	CCCN
	'Temptation'	CCCN
	tetrandra	CExl
	× ***tresederi***	see *P.* × *violacea* 'Tresederi'
	trifasciata	CCCN
	tripartita B&SWJ 14768	WCru
	- B&SWJ 14807	WCru
	tucumanensis tetraploid	CCCN
	tulae	CCCN
	venusta	CCCN
§	× ***violacea*** ♀^{H2}	CCCN CRHN
	- 'Eynsford Gem'	CCCN
	- 'Lilac Lady'	see *P.* × *violacea* 'Tresederi'
	- 'Sabin'	CCCN
§	- 'Tresederi'	CCCN ELan
	- 'Twin Star'	CCCN
	- 'Victoria'	CCCN CSBt NLar
	vitifolia (F)	CCCN
	- 'Innocentiae'	CCCN
	'White Queen'	CCCN
	'White Surprise'	CCCN
	'White Wedding'	CCCN
	'Wilgen Heintje'	CCCN
	'Wilgen K Verhoeff'	CCCN
	'Wilgen Marieke'	CCCN
	'Winterland'	CCCN

passion fruit see *Passiflora*

passion fruit, banana see *Passiflora mollissima* (Kunth) L.H. Bailey

Pastinaca (*Apiaceae*)

sativa	CHab SPhx SVic WCot
- subsp. ***sylvestris***	NGrd

Patersonia (*Iridaceae*)

occidentalis	LRHS SPlb

Patrinia ✿ (*Caprifoliaceae*)

gibbosa	CSam CSpe EBee EMor GEdr MMrt MMuc NLar SBut SPhx WFar WPnP
- B&SWJ 874	ESwi WCru
heterophylla	GKev
intermedia	EBee
cf. ***monandra***	EBee ESwi
punctiflora new	CSpe SDix
aff. ***punctiflora***	ECha NDov
rupestris B&SWJ 12654	WCru
scabiosifolia	CElw CKno CMiW CSpe ECha ECtt EMor ESwi EWld LRHS MAvo MHol NBir NLar SBut SDix SPhx WFar WHoo
- B&SWJ 8740	WCru
- 'Nagoya'	MNrw
triloba	CMiW CSpe EHyd EMor GEdr LRHS MMrt NLar SBut WFar
- var. ***palmata***	EBee GKev
villosa	CExl EBee IMou SBut SPhx

Paulownia (*Paulowniaceae*)

catalpifolia	EBee NLar SAko
elongata	CBcs NLar WLov
fargesii misapplied	see *P. tomentosa* 'Lilacina'
fargesii ambig.	WCot
fortunei	MBlu SPlb
- NMWJ 14533 **new**	WCru
- FAST BLUE ('Minfast') ♀H5	CExl EBee LSRN
kawakamii	CBct CMCN EPfP ESwi SChF WPGP
- NMWJ 14552 **new**	WCru
- RWJ 9909	WCru
'Purple Spendour'	SAko SPer
taiwaniana NMWJ 14529 **new**	WCru
tomentosa ♀H5	Widely available
- W 769	WPGP
- 'Coreana'	ESwi WCru
§ - 'Lilacina'	CBcs

Pavonia (*Malvaceae*)

multiflora ambig.	CCCN
praemorsa	CCCN
strictiflora	CCCN
* ***volubilis***	CCCN

pawpaw (false banana) see *Asimina triloba*

pawpaw (papaya) see *Carica papaya*

pea see AGM Vegetables Section

peach see *Prunus persica*

pear see *Pyrus communis*; also AGM Fruit Section

pear, Asian see *Pyrus pyrifolia*

pecan see *Carya illinoinensis*

Pedicularis (*Orobanchaceae*)

bicornata	CPla

Pelargonium ✿ (*Geraniaceae*)

'A.M. Mayne' (Z/d)	WFib
'Aaron West' (St)	WFib
'Abba' (Z/d)	WFib
'Abbie Hillier' (R)	WFib
'Abel Carrière' (I/d)	WFib
abrotanifolium (Sc)	ENfk MHer SEdd SVen WFib WGwG
acetosum	EPPr MHer WFib
'Ada Green' (R)	WFib
'Ada Sutterby' (Dw/d)	WFib
'Ade's Elf' (Z/St)	WFib
'Ainsdale Beauty' (Z)	WFib
alchemilloides	WFib
'Aldwyck' (R) ♀H1c	WFib
'Alex Kitson' (Z)	WFib
'Algenon' (Min/d)	WFib
I 'Alice' (Min)	WFib
'Alison March' (Dw/Z/v/d)	WFib
'Allesley Shadow' (Dw/d)	ECtt WFib
'Allwoods Lemon Drizzle' (Z/Min) **new**	SAll
'Alma' (Dw/C)	SSea
alpinum	MHer WOld
'Alta Bell' (R)	ELan
'Amari' (R)	WFib
'Ambrose' (Min/d)	WFib
AMELIT ('Pacameli'PBR) (I/d)	SSea
'American Prince of Orange' (Sc)	SPet
'Amethyst' (R)	SCoo WFib
I 'Amy' (Dw)	WFib
(Angeleyes Series)	MCot
ANGELEYES BICOLOR ('Pacbicolor'PBR) (A)	
- ANGELEYES RANDY ('Pacra') (A)	SSea
'Angelique' (Dw/d)	WFib
'Ann Hoystead' (R) ♀H1c	WFib
'Annabelle Stephenson' (Dw/d)	WFib
'Annsbrook Beauty' (A/C)	SPet WFib
'Annsbrook Jupitor' (Z/St)	WFib
(Antik Series) ANTIK ORANGE ('Tikorg'PBR) (Z) ♀H1c	SPoG
- ANTIK PINK ('Tikpink'PBR) (Z)	SPoG
- ANTIK SCARLET ('Tikscarl'PBR) (Z)	SPoG
- ANTIK VIOLET ('Tikvio'PBR) (Z)	SPoG
'Antoine Crozy' (I × Z/d)	WFib
'Apache' (Z/d)	WFib
appendiculatum	MHer
'Apple Betty' (Sc)	NWsh WFib
'Apple Blossom Rosebud' (Z/d) ♀H1c	ECtt EShb MHer WFib
'Apricot Fool' (U/Sc)	WFib
'Apricot Glace' (U/Sc)	MHer WFib
'April Hamilton' (I)	LCro LOPS WFib
'April Showers' (A)	WFib
'Arctic Frost' (I)	WFib
§ 'Arctic Star' (St) ♀H1c	CSpe WBrk WFib
'Ardens' ♀H1c	CBod CDow CNor CPbh CSpe EBee ELan LCro LOPS MCot MHer SEdd SWvt WCAu WCot WFib WOld WWFP
'Ardwick Cinnamon' (Sc)	ENfk MHer NWsh SPet SRms WFib
'Arnside Fringed Aztec' (R)	MHer WFib
'Ashby' (Dec/Sc) ♀H1c	ECtt ENfk MHer SPet WFib
'Ashfield Jubilee' (Z/C)	WFib
'Ashfield Serenade' (Z) ♀H1c	WFib
'Askham Fringed Aztec' (R) ♀H1c	WFib
asperum Ehr. ex Willd.	see *P.* 'Graveolens'
§ 'Atomic Snowflake' (Sc/v)	ECtt ENfk MNHC NWsh SPet SRms WFib
'Atrium' (U)	MHer NWsh WFib
'Attar of Roses' (Sc) ♀H1c	CCBP CCht CLau CSpe ECtt ENfk LCro LOPS MCot MHer MNHC MPri NCou NWsh SEdi SGro SPet SPoG SRms WBrk WFib WGwG
'Aurora' (Z/d)	ECtt
australe	MCot MHer NWsh WFib
'Australian Mystery' (R/Dec) ♀H1c	CSpe ECtt WFib
'Aztec' (R) ♀H1c	WFib
'Baby Bird's Egg' (Min)	WFib
'Baby Harry' (Dw/v)	WFib
'Balcon Lilas'	see *P.* 'Roi des Balcons Lilas'
'Balcon Rose'	see *P.* 'Hederinum'
'Ballerina' (R)	see *P.* 'Carisbrooke'
I 'Ballerina' (Min)	WFib
'Barbara Eldridge' (Z)	WFib

§	'Barbe Bleu' (I/d) ♀H1c	LCro LOPS WFib
	barklyi	WFib
	'Baronne A. de Rothschild' (Z/d)	WFib
	'Bath Beauty' (Dw)	CSpe
	'Beatrice Cottington' (I/d)	WFib
	'Beauty of Calderdale' (Z/C)	WFib
	'Beauty of Eastbourne' misapplied	see *P.* 'Lachskönigin', *P.* 'Eastbourne Beauty'
	BELLADONNA ('Fisopa') (I/d)	SCoo
	'Bembridge' (Z/St/d)	CDow WFib
	'Ben Matt' (R)	WFib
§	'Bergpalais' (Z/d)	SSea
	'Berkswell Bolero' (A) **new**	WFib
	'Berkswell Carnival' (A)	ELan
	'Berkswell Lace' (A)	MHer
	'Beromünster' (Dec)	ECtt MHer WFib
	'Bert Pearce' (R)	WFib
	'Beryl Gibbons' (Z/d)	WFib
	'Beryl Reid' (R)	WFib
	betulinum	CPbh WFib
	'Betwixt' (Z/v)	WFib
	'Big Apple' (Sc)	SRms
	'Bird Dancer' (Dw/St) ♀H1c	CSpe MHer MNHC SIvy WBrk
	(Birdbush Series) 'Birdbush Bobby' (Sc)	SRms
	- 'Birdbush Bold and Beautiful' (Sc)	SRms
	- 'Birdbush Eleanor' (Z)	WFib
	- 'Birdbush Nutty' (Sc)	SRms
	'Birthday Girl' (R) ♀H1c	ECtt WFib
	'Bitter Lemon' (Sc)	ECtt WFib
	'Black Butterfly'	see *P.* 'Brown's Butterfly'
	'Black Country Bugle' (Z/d)	WFib
	'Black Knight' (A)	SPet
	'Black Knight' (R)	ECtt MHer
	'Black Prince' (R/Dec)	CSpe WFib
	'Black Vesuvius'	see *P.* 'Red Black Vesuvius'
	'Blackcurrant Yhu' (Dec)	MPtG
	BLANCHE ROCHE ('Guitoblanc') (I/d)	MBros MHer SCoo SSea
§	'Blandfordianum' (Sc)	MHer NWsh
I	'Blandfordianum Album' (Sc)	WFib
	'Blandfordianum Roseum' (Sc)	MHer WFib
	'Blazonry' (Z/v)	WFib
	(Blizzard Series) BLIZZARD BLUE ('Fisrain'[PBR]) (I)	SCoo
	- BLIZZARD RED ('Fizzard') (I)	SCoo
	- BLIZZARD WHITE ('Fisbliz'[PBR]) (I)	SCoo
	'Blue Beard'	see *P.* 'Barbe Bleu'
	BLUE WONDER ('Pacbla'[PBR]) (Z/d)	SSea
	'Bob Newing' (Min/St)	WFib
	'Bobberstone' (Z/St)	WFib
	'Bold Ann' (Dw/Z/d)	WFib
	'Bold Appleblossom' (Z)	WFib
	'Bold Bridesmaid' (Dw/d)	WFib
	'Bold Carousel' (Z/d)	WFib
	'Bold Cherie' (Dw/d)	WFib
	'Bold Cherub' (Z/d)	WFib
	'Bold Cyclamen' (Dw/d)	WFib
	'Bold Debonair' (Dw/d)	WFib
	'Bold Dove' (Dw)	WFib
	'Bold Flame' (Z/d)	WFib
	'Bold Gem' (Z/d)	WFib
	'Bold Limelight' (Z/d)	WFib
	'Bold Minstrel' (Z/d)	WFib
	'Bold Moonlight' (Dw)	WFib
	'Bold Pixie' (Dw/d)	WFib
	'Bold Princess' (Z/d)	WFib
	'Bold Special' (Z)	WFib
	'Bold Spirit' (Z)	WFib
	'Bold Sunset' (Z/d) ♀H1c	WFib
	'Bolero' (U) ♀H1c	MPtG WFib
	'Bon Bon' (Min/St)	WFib
	'Bontrosai'[PBR] (Sc)	MCot
	'Bosham' (R)	WFib
	'Both's Snowflake' (Sc/v)	WFib
	'Bourbon Rose' (Sc)	MHer
	bowkeri	WFib
	BRAVO ('Fisbravo') (Z/d)	WFib
	'Brenda' (Min/d)	WFib
	'Brenda Hyatt' (Dw/d)	WFib
	'Brian West' (Min/St/C)	WFib
	'Brian West Butterfly' (Z/St) ♀H1c	WFib
	'Bright Eyes' ambig. (Dw)	WFib
	'Brightstone' (Z/d)	ECtt WFib
	'Brilliant' (Dec)	ENfk SPet WFib
	'Brilliantine' (Sc)	ENfk MHer SRms WFib
	'Britannia' (R)	WFib
	'Brixworth Pearl' (Z)	WFib
	'Brook's Purple'	see *P.* 'Royal Purple'
	'Brookside Flamenco' (Dw/d)	WFib
	'Brookside Primrose' (Min/C/d)	WFib
	'Brookside Serenade' (Dw)	WFib
§	'Brown's Butterfly' (R)	WFib
	'Brunswick' (Sc)	MHer WFib
	'Bushfire' (R) ♀H1c	WFib
	BUTTERFLY ('Fisam') (I)	SCoo
	caespitosum	MHer
	caffrum	WFib
	- 'Diana'	MHer WOld
	'Cal'	see *P.* 'Salmon Irene'
	'California Brilliant' (U)	MHer
	'Calignon' (Z/St)	WFib
	'Cameo' (Dw/d)	WFib
	'Camphor Rose' (Sc) ♀H1c	SRms
	'Can-can' (I/d)	WFib
	canescens	see *P.* 'Blandfordianum'
	'Cape Town' (Dw/Z/v)	WFib
	capitatum	ENfk WFib
	'Capri' (Sc)	WFib
	'Captain Starlight' (A) ♀H1c	EShb MHer SPet WFib
	'Carefree' (U) ♀H1c	ECtt WFib
§	'Carisbrooke' (R) ♀H1c	WFib
	'Carmel' (Z)	WFib
	carnosum	MHer
	'Carole Munroe' (Z/d)	WFib
	'Caroline' (Dec)	WFib
	'Caroline Schmidt' (Z/d/v)	ECtt MCot WBrk WFib
	'Carolyn Hardy' (Z/d)	WFib
	CASCADE LILAC	see *P.* 'Roi des Balcons Lilas'
	CASCADE PINK	see *P.* 'Hederinum'
	'Catford Belle' (A)	MHer
	caucalifolium subsp. ***caucalifolium***	MHer
	- subsp. ***convolvulifolium***	WFib
	'Cedric Morris Corvette' (Z)	WFib
	'Celebration' (Z/d)	WFib
	'Celestial Rose' (Z/d)	WFib

	'Cézanne' (R)	MCot
	'Charity' (Sc) ♀H1c	EHDe ENfk MCot MHer MNHC NWsh SPet SRms WFib
	'Charlotte Bronte' (Dw/v)	WFib
	'Charmay Cocky' (Z/d)	WFib
	'Charmay Hampshire' (Z/d)	WFib
	'Charmay Snowflake' (Sc/v)	SRms
	'Charmay Snowflurry' (Sc/v)	WFib
	'Chavarri Hermanos' (Z/d)	WFib
	'Chelsea Gem' (Z/d/v) ♀H1c	WFib
	'Chelsea Morning' (Z/d)	WFib
	'Cherry' (Min)	WFib
	'Cherry Baby' (Dec) ♀H1c	ECtt WFib
	'Cherry Orchard' (R)	WFib
	'Chew Magna' (R)	WFib
	'Chieko' (Min/d)	WFib
	'Chinese Cactus' (Z/St)	WFib
§	'Chocolate Peppermint' (Sc)	ECtt ELan ENfk MCot MHer NWsh SPet SRms WFib
	'Chocolate Tomentosum'	see *P.* 'Chocolate Peppermint'
	'Choun Cho' (I)	LCro LOPS WFib
	'Chrissie' (R)	WFib
	'Cindy' (Dw/d)	WFib
	'Citriodorum' (Sc) ♀H1c	ELan MCot MHer WFib
	'Citronella' (Sc)	SRms WFib
	'Claret Rock Unique' (U)	WFib
	'Clorinda' (U/Sc)	ENfk MCot MHer MNHC NWad SPet SRms WFib
	'Clown' (R)	WFib
	'Coddenham' (Dw/d)	WFib
	'Cola Bottles'	CDow CPla ELan NPer SPet SPoG WABo WFib
§	'Colonel Baden-Powell' (I/d)	WFib
	COLORADO NOVA ('Genu'PBR) (Z)	SSea
	COLUMBIA (St)	WFib
	'Colwell' (Min/d)	WFib
	'Concolor Lace'	see *P.* 'Shottesham Pet'
	'Conron' (Sc) **new**	NWsh
	'Contrast' (Z/C/v)	SCoo SPoG WFib
	'Cook's Peachblossom' (Z/d)	WFib
	'Copthorne' (U/Sc) ♀H1c	CDow MCot MHer NWsh SPet SRms WFib
	cordifolium	WFib
	- var. ***rubrocinctum***	MHer NWsh
	coriandrifolium	see *P. myrrhifolium* var. *coriandrifolium*
	'Cornell' (I/d)	WFib
	cortusifolium	MHer
	'Costanza da Schio' **new**	SAll
	'Cotta Lilac Queen' (I/d)	ECtt
	'Cottenham Bliss' (A)	WFib
	'Cottenham Cynthia Haird' (A)	WFib
	'Cottenham Delight' (A)	WFib
	'Cottenham Glamour' (A) ♀H1c	MHer
	'Cottenham Harmony' (A)	EHDe WFib
	'Cottenham Jubilee' (A)	MHer
	'Cottenham Surprise' (A) ♀H1c	MPtG SPet
	'Cottenham Wonder' (A) ♀H1c	SPet WFib
	cotyledonis	WFib
	'Countess of Scarborough'	see *P.* 'Lady Scarborough'
	'Cover Girl' (Z/d)	WFib
	'Covina' (R)	WFib
	'Cramdon Red' (Dw)	WFib
	'Crampel's Master' (Z)	WFib
	'Creamery' (d)	WFib
	'Creamy Nutmeg' (Sc/v)	ENfk EShb MHer NWad SEND SRms
	'Credo' (Z)	WFib
	'Crimson Unique' (U) ♀H1c	CSpe ELan ENfk MCot MHer WFib
§	***crispum*** (Sc)	GPoy
	- 'Cy's Sunburst' (v) ♀H1c	CLau ECtt MHer NWsh SPet WFib
§	- 'Golden Well Sweep' (Sc/v)	WFib
	- 'Major' (Sc)	WFib
	- 'Peach Cream' (Sc/v)	ENfk WFib
	- 'Prince Rupert' (Sc)	NWsh
	- 'Variegatum' (Sc/v) ♀H1c	ECtt EHDe ENfk GPoy MHer SPet SRms WCot WFib
	crithmifolium	MHer
	'Crock O Day' (I/d)	ECtt
	'Crocodile' (I/C/d) ♀H1c	CDow ECtt ELan MHer MNHC NWad WFib
	'Crowfoot Rose' (Sc)	WFib
	'Crystal Palace Gem' (Z/v)	CDow ECtt WFib
	cucullatum	WFib
	- 'Flore Pleno' (d)	MHer WFib
	'Cupid' (Min/Dw/d)	WFib
	'Cynthia'PBR (R) **new**	LCro LOPS
§	'Czar' (Z/C)	SCoo
	'Dainty Maid' (Sc)	ECtt ENfk SPet
	'Dale Queen' (Z)	WFib
	'Dark Delight' (I) **new**	SAll
	'Dark Red Irene' (Z/d)	WFib
	'Dark Secret' (R)	CSpe WFib
	'Dark Venus' (R)	WFib
	'Davina' (Min/d)	WFib
	'Deacon Avalon' (Dw/d)	WFib
	'Deacon Barbecue' (Z/d)	WFib
	'Deacon Bonanza' (Z/d)	WFib
	'Deacon Clarion' (Z/d)	WFib
	'Deacon Coral Reef' (Z/d)	WFib
	'Deacon Fireball' (Z/d)	WFib
	'Deacon Gala' (Z/d)	WFib
	'Deacon Golden Bonanza' (Z/C/d)	WFib
	'Deacon Golden Lilac Mist' (Z/C/d)	WFib
	'Deacon Lilac Mist' (Z/d)	WFib
	'Deacon Mandarin' (Z/d)	WFib
	'Deacon Minuet' (Z/d)	WFib
	'Deacon Peacock' (Z/C/d)	WFib
	'Deacon Picotee' (Z/d)	WFib
§	'Deacon Summertime' (Z/d)	WFib
	'Deborah Miliken' (Z/d) ♀H1c	WFib
	'Decora Lavender'	see *P.* 'Decora Lilas'
§	'Decora Lilas' (I)	ECtt
	'Decora Mauve'	see *P.* 'Decora Lilas'
	'Decora Pink'	see *P.* 'Decora Rouge'
	'Decora Red'	see *P.* 'Decora Rouge'
§	'Decora Rose' (I)	ECtt
§	'Decora Rouge' (I)	ECtt
	'Deerwood Angel Wings' (A)	WFib
	'Deerwood Darling' (Min/v/d)	WFib
	'Deerwood Lavender Lad' (Sc)	ENfk MHer SPet WFib
	'Deerwood Lavender Lass' (Sc)	MCot MHer SRms
	'Deerwood Pink Puff' (St/d)	WFib
	'Delightful' (R)	WFib

'Delli' (R) ♀H1c	MHer MPtG NPer WFib
denticulatum	MHer
§ - 'Filicifolium' (Sc)	ELan ENfk EPri MCot MHer NWsh SPet WFib
'Diana Louise' (Z/d)	WFib
'Diana Palmer' (Z/d)	WFib
dichondrifolium (Sc)	WFib
'Dick Key' (Z/d)	WFib
'Display' ambig. (Dw/v)	WFib
'Distinction' (Z)	SPoG WFib WMal
'Dodd's Super Double' (Z/d)	WFib
'Dolly' (R)	WFib
'Dolly Varden' (Z/v) ♀H1c	ECtt WFib
'Don Franco'PBR (R) **new**	LCro LOPS
'Don Palido'PBR (R) **new**	LCro LOPS
'Don Valentino'PBR (R) **new**	LCro LOPS
'Don's Helen Bainbridge' (Z/C)	MHer WFib
'Don's Richard A. Costain' (Z/C)	WFib
'Don's Stokesley Gem' (Z/C)	WFib
'Doris Hancock' (R)	WFib
'Doris Shaw' (R)	ELan WFib
'Dorothy Baker' (R)	WFib
'Double New Life' (Z/d)	WFib
'Double Pink' (R/d)	WFib
'Dovedale' (Dw/C)	WFib
'Downlands' (Z/d)	WFib
'Dresden Pink' (Dw)	MHer
'Dresden White' (Dw)	MHer WFib
'Dubonnet' (R)	WFib
'Duchess of Devonshire' (U)	WFib
'Duke of Buckingham' (Z/d)	WFib
'Duke of Edinburgh'	see *P.* 'Hederinum Variegatum'
'Dunkery Beacon' (R)	WFib
'E. Dabner' (Z/d)	WFib
§ 'Eastbourne Beauty' (I/d)	WFib
echinatum	MHer WFar
- 'Album'	WFib
'Eclipse' (Dw/d)	ECtt
'Eden Gem' (Min/d)	WFib
'Edmond Lachenal' (Z/d)	WFib
'Edward Hockey' (Z)	WFib
'Eileen Postle' (R) ♀H1c	WFib
'Elaine Ward' (R)	WFib
'Elizabeth Taylor' (Z)	WFib
'Ella Jane' (Z/d)	WFib
'Elmsett' (Dw/C/d)	ECtt WFib
'Els' (Dw/St)	WBrk
'Elsi' (I × Z/d/v)	WFib
'Elsie Gillam' (St)	WFib
'Elsie Taylor' (R) **new**	WFib
'Embassy' (Min)	WFib
EMILIA ('Pactina'PBR) (Z)	SSea
'Emma Hössle'	see *P.* 'Frau Emma Hössle'
'Emma Jane Read' (Dw/d)	WFib
'Emma Louise' (Z)	WFib
'Emperor Nicholas' (Z/d)	WFib
endlicherianum	MHer WCot XEll
'Endsleigh' (Sc)	WFib
'Eros' **new**	SAll
'Eskay Gold' (A)	WFib
'Eskay Jewel' (A)	WFib
'Eskay Sugar Candy' (A)	WFib
'Eskay Verglo' (A)	WFib
EVENING GLOW	see *P.* 'Bergpalais'

'Evka'PBR (I/v)	ECtt SCoo
'Exotica' **new**	SAll
exstipulatum	MHer
'Fair Ellen' (Sc)	MHer WFib
'Fairlee' (Dw)	WFib
'Fairy Orchid' (A)	SPet WFib
'Fallen Angel' (Z/St)	ECtt
'Fandango' (Z/St)	WFib
'Fanny Eden' (R)	WFib
'Fantasia' white-flowered (Dw/d) ♀H1c	WFib
'Fareham' (R) ♀H1c	WFib
'Femme Fatale' **new**	SAll
'Fern Mint' (Sc)	MHer SRms
'Fiat Queen' (Z/d)	WFib
'Fieldings Unique' (U)	SPet
'Fiery Sunrise' (R)	WFib
'Fifth Avenue' (R)	SGro WFib
'Filicifolium'	see *P. denticulatum* 'Filicifolium'
'Fir Trees Catkins' (A)	MHer
'Fir Trees Ellie'	MPtG
'Fir Trees Fiesta' (R) ♀H1c	ECtt MPtG
'Fir Trees Hayley' (R)	WFib
'Fir Trees Mark' (R/Dec/v) ♀H1c	MPtG
'Fir Trees Muffin' (Sc) ♀H1c	MPtG
'Fir Trees Pearl Anniversary' (Z/C)	WFib
'Fir Trees Silver Wedding' (Z/C/d)	WFib
'First Blush' (R)	WFib
FIRST YELLOW ('Pacyell'PBR) (Z/d)	WFib
'Fleetlands' (St/v) **new**	SAll
'Fleur d'Amour' (R)	WFib
'Fleurisse' (Z)	WFib
(Flower Fairy Series) FLOWER FAIRY BERRY ('Sweberry'PBR) (Z)	SSea
- FLOWER FAIRY VELVET ('Swevel'PBR) (Z)	SSea
- FLOWER FAIRY WHITE SPLASH ('Swewhi'PBR) (Z)	SSea
fragrans	CDow ECtt ENfk MBow SPet SRms
Fragrans Group (Sc)	CDow GPoy MCot MHer NWsh WFib WGwG
§ - 'Fragrans Variegatum' (Sc/v) ♀H1c	MCot NWsh SPet SPoG WFib
- 'Snowy Nutmeg'	see *P.* (Fragrans Group) 'Fragrans Variegatum'
'Fraiche Beauté' (Z/d)	WFib
'Francis Gibbon' (Z/d)	WFib
'Francis Parmenter' (Min/I/v)	CDow
'Francis Parrett' (Min/d) ♀H1c	WFib
'Frank Bolton' (Z/d) **new**	MHer
'Frank Headley' (Z/v) ♀H1c	ECtt EShb MCot NPer SCoo SPoG WFib WOld
§ 'Frau Emma Hössle' (Dw/d)	WFib
'Freak of Nature' (Z/v)	MHer WFib
'Frensham' (Sc)	ENfk MHer NWsh WFib
'Freshwater' (St/C)	WFib
'Friary Wood' (Z/C/d)	WFib
'Friesdorf' (Dw/Fr)	MCot MHer WBrk WFib WMal
'Fringed Apple' (Sc)	WFib
'Fringed Aztec' (R) ♀H1c	WFib
'Frosty' misapplied	see *P.* 'Variegated Kleine Liebling'
'Frosty Petit Pierre'	see *P.* 'Variegated Kleine Liebling'

'Fruity' (Sc)	SRms
'Frumpy' (Z/Min) **new**	SAll
frutetorum	MHer
fruticosum	CDow SEdd WFib
fulgidum	MCot MHer WFib
'Gabriel' (A)	WFib
'Galway Star' (Sc/v) 🏆H1c	MHer WFib
'Ganther' (Dec)	WFib
'Gareth Mark Pratt' (Z/C)	WFib
'Garland' (R)	WFib
'Garnet' (Min)	MPri
'Garnet Rosebud' (Min/d)	WFib
'Garnet Wings' (R)	WFib
'Gartendirektor Herman' (Dec) 🏆H1c	ELan MHer MPtG WFib
'Gaudy' (Z)	WFib
'Gemini' (Z/St/d) 🏆H1c	WFib
'Gemstone' (Sc) 🏆H1c	ENfk MHer SPet WFib
'Genie' (Z/d)	WFib
'Gentle Georgia' (R)	WFib
'Georgia' (R)	WFib
'Georgia Peach' (R)	WFib
'Georgina Blythe' (R) 🏆H1c	WFib
'Georgina Forever' (A) **new**	WFib
'Giant Butterfly' (R)	WFib
gibbosum	CSpe EHDe MHer NWsh WFib
'Gillian Shaw' (R)	WFib
'Glacis' (Quality Series) (Z/d)	SSea
'Gladys Evelyn' (Z/d)	WFib
'Gladys Weller' (Z/d) 🏆H1c	WFib
glaucum	see *P. lanceolatum*
§ ***glutinosum***	WFib
'Goblin' (Min/d)	MHer
'Goesta' (Z/d)	SSea
GOLDEN ANGEL	see *P.* 'Sarah Don'
'Golden Brilliantissimum' (Z/v)	WFib
'Golden Chalice' (Min/v)	WFib
'Golden Clorinda' (U/Sc/C)	NWsh SEND SPet WFib
'Golden Ears' (Dw/St/C) 🏆H1c	NPer WFib
'Golden Edinburgh' (I/v)	WFib
'Golden Lilac Gem' (I/d)	WFib
'Golden Princess' (Min/C)	WFib
'Golden Square' (Dw/St)	WFib
'Golden Staphs' (Z/St/C)	MHer
'Golden Well Sweep'	see *P. crispum* 'Golden Well Sweep'
'Gooseberry Leaf'	see *P. grossularioides*
'Gosport' (Z/v)	WFib
'Grace Thomas' (Sc) 🏆H1c	MHer WFib
'Grace Wells' (Min)	WFib
'Grainger's Antique Rose' (Z/d) **new**	WFib
'Grand Slam' (R) 🏆H1c	WFib
'Grandad Mac' (Dw/St) 🏆H1c	MPtG
GRANDEUR BUTTERFLY BICOLOUR RED (I) **new**	LSou
GRANDEUR BUTTERFLY IVY WHITE (I) **new**	LSou
GRANDEUR BUTTERFLY NEON (I) **new**	LSou
GRANDEUR BUTTERFLY PINK (I) **new**	LSou
GRANDEUR BUTTERFLY PURPLE (I) **new**	LSou
grandiflorum	MCot MHer WFib
'Granny Barter' (Z) **new**	SAll
graveolens L'Hér.	see *P.* 'Graveolens'
graveolens ambig.	SEND SGro
graveolens *sensu* J.J.A. van der Walt	WFib
§ 'Graveolens' (Sc)	ENfk GPoy MHer SVen WBrk WFib
'Green Eyes' (I/d)	MHer
'Greetings' (Min/v)	WFib
GRETA ('Pacgret') (Darkline Series) (Z) **new**	SSea
'Grey Lady Plymouth' (Sc/v)	CPbh LCro LOPS MCot MHer NWsh WFib
'Grey Sprite' (Min/v)	WFib
§ ***grossularioides***	MHer
§ 'Hannaford Star' (Z/St)	WFib
'Hansen's Pinkie' (Dec)	WFib
'Hansen's Wild Spice' (Sc)	NWsh WFib
'Happy Thought' (Z/v) 🏆H1c	ECtt MCot SCoo WFib
'Harbour Lights' (R)	WFib
'Harewood Slam' (R)	WFib
'Harlequin Pretty Girl' (I × Z/d)	WFib
'Harlequin Rosie O'Day' (I)	ECtt WFib
'Harvard' (I/d)	WFib
'Hazel' (R)	WFib
'Hazel Cherry' (R)	WFib
'Hazel Dean' (R)	ECtt
'Hazel Glory' (R)	WFib
'Hazel Gypsy' (R)	WFib
'Hazel Peach' (R)	WFib
'Hazel Star' (R)	WFib
'Hazel's Finale' (Dec)	WFib
§ 'Hederinum' (I)	SAll
§ 'Hederinum Variegatum' (I/v)	ECtt WFib
'Helen Christine' (Z/St) 🏆H1c	MHer WFib WOld
'Henry Weller' (A) 🏆H1c	WFib
'Hermanus Show' (Sc)	WFib
'Hermione' (Z/d)	WFib
'Highfields Attracta' (Z/d)	WFib
'Highfield's Cameo' (Z) **new**	SAll
'Highfields Candy Floss' (Z/d)	ECtt WFib
'Highfields Choice' (Z) 🏆H1c	WFib
'Highfields Delight' (Z)	WFib
'Highfields Festival' (Z/d) 🏆H1c	ECtt WFib
'Highfields Flair' (Z/d)	WFib
'Highfields Melody' (Z/d)	WFib
'Highfields Pink' (Z)	WFib
'Highfields Pride' (Z)	WFib
'Highfields Snowdrift' (Z)	WFib
'Highfields Symphony' (Z)	WFib
'Highfields Vogue' (Z)	WFib
'Hilda's Memory' (Dw/Z/d)	WFib
'Hills of Snow' (Z/v)	MHer WFib
'Hindoo' (R × U) 🏆H1c	SAll WFib
hispidum	MHer
'Hit Parade' (I/d)	WFib
'Hitcham' (Min/d)	WFib
'Holbrook' (Dw/C/d)	WFib
'Honeywood Lindy' (R)	WFib
Horizon Series (Z) **new**	MBros
- 'Horizon Deep Salmon Improved' (Z) **new**	MBros
- 'Horizon Deep Scarlet' (Z) **new**	MBros
- 'Horizon Lilac Rose' (Z) **new**	MBros
'House and Garden' (R)	ECtt
'Hula' (R × U)	WFib

	Name	Suppliers
	'Icecrystal' (Sweetheart Series) (Z/d)	SSea
	'Icing Sugar' (I/d)	WFib
	ignescens	WFib
	'Immaculatum' (Z)	WFib
	'Imperial Butterfly' (A/Sc) ♀H1c	ENfk MPtG SPet SRms WFib
	ionidiflorum	CSpe EShb MCot MHer MNHC SRms WAvo WOld
	'Irene' (Z/d)	WFib
	'Irene Cal' (Z/d)	WFib
	'Irene Toyon' (Z)	WFib
	'Isabel Pearce' (Z) **new**	SAll
	'Islington Peppermint' (Sc)	SPet SRms WFib
	'Italian Mystery' **new**	SAll
	'Ivalo' (Z/d)	WFib
	'Ivory Snow' (Z/d/v)	WFib
	'Jack of Hearts' (I × Z/d)	WFib
	'Jack Phillips' (Z/d)	WFib
§	'Jackie' (I/d) ♀H1c	SAll WFib
	'Jackie Gall'	see *P.* 'Jackie'
	'Jackie Totlis' (Z/St)	WFib
	'Jackpot Orchid Mist' (Z) **new**	SAll
	'Jackpot Wild Rose' (Z/d)	WFib
	'Jane Chapman' (Z/d) **new**	SAll
	'Jane Innes' (I/d)	WFib
	'Janet Hofman' (Z/d)	WFib
	'Janet Kerrigan' (Min/d)	WFib
	'Jayne Eyre' (Min/d)	WFib
§	'Jeanne d'Arc' (I/d)	WFib
	'Jer'Rey' (A)	WFib
	'Jip's Bishops Wood' (Dw/d)	WFib
	'Jip's Desert Poppy' (Z/Min)	WFib
	'Jip's Eleanor Renton' (Dw/d)	WFib
	'Jip's Little Lady' (Dw)	WFib
	'Jip's Megan' (Z/C/D)	ECtt
	'Jip's Pippin' (Dw)	WFib
	'Jip's Proud Sentinel' (Dw/d)	WFib
	'Jip's Sky Gipsy' (Dw)	WFib
	'Jip's Twilight' (Dw)	WFib
	'Joan Fontaine' (Z)	WFib
	'Joan Morf' (R) ♀H1c	WFib
	'Joan of Arc'	see *P.* 'Jeanne d'Arc'
	'Joy' (R) ♀H1c	CSpe ECtt WFib
	'Joy Lucille' (Sc)	NWsh
	'Julie Smith' (R)	WFib
	'Juniper' (Sc)	WFib
	'Just Beth' (Z/C/d)	WFib
	'Just Jip' (Dw/Z)	WFib
	'Just Joss' (Dw/d)	WFib
	'Just William' (Min/C/d)	WFib
	'Kamahl' (R)	WFib
	'Karl Hagele' (Z/d)	WFib
	'Karmin Ball'	WFib
	'Karrooense'	see *P. quercifolium*
	'Katie Hillier' (R)	WFib
	'Kaufman's Bonfire' (R)	WFib
	'Keepsake' (Min/d)	WFib
	'Kenny's Double' (Z/d)	ECtt WFib
	'Kerensa' (Min/d)	WFib
	'Kesgrave' (Min/d)	WFib
	'Kewense' (Z)	EShb WFib
	'Key's Unique' (U)	WFib
	'Kimono' (R) ♀H1c	ECtt
	'King Edmund' (R) ♀H1c	WFib
	'King of Balcon'	see *P.* 'Hederinum'
	'King of Denmark' (Z/d)	WFib
	'King Solomon' (R)	WFib
	'King's Ransom' (R)	WFib
§	'Kleine Liebling' (Min)	WFib
	'La France' (I/d) ♀H1c	ECtt LCro LOPS WFib
	'La Jolla' (Z/d)	WFib
	'La Paloma' (R)	WFib
§	'Lachskönigin' (I/d)	WFib
	'Lady Ilchester' (Z/d)	WFib
	'Lady Love Song' (R)	WFib
	'Lady Mary' (Sc)	MHer SRms WFib
	'Lady Mavis Pilkington' (Z/d)	WFib
	'Lady Plymouth' (Sc/v) ♀H1c	CPbh CSpe ECtt EHDe ELan ENfk GLog MCot MHer NWad NWsh SEND SPet SRms WFib WGwG
§	'Lady Scarborough' (Sc)	ENfk MHer SRms WFib
	laevigatum	MHer
	'Lancastrian' (Z/d)	ECtt WFib
§	***lanceolatum***	MHer
	'Lara Ballerina' (Sc/d) ♀H1c	SPet SRms
	'Lara Candy Dancer' (Sc) ♀H1c	MAsh NWsh SPet WFib
	'Lara Dora Price' (Za) **new**	WFib
	'Lara Jester' (Sc)	ECtt ENfk NWsh WFib
	'Lara Largo' (Za) **new**	WFib
	'Lara Mandarin' (Za/d) **new**	WFib
	'Lara Marjorie' (Za) **new**	WFib
	'Lara Starshine' (Sc) ♀H1c	ENfk MHer SPet SRms WFib
	'Lara Susanne' (Za) **new**	WFib
	'Lara Waltz' (R/d)	WFib
	'Laurel Hayward' (R)	WFib
	'Lauren Alexandra' (Z/d)	WFib
	'Lavender Lindy' (Sc)	CDow NWsh SPet WFib
	'Lavender Mini Cascade'	see *P.* LILAC MINI CASCADE
	'Lavender Sensation' (R)	WFib
	'Lawrenceanum'	LCro LOPS WFib
	laxum	WFib
	'L'Élégante' (I/v) ♀H1c	CDow MCot MHer WFib
	'Lemon Air' (Sc)	WFib
	'Lemon Crisp'	see *P. crispum*
	'Lemon Fancy' (Sc) ♀H1c	MHer NWad NWsh SPet WFib
	'Lemon Kiss' (Sc)	CSpe NWsh WFib
	'Lemon Meringue' (Sc)	WFib
	'Letitia' (A)	ENfk
	LILA COMPAKT-CASCADE	see *P.* 'Decora Lilas'
	LILAC ('Paclilac'PBR) (I)	SSea
	LILAC CASCADE	see *P.* 'Roi des Balcons Lilas'
	'Lilac Gem' (Min/I/d)	ENfk
§	LILAC MINI CASCADE ('Lilamica'PBR) (I) ♀H1c	CDow
	'Lilian Pottinger' (Sc) ♀H1c	ENfk MHer NWsh WFib
	'Lilian Woodberry' (Z)	WFib
	'Limoneum' (Sc)	ENfk MHer SPet WFib
	'Lincolnshire Lady' (R)	ECtt
	'Lipstick' (St)	WFib
	'Lisa' (Min/C)	WFib
	'Lisa Jo' (St/v/Dw/d)	WFib
	'Little Alice' (Dw/d) ♀H1c	WFib
	'Little Gem' (Sc)	ENfk MHer WFib
	'Little Jip' (Z/d/v) ♀H1c	WFib
	'Little Spikey' (St/Min/d)	MHer WFib
	'Lizzie Hillier' (R)	WFib
	'Lollipop' (Z/d)	WFib
	'Lord Baden-Powell'	see *P.* 'Colonel Baden-Powell'
	'Lord Bute' (R) ♀H1c	CSpe ECtt ELan LCro LOPS MCot MHer MPtG NPer SGro SVen WABo WFib WGwG

	'Lord de Ramsey'	see *P.* 'Tip Top Duet'
	'Lord Roberts' (Z)	WFib
	'Lottie Lungburgh' (Z/St)	WFib
	'Lotusland' (Dw/St/C) 🏆^{H1c}	ECtt SPoG WFib
I	'Louise' (R) 🏆^{H1c}	ECtt MPtG WFib
	'Love Song' (R/v)	WFib
	'Lovely Greta' (Za) **new**	WFib
	'Lovely Wera' (Za/d) **new**	WFib
	'Lucy Gunnett' (Z/d/v) 🏆^{H1c}	ECtt WFib
	'Lyewood Bonanza' (R)	WFib
	'Lyric' (Min/d)	WFib
	'Mabel Grey' (Sc) 🏆^{H1c}	CSpe ECtt ENfk MHer MNHC NPer NWsh SPet WFib
§	'Madame Auguste Nonin' (U/Sc)	ENfk MHer NWsh SPet WFib
	'Madame Crousse' (I/d) 🏆^{H1c}	WFib
	'Madame Layal' (A) 🏆^{H1c}	WFib
	'Madame Margot'	see *P.* 'Hederinum Variegatum'
	'Madame Recamier' (Z/d)	ECtt
	magenteum	MHer
	'Magnum' (R)	WFib
	'Majestic' (Z/d)	WFib
	'Mandarin' (R)	ECtt
	'Mangles' Variegated' (Z/v)	WFib
	'Mani di Fata' (St) **new**	SAll
	'Maple Leaf' (Sc)	NWsh
	'Maréchal MacMahon' (Z/C)	ENfk
	'Margaret Soley' (R) 🏆^{H1c}	WFib
	'Margaret Waite' (R)	WFib
	'Margery Stimpson' (Min/d)	WFib
	'Marie Thomas' (Sc)	SGro
	MARIMBA ('Fisrimba'^{PBR})	SCoo
	'Marion Saunders' (Dec)	WFib
	'Mariquita' (R)	WFib
	'Mark' (Dw/d)	WFib
	'Marmalade' (Min/d)	WFar
	'Marquis of Bute' (R/v)	MHer
	'Martin Parrett' (Min/d)	WFib
	'Mary Harrison' (Z/d)	WFib
I	'Maureen' Hoddinott (Z/d)	MHer
	'Mauve Beauty' (I/d)	WFib
	'Maxime Kovalevski' (Z)	WFib
	'May Day' (R)	WFib
	'May Magic' (R)	WFib
	'Meadowside Dark and Dainty' (St)	WFib
	'Meadowside Midnight' (St/C)	WFib
	'Medley' (Min/d)	WFib
	MELOCHERRY ('Pacmel'^{PBR}) (Tempo Series) (Z/d)	SSea
	'Memento' (Min/d)	WFib
	'Mendip' (R)	WFib
	'Mendip Barbie' (R) 🏆^{H1c}	MPtG
	'Mendip Candy Floss' (R)	WFib
	'Mendip Royale' (R)	WFib
	'Meon Maid' (R)	WFib
	'Mere Casino' (Z)	WFib
	'Mexican Beauty' (I)	WFib
	'Mexicana'	see *P.* 'Rouletta'
	'Mexicanerin'	see *P.* 'Rouletta'
	'Michael' (A) 🏆^{H1c}	MHer SPet
	'Michelle West' (Min)	WFib
	'Mike West' (St)	WFib
	'Millfield Gem' (I/d)	WFib
	'Millmoor Clover' **new**	SAll
	'Millmoor Porcelain' **new**	SAll
	'Mimfy' (Z) **new**	SAll
	'Mini Czech' (Cas/Min)	ECtt WBrk
	'Minnie' (Z/d/St)	WBrk WFib
	'Minstrel Boy' (R)	WFib
	'Minx' (Min/d)	WFib
	'Miss Burdett Coutts' (Z/v)	MHer WFib
	'Miss Muffett' (Min/d)	WFib
§	'Miss Stapleton'	LCro LOPS MHer WFib
	'Misterioso' (R)	WFib
	'Misty Morning' (R)	WFib
	'Modesty' (Z/d)	WFib
	'Mohawk' (R)	WFib
	'Mole'	see *P.* 'The Mole'
	'Molly' (A)	ENfk
	'Monique McEwan' (Z/St)	WFib
	'Monsieur Ninon' misapplied	see *P.* 'Madame Auguste Nonin'
§	'Monsieur Ninon' (U)	WFib
	'Mont Blanc' (Z/v)	CDow WFib
	'Montague Garabaldi Smith' (R)	WFib
	'Monty's Magic' (R)	ECtt ELan
	'Moon Maiden' (A)	WFib
	'More's Victory' (U/Sc)	WFib
	'Morval' (Dw/C/d) 🏆^{H1c}	WFib
	'Morwenna' (R)	MHer WCot WFib
	'Mosaic Gay Baby' (I/v/d)	WFib
	'Mr Henry Cox' (Z/v) 🏆^{H1c}	MHer WFib
	'Mr Wren' (Z)	ECtt ELan EShb SIvy WFib WOld
	'Mrs Cannell' (Z)	WFib
	'Mrs Farren' (Z/v)	MCot
	'Mrs G.H. Smith' (A) 🏆^{H1c}	ECtt SPet WFib
	'Mrs J.C. Mappin' (Z/v) 🏆^{H1c}	ECtt
	'Mrs Kingsbury' (U)	WFib
	'Mrs Martin' (I/d)	WFib
	'Mrs McKenzie' (Z/St)	WFib
	'Mrs Morf' (R)	ECtt
	'Mrs Parker' (Z/d/v)	ECtt WFib
	'Mrs Pollock' (Z/v)	ECtt ELan MBros MCot SCoo WBrk WFib
	'Mrs Quilter' (Z/C) 🏆^{H1c}	ECtt WBrk WFib
	'Mrs W.A.R. Clifton' (I/d)	WFib
	multibracteatum	WFib
	multiradiatum	WFib
	mutans	WFib
	'My Chance' (Dec)	WFib
§	***myrrhifolium*** var. ***coriandrifolium***	MHer WFib
	'Mystery' (U) 🏆^{H1c}	ECtt LCro LOPS WFib
	'Narina' (I)	SCoo
	'Needham Market' (A)	ENfk SPet
	'Nellie Nuttall' (Z)	WFib
	NEONA ('Pacneon'^{PBR}) (Z)	SSea
	'Nervous Mabel' (Sc) 🏆^{H1c}	MHer WFib
	'New Gypsy' (R)	ELan
	'Newchurch' (Z/St)	WFib
	'Nicor Star' (Min)	WFib
	'Noele Gordon' (Z/d)	WFib
	'Occold Shield' (Dw/C/d) 🏆^{H1c}	ECtt MHer WBrk WFib
	'Occold Tangerine' (Z)	WFib
	'Occold Volcano' (Dw/C/d)	WFib
	odoratissimum (Sc) 🏆^{H1c}	ENfk GPoy MHer SPet SRms WFib
	'Odyssey' (Min)	WFib
	'Old Spice' (Sc/v)	ENfk SPet WFib
	'Oldbury Duet' (A/v) 🏆^{H1c}	MHer SPet
	'Olivia' (R)	WFib
	'Opera House' (R)	WFib
	'Orange Fizz' (Sc) 🏆^{H1c}	MHer NWsh SPet SRms WFib WGwG
	'Orange Parfait' (R)	WFib
	'Orangeade' (Dw/d)	WFib
	'Orchid Clorinda' (Sc)	WFib

'Orchid Paloma' (Dw/d)	WFib
'Orion' (Min/d)	WFib
'Orsett' (Sc) 🏆H1c	GLog
otaviense	WFib
'Our Flynn' (Z/St)	WFib
'Our Henry' (Dw/d)	WFib
PAC cultivars	see under selling name
'Pagoda' (Z/St/d)	MHer WFib
'Paisley Red' (Z/d)	WFib
Palladium Series (Z) **new**	MBros
'Pamela Vaughan' (Z/St)	WFib
'Pampered Lady' (A)	SPet
panduriforme	WFib
papilionaceum	ELan EShb MCot MHer WFib
'Parisienne' (R) 🏆H1c	WFib
'Party Dress' (Z/d)	WFib
'Pat Hannam' (St)	WFib
'Paton's Unique' (U/Sc) 🏆H1c	CDow ECtt ELan ENfk MCot MHer SPet SVen WCot WFib
'Patricia Andrea' (Z/T) 🏆H1c	NPer WFib
patulum	WFib
'Paul Crampel' (Z) 🏆H1c	MCot MHer WFib
'Paul West' (Min/d)	NWad SGro
'Pauline Harris' (R)	WFib
'Peace' (Min/C)	WFib
'Peach Princess' (R)	ECtt
PELFI cultivars	see under selling name
peltatum	SIvy WFib
'Penny' (Z/d)	WFib
'Penny Lane' (Z)	WFib
'Pensby' (Dw)	WFib
'Peppermint Lace' (Sc)	NWsh SPet
'Perfect' (Z)	WFib
'Pershore Princess'	WAvo WBrk
'Petals' (Z/v)	SPoG
'Peter Godwin' (R)	WFib
'Peter's Choice' (R)	WFib
'Petit Pierre'	see *P.* 'Kleine Liebling'
'Phyllis Richardson' (R/d)	WFib
'Phyllis Variegated' (U/v)	ECtt ENfk MHer SPet WCot WFib
'Pink Aurore' (U)	WFib
'Pink Bonanza' (R)	WFib
'Pink Capitatum'	see *P.* 'Pink Capricorn'
§ 'Pink Capricorn' (Sc)	CCBP ENfk LCro LOPS MPri NWsh SRms WFib
'Pink Cascade'	see *P.* 'Hederinum'
'Pink Champagne' (Sc)	MHer
'Pink Dolly Varden' (Z/v)	ECtt WFib
'Pink Fondant' (Min/d)	WFib
'Pink Gay Baby'	see *P.* 'Sugar Baby'
'Pink Happy Thought' (Z/v)	ECtt WFib
'Pink Needles' (Min/St)	MHer WFib
'Pink Pandora' (T)	WFib
'Pink Pet' (U)	ECtt
'Pink Rambler' (Z/d)	WFib
'Pink Rosebud' (Z/d)	WFib
'Playboy Cherry' **new**	SAll
'Playmate' (Min/St)	WFib
'Plum Rambler' (Z/d)	ECtt EShb WBrk WFib
'Polka' (U) 🏆H1c	SPet WFib
'Pompeii' (R)	WFib
'Poquita' (Sc)	SRms
'Porchfield' (Min/St)	WBrk
praemorsum	WFib
'Preseli Lottie' (Z/d)	WFib
'Preston Park' (Z/C)	WFib
'Pretty Polly' (Sc)	WFib
'Prim' (Dw/St/d)	WFib
'Prince of Orange' (Sc) 🏆H1c	CCBP ECtt ENfk GPoy MCot MHer MPri MPtG NWsh SPet SRms WFib
'Princeanum' (Sc) 🏆H1c	WFib
'Princess Abigail' (Dw/d)	ECtt WFib
'Princess Josephine' (R)	WFib
'Princess of Balcon'	see *P.* 'Roi des Balcons Lilas'
'Princess of Wales' (R)	WFib
'Princess Virginia' (R/v)	WFib
'Priory Beacon' **new**	SAll
'Priory Salmon' (St/d)	EShb
'Priory Star' (St/Min/d)	WFib
pseudoglutinosum	WFib
'Pulsar Salmon Splash' (Pulsar Series) (Z)	EHyd LRHS
'Pungent Peppermint' (Sc)	SRms
'Purple Rogue' (R)	WFib
'Purple Unique' (U/Sc)	ECtt ENfk MCot MHer SPet SVen WFib
'Pygmalion' (Z/d/v)	WFib
'Quantock' (R)	WFib
'Quantock Angelique' (A)	SPet
'Quantock Butterfly' (A)	SPet
'Quantock Candy' (A) 🏆H1c	ELan SPet
'Quantock Clare' (A)	SPet
'Quantock Double Dymond' (A/d) 🏆H1c	MPtG WFib
'Quantock Kendy' (A) 🏆H1c	MPtG
'Quantock Kennedy'	MPtG
'Quantock Kirsty' (A) 🏆H1c	SPet
'Quantock Marjorie' (A) 🏆H1c	SPet
'Quantock Matty' (A) 🏆H1c	MPtG
'Quantock Perfection' (A) 🏆H1c	MPtG SPet WFib
'Quantock Sally' (A/d)	SPet
'Queen of Denmark' (Z/d)	WFib
'Queen of Hearts' (I × Z/d)	WFib
quercifolium (Sc)	ECtt EHDe ELan GPoy SEdd WFib WSMil
quinquelobatum	WFib
radens (Sc)	ENfk WFib
'Radula' (Sc) 🏆H1c	CCBP ELan MHer SPet SRms WFib
'Radula Roseum' (Sc)	WFib
'Ray Bidwell' (Min)	WFib
§ 'Red Black Vesuvius' (Min/C)	MHer WFib WSMil
'Red Cascade' (I) 🏆H1c	SAll WFib
'Red Gables'	WAvo
'Red Pandora' (Z/T) 🏆H1c	WFib
'Red Pimpernel' (Z/T)	WFib
'Red Rambler' (Z/d)	WBrk WFib
'Red Robin' (R)	ENfk WCot
'Red Spider' (Dw/Ca)	WFib
'Red Startel' (Z/St/d)	WFib
'Red Susan Pearce' (R)	WFib
'Red Victus Spider' **new**	SAll
'Red Witch' (Dw/St/d)	MHer WBrk WFib
§ RED-MINI-CASCADE ('Rotemica') (I)	CDow
'Reflections' (Z/d)	WFib
'Regina' (Z/d) 🏆H1c	WFib
'Rembrandt' (R)	WFib
'Renate Parsley' 🏆H1c	LCro LOPS MHer WFib
reniforme	MHer WFib
'Reunion Rose' (Sc)	WFib
ribifolium	EShb
'Richard Gibbs' (Sc)	ENfk MHer SPet
'Richard Key' (Z/d/C)	WFib
'Rietje van der Lee' (A)	ENfk WFib
'Rimfire' (R) 🏆H1c	ELan LCro LOPS MHer NWad WFib
'Rio Grande' (I/d)	MHer WFib
'Rober's Lemon Rose' (Sc)	ENfk MHer SEND SPet SRms WBrk WFib

'Robert Fish' (Z/C)	SCoo
'Robert McElwain' (Z/d)	WFib
'Robin' (R)	ECtt
'Robin's Unique' (U)	MHer WFib
'Robyn Hannah' (St/d) ♀H1c	MHer MPtG
'Rogue' (R)	WFib
'Roi des Balcons'	see *P.* 'Hederinum'
§ 'Roi des Balcons Lilas' (I)	SAll
'Roi des Balcons Rose'	see *P.* 'Hederinum'
'Roller's Echo' (A)	WFib
'Roller's Pioneer' (I/v)	ENfk
'Roller's Satinique' (U)	MHer
'Rollison's Unique' (U)	MHer WFib
'Rookley' (St/d) ♀H1c	MPtG
'Rose Bengal' (A)	ENfk
'Rose Eye' (Dw)	WFib
'Rose of Amsterdam' (Min/d)	WFib
'Rose Silver Cascade' (I)	ECtt MCot MHer
'Rosebud Supreme' (Z/d)	WFib
'Rosmaroy' (R)	WFib
'Rosy Dawn' (Min/d)	WFib
'Rote Mini-cascade'	see *P.* RED-MINI-CASCADE
§ 'Rouletta' (I/d)	WFib
'Royal Ascot' (R)	SPet
'Royal Oak' (Sc) ♀H1c	CPbh ECtt ENfk MCot MHer MNHC NWad NWsh SPet SPoG SRms SVen WFib
§ 'Royal Purple' (Z/d)	SAll WFib
(Royal Series) ROYAL CANDY CANE ('Klep01028') (I)	SSea
- ROYAL LAVENDER ('Klepp07196'PBR) (I)	SSea
- ROYAL RED ('Kleroder'PBR) (I)	SSea
'Royal Sovereign' (R)	WFib
'Royal Surprise' (R) ♀H1c	MPtG
'Ruby' (Min/d)	WFib
'Rushmere' (Dw/d)	WFib
'Rushmoor Golden Rosebud' (Za)	ECtt WFib
'Rushmoor Mrs Eve Scott' (Za/d)	ECtt WFib
(Rushmoor River Series) 'Rushmoor Amazon' (Za/d) **new**	WFib
- 'Rushmoor Amur' (Za) **new**	WFib
- 'Rushmoor Avon' (d/Za) **new**	WFib
- 'Rushmoor Beautiful' (d/Za) **new**	WFib
- 'Rushmoor Colorado' (d/Za) **new**	WFib
- 'Rushmoor Congo' (Za/d) **new**	WFib
- 'Rushmoor Danube' (Za) **new**	WFib
- 'Rushmoor Euphrates' (Za) **new**	WFib
- 'Rushmoor Ganges' (Za) **new**	WFib
- 'Rushmoor Indus' (Za) **new**	WFib
- 'Rushmoor Irtysh' (Za) **new**	WFib
- 'Rushmoor Krishna' (Za) **new**	WFib
- 'Rushmoor Main' (Za) **new**	WFib
- 'Rushmoor Mekong' (Za/d) **new**	WFib
- 'Rushmoor Mississippi' (Za) **new**	WFib
- 'Rushmoor Missouri' (Za) **new**	WFib
- 'Rushmoor Morava' (Za) **new**	WFib
- 'Rushmoor Mosman' (Za) **new**	WFib
- 'Rushmoor Murray' (Za) **new**	WFib
- 'Rushmoor Niger' (Za) **new**	WFib
- 'Rushmoor Nile' (Za/d) **new**	WFib
- 'Rushmoor Orinoco' (Za/d) **new**	WFib
- 'Rushmoor Paraná' (Za) **new**	WFib
- 'Rushmoor Rhine' (Za/d) **new**	WFib
- 'Rushmoor Rhone' (Za/d) **new**	WFib
- 'Rushmoor Ribble' (Za/d) **new**	WFib
- 'Rushmoor Rio Grande' (Za) **new**	WFib
- 'Rushmoor Saint Lawrence' (Za/d) **new**	WFib
- 'Rushmoor Salween' (Za/d) **new**	WFib
- 'Rushmoor Sava' (Za) **new**	WFib
- 'Rushmoor Severn' (Za/d) **new**	WFib
- 'Rushmoor Thames' (Za/d) **new**	WFib
- 'Rushmoor Tiber' (Za/d) **new**	WFib
- 'Rushmoor Vistula' (Za/d) **new**	WFib
- 'Rushmoor Wheaton' (Za) **new**	WFib
- 'Rushmoor Yamuna' (Za/d) **new**	WFib
- 'Rushmoor Yangtze' (Za/d) **new**	WFib
- 'Rushmoor Yarra' (Za/d) **new**	WFib
- 'Rushmoor Yenisei' (Za/d) **new**	WFib
- 'Rushmoor Zambezi' (Za/d) **new**	WFib
'Saint Elmo's Fire' (St/Min/d)	MHer WFar WFib
SAINT MALO ('Guisaint') (I)	ECtt
'Salmon Beauty' (Dw/d)	WFib
§ 'Salmon Irene' (Z/d)	WFib
'Salmon Queen'	see *P.* 'Lachskönigin'
SALMON QUEEN ('Pacsalque'PBR) (Z)	SSea
salmoneum	WFib
'Samantha' (R)	WFib
'Samantha Stamp' (Dw/C/d)	WFib
SAMELIA ('Pensam'PBR) (Dark Line Series) (Z/d)	SSea
'Sammi Brougham' (Dw/Z)	WFib
'Sancho Panza' (Dec)	CSpe WFib

	Name	Suppliers
	'Sandra Lorraine' (I/d)	WFib
	SANGRIA NOVA ('Gendana'PBR) (Z)	SSea
	'Sanguineum'	CSpe
§	'Sarah Don' (A/v)	ECtt WFib
	'Sarah Jane' (Sc)	WFib
	'Satsuki' (R) ♀H1c	ECtt
	'Saxifragoides'	WFib
	'Scarlet Gem' (Z/St)	WBrk WFib
	'Scarlet Pet' (U) ♀H1c	CDow ECtt ENfk NWsh SPet
	'Scarlet Rambler' (Z/d)	ECtt EShb WFib
	'Scarlet Unique' (U)	CSpe MCot MNHC WFib
	schizopetalum	MHer WFib
	'Schottii' ♀H1c	CPbh MHer WFib
	'Scottow Star' (Z/C)	WFib
	'Seaview Silver' (Min/St)	WFib
	'Seaview Sparkler' (Z/St)	WFib
	'Secret Love' (Sc)	SRms
	'Seeley's Pansy' (A)	MHer
	'Sefton' (R) ♀H1c	WFib
	'Shannon'	WFib
	'Shelley' (Dw)	WFar
§	'Shottesham Pet' (Sc)	CCBP ENfk MHer NWad SPet SRms WGwG
	sidoides ♀H1c	CDow CPbh CSpe CWCL EAJP ECtt EHDe ELan ENfk LCro LOPS MCot MHer NWsh SChr SDix SGro SPhx SPlb SVen WAvo WFib WHer WKif WOld
	'Silver Blazon' (Z/Dw/C/v)	WFib
	'Silver Delight' (v/d)	WFib
	'Silver Kewense' (Dw/v)	WFib
	'Silver Snow' (Min/St/d)	WFib
	'Skelly's Pride' (Z)	WFib
	'Skies of Italy' (Z/C/d)	WFib
	'Snow Flurry' (Sc)	WFib
	'Snowbaby' (Min/d)	WFib
	'Snowdrift' (I/d)	WFib
	'Snowflake' (Min)	see *P.* 'Atomic Snowflake'
	'Snowstorm' (Z)	WFib
	'Sofie'	see *P.* 'Decora Rose'
	'Solferino' (A)	ENfk
	'Something Special' (Z/d) ♀H1c	WFib
	'Sophia' (Z)	WGwG
	SOPHIE CASADE	see *P.* 'Decora Rose'
	'Sophie Dumaresque' (Z/v) ♀H1c	WFib
	'Sophie Emma' (Z)	WFib
	'Sophie Marion' (Dw/Z)	WFib
	'South American Bronze' (R) ♀H1c	WFib
	'Southern Rosina' (Dw)	WFib
	'Spanish Angel' (A) ♀H1c	MHer SPet WFib
	'Spellbound' (R)	WFib
	'Spital Dam' (Dw/d)	WFib
	'Spitfire' (Z/Ca/d/v)	CDow ECtt WFib
§	'Splendide' ♀H1c	CPbh CSpe MHer SWvt WFib
	'Spot-on-bonanza' (R) ♀H1c	ECtt WFib
	'Springfield Black' (R)	MCot
	'Springtime' (Z/d)	WFib
	'Stadt Bern' (Z/C) ♀H1c	CSpe
	× ***stapletoniae***	see *P.* 'Miss Stapleton'
	'Startel Salmon' (Z/St)	MHer
	'Stellar Arctic Star'	see *P.* 'Arctic Star'
	'Stellar di Formosa' **new**	SAll
	'Stellar Hannaford Star'	see *P.* 'Hannaford Star'
	'Stewart Meehan' (R)	WFib
	'Strawberry Fayre' (Dw/St)	WFib
§	'Sugar Baby' (DwI)	MHer WFib

	Name	Suppliers
	'Summer Cloud' (Z/d)	WFib
	SUMMER RAIN (mixed) (I)	MBros MPri
	'Summertime' (Z/d)	see *P.* 'Deacon Summertime'
	'Sun Rocket' (Dw/d)	WFib
	'Sundridge Moonlight' (Z/C)	WFib
	'Sundridge Surprise' (Z)	WFib
	'Sunraysia' (Z/St)	WFib
	'Sunset Snow' (R)	WFib
	'Sunspot Petit Pierre' (Min/v)	WFib
	'Sunstar' (Min/d)	WFib
	'Supernova' (Z/St/d)	WFib
	'Surcouf' (I)	WFib
	'Susan Hillier' (R)	WFib
	'Susan Payne' (Dw/d)	MHer
	'Susie' (Z/C)	WFib
	'Sussex Gem' (Min/d)	WFib
	'Sussex Lace'	see *P.* 'White Mesh'
	'Swanland Lace' (I/d/v)	WFib
	'Swedish Angel' (A)	WFib
	'Sweet Annette' (Z) **new**	SAll
	'Sweet Mimosa' (Sc) ♀H1c	CCBP CPbh ECtt ELan ENfk MCot MHer NWsh SPet SRms WFib
	'Sweet Sixteen' (R)	WFib
	'Sybil Holmes' (I/d)	ECtt WFib
	'Tammy' (Dw/d)	WFib
	'Tara Caws' (Z)	WFib
	tetragonum	EShb MHer WFib
	'The Boar' (Fr) ♀H1c	EShb MCot WFib
	'The Culm' (A)	MHer WFib
	'The Czar'	see *P.* 'Czar' (Z/C)
	'The Joker' (I/d)	WFib
	'The Marchioness of Bute' (R)	MHer WFib
§	'The Mole' (A)	WFib
	'The Tamar' (A)	MHer
	'The Yar' (Z/St)	WFib
	'Thomas Earle' (Z)	WFib
	'Tinker West' (Z/St/Dw)	WFib
§	'Tip Top Duet' (A) ♀H1c	MHer WFib
	'Tirley Garth' (A)	WFib
	tomentosum (Sc) ♀H1c	CPbh CSpe ENfk EShb GLog GPoy LCro LOPS MCot MHer NWad NWsh SIvy SPet WABo WFib
	- 'Chocolate'	see *P.* 'Chocolate Peppermint'
	TOMMY ('Pactommy') (I)	ELan SSea
	tongaense	WFib
	'Topscore' (Z/d)	WFib
	'Tornado' (R) ♀H1c	LCro LOPS WFib
	'Torrento' (Sc)	MHer NWsh SPet SRms WFib
	'Tortoiseshell' (R)	WFib
	transvaalense	CPbh
	'Treasured Memories' (A) **new**	SAll
	tricolor misapplied	see *P.* 'Splendide'
	tricolor Curt.	CPbh
	tricuspidatum	MHer WFib
	trifidum	WFib
	'Trino' **new**	SAll
	'Triomphe de Nancy' (Z/d)	WFib
	triste	MHer WFib
	'Trudie' (Dw/Fr)	MHer WFib
	'Turkish Coffee' (R)	WFib
	'Turkish Delight' (Dw/C)	WFib
	'Turtle's Surprise' (Z/d/v)	WBrk
	'Two Dees' (Dw/d)	WFib
	'Unicorn Bride' (Za/d) **new**	WFib
	'Unicorn Diva' (Za) **new**	WFib
	'Unicorn Frills' (Za) **new**	WFib

	'Unicorn Gold' (Za) **new**	WFib
	'Unicorn Hot Butter' (Za/d) **new**	WFib
	'Unicorn Hot Pepper' (Za/d) **new**	WFib
	'Unicorn Rose' (Za/d) **new**	WFib
	'Unique Aurore' (U)	MHer
	'Unique Mons Ninon'	see *P.* 'Monsieur Ninon'
	'Urchin' (Min/St)	WFib
	'Ursula Key' (Z/c)	WFib
	'Ursula's Choice' (A)	SPet WFib
	'Val Merrick' (Dw/St)	WFib
	'Valentine' (Z/C)	WFib
	'Vancouver Centennial' (Dw/St/C) ♀H1c	ECtt MHer SCoo SPoG SSea WFib
	'Vandersea' (Sc)	MCot MHer NWsh
	'Variegated Clorinda' (Sc/v)	WFib
	'Variegated Fragrans'	see *P.* (Fragrans Group) 'Fragrans Variegatum'
§	'Variegated Kleine Liebling' (Min/v)	WFib
	'Variegated Petit Pierre' (Min/v)	MHer WFib
	'Vectis Glitter' (Z/St) ♀H1c	WBrk WCot WFib
	'Vectis Pink' (Dw/St)	WFib
	'Vectis Purple' (Z/d)	WFib
	'Vectis Starbright' (Dw/St)	WFib
	'Vectis Volcano' (Z/St)	WFib
	'Vicki Town' (R)	WFib
	'Vicky Claire' (R)	WFib
	VICKY ('Pacvicky'PBR) (I)	SSea
	'Ville de Paris'	see *P.* 'Hederinum'
	'Vina' (Dw/C/d)	WFib
	violareum misapplied	see *P.* 'Splendide'
	'Viscossisimum' (Sc)	MHer
	viscosum	see *P. glutinosum*
	'Vivat Regina' (Z/d)	WFib
	'Voodoo' (U) ♀H1c	CPbh CSpe ECtt MCot MHer SIvy SPet WCot WFib
	'Wallis Friesdorf' (Dw/C/d)	WFib
	'Wantirna' (Z/v) ♀H1c	ECtt
	'Warrenorth Coral' (Z/C/d)	WFib
	'Wayward Angel' (A)	SPet
	'Wedding Royale' (Dw/d)	WFib
	'Welling' (Sc)	ENfk SPet WFib
	'Wendy Jane' (Dw/d)	WFib
	'Wendy Read' (Dw/d)	WFib
	'Westdale Appleblossom' (Z/C/d)	ECtt MHer WFib
	'Westside' (Z/d)	MHer WFib
	'Westwood' (Z/St)	WFib
	'Whisper' (R)	WFib
	'White Bird's Egg' (Z)	WFib
	'White Boar' (Fr)	CSpe ECtt EShb WFib
	'White Bonanza' (R)	WFib
	'White Eggshell' (Min)	WFib
	'White Feather' (Z/St)	MHer
§	'White Mesh' (I/v)	CDow
	'White Unique' (U)	SPet WFib
	'Wilhelm Kolle' (Z)	WFib
	'Wilhelm Langath' (Z/v)	ECtt EShb SCoo WBrk
	'Willa' (Dec)	WFib
	'Wirral Moonlight' (Z/C/d)	WFib
	'Wolverton' (Z)	WFib
	'Yale' (I/d) ♀H1c	WFib
	'Yan le Grounch' (Z/C)	WFib
	'Yhu' (R)	WFib
	'York Florist' (Z/d/v)	ECtt
	'Yvonne' (Z)	WFib
	'Zinc' (Z/d)	WFib
	zonale	WFib
	'Zulu King' (R)	WFib
	'Zulu Warrior' (R)	WFib

Peliosanthes (*Asparagaceae*)

	arisanensis B&SWJ 3639	WCru
	caesia B&SWJ 5183	WCru
	teta subsp. ***humilis*** RWJ 10044	WCru

Pellaea (*Pteridaceae*)

	falcata	EShb ISha
	ovata	SPlb
	paradoxa 'Glowstar'	ISha
	rotundifolia ♀H2	CAby CLAP CRos CTsd EHyd EShb ISha LEdu LLWG LRHS MAsh NRHS WBor WCot
	viridis	LEdu WPGP

Peltandra (*Araceae*)

	undulata	see *P. virginica* (L.) Schott
§	***virginica*** (L.) Schott	LLWG NPer

Peltaria (*Brassicaceae*)

	alliacea	CSpe LEdu WCot

Peltiphyllum see *Darmera*

Peltoboykinia (*Saxifragaceae*)

§	***tellimoides***	MPnt NBir WFar WPnP
	watanabei	CElw CPla CSpe EBee GEdr GPSL IMou LEdu MBriF MMrt NLar SPad WCru WPnP

Pennellianthus see *Penstemon*

Pennisetum ✿ (*Poaceae*)

	× ***advena*** 'Fireworks'PBR (v)	CBcs CBod EBee EHyd EPfP LRHS MAsh MCot NRHS SWvt
§	- 'Rubrum' ♀H3	CBcs CBct CExl CKno EBee EHyd EShb LCro LOPS LRHS MAsh MBros NRHS NWsh SCoo SMad SWvt
§	***alopecuroides***	CBcs CBod CWCL ECha EHyd EPfP EWhm LRHS NGdn NRHS SCob SLim SPer SPlb SWvt XLum XSen
	- AUTUMN WIZARD	see *P. alopecuroides* 'Herbstzauber'
	- 'Black Beauty'	CKno CSpe ECha IPot SMHy SMea SSut WHoo
	- 'Cassian's Choice' ♀H3	CKno EWes GWyn ILea MAsh SHar
	- 'Caudatum'	CKno
	- 'Dark Desire'	CKno CRos CSde EHyd EPfP LEdu LRHS MAsh NRHS
	- 'Foxtrot'	EPPr
	- 'Gelbstiel'	CKno EBee EHyd ELon EPfP LRHS NRHS
	- 'Goldstrich'	ELon SAko XSen
	- 'Hameln'	Widely available
	- 'Hameln Gold'PBR	CKno ELon XSen
§	- 'Herbstzauber'	CBod CKno EAJP EBee ELon NLar XLum XSen
	- 'Js Jommenik'PBR **new**	EBee ELon
	- 'Little Bunny'	CBod CSde EBee EHyd ELan ELon EPfP LRHS LSRN MAsh NGdn NRHS SCob SMea SWvt XCre XSen
	- 'Little Honey' (v)	ELan ELon LRHS XLum XSen
	- 'Magic'	CBod EBee ELon SMea
	- 'Moudry'	CBod CExl CSde EAJP EBee ELon EPPr EPfP EShb LRHS NLar XLum
	- 'Red Head'	CKno CMea CRos EBee EHyd ELan ELon EPfP EWes LEdu LRHS LSun

	MAsh MAvo MBel NLar NRHS NSti SEdd SMad SMea SPoG WCot XSen
- f. ***viridescens***	CBod EAJP EHyd ELan ELon EPPr EShb LEdu LRHS LSun NRHS SCob SMad SPtp XCre XLum XSen
- 'Weserbergland'	CKno EBee ELon SAko XCre
- 'Woodside'	CKno SMad XLum
clandestinum	EShb
compressum	see *P. alopecuroides*
'Fairy Tails'	CKno CRos EBee EHyd ELon EPPr EPfP LCro LOPS LPla LRHS MAsh MAvo MBel NDov NRHS NWsh SEdd SMHy SMea SPoG WCot WHoo
flaccidum	EPPr
glaucum 'Purple Majesty'	CSpe SWvt
incomptum	XCre XLum
longistylum misapplied	see *P. villosum*
macrourum	CBod CKno CSam CSde CSpe EAJP EBee ECha EHyd EPPr EPfP EShb LEdu LRHS MAvo MNrw NDov NRHS NWsh SDix SEND SMHy SMad SPtp WABo WPGP XCre
- 'Short Stuff'	CKno
massaicum 'Red Bunny Tails'	CChe LRHS NRHS SRms
- 'Red Buttons'	see *P. thunbergii* 'Red Buttons'
orientale ♀H3	CBod CKno CRos CSde CSpe ECha EHyd EPfP LRHS LSun MRav NBir NRHS NWsh SEND SPer SRkn SWvt WABo WKif XLum XSen
- 'Flamingo'	CRos EHyd IPot NRHS SMea
- 'Karley Rose'PBR	CKno CPar CSpe EWes IMou LRHS MAsh MAvo NDov NRHS SCob SMad SWvt WPGP XCre
I - 'Robustum'	EPPr MAvo WPGP
- 'Shogun'	CKno CRos CSam EHyd EPfP IPot LRHS MAsh NRHS SMHy SMea
- 'Tall Tails'	EBee EHyd EPPr EShb EWes GMaP LRHS NDov SMea XCre XLum
'Paul's Giant'	EBee ELon XLum
purpureum	SRms
rueppellii	see *P. setaceum*
§ ***setaceum***	SWvt
- 'Rubrum'	see *P.* × *advena* 'Rubrum'
thunbergii	CAby CBod EHyd GKev LRHS
§ - 'Red Buttons'	CKno CRos CSde EHyd ELon EPPr EPfP EShb LEdu LRHS MAsh MAvo MGos MNrw NRHS SCob SMHy SMea SPoG SSut WAvo WHoo XCre
VERTIGO ('Tift-8'PBR)	MCot
§ ***villosum*** ♀H3	Widely available

pennyroyal see *Mentha pulegium*

Penstemon ✿ (*Plantaginaceae*)

'Abbotsmerry'	ECtt ELon MBNS MCot SIvy SLon
§ 'Alice Hindley'	CBar CRos CSpe CTri EAJP EHyd ELan EPfP LRHS LSRN MCot MRav NBir NRHS SIvy SLon SRms SWvt WAvo WBrk WCAu WCot WHoo WKif XLum
alpinus	GWyn
'Amy Gray'	WAvo WBrk
§ 'Andenken an Friedrich Hahn' ♀H5	Widely available
§ ***angustifolius***	CSpe
'Apple Blossom' misapplied	see *P.* 'Thorn'
'Apple Blossom'	Widely available
'Arabesque Appleblossom'	EHyd LRHS NRHS
'Arabesque Orchid' **new**	CRos
'Arabesque Pink'	CBod EHyd LRHS MHol NRHS
'Arabesque Red'	CBod EHyd LRHS NRHS
'Arabesque Violet'	CBod EHyd LRHS MHol NRHS
arizonicus	see *P. whippleanus*
'Ashton'	WAvo
attenuatus subsp. ***militaris***	SPlb
'Audrey Cooper'	CMac WAvo
'Avon Belle'	WHrl
'Axe Valley Penny Mitchell'	ECtt
'Axe Valley Pixie'	SBut
azureus	GKev
'Barbara Barker'	see *P.* 'Beech Park'
§ ***barbatus***	SPer SRms SSut XSen
- 'Coccineus'	CSde CSpe GBin SBut XLum
- 'Iron Maiden'	LRHS
- 'Jingle Bells'	EPfP SPeP
- orange-flowered	SPlb
- Pinacolada Series	EHyd LRHS NRHS
- - 'Pinacolada Blue'	CRos
- - 'Pinacolada Dark Rose'	EHyd LRHS NRHS
- - 'Pinacolada Light Rose'	CRos
- - 'Pinacolada Rosy Red'	EHyd LRHS NRHS
- - 'Pinacolada White'	EHyd LRHS NRHS SRms
- var. ***praecox*** f. ***nanus*** 'Rondo'	EAJP LRHS
- 'Roseus' **new**	SHar
'Beckford'	EWes MBNS
§ 'Beech Park' ♀H4	EBee EHyd ELan EMor EPfP LRHS SRms WAvo
'Bisham Seedling'	see *P.* 'White Bedder'
'Blackbird' (Bird Series)	Widely available
'Blue Riding Hood'PBR (Riding Hood Series)	SPoG
'Blue Spring' misapplied	see *P. heterophyllus* 'Blue Spring'
'Blueberry Taffy'PBR	ECtt EHyd LRHS NRHS
'Bodnant' ♀H4	WAvo WBrk WHoo
'Boysenberry Taffy'PBR	EHyd LRHS NRHS
'Bredon'	WAvo
'Bubblegum' (Ice Cream Series)	CAby
'Burford Purple'	see *P.* 'Burgundy'
'Burford Seedling'	see *P.* 'Burgundy'
'Burford White'	see *P.* 'White Bedder'
§ 'Burgundy'	CMac ECtt GMaP LRHS NBir NPer SRms WAvo XLum
caeruleus	see *P. angustifolius*
§ ***campanulatus***	CRos EHyd EPot EWes GKev IMou LRHS NRHS SHar SRms
- PC&H 148	SDys
- 'Roseus' misapplied	see *P. kunthii*
'Candy Pink'	see *P.* 'Old Candy Pink'
cardinalis subsp. ***regalis***	GKev
cardwellii	EWes
'Castle Forbes'	GMaP MBNS SRms WAvo
'Cathedral Rose'	EBee EHyd ELan EPfP LRHS
'Catherine de la Mare'	see *P. heterophyllus* 'Catherine de la Mare'
'Centra'	WAvo
'Cha Cha Cherry'PBR **new**	LSou
'Cha Cha Lavender'PBR **new**	CBod LSou
'Cha Cha Purple'PBR **new**	LSou
'Charles Rudd'	ECtt ELan ELon EPfP LSRN MBNS MHer NLar SRms SWvt WAvo
§ 'Cherry'	ECtt MBNS SHar WAvo
'Cherry Ripe' misapplied	see *P.* 'Cherry'
§ 'Chester Scarlet'	ECtt MBNS WAvo WCFE WKif
'Choirboy'	EWes
cobaea	CSpe

	'Comberton'	WAvo
	confertus	CTri EBee EPot GKev MMuc
	- RCB/MO A-7	WCot
	'Connie's Pink' ♀H4	SRms WAvo
	'Coral Sea'	LSou MBros WFar
	'Cottage Garden Red'	see *P.* 'Windsor Red'
§	'Countess of Dalkeith'	ECtt ELan GBin MCot MRav SHar SRms SWvt WAvo WCFE
	'Craigieburn Taffeta'	WAvo
	cristatus	see *P. eriantherus*
*	***cyananthus*** var. ***utahensis***	WCot
	'Dark Towers'PBR	CAbb CWGN EBee ECtt EHyd EMor EPfP EWTr LRHS MBNS MBel MHol MNrw MPri NCou NHpl NRHS SLon SMad SPad SPoG WBrk WCot WHoo
	davidsonii	EPot EWes GEdr
	- var. ***davidsonii***	WAbe
	- var. ***menziesii*** 'Microphyllus'	CPBP EPot GEdr NWad WAbe
	- var. ***praeteritus***	GEdr
	- 'Silverwells'	EPot GEdr
	'Dazzler'	SWvt WAvo
	'Delfts Blue Riding Hood'PBR (Riding Hood Series)	LCro LOPS MPri
	'Devonshire Cream'	WAvo
	diffusus	see *P. serrulatus*
	digitalis	SRms
	- 'Goldfinger' **new**	MBNS
§	- 'Husker Red'	Widely available
	- 'Isa'	WCot
	- 'Joke'	MAvo
	- 'Mystica'	EBee EHyd EPfP LRHS NRHS SRms STPC
	- 'Purpureus'	see *P. digitalis* 'Husker Red'
§	'Drinkstone Red'	SDix SDys SRms WAvo
	'Drinkwater Red'	see *P.* 'Drinkstone Red'
	eatonii	GKev
	(Elgar Series) 'Elgar Crown of India'	WCot
	- 'Elgar Firefly'	WCot
	- 'Elgar Light of Life'	WCot
	- 'Elgar Nimrod'	WCot
	'Ellenbank Amethyst'	SDys
	'Ellenbank Cardinal'	WKif
	'Ellwood Red Phoenix'	WAvo
	'Elmley'	WAvo WBrk
§	***eriantherus***	SPlb
	ETNA ('Yatna') (Volcano Series)	ECtt EPfP LRHS NRHS SPad SRms
	euglaucus	GKev
§	'Evelyn' ♀H4	ECha ELan ELon EPfP LRHS LSRN MBNS MCot MHer MRav SPer SPoG SRms SWvt WAvo WBrk WKif WSHC XLum
	'Fanny's Blush'	SWvt
	'Firebird'	see *P.* 'Schoenholzeri'
	'Flame'	WAvo
	'Flamingo'	CPla CRos ECtt ELon EPfP EWes GBin LRHS MBNS NLar SGbt SHar SRms SWvt WAvo
§	***fruticosus*** var. ***scouleri*** ♀H4	MAsh
	- - 'Albus' ♀H4	WAbe
	- - 'Amethyst'	WAbe
	FUJIYAMA ('Yayama'PBR)	CChe ECtt EPfP LRHS MAvo MBow SLon SPad SRms SWvt
	'Garden Red'	see *P.* 'Windsor Red'
	'Garnet'	see *P.* 'Andenken an Friedrich Hahn'

	gentianoides B&SWJ 10271	WCru
	'Geoff Hamilton'	CElw ECtt MBNS SLon SPoG WAvo
§	'George Home' ♀H3	EWes GBin MBNS SRms WAvo
	'George Moon'	SPad
	glaber	CMea EWld MBow SPlb
	- 'Roundway Snowflake'	SHar SRms
	'Gloire des Quatre Rues'	XLum
	'Grape Taffy'PBR	EHyd LRHS NRHS
	hallii	EPot EWes SPlb
	hartwegii 'Albus'	SHar SRms
	- 'Picotee Red'	CRos EHyd LRHS NRHS
§	***heterophyllus***	LRHS NBir SRkn SRms
	- 'Blue Gem'	CElw
§	- 'Blue Spring'	CFis CSpe EHyd EPfP LRHS MRav
§	- 'Catherine de la Mare'	CRos EBee EHyd ELan GBin LRHS LSRN NLar NRHS SCob SHar SPer SWvt WKif WSMil WSpi XLum
	- 'Electric Blue'	CBod CRos EHyd LRHS LSou MHol NRHS SLon WFar
	- 'Heavenly Blue'	Widely available
	- 'Jeanette'	CMea
	- 'True Blue'	see *P. heterophyllus*
	- 'Züriblau'	SPlb WHil
§	'Hewell Pink Bedder' ♀H4	CMea CRos EHyd EPfP GBin LRHS MBNS MRav NCou NRHS SHar SIvy SRms SWvt WAvo WHil
	'Hidcote Pink' ♀H3	Widely available
	'Hidcote Purple'	SHar WHoo XLum
	'Hidcote White'	MHer SWvt WBrk
	'Hillview Pink'	SLon XLum
§	***hirsutus***	EBee SBut XLum
	- 'Blue Foam'	GWyn
	- var. ***pygmaeus***	CMea EDAr EPfP NHpl NRya SBut SPlb SRms WHoo
*	- - f. ***albus***	WHoo
	- - 'Purpureus'	WAbe
	'Hopleys Variegated' (v)	SWvt
	'Hot Pink Riding Hood'PBR (Riding Hood Series)	EHyd LCro LOPS LRHS NRHS
	JEAN GRACE ('Penbow')	ECtt
	'John Nash' misapplied	see *P.* 'Alice Hindley'
	'John Nash'	SRms
	'Juicy Grape' (Ice Cream Series)	CPla WCot
	'June'	see *P.* 'Pennington Gem'
	'Jupiter'	XLum
	KILIMANJARO ('Yajaro') (Volcano Series)	CRos EPfP LRHS SLon SRms WFar
	'King George V'	Widely available
§	***kunthii***	MAsh
§	***laetus*** subsp. ***roezlii***	EPot MAsh
§	'Le Phare'	WAvo XLum
	'Lilac and Burgundy'	SHar SRms SWvt WAvo
	'Lilac Frost'	EPfP
	linarioides 'Marilyn Ross'	ECtt
	'Lord Home'	see *P.* 'George Home'
	lyallii	GAbr GWyn SRms
	'Lynette'	SGro WAvo
	'Macpenny's Pink'	CMac MBNS WAvo XLum
	'Madame Golding'	XLum
	'Margery Fish' ♀H3	CFis ECtt EWes
	'Maurice Gibbs' ♀H3	CBcs ELon EPfP EWes LSRN MBNS NGBl SRms
	'Melting Candy' (Ice Cream Series)	WCot
	mensarum	GLog LRHS WKif
	Mexicali hybrids	SBut
	- (Carillo Series) 'Carillo Purple'	CRos EHyd LRHS NRHS

	- - 'Carillo Red'	CRos EHyd LRHS NRHS
	× ***mexicanus*** 'Sunburst Amethyst'	ELan SRms XLum
	- 'Sunburst Ruby'	EBou ELan
	'Midnight'	ECtt ELan EMor MBel MRav MSwo SEND SHar SIvy SWvt WAvo WCFE XLum
	'Modesty'	SRms
	'Mother of Pearl'	CBcs CTri EHyd ELan EMor EPfP GMaP LRHS LSRN MCot MSwo MWat SHar SRms SWvt WAvo
	'Mrs Morse'	see *P.* 'Chester Scarlet'
	'Mrs Oliver'	EWes
	multiflorus	EBee
§	'Myddelton Gem'	MWat SRms
	'Myddelton Red'	see *P.* 'Myddelton Gem'
	newberryi ♀H5	GKev
	- f. ***humilior***	EPot
§	- subsp. ***sonomensis***	SRms WAbe
	'Newbury Gem'	SHar SWvt
	'Oaklea Red'	WAvo
§	'Old Candy Pink'	SWvt WAvo
	'Osprey' (Bird Series) ♀H3	CWGN EAJP ECtt EHyd ELan EMor EPfP EWes LRHS NBir SHar SRms SWvt WAvo
	ovatus	CMac SPhx SRms WKif
	'Overbury'	SRms WAvo WBrk
	'Papal Purple'	MBNS SBut SHar SRms WAvo XLum
	'Patio Wine'	WAvo
	'Peace'	GBin
§	'Pennington Gem'	CTri MHer NBir SHar SRms SWvt WAvo
	(Pensham Series) 'Pensham Amelia Jane'	CAby CRos CWGN ECtt EHyd ELon EPau EPfP GWyn LRHS MTis NLar NRHS SLon SPer SRms SWvt WCav
	- 'Pensham Arctic Fox'	CSpe ECtt ELon LRHS SBut SLon SPoG
	- 'Pensham Avonbelle' ♀H4	SRms
	- 'Pensham Bilberry Ice'	SWvt
	- 'Pensham Blackberry Ice'	ECtt SLon SRms
	- 'Pensham Blueberry Ice'	ECtt SWvt
	- 'Pensham Charlotte Louise'	ECtt SRms
	- 'Pensham Czar'	CAby CRos ECtt EHyd ELon EPfP GWyn LRHS LSun MBNS MCot MGos MTis MWat NLar NRHS SGbt SLon SPer SPoG SRkn SRms SWvt WBor WFar WHil WHoo
	- 'Pensham Eleanor Young'	CRos ECtt EPfP LRHS SLon SWvt
	- 'Pensham Freshwater Pearl'	SRms WHoo
	- 'Pensham Great Expectations'	ECtt
	- 'Pensham Jessica Mai'	ECtt SCob SPer SRms SWvt
	- 'Pensham Just Jayne' ♀H4	ECtt ELon EPfP LRHS SLon SRms SWvt WBrk WHoo WSpi XLum
	- 'Pensham Laura'	CAby CDor CPla CRos CWGN ECtt EHyd EPfP LCro LOPS LRHS LSun MAvo MBNS MPri NRHS SCob SLon SPer SRms SWvt WBor WBrk WFar WHoo
	- 'Pensham Loganberry Ice'	SLon
	- 'Pensham Miss Wilson'	SRms
	- 'Pensham Plum Jerkum'	CAby CDor CRos CWGN EBee ECtt EHyd ELon EPfP LCro LOPS LRHS MBNS MBel MCot MHer MPie NLar NRHS SCob SDix SLon SPer SRms SWvt WFar WHil WHoo
	- 'Pensham Raspberry Ice'	SLon
	- 'Pensham Skies'	SRms
	- 'Pensham Son of Raven'	WAvo WBrk
	- 'Pensham Tayberry Ice'	ECtt SLon SRms
	- 'Pensham Ted's Purple'	WCFE
	- 'Pensham Twilight'	CBod
	- 'Pensham Victoria Plum' ♀H4	CElw SGro SHar SRms WHoo
	- 'Pensham Wedding Bells'	ELon SRms
	- 'Pensham Wedding Day'	EBee ECrN EHyd EPfP LRHS LSRN MCot MNHC NRHS SLon SPer SPoG WFar WHoo
	- 'Pensham Westminster Belle'	ECtt LBuc MTis SCob SRms
	(Pentastic Series) PENTASTIC PINK ('Yapmine') **new**	LCro LOPS LSou MHol NDov
	- PENTASTIC RED ('Yapruby') **new**	CWGN LCro LOPS LSou MHol NDov
	- PENTASTIC ROSE ('Yaprose') **new**	CWGN LCro LOPS LSou MHol NDov
	(PepTalk Series) 'Pep Talk Cerise'	MPri
	- 'Pep Talk Hot Pink'	MPri
	- 'Pep Talk Pink'	MPri
	- 'Pep Talk Purple'	MPri
	'Pershore Anniversary'	WAvo
	'Pershore Carnival'	SRms WAvo WHrl
	'Pershore Fanfare'	WAvo WHrl
	'Pershore Festival'	WAvo
	'Pershore Pink Necklace'	SRms SWvt WAvo WHrl
	'Phare'	see *P.* 'Le Phare'
	(Phoenix Series) PHOENIX APPLEBLOSSOM 09 ('Peni Ablos09')	CRos EHyd LRHS NRHS
	- PHOENIX LAVENDER ('Peni Laver')	EHyd LRHS
	- PHOENIX MAGENTA 09 ('Peni Mag09')	CRos EHyd LRHS NRHS
	- PHOENIX MAGENTA ('Pheni Magna') **new**	EPfP
	- PHOENIX PINK ('Pheni Pinka')	CRos EHyd LRHS NRHS
	- PHOENIX RED ('Pheni Reeda'PBR)	CRos EHyd LRHS NRHS SRms
	- PHOENIX ROSE ('Penharros'PBR)	LRHS
	- PHOENIX VIOLET 09 ('Peni Vio09'PBR)	CRos EHyd EPfP LRHS NRHS
	- PHOENIX VIOLET ('Pheni Vio') **new**	SRms
	'Phyllis'	see *P.* 'Evelyn'
	pinifolius ♀H4	CMea CRos CTri EHyd EMor EPot GKev LRHS MMuc NRHS NSla SRms WFar WHoo
	- 'Mersea Yellow'	CMea EHyd ELan EPfP EPot GKev LRHS MHer MMuc NRHS SPlb SRms WIce XLum
	- 'Wisley Flame' ♀H4	EPfP EPot EWes GKev MBNS MHer NHpl NSla
	'Pink Bedder'	see *P.* 'Hewell Pink Bedder', 'Sutton's Pink Bedder'
	'Port Wine' ♀H3	CTri ELon EPfP GMaP LRHS MWat NBir SPoG SWvt WAvo WKif
	'Powis Castle'	ECtt WAvo WBrk
	'Prairie Twilight'PBR	MHol
	'Precious Gem'	WHrl
	procerus var. ***brachyanthus***	GKev
§	- var. ***formosus***	SRms WAbe
	- 'Hawkeye'	CPBP

§	– 'Roy Davidson' ♀H5	CMea EPot MMrt WAbe
	– var. ***tolmiei***	EPot GEdr GKev WAbe
	pseudospectabilis	XSen
	pubescens	see *P. hirsutus*
	pulchellus Greene	see *P. procerus* var. *formosus*
	pulchellus Lindl.	see *P. campanulatus*
	'Purple and White'	see *P.* 'Countess of Dalkeith'
	'Purple Bedder'	CMac CRos EHyd ELan EPfP GBin LRHS LSRN MWat NBir NRHS SPoG SRkn SRms SWvt XLum
	'Purple Passion'	CElw CRos EBee EHyd ELan ELon EPfP LRHS NRHS SCob
	'Purple Riding Hood'PBR (Riding Hood Series)	CRos EHyd LCro LOPS LRHS MPri NRHS
	'Purple Sea'	MBros MHol WFar
	'Purpureus Albus'	see *P.* 'Countess of Dalkeith'
	'Raven' (Bird Series) ♀H3	Widely available
	'Razzle Dazzle'	SPlb SRms WAvo WCot
	'Red Emperor'	WAvo
	'Red Knight'	WAvo
	'Red Riding Hood'PBR (Riding Hood Series)	CRos EHyd EPfP LCro LOPS LRHS MPri NRHS SPoG
	RED ROCKS ('P008s')	WCot
	'Red Sea'	LSou MBros MHol WFar
	'Rich Purple'	MBNS SPlb XLum
	'Rich Ruby' ♀H3	CAby CFis CRos EHyd ELan EPfP EWes GBin LRHS MBel NBir NRHS SBut SHar SPlb SWvt WAvo XLum
	'Ridgeway Red'	WAvo
	roezlii Regel	see *P. laetus* subsp. *roezlii*
	'Roger Skipper'	ECtt
	'Ron Sidwell'	WAvo WBrk
	'Rosy Blush'	MBNS SPlb WAvo
	'Roy Davidson'	see *P. procerus* 'Roy Davidson'
	'Royal White'	see *P.* 'White Bedder'
	'Rubicundus' ♀H4	CRos EHyd ELan ELon EPfP LRHS LSRN NRHS SRms SWvt WBor
	'Ruby' misapplied	see *P.* 'Schoenholzeri'
	'Ruby Candle'	ECtt
	rupicola ♀H5	NSla
	– 'Conwy Lilac'	WAbe
	– 'Conwy Rose'	EPot WAbe
	'Russian River'	ECtt EPfP LRHS SPlb SWvt XLum
	rydbergii	SPlb
	'Samsong'	WCFE
§	'Schoenholzeri' ♀H4	CBcs CDor CMea CRos CSam ECtt EHyd ELon EPfP GMaP LRHS MBel MGil MHer MMuc NBir NGdn NRHS SCob SEND SPer SPhx SPlb SPoG SRms SWvt WAvo WFar WHoo XLum
	scouleri	see *P. fruticosus* var. *scouleri*
§	***serrulatus***	EWes GKev XLum
	'Sherbourne Blue'	WAvo
	'Sissinghurst Pink'	see *P.* 'Evelyn'
	'Six Hills'	EPot GBin SDys WAbe WOld
	smallii	EBee EHyd EMor EPPr EPfP EWes LRHS LSRN MHer SPhx
	'Snow Storm'	see *P.* 'White Bedder'
	'Snowflake'	see *P.* 'White Bedder'
	sonomensis	see *P. newberryi* subsp. *sonomensis*
	'Sour Grapes' misapplied	see *P.* 'Stapleford Gem'
	'Sour Grapes' ambig.	CAby CBcs CDor CTri MSCN NGdn SCob SPoG WCAu
§	'Sour Grapes' M. Fish ♀H4	CBod CMac CRos CWld EBee ECha EHyd ELan ELon EPau EPfP GBin GMaP LCro LOPS LRHS LSRN MBel MGil MSwo NLar NRHS SEND SHar SPer SPtp SRms WBrk WKif
	'Southcombe Pink'	WAvo
	'Southgate Gem'	GWyn MHCG MWat SRms SWvt WAvo
	'Souvenir d'Adrian Regnier'	MHCG
	'Souvenir d'André Torres' misapplied	see *P.* 'Chester Scarlet'
	spectabilis	CSpe
§	'Stapleford Gem' ♀H4	CFis CMac CSpe LRHS MBel MRav SBut SHar SRms SWvt WAvo WBrk WFar WHoo
	'Storm'	WHrl
	'Strawberries and Cream' (Ice Cream Series)	EMor EPfP MTis NLar WCot
	'Strawberry Fancy'	SRms
	'Strawberry Fizz'	SRms
	strictus	EBee EPfP MMuc SBut SPhx XSen
	STROMBOLI ('Yaboli') (Volcano Series)	CTri
§	'Sutton's Pink Bedder'	WAvo
	'Sweet Cherry' (Ice Cream Series)	CPla ECtt SCob WCot
	tall, pink-flowered	see *P.* 'Welsh Dawn'
	teucrioides	CPBP
	'The Juggler'	ECtt SWvt
§	'Thorn'	ECtt LRHS MWat SRms SWvt WAvo WHrl
	'Threave Pink'	ECtt SHar SRms SWvt WAvo
	'Thundercloud'	ECtt WAvo WBrk
	'Tiger Bell Coral'	NChi
	'Torquay Gem'	WAvo
	'True Sour Grapes'	see *P.* 'Sour Grapes' M. Fish
	'Tubular Bells Red'	MHol
	'Vanilla Plum' (Ice Cream Series)	EMor SCob
	venustus purple-flowered	SBrt
	VESUVIUS ('Yasius') (Volcano Series)	CRos EPfP LRHS NRHS SLon SRms WFar
	virgatus 'Blue Buckle'	EMor GEdr SPlb WFar
	'Watermelon Taffy'PBR (Taffy Series)	ECtt EHyd EMor LRHS NRHS
§	'Welsh Dawn'	MBNS
§	***whippleanus***	EAJP GEdr LRHS MHer MMuc SBut SPlb
	– 'Chocolate Drop'	SIvy
§	'White Bedder'	Widely available
	'Whitethroat' Sidwell	MBNS WHoo
	'Willy's Purple'	ECtt
§	'Windsor Red'	CTri ECtt EPfP LRHS SLon SRms SWvt WAvo WBrk WCot
	'Woodpecker'	ECtt ELon EMor IPot SRms WAvo WBrk WHoo

Pentaglottis (*Boraginaceae*)

§	***sempervirens***	EPfP SRms WSFF

Pentapanax see *Aralia*

Pentapterygium see *Agapetes*

Pentas (*Rubiaceae*)

lanceolata	CCCN EShb

Peperomia ✿ (*Piperaceae*)

ferreyrae	EShb
graveolens new	EShb
polybotrya 'Raindrop' new	CDoC LCro LOPS

pepino see *Solanum muricatum*

peppermint see *Mentha* × *piperita*

Perezia (*Asteraceae*)

recurvata	EPot

Pericallis (*Asteraceae*)

× ***hybrida*** Senetti Series	MPri NPer SPoG
- - SENETTI BLUE BICOLOR ('Sunseneribuba'PBR)	MGos SPoG
- - SENETTI BLUE ('Sunsenebu'PBR)	SPoG
- - SENETTI MAGENTA BICOLOR ('Sunsenereba'PBR)	MGos SPoG
- - SENETTI MAGENTA ('Sunsenere'PBR)	SPoG
§ ***lanata*** (L'Hér.) B. Nord.	EShb
- Kew form	CSpe

Perilla (*Lamiaceae*)

frutescens	WJek
§ - var. ***crispa*** 🏆H3	CLau CSpe
- var. ***nankinensis***	see *P. frutescens* var. *crispa*
- var. ***purpurascens***	CLau WJek

Periploca (*Apocynaceae*)

graeca	CBcs CBod CCCN CPla EBee MGil
sepium	CExl

Pernettya see *Gaultheria*

Perovskia (*Lamiaceae*)

abrotanoides	XLum
atriplicifolia	CMea ELan LSun MGil MHer MNHC WKif
- 'Blue Shadow'	CRos EHyd LRHS NLar
'Blue Spire' 🏆H5	Widely available
'Filigran'	CBod CRos EHyd ELan EPfP GBin LRHS LSou MBel NLar NRHS SBrt SPoG WGrn WSpi XSen
'Hybrida'	LRHS WMal
LACEY BLUE ('Lisslitt'PBR)	CRos EBee EHyd EMor EPfP LPla LRHS MAsh NLar NRHS SCob SGsty SWvt XSen
'Little Spire'PBR	CBcs CBod CMac CRos CSBt CSpe EBee EHyd ELon EMor EPfP EWes GMaP LCro LOPS LRHS LSRN MAsh MAvo MHed NLar NRHS SCob SEdd SPer SPoG SRkn WCAu WSpi
'Longin'	LRHS XLum
SILVERY BLUE ('Lissvery'PBR)	CBod CMac CRos EHyd EMor LRHS NLar NRHS SNig WNPC XSen

Persea (*Lauraceae*)

americana	CCCN SVic
indica	CCCN
- B&SWJ 12535	WCru
japonica B&SWJ 12789	WCru
thunbergii B&SWJ 12747	WCru

Persicaria (*Polygonaceae*)

B&SWJ 11268 from Sumatra	WCru
§ ***affinis***	CBcs CSBt GAbr MSCN NBro SCob WFar
- 'Darjeeling Red' 🏆H7	Widely available
- 'Dimity'	see *P. affinis* 'Superba'
- 'Donald Lowndes' 🏆H7	Widely available
- 'Kabouter'	EBee GBin GWyn NLar WBor
§ - 'Superba' 🏆H7	Widely available
alata	see *P. nepalensis*
alpina 🏆H6	CBcs CBct EBee ECha EPPr EPfP EWhm GBin GMaP GQue IPot LEdu LRHS MAvo MHol MRav NDov SCob SDix SMad SPoG WCAu WCot WPnP WSpi
amphibia	EWat LLWG XLum
§ ***amplexicaulis***	CBre CCBP CKno CRos ELan EWes GMaP GWyn ILea MBel MCot NChi WBor WBrk WFar WRHF WWtn XLum
- 'Alba'	Widely available
- 'Amethyst'	CKno LPla
- 'Ample Pink'	MAvo
- 'Anouk'	EBee
- 'Arends Pride' **new**	SDix
- 'Atrosanguinea'	CBod CKno CMac CTri ECha EHyd ELan ELon EPfP GLog LRHS MMuc MRav MSpe NBir NLar NRHS SEND SPer SRms SWvt WFar WOld XLum
- 'Betty Brandt'	GWyn
- 'Black Adder'	ELon
- 'Blackfield'PBR	Widely available
- 'Clent Charm'	MBriF MHCG MSpe NChi WOut
- 'Cottesbrooke Gold'	ECtt EWhm MAvo
- 'Dikke Floskes'	CBct CBod CKno EBee ECtt ELon EPPr GBin LRHS MHol MSpe SRms WBrk WCot WHoo WMal
- 'Early Pink Lady'	ELon
- 'Eastfield' (v)	EPPr WCot WFar
- 'Fascination'	ELon MAvo WCot
- 'Fat Domino'PBR	CBct CBod CKno CRos EBee ECtt EHyd ELan EMor EPfP GQue ILea IPot LPla LRHS MAvo MBel MCot MHol MNrw MSCN NCou NDov NLar NRHS SEdd SHeu SPoG WCAu WCot
- 'Fat White'	ELon GBin
- 'Firedance'	CAby CKno ECtt ELon EPPr GQue IPot MSpe NDov SMHy SPhx SRms WCot WFar
- 'Firetail'	Widely available
- 'Golden Arrow' (v)	CBct CBod EBee ECtt EHyd ELon EMor GBin LRHS MBel MSCN NEoE NSti SCob SPoG SRms WFar WHil WPnP WTor
- 'High Society'	CKno SEdd SPoG SRms WCAu
- 'Inverleith'	CBct CBod CBre CKno EBee ECha ECtt EHyd ELon EPed GBin GMaP GQue LRHS MAvo MMuc MSpe NBPC NBid NBir NGrd NRHS SGbt SPoG WBor WCAu WPnP
I - 'Jo and Guido's Form'	ELon MSpe NLar WCAu WFar
- 'JS Caliente'PBR	CBod CKno ECtt ELon EMor GQue LRHS LSun MNrw NBir SAko SCob SHar SHeu SRms WCot WPnP WSpi
- 'JS Calor'PBR	EBee GQue GWyn
- 'JS Delgado Macho'PBR	CKno EBee ELon MBel MNrw SHeu SRms
- 'Lisan'	CBod EPPr MNrw WCAu
- ORANGE FIELD ('Orangofield'PBR)	CBct CBod CKno CMea CRos EBee ECtt EHyd ELan ELon EMor EPfP EShb EWTr GMaP GQue LRHS MCot MHol MNrw NLar NRHS SAko SCob SGbt WBor WCAu WHoo WWtn
- var. ***pendula***	EBee ELon GBin IMou NBir SMHy WFar
- - HWJK 2255	WCru

- 'Pink Elephant' see *P.* 'Pink Elephant'
- 'Pink Knot' CRos EHyd LRHS NRHS
- 'Pink Lady' MPie
- 'Pink Mist' WGoo
- 'Rosea' Widely available
- 'Rowden Gem' EBee ELon GBin IPot MSpe WCAu WOut
- 'Rubie's Pink' ECha
- 'September Spires' CKno NDov WGoo
- 'Seven Oaks Village' EBee
- 'Summer Dance' CKno EBee ECtt ELon EPPr SMHy
- TAURUS ('Blotau') CElw CRos CSam ECha ECtt EHyd ELon EPPr GBin IPot LRHS MCot NLar NRHS NSti SMHy SRkn SRms WCAu WFar WHoo
- 'White Eastfield' CKno ECha ELan NDov NLar SAko WCAu

§ ***bistorta*** GPoy MHer MMuc NBir NGrd NLar SEND SRms WFar
- subsp. ***carnea*** CBod CRos EBee ECha EHyd ELon EPPr EWhm GPSL LRHS MBNS MMuc MPie NBir NBro NRHS WCot
- 'Hohe Tatra' CBod CRos EBee ECtt EHyd EMor EPPr GMaP LRHS LSun MBel MCot MHol NCou NDov NRHS SDix SEdd SPoG WCot WFar
- 'Superba' ♀H7 Widely available

campanulata CBod CElw EBee ECha ECtt EMor GAbr GMaP MAvo MMuc MRav NSti SPer WFar WOut WWFP
- Alba Group CElw MPie
- 'Madame Jigard' ECha GBin WMal
- 'Rosenrot' CBre ILea NBir WOld
- 'Southcombe White' ECha

§ ***capitata*** XLum
- 'Pink Bubbles' CPla ELon LPot NBir SWvt

chinensis B&SWJ 11268 WCru

dshawachischwilii LPla SMHy

× ***fennica*** 'Johanniswolke' EBee IPot

* ***hydropiper*** var. ***rubra*** WJek

'Indian Summer' EBee LPla SBrt WCot WFar WMal WOld

* ***kahil*** GBin MCot NLar WCot

microcephala MHer MPie
- 'Dragon's Eye'PBR EBee WNPC
- 'Red Dragon'PBR Widely available

milletii CRos EBee EHyd LRHS MAvo NDov NRHS WCru

§ ***mollis*** WPGP

neofiliformis EShb MSpe

§ ***nepalensis*** CExl EMor EPPr EShb IMou

'October Pink' CSam SMHy

§ ***odorata*** CLau ENfk GPoy LLWG MHer MNHC NGrd SEdi SPre SRms WHer WJek XAbr

orientalis CSpe SPhx
- 'Variegata' (v) CSpe

§ 'Pink Elephant' CSam ELon EMor EPPr EPed GBin ILea MNrw NDov NLar SAko SCob SEdd SHeu SRms WCAu WFar WHoo WMal WNPC WSpi

polystachya see *P. wallichii*

'Red Baron' ECtt ELon EMor EPPr

§ ***runcinata*** EBee MMuc NBir WFar
- 'Purple Fantasy' CBod CDTJ CPla ECtt ELan EMor EShb LPla MAvo MBriF MHol MNrw MSpe NSti SCob SDix SEdd SMad SPtp WFar WHil WMal WNPC

scoparia see *Polygonum scoparium*

'Silver Dragon'PBR CBct CBod EMor LPla LSun MAvo MBel NSti SEdd SPoG WCot

tenuicaulis CBre GBin SBrt SGro WCru

§ ***tinctoria*** WSFF

§ ***vacciniifolia*** ♀H5 CBcs CSBt CTri EBou ECha ECtt GAbr GEdr GKev GMaP MCot MHer MMuc NBid NBir NLar SCob SDix SPlb SRms SWvt WAbe WBor WFar WHoo WIce WSpi

§ ***virginiana*** LEdu LSun WWtn
- 'Alba' EPPr
- 'Brushstrokes' SDix
- var. ***filiformis*** CAby CBod CSam CSpe ELan LEdu MBel MPie NChi SBrt SPoG SPtp SRkn SWvt WAul WCot WHil
- - 'Ballet' WCot
- - 'Batwings' SPtp
- - 'Compton's Red' CSam ECha ECtt EMor EPPr EShb MAvo WAul WCot WFar
- - 'Guizhou Bronze' LEdu
- - 'Lance Corporal' CMac CMea EPPr EShb LPot MAvo NLar
- Variegated Group (v) ECha EShb MBNS WCot WFar
- - 'Painter's Palette' (v) CBod CDTJ CMac EBee ECha ECtt ELan EMor EPPr EPed EShb GWyn LRHS MHol MPie MRav NBid NRHS NSti SPer SRms SWvt WAul WCot WFar WMal XLum

§ ***wallichii*** CSpe MMuc NLar SDix SEND WCot XLum

§ ***weyrichii*** NBir NBro NLar WFar XLum

persimmon see *Diospyros virginiana*

persimmon, Japanese see *Diospyros kaki*

Pertya (*Asteraceae*)

sinensis new IArd

Petalostemon see *Dalea*

Petamenes see *Gladiolus*

Petasites (*Asteraceae*)

albus GPoy MHer NSti

fragrans ELan SRms WHer XLum

§ ***frigidus*** var. ***palmatus*** NLar WCot
- - 'Golden Palms' WBor

hybridus 'Variegatus' (v) XLum

japonicus CAgr CBcs GPoy
- var. ***giganteus*** ECha EPfP LEdu MBel WCru

§ - - 'Nishiki-buki' (v) CMac EBee ECha EWld GQue LEdu MHer NBir NSti SMad WBor WFar XLum
- - 'Variegatus' see *P. japonicus* var. *giganteus* 'Nishiki-buki'

palmatus see *P. frigidus* var. *palmatus*

paradoxus EWld LEdu LPot MBel SBrt WCot WFar WPGP

Petrea (*Verbenaceae*)

volubilis CCCN

Petrocallis (*Brassicaceae*)

lagascae see *P. pyrenaica*

§ ***pyrenaica*** WAbe
- white-flowered WAbe

Petrocoptis (*Caryophyllaceae*)

pyrenaica EWes SRms

Petrocosmea ✿ (*Gesneriaceae*)

	barbata	WDib
	begoniifolia	WAbe WDib
	coerulea	WDib
§	***cryptica***	WAbe WDib
	- 'Yumebutai'	WDib
	flaccida	WDib
	'Fluffer Nutter'	WDib
	forrestii	WAbe WDib
	grandiflora	WAbe WDib
	- 'Crème de Crûg'	WCru
	'Ht-2'	WDib
	iodioides 𝕐^{H1c}	WDib
	kerrii	WDib
	'Keystone's Angora'	WDib
	'Keystone's Bantam'	WDib
	'Keystone's Barnswallow'	WDib
	'Keystone's Belmont'	WDib
	'Keystone's Blue Jay'	WDib
	'Keystone's Lafayette' **new**	WDib
	'Keystone's Magic'	WDib
	minor	WDib
	parryorum	WDib
	'Paul Kroll'	WDib
	'Rosemary Platz'	WDib
	rosettifolia misapplied	see *P. cryptica*
	sericea	WDib
	'Yuki-no-sei' **new**	WDib

Petromarula (*Campanulaceae*)

	pinnata	EBee

Petrophytum (*Rosaceae*)

	caespitosum	CMea WAbe
	cinerascens	WFar
§	***hendersonii***	WAbe

Petrorhagia (*Caryophyllaceae*)

	saxifraga 𝕐^{H4}	CSpe EPPr GLog MBel NLar NSla SBut SRms XLum

Petroselinum (*Apiaceae*)

§	***crispum***	CLau EMor ENfk GPoy LCro LOPS MNHC MPri NPol SPoG SRms XAbr
	- 'Bravour' 𝕐^{H6}	LRHS MHer
	- 'Champion Moss Curled'	MBros SVic
	- 'Curlina' 𝕐^{H4} **new**	LCro LOPS
	- 'Extra Moss Curled' **new**	LCro LOPS
	- French	CCBP CLau EMor ENfk LCro LOPS MBros MHer MNHC MPri SPoG SRms
	- 'Italian'	see *P. crispum* var. *neapolitanum*
	- 'Laura'^{PBR}	CLau
	- 'Moss Curled' 𝕐^{H6}	CHby EHyd EKin LRHS MCtn NRHS NRob SRms
§	- var. ***neapolitanum***	CLau ENfk LCro LOPS SPoG SRms SVic
§	- var. ***tuberosum***	CLau SRms SVic
	hortense	see *P. crispum*
	tuberosum	see *P. crispum* var. *tuberosum*

Petteria (*Papilionaceae*)

	ramentacea	CPla EBtc

Petunia (*Solanaceae*)

	AMORE QUEEN OF HEARTS (Amore Series) **new**	MBros
	× ***atkinsiana*** 'Storm Lavender' 𝕐^{H2} **new**	LCro LOPS
	BABYDOLL ('Kleph17342') **new**	MPri SCob
	BALCONY MIX **new**	LCro LOPS
	BEDDING STRIPED MIX **new**	LCro LOPS
	BLACK VELVET ('Balpevac'^{PBR})	MBros
	'Buzz Purple' (Designer Series)	LSou MBros MPri
	(Cascadias Series) CASCADIAS INDIAN SUMMER ('Dcas303'^{PBR})	LSou
	- CASCADIAS RIM MAGENTA ('Dcas298'^{PBR})	LSou MPri
	CRAZYTUNIA MANDEVILLE ('Wespecramand') (Crazytunia Series)	MBros
	Double Pirouette Series (d) **new**	LCro LOPS
	- 'Double Pirouette Rose' (d) **new**	LCro LOPS
	Duo Series **new**	MBros
	(Easy Wave Series) EASY WAVE BERRY VELOUR ('Pas982903')	MBros MPri
	- EASY WAVE BLUE ('Pas320593')	MPri
	- EASY WAVE BUBBLEGUM	see *P.* EASY WAVE PINK PASSION
	- EASY WAVE BURGUNDY STAR ('Pas760702')	MPri
	- EASY WAVE BURGUNDY VELOUR ('Pas933562')	MPri
	- EASY WAVE GRAND RAPIDS **new**	MPri
	- EASY WAVE NEON ROSE ('Pas760700')	MPri
§	- EASY WAVE PINK PASSION ('Pas882697')	MPri
	- EASY WAVE PLUM VEIN ('Pas739163')	MPri
	- EASY WAVE RED VELOUR ('Pas933560')	MPri
	- EASY WAVE SILVER ('Pas1016992')	MPri
	- EASY WAVE VIOLET ('Pas760717')	MPri
	exserta	CSpe WCot
	FANTASIA MIX **new**	LCro LOPS
	Frenzy Series	MBros
	- FRENZY REFLECTION MIX **new**	LCro LOPS
	LITTLETUNIA PINK FRILLS (Littletunia Series) **new**	LSou
	MARGARITA ('Kermar') (Tumbelina Series)	MBros
	NIGHTSKY ('Kleph15313') 𝕐^{H3}	LSou MBros MPri SCob
	(Ovation Series) 'Ovation Dark Heart' (Ovation Series)	MPri
	- 'Ovation Lilac' **new**	MPri
	- 'Ovation Pink' **new**	MPri
	- 'Ovation White' **new**	MPri
	patagonica	SPlb WAbe
	PHANTOM ('Balpephan'^{PBR})	MBros
	PINSTRIPE ('Balpepin'^{PBR}) **new**	MBros
	'Prism Sunshine' (Prism Series) **new**	MBros
	'Purple Flash' (Designer Series)	MBros

(Surfinia Series) SURFINIA BLUE ('Sunblu')	LSou MPri
- SURFINIA BLUE TOPAZ ('Sunsurfbupa'PBR)	MBros
- SURFINIA BLUE VEIN ('Sunsolos'PBR)	MBros
- SURFINIA BURGUNDY ('Keiburtel'PBR)	MBros
- SURFINIA GIANT PURPLE ('Sunlapur'PBR)	MBros
- SURFINIA HEAVENLY BLUE ('Sunsurf Skytatsu'PBR)	LSou
- SURFINIA HOT PINK 06 ('Sunrovein'PBR)	MBros MPri
- SURFINIA HOT PINK ('Marrose')	LSou
- SURFINIA HOT RED ('Sunhore'PBR)	LSou MBros
- SURFINIA LIME ('Keiyeul'PBR)	MBros
- SURFINIA PINK VEIN ('Suntosol') ♀H2	MBros
- SURFINIA PURPLE ('Shihi Brilliant') ♀H2	LSou MPri
- SURFINIA ROSE VEIN ('Sunrove'PBR)	MBros
- SURFINIA IMPULZ SNOW ('Sunsurfkuri'PBR)	MBros MPri
- SURFINIA VARIEGATED MINI PURPLE (v)	LSou
- SURFINIA WHITE ('Kesupite')	LSou
- SURFINIA YELLOW DREAM	MBros
TRIXI EARLY SUNSET **new**	MPri
(Tumbelina Series) TUMBELINA ANNA (d)	MPri
- TUMBELINA BELINDA (d)	MBros
- TUMBELINA CANDYFLOSS ('Kercan'PBR) (d)	MBros
- TUMBELINA CHERRY RIPPLE ('Kerripcherry'PBR) (d)	LSou
- TUMBELINA DAMSON RIPPLE	LSou
- TUMBELINA INGA (d)	MBros
- TUMBELINA MARIA (d)	MBros MPri
- TUMBELINA PRISCILLA ('Kerpril'PBR) (d) ♀H1c	LSou MBros

Peucedanum (*Apiaceae*)

* ***aromaticum***	IMou
litorale	see *Kitagawia litoralis*
officinale	CSpe EHyd GBin LRHS SPhx SPlb
ostruthium	GPoy LEdu
- 'Daphnis' (v)	CSpe EBee ECha EWhm LEdu MAvo MBriF MNrw NChi NGrd NLar SPtp WAvo WCFE WCot WHrl WSHC XLum
rablense	EPPr GBin LEdu NDov SPhx
verticillare	CRos CSam CSpe EBee EHyd EMor GBin GWyn IMou LEdu LPla LRHS MAvo MBel MBriF NDov NRHS SBrt SDix SPhx WCot WKif

Phacelia (*Boraginaceae*)

bolanderi	CPla EWes GEdr SBut
tanacetifolia	LCro SVic WSFF

Phaedranassa (*Amaryllidaceae*)

viridiflora	WCot

Phaenocoma (*Asteraceae*)

prolifera	SPlb

Phaenosperma (*Poaceae*)

globosa	CBod CSam CSpe ECha EPPr EShb GBin GQue LRHS MMuc NWsh WCot WPGP WSMil WWtn XCre XLum

Phaiophleps see *Olsynium*

nigricans	see *Sisyrinchium striatum*

Phalaris (*Poaceae*)

arundinacea	MBNS SPlb SVic
- 'Elegantissima'	see *P. arundinacea* var. *picta* 'Picta'
- var. ***picta***	CTri NBir NPer WFar XLum
- - 'Arctic Sun' (v)	CKno EBee EPPr EShb GBin LLWG LRHS MAsh MMuc NEoE SEND SPoG
- - 'Aureovariegata' (v)	MRav NPer XLum
- - 'Feesey' (v) ♀H7	Widely available
- - 'Luteopicta' (v)	EPPr MMuc XLum
§ - - 'Picta' (v)	CBod EHyd ELan EPfP GBin LRHS MMuc NRHS SCob SEND SPer
- - 'Streamlined' (v)	EPPr NWsh

Phanerophlebia ✿ (*Dryopteridaceae*)

caryotidea	see *Cyrtomium caryotideum*
falcata	see *Cyrtomium falcatum*
fortunei	see *Cyrtomium fortunei*

Pharbitis see *Ipomoea*

Phaseolus (*Papilionaceae*)

caracalla	see *Cochliasanthus caracalla*

Phedimus see *Sedum*

Phegopteris (*Thelypteridaceae*)

§ ***connectilis***	CLAP EFer LEdu
decursive-pinnata	CBdn CBod CRos EBee EHyd LEdu LRHS MMuc NRHS SEND WFib WPnP
hexagonoptera	CBdn

Phellodendron (*Rutaceae*)

amurense	CBcs CCCN CMCN EBee EPfP GBin LMaj MBlu WBor
- B&SWJ 11000	WCru
japonicum B&SWJ 11175	WCru

Phemeranthus (*Portulacaceae*)

sediformis	GKev

Phenakospermum (*Strelitziaceae*)

guianense	XBlo

Pherosphaera ✿ (*Podocarpaceae*)

fitzgeraldii	CKen WPav WThu

Philadelphus ✿ (*Hydrangeaceae*)

SDR 2823	CExl
SDR 4946	CExl
'Atlas' (v)	NLar
'Avalanche'	CExl MMuc NLar SPer SRms
'Beauclerk' ♀H6	CBod CBrac CCCN CDoC CTri EBee ECrN EPfP LRHS MGos MMuc MRav NLar SCob SLim SPer SRms SWvt WSpi

'Belle Étoile' ♀H6	Widely available
'Bialy Sopel'	CCCN WAvo
'Bicolore'	NLar WAvo WSpi
'Bouquet Blanc'	MRav NLar SGol SRms WLov
brachybotrys	MRav
'Buckley's Quill' (d)	CAby EBee EPfP EWes LRHS MRav SMad SWvt
'Burfordensis'	MMuc MRav SEND WSpi
'Casa Azul' **new**	WPGP
coronarius	CBcs CBod EPfP LBuc LRHS MRav SPer WSpi
- 'Aureus' ♀H6	Widely available
- 'Bowles's Variety'	see *P. coronarius* 'Variegatus'
§ - 'Variegatus' (v) ♀H6	CMac CRos ELan ELon EPfP EWTr GBin LPot LRHS MGil MGos MMuc MRav MSwo NBir NLar SCob SPer SPoG SRms WAvo WCFE WCot WFar WKif WLov WSpi
coulteri	EBee SBrt SMad WPGP
'Coupe d'Argent'	MRav
'Dainty Lady'PBR	GBin LCro LOPS LRHS SLon
'Dame Blanche' (d)	ECrN EPfP MRav NLar WFar
delavayi	EPfP EWTr GBin LEdu NLar SPer WLov WPGP WSpi
- var. ***calvescens***	MRav SPtp
- - BWJ 8005	WCru
- f. ***melanocalyx***	EPfP MRav SChF WPGP
- - B&L 12168	EBee WPGP
- - 'Nyman's Variety' ♀H6	CExl CTho WKif WLov WPGP
aff. ***delavayi***	SBrt
'Enchantement' (d)	MRav SDix
'Erectus'	CSBt EBee ELan ELon EPfP LRHS MRav NLar SBrt SPer SPoG WAvo WSpi
'Étoile Rose'	WAvo
'Falconeri'	MRav
'Frosty Morn' (d)	CBcs EShb EWTr LEdu MBlu MMuc MRav SEND SPer SPoG
incanus B&SWJ 8616	WCru
§ 'Innocence' (v) ♀H6	CAgr CExl CMac CRos CTsd CWGN EHyd ELan EPfP LRHS MAsh MGos MMuc MRav MSwo NEoE NLar NRHS SEND SGol SPad SPer SPoG SRms WFar WLov
'Innocence Variegatus'	see *P.* 'Innocence'
§ ***insignis***	MRav
'Karolinka' **new**	NLar
karwinskianus F&M 152	WPGP
'Lemoinei'	CBcs CBod CTri MGos SCob SGol WSpi
lewisii	CExl SPhx
- L 1896	CExl
- 'Snow Velvet'	EPfP LRHS
- 'Waterton'	ELon WAvo WSpi
'Limestone'	MRav
'Little White Love'	SGol
maculatus 'Mexican Jewel'	CBcs CBod CExl CRos EBee ELan ELon EPfP GBin LEdu LRHS MNHC NLar SChF SMad SPad WGob WKif WLov WPGP WSHC
- 'Scented Storm'	EBee WPGP
- 'Sweet Clare' ♀H5	CRos EHyd EPfP LCro LOPS LRHS NRHS SPoG WSpi
madrensis	EBee MRav
- F&M 326	WPGP
'Manteau d'Hermine' (d) ♀H6	Widely available
'Marjorie'	NLar
mexicanus B&SWJ 10253	WCru
- 'Rose Syringa'	CExl SBrt WLov WPGP
mexicanus* × *palmeri	EBee WPGP
microphyllus	CAby CBrac CMCN CTho CTri EBee ELan ELon EPfP GBin LRHS MGos MRav NLar SLon SPer SPoG WFar WKif
'Minnesota Snowflake' (d)	CBcs CRos EHyd ELon EPfP EWes LRHS LSRN MMuc MRav NLar NRHS SEND SGol WFar
'Mont Blanc'	CBcs GKin MRav NLar
'Mrs E.L. Robinson' (d)	CMac CRos EHyd ELon EPfP GLog LRHS MGos NRHS WAvo WCFE WLov
myrtoides B&SWJ 10436	WCru
'Natchez' (d)	CBod CMac NLar WLov
'Norma'	WLov
palmeri	EBee WPGP
'Patricia'	WAvo WLov
pekinensis	CExl NLar
'Perryhill'	MRav
'Polar Star'	NLar WKif
purpurascens	CExl CJun EBee EPfP EWes GLog LEdu MGos MRav NLar SChF WCFE WLov WPGP
- BWJ 7540	WCru
'Purpureomaculatus'	ELon MRav NLar WPGP
'Pyramidal' (d) **new**	CBrac
satsumi	NLar
- B&SWJ 10811	WCru
- B&SWJ 11004	WCru
schrenkii	NLar
- B&SWJ 8465	ESwi WCru
sericanthus	NLar
§ 'Silberregen' ♀H6	CMac CRos EBee ELan ELon EPfP LEdu LRHS MAsh MGos MMuc MRav NEoE NLar SCob SEND SGol SMad SPoG SRms SWvt
SILVER SHOWERS	see *P.* 'Silberregen'
'Snowbelle' (d)	CCCN CDoC EHyd EPfP EWTr LCro LOPS LRHS MAsh MPri NLar NOra SCob SPoG SRms SWvt SavN WLov
'Snowgoose'	LRHS SGol
'Souvenir de Billiard'	see *P. insignis*
'Starbright'PBR	CAby CBcs CCCN EBee EHyd EPfP LRHS MAsh SCob SPoG
subcanus	CExl SPtp
- L 524	CExl
'Sybille' ♀H6	CMac CRos ECrN EHyd EPfP LRHS MRav MSwo SDix SPer SRms WAvo WKif WLov WSpi
tomentosus	CExl
- B&SWJ 2707	WCru
- GWJ 9215	WCru
'Velléda'	WAvo
'Virginal' (d)	Widely available
× ***virginalis***	SReu
'Voie Lactée'	MRav NLar WSpi
WHITE ROCK ('Pekphil') ♀H6	CMac CRos EBee LRHS LSRN MRav NLar SPer
'Yellow Cab'	EBee
'Yellow Hill'	CMac EPfP LRHS

Philesia (*Philesiaceae*)

buxifolia	see *P. magellanica*
§ ***magellanica***	CExl CRHN GEdr GGGa MGil WCru
- 'Rosea'	CRHN

Phillyrea (*Oleaceae*)

angustifolia	CBcs CMCN CRos CSpe EBee EHyd ELan ELon EPfP EShb LRHS LTop

		MGos MRav NLar SArc SEND SPer SWeb WLov WPGP XSen
	- f. ***rosmarinifolia***	CCCN CCoa CExl
	- - 'French Fries'	EBee EPfP WPGP
	decora	see *Osmanthus decorus*
§	***latifolia***	CBcs CBod CCCN CDoC CRos CTho EBee EHyd ELan EPfP LRHS LTop SArc SEND WPGP XSen
	media	see *P. latifolia*

Philodendron (*Araceae*)

	'Angra dos Reis'	see *P. cordatum*
§	***angustisectum*** ♀H1a	XBlo
	bipennifolium	SPlb
	bipinnatifidum ♀H2	XBlo
	corcovadense	XBlo
§	***cordatum***	XBlo
	elegans	see *P. angustisectum*
	erubescens 'Red Emerald'	XBlo
*	***radiatum***	XBlo
	var. ***pseudoradiatum*** 'Simmonds'	
*	***rubrum***	XBlo
	scandens ♀H1b	LCro LOPS
	- 'Green Emerald'	XBlo
	- 'Mica'	XBlo
	tripartitum	XBlo
	xanadu	LCro LOPS NGBl XBlo

Philotheca (*Rutaceae*)

§	***myoporoides***	ILea LRHS

Phlebodium (*Polypodiaceae*)

§	***aureum*** ♀H1b	CSpe SPlb WCot
	- var. ***areolatum***	EShb
	- 'Blue Star'	ISha
	- 'Glaucum'	CSpe WCot
	pseudoaureum	ISha LEdu MAsh WCot
	- 'Virginia Blue' **new**	LEdu

Phleum (*Poaceae*)

	phleoides	EHyd LRHS NRHS
	pratense	WSFF

Phlomis ✿ (*Lamiaceae*)

	alpina	SPlb
*	***anatolica***	EHyd LRHS
	- 'Lloyd's Variety'	see *P. grandiflora* 'Lloyd's Silver'
	anisodonta white-flowered	XSen
	armeniaca	XSen
	atropurpurea	IMou
	- BWJ 7922	WCru
	bourgaei	XSen
	- NJM 12.008	WPGP
	bovei subsp. ***maroccana***	SEND WHal XLum
	capitata	XSen
	cashmeriana	CBod CRos EBee ECha EHyd EPfP ILea LRHS MCot MHol NQui NRHS SMad WAvo WCFE WSpi XSen
	chrysophylla ♀H5	ECha EHyd ELan EPfP LRHS MAsh MRav NLar WCFE WSpi XSen
	cretica	SVen WMal
	× ***cytherea***	XSen
	'Edward Bowles'	CBod EBee ECha EHyd EPfP GBin LRHS MRav NLar SEND SWvt WAvo WCFE WSpi XSen
*	'Elliot's Variety'	CExl
	fruticosa ♀H5	Widely available
	- white-flowered	CBcs
	aff. ***fruticosa***	EPed WSpi
	grandiflora	EBee EPfP MMuc MNrw SEND XSen
	- NJM 10.014	WPGP
§	- 'Lloyd's Silver' ♀H5	CSam EHyd ELan LRHS MAsh NLar
	herba-venti	XSen
	italica	Widely available
	lanata	CRos CSde EBee EHyd EPfP LRHS SBrt XSen
	- 'Pygmy'	XSen
	'Le Chat' **new**	XSen
	'Le Sud'	WCot XSen
	leucophracta	SVen
*	***libanotica***	EBee
	longifolia	CBod CDoC EBee EHyd EPfP LRHS MNrw SEND SPer WPGP XSen
	- var. ***bailanica*** ♀H4	CSam EHyd EPfP LRHS NRHS XLum
	- var. ***longifolia***	WSpi
	lychnitis	XSen
	lycia	XSen
	- NJM 10.016	WPGP
	macrophylla	SPhx
	× ***margaritae***	XSen
	'Marina'	XSen
	monocephala	XSen
	nissolei	XSen
	pratensis	CPla
	purpurea	CBod CExl EHyd ELan EPfP LRHS MAsh MMuc NBir NRHS SEND WCot XSen
I	- 'Alba'	CBod ELan GBin LRHS MMrt
	- subsp. ***almeriensis***	XSen
§	***russeliana*** ♀H6	Widely available
	- PAB 7444	LEdu
	- 'Dappled Shade' (v)	WCot
	samia Boiss.	see *P. russeliana*
	samia L.	CBod CMac EHyd LRHS MMrt MMuc MNrw NBir NGdn NLar NRHS SAko SBrt SEND SPtp WMal XSen
	- JMT	EPPr
	- 'Green Glory'	WCot
	taurica	SEND
	× ***termessi***	XSen
	'Toob'	SBrt WPGP
	'Tramuntana'	XSen
	tuberosa	CBcs CBod CPou EHyd ELan EPed EWTr ILea LEdu LRHS LSRN MMuc MPnt NGdn SDix SPhx WCAu WMal XLum XSen
	- 'Amazone' ♀H5	CBod CKno EBee ECha EPfP GBin GMaP LCro LOPS LPla MAvo MBel MNrw MRav NBPC NBid NDov NGBl NSti SMad SPeP SPer SRms WCAu WCot WFar WHil WSHC WSpi
	- 'Bronze Flamingo'	CMac CRos EMor EPfP GBin ILea LRHS MBel MNrw MPnt MRav NLar SPoG SPtp WSpi
	viscosa misapplied	see *P. russeliana*

Phlox ✿ (*Polemoniaceae*)

	adsurgens 'Alba'	WFar
	- 'Wagon Wheel'	CBor ECtt EHyd EPot EWes LRHS NHpl NRHS SPlb SRms WIce
	amplifolia	MSpe WCot XLum
	- 'Augenstern' **new**	WFar
	- 'Winnetou'	IPot
	× ***arendsii*** 'Andrew'	WCot
	- 'Autumn's Pink Explosion'	WCot
	- 'Babyface'	ELon NGdn NLar

	- 'Casablanca'	NDov
	- 'Dylan'	WCot
	- 'Eyecatcher'	NBro
	- 'Gary'	WCot
	- 'Hesperis'	CMiW ECha ELon GWyn LRHS MAvo MNrw MTis NDov NLar SHar SPhx WHil WSHC
	- 'Luc's Lilac' ♀H7	CWld ECtt EPPr MCot NBro NDov NGdn NSti SDix SGbt SPhx WAul WCot
§	- 'Miss Jill' (Spring Pearl Series)	ELan EPfP WCot
§	- 'Miss Karen' (Spring Pearl Series)	EBee ELan NBro
§	- 'Miss Mary' (Spring Pearl Series) ♀H7	EBee EHyd ELan EPfP ILea LRHS MSpe NLar SRkn WRHF
§	- 'Miss Wilma' (Spring Pearl Series)	EBee ELan EPfP
	- 'Paul'	MNrw WCot WSHC
	- 'Ping Pong'	SGbt
	- 'Pink Attraction'	LRHS NBro
	- 'Utopia' ♀H7	CSpe EBee ELon GBin IMou LPla MAvo NDov SPhx WCot
	austromontana	EPot NWad
	bifida 'Ralph Haywood'	ECtt EPot
	- 'Thefi'	ECtt
	borealis	see *P. sibirica* subsp. *borealis*
	caespitosa	CMea CPBP EWes
	- subsp. ***pulvinata***	see *P. pulvinata*
	- 'Zigeunerblut'	CMea ECtt EPot NWad WAbe WHal WHoo
	canadensis	see *P. divaricata*
	carolina 'Bill Baker'	see *P. glaberrima* 'Bill Baker'
	- 'Magnificence'	EBee EWes GWyn SMad SPlb WCot
	- 'Miss Lingard' ♀H6	CBod CDor CSam ECtt EHyd GBee LRHS LSou MMuc MRav MTis MWat NBir NGdn NLar NRHS NSti SGbt WCAu WCot
	'Chattahoochee'	see *P. divaricata* subsp. *laphamii* 'Chattahoochee'
	'Daniel's Cushion'	see *P. subulata* 'McDaniel's Cushion'
	diffusa	EPot
§	***divaricata*** ♀H5	SPlb
	- 'Blue Dreams'	ECtt LSou MNrw WFar
	- 'Blue Moon' **new**	CWCL
	- 'Blue Perfume'	EBee ECtt GWyn LCro LOPS
	- 'Charles'	XLum
	- 'Clouds of Perfume'	Widely available
	- 'Dirigo Ice'	EHyd LRHS NRHS SAko WSHC
	- 'Fuller's White'	CWCL
	- subsp. ***laphamii***	CWCL EBee EWes WFar
§	- - 'Chattahoochee' ♀H5	CBcs CPBP CPla CWCL EAJP ECtt EHyd ELan EMor EPfP EShb EWes GBin GWyn ILea LCro LOPS LRHS MCot MNrw NDov NHpl NLar NRHS NSla SPoG SWvt WCFE WSpi
	- 'May Breeze'	CWCL EAJP ECtt EHyd GMaP LRHS MNrw MPnt NRHS WAvo WSHC
	- 'Plum Perfect'	ECtt
	- 'White Perfume'	CWCL EBee EHyd EPfP EWes ILea LRHS MBel MMrt MTis NDov NLar SBut SPoG WAul WFar XLum
	douglasii	SRms
	- 'Apollo'	CBor CTri ECtt
	- 'Boothman's Variety' ♀H6	ECtt ELan ITim SRms
	- 'Crackerjack' ♀H6	CMea CPBP CTri EBou ECtt EHyd ELan ELon EPot GKev GMaP ITim LRHS MAsh MHol NBir NHol NHpl NRHS NSla SPoG WIce
	- 'Eva'	CBor EBou ECtt EHyd ELon EPot GMaP ITim LRHS LSRN MAsh MHol NBir NHpl NLar NRHS NSla NWad WFar WIce
	- 'Georg Arends'	CBor ECtt WFar
	- 'Ice Mountain'	CBor CMea ECtt ELan EPot GKev ITim NHol NWad SPoG WCav WFar
	- 'J.A. Hibberson'	EPot EWes NWad
	- 'Lilac Cloud'	ECtt
	- LILAC QUEEN	see *P. douglasii* 'Lilakönigin'
§	- 'Lilakönigin'	CTri
	- 'Napoleon'	ECtt EPot ITim NWad
	- 'Ochsenblut'	CBor CSma ECtt EHyd LRHS NLar NRHS NSla NWad WIce
	- 'Red Admiral' ♀H5	ECtt ELan EPfP EWes GMaP MHol NWad WCFE WFar
	- 'Rose Cushion'	EWes
	- 'Rosea'	ELan MMuc NHpl WIce
	- 'Sprite'	SRms
	- 'Tycoon'	see *P. subulata* 'Tamaongalei'
	- 'Waterloo'	CBor CPBP EBou ECtt EHyd EPot LRHS NRHS
I	- 'White Admiral'	CRos CTri ECtt EHyd ELan EPfP GBin LRHS LSRN MHol NRHS
	drummondii POPSTARS MIXED	LSou
	- SURPHLOX PINK ('Sunphlopin')	MHol
	(Fashionably Series) 'Fashionably Early Crystal' **new**	LCro LOPS
	- 'Fashionably Early Princess' **new**	LCro LOPS
	- 'Fashionably Lavender Ice' **new**	LCro LOPS
	'Flare'	see *P. paniculata* 'Neon Flare'
§	***glaberrima*** 'Bill Baker' ♀H6	CSam EAJP ECha ECtt ELon EPfP GMaP MAsh MBow MNrw NBir NGdn NSti SBut SWvt WCAu WFar WMal XLum
	- 'Morris Berd'	EBee WFar WSHC
	- var. ***triflora*** 'Triple Play' (v) **new**	SPtp
	hendersonii	WAbe
	hoodii	WAbe
	'Jeff's Pink'	ECtt NLar
	'Kelly's Eye' ♀H5	EBou ECtt EHyd EPot LRHS NBir NRHS SPoG
	kelseyi 'Lemhi Purple'	CPBP EPot WAbe
	- 'Rosette'	NWad
	LIGHT PINK FLAME ('Bareleven'PBR)	CBod ECtt EHyd LRHS SPoG
	LILAC FLAME ('Barten'PBR)	EHyd LRHS NRHS SCob
	maculata 'Alba'	SAko WAul
	- 'Alpha' ♀H6	CSam CWCL EBee ECha ECtt EHyd EMor EPfP GMaP ILea LEdu LRHS LSou NLar NRHS SGbt SPer SWvt WAul WCAu WFar WSHC WTyc XLum
	- AVALANCHE	see *P. maculata* 'Schneelawine'
	- 'Delta'	EAJP EHyd LRHS NLar SAko SGbt SPer SRkn SWvt
	- 'Natascha' ♀H6	CMac CSam CWld EBee ECtt EHyd ELon EPfP EWes GMaP LRHS LSRN NGdn NHol NLar NRHS NWad SAko SGbt SMad SPer SRkn SWvt WCAu WFar WHil WTyc
	- 'Omega' ♀H6	CExl CMac ECtt ILea LEdu MCot MMuc MNrw MPie NGdn NLar

	SGbt SPer SWvt WCAu WFar WSpi WTyc
- 'Princess Sturdza' ♀H6	NDov SDix
- 'Reine du Jour'	CSam MAvo NDov SPhx WSHC
- 'Rosalinde'	ECtt LRHS LSou MCot NLar SAko SWvt WSHC
§ - 'Schneelawine'	EHyd LRHS SPlb WSpi
'Millstream'	see *P.* × *procumbens* 'Millstream'
'Minnie Pearl'	EWes LPla MAvo MPie NDov WCot
nivalis 'Nivea'	WAbe
paniculata	LEdu NBid NDov SDix WCot
- 'A.E.Amos'	ELon
- (Adessa Series) 'Adessa Orange' **new**	NLar WHil
- - 'Adessa Pink Star'	NLar NRHS WHil
- - 'Adessa Red' **new**	NLar
- - 'Adessa Rose Eye'	NLar WHil
- - 'Adessa Special Deep Purple'	WHil
- - 'Adessa Special Fire'	NLar WHil
- - 'Adessa Special Lilac Twist'	WHil
- 'Aida'	EBee
- var. ***alba***	SDix WCot
- 'Alba Grandiflora' ♀H7	MAvo MNrw NChi WCot WHoo
- 'Alexandra'PBR	LCro LOPS
- 'All in One'	MAvo
- 'Amethyst' misapplied	see *P. paniculata* 'Lilac Time'
- 'Amethyst' Foerster	ELon GWyn LRHS MRav MTis NBir NLar WCAu
- 'André'	LRHS
- 'Anne'	ELon
- 'Argus'	ECtt
- 'Balmoral'	CMac EBee ECtt ELon NCou NSti SWvt
- BAMBINI CANDY CRUSH ('Verscan') **new**	CWGN
- BAMBINI DESIRE ('Versde') **new**	CWGN
- 'Becky Towe'PBR (v) ♀H7	ECtt EMor MHer MHol MNrw NHol NSti SMad SPoG WCot
- 'Blauer Morgen'	XLum
- 'Blue Boy'	CRos EBee ECtt EHyd ELan ELon EMor EPfP GMaP GWyn LRHS MSpe NBir NRHS SWvt WCAu WFar
- 'Blue Evening'	ELon LCro LOPS MSpe NLar
- BLUE FLAME	MPri
- 'Blue Moon'	ELon
- 'Blue Paradise'	Widely available
- 'Blushing Bride'	SRms
- 'Bonny Maid'	MAvo
- 'Border Gem'	CAby CBcs CBod CMac ECtt ELon EShb LRHS MRav MTis SDix SWvt WBrk WCot
- 'Bosvigo Pink'	ELon MAvo SHar
- 'Brigadier'	CTri EBee ECtt ELan LRHS MAvo MSpe NGdn SPer SRms
- 'Bright Eyes'	Widely available
- 'Burgi'	SDix
- 'Butonik'	ELon
- 'Cardinal'	MTis NDov
- 'Caroline van den Berg'	SRms
- 'Charlotte'	MSpe WGoo
- 'Cheriton'	EHyd NRHS
- 'Chintz'	EHyd LRHS MRav NRHS SRms
- 'Cinderella'	ECtt
- 'Cleopatra'PBR	NLar
- COMPACT LILAC	see *P. paniculata* SWEET SUMMER FAVOURITE
- COMPACT ROSE WHITE	see *P. paniculata* SWEET SUMMER CANDY
- 'Cool Best'	NDov NLar
- 'Cool Water'	NLar
- CORAL FLAME ('Barsixtytwo'PBR) (Flame Series)	CBod CMac LSou MHol NLar SCob SPad SRkn WHil
- 'Coral Queen'	SRms
- 'Cosmopolitan'PBR	MNrw NLar
- COUNT ZEPPELIN	see *P. paniculata* 'Graf Zeppelin'
- 'Danielle' ♀H7	LRHS NRHS SHar
- 'Darwin's Choice'	see *P. paniculata* 'Norah Leigh'
- 'David' ♀H7	Widely available
- 'David's Lavender' ♀H7	CRos EHyd ELon IPot LRHS NLar NRHS WSpi
- 'Delilah'PBR	CWGN ECtt NHpl
- 'Discovery'	EShb EWes LCro LOPS LPla LRHS MRav MSpe SHar
- 'Dodo Hanbury-Forbes'	MNrw
- 'Doghouse Pink'	SDix
- 'Drakon'	ELon
- 'Dresden China'	SHar
- 'Duchess of York'	MAvo MNrw MSpe SDix
§ - 'Düsterlohe'	CSam CSpe EBee ECtt EHyd ELon EMor GBin GQue GWyn ILea IPot LRHS MHer MRav MTis NBir NDov NLar NRHS NSti SPer SRkn SRms WCAu WCot WSpi XLum
- (Early Series) EARLY CERISE **new**	WHil
- - EARLY LIGHT PINK	IPot
- - EARLY PINK CANDY **new**	WHil
- - EARLY PINK DARK EYE ('Barphlearpideye'PBR)	WHil
- - EARLY RED **new**	WHil
- 'Eclaireur' misapplied	see *P. paniculata* 'Düsterlohe'
- 'Eclaireur' Lemoine	MAvo
- 'Eden's Flash'	CElw ECtt MPie MSpe
- 'Eden's Smile'	ECtt
- 'Edentuin'	IPot
- 'Elisabeth' (v)	LSRN NWad
- 'Elizabeth Arden'	ECtt ELon LPla MTis NLar
- 'Elizabeth Campbell'	EHyd LRHS
- 'Ending Blue'	MAvo
- 'Etoile de Paris'	see *P. paniculata* 'Toits de Paris' Symons-Jeune
- 'Europa'	EBee ECtt ELan ELon IPot NBir NGdn NLar SPer WCAu WSHC
- 'Eva Cullum' ♀H7	CBod CRos CSam EBee ECtt EHyd ELan ELon EPfP GMaP GWyn LRHS MHer NHpl NRHS SAko SDix SPer WCAu WCot WFar
- 'Eva Foerster' ♀H7	CRos EBee EHyd GWyn LRHS NRHS XLum
- 'Eventide'	CMac CRos CSam ECtt EHyd EPfP LRHS MArl MAvo MBel MNrw MRav MWat NRHS SPer WFar
- 'Fairytale of the Ural'	see *P. paniculata* 'Uralskie Skazy'
- 'Ferris Wheel'	EBee
- FLAME LIGHT BLUE (Flame Series) **new**	WHil
- 'Flamingo' ♀H7	EBee ECtt ELon MSpe NLar SWvt XLum
- 'Fondant Fancy'PBR	NLar
- 'Franz Schubert' ♀H7	CDor CRos CWld ECtt EHyd ELan EMor EPfP EWTr GBin GWyn ILea LCro LRHS MAvo MCot MSpe MTis MWat NBir NChi NGdn NLar NRHS NSti SPer SWvt WCot WFar WHoo

§ - 'Frau Alfred von Mauthner' GKev
- 'Fujiyama' see *P. paniculata* 'Mount Fuji'
- 'Gamlingay Purple' **new** MAvo
- 'Glebe' CSam
- 'Goldmine'PBR (v) EHyd LRHS MHol MNrw NHpl SPoG SRms WCot
§ - 'Graf Zeppelin' ECtt ELon MSpe MTis NHol NLar SRms XLum
- 'Grenadine Dream'PBR ♀H7 CWGN EHyd LRHS MNrw NHpl WCot
- 'Grey Lady' ♀H7 CRos EHyd LRHS MNrw NRHS WGoo
- 'Harlequin' (v) CMac CWGN ECha ECtt GBee MHol WCot
- 'Herbstwalzer' ELon IPot WCot
- 'Ice Cream' CWGN ELon
- 'Irene Mast' CSam
- 'Iris' MNrw SRms WCot
- 'Jade' ECtt ELon EMor GQue LRHS MHol MNrw NLar NSti WCot WHil
- 'Jeana' MNrw
- 'Jeff's Blue' MHol NLar WCot
- 'Judy' LSRN
§ - 'Juliglut' EHyd ELon LRHS NRHS WCot
- JULY GLOW see *P. paniculata* 'Juliglut'
- 'Junior Bouquet' MHol NLar
- 'Junior Dream' NLar
- 'Katherine' EHyd IPot LRHS MSpe NLar NRHS
- 'Katja' IPot NLar
- 'Kimbers' **new** MAvo
- 'Kirchenfürst' CElw CRos EHyd ELon LCro LOPS LRHS MSpe MTis NBir NLar NRHS SAko WCAu WFar
- 'Kirmesländler' ECtt IPot NLar SAko
- 'Ksenija' ELon
- 'Lads Pink' SDix
- 'Lady Clare' SRms
- 'Landhochzeit' WFar
- 'Larissa'PBR LCro LOPS LSou MNrw
- 'Laura' see *P. paniculata* 'Uspekh'
§ - 'Lavendelwolke' LRHS MSpe NBir NLar WCot
- LAVENDER CLOUD see *P. paniculata* 'Lavendelwolke'
- 'Le Mahdi' ♀H7 MTis NLar SRms WBor
- 'Lichtspel' LPla NDov SPhx
§ - 'Lilac Time' CBod CElw CRos ECtt EHyd EPfP GKev GMaP LRHS MMuc MTis NLar NRHS SCob SPer SWvt WSpi
- 'Little Boy' CElw ELon MNrw NLar SGbt WHil
- 'Little Laura' CBod ECtt LSRN MNrw MSpe NLar WCot WHoo
- 'Little Princess' ELon NLar
- 'Little Sara' NDov
- 'Logan Black' SHar WSHC
- 'Long Border Mauve' SDix
- MAGICAL DREAM see *P. paniculata* SWEET SUMMER DREAM
- MAGICAL FAVORITE see *P. paniculata* SWEET SUMMER FAVOURITE
- MAGICAL SURPRISE see *P. paniculata* SWEET SUMMER SURPRISE
- 'Manoir d'Hézèques' WCot
- 'Mardi Gras' EPfP
- 'Mary Christine' (v) LRHS MAvo MPie NBid NRHS
- 'Maude Stella Dagley' ELon MSpe
- 'Mia Ruys' MArl
- 'Mies Copijn' ELon MTis
- 'Mike's Favourite' EBee
- 'Milly van Hoboken' MAvo WKif
- 'Miss Holland' NGdn SGbt XLum
- 'Miss Jill' see *P.* × *arendsii* 'Miss Jill'
- 'Miss Karen' see *P.* × *arendsii* 'Miss Karen'
- 'Miss Kelly' EShb MSpe NLar
- 'Miss Mary' see *P.* × *arendsii* 'Miss Mary'
- 'Miss Pepper' ♀H7 CRos ECtt EHyd ELon LRHS MMuc MSpe NGdn NLar NRHS
- 'Miss Universe' ELon
- 'Miss Wilma' see *P.* × *arendsii* 'Miss Wilma'
- 'Modern Art' **new** MNrw
- 'Monica Lynden-Bell' ♀H7 CAby CDor CWGN EBee ELon EWTr GMaP GWyn LRHS LSun MBriF MHol MNrw MPie MRav NBid NChi NDov NLar NSti SGbt SMad WAul WCot WKif
- 'Monte Cristallo' GWyn MSpe
- 'Mother of Pearl' ♀H7 GQue GWyn IPot LRHS WSpi
§ - 'Mount Fuji' Widely available
- 'Mount Fujiyama' see *P. paniculata* 'Mount Fuji'
- 'Mrs A.E. Jeans' SRms
- 'Nadia' LRHS
- 'Natural Feelings'PBR (Feelings Series) NLar
§ - 'Neon Flare' (Neon Series) CWGN WHil
- 'Newbird' EBee ECtt MSpe SRms
- 'Nicky' see *P. paniculata* 'Düsterlohe'
- 'Nirvana' CSam
§ - 'Norah Leigh' (v) ♀H7 CElw CMac CRos CWGN EBee ECha ECtt ELan EMor EPfP EWes GWyn LRHS MHer MHol NPer NRHS NSti NWad SDix SPer SPoG SRms SWvt WCAu WCFE WCot WFar WOld
- 'Oljenka' ELon
- 'Orange Perfection' see *P. paniculata* 'Prince of Orange'
- 'Othello' CSam ECtt ELon MSpe NGdn WHoo
- 'Otley Choice' CSam ECtt GWyn LRHS MRav NCou NLar NSti SDix
- 'Otley Purple' MHer NCou
- 'P.D. Williams' WCot
- 'Pallas Athene' IPot
- 'Pastorale' WCot
- (Peacock Series) PEACOCK CHERRY RED ♀H7 CRos EHyd LRHS NRHS WCFE WTor
- - PEACOCK LILAC ♀H7 CRos EHyd LRHS NRHS
- - PEACOCK NEON PURPLE ♀H7 CRos EHyd LRHS NRHS
- - PEACOCK PURPLE BICOLOR CRos EHyd LRHS NRHS
- - PEACOCK WHITE ♀H7 CRos EHyd LRHS NRHS WTor
- 'Peppermint Twist' CWGN EBee EHyd ELon GKev GWyn LRHS MHol MNrw NLar SWvt WFar
- 'Picasso' CWGN ECtt IPot NLar
- 'Pina Colada'PBR CWGN EBee ECtt MPri WCAu WFar WHil
- PINK EYE FLAME ('Barthirtyfive'PBR) ♀H7 EHyd EPfP LRHS NRHS SPoG SRkn SRms
- 'Pink Lady'PBR WFar
- 'Pink Posie' (v) WCot
- PINK RED EYE FLAME ('Barthirtyfour') SPoG
- 'Polarstern' CSam
- 'Popeye' IPot LPla WCot
- 'Prime Minister' ELon
§ - 'Prince of Orange' ♀H7 CBcs CBod CRos CSBt CWld EBee ECtt EHyd EMor EPfP LRHS MAvo MHol MRav MSCN MSpe MWat NLar NRHS SCob SGbt SPer SRms SWvt WCAu WCot XLum
- 'Prospero' ♀H7 CElw CSpe EBee GWyn MRav NBid

- PURPLE EYE FLAME ('Barthirtythree'PBR) ♀H7 — EHyd LRHS NRHS SPad SRkn SWvt WCAu WFar
- 'Purple Kiss'PBR — CWGN ECtt MHol MPri NHpl NLar WFar WHil
- 'Purple Paradise' — LRHS
- 'Rainbow' — ELon NLar
- 'Rainbow Dancer' — LSou
- 'Red Caribbean' — ECtt MPri NLar
- 'Red Feelings' (Feelings Series) — CBod CWld LRHS SGbt
- 'Red Flame' — CWGN ECtt EHyd EPfP LRHS MHol MNrw MPri SAko SRkn WFar
- 'Red Riding Hood' — see *P.* × *arendsii* 'Miss Mary'
- I - 'Reddish Hesperis' — MAvo
- 'Rembrandt' — CExl CRos EHyd ELon EPfP LCro LOPS LRHS MAvo NRHS WCAu XLum
- 'Rijnstroom' — CBcs ECha ECtt ELon MArl NLar SCob WBrk WCAu
- 'Robert Poore' — ECtt ELon
- 'Roberta' — LCro LOPS
- 'Rosa Goliath' — CSam
- 'Rosa Pastell' ♀H7 — CAby CDor CEnd CSpe ECtt ELon EMor GBin GQue IPot LRHS MAvo MHol MPie MTis NBid NLar SPer SPtp WAul WCot
- 'Rowie' — NBid
- 'Sandringham' — ECtt LRHS MArl MRav NBir NCou NRHS SPer SWvt
- § - 'Schneerausch' — LPla SPhx
- 'Septemberglut' — CRos EBee EHyd ELon EPfP LRHS NRHS
- 'Sherfield' **new** — SDix
- 'Shockwave' (v) — WCot
- SNOWDRIFT — see *P. paniculata* 'Schneerausch'
- 'Spätsommer' — IPot
- 'Speed Limit 45' — WCot
- 'Spitfire' — see *P. paniculata* 'Frau Alfred von Mauthner'
- 'Starfire' ♀H7 — Widely available
- I - 'Stars and Stripes' — LRHS
- 'Steeple Bumpstead' — WCot
- I - 'Stellata' — EHyd LRHS
- 'Sterling Brocade' (v) — WCot
- 'Sternhimmel' — LPla MSpe MTis
- 'Strawberry Daiquiri'PBR — WFar
- § - (Sweet Summer Series) SWEET SUMMER CANDY ('Ditosdre'PBR) — WHil
- § - - SWEET SUMMER DREAM ('Ditomdre'PBR) — MAvo NLar WCAu
- - - SWEET SUMMER FANTASY ('Ditopur'PBR) — MAvo WCAu WTor
- § - - SWEET SUMMER FAVOURITE ('Ditomfav'PBR) ♀H7 — NLar WCAu WHil
- - - SWEET SUMMER FRAGRANCE ('Ditomfra'PBR) — WHil
- - - SWEET SUMMER PURPLE WHITE — see *P. paniculata* (Sweet Summer Series) SWEET SUMMER TEMPTATION
- - - SWEET SUMMER QUEEN ('Ditoran'PBR) — NLar WHil
- § - - SWEET SUMMER SURPRISE ('Ditomsur'PBR) — ECtt WCAu
- § - - SWEET SUMMER TEMPTATION ('Ditostem'PBR) — WHil
- - - SWEET SUMMER WINE ('Ditowine'PBR) — ECtt IPot MAvo NLar WHil
- 'Swizzle' — CWGN ECtt MPri WFar
- 'Tatjana' — IPot
- 'Tenor' — CRos CTri ECtt ELon EPfP LEdu LRHS NLar NRHS SGbt SRms SWvt WCAu WSHC
- 'Tequila Sunrise'PBR — EBee ECtt MNrw
- 'The King' ♀H7 — EBee ECtt MAvo MSpe NLar WSHC WSpi
- 'Tiara'PBR (d) — ECtt LRHS MPie NGdn SWvt WCot
- § - 'Toits de Paris' Symons-Jeune — WSHC
- 'Twister' — EBee MNrw WFar
- § - 'Uralskie Skazy' — IPot
- § - 'Uspekh' ♀H7 — Widely available
- 'Valentina' — EBee
- 'Veg Plot Pink' — SMHy
- 'Veg Plot White' — SMHy
- 'Velvet Flame' ♀H7 — EHyd LRHS NRHS
- 'Vintage Wine' — MNrw
- 'Violetta Gloriosa' — ELon WFar
- 'Visions' ♀H7 — EHyd LRHS
- 'Volcano Betty' — MNrw
- 'Watermelon Punch' — ECtt MPri NLar WFar
- 'Wendy House' — MAvo MNrw NHol
- 'White Admiral' ♀H7 — CBcs CElw CRos EBee ECtt EHyd ELan ELon EMor EPfP GKev GMaP LRHS MHer MNrw MSpe MWat NGrd NLar NRHS SCob SGbt SPer SPhx SRms SWvt WCAu WFar XLum
- WHITE FLAME ('Bartwentynine'PBR) ♀H7 — CDor CWGN EHyd EPfP IPot LBuc LRHS LSou NLar NRHS SCob SWvt WCot
- 'White Pepper' — MAvo
- 'Wilhelm Kesselring' — ECtt EHyd ELon LRHS MTis NChi
- 'Willow Lodge' — SHar
- 'Windsor' — EBee ECtt ELon EMor EPfP NCou NHol SRms SWvt WCAu
- (Younique Series) YOUNIQUE BICOLOR ('Versbicolor') — WFar
- - - YOUNIQUE MAUVE ('Versmauve') — LCro LOPS
- - - YOUNIQUE OLD BLUE ('Versoldblue') — MBros WFar
- - - YOUNIQUE OLD CERISE ('Verscerise') — MBros WFar
- - - YOUNIQUE OLD PINK ('Versoldpink') — MBros WFar
- - - YOUNIQUE OLD PURPLE — WFar
- - - YOUNIQUE WHITE ('Verswhite'PBR) — LEdu MBros MNrw WFar

'Peppermint Candy' — WFar
'Petticoat' — CSma ECtt WIce
PINK FLAME ('Bartwelve'PBR) — EHyd EPfP LRHS LSou MPri NLar SCob SRkn SRms WHil
'Pride of Rochester' — CBor EBou ECtt EHyd LRHS NRHS
§ × ***procumbens*** 'Millstream' ♀H5 — ECtt
- 'Variegata' (v) — EBou ECha ECtt WCav
§ ***pulvinata*** — SPlb WAbe
PURPLE FLAME ('Barfourteen'PBR) — EHyd EPfP GWyn LRHS LSou NRHS SCob SRkn SRms WFar WHil
× ***rugelii*** — EWld
'Sherbet Cocktail'PBR — CWGN MSCN NHol
§ ***sibirica*** subsp. ***borealis*** — CPBP WAbe
'Sileniflora' — WAbe
'Special Purple Star' (Adessa Series) — NRHS

	stolonifera	MNrw
I	– 'Alba'	EPfP NLar WFar WKif
	– 'Ariane'	ECha ECtt MCot MNrw
	– 'Blue Ridge' 🏆H6	CExl ECha ECtt EPfP LRHS LSRN MHol MRav SRms WFar
	– 'Fran's Purple'	ECtt EWld MNrw WAvo WBrk WFar WKif
	– 'Home Fires'	ECtt EPfP LEdu LRHS MNrw SPlb
	– 'Janusz'	NWad
	– 'Pink Ridge'	WFar XLum
	– 'Purpurea'	EPfP LEdu
	subulata 'Alexander's Surprise'	CMea ECtt EHyd EPfP EPot LRHS MAsh NBir NRHS
	– 'Amazing Grace'	CTri CWCL ECtt EHyd EPfP EWes IPot LRHS NDov NRHS NSla NWad SPoG WCav WFar WHoo WIce
	– 'Apple Blossom'	NHol SPoG SRms
	– 'Atropurpurea'	EPfP SPoG XLum
	– 'Bavaria'	CBor CMea CPBP CRos ECtt EHyd EPfP EPot LCro LOPS LRHS MBel NRHS WFar
	– BEAUTY OF RONSDORF	see *P. subulata* 'Ronsdorfer Schöne'
	– 'Blue Eyes'	see *P. subulata* 'Oakington Blue Eyes'
	– 'Bonita'	ECtt EHyd EPot GWyn LRHS MAsh NRHS WHoo WIce
	– 'Bressingham Blue Eyes'	see *P. subulata* 'Oakington Blue Eyes'
	– 'Candy Stripe'	see *P. subulata* 'Tamaongalei'
	– 'Cavaldes White'	ECtt
	– 'Coral Eye'	ECtt
	– 'Daisy Hill'	XLum
	– 'Drumm'	see *P. subulata* 'Tamaongalei'
	– (Early Spring Series) EARLY SPRING LIGHT PINK ('Barsixtyfour'PBR)	CBod NSla
	– – EARLY SPRING PURPLE ('Barseventyfour'PBR)	CBod EHyd EPfP LRHS NRHS
	– – EARLY SPRING WHITE ('Barseventythree'PBR)	CBod NSla
	– 'Emerald Cushion'	CBod CTri EBou ECtt ELon EPfP LRHS MHol NHol NHpl NLar NSla SGbt WCFE WTor XLum
	– 'Emerald Cushion Blue'	CExl CTri EBou ECtt EHyd ELan EPfP LRHS MAsh MHCG MHol NBir NRHS SEdd SPlb SPoG WCAu WCav WFar
	– 'Fabulous Blue Violet' **new**	IPot
	– 'Fort Hill'	ECtt
	– 'G.F. Wilson'	see *P. subulata* 'Lilacina'
	– 'Holly'	EPot ITim NHol NWad
	– 'Kimono'	see *P. subulata* 'Tamaongalei'
§	– 'Lilacina'	CMea ECha MAsh MBNS MBel
§	– 'Maischnee'	CPBP CTri ECtt MAsh SPlb
	– 'Marjorie'	EBou ECtt GKev MHer NBir SPoG WRHF
	– MAY SNOW	see *P. subulata* 'Maischnee'
§	– 'McDaniel's Cushion' 🏆H6	CExl CRos CTri EBou ECha ECtt EDAr EHyd ELan ELon EPfP EPot GMaP LRHS MAsh MMuc NLar NRHS SPlb SPoG WCAu WCav WFar WHil WHoo WIce
	– 'Mikado'	see *P. subulata* 'Tamaongalei'
	– 'Millstream Daphne'	ECtt IPot
	– 'Moerheimii'	IPot
	– 'Nettleton Variation' (v)	CRos ECtt EHyd ELon EPot EWes LRHS MMuc NRHS SPoG SRms WFar WHoo
§	– 'Oakington Blue Eyes'	CTri GWyn SRms
	– 'Purple Beauty'	CMea ECtt EHyd EPfP GMaP LRHS NRHS NWad SPoG WCFE WFar WHoo XLum
	– 'Red Wings' 🏆H6	ECtt EPfP MHol SRms
§	– 'Ronsdorfer Schöne'	ECtt EPfP NBir
	– 'Samson'	LSRN WOld
	– 'Scarlet Flame'	CBod CMea EBou ECtt ELon EMor EPfP MAsh MHol NHol NHpl WCAu
	– 'Snow Queen'	see *P. subulata* 'Maischnee'
§	– 'Tamaongalei'	CBod CMea CTri EBou ECtt EHyd ELan ELon EWes GKev LRHS MAsh MHol MMuc NRHS NWad WCFE WCav WFar WHil WIce XLum
	– 'Temiskaming'	CTri ECtt EHyd EWes LRHS MBel NRHS NSla SRms WSHC
	– 'White Delight'	CBod CMea ECtt EHyd ELan ELon EPfP SPoG WCAu
	SWEET SUMMER SENSATION ('Ditosse'PBR) (Sweet Summer Series)	WCAu WHil
	'Swirly Burly'	MTis
	'Tiny Bugles'	CPBP
	VIOLET FLAME ('Barsixtyone'PBR)	CBod CDor CSpe EPfP LPla LRHS LSou LSun MAvo MHol MPri NLar SPer SPoG WCot WHil WRHF
	'Violet Pinwheels' **new**	CBor WFar
	WHITE EYE FLAME ('Barsixty'PBR)	CDor CWGN EPau EPfP IPot LRHS LSou MPri NLar WHil
	'White Kimono'	CRos EHyd LRHS NRHS
	'Zwergenteppich'	CBor CPBP CRos EHyd EPfP LRHS NRHS SPoG WFar

Phoenix (*Arecaceae*)

	canariensis 🏆H2	CBcs CDoC CExl EPfP SArc SEND SGsty SPalm SPlb SPoG SWeb WSMil
	dactylifera (F)	SPalm
	– 'Mazafati'	XBlo
	reclinata	XBlo
	roebelenii 🏆H1b	CDTJ LCro LOPS
	– 'Multistem'	XBlo
	theophrasti	CPHo SPalm

Phormium ✿ (*Hemerocallidaceae*)

§	'Alison Blackman'PBR	CBcs CBod EBee EHyd EPfP LRHS LSRN MAsh MGos NLar SCob SCoo SEND SPoG SWvt
	'Amazing Red'	SPer
	'Apricot Queen' (v)	CAbb CBcs CBod CBrac CCCN CDoC CSBt EHyd EPfP LCro LOPS LRHS LSRN MGos NBPC NLar NRHS SCob SEND SGbt SGsty SPer SPoG
	BACK IN BLACK ('Seilack'PBR)	CBcs CPla EHyd LRHS SCob SPeP WFar
	'Black Adder'PBR	EBee EHyd EPfP ILea LRHS LSRN MAsh NRHS SCob SEND SGbt SPoG
	'Black Rage'	CBcs EPfP
	BLACK VELVET ('Seivel'PBR)	CBcs CBod CTsd EHyd LRHS MSwo WCot
	'Bronze Baby'	CBcs CBod CCCN CDoC CSBt EBee EHyd ELan EPfP LRHS LSRN MGos MSwo NBPC NLar NRHS SCob SLim SPer SPoG SWvt
	'Buckland Ruby'	EBee
	'Chocomint'PBR	CBod CDoC ELan NLar SCob
	colensoi	see *P. cookianum*
§	***cookianum***	GAbr SArc

	- 'Alpinum Purpureum'	see *P. tenax* 'Nanum Purpureum'
	- subsp. ***hookeri*** 'Cream Delight' (v) 🏆H4	CAbb CBcs CCCN CDoC CEnd CSBt EBee EHyd EPfP LRHS LSRN MAsh MGos MSwo NRHS SCob SCoo SGol SWvt WFar
	- - 'Tricolor' (v) 🏆H4	CBcs CBrac CChe CDTJ CDoC CRos CSBt EBee EHyd ELan EPfP LCro LOPS LRHS MGos MMuc NBPC NRHS SArc SCob SEND SGol SLim SPalm SPer SPoG SRms SWvt WFar
	'Crimson Devil'	CBcs EHyd LRHS NRHS
	'Dark Delight'	CBcs
	'Duet' (v) 🏆H3	CBcs CCCN NBPC SEND SWvt
	'Dusky Chief'	CSBt EBee
	'Evening Glow' (v)	CBcs CCCN CDoC EHyd EPfP LRHS LSRN MGos NBPC NLar NRHS SPalm SPoG SRms SWvt
	'Firebird'	LSRN SWvt
	'Flamingo' (v)	CBcs CBod CCCN CDTJ CDoC EPfP LRHS MGos MHol NLar SCob SGbt SLim SPoG
	'Gold Ray' (v)	CBcs CBrac CTsd EHyd EPfP LRHS NRHS SCoo SWvt WLov
	'Gold Sword' (v)	CBcs CCCN CSBt EHyd EPfP LRHS SCob SGbt
	'Golden Alison'	see *P.* 'Alison Blackman'
	'Green Sword'	CCCN
	'Jack Spratt' (v)	SWvt
	'Jester' (v)	CBcs CBod CBrac CCCN CChe CDoC CRos CSBt EHyd ELan EPfP LRHS LSRN MAsh MGos MSwo NRHS SCob SCoo SGbt SLim SPalm SPoG SRkn SRms WSMil
	'Limelight'	SEND SWvt
§	'Maori Chief' (v)	CRos CSBt EPfP LRHS SWvt WFar
§	'Maori Maiden' (v)	CCCN CDoC CTri EBee EHyd EPfP LRHS MSwo NBPC SRms SWvt
§	'Maori Queen' (v)	CBcs CBod CBrac CCCN CDTJ CDoC EBee EHyd ELan EPfP ILea LCro LOPS LRHS MGos MSwo NBPC NRHS SCoo SEND SGbt SPer SWvt WFar
§	'Maori Sunrise' (v)	CBcs CCCN CDoC CPla EHyd IArd LCro LOPS LRHS LSRN MGos NBPC SCoo SLim SRms SWvt
	'Margaret Jones' PBR	CCCN LSRN
	'Moonraker' PBR	CBcs MHol SCob
	'Pink Panther' (v)	CAbb CBcs CCCN EHyd EPfP LRHS LSRN MGos NBPC NLar SPoG SRms
	'Pink Stripe' (v)	CBcs CBod CSBt EHyd EPfP LRHS MAsh MGos NRHS SCob SGbt SPalm SPoG SWvt
	'Platt's Black'	CCCN EHyd EPfP LCro LOPS LRHS LSRN MGos MSwo NBir NLar SCob SLim SPer SPoG SSta SWvt WFar WLov
	'Rainbow Chief'	see *P.* 'Maori Chief'
	'Rainbow Maiden'	see *P.* 'Maori Maiden'
	'Rainbow Queen'	see *P.* 'Maori Queen'
	'Rainbow Sunrise'	see *P.* 'Maori Sunrise'
	'Red Sensation'	CDoC LSRN NBPC SPeP
	'Sundowner' (v) 🏆H3	CBcs CCCN CSBt CTsd EBee EHyd EPfP LCro LOPS LRHS MAsh MGos NBir NRHS SCob SCoo SEND SLim SPer SPoG SWvt WLov
	'Sunset' (v)	CBcs CCCN CSBt SWvt
	'Surfer' (v)	CDoC
	'Surfer Bronze'	CCCN
	'Surfer Green'	CCCN
	'Sussex Velvet'	SCoo SLim
	tenax	CAgr CBcs CBrac EHyd EPfP LCro LOPS LRHS MGos MPri MSwo NGdn SArc SCob SEND SGol SGsty SPer SPlb SPoG SWeb SWvt
	- 'All Black'	MGos SCoo
	- 'Bronze'	CTsd SWvt
	- 'Co-ordination' (v)	CBcs CCCN NBPC
	- 'Croce di Malta'	SArc
	- 'Joker' (v)	CBcs CBod CDoC EBee NLar SCob
*	- ***lineatum***	SEND
§	- 'Nanum Purpureum'	SArc
	- Purpureum Group 🏆H5	CBod CBrac CDoC EBee EHyd ELan EPfP GAbr LRHS MGil MMuc MSwo NLar SCob SEND SGol SGsty SLim SLon SPer SPlb SWeb WFar XLum
	- 'Thumbelina'	CCCN
	- 'Tiny Tiger' (v)	EPfP
	- 'Variegatum' (v) 🏆H5	CDTJ CDoC CPla EBee EPfP MGos MMuc MPri SArc SCob SEND SGsty SRms SWeb
	- 'Yellow Queen' (v)	WFar
	'Yellow Wave' (v) 🏆H4	CAbb CBcs CBod CBrac CChe CDoC CEnd EBee EHyd ELon EPfP LRHS LSRN MAsh MGos MSwo NBPC NRHS SCob SEND SGbt SLim SPalm SPer SPoG SWvt

Photinia ✿ (*Rosaceae*)

	arbutifolia	see *Heteromeles salicifolia*
	arguta var. ***arguta***	SMad
	- - KR 10738	WPGP
	beauverdiana	CJun
	var. ***notabilis***	
	davidiana	CMac CTri ELan EPfP GKev IDee MGil MRav NLar SPtp SRms SVen WPav
	- PAB 8097	LEdu
	- 'Palette' (v)	CBcs CBrac CMac ELan ELon EPfP LRHS MAsh MGos MMuc MSwo NLar SGol SMad SPer SPoG SRms SWvt WFar WMat
	- Salicifolia Group	WPav
	- var. ***undulata*** 'Fructu Luteo'	MMuc MRav NLar
	- - 'Prostrata'	CMac CTri MRav NLar WCFE
	'Diamond Red' **new**	CDoC
	× ***fraseri***	WTSh
I	- 'Atropurpurea Nana'	CBcs CDoC MGos
	- 'Birmingham'	CMac EWes SRms
	- 'Canivily' 🏆H5	CEnd CRos EHyd LRHS MGos NLar NRHS SGol
*	- 'Ilexifolium'	ESwi
	- 'Little Red Robin'	Widely available
	- 'Louise' (v)	CBod CRos CSBt EBee EHyd LBuc LRHS MAsh MGos MHed NLar NRHS SCob WFar
	- MAGICAL VOLCANO ('Kolmavoca' PBR)	LRHS MAsh NLar SGol SMad SPoG
	- PINK MARBLE ('Cassini') (v) 🏆H5	CBcs CBrac CDoC CEnd CRos EBee EHyd ELan EPfP LBuc LCro LOPS LRHS MAsh MGos MMuc MSwo NLar NRHS SCob SGbt SGol SGsty SLim SLon SPer SPoG SRms
	- 'Red Robin' 🏆H5	Widely available
	- 'Red Robin Variegated' (v) **new**	SavN
	- 'Red Select'	WFar
	- 'Robusta'	CMac EPfP LRHS SRms SWvt
I	- 'Robusta Compacta'	LSRN

glabra	SArc
§ - 'Parfait' (v)	CMac EBee MAsh
- 'Pink Lady'	see *P. glabra* 'Parfait'
- 'Rubens'	CRos EHyd EPfP LRHS MAsh MRav
- 'Variegata'	see *P. glabra* 'Parfait'
lasiogyna	CMCN
lucida	WCru
microphylla B&SWJ 11837	WCru
- HWJ 564	WCru
niitakayamensis	SPtp
- CWJ 12435	WCru
cf. ***prionophylla*** 'Bodnant' **new**	SBrt
'Redstart'	CMac ELan EPfP LRHS MMuc NLar SLon SPer SWvt WFar
§ ***serratifolia***	CBcs CMCN EPfP NLar SArc SEND SPer WFar WPGP
- var. ***ardisiifolia*** NMWJ 14513	WCru
- CRUNCHY ('Rev100'PBR)	LBuc SCob
- CURLY FANTASY ('Kolcurl'PBR)	LRHS MAsh MRav NLar SavN
- 'Jenny'	NLar SavN WFar
- PINK CRISPY ('Oploo5'PBR)	ELan SPoG SavN
serrulata	see *P. serratifolia*
SUPER HEDGE ('Branpara'PBR)	LRHS MSwo WFar
'Super Red'	CAby CSBt NLar
villosa	CTho EPfP WPav
- B&SWJ 8665	WCru
- var. ***coreana*** B&SWJ 8789	WCru
- var. ***laevis***	CExl EPfP WPGP
- - B&SWJ 8877	WCru
- f. ***maximowicziana***	CDoC CJun NLar
* - var. ***zollingeri*** B&SWJ 8903	WCru

Phragmites (*Poaceae*)

sp.	CHab
from Sichuan, China	EPPr
§ ***australis***	CBen CHab CWat NMir SVic WMAq WPnP XLum
- subsp. ***australis*** var. ***striatopictus***	EPPr
- - 'Variegatus' (v)	CWat EPPr LLWG MMuc NBir SEND SMad XLum
- subsp. ***humilis***	CHab
- subsp. ***pseudodonax***	EPPr
communis	see *P. australis*

Phuopsis (*Rubiaceae*)

§ ***stylosa***	CBod CCBP CTri EBee EBou ECha ELan ELon EPPr EPfP GAbr GMaP MHer MHol MMuc MSpe NBid NBir NBro NChi NSti SEND SPhx SRms SWvt WCAu WMal WWFP XLum
- 'Purpurea'	EBee MNrw MRav NChi

Phygelius (*Scrophulariaceae*)

aequalis	MRav
- 'Aureus'	see *P. aequalis* 'Yellow Trumpet'
- 'Cream Trumpet'	see *P. aequalis* 'Yellow Trumpet'
- 'Indian Chief'	see *P. × rectus* 'African Queen'
- 'Sani Pass'	ELon MHer SIvy SPer SPlb
- 'Trewidden Pink' ♀H4	EHyd ELan ELon GBin LRHS MHer MSCN NRHS SWvt XLum
§ - 'Yellow Trumpet' ♀H4	CSBt ELan ELon GMaP LSRN MAsh MGil MMuc SDix SEND SGbt SLim SWvt WAvo
CANDY DROPS SALMON ORANGE ('Kerphysalm'PBR) (Candy Drops Series)	SRms
capensis	CTri MHer SRms WOut WRHF
'Golden Gate'	see *P. aequalis* 'Yellow Trumpet'
Logan form	GBin
NEW SENSATION ('Blaphy'PBR)	EPfP MRav SRms SWvt
'Passionate'PBR	NLar
§ × ***rectus*** 'African Queen' ♀H5	CTri ECrN EHyd ELan EPfP LRHS MGil MRav MSwo NBir NGdn SCob SDix SEND SPlb SWvt WAvo WCav WKif WLov XLum
- 'Devil's Tears' ♀H4	CBcs CPla MMuc SCob SEND SLim SWvt
- 'Ivory Twist'	ELon SPer
- 'Jodie Southon'	ELon LSou SDys WCot
- 'Moonraker'	CAby CBcs CTri ELan ELon EPfP GBin GWyn MAsh MGil MHer MRav NGdn NLar SCob SEND SPer SPlb SRms WKif XLum
- 'Salmon Leap' ♀H5	CBcs CTri EHyd ELan EPfP LRHS LSRN MGos MRav NRHS SBut SCob SLim SPlb SRms SWvt
- (Somerford Funfair Series) SOMERFORD FUNFAIR APRICOT ('Yapapr')	SWvt
- - SOMERFORD FUNFAIR CORAL ('Yapcor'PBR)	EHyd EPfP LRHS MAsh MBros NLar SLim SRkn SWvt
- - SOMERFORD FUNFAIR CREAM ('Yapcre'PBR)	CBod EHyd EPfP LRHS MBros NLar SLim SPoG SWvt
- - SOMERFORD FUNFAIR ORANGE ('Yapor'PBR)	CBod CPla EBou EHyd EPfP LRHS MAsh NLar SCob SLim SRms SWvt
- - SOMERFORD FUNFAIR WINE ('Yapwin')	CAby CBod CChe ECrN EHyd ELan EPfP LRHS MAsh NRHS SCob SLim SPoG SWvt
- - SOMERFORD FUNFAIR YELLOW ('Yapyel'PBR)	CChe EHyd EPfP LRHS MAsh SLim SWvt
§ - 'Winchester Fanfare'	CSBt GWyn MGos MRav NLar SEND SLim SWvt
- 'Winton Fanfare'	see *P. × rectus* 'Winchester Fanfare'
'Rory'PBR	SRms

Phyla (*Verbenaceae*)

lanceolata	LLWG
§ ***nodiflora***	ECha MBow MHer SRms WJek XSen
- 'Alba'	MMuc SEND
§ - var. ***canescens***	XLum

Phylica (*Rhamnaceae*)

arborea	LRHS
pubescens	CPbh

× *Phylliopsis* (*Ericaceae*)

'Coppelia' ♀H5	EPot ITim
hillieri 'Askival'	EPot GKev WThu
- 'Pinocchio'	EPot GEdr GKev WThu
- 'Sugar Plum'	CCCN GEdr SWvt
'Hobgoblin'	ITim
'Mermaid'	EPot GRum ITim
'Puck'	EPot
'Sprite'	EPot ITim
'Swanhilde'	WThu

Phyllitis see *Asplenium*

Phyllocladus ✿ (*Podocarpaceae*)

aspleniifolius	WPav

trichomanoides var. ***alpinus***	WThu
- - 'Blue Blades'	MGil SLim
- - 'Highland Lass'	MGil SLim
- - 'Highlander'	MGil SLim

Phyllodoce (*Ericaceae*)

aleutica	WThu
§ - subsp. ***glanduliflora***	EPot
§ - - 'Flora Slack'	GRum WThu
- - white-flowered	see *P. aleutica* subsp. *glanduliflora* 'Flora Slack'
× ***alpina***	GRum
caerulea japonica	see *P. nipponica*
- 'W.M. Buchanan's Peach Seedling'	GRum
empetriformis	WThu
glanduliflora	see *P. aleutica* subsp. *glanduliflora*
× ***intermedia*** 'Fred Stoker'	GRum
§ ***nipponica***	GRum WThu
'Peach'	NLar

× *Phyllosasa* (*Poaceae*)

tranquillans	MMuc MWht SEND
- 'Shiroshima' (v)	CAbb CDTJ CDoC EPfP MBrN MMuc MWht SEND XCre

Phyllostachys ✿ (*Poaceae*)

angusta	MWht
arcana 'Luteosulcata'	MMuc MWht XCre
§ ***atrovaginata***	CBdn SGol XCre
aurea ♀H6	Widely available
- 'Albovariegata' (v)	EPfP LRHS MWht SPoG XCre
- 'Flavescens Inversa'	MWht XCre
- 'Holochrysa'	CDTJ CJun MMuc MWht NLar XCre
- 'Koi'	CDTJ MWht SGol XCre
aureocaulis	see *P. aureosulcata* f. *aureocaulis*, *P. vivax* f. *aureocaulis*
aureosulcata	XCre
- f. ***alata***	see *P. aureosulcata* f. *pekinensis*
§ - f. ***aureocaulis***	CAbb CBcs CBdn CBod CJun CRos CTsd ELon EPfP LCro LOPS LRHS LSRN MGos MSwo MWht NRHS SArc SCob SEWo SGol SGsty SPoG SWvt XCre
- 'Harbin'	XCre
- 'Lama Tempel'	CDTJ CJun XCre
§ - f. ***pekinensis***	XCre
- f. ***spectabilis*** ♀H5	Widely available
bambusoides	CDTJ
- 'Allgold'	see *P. bambusoides* 'Holochrysa'
- 'Castillonii' ♀H5	CBct EWes LEdu MMuc MWht SEND XCre
- 'Castillonii Inversa'	LEdu MWht XCre
§ - 'Holochrysa' ♀H5	CDTJ MMuc MWht SEND WPGP XCre
- f. ***lacrima-deae***	CDTJ
- 'Marliacea'	CBdn WPGP XCre
- 'Sulphurea'	see *P. bambusoides* 'Holochrysa'
- 'Tanakae'	CDTJ XCre
bissetii ♀H5	CAbb CAgr CBcs CBdn CBod CCVT CDoC EPfP LCro LOPS LRHS MAvo MBrN MGos MMuc MSwo MWht NLar NRHS SEND SGol SGsty SPlb SWeb WPGP WSMil XCre
circumpilis	XCre
congesta misapplied	see *P. atrovaginata*
decora	MMuc MWht XCre
dulcis	CBdn EPfP MWht XCre
§ ***edulis***	CAgr CBct SPlb XCre
§ - 'Heterocycla'	XBlo
- f. ***pubescens***	see *P. edulis*
flexuosa	CBcs MWht SGol XCre
glauca	EPfP MWht XCre
- f. ***yunzhu***	MWht XCre
heteroclada 'Solid Stem' misapplied	see *P. purpurata* 'Straight Stem'
heterocycla	see *P. edulis* 'Heterocycla'
- var. ***pubescens***	see *P. edulis*
humilis	CBdn MMuc MWht SEND XCre
iridescens ♀H5	MWht XCre
kwangsiensis	XCre
lofushanensis	XCre
mannii	MWht
nidularia	XCre
nigra ♀H5	Widely available
- 'Boryana'	CBdn CCVT CEnd EPfP MGos MMuc MWht NLar SEND SWvt XCre
- 'Hale'	CBct MWht
- f. ***henonis*** ♀H5	CBdn MMuc MWht NLar SEND SGol WPGP XCre
- 'Megurochiku'	MWht XCre
- f. ***punctata***	MAvo MMuc SEND
nuda	MWht XCre
- f. ***localis***	MWht
parvifolia	MWht
platyglossa	XCre
praecox f. ***prevernalis***	XCre
- f. ***viridisulcata***	XCre
propinqua	MWht
§ ***purpurata*** 'Straight Stem'	MWht
reticulata	XCre
robustiramea	XCre
rubromarginata	MMuc MWht XCre
stimulosa	MWht XCre
sulphurea 'Houzeau'	MMuc SEND
§ - f. ***sulphurea***	XCre
- 'Sulphurea'	see *P. sulphurea* f. *sulphurea*
§ - f. ***viridis***	XCre
violascens	CAgr MWht XCre
virella	XCre
viridiglaucescens	CAgr CDTJ MMuc MWht SEND WCot XCre
viridis	see *P. sulphurea* f. *viridis*
vivax	EPfP MWht NLar XCre
§ - f. ***aureocaulis*** ♀H5	CAbb CAgr CBcs CCVT CDoC CEnd EPfP LEdu LRHS LSRN MGos MMuc MWht NLar SCob SEND SGol SWeb WPGP XCre
- - 'Huangwenzhu'	CDTJ MWht XCre
- 'Katrin'	LEdu
* - 'Sulphurea'	XBlo

Phymatosorus (*Polypodiaceae*)

diversifolius	see *Microsorum diversifolium*

Phymosia (*Malvaceae*)

§ ***umbellata***	EBee LEdu LRHS MPkF WPGP

Phyodina see *Callisia*

Physalis (*Solanaceae*)

alkekengi ♀H7	CTri EPfP NBir NLar SWvt WMal
- var. ***franchetii***	CBcs CMac CRos CSBt CTri EBee ECha EHyd ELan EPfP LCro LOPS LRHS MBel MNrw NBir NBro NRHS SCob SPer SPoG SRms WFar WOld
- - dwarf	EHyd LRHS NLar

	- - 'Gigantea'	CBct CBod CRos CWld EHyd LRHS MBros NLar NRHS SPlb WFar
	- - 'Gnome'	see *P. alkekengi* var. *franchetii* 'Zwerg'
	- - 'Variegata' (v)	EWes LEdu SEND WPGP
§	- - 'Zwerg'	CDor EBee EBou EHyd ELon LRHS LSun SEdi
	- 'Halloween King'	EBee NLar
	- 'Halloween Queen'	NLar
	edulis	see *P. peruviana*
§	***peruviana*** (F)	CCCN CSpe SPlb SVic WOld XAbr

Physaria (*Brassicaceae*)

	alpina	SPlb
	didymocarpa	CPla

Physocarpus (*Rosaceae*)

	'Brown Sugar' **new**	CBod WNPC
	capitatus 'Tilden Park'	EBee
	LITTLE DEVIL	see *P. opulifolius* 'Donna May'
	'Midnight'	CBod GBin LRHS MAsh MMrt WFar
	opulifolius AMBER JUBILEE ('Jefam'[PBR])	CBod CDoC LCro LOPS NEoE SCob SRms
	- 'Angel Gold'	CDoC CRos EHyd LRHS MAsh MPri NRHS SPoG
	- 'Anny's Gold'[PBR]	EBee NLar SRms
	- 'Burning Embers'	CDoC SRms
	- 'Chameleon'	EBee EMil GBin NEoE SCob SGol
	- COPPERTINA	see *P. opulifolius* DIABLE D'OR
	- 'Dart's Gold' [H7]	CBcs CBod CDoC CExl CMac CRos CSBt CTri ELan EPfP LRHS MGos MMuc MSwo NHol NLar SCob SGbt SGol SGsty SLim SLon SPer SPoG SRms SWvt SavN WCot WFar WSpi
§	- DIABLE D'OR ('Mindia'[PBR])	CBar CBod CDoC CRos EBee EHyd EPfP ILea LCro LOPS LRHS LSRN MAsh MBlu MGos NLar NOra NRHS SGbt SGol WLov
	- 'Diabolo'[PBR] [H7]	Widely available
§	- 'Donna May'[PBR]	CBod ELan EPfP EShb LSou MAsh NEoE SCob WFar
	- 'Firebrand'	NEoE
§	- LADY IN RED ('Tuilad'[PBR]) [H7]	Widely available
	- LITTLE ANGEL ('Hoogi016'[PBR])	CWGN EMil EPfP LCro LOPS SCob SPad SPoG
	- LITTLE JOKER ('Hoogi021') **new**	NLar
	- MIDNIGHT ('Jonight'[PBR])	CBcs MGil SCob
	- 'Red Baron'	WFar
	- RUBY SPICE	see *P. opulifolius* LADY IN RED
	- SUMMER MOON ('Tuimon')	CBcs NEoE SGol WFar
	- SUMMER WINE ('Seward'[PBR])	CDoC EBee EPfP EWTr EWes LRHS MAsh NLar SGsty WSpi
	- TINY WINE ('Smpotw'[PBR])	EPfP MAsh NLar

Physochlaina (*Solanaceae*)

	orientalis	GEdr WCot

Physostegia (*Lamiaceae*)

	angustifolia	NBre
I	'Aquatica'	LLWG
§	***virginiana***	CBod CSBt CTri GMaP ILea MBel SBut SRms WCFE WOld
	- 'Alba'	CAby CMac CSBt CTri EBee ELon EMor GAbr GMaP LEdu MBros SPlb WCav WOut XLum
§	- 'Crown of Snow'	CRos EHyd EPfP GWyn LRHS MHer MRav NRHS SWvt
	- 'Crystal Peak White'	LRHS WFar
	- 'Miss Manners'	CBod EBee ECtt EHyd LRHS MCot MPie NBPC NBre NGdn NLar NRHS SGbt
	- 'Pink Manners'	NLar STPC
	- 'Red Beauty'	NLar
	- 'Rose Crown'	SPer
	- 'Rose Queen'	CBod CTri EMor NBre WFar
	- 'Rosea'	CRos EHyd EPfP GJos GPSL GWyn LRHS LSun MMuc NChi NCou NGdn NRHS SHar SPoG SWvt WFar WHrl
	- SCHNEEKRONE	see *P. virginiana* 'Crown of Snow'
	- 'Snow Queen'	see *P. virginiana* 'Summer Snow'
§	- var. ***speciosa*** 'Bouquet Rose'	CBod CRos EBee ECha EPfP LEdu LRHS MRav NBir NLar NRHS SGbt SPer SRms SWvt WCAu WFar WRHF XLum
	- - ROSE BOUQUET	see *P. virginiana* var. *speciosa* 'Bouquet Rose'
	- - 'Variegata' (v)	CBod CMac EBee ECtt ELan ELon EPfP GLog MRav NBPC NBir NGdn NHol SPer SPoG SRms WCAu WCot WFar XLum
§	- 'Summer Snow' [H7]	CBcs CCBP ECha ELan EPfP LRHS NGBl NLar SPer SRms WCAu WCot
	- 'Vivid' [H7]	Widely available

Phyteuma (*Campanulaceae*)

	balbisii	see *P. cordatum*
	betonicifolium	WHoo
§	***cordatum***	GJos
	halleri	see *P. ovatum*
	hemisphaericum	NSla
	humile	WThu
	nigrum	GEdr NBid SBrt WBor
	orbiculare	CPla CWld GEdr GJos
§	***ovatum***	SPlb
	scheuchzeri	EBee EBou EDAr ELan EPfP EWld GEdr GJos GWyn MMrt MSCN SMad SPad SRms WCot WIce XLum
	spicatum	GJos NBro
	- subsp. ***coeruleum***	GJos

Phytolacca (*Phytolaccaceae*)

	acinosa	EWld SBrt
	- HWJ 647	WCru
§	***americana***	CAby CBcs CCBP EBee ELan EMor EPfP ESwi GPoy MBNS MHer MPie NChi SPlb SRms
	- B&SWJ 8817A	WCru
	- B&SWJ 12743 **new**	ESwi
	- 'Silberstein' (v)	EBee MHol WHer
	bogotensis B&SWJ 14221	ESwi WCru
	clavigera	see *P. polyandra*
	decandra	see *P. americana*
	dioica	CExl SPlb
	esculenta	LEdu SEND
	icosandra Purpurascens Group B&SWJ 11251	WCru
	japonica B&SWJ 3005	NBid WCru
	- B&SWJ 3522	WCru
§	***polyandra***	GAbr NBid NBro SRms

Picea ✿ (*Pinaceae*)

§	***abies***	CCVT CLnd CMac CSBt CTho CTri EPfP GBin GQue LBuc LMaj MMuc SCoo SEND SPoG WMou WTSh

	- 'Acrocona' ♀H7	LRHS NLar XLot
	- 'Archer'	CKen
	- 'Bago'	CKen
	- 'Bally' **new**	CKen
	- 'Barus'	NLar
	- 'Brunn'	NLar
	- 'Capitata'	CKen
	- 'Clanbrassiliana' ♀H7	CKen ELan EPfP LRHS NWad
	- Columnaris Group	LRHS
I	- 'Congesta'	CKen
	- 'Crippsii'	CKen
I	- 'Cruenta'	CKen
	- 'Cupressina'	CKen
	- 'Diffusa'	CKen
	- 'Dumpy'	CKen NHol
	- 'Echiniformis' **new**	CKen
	- 'Excelsa'	see *P. abies*
	- 'Fahndrich'	CKen CMen
	- 'Formanek'	SAko
	- 'Four Winds'	CKen
	- 'Frohburg'	CKen LRHS XLot
	- 'Gold Drift'	NLar XLot
	- 'Gold Finch'	NLar
	- 'Gregoryana'	CKen XLot
	- 'Hasin'	SAko
	- 'Heartland Gem'	CKen
	- 'Honey Pot'	NLar
	- 'Horace Wilson'	CKen CMen
	- 'Humilis'	CKen
	- 'Humphrey's Gem' **new**	CKen
	- 'Hystrix'	CMen LRHS NLar NWad
	- 'Inversa' ♀H7	CKen MBlu SLim XLot
	- 'J.W. Daisy's White'	see *P. glauca* var. *albertiana* 'J.W. Daisy's White'
	- 'Jana'	CKen NLar
	- 'Jermyns Broom No. 1'	CKen
	- 'Kral'	CKen
	- 'Krenek'	NLar
	- 'Lemon Drop'	NLar
	- 'Little Gem' ♀H7	CKen CMen ELan EPfP GEdr LRHS MAsh MGos NHol NLar NWad SCoo SLim XLot
	- 'Lucky Strike'	CKen LRHS MAsh NLar XLot
	- 'Marcel'	CKen
	- 'Mini Kalous'	CKen
	- 'Nana Compacta'	CKen CMen MAsh
	- 'Nidiformis' ♀H7	CKen CMac CMen CSBt CTri LRHS MGos SRms XLot
	- 'Norrköping'	CKen
	- 'Ohlendorffii'	CKen
	- 'Pachyphylla'	CKen
	- 'Parsonsii'	SAko
	- 'Pseudomaxwellii'	LRHS
	- 'Pumila'	WCFE
	- 'Pusch'	CKen CMen NLar
	- 'Pygmaea'	CKen NWad
	- 'Remontii'	NLar XLot
	- 'Ripley Broom'	CKen
	- 'Roseospicata'	NLar
	- 'Rydal' ♀H7	CBcs CKen LRHS MAsh NLar
	- 'Spring Fire'	CKen
	- 'Tompa'	NLar
	- 'Tutsberg'	NLar
	- 'Typner'	CKen NLar
	- 'Vermont Gold'	CKen LRHS NLar
	- 'Wagner'	NLar
	- 'Wichtel'	CKen
	- WILL'S DWARF	see *P. abies* 'Wills Zwerg'
§	- 'Wills Zwerg'	ELan LRHS NLar
§	***alcoquiana*** var. ***alcoquiana***	SLim
	asperata 'Mongolei'	NLar
	bicolor	see *P. alcoquiana* var. *alcoquiana*
	breweriana ♀H7	CMac CTho EPfP GKin IDee LEdu LRHS MBlu MGos NLar SLim SSta WCFE WTSh
	- 'Frühlingsgold'	CKen
	- 'Kohout's Dwarf'	CKen NLar
	engelmannii 'Bush's Lace'	NLar
	- 'Cienega'	CKen
	- 'Compact'	SLim
	- subsp. ***engelmannii***	CKen
	- Glauca Group **new**	LMaj
	- 'Jasper'	CKen NLar
	glauca	SWvt
	- var. ***albertiana*** ALBERTA BLUE ('Haal'PBR)	CKen LRHS
	- - 'Alberta Globe' ♀H7	CBrac GKin LRHS MAsh MGos NHol NWad SCoo SPoG XLot
	- - 'Conica' ♀H7	CBcs CBrac CMac CSBt EPfP LCro LOPS LRHS MAsh MGil MGos MMuc NHol NLar NOrn SCob SEND SLim SPoG SRms SVic SWvt WCFE XLot
	- - 'Gnome'	CKen
§	- - 'J.W. Daisy's White' ♀H7	CBcs CBod CBrac CKen ELan EPfP GKin LRHS MAsh MGos NHol NLar NOrn SCoo SLim SPoG XLot
	- - 'Laurin' ♀H7	CKen NWad SLim
	- - 'Lilliput'	CKen NLar NWad SPoG
	- - 'Piccolo'	CKen NLar NWad SLim
	- - 'Sander's Blue'	CBod CKen EPfP GKin LRHS NLar NRya SAko SPoG SVic XLot
	- - 'Tiny'	CKen MGil NWad
	- 'Arneson's Blue Variegated' (v)	CKen MAsh SLim
	- 'Biesenthaler Frühling'	CKen SLim
	- 'Blue Planet'	CKen
	- 'Blue Teardrop'	NLar
	- 'Cy's Wonder'	CKen
	- 'Dendroforma Gold'	CKen NLar
	- 'Eagle Rock'	NLar
	- 'Echiniformis' ♀H7	CKen LRHS NLar XLot
	- 'Goldilocks'	CKen NLar
	- 'Jalako Gold'	LRHS
I	- 'Julian Potts Monstrosa'	NLar
	- 'Milford'	CKen
§	- 'Nana'	CKen
	- 'Pendula'	CKen
	- PERFECTA ('Hb07'PBR) **new**	XLot
	- 'Pixie'	CKen
	- 'Pixie Dust'	CKen
	- 'Rainbow's End' (v)	CKen NLar XLot
	- 'Spring Surprise'	CKen
	- 'Zuckerhut'	LRHS XLot
	glehnii 'Shimezusei'	CKen
	jezoensis	CKen CMen
	- 'Aurea'	SLim
	- subsp. ***hondoensis***	CMen
	- 'Marianbad'	CKen
	- 'Mariánské Làzně'	NLar
	- 'Pygmy' **new**	CKen
	- 'Yatsabusa'	CKen CMen
	kosteri 'Glauca'	see *P. pungens* (Glauca Group) 'Koster'
	koyamae 'Bedgebury Cascade'	SLim
	likiangensis	CMCN EPfP NLar
	- var. ***balfouriana***	see *P. likiangensis* var. *rubescens*

§	- var. ***rubescens***	LRHS SLim XLot
	mariana	EPfP
	- 'Austria Broom'	CKen
	- 'Bill Archer'	NWad
	- 'Blue Teardrop'	CKen
	- 'Fastigiata'	CKen
	- 'Nana' 🏆H7	CKen CMac CMen EPfP GEdr MGos MMuc NHol NWad SCoo SLim SPoG
I	- 'Pygmaea'	CKen NWad SLim
	meyeri	CTho EPfP
	morrisonicola	CKen
	obovata var. ***coerulea***	EPfP
	omorika 🏆H7	CBcs CCVT CJun CMCN CTho EPfP EWTr EWhm LBuc MMuc NLar SCob SEND SEWo WCFE WMou XLot
	- 'Berliner's Weeper' witches' broom	NLar
	- 'Cinderella'	NLar
	- 'Elegance'	SAko
	- 'Frohnleiten'	CKen
	- 'Frondenberg'	CKen
	- 'Halone'	CKen
	- 'Karel'	CKen LRHS SLim XLot
	- 'Minimax'	CKen
	- 'Nana' 🏆H7	LRHS SLim WCFE XLot
	- 'Pendula' 🏆H7	LRHS MBlu SSta XLot
	- 'Pendula Bruns'	MBlu NLar SAko SLim
	- 'Pévé Tijn'	LRHS NLar SLim
	- 'Pimoko'	CKen NLar SLim XLot
	- 'Pygmy'	CKen
	- 'Schneverdingen'	CKen SAko
	- 'Tijn'	CKen SLim
	- 'Treblitsch'	CKen NLar SAko SLim
	orientalis 🏆H7	WThu
	- 'Aurea' (v) 🏆H7	ELan SMad
	- 'Aureospicata'	CTho MAsh MBlu SLim XLot
	- 'Bergman's Gem'	CKen
	- 'Golden Start'	SLim XLot
	- 'Gowdy Gold'	NLar
	- 'Gracilis'	XLot
	- 'Juwel'	CKen NLar
	- 'Kenwith'	CKen
	- 'Mount Vernon'	CKen NLar
	- Nana Group	GKin
	- 'Pévé Tiny Gold'	CKen NLar
	- 'Professor Langner'	CKen NLar
	- 'Shadow's Broom'	CKen CMen
§	- 'Silver Seedling'	NLar
	- 'Skylands' 🏆H7	CKen MAsh NLar NOra SLim XLot
	- 'Spring Grove'	NLar
	- 'Sulphur Flush'	see *P. orientalis* 'Silver Seedling'
	- 'Tom Thumb'	CKen NLar
	- 'Wittboldt'	CKen LRHS NLar XLot
	pungens	CCVT EWhm LMaj
	- 'Anton'	NLar
	- 'Blaukissen'	CKen NLar
	- 'Blue Diamond'	LRHS SPoG
	- 'Blue Pearl'	CKen
	- 'Donna's Rainbow'	NLar
	- 'Edith' 🏆H7	CKen NLar NOra NOrn SCoo SLim WMat XLot
	- 'Erich Frahm'	CCVT MAsh NLar NOra SCoo SPoG WMat XLot
	- 'Fat Albert' 🏆H7	CCVT LMaj LRHS NLar SLim SPoG
	- 'Frieda'	SLim
	- Glauca Group	CBrac CCVT CMac EWTr MMuc SCoo SPoG WMou WTSh XLot
	- - 'Glauca Procumbens'	CKen
§	- - 'Glauca Prostrata'	SLim
I	- - 'Globosa' 🏆H7	CBcs CCVT CKen CSBt EPfP LRHS MAsh NHol SCoo SGsty SLim SPoG SWeb XLot
	- - 'Hoopsii' 🏆H7	EPfP GKin LRHS MAsh MGos NOrn SCoo SPoG SWvt WMat XLot
	- - 'Iseli Fastigiate'	CCVT GKin LRHS MAsh SCoo SLim SPoG XLot
§	- - 'Koster'	EPfP SPoG
	- - 'Oldenburg'	SLim XLot
	- 'Globe'	CKen CMen
	- 'Gloria'	CKen SLim
	- 'Hermann Naue'	CKen
	- 'Maigold' (v)	CKen LRHS NLar SLim XLot
	- 'Montgomery'	CKen
	- 'Mrs Cesarini'	CKen NLar SLim
	- 'Niemitz'	NLar
	- 'Nimetz'	CKen
	- 'Porcupine'	NLar
	- 'Prostrata'	see *P. pungens* (Glauca Group) 'Glauca Prostrata'
	- 'Saint Mary's Broom'	CKen
	- 'The Blues'	CKen NLar
	- 'Waldbrunn'	CKen NLar
	- 'Yvette'	NLar
	purpurea	EPfP LRHS
	schrenkiana	CMCN
	sitchensis	MAsh MMuc WTSh
	- 'Nana'	NLar
	- 'Papoose'	EPfP SLim
	- 'Pévé Wiesje'	NLar
	- 'Silberzwerg'	CKen SAko SLim
	- 'Strypemonde'	CKen
	- 'Tenas'	CKen SLim SPoG XLot
	smithiana	CTho EPfP
	- 'Sunray'	LRHS NLar SLim
	wilsonii	CKen

Picrasma (*Simaroubaceae*)

	ailanthoides	see *P. quassioides*
§	***quassioides***	CMCN EBee EPfP WPGP

Picris (*Asteraceae*)

	echioides	see *Helminthotheca echioides*

Picrorhiza (*Plantaginaceae*)

	kurrooa	GPoy LEdu

Pieris (*Ericaceae*)

	'Balls of Fire'	CMac
	'Bert Chandler'	CMac WSpi
	'Brouwer's Beauty'	LRHS NLar SPoG
	'Firecrest' 🏆H5	GKev NLar SCob
	'Flaming Silver' (v) 🏆H5	Widely available
	floribunda	CBrac
	'Forest Flame' 🏆H5	Widely available
	formosa B&SWJ 2257	WCru
	- var. ***forrestii***	CDoC SCob
	- - 'Charles Michael'	CExl
	- - 'Jermyns'	CMac MRav
	- - 'Wakehurst' 🏆H5	CCCN CExl CMac CRos CTri EHyd ELon EPfP GKin LMil LRHS MAsh MGos MRav NOra SAko SCob SPer WSpi
	HAVILA ('Mouwsvila') (v)	CCCN CMac MAsh NWad SCob
	japonica	CMac CPla SavN
	- 'Bonfire' 🏆H5	CBod CBrac CCCN CRos EHyd ELan EPfP ILea LRHS MAsh MGos MPkF NLar NRHS SCob SGbt SLim SPer SPoG

	- 'Carnaval' (v) 🏆H5	CCCN CDoC CMac CRos CSBt EHyd ELan ELon EPfP EShb LBuc LRHS LSRN MAsh MGos MPri NLar NRHS SCoo SLim SPoG SWvt WFar
§	- 'Christmas Cheer'	CMac EPfP LSRN SCob
	- 'Cupido'	LRHS MAsh NLar SLim WFar WGwG
	- 'Debutante' 🏆H5	CBcs CDoC CRos ELan GKin LRHS MAsh MGos NLar SCob SCoo SWvt WFar
	- 'Don'	see *P. japonica* 'Pygmaea'
	- 'Dorothy Wyckoff'	NLar SCob SGbt SSta
	- 'Erik'	SAko
	- 'Flaming Star'	SGbt SWvt
	- 'Flamingo'	CMac
	- 'Hino Crimson' **new**	SWeb
I	- 'Katsura' PBR	CBcs CBod CDoC CMac CRos EHyd ELan EPfP GKin LBuc LMil LRHS LSRN MAsh MBlu MGos NHol NLar NRHS SCoo SLim SPer SPoG SWvt WFar
	- 'Little Heath' (v)	CBcs CBod CDoC CEnd CMac CRos CSBt EHyd ELan ELon EPfP GKin LRHS MAsh MGos MPri NHol NLar NRHS NWad SArc SCob SLim SPer SPoG SRms SWeb SWvt WFar WSMil
	- 'Little Heath Green'	CBrac CCCN CMac ELon GKin MAsh MGos MMuc SCob SPer SPoG SWvt WFar
	- 'Minor'	GKev NWad WFar WThu
	- 'Mountain Fire' 🏆H5	Widely available
	- 'Passion' PBR	CBcs CBod CEnd CRos CSBt EBee EHyd EPfP LCro LMil LOPS LRHS LSRN MAsh NLar NRHS SAko SPer
	- 'Pink Delight' 🏆H5	CDoC CRos LMil LRHS LSRN MAsh MRav SCob SRms
	- 'Prelude' 🏆H5	CRos CSBt EHyd EPfP LMil LRHS MAsh WAbe
	- 'Purity' 🏆H5	CBcs CBod CCCN CMac MAsh MGos NLar SArc SCob SLim SWvt WFar
§	- 'Pygmaea'	NWad
	- 'Ralto' PBR	CRos EHyd LCro LMil LOPS LRHS MAsh MRav NLar NRHS SCob SPoG
	- RALTO ROSE ('Opstal10')	MPkF
	- RED MILL ('Zebris')	CEnd SLim SPer
	- 'Sarabande' 🏆H5	ILea MAsh SCob SPer
	- 'Scarlett O'Hara'	CSBt NLar
	- Taiwanensis Group	CMac GKin NLar SRms WFar
	- 'Temple Bells'	CSBt
	- 'Valley Rose'	CSBt ELan GKin MAsh NLar
	- 'Valley Valentine' 🏆H5	CBcs CDoC CMac CRos CSBt EHyd EPfP LCro LMil LOPS LRHS LSRN MAsh MGos MPkF NHpl NLar NOra NRHS SAko SCob SCoo SLim SPer SPoG SRkn SWvt WFar
	- 'Variegata' misapplied	see *P. japonica* 'White Rim'
	- 'Variegata' ambig.	CBrac LMil SPer
	- 'Variegata' (Carrière) Bean (v)	CRos EHyd LRHS NRHS
	- 'Wada's Pink'	see *P. japonica* 'Christmas Cheer'
	- 'White Cascade'	SCob
	- 'White Pearl'	CMac SCob
§	- 'White Rim' (v)	CMac MAsh SCob SPlb
	- 'William Buchanan'	NWad WThu
	- var. ***yakushimensis***	NLar
	nana	WThu
	'Tilford'	CMac

Pilea (*Urticaceae*)

	cadierei 🏆H1c	EShb
	libanensis	EShb
	peperomioides 🏆H1c	CCBP CDoC LCro LOPS
	platanifolia 'Pelling' **new**	MHid

Pileostegia (*Hydrangeaceae*)

	viburnoides	Widely available
	- B&SWJ 3565	WCru
	- B&SWJ 3570 from Taiwan	WCru
	- B&SWJ 7132	WCru
	- variegated (v)	LRHS

Pilgerodendron (*Cupressaceae*)

	uviferum	IDee

Pilosella (*Asteraceae*)

§	***aurantiaca***	CBor EBou ELan GJos IRos LCro LEdu LOPS LPot LRHS MBow MHer MNHC NBid SPhx SRms WCot WHer WOut WSFF
§	- subsp. ***carpathicola***	MMuc SEND
§	***officinarum***	NRya XSen

Pimelea (*Thymelaeaceae*)

	coarctata	see *P. prostrata*
	drupacea	IDee
	ferruginea	SVen
	oreophila	WThu
§	***prostrata***	EPot EWes GEdr GRum
	tomentosa	LRHS

Pimpinella (*Apiaceae*)

	anisum	SPhx SVic XAbr
	major	LEdu
	- 'Rosea'	Widely available
	saxifraga	CHab EBou SPhx WSFF
	siifolia	WHil
	tripartita	SPhx
	- PAB 6112	LEdu WPGP
	- PAB 7261	WPGP

pineapple see *Ananas comosus*

pineapple guava see *Acca sellowiana*

Pinellia (*Araceae*)

	cordata	LEdu WCru XLum
	pedatisecta	GKev MRav
	peltata **new**	GKev
	pinnatisecta	see *P. tripartita*
	ternata	EBee GEdr GKev NLar
	- B&SWJ 3532	WCru
§	***tripartita***	CExl GKev WCot
	- B&SWJ 1102	WCru
	- 'Purple Face'	WCru

Pinguicula (*Lentibulariaceae*)

	ehlersiae	SPlb
	grandiflora 🏆H4	EECP EPot EWld GKev NRya

pinkcurrant see *Ribes rubrum* (P)

Pinus ✿ (*Pinaceae*)

	albicaulis 'Flinck'	CKen
	- 'Nana'	see *P. albicaulis* 'Noble's Dwarf'
	- 'No 3'	CKen
§	- 'Noble's Dwarf'	CKen
	aristata ambig.	LRHS SAko SEND WHwl

	aristata Engelm.	CMCN CMen
	- 'Bashful'	CKen
	- 'Cecilia'	CKen
	- 'Kohout's Mini'	CKen
	- 'Sherwood Compact'	CKen MAsh NLar SLim
	armandi	CMCN EPfP LRHS WHwl
	austriaca	see *P. nigra* subsp. *nigra*
	ayacahuite	CKen
	balfouriana dwarf	CKen
	banksiana 'Chippewa'	CKen
I	- 'Compacta'	CKen
	- 'Neponset'	CKen
	- 'Schneverdingen'	NLar
	- 'Schoodic'	NLar SLim
	bhutanica	WPGP
	- KR 10358	WPGP
	bungeana	CMCN EPfP MBlu MGil SPtp
	- 'Diamant'	CKen
	- 'June's Broom'	CKen
	cembra	CAgr EPfP LRHS MCoo WHwl XLot
	- 'Aurea'	see *P. cembra* 'Aureovariegata'
§	- 'Aureovariegata' (v)	SLim
	- 'Barnhourie'	CKen
	- 'Blue Mound'	CKen
	- 'Inverleith'	CKen
	- 'Jermyns'	CKen
	- 'King's Dwarf'	CKen
	- 'Ortler'	CKen
	- 'Stricta'	CKen LRHS NLar XLot
	- witches' broom	CKen
	cembroides NJM 09.022A	WPGP
	- 'Fancy Nancy'	CKen
	contorta	CBcs GJos SPlb WHwl
	- 'Asher'	CKen LRHS
	- 'Chief Joseph' ℽH6	CKen MAsh NLar SLim
	- 'Fordham's Dwarf Rug' **new**	CKen
	- 'Frisian Gold'	NLar
	- 'Spaan's Dwarf'	CKen SLim
	- 'Taylor's Sunburst'	CKen NLar
	coulteri	EPfP WPGP
	densiflora	EBtc WHwl
	- 'Alice Verkade' ℽH7	CMen LRHS MAsh NLar WFar
I	- 'Bedgebury Sport Broom'	CKen
	- 'Golden Ghost'	NLar
	- 'Haybud'	MMrt
	- 'Jim Cross'	CKen
	- 'Kim'	NLar
	- 'Low Glow'	CKen LRHS NLar SLim SPoG
	- 'Oculus-draconis' (v)	SLim XLot
	- 'Pendula'	CKen MBlu MGil SLim
	- 'Pumila'	LRHS
	- 'Rata'	NLar
	- 'Umbraculifera'	CMen MAsh WHwl XLot
	× ***densithunbergii***	CMen LRHS NLar NOra SLim SPoG
	'Jane Kluis' ℽH7	XLot
	edulis	CMCN
	- 'Juno'	CKen
	elliottii var. ***densa***	CKen
	fenzeliana	CKen
	flexilis 'Cesarini Blue'	NLar
	- 'Cow Creek'	NLar
	- 'Firmament'	NOra SLim WMat
	- 'Glenmore Dwarf'	CKen
	- 'Lil Wolf'	NLar
	- 'Nana'	CKen
	- 'Ririe'	CKen MAsh
	- 'Tarryall'	CKen
	- 'Vanderwolf's Pyramid'	CCVT NLar SLim
	- WB No 1	CKen
	- WB No 2	CKen
	greggii	EBtc
	griffithii McClell.	see *P. wallichiana*
	halepensis	SEND XSen
§	***heldreichii***	EPfP NOra SLim WMat
	- 'Atze Saule' **new**	NLar
	- 'Aureospicata'	NLar
	- 'Compact Gem' ℽH6	CKen LRHS NLar SLim XLot
	- 'Dolce Dorme'	CKen
	- 'Emerald Arrow'	NLar
	- 'Green Giant'	NLar XLot
	- 'Green Pyramid'	NLar
	- 'Groen'	CKen
	- var. ***leucodermis***	see *P. heldreichii*
	- - 'Irish Bell'	CKen NLar
	- - 'Pirin No 3'	SAko
	- 'Little Dracula' **new**	NLar
	- 'Malink'	CKen
	- 'Pygmy'	CKen
	- 'Satellit' ℽH6	CKen MAsh NLar SLim XLot
	- 'Schmidtii'	see *P. heldreichii* 'Smidtii'
§	- 'Smidtii' ℽH6	CKen CMen LRHS MAsh NLar NPoe SLim SPoG
	- 'Zwerg Schneverdingen'	CKen SLim
	× ***holfordiana***	EBee EPfP WPGP
	jeffreyi 'Joppi'	CKen NLar SLim
	- 'Misty Lemon'	NLar
	koraiensis	LEdu
	- 'Baishan'	NLar
	- 'Bergman'	CKen LRHS
	- 'Blue Ball'	CKen NLar
	- 'China Boy'	NLar
	- 'Dongling'	NLar
	- 'Dragon Eye'	CKen SLim
	- 'Jack Corbit'	CKen WFar
	- 'Shibamichi' (v)	CKen
	- 'Silveray'	CKen NLar
	- 'Silvergrey'	CKen
	- 'Spring Grove'	CKen
	- 'Tong Hua'	NLar
	- 'Tsingtao'	NLar
	- 'Winton'	CKen NLar XLot
	leucodermis	see *P. heldreichii*
	'Marie Bregéon' PBR	LRHS
	monophylla 'Wrinkle'	NLar
	montezumae Lamb.	SArc WPGP
	- NJM 09.016	WPGP
	- 'Sheffield Park'	SLim
	monticola 'Crawford'	NLar
	- 'Ondulata'	NLar
	- 'Pendula'	CKen
	- 'Pygmy'	see *P. monticola* 'Raraflora'
§	- 'Raraflora'	CKen
	- 'Strobicola'	EPfP
	- 'Windsor Dwarf'	CKen
	mugo	CBcs EPfP MGos SCob SGsty SWeb WHwl
	- 'Allgäu'	CKen NLar XLot
	- 'Alpen Hexe'	NLar
	- 'Árpád' **new**	XLot
	- 'Benjamin'	CKen LRHS NLar XLot
	- 'Bonita'	LRHS
	- 'Brownie'	CKen
	- 'Carsten' ℽH7	CKen EPfP LRHS MAsh NLar NOra SCoo SLim SPoG XLot
	- 'Columbo'	WHwl XLot
	- 'Corley's Mat'	CKen NLar NOra SLim XLot
	- 'Dezember Gold'	SLim
	- 'Echiniformis' **new**	XLot
	- 'Flanders Belle'	SLim

	- 'Gnom'	ELan EPfP GKin LRHS MAsh MGos SCoo SLim XLot
	- 'Gold Star'	CMen NLar XLot
	- 'Golden Glow'	NLar SLim SPoG XLot
	- 'Grüne Kugel' **new**	NLar XLot
	- 'Heinis Triumph'	XLot
	- 'Hesse'	SCoo
	- 'Hoersholm'	CKen
	- 'Hulk'	CKen
	- 'Humpy' ♀H7	CKen CMen CRos MAsh SCoo SLim
	- 'Ironsides'	CKen
	- 'Jacobsen'	CKen NLar SLim
	- 'Janovsky'	CKen
	- 'Kissen' ♀H7	EPfP NHol SLim
	- KLOSTERGRUN	see *P. mugo* 'Klosterkötter'
§	- 'Klosterkötter'	LRHS
	- 'Krauskopf'	CKen XLot
	- 'Laarheide'	SPoG
	- 'Laurin'	CKen
	- 'Lemon'	NLar
	- 'Little Gold Star'	CKen
	- 'March'	CKen NLar XLot
	- 'Mini Mini'	CKen
	- 'Mini Mops'	CKen SLim
	- 'Minikin'	CKen
	- 'Mitsch Mini' **new**	CKen
	- 'Mops' ♀H7	CMen EPfP LRHS MAsh MBlu MGos NOra SCob SCoo SGsty SLim SPoG WHwl XLot
	- 'Mops Gold'	NLar
	- 'Mops Midget'	CMen MAsh XLot
	- var. ***mughus***	see *P. mugo* subsp. *mugo*
§	- subsp. ***mugo***	CBod CSBt SCob SGol XLot
	- - 'Milky Way'	CKen NLar
	- 'Mumpitz'	CKen LRHS XLot
	- 'Northern Lights'	CKen
	- 'Ophir' ♀H7	CBcs CMen ELan EPfP LRHS MAsh MGos SCoo SLim SPoG SSta XLot
	- 'Pal Maleter' (v)	SCoo SLim SPoG XLot
	- 'Paul's Dwarf'	CKen
	- 'Picobello'	LRHS MAsh NHol NLar SLim XLot
	- 'Piggelmee'	CKen
	- 'Pincushion'	LRHS
	- Pumilio Group	ELan EPfP LRHS MGos MMuc NLar SCob SEND SPad XLot
	- - 'David Compressa'	SAko
	- - 'Emerald Dwarf'	NLar
	- 'Rigi' **new**	NLar XLot
	- 'Rock Garden'	NLar
	- var. ***rostrata***	see *P. mugo* subsp. *uncinata*
	- subsp. ***rotundata*** 'Ježek'	CKen MAsh NLar
	- 'Ruze'	LRHS
	- 'Sandy'	NLar
	- 'Sherwood Compact'	NLar SLim
	- 'Sherwood Compact No 5'	SAko
	- 'Spaan'	CKen
	- 'Sunshine' (v)	NLar
	- 'Suzi'	CKen NLar
	- 'Tuffet'	CKen LRHS NHol SLim
	- 'Uelzen'	CKen LRHS
§	- subsp. ***uncinata***	IDee
	- - 'Etschtal'	CKen
	- - 'Grüne Welle'	CKen NLar SLim XLot
	- - 'Heideperle'	NLar
	- - 'Kostelnicek'	CKen NLar
	- - 'Leuco-like'	CKen
	- - 'Litomysl'	NLar
	- - 'Offenpass'	CKen
	- - 'Paradekissen'	CKen NLar
	- - 'Süsse Perle'	CKen
	- 'Varella'	LRHS NLar SCoo SLim XLot
	- 'White Tip'	CKen
	- 'Winter Gold'	EPfP LRHS MGos NHol SSta
	- 'Winter Sun'	LRHS MAsh NLar
	- 'Winzig'	CKen
	- 'Yellow Tip' (v)	NHol SLim
	- 'Zundert'	CKen SPoG XLot
	- 'Zwergkugel'	CKen NLar SAko
	nigra	CBcs CLnd CMac CTri EPfP LRHS MAsh MGos NOrn SArc SGol
	- var. ***austriaca***	see *P. nigra* subsp. *nigra*
	- 'Bambino'	CKen
	- 'Black Prince' ♀H7	CKen NOra SLim WMat
	- 'Bobo'	CKen
	- var. ***calabrica***	see *P. nigra* subsp. *laricio*
	- 'Cebennensis Nana'	CKen
	- var. ***corsicana***	see *P. nigra* subsp. *laricio*
	- 'Frank'	CKen
	- 'Green Tower'	LRHS NLar SLim WHwl XLot
	- 'Helga'	NLar
	- 'Hornibrookiana'	CKen XLot
	- 'Keightley Broom' **new**	SLim
	- 'Komet'	NLar SAko SLim
§	- subsp. ***laricio***	CCVT CMac MMuc SCob SEND SLim
	- - 'Aurea'	MBlu
	- - 'Bobby McGregor'	CKen
	- - 'Goldfinger'	NLar
	- - 'Pygmaea'	CKen
	- - 'Wurstle'	CKen
	- subsp. ***maritima***	see *P. nigra* subsp. *laricio*
	- 'Moran'	NLar
	- 'Moseri'	CKen NLar
	- 'Nana'	LRHS XLot
§	- subsp. ***nigra***	CBrac CCVT CLnd CTho EWTr LMaj LRHS MMuc SCob SEND SEWo SGol SGsty WHwl
	- - 'Birte'	CKen
	- - 'Helga'	NLar
	- - 'Schovenhorst'	CKen
	- - 'Skyborn'	CKen
	- - 'Strypemonde'	CKen
	- - 'Yaffle Hill'	CKen
	- 'Obelisk'	CKen NLar
	- 'Ola'	CKen
	- 'Oregon Green'	CKen NLar WHwl
	- subsp. ***pallasiana*** 'Pyramidalis'	XLot
	- 'Pierrick Bregéon'PBR	LRHS
	- 'Richard'	CKen NLar SLim
	- 'Spielberg'	LRHS NLar XLot
	parviflora	SPlb WHwl
	- 'Aaba-jo'	CKen
	- 'Adcock's Dwarf' ♀H7	CKen SLim
	- 'Al Fordham'	CKen
	- 'Aoi'	CKen CMen
	- 'Ara-kawa'	CKen CMen
	- 'Atco-goyo'	CKen
	- Azuma-goyo Group	CKen CMen LRHS
I	- 'Baasch's Form'	CKen MGil
	- 'Beran' **new**	SLim
	- 'Bergman'	MAsh NLar SLim
	- 'Blue Angel'	MBlu
	- 'Blue Giant'	IArd MBlu XLot
	- 'Blue Lou'	NLar
	- 'Bonnie Bergman' ♀H7	CKen EPfP LRHS NHol NLar
	- 'Catherine Elizabeth'	CKen NLar
	- 'Dai-ho'	CKen
	- 'Daisetsusan'	CKen
	- 'Debbie'	NLar

	- 'Dougal'	CKen
	- 'Fukai' (v)	CKen NHol SLim
	- 'Fukiju'	CKen
	- Fukushima-goyo Group	CKen CMen
	- 'Fuku-zu-mi'	CKen
	- 'Fu-shiro'	CKen
	- 'Gemstar'	CKen
	- 'Gin-sho-chuba'	CKen
	- Glauca Group	LMaj LRHS MAsh MBlu
	- - 'Glauca' ♀H7	XLot
I	- - 'Glauca Nana'	CKen
	- 'Goykuri'	CKen LRHS
	- 'Gyok-kasen'	CKen
	- 'Gyo-ko-haku'	CKen
	- 'Gyokusen Sämling'	CKen
	- 'Gyo-ku-sui'	CKen CMen
	- 'Hagaromo Seedling'	CKen CMen
	- 'Hakko'	CKen
	- 'Hatchichi'	CKen
	- 'Ha-tzumari'	MGil NLar SLim
	- 'Hobbit'	CKen
	- 'Ibo-can'	CKen CMen
	- 'Ichi-no-se'	CKen
	- 'Iona' **new**	CKen
	- 'Iri-fune'	CKen
	- Ishizuchi-goyo Group	CKen
	- 'Jade Tiers'	LRHS
	- 'Jim's Mini Curls'	CKen NLar
	- 'Ka-ho'	CKen
	- 'Kanrico'	CKen
	- 'Kanzan'	CKen
	- 'Kenwith' **new**	NLar
	- 'Kin-po'	CKen NLar
	- 'Kiyomatsu'	CKen
	- 'Kobe'	CKen
	- 'Kokonoe'	CKen CMen
	- 'Kokuho'	CKen
	- 'Kusu-dama'	CKen
	- 'Little Hedgehog'	CKen
	- 'Lorraine'	CKen
	- 'Masami'	CKen
	- 'Meiko'	CKen CMen
	- 'Michinoku'	CKen
	- 'Momo-yama'	CKen NLar
	- 'Myo-jo'	CKen
	- Nasu-goyo Group	CKen
	- 'Negishi' ♀H7	CKen CMen LRHS MAsh NLar SLim
	- 'Ogon-goyo'	CKen
	- 'Ōgon-janome'	CKen MAsh SLim
	- 'Ossorio Dwarf'	CKen
	- 'Perido'	NLar
	- 'Regenhold Broom'	CKen
	- 'Richard Lee'	CKen MAsh NLar
	- 'Ryo-ku-ho'	CKen
	- 'Ryu-ju'	CKen
	- 'Sa-dai-jin'	CKen
	- 'San-bo'	CKen
§	- 'Saphir'	CKen NLar
	- 'Schoon's Bonsai'	LRHS NHol NLar
	- 'Setsugekka'	CKen SAko
	- 'Shika-shima'	CKen
	- Shikoku-goyo Group	LRHS
	- 'Shimada'	CKen
	- 'Shin Sen'	LRHS
	- 'Shin Sho'	LRHS
	- Shiobara-goyo Group	CKen
	- 'Shiro-Janome' (v) **new**	CKen
	- 'Shizukagoten'	CKen SLim
	- 'Shu-re'	CKen
	- 'Sieryoden'	CKen
	- 'Smout'	CKen
	- 'Tani-mano-uki'	CKen
	- 'Tempelhof'	NLar NOrn
	- 'Tenysu-kazu'	CKen EPfP LRHS MAsh NLar SLim
	- 'Tokyo Dwarf'	CKen
	- 'Walker's Dwarf'	CKen
	- 'Watnong'	CKen
	- 'Zelkova'	CMen
	- 'Zui-sho'	CKen
	patula ♀H4	CBcs CBod CCCN CMCN ECre EPfP IDee SArc SCoo SIvy SLim SMad SPlb SPoG WMat WPGP
	peuce	EPfP SEND
	- 'Arnold Dwarf'	CKen
	- 'Cesarini'	CKen NLar
	- 'Daniel'	CKen NLar
	- 'Harlekin'	NLar
	- 'Thessaloniki Broom'	CKen
	'Pichounet'	NLar
	pinaster	CBcs EPfP MMuc SEND
	pinea ♀H4	CAgr CCVT CLnd EPfP LMaj MGos MMuc SArc SCob SCoo SEND SEWo SGsty SPlb SWeb WPGP XSen
	- 'Queensway'	CKen
	ponderosa	EPfP LRHS
	- SDL2	NLar
	pumila 'Blue Mops' **new**	NLar
	- 'Blue Note'	NLar
	- 'Buchanan'	CKen
I	- 'Compacta'	XLot
	- 'Draijer's Dwarf'	SLim XLot
	- 'Dwarf Blue'	NHol
	- 'Glauca' ♀H7	CKen MAsh XLot
	- 'Globe'	MAsh NLar SLim XLot
	- 'Jeddeloh'	CKen
	- 'Pinocchio'	CKen
	- 'Säntis'	CKen
	- 'Saphir'	see *P. parviflora* 'Saphir'
	radiata	CBcs CBod CBrac CCVT CCoa CLnd CMCN CMac CSBt CSde CTho ELan EPfP LMaj MMuc NOrn SArc SCoo WHwl WMat
	- Aurea Group	SCoo SLim SPoG WMat
	- - 'Aurea' ♀H5	CKen LRHS NOra
	- 'Bodnant'	CKen
	- 'Marshwood' (v)	CKen SLim
	resinosa 'Don Smith'	CKen
	- 'Joel's Broom'	CKen
	- 'Quinobequin'	CKen
	× ***schwerinii***	CKen
	- 'Wiethorst' ♀H7	CKen IDee LRHS NLar SLim WMat XLot
	sibirica 'Blue Smoke'	CKen
	- 'Mariko'	CKen
	strobiformis 'Coronado'	CKen
	- 'Loma Linda'	CKen SLim
	strobus	CBcs CCVT CMen EPfP LMaj LRHS MGos MMuc SCob SEND WHwl XLot
§	- 'Alba'	SLim
	- 'Amelia's Dwarf'	CKen
	- 'Angel Falls'	CKen NLar
	- 'Anna Fiele'	CKen
	- 'Bergman's Mini'	CKen LRHS NLar SLim
	- 'Bergman's Pendula Broom'	CKen
I	- 'Bergman's Sport of Prostrata'	CKen
	- 'Beth'	CKen
	- 'Bloomer's Dark Globe'	CKen

– 'Blue Shag' 🏆H7	ELan LRHS NLar NWad SCoo SLim XLot
– 'Bob's Wishes'	NLar
– 'Brevifolia'	CKen SArc
– 'Cedar Ridge Broom' **new**	SLim
– 'Cesarini'	CKen
– 'Densa'	CKen
– 'Densa Hill' **new**	SLim
– 'Diablo'	NLar
– 'Ed's Broom'	CKen
– 'Elf'	NLar
– 'Elkins Dwarf'	CKen LRHS
– 'Fastigiata'	CKen MBlu
– 'Golden Candles'	NLar
– 'Golden Showers'	NLar
– 'Green Curls'	CKen
– 'Green Twist'	CKen NLar SLim
– 'Greg'	CKen
– 'Ground Hugger'	NLar
– 'Hershey'	CKen
– 'Hillside Gem'	CKen
– 'Horsford'	CKen SLim
– 'Horsford Sister'	CKen
– 'Jamaican Curls'	CKen
– 'Joe's Best Blue'	NLar
– 'Julian Pott'	CKen
– 'Julian's Dwarf'	CKen
– 'Krügers Lilliput'	LRHS NLar NWad SLim
– 'Louie'	CKen MAsh NLar SLim XLot
– 'Macopin'	LRHS NLar WFar
– 'Mary Butler'	CKen NLar
– 'Mary Sweeny'	NLar
– 'Merrimack'	CKen
– 'Minima' 🏆H7	CKen LRHS LSRN MBlu SLim SPoG XLot
– 'Minuta'	CKen LRHS SLim
– Nana Group	SEWo
– 'Niagara Falls'	CKen NLar
– 'Nivea'	see *P. strobus* 'Alba'
– 'Northway Broom'	CKen
– 'Paul Waxman'	NLar
– 'Pendula'	CKen ELan LRHS MBlu
I – 'Pendula Broom'	CKen
– 'Pygmaea'	LRHS MGil
– 'Reinshaus'	CKen
– 'Sayville'	CKen
– 'Sea Urchin'	CKen MAsh NLar SLim
– 'Secrest'	LRHS
– 'Smokey Hollow'	NLar
– 'Soft Touch' **new**	SLim
– 'Squiggles'	NLar
– 'Stowe Pillar'	NLar SLim
– 'Tiny Kurls'	CKen LRHS MAsh NLar SLim XLot
– 'Torulosa'	MBlu
– 'Uncatena'	CKen
– 'Verkade's Broom'	CKen
– 'White Mountain'	MBlu SAko
sylvestris	CBcs CBrac CCVT CHab CMac CSBt CTho CTri ELan EPfP EWTr LBuc LMaj MGos MMuc NOrn SCob SEND SEWo SGol SGsty SPlb SWeb WFar WHwl WMou WTSh
– 'Abergeldie'	CKen
– 'Albyns'	XLot
– 'Alderly Edge'	CMen
– 'Andorra'	CKen
– 'Anny's Wintersun'	NLar
– Aurea Group	CKen CMen MBlu SLim SSta WMat
– – 'Aurea' 🏆H7	MAsh
– 'Avondene'	CKen
– 'Bergfield'	CMen
– 'Beuvronensis' 🏆H7	CMen SLim
– 'Buchanan's Gold'	CKen
– 'Burghfield'	CMen
– 'Candlelight'	NLar
– 'Chantry Blue'	CCVT EPfP LRHS MAsh MGos NLar NOra NOrn SCoo SLim SPoG WMat
– 'Clumber Blue'	CKen
– 'Denny Boy'	NLar
– 'Dereham'	CKen LRHS NLar
– 'Doone Valley'	CKen
– 'Edwin Hillier'	NOra SLim WMat WPGP
– Fastigiata Group	CEnd CKen CMen LRHS NLar SCoo SLim WCFE WHwl
– 'Frensham' 🏆H7	CKen MAsh XLot
– 'Gold Coin' 🏆H7	CKen EPfP SPoG
– 'Gold Medal'	CKen
– 'Grand Rapids'	CKen
– 'Green Penguin'	NLar
– 'Gwydyr Castle'	CKen
– 'Hillside Creeper'	CKen SLim
– 'Humble Pie'	CKen LRHS
– 'Jeremy'	CKen
– 'John Boy'	CMen
– 'Kelpie'	SLim
– 'Kenwith'	CKen
– 'Lodge Hill'	CMen MAsh SLim
– 'Longmoor'	CKen
– 'Martham'	CKen CMen
– 'Meffen Gold'	NLar
– 'Mitsch Weeping'	CKen
– 'Nana' misapplied	see *P. sylvestris* 'Watereri'
– Nana Group	SWeb
– – 'Nana Compacta'	CMen
§ – 'Nisbet's Gem'	CKen CMen
– 'Padworth'	CMen
– 'Piskowitz'	CKen
– 'Pixie'	CKen
I – 'Prostrata'	SLim
– 'Repens'	CKen
– 'Saint George'	CKen
– 'Sandringham'	NLar
– 'Saxatilis'	CKen CMen NLar
– 'Scott's Dwarf'	see *P. sylvestris* 'Nisbet's Gem'
– 'Sentinel'	CKen
– 'Skjak I'	CKen
– 'Skjak II'	CKen SLim
– 'Spaan's Slow Column'	CKen SLim
– 'Tage'	CKen
– 'Tanya'	CKen
– 'Tilhead'	CKen
– 'Treasure'	CKen
– 'Trefrew Quarry'	CKen LRHS
– 'Trollguld'	CKen LRHS NLar
§ – 'Watereri'	CCVT LMaj LRHS NLar SCoo SLim WHwl XLot
– 'Westonbirt'	CKen CMen MAsh
– 'Wittichenau'	CKen
– 'Xavery'	NLar
tabuliformis	SLim
taiwanensis	EPfP
tecunumanii	SLim
thunbergii	CLnd CMen ELan MMuc SGsty
– 'Akame'	CKen CMen
– 'Akame Yatsabusa'	CMen
– 'Aocha-matsu' (v)	CKen CMen
– 'Arakawa-sho'	CKen CMen
– 'Banshosho'	CKen CMen NLar SLim XLot
– 'Beni-kujaku'	CKen CMen
– 'Compacta'	CKen CMen

- var. ***corticosa*** 'Fuji'	CMen
- - 'Iihara'	CMen
- 'Dainagon'	CKen CMen
- 'Hayabusa'	CMen
- 'Iwai'	CMen
- 'Janome' (v)	CMen
- 'Katsuga'	CMen
- 'Kotobuki'	CKen CMen NLar XLot
- 'Koyosho'	CMen
- 'Kujaku'	CMen
- 'Kyokko'	CKen CMen
- 'Kyushu'	CKen CMen
- 'Maijima'	LRHS
- 'Mikawa'	CMen MBlu
- 'Miyajuna'	CKen CMen
- 'Nishiki-ne'	CKen CMen
- 'Nishiki-tsusaka'	CMen
- 'Ogi-matsu'	CKen
- 'Ōgon'	CMen LRHS NLar SLim
- 'Porky'	CKen CMen
§ - 'Sayonara' ♀H7	CMen MAsh SLim XLot
- 'Senryu'	CKen CMen
- 'Shinsho'	CKen CMen
- 'Shio-guro'	CKen CMen XLot
- 'Suchiro Yatabusa'	CKen CMen
- 'Sunsho'	CKen CMen
- 'Taihei'	CMen
I - 'Thunderhead' ♀H7	CKen CMen NLar SLim XLot
- witches' broom	CKen
- 'Yatsubusa'	see *P. thunbergii* 'Sayonara'
- 'Ye-i-kan'	CKen
- 'Yoshimura'	CMen
- 'Yumaki'	CKen CMen
torreyana	CBcs
uncinata	see *P. mugo* subsp. *uncinata*
virginiana 'Driscoll'	NLar
- 'Wate's Golden'	CKen
§ ***wallichiana*** ♀H6	CBcs CCVT CLnd CMCN CTho EPfP IDee LMaj LRHS MBlu MGil MGos MHid MMuc NHol NLar NOra NOrn SCob SEND SEWo SGol SGsty SLim SMad WHwl WMat WPGP XLot
- 'Densa Hill'	LMaj LRHS NLar
- 'Frosty'	CKen
- 'Kenwith Cascade' **new**	CKen
- 'Nana' ♀H6	CKen LRHS NLar SCoo SLim
- 'Umbraculifera'	MAsh
- 'Winter Light'	NLar
- 'Zebrina' (v)	LRHS MBlu NHol NLar
yunnanensis	LRHS
- var. ***yunnanensis*** **new**	SLim

Piper (*Piperaceae*)

auritum	GPoy LEdu
betle	GPoy
excelsum	see *Macropiper excelsum*
heydei B&SWJ 10445	WCru

Piptanthus (*Papilionaceae*)

forrestii	see *P. nepalensis*
laburnifolius	see *P. nepalensis*
§ ***nepalensis***	CBcs CRos CSpe EBee EHyd ELan EPfP EWld GKev IDee LRHS MGil MGos NBid NLar SBrt SPer SRms WAvo
aff. ***nepalensis***	SWvt

Pistacia (*Anacardiaceae*)

chinensis	CBcs EBee EPfP IDee WPGP XSen
lentiscus	CBcs CCCN LRHS SEND SVen XSen
terebinthus	XSen
- NJM 11.004	WPGP
vera	CBcs CTsd EBee

Pistia (*Araceae*)

stratiotes	LCro LLWG LOPS NPer SCoo SVic
- variegated	LLWG

Pitavia (*Rutaceae*)

punctata	IArd IDee

Pitcairnia (*Bromeliaceae*)

heterophylla	WCot
pungens	WCot
punicea **new**	WCot
ringens	WCot

Pittosporum ✿ (*Pittosporaceae*)

adaphniphylloides	CBcs
anomalum	CCCN CTrC CTsd GBin SEle SIvy
'Arundel Green' (f) ♀H4	CBrac CDoC CRos EHyd ELon EPfP LRHS MAsh NOra NRHS SCob SLim SPer SWvt
bicolor	CTsd
'Bicton Silver' (m/v)	CCCN
buchananii	SVen
'Collaig Silver'	CRos EHyd EPfP LRHS MAsh NRHS SLim
crassifolium	CBcs CCCN CCoa CSde CTsd IDee SPlb
- 'Variegatum' (v)	CBcs CBod CCCN MGil WAvo
'Crinkles' (f)	SPer SVen
dallii	CCCN SPlb
daphniphylloides	ELan WPGP
- B&SWJ 6789	WCru
- CWJ 12404	WCru
- RWJ 9913	WCru
eugenioides	CCoa CMCN CSam CSde ELon SEND
- 'Platinum' (v)	CCCN
- 'Variegatum' (v) ♀H3	CBcs CCCN CCoa CDoC CMac CRos CSde EHyd ELan EPfP LRHS MGos NLar NRHS SAko SEND SLim SNig SVen WAvo
'Garnettii' (v) ♀H3	Widely available
glabratum	WPGP
- var. ***neriifolium*** B&SWJ 11685	WCru
heterophyllum	CBod ECrN EPfP EWes LRHS MMrt SEND
- variegated (v)	CCCN CRos EBee EHyd EPfP LRHS WSHC
illicioides	WPGP
var. ***angustifolium***	
- - B&SWJ 14560 **new**	WCru
- - RWJ 9846	WCru
- var. ***illicioides*** B&SWJ 6712	WCru
- - PAB 9004	LEdu WPGP
× ***intermedium***	SWvt
- 'Craxten' (f)	CCCN EBee
'Nanum Variegatum'	see *P. tobira* 'Variegatum'
napaulense	WCru
oblongilimbum DJHV 06137	WCru
'Oliver Twist'	CRos CTrC EHyd EPfP LRHS LSRN MAsh NRHS SCoo SSta
omeiense	EWes

– VdL 80626	EBee WPGP
parvilimbum **new**	WPGP
patulum	WPGP
phillyreoides	CTsd
ralphii	CCCN CMCN CTsd
– 'Variegatum' (v)	CCCN LRHS WPGP
'Saundersii' (v)	SCoo
tenuifolium	Widely available
– 'Abbotsbury Gold' (f/v)	CAbb CBcs CBod CBrac CCCN CDoC CMac CRos CSde CTri ELan EPfP EWes LRHS LSRN MAsh MGil MGos MSwo NRHS SCob SEND SGbt SGol SGsty SLim SPer SWvt WAvo WHwl
– 'Atropurpureum'	CBcs ELan
– 'Brockhill Compact'	CCCN LRHS SAko
– 'Cornish Mist'	CTsd
– 'County Park'	CBrac CCCN SRms
– 'County Park Dwarf'	MAsh NOra
– 'County Park Green'	ELon
– 'Cratus' **new**	SArc
– 'Elizabeth' (m/v)	CBcs CBod CCoa CDoC CMac CRos CTrC EHyd ELon EPfP EWTr IArd LRHS LSRN MAsh MGos MRav MSwo NOra NRHS SCob SCoo SEND SGbt SGol SGsty SLim SPer SPoG SRms
– EMERALD DOME ('Minpitto'PBR)	EWTr SGsty
– 'French Lace'	CBcs CCCN CCoa CDoC CSde ELan SCob WFar WHwl
– 'Gold Star'	CBcs CBod CBrac CCoa CRos CSde EHyd ELan EPfP LRHS MAsh MGil MGos NOra NRHS SCob SCoo SEle SGbt SLim SPer SPoG SRms SWvt SavN WFar WHwl WLov
– 'Golden Ball' **new**	CRos
– 'Golden King'	CBrac CCCN CMac CRos CSBt EPfP LRHS MAsh MGos NOra NRHS SLim SRms
– 'Golf Ball'PBR	CBcs CDoC CRos EHyd ELan EPfP LCro LOPS LRHS LSRN MGil MGos NOra NRHS SArc SCob SGbt SPer SPoG SWvt WFar
– 'Green Thumb'	CCCN CMac EBee EPfP
– 'Irene Paterson' (m/v) ♈H4	Widely available
– 'James Stirling'	CCCN SEND
– 'John Flanagan'	see *P. tenuifolium* 'Margaret Turnbull'
– 'Limelight' (v)	CBcs CBrac CCCN CRos CSBt EBee EPfP LRHS LSRN SLim SPoG
– 'Loxhill Gold'	CCCN CCoa EHyd EPfP LRHS NOra SGol SGsty
§ – 'Margaret Turnbull' (v)	CTrC EWes LRHS MGos NOra SGol SGsty
– 'Marjory Channon' (v)	CRos EHyd LRHS NRHS
– 'Moonlight' (v)	CBod LRHS MRav
– 'Mountain Green'	CMac
– 'Nutty's Leprechaun'	CBod CCCN CTrC WRHF
– 'Pompom'	CCCN CRos EHyd LRHS LSRN NRHS
– 'Purpureum' (m)	CBar CBrac CCCN CDoC CMac CRos CSBt CTri EHyd ELon EPfP GBin LRHS LSRN MAsh MGil MMuc NRHS SAko SCob SEND SPer SPoG SRms WAvo WFar
– 'Silver Ball' (v) **new**	CBod CRos LSRN
– 'Silver Magic' (v)	CBcs EPfP LRHS SEle SRkn
– 'Silver Queen' (f/v) ♈H4	Widely available
– 'Silver Sheen' (m)	CBcs CBod CMac CRos EHyd LRHS NRHS SCob SWvt
– 'Stevens Island'	CBcs CBod CCoa CTrC
– 'Tandara Gold' (v)	CBcs CBod CCCN CCht CCoa CDoC CMac CRos CSBt CTrC EBee EHyd ELan ELon EPfP LRHS MAsh MGil MGos NRHS SCoo SEND SRms WAvo WHwl
– 'Tiki' (m)	CCCN
– 'Tom Thumb' ♈H4	Widely available
– 'Tresederi' (f/m)	CCCN CTsd
– 'Variegatum' (m/v)	CBcs CBod CRos CSBt EBee EHyd ELon EWTr LCro LOPS LRHS LSRN MGos MSwo NOra NRHS SArc SCob SEND SGbt SGsty SLim SWeb SWvt WFar
– 'Victoria' (v)	CBcs CBod CCCN CRos EBee LRHS LSRN WFar
– 'Warnham Gold' (m) ♈H4	CBcs CBod CBrac CCCN CDoC CMac CRos CSde EBee EHyd ELan EPfP LRHS MAsh MGos NRHS SCob SLim SNig SPoG SRms SVen WHwl
– 'Wendle Channon' (m/v)	CCCN CMac CRos CSBt EPfP LRHS MAsh NOra SGol WHwl WSHC
– 'Wrinkled Blue'	CBcs CBod CDoC CRos EHyd EPfP LRHS MAsh MRav MSwo NRHS SPoG SWvt
tobira ♈H3	Widely available
– B&SWJ 12758	WCru
* – 'Nanum'	CBcs CCCN CCoa CMac CRos EHyd ELan EPfP LCro LOPS LRHS LSRN MGos NOra SCob SLim SPer SPoG SWeb WHwl XSen
§ – 'Variegatum' (v) ♈H3	CBcs CCCN CCoa CMac CRos CSde EHyd ELan EPfP LRHS LSRN MGos SArc SCob SEND SLim SLon SPer SPoG WSHC
– 'West Acre Gold' **new**	CBod
'Trim's Hedger'	ELan
truncatum	CCCN CExl
undulatum	WAvo WHwl WLov
viridiflorum	EShb

Pityrogramma (*Pteridaceae*)

calomelanos **new**	WCot

Plagianthus (*Malvaceae*)

betulinus	see *P. regius*
lyallii	see *Hoberia lyallii*
§ ***regius***	CBcs

Plagiorhegma see *Jeffersonia*

Planera (*Ulmaceae*)

aquatica	IDee

Plantago (*Plantaginaceae*)

coronopus	CAgr
holosteum	GKev
lanceolata	CAgr CHab WSFF
major	GPoy WSFF
– 'Atropurpurea'	see *P. major* 'Rubrifolia'
– 'Bowles's Variety'	see *P. major* 'Rosularis'
– 'Frills'	NPoe
– 'Purple Perversion'	CSpe
– 'Rosenstolz'	NChi
§ – 'Rosularis'	CBre CFis CSpe LEdu NBro NPoe SRms WHer

§	- 'Rubrifolia'	CBod CBre CSpe EShb MMuc NBid NPoe SHar SRms WSFF XLum
	- 'Tony Lewis'	CNat
	media	CHab MHer
	nivalis	EDAr GEdr
	rosea	see *P. major* 'Rosularis'
	subulata	EDAr
	triandra 'Wanaka'	IMou

Platanus ✿ (*Platanaceae*)

	× ***acerifolia***	see *P.* × *hispanica*
§	× ***hispanica*** ♀H6	CBcs CCVT CLnd CMCN ECrN ELan EPfP LMaj MGos MMuc SArc SCob SEND SEWo SGol SPer WMat WMou WTSh
	- 'Pyramidalis'	LMaj
	orientalis	CCVT CLnd CMCN EPfP WPGP
	- PAB 346	LEdu
§	- f. ***digitata*** ♀H6	CCVT CLnd CMCN CTho EBee EPfP WMou
	- var. ***insularis***	SMad WPGP
	- 'Laciniata'	see *P. orientalis* f. *digitata*
	- 'Mirkovec'	EPfP IArd

Platycarya (*Juglandaceae*)

	strobilacea	SPtp

Platycerium (*Polypodiaceae*)

	alcicorne misapplied	see *P. bifurcatum*
§	***bifurcatum*** ♀H1b	CCCN CDoC NCft XBlo
	grande hort.	see *P. superbum*
§	***superbum*** ♀H1a	CCCN EShb NCft

Platycladus (*Cupressaceae*)

§	***orientalis***	LEdu
§	- 'Aurea Nana' ♀H7	CBrac CKen CMac CSBt EPfP LBee LRHS MAsh MGos NWad SGol SGsty SLim SPoG WCFE XLot
	- 'Autumn Glow'	CKen
	- 'Beverleyensis'	NLar
	- 'Conspicua'	CKen CSBt
	- 'Elegantissima'	LRHS
	- 'Flame'	LRHS
	- 'Franky Boy' ♀H7	NLar SPoG
	- 'Golden Pygmy'	CKen
	- 'Kenwith'	CKen
	- 'Meldensis'	CTri
	- 'Miller's Gold'	see *P. orientalis* 'Aurea Nana'
	- 'Minima Glauca'	CKen
I	- 'Pyramidalis Aurea'	LBee LRHS
	- 'Rosedalis'	CKen CSBt EPfP LBee MAsh SLim
	- 'Sanderi'	WCFE
	- 'Shirley Chilcott'	MAsh
	- 'Southport'	LBee LRHS
	- 'Summer Cream'	CKen

Platycodon (*Campanulaceae*)

	grandiflorus ♀H5	CTri CTsd ECha EPfP GKev MHer SRms XAbr
	- 'Albus'	EPfP GKev SPer SWvt
	- Apoyama Group ♀H5	WHoo WThu
	- - 'Fairy Snow'	EBou WHoo
	- (Astra Series) 'Astra Blue'	CRos CSpe EHyd EPfP LRHS NRHS SPoG
	- - 'Astra Pink'	SPoG
	- - 'Astra White'	SPoG
	- 'Fuji Blue'	WHoo XLum
	- 'Fuji Pink'	MRav SWvt WHoo XLum
	- 'Hakone'	MRav
	- 'Hakone Blue'	EPfP NBre
	- 'Hakone Double Blue' (d)	SRms
	- 'Hakone White'	EPfP LSun MRav
	- 'Mariesii' ♀H5	CSBt EPfP MRav NBir SPer SPlb SRms SWvt WAul WHoo WSHC
	- MOTHER OF PEARL	see *P. grandiflorus* 'Perlmutterschale'
§	- 'Perlmutterschale'	MRav
	- pink-flowered	GKev
	- 'Sentimental Blue'	XLum
	- 'Shell Pink'	see *P. grandiflorus* 'Perlmutterschale'
	- 'Willy'	XLum
	- 'Zwerg'	CSpe NBre

Platycrater (*Hydrangeaceae*)

	arguta	WCru WPGP
	- B&SWJ 6266	WCru

Plecostachys (*Asteraceae*)

§	***serpyllifolia***	LSou

Plectranthus (*Lamiaceae*)

	ambiguus	EGeo
	- 'Nico'	CBct CSam EGeo SDix
	amboinicus	CCBP EGeo MNHC
	- 'Variegatus' (v)	EGeo
	- 'Well Sweep Wedgewood' (v)	EGeo
	argentatus ♀H1c	CBct CDTJ CSam CSpe EGeo EWld IDee MCot SEND SRkn WKif
	- 'Hill House' (v)	CSam EShb MPie
	- 'Silver Shield'	EShb MCot MPie
	australis misapplied	see *P. verticillatus*
	barbatus	EGeo
	behrii	see *P. fruticosus*
	BLUE ANGEL ('Edelblau') (Cape Angels Series)	EGeo
	caninus	SPoG
	ciliatus	CPbh EGeo EShb SRkn
	- 'Easy Gold' (v) ♀H1c	EGeo
	- 'Sasha' (v)	CCCN CSam ECtt EShb MPie
	coleoides 'Marginatus'	see *P. forsteri* 'Marginatus'
	- 'Variegatus'	see *P. madagascariensis* 'Variegated Mintleaf'
	Cuban oregano	CSam
	ernstii	EGeo EWld
	- blue-flowered	WCot
§	***forsteri*** 'Marginatus'	EGeo
§	***fruticosus***	CPbh CSam
	- 'Behr's Pride'	CSam EGeo
	- blue-flowered	EGeo
	- 'James' ♀H2	CSam EGeo WKif
	hadiensis var. ***tomentosus***	EGeo
	- - 'Carnegie'	EGeo
	- - green-leaved	EGeo
	- - 'Penge' (v)	EGeo
	madagascariensis	EGeo EShb WKif
	- 'Lothlorien' (v)	EGeo
§	- 'Variegated Mintleaf' (v) ♀H1c	CSam MNHC SRms
	'Marble Ruffles'	EGeo
	menthol-scented, large-leaved	EGeo
	MONA LAVENDER ('Plepalila'PBR) ♀H1b	EGeo WKif WWFP
	mutabilis	EGeo
	neochilus	CSpe
§	***oertendahlii*** ♀H1c	CPbh CSam EBak EGeo
	ornatus	EGeo
	prostratus	EGeo
	purpuratus ♀H1c	EGeo

	saccatus subsp. ***longitubus***	EGeo
	- subsp. ***pondoensis***	WKif
	sinensis	EHyd LRHS
	spicatus	EGeo
	Swedish ivy	see *P. oertendahlii*
	venteri	EGeo
§	***verticillatus***	EGeo
	- 'Barberton'	EGeo
	Vick's plant	EGeo
	zuluensis	CPbh CWCL EGeo EWld SDix SRkn WBor

Pleioblastus (*Poaceae*)

	altiligulatus **new**	XCre
§	***argenteostriatus*** f. ***pumilus***	CBod GMaP MMuc MWht NLar NWad SCob SPlb XCre
	auricomus	see *P. viridistriatus*
	- 'Vagans'	see *Sasaella ramosa*
	chino f. ***angustifolius***	see *P. chino* 'Murakamianus'
	- f. ***elegantissimus***	CBcs CBdn EPfP EShb MMuc SEND
	- var. ***hisauchii***	MWht XCre
§	- 'Murakamianus'	XCre
	fortunei	see *P. variegatus* 'Fortunei'
	'Gauntlettii'	see *P. argenteostriatus* f. *pumilus*
	glaber 'Albostriatus'	see *Sasaella masamuneana* 'Albostriata'
	gramineus	XCre
§	***hindsii***	XCre
	humilis var. ***pumilus***	see *P. argenteostriatus* f. *pumilus*
	juxianensis	XCre
	kongosanensis 'Aureostriatus' (v)	MWht
	linearis	EShb MCot MWht XCre
	longifimbriatus	see *Sinobambusa intermedia*
	oleosus	XCre
§	***pygmaeus***	CTri ELan GMaP MBrN SCob SGol SPer SRms XCre
§	- 'Distichus'	XCre
§	- 'Mirrezuzume'	CExl
*	- var. ***pygmaeus*** 'Mini'	MMuc WCot
§	***simonii***	CAgr CRos EHyd LRHS MMuc MWht NRHS SEND SPoG XBlo XCre
	- 'Variegatus' (v)	CBcs CRos EHyd LRHS NRHS SPer SPoG XCre
§	***variegatus*** (v) ♀H5	CBcs CBdn CBod ELan EPfP GMaP LRHS MBrN MWht SCob SDix SLim SPlb SWvt WFar XBlo XCre
§	- 'Fortunei' (v)	CTsd MMuc SEND SGol
	- 'Tsuboii' (v)	CAbb CDTJ MBrN SGol
§	***viridistriatus*** ♀H5	CBcs CBod CExl ECha ELon EPfP GMaP LRHS MMuc MRav MWht NWsh SCob SDix SEND SGol SPer SRms WFar WSMil XBlo XCre
	- f. ***variegatus*** (v)	CTsd SWvt

Pleione (*Orchidaceae*)

	sp.	NDav
	Alishan gx 'Merlin'	LYaf
	- 'Mother's Day'	GEdr LYaf
	- 'Mount Fuji'	LYaf
	Asama gx 'Red Grouse'	GEdr LYaf
	Ascension gx	LYaf
	Askia gx	GEdr
	- 'Goldfinch' **new**	LYaf
	aurita	GEdr GKev SDir
	× ***barbarae***	GKev LYaf
	Barcena gx	LYaf
	Berapi gx 'Purple Sandpiper'	LEdu LYaf WPGP
	Bonobo gx	LYaf
	Brigadoon gx 'Stonechat'	LEdu WPGP
	Britannia gx 'Doreen'	GEdr LEdu LYaf WPGP
§	***bulbocodioides***	CExl GEdr GKev LYaf
	- 'New Forest'	GEdr
§	- 'Yunnan'	GEdr
	Burnsall gx	GEdr
	Captain Hook gx	LYaf
	Caroli gx 'Cape Robin'	LYaf
	chunii	GEdr
	Confirmation gx	LYaf
	Eiger gx	GEdr LYaf
	El Pico gx 'Pheasant'	LYaf
	Erebus gx 'Redpoll'	GEdr
	Fancy Pants gx	LYaf
	formosana ♀H3	EPot GKev LCro LEdu LOPS LRHS MHer NHpl SDeJ SDir WFar WPGP
	- Alba Group	GKev WFar
	- - 'Claire'	LEdu LYaf WPGP
	- - 'Snow Bunting'	LEdu LYaf WPGP
	- 'Blush of Dawn'	NHpl
	- 'Greenhill'	LYaf
	- 'Pitlochry'	LYaf
	- (Pricei Group) 'Oriental Grace'	LYaf
	- - 'Oriental Splendour'	LYaf
	- 'Snow White'	CExl LEdu LYaf WPGP
	forrestii	EPot GKev NHpl SDir
	Gerry Mundey gx	GEdr
	- 'Tinney's Firs'	LYaf
	Glacier Peak gx	LYaf
§	***grandiflora***	GKev
	Hekla gx 'Locking Stumps'	GEdr
	- 'Partridge'	GEdr
	- 'Partridge' × **Zeus Weinstein gx**	GEdr
	hookeriana	GKev
	humilis	LYaf
	- orange-red-flowered	GKev
	Irazu gx 'Cheryl'	GEdr
	Jake Butterfield gx	LYaf
	- 'Kingfisher'	LYaf
	Jorullo gx 'Long-tailed Tit'	GEdr LYaf
	Katmai gx 'Crossbill'	LYaf
	Keith Rattray gx 'Kelty'	LYaf
	Kelut gx	LYaf
	Kenya gx 'Bald Eagle'	LYaf
	- 'Wood Owl'	LYaf
	Krakatoa gx	LYaf
	- 'Wheatear'	LYaf
	Lascar gx 'Purple Finch'	LYaf
	Leda gx 'Golden Pipit'	LYaf
	- 'Palm Thrush'	LYaf
	Lhasa gx 'Blushes'	LYaf
	limprichtii ♀H2	GKev LEdu
	maculata	GKev LYaf
	Mageik gx 'Black Kite'	LYaf
	Mandalay gx 'Purple Rain'	LYaf
	- 'Strawberry Fields'	LYaf
	Marion Johnson gx 'Bubs'	LYaf
	- 'Oxpecker'	LYaf
	- 'Whinchat'	LYaf
	Mauna Loa gx 'Glossy Starling'	LYaf
	Mawenzi gx	LYaf
	Michael Butterfield gx	LYaf
	- 'Crowned Eagle' **new**	LYaf

- 'Red Kite' **new**	LYaf
Myojin gx	GEdr
Novarupta gx 'Raven'	LYaf
Orinoco gx 'Gemini'	GEdr
Orizaba gx	GEdr
- 'Fish Eagle'	LYaf
pinkepankii	see *P. grandiflora*
Piton gx	EPot LYaf
§ ***pleionoides***	LYaf
pogonioides misapplied	see *P. pleionoides*
pogonioides (Rolfe) Rolfe	see *P. bulbocodioides*
praecox	GKev
Quizapu gx 'Peregrine'	LYaf
Rakata gx 'Blackbird'	MHer
- 'Locking Stumps'	GEdr
- 'Redwing'	LYaf
- 'Shot Silk'	GEdr LYaf
- 'Skylark'	LEdu WPGP
Red Colobus gx	LYaf
'Rossini'	GKev SDir
Salek gx 'Eagle Owl'	LYaf
Santa Maria gx 'Nightjar'	LYaf
Santorini gx	LYaf
- 'Yellow Wagtail'	LYaf
Semeru gx	LYaf
Shantung gx	NHpl
- 'Double Cream'	LYaf
- 'Ducat'	LYaf
- 'Gerry Mundey'	LYaf
- 'Muriel Harberd' ♀H2	GEdr
- 'Silver Anniversary'	LYaf
Sharon Ann Winter gx 'Marsh Owl' **new**	LYaf
Shasta gx	LYaf
Sinope gx	LYaf
Sirena gx	LYaf
Sorea gx	GEdr
Soufrière gx	GEdr
speciosa Ames & Schltr.	see *P. pleionoides*
Steve James gx 'Plum Perfection'	LYaf
Stromboli gx 'Fireball'	CExl EPot LEdu WPGP
Suswa gx 'Sand Plover'	LYaf
Taal gx 'Red-tailed Hawk'	LYaf
× ***taliensis***	LYaf
Tibesti gx	LYaf
Tolima gx 'Moorhen'	LEdu LYaf WPGP
Tongariro gx	CPBP EPot GEdr GKev LCro LEdu LOPS LRHS MHer MNrw WPGP
Ueli Wackernagel gx 'Pearl'	LYaf
'Verdi'	GKev
Versailles gx 'Bucklebury'	GEdr LEdu WPGP
- 'Muriel Turner'	GEdr
Vesuvius gx 'Leopard'	LYaf
- 'Phoenix'	LYaf
- 'Tawny Owl'	GEdr
'Vivaldi'	GKev
Volcanello gx 'Honey Buzzard'	GEdr LYaf
- 'Song Thrush'	LYaf
Whakari gx	LYaf
- 'Dusky Sunbird'	LYaf
- 'Mountain Pipit'	LYaf
Wharfedale gx 'Pine Warbler'	LYaf
yunnanensis misapplied	see *P. bulbocodioides* 'Yunnan'
yunnanensis ambig.	GEdr GKev SDir
Zeus Weinstein gx 'Egret' **new**	LYaf

Pleomele see *Dracaena*

Pleurospermum (*Apiaceae*)

SDR 7941	GKev
SDR 7985	GKev
benthamii B&SWJ 2988	WCru
camtschaticum B&SWJ 12627	WCru
yunnanense BWJ 7952A	WCru

plum see *Prunus domestica*; also AGM Fruit Section

Plumbago (*Plumbaginaceae*)

§ ***auriculata*** ♀H2	CBcs CCCN CSBt CSpe CTri CWCL EBak ELan EPfP EPri EShb MGil MRav SEND SPer SPoG SRms WAvo WFib
- f. ***alba*** ♀H2	CBcs CCCN CRHN EPfP EShb IDee SEND WFib
- 'Crystal Waters'	CCCN CSam EShb
- dark blue-flowered	CRHN WFib
- (Escapade Series) 'Escapade Blue'	CWGN EShb SPre
- - 'Escapade White'	EShb
capensis	see *P. auriculata*
larpentiae	see *Ceratostigma plumbaginoides*

Plumeria (*Apocynaceae*)

rubra ♀H1b	CCCN WSFF XBlo
- 'Golden Glow'	XBlo
- 'Velvet Red'	XBlo

Poa (*Poaceae*)

alpina	XLum
chaixii	EPPr
cita	IMou XCre
glauca 'Blue Hills' **new**	CBod
labillardierei	CKno CWCL ECha EHyd ELan ELon EPPr EPfP EShb IMou LRHS MBel MMuc SEND XCre XLum
pratensis	CHab

Podalyria (*Papilionaceae*)

calyptrata	SPlb
sericea	SPlb

Podanthus (*Asteraceae*)

ovatifolius	SVen

Podocarpus ✿ (*Podocarpaceae*)

acutifolius	LRHS
andinus	see *Prumnopitys andina*
'Autumn Shades' (m)	NLar
'Blaze' (f)	LEdu
chilinus	see *P. salignus*
'Chocolate Box' (f)	ELan LRHS MAsh NLar NOra SLim
'County Park Fire' PBR (f) ♀H6	CBcs EPfP LRHS MAsh MGos NHol NLar NOra SCoo SLim SRms SWvt WFar
cunninghamii	see *P. laetus*
dacrydioides	see *Dacrycarpus dacrydioides*
elongatus	CTrC
- 'Blue Chip'	CBcs
'Flame' (m)	NLar NOra SLim
'Guardsman'	LRHS SLim
hallii	see *P. laetus*
henkelii	CBcs CTrC
'Jill' (f)	CBcs
laetus 'Roro' (m)	CBcs

lawrencei	CBcs
- 'Blue Gem' (f)	CJun LRHS MAsh MMuc NOra SCoo SLim WFar
- 'Red Tip'	LRHS NOra SPad
macrophyllus	SArc WPGP
- 'Aureus'	CBcs
nivalis	CBcs CTrC NGKo SRms WThu
- 'Jack's Pass' (m)	LRHS
- 'Kilworth Cream' (m/v) ♀H6	CBcs LRHS NHol SLim SWvt WCot
- 'Livingstone' (f)	CBcs
- 'Otari' (m)	MAsh
- 'Ruapehu' (m)	MGil
'Red Embers' (f)	NOra SCoo SLim
§ ***salignus*** ♀H4	CBcs CExl EPfP IDee LRHS MGil SArc SLim WPGP WPav WThu
'Spring Sunshine' (f)	CBcs
totara	CBrP CTrC LEdu WPGP
- 'Albany Gold'	CTrC
- 'Aureus'	CBcs LRHS
- 'Pendulus'	LRHS MGil WFar
'Young Rusty' (f)	CBcs LRHS MAsh SLim WFar

Podophyllum (Berberidaceae)

aurantiocaule	CExl EBee GGGa SBrt
- subsp. ***aurantiocaule***	GEdr
§ ***delavayi***	CDTJ CExl WSHC
difforme	LEdu
- 'Hunan' **new**	WFar
emodi	see *Sinopodophyllum hexandrum* var. *emodi*
- var. ***chinense***	see *Sinopodophyllum hexandrum* var. *chinense*
hexandrum	see *Sinopodophyllum hexandrum*
- var. ***chinense***	see *Sinopodophyllum hexandrum* var. *chinense*
'Kaleidoscope' (v)	CAby CBcs CBct CMiW EBee ECtt ELan EMor EPot ESwi GBin IPot LEdu MAvo MBNS MHol MPnt NHpl NLar WCot WFar
peltatum	CAby CBct CBro CMiW CWCL EBee EMor EPfP EWld GBin GKev GPoy ILea LEdu MBel NLar NSti SPhx SPtp WCru WPGP WPnP
pleianthum ♀H4	CAby GEdr WCot WCru WPGP
- B&SWJ 282 from Taiwan	WCru
- var. ***album***	GEdr
- short	WCru
veitchii	see *P. delavayi*
versipelle	LEdu WCru
- 'Spotty Dotty'PBR (v) ♀H4	Widely available
- subsp. ***versipelle***	GKev

Podranea (Bignoniaceae)

§ ***ricasoliana*** ♀H1c	CBcs EShb SPoG WBor

Pogonatherum (Poaceae)

* ***distichum***	XBlo

Pogonia (Orchidaceae)

sp.	NDav

Pogostemon (Lamiaceae)

§ ***cablin***	EOHP GPoy
patchouly	see *P. cablin*

Polemonium ✿ (Polemoniaceae)

ambervicsii	see *P. pauciflorum* subsp. *hinckleyi*
'Apricot Beauty'	see *P. carneum* 'Apricot Delight'
archibaldiae ♀H5	CBod NBir SRms WSHC
'Blue Pearl'	EBee EHyd ELan EPfP EWld GJos LRHS MAsh MBel MHol NBro NGdn NLar SPer WFar WSpi
§ ***boreale***	NPol SWvt
- 'Heavenly Habit'	EHyd GJos
brandegeei misapplied	see *P. pauciflorum*
§ ***brandegeei*** Greene	GKev
- subsp. ***mellitum***	see *P. brandegeei* Greene
§ ***caeruleum***	CBod CTri ECha EHyd ELan ENfk EPfP GKev GMaP GPoy LCro LOPS LRHS MBow MHer MMuc MNHC NBro NGrd NLar NPol NRHS SPer SPlb SPoG SRms SWvt WCAu WSpi
- subsp. ***amygdalinum***	see *P. occidentale*
- - 'Album'	see *P. caeruleum* subsp. *caeruleum* f. *album*
- 'Bambino Blue'	CBod SRms SWvt
- BRISE D'ANJOU ('Blanjou'PBR) (v)	CMac CMea CRos ECtt EHyd ELan EMor EPfP EShb EWes LRHS MAsh MHol MPri NBir NGdn NRHS SCob SPer SPoG SWvt
- subsp. ***caeruleum***	GKev
§ - - f. ***album***	CBre CCBP CRos CWCL EBee ECha EHyd ELan EPfP GKev GQue LRHS MBNS MBel MHer MRav NBro NRHS SCob SGbt SPer SPoG SRms WBrk WCAu WSpi
- - - 'White Pearl'	GWyn
- 'Days of Thunder'	EBee
I - f. ***dissectum***	NPol
- 'Filigree Skies'	MWat NGdn
§ - subsp. ***himalayanum*** CC 7325	EWld
- 'Humile'	see *P.* 'Northern Lights'
- 'Snow and Sapphires' (v)	CWGN ECtt MPnt NPer SWvt
- 'Southern Skies'	NPol
- subsp. ***vulgare***	NPol
- white-flowered	GJos MMuc
carneum	CElw CTri ECha EHyd EWld LRHS NPol
§ - 'Apricot Delight'	EMor GJos GMaP MNHC MNrw NGdn NPol NQui SBut SGbt SIvy SRms WSpi
cashmerianum	see *P. caeruleum* subsp. *himalayanum*
'Churchills'	CBre NPol WSHC
'Dawn Flight'	NPol
'Eastbury Purple'	CElw NPol
'Elworthy Amethyst'	CElw EBee NPol
flavum	see *P. foliosissimum* var. *flavum*
foliosissimum misapplied	see *P. archibaldiae*
foliosissimum A. Gray	NPol
- var. ***albiflorum***	see *P. foliosissimum* var. *alpinum*
§ - var. ***alpinum***	NPol
- 'Cottage Cream'	LEdu NPol WCot WFar
§ - var. ***flavum***	NPol
- var. ***foliosissimum***	NPol WSpi
- 'Scottish Garden'	NPol
- 'White Spirit'	NPol
'Glebe Cottage Lilac'	CDor EBee NBir NPol
'Glebe Cottage Violet'	NPol
'Hannah Billcliffe'	ECtt MBrN NChi NPol SWvt WFar
'Heaven Scent'PBR	CRos EBee ECtt EHyd EMor LRHS LSou MPri NDov NLar NRHS WCAu WCav WGrn
§ 'Hopleys'	EBee MNrw NChi
× ***jacobaea***	EPPr EWes WCot
'Katie Daley'	see *P.* 'Hopleys'
'Lambrook Mauve'	Widely available
'Mary Mottram'	NPol

	mellitum	see *P. brandegeei* Greene
	'North Tyne'	NChi NPol NWad
§	'Northern Lights' ♀H7	Widely available
	'Norwell Mauve'	MNrw NPol WBrk WFar
§	***occidentale***	NPol
§	***pauciflorum***	ECtt ELan NBir WHil
§	- subsp. ***hinckleyi***	GKev NPol NQui
§	- subsp. ***pauciflorum***	NPol
	- silver-leaved	see *P. pauciflorum* subsp. *pauciflorum*
	- 'Sulphur Trumpets'	SWvt
	- subsp. ***typicum***	see *P. pauciflorum* subsp. *pauciflorum*
	'Pink Beauty'	EBee ECtt EHyd ELan EPfP NGdn NPol
	pulchellum Salisb.	see *P. reptans*
	pulchellum Turcz.	see *P. caeruleum*
	pulcherrimum misapplied	see *P. boreale*
	- 'Tricolor'	see *P. boreale*
§	***reptans***	GPoy MHer NBro NPol SRms
	- 'Album'	see *P. reptans* 'Virginia White'
	- 'Blue Ice'	NPol
	- 'Jacob's Gold' (v)	EBee EHyd ELan EMor EPfP NPol NRHS SCob
*	- 'Sky Blue'	NBro
	- 'Stairway to Heaven'PBR (v)	Widely available
	- 'Touch of Class'PBR (v)	CWGN EMor EWTr MBel MHol MPri NLar SCob SPoG
§	- 'Virginia White'	CBre EWes MAvo NChi NPol NQui
	- 'White Pearl'	MHol
	'Ribby'	NPol
	× ***richardsonii*** misapplied	see *P.* 'Northern Lights'
	richardsonii Graham	see *P. boreale*
	'Sapphire'	CBre EHyd LRHS
	'Sonia's Bluebell'	CWCL ECtt EPPr EWes EWld LSou MNrw MPie NDov NPol NSti SGro WFar
	'Sunnyside Storm'	NPol
	'Theddingworth'	NPol
	viscosum	NPol SPlb
	- f. ***leucanthum***	NPol
	yezoense	NBre NPol WFar
	- var. ***hidakanum***	GAbr NPol
	- - BRESSINGHAM PURPLE ('Polbress')	Widely available
	- - 'Halfway to Paradise'	SCob WGrn
	- - 'Purple Rain'	CCBP CDor CMac CSpe EAJP EHyd ELan ELon EMor EPfP EWes GMaP GWyn LEdu LRHS LSRN LSun MHol MRav MWat NLar NPol NRHS SCob SRkn SRms WCot WFar WKif
	- 'Kaleidoscope' (v) **new**	NPol WNPC

Polianthes (*Asparagaceae*)

elongata	WCot
tuberosa	CBcs CCCN GKev LCro LOPS XLum
- 'Cinderella'	GKev
- 'Golden Harvest'	GKev
- 'Pink Sapphire'	GKev WCot
- 'Sensation'	EShb GKev SDeJ
- 'Super Gold'	SDeJ
- 'The Pearl' (d)	EShb GKev LCro LOPS SDeJ XLum
- 'Yellow Baby'	GKev WCot

Poliomintha (*Lamiaceae*)

bustamanta	NBir SPhx WSHC

Poliothyrsis (*Salicaceae*)

sinensis	CBcs CMCN EBtc EPfP

Pollia (*Commelinaceae*)

japonica	ESwi IMou WCot

Polygala (*Polygalaceae*)

	'Africana'PBR	CPbh
	africana 'Nana'	LRHS
	arillata	LEdu
	calcarea	WAbe
	- Bulley's form	EPot WFar
	- 'Lillet' ♀H7	EHyd EPot GEdr LRHS NRHS WAbe
	chamaebuxus	see *Polygaloides chamaebuxus*
§	× ***dalmaisiana*** ♀H1c	CAbb CCCN CSde CSpe CTsd ECre ELan LRHS SEND SIvy WCFE
	'Dolomite'	GAbr GEdr
	myrtifolia ♀H1c	CCCN CPbh CTrC ILea LRHS MGos SAdn SPlb WSMil
	- BIBI PINK ('Polylap')	CTrC
	- 'Grandiflora'	see *P.* × *dalmaisiana*
	'Purple Passion'	CCCN LRHS SRms WFar
	virgata	CCCN ELan SIvy

Polygaloides (*Polygalaceae*)

§	***chamaebuxus*** ♀H7	GKev MAsh MGos NLar NSla NWad SRms WIce WThu
I	- ***alba***	NLar WAbe
§	- 'Grandiflora' ♀H7	CBcs EPfP EPot GAbr GEdr GKev MAsh MGos NBir NHpl NSla SPlb SPoG WAbe WFar WIce
	- 'Kamniski'	EPot
	- 'Loibl'	EPot WFar
	- 'Purpurea'	see *P. chamaebuxus* 'Grandiflora'
	- 'Rhodoptera'	see *P. chamaebuxus* 'Grandiflora'

Polygonatum ✿ (*Asparagaceae*)

	SBQE 310	LEdu MAvo
	acuminatifolium 'Ogon'	EBee
	altelobatum B&SWJ 1886	WCru
	- B&SWJ 286	WCru
	annamense B&SWJ 9752	WCru
	arisanense B&SWJ 271	WCru
	- B&SWJ 3839	WCru
§	***biflorum***	CPou CRos CWCL EBee ECtt EHyd ELan EMor EPfP GBin GKev GMaP ILea LRHS MAvo NLar NRHS NWad SPoG SWvt WCru WFar WPnP WSMil XLum
	- dwarf	EHyd LRHS
	brevistylum B&SWJ 2421	WCru
	canaliculatum	see *P. biflorum*
	cathcartii B&SWJ 2429	WCru
	- yellow-flowered B&SWJ 2412	WCru
	cirrhifolium	EBee EMor EPot GAbr GEdr GKev LEdu MAvo MNrw NHpl NWad SBut WCru WPGP
	- ARGS 320	EPPr
	- from China	WCru
	- red-flowered	NLar
	commutatum	see *P. biflorum*
	costatum B&SWJ 6599	WCru
	cryptanthum	WCru
	curvistylum	CAby CAvo CBct EPPr ESwi EWld GEdr GKev ILea IMou LEdu MAvo NBPC NLar NRya WCru WFar WSHC
	cyrtonema misapplied	see *Disporopsis pernyi*
	cyrtonema Hua	WCru

	- B&SWJ 271	LEdu MAvo
*	***desoulavyi*** var. ***yezoense*** B&SWJ 764	WCru
	falcatum misapplied	see *P. humile*
	falcatum A. Gray	EBee NHpl NRya
	- B&SWJ 1077	CBct WCru
	- B&SWJ 5054	WCru
	- NJM 11.012 **new**	WPGP
	- 'Shikoku Silver'	CBct LEdu SMHy WCru
	- 'Silver Mist'	LEdu
	- 'Variegatum'	see *P. odoratum* var. *pluriflorum* 'Variegatum'
	'Falcon'	see *P. humile*
	filipes	EBee EPPr LEdu WCru
	fuscum	WCru
	geminiflorum	CBct LEdu LPla WCru WFar
	giganteum	see *P. biflorum*
	glaberrimum	WCot
	'Golden Gift'	CBct LPla
§	***graminifolium***	CAby CBct CPBP GKev IMou WCru WThu
§	***hirtum***	CAby CBct EHyd EMor EPPr LEdu LRHS WCru
	- W&B BG C-2 **new**	WCot
	- 'Robustum'	WCru
	hookeri	CAby CBct CExl CPBP EBee EHyd EPPr EPot EWld GBin GEdr GKev GQue LEdu LRHS NBid NHpl NLar NRya NSla NWad SPhx SPtp WCru WFar
§	***humile***	CBct CWCL EBee ELan EMor EPPr EPfP EPot EWTr GKev ILea ITim LEdu MAvo NGdn NLar SPtp SWvt WCav WCru WHil WPGP WTor XLum
	- 'Shiro-shima-fu' (v) **new**	WFar
I	- 'Variegatum' (v)	CMac WCot
§	× ***hybridum*** ♀H7	Widely available
	- 'Bere'	LEdu WPGP
	- 'Betberg'	CSpe ECha ELon EPPr IMou IPot LEdu LPla MAvo MBriF NBir WCot WFar
	- 'Flore Pleno' (d)	WHer
	- 'Nanum'	CBct MRav WCot
	- 'Purple Katie'	MAvo MMrt
§	- 'Striatum' (v)	Widely available
	- 'Variegatum'	see *P.* × *hybridum* 'Striatum'
	- 'Wakehurst'	LEdu
	- 'Weihenstephan'	EPPr GKev ILea LEdu MAvo
	- 'Welsh Gold' (v)	CAvo EBee ESwi
	inflatum	WCru
	- B&SWJ 922	WCru
	involucratum	WCru
	- B&SWJ 4285	WCru
	japonicum	see *P. odoratum*
	kingianum	IMou LEdu WMal
	- red-flowered **new**	GKev
	- yellow-flowered B&SWJ 6545	WCru
	- - B&SWJ 6562	WCru
	'Langthorn's Variegated' (v)	ELan
	lasianthum	SMHy WCru
	- B&SWJ 671	WCru
	latifolium	see *P. hirtum*
	maximowiczii	EPPr LEdu LPla WCru WPGP
	mengtzense f. ***mengtzense*** HWJ 588	WCru
	- - HWJ 861	LEdu WCru
	- f. ***tonkinense*** B&SWJ 8246	LEdu WCru

	- - HWJ 551	WCru
	- - HWJ 567	WCru
	- - HWJ 573	CBct EPot WCru
	- - HWJ 861	LEdu
	'Multifide'	EBee GKev
	multiflorum misapplied	see *P.* × *hybridum*
	multiflorum L.	CAby CAgr CBcs CDoC CHab CMac CSBt CWCL ECha EMor EPfP GAbr GKev LSou LSun MHol MRav NGdn NLar SEdd SPlb SRms SWvt WCAu WCru WFar WHer XLum
	- CC 4572	WCot
	- 'Flore Pleno' (d)	WFar
	- ***giganteum*** hort.	see *P. biflorum*
	- 'Ramosissima'	LEdu MAvo SMHy WCru
	- var. ***ramosum***	LEdu
*	***nanum*** 'Variegatum' (v)	CBcs
	nodosum	WCru
§	***odoratum***	CAvo CBct CBro CTsd EBee EPfP GKev GMaP LEdu MBriF MPnt NBid NLar NRya WCru
	- RBG 93-101	EBee
	- 'Byakko' (v)	GEdr GKev
	- 'Dai Koga' (v) **new**	WFar
	- 'Dusky Bere'	WPGP
§	- dwarf	EBee LEdu
	- 'Flatmate'	ESwi LEdu MAvo WCru
	- 'Flore Pleno' (d)	CAby CAvo GKev LEdu MBriF MHer WCot WHoo
	- 'Georgia'	WPGP
	- 'Goldilocks' (v) **new**	WCot
	- 'Grace Barker'	see *P.* × *hybridum* 'Striatum'
	- Kew form	EPot
	- 'Koryu'	GEdr
	- var. ***odoratum***	GKev
§	- var. ***pluriflorum*** 'Variegatum' (v)	Widely available
	- 'Pruhonice'	IMou
	- 'Red Stem'	CMea LEdu MAvo WCru
	- 'Silver Wings' (v)	CBct ECha IPot LEdu NBPC NBir NLar WFar WSHC
	- var. ***thunbergii***	IMou WCru
	- 'Triglav'	MAvo
	- 'Ussuriland'	EBee EPPr LEdu LPla MAvo
	- 'Ussuriland Roundleaf'	EBee ESwi LEdu MAvo
	officinale	see *P. odoratum*
	oppositifolium B&SWJ 2537	WCru
§	***orientale***	CAvo GKev
	- S&F 364	WCot
	pluriflorum	see *P. graminifolium*
	polyanthemum	see *P. orientale*
	prattii	EBee EPot GKev ILea WCru
	- CLD 325	LEdu
	pubescens	CBct LEdu WCru WThu
	pumilum	see *P. odoratum* dwarf
	punctatum ambig.	LEdu NBid WPGP
	punctatum Royle ex Kunth	WCot
	- B&SWJ 2395	CBct WCru
	racemosum	CBct IMou
	roseum	EMor EPPr GKev MAvo SMHy WCru
	sewerzowii	EMor EPPr
	sibiricum	CAvo CBct ESwi GKev WCru WFar
	- DJHC 600	EBee LEdu MAvo WPGP
	singalilense	WCru
	stenanthum B&SWJ 11425	WCru
	- B&SWJ 5727	LEdu WCru
	stenophyllum	IMou WCru

stewartianum	EBee EPPr ILea MAvo NRya
tessellatum PAB 8336	LEdu
verticillatum	CBct CBro EBee ECha EHyd EPPr EPfP ESwi GEdr GKev LEdu LRHS MBriF MNrw MRav SMad WCru WFar WPGP WSMil WWtn
- B&SWJ 2147	WCru
- CLD 1308	EPPr
- PAB 2455	LEdu
- 'Giant One'	IMou XEll
- 'Himalayan Giant'	EMor EPPr GKev MAvo WPnP
- 'Krynica'	LEdu WPGP
* - 'Roseum'	CAvo LRHS
- 'Rubrum'	CAby CBct CSpe EHyd EMor EPPr EThi GEdr ILea LEdu LRHS MAvo MBel MHid NBPC NBid NChi NLar WCot WCru WFar WHoo
- 'Serbian Dwarf'	CBct ESwi GKev LEdu WPGP
aff. ***verticillatum***	CSpe
yunnanense	CBct EBee ESwi LEdu WPGP
zanlanscianense	EBee EWld IMou LEdu MAvo WCru

Polygonum (*Polygonaceae*)

affine	see *Persicaria affinis*
amplexicaule	see *Persicaria amplexicaulis*
aubertii	see *Fallopia baldschuanica*
baldschuanicum	see *Fallopia baldschuanica*
bistorta	see *Persicaria bistorta*
capitatum	see *Persicaria capitata*
compactum	see *Fallopia japonica* var. *compacta*
equisetiforme misapplied	see *P. scoparium*
filiforme	see *Persicaria virginiana*
forrestii	EBee GKev
molle	see *Persicaria mollis*
multiflorum	see *Fallopia multiflora*
odoratum	see *Persicaria odorata*
polystachyum	see *Persicaria wallichii*
runciforme	see *Persicaria runcinata*
§ ***scoparium***	EPPr ESwi EWes SDys SVen WFar WOld XLum
tinctorium	see *Persicaria tinctoria*
vacciniifolium	see *Persicaria vacciniifolia*
weyrichii	see *Persicaria weyrichii*

Polylepis (*Rosaceae*)

australis	CBcs EBee IDee IMou SMad
- tall	WPGP

Polymnia (*Asteraceae*)

sonchifolia 'Red China'	WPGP

Polypodiodes (*Polypodiaceae*)

formosana	WCot

Polypodium ✿ (*Polypodiaceae*)

aureum	see *Phlebodium aureum*
australe	see *P. cambricum*
- Pat's form	EBee
azoricum new	WCot
californicum	EBee LEdu
§ ***cambricum***	CLAP EFer WCot WFib
- GG 20131	SMHy
- 'Barrowii'	CLAP WAbe WFib WGwG
- 'Bob's Choice'	WCot
I - 'Cambricum' ♀H7	WAbe
- 'Conwy'	EBee WFib
- 'Cristatum'	EBee WCot WFib
- (Cristatum Group) 'Grandiceps Fox' ♀H7	MRav WFib
- 'Hornet'	WFib
- 'Macrostachyon'	NBid WFib
- 'Oakleyae'	EBee EWld SMHy WCot
- 'Omnilacerum Oxford'	EBee
- 'Prestonii'	CLAP WCot WFib
- Pulcherrimum Group	SDys WAbe
- - bifid	EBee
- - 'Pulcherrimum Addison'	EBee LEdu WCot WFib WPGP
- - 'Pulchritudine'	LLWG WCot
- 'Richard Kayse' ♀H7	CLAP EShb EWes SMHy WAbe WCot WFib WPGP
- Semilacerum Group	EFer
- - 'Carew Lane'	WFib
- - 'Falcatum O'Kelly'	WCot
- - 'Robustum'	EBee WFib
- 'Whilharris' ♀H7	SMHy WAbe WCot
I × ***coughlinii*** bifid	WFib
formosanum	GBin SPlb
glycyrrhiza	EMor GPoy SMHy WFib
- bifid	see *P.* × *coughlinii* bifid
- 'Lawrence Crocker'	WCot
- 'Longicaudatum' ♀H7	EFer EShb WBrk WCot WFib
- 'Malahatense'	CLAP
- 'Malahatense' (sterile)	EBee WCot WPGP
glycyrrhiza × ***scouleri***	EBee
guttatum	SPlb
interjectum	EFer EMor EShb MRav WCot
- 'Glomeratum Mullins'	WFib
macaronesicum	WCot
× ***mantoniae***	CLAP WFib
- 'Bifidograndiceps'	NBid WFib
- 'Cornubiense' ♀H7	CLAP EShb EWld LEdu MHost NBid NBir SMHy
pseudoaureum 'Virginia Blue'	EHyd LRHS NRHS
scouleri	CBdn CLAP EBee EFer EHyd EShb ISha LEdu LRHS MAsh MRav NBro NRHS WCot WPGP
vulgare	Widely available
- 'Bifidocristatum'	CAby CBdn CLAP CWCL ELon EMor EPfP GBin GEdr ISha LEdu LLWG MAsh MGos MRav NLar SEND WBrk
- 'Bifidomulticeps'	WCot
* - 'Congestum Cristatum'	SRms
- 'Cornubiense Grandiceps'	SRms
* - 'Cornubiense Multifidum'	WCot
- 'Elegantissimum'	NBid WFib
- 'Parsley'	WCot
- 'Ramosum Hillman'	WCot
- 'Trichomanoides Backhouse'	CLAP WAbe WFib
'Whitley Giant'	EBee ECtt EMor EShb ESwi GBin GEdr GQue ISha ITim LEdu LLWG LPla LSun MHol MMuc MPie NBid NCou SEND SEdd SMad WCot WPnP

Polypompholyx see *Utricularia*

Polyspora (*Theaceae*)

§ ***axillaris***	CCCN CTsd EBee LRHS
longicarpa B&SWJ 11704	WCru
- WWJ 11604	WCru
- WWJ 11894	WCru
speciosa B&SWJ 11708 from Vietnam	WCru
- B&SWJ 11750	WCru
- WWJ 11934	WCru

Polystichum ✿ (*Dryopteridaceae*)

	acrostichoides	CDTJ CLAP EBee EHyd EMor IBal LEdu LRHS NBro NLar NRHS WCot WPGP XLum
	aculeatum ♀H7	CLAP CRos ECha EFer EHyd ELan EMor EShb GMaP IBal LCro LEdu LRHS MAsh MGos MMuc NBid NLar NRHS SCob SPoG SRms SWvt WBrk WFib XLum
I	- Densum Group	EFer
	- 'Portia'	WFib
	andersonii	CLAP EMor NBro WCot
	biaristatum	WPGP
	bissectum	CExl
	braunii	CBcs CBdn CDoC CDor CLAP CMac CRos CWCL EHyd EMor EPfP GMaP IBal LRHS MAsh NBid NBro NLar NRHS SPoG WFib WPnP XLum
	caryotideum	see *Cyrtomium caryotideum*
	× ***dycei*** ♀H5	CLAP EBee EHyd ISha LEdu LRHS MAsh NRHS WCot WPGP
	falcatum	see *Cyrtomium falcatum*
	falcinellum	EBee
	fortunei	see *Cyrtomium fortunei*
	imbricans	CLAP
	interjectum	MRav
	luctuosum	ISha
	makinoi	CBdn CCCN CLAP CRos EHyd EMor IBal ISha LLWG LRHS MAsh NBid NBro NRHS SPlb WCot WFib
	mayebarae	CBdn CLAP EBee ISha
	munitum ♀H7	Widely available
	neolobatum	CBdn CLAP EBee WCot WFib WPGP
	- BWJ 8182	WCru
	polyblepharum ♀H7	Widely available
	- 'Jade'	EBee LRHS
	proliferum misapplied	see *P. setiferum* Acutilobum Group
	proliferum (R. Br.) C. Presl	CLAP LBuc WAbe WFib WPGP
*	- ***plumosum***	SWvt
	rigens	CAby CBdn CBod CLAP CRos CWCL EFer EHyd ELon EMor EPau IBal ISha LEdu LRHS NBro NLar NRHS SRms WFib
	setiferum ♀H7	Widely available
§	- Acutilobum Group	CRos ECha EHyd EMor GMaP IBal LLWG LRHS NRHS SCob SDix SPad SPer SRms WBor WPGP XLum
	- Congestum Group	CDor CLAP ELon EMor EWTr NBro NHol NLar SPer SRms WBrk WFib
	- - 'Congestum'	CWCL EHyd ELan EPfP EPot IBal ISha LEdu LRHS MAsh MRav NBir NGdn NHol NRHS SPad SPoG XLum
	- 'Cristatopinnulum'	CLAP WPGP
	- Cristatum Group	CLAP SRms
	- - 'Multifidum Polydactylum'	LEdu
	- (Decompositum Group) 'Proliferum'	CWCL
	- Divisilobum Group ♀H7	CLAP EBee EFer ELan MCot MGos SRms WAbe WFar WFib WHoo WPGP
	- - 'Caernarfon'	EBee
	- - 'Dahlem'	CRos EBee ECha ECtt EFer EHyd ELan ELon EMor EPfP GMaP IBal LRHS LSRN NBid NLar NRHS SPer WFib XLum
	- - 'Divisilobum Densum' ♀H7	EPfP MRav NBir
	- - 'Divisilobum Grandiceps'	CLAP
	- - 'Divisilobum Iveryanum' ♀H7	CLAP EFer SRms WFib
	- - 'Divisilobum Laxum'	EBee
§	- - 'Divisilobum Wollaston'	CDTJ CLAP CRos CWCL ECtt EHyd EMor GBin IBal ISha LEdu LRHS MGos MRav NBid NLar NRHS SCob WCot
	- - 'Herrenhausen'	Widely available
	- - 'Proliferum'	NLar
	- Foliosum Group	EFer
	- 'Gracile'	MRav NBir
§	- 'Gracillimum'	CLAP
	- 'Grandiceps'	EFer
	- GREEN LACE	see *P. setiferum* 'Gracillimum'
	- 'Hamlet'	WFib
	- 'Helena'	WFib
	- 'Hirondelle'	SRms
	- Lineare Group	WFib
	- Multilobum Group	SRms WFib
	- 'Othello'	WFib
	- Perserratum Group	NBid WFib
	- 'Plumo-Densum'	see *P. setiferum* Plumosomultilobum Group
	- 'Plumosodensum'	see *P. setiferum* Plumosomultilobum Group
	- Plumosodivisilobum Group	EBee ECha MPnt NBid NBro SMHy WAbe WFib WRHF
	- - 'Baldwinii'	WFib
	- - 'Bland'	WFib
§	- Plumosomultilobum Group	CDor CWCL EBee EMor EPfP GQue IBal ISha LCro LOPS LPla MCot MGos NBir NLar SMad WCot WFib WHoo WPnP
I	- - 'Plumosomultilobum Densum'	CAby CLAP CRos ECtt EHyd IBal LLWG LRHS LSun MBel MSCN NRHS SEdd SMad WBrk WCot WFar
	- Plumosum Group	CMac CSpe EFer EHyd ELon EMor EPfP LLWG LRHS NRHS SArc
	- - dwarf	CSBt
*	- ***plumosum grande*** 'Moly'	SRms
	- Proliferum Group	see *P. setiferum* Acutilobum Group
	- 'Proliferum Wollaston'	see *P. setiferum* (Divisilobum Group) 'Divisilobum Wollaston'
	- 'Pulcherrimum Bevis' ♀H7	CBdn CLAP EBee EFer EHyd ELon EShb ESwi ISha LEdu LRHS MMuc MPie NLar NRHS SArc SEND SWvt WFib WLov WPGP
	- (Pulcherrimum Group) 'Pulcherrimum'	ISha
	- (Rotundatum Group) 'Cristatum'	CLAP ISha
	- 'Smith's Cruciate'	MRav WFib
	- 'Wakeleyanum'	EFer SRms
	'Spiny Holly'	CLAP
	tsussimense ♀H6	Widely available
	- 'K Rex'	CRos EHyd NRHS
	wawranum new	LEdu WPGP
	xiphophyllum	CBdn CLAP WPGP

Polytaenia (*Apiaceae*)

nuttallii new	SPhx

Pomaderris (*Rhamnaceae*)

apetala	CExl
elliptica	CExl

pomegranate see *Punica granatum*

Poncirus see *Citrus*

Ponerorchis see *Hemipilia*

Pontederia (*Pontederiaceae*)

cordata 🏆H5	CBen CWat EPfP EWat LCro LOPS MWts NPer SPlb WMAq WPnP WWtn XLum
- f. ***albiflora***	CWat EPfP EWat LLWG XLum
§ - var. ***lancifolia***	CBen CWat EWat LLWG MNrw MWts NPer WWtn
- pink-flowered	LLWG
- 'Sunsplash' (v)	LLWG
dilatata	see *Monochoria hastata*
lanceolata	see *P. cordata* var. *lancifolia*

Populus ✿ (*Salicaceae*)

× ***acuminata***	WMou
alba	CBcs CCVT CLnd CTho CTri ECrN EPfP LBuc MMuc SCob SEWo SGol SPer WMou WTSh
- 'Bolleana'	see *P. alba* 'Pyramidalis'
§ - 'Pyramidalis'	WMou
§ - 'Raket'	CCVT CTho ECrN ELan SPer
- 'Richardii'	EBtc SDix WCot WMou
- ROCKET	see *P. alba* 'Raket'
§ 'Balsam Spire' (f)	CTho WMou
§ ***balsamifera***	CCVT CLnd CSBt CTri GAbr SPer WCot
- 'Vita Sackville West'	MBlu
× ***canadensis***	ECrN
§ - 'Aurea' 🏆H7	ECrN SPer WMat WMou
- 'Aurea' × (× ***jackii*** 'Aurora')	CCCN ELan WFar
- 'Columbia'	WMou
- 'Eugenei' (m)	WMou
- 'Robusta' (m)	CCVT CLnd LBuc WMou
- 'Serotina' (m)	WMou
× ***canescens***	CLnd WMou
- 'Tower'	WMat
deltoides 'Fuego'	SGol
- 'Purple Tower'^PBR	CBcs CLnd EBee ELan EPfP IArd LRHS MBlu MMuc NOra SLim WCot WMat
× ***generosa*** 'Beaupré'	WMou
glauca	SPtp WPGP
- KR 3993	WPGP
- MF 20088	WPGP
× ***jackii*** 'Aurora' (f/v)	CBcs CCVT CLnd CMac CSBt CTsd MGos MMuc NOrn SPer WFar WMou
lasiocarpa	CBcs CExl CMCN CTho EPfP IArd IDee MBlu SGol SMad SPtp WMou WPGP
- (m/f)	WPGP
maximowiczii	SPtp WMou
nigra	CHab CTho CTri NOrn WSFF
- (f)	ECrN MMuc
- (m)	MMuc
- subsp. ***betulifolia***	CCVT CHab CLnd WMou
- - (f)	EBtc WMou
- - (m)	EBtc WMou
§ - 'Italica' (m) 🏆H7	CCVT CLnd CMac CSBt CTho CTri ECrN ELan LBuc MGos MMuc SCob SEWo SPer WMou
- 'Pyramidalis'	see *P. nigra* 'Italica'
purdomii	SPtp WPGP
'Serotina Aurea'	see *P.* × *canadensis* 'Aurea'
simonii 'Fastigiata'	WMou
szechuanica	WMou
§ - var. ***tibetica***	WMou WPGP
tacamahaca	see *P. balsamifera*
'Tacatricho 32'	see *P.* 'Balsam Spire'
tomentosa	WMou
tremula	CCVT CHab CLnd CMac CTho CTri ELan EWTr GAbr LBuc LMaj MMuc SCob SEWo SPer WMou WSFF WTSh
§ - 'Erecta' 🏆H7	CEnd CLnd MBlu MMuc NOrn WMat WMou
- 'Fastigiata'	see *P. tremula* 'Erecta'
- 'Pendula' (m)	CEnd CTho WMou
trichocarpa	SPer
- 'Fritzi Pauley' (f)	CTho WMou
violascens	see *P. szechuanica* var. *tibetica*
× ***wilsocarpa*** 'Beloni'	WPGP
wilsonii	WPGP
yunnanensis	WMou

Porophyllum (*Asteraceae*)

ruderale	WJek

Portulaca (*Portulacaceae*)

grandiflora	SVic
oleracea	ENfk SSim SVic
- var. ***aurea***	MNHC

Portulacaria (*Didiereaceae*)

afra	CDoC EShb
- 'Variegata' (v)	CDoC EShb SSim

Potamogeton (*Potamogetonaceae*)

crispus	CWat LLWG WMAq WSFF
lucens **new**	LLWG
malainus	LLWG
natans	LLWG WSFF XLum
perfoliatus	LLWG
schweinfurthii	XBlo

potato see AGM Vegetables Section

Potentilla ✿ (*Rosaceae*)

alba	CTri ECha ELan LPot MBel MRav NChi NWad SPer WSHC
alchemilloides	CMac
alpina (Willk.) Zimmeter	see *P. aurea*
alpina Dalla Torre **new**	WSHC
ambigua	see *P. cuneata*
ancistrifolia var. ***dickinsii***	GEdr
anserina	CAgr MHer NMir WHer XLum
- 'Golden Treasure' (v)	NSti
arbuscula misapplied	see *P. fruticosa* (Sulphurascens Group) 'Elizabeth'
- 'Beesii'	see *P. fruticosa* 'Beesii'
'Arc-en-ciel'	CKno CWCL ECtt EHyd ELan ELon EPfP EShb ILea LRHS LSRN MAvo MBNS MBel MHol MNrw MPnt MSCN NBPC NEoE NLar NQui NRHS SGbt SRkn SRms WBor WCAu WFar WGwG
argentea	SPlb WFar XLum
argyrophylla	see *P. atrosanguinea* var. *argyrophylla*
atrosanguinea	Widely available
§ - var. ***argyrophylla***	CDor CSam CWCL EBee EBou ECha ELan EPfP GKev GPSL LPot

		MMuc MRav NBPC NBir NBro NChi NLar SRms WOut XLum
	- - 'Golden Starlit'	CBod EDAr SVic
§	- - 'Scarlet Starlit'	CAby CBod CDor EBou EDAr EHyd ELon EPfP GJos LLWG LRHS NEoE SVic
	- var. ***leucochroa***	see *P. atrosanguinea* var. *argyrophylla*
*	- 'Sundermannii'	NWad SBrt
§	***aurea***	ECtt GBin
	- 'Aurantiaca'	NLar
§	- 'Goldklumpen'	ECtt
	- 'Plena' (d)	NRya
	'Blazeaway'	ECtt EHyd EPfP LRHS MArl MBel NEoE NGdn NRHS SRms
	calabra	ECha EWes SPhx
§	***cinerea***	CTri
§	***crantzii***	CMea EBou SRms
	- 'Nana'	see *P. crantzii* 'Pygmaea'
§	- 'Pygmaea'	ECtt
§	***cuneata*** ♀H7	GKev
	davurica 'Abbotswood'	see *P. fruticosa* 'Abbotswood'
	dombeyi	IMou
	'Emilie' (d)	CRos CWCL ECtt GWyn IPot MBNS MBel MNrw MTis NBPC NLar SWvt WBor WFar
§	***erecta***	GPoy MBow MNHC SRms
	eriocarpa	CPBP EPot NSla WAbe WIce
	'Esta Ann'	CBod CMac ECtt LRHS MArl MBel MNrw MSCN MTin NBPC NLar NRHS WCAu
	'Etna'	CWCL ECtt EHyd ELan LRHS MNrw MTin NBir NLar NRHS WFar WHrl
	'Everest'	see *P. fruticosa* 'Mount Everest'
	'Fireflame'	EBee NBPC NLar
	fissa	MNrw NBir NLar SPhx
	'Flambeau' (d)	CWCL ECtt EHyd EPfP EShb ILea LRHS MArl MRav NChi NGdn NLar NRHS NSti WCAu XEll
	'Flamboyant' (d)	EBee MSCN
	'Flamenco'	CRos CSam CTri ECtt EHyd IPot LRHS MArl MBNS MMrt MRav NBir NRHS WFar
	fragariiformis	see *P. megalantha*
	fruticosa	LBuc
§	- 'Abbotswood' ♀H7	Widely available
	- 'Annette'	NEoE NLar
	- var. ***arbuscula*** hort.	see *P. fruticosa* (Sulphurascens Group) 'Elizabeth'
	- 'Argentea Nana'	see *P. fruticosa* 'Beesii'
§	- 'Beesii'	CRos EHyd EPfP LRHS MAsh NRHS
	- BELLA SOL ('Hanchdon') **new**	SPad
	- BELLISSIMA ('Hachliss'^{PBR}) **new**	CBod
	- 'Bewerley Surprise'	WFar
	- 'Bo-Peep'	CEnd EBee EHyd LRHS LSRN WFar
	- 'Chelsea Star' ♀H7	CDoC CMac CRos EHyd EPfP LRHS LSRN MAsh NRHS SPoG
	- 'Clotted Cream'	SGbt
	- var. ***dahurica*** 'Hersii'	see *P. fruticosa* 'Snowflake'
	- 'Dakota Sunrise'	WFar
	- DANNY BOY ('Lissdan'^{PBR})	CRos EBee EHyd EMil LCro LOPS LRHS MAsh NEoE NRHS SCob SLon SPad SPoG
	- 'Daphne'	NWad
	- 'Dart's Golddigger'	CTri
	- 'Daydawn'	CBcs CBrac CMac CRos CTri EHyd ELan EPfP LRHS MAsh MGil MMuc MRav MSwo NBir NLar NRHS NWad SCob SGol SLim SPer SRms SWvt WFar
	- 'Farreri'	see *P. fruticosa* 'Gold Drop'
	- 'Friedrichsenii'	CBrac
	- 'Glenroy Pinkie'	MRav
§	- 'Gold Drop'	CMac NHol
	- 'Goldfinger'	CAgr CBod CBrac CChe CDoC CRos CSBt EHyd EPfP LRHS MAsh MGos MMuc MRav MSwo NRHS SCob SCoo SLim SPer SPlb SPoG WFar XSen
	- GOLDKUGEL	see *P. fruticosa* 'Gold Drop'
	- 'Goldstar'	EHyd IArd LRHS MMuc MPri SCob SEND SLim SLon SNig SRms WFar
	- 'Goldteppich'	LBuc
	- 'Grace Darling'	EPfP EWes NBir SWvt
	- 'Groneland' ♀H7	CRos EHyd ELan EPfP LRHS MAsh NRHS SCoo SPoG
	- 'Hopleys Orange' ♀H7	CBrac CDoC CRos EHyd EPfP EWes LRHS MPri NHol NRHS SGbt SGol SNig SRms WFar
	- 'Jackman's Variety' ♀H7	CRos EHyd EPfP LRHS MAsh SRms
	- 'Katherine Dykes'	CRos CTri EBee EHyd EPfP GKin LRHS LSRN MAsh NRHS SCob SCoo SGbt SLim SPer SRms WAvo WFar
	- 'King Cup' ♀H7	CRos EHyd EPfP LRHS MAsh
§	- 'Klondike'	CBcs CBrac
	- 'Kobold'	CDoC NLar
	- 'Lemon and Lime'	see *P. fruticosa* 'Limelight'
§	- 'Limelight' ♀H7	CRos CSBt EBee EHyd EPfP GKin LRHS MAsh MRav MSwo NEoE NRHS NWad SRms WAvo WFar WLov
	- 'Lovely Pink'	see *P. fruticosa* 'Pink Beauty'
§	- 'Maanelys'	CBrac CSBt SPer
	- 'Macpenny's Cream'	CMac SRms
§	- 'Manchu'	CMac MRav SPer SRms WCFE
	- MANGO TANGO ('Uman'^{PBR})	CRos CSBt EHyd EPfP LRHS LSRN MAsh NEoE NLar NRHS SCob SGol SPoG WFar
§	- MARIAN RED ROBIN ('Marrob'^{PBR}) ♀H7	CDoC CRos EHyd ELan EPfP GKin LCro LOPS LRHS MAsh MPri MRav MSwo NRHS SCoo SLim SLon SNig SPer SRms SWvt WLov
	- 'McKay's White'	NLar
	- 'Medicine Wheel Mountain' ♀H7	CBod CRos EBee EHyd ELan EWes IArd LRHS MAsh MRav MTin NEoE NLar NRHS NWad SCoo SGol SLim SPer SPoG WFar
	- MOONLIGHT	see *P. fruticosa* 'Maanelys'
§	- 'Mount Everest'	CMac CTri MMuc SLon
	- 'Nana Argentea'	see *P. fruticosa* 'Beesii'
	- 'New Dawn'	CBcs GKin MAsh
	- 'Orangeade'	CRos EHyd EPfP LRHS MAsh NLar SCoo SPoG
*	- 'Peachy Proud'	NEoE
§	- 'Pink Beauty'^{PBR} ♀H7	CBar CDoC CRos CSBt EHyd ELan EPau EPfP GKin LCro LOPS LRHS LSRN MAsh MMuc MPri MRav NHol NRHS SCob SCoo SLim SPer SPoG SRkn SRms SWvt WFar
	- PINK PARADISE ('Kupinpa'^{PBR})	SCob
	- 'Pink Pearl'	WFar
	- 'Pink Queen'	NLar
	- 'Pink Whisper'	NEoE SRms
	- 'Pretty Polly'	CRos EHyd ELan EPfP LRHS MSwo NHol NLar NWad WFar
	- 'Primrose Beauty' ♀H7	CBod CDoC CMac CRos EBee EHyd ELan EPfP GWyn LCro

		LOPS LRHS LSRN MAsh MGil MMuc MRav MSwo NHol NRHS SCoo SEND SGbt SGol SLim SPer SPlb WFar
§	- PRINCESS ('Blink')	CBcs CDoC CRos EBee EHyd ELan EPfP LRHS MAsh MRav NRHS SCob SCoo SGol SLim SRms WFar
	- var. ***pumila***	WAbe
	- 'Red Ace'	Widely available
	- 'Red Lady'PBR	CRos EBee EHyd ELan EPfP LRHS MAsh NEoE NHol NRHS SPoG
	- RED ROBIN	see *P. fruticosa* MARIAN RED ROBIN
	- 'Red Surprise'	WFar
	- 'Royal Flush'	NWad
	- 'Snowbird'	NEoE SLim WFar
§	- 'Snowflake'	CBcs
	- 'Sommerflor' ♀H7	CRos EHyd EPfP LRHS MAsh NRHS
	- 'Sophie's Blush'	MGil MRav
§	- (Sulphurascens Group) 'Elizabeth'	CBcs CBod CMac CRos EPfP LRHS LSRN MGos MSwo NHol SCob SGbt SGol SLim SPer SRms SWvt WCFE WFar
	- - 'Longacre Variety'	CMac CTri IArd MSwo NLar
	- 'Sunset'	CBcs CBrac CMac GKin LSRN NBir SCoo SLim SPer SRms WFar
	- 'Tangerine'	CBcs CBod CBrac CDoC CMac CRos CTri EHyd EPfP GBin LRHS MAsh MGos MMuc MRav MSwo NBir NHol NRHS SCob SLim SPer SPlb SRms SWvt WFar
	- 'Tilford Cream'	CDoC CRos CSBt CTri EBee EHyd ELan EPfP GKin LRHS LSRN MRav MSwo NBir NHol NRHS SCob SGbt SGol SLim SNig SPer SRms WCFE WFar
	- 'Tom Conway'	CMac SRms
	- var. ***veitchii***	CSBt
	- 'Vilmoriniana'	CMac CRos CTri EHyd ELan EPfP LRHS MAsh MRav NLar SPer SPoG SWvt WKif WSpi
	- 'Whirligig'	CMac
	- 'White Lady'PBR	CBod NEoE
	- 'Yellow Bird' ♀H7	CRos EHyd LRHS MAsh
	'Gibson's Scarlet' ♀H7	Widely available
§	***glandulosa*** subsp. ***nevadensis***	CTri MAsh
	'Gloire de Nancy' (d)	EBee MRav NBir NChi NLar
	'Gold Clogs'	see *P. aurea* 'Goldklumpen'
	'Herzblut'	NLar
	hippiana	EBee
	× ***hopwoodiana***	CMea CSpe CWCL EBee ECha ECtt ELan EPPr GMaP ILea MAvo MBel MCot MNrw MRav NBir NChi NDov NLar SPer WCAu WFar
	× ***hybrida*** 'Jean Jabber'	EBee GLog MBow MRav NEoE NLar WFar
	hyparctica	GJos
	kurdica	XLum
	'Light My Fire'	EBee ECtt MAsh MNrw NBPC
	'Mandshurica'	see *P. fruticosa* 'Manchu'
§	***megalantha***	CBod CBro CRos EAJP EBou ECtt EDAr EHyd ELan EPfP EPri GQue LEdu LRHS MBNS MRav NBir NBro NRHS NSti SGbt SRms XLum
	- 'Gold Sovereign'	EBee LRHS WMal
	'Melton Fire'	EPfP GJos GKin GPSL MNrw NBPC NBir
	micrantha 'Purple Haze'	LEdu
	- 'Purple Heart'	WPGP
	'Monarch's Velvet'	see *P. thurberi* 'Monarch's Velvet'
	'Monsieur Rouillard' (d)	CElw CMac CRos CSam ECtt EHyd GPSL LRHS MArl MNrw MPie MRav NBPC NGdn NLar NRHS WHoo
	'Mont d'Or'	EBee MRav NLar
	nepalensis	CRos EHyd LRHS NBro NChi NRHS WMal XLum
	- 'Helen Jane'	CDor EWld GBin GQue LEdu NBir NHol NLar NWad WFar WHrl
§	- 'Miss Willmott'	Widely available
	- 'Ron McBeath'	CDor CKno CRos CWCL ECtt EHyd ELan EPfP EWld GAbr GBin ILea LRHS MAvo MRav NHol NLar NRHS NSti SRkn SRms SWvt WGwG WHoo
	- 'Roxana'	ELan EWTr GJos MRav NBro SBut
	- 'Shogran'	CRos EBou EHyd GJos LRHS NChi NHol NLar NRHS WRHF
§	***neumanniana***	CPBP MAsh NBir NPoe WCav
	- 'Goldrausch'	IMou XLum
§	- 'Nana'	EBou EPot MAsh NRya NWad SPlb SRms WFar WHoo WIce XLum
	nevadensis	see *P. glandulosa* subsp. *nevadensis*
	nitida	EPot MAsh WAbe
	- 'Alba'	EPot
	- 'Rubra'	CMea EDAr GEdr NBir WAbe
	palustris	CWat EBee EWat LLWG MWts NAts NLar XLum
	parvifolia 'Klondike'	see *P. fruticosa* 'Klondike'
	pedata	NChi XLum
	'Pink Panther'	see *P. fruticosa* PRINCESS
	aff. ***polyphylla***	GKev
	porphyrantha	GEdr GJos
	recta	CBod SRms XLum
	- 'Alba'	GMaP
	- 'Citrina'	see *P. recta* var. *sulphurea*
	- 'Macrantha'	see *P. recta* 'Warrenii'
§	- var. ***sulphurea***	CMea EAJP EPPr EWTr GAbr GWyn LSun MCot MNrw NBir NLar NSti NWad SPhx SRkn WBrk WCAu WHal WHoo WHrl WMal XLum
§	- 'Warrenii'	CSBt EHyd EPfP GMaP LRHS MRav NBir SHar SPer SRms WHal WHrl XLum
	'Roxanne' (d)	LRHS MHer
	rupestris	CMea ECha EPPr EWTr GJos LSun MHer NSti SBut WCAu WFar WHal
	× ***russelliana***	EHyd LRHS
	'Scarlet Starlet'	see *P. atrosanguinea* var. *argyrophylla* 'Scarlet Starlit'
	speciosa	EWes
	sterilis	WHer WSFF
*	***sundermanii***	WHrl
	tabernaemontani	see *P. neumanniana*
	thurberi	CRos LRHS NLar NRHS SPhx XLum
§	- 'Monarch's Velvet'	Widely available
	tommasiniana	see *P. cinerea*
	× ***tonguei*** ♀H5	Widely available
	tormentilla	see *P. erecta*
	tridentata	see *Sibbaldiopsis tridentata*
	'Twinkling Star'	CBod EBee LSou MHol NEoE
	verna misapplied	see *P. neumanniana*
	- 'Pygmaea'	see *P. neumanniana* 'Nana'
	'Versicolor Plena' (d)	NLar
	villosa	see *P. crantzii*
	'Vogue'	EBee
	'Volcan'	CAby CWCL EWes MAvo NChi WCAu WFar WHal WTor
	'White Queen'	GLog MRav SBut SHar SRms

	'William Rollisson' ♀H7	Widely available
	willmottiae	see *P. nepalensis* 'Miss Willmott'
	'Yellow Queen'	CMac CTri EHyd GKin GMaP LPot LRHS MNrw MRav NLar NRHS SPer SRms WCAu

Poterium see *Sanguisorba*

	sanguisorba	see *Sanguisorba minor*

Prangos (*Apiaceae*)

	ferulacea	WCot

Pratia (*Campanulaceae*)

§	***angulata***	MBel
§	- 'Treadwellii'	ECha ECtt ELan SPlb SRms WFar WHal
	montana	see *Lobelia montana*
§	***pedunculata***	CTri EBou ECha ECtt EDAr EPfP LLWG LSun MAsh NHpl SPlb SRms WFar WIce
I	- 'Alba'	CBod EWes NHpl SRms WFar WIce
	- 'County Park'	CExl CMea CSpe CTri EBou ECha ECtt EDAr ELan EPfP GWyn LLWG MAsh NHpl SPlb SPoG SRms WCav WFar WIce XLum
	- 'White Stars'	LLWG

Preslia see *Mentha*

Primula ✿ (*Primulaceae*)

	(Si)	MAsh
	acaulis	see *P. vulgaris*
	'Adrian Jones' (Au)	EPot
	'Alan Robb' (Pr/Prim/d)	ECtt NGdn
	'Alexina' (*allionii* hybrid) (Au)	NHar XBar
§	***allionii*** (Au)	GKev WAbe
	- 'Aire Waves'	see *P.* × *loiseleurii* 'Aire Waves'
	- 'Allen Charm' (Au)	ITim
	- 'Allen Moonbeam' (Au)	GAbr ITim NHar
	- 'Allen Queen' (Au)	XBar
	- 'Anna Griffith' (Au)	CPBP WAbe
	- 'Apple Blossom' (Au)	GKev NHpl
	- 'Archer' (Au)	ITim
	- 'Ares' (Au)	NHar
	- 'Aries Violet' (Au)	ITim NHar
	- 'Bill Martin' (Au)	EPot ITim
	- 'Blood Flake' (Au)	ITim
	- 'Blush' (Au)	CPBP
	- 'Broadwell No 4' (Au)	CPBP
	- 'Cherry' (Au)	CPBP WAbe
	- 'Chivalry' (Au)	CPBP WAbe
	- 'Circe's Flute' (Au)	NHar
	- 'Cissie' (Au)	CPBP ITim NHar
	- 'Crusader' (Au)	EPot
	- 'Crystal' (Au)	CPBP
	- 'Daniel Burrow' (Au)	CPBP
	- 'David Philbey' (Au)	CPBP
	- 'Eliza' (Au)	EPot
	- 'Elizabeth Burrow' (Au)	WAbe
	- 'Emily Jane' (Au)	EPot
	- 'Eureka' (Au)	CPBP EPot WAbe
	- 'Eveline Burrow' (Au)	WAbe
	- 'Fanfare' (Au)	MAsh NHar
I	- 'Forma' (Au)	XBar
	- 'Gilderdale Glow' (Au)	CPBP NHar
	- 'Hartside 6' (Au)	ITim
	- 'Hemswell' (Au)	NHpl
	- 'Henry Burrow' (Au)	WAbe
	- 'Herald' (Au)	ITim
	- 'Horwood' (Au)	ITim
	- 'Jenny' (Au)	GKev
	- 'John Burrow' (Au) **new**	EPot
	- 'Kate Evans' (Au)	CPBP
	- 'Lee Mayers' (Au) **new**	WFar
	- 'Lepus' (Au)	WAbe
	- 'Lucy' (Au)	NHar
	- 'Malcolm' (Au)	ITim
	- 'Marion' (Au)	XBar
	- 'Marjorie Wooster' (Au)	CPBP XBar
	- 'Mary Berry' (Au)	CPBP
	- 'Neon' (Au)	CPBP
	- 'Neptune's Wave' (Au)	NHar
	- 'New Dawn' (Au)	ITim
	- 'Peace' (Au)	NHar
	- 'Peggy Wilson' (Au)	EPot GKev WThu
	- 'Pennine Pink' (Au)	CPBP
	- 'Phoebe's Moon' (Au)	NHar
	- 'Pink Ice' (Au)	LRHS
	- 'Pinkie' (Au)	WAbe
	- 'Raymond Wooster' (Au)	GKev
	- 'Snowflake' (Au)	CPBP GKev WSHC
	- 'Steven Burrow'	CPBP
	- 'Timsbury Glow' (Au)	CPBP
	- 'Tranquillity' (Au)	CPBP ITim
	- 'Viscountess Byng' (Au)	CPBP
	- 'William Earle' (Au)	CPBP XBar
	allionii* × *auricula misapplied 'Old Red Dusty Miller' (Au)	WFar
	allionii × 'Lismore Jewel' (Au)	CPBP
	allionii × 'Lismore Treasure' (Au)	GKev ITim NHpl
	allionii* × *pubescens (Au)	NHpl
	allionii* × *pubescens 'Harlow Car' (Au)	WFar
	allionii × 'White Linda Pope' (Au)	NHpl
	alpicola (Si) ♀H6	CAby CTsd CWCL GAbr GKev GQue MMuc NBid NGdn NWad WTyc XBar
	- var. ***alba*** (Si)	CPla CTsd GAbr GKev NBid NChi
§	- var. ***alpicola*** (Si)	EBee GKev
	- hybrids (Si)	NHpl
	- 'Kevock Sky' (Si)	EBee GKev
	- var. ***luna***	see *P. alpicola* var. *alpicola*
	- var. ***violacea*** (Si)	EBee EWld GAbr GKev MNrw NBid NWad
	- - 'Royal Blue' (Si) **new**	GKev
	- - wine-red-flowered (Si)	GKev
	'Altaica'	see *P. elatior* subsp. *meyeri*
	altaica grandiflora	see *P. elatior* subsp. *meyeri*
	amoena	see *P. elatior* subsp. *meyeri*
	'Amy Smith' (Pr/Prim)	GAbr
	angustifolia (Pa)	GKev WAbe
	anisodora	see *P. wilsonii* var. *anisodora*
	× ***anisodoxa*** 'Kevock Surprise' (Pf)	CWCL EBee GKev
	'Annemijne' (Pr/Poly)	WCot
	apoclita (Mu)	GKev XBar
	× ***arctotis***	see *P.* × *pubescens*
	aurantiaca (Pf)	CPla EBee GKev NHpl XBar
	- 'Harperley Pink' (Pf)	GBin MPnt NHpl
	aurantiaca* × *pulverulenta (Pf) **new**	GRum

aureata (Pe)	NHar
auricula L. (Au) 🏆^{H5}	CRos EDAr EHyd EWld GKev LRHS MAsh NRHS NSla SPer SPlb SPoG
- subsp. ***bauhinii*** (Au)	CWCL GKev
auricula misapplied (Au)	EBou ECha EHyd LRHS MBow NRHS WCav
- A74 (Au)	MMuc SEND
I - '1-2-3' (Au)	EBee
- 'Abdor' (Au/St)	NDro
- 'Abundance' (Au/A)	NDro
- 'Achates' (Au/A)	WAln
- 'Admiral' (Au/A)	NDro WAln
- 'Adrian' (Au/A)	ITim NDro WHil XBar
- 'Adrienne' (Au/A)	GKev
- 'Adrienne Ruan' (Au/A)	NDro WAln
- 'After Glow' (Au/St)	NDro
- 'Aga Khan' (Au/A)	NDro WAln
- 'Airy Fairy' (Au/S)	NDro
- 'Alamo' (Au/A)	NDro
- 'Alan Ravenscroft' (Au/A)	WHil
- 'Albert Bailey' (Au/d)	GAbr ITim NDro WFar WHil XBar
- 'Alchemist' (Au/S)	NDro
- 'Aldgate' (Au/S)	NDro
- 'Alexandra Georgina' (Au/A)	WAln
- 'Alf' (Au/A)	NDro WHil
- 'Alfred Charles' (Au/A)	WAln
- 'Alice' (Au/d)	NDro
- 'Alice Haysom' (Au/S)	ELan GAbr ITim NDro WHil XBar
- 'Alicia' (Au/A)	GAbr NDro XBar
- 'Alien' (Au/S)	NDro
- 'Alison' (Au/S)	NDro
- 'Alison Jane' (Au/A)	NDro WHil XBar
- 'Alison Rose' (Au/B)	NDro
- 'Alison Telford' (Au/A)	WHil
- 'All the Way' (Au/St) **new**	NDro
- 'Allard' (Au/A)	WAln
- 'Alloway' (Au/d)	WAln
- 'Amber Light' (Au/S)	WAln
- 'Amicable' (Au/A)	NDro WHil XBar
- 'Amie Rosalind' (Au/B)	NDro
- 'Amore' (Au/St)	NDro
- 'Ancient Order' (Au/A)	WAln
- 'Ancient Society' (Au/A)	NDro WHil XBar
- 'Andrea Julie' (Au/A)	NDro WHil
- 'Andrew Hunter' (Au/A)	NDro XBar
- 'Andy Cole' (Au/A)	NDro WAln
- 'Angel Eyes' (Au/St)	NDro
- 'Angel Islington' (Au/S)	NDro
- 'Angela Gould' (Au/B)	NDro WHil XBar
- 'Angela Grace' (Au/d)	XBar
- 'Angostura' (Au/d)	EBee WHil
- 'Ann Brookes' (Au/d)	WAln
- 'Ann Taylor' (Au/A)	WAln
- 'Anna' (Au/B)	NDro
- 'Anne Hyatt' (Au/d)	NDro
- 'Annette' (Au/B)	NDro
- 'Ansells' (Au/S)	WAln
- 'Anwar Sadat' (Au/A)	NDro WHil
- 'Apple Blossom' (Au/B)	NDro WHil
- 'Applecross' (Au/A)	NDro NHpl WHil
- 'April Moon' (Au/S)	NDro WHil
- 'Arab Prince' (Au/A)	WAln
- 'Arab Queen' (Au/A)	WAln
- 'Arabian Night' (Au/A)	NDro WAln
- 'Arctic Fox' (Au/A)	WAln WHil XBar
- 'Argentine' (Au/S)	XBar
- 'Argus' (Au/A)	ITim LSun NDro NWad WHil XBar
- 'Arlene' (Au/A)	WAln
- 'Armorique' (Au/d)	XBar

- 'Arras' (Au/d) **new**	WHil
- 'Art Deco' (Au/B)	NDro WAln
- 'Arthur Delbridge' (Au/A)	NDro WHil XBar
- 'Artwork' (Au/S)	NDro
- 'Arundell' (Au/S/St)	EBee ITim NDro WFar WHil XBar
- 'Ascot Gavotte' (Au/S)	NDro
- 'Ashcliffe Gem' (Au/A)	NDro WAln
- Ashwood strain (Au) **new**	MAsh
- 'Astolat' (Au/S)	EBee NDro NHpl WHil XBar
- 'Athene' (Au/S)	ITim NDro
- 'Atlantic' (Au/S)	NDro
- 'Aubergine' (Au/B)	NDro
- 'Audacity' (Au/d)	NDro WAln
- 'Audrey' (Au/S)	NDro
- 'Aurora' (Au/A)	EDAr WAln
- 'Austin' (Au/A)	WAln
- 'Autumn Fire' (Au/A)	GAbr
- 'Autumn Glow' (Au/d)	NDro
- 'Autumn Jewels' (Au/d)	XBar
- 'Avon Citronella' (Au/d)	XBar
- 'Avonwick' (Au/B)	NDro
- 'Avril' (Au/A)	NDro WAln WHil XBar
- 'Avril Hunter' (Au/A)	ITim MHer NDro WHil XBar
- 'Aztec' (Au/d)	WAln
- 'Baby Blue' (Au)	NDro WHil
- 'Bacchante' (Au/d)	WAln
- 'Bacchus' (Au/A)	NDro WHil
- 'Baggage' (Au/St)	ITim NDro WHil
- 'Bailey Boy' (Au/B)	NDro
- 'Bakerloo Line' (Au/S)	NDro WHil
- 'Balbithan' (Au/B)	NDro
- 'Ballynahinch' (Au)	ITim
- 'Baltic Amber' (Au/d)	GAbr NDro WAln WHil XBar
- 'Bank Error' (Au/S)	NDro WAln
- 'Barbara Mason' (Au)	NDro WAln
- 'Barbarella' (Au/S)	NDro XBar
- 'Barber's Pole' (Au/St)	NDro
- Barnhaven Border hybrids (Au/B)	XBar
- Barnhaven doubles (Au/d)	GAbr XBar
- 'Barr Beacon' (Au/A)	ITim NDro
- 'Bartl' (Au/A)	EBee MAvo
- 'Basilio' (Au/S)	NDro
- 'Basuto' (Au/A)	ITim WHil XBar
- 'Beatrice' (Au/A)	CTri NDro NHpl WFar WHil XBar
- 'Beauty of Bath' (Au/S)	WAln
- 'Beckminster' (Au/A)	WAln
- 'Bedford Lad' (Au/A)	NDro
- 'Beechen Green' (Au/S)	ITim
- 'Beeches Variegated' (Au/A/v)	EBee WFar
- 'Beervelde' (Au/B) **new**	WHil
- 'Belgravia Gold' (Au/B)	NDro
- 'Bellamy Pride' (Au/B)	NDro
- 'Belle Zana' (Au/S)	NDro
- 'Bellini' (Au/d)	XBar
- 'Ben Wyves' (Au/S)	NDro
- 'Bendigo' (Au/S)	NDro WAln
- 'Benny Green' (Au/S)	NDro XBar
- 'Beppi' (Au/B)	NDro WHil
- 'Bessie' (Au/d)	XBar
- 'Best Wishes' (Au/F)	NDro
- 'Bethan McSparron' (Au/B)	NDro
- 'Betty Sherriff' (Au/B)	GAbr
- 'Betty Stewart' (Au/A)	WAln
- 'Betty Wilson' (Au/St)	NDro
- 'Bewitched' (Au/A)	NDro WAln XBar
- 'Bielfeld' (Au/B) **new**	NDro
- 'Big Thrill' (Au)	WFar

- 'Bilbao' (Au/A) WAln
- 'Bilbo Baggins' (Au/A) NDro WAln
- 'Bill Bailey' (Au/d) NDro
- 'Bingley Folk' (Au/B) NDro
- 'Bingley Snowflake' (Au/B) NDro
- 'Bisto' (Au/S) WAln
- 'Bizarre' (Au) NDro
- 'Black Diamond' (Au/d) WHil XBar
- 'Black Jack'[PBR] (Au/d) CBct CWCL ECtt MHol NHpl NLar SEdd WIce WTor
- 'Blackberry Crush' (Au) NDro
- 'Blackhill' (Au/S) ITim NHpl
- 'Blackpool Rock' (Au/St) CWCL NDro XBar
- 'Blairside Yellow' (Au/B) NDro NSla WAbe
- 'Blakeney' (Au/d) NDro
- 'Blossom' (Au/A) XBar
- 'Blue Bella' (Au/B) NDro
- 'Blue Belle' (Au/B) NDro
- 'Blue Bonnet' (Au/A/d) NDro WAln XBar
- 'Blue Boy' (Au/S) WHil
- 'Blue Chip' (Au/S) GAbr NDro WHil
- 'Blue Cliff' (Au/S) NDro WAln
- 'Blue Frills' (Au/d) NDro WAln
- 'Blue Heaven' (Au/A) NDro XBar
- 'Blue Lace' (Au/A) WAln
- 'Blue Merle' (Au/B) NDro
- 'Blue Mist' (Au/B) NDro
- 'Blue Night' (Au/B) ITim NDro
- 'Blue Ridge' (Au/A) NDro
- 'Blue Skies' (Au/St) NDro
- 'Blue Velvet' (Au/B) GQue NDro NHpl WHil XBar
- 'Blue Wave' (Au/d) CBor
- 'Blue Waves' (Au/B) NDro
- 'Blue Yodeler' (Au/A) NDro WFar WHil XBar
- 'Blue Yonder' (Au/S) ITim
- 'Blush Baby' (Au/St) EBee NDro NWad WHil XBar
- 'Blyth Spirit' (Au/A) NDro WAln XBar
- 'Bob Lancashire' (Au/S) GAbr ITim NDro WHil XBar
- 'Bokay' (Au/d) WAln
- 'Bold Tartan' (Au/St) NDro
- 'Bolero' (Au/A) WAln
- 'Bonafide' (Au/d) WAln
- 'Bonanza' (Au/S) WAln
- 'Bonnie the Cat' (Au) **new** WHil
- 'Bookham Firefly' (Au/A) NDro WHil XBar
- 'Border Bandit' (Au/B) GAbr NDro XBar
- 'Border Beauty' (Au/St) NDro
- 'Border Blue' (Au/B) NDro
- 'Border Patrol' (Au/B) ITim NDro
- 'Border Tawny' (Au/B) NDro
- 'Boromir' (Au/A) NDro WAln
- 'Bournebrook' (Au/A) WAln
- 'Bowen's Blue' (Au/B) NDro SMHy
- 'Bradford City' (Au/A) CFis EBee MAvo NDro WFar WHil XBar
- 'Bradmore Bluebell' (Au/B) GAbr NDro
- 'Bramshill' (Au/S) NDro
- 'Bran' (Au/B) NDro
- 'Brandaris' (Au/A) WAln
- 'Branston' (Au/d) XBar
- 'Brasso' (Au/S) NDro WAln XBar
- 'Brazen Hussy' (Au/d) WAln
- 'Brazil' (Au/S) EBee GAbr NDro WHil
- 'Brazos River' (Au/A) NDro WHil
- 'Breckland Joy' (Au/A) NDro WAln
- 'Brenda's Choice' (Au/A) NDro
- 'Brenda's Dilemma' (Au/S) NDro
- 'Brentford Bees' (Au/St) NDro
- 'Brick Lane' (Au/S) **new** NDro
- 'Bright Eyes' (Au/A) XBar
- 'Bright Ginger' (Au/S) NDro WAln
- 'Brigitte' (Au/A) XBar
- 'Brimstone and Treacle' (Au/d) WAln
- 'Brixton' (Au/S) NDro
- 'Broad Gold' (Au/A) NDro XBar
- 'Broadwell Gold' (Au/B) GAbr NDro
- 'Brocade' (Au/St) NDro
- 'Brookfield' (Au/S) GAbr NDro NHpl WHil XBar
- 'Broughton' (Au/S) NDro
- 'Brown Ben' (Au/A) WFar WHil
- 'Brown Bess' (Au/A) GAbr ITim WHil
- 'Brownie' (Au/B) GAbr NBir NDro WHil XBar
- 'Brownie Guider' (Au/B) NDro
- 'Brownie Point' (Au/B) NDro
- 'Brunhilde' (Au/B) NDro
- 'Bucks Green' (Au/S) GAbr NDro
- 'Buffy' (Au/St) NDro
- 'Bunny Black' (Au) **new** GKev
- 'Buoyance' (Au/A) WAln
- 'Burnished Gold' (Au/d) WAln
- 'Bush Baby' (Au/B) NDro
- 'Buttermere' (Au/d) WAln
- 'Butterwick' (Au/A) GAbr ITim NDro XBar
- 'C.G. Haysom' (Au/S) NDro WHil
- 'C.W. Needham' (Au/A) ITim NDro XBar
- 'Cadiz Bay' (Au/d) WAln
- 'Café au Lait' (Au/A) XBar
- 'Calico' (Au/d) XBar
- 'Calypso' (Au/d) NDro WAln
- 'Cambodunum' (Au/A) NDro WFar WHil
- 'Cambrai' (Au/d) **new** WHil
- 'Camelot' (Au/d) NDro WFar WHil XBar
- 'Cameo' (Au/A) NHpl
- 'Cameo Beauty' (Au/d) NDro
- 'Candy Stripe' (Au/St) NDro
- 'Cannelle' (Au/d) XBar
- 'Caramel' (Au/A) GAbr WAln
- 'Cardinal Red' (Au/d) NDro
- 'Cardington' (Au/A) WAln
- 'Carioca' (Au/A) WAln
- 'Carmel' (Au/d) NDro WAln
- 'Carnaval' (Au/B) WHil XBar
- 'Carne' (Au/d) NDro
- 'Carnival' (Au/A) WAln
- 'Carole' (Au/A) WHil
- 'Carousel' (Au/B) NDro WHil
- 'Carreras' (Au) NDro
- 'Carsa Wakes' (Au/d) NDro WAln
- 'Carzon' (Au/A) NDro
- 'Catherine Wheel' (Au/St) NDro
- 'Cathy McKay' (Au/B) NDro
- 'Catta Ha' (Au/d) NDro
- 'Celtic One' (Au/St) NDro
- 'Ceri Nicolle' (Au/B) NDro
- 'Chaffinch' (Au/S) GAbr NDro
- 'Chamois' (Au/B) GAbr NDro WHil
- 'Chanel' (Au/S) WAln
- 'Charisma' (Au/St) NDro
- 'Charles Bronson' (Au/d) NDro XBar
- 'Charles Rennie' (Au/B) NDro WHil XBar
- 'Charlie's Aunt' (Au/A) NDro WAln
- 'Charlotte' (Au/B) NDro
- 'Charlotte Brookes' (Au/d) WAln
- 'Checkmate' (Au/d) WAln XBar
- 'Chelsea Bridge' (Au/A) NDro WHil
- 'Chelsea Girl' (Au/d) NDro
- 'Cheops' (Au/A) NDro XBar
- 'Cherille' (Au/S) NDro

- 'Cherry' (Au/S) NDro
- 'Cherry Picker' (Au/A) NDro
- 'Chestnut' (Au/B) NDro
- 'Cheyenne' (Au/S) NDro
- 'Chiffon' (Au/S) NDro
- 'Chiquita' (Au/d) NDro
- 'Chirichua' (Au/S) WAln
- 'Chloë' (Au/S) GRum NDro NHpl
- 'Choir Boy' (Au/A) WAln
- 'Chorister' (Au/S) EBee ITim NDro WHil
- 'Chyne' (Au) NDro
- 'Cicero' (Au/A) WAln
- 'Cinders' (Au/St) NDro
- 'Cindy' (Au/A) NDro
- 'Cinnamon' (Au/d) ITim NDro WFar WHil XBar
- 'Ciribiribin' (Au/A) WAln
- 'Clara' (Au/d) WFar
- 'Clare' (Au/S) NDro
- 'Classy Stripe' (Au/St) ITim
- 'Clatter-Ha' (Au/d) WHil
- 'Claud Wilson' (Au/St) NDro
- 'Cleft Stick' (Au) NDro
- 'Cloth of Gold' (Au/A) NDro
- 'Clotted Cream' (Au/B) NDro
- 'Clouded Yellow' (Au/S) GAbr NDro WHil
- 'Cloudscape' (Au/S) **new** NDro
- 'Cloudy Bay' (Au/B) GAbr NDro WCot
- 'Cloverdale' (Au/d) WAln
- 'Clunie' (Au/S) NDro XBar
- 'Cobbydale Orange' (Au/B) NDro
- 'Cobden Meadows' (Au/A) WAln
- 'Cocoa' (Au/d) XBar
- 'Coffee' (Au/S) NDro WFar WHil
- 'Colbury' (Au/S) NDro
- 'Colonel Champney' (Au/S) NDro
- 'Colonel Mustard' (Au/d) XBar
- 'Comet' (Au/S) NDro
- 'Connaught Court' (Au/A) NDro
- 'Conquistador' (Au/A) NDro WAln
- 'Conservative' (Au/S) NDro
- 'Consett' (Au/S) WHil
- 'Cooper's Gold' (Au/B) NDro
- 'Coppi' (Au/A) NDro
- 'Coral' (Au/S) ITim
- 'Cornish Cream' (Au/B) NDro
- 'Cornmeal' (Au/S) NDro WHil XBar
- 'Corntime' (Au/S) WAln
- 'Corrie Files' (Au/d) WAln
- 'Cortina' (Au/S) ITim NDro WHil
- 'County Park Red' (Au/B) NDro
- 'Coventry Street' (Au/S) NDro
- 'Crackling Rosie' (A/d) WAln
- 'Craig Nordie' (Au/B) NDro
- 'Craig Vaughan' (Au/A) NDro XBar
- 'Cranborne' (Au/A) WAln
- 'Crimple' (Au/S) NDro WHil
- 'Crimson Glow' (Au/d) EBee ITim LCro LOPS NDro WHil XBar
- 'Crinoline' (Au/S) NDro
- 'Cuckoo Fair' (Au/S) ECtt NDro WFar
- 'Cuddles' (Au/A) NDro WAln
- 'Curry Blend' (Au/B) NDro NWad WHil
- 'Cutie Pie' (Au/St) NDro
- 'D.S.J.' (Au/S) NDro
- 'Daftie Green' (Au/S) NDro
- 'Dales Red' (Au/B) NDro NHpl WHil
- 'Dan Tiger' (Au/St) NDro WHil

I - 'Daniel' (Au/d) XBar
- 'Daniel' (Au/A) NDro WAln
- 'Daniel T. Taylor' (Au/A) NDro WAln
- 'Darent Tiger' (Au/St) NDro XBar
- 'Dark Eyes' (Au/d) NDro WHil
- 'Dark Lady' (Au/A) WAln
- 'D'Artagnan' (Au/B) NDro
- 'Darth Vader' (Au/d) XBar
- 'David Beckham' (Au/d) NDro WAln
- 'David McSparron' (Au/B) NDro
- 'Day by Day' (Au/St) NDro
- 'Deal' (Au/S) NDro
- 'Deckchair' (Au/St) NDro
- 'Dedham' (Au/d) WAln
- 'Del Boy' (Au/A) WAln
- 'Delilah' (Au/d) ITim NDro WFar WHil
- 'Denise' (Au/S) WAln
- 'Denna Snuffer' (Au/d) NDro
- 'Derek's Fanfare' (Au/St) NDro
- 'Derrill' (Au/B) NDro
- 'Derwent Water' (Au/S) NDro
- 'Deuce of Hearts' (Au/St) NDro
- 'Devon Cream' (Au/d) NDro XBar
- 'Diamond Dust' (Au/B) NDro
- 'Diane' (Au/A) NDro
- 'Dick Rogers' (Au/B) NDro
- 'Dido' (Au/B) XBar
- 'Digby' (Au/d) NDro WAln
- 'Digit' (Au/d) NDro WAln
- 'Dill' (Au/A) NDro WHil
- 'Dilly Dilly' (Au/A) NDro
- 'Divint Dunch' (Au/A) NDro WHil XBar
- 'Doctor Lennon's White' (Au/B) GAbr MHer NDro NWad WHil XBar
- 'Dolly' (Au/B) NDro

I - 'Dolly Mixture' (Au/B) XBar
- 'Dolly Viney' (Au/d) WAln
- 'Don Carlos' (Au/d) XBar
- 'Donhead' (Au/A) ITim NDro WHil
- 'Donn' (Au/d) WAln
- 'Donna Clancy' (Au/S) NDro XBar
- 'Doreen Stephens' (Au/A) NDro
- 'Doris Jean' (Au/A) NDro
- 'Doublet' (Au/d) NDro WHil
- 'Doubloon' (Au/d) XBar
- 'Doublure' (Au/d) GAbr NDro WHil
- 'Douglas Bader' (Au/A) ITim NDro WHil
- 'Douglas Black' (Au/S) CPla GAbr NDro WHil
- 'Douglas Green' (Au/S) NDro
- 'Dovedale' (Au/S) NDro
- 'Doyen' (Au/d) ITim NDro NHpl WAln WHil
- 'Dragon's Hoard' (Au/A) WAln
- 'Drax' (Au/A) WAln
- 'Dubarii' (Au/A) NDro WAln
- 'Duke of Edinburgh' (Au/B) NDro
- 'Dusky Girl' (Au/A) NDro WAln
- 'Dusky Maiden' (Au/A) NDro WHil
- 'Dusky Yellow' (Au/B) NDro
- 'Dusty Miller' (Au/B) EBee NBir
- 'Eastern Promise' (Au/A) NDro WHil
- 'Eaton Dawn' (Au/S) XBar
- 'Ed Spivey' (Au/A) NDro
- 'Eddy Gordon' (Au/A) WAln
- 'Eden Alexander' (Au/B) NDro XBar
- 'Eden Amethyst' (Au/B) NDro
- 'Eden Aramis' (Au/B) NDro
- 'Eden Blue Star' (Au/B) GAbr NDro WFar WHil
- 'Eden Bramley' (Au/B) NDro
- 'Eden Carmine' (Au/B) MHer NDro NWad WHil XBar

- 'Eden Dark Eyes' (Au/B) NDro
- 'Eden David' (Au/B) NDro WFar WHil
- 'Eden Ensign' (Au/B) NDro WFar
- 'Eden Fanfare' (Au/B) NDro WFar
- 'Eden Glow' (Au/B) NDro
- 'Eden Goldfinch' (Au/B) NDro WFar WHil
- 'Eden Greenfinch' (Au/B) NDro WHil XBar
- 'Eden Lilactime' (Au/B) NDro WFar
- 'Eden Moonlight' (Au/B) NDro WHil XBar
- 'Eden Porthos' (Au/B) NDro
- 'Eden Rhiann' (Au/B) NDro
- 'Eden Royalty' (Au/B) WFar
- 'Eden Ruby Star' (Au/B) NDro
- 'Eden Simon' (Au/B) NDro
- 'Eden Sunrise' (Au/B) NDro
- 'Eden Surprise' (Au/B) NDro
- 'Eden Wendy' (Au/B) **new** NDro
- 'Edinburgh' (Au/A) WAln
- 'Edith Major' (Au/d) WHil
- 'Edward Sweeney' (Au/S) WAln
- 'Eglinton' (Au) NDro
- 'Eileen K' (Au/S) NDro
- 'Elegance' (Au/S) WFar
- 'Eli Jenkins' (Au) WAln
- 'Elizabeth Ann' (Au/A) NDro
- 'Ellen Thompson' (Au/A) NDro WHil XBar
- 'Ellie May' (Au/S) XBar
- 'Elsie May' (Au/A) ITim NDro
- 'Embley' (Au/S) NDro NHpl
- 'Emery Down' (Au/S) NDro
- 'Emily Mary' (Au/B) **new** NDro
- 'Emmett Smith' (Au/A) NDro WAln
- 'Ems Blue' (Au/B) NDro
- 'Ems Funny Face' (Au/B) NDro
- 'Enlightened' (Au/A) NDro
- 'Erica' (Au/A) NDro WHil XBar
- 'Erjon' (Au/S) NDro
- 'Error' (Au/S) NDro
- 'Eschman Starflower' (Au/S) WHil
- 'Esso' (Au/S) WAln
- 'Ethel' (Au) CBor NDro
- 'Ethel Wilkes' (Au/d) WAln
- 'Etna' (Au/S) NDro
- 'Euston Road' (Au/S) NDro
- 'Eve Guest' (Au/A) NDro WAln
- 'Everest Blue' (Au/S) NDro XBar
- 'Everso Lovely Blue' (Au/B) **new** NDro
- 'Excalibur' (Au/d) NDro
- 'Exhibition Blau' (Exhibition Series) (Au/B) WHil
- 'Eye Candy' (Au/St) NDro
- 'Eyeopener' (Au/A) NDro WHil
- 'Fabuloso' (Au/St) NDro
- 'Fairy' (Au/A) WAln
- 'Fairy Dust' (Au/D) **new** XBar
- 'Fairy Light' (Au/S) NDro
- 'Fairy Moon' (Au/S) NDro
- 'Fairy Queen' (Au/S) NDro
- 'Faliraki Fanciful' (Au) NDro
- 'Falstaff' (Au/d) WAln
- 'Fanciful' (Au/S) NDro WHil XBar
- 'Fancy Pants' (Au/S) NDro
- 'Fandancer' (Au/A) WAln
- 'Fandango' (Au/St) NDro
- 'Fanfare' (Au/S) NDro WHil
- 'Fanny Meerbeck' (Au/S) GAbr NDro WHil
- 'Fantasia' (Au/d) NDro
- 'Faro' (Au/S) NDro
- 'Favourite' (Au/S) GAbr ITim NDro WHil XBar
- 'Fearless' (Au/S) WAln
- 'Femme Fatale' (Au/St) NDro
- 'Ferrybridge' (Au/A) NDro WAln
- 'Festubert' (Au/d) **new** WHil
- 'Fiddler's Green' (Au/d) NDro NWad WCot XBar
- 'Figaro' (Au/S) NDro XBar
- 'Figurine' (Au/d) WAln
- 'Finchfield' (Au/A) GAbr NDro WAln
- 'Fine Art' (Au/S) NDro
- 'Finley' (Au/B) NDro
- 'Firecracker' (Au) WAln
- 'Firsby' (Au/d) NDro WHil
- 'First Lady' (Au/A) WAln WFar
- 'First Light' (Au/B) NDro
- 'Fleet Street' (Au/S) NDro WFar WHil
- 'Fleminghouse' (Au/S) NDro
- 'Flirty' (Au/St) NDro
- 'Florence Baker' (Au/S) NDro
- 'Florence Brown' (Au/S) NDro
- 'Fluffy Duckling' (Au/S) NDro
- 'For You' (Au/St) NDro
- 'Forest Autumn Glow' (Au/d) **new** WHil
- 'Forest Beauty' (Au/d) **new** WHil
- 'Forest Beech' (Au/d) WHil
- 'Forest Blush' (Au/d) **new** WHil
- 'Forest Bordeaux' (Au/d) WHil
- 'Forest Bracken' (Au/d) WHil
- 'Forest Brown Sugar' (Au/d) **new** WHil
- 'Forest Burgundy' (Au/d) WHil
- 'Forest Burnt Gold' (Au/d) WHil
- 'Forest Buttercup' (Au/d) **new** WHil
- 'Forest Cappuccino' (Au/d) WHil
- 'Forest Coffee' (Au/d) NDro WHil
- 'Forest Dawn' (Au/d) **new** WHil
- 'Forest Delight' (Au/d) **new** WHil
- 'Forest Diamond' (Au/d) **new** WHil
- 'Forest Disco Dancer' (Au/d) **new** WHil
- 'Forest Dream' (Au/d) **new** WHil
- 'Forest Duet' (Au/d) NDro WFar WHil
- 'Forest Dusk' (Au/d) **new** WHil
- 'Forest Emperor' (Au/d) **new** WHil
- 'Forest Fall' (Au/d) **new** WHil
- 'Forest Fancy That' (Au/d) **new** WHil
- 'Forest Fantasy' (Au/d) **new** WHil
- 'Forest Fire' (Au/d) GAbr WHil
- 'Forest Flame' (Au/d) **new** WHil
- 'Forest Foxy Girl' (Au/d) **new** WHil
- 'Forest Frost' (Au/d) **new** WHil
- 'Forest Garnet' (Au/d) WHil
- 'Forest Gingernut' (Au/d) **new** WHil
- 'Forest Glade' (Au/d) WHil
- 'Forest Golden Crown' (Au/d) **new** WHil
- 'Forest Gorse' (Au/d) WHil
- 'Forest Greenfinch' (Au/d) **new** WHil

- 'Forest Heartbreaker' (Au) **new** WHil
- 'Forest Hint of Pink' (Au/d) **new** WHil
- 'Forest Hot Stuff' (Au/d) **new** WHil
- 'Forest Kingcup' (Au/d) **new** WHil
- 'Forest Lemon' (Au/d) WHil
- 'Forest Lemon Sorbet' (Au/d) **new** WHil
- 'Forest Lime' (Au/d) WHil
- 'Forest Love' (Au/d) **new** WHil
- 'Forest Mayday' (Au/d) **new** WHil
- 'Forest Old Thumper' (Au/d) **new** WHil
- 'Forest Peach' (Au/d) **new** WHil
- 'Forest Pecan' (Au/d) WHil
- 'Forest Pink Lustre' (Au/d) **new** WHil
- 'Forest Pink Sensation' (Au/d) **new** WHil
- 'Forest Pink Surprise' (Au/d) **new** WHil
- 'Forest Plum' (Au/d) **new** WHil
- 'Forest Prince' (Au/d) **new** WHil
- 'Forest Purple Penny' (Au/d) **new** WHil
- 'Forest Red Beret' (Au/d) **new** WHil
- 'Forest Red Mist' (Au/d) **new** WHil
- 'Forest Red 'n' Fred' (Au/d) **new** WHil
- 'Forest Redstart' (Au) **new** WHil
- 'Forest Rocket' (Au/d) **new** WHil
- 'Forest Sage' (Au/d) **new** WHil
- 'Forest Scarlet Woman' (Au/d) **new** WHil
- 'Forest Shade' (Au/d) WHil
- 'Forest Sherbek' (Au/d) **new** WHil
- 'Forest Shy Girl' (Au/d) **new** WHil
- 'Forest Smokey' (Au/d) **new** WHil
- 'Forest Sorcerer' (Au/d) **new** WHil
- 'Forest Starlet' (Au/d) **new** WHil
- 'Forest Sunbeam' (Au/d) **new** WHil
- 'Forest Sunburst' (Au/d) WHil
- 'Forest Sunfire' (Au/d) WHil
- 'Forest Sunlight' (Au/d) WHil
- 'Forest Sunshade' (Au/d) **new** WHil
- 'Forest Sunshine' (Au/d) WHil
- 'Forest Thatch' (Au/d) **new** WHil
- 'Forest Twilight' (Au/d) WHil
- 'Forest Way' (Au/d) **new** WHil
- 'Forest Zest' (Au/d) **new** WHil
- 'Foundling' (Au) ITim
- 'Foxfire' (Au/A) WAln
- 'Foxy' (Au/B) NDro
- 'Fradley' (Au/A) NDro WAln WFar WHil
- 'Françoise' (Au/d) XBar
- 'Frank Bailey' (Au/d) WAln
- 'Frank Crosland' (Au/A) NDro WHil
- 'Frank Faulkner' (Au/A) WAln
- 'Frank Hemmingway' (Au/B) NDro
- 'Frank Jenning' (Au/A) NDro WAln
- 'Fred Booley' (Au/d) GRum NDro WFar WHil XBar
- 'Fred Livesley' (Au/A) WAln
- 'Fresco' (Au/A) WAln
- 'Freya' (Au/S) NDro XBar
- 'Fridl' (Au) EBee
- 'Friends of Ashwood' (Au/S) NDro
- 'Friskney' (Au/d) WAln
- 'Frittenden Yellow' (Au/B) NDro
- 'Fromelles' (Au/d) **new** WHil
- 'Frosty' (Au/S) NDro
- 'Fuller's Red' (Au/S) NDro WHil XBar
- 'Funny Valentine' (Au/d) NDro WHil
- 'G.L.Taylor' (Au/A) NDro
- 'Gaia' (Au/d) WHil
- 'Gail Atkinson' (Au/A) WAln
- 'Galator' (Au/A) WAln
- 'Ganymede' (Au/d) WAln
- 'Gary Pallister' (Au/A) WAln
- 'Gay Crusader' (Au/A) NDro WFar WHil
- 'Gazza' (Au/A) WAln
- 'Gee Cross' (Au/A) NDro
- 'Geldersome Green' (Au/S) GRum NDro
- 'Geldersome Green No. 2' (Au/S) ITim
- 'Gemini' (Au/S) NDro
- 'Generosity' (Au/A) NDro WHil
- 'Geordie' (Au/A) WAln
- 'George Edge' (Au/B) NDro
- 'George Harrison' (Au/B) NDro
- 'George Jennings' (Au/A) NDro
- 'George Swinford's Leathercoat' (Au/B) NDro
- 'Geronimo' (Au/S) GAbr NDro WHil
- 'Ghost Ridge' (Au/B) **new** NDro
- 'Gild Green' (Au/S) NDro
- 'Gimli' (Au/A) WAln
- 'Ginger Spice' (Au/B) NDro WHil
- 'Girl Guide' (Au/S) WHil
- 'Gizabroon' (Au/S) CBor CFis EBee GAbr NDro NLar WHil XBar
- 'Gleam' (Au/S) EDAr NDro WHil XBar
- 'Glencoe' (Au/S) NDro
- 'Gleneagles' (Au/S) GRum NDro
- 'Glenelg' (Au/S) GAbr ITim NDro WHil XBar
- 'Glenluce' (Au/S) NDro
- 'Gloire de Dijon' (Au/S) XBar
- 'Gnome' (Au/B) GAbr NDro
- 'Goeblii' (Au/B) NDro WHil XBar
- 'Gold Seam' (Au/A) WAln WHil
- 'Gold Star' (Au/St) NDro
- 'Golden Boy' (Au/A) NDro WAln
- 'Golden Chartreuse' (Au/d) NDro
- 'Golden Fleece' (Au/S) NDro
- 'Golden Girl' (Au/A) WAln
- 'Golden Glory' (Au/A) NDro WAln
- 'Golden Hill' (Au/S) ITim
- 'Golden Hind' (Au/d) GAbr NDro WHil
- 'Golden Splendour' (Au/d) ITim NDro WFar WHil
- 'Golden Wedding' (Au/A) NDro WAln WHil XBar
- 'Goldie' (Au/S) NDro
- 'Goldwin' (Au/A) NDro
- 'Gollum' (Au/A) NDro WAln WFar

	- 'Good Report' (Au/A)	NDro WFar WHil
	- 'Goody Goody' (Au/St)	NDro
	- 'Googie' (Au/d)	WHil
	- 'Gordon Files' (Au/S)	WAln
	- 'Gorey' (Au/A)	NDro WHil
	- 'Grabley' (Au/S)	NDro
	- 'Grace Ellen' (Au/S)	NDro
	- 'Gracie Lou' (Au/B)	NDro
	- 'Grandad's Favourite' (Au/B)	NDro
	- 'Grasmere' (Au/d)	NDro
	- 'Green Goddess' (Au/St)	NDro
	- 'Green Isle' (Au/S)	GAbr NDro XBar
	- 'Green Jacket' (Au/S)	NDro
	- 'Green Lane' (Au/S)	XBar
	- 'Green Mustard' (Au/S)	NDro
	- 'Green Parrot' (Au/S)	GAbr WHil
	- 'Green Shank' (Au/S)	NDro WHil XBar
	- 'Greenfield's Fancy' (Au)	EBee
	- 'Greenpeace' (Au/S)	GAbr NDro XBar
	- 'Grenache' (Au/B)	XBar
	- 'Greta' (Au/S)	GAbr NDro WHil XBar
	- 'Grey Cloud' (Au/B)	NDro
	- 'Grey Day' (Au/S)	NDro
	- 'Grey Hawk' (Au/S)	NDro
	- 'Grey Lag' (Au/S)	WHil XBar
	- 'Grey Monarch' (Au/S)	GAbr WHil XBar
	- 'Grey Owl' (Au/S)	NDro
	- 'Grey Shrike' (Au/S)	NDro
	- 'Grüner Veltliner' (Au/S)	GAbr
	- 'Guinea' (Au/S)	GAbr ITim NDro
	- 'Gwai Loh' (Au/B)	NDro
	- 'Gwen' (Au/A)	NDro WAln XBar
	- 'Gwen Baker' (Au/d)	NDro
	- 'Gwenda' (Au/A)	NDro WAln WHil
	- 'Gypsy Boy' (Au/A)	WAln
	- 'H Old Gold' (Au/S)	NDro
	- 'Habanera' (Au/A)	NDro WFar
	- 'Haffner' (Au/S)	NDro
	- 'Hallmark' (Au/A)	NDro WAln
	- 'Handsome Lass' (Au/St)	NDro XBar
	- 'Hannah' (Au/A)	WAln
	- 'Harlequin' (Au/B)	NDro
	- 'Harmony' (Au/B)	NDro XBar
	- 'Harry Armitage' (Au/B)	NDro
	- 'Harry Hotspur' (Au/A)	NDro WFar WHil XBar
	- 'Harry 'O'' (Au/S)	NDro
	- 'Harthorpeburn' (Au/B)	NDro
	- 'Harvest Glow' (Au/S)	NDro WFar WHil
	- 'Hawkwood' (Au/S)	EBee NDro WHil XBar
	- 'Hazel' (Au/B)	NDro XBar
	- 'Hazel' (Au/A)	NDro WHil
	- 'Heady' (Au/A)	NDro WHil XBar
	- 'Heart of Gold' (Au/A)	NDro WAln
	- 'Hearts of Oak' (Au/A)	WAln
	- 'Heaven Scent' (Au)	NDro
	- 'Hebers' (Au)	NDro WAln
	- 'Helen' (Au/S)	GAbr NDro WHil
	- 'Helen Barter' (Au/S)	NDro WHil
	- 'Helen Ruane' (Au/d)	GQue WFar
	- 'Helena' (Au/S)	NDro WAln WHil
	- 'Helena Dean' (Au/d)	WAln
	- 'Henry's Bane' (Au/St)	NDro
	- 'Her Nibs' (Au/St)	NDro
	- 'Hermes the Cat' (Au)	WHil
	- 'Hermia' (Au/A)	WHil
	- 'Hetty Woolf' (Au/S)	GAbr NDro
	- 'Hew Dalrymple' (Au/S)	NDro
	- 'Highland Park' (Au/A)	NDro WHil XBar
	- 'Hillhook' (Au/A)	WAln
	- 'Hillview Hermes' (Au/S)	NDro WHil
	- 'Hinton Admiral' (Au/S)	GAbr NDro WHil XBar
	- 'Hinton Fields' (Au/S)	EBee GAbr MAvo NDro WFar WHil
	- 'Hobby Horse' (Au/St)	ITim
	- 'Holyrood' (Au/S)	GAbr ITim NDro NHpl XBar
	- 'Honey' (Au/d)	GAbr NDro
	- 'Honeydawn' (Au/B)	NDro
	- 'Hopleys Coffee' (Au/d)	GAbr NDro WAln
	- 'Hopton Gem' (Au/B)	NDro
	- 'Hughie' (Au/A)	WAln
	- 'Hurstwood Midnight' (Au)	XBar
*	- 'Hyacinth' (Au/S)	EBee NDro WCAu
	- 'Ian Greville' (Au/A)	NDro XBar
	- 'Ibis' (Au/A)	WAln
	- 'Ice Cap' (Au/d)	XBar
	- 'Ice Maiden' (Au/A)	GAbr NDro WHil
	- 'Idgy' (Au/d) **new**	WHil
	- 'Idmiston' (Au/S)	GAbr NDro WHil XBar
	- 'Imari Stripe' (Au/St)	NDro WHil
	- 'Immaculate' (Au/A)	NDro WHil
	- 'Impassioned' (Au/A)	XBar
	- 'Imperturbable' (Au/A)	NDro
	- 'Indian Love Call' (Au/A)	GAbr ITim NDro WHil
I	- 'Innominata' (Au/S)	NDro
	- 'Innsworth' (Au/A)	WAln
	- 'Iris Scott' (Au/A)	ITim NDro
	- 'Isabel' (Au/S)	WAln
	- 'Isabella' (Au/A)	NDro WAln
	- 'Jack Dean' (Au/A)	WFar WHil XBar
	- 'Jack Horner' (Au)	NDro
	- 'Jack Redfern' (Au/A)	NDro
	- 'Jaffa' (Au/A)	NDro WAln
	- 'James Arnot' (Au/S)	GAbr NDro XBar
	- 'James Wattam' (Au/S)	NDro
	- 'Jane' (Au/S)	WAln
	- 'Jane Myers' (Au/d)	WAln WHil
	- 'Janet Watts' (Au/B)	NDro
	- 'Janie Hill' (Au/A)	XBar
	- 'Jb' (Au)	GAbr
	- 'Je t'adore' (Au/St)	NDro
	- 'Jealous Lover' (Au/St)	NDro
	- 'Jean Fielder' (Au/A)	NDro WAln
	- 'Jean Jacques' (Au/A)	NDro WAln
I	- 'Jean Jacques' (Au/d)	XBar
	- 'Jean-Claude' (Au/d)	XBar
	- 'Jeannie Jingles II' (Au/St)	NDro
	- 'Jeannie Telford' (Au/A)	NDro
	- 'Jeff Scruton' (Au/A)	WAln
	- 'Jenny' (Au/A)	NDro WFar
	- 'Jersey Bounce' (Au/A)	ITim NDro WHil
	- 'Jessie' (Au/d)	NDro
	- 'Jilting Jessie' (Au/St)	NDro
	- 'Joanne' (Au/d)	NDro
	- 'Joanne' (Au/A)	GAbr NDro
	- 'Joe Perks' (Au/A)	ITim NDro WHil XBar
	- 'Joel' (Au/S)	ITim NDro XBar
	- 'Johann Bach' (Au/B)	NDro
	- 'John Hart' (Au/A)	NDro
	- 'John Wayne' (Au/A)	NDro WHil
	- 'John Woolf' (Au/S)	NDro
	- 'Jonathon' (Au/A)	NDro WAln
	- 'Joy' (Au/A)	NDro NWad WHil XBar
	- 'Joyce' (Au/A)	GAbr NDro WFar WHil XBar
	- 'Judith Borman' (Au/d)	NDro
	- 'Julia Jane' (Au/B)	NDro
	- 'Julie Nuttall' (Au/B)	GAbr NDro WHil
	- 'June' (Au/A)	NDro
	- 'Jungfrau' (Au/d)	NDro WAln
	- 'Jupp' (Au/d)	EBee
	- 'Jura' (Au/A)	WAln

- 'Just Steven' (Au/A)	WAln
- 'Justin Case' (Au/B)	NDro
- 'K S' (Au/S)	NDro
- KALEIDOSCOPE (mixed) (Au)	EDAr EWTr
- 'Karen Cordrey' (Au/S)	EBee GAbr GKev NDro WHil
- 'Karen McDonald' (Au/A)	NDro
- 'Kate Haywood' (Au/B)	NDro WHil
- 'Kelvin's Variegated' (Au) **new**	WHil
- 'Ken Chilton' (Au/A)	NDro WHil
- 'Kentucky Blues' (Au/d)	NDro WAln
- 'Kersey' (Au/S)	NDro
- 'Kevin' (Au/A)	WAln
- 'Kevin Keegan' (Au/A)	NDro WHil XBar
- 'Key West' (Au/A)	NDro WAln
- 'Khachaturian' (Au/A)	NDro WAln
- 'Khaki' (Au) **new**	WHil
- 'Kilby' (Au/A)	NDro
- 'Kim' (Au/A)	NDro WHil
- 'Kimberworth Boy' (Au/A)	NDro WAln
- 'Kingcup' (Au/A)	NDro
- 'Kingfisher' (Au/A)	NDro WHil
- 'Kingpin' (Au/St)	NDro
- 'Kirklands' (Au/d)	ITim NDro WHil
- 'Kitterford Cross' (Au/B)	NDro
- 'Kiwi' (Au/B) **new**	NDro
- 'Kohinoor' (Au/A)	WHil
- 'Königin der Nacht' (Au/St)	NDro WHil
- 'Krithia' (Au/d) **new**	WHil
- 'Lady Daresbury' (Au/A)	NDro WHil XBar
- 'Lady Day' (Au/d)	WAln
- 'Lady Diana' (Au/S)	NDro
- 'Lady Emma Monson' (Au/S)	NDro
- 'Lady Joyful' (Au/S)	NDro
- 'Lady of the Vale' (Au/A)	NDro WAln
- 'Lady Penelope Sitwell' (Au/St)	NDro
- 'Lady Zoë' (Au/S)	NDro
- 'Lambert's Gold' (Au/B)	GAbr WHil
- 'Lambrook Gold' (Au/B)	NDro
- 'Lamplugh' (Au/d)	WHil
- 'Landy' (Au/A)	NDro
- 'Langley Park' (Au/A)	NDro WHil
- 'Laphroaigh' (Au/S)	WAln
- 'Lara' (Au/A)	NDro XBar
- 'Laredo' (Au/A)	WAln
- 'Larry' (Au/A)	NDro WFar XBar
- 'Late Romantic' (Au/d)	CBct CDor ECtt GAbr GRum MHol NHpl NLar SEdd WIce
- 'Lavender Hill' (Au/St)	NDro
- 'Lavender Lady' (Au/B)	NDro
- 'Lavender Ridge' (Au/B)	NDro WAln
- 'Lavenham' (Au/S)	WAln
- 'Laverock' (Au/S)	NBir WHil
- 'Laverock Fancy' (Au/S)	GAbr NDro XBar
- 'Lazy River' (Au/A)	NDro WAln
- 'Le Cateau' (Au/d) **new**	WHil
- 'Leather Jacket' (Au/B)	GAbr WHil
- 'Lechistan' (Au/S)	WHil
- 'Lee' (Au/A)	NDro WAln
- 'Lee Clark' (Au/A)	NDro WAln
- 'Lee Paul' (Au/A)	NDro WHil XBar
- 'Lee Sharpe' (Au/A)	NDro WAln
- 'Legolas' (Au/A)	WAln
- 'Leicester Square' (Au/S)	NDro
- 'Lemon Drop' (Au/S)	ITim NDro
- 'Lemon Ridge' (Au/B)	WAln
- 'Lemon Sherbet' (Au/B)	GAbr GRum NDro WHil
- 'Lemon Sorbet' (Au)	NDro
- 'Lepton Jubilee' (Au/S)	GAbr NDro WAln
- 'Leroy Brown' (Au/A)	WAln
- 'Lester' (Au/d)	WAln WHil
- 'Light Fantastic' (Au/S)	NDro
- 'Light Hearted' (Au/A)	NDro XBar
- 'Light Music' (Au/d)	WAln
- 'Lila' (Au/S)	NDro WAln
- 'Lilac Domino' (Au/S)	GAbr NDro NWad WHil
- 'Lilac Ladywood' (Au/d)	WFar
- 'Lilac Mist' (Au/d)	XBar
- 'Lillian Hill' (Au/A)	WAln
- 'Lillibet' (Au/A)	NDro
- 'Lima' (Au/d)	WAln
- 'Lime 'n' Lemon' (Au)	ITim NDro
- 'Lime Ridge' (Au)	NDro WAln
- 'Limelight' (Au/A)	NDro
- 'Limelight' (Au/S)	NDro
- 'Lincoln Bullion' (Au/d)	NDro WHil XBar
- 'Lincoln Chestnut' (Au/d)	NDro XBar
- 'Lincoln Cuckoo' (Au/d)	NDro
- 'Lincoln Imp' (Au/d)	NDro
- 'Lincoln Imperial' (Au/d)	NDro
- 'Lincoln Melody' (Au/St/d)	NDro XBar
- 'Lincoln Poacher' (Au/d)	NDro
- 'Lincoln Whisper' (Au/d)	NDro
- 'Linda' (Au/A)	WAln WHil
- 'Lindley' (Au/S)	NDro
- 'Ling' (Au/A)	GAbr NDro
- 'Linnet' (Au/B)	NDro
- 'Lintz' (Au/B)	NDro WHil XBar
- 'Linze 2' (Au/S)	NDro
- 'Lisa' (Au/A)	NDro WFar WHil XBar
- 'Lisa Clara' (Au/S)	NDro NHpl WFar XBar
- 'Lisa's Smile' (Au/S)	NDro WHil
- 'Little Bo Peep' (Au)	NDro
- 'Little Rosetta' (Au/d)	GAbr NDro WHil
- 'Lizzie Files' (Au/A)	WAln
- 'Lockyer's Gem' (Au/B/St)	NDro
- 'Lofty' (Au/St)	NDro
- 'Lolita' (Au/St)	NDro WHil XBar
- 'Lord Saye and Sele' (Au/St)	GAbr NDro NWad WHil XBar
- 'Loudhailer' (Au/B) **new**	NDro
- 'Louis' (Au/d)	XBar
- 'Louise Jordan' (Au/A)	NDro
- 'Lovebird' (Au/S)	GAbr NDro NHpl XBar
- 'Lowther Show' (Au/St)	NDro
- 'Luca' (Au/d) **new**	WHil
- 'Lucia' (Au/B)	XBar
- 'Lucy Locket' (Au/B)	EBee GAbr ITim LCro MPnt NDro WHil
- 'Ludlow' (Au/S)	GAbr NDro
- 'Lunar Eclipse' (Au/d)	CBct CWCL GRum MHol NLar WHil WTor
- 'Lune Tiger' (Au/St)	NDro
- 'Lupy Minstrel' (Au/S)	NDro
- 'Lynn' (Au/A)	WAln
- 'Lypiard' (Au/B) **new**	NDro
- 'MacWatt's Blue' (Au/B)	GAbr NDro NWad WHil XBar
- 'Macy the Cat' (Au/S)	WHil
- 'Maggie' (Au/S)	GAbr NDro
- 'Magnolia' (Au/B)	WHil
- 'Mametz' (Au/d) **new**	WHil
- 'Mamm-Gozh' (Au/d)	XBar
- 'Mandarin' (Au/A)	GAbr NDro WFar WHil XBar
- 'Mandy' (Au/S)	NDro
- 'Marble Arch' (Au/S)	NDro
- 'Mardi Gras' (Au/d)	WAln
- 'Margaret' (Au/S)	GAbr

- 'Margaret Faulkner' (Au/A) GAbr XBar
- 'Margaret Martin' (Au/S) ITim NDro
- 'Margaret Merril' (Au) GAbr
- 'Margot' (Au/S) WAln
- 'Margot Fonteyn' (Au/A) GAbr WHil
- 'Mariandl' (Au/A) EBee MAvo
- 'Marie Crousse' (Au/d) CFis CMea ITim NDro WCot WFar WHil
- 'Marie Pierre' (Au/d) XBar
- 'Marion Tiger' (Au/St) NDro
- 'Mark' (Au/A) GAbr NDro
- 'Marmion' (Au/S) GAbr ITim NDro WHil XBar
- 'Mars Bars' (Au/St) NDro
- 'Martha's Choice' (Au/A) WAln
- 'Martin Luther King' (Au/S) NDro WHil XBar
- 'Mary' (Au/d) GAbr NDro
- 'Mary Poppins' (Au/S) NDro
- 'Mary Taylor' (Au/S) NDro
- 'Mary Zach' (Au/S) NDro WAln WHil
- 'Matthew' (Au) GKev
- 'Matthew Yates' (Au/d) GAbr ITim NDro NHpl WCot WHil
- 'Maureen Millward' (Au/A) NDro
- 'May' (Au/A) NDro
- 'Mazetta Stripe' (Au/S/St) GAbr NDro NWad WHil
- 'Meadow Sweet' (Au/S) NDro
- 'Meadowlark' (Au/A) ITim NDro WHil XBar
- 'Mehta' (Au/A) NDro WAln
- 'Mellifluous' (Au/A) WHil
- 'Melody' (Au/S) NDro
- 'Merlin' (Au/S) EBee WFar
- 'Merlin Stripe' (Au/St) NDro WHil XBar
- 'Merridale' (Au/A) GAbr WHil
- 'Mersey Tiger' (Au/S) ITim NDro WHil XBar
- 'Mexicano' (Au/A) NDro WAln
- 'Michael' (Au/S) WAln WHil
- 'Michael Wattam' (Au/S) NDro
- 'Mick' (Au/A) WHil
- 'Midland Marvel' (Au/St) NDro
- 'Midnight' (Au/A) WAln
- 'Mikado' (Au/S) WHil XBar
- 'Milkmaid' (Au/A) WMAq
- 'Millicent' (Au/A) NDro WHil
- 'Mini Ha Ha' (Au/St) **new** NDro
- 'Mink' (Au/A) NDro
- 'Minley' (Au/S) GAbr NBir NDro
- 'Minstrel' (Au/S) ITim NDro
- 'Mirabella Bay' (Au/A) WAln
- 'Mirandinha' (Au/A) NDro
- 'Mish Mish' (Au/d) NDro WHil
- 'Miss Bluey' (Au/d) NDro WAln XBar
- 'Miss Jones' (Au/St) NDro
- 'Miss Newman' (Au/A) NDro
- 'Miss Pinky' (Au/d) NDro
- 'Miss Teak' (Au/S) NDro
- 'Misty' (Au/d) NDro
- 'Mojave' (Au/S) GAbr GEdr GKev GRum ITim NDro NHpl XBar
- 'Mollie Langford' (Au/A) NDro WHil XBar
- 'Mondeo' (Au/A) WAln
- 'Monet' (Au/S) NDro
- 'Moneymoon' (Au/S) GAbr NDro WHil
- 'Monk' (Au/S) NDro WHil XBar
- 'Monmouth Star' (Au/St) WHil
- 'Mons' (Au/d) **new** WHil
- 'Moon Fairy' (Au/S) NDro
- 'Moondance' (Au/d) WAln
- 'Moonglow' (Au/S) GAbr
- 'Moonlight' (Au/S) WAln
- 'Moonrise' (Au/S) NDro
- 'Moonriver' (Au/A) WHil
- 'Moonshine' (Au/d) WAln
- 'Moonshot' (Au/d) NDro
- 'Moonstone' (Au/d) WAln
- 'Morello' (Au/d) XBar
- 'Morning Glory' (Au/B) NDro
- 'Morven' (Au) GAbr
- 'Moselle' (Au/S) NDro
- 'Mr A' (Au/S) NDro WHil
- 'Mr Bojangles' (Au/d) WAln
- 'Mr Hollis' (Au/St) NDro
- 'Mrs Cairn's Blue' (Au/B) NDro
- 'Mrs Dargan' (Au/d) NDro
- 'Mrs Harris' (Au/B) NDro
- 'Mrs L. Hearn' (Au/A) GAbr ITim NDro WHil XBar
- 'Mrs Lowry' (Au/B) NDro
- 'Mrs R. Bolton' (Au/A) WHil
- 'Mrs Wilson' (Au) GAbr
- 'Murray Lakes' (Au/A) NDro WAln
- 'Mustard Sauce' (Au/B) NDro
- 'My Fair Lady' (Au/A) NDro
- 'My Friend' (Au/B) GAbr NDro
- 'Myrtle Park' (Au/A) WAln
- 'Mystery' (Au) GAbr
- 'Nancy Dalgetty' (Au/B) NDro
- 'Nantenan' (Au/S) GAbr NDro
- 'Neat and Tidy' (Au/S) GAbr ITim NDro NWad XBar
- 'Nefertiti' (Au/A) NDro WHil
- 'Nessun Dorma' (Au/A) NDro WAln
- 'Neville Telford' (Au/S) GAbr NDro WFar
- 'Newbottle' (Au/S) WHil
- 'Newsboy' (Au/A) WAln
- 'Newton Harcourt' (Au/A) NDro WHil
- 'Nicholas van Zanten' (Au/B) NDro
- 'Nick Drake' (Au/d) NDro
- 'Nickity' (Au/A) GAbr ITim NDro WHil XBar
- 'Nicola Jane' (Au/A) WAln
- 'Nigel' (Au/d) GAbr NDro
- 'Nightwink' (Au/S) WAln
- 'Nina' (Au/A) NDro WAln
- 'Nita' (Au/d) WAln
- 'No 21' (Au/S) NDro
- 'Nocturne' (Au/S) NDro
- 'Noelle' (Au/S) EBee NDro
- 'Nona' (Au/d) NDro WHil
- 'Nonchalance' (Au/A) NDro WHil
- 'Norma' (Au/A) NDro
- 'Northern Lights' (Au/S) GAbr NDro
- 'Nymph' (Au/d) GAbr GRum NDro WHil
- 'Oakie Dokie' (Au/St) **new** NDro
- 'Oban' (Au/S) NDro XBar
- 'Odette' (Au/d) WHil
- 'O'er the Moon' (Au/S) WAln
- 'Oikos' (Au/B) NDro
- 'Old Black Isle Dusty Miller' (Au/B) NDro WHil
- 'Old Buffer' (Au/St) NDro
- 'Old Clove Red' (Au/B) GAbr NDro NWad WHil
- 'Old Cottage Blue' (Au/B) GAbr NDro WFar
- 'Old Dublin Blue' (Au/B) NDro
- 'Old England' (Au/S) GAbr NDro
- 'Old Fashioned Sally' (Au/B) **new** NDro
- 'Old Gold' (Au/S) GAbr NDro WFar
- 'Old Gold Dusty Miller' (Au/B) NDro
- 'Old Irish Blue' (Au/B) NDro WCot
- 'Old Irish Green' (Au/B) GAbr NDro
- 'Old Irish Scented' (Au/B) GAbr NDro NWad WHil XBar
- 'Old Irish Yellow' (Au/B) NDro NHpl

- 'Old Kent Road' (Au/S)	NDro
- 'Old Mustard' (Au/B)	GAbr NDro SMHy
- 'Old Pink Dusty Miller' (Au/B)	GAbr
§ - 'Old Purple Dusty Miller' (Au/B)	GAbr
- 'Old Red Dusty Miller' (Au/B)	GAbr NDro WFar WHil
- 'Old Red Elvet' (Au/S)	GAbr
- 'Old Smokey' (Au/A)	NDro WHil XBar
- 'Old Suffolk Bronze' (Au/B)	GAbr NDro NWad WHil
- 'Old Yellow Dusty Miller' (Au/B)	EWes GAbr NDro NWad WHil
- 'Old-Fashioned' (Au/B)	NDro
- 'Olton' (Au/A)	NDro WFar XBar
- 'Optimist' (Au/St)	GAbr NDro
- 'Opus One' (Au/A)	WAln
- 'Orb' (Au/S)	GRum WHil XBar
- 'Ordvic' (Au/S)	NDro
- 'Orlando' (Au/S)	NDro
- 'Orwell Tiger' (Au/St)	NDro XBar
- 'Osborne Green' (Au/B)	GAbr GQue NDro WHil
- 'Ossett Sapphire' (Au/A)	NDro
- 'Otto Dix' (Au/A)	WAln
- 'Our Sophie' (Au/B)	NDro
- 'Overdale' (Au/A)	NDro WAln
- 'Oyster' (Au/B)	NDro
- 'Paddlin' Madeleine' (Au/A)	NDro WAln XBar
- 'Pageboy' (Au/A)	WAln
- 'Pale Blue' (Au/B) **new**	WHil
- 'Paleface' (Au/A)	NDro
- 'Pall Mall' (Au/St)	NDro WHil
- 'Palpatine' (Au/D) **new**	XBar
- 'Panache' (Au/S)	WAln
- 'Pang Tiger' (Au/St)	NDro
- 'Paradise Yellow' (Au/B)	GAbr NDro
- 'Paragon' (Au/A)	WHil
- 'Parakeet' (Au/S)	NDro
- 'Party Animal' (Au/St)	NDro XBar
- 'Passchendaele' (Au/d)	WHil
- 'Passing Cloud' (Au/d)	WAln
- 'Pastures New' (Au)	NDro
- 'Pat Mooney' (Au/d)	NDro
- 'Patience' (Au/S)	WHil
- 'Pauline' (Au/A)	NDro
- 'Pavarotti' (Au/A)	ITim NDro
- 'Paxton's Blue Eden' (Au/B)	NDro
- 'Pearl the Cat' (Au) **new**	WHil
- 'Pegasus' (Au/d)	NDro
- 'Peggy' (Au/A)	GAbr ITim WHil
- 'Pen Pink Stripe' (Au/St) **new**	WHil
- 'Pendeford Yellow' (Au/B)	NDro
- 'Pendle Promise' (Au/A)	NDro
- 'Penelope' (Au/d) **new**	WHil
- 'Pequod' (Au/A)	NDro
- 'Perirot' (Au)	ITim
- 'Persephone' (Au/B)	NDro
- 'Phantom' (Au/d)	WAln
- 'Pharaoh' (Au/A)	GAbr NDro XBar
- 'Phoenix' (Au/A)	WAln
- 'Phyllis Douglas' (Au/A)	NDro WHil
- 'Piccadilly' (Au/S)	NDro
- 'Piccalilli' (Au/d)	XBar
- 'Pierot' (Au/A)	NDro WHil XBar
- 'Piers Telford' (Au/A)	EBee GAbr MAvo NDro WFar WHil XBar
- 'Piglet' (Au/d)	GAbr NDro WHil XBar
- 'Pikey' (Au/S)	NDro
- 'Pimroagh' (Au/A)	GAbr
- 'Pink Floyd' (Au/A)	XBar
- 'Pink Fondant' (Au/d)	NDro
- 'Pink Hint' (Au/B)	NDro
- 'Pink Lady' (Au/A)	GAbr WHil
- 'Pink Lilac' (Au/A/S)	NDro
- 'Pink Triumph' (Au/B)	NDro WHil
- 'Pinkie' (Au/A)	WHil
- 'Pinkie Dawn' (Au/B)	NDro
- 'Pinstripe' (Au)	GAbr NDro
- 'Pioneer Stripe' (Au/S)	GAbr
- 'Pippin' (Au/A)	GAbr NDro WHil XBar
- 'Pixie' (Au/A)	NDro
- 'Playboy' (Au/A)	NDro WAln
- 'Plum Pudding' (Au/d)	WAln
- 'Plums and Custard' (Au/B)	XBar
- 'Poacher's Lady' (Au/d)	NDro
- 'Poacher's Sky' (Au/d) **new**	XBar
- 'Poacher's Starlight' (Au/d)	NDro XBar
- 'Polar Sight' (Au/B)	NDro
- 'Polestar' (Au/A)	NDro WHil XBar
- 'Polly' (Au/B)	GKev NDro WHil
- 'Porcelain' (Au/d)	GRum
- 'Portree' (Au/S)	GAbr
- 'Pot o' Gold' (Au/S)	EBee NDro WHil XBar
- 'Powder and Paint' (Au/A)	WAln
- 'Powder Puff' (Au/B)	NDro WHil
- 'Powys' (Au/St) **new**	NDro
- 'Prague' (Au/S)	GAbr NBir NDro
- 'Pretty Prop' (Au/St)	NDro
- 'Pretty Purple' (Au/d)	NDro WAln
- 'Prima' (Au/d)	NDro
- 'Prince Bishops' (Au/S)	WAln
- 'Prince Charming' (Au/S)	NDro
- 'Prince John' (Au/A)	NDro WHil
- 'Proctor's Yellow' (Au/B)	GAbr NDro NWad WHil
- 'Prometheus' (Au/d)	GAbr ITim NDro WHil
- 'Provence' (Au/d)	WHil
- 'Psyche' (Au/S)	NDro
- 'Pumpkin' (Au)	GAbr NHpl
- 'Purple Dusty Miller'	see *P. auricula* 'Old Purple Dusty Miller'
- 'Purple Glow' (Au/d)	WAln
- 'Purple Knight' (Au/S)	WAln
- 'Purple Pip' (Au/d)	CBct CWCL GRum MHol NLar SEdd
- 'Purple Prolific' (Au/B)	NDro
- 'Purple Promise' (Au/B)	GAbr ITim NDro
- 'Purple Prose' (Au/St)	WHil
- 'Purple Rose' (Au/d)	ITim WAln
- 'Purple Royale' (Au/B)	GAbr NDro
- 'Purple Sage' (Au/S)	ITim NDro WHil
- 'Purple Velvet' (Au/S)	NDro
- 'Quality Street' (Au/d) **new**	XBar
- 'Queen Alexandra' (Au/B)	GAbr NDro WHil
- 'Queen Bee' (Au/S)	GAbr NDro
- 'Quintessence' (Au/A)	NDro WHil
- 'R.L. Bowes' (Au/A)	NDro
- 'Rab C. Nesbitt' (Au/A)	WAln
- 'Rabley Heath' (Au/A)	GAbr ITim NDro WHil
- 'Rachel' (Au/A)	NDro WAln
I - 'Rachel' (Au/d)	XBar
- 'Rachel Labouchere' (Au/S)	WAln
- 'Radiant' (Au/A)	NDro
- 'Rag Doll' (Au/S)	NDro
- 'Ragnald the Magnificent' (Au/S)	WAln

- 'Rainy Days' (Au/B) NDro
- 'Rajah' (Au/S) GAbr NHpl WHil XBar
- 'Raleigh Stripe' (Au/St) GAbr
- 'Rameses' (Au/A) NDro
- 'Randall's White' (Au/B) new NDro
- 'Rebecca Baker' (Au/d) WHil
- 'Red Admiral' (Au/S) NDro WAln
- 'Red Arrows' (Au/S) NDro WAln
- 'Red Baron' (Au/S) WAln
- 'Red Bordeaux' (Au/S) NDro
- 'Red Diamond' (Au/d) WAln
- 'Red Embers' (Au/S) WAln
- 'Red Ensign' (Au/B) NDro
- 'Red Gauntlet' (Au/S) GAbr NDro
- 'Red King' (Au/S) WAln
- 'Red Mark' (Au/A) WHil XBar
- 'Red Rum' (Au/S) GAbr WAln
- 'Red Wire' (Au/St) NDro
- 'Red Wrekin' (Au/S) NDro
- 'Redcar' (Au/A) GAbr NDro XBar
- 'Reddown Apricot' (Au/B) NDro
- 'Reddown Barley Meal' (Au/B) NDro
- 'Reddown Brownie' (Au/B) new NDro
- 'Reddown Dark Pink' (Au/B) NDro
- 'Reddown First Swallow' (Au/B) NDro
- 'Reddown Rainman' (Au/B) NDro
- 'Reddown Tickled Pink' (Au/B) NDro
- 'Redstart' (Au/S) EBee GKev NDro WHil
- 'Regency' (Au/A) NDro WHil
- 'Regency Carousel' (Au/St) NDro
- 'Regency Emperor' (Au/St) NDro WHil XBar
- 'Regency Paperchase' (Au/St) NDro
- 'Regency Saint Clements' (Au/St) NDro
- 'Remus' (Au/S) ITim NDro WHil XBar
- 'Rene' (Au/A) GAbr NDro WHil XBar
- 'Renown' (Au/A) NDro WAln
- 'Requiem' (Au/d) WAln
- 'Resi' (Au/A) WHil
- 'Respectable' (Au/A) WAln
- 'Reverie' (Au/d) WAln
- 'Reynardine' (Au/d) WAln
- 'Rhinegold' (Au/d) XBar
- 'Rhubarb Rock' (Au/B) WHil
- 'Riatty' (Au/d) GAbr NDro
- 'Richard Shaw' (Au/A) NDro
- 'Ring of Bells' (Au/S) WAln
- 'Ring of Fire' (Au/A) WAln
- 'Rintein' (Au/B) NDro
- 'Risdene' (Au/A) WAln
- 'Rivendell' (Au/A) WAln
- 'Robbo' (Au/B) GAbr NDro
- 'Robert Green' (Au/S) NDro
- 'Robert Lee' (Au/A) WAln
- 'Roberto' (Au/S) NDro WHil
- 'Robin Hood Stripe' (Au/St) NDro
- 'Robinette' (Au/d) GAbr
- 'Rock Sand' (Au/S) GAbr ITim NDro WHil
- 'Rodeo' (Au/A) GAbr
- 'Rolts' (Au/S) GAbr NDro WHil XBar
- 'Rondy' (Au/S) ITim WHil
- 'Ronnie Johnson' (Au) WAln
- 'Rosalie Edwards' (Au/S) NDro
- 'Rose Conjou' (Au/d) GAbr NDro WHil XBar
- 'Rose Kaye' (Au/A) GAbr
- 'Rose Petal' (Au/d) XBar
- 'Rosebud' (Au/S) GAbr NDro
- 'Rosemarket Rackler' (Au/B) NDro
- 'Rosemary' (Au/S) GAbr NDro WHil
- 'Rosewood' (Au/d) WAln
- 'Rosie' (Au/S) NDro
- 'Rostock' (Au/B) NDro
- 'Rouge Gorge' (Au/B) XBar
- 'Rowena' (Au/A) NDro WHil
- 'Roxburgh' (Au/A) NDro
- 'Roxie' (Au/d) new WHil
- 'Roy Keane' (Au/A) WAln
- 'Royal Mail' (Au/S) NDro XBar
- 'Royal Marine' (Au/S) WAln
- 'Royal Scot' (Au/S) NDro
- 'Royal Velvet' (Au/S) GAbr NDro WFar WHil
- 'Ruby Hyde' (Au/B) GAbr NDro WHil
- 'Ruddy Duck' (Au/S) NDro
- 'Runwell' (Au/B) NDro
- 'Rusty Dusty' (Au) GAbr NDro
- 'Rusty Red' (Au/B) NDro
- 'Ryecroft' (Au/A) WAln
- 'Sabrina' (Au/A) WAln
- 'Saginaw' (Au/A) WAln
- 'Sailor Boy' (Au/S) NDro WAln WHil
- 'Saint Boswells' (Au/S) GAbr
- 'Saint Elmo' (Au/A) GAbr
- 'Saint-Émilion' (Au/d) XBar
- 'Salad' (Au/S) GAbr
- 'Sale Green' (Au/S) NDro
- 'Sally' (Au/A) NDro
- 'Sam Brown' (Au/S) WAln
- 'Sam Gamgee' (Au/A) NDro WAln
- 'Sam Hunter' (Au/A) NDro
- 'Samantha' (Au/A) NDro WAln
- 'Samantha' (Au/d) NDro WFar XBar
- 'San Antonio' (Au/A) NDro
- 'San Gabriel' (Au/A) WAln
- 'Sanctuary Wood' (Au/d) WHil
- 'Sandhills' (Au/A) WHil
- 'Sandra' (Au/A) GAbr NDro WHil XBar
- 'Sandwood Bay' (Au/A) GAbr NDro WHil
- 'Sarah Gisby' (Au/d) NDro
- 'Sarah Humphries' (Au/d) WAln
- 'Sarah Lodge' (Au/d) GAbr NDro WHil
- 'Sarah Millington' (Au) new WHil
- 'Sarah Suzanne' (Au/B) NDro
- 'Saruman' (Au/A) WAln
- 'Sasha Files' (Au/A) WAln
- 'Satsuma' (Au/d) WAln
- 'Scaraben' (Au) GAbr
- 'Schaumburg' (Au/B) NDro
- 'Schicchi' (Au/d) XBar
- 'Scipio' (Au/S) NDro
- 'Scorcher' (Au/S) GAbr WHil XBar
- 'Scrumpy' (Au/St) NDro
- 'Second Victory' (Au/S) NDro WHil XBar
- 'Seen-a-Ghost' (Au/S) NDro
- 'Serenity' (Au/S) WHil XBar
- 'Shadow Boxer' (Au/St) NDro
- 'Shalford' (Au/d) GAbr WCot WHil

- 'Shaun' (Au/d)	CBct ECtt GAbr MHol NHpl NLar WIce
- 'Sheila' (Au/S)	GAbr NDro WHil
- 'Shere' (Au/S)	NDro
- 'Shergold' (Au/A)	WHil
- 'Sherwood' (Au/S)	GAbr NDro NHpl WHil XBar
- 'Shirley' (Au/S)	NDro
- 'Show Bandit' (Au/St)	NDro
- 'Showtime' (Au/S)	NDro
- 'Sibsey' (Au/d)	NDro WFar
- 'Sidney' (Au/A)	WAln
- 'Silas' (Au/B)	NDro
- 'Silbermond' (Au/B)	NDro
- 'Silmaril' (Au/d)	WAln
- 'Silverway' (Au/S)	GKev NDro WHil
- 'Simply Red' (Au/S)	NDro WHil XBar
- 'Sir John' (Au/A)	NDro WHil
- 'Sir Robert' (Au/d)	GAbr WAln
- 'Sir Titus Salt' (Au/S)	WAln
- 'Sirbol' (Au/A)	GAbr NDro WHil
- 'Sirius' (Au/A)	GAbr MHer NDro NWad WHil XBar
- 'Skylark' (Au/A)	GAbr ITim NDro WHil XBar
- 'Skyliner' (Au/A)	NDro
- 'Slack Top Red' (Au)	NDro NSla WHil
- 'Slim Whitman' (Au/A)	NDro WHil
- 'Slioch' (Au/S)	GAbr WFar WHil XBar
- 'Slip Anchor' (Au/A)	WAln
- 'Smoothy' (Au/St)	NDro
- 'Snips' (Au/St)	NDro
- 'Snooty Fox II' (Au/A)	NDro
- 'Snow Maiden' (Au/d)	WAln
- 'Snowstorm' (Au/S)	NDro
- 'Snowy Owl' (Au/S)	NDro XBar
- 'Snowy Ridge' (Au/B)	NDro
- 'Soliloquy' (Au/B)	NDro
- 'Somme' (Au/d) **new**	WHil
- 'Soncy Face' (Au/A)	WHil
- 'Sonia Nicolle' (Au/B)	NDro
- 'Sonja' (Au/S)	NDro
- 'Sonny Boy' (Au/A)	NDro WAln
- 'Sooty' (Au/d)	NDro XBar
- 'Sophie' (Au/d)	WAln
- 'Sophie' (Au/A)	NDro
- 'South Barrow' (Au/d)	GAbr WHil
- 'Southport' (Au/B)	GAbr NDro WHil
- 'Sparky' (Au/A)	NDro WAln
- 'Spider' (Au/S)	NDro
- 'Splash' (Au)	WHil
- 'Splendide' (Au/d) **new**	XBar
- 'Split Ends' (Au/St)	NDro
- 'Spring Meadows' (Au/S)	GAbr GKev NDro WHil
- 'Stafford Blue' (Au/B)	NDro
- 'Standish' (Au/d)	GAbr
- 'Stant's Blue' (Au/S)	NDro
- 'Star Spangle' (Au/St)	NDro
- 'Star Wars' (Au/S)	GAbr NDro WHil XBar
- 'Starburst' (Au/S)	NDro
- 'Stardust' (Au/S)	NDro
- 'Starling' (Au/B)	GAbr NDro
- 'Steiff' (Au/S)	NDro
- 'Stella Coop' (Au/d)	NDro
- 'Stella North' (Au/A)	WAln
- 'Stella South' (Au/A)	NDro WFar
- 'Stepney Green' (Au/S)	NDro
- 'Stetson' (Au/A)	WAln
- 'Stirling Castle' (Au/St)	NDro
- 'Stoke Poges' (Au/A)	NDro
- 'Stoney Cross' (Au/S)	WAln
- 'Stonnal' (Au/A)	NDro WHil
- 'Stormin' Norman' (Au/A)	NDro WHil

- 'Strand' (Au/St)	NDro
- 'Strawberry Fields' (Au/S)	NDro
- 'Stripe U Like' (Au/St)	NDro
- 'Striped Ace' (Au/St)	NDro WHil
- 'Stripey' (Au/d)	NDro
- 'Stromboli' (Au/d)	GAbr ITim NDro WCot WHil XBar
- 'Subliminal' (Au/A)	NDro
- 'Sugar Plum Fairy' (Au/S)	GAbr NDro WHil
- 'Summer Sky' (Au/A)	NDro
- 'Summer Wine' (Au/A)	NDro XBar
- 'Sumo' (Au/A)	GAbr NDro WHil XBar
- 'Sunflower' (Au/A/S)	GAbr ITim NDro WHil
- 'Sunlight' (Au/A)	WAln
- 'Sunlit Tiger' (Au/S)	GAbr NDro
- 'Sunspot' (Au/A)	WAln
- 'Sunstar' (Au/S)	NDro
- 'Super Para' (Au/S)	GAbr NDro WHil
- 'Superb' (Au/S)	XBar
- 'Surething' (Au/A)	WAln
- 'Susan' (Au/A)	NDro
- 'Susannah' (Au/d)	NDro WFar WHil XBar
- 'Sweet Georgia Brown' (Au/A)	NDro WAln
- 'Sweet Lorraine' (Au/S)	NDro
- 'Sweet Pastures' (Au/S)	GAbr NDro
- 'Swiss Royal Velvet' (Au/B)	NDro
- 'Sword' (Au/d)	GAbr NDro WFar XBar
- 'Symphony' (Au/A)	ITim NDro WHil XBar
- 'T.A. Hadfield' (Au/A)	NDro WHil
- 'Taffeta' (Au/S)	EBee GAbr LCro LOPS NDro WFar WHil
- 'Tally-ho' (Au/A)	WAln
- 'Tamar Mist' (Au/d)	WHil
- 'Tamino' (Au/S)	NDro
- 'Tango' (Au/d)	NDro WAln
- 'Tarantella' (Au/A)	GAbr NDro
- 'Tawny Owl' (Au/B)	GAbr
- 'Tay Tiger' (Au/St)	GAbr NDro WHil XBar
- 'Taylor's Grey' (Au/S)	NDro
- 'Teawell Pride' (Au/d)	ITim NHpl WHil
- 'Ted Gibbs' (Au/A)	NDro WHil
- 'Ted Roberts' (Au/A)	CBor ITim NDro WHil XBar
- 'Teem' (Au/S)	GAbr NDro XBar
- 'Telford's Surprise' (Au/A)	WAln
- 'Temeraire' (Au/A)	WHil
- 'Tenderly' (Au/St)	NDro
- 'Terpo' (Au/A)	NDro WAln WHil
- 'Tess' (Au/A)	XBar
- 'The Argylls' (Au/St)	NDro
- 'The Baron' (Au/S)	GAbr GKev WHil XBar
- 'The Bishop' (Au/S)	ITim WAln WHil XBar
- 'The Bride' (Au/S)	NDro
- 'The Cardinal' (Au/d)	WAln
- 'The Czar' (Au/A)	GAbr NDro
- 'The Egyptian' (Au/A)	NDro WHil XBar
- 'The Hobbit' (Au/A)	WAln
- 'The Lady Galadriel' (Au/A)	NDro
- 'The Raven' (Au/S)	ITim WHil
- 'The Sneep' (Au/A)	GAbr ITim NDro XBar
- 'The Snods' (Au/S)	NDro
- 'Thea' (Au/B)	XBar
I - 'Theodora' (Au/S)	XBar
- 'Thetis' (Au/A)	XBar
- 'Thisbe' (Au/A)	NDro
- 'Three Way Stripe' (St)	GAbr WHil
- 'Thutmoses' (Au/A)	NDro WAln
- 'Tiana' (Au/B) **new**	XBar
- 'Tim' (Au/d)	GAbr ITim NDro

– 'Timpany Blues' (Au/B)	ITim NDro
– 'Timpany Dawn' (Au/B) **new**	NDro
– 'Tim's Fancy' (Au/S)	NDro
– 'Tinker' (Au/S)	NDro WAln
– 'Tinkerbell' (Au/S)	NDro
– 'Tiptoe' (Au/St)	NDro
– 'Toffee Apple' (Au/d)	NDro
– 'Toffee Crisp' (Au/A)	GAbr NDro XBar
– 'Tomboy' (Au/S)	NDro
– 'Toolyn' (Au/S)	NDro WAln
– 'Topaz' (Au/B) **new**	NDro
– 'Tosca' (Au/S)	GAbr NDro WHil XBar
– 'Trafalgar' (Au/S)	NDro
– 'Trafalgar Square' (Au/S)	GAbr NDro XBar
– 'Tregor Orange' (Au/d)	WCot
– 'Tregor Stripe' (Au/St)	XBar
– 'Trish' (Au)	GAbr
– 'Trojan' (Au/S)	EBee
– 'Trouble' (Au/d)	GAbr GQue NDro WHil
– 'Troy Aykman' (Au/A)	NDro WAln WHil XBar
– 'Trudy' (Au/S)	GAbr ITim NDro WHil
– 'True Briton' (Au/S)	NDro
– 'Truman' (Au/B)	NDro
– 'Trumpet Blue' (Au/S)	NDro WAln WHil
– 'Tudor Rose' (Au/S)	WAln XBar
– 'Tumbledown' (Au/A)	NDro
– 'Tummel' (Au/A)	GAbr NDro WHil
– 'Tupelo Honey' (Au/d)	WAln
– 'Twiggy' (Au/S)	GAbr NDro WFar XBar
– 'Typhoon' (Au/A)	WHil
– 'Uncle Arthur' (Au/A)	WAln WHil
– 'Upper Crust' (Au/St)	NDro
– 'Upperfields' (Au/B)	NDro
– 'Ursula' (Au/d)	WAln
– 'Valerie' (Au/A)	ITim
– 'Valerie Clare' (Au/S)	WAln WHil
– 'Vee Too' (Au/A)	GAbr NDro WHil
– 'Vega' (Au/A)	WAln
– 'Velvet Moon' (Au/A)	WAln
– 'Venetian' (Au/A)	ITim NDro WHil
– 'Venus' (Au/A)	WAln
– 'Vera' (Au/A)	NDro WAln
– 'Vera Eden' (Au)	WAln
– 'Vera Hill' (Au/A)	WAln
– 'Verdi' (Au/A)	WAln
– 'Vesuvius' (Au/d)	GAbr NDro
– 'Victoria de Wemyss' (Au/A)	NDro WHil XBar
– 'Victoria Jane' (Au/A)	WAln
– 'Victoria Park' (Au/A)	WAln XBar
– 'Vienna' (Au/B)	NDro
– 'Violet Surprise' (Au/St)	NDro
– 'Voodoo Mama' (Au/St)	NDro
– 'Vroni' (Au/A)	EBee
– 'Vulcan' (Au/A)	NDro XBar
– 'Walhampton' (Au/S)	NDro
– 'Walton' (Au/A)	GAbr NDro WHil XBar
– 'Walton Heath' (Au/d)	GAbr NDro WCot WFar WHil
– 'Wanda's Moonlight' (Au/d)	WAln
– 'Warpaint' (Au/St)	NDro
– 'Watchett' (Au/S)	NDro
– 'Weirdo' (Au) **new**	NDro
– 'Wentworth' (Au/A)	WAln
– 'Werner Müller' (Au/B)	NDro
– 'West Harrow' (Au/S)	NDro
– 'Westbourne Park' (Au/S)	NDro
– 'Wheal' (Au/S)	NDro
– 'Whistlejacket' (Au/S)	NDro
– 'White Ensign' (Au/S)	GAbr NDro NWad WHil
– 'White Pyne' (Au/B)	NDro
– 'White Satin' (Au/S)	NDro
– 'White Water' (Au/A)	NDro WHil
– 'White Wings' (Au/S)	ITim NDro NHpl
– 'Whoopee' (Au/A)	NDro WAln
– 'Wichita Falls' (Au/A)	NDro WAln
– 'Wide Awake' (Au/A)	NDro
– 'Wild and Grey' (Au/S)	NDro
– 'Wilf Booth' (Au/A)	XBar
– 'William Gunn' (Au/d)	NDro WAln
– 'Willow Tree' (Au/S)	WAln
– 'Wincha' (Au/S)	ITim NDro
– 'Windward Blue' (Au)	NDro
– 'Windways Mystery' (Au/B)	GAbr NDro
– 'Windy Border' (Au/B) **new**	NDro
– 'Windy Goldtop' (Au/A)	WAln
– 'Winifred' (Au/B)	see *P.* × *pubescens* 'Winnifred'
– 'Winifrid' (Au/A)	NDro NWad WHil
– 'Wonderous One' (Au/St)	NDro
– 'Woodlands Lilac' (Au/B)	NDro WHil
– 'Woodmill' (Au/A)	NDro WHil XBar
– 'Wookey Hole' (Au/A)	NDro
– 'Wycliffe Harmony' (Au/B)	NDro
– 'Wycliffe Midnight' (Au/B)	GAbr ITim NDro WHil
– 'Wye Hen' (Au/St)	NDro
– 'X2' (Au/S)	WHil
– 'Xavier' (Au/d)	EBee
– 'Yellow Ace' (Au)	GAbr
– 'Yellow Hammer' (Au/S)	WAln
– 'Yellow Isle' (Au/S)	WAln
– 'Yellow Muff' (Au/S)	NDro
– 'Yellow Ribbon' (Au)	WAln
– 'Yitzhak Rabin' (Au/A)	NDro WHil
– 'Yorkshire Grey' (Au/S)	GAbr NDro
– 'Young Ian' (Au/B)	NDro
– 'Young Love' (Au/B) **new**	NDro
– 'Zambia' (Au/d)	GAbr ITim NDro
– 'Zephyr' (Au/St)	NDro
– 'Ziggy' (Au/St)	NDro
– 'Zircon' (Au/S)	NDro
– 'Zoe' (Au/A)	WAln
– 'Zoe Ann' (Au/S)	WAln
I – 'Zona' (Au/A)	NDro
– 'Zorro' (Au/St)	NDro
auriculata (Or)	GKev SVic
balbisii (Au)	CWCL GKev
'Balmoral' (Royal Oakleaf Series) (Pr/Poly) **new**	MMrt
'Barbara Midwinter' (Pr)	EBee GAbr SHar WCot
Barnhaven Blues Group (Pr/Prim)	XBar
Barnhaven doubles (Pr/Prim/d)	XBar
Barnhaven Gold Group (Pr/Prim)	XBar
Barnhaven Gold-laced Group	see *P.* Gold-laced Group Barnhaven
Barnhaven Pixies Group (Pr/Prim)	XBar
'Beatrice Wooster' (Au)	EHyd GAbr LRHS NRHS WFar XBar
'Beeches' Pink' (Prim/Poly)	GAbr
beesiana (Pf) ♀H6	Widely available
(Belarina Series) BELARINA AMETHYST ICE ('Kerbelpicotee'[PBR]) (Pr/Prim/d)	CDor LRHS LSou MHol WHil WTor

- BELARINA BUTTER YELLOW ('Kerbelbut'PBR) (Pr/Prim/d)	CAby CDor CExl CWCL ELon EPfP LRHS LSou MHol NLar WCav WHil
- BELARINA BUTTERMILK ('Kerbelmilk'PBR) (Pr/Prim/d)	LSou NLar
- BELARINA COBALT BLUE ('Kerbelcob'PBR) (Pr/Prim/d)	CAby CExl CWCL LRHS LSou NHpl NLar WHil
- BELARINA CREAM ('Kerbelcrem'PBR) (Pr/Prim/d)	CAby CDor CExl CWCL ELon LRHS NHpl WBor
- BELARINA PINK CHAMPAGNE ('Kerbelchamp'PBR) (Pr/Prim/d)	CWCL LSou WHil
- BELARINA PINK ICE ('Kerbelpice'PBR) (Pr/Prim/d)	CAby CDor CWCL ELon LSou MAvo NHpl NLar WBor WHil WTor
- BELARINA ROSETTE NECTARINE ('Kerbelnec'PBR) (Pr/Prim/d)	CAby CDor CExl CWCL ECtt ELon LRHS MHol NLar SPad WCav WHil
- BELARINA VALENTINE ('Kerbelred'PBR) (Pr/Prim/d)	CAby CDor CWCL LRHS LSou MHol NLar WHil WTor
bellidifolia (Mu)	GKev NGdn
beluensis	see *P.* × *pubescens* 'Freedom'
× ***berninae*** (Au)	GKev
'Bewerley White'	see *P.* × *pubescens* 'Bewerley White'
bhutanica	see *P. whitei* 'Sherriff's Variety'
bileckii	see *P.* × *forsteri* 'Bileckii'
'Blindsee' (Au)	EPot NHar XBar
blinii (Y)	GKev
'Blue Ice' (Pr/Prim/d)	XBar
Blue Julians Group (Pr/Prim)	XBar
'Blue Riband' (Pr/Prim)	GAbr WFar
'Blue Sapphire' (Pr/Prim/d)	CMiW XBar
'Bon Accord Cerise' (Pr/Poly/d)	GAbr
'Bon Accord Purple' (Pr/Poly/d)	CMiW WRHF
'Bonheur' (Pr/Prim/d)	XBar
boothii 'Renfe' (Pe)	WCot
- subsp. ***repens*** (Pe)	GKev MNrw
'Boothman's Ruby'	see *P.* × *pubescens* 'Boothman's Variety'
boveana (Sp)	GKev
bracteata (Bu)	EPot GKev WAbe
§ - subsp. ***dubernardiana*** (Bu)	WAbe
brevicula (Cy) SDR 4452	GKev
'Brittany Blue' (Pr/Prim/d)	XBar
'Broadwell Chameleon' (Au)	ITim NHar
'Broadwell Milkmaid' (Au) 🏆H5	ITim WAbe
'Broadwell Ruby' (Au)	ITim WAbe
'Broadwell Snowstorm' (Au)	ITim
'Broxbourne' (Au) 🏆H5	ITim
'Buckland Wine' (Pr/Prim)	CElw CFis EBee ECtt EPfP GAbr GEdr XBar
bullata (Bu)	GKev
× ***bulleesiana*** (Pf)	CAby CDor CTsd CWCL EHyd EPfP EShb EWTr GKev GMaP GWyn LRHS MCot MWts NChi NGdn NHol NRHS NWad SAko SCob WFar WPnP XBar
bulleyana (Pf) 🏆H7	Widely available

- hybrids (Pf)	GKev
'Burgundy Ice' (Pr/Prim/d)	XBar
burmanica (Pf)	CWCL GAbr GKev MMuc NChi WHoo XBar
'Butter's Baby' **new**	WOut
'Butter's Bronze' (Pr/Prim)	WOut
Butterscotch Group (Pr/Prim)	XBar
'Caerulea Plena' (Pr/Prim)	NBid
calderiana purple-flowered (Pe)	GKev
- subsp. ***strumosa*** (Pe)	GKev
calliantha (Cy)	GKev
'Camaieu' (Pr/Prim/d)	XBar
Candelabra hybrids (Pf)	CBre CPla GAbr ITim MBriF NBir NGdn NHpl WCav
Candy Pinks Group (Pr/Prim)	XBar
capitata (Ca)	CBcs CPla EPfP GKev LRHS MPie NGBl NHpl SPer WCAu WCot
- CC 3843	SRms
- subsp. ***capitata*** (Ca)	CAvo
- subsp. ***crispata*** (Ca)	GKev
- subsp. ***mooreana*** (Ca)	CAby CExl CSpe CTsd EDAr EPfP GKev NChi NGdn NHpl NLar SPlb WAbe XBar
- 'Noverna Blue' (Ca)	MHol
- 'Noverna Deep Blue' (Ca)	SRms WCav
- subsp. ***sphaerocephala*** (Ca) 🏆H7	GKev
'Captain Blood' (Pr/Prim/d)	CMiW NHpl
Carnation Victorians Group (Pr/Poly)	XBar
carniolica (Au)	GKev WCot
cawdoriana (So)	GKev
cernua (Mu)	XBar
Chartreuse Group (Pr/Poly)	XBar
'Cherry' (Pr/Prim)	GAbr
§ ***chionantha*** (Cy) 🏆H6	GAbr GEdr GKev NBir NGdn WFar XBar
- subsp. ***chionantha*** (Cy)	EBee GKev MHol
- subsp. ***melanops***	see *P. melanops*
§ - subsp. ***sinoplantaginea*** (Cy)	NLar
§ - subsp. ***sinopurpurea*** (Cy)	EBee GKev NBir
chungensis (Pf)	CBod CDor CTsd EBee ELan ELon EPfP GBin GKev GLog GWyn MHol NGdn NHol NLar SPtp SWvt WFar WMAq XBar
§ ***chungensis*** × ***pulverulenta*** (Pf)	GBin GKev MPnt SAko WSpi
× ***chunglenta***	see *P. chungensis* × *pulverulenta*
'Cisca' (Pr)	WCot
'Clarence Elliott' (Au) 🏆H5	GKev MPnt NRya NWad WFar WIce
'Clarissa White' (Pr/Poly)	XBar
clarkei (Or)	GKev WAbe
clusiana (Au)	GKev WAbe
- 'Murray-Lyon' (Au)	NDro NHar
cockburniana (Pf) 🏆H6	CSpe CTsd GAbr NWad WCot XBar
- SDR 1967	EBee GKev
- 'Kevock Sunshine' (Pf)	GKev NWad XBar
- orange-flowered (Pf)	GKev
concholoba (Mu)	EBee GKev XBar
'Corporal Baxter' (Pr/Prim/d)	CMiW ECtt GMaP XBar
cortusoides (Co)	CAby EBee GKev XBar
'Cottage Cream' (Pr)	LSou MBros SVic
Cowichan Amethyst Group (Pr/Poly)	XBar

	Cowichan Blue Group (Pr/Poly)	XBar
	Cowichan Garnet Group (Pr/Poly)	MBriF XBar
	Cowichan strain (Pr/Poly)	CElw
	Cowichan Venetian Group (Pr/Poly)	XBar
	Cowichan Yellow Group (Pr/Poly)	XBar
	'Craddock White' (Pr/Prim)	CFis CMiW
	'Crème du Tregor' (Pr/Prim/d)	XBar
	'Crimson Velvet' (Au)	WThu XBar
	crispa	see *P. glomerata*
	cuneifolia (Cu)	GKev
	- subsp. ***heterodonta*** (Cu)	GKev
	'Custard the Cat' **new**	WHil
	darialica (Al)	GKev
	'Dark Rosaleen' (Pr/Poly)	CAby CElw CExl CRos CWGN ECtt EHyd EMor EPfP EWTr GAbr LRHS MBNS MBriF MHol MMuc MNrw MPie NDov NHpl NLar NRHS NWad SAko SPoG WBrk WCot WFar XBar
	'David Green' (Pr/Prim)	CMiW
	'David Valentine' (Pr/Poly)	CFis GAbr WCot WOld XBar
	'Dawn Ansell' (Pr/Prim/d)	CAby CDor CMiW ECtt EPfP MBNS MBow MHol NBir NHpl WCAu WHer WHil XBar
	Daybreak Group (Pr/Poly)	XBar
	'Dentelle' (Pr/Prim/d)	XBar
	denticulata (De) [H6]	Widely available
	- var. ***alba*** (De)	CAby CAvo CBcs CRos CTri EBee EBou ECha EHyd EPfP GAbr GMaP GWyn LRHS LSun MBel MMuc MPri NGdn NLar NRHS SCob SGbt SPer SPoG WFar WGwG WWtn
	- blue-flowered (De)	CAvo EPfP GAbr GBin GWyn MPri NLar
	- 'Bressingham Beauty' (De)	EBee EHyd LRHS
	- var. ***cachemiriana*** hort. (De)	GRum NWad
	- 'Glenroy Crimson' (De)	EBee
	- hybrids	WFar XBar
	- 'Karryann' (De/v)	WCot WHil
	- lavender-flowered (De)	CAby
	- lilac-flowered (De)	CRos EHyd EPfP EShb LRHS NHol NRHS SCob WTor
	- red-flowered (De)	CAby CAvo EPfP NBir SCob
	- 'Rubin' (De)	CRos CWCL CWat EBee EBou EHyd EPfP GAbr GMaP LRHS MBel NChi NLar NRHS SPer SPoG SRms XLum
	- 'Rubinball' (De)	NHol
	Desert Sunset Group (Pr/Poly)	XBar
	dickieana (Am)	GKev
	× ***digenea*** (Pr) **new**	XBar
	'Don Keefe' (Pr/Poly)	CBcs CBod EBee ECtt GAbr MBNS MBel MBriF MHol MMuc MNrw MPie NGBl NHpl NLar NWad WCot WFar
	'Double Lilac'	see *P. vulgaris* 'Lilacina Plena'
	dubernardiana	see *P. bracteata* subsp. *dubernardiana*
	'Duchess of York' (Pr/Poly)	CMiW ECtt GAbr MHCG NLar WCot
	'Duckyls Red' (Pr/Prim)	NBir WHal
	'Easter Bonnet' (Pr/Prim)	LRHS MMuc SEND
	edgeworthii	see *P. nana*
§	***elatior*** (Pr) [H6]	CAby CBod CDor CMac EPfP GAbr GJos GKev GMaP LCro LOPS MBel MBow MHer MHol MNHC MNrw MPri NAts NChi NLar SPer SPoG SRms SWvt WBrk WCav WHoo
	- hose-in-hose (Pr/d)	NBid
	- hybrids (Pr)	SPlb
	- 'Magnifica' (Pr)	GKev
§	- subsp. ***meyeri*** (Pr)	SBrt
I	- - 'Alba' (Pr) **new**	GRum
	- subsp. ***pallasii*** (Pr)	GKev SPhx
	- subsp. ***pseudoelatior*** (Pr)	GKev WAbe
	'Elizabeth Browning' (Pr/Poly)	ECtt GAbr WCot
	'Elizabeth Killelay'[PBR] (Pr/Poly/d)	CAby CBct CDor CExl CMiW CPla CWCL CWGN ECtt ELan MNrw MPie NBir NDov NGdn NHpl NLar NWad SPer WCot WFar
	'Ethel Barker' (Au)	NWad
	'Eugénie' (Pr/Prim/d)	ECtt MRav
	'Fairy Rose' (Au)	NWad
	fangii (Pu) **new**	GKev
	farinosa (Al)	GKev NGdn XBar
	- var. ***denudata*** (*Al*)	GKev
	fasciculata (Ar)	SPlb
	- CLD 345	GEdr WAbe
	'Feuerkönig' (Au)	NDro
	'Fire Opal' (Pr/Poly)	CRos EHyd LRHS NRHS
	Firefly Group (Pr/Poly)	WCot XBar
§	***firmipes*** (Si)	LPot
§	***flaccida*** (Mu)	GEdr GKev NHpl WHil
	Flamingo Group (Pr/Poly)	XBar
	floribunda (Sp) **new**	EWTr
	florindae (Si) [H7]	Widely available
	- bronze-flowered (Si)	NBir
	- 'Dave's Red' (Si)	LEdu
	- hybrids (Si)	CMac EShb WFar WHil WWtn XBar
	- Keillour hybrids (Si)	NGdn SWvt WBor
	- orange-flowered (Si)	GPSL LLWG MNrw SRms WPnP
	- peach-flowered (Si)	CSpe
	- 'Ray's Ruby' (Si)	CTsd GAbr MNrw NBir NChi WCot
	- red and copper hybrids (Si)	MWts SWvt WHoo
	- 'Red Shades' (Si)	CRos NWad
	- red-flowered (Si)	CSpe GKev GPSL LLWG MMuc NBid NLar WFar
	- terracotta-flowered (Si)	NGdn
	Footlight Parade Group (Pr/Prim)	XBar
	forbesii (Mo)	WCot
	- CC 4084	CExl
	forrestii (Bu)	EPot GKev
	- SDR 4304	CExl
§	× ***forsteri*** (Au)	NHpl NLar
§	- 'Bileckii' (Au)	GMaP NBir NHar NSla
	- 'Dianne' (Au)	GAbr GKev NRya WAbe
	'Francisca' (Pr/Poly) [H7]	CAby CBod CExl CMac CWCL CWGN EBee ECtt EPfP GBin LPot MBNS MBel MHol NChi NHpl NLar NSti NWad SPad WBrk WCAu WCFE WCot WFar WRHF XBar XLum
	'Fred Salter' (Au)	NRya
	frondosa (Al) [H5]	EWTr MHol MPnt WAbe
	'Frou-frou' (Pr/Prim/d)	XBar
	Fuchsia Victorians Group (Pr/Poly)	XBar
	'Garnet' (*allionii* hybrid) (Au)	XBar
	'Garryarde Guinevere'	see *P.* 'Guinevere'
	geraniifolia (Co)	GKev

	'Gigha' (Pr/Prim)	EBee GKev MNrw WFar
	'Gilded Garnet' (Pr/Poly/d)	NHpl
	Gilded Ginger Group (Pr/Poly)	XBar
	'Ginger Spice' (Au)	NDro WHil
§	***glomerata*** (Ca)	GKev XBar
	'Glowing Embers' (Pf)	GKev NBir
	glutinosa All.	see *P. allionii*
	Gold-laced Group (Pr/Poly)	CBod CBre CDor CRos CTsd CWCL ECtt EHyd ELan EMor EPfP GAbr GQue LRHS LSRN MAsh MMuc MNHC NGdn NHpl NLar NRHS SEND SPer SPlb SPoG WCAu WFar
§	- Barnhaven (Pr/Poly)	MAsh NBir XBar
	- - 'Gold-laced Jack in the Green'	XBar
	- Beeches strain (Pr/Poly)	XBar
	- hose-in-hose (Pr/Poly) **new**	XBar
	- 'Lightly Laced' (Pr/Poly) **new**	NWad
	- red-flowered (Pr/Poly)	ELan XEll
	gracilipes (Pe)	GKev WFar
	- 'Minor'	see *P. petiolaris* Wall.
	graminifolia	see *P. chionantha*
	Grand Canyon Group (Pr/Poly)	CWCL XBar
	grandis (Sr)	GKev XBar
	'Green Lace' (Pr/Poly)	ECtt
	'Groenekan's Glorie' (Pr/Prim)	CFis EBee ECtt GAbr NBir WFar XBar
	'Guernsey Cream' (Pr/Prim/d)	XBar
§	'Guinevere' (Pr/Poly) 🏆H6	Widely available
	'Hall Barn Blue' (Pr/Prim)	CSam EBee ELan EWhm GAbr GEdr GMaP MHCG MMuc SEND WCot WOld
§	***halleri*** (Al)	EBee GAbr GKev XBar
	- 'Longiflora'	see *P. halleri*
	- subsp. ***platyphylla*** (Al)	GKev
	handeliana × ***maximowiczii*** (Cy)	GKev
	Harbinger Group (Pr/Prim)	XBar
	Harbour Lights Group (Pr/Poly)	XBar
	Harlow Car hybrids (Pf)	CRos EHyd EPfP LRHS NRHS NSla NWad WHil XBar
	Harvest Yellows Group (Pr/Poly)	CWCL XBar
	helodoxa	see *P. prolifera*
	'Hemswell Blush' (Au)	NHpl WFar
	'Hemswell Ember' (Au)	CPBP ECtt
	'Heritage Cream' (Pr/Prim)	EPfP
	heucherifolia (Co) SDR 3224	GKev
	hidakana (R)	GEdr
	'High Point' (Au)	CPBP
	hirsuta (Au)	GKev MMuc SEND
	- red-flowered (Au)	GKev
	- subsp. ***valcuvianensis*** (Au)	EPot
	- white-flowered (Au)	NRya
	hirsuta × ***minima***	see *P.* × *forsteri*
	hoffmanniana	SPlb
	hose-in-hose (Pr/Poly/d)	EWes MNrw
	- Barnhaven (Pr/Poly/d)	XBar
§	Husky Series (Pr/Prim) 🏆H5	SVic
	ianthina	see *P. prolifera*
	Indian Reds Group (Pr/Poly)	CWCL XBar
	'Ingram's Blue' (Pr/Poly)	CFis CMiW EBee EPfP MHol
	Inshriach hybrids (Pf)	CAby GBin SPer WBor
	integrifolia (Au)	GKev
§	'Inverewe' (Pf)	EBee GBin GEdr GKev MPnt NBir NHpl XBar
	involucrata	see *P. munroi*
	'Iris Mainwaring' (Pr/Prim)	CFis EBee ECtt ELan GAbr GKev
	irregularis (Pe)	ITim WAbe
	Jack-in-the-Green Group (Pr/Poly)	GAbr MNrw WBor
	- Barnhaven (Pr/Poly)	XBar
	- red-flowered (Pr/Poly)	MMuc WHil
	'Jack-the-Lad' (Pr/Prim/d)	XBar
	'Janet Aldrich' (Au)	CPBP
	japonica (Pf)	CSam ECha LRHS MSCN MWts NBro NGdn
	- 'Alba' (Pf)	CAby CBod CPla CTri CTsd EHyd EPfP EShb LLWG LRHS MBel MHol NChi NGdn NLar NWad SPer WCAu WFar WHil
	- 'Apple Blossom' (Pf)	Widely available
*	- 'Carminea' (Pf)	CDor GKev MSCN NBro NGdn NWad SPer WFar
	- 'Fuji' (Pf)	GKev NBro
	- hybrids (Pf)	CMac WFar
	- 'Jim Saunders' (Pf)	SLon
	- 'Miller's Crimson' (Pf) 🏆H6	Widely available
	- 'Oriental Sunrise' (Pf)	GKev ITim XBar
	- pale pink-flowered (Pf)	ITim
	- 'Postford White' (Pf) 🏆H6	CBcs CBod CCBP CDor CPla CRos CSam EBee EHyd ELan EPfP GAbr GKev GMaP ITim LRHS LSRN NBir NRHS SCob SPer SPoG SRms SWvt WBor WBrk XBar
	- 'Valley Red' (Pf)	GKev
	- Violet Oriental Group (Pf)	XBar
	- violet-flowered (Pf)	GKev
	jesoana (Co)	GKev
	- var. ***pubescens*** (Co)	GKev
	'Jewel' (Pr)	GAbr
	'Joan Hughes' (*allionii* hybrid) (Au)	WAbe
	'Joanna' (Pr/Poly)	ECtt MPnt
	'Johanna' (Pu)	GKev LEdu NGdn WAbe
	'John Fielding' (Pr)	CBro CElw EBee GAbr NWad
	'Jo-Jo' (Au)	CPBP ITim WAbe XBar
	'Jubilee' (Pr/Prim/d)	XBar
	juliae (Pr)	EHyd GKev LRHS NBid NHpl NRHS SPlb WAbe
I	- 'Millicent' (Pr)	WCot
	'Ken Dearman' (Pr/Prim/d)	CMiW ECtt EWTr NBir NHpl XBar
	× ***kewensis*** (Sp) 🏆H3	CPla GKev XBar
	'Kingscote' (Au)	NDro
	'Kinlough Beauty' (Pr/Poly)	CFis EBee ECtt GMaP XBar
§	***kisoana*** (Co)	CExl GEdr GKev
	- var. ***alba*** (Co)	GEdr NHar XBar
	- 'Barnhaven Blush' (Co)	XBar
	- 'Iyo-beni' (Co)	GEdr NHar XBar
	- 'Noushoku' (Co)	GEdr XBar
	- var. ***shikokiana***	see *P. kisoana*
	kitaibeliana (Au)	GKev
	komarovii (Pr)	SPlb
	'Kusum Krishna' (Au)	GEdr GRum MAvo MBNS MHol MPie NHpl NRya NWad WCot WFar
	'Lady Greer' (Pr/Poly) 🏆H5	CBod CMac CMiW CSam EBee ECtt ELan EMor EPPr EPfP GAbr GKev GMaP GWyn MHer MTin NChi NGdn NLar WCAu WFar XBar
	'Lambrook Mauve' (Pr/Poly)	CElw CFis GAbr
§	***latifolia*** (Au)	GKev
	latisecta (Co)	GEdr GKev

§	***laurentiana*** (Al)	EWes GKev
	'Lea Gardens' (*allionii* hybrid) (Au)	NWad
	'Lee Myers' (*allionii* hybrid) (Au)	WFar XBar
	'Lemon and Lime'	CMea
	leucophylla	see *P. elatior*
	'Lilac Lover' (Au) **new**	CPBP
	lilacina (Mu)	EPot GKev
	'Lilian Foster' (Pr/Prim)	WCot
	'Lilian Harvey' (Pr/Prim/d)	CMiW
	'Lindum Angelic' (Au)	NHar
	'Lindum Celebration' (Au)	NHar
	'Lindum Crepes Suzette' (Au)	ITim NHar
	'Lindum Destiny' (Au) **new**	CPBP
	'Lindum Dove' (Au)	NHar
	'Lindum Finale' (Au)	ITim NHar
	'Lindum First Kiss' (Au)	ITim
	'Lindum Frosty Moon' (Au)	ITim
	'Lindum Gecko' (Au)	NHar
	'Lindum Golden Orb' (Au)	NHar
	'Lindum Heavenly' (Au)	XBar
	'Lindum Lancelot' (Au)	WMal
	'Lindum Lavender Mist' (Au)	XBar
	'Lindum Limelight' (Au)	ITim
	'Lindum Lyric' (Au)	NHar
	'Lindum Moonlight' (Au)	WMal XBar
	'Lindum Morning Flight' (Au)	NHar
	'Lindum Rapture' (Au)	NHar
	'Lindum Storm Cloud' (Au)	NHar
	'Lindum Wedgwood' (Au)	ITim NHar
	'Lingwood Beauty' (Pr/Prim)	CAby CElw CFis
	'Lismore' (Au)	NWad
	'Lismore Peardrop' (Au)	EPot
	'Lismore Pink Ice' (Au)	NWad
	Little Egypt Group (Pr/Poly)	XBar
	littoniana	see *P. vialii*
	'Lizzie Green' (Pr/Prim)	NLar
	× ***loiseleurii*** 'Aire Mist' (Au) ♀^{H5}	ITim NHpl NRya NSla WFar XBar
§	- 'Aire Waves' (Au)	CWCL ITim NHar NRya
	- 'Lismore Yellow' (Au)	XBar
	- 'Pink Aire Mist' (Au)	ITim
	longiflora	see *P. halleri*
	'Lopen Red' (Pr/Prim)	CMiW XBar
	lutea (Au)	GKev
	luteola (Or)	GKev NGdn NHpl XBar
	macrocalyx	see *P. veris*
	macrophylla (Cy)	EWes GKev
	- var. ***moorcroftiana*** (Cy)	EWld GKev
	'MacWatt's Claret' (Pr/Poly)	ECtt GAbr
	'MacWatt's Cream' (Pr/Poly)	CFis CRos EBee EHyd GAbr GEdr LEdu LRHS NLar NRHS WCot WHil
	'Mademoiselle Zia' (Pr/Poly)	XBar
	magellanica (Al)	GKev SPlb
	mairei (Al)	GKev
	'Maisie Michael' (Pr/Prim)	EPot GEdr NHpl WAbe
	malacoides (Mo) ♀^{H2}	XBar
	malvacea (Ma)	GKev
	marginata (Au) ♀^{H5}	CRos EHyd LRHS MMuc NRHS NSla SEND WAbe
	- 'Adrian Evans' (Au)	GEdr WIce
	- 'Adrian Jones' (Au)	XBar
	- 'Alba' (Au)	EHyd GEdr LRHS NBro NRHS NRya NWad XBar
	- 'Ardfearn' (Au)	GEdr
	- 'Baldock's Purple' (Au)	NRya XBar
	- 'Barbara Clough' (Au)	GEdr NRya NWad XBar
	- 'Beamish' (Au) ♀^{H5}	GEdr NBro NRya NSla NWad
	- 'Beatrice Lascaris' (Au)	EHyd GEdr LRHS NRHS NRya WAbe
	- 'Bill Crow' (Au)	GEdr NRya
	- 'Caerulea' (Au)	GEdr NRya NWad XBar
	- 'Casterino' (Au)	WAbe
	- 'Clear's Variety' (Au)	GKev XBar
	- 'Crookes Variety' (Au)	NRya
	- 'Doctor Jenkins' (Au)	NRya NWad
	- 'Dolomites' (Au)	NWad
	- 'Drake's Form' (Au)	NRya XBar
	- dwarf (Au)	EHyd GEdr LRHS NRHS NRya
	- 'Earl L. Bolton'	see *P. marginata* 'El Bolton'
§	- 'El Bolton' (Au)	NRya NWad
	- 'Elizabeth Fry' (Au)	GEdr
	- 'Grandiflora' (Au)	NWad
	- 'Highland Twilight' (Au)	NSla
	- 'Holden Variety' (Au)	NRya NWad XBar
	- 'Holly Leaf' (Au)	GEdr
	- 'Ivy Agee' (Au)	NRya
	- 'Janet' (Au)	GEdr NWad
	- 'Johannes Holler' (Au)	ITim NRya
	- 'Kesselring's Variety' (Au)	CMea ITim NWad WAbe WFar WIce XBar
	- 'Laciniata' (Au)	EHyd GKev GRum LRHS NRHS XBar
	- 'Linda Pope' (Au) ♀^{H5}	GEdr NBir WThu XBar
	- maritime form (Au)	XBar
	- 'Millard's Variety' (Au)	ITim NWad
	- 'Mrs Carter Walmsley' (Au)	NRya NWad
	- 'Mylene' (Au)	CPBP NRya
	- 'Napoleon' (Au)	GEdr ITim NRya NWad
	- 'Peggy Fell' (Au)	NWad
	- 'Prichard's Variety' (Au) ♀^{H5}	GEdr GPSL ITim NRya WAbe
	- 'Sheila Denby' (Au)	NRya NWad
	- 'The President' (Au)	NWad
	- 'Waithman's Variety' (Au)	NRya NWad
	'Maria Talbot' (*allionii* hybrid) (Au)	CPBP
	'Marianne Davey' (Pr/Prim/d)	WKif
	Marine Blues Group (Pr/Poly)	XBar
	'Mars' (*allionii* hybrid) (Au)	XBar
	'Mary Anne' (Pr)	GAbr
	matthioli	see *Cortusa matthioli*
	Mauve Victorians Group (Pr/Poly)	XBar
	maximowiczii (Cy)	EDAr GEdr NGdn
§	- var. ***maximowiczii*** (Cy)	GKev NHpl
	- Red-flowered Group	see *P. maximowiczii* var. *maximowiczii*
	maximowiczii × ***tangutica*** (Cy)	GKev
	megaseifolia (Pr)	GKev
	melanantha (Cy)	GKev
	- 'Moonshine' (Cy)	GKev
§	***melanops*** (Cy)	GKev
	'Melenoc'h' (Pr/Prim/d)	MBow XBar
	Midnight Group (Pr/Prim)	XBar
	'Miel' (Pr/Prim/d)	XBar
	'Millstream Cream' (Au)	NLar
	'Millwood Blush' (Pr/Prim) **new**	CMiW
	'Millwood Double' (Pr/Prim/d) **new**	CMiW
	'Millwood Lemon' (Pr/Prim) **new**	CMiW
	minima (Au)	GKev NBro

	minor (Cy)	GKev
	'Miss Doris' (Pr/Prim/d)	XBar
	'Miss Indigo' (Pr/Prim/d)	CMiW CTsd CWCL ECtt EPfP GMaP MBNS MBow MHol NHpl WCAu XBar
	mistassinica (Al)	XBar
	- var. ***macropoda***	see *P. laurentiana*
	miyabeana (Pf)	GKev
	modesta (Al)	XBar
	- var. ***faurieae*** (Al)	GKev
	- var. ***samanimontana*** (Al)	GKev
	'Moerheimii' (Pr/Prim)	GAbr GEdr
	moupinensis (Pe)	CExl
	- subsp. ***barkamensis*** (Pe)	GKev
	'Mrs Eagland' (Pr/Prim)	GAbr
	'Mrs Frank Neave' (Pr/Prim)	GAbr WFar
	'Mrs McGillivray' (Pr/Prim)	GAbr
§	***munroi*** (Ar)	GKev WAbe XBar
	- subsp. ***munroi*** (Ar) CC 5311	GKev
	- white-flowered (Ar)	WAbe
§	- subsp. ***yargongensis*** (Ar)	EBee GKev XBar
	muscarioides (Mu)	GKev
	Muted Victorians Group (Pr/Poly)	XBar
	'Myline'	WThu
§	***nana*** (Pe)	NHar
	New Pinks Group (Pr/Poly)	XBar
	'Nightingale' (Au)	ITim
	nivalis Pallas	see *P. chionantha*
	nutans Delavay ex Franch.	see *P. flaccida*
	obconica subsp. ***werringtonensis*** (Ob)	GKev
	obtusifolia (Cy)	GKev
	'Old Port' (Pr/Poly)	CSam GKev GQue
	Old Rose Victorians Group (Pr/Poly)	XBar
	'Ooh La La Blood Orange' (Ooh La La Series)	WHil
	'Ooh La La Pastel Pink' (Ooh La La Series)	LCro WHil
	optata (Cy)	GKev
	'Orange Flame' (Pf)	GKev
	orbicularis (Cy)	GKev NHpl
	Osiered Amber Group (Pr/Prim)	CWCL NWad XBar
	'Our Pat' (Pr/Poly/d)	CMiW
	Pacific Giants Series (Pr/Poly) **new**	SVic
	palinuri (Au)	WMal
	palmata (Co)	GEdr GKev
	Paris '90 Group (Pr/Poly)	XBar
	parryi (Pa)	GEdr GKev
	pedemontana 'Alba' (Au)	GEdr WThu XBar
	'Perle von Bottrop' (Pr/Prim)	ECtt GBin WCot
	'Peter Klein' (Or)	ECtt GKev
	petiolaris misapplied	see *P.* 'Redpoll'
§	***petiolaris*** Wall. (Pe)	NHar
	- Sherriff's form	see *P.* 'Redpoll'
	'Petticoat' (Pr/Prim/d)	CMiW ECtt NWad WCot XBar
	'Pink Aire' (Au)	XBar
	'Pink Fairy' (Au)	ITim
	'Pink Grapefruit' (Pr/Prim/d)	XBar
	'Pink Ice' (*allionii* hybrid) (Au)	GKev NWad XBar
	'Pink' (Primlet Series) (Pr/Prim)	EHyd LRHS NRHS
	'Pink Star' (Pr/Prim/d)	XBar
	poissonii (Pf)	CDoC CDor CFis CTri CTsd EDAr EHyd EPfP GKev LRHS NGdn NHpl NRHS WShi WWtn
	polyanthus (Pr/Poly)	MMuc SVic
	polyneura (Co)	CBod CTsd EBee GKev MHol NGdn WCot XBar
	'Port Wine' (Pr)	GAbr
	'Powdery Pink' (Pf)	CRos EHyd LRHS NRHS
	prenantha (Pf) SDR 3909	GKev
	'Primadiente Rose' (Co) **new**	WHil
	Primlet Series (Pr/Prim)	SVic
§	***prolifera*** (Pf) ♀H4	EHyd ELan EPfP GKev LRHS MNrw NGdn NHpl NWad SPtp XBar
	- purple-flowered B&SWJ 13951	WCru
§	× ***pubescens*** (Au) ♀H5	CDor EHyd LRHS MHer NGdn NRHS
§	- 'Bewerley White' (Au)	EBee EPfP NDro
§	- 'Boothman's Variety' (Au)	CTri EPfP GKev NSla WBrk WHoo
	- 'Carmen'	see *P.* × *pubescens* 'Boothman's Variety'
	- 'Christine' (Au)	CMea GKev MHer NBir WCot
	- 'Cream Viscosa' (Au)	SPlb WFar
	- 'Faldonside' (Au)	NSla
§	- 'Freedom' (Au)	CTri GKev NBir NSla XBar
	- 'Harlow Car' (Au)	CMea MPnt NWad
	- 'Hazel's White' (Au)	GAbr
	- 'Joan Danger' (Au)	NDro
	- 'Joan Gibbs' (Au)	NHpl XBar
	- 'Lilac Fairy' (Au)	GKev ITim NWad WThu
	- 'Moonlight' (Au)	NDro
	- 'Mrs J.H. Wilson' (Au)	NRya XBar
	- 'Pat Barwick' (Au)	NDro NWad
	- 'Rufus' (Au) ♀H5	GAbr GEdr NDro WThu XBar
	- 'Rumbling Bridge' (Au) **new**	GRum
	- 'Sid Skelton' (Au)	NRya
	- 'Slack Top Violet' (Au)	NSla
	- 'Snowcap' (Au)	ITim XBar
	- 'The General' (Au)	CTri GEdr
§	- 'Wedgwood' (Au)	GAbr NDro XBar
§	- 'Winnifred' (Au)	GAbr NDro
	pulchella (Pu)	GKev
	pulverulenta (Pf) ♀H6	Widely available
	- Bartley hybrids (Pf) ♀H6	CPla EWTr GKev GWyn NHpl NWad
	- 'Bartley Pink' (Pf)	CPla
	'Purple' (Primlet Series) (Pr/Prim)	EHyd LRHS NRHS
	'Purple Storm' (Pr/Prim/d)	WFar XBar
	'Quaker's Bonnet'	see *P. vulgaris* 'Lilacina Plena'
	'Rachel Kinnen' (Au)	GAbr WFar XBar
	Ramona Group (Pr/Poly)	XBar
	'Raspberry Ripple' (Pr/Prim/d)	EHyd LRHS MBow XBar
	'Ravenglass Vermilion'	see *P.* 'Inverewe'
	'Red' (Primlet Series) (Pr/Prim)	CRos EHyd LRHS NRHS
	'Red Ruffles' (Pr/Poly/d)	ECtt
§	'Redpoll' (Pe)	GEdr NHar
	'Reenie' (Au)	EPot
	reidii (So)	GEdr GKev XBar
	- var. ***williamsii*** (So)	GEdr GKev
*	- - ***alba*** (So)	GEdr
	reticulata (Si)	EBee GKev
	Reverie Group (Pr/Poly)	XBar
	'Rheniana' (Au)	NRya
	'Romance' (Pr/Prim/d) **new**	WHil
	'Romeo' (Pr/Prim)	GAbr NWad WCot

'Rose' (Primlet Series) (Pr/Prim)	CRos EHyd LRHS NRHS
rosea (Or) 🏆H5	CAby CBod EPfP GKev GLog GMaP MMuc NBid NBir NRya SCob WPnP XBar
- CC 5260	MAsh
- 'Gigas' (Or)	GAbr WMAq
- 'Grandiflora' (Or)	CBod CMac EMor EPfP GKev GPSL LRHS MBel NLar SPoG SRms XLum
'Rosemary Cottage' (Pr/Poly)	WCot
I 'Rowena' (Pr/Prim)	CFis GAbr WCot
'Roy Cope' (Pr/Prim/d)	NBir
rubra	see *P. firmipes*
'Ruby Tuesday' (Au)	NDro
rupicola (Y)	GKev
rusbyi (Pa)	GKev
- subsp. ***ellisiae*** (Pa)	GKev
'Sapphire' (Au)	XBar
scandinavica (Al)	GKev
scapigera (Pe)	WFar
§ 'Schneekissen' (Pr/Prim)	CAby CBod CMiW CRos CSam CWCL EBee EHyd LRHS MHer NBro NChi NRHS WFar WTor
scotica (Al)	EMor GKev GPoy NSla SPlb WAbe
secundiflora (Pf)	CTsd ELan EWes GKev LLWG NBir NChi NWad SPlb WBrk XBar
serratifolia (Pf)	GKev
sharmae (Al)	GKev
'Sheryl Louise' (Pr/Prim) **new**	NHar
sibthorpii	see *P. vulgaris* subsp. *sibthorpii*
sieboldii (Co) 🏆H5	EHyd EWld GKev MAsh MNrw NHpl NRHS SGro SRms
- 'Aiaigasa' (Co)	CSta
- 'Aka Tonbo' (Co)	CSta
- 'Aki-no-yosooi' (Co)	CSta
- 'Andromeda' (Co)	EBee
- 'Aoba-no-fue' (Co)	CAby CSta
- 'Aoi-no-ue' (Co) **new**	CSta
- 'Aoyagi-zome' (Co)	XBar
- 'Appare' (Co) **new**	CSta
- 'Apple Blossom' (Co) **new**	XBar
- 'Ariake' (Co) **new**	CSta
- 'Arimayama' (Co)	CSta WFar WHil
- 'Asahi' (Co)	CSta WFar
- 'Asahigata' (Co)	CSta WHil
- 'Ayanami' (Co)	WFar
- 'Ayasegawa' (Co)	CSta WFar WHil
- 'Beeches Star' (Co)	EBee
- 'Benjamin' (Co)	CSta WFar WHil
- 'Bide-a-Wee Blue' (Co)	NBid
- 'Bide-a-Wee Lace' (Co)	NBid
- 'Bijyonomai' (Co)	GWyn WFar
I - 'Blue Lagoon' (Co)	CBor CRos CSta EBee EHyd EPfP LRHS NLar NRHS WFar WHil
- 'Blue Shades' (Co)	CWCL
- blue-flowered (Co)	CSta WHil
- 'Blush' (Co)	CSta WFar
- 'Bonbori' (Co) **new**	WFar
- 'Bureikou' (Co)	CSta WFar
- 'Carefree' (Co)	CSta ECtt NBro NLar WFar WHil XBar
- 'Carmine Pink' (Co)	WHil
- 'Cherubim' (Co)	CSta EBee EHyd LRHS
- 'Chidoriasobi' (Co) **new**	CSta
- 'Daikoshi' (Co)	CSta WFar
- 'Daiminnishiki' (Co)	CSta WFar
- 'Dancing Ladies' (Co)	ECtt GWyn NBro WFar WHil XBar
- 'Dart Rapids' (Co)	CSta WFar WHil
- 'Duane's Choice' (Co)	CAby CSta
- 'Edasango' (Co)	GWyn WFar
- 'Edomurasaki' (Co)	CSta GWyn NPnk WFar WHil
- 'Elegance' (Co) **new**	CSta WFar
- 'Emerald Sun' (Co)	WFar
- 'Essie' (Co)	CSta
- 'Flamenco' (Co/d)	GEdr WFar XBar
- 'Frilly Blue' (Co)	CBor CRos CSta EBee EHyd GEdr GWyn LRHS NRHS WFar
- 'Frilly White' (Co) **new**	WFar
- 'Fuji Shishi' (Co/d)	WFar XBar
- 'Fukiagezakura' (Co) **new**	CSta
- 'Fukuju' (Co) **new**	CSta
- 'Galactic' (Co)	CSta
- 'Galaxy' (Co)	NBro
- 'Geisha Girl' (Co)	CDor CRos CSpe CSta EBee ECtt EHyd GEdr GWyn LRHS NLar NRHS WFar WHil
- 'George' (Co) **new**	CSta
- 'Ginfukurin' (Co) **new**	CSta
- 'Gin-kaji-oku' (Co) **new**	WFar
- 'Gin-pukurin' (Co)	CAby CSta WFar WHil
- 'Girl of the Limberlost' (Co)	WFar XBar
- 'Gloaming' (Co)	WFar XBar
- 'Gunma' (Co) **new**	WFar
- 'Gunma Niizatia' (Co)	CSta
- 'Gyokk-bai' (Co) **new**	CSta
- 'Hakutaka' (Co) **new**	CSta
- 'Hana-angya' (Co/d)	WFar XBar
- 'Hanaguruma' (Co)	CSta WFar
- 'Hana-monyo' (Co) **new**	CSta
- 'Hana-nishiki' (Co) **new**	CSta
- 'Haru-no-yoi' (Co) **new**	WFar
- 'Harutugedoric' (Co)	GWyn WFar
- 'Hatu-garasu' (Co)	CSta WFar
- 'Hatu-goromo' (Co)	CSta WFar
- 'Heart's Desire' (Co)	EBee WFar
- 'Hidamari' (Co) **new**	CSta
- 'Higurasi' (Co)	WFar
- 'Hinomaru' (Co) **new**	CSta
- 'Hokutosei' (Co) **new**	CSta
- 'Ikoko-no-e-beni' (Co) **new**	WFar
- 'Inukima Mincura' (Co)	CSta GWyn WFar
- 'Inukine White' (Co) **new**	CSta
- 'Isamijishi' (Co) **new**	CSta
- 'Iso-botan' (Co)	CSta GEdr WFar XBar
- 'Izutu' (Co)	CSta
- 'Janomegasa' (Co) **new**	CSta
- 'Jessica' (Co)	CSta WFar WHil
- 'Jintsūriki' (Co) **new**	CSta
- 'Jisshū-no-sora' (Co) **new**	CSta
- 'Kafajin' (Co) **new**	CSta
- 'Kakuremino' (Co) **new**	CSta
- 'Kamiyo-no-kanmuri' (Co) **new**	CSta
- 'Kansenden' (Co)	WFar
- 'Karafune' (Co) **new**	CSta
- 'Karakoromo' (Co)	CSta
- 'Kashima' (Co)	CAby CSta WFar
- 'Kassai' (Co) **new**	WFar
- 'Keepsake' (Co) **new**	CSta
- 'Kenkou' (Co) **new**	CSta
- 'Kihi-no-yume' (Co)	CSta
- 'Kiraboshi' (Co)	WFar XBar
- 'Koenji' (Co) **new**	CSta
- 'Kohara-biyori' (Co) **new**	CSta
- 'Kokoroiki' (Co)	CSta GWyn WFar
- 'Komodo-ne' (Co) **new**	WFar
- 'Kotobuki' (Co)	CSta GEdr WFar

- 'Kotonoshirabe' (Co)	CSta WFar
- 'Kotyou-no-mail' (Co) **new**	CSta
- 'Kourohou' (Co)	GWyn WFar
- 'Kozakura-genji' (Co) **new**	CSta
- 'Kumoizuru' (Co) **new**	CSta
- 'Kurama' (Co)	GWyn WFar
- 'Ky-kanoko' (Co) **new**	CSta
- 'Laced Lady' (Co)	WFar
- 'Lacewing' (Co)	CSta WHil
- f. ***lactiflora*** (Co)	CSta EHyd GWyn LRHS NBro WHil
- 'Lilac Blue' (Co)	CSta
- 'Lilac Crinoline' (Co)	WFar XBar
- 'Lilac Sunbonnet' (Co)	EPfP WFar
- 'Mai-momiji' (Co) **new**	CSta WFar
- 'Mai-ōgi' (Co) **new**	CSta
- 'Makazebeni' (Co)	GWyn WFar
- 'Maki-no-o' (Co) **new**	CSta
- 'Managuruma' (Co)	WFar
- 'Manakoora' (Co)	CAby ECtt NBro WFar XBar
- 'Mangeto' (Co)	CSta WFar
- 'Martin Nest Blue' (Co)	CSta WFar WHil
- 'Martin Nest Pale Pink' (Co)	WHil
- 'Martin Nest Pink' (Co) **new**	CSta
- 'Matu-no-yuki' (Co)	CSta WFar WHil
- 'Mejirodai' (Co) **new**	CSta
- 'Miho-no-koji' (Co)	CSta WFar
- 'Mikado' (Co)	CSta EBee ECtt EHyd GEdr LRHS WFar WHil
- 'Mikini-no-mare' (Co)	CSta GWyn WFar
- 'Mikuni-beni' (Co) **new**	CSta
- Minuet Group (Co)	XBar
- 'Mitajiman' (Co)	CSta
- 'Miyakowakare' (Co)	WFar
- 'Miyuki' (Co)	GWyn WFar
- 'Molly' (Co) **new**	CSta
- 'Momijbashi' (Co) **new**	CSta
- 'Momo-kagari' **new**	WFar
- 'Mukashi-no-ume' (Co) **new**	WFar
- 'Musashino' (Co)	CSta WHil
- 'Musasi' (Co)	CSta
- 'Naka-fu' (Co) **new**	WFar
- 'Nami-no-ue' (Co) **new**	CSta
- 'Nankin-kozakura' (Co)	CSta GEdr WFar XBar
- 'Nirvana' (Co)	WFar XBar
- 'Noboruko' (Co)	CSta WHil
- 'Nuretubame' (Co)	CSta WFar XBar
- 'Ochibagoromo' (Co) **new**	CSta
- 'Okinanotomo' (Co)	WFar
- 'Okinosabi' (Co)	WFar
- 'Old Vienna' (Co)	WFar XBar
- 'Oni-gokko' (Co)	CSta WFar XBar
- 'Oshibori' (Co)	CSta GKev GWyn MNrw WFar WHil
- 'Our White' (Co)	WFar WHil
- 'Pago-Pago' (Co)	CSta ECtt NBro WFar XBar
- 'Pale Moon' (Co)	WFar XBar
- 'Pink Laced' (Co)	GWyn WFar
- 'Pink Ladies' (Co)	WHil
- pink-flowered (Co)	NBir NRya
- 'Purity' (Co)	WFar
- 'Purple Dusk' (Co)	WFar XBar
- 'Raspberry Buttons' (Co) **new**	WFar
- 'Rasyoumon' (Co)	WFar
- 'Rock Candy' (Co)	CSta WFar
- 'Romance' (Co)	XBar
- 'Ryokuryū' (Co) **new**	CSta
- 'Saiun' (Co)	CSta WFar WHil
- 'Sakuragawa' (Co)	CSta GWyn WFar
- 'Sakura-no-miya' (Co)	WFar
- 'Sangoguko'	GBin GKev GWyn MNrw
- 'Sato-zakura' (Co)	WFar XBar
- 'Sekidaiko' (Co)	CSta
- 'Senshō' (Co)	CSta GWyn WFar
- 'Sen-yū' (Co) **new**	CSta
- 'Seraphim' (Co)	CRos CSta EBee EHyd LRHS NLar NRHS WFar
- 'Seto-no-ume' (Co)	CSta WHil
- 'Shibori Gasane' (Co/d)	XBar
- 'Shibori-tatuta' (Co) **new**	CSta
- 'Shiokemuri' (Co)	CSta WHil
- 'Shira-tonbo' (Co) **new**	CSta
- 'Shira-washi' (Co)	CSta
- 'Shiro-tombo' (Co)	GEdr XBar
- 'Shirousagi' (Co)	WFar
- 'Shishi-funjin' (Co)	CSta WFar WHil
- 'Sikoubai' (Co)	WFar
- 'Sinakatonba' (Co)	GWyn WFar
- 'Sinipukurn' (Co)	GWyn WFar
- 'Sinnkirou' (Co)	WFar
- 'Sinseto' (Co)	WFar
- 'Siritonbo' (Co)	GWyn WFar
- 'Sitikenjin' (Co)	WFar
- 'Snow Flakes' (Co)	CSta
- 'Snowbird' (Co)	XBar
- 'Snowdrop' (Co)	CBod CDor CSta ECtt GBin GKev GWyn LSou MBel MHol MNrw MPie SEdd WCot WFar WOld
- 'Snowflake' (Co)	CSta EBee EHyd EPfP GKev GWyn LRHS NLar SBut WFar
- 'Sorcha's Pink' (Co)	CSta WFar
- 'Sōshiari' (Co)	CSta WFar
- 'Sotodorihime' (Co)	WFar
- 'Spring Blush' (Co)	CSta
- 'Spring Song' (Co)	CSta WFar WHil
- 'Suibijin' (Co)	WFar
- 'Suiloijiw' (Co)	GWyn
- 'Sumida-no-hatu' (Co)	GWyn WFar
- 'Sumisonegawa' (Co)	WFar
- 'Sumizomegenji' (Co)	CSta WFar WHil XBar
- 'Sun Bonnets' (Co)	GEdr
- 'Sweetie' (Co)	CSta WFar
- 'Syosin' (Co)	CSta
- 'Syutyuka' (Co)	CSta
- 'Tagonoura' (Co)	CSta GWyn WFar WHil
- 'Tah-ni' (Co)	NBro WHil XBar
- 'Tairou-no-tsuki' (Co) **new**	CSta
- 'Takane-no-yuki' (Co) **new**	CSta
- 'Tamagawa-zome' (Co) **new**	CSta
- 'Tamashiki-no-miya' (Co) **new**	CSta
- 'Taoyami' (Co)	CSta
- 'Tatsuta-no-yū' (Co) **new**	CSta
- 'Tatuta-no-yūbe' (Co)	CSta WFar
- 'Tobitake' (Co) **new**	CSta
- 'Tokasamesi' (Co)	WFar
- 'Tokimeki' (Co/d)	WFar XBar
- 'Toyonoharu' (Co)	GWyn WFar
- 'Trade Winds' (Co)	WFar XBar
- 'Tsuki-no-miyake' (Co) **new**	CSta
- 'Tsukumo-jishi' (Co) **new**	CSta
- 'Tukasamesi' (Co)	CSta
- 'Turu-no-kegoromo' (Co)	CSta WHil
- 'Ue-no-ume' (Co) **new**	CSta
- 'Ukima Aka' (Co) **new**	CSta
- 'Ukimashiro' (Co) **new**	CSta

- 'Usujanome' (Co)	CSta
- 'Vilia' (Co)	XBar
- 'Vivid Pink' (Co)	CSta WFar WHil
- 'White Buttons' (Co) **new**	WFar
- 'Winter Dreams' (Co)	CAby CWCL ECtt GWyn MBel NBid NBro WFar
- 'Yugeshiki' (Co)	WFar
- 'Yūhi-beni' (Co)	CSta WFar
- 'Yukiguruma' (Co)	GWyn WFar
- 'Yukizakura' (Co) **new**	CSta
sikkimensis (Si) ♀H6	CBcs EBee EHyd EPfP GAbr GKev LRHS MMuc NGdn SPoG
- peach-flowered (Si)	GKev
- pink-flowered (Si)	GKev
- var. ***pseudosikkimensis*** (Si)	GKev
- var. ***pudibunda*** (Si)	GKev NWad
- red-flowered (Si)	GKev
aff. ***sikkimensis*** (Si)	NGdn XBar
Silver-laced Group (Pr/Poly)	CBod EPfP MMuc SEND SPoG SWvt WFar XBar
- black-flowered (Pr/Poly)	EMor WCAu XEll
simensis (Sp)	XBar
sinoplantaginea	see *P. chionantha* subsp. *sinoplantaginea*
sinopurpurea	see *P. chionantha* subsp. *sinopurpurea*
'Sir Bedivere' (Pr/Prim)	EBee WCot
smithiana	see *P. prolifera*
'Snow Carpet'	see *P.* 'Schneekissen'
'Snow Ruffles' (Au)	ITim XBar
'Snow White' (Pr/Poly)	GBin MRav
SNOWCUSHION	see *P.* 'Schneekissen'
'Snowgoose' (Pr/Prim/d)	XBar
sonchifolia (Pe)	GKev
- subsp. ***emeiensis*** (Pe)	GKev
sorachiana	see *P. yuparensis*
Sorbet Group (Pr/Poly)	XBar
spectabilis (Au)	GKev
Spice Shades Group (Pr/Poly)	XBar
× ***steinii***	see *P.* × *forsteri*
Stella Series (Pr/Poly) **new**	LCro LOPS
stenocalyx (Pu)	GKev
stenodonta (Pf)	CPla GKev
'Stradbrook Charm' (Au)	CWCL EPot NRya XBar
'Stradbrook Dainty' (Au)	WFar XBar
'Stradbrook Dream' (Au)	ITim WFar XBar
'Stradbrook Lilac Lustre' (Au)	CPBP EPot
'Stradbrook Lucy' (Au)	GEdr ITim NWad
'Strawberries and Cream' (Pr/Prim)	XBar
stricta (Al)	GKev
Striped Victorians Group (Pr/Poly)	XBar
'Strong Beer' (Pr/Prim/d)	CBod CMiW EBee ECtt EPfP GBin GEdr GWyn MHol MMuc MPie NHpl NWad SAko SEdd WBrk WCot WFar WHil WKif XBar
'Sue Jervis' (Pr/Prim/d)	CMiW NBir NGrd NHpl XBar
suffrutescens (Su)	WAbe
'Sundae' (Pr/Prim/d)	MBow XBar
'Sunny Evans'	EPot
'Sunrise' (Au)	CRos EHyd LRHS NRHS
'Sunshine Susie' (Pr/Prim/d)	CMiW GMaP XBar
SWEETHEART (mixed) (Pr/Prim) **new**	LCro LOPS
takedana (Bu)	GEdr
Tango Group (Pr/Poly)	NDro XBar
tangutica (Cy)	GKev
'Tantallon' (Pe)	NHar
Tartan Reds Group (Pr/Prim)	XBar
'Tatyana' (Pr/Prim)	EBee GKev
'Tawny Port' (Pr/Poly)	CElw CFis EBee ELan
'Theodora' (Pr)	CBre EBee ELan GAbr WFar
'Tie Dye' (Pr/Prim)	CBod ELan MHol MMrt MNrw NLar NWad SAko WCot WFar WKif
'Tinney's Moonlight' (Pe)	NHar SGro
'Tipperary Purple' (Pr/Prim)	ECtt NHpl
'Tomato Red' (Pr/Prim)	CAby CMil EBee NHpl WCAu WCot WFar
'Tony' (Au) ♀H5	XBar
'Tortoiseshell' (Pr/d)	ECtt
Traditional Yellows Group (Pr/Prim)	CWCL XBar
tyrolensis (Au)	GKev
'Val Horncastle' (Pr/Prim/d)	CMiW ECtt EPfP EShb GMaP NHpl XBar
Valentine Victorians Group (Pr/Poly)	XBar
× ***venusta*** (Au)	GKev
'Vera Maud' (Pr)	MBriF XBar
§ ***veris*** (Pr) ♀H5	Widely available
- PAB 3777	LEdu NRHS
- subsp. ***columnae*** (Pr)	GKev
- Coronation Cowslips Group (Pr/Poly)	MBros XBar
- hose-in-hose (Pr/d)	EWes WBrk WHoo
- 'Katy McSparron' (Pr/d)	CExl CMiW ECtt GBin MHol MNrw MPie NHpl NLar NSti SPer WCot WFar
- 'Lady Agatha' (Pr)	XBar
- Lord Alfred Group hose-in-hose (Pr)	XBar
- subsp. ***macrocalyx*** (Pr)	NWad
- red-flowered (Pr)	NBid NGdn
- 'Sunset Shades' (Pr)	CDor EAJP EMor EPfP NGdn NLar SWvt XEll
- subsp. ***veris*** (Pr)	CPla LSou
vernalis	see *P. vulgaris*
verticillata (Sp)	GKev
§ ***vialii*** (So) ♀H5	Widely available
- 'Alison Holland' (So)	MPnt NHpl
§ ***villosa*** (Au)	GKev
- var. ***commutata*** (Au)	GKev
- var. ***cottia***	see *P. villosa*
'Vintage' (Pr/Prim/d)	XBar
violacea (Mu)	GKev
Violet Victorians Group (Pr/Poly)	XBar
viscosa All.	see *P. latifolia*
§ ***vulgaris*** (Pr/Prim) ♀H7	Widely available
- var. ***alba*** (Pr/Prim)	WBrk
- 'Alba Plena' (Pr/Prim/d)	CMiW GAbr
- 'Avoca' (Pr/Prim)	NHar WFar
- 'Avondale' (Kennedy Irish Series) (Pr/Prim)	CAby CDor EBee GJos MAvo MBriF MHol MNrw NHar WCot
- 'Blarney Castle Blush' (Pr/Prim)	NHar WFar
- 'Blarney Castle Pink' (Pr/Prim)	NHar NHpl
- 'Blarney Castle Red' (Pr/Prim)	NHar NHpl XBar
- 'Carrigdale' (Pr/Prim)	CDor MBriF NHar WCot WFar
- 'Catherine Thompson' (Pr/Prim)	NBir
- 'Claddagh' (Pr/Prim)	MBriF NHar NHpl WCot

- Cornish pink (Pr/Prim) GKev
- DRUMCLIFFE ('K74'PBR) (Pr/Prim) ECtt ELan EMor GBin GMaP MBel MHol MNrw NHpl NLar NSti SEdd WCot WFar XBar
- 'Dunbeg' (Kennedy Irish Series) (Pr/Prim) CAby CDor ELan EPfP GAbr GBin MBriF NLar WCot WHil
- 'Glengarriff' (Kennedy Irish Series) (Pr/Prim) MBriF NHar NHpl WCot
- 'Golden Gem' (Pr/Prim/d) WCot
- 'Finella' (mixed) (Pr/Prim) **new** SVic
- green-flowered see *P. vulgaris* 'Viridis'
- hybrids (Pr/Prim) CTsd
- INNISFREE ('K72'PBR) (Pr/Prim) CAby CDor CMil ECtt EMor EPfP GAbr GBin GMaP GWyn MBel MMuc MNrw NHpl NLar SEdd WCot WFar XBar
§ - 'Lilacina Plena' (Pr/Prim/d) CMiW NHpl WHer XBar
- 'Lutea' (Pr/Prim) CBor
- 'Moneygall' (Kennedy Irish Series) (Pr/Poly/d) NHar NHpl WFar
- 'Mount Juliet' (Pr/Prim) NHar
§ - subsp. ***sibthorpii*** (Pr/Prim) ♀H5 CAby CDor CMiW CRos CSam EBee EHyd ELan ELon EMor EPfP GAbr GBin GKev LRHS MBriF MCot MHer MNrw NBro NChi NRHS NWad SPtp SRms WFar WHil WOld
- 'Taigetos' (Pr/Prim) ♀H7 CBro CExl
- 'Tara' (Pr/Prim) NHar NHpl
- 'Tarragem Sparkling Ruby' (Pr/Prim/d) CRos CWCL MBriF NHpl WCot
- 'Vanilla Cream' (Pr/Prim) MBriF WCot
§ - 'Viridis' (Pr/Prim/d) MNrw
- subsp. ***vulgaris*** (Pr/Prim) ♀H7 MBriF WCav WMAq
waltonii (Si) EPfP GAbr GKev MNrw
'Wanda' (Pr/Prim) ♀H7 CBcs CRos CTri EHyd ELan GAbr GBin GKev GQue GWyn LRHS MBel MHer MMuc NBid NRya SRms WBrk WCFE WCot WGwG XBar
Wanda Group (Pr/Prim) NBro
- 'Wanda Hose-in-hose' (Pr/Prim/d) CMiW NBir
- 'Wanda Jack-in-the-Green' (Pr/Prim) WCot
- 'Wanda Tomato Red' (Pr/Prim) CBod CMiW EMor GAbr MBriF MPie NHpl
wardii see *P. munroi*
warshenewskiana (Or) EWes GJos GKev NRya WAbe WGwG
watsonii (Mu) CPla EBee GKev XBar
- maroon-flowered (Mu) GKev
'Wedgwood' see *P.* × *pubescens* 'Wedgwood'
Westonbury Mill hybrids WWtn
'Wharfedale Bluebell' (Au) NBir
'Wharfedale Buttercup' (Au) ITim
'Wharfedale Gem' (*allionii* hybrid) (Au) EPot WIce XBar
'Wharfedale Ling' (*allionii* hybrid) (Au) EPot XBar
'Wharfedale Sunshine' (Au) GKev WFar
'Wharfedale Superb' (*allionii* hybrid) (Au) XBar
'Wharfedale Village' (Au) MPnt
'White Linda Pope' (Au) GEdr NSla
'White Wanda' (Pr/Prim) XBar
'White Waves' (*allionii* hybrid) (Au) ITim
§ ***whitei*** 'Sherriff's Variety' (Pe) NHar
wilsonii (Pf) CTri GAbr LLWG NBir NGdn NWad WBrk WTyc WWtn XBar
- SDR 7824 GKev
§ - var. ***anisodora*** (Pf) GKev GLog NGdn NHpl NWad XBar
- var. ***wilsonii*** (Pf) GKev NWad
Winter White Group (Pr/Prim) **new** CWCL XBar
'Wisley Crimson' see *P.* 'Wisley Red'
§ 'Wisley Red' (Pr/Prim) CElw CMiW
'Woodland Walk' (Pr/Prim) EPfP SRms
wulfeniana (Au) CWCL GKev
yargongensis see *P. munroi* subsp. *yargongensis*
'Yellow' (Primlet Series) (Pr/Prim) CRos EHyd LRHS NRHS
yunnanensis (Y) GKev
§ ***yuparensis*** (Al) GKev WHil
zambalensis (Ar) GKev
'Zebra Blue' (Pr/Prim) EPfP WHil

Primulina (*Gesneriaceae*)

tabacum 'Deco' WDib

Prinsepia (*Rosaceae*)

sinensis MBlu NLar SLon WSHC

Prionosciadium (*Apiaceae*)

thapsoides SDix

Pritchardia (*Arecaceae*)

affinis XBlo
pacifica XBlo

Pritzelago see *Hornungia*

Prosartes (*Liliaceae*)

§ ***hookeri*** CMiW EBee MNrw
§ - var. ***oregana*** EBee WCru
§ ***lanuginosa*** EHyd EMor EPPr LEdu LRHS WCru WFar WPGP
§ ***maculata*** CAby LEdu MNrw NLar WCru
§ ***smithii*** EBee EPfP GAbr GKev GLog IMou LEdu LRHS MAvo MNrw NBir NLar WCru WPGP WSHC
§ ***trachycarpa*** SDR 8177 GKev

Prostanthera (*Lamiaceae*)

aspalathoides CCCN CTsd
'Badja Peak' CCCN CCht CTrC CTsd MAsh MGil
baxteri CTrC
cuneata ♀H4 Widely available
- 'Alpine Gold' (v) MAsh
- 'Blushing Bride' CMac CTrC LBuc MHtn
denticulata CTsd
* ***digitiformis*** CTsd
incana CTsd
incisa CTsd
lasianthos CBcs CCCN CTsd GKev SPlb SVen
- 'Badja Point' CSpe
- 'Kallista Pink' CTsd
- var. ***subcoriacea*** CExl
latifolia CTsd
melissifolia CTsd
§ - var. ***parvifolia*** CCCN CTsd
'Mint Royale' CCCN LEdu LRHS
'Mint-Ice' LRHS

	ovalifolia ♀H3	CCCN SEle WAvo
I	- 'Variegata' (v)	CBcs CBod CCCN CExl CMac CTrC CTsd ELan LRHS LSou MAsh MGil SEle SIvy SNig WAvo WGrn
	phylicifolia	CBcs CTrC CTsd
	'Poorinda Ballerina'	CCCN CRos CTsd EBee ELan LRHS MAsh SEle SRkn
	'Poorinda Petite'	CBod CCCN CRos CTsd ELan LRHS
	rhombea	CTsd
	rotundifolia ♀H2	CAbb CBod CCCN CCht CTri CTsd EBee MGil MNHC SEle SIvy SNig SPer SVen WCFE WGrn WKif
	- 'Chelsea Girl'	see *P. rotundifolia* 'Rosea'
§	- 'Rosea' ♀H2	CCCN CTrC CTsd EPfP LRHS SEND SIvy
	rugosa	CTsd
	sericea	LRHS
	sieberi misapplied	see *P. melissifolia* var. *parvifolia*
	sieberi Benth.	CTsd
I	- 'Variegata' (v)	CTsd
	spinosa	CTrC CTsd
	'Starlight' (v)	CTsd
	walteri	CBcs CCCN CTsd EBee LRHS MNHC SIvy SPhx

Protea (*Proteaceae*)

	aurea	CTrC SPlb
	- subsp. ***aurea***	CPbh
	burchellii	SPlb
	'Clark's Red'	LRHS
	coronata	CPbh SPlb
	cynaroides	CCCN CCtw CPbh CTrC SPlb
	- 'King Pine'	CCCN
	- 'King White'	CCCN
	- 'Little Prince'PBR	CBcs CCCN
	- 'Madiba'	CCCN
	- 'Mini King'	CCCN
	- 'White Crown'PBR	CCCN
	effusa	SPlb
	eximia	CCCN CCtw CPbh SPlb
	grandiceps	CCCN CCtw CPbh SPlb
	'Juliet'	CCCN
	lacticolor	CPbh SPlb
	laurifolia	SPlb
	lepidocarpodendron	CPbh
	longifolia	CPbh
	nana	SPlb
	neriifolia	CCCN CPbh CTrC SPlb
	- 'Snowcrest'	CPbh
	obtusifolia	SPlb
	repens	CPbh LRHS SPlb
	- 'Ruby Blush'	CCCN
	scolymocephala	SPlb
	'Southern Cross'	CCCN
	'Special Pink Ice'	CCCN
	subvestita	CPbh SPlb
	susannae	CPbh CTrC SPlb
	'Susara'	CCCN LRHS
	'Sylvia'	CCCN

Prumnopitys ✿ (*Podocarpaceae*)

§	***andina***	CBcs IDee WFar
	elegans	see *P. andina*

Prunella (*Lamiaceae*)

§	***grandiflora***	CHby ECha ELan SCob SPhx SRms
	- 'Alba'	CBod CBre EBee ECha ELan EPfP GMaP NBid NLar SPer SRms WCAu
	- 'Altenberg Rosa'	WCAu
	- 'Blue Loveliness'	SWvt
	- 'Blue Pearl'	MHol
	- 'Carminea'	EBee MRav
	- 'Freelander'	WHil
	- 'Gruss aus Isernhagen'	GBee
	- 'Loveliness'	CMac ECha ELan GMaP MRav NBro NGdn NSti SPer SPlb WCAu WFar
	- 'Pagoda'	CSpe NLar
	- 'Pink Loveliness'	CRos SRms WFar
	- 'Rosea'	SBut WFar
	- 'Rubra'	CBod NLar WOut
	- violet-flowered	NSti
	- 'White Loveliness'	CMac SRms
	'Icing Sugar'	WFar
	incisa	see *P. vulgaris*
	SUMMER DAZE ('Binsumdaz'PBR)	ECtt LSou STPC
§	***vulgaris***	CBod CCBP CHab CTri EBou ENfk GPoy MBow MMuc MNHC NMir SRms WHer WOut WWild XAbr
	- f. ***leucantha***	WHer
	- 'Rose Pearl'	CBod EBou LSRN MHol NHpl SRms WCav
	× ***webbiana***	see *P. grandiflora*

Prunus ✿ (*Rosaceae*)

	'Accolade' (d) ♀H6	Widely available
§	'Amanogawa' ♀H6	Widely available
	amygdalus	see *P. dulcis*
	'Aprimira' (miracot) (F) **new**	MAsh
	'Aprisali' (aprium) (F) **new**	NOra
	armeniaca	MPri SGsty
	- 'Alfred' (F)	SKee SPer
	- 'Bergeron' (F)	NOra SKee WMat
	- 'Bredase' (F)	ELan
	- COMPACTA (F) **new**	NOra
	- 'De Nancy'	see *P. armeniaca* 'Gros Pêche'
	- 'Delicot' (F)	SSFr
	- 'Early Moorpark' (F)	CAgr EPfP LEdu NOra SEND SLon SSFr SWeb WMat
	- FLAVORCOT ('Bayoto'PBR) (F)	CAgr EPfP EPom MCoo NOra SKee SPer SSFr SWeb WMat
	- 'Garden Aprigold' (F)	EPom SSFr WMat
	- 'Goldcot' (F)	CAgr CTho LRHS MCoo NOra SKee SPoG SSFr WMat
	- 'Golden Glow' (F)	CAgr CTho CTri EPfP EPom LRHS MAsh MCoo NOra SGbt SKee SSFT WMat
	- 'Goldrich' (F)	CAgr
§	- 'Gros Pêche' (F)	SVic
	- 'Hargrand' (F)	CAgr SVic
	- 'Harogem' (F)	CAgr
	- 'Helena de Roussilon' (F)	CAgr
	- 'Hemskirke' (F)	SKee
	- 'Hongaarse' (F)	ELan
	- 'Kioto'PBR (F) **new**	NOra
	- 'Moorpark' (F)	CHab CSBt CTri ELan LBuc MPri MRav SEdi SKee
	- 'New Large Early' (F)	SEND SEdi
	- ORANGE SUMMER ('Zaitorde'PBR) (F)	EPom
	- 'Petit Muscat' (F)	EPom SKee
	- 'Robada'PBR (F)	CAgr MWat
	- 'Tomcot' (F)	CAgr CTri EPfP EPom LBuc LSRN MCoo NOra SKee SPer SPoG SSFr WMat
	- 'Tross Orange' (F)	ELan
	- 'Vigama' (F)	MCoo NOra WMat
	'Asano'	CLnd
	avium	Widely available
	- 'Alba'	SKee

- 'Amber Heart' (F)	CArg NOra SKee WMat
- 'Bigarreau Gaucher' (F)	SKee WMat
§ - 'Bigarreau Napoléon' (F)	CArg EPom LMaj NOra SEdi SKee SSFr SVic WMat
- 'Birchenhayes'	see *P. avium* 'Early Birchenhayes'
- 'Black Elton' (F)	SKee
- 'Black Tartarian' (F)	SKee
- 'Bradbourne Black' (F)	SKee
- 'Bullion' (F)	CEnd CTho
- 'Burcombe' (F)	CEnd CTho
- 'Cariad' (F)	WGwG
- CELESTE ('Sumpaca'^{PBR}) (D)	CAgr CArg CMac CTri MCoo MWat NLar NOra SGbt SLim SPoG WMat
- 'Cherokee'	see *P. avium* 'Lapins'
- 'Colney' (F)	CArg EPom NOra SSFr WJas WMat
- 'Danelia' (D)	WMat
- 'Dun' (F)	CHab CTho WMat
§ - 'Early Birchenhayes' (F)	CEnd
- 'Early Rivers' (F)	CSBt IArd LSRN NOra SEdi SKee SSFr SVic WMat
- 'Emperor Francis' (F)	SKee
- 'Fice' (F)	CEnd CTho
- 'Florence' (F)	SKee
- 'Garden Bing' (F)	EPom
- 'Giorgia' (D)	WMat
- 'Grandiflora'	see *P. avium* 'Plena'
- 'Hannaford' (D/C)	CHab
- 'Hertford' (F)	NOra SEdi SSFr WMat
- 'Ironsides' (F)	SKee
- 'Karina' (D)	WMat
- 'Kentish Red' (F)	SKee
- 'Knight's Early Black' (D)	CArg WMat
- 'Kordia' (D) ♀H6	CArg EPom NOra SKee WMat
- 'Kozerska' (F)	WMat
§ - 'Lapins' (F) ♀H6	CAgr CArg CLnd CTho ECrN EPfP EPom MRav MWat NLar NOra SEdi SKee SSFT SSFr WJas WMat WWct
- 'May Duke'	see *P.* × *gondouinii* 'May Duke'
- 'Merchant' (F) ♀H6	NOra SEdi SKee SSFT SSFr WMat WWct
- 'Merton Bigarreau' (F)	CArg NOra SKee SSFr WMat
- 'Merton Favourite' (F)	SKee
- 'Merton Glory' (F)	CAgr CArg CSBt EPfP NOra SEWo SEdi SKee SLim SSFr WMat WWct
- 'Merton Premier' (F)	SVic
- 'Merton Reward'	see *P.* × *gondouinii* 'Merton Reward'
- 'Mizia' (D)	WMat
- 'Nabella' (F)	MAsh WJas
- 'Napoléon'	see *P. avium* 'Bigarreau Napoléon'
- 'Noble' (F)	SKee
- 'Noir de Guben' (F)	SKee WMat
- 'Octavia' (D)	WMat
- 'Old Black Heart' (F)	SKee
- 'Penny'^{PBR} (F) ♀H6	CAgr CArg CTri EPom MCoo MWat NOra SKee WMat WWct
- 'Petit Noir' (F)	CArg NOra WMat
§ - 'Plena' (d) ♀H6	Widely available
- 'Regina' (F)	EPom NLar NOra SKee WMat
- 'Ronald's Heart' (F)	SKee
- 'Roundel Heart' (F)	SKee WMat
- 'Sasha' (F)	MCoo
- 'Skeena'^{PBR} (F)	CArg MCoo NOra WMat
- 'Small Black' (F)	CHab
- STARDUST ('13-7-70') (F)	LCro LOPS NOra
- 'Stella' (F) ♀H6	Widely available
- 'Stella Compact' (F)	ECrN LSRN SEdi
- 'Summer Sun' (D) ♀H6	CAgr CArg CLnd CMac CTho CTri EPom LBuc MAsh MCoo MGos MWat NLar NOra SCoo SKee SLim SPoG SSFT SSFr WMat WWct
- 'Summit' (F)	CLnd SEdi SKee SSFr WMat
- 'Sunburst' (D)	Widely available
- 'Sweetheart' (F) ♀H6	CAgr CArg CLnd CTri EPom LCro LMaj LOPS LRHS LSRN MAsh MWat NOra NRHS SEWo SKee SLim SPoG SVic WMat
- 'Sylvia' (F)	CAgr NOra WMat
- 'Turkish Black' (F)	SKee
- 'Ursula Rivers' (F)	SKee
- 'Van' (F)	CAgr CArg CSBt EPom NLar NOra SEdi SKee WMat
- 'Vanda'^{PBR} (F)	NOra WMat
- 'Vega' (F)	CAgr CArg NOra SEdi SKee SSFr WJas WMat
- 'Waterloo' (F)	NOra SKee
- 'White Heart' (F)	CHab SKee
§ 'Beni-tamanishiki' ♀H6	CBcs NOra WMat
'Beni-yutaka' ♀H6	CBcs CCVT CTho MAsh MRav MSwo NOra NOrn NRHS SCoo SLim WHwl WMat WMou
besseyi	WKor
'Blaze'	see *P. cerasifera* 'Nigra'
× ***blireana*** (d) ♀H5	CEnd CLnd CTri EPfP LCro LOPS MGos MRav MSwo SCob SCoo SPer SPoG WMou
- 'Moseri' (d)	WTSh
BLUSHING BRIDE	see *P.* 'Shōgetsu'
campanulata 'Felix Jury'	EBee NOra WMat
CANDY FLOSS	see *P.* 'Matsumae-beni-murasaki'
caroliniana	LMaj SArc
cerasifera (F)	CAgr CBrac CHab CTri ECrN EPfP EPom LBuc SCob SKee SPer WKor
- 'Countess' (F)	EPom NOra
- CRIMSON POINTE ('Cripoizam')	EBee LRHS NLar NOra SPoG
- 'Golden Sphere' (F)	CAgr CArg CTho CTri EPom NOra SKee SPer SSFr WMat
- 'Gypsy' (F)	CAgr CTho LRHS NOra SKee SSFr WMat
- 'Hessei' (v)	LRHS MRav NOrn SEle
- 'Kentish Red' (F)	MMuc SEND
§ - Myrobalan Group (F)	MRav SPre SVic WMat
§ - 'Nigra' ♀H6	Widely available
- 'Pendula'	ECrN SWvt
§ - 'Pissardii'	CDoC EPfP LCro LMaj LSRN NOrn SCoo SGsty SLon SWvt WFar WJas WMou
- 'Ruby' (F)	CAgr EPom SKee SPer
- 'Woodii'	CSBt
cerasus 'Maynard'	SSFr
- 'Meteor Korai'	CAgr LRHS MCoo NOra NRHS WMat
- 'Montmorency' (F)	NOra SKee
- 'Morello' (C) ♀H6	Widely available
- 'Nabella' (F)	SKee
- 'Semperflorens'	CLnd
'Cheal's Weeping'	EBar
CHOCOLATE ICE	see *P.* 'Matsumae-fuki'
§ × ***cistena*** ♀H6	CBcs CDoC CRos EBee EHyd ELan EPfP LRHS MAsh MGos MSwo NRHS SCob SCoo SGol SPoG SWvt WFar
- 'Crimson Dwarf'	see *P.* × *cistena*
'Collingwood Ingram' ♀H6	EPfP LRHS MBlu NOra NOrn SLim WHwl WMat
'Cot 'n 'Candy' (aprium) (F)	CAgr EPom
'Daikoku'	CBcs EBee LRHS NOra WMat
davidiana	SPlb

'Delma'^{PBR} (F)	CSBt EBee NOra WMat
domestica (D/C)	SPre
- 'Angelina Burdett' (D)	CHab SKee
- 'Anna Späth' (C/D)	SKee
- 'Ariel' (C/D)	SKee
- 'Autumn Compote' (C)	SKee
- 'Avalon' (D)	CAgr CCVT CLnd LBuc NOra SEdi SKee SSFr WMat
- 'Belgian Greengage' (F)	CHab
- 'Belle de Louvain' (C)	CArg CHab CLnd CTri NOra SEdi SKee WMat WWct
- 'Birchenhayes' (F)	CEnd
- 'Blaisdon Red' (C)	NOra SKee WMat
- 'Blue Rock' (C/D) 🏆^{H5}	SKee
- 'Blue Tit' (C/D) 🏆^{H5}	CAgr EPom MMuc NOra SEND SKee SSFr WMat WWct
- 'Bohemian' (C)	SKee
- 'Bonne de Bry' (D)	SKee
§ - 'Bountiful' (C)	SEdi
- 'Bryanston Gage' (D)	WMat
- 'Burbank's Giant'	see *P. domestica* 'Giant Prune'
- 'Burcombe' (F)	CEnd
- 'Cambridge Gage' (D) 🏆^{H5}	CAgr CArg CCVT CEnd CHab CLnd CMac CTri EBee ECrN EPfP EPom LCro LRHS LSRN MAsh MMuc MWat NOra SCoo SEND SEWo SEdi SKee SLim SPer SSFr WJas WMat WWct
- 'Coe's Golden Drop' (D)	CAgr CArg CHab CLnd EPom MGos MRav NOra SEdi SKee SPer WMat WWct
- 'Conwy Castle' (F)	WMat
- 'Count Althann's Gage' (D)	CHab SKee SSFr WWct
- 'Crimson Drop' (D)	SKee
- 'Cropper'	see *P. domestica* 'Laxton's Cropper'
- 'Curlew' (C)	SKee
- 'Czar' (C) 🏆^{H6}	Widely available
- 'Delicious'	see *P. domestica* 'Laxton's Delicious'
- 'Denbigh' (C)	CHab WGwG
- 'Denniston's Superb'	see *P. domestica* 'Imperial Gage'
- 'Diamond' (C)	SKee
- 'Dittisham Ploughman' (C)	CTho SKee WMat
- 'Dunster Plum' (F)	CTho CTri WMat
- 'Early Laxton' (C/D)	CHab MMuc SEND SEdi SKee
- 'Early Prolific'	see *P. domestica* 'Early Rivers'
§ - 'Early Rivers' (C)	CAgr CArg CHab CSBt CTho CTri EBee ELan EPom LSRN NOra SCoo SEdi SKee SPer SSFr WMat WWct
- 'Early Transparent Gage' (C/D)	CAgr CEnd CMac CSBt CTho ECrN LBuc LRHS MCoo NOra SCoo SKee SSFr WMat
- 'Early Victoria' (C/D)	SGbt
- 'Edda' (D)	NOra WMat
- 'Edwards' (C/D)	CTri SEdi SKee SSFr
- 'Excalibur' (D)	CAgr EPom IArd LBuc LSRN NOra SEdi SKee WMat
- 'Finger Plum' (F)	WMat
§ - German Prune Group (C)	MCoo NOra SKee WMat
§ - 'Giant Prune' (C)	MMuc SEND SEdi SKee SSFr
- 'Gold Dust' (F)	WMat
- 'Golden Transparent' (D)	MCoo SKee
- 'Goldfinch' (D)	MCoo MMuc SEND SKee
- 'Gordon Castle'	NLar WMat
- Green Gage Group	see *P. domestica* Reine-Claude Group
- - 'Lindsey Gage' (F)	NOra SKee
- 'Grove's Late Victoria' (D)	SKee WWct
- 'Guinevere' (C)	CAgr CEnd EPom LRHS MCoo NOra SKee WMat
- 'Guthrie's Late Green' (D)	SKee
- 'Haganta'^{PBR} (F) 🏆^{H5}	CAgr MCoo NOra WMat
- 'Herman' (D)	CAgr CEnd CMac EPom LRHS MCoo NOra SKee WMat
- 'Heron' (C)	NOra WMat WWct
§ - 'Imperial Gage' (D) 🏆^{H5}	CAgr CArg CLnd CMac CSBt CTho CTri EPom LRHS MMuc NOra SEND SKee SSFT SSFr WMat
- 'Jan James' (F)	CEnd
- 'Jefferson' (D) 🏆^{H5}	CAgr CArg CHab CLnd NOra SKee SSFr SVic WMat
* - 'Jubilaeum' (D)	CAgr CLnd CMac EPom LBuc LRHS NOra SCoo SEWo SKee SSFr
- 'Kea' (C)	CLnd CTho SKee WMat
- 'Kirke's' (D)	CHab ELan NOra SKee SSFr WMat
- 'Kulinaria' (D)	SPoG
- 'Landkey Yellow' (F)	CTho WMat
- 'Langley Gage' (D)	CAgr
- 'Late Muscatelle' (D)	SKee
- 'Late Transparent Gage' (D)	SKee
- 'Lawson's Golden' (D)	SKee
- 'Laxton's Bountiful'	see *P. domestica* 'Bountiful'
§ - 'Laxton's Cropper' (C)	CHab SEdi SKee
§ - 'Laxton's Delicious' (D)	CHab
- 'Laxton's Early Gage' (D/C)	SKee
- 'Laxton's Jubilee' (C/D)	CEnd CSBt SGbt SSFr WMat
- 'Mallard' (D) 🏆^{H6}	NOra SKee WMat
- 'Manaccan' (C)	CTho WMat
- 'Manns No. 1' (C/D)	SKee WMat
- 'Marjorie's Seedling' (C) 🏆^{H5}	Widely available
- 'Meritare' (F)	NOra WMat
- 'Merton Gage' (D)	SKee
- 'Merton Gem' (D)	SKee
- 'Miraclaude' (F)	EPom
- (Myrobalan Group) 'Myrobalan B' (F)	WTSh
- Old English gage	CLnd EBee ECrN EPom MAsh SEdi
- 'Olympia' (C/D)	SKee
- 'Opal' (D) 🏆^{H6}	Widely available
- 'Orleans' (C)	SKee
- 'Oullins Gage' (C/D) 🏆^{H5}	Widely available
- 'Pershore' (C)	CAgr CHab NOra SEdi SKee WMat WWct
- 'Pershore Emblem' (F)	WWct
- 'Pozegaca' (D)	SKee
- 'President' (C)	CHab LMaj MMuc SEND SKee SSFr
- 'Purple Pershore' (C) 🏆^{H5}	CAgr CHab CTri IArd NOra SKee WMat WWct
- 'Queen's Crown' (C/D)	WMat
- 'Quetsche d'Alsace'	see *P. domestica* German Prune Group
- 'Reeves' (C)	NOra SKee
- 'Reine-Claude Dorée'	see *P. domestica* Reine-Claude Group
§ - Reine-Claude Group (D)	ECrN ELan MMuc NOra SEND SKee SLim SPer WMat
- - 'Ingall's Grimoldby Green Gage' (D)	SKee
- - 'Old Green Gage'	see *P. domestica* (Reine-Claude Group) 'Reine-Claude Vraie'
- - 'Reine-Claude de Bavais' (D)	CArg CLnd CTri NOra SKee WMat
- - 'Reine-Claude de Moissac' (D)	SKee
- - 'Reine-Claude de Vars' (D)	SVic
- - 'Reine-Claude Violette' (D)	SGsty SKee

§	- - 'Reine-Claude Vraie' (C/D)	CAgr CArg CRos CSBt EPom LBuc LCro LOPS LRHS LSRN MPri NOra SEWo SGbt SSFT SSFr WJas WMat
§	- - 'Willingham Gage' (C/D)	EBee LSRN MAsh NOra SKee WMat
	- 'Sanctus Hubertus' (D)	CTri SKee WWct
	- 'Seneca' (D)	EPom NOra SKee SSFr WMat
	- 'Severn Cross' (D)	SSFr
	- 'Stanley' (C/D)	LMaj SGsty SVic
	- 'Stella' (F)	CCVT LOPS LSRN MPri SLim
	- 'Stella's Star' (D)	MAsh MCoo NOra WMat
	- 'Swan' (C)	NOra WMat WWct
	- 'Syston White' (F)	MGos
	- 'Thames Cross' (D)	NOra
	- 'Transparent Gage' (D)	SKee
	- 'Valor' (D) ♀H5	NOra SKee
	- 'Verity' (C/D)	SKee WMat
	- 'Victoria' (D) ♀H5	Widely available
	- 'Violetta'^{PBR} (D)	CAgr
	- 'Warwickshire Drooper' (C)	CAgr CHab CTho MAsh NOra SKee SLon SSFr WMat WWct
	- 'Willingham'	see *P. domestica* (Reine-Claude Group) 'Willingham Gage'
	- 'Zimmers Frühzwetsche' (F)	SKee
§	***dulcis***	CHab CLnd CTri ELan EPfP EPom LMaj LRHS MGos MMuc SCob SCoo SEND SWvt WMou
	- 'Ai' (F)	CAgr
	- 'Ardéchoise' (F)	CAgr
	- 'Ferraduel' (F)	CAgr
	- 'Ferragnès' (F)	CAgr
*	- 'Phoebe' (F)	CAgr
	- 'Princesse' (F)	SKee
	- 'Sultane' (F)	SKee
	- 'Supernova' (F)	CCCN
	- 'Tuono' (F)	CCCN
	EASTER BONNET ('Comet'^{PBR})	CTri LRHS
	'Flavor King' (Pluot Series) (D)	CAgr LCro LOPS WMat
	'Flavour Supreme' (F)	EPom
	FRAGRANT CLOUD	see *P.* 'Shizuka'
	FRILLY FROCK ('Fpmspl') (v)	EBee LRHS MPri NLar NOra SGbt SPoG WMat
	fruticosa	WFar
	'Fugenzō' misapplied	see *P.* 'Kofugen'
§	'Fugenzō' ♀H6	Widely available
	glandulosa 'Alba Plena' (d)	CEnd CMac CSBt SDix SGol SPlb SRms SWvt WCFE
	- 'Rosea Plena'	see *P. glandulosa* 'Sinensis'
§	- 'Sinensis' (d)	CEnd CExl CSBt SGol SRms
§	× ***gondouinii*** 'May Duke' (F)	SKee
§	- 'Merton Reward' (F)	SEdi SKee
	grayana B&SWJ 10903	WCru
	'Gyoikō'	CBcs CEnd CLnd EBee LRHS NOra WMat
	'Hally Jolivette'	CEnd EBee LRHS MAsh NOra NOrn SPoG WHwl WMat
§	'Hanagasa' ♀H6	CBcs CEnd EPfP NLar NOra SGbt WMat WMou
	'Hillieri Spire'	see *P.* 'Spire'
	'Hilling's Weeping'	LCro LOPS SLon
	himalaica	CJun EBee LRHS NLar NOra WMat WPGP
	'Hokusai' ♀H6	CBcs CBrac EBee EPfP LRHS NOra SGol WMat
	HOLLYWOOD	see *P.* 'Trailblazer'
	'Horinji'	CBcs NLar NOra SCoo WMat
	'Howard No. 3'	WMat
	'Ichiyo' (d) ♀H6	CBcs CLnd EPfP NOra SCoo SPer WMat
	ilicifolia subsp. ***lyonii***	WPGP
	× ***incam*** 'Okamé' ♀H6	Widely available
	- 'Shosar' ♀H6	CEnd SCoo SPer
	incisa	CTri
	- 'Beniomi'	MRav
	- 'February Pink'	CJun SGol
	- 'Fujimae' ♀H6	NLar
	- 'Kojo-no-mai' ♀H6	Widely available
	- 'Mikinori'	CEnd CJun CMac CSBt EPfP MAsh MBlu NLar NOra NOrn SCoo SEWo WMat
	- 'Oshidori' (d) ♀H6	CAby CMac CSBt ELon EPfP LRHS MMrt MRav NLar NOra NQui SRms WMat WSpi
	- 'Paean'	NLar WFar
	- 'Pendula' ♀H6	LRHS NOra SCoo WMat
	- 'Praecox'	CSBt CTho EPfP SCoo WMat
§	- f. ***yamadei*** ♀H6	CJun MAsh NOrn WSpi
	insititia (F)	MWht
	- 'Abergwyngregin' (C)	WMat
	- 'Aylesbury Prune' (C)	NOra SKee WMat
	- 'Blue Violet Damson' (C)	CAgr MCoo NOra SKee WMat
§	- 'Bradley's King Damson' (C)	CArg CLnd MCoo NLar NOra SKee WMat
	- bullace (C)	LEdu SEdi
	- 'Countess' (C)	CTri
	- 'Dittisham Damson' (C)	WMat
	- 'Farleigh Damson' (C) ♀H6	CAgr CArg CHab EPfP EPom LBuc LEdu NLar NOra SEdi SKee SPer SVic WJas WMat WWct
	- 'King of Damsons'	see *P. insititia* 'Bradley's King Damson'
	- 'Langley Bullace' (C)	CAgr CTri LEdu NOra SKee SSFr WMat
	- 'Lisna' (C)	CTri WMat
	- 'Merryweather Damson' (C)	Widely available
	- 'Mirabelle Countess' (C)	EPom WMat
	- 'Mirabelle de Metz' (C)	SKee
	- 'Mirabelle de Nancy' (C)	CAgr EPom MWat NOra SEWo SKee WMat
	- 'Mirabelle Ruby' (C)	CArg LRHS NOra SPoG WMat
§	- 'Prune Damson' (C) ♀H6	CAgr CArg CHab CLnd CMac CTho CTri EBee EPom LBuc LCro LRHS MAsh MMuc MWat NLar NOra SEND SEWo SGbt SKee SPer SSFr WJas WMat WWct
	- 'Shepherd's Bullace' (C)	MCoo SKee
	- 'Shropshire Damson'	see *P. insititia* 'Prune Damson'
	- 'Small Bullace' (C)	SKee
	- 'Westmorland Prune' (C)	CHab NLar
	- 'Yellow Apricot' (C)	SKee
	'Jacqueline'	EBee LRHS NLar NOra WMou
	'Jō-nioi'	CEnd CLnd CTho LRHS
	kansuensis	IArd
§	'Kanzan' (d) ♀H6	Widely available
§	'Kiku-shidare-zakura'	Widely available
	'Kobuku-zakura'	EWTr NOra WMat
§	'Kofugen'	CSBt LRHS NOra WMat
	Korean hill cherry	see *P. verecunda*
	'Kursar'	CLnd CSBt CTri EPfP GKin LRHS LSRN NOrn SCoo SGbt SLim SLon SPer SSFr SWvt WHwl WMat WSpi
	laurocerasus	CBcs CBrac CCVT CDoC CMac EBee ECrN ELan EPfP EShb GKin LMaj MGos MHed MPri MRav SArc SCob SGbt SGol SGsty SPer WMat WMou WTSh

- 'Angustifolia'	CDoC SCob
- 'Camelliifolia'	CMac CTri MBlu WCFE
- 'Castlewellan' (v)	CBrac CDoC CTri ELon EPfP EShb MGos MRav MSwo NLar NWad SCob SDix SPer SPoG SSta WAvo WFar WRHF
- 'Caucasica'	CEnd ECrN LMaj NLar SEND SGol SGsty
- 'Cherry Brandy'	SGol
- ETNA ('Anbri'PBR) ♀H5	CBod CMac EHyd LBuc LRHS MAsh SCob SWvt
- 'Gajo'PBR	CBod
- GENOLIA ('Mariblon'PBR)	LMaj SGol
- GORIS GOLD ('Goris11'PBR) **new**	CBod
- 'Green Marble' (v)	CTri EBee
- 'Ivory'PBR	CBod
§ - 'Latifolia'	LMaj WCFE WMou
- 'Magnoliifolia'	see *P. laurocerasus* 'Latifolia'
- 'Mano'	LMaj
- 'Marbled White'	see *P. laurocerasus* 'Castlewellan'
- 'Miky'	CJun
- 'Mount Vernon'	CTri MBlu
- 'Novita'	CBod CBrac CDoC ECrN EPfP LMaj LSRN MPri NLar NOrn SCob SGsty SWeb
- 'Otto Luyken' ♀H5	CBcs CBod CBrac CCVT CMac CTri EBee ELan EPfP LBuc LRHS MAsh MGos MSwo NBir NLar SArc SCob SGol SPer SPlb WCFE WFar
- 'Piranha'PBR	NEoE
- 'Reynvaanii'	LMaj
- 'Rotundifolia' ♀H5	Widely available
- 'Variegata' misapplied	see *P. laurocerasus* 'Castlewellan'
- 'Variegata' ambig. (v)	SRms
- 'Whitespot'	MMuc
- 'Zabeliana'	CMac CTri MSwo SCob SRms WCFE
litigiosa	EBee LRHS NLar NOra WMat
'Little Pink Perfection'	EPom LCro LOPS NLar NOra NOrn SCoo SPoG WMat
* ***longipedunculata***	WHwl
lusitanica ♀H5	Widely available
- subsp. ***azorica***	CExl EBee LRHS WMou WPGP
- 'Brenelia'PBR	SGsty
- 'Myrtifolia' ♀H5	CBar CDoC CRos CTri ECrN EHyd EPfP EShb LMaj LRHS MRav NLar NOra SArc SCob SGol SGsty SLon SPoG SWvt WCFE WMat
- 'Variegata' (v)	CBar CBod CBrac CMac ELan ELon MGos MRav MSwo SCob SGol SGsty SPer SPoG SSta SWvt WFar
maackii	LMaj NOrn
- 'Amber Beauty'	EBee EPfP LMaj MMuc MRav NOra SEND SGol SLon WMat WMou
maritima	WKor
§ 'Matsumae-beni-murasaki'	CBcs LRHS NLar NOra WMat
'Matsumae-beni-tamanishiki'	see *P.* 'Beni-tamanishiki'
§ 'Matsumae-fuki' ♀H6	CBcs EBee LSRN NLar NOra NOrn NRHS SLim WHwl WMat
'Matsumae-hanagasa'	see *P.* 'Hanagasa'
maximowiczii B&SWJ 10967	WCru
'Mount Fuji'	see *P.* 'Shirotae'
mume	CMen ELon MMrt
- 'Beni-chidori' ♀H5	CBcs CEnd CMac CSBt ELan ELon EPfP LCro LOPS LRHS MBlu NLar NOra NOrn SCoo SPoG WCot WJas WMat
§ - 'Omoi-no-mama' (d)	CEnd CMen EBee NOrn SAko
- 'Omoi-no-wac'	see *P. mume* 'Omoi-no-mama'
myrobalana	see *P. cerasifera* Myrobalan Group
nigra	WMat
nipponica var. ***kurilensis*** 'Brillant'	CBcs CBod CDoC CRos CSBt EHyd ELon LRHS NHol NLar NOrn NRHS SPoG
- - 'Ruby'	LSRN
'Okame Harlequin' (v)	WMou
'Oku-miyako' misapplied	see *P.* 'Shōgetsu'
padus	CArg CCVT CHab CLnd CMac CSBt ECrN LBuc MGos MMuc MSwo NLar SCob SEND SEWo SGsty WKor WMou WTSh
- 'Albertii'	CCVT NOra WMat
- 'Colorata' ♀H6	CArg CEnd CMac CTho ECrN ELan MGos MMrt MMuc MPri MRav NLar SEND SGol SPer SWvt WCot
- 'Grandiflora'	see *P. padus* 'Watereri'
- 'Le Thoureil'	LRHS MMrt NOra
- 'Purple Queen'	ECrN SGol
§ - 'Watereri' ♀H6	CArg CCVT CEnd CLnd CMCN CMac CTho ELan EPfP LMaj MMuc SCob SEND SEWo SGol SPer WMat WMou
'Pandora' ♀H6	CBrac CCVT CLnd CSBt EBee EPfP EPom LCro LMaj LOPS LRHS MGos MMuc MRav MSwo NOra NOrn SCob SCoo SEND SEWo SLim SPer SPoG SSFr WMat WMou
§ ***pendula*** f. ***ascendens*** 'Rosea' ♀H6	LRHS MRav NOra WMat
- 'Pendula Plena Rosea' (d)	NOra WHwl WMat
§ - 'Pendula Rosea'	CEnd CLnd CTri EPfP SGsty SPer WJas
§ - 'Pendula Rubra' ♀H6	CCVT CLnd CMac CSBt EBee ELan EPfP EPom LRHS MSwo NOra NOrn SCob SCoo SGbt SLim SPer SPoG WMat
§ - 'Stellata' ♀H6	EPfP LRHS NOra SGbt WMat
persica	SGsty SPre
- 'Amsden June' (F)	CLnd NOra SEdi SKee WMat
- 'Avalon Pride' (F)	CAgr EPom MCoo NOra SKee SPoG SSFr
- 'Bellegarde' (F)	NOra SKee WMat
- 'Bonanza' (F)	EPom LSRN
- 'Carman' (F)	WMat
- 'Champion' (F)	CLnd
- 'Crimson Bonfire' (F)	EPom
- 'Crimson Cascade' (F)	ELan
- 'Darling' (F)	SVic
- 'Diamond' (F)	EPom
- 'Dixi Red' (F)	CAgr SGsty
- 'Duke of York' (F)	CTri SKee SSFr
- 'Francis' (F)	SKee
- 'Frost' (F)	WMat
- 'Garden Lady' (F)	EPom NOra SLim WMat
- 'Gorgeous' (F)	NOra WMat
- 'Hale's Early' (F)	MMuc MRav NOra SEdi SKee SLim SPer WMat
- 'Jalousia' (F)	EPom SVic
- 'Lacrima' (F)	EPom
- 'Melred' (F)	WMou
- 'Mesembrine'PBR (F)	EPom NOra
- var. ***nectarina***	SGsty
- - 'Earliglo' (F)	NOra WMat
- - 'Early Rivers' (F)	LSRN WMat
- - 'Fantasia' (F)	SSFr
- - 'Flavortop' (F)	SSFr
- - 'Garden Beauty' (F/d)	WMat
- - 'Honey Kist'PBR (F)	EPom
- - 'Humboldt' (F)	CAgr SEdi WMat

- - 'Lord Napier' (F)	CAgr CSBt CTri EPfP EPom LRHS MGos MWat NOra SEND SEdi SGbt SKee SLim SPer SSFT SSFr SVic WMat
- - 'Madame Blanchet' (F)	SVic
- - 'Nectarella' (F)	EPom LSRN NOra SLim WMat
- - 'Pineapple' (F)	CAgr CTri LRHS NOra SKee WMat
- - RUBIS ('Necta Zee'[PBR]) (F)	EPom
- - 'Sauzee Bel' (F)	EPom
- - 'Sauzee King' (F)	EPom
- - 'Snow Baby' (F)	EPom
- - 'Snow Queen' (F)	SSFr
- - 'Terrace Ruby' (F)	MGos WMat
- 'Peregrine' (F)	CAgr CLnd CSBt CTri ELan EPfP EPom LRHS LSRN MAsh MGos MMuc NLar NOra SEND SEdi SGbt SKee SLim SPer SSFT SSFr SWeb WJas WMat
- 'Redhaven' (F)	CAgr NOra SKee SVic WMat
- 'Redlate Necta'[PBR] (F) new	SEdi
- 'Redwing' (F)	CAgr
- 'Robin Redbreast' (F)	CAgr
- 'Rochester' (F)	CAgr CLnd CSBt CTri ELan EPom LRHS LSRN MGos NLar NOra SEdi SKee SLim SPer SSFT SSFr SWeb WMat
- 'Sanguine de Savoie' (F)	EPom LRHS NOra WMat
- 'Saturne' (F)	CAgr CLnd EPom LRHS MAsh NOra SKee SSFr WMat
§ - 'Spring Snow'[PBR] new	NLar
- 'Terrace Amber' (F)	WMat
- 'Terrace Diamond' (F)	WMat
- 'Terrace Garnet' (F)	MGos WMat
× ***persicoides*** 'Ingrid' (F)	CAgr CEnd ECrN MCoo MGos NOra SCoo SKee SSFr WMat
- 'Pollardii'	WJas
- 'Robijn' (F)	CAgr EPom LBuc LEdu NOra SKee SVic
- 'Spring Glow'	CCVT CEnd CLnd EBee EMil EPfP MSwo NOra SCoo SEND SLim SLon WJas WMat
phaeosticta NJM 10.072	WPGP
'Pink Candy' (F)	EPom
PINK PARASOL	see *P.* 'Hanagasa'
'Pink Perfection' ♀[H6]	CBcs CBrac CLnd CSBt ELan ELon EPfP EPom GQue LRHS MGos MSwo NOra NOrn SCob SGbt SGsty SPer SSFr WJas WMat WMou
'Pink Shell'	CLnd EPfP EPom EWTr NOra SPer SSFr WMat
PINK SNOW SHOWERS ('Pisnshzam')	EPom
pissardii	see *P. cerasifera* 'Pissardii'
'Pissardii Nigra'	see *P. cerasifera* 'Nigra'
prostrata	WCot
pumila var. ***depressa***	MRav SAko
'Royal Burgundy' (d) ♀[H6]	Widely available
rufa	CBcs CJun CLnd CRos MAsh NOra SLon WLov WMat
salicina 'Lizzie' (F)	EPom
- 'Methley' (D)	CAgr NOra WMat
sargentii	CBcs CCVT CLnd CMac CSBt CTho CTri ECrN ELan EPfP EPom LBuc LCro LEdu LMaj LRHS MBlu MGos MMuc MRav MSwo SCob SEND SEWo SGol SSta WFar WJas WMat WTSh
- 'Charles Sargent' ♀[H6]	CMCN LMaj LSRN MBlu
- 'Columnaris'	EBee LRHS WMat
- 'Rancho'	CLnd LMaj MAsh NOrn SCoo SLim SPer SPoG WMat
× ***schmittii***	CBcs CCVT EBee LMaj LRHS NOra SCob WJas WMat
'Sekiyama'	see *P.* 'Kanzan'
§ ***serrula***	Widely available
- 'Branklyn' ♀[H6]	EBee EPfP LRHS MGos NOra
- 'Dorothy Clive' ♀[H6]	EBee
- 'Princesse Sturdza'	MBlu
- var. ***tibetica***	see *P. serrula*
serrula × ***serrulata***	WPGP
serrulata 'Erecta'	see *P.* 'Amanogawa'
- 'Grandiflora'	see *P.* 'Ukon'
- 'Longipes'	see *P.* 'Shogetsu'
- 'Miyako' misapplied	see *P.* 'Shogetsu'
- var. ***pubescens***	see *P. verecunda*
- 'Rosea'	see *P.* 'Kiku-shidare-zakura'
'Shidare-zakura'	see *P.* 'Kiku-shidare-zakura'
'Shimizu-zakura'	see *P.* 'Shogetsu'
'Shirofugen'	see *P.* 'Fugenzo'
§ 'Shirotae' ♀[H6]	Widely available
§ 'Shizuka' ♀[H6]	CBcs ECrN ELon LBuc LRHS MSwo NLar NOra NOrn SCob SCoo SGbt SLim SPer WHwl WMat WMou
§ 'Shōgetsu' ♀[H6]	CBcs CEnd CLnd CMCN CMac CSBt CTho ELan EPfP EPom LMaj LRHS LSRN MAsh MMuc NLar NOra NOrn SCob SEWo SLim SPer WHwl WMat WMou
× ***sieboldii*** 'Caespitosa'	see *P.* 'Takasago'
SNOW FOUNTAINS ('Snofozam')	SGsty SPer
'Snow Goose'	CMac CRos CTho EBee ELan EPfP EPom EWTr LCro LOPS LRHS MBlu MMuc NLar NOra NOrn SCoo SGol SPoG WMat
'Snow Showers'	CCVT CEnd CMac EBee ELan EPom LCro LRHS LSRN MAsh MGos MPri NLar NOra NOrn SEND SLim SPer SPoG WHwl WMat
spinosa	CArg CBrac CCVT CHab CMac CTri ECrN EPfP EPom GAbr LBuc LCro LMaj LOPS LSRN MBlu NLar NPol SCob SEWo SGsty SPer SPoG SVic WKor WMat WMou WSFF WTSh
- 'Plena' (d)	CEnd MBlu
- 'Purpurea'	MBlu WMou
§ 'Spire' ♀[H6]	CCVT CLnd CMCN CMac CSBt CTho ELon EPfP LBuc LCro LMaj LOPS LRHS MBlu MGos MMuc MPri MSwo NOrn NRHS SCob SCoo SEND SGol SPer WFar WJas WMat
SPRING SNOW	see *P.* 'Beni-tamanishiki'
'Spring Snow'	see *P. persica* 'Spring Snow'
'Stefania'	WMat
× ***subhirtella*** var. ***ascendens***	see *P. pendula* f. *ascendens*
- 'Autumnalis'	Widely available
- 'Autumnalis Rosea'	Widely available
- 'Falling Stars'	SLon
- 'Fukubana'	CLnd CMac ELon EPfP NLar WHwl WMat WMou
- 'Pendula' misapplied	see *P. pendula* 'Pendula Rosea'
- 'Pendula Rosea'	see *P. pendula* 'Pendula Rosea'
- 'Pendula Rubra'	see *P. pendula* 'Pendula Rubra'
- 'Rosea'	see *P. pendula* f. *ascendens* 'Rosea'

	- 'Stellata'	see *P. pendula* 'Stellata'
	'Sunset Boulevard' ♀H6	CCVT CLnd EBee ELan EPfP LMaj LRHS LSRN MGos NLar NOra SCob WMat
	'Tai-haku' ♀H6	Widely available
§	'Takasago'	EBee
	'Taoyame' ♀H6	CLnd
	tenella	ECha WCot
	- 'Alba'	WFar
	- 'Fire Hill'	CBcs ELan EPfP LRHS MGos NLar SPer WCot WJas WSpi
	'The Bride' ♀H6	CBcs CBrac CEnd CJun CTho EBee EPfP EPom LCro LOPS LRHS MAsh NOra NOrn SChF SCoo SEWo SGbt SPer WMat WMou
	tibetica	see *P. serrula*
	'Tiltstone Hellfire'	EBee GBin LRHS NLar NOra WMat
	tomentosa	WKor
§	'Trailblazer' (C/D)	CEnd CLnd CMac EMil MRav MSwo SCob SLon
	triloba	CBcs ECha LCro LOPS MBlu MGos
	- 'Multiplex' (d)	SRms WAvo WJas
§	'Ukon' ♀H6	CBcs CLnd CMCN CMac CTho CTri EBee ECrN EPfP EWTr LCro LOPS LRHS MAsh MGos MRav NLar NOra NOrn SCob SGol SLim SPer WFar WMat
	'Umineko'	CCVT CLnd ECrN LMaj MGos MMuc SCob SEND SEWo SPer
§	***verecunda***	CLnd WJas
	- 'Autumn Glory' ♀H6	CTho
	'Victoria Willis'	WMat
	virginiana	WKor
	- 'Schubert'	ELan MMuc
	'Woodfield Cluster'	IArd
	yamadae	see *P. incisa* f. *yamadei*
	× ***yedoensis***	CCVT CLnd CSBt ELan LMaj MRav NOra SCob SEWo SGsty SLon SPer WMat
	- 'Ivensii'	CSBt EPom LMaj SCoo SPer
	- 'Pendula'	see *P.* × *yedoensis* 'Shidare-Yoshino'
	- 'Perpendens'	see *P.* × *yedoensis* 'Shidare-Yoshino'
§	- 'Shidare-Yoshino'	CCVT CMac CSBt EBee ECrN LRHS MGos MRav MSwo NOrn SGsty SLim SLon SPer WMat
§	- 'Somei-Yoshino' ♀H6	CCVT CMCN CTho CTri SLim SSFr WJas
	'Yoshino'	see *P.* × *yedoensis* 'Somei-Yoshino'
	'Yoshino Pendula'	see *P.* × *yedoensis* 'Shidare-Yoshino'

Pseudocydonia (*Rosaceae*)

§	***sinensis***	CBcs CMen SEND SSta WKor

Pseudofumaria see *Corydalis*

	alba	see *Corydalis ochroleuca*

Pseudogynoxys (*Asteraceae*)

§	***chenopodioides***	CCCN CSpe ECre SVen

Pseudolarix (*Pinaceae*)

	amabilis ♀H7	CMen CTho EPfP MBlu MPkF SLim SMad
	kaempferi (Lamb.) Gordon	see *Larix kaempferi*

Pseudomuscari see *Muscari*

Pseudopanax ✿ (*Araliaceae*)

	(Adiantifolius Group) 'Adiantifolius'	CAbb CBcs CCCN CTrC EBee SVen
	- 'Cyril Watson' ♀H3	CBcs EBee ELon SVen
	arboreus	see *Neopanax arboreus*
	'Chainsaw' **new**	CBct
	chathamicus	SArc
	crassifolius	CBrP CCCN CDTJ CRos ELon GBin LRHS SArc WPGP
	- var. ***trifoliolatus***	CBcs CDTJ EBee WPGP
	'Dark Star'	CBcs CTrC LRHS
	discolor	LEdu
	ferox	CBrP CDTJ CTrC CTsd GBin LCro LOPS LRHS SVen
	laetus	see *Neopanax laetus*
	lessonii	CBcs CBrP
	- 'Gold Splash' (v) ♀H3	CBcs CBod CCCN CTrC EBee ELon EPfP LRHS SEND SVen
	- 'Nigra'	CTrC
	- 'Rangitira'	CBcs CTrC LRHS
	'Linearifolius'	CTrC IDee LEdu
	'Moa's Toes'	CBcs CBct CTrC CTsd MHtn SCob SEND SPad WCot WPGP
	'Purpureus' ♀H3	CCCN CDTJ CTrC CTsd EBee ELon EPfP IDee IMou SEND SVen
	'Sabre'	CAbb CBcs CCCN CDTJ CTrC EBee ELon EPfP IDee LRHS SEND
	'Trident' ♀H3	CTrC IMou SVen
	'Tuatara'	CAbb CBcs CCht CTrC GBin MHtn SCob WPGP

Pseudosasa (*Poaceae*)

	amabilis misapplied	see *Arundinaria gigantea*
	- var. ***tenuis***	XCre
	cantorii	XCre
§	***japonica*** ♀H5	CAbb CAgr CBcs CBdn CBod CRos CSBt CTsd EHyd EPfP GBin LCro LOPS LRHS MMuc MWht NLar NRHS SArc SCob SEND SGsty SPoG SWeb WFar XCre
§	- 'Akebonosuji' (v)	CBdn SWeb WPGP XCre
I	- var. ***pleioblastoides***	MWht
	- 'Tsutsumiana'	ELon MWht NLar XCre
	- 'Variegata'	see *P. japonica* 'Akebonosuji'
	viridula	MWht XCre

Pseudotaxus (*Taxaceae*)

	chienii	CBcs SPtp WPGP

Pseudotsuga (*Pinaceae*)

§	***menziesii***	CBcs CLnd ECrN ELan EPfP MBlu MMuc SCob WTSh
	- 'Bhiela Lhota'	CKen
	- 'Blue Wonder'	CKen
	- 'Dandy Doug'	NLar
	- 'Densa'	CKen
	- 'Fastigiata'	CKen
	- 'Fletcheri'	CKen SLim
	- 'Foxy Fir'	SLim
	- 'Glauca Pendula'	LRHS MBlu
	- 'Gollen' **new**	SLim
I	- 'Gotelli's Pendula'	CKen
	- 'Graceful Grace'	CKen
	- 'Hillside Pride'	NLar
	- 'Idaho Gem'	NLar
	- 'Julie'	CKen
	- 'Knaphill'	LRHS
	- 'Les Barres' **new**	SLim
	- 'Little Jamie'	CKen
	- 'Lohbrunner'	CKen SLim
	- 'Moerheimii' **new**	NLar
	- 'Nana'	CKen
	- 'Nýřany' **new**	SLim
	- 'Pannenhoef' **new**	SLim

- 'Seattle Mountain' **new** — SLim
- 'Serpentine' — MBlu NLar SLim
- 'Stairii' — CKen
- 'Uwes Golden' — SLim

taxifolia — see *P. menziesii*

Pseudowintera (*Winteraceae*)

§ ***colorata*** — CBcs CCCN CDoC CExl CMac CPla CTrC EBee GAbr GKin MRav NLar SBrt SEle WFar WSHC
- 'Marjorie Congreve' — CBcs CDoC GKin IArd LRHS
- 'Moulin Rouge' — CBcs CTrC SEle
- 'Red Glow' — CBcs
- 'Red Leopard' — CAby CBcs CTrC LRHS MPkF NLar SEle WFar

Psidium (*Myrtaceae*)

cattleyanum — see *P. littorale* var. *longipes*
guajava (F) — CCCN CMCN SPlb SVic XBlo
littorale var. ***littorale*** (F) — WKor
§ - var. ***longipes*** (F) — CCCN WKor XBlo

Psophocarpus (*Papilionaceae*)

tetragonolobus — LOPS SPhx

Psoralea (*Papilionaceae*)

aphylla — SVen
* ***fleta*** — SPlb
glabra — SPlb
glandulosa — SPlb WSHC
oligophylla — SPlb
pinnata — CExl IArd

Psychotria (*Rubiaceae*)

capensis — CExl

Psylliostachys (*Plumbaginaceae*)

suworowii — LRHS SPhx

Ptelea (*Rutaceae*)

trifoliata — CBcs CLnd EPfP MBlu SPer SRms WPGP
- 'Aurea' 🏆H6 — CBcs CExl CJun CLnd ELan EPfP MBlu MMuc SPer WBor WPGP

Pteracanthus see *Strobilanthes*

Pteridium (*Dennstaedtiaceae*)

aquilinum — XLum

Pteridophyllum (*Papaveraceae*)

racemosum — CMiW GEdr LEdu NHpl WCru

Pteris ✿ (*Pteridaceae*)

cretica var. ***albolineata*** — see *P. nipponica*
- 'Mayi' (v) — CRos EHyd LRHS NRHS
- 'Ouvradii' — SPlb
- 'Parkeri' — CBdn EHyd LRHS
- 'Rivertoniana' — EHyd LRHS NRHS
- 'Rowei' — CRos EHyd LRHS NRHS XBlo
- 'Wimsettii' — CRos EHyd LEdu LRHS MAsh NRHS WCot

ensiformis 'Evergemiensis' (v) — EShb
gallinopes — EBee
incompleta **new** — LEdu WPGP
§ ***nipponica*** 🏆H1c — CRos EHyd EShb LLWG LRHS MAvo MBel NRHS SEdd WCot XBlo
* ***staminea*** — XBlo
tremula — EShb NBro
tricolor — EShb
umbrosa — CAby CCht CLAP CRos CTsd EHyd LLWG LRHS MAsh MHol NBro NRHS WCot WLov WPGP WSMil
wallichiana — SMad WCot WPGP

Pterocactus (*Cactaceae*)

hickenii F&W 10240 — WCot

Pterocarya ✿ (*Juglandaceae*)

fraxinifolia — CBcs CCVT CLnd CMCN CTho EBee ECrN EPfP IArd IDee LMaj LRHS MBlu MCoo MMuc MRav SChF WTSh
- NJM 13.007 — WPGP
- PAB 13.052 — LEdu
- 'Abbotsbury Giant' — WPGP

macroptera var. ***insignis*** — CExl EBee SMad WPGP
× ***rehderiana*** — CTho MBlu WMou
rhoifolia — CMCN IArd SEND
stenoptera — CBcs CDTJ CMCN CTho NLar WMou
- 'Fern Leaf' 🏆H6 — CDoC CExl EBee MBlu WPGP

tonkinensis — WPGP

Pterocephalus (*Caprifoliaceae*)

parnassi — see *P. perennis*
§ ***perennis*** — CMea MHer NBir SRms WHoo
pinardii — CPBP
spathulatus — WAbe

Pterostylis (*Orchidaceae*)

curta 🏆H2 — CBro SGro

Pterostyrax (*Styracaceae*)

corymbosa — CBcs CMCN GBin MBlu NLar
- CWJ 12838 — WCru

hispida 🏆H5 — CBcs CMCN EPfP ESwi MBlu MRav NLar SAko WFar
psilophyllus — CMCN IArd SPtp WPGP
- var. ***leveillei*** — WPGP
- trilobed — EBee WPGP

Ptilostemon (*Asteraceae*)

§ ***diacantha*** — CBod EBee EHyd EMor LRHS
echinocephalus — CBod

Ptilotrichum see *Alyssum*

Ptilotus (*Amaranthaceae*)

exaltatus — SPlb

Pulicaria (*Asteraceae*)

§ ***dysenterica*** — CHab LLWG NGrd NMir WHer WSFF

Pulmonaria (*Boraginaceae*)

angustifolia 🏆H6 — CTri EPfP GKev GMaP MNrw NWad SHeu SRms
- 'Azurea' — CElw ELan EPPr EPfP GAbr GMaP LRHS MCot MMuc MRav NBro NGrd NLar SRms WCAu WSpi
- 'Blaues Meer' — EBee ECtt EHyd LRHS MNrw NRHS NSti SGbt SHeu WSpi
- 'Munstead Blue' — MCot MRav NRya SRms

'Apple Frost' — LRHS SHeu
'Ballyrogan Blue' 🏆H6 — EHyd LRHS
'Barfield Regalia' — NChi NSti
'Benediction' — MBriF MNrw NSti WBrk WCot WMal
'Beth Chatto' — CElw

	'Beth's Pink'	GAbr
	'Blake's Silver'	CBre CDor MHol MNrw NSti SCob WBrk WCot WHoo WOld
	'Blauer Hügel'	NSti
	'Blue Crown'	CElw EWes WBrk
	'Blue Ensign' ♀H6	Widely available
	'Blue Moon'	see *P. officinalis* 'Blue Mist'
	'Blue Pearl'	EHyd LRHS NRHS XEll
	'Bubble Gum'PBR	CDor EHyd LRHS SCob SHeu
	'Cleeton Red'	MNrw
	'Coral Springs'	NLar
	'Cotton Cool' ♀H6	EBee ECha ECtt EHyd EShb GBin GQue LRHS MAvo MBNS MBel MBriF MCot MHer MRav MTin NHol NRHS NSti NWad SGbt SHeu SSut WCAu WGwG WSMil WWtn
	'Dark Vader'	CWCL ECtt EHyd LRHS SHeu SPoG
	'Diana Clare' ♀H6	Widely available
	'Elworth Sentinel' **new**	MBriF
	'Excalibur'	ECtt NLar SHeu SRms
	'Fiona'	MNrw
	'Gavin Compton' (v)	MNrw
	'Glacier'	EPfP NChi WCot
	'High Contrast'	ECtt SHeu
	'Highdown'	see *P.* 'Lewis Palmer'
	'Ice Ballet' (Classic Series)	CDor EBee ECtt EMor EPfP MBriF MNrw SCob SHar SHeu WCAu
	'Joan Curtis'	EWld MNrw
§	'Lewis Palmer' ♀H6	CBro CDor CTri CWCL GMaP LRHS MNrw NBir SRms WAvo WBrk WHoo
	'Little Star' ♀H6	CElw CRos EBee ECha EHyd LRHS MAvo NRHS NSti SHeu WFar
	longifolia	CBod ECha ECtt EHyd ELan EPfP GBin GKev LRHS LSou MHer NBir NLar NRHS NSti SRms WCav
§	- 'Ankum'	CElw NBir WCot
	- 'Bertram Anderson'	EBee ECtt EMor GMaP LRHS NBir NLar NRHS SHeu SPer SRms SWvt
	- subsp. ***cevennensis***	EHyd EMor ILea LRHS NLar NRHS SHeu WBrk WFar WSpi
	- 'Coen Jansen'	see *P. longifolia* 'Ankum'
	- 'Dordogne'	NBir NLar
	- 'Howard Eggins'	WAvo WBrk
	- 'Juliett M.'	XEll
	'Mado'	ECha
	'Majesté'	CBod CDor CMiW CRos ECha EHyd ELan EMor EPfP EWes GMaP LRHS MBel MRav NBir NLar NRHS NSti SCob SEdd SHeu SPer SPoG SRms WCAu WCot WFar
	'Margery Fish'	CDor LRHS NChi SHeu WBrk
	'Mary Mottram'	NBir NSti SHeu WCot
	'Mawson's Blue'	EWes NBir NChi SWvt
	'Milky Way'	CWCL ECtt EMor EPfP SHeu SPoG
	'Miss Elly'	MAvo
	mollis	CBod EHyd GBin IMou LRHS MNrw NSti WCAu
	- 'Royal Blue'	MRav
	'Monksilver'	CElw
	'Moonshine'PBR	CRos ECtt EHyd EPfP GKev LRHS MAsh MBel NRHS NSti SHeu
	'Moonstone'	CElw
	'Mrs Kittle'	CWCL EHyd GPSL IMou LRHS MBel MBriF MRav NBir NGdn NHol NRHS NSti SHeu SSut WSMil
	'Netta Statham'	MAvo
	'Nürnberg'	CDor
	officinalis	CHby NChi NGrd WBrk WCFE XAbr
	- 'Alba'	WBrk
§	- 'Blue Mist'	GMaP NBir WAvo WCot
	- 'Bowles's Blue'	see *P. officinalis* 'Blue Mist'
	- Cambridge Blue Group	EPfP LRHS MRav NBir NGdn WCot WWtn
	- 'White Wings'	NLar
	OPAL ('Ocupol') ♀H6	Widely available
	'Pierre's Pure Pink'	EBee EHyd LRHS SHeu
	'Pink Haze'PBR	ECtt MHol NLar SWvt
	'Purple Haze'	SCob
	'Raspberry Splash'PBR	CBod CRos CWCL ECtt ECul EMor EPfP LCro LOPS LRHS MMuc MNHC MNrw NBir NLar SCob SHeu SWvt WCAu WPnP
*	'Rowlatt Choules'	MNrw
	'Roy Davidson'	CBod CDor ECtt EHyd EPPr EPfP LRHS MBow NBir NChi NHol NRHS SRms SWvt
	rubra	CBcs CElw CWCL ECha ELan GAbr LCro LOPS MMuc MNrw NBid NChi NLar NSti SHeu SRms WBrk WCAu
	- var. ***alba***	see *P. rubra* var. *albocorollata*
§	- var. ***albocorollata***	EHyd EPfP GBin LRHS NBid
	- 'Ann'	GBin GQue
	- 'Barfield Pink'	MNrw NBir NLar SHeu
	- 'Bowles's Red'	CBod GPSL LRHS MNrw MRav NBir WFar WWtn
	- 'David Ward' (v)	CWCL ECha ECtt EHyd ELan EMor LRHS MBel MRav NBir NSti SCob SHeu SMad SPoG SRms WCAu WCFE WCot
	- 'Rachel Vernie' (v)	NQui WAvo
	- 'Redstart'	CBod CCBP CDor CSam ECtt GMaP ILea LRHS MNrw MRav NBir NGrd NLar SCob SHeu SRms SWvt WBrk WCAu WFar
§	***saccharata***	ECha GMaP MMuc SRms
	- 'Alba'	CElw MMuc SRms
	- Argentea Group ♀H6	CTri EPfP GMaP LRHS MMuc MRav NGdn
	- 'Clent Skysilver'	WAvo WBrk
	- 'Dora Bielefeld'	CAby CBod ECha EPfP EWTr EWes EWld GMaP IMou LRHS MBriF MNrw MRav NBir NChi NGdn NHol NRHS NSti SHeu SPer SWvt WCav WFar
	- 'Frühlingshimmel'	CDor LPla MRav
	- 'Glebe Cottage Blue'	CElw
	- 'Leopard'	CAby CDor CMea CRos CSam CWCL ECtt EHyd EMor EPfP GMaP LRHS MBel MNrw NBir NGdn NLar NRHS NSti SHeu SWvt WCAu WCot WGwG WHoo WSpi
	- 'Mrs Moon'	CBod CTri ECtt EHyd EMor EPfP GMaP LCro LOPS LRHS MBriF MNHC NLar SCob SHeu SPer SWvt WCAu WCav
	- 'Old Rectory Silver'	NBir
	- 'Picta'	see *P. saccharata*
	- 'Reginald Kaye'	ECha
	- 'Silverado'PBR	ECtt LRHS NGdn NLar SCob SHeu SWvt
	- 'Stanhoe'	EWes
	'Saint Ann's'	CRos EHyd LRHS NRHS NSti
	'Samurai' ♀H6	CBod CWCL IMou LRHS MNrw NLar NSti SHeu WFar WGrn
	'Silver Bouquet'PBR	ECtt ECul EPfP LCro LOPS LSou MAsh NHpl NSti SHeu
	'Silver Lance'	SHeu

'Silver Shimmers'PBR	SHeu
'Sissinghurst White' ♀H6	Widely available
'Smoky Blue'	ECtt MRav SCob SHeu
'Spilled Milk'	SHeu
'Stillingfleet Meg'	CDor CRos ECtt EHyd EPfP LRHS LSou MBNS MBriF MHer NGdn NRHS NSti NWad SHar SHeu WCAu WGwG WWtn
'Trevi Fountain' ♀H6	Widely available
'Vera May' ♀H6	MBriF MNrw
'Victorian Brooch'PBR	CBod CRos CWCL ECtt EHyd EPau EPfP GKev GMaP LRHS MAsh MHol MNrw NCou NRHS SHeu SPad SPoG WCAu WSpi
'Weetwood Blue'	EHyd LRHS MNrw NRHS WMal
'Wendy Perry'	EHyd LRHS

Pulsatilla (*Ranunculaceae*)

albana	EHyd GKev LRHS NRHS
- 'Lutea'	EBee NSla
alpina	SPlb SRms
§ - subsp. ***apiifolia***	GKev
- subsp. ***sulphurea*** misapplied	see *P. alpina* subsp. *apiifolia*
ambigua	GEdr
bungeana	SBrt
campanella	EBee GEdr
caucasica	EHyd EWld LRHS NRHS
halleri ♀H5	EBee GKev WHal WSHC
- subsp. ***slavica*** ♀H5	EPot
- subsp. ***taurica***	GEdr
lutea	see *P. alpina* subsp. *apiifolia*
montana	SPlb XEll
occidentalis	GEdr
§ ***patens***	NGdn
- subsp. ***flavescens***	GEdr
pratensis	GPoy SRms
- subsp. ***nigricans***	EBee GEdr WAbe
red-flowered	CTri
rubra	CAvo CMea CRos EAJP EBou EHyd ELan EMor EPfP GJos GKev GMaP LRHS MHer NBir NGdn NLar NRHS SPer SPoG SRms WHoo WIce
* ***serotina***	EBee GKev
sugawarae **new**	GEdr
tatewakii	NSla
turczaninovii	NSla SHar XEll
§ ***vernalis***	GEdr NLar NSla WAbe XEll
violacea	CBcs
§ ***vulgaris*** ♀H5	Widely available
- 'Alba'	CAby CAvo CRos EBee ECha EHyd ELan EPfP EShb GKev LRHS LSun MBel MHer NBir NGdn NRHS NSla SPer SPoG SWvt WFar WGwG WIce XEll XLum
- 'Barton's Pink'	CRos EHyd LRHS NRHS
- 'Blaue Glocke'	CAby CRos EHyd GEdr LRHS NRHS SHar SWvt
- blue-flowered	CTri
- 'Eva Constance'	CRos EHyd LRHS NRHS
- subsp. ***grandis***	CFis CRos EHyd EPot GEdr LRHS NRHS NSla
- - 'Papageno'	CDor CSpe EAJP ELon EMor GEdr IPot LSou MBel MHol NHol NHpl NLar NSla WIce
- Heiler hybrids	EShb MArl MRav MWat NGdn NSla SGbt SVic WGwG
- 'Perlen Glocke'	EDAr EHyd GEdr LRHS NLar NRHS WIce
- pink-flowered	EAJP GKev WFar
- (Pinwheel Series) PINWHEEL BLUE VIOLET SHADES	CBod EHyd NRHS
- - PINWHEEL WHITE	MHol WFar
- RED CLOCK	see *P. vulgaris* 'Röde Klokke'
- red-flowered	CTsd EBee GAbr SGbt WFar
§ - 'Röde Klokke'	CAby CRos ECtt EHyd EPfP GEdr GWyn LRHS LSun MBel MCot NRHS NSla SHar SWvt XEll XLum
- ROTE GLOCKE	see *P. vulgaris* 'Röde Klokke'
- 'Violet Bells'	EBou
- violet-blue-flowered	CRos EHyd EPfP LRHS NRHS
§ - 'Weisse Schwan'	EPfP GEdr GMaP
- 'White Bells'	NHol WFar
- WHITE SWAN	see *P. vulgaris* 'Weisse Schwan'

Pultenaea (*Papilionaceae*)

daphnoides	SVen
juniperina	SPlb SVen

pummelo see *Citrus maxima*

Punica (*Lythraceae*)

granatum	CBcs CCCN CMCN CMen ELan EPfP LMaj SEND SIvy SPre SVic SWeb SWvt WLov
- 'Chico' (d)	CBcs
- 'Fina Tendral' (F)	CCCN EShb XSen
- 'Legrelleae' (F/d)	SEND
- 'Maxima Rubra' (d)	EShb
- 'Mollar de Elche'	XSen
- var. ***nana*** ♀H3	CAby CCCN CMen CTsd EHyd EPfP EShb LEdu LRHS MHer SRms SVen SVic SWeb WKor WLov
- f. ***plena*** (d)	CBcs EPfP LRHS MRav SPer WCFE
- - 'Flore Pleno Luteo' (d)	LRHS
- 'Provence' (F)	EPom XSen
- 'Wonderful' (F)	CAgr XSen

Puschkinia (*Asparagaceae*)

scilloides	NBir
- 'Aragat's Gem'	GKev
- blue-flowered **new**	GKev
- large-flowered clone	GKev
- var. ***libanotica*** ♀H6	CRos EHyd EPot ERCP GKev LCro LOPS LRHS MPie NRHS SDeJ SEND WShi
- - 'Alba'	EPot GKev SDeJ

Puya ✿ (*Bromeliaceae*)

RH 1809	WCot
RH 2910A	WCot
RH 2961C	WCot
RH 3425B	WCot
alpestris	CCCN CPla EShb SPlb
§ - subsp. ***zoellneri***	CAbb CCCN CDTJ EShb SPlb SVen WCot
berteroana misapplied	see *P. alpestris* subsp. *zoellneri*
bicolor B&SWJ 14869	WCru
boliviensis	WCot
castellanosii	WCot
chilensis	CAbb CCCN CDTJ CPla LRHS SPlb SVen WCot
coerulea	CCCN CDTJ CPla CTsd SPlb WSMil
dyckioides	LRHS WCot
- red-bracted	WCot
ferruginea	SPlb WCot
grantii B&SWJ 14819	WCru
hromadnikii	SPlb
humilis **new**	WCot
killipii B&SWJ 14801	WCru

laxa SPlb WCot
lineata B&SWJ 14878 WCru
mirabilis CAbb CDTJ GBin SPlb WSMil
- B&SWJ 14825 WCru
- B&SWJ 14827 WCru
aff. ***nitida*** B&SWJ 14396 WCru
- B&SWJ 14887 WCru
ochroleuca WCru
B&SWJ 14716 new
santosii B&SWJ 14783 WCru
trianae B&SWJ 14818 WCru
- B&SWJ 14921 WCru
venusta CCCN CCht CDTJ CPla LRHS SPlb SVen WCot
yakespala LRHS WCot

Pycnanthemum (*Lamiaceae*)

albescens new ECha
curvipes LEdu
muticum LEdu SBrt SPhx WPGP
pilosum CLau EBou MHer SPhx WFar WJek XLum
- 'Bees' Friend' MNrw
tenuifolium NLar SBrt SPhx
virginianum EBee SPhx

Pycnostachys (*Lamiaceae*)

urticifolia EWes

Pygmea see *Chionohebe*

Pyracantha (*Rosaceae*)

ALEXANDER PENDULA ('Renolex') MRav MSwo SRms
angustifolia WCFE
- KR 2481 WPGP
§ ***atalantioides*** SPlb WCFE
coccinea 'Lalandei' CMac
- 'Red Column' Widely available
- 'Red Cushion' ELan SArc SRms
crenulata WCFE
DART'S RED ('Interrada') CSBt
'Fiery Cascade' CRos EHyd LRHS NRHS SPoG WFar
gibbsii see *P. atalantioides*
'Golden Charmer' CDoC CMac CRos EHyd EPfP LBuc LRHS MGos MSwo NLar SCoo SGol SPer SPoG SRms SWvt WFar
'Golden Glow' SGol
'Golden Paradise'PBR CBod NEoE SHar
'Golden Sun' see *P.* 'Soleil d'Or'
'Harlequin' (v) CMac SGol WFar
'Knap Hill Lemon' MBlu
koidzumii 'Victory' ECrN NLar WAvo
'Mohave' CRos CTri ECrN EHyd ELan ELon LRHS MAsh NRHS SCob SGol SLim SRms SWvt WFar
'Mohave Silver' (v) CMac CRos EHyd ELan EShb LRHS NHol NRHS
'Navaho' LMaj SGsty
'Orange Charmer' CBrac CMac CTri ELan LRHS MGos NHol NLar SCob SGol SPer SPlb WFar
'Orange Glow' ♀H6 CArg CBod CBrac CRos CSBt CTri ECrN EHyd EPfP EShb LBuc LRHS MAsh MGos MMuc MSwo NLar NRHS SArc SCob SEND SEWo SGol SLim SPer SRms SWvt WAvo WFar
'Red Charmer' NHol
* 'Red Pillar' SGbt
'Red Star' NRHS
rogersiana 'Flava' ♀H5 CRos CSBt EHyd EPfP LRHS MAsh NRHS SPoG SWvt WAvo
'Rosedale' CRos EHyd LRHS WAvo
SAPHYR JAUNE ('Cadaune') CBcs CCVT CDoC CEnd EBee EPfP ILea LCro LOPS LRHS MAsh MGos MRav NHol SCob SGbt SGol SPer SWeb
SAPHYR ORANGE ('Cadange') ♀H6 CBcs CCVT CDoC CEnd CMac CRos CSBt EBee ECrN EHyd EPfP ILea LCro LOPS LRHS MAsh MGos MRav NRHS SCob SCoo SGbt SGol SPer SWeb
SAPHYR ROUGE ('Cadrou'PBR) ♀H6 Widely available
'Shawnee' CMac MSwo
§ 'Soleil d'Or' CBod CTri ECrN EHyd ELan EPfP LRHS MAsh MRav NLar SCob SEND SEWo SGol SLim SLon SPer SPlb SRms SWvt WAvo WFar
'Sparkler' (v) CMac SMad SPoG
'Teton' ♀H6 CMac CRos EHyd ELan EPfP LRHS MAsh MGos MSwo NRHS SGol SPoG SRms WFar
'Watereri' WSpi
'Yellow Sun' see *P.* 'Soleil d'Or'

× *Pyracomeles* (*Rosaceae*)

vilmorinii IDee SAko

Pyrethropsis see *Rhodanthemum*

Pyrethrum see *Tanacetum*

+ *Pyrocydonia* (*Rosaceae*)

'Danielii' (F) SAko

Pyrola (*Ericaceae*)

rotundifolia LEdu WHer

× *Pyronia* (*Rosaceae*)

veitchii SAko

Pyrrosia (*Polypodiaceae*)

hastata CMen WCot
- 'Harima Jishi' CMen
- 'Ryujin' CMen
- 'Shikoku Jishi' CMen
- 'World Champion' CMen
linearifolia 'Urakoryu Jishi' CMen
lingua CMen WPGP
- 'Hiryu' CMen
- 'Ōgon Nishiki' (v) WCot
- 'Tachiba Koryu' CMen
polydactyla CMen WCot
sheareri EHyd LRHS WCot

Pyrus ✿ (*Rosaceae*)

amygdaliformis CMCN
- W&B B-10 WCot
- var. ***cuneifolia*** CLnd
calleryana SGol
- 'Bradford' CLnd
- 'Chanticleer' Widely available
- 'Chanticleer' variegated (v) MAsh
- 'Redspire' CCVT ELan SCob SPer
caucasica WMat
communis (F) CCVT CTri ECrN LBuc LMaj SPer SPlb WMou WTSh
- 'Abbé Fétel' (D) SGsty SKee

	- 'Bambinella' (D)	SKee
	- 'Barland' (Perry)	CHab
	- 'Barnet' (Perry)	CHab
	- 'Baronne de Mello' (D)	NOra SKee WMat
	- 'Beech Hill' (F)	EBee ECrN LMaj SCob SPer
	- 'Belle Guérandaise' (D)	SKee
	- 'Belle Julie' (D)	SKee
	- BENITA ('Rafzas') (F)	LCro LOPS LRHS MCoo WMat
	- 'Beth' (D) 🏆^{H6}	CAgr CArg CHab CMac CSBt CTri EBee EPfP EPom IArd LBuc LRHS MAsh MGos MPri NLar NOra SEdi SGbt SKee SLim SPer SSFT SSFr WMat
	- 'Beurré Bedford' (D)	SKee
	- 'Beurré Clairgeau' (C)	SKee
	- 'Beurré d'Anjou' (F)	SKee
	- 'Beurré d'Avalon' (D)	SKee
	- 'Beurré de Beugny' (D)	SKee
	- 'Beurré de l'Assomption' (D)	SKee
	- 'Beurré de Naghin' (C/D)	SKee
	- 'Beurré Dubuisson' (D)	SKee
	- 'Beurré Dumont' (D)	CAgr
	- 'Beurré Giffard' (D)	CAgr
	- 'Beurré Hardy' (D) 🏆^{H6}	CAgr CArg CCVT CMac CSBt CTri ELan EPfP EPom IArd LMaj MCoo MMuc MWat NOra SEND SEdi SKee SPer SSFT SSFr WMat WWct
	- 'Beurré Six' (D)	SKee
	- 'Beurré Superfin' (D) 🏆^{H6}	SKee SSFr
	- 'Bianchettone' (D)	SKee
	- 'Bishop's Thumb' (D)	SKee
	- 'Black Worcester' (C)	CHab NOra SKee WJas WMat WWct
	- 'Blakeney Red' (Perry)	CHab NOra SKee WMat
	- 'Brandy' (Perry)	CAgr CArg CHab NOra SKee SVic WMat
	- 'Bristol Cross' (D)	CAgr CHab SKee
	- 'Butt' (Perry)	CHab
	- 'Calebasse Bosc' (D)	NOra SKee
	- 'Canal Red' (D)	SKee
	- 'Cannock' (F)	CArg WMat
	- 'Catillac' (C)	CAgr CHab NOra SKee WMat
	- 'Charneaux' (F)	LMaj
	- 'Citron des Carmes' (C)	SKee
	- 'Clapp's Favourite' (D)	CHab CTho LMaj NOra SEdi SKee SVic WMat
	- 'Concorde' (D) 🏆^{H6}	Widely available
	- 'Conference' (D) 🏆^{H6}	Widely available
	- 'Docteur Jules Guyot' (D)	CAgr SKee
	- 'Doyenné Blanc' (F)	SKee
	- 'Doyenné Boussoch' (D)	SKee
	- 'Doyenné d'Été' (D)	MCoo SKee
	- 'Doyenné du Comice' (D) 🏆^{H6}	Widely available
	- 'Doyenné Georges Boucher' (D)	SKee
	- 'Duchesse d'Angoulême' (D)	SKee
	- 'Durondeau' (D)	NOra SKee WMat
	- 'Emile d'Heyst' (D)	MCoo SKee WMat
	- 'Fertility' (D)	CLnd
	- 'Fertility Improved'	see *P. communis* 'Improved Fertility'
	- 'Fondante d'Automne' (D)	CAgr CTho NOra SKee WMat
	- 'Forelle' (D)	SKee
	- 'Garden Gem' (F)	SGsty WMat
	- 'Gieser Wildeman' (F)	LMaj
	- 'Gin' (Perry)	CHab WMat
	- 'Glou Morceau' (D)	CAgr CArg MCoo MWat NOra SKee SSFT SSFr WMat
	- 'Gorham' (D) 🏆^{H6}	CAgr CTho NOra SKee SSFT SSFr WMat
	- 'Green Horse' (Perry)	CHab WMat
	- 'Green Pear of Yair' (D)	SKee
	- 'Hacon's Incomparable' (D)	SKee
	- 'Harvest Queen' (D/C)	CAgr
	- 'Hellen's Early' (Perry)	CArg CHab SKee WMat
	- 'Hendre Huffcap' (Perry)	CAgr CHab EPom NOra SKee WMat
	- 'Hessle' (D)	CAgr CHab SEdi SKee
	- HUMBUG ('Pysanka') (D)	CArg EPom LRHS NOra SSFT WMat
§	- 'Improved Fertility' (D)	CAgr SKee
	- INVINCIBLE ('Delwinor') (D/C)	CAgr CArg CTho EPom LBuc MCoo NOra SLim SSFT WMat
	- 'Jargonelle' (D)	CAgr CHab SKee WMat
	- 'Joséphine de Malines' (D) 🏆^{H6}	CAgr IArd NOra SKee
	- 'Judge Amphlett' (Perry)	EPom NOra SKee WMat
	- 'Laxton's Foremost' (D)	CAgr
	- 'Légipont' (F)	CAgr
	- 'Louise Bonne of Jersey' (D)	CAgr CArg CLnd CMac CTri ECrN EPfP EPom IArd MGos NOra SEdi SKee SSFr WMat WWct
	- 'Magyar Kobak' (C)	SKee
	- 'Marie-Louise' (D)	SKee
	- 'Merrylegs' (Perry)	CHab
	- 'Merton Pride' (D)	CAgr CArg CLnd EPom MCoo NOra SKee SSFr WMat
	- 'Merton Star' (D)	SKee
	- 'Monsieur le Curé'	see *P. communis* 'Vicar of Winkfield'
	- 'Moonglow' (F)	CAgr NOra SKee WMat
	- 'Moorcroft' (Perry)	SKee
	- 'Nouveau Poiteau' (C/D)	CAgr SKee
	- 'Nuvar Celebration' (F)	SKee WMat
	- 'Nye Russet Bartlett' (F)	CAgr
	- 'Obelisk' (D)	EPom LCro LOPS NOra SPoG
	- 'Old Home' (Perry)	WMat
	- 'Oldfield' (Perry)	CHab
	- 'Onward' (D)	CAgr CArg CHab CLnd CTri EBee EPom IArd LRHS NOra SKee SSFT SSFr WMat WWct
	- 'Ovid' (D)	CAgr
§	- 'Packham's Triumph' (D)	CAgr CLnd CTri EPom NOra SEdi SKee SSFr WMat
	- 'Parsonage' (Perry)	CHab
	- 'Passe Crassane' (D)	SKee
	- 'Pear Apple' (D)	CHab
	- 'Penrhyn' (D)	WGwG WMat
	- 'Pero Nobile' (D)	SKee
I	- 'Petite Poire' (D)	EPom SVic
	- 'Pitmaston Duchess' (C/D)	MCoo SKee WMat WWct
	- 'Précoce de Trévoux' (D)	SKee
	- 'Red Beurre Hardy' (C)	SKee
	- 'Red Comice' (D/C)	SKee
	- 'Red Pear' (Perry)	CHab WMat
	- 'Red Sensation Bartlett' (D/C)	CArg EPom LBuc LRHS NOra SKee SSFT WMat
	- 'Robin' (C/D)	SEdi SKee WMat
	- 'Seckel' (D)	NOra SKee
	- 'Shipova'	see × *Sorbopyrus auricularis* 'Shipova'
	- 'Sierra' (D)	CAgr
	- 'Snowdon Queen' (D)	CHab WGwG
	- 'Sommer Blutbirne' (D)	SAko
	- 'Starkrimson' (D)	SKee
	- 'Swan's Egg' (D)	SKee
	- 'Taynton Squash' (Perry)	NOra WMat
	- 'Terrace Pearl' (D)	WMat
	- 'Thorn' (Perry)	CAgr CHab EPom SKee WMat

- 'Triumph'	see *P. communis* 'Packham's Triumph'
- 'Uvedale's St Germain' (C)	SKee
- 'Verdi' (F)	EPom
§ - 'Vicar of Winkfield' (C)	ECrN SKee
- 'Williams' Bon Chrétien' (D/C)	Widely available
- 'Williams' Red' (D/C)	MPri SEdi SGsty SKee
- 'Williams' Rouge Delbard' (F)	EPom
- 'Winnal's Longdon' (Perry)	EPom SKee WMat
- 'Winter Nelis' (D)	CAgr CArg CHab CTri LRHS NLar NOra SKee WMat WWct
- 'Woodhall' (F)	WMat
- 'Zéphirin Grégoire' (D)	SKee
elaeagnifolia	LMaj MAsh
- var. ***kotschyana***	NOrn SLim WHwl
- 'Silver Sails'	CLnd CMac EBee EMil LRHS NOra NOrn SCoo WMat WPGP
× ***michauxii***	SVen
nivalis	CLnd CTho EBee EPfP LEdu LMaj SPer WHwl
- 'Catalia'	CLnd MAsh WMat
pashia	CBcs CMCN EBee LEdu NLar WMat
pyraster	CHab
pyrifolia '20th Century'	see *P. pyrifolia* 'Nijisseiki'
- 'Chojuro' (F)	CAgr
- 'Hosui' (F)	CAgr SVic
- 'Kosui' (F)	SVic
- 'Kumoi' (F)	CAgr EPom MAsh MCoo SKee WMat
§ - 'Nijisseiki' (F)	SKee SVic
- 'Shinko' (F)	CAgr SVic
- 'Shinseiki' (F)	CAgr CTri SKee SVic WMat
- 'Shinsui' (F)	SKee
salicifolia	LMaj
* - var. ***orientalis***	CTho
- 'Pendula' 🏆^{H6}	Widely available

Pyrus × *Sorbus* see × *Sorbopyrus*

Q

Qiongzhuea see *Chimonobambusa*

Quercus ✿ (Fagaceae)

acerifolia	EPfP
§ ***acuta***	CBcs CMCN
acutissima	CBcs CLnd CMCN EPfP LMaj NLar
- PAB 7957	LEdu
- 'Gobbler'	ESwi
- subsp. ***kingii***	EBee
- - NJM 13.077	WPGP
aegilops	see *Q. ithaburensis* subsp. *macrolepis*
affinis 🏆^{H5}	CMCN EPfP
agrifolia	CMCN EBtc LMaj
ajudaghiensis	see *Q. hartwissiana*
alba	CMCN EBee EBtc WPGP
* ***alentejana***	CMCN
aliena	CMCN LEdu
- NJM 13.075	WPGP
- PAB 13.383	LEdu
- PAB 8972	LEdu
alnifolia	CMCN
anatolica	see *Q. pubescens* subsp. *crispata*
× ***beadlei***	see *Q.* × *saulii*
'Bear Creek Ranch'	MBlu
benthamii new	CMCN
berberidifolia	CMCN
bicolor	CLnd CMCN EPfP IArd IDee LMaj MBlu WPGP
§ × ***bimundorum*** 'Crimschmidt'	CLnd EPfP MBlu SGol
borealis	see *Q. rubra*
brantii	CMCN
breweri	see *Q. garryana* var. *breweri*
buckleyi	CMCN EPfP
- 'Dazzling Red'	EPfP MBlu SReu
× ***bushii***	CMCN EPfP MBlu
- 'Seattle Trident'	EPfP MBlu SAko WCot WPGP
canariensis 🏆^{H5}	CLnd CMCN EPfP SReu WPGP
canbyi	CMCN
candicans	CMCN
castaneifolia	CMCN EBtc WMou
- 'Green Spire' 🏆^{H6}	CLnd CMCN EBee EPfP MBlu SEND
cerris	CArg CBcs CCVT CMCN CTho ECrN EPfP LMaj MGos SCob SEND SGol SPer
- 'Afyon Lace'	MBlu
§ - 'Argenteovariegata' (v)	CEnd CMCN EBee ELan EPfP MAsh MBlu
- 'Athena'	MBlu
- 'Bolte's Obelisk'	MBlu
- 'Variegata'	see *Q. cerris* 'Argenteovariegata'
- 'Wodan'	MBlu
chenii	CMCN
chrysolepis	CBcs CMCN
coccifera	CMCN EPfP LEdu SGol SVen WCot WPGP XSen
- NJM 12.006	WPGP
- subsp. ***calliprinos***	CMCN
coccinea	CBcs CLnd CMCN CTho CTri EBee EPfP IArd LMaj MBlu MWht SCob SEWo WTSh
- 'Splendens' 🏆^{H6}	CEnd CMCN CTri EBee ELan EPfP MBlu NLar SGol SPer SPoG
crassifolia	CMCN WPGP
§ × ***crenata*** new	SReu
- 'Ambrozyana'	CMCN NLar
- 'Diversifolia'	CMCN EPfP MBlu
- 'Fulhamensis'	CMCN MBlu MMuc SEND SGol WMou
§ - 'Lucombeana' 🏆^{H6}	CMCN CSBt CTho EBee EPfP MBlu MMuc SPer
- 'Suberosa'	CTho
- 'Waasland Select'	NLar NOrn SGol WMou
- 'Wageningen'	CMCN LMaj
CRIMSON SPIRE	see *Q.* × *bimundorum* 'Crimschmidt'
dentata	CMCN IArd
- 'Carl Ferris Miller'	CBcs CLnd CMCN EPfP MBlu MMuc WCot WLov WPGP
- 'Pinnatifida'	CMCN EPfP LMaj MBlu MPkF NLar WCot WLov
- 'Sir Harold Hillier'	CMCN MBlu
- subsp. ***yunnanensis***	CMCN MBlu
dolicholepis	CMCN
douglasii	CMCN EBtc
durata	CMCN
× ***egglestonii***	CMCN
ellipsoidalis	CMCN NLar SGol
- 'Hemelrijk' 🏆^{H6}	CMCN EPfP MBlu
engleriana NJM 11.028	WPGP
fabrei	CMCN

	faginea	WPGP
	falcata	CMCN EBtc WPGP
	- var. ***pagodifolia***	see *Q. pagoda*
	× ***fernaldii***	CMCN EPfP MBlu
	'Fire Water'	MBlu
	frainetto	CLnd CMCN CTho EBee EPfP LMaj SGol SPer WMou
	- 'Hungarian Crown' 🏆H6	CMCN EPfP MBlu
	- 'Trump'	CMCN MMuc
	franchetii	WPGP
	gambelii	CMCN EBtc
	garryana	CMCN EPfP
§	- var. ***breweri***	CMCN
	- var. ***fruticosa***	see *Q. garryana* var. *breweri*
	georgiana	CMCN
	germana	WPGP
	gilva	CMCN
	glabrescens	CMCN WPGP
	glandulifera	see *Q. serrata* Thunb.
	glauca	CMCN EPfP NLar
	- from Korea	WPGP
	gravesii	CMCN EPfP
	greggii	WPGP
	grisea	CMCN
§	***hartwissiana***	CMCN EPfP
	× ***hastingsii***	CMCN
	hemisphaerica	CMCN EPfP
	× ***heterophylla***	CLnd CMCN EPfP
	× ***hickelii***	CMCN EPfP
	hintoniorum new	CMCN
	hirtifolia	WPGP
	× ***hispanica*** misapplied	see *Q. crenata*
	× ***humidicola***	CMCN
	hypoleucoides	CMCN EPfP
	ilex	Widely available
	- 'Fordii'	CLnd
	ilicifolia	CMCN EPfP
	imbricaria	CBcs CLnd CMCN EPfP IArd WPGP
	incana Roxb.	see *Q. leucotrichophora*
§	***incana*** Bartram	CMCN
§	***ithaburensis*** subsp. ***macrolepis***	CMCN LEdu
	- subsp. ***macrolepis*** 'Hemelrijk Silver'	EPfP MBlu WCot WPGP
	kelloggii	CBcs CMCN EPfP
	× ***kewensis*** 🏆H6	CMCN SEND WMou
	laevigata	see *Q. acuta*
	laevis	CMCN EPfP
§	***laurifolia***	CMCN EPfP
	laurina	CMCN WPGP
	- NJM 05.013A new	WPGP
	× ***leana***	CMCN
§	***leucotrichophora***	LEdu
	× ***libanerris*** 'Rotterdam'	CMCN
	libani	CMCN EPfP SEND
	lobata	CMCN
	× ***lucombeana***	see *Q.* × *crenata* 'Lucombeana'
	- 'William Lucombe'	see *Q.* × *crenata* 'Lucombeana'
	× ***ludoviciana***	EPfP
	lyrata	CMCN
	- 'Arnold'	MBlu
	macranthera	CMCN EPfP WMou
	- PAB 13.002	LEdu
	macrocarpa	CMCN EPfP WPGP
	macrolepis	see *Q. ithaburensis* subsp. *macrolepis*
	marilandica	CMCN EPfP MBlu
	'Mauri'	LMaj MBlu
	'Maya' 🏆H5	CBcs EPfP IArd NLar SGol SLim WHwl WMat WMou WPGP
	× ***megaleia***	CMCN
	mexicana	CMCN
§	***michauxii***	CMCN EPfP MBlu
	mongolica	EPfP MBlu
	- subsp. ***crispula***	CMCN
	'Monument'	WCot
	muhlenbergii	CMCN MBlu WPGP
	- 'Dallas'	EPfP
	myrsinifolia	CBcs CMCN EBee IArd LMaj NLar SArc
	myrtifolia	WPGP
	nigra	CMCN EBtc EPfP WMou
	- 'Beethoven'	MBlu
	- 'Thierry'	MBlu
	nuttallii	see *Q. texana*
	obtusa	see *Q. laurifolia*
	oglethorpensis	CMCN
§	***pagoda***	CMCN WPGP
	palustris 🏆H6	CArg CCVT CLnd CMCN CTho ELan EPfP IArd LMaj MBlu MMuc NLar NOrn SCob SEWo SGol SPer SReu WMou WTSh
	- 'Flaming Suzy'	MBlu
	- 'Green Dwarf'	CMCN LCro LMaj LOPS MBlu NLar
	- GREEN PILLAR ('Pringreen')	CDoC CTho EBee EPfP IArd LMaj MAsh MBlu NLar NOra NOrn SGol WMat WMou
	- 'Isabel'	EPfP WMat
	- 'Pendula'	CEnd CMCN
	- 'Swamp Pygmy'	CMCN EPfP ESwi MBlu
	- 'Windischleuba'	MBlu
	pedunculata	see *Q. robur*
	pedunculiflora	see *Q. robur* subsp. *pedunculiflora*
§	***petraea***	CArg CHab CLnd CTri ECrN EPfP GAbr LMaj MBlu SCob SGol SPer WFar WMou WTSh
	- 'Laciniata'	see *Q. petraea* 'Laciniata Crispa'
§	- 'Laciniata Crispa'	CEnd CMCN EPfP MBlu
	- subsp. ***polycarpa*** NJM 13.025	WPGP
§	- 'Purpurea'	CMCN EPfP MBlu
	- 'Rubicunda'	see *Q. petraea* 'Purpurea'
§	***phellos***	CLnd CMCN EPfP IArd LMaj MBlu NLar
	- HIGHTOWER ('Qpsta')	SGol
	- var. ***latifolia***	see *Q. incana* Bartram
	phillyreoides	CBcs CLnd CMCN EPfP
	polymorpha	CMCN WPGP
	Pondaim Group	CMCN NOra WMou
	- 'Pondaim Giant'	MBlu
	pontica	CMCN EPfP LMaj MBlu
	prinoides	CMCN
	prinus misapplied	see *Q. michauxii*
§	***prinus*** L.	CMCN
	pubescens	CMCN LMaj MMuc SEND
§	- subsp. ***crispata*** NJM 12.016	WPGP
	- - NJM 12.017	WPGP
	pumila Michx.	see *Q. prinus* L.
	pumila Walt.	see *Q. phellos*
	pungens	CMCN
	pyrenaica	CMCN MMuc SEND
	- NJM 12.001	WPGP
	- 'Pendula' 🏆H6	CMCN EPfP
	rhysophylla	see *Q. rysophylla*
§	***robur***	Widely available
	- 'Argenteomarginata' (v)	CMCN MBlu
	- 'Atropurpurea'	EBtc
	- 'Blue Gnome'	MBlu
	- 'Compacta'	MBlu

- 'Concordia'	CBcs CEnd CMCN ELan EPfP MBlu NLar
- Cristata Group	CMCN
- 'Dissecta'	CMCN
- Fastigiata Group	CLnd EBee ECrN IArd MGos SGol SLim SPer
- - 'Koster' ♀H6	CMCN CMac CTri EPfP LMaj MBlu MRav SCob WMat
- 'Filicifolia' misapplied	see *Q. robur* 'Pectinata'
- 'Filicifolia' Hort. ex Loud.	CEnd
- 'Irtha'	EPfP MBlu
- 'Menhir'	MBlu WLov
§ - 'Pectinata'	EPfP MBlu
§ - subsp. ***pedunculiflora***	CMCN
- 'Pendula'	CEnd CMCN MBlu
- 'Purpurascens'	CEnd CMCN
- 'Purpurea'	MBlu
- 'Raba'	CMCN
§ - 'Salfast'	MBlu
- 'Salicifolia Fastigiata'	see *Q. robur* 'Salfast'
- 'Strypemonde'	CMCN
- 'Timuki'	MBlu
- 'Tromp Dwarf'	MBlu
- (Variegata Group) 'Fürst Schwarzenburg' (v)	MBlu
× ***rosacea*** 'Columna'	WMou
rotundifolia	CAgr CMCN EPfP WPGP
§ ***rubra***	Widely available
- 'Aurea'	CEnd CMCN EPfP MBlu
- 'Bolte's Gold'	MBlu NOra SMad WHwl WMat
- 'Magic Fire' ♀H6	CMCN EPfP MBlu
- 'Red Queen'	EPfP MBlu
* - 'Sunshine'	CMCN MBlu WCot
× ***runcinata***	CMCN
§ ***rysophylla***	CMCN EPfP IArd MBlu WPGP
sadleriana	CMCN WPGP
salicina	WPGP
× ***sargentii*** 'Thomas'	EPfP MBlu
sartorii	CMCN
§ × ***saulii***	CMCN
× ***schochiana***	EPfP MBlu
schottkyana	WPGP
seemanii new	CMCN
semecarpifolia	CBcs CMCN MBlu WPGP
§ ***serrata*** Thunb.	CMCN EPfP
- 'Herkenrode'	MBlu
sessiliflora	see *Q. petraea*
shumardii	CLnd CMCN EPfP LMaj MBlu NLar SGol
- 'Del Rio'	MBlu
stellata	CMCN EPfP
suber	CAgr CBcs CMCN CTsd EBee ELan EPfP IArd LEdu LMaj MBlu MGos SArc SCob SEND SPer SWeb WCot WHwl WMou WPGP
- 'Sopron'	EPfP MBlu
× ***substellata***	CMCN
§ ***texana***	CMCN EPfP NOra WPGP
- 'New Madrid'	CTho EPfP ESwi MBlu WMat WMou WPGP
trojana	CMCN WPGP
turbinella	CMCN
× ***turneri***	CLnd CMCN CTho EPfP WSpi
- 'Pseudoturneri' ♀H5	CBcs EBee ELan MBlu SEND SGol WMou
vacciniifolia	CMCN
variabilis	CMCN EPfP SGol
velutina	CBcs CMCN CTho EPfP NLar
- 'Albertsii'	MBlu
- 'Oakridge Walker'	MBlu
- 'Rubrifolia'	CMCN EPfP
'Vilmoriana'	CMCN
virginiana	CBcs CMCN
× ***warburgii***	EBee EPfP
× ***warei***	CMCN
- 'Chimney Fire'	EPfP MBlu
- KINDRED SPIRIT	see *Q.* × *warei* 'Nadler'
§ - 'Long'	EBee ELan EPfP MBlu NLar NOra WMat
§ - 'Nadler'	SGol
- REGAL PRINCE	see *Q.* × *warei* 'Long'
- 'Windcandle'	LMaj MBlu
wislizeni	CMCN NLar

Quillaja (*Quillajaceae*)

saponaria	CCCN EBee SPlb

quince see *Cydonia oblonga*

Quisqualis (*Combretaceae*)

indica	CCCN

R

Racosperma see *Acacia*

Radermachera (*Bignoniaceae*)

sinica ♀H1b	EShb

radish see AGM Vegetables Section

Ramonda (*Gesneriaceae*)

§ ***myconi*** ♀H5	EMor EWes NSla SRms WAbe
- var. ***alba***	WThu
- 'Jim's Shadow'	WAbe
nathaliae ♀H5	WAbe WThu
- 'Alba'	NSla WAbe XEll
pyrenaica	see *R. myconi*
serbica	WThu

Ranunculus (*Ranunculaceae*)

aconitifolius	CMiW EBee GMaP NLar SBut SHar WFar WHal WSHC
- Cally form	MNrw
- 'Flore Pleno' (d) ♀H7	Widely available
acris	CHab NBir NMir NPer SRms WSFF
- subsp. ***acris*** new	SBut
- - 'Stevenii'	SDix WHal
- 'Citrinus'	CElw CMiW EAJP EMor GQue LLWG LPot LSun MHol WCot WHal WHrl WMal
- 'Flore Pleno' (d) ♀H7	CDor CWCL EBee ECha ELan EPfP GMaP LEdu LLWG LPot MCot MRav NBid NBro NGdn NRya SPoG SRms WCAu WFar WSHC XLum
- 'Hedgehog'	MMrt MNrw
- 'Sulphureus'	CBre EBee WCAu WHal
alpestris	GEdr NSla SBrt WFar
- 'Flore Pleno' (d)	GEdr
amplexicaulis	EBee GEdr GKev NSla WCot
aquatilis	CWat EWat LLWG MWts WMAq WSFF
asiaticus	ERCP
- var. ***albus***	GKev
- 'Aviv Orange'	SDeJ
- 'Aviv Red'	LCro LOPS

- 'Aviv Rose'	LCro LOPS
- 'Aviv White'	LCro LOPS
- 'Bloomingdale Pink Shades' (Bloomingdale Series)	SDeJ
- Tolmer's hybrids (d)	GKev
bilobus	WAbe
§ ***bulbosus*** 'F.M. Burton'	CElw NRya WCot WMal
- 'Speciosus Plenus'	see *R. constantinopolitanus* 'Plenus'
calandrinioides ♀H5	EWes GKev NBir SBrt SGro WAbe
circinatus	LLWG
§ ***constantinopolitanus*** 'Plenus' (d)	CMiW EBee GAbr GMaP MNrw MRav NBid NBro NLar WCot WMal WSHC
cortusifolius	CPla ECre SBrt SHar
crenatus	GEdr
ficaria	see *Ficaria verna* subsp. *verna*
flammula	CBen CHab CWat LLWG MWts
- subsp. ***minimus***	EWat
gouanii	NRya
'Gowrie'	GEdr
gramineus ♀H7	EBee EHyd GEdr GMaP LRHS NRHS NRya SRms WOut XEll
- 'Pardal'	SMHy WCot WSHC
illyricus	WHal
lanuginosus	EPPr NGrd
lingua	SPlb WSFF
- 'Grandiflorus'	CBen LLWG NPer WHal WMAq WPnP
lyallii	GKev LSun
millefoliatus	CPBP WAbe
montanus double-flowered (d)	SHar WCot WSHC
- 'Miss Austria' (d)	NHpl
- 'Molten Gold' ♀H5	GEdr GMaP MMrt MRav WFar
aff. ***nigrescens*** 'Cazorla'	SBrt
nivicola	WCot
parnassiifolius	GAbr GEdr MNrw WAbe WCot
platanifolius	CRos EBee EHyd LRHS NRHS SBrt SMHy
× ***prietoi*** 'Moonlight'	LEdu MMrt WCot
'Purple Heart' (d)	EPfP LCro LOPS SDeJ
repens 'Buttered Popcorn' (v)	EBee
- 'Gloria Spale'	CBre
- var. ***pleniflorus*** (d)	CBre LLWG MSCN NGrd
- 'Timothy Clark' (d)	CBre WMal
seguieri	EHyd GEdr LRHS NRHS WAbe
speciosus 'Flore Pleno'	see *R. constantinopolitanus* 'Plenus'
traunfellneri	WAbe

Ranzania (*Berberidaceae*)

japonica	GEdr WCru

Raoulia (*Asteraceae*)

australis misapplied	see *R. hookeri*
australis ambig.	EPot GAbr GKev GMaP GQue NHpl WCot WTor
australis Hook.f. ex Raoul	ITim MAsh
§ - Lutescens Group	ECha SPlb
§ ***hookeri***	CMea ECha EPot EWes MAsh SPlb SRms WAbe
× ***loganii***	see × *Leucoraoulia loganii*
lutescens	see *R. australis* Lutescens Group
petriensis	SPlb WAbe
× ***petrimia*** 'Margaret Pringle'	EPot WAbe
tenuicaulis	ECha SPlb

raspberry see *Rubus idaeus*; also AGM Fruit Section

Ratibida (*Asteraceae*)

columnifera	CRos EHyd ELan EPfP LRHS NRHS
- f. ***pulcherrima***	EHyd EPfP LRHS NRHS XLum
- - 'Red Midget'	CSpe EHyd EMor LRHS NGBl
mexicana	CSam EBee EHyd LRHS NRHS SPhx
pinnata	CSam CSpe EPfP LRHS NBir NGBl SIvy SPhx SPlb WCot

Raukaua (*Araliaceae*)

laetevirens	WPGP

Ravenala (*Strelitziaceae*)

madagascariensis	SPlb XBlo

Ravenea (*Arecaceae*)

rivularis	CCCN XBlo

Rechsteineria see *Sinningia*

redcurrant see *Ribes rubrum* (R); also AGM Fruit Section

Regelia (*Myrtaceae*)

velutina	SPlb

Rehderodendron (*Styracaceae*)

indochinense B&SWJ 12115	WCru
- NJM 09.116	WPGP
- WWJ 11869	WCru
kwangtungense WWJ 11940	WCru
kweichowense WWJ 12019	WCru
macrocarpum	CBcs CJun EBee LEdu WPGP
- B&SWJ 11841	WCru
- KWJ 12310	WCru
- WWJ 11952	WCru

Rehmannia (*Plantaginaceae*)

angulata misapplied	see *R. elata*
§ ***elata*** ♀H3	CBod CDor CPla CSpe CTsd EHyd ELan EPfP LRHS LSun MNHC SAdn SDys SRms WGwG WKif XLum
henryi	CSpe EBee LRHS
WALBERTON'S MAGIC DRAGON ('Walremadra'PBR)	CRos EHyd EPfP LBuc LRHS NRHS SHar SPad SPoG SRms

Reineckea (*Asparagaceae*)

§ ***carnea***	CAby CDor CExl ECha ELan EPPr GEdr GKev IMou LEdu MMuc MPie NSti SDys SEND SPlb WCot WPGP XLum
- B&SWJ 4808	ELon WCru
- 'Baoxing Booty'	IMou WCru
- 'Crûg's Broadleaf'	WCru
- 'Jinfo Jewel' **new**	WCru
- 'Variegata' (v)	WCot
aff. ***carnea*** from Sichuan	WCot
incurva 'Crug's Linearleaf'	ESwi WCru
yunnanense	see *R. carnea*

Reinwardtia (*Linaceae*)

§ ***indica***	CCCN CExl SAdn SEle
trigyna	see *R. indica*

Remusatia (*Araceae*)

hookeriana B&SWJ 2529	WCru
pumila	MPie
vivipara	MPie

Reseda (*Resedaceae*)

alba	SPhx
lutea	CWld SPhx SRms
luteola	CBod CHab CHby GPoy MHer MNHC WSFF
odorata new	SVic

Restio (*Restionaceae*)

festuciformis	CCtw CPbh LRHS
paniculatus	CBod CCCN CCtw CDTJ CPbh CTrC LRHS
quadratus	CCtw
similis	CPbh
subverticillatus	CCtw CPbh LRHS
tetraphyllus	see *Baloskion tetraphyllum*
- 'Cornish Gold'	see *Baloskion tetraphyllum* 'Cornish Gold'

Retama (*Papilionaceae*)

sphaerocarpa	SBrt

Reynoutria see *Fallopia*

Rhamnus (*Rhamnaceae*)

alaternus	XSen
§ - 'Argenteovariegata' (v) ♀H5	Widely available
- 'Variegata'	see *R. alaternus* 'Argenteovariegata'
cathartica	CCVT CHab CLnd CTri ECrN EPfP LBuc MCoo NLar SCob SEWo WMou WSFF WTSh
davurica B&SWJ 12609	WCru
§ ***erythroxyloides***	NLar
frangula	see *Frangula alnus*
grandifolia	SPtp
ilicifolia	SBrt
imeretina	WCot WPGP
ludovici-salvatoris	SBrt
lycioides	SBrt
- subsp. ***oleoides***	XSen
microcarpa new	GKev
pallasii	see *R. erythroxyloides*
taquetii	NLar

Rhaphidophora (*Araceae*)

decursiva	XBlo

× *Rhaphiobotrya* (*Rosaceae*)

§ 'Coppertone'	CDoC ELan LMaj SArc SEND SGsty WPGP

Rhaphiolepis (*Rosaceae*)

× ***delacourii***	EBee EPfP SEND
- 'Coates' Crimson'	CDoC CRos EBee ELan EPfP LRHS MAsh MGil SEle WLov
- ENCHANTRESS ('Moness')	CCCN ELan EPfP LRHS MAsh MRav SLon
- 'Pink Cloud'	EPfP LRHS
indica	SEND
- B&SWJ 8405	WCru
- 'Coppertone'	see × *Rhaphiobotrya* 'Coppertone'
- SPRINGTIME ('Monme')	CBcs CRos EPfP LCro LOPS LRHS WSMil
integerrima	CMCN
minor B&SWJ 14669	WCru
umbellata	CBcs CBod CTri EBee ELan EPfP GBin LEdu MAsh MGil MRav SEND SLon SVen SavN WLov WPGP
- f. ***ovata*** B&SWJ 4706	WCru

Rhaphithamnus (*Verbenaceae*)

cyanocarpus	see *R. spinosus*
§ ***spinosus***	CBcs EBee EPfP LEdu MGil SMad SPoG WPGP WPav

Rhapidophyllum (*Arecaceae*)

hystrix	CBrP CPHo SPalm WSMil

Rhapis ✿ (*Arecaceae*)

§ ***excelsa*** ♀H1b	CCCN LCro LOPS SEND SPalm SPlb WSMil XBlo

Rhaponticum (*Compositae*)

§ ***centaureoides***	CBod CDor EBee ECha ELon LRHS MAvo MHer MHol MSpe MTis NBid NSti SBrt SEND WCAu WCot WMal WSpi
§ ***exaltatum***	SPhx WHil

Rhazya (*Apocynaceae*)

orientalis	see *Amsonia orientalis*

Rheum ✿ (*Polygonaceae*)

Chen Yi	WCot
GWJ 9329 from Sikkim	WCru
§ 'Ace of Hearts' ♀H6	Widely available
'Ace of Spades'	see *R.* 'Ace of Hearts'
acuminatum HWJCM 252	WCru
- HWJK 2354	WCru
- PAB 2487	LEdu WPGP
alexandrae	CBct EWes GBin GEdr GKev IMou MMrt NLar SPlb WFar
- KGB 767	WPGP
- SDR 2924	EBee
altaicum PAB 1055	LEdu
§ ***australe***	CRos EBee EHyd GEdr LRHS NLar NRHS WCot WFar
- CC 7492	GKev
- 'Pink Marble' (v)	WCot
'Cally Giant'	ELon EWes
delavayi	NBPC NLar
- BWJ 7592	WCru WFar
emodi	see *R. australe*
'Great Bere'	LEdu WPGP
* ***henryi***	EBee
× ***hybridum*** 'Apple Delight' new	CRos LCro LOPS
- 'Brandy Carr Scarlet'	CTri LEdu MRav
- 'Champagne'	CAgr EPfP EPom LCro LEdu LOPS LRHS NLar NRHS SGbt SKee SPer SPoG SRms SVic WMat
* - 'Champagne Rood'	NRHS
- 'Early Victoria'	SRms
- 'Fenton's Special'	CTri LEdu MRav
- 'Glaskin's Perpetual'	CAgr CRos CTsd EHyd EMor LBuc LRHS NRHS SRms SVic
- 'Goliath'	EBee
- 'Grandad's Favorite' ♀H5	CRos EHyd LRHS NRHS
- 'Hawke's Champagne' ♀H5	WCot
- 'Holstein Bloodred'	EMor
- 'Holsteiner Blut'	EBee NLar SPoG
- 'Livingstone'PBR	EPom LCro LOPS

- 'Pink Champagne' EBee EPfP
- 'Raspberry Red' ♀H5 CMac CRos EMil EPfP EPom LCro LOPS LRHS NRHS SPoG
- 'Red Champagne' ELan EMor EPfP LBuc WSpi
- 'Stein's Champagne' NRob
- 'Stockbridge Arrow' CArg CTri ECrN
- 'Strawberry' LCro LOPS NBir
- 'Thompson's Terrifically Tasty' EPom
- 'Timperley Early' ♀H5 Widely available
- 'Timperley Early 1' SRms
- 'Victoria' Widely available
- 'Vroege Engelse' LEdu

kialense EBee LEdu NBid NSti
moorcroftianum GEdr
nobile GKev IMou
officinale CBct
palmatum CBcs CRos EBee ECha ELan EPfP GKev LRHS MGos MRav NGdn NRHS SCob SHar SRms

- 'Atropurpureum' see *R. palmatum* 'Atrosanguineum'
§ - 'Atrosanguineum' CBct CDor CMac CRos ECha EHyd ELan EPfP EShb LEdu LRHS MBel MGos MMuc MRav NBid NBro NRHS NWad SCob SPer SPlb SPoG WCru WFar WSMil WSpi
- 'Bowles's Crimson' ♀H7 MRav NBid WCot
- 'Ferguson's Red' CBct WCot
- 'Hadspen Crimson' ♀H6 CBct CBod EBee ECtt MHol MNrw NBid WCot
- var. ***palmatum*** CPla
- 'Red Herald' CBct WCot WPGP
- 'Rubrum' CBct EHyd LRHS NBir NRHS
- 'Savill' ♀H7 CBct MRav
- var. ***tanguticum*** Widely available

pumilum XEll
rhaponticum NLar
ribes WCot WCru
tanguticum EMor
tataricum LEdu WPGP

Rhinanthus (*Orobanchaceae*)

minor CHab LCro LOPS WSFF

Rhodanthe (*Asteraceae*)

§ ***anthemoides*** IMou
chlorocephala subsp. ***rosea*** 'Pierrot' CSpe

Rhodanthemum (*Asteraceae*)

'African Eyes' ELan EPfP MBrN MGos MHol MPri SCoo SVen WMal
'African Spring' **new** CDoC
§ ***atlanticum*** EWes
'Casablanca'PBR (Atlas Daisy Series) CDoC CRos EPfP LRHS MPri NRHS SCoo SPoG
§ ***catananche*** CCCN CPBP EPot EWes WAbe
§ - 'Tizi-n-Test' WAbe
- 'Tizi-n-Tichka' CRos EHyd EWes LRHS NRHS WAbe
§ ***gayanum*** CCCN EWes
- 'Flamingo' see *R. gayanum*
- 'Pretty in Pink' CBcs MHol MPri SPoG
§ ***hosmariense*** ♀H4 CCCN CRos EBou ECha EHyd ELan ELon EPfP EPot GMaP LRHS MCot MHol NRHS SEND SPer SPhx SRms WCav WHoo WIce
'Marrakech' (Atlas Daisy Series) CDoC MPri SCoo SPad SPoG

Rhodiola (*Crassulaceae*)

SSSE 10 NWad
chrysanthemifolia WJC 13669 WCru
crassipes see *R. wallichiana*
cretinii HWJK 2283 WCru
§ ***fastigiata*** CSpe WCot WThu
- BWJ 7544 WCru
§ ***heterodonta*** MRav WCot
himalensis misapplied see *R.* 'Keston'
himalensis (D. Don) Fu CTri
- WJC 13723 WCru
§ ***integrifolia*** SPlb
§ 'Keston' CTri
§ ***kirilowii*** EHyd LRHS
- var. ***rubra*** EBee EHyd EPfP LRHS NRHS
§ ***pachyclados*** CRos ECtt EHyd EPPr GBin GMaP GWyn LRHS MHer MMuc NBir NHpl NRHS NRya NWad SEND SPlb SSim SWvt WCot WFar XLum
rhodantha NLar
§ ***rosea*** Widely available
§ ***saxifragoides*** EHyd EPot LRHS NRHS SPlb
semenovii GKev NLar
sinuata HWJK 2318 WCru
- HWJK 2326 WCru
tibetica **new** GKev
trollii see *R. saxifragoides*
§ ***wallichiana*** NBid
- GWJ 9263 WCru
- HWJK 2352 WCru
§ ***yunnanensis*** BWJ 7941 WCru

Rhodochiton (*Plantaginaceae*)

§ ***atrosanguineus*** ♀H2 CBcs CCCN CSpe EPfP GBee IDee LBuc LCro LOPS MBow MGil MPri SPoG
volubilis see *R. atrosanguineus*

Rhodocoma (*Restionaceae*)

arida CCCN CCtw
capensis CAbb CCCN CCht CCtw CPbh CTrC CTsd
foliosa LRHS
gigantea CCCN CCht CCtw CPbh CTrC LRHS SPlb

Rhododendron ✿ (*Ericaceae*)

'A.J. Ivens' see *R.* 'Arthur J. Ivens'
aberconwayi LMil MHid SLdr
- 'His Lordship' GGGa IDee LMil
'Abigale' (A) SLdr
acuminatum **new** SReu
'Addy Wery' (EA) SPer
adenogynum GKev LMil
adenosum GGGa
'Admiral Piet Hein' SSta
'Adonis' (EA/d) ♀H5 CBcs CMac SLdr
'Advance' (EA) SLdr
aeruginosum see *R. campanulatum* subsp. *aeruginosum*
aganniphum var. ***aganniphum*** MHid
'Airy Fairy' LMil
'Aksel Olsen' CTri GEdr
'Aladdin' (EA) SLdr
'Aladdin' (*auriculatum* hybrid) SSta

	(Albatross Group) 'Albatross'	SSta
	- 'Albatross Townhill Pink'	LMil
	'Albert Schweitzer' ♀H5	CDoC LMil LRHS LSRN NLar SCob SLdr SLim SPer
	albrechtii (A)	CBcs GGGa GKev LMil
	- Whitney form (A)	LMil
	'Alexander' (EA) ♀H4	LMil LSRN SLdr
	'Alfred'	LMil
	'Alice' ♀H5	LMil SLdr
	Alison Johnstone Group	SLdr
	- 'Alison Johnstone'	LMil WThu
	'All Gold'	GGGa
	'Al's Picotee' (EA/d)	MPkF
	'Altaclerense'	LMil
	alutaceum var. ***iodes*** 'White Plains' **new**	MHid
	amagianum (A)	LMil
	ambiguum	LMil MHid
	- 'Golden Summit'	GGGa
	- 'Jane Banks'	LMil
	'Ambrosia' (EA)	CSBt
	'Amity'	LMil MMuc
	Amor Group	SLdr
	'Anah Kruschke'	LCro MAsh SPoG
	'Analin'	see *R.* 'Anuschka'
	'Anchorite' (EA)	SLdr
	Angelo Group	GGGa LMil
	- 'Angelo'	LMil SLdr SSta
	'Ann Lindsay'	SLdr
	'Anna Baldsiefen'	SPoG
	'Anna Rose Whitney'	CBcs CTri EPfP LRHS LSRN MAsh MPri SLim WFar
	'Annabella' (K)	SSta
	annae	LMil LRHS
	'Anne de Rothschild' **new**	SReu
	'Anne Frank' (EA)	CDoC WFar
	'Anneke' (A)	CDoC LMil LRHS MGos MMuc MPkF NHol NLar SCob SPer SSta
	'Anouk' (EA)	CDoC
	anthopogon	LMil
	- 'Betty Graham'	GGGa
	- subsp. ***hypenanthum*** 'Annapurna'	GGGa IDee ITim LMil WAbe WThu
	anthosphaerum	GKev
	'Antilope' (Vs) ♀H6	CBcs LMil LRHS MMuc SLdr SSta
§	'Anuschka'	LMil MAsh
	anwheiense	GGGa LMil
	apodectum	see *R. dichroanthum* subsp. *apodectum*
	'Apotrophia'	SLdr
	'Apple Blossom' ambig.	CMac GKin
	'Appleblossom' (EA)	see *R.* 'Ho-o'
	'Apricot Blaze' (A)	SSta
	'Apricot Fantasy'	LMil SSta
	'Apricot Surprise'	CAby CSBt CTri MAsh MMuc
	'April Showers' (A)	LMil
	'Aquamarin'	NLar
	'Arabesk' (EA)	CDoC GKin ILea MAsh MGos MPkF NLar SWeb
	arborescens (A) ♀H6	GGGa LMil
	arboreum	GGGa GKev IDee LMil SLdr SReu
	- B&SWJ 2244	WCru
	- subsp. ***arboreum***	MHid
	- subsp. ***cinnamomeum*** ♀H4	GGGa LMil
	- - Sch 2049	LMil
	- - WJC 13821	WCru
	- - var. ***album***	GGGa GKev
	- - 'Everest Reunion'	LMil
	- - var. ***roseum***	GGGa
	- - - SDR 749	GKev
	- - - 'Tony Schilling'	GKin LMil LRHS SSta
	- subsp. ***delavayi***	GGGa LMil SLdr
§	- subsp. ***nilagiricum***	MHid
	- 'Rubaiyat'	GKin LMil
§	- subsp. ***zeylanicum***	GGGa
	'Arctic Fox' (EA)	LMil SReu
	'Arctic Tern' ♀H5	CDoC CRos CSBt CTri LCro LMil LOPS MGos NLar NWad WThu
	'Ardeur' (EA)	NLar
§	***argipeplum***	GGGa LMil MHid
	- 'Fleurie'	LMil
	(Argosy Group) 'Argosy'	LMil
	argyrophyllum	SLdr SReu
	- subsp. ***argyrophyllum***	GGGa SLdr
	- subsp. ***nankingense***	GGGa
	- - 'Chinese Silver' ♀H5	LMil MHid SLdr
	arizelum	GGGa LMil MHid WPGP
	- subsp. ***arizelum*** Rubicosum Group	GGGa
	aff. ***arizelum*** KR 10420	WPGP
	'Arneson Gem' (A) ♀H6	CBcs CDoC GGGa GKin LMil LRHS MPkF NLar
§	(Aronense Group) 'Fumiko' (EA)	CBcs CDoC CRos CSBt LCro LMil NLar SCob SLdr SReu WFar
§	- 'Hanako' (EA)	WFar
§	- 'Kazuko' (EA)	CDoC CPla NLar
§	- 'Momoko' (EA)	LRHS WFar
§	- 'Satschiko' (EA) ♀H5	CBcs CDoC CSBt GGGa LMil LRHS MPri NLar NRHS SReu
	'Arpège' (Vs)	LMil NLar
	'Arthur Bedford'	CSBt
§	'Arthur J. Ivens'	SLdr
	'Arthur Stevens'	SLdr
	'Asa-gasumi' (Kurume) (EA)	SLdr
	asterochnoum	GGGa MHid
	'Astrid'	LSRN SReu
	atlanticum (A)	GGGa LMil WFar
	- 'Seaboard' (A)	LMil
	atlanticum × ***canescens***	GKev
	'August Lamken'	LMaj
	augustinii	CBcs CTsd GGGa LMil NLar SLdr SReu SSta
	- subsp. ***augustinii*** **new**	MHid
	- 'Bowood Blue'	LMil
§	- subsp. ***chasmanthum***	GGGa
	- Electra Group	LMil SLdr
§	- - 'Electra' ♀H4	GGGa
	- Exbury form	GGGa LMil
§	- subsp. ***hardyi***	GGGa
	- Reuthe's dark form	SReu
§	- subsp. ***rubrum***	MHid
*	- 'Trewithen'	GGGa LMil
I	- 'Werrington'	CExl SSta
	auriculatum	GGGa LMil MHid SLdr SReu SSta
	- Reuthe's form	SReu
	auritum	SLdr
	austrinum (A)	IDee LMil NLar
	'Autumn Gold'	SLdr
	(Avalanche Group) 'Avalanche'	LMil
	Avocet Group	LMil SLdr
	'Award'	LMil
	Azrie Group	SLdr
§	'Azuma-kagami' (Kurume) (EA)	LMil LRHS SCob SLdr
	'Azurika'	MPkF
	'Azurro'	IDee LMil LRHS MMuc SLdr
	'Babette'	see *R.* (Volker Group) 'Babette'
	'Babuschka'	LMil

'Baden-Baden' 🏆H6	CMac CPla CTri GEdr GKin LCro LMil MAsh SLdr WFar
balfourianum	MHid
'Baltic Amber' (A)	CDoC
'Balzac' (K)	GKin MAsh
'Barbara Reuthe'	SReu SSta
'Barbarella'	LMil LRHS
barbatum	GGGa LMil MHid SReu
- WJC 13686	WCru
'Barbecue' (K)	LMil
'Barmstedt'	MAsh
'Barnaby Sunset'	LRHS MAsh
'Bashful' 🏆H5	CSBt
§ ***basilicum***	LMil MHid
'Bastion'	LMil
bauhiniiflorum	see *R. triflorum* var. *bauhiniiflorum*
beanianum	LMil
- compact	see *R. piercei*
'Beatrice Keir'	LMil SSta
'Beattie' (EA)	SLdr
(Beau Brummell Group) 'Beau Brummell'	LMil
beesianum	MHid
'Beethoven' (Vuykiana) (EA)	SLdr
BELAMI ('Hachbela')	LMil LRHS
'Belkanto'	GKin MMuc NLar SLdr
'Bellini'	LMaj LMil
'Ben Cruachan' (K)	GGGa
'Ben Lawers' (K)	GGGa
'Ben Lomond' (K)	GGGa
'Ben Morrison' (EA)	LMil SReu
'Bengal'	CDoC CRos GEdr LRHS LSRN MAsh NLar SLdr SLim
'Bengal Beauty' (EA)	SLdr
'Bengal Fire' (EA)	CMac SLdr
benhallii 'Honshu Blue'	GGGa
- 'Plum Drops'	GGGa
- 'Slieve Donard'	CMac
- 'Ylva'	GGGa
'Beni-giri' (Kurume) (EA)	CMac SLdr
'Beni-kirishima' (A) **new**	SWeb
'Benny Gery' (EA)	NLar
'Bergensiana'	SSta
'Bergie Larson' 🏆H4	LMil
bergii	see *R. augustinii* subsp. *rubrum*
'Bernard Shaw'	SSta
'Bernstein'	MAsh
'Berryrose' (K) 🏆H6	CBcs CDoC CMac CSBt CTri EPfP GKin LMil LRHS MAsh MGos MPkF SCob SSta WFar
'Bert's Own'	CBcs
'Betty' (Kaempferi) (EA)	SLdr
'Betty Anne Voss' (EA)	LMil LSRN MAsh SCoo SLdr SReu
'Betty Wormald'	CMac
bhutanense	GGGa
Bibiani Group	LMil LRHS
'Bijou de Ledeberg' (Indian) (EA/v)	CMac
'Birthday Girl'	LMil LSRN MAsh
(Biskra Group) 'Biskra'	GGGa LMil
'Blaauw's Pink' (Kurume) (EA) 🏆H4	CMac CSBt EPfP GKin LCro LMil LOPS MMuc SCob SLdr SPer SPlb SPoG
'Black Knight' (EA)	SLdr
'Black Magic'	CAby CTsd GKin LMil MMuc WTyc
'Black Widow'	SReu SSta
'Blaney's Blue'	MPkF
'Blattgold' (v)	LMil
BLAUE DONAU	see *R.* 'Blue Danube'
'Blaue Jungs'	GGGa
'Blewbury' 🏆H5	LMil
BLOOMBUX ('Microhirs3'PBR)	LCro LMil LOPS
'Blue Boy'	LMil
§ 'Blue Danube' (EA) 🏆H3	CBcs CDoC CMac CPla CRos CSBt CTri EPfP GKin LCro LMil LOPS LRHS MAsh MGos MPri NLar SCob SLdr SLim SPer SPoG SReu SSta WFar
Blue Diamond Group	CBcs EPfP
- 'Blue Diamond'	CSBt LRHS LSRN MAsh NRHS SLdr WGwG
'Blue Monday' (EA)	SLdr
'Blue Peter' 🏆H6	CBcs CSBt LCro LMil LOPS MAsh NHol SCob SReu SSta
'Blue Pool'	LMil
Blue Ribbon Group	SLdr
'Blue Silver'	GGGa LMil MAsh
'Blue Steel'	see *R. fastigiatum* 'Blue Steel'
Blue Tit Group	CBcs CDoC CMac EPfP GGGa LMaj LRHS MAsh MGos NLar NRHS SLdr SLim SPer SSta
Bluebird Group	CSBt SLdr
'Blueshine Girl'	SLdr
'Blutopia'	LMil LRHS
'Boddaertianum'	LMil
BOHLKEN'S JUDITHA	LMil
BOHLKEN'S KRONJEWEL	LMil
BOHLKEN'S LUPINENBERG	LMil
BOHLKEN'S LUPINENBERG LAGUNA	IDee LMil LRHS NLar
BOHLKEN'S SNOW FIRE	LMil LRHS NLar
Bo-peep Group	CBcs
- 'Bo-peep'	LMil SLdr
'Boskoop Ostara'	LMil
'Boule de Neige'	CRos SPer
'Bouquet de Flore' (G) 🏆H6	LMil
Bow Bells Group	SCob
- 'Bow Bells' 🏆H4	EPfP GEdr LMil LRHS MAsh MGos NHol SLdr
§ ***brachycarpum*** subsp. ***fauriei*** B&SWJ 4326	WCru
'Brazier' (EA)	SLdr
'Bremen'	LMil
'Bright Forecast' (K)	MPkF SLdr
'Brigitte'	LSRN MAsh
'Brilliant' **new**	NLar
'Brilliant Blue' (EA)	MAsh
'Britannia'	CSBt NHol SCob SSta
BROCÉLIANDE PERCEVAL	SEE *R.* WALBERTON'S MAUVE RUFFLES
BROCÉLIANDE VIVIANE	see *R.* WALBERTON'S SNOW RUFFLES
'Bronze Fire' (A)	NHol SSta
'Brown Eyes'	MAsh MMuc
'Bruce Brechtbill'	GKin MAsh MMuc NLar
§ 'Bruns Gloria'	LMil NLar
'Bruns Schneewitchen'	SSta
'Buccaneer' (Glenn Dale) (EA)	SLdr
bullatum	see *R. edgeworthii*
'Bungo-nishiki' (Wada) (EA/d)	CMac
bureavii 🏆H6	CBcs GGGa LMil MHid SReu SSta
- hybrid **new**	SReu
bureavii* × *yakushimanum	SReu
bureavioides	GKev MHid
burmanicum	CBcs

	Bustard Group	LMil
	'Butter Brickle'	LMil NLar
	'Butterfly'	SLdr
	'Buttermint'	SLdr
	'C.B. van Nes'	SLdr
	calendulaceum (A)	GGGa IDee LMil
	- red-flowered (A)	LMil
	- yellow-flowered (A)	LMil
	(Calfort Group) 'Calfort'	GGGa
	callimorphum	GKev
	calophytum 🏆H5	GGGa LMil SLdr SReu
	calostrotum	SReu
	- 'Gigha' 🏆H6	GGGa LMil SReu WAbe
§	- subsp. ***keleticum*** 🏆H6	GEdr ITim LCro LOPS WThu
	- - R 58	GGGa LMil
§	- - Radicans Group	GEdr GGGa ITim NWad WAbe WThu
	- subsp. ***riparioides***	LMil
	- subsp. ***riparium***	ITim
§	- - Nitens Group	CBcs GGGa WThu
	Calstocker Group	LMil
	camelliiflorum	GGGa MHid
	campanulatum	GKev LMil SLdr SReu
	- B&SWJ 13934	WCru
	- HWJCM 195	WCru
	- HWJCM 409	WCru
§	- subsp. ***aeruginosum***	LMil MHid
	- subsp. ***campanulatum***	MHid
	- hybrid **new**	SReu
	'Campfire' J.B. Gable (EA)	SLdr
	campylocarpum	CBcs IDee LMil
	- subsp. ***campylocarpum***	MHid
	campylogynum	LCro LMil LOPS LRHS SReu
	- SBEC 0519	GGGa
	- 'Album'	see *R.* 'Leucanthum'
	- Charopoeum Group	WThu
	- - 'Patricia'	GEdr
	- (Cremastum Group) 'Bodnant Red'	GGGa
	- Myrtilloides Group 🏆H5	GGGa LMil WAbe WThu
	aff. ***campylogynum*** **new**	SReu
	camtschaticum	GGGa GKev IDee LMil WAbe
	- 'Glendoick Lilac' **new**	GKev
	- red-flowered	GGGa
	canadense (A)	GGGa
	- f. ***albiflorum*** (A)	GGGa LMil
	- dark-flowered (A)	LMil
	CANDY LIGHTS ('UMinn's Candy Lights') (A)	LRHS
§	***canescens*** (A)	LMil MPkF
	'Cannon's Double' (K/d) 🏆H6	CDoC GKin LMil LRHS MGos NLar SPer
	'Canzonetta' (EA/d) 🏆H5	CEnd CRos EPfP GGGa LMil LRHS MAsh NLar NRHS SAko SLdr
	'Captain Jack'	GGGa
	'Carat' (A)	NLar
	(Carita Group) 'Golden Dream'	LMil
	(Carmen Group) 'Carmen' 🏆H6	GEdr GGGa GKin LMil MAsh MMuc SLdr
	'Caroline Allbrook'	MAsh NLar WFar
	'Cary Ann'	CTri LRHS MAsh
	'Casablanca' (EA)	SLdr
	'Cassley' (Vs)	LMil
	catawbiense	CMCN SLdr
	'Catawbiense Album'	CTri MAsh
	'Catawbiense Boursault'	LMaj
	'Catawbiense Grandiflorum'	LMil MAsh
	'Catharine van Tol'	LMaj
	'Caucasicum Pictum'	IDee LMil SLdr

	'Cayenne' (EA)	SLdr
	'Cecile' (K) 🏆H6	CBcs CMac CTri GKin LMil LSRN MMuc MPkF
	'Celestial' (EA)	CMac
	cephalanthum	LMil
	- subsp. ***cephalanthum*** SBEC 0751	WThu
	- - Crebreflorum Group	GGGa LMil WAbe WThu
	cerasinum	LMil MHid SReu
	- 'Cherry Brandy'	GGGa
	- 'Coals of Fire'	GGGa
	chaetomallum	see *R. haematodes* subsp. *chaetomallum*
	'Chanel' (Vs)	NLar SSta
	'Chanticleer' (Glenn Dale) (EA)	SLdr
	chapaense	see *R. maddenii* subsp. *crassum*
	charitopes	LMil
	- F 25570	LMil
	- subsp. ***charitopes***	MHid
*	'Charlotte de Rothschild' (EA)	SLdr
	'Charlotte Megan' (A)	LMil
	chasmanthum	see *R. augustinii* subsp. *chasmanthum*
	'Cheer'	MAsh MMuc
	'Chelsea Reach' (K/d) 🏆H6	LMil
	'Chelsea Seventy'	SLdr
	'Cherokee' (EA)	SLdr
	'Cherry Drops' (EA)	EPfP MAsh SPoG
	CHERRY KISS ('Hachcher'PBR)	GGGa IDee LMil LRHS SAko
	'Chetco' (A)	LMil MGos
	'Chevalier Félix de Sauvage'	LMil
	'Chikor'	CDoC GKin MGos
	'Chionoides'	SLdr
	'Chipmunk' (EA/d)	LRHS MAsh NRHS
	'Chippewa' (Indian) (EA)	CTri LMil SAko
	'Chocolate Dane' **new**	LMil
	Choptank River Group (A)	GKev
	(Choremia Group) 'Choremia' 🏆H5	LMil
	'Christina' (Vuykiana) (EA/d)	SLdr
	'Christmas Cheer' (EA/d)	see *R.* 'Ima-shojo'
	'Christmas Cheer' (*caucasicum* hybrid) 🏆H5	CBcs CDoC CSBt EPfP GGGa GKin LCro LMil LOPS MAsh MGos MPri NLar SLdr SPer
	'Christopher Loder'	SLdr
	chryseum	see *R. rupicola* var. *chryseum*
	ciliatum	CBcs SLdr
	- deep rose-flowered	SLdr
	- white-flowered	SLdr
	Cilpinense Group	CBcs
	- 'Cilpinense' 🏆H5	CMac CSBt EPfP LMil LRHS MAsh MMuc MPri SLdr
	cinnabarinum	LMil SLdr SReu
	- subsp. ***cinnabarinum***	MHid SReu
	- - BL&M 234	LMil
I	- - 'Mount Everest'	SReu
	- - 'Nepal'	LMil SReu
	- - Roylei Group	GGGa LMil
	- - - B&SWJ 13972	WCru
	- - - 'Vin Rosé'	LMil
	- Cinzan Group	LMil
§	- (Conroy Group) 'Conroy'	CTsd LMil
§	- subsp. ***xanthocodon***	CBcs GGGa GKev LMil WPGP
	- - 'Apricot Belle' **new**	LMil
§	- - Concatenans Group	GGGa LMil SLdr
	- - - KW 5874	LMil
	- - Purpurellum Group	GGGa SLdr

	citriniflorum	LMil
	- R 108	LMil
	- var. ***citriniflorum***	LMil
	clementinae F 25705	LMil
	'Cliff Garland'	LMil
	'Coccineum Speciosum' (G) ♀H6	CMac LMil LRHS SReu SSta
	'Cockatoo' (K)	LMil
	coeloneurum	LMil MHid
	- EGM 334	LMil
	'Colin Kenrick' (K/d)	LMil
	'Colonel Coen'	MMuc
	Colonel Rogers Group	SLdr
	columbianum	SLdr
	'Colyer' (EA)	SLdr
	Comely Group	SLdr
	concatenans	see *R. cinnabarinum* subsp. *xanthocodon* Concatenans Group
	concinnum	MHid
	- Pseudoyanthinum Group ♀H5	GGGa
	'Connie' (Kaempferi) (EA)	SSta
	'Conroy'	see *R. cinnabarinum* (Conroy Group) 'Conroy'
	'Contina'	LMil
	'Conversation Piece' (EA)	CEnd SLdr
	'Coral Seas' (V)	GGGa LMil
	'Corany' (A)	CDoC LMil NLar
	coriaceum	GGGa LMil
	'Corneille' (G/d)	CSBt LMil LRHS
	'Coronation Day'	LMil
	'Coronation Day' × ***yakushimanum***	SReu
	'Cosmopolitan'	CDoC LCro LOPS MGos MMuc NLar SCob SPer SPoG
	'Cotton Candy'	LMil
	'Countess of Athlone'	CMac
	'Countess of Haddington'	CBcs LMil LRHS
	Cowslip Group	CTri LMil MAsh MGos
	- 'Cowslip' ♀H4	CDoC CRos EPfP LRHS NLar
	'Crane' ♀H5	CRos EPfP GGGa IDee LMil LRHS MAsh
	crassum	see *R. maddenii* subsp. *crassum*
	'Cream Crest'	CDoC GKin SLim
	'Creamy Chiffon'	NLar
	'Crest' **new**	SReu
	crinigerum	LMil
	'Crinoline' (EA)	SLdr
	'Croceum Tricolor' (G)	LMil
	Crossbill Group	CBcs SLdr
	'Crosswater Belle'	LMil
	'Crosswater Red' (A) ♀H6	LMil
	cubittii	see *R. veitchianum* Cubittii Group
	cucullatum	see *R. roxieanum* var. *cucullatum*
	cumberlandense (A)	LMil
	- 'Sunlight'	LMil
	'Cunningham's White'	CBcs CDoC CTri ELan EPfP GGGa LCro LMil LOPS LRHS MAsh MGos MMuc MPri NHol NLar SArc SCob SGsty SLdr SLim SPer SPoG SReu SSta
	'Curlew' ♀H5	CMac GEdr GKin LMil MAsh MMuc NHol SCob SLdr
	cyanocarpum	GGGa GKev
	'Cynthia' ♀H6	CBcs CMac CSBt GGGa LMil LSRN SCob SLdr SSta
	'Daisetsuzan' (EA)	MPkF
	dalhousieae	NLar SReu
	(Damozel Group) 'Damozel'	LMil
	'Darkness' (EA) **new**	SWeb
	'Dartmoor Pixie'	WThu
	'Dartmoor Shepherd's Delight'	SSta
	dasycladum	see *R. selense* subsp. *dasycladum*
	dauricum	SReu
	- 'Album'	see *R. dauricum* 'Hokkaido'
§	- 'Hokkaido'	LMil
	- 'Mid-winter' ♀H6	GGGa LMil
	davidii	LMil
	davidsonianum ♀H5	CMac LMil MHid SReu
	- Bodnant form	LMil
	- 'Caerhays Blotched'	GGGa
	- 'Ruth Lyons'	LMil
	'Daviesii' (G) ♀H6	CBcs CDoC CEnd CRos CSBt CTho CTri ELan EPfP GKin LCro LMil LOPS LRHS MAsh MMuc MPkF MPri NLar SCob SPer SPoG SSta
	'Daybreak' (EA/d)	see *R.* 'Kirin'
	'Dear Barbara'	LSRN
	'Dear Grandad' (EA)	CTri LMil LSRN SReu
	'Dear Grandma' (EA)	LMil LSRN SReu
	'Dearest' (EA)	LMil LRHS MAsh MPri NRHS
	'Debutante'	SSta
	decorum ♀H6	CBcs GGGa IDee LMil LRHS SLdr SReu
	- subsp. ***cordatum***	MHid
	- - C&H 7132	GGGa
	- subsp. ***decorum***	MHid
§	- subsp. ***diaprepes***	MHid
	- - 'Gargantua'	SLdr
	- hybrid	SReu
	- pink-flowered	GGGa
	aff. ***decorum*** **new**	SReu
	decorum × ***yakushimanum***	SReu
§	***degronianum*** subsp. ***degronianum***	LMil
§	- subsp. ***heptamerum***	SReu
	- - 'Ho Emma'	LMil LRHS
	- - 'Oki Koki' **new**	LMil
	- 'Rae's Delight'	LMil
	'Delicatissimum' (O) ♀H5	GGGa GKin LRHS MPkF
	'Delta'	CDoC MGos MMuc NLar SLdr SLim WFar
	dendrocharis	LMil
	- Cox 5016	WAbe
	- GLENDOICK GEM ('Gle002')	GGGa
*	'Denny's Rose' (A)	LMil SSta
	'Denny's Scarlet'	NHol SSta
	'Denny's White' (A)	LMil NHol SSta
	denudatum	LMil MHid
	- EGM 294	LMil
	'Devisiperbile' (EA)	SLdr
	Diamant Group lilac-flowered (EA)	LMil
§	- red-flowered (EA)	SLdr
	'Diamant Rot'	see *R.* Diamant Group red-flowered
I	'Diana'	SLdr SWeb
	diaprepes	see *R. decorum* subsp. *diaprepes*
	dichroanthum	LMil
§	- subsp. ***apodectum***	GGGa LMil
§	- subsp. ***scyphocalyx***	LMil
	didymum	see *R. sanguineum* subsp. *didymum*
	'Diorama' (Vs)	SSta
	discolor	see *R. fortunei* subsp. *discolor*
	'Doc'	CBcs CMac SLdr SSta
	'Doctor Arnold W. Endtz'	SSta

	'Doctor H.C. Dresselhuys'	MMuc
	'Doctor M. Oosthoek' (M)	GKin
	'Doctor Reiger'	CDoC CRos NLar
	'Dopey' ♀H5	CBcs CDoC EPfP GGGa LMil LRHS MAsh MGos NHol NLar SCob SLdr SLim SReu SSta
	'Dora Amateis' ♀H6	CBcs GGGa LMil LRHS MAsh MGos MMuc MPri NRHS SAko SCob SLdr SLim
	Dormouse Group	LMil MAsh
	'Dorothy Hayden' (EA)	SLdr SWeb
	'Dotella'	GGGa SSta
	'Double Beauty' (Vuykiana) (EA/d)	SSta
	'Dracula' (K)	LMil
	Dragonfly Group	SSta
	'Dreamland' ♀H5	CBcs CDoC CRos EPfP LCro LMil LOPS LRHS MAsh MGos MMuc NLar NRHS SCob SLdr SLim SPoG SReu SSta WFar
	'Driven Snow' (EA)	SLdr
	'Dufthecke'	see *R.* WHITE DUFTHECKE
	'Dufthecke Yellow'	LMil
	'Dusty Miller'	MAsh SLdr WFar
	'Earl of Donoughmore'	SSta
	'Easter Parade' (EA)	SLdr
	'Ebony Pearl'	SLdr
	eclecteum	GGGa LMil MHid
§	***edgeworthii*** ♀H3	CBcs GGGa LMil MPkF SReu
	- hybrid **new**	SReu
	'Edith Bosley'	CDoC LRHS NLar SLdr SPer
	'Edna Bee' (EA)	LMil SLdr
	'Egret' ♀H4	GEdr GGGa LMil SLdr
	'Eiger' (EA)	CRos
	'El Camino'	SLdr
	(Eleanore Group) 'Eleanore'	SLdr
	'Electra'	see *R. augustinii* (Electra Group) 'Electra'
	elegantulum	LMil MHid
	(Elisabeth Hobbie Group) 'Elisabeth Hobbie' ♀H5	CDoC LMil NLar SLdr
	'Elizabeth' (EA)	CMac CSBt EPfP SCob SLdr
	Elizabeth Group	CBcs LMil MAsh SLdr
§	- 'Creeping Jenny'	GGGa SLdr
	- 'Elizabeth'	CTri LRHS LSRN NHol NRHS
	'Elizabeth Jenny'	see *R.* (Elizabeth Group) 'Creeping Jenny'
	'Elizabeth Lockhart'	GAbr
	'Elizabeth Red Foliage'	CTri LMil MAsh MPkF SGsty SLdr
	'Elizabeth' × ***yakushimanum***	SReu
	elliottii	SReu
	'Elsie Lee' (EA/d) ♀H5	CEnd CSBt EPfP LMil MAsh SCob SLdr WFar
	'Emasculum'	SLdr
	'Endsleigh Pink'	LMil
	eriocarpum 'Gumpō' (EA)	CMac SLdr
	eriogynum	see *R. facetum*
	'Esmeralda'	CMac
	'Esther May' (A)	SSta
	'Etna' (EA)	SLdr
	'Etta Burrows'	GGGa SLdr
	'Eucharis' (Glenn Dale) (EA)	MPkF
	'Eunice Ann' (A)	SSta
	'Europa'	LMil SSta
	'Eurydice'	LMil
	'Evelyn Hyde' (EA)	SLdr
	'Everbloom' (EA)	SLdr
	'Everitt Hershey' (A)	SLdr
	EVERRED ('851C'PBR)	GGGa

	exasperatum KW 6855	LMil
	Exburiense Group	MMuc
	'Exbury Calstocker'	LMil
	excellens	GGGa LMil
	eximium	see *R. falconeri* subsp. *eximium*
	'Exquisitum' (O) ♀H5	CTho GGGa GKin LMil
	exquisitum	see *R. oreotrephes* Exquisitum Group
	'Extraordinaire'	LMil SSta
	(Fabia Group) 'Fabia' ♀H4	CMac GGGa GKin LMil SLdr
§	- 'Fabia Tangerine'	CMac
	- 'Fabia Waterer'	LMil
§	***facetum***	GGGa LMil LRHS
	'Faggetter's Favourite' ♀H5	LMil LRHS SSta
	Fairy Light Group	LMil LRHS SLdr
	faithae CGG 14142	GGGa
	falconeri ♀H4	GGGa IDee LMil SLdr SReu
	- KR 10420	WPGP
	- WJC 13825	WCru
	- from East Nepal	SReu
§	- subsp. ***eximium***	GGGa GKev LMil MHid
	- subsp. ***falconeri***	MHid
	- hybrid **new**	SReu
	'Falling Snow'	SAko SReu
	'Fanal' (K)	NLar
	'Fanny'	see *R.* 'Pucella'
	'Fantastica' ♀H6	CDoC CRos ELan GGGa LMil MAsh MGos MMuc MPri NLar SCob SLim SPoG
	fargesii	see *R. oreodoxa* var. *fargesii*
	fastigiatum	GEdr LMil SLdr WAbe
	- SBEC 0804	WThu
	- SDR 7990	GKev
§	- 'Blue Steel' ♀H6	CRos CTri GKin LMil LRHS MAsh MPri NRHS SLdr SPlb WAbe
	- 'Indigo Steel'	GGGa
	'Fastuosum Flore Pleno' (d) ♀H6	CBcs CMac CSBt GGGa IDee LMil SCob SLdr SPer SSta
	fauriei	see *R. brachycarpum* subsp. *fauriei*
	'Favorite' ambig. (EA)	SLdr
	'Fawley' (K)	SLdr
	'Fay Norman'	LMil
	ferrugineum	LMil LRHS
	'Feuerwerk' (K)	MMuc NLar
	fictolacteum	see *R. rex* subsp. *fictolacteum*
	'Fire Bird'	SLdr
	'Fire Rim'	LRHS MAsh
	'Fireball' (K) ♀H6	CBcs CDoC CRos CTri EPfP GBin GGGa GKin IDee LMil LRHS MAsh MGos MMuc MPri NLar SCob SPer SPoG SReu
	'Fireball' (hybrid)	CBod MPkF
	'Firecracker' (A)	LRHS MAsh
	'Fireglow' (EA)	GKin LMil
	'Firelight' (EA) **new**	CDoC CRos
	'Firelight' (hybrid)	GKin LMil NLar SPer
§	'Firestorm'	MPri
	'Flaming Gold'	LMil LRHS LSRN MAsh SLdr
	'Flanagan's Daughter'	LMil MAsh
	Flava Group	see *R.* Volker Group
	flavidum	MMuc
	fletcherianum 'Yellow Bunting'	GGGa
	floccigerum	LMil
	floribundum	GGGa LMil
	'Florida' (EA/d) ♀H4	CDoC CMac LMil SCob SLdr
	'Flower Arranger' (EA)	LMil MAsh SCoo
	formosum	CBcs
§	- var. ***formosum*** Iteaphyllum Group	GGGa

forrestii subsp. ***forrestii***	LMil
- - Repens Group	LMil
- - - 'Seinghku'	GGGa
- Tumescens Group	WThu
Fortune Group	SLdr
fortunei 🏆H5	GGGa LMil SLdr SReu
§ - subsp. ***discolor*** 🏆H5	CBcs LMil MHid
- - (Houlstonii Group) 'John R. Elcock'	LMil
- - var. ***kwangfuense*** AC 5208	LMil
- subsp. ***discolor*** × 'Lodauric Iceberg'	GKin
- subsp. ***fortunei*** **new**	MHid SReu
- hybrid **new**	SReu
- 'Mrs Butler'	see *R.* 'Sir Charles Butler'
fragariiflorum	GGGa
'Fragrance'	SReu
'Fragrant Memories'	LMil
'Fragrant Star' (A)	LRHS MPkF
'Fragrantissimum' 🏆H3	CBcs CDoC CEnd CMac CSBt CTsd GGGa LMil LRHS MPkF MRav NLar SLdr SReu
'Frank Galsworthy'	SCob
Fraseri Group (M)	SReu
- 'Fraseri' (M)	LMil
'Fred Peste' 🏆H4	LMil MGos MMuc SCob SLdr SLim
(Fred Wynniatt Group) 'Fred Wynniatt'	LMil
'Fred Wynniatt Stanway'	see *R.* 'Stanway'
'Freya' (R/d)	LMil LSRN
'Fridoline' (EA)	SAko
'Frigate' (EA)	SLdr
'Frilly Lemon' (Ad)	ELan EPfP LRHS MPkF
'Frosted Orange' (EA)	LMil MAsh
'Frosthexe'	WAbe
'Fulbrook'	LMil
fulgens	LMil MHid
fulvum 🏆H5	GGGa IDee LMil LRHS SReu SSta
'Furious Fujiori'PBR (EA) **new**	MPkF
'Furnivall's Daughter' 🏆H5	CBcs CMac CSBt IDee LMaj LMil MMuc NHol SLdr SPer SSta
fuyuanense	GGGa
'Gabrielle Hill' (EA)	MAsh SLdr
'Gaiety' (Glenn Dale) (EA)	LMil SLdr
galactinum	GGGa LMil
'Galathea' (EA)	MMuc
'Gandy Dancer'	SLdr
'Garden State Glow' (EA/d)	SLdr
'Gartendirektor Glocker'	CDoC CMac CRos LMil MGos NLar SCob SLim
'Gartendirektor Rieger' 🏆H5	CBcs GGGa LMil NLar
'Geisha' (EA)	SReu
'Geisha Lilac'	see *R.* (Aronense Group) 'Hanako'
'Geisha Orange'	see *R.* (Aronense Group) 'Satschiko'
'Geisha Pink'	see *R.* (Aronense Group) 'Momoko'
'Geisha Purple'	see *R.* (Aronense Group) 'Fumiko'
'Geisha Red'	see *R.* (Aronense Group) 'Kazuko'
Gelb Dufthecke ('Rhodunter 150'PBR) (Inkarho) **new**	NLar
'Gena Mae' (A/d) 🏆H6	SLdr
'General Practitioner'	CMac SLdr
'General Wavell' (EA)	CMac
'Gene's Favourite'	SSta
genestierianum	GGGa
'Geoffroy Millais'	LMil
'Georg Arends' (A)	CDoC EPfP LMil LRHS MAsh NLar
'George Hyde' (EA)	EPfP LRHS LSRN MAsh SCoo
§ × ***geraldii***	SLdr
'Germania'	CBcs CDoC LRHS MAsh MGos MPri NLar SCob SPoG SSta
Gertrud Schäle Group	CDoC CTri NLar
'Gibraltar' (K) 🏆H6	CBcs CBod CDoC CSBt CTri EPfP GGGa GKin IDee LMil LRHS MAsh MGos MPkF NHol NLar SCob SLim SPer SSta
Gibraltar Group	LMil WFar
'Gilbert Mullie' (EA)	CDoC LMil NLar SLim SSta
'Gillian Bramley'	SLdr
'Ginger' (K)	LMil SReu
'Ginny Gee' 🏆H5	CBcs CDoC CPla CRos EPfP GEdr GGGa GKin LMil LRHS MAsh MGos NLar NRHS NWad SSta WFar
§ 'Girard's Hot Shot' (EA)	LRHS MPkF NRHS SReu SSta
§ 'Girard's Variegated Hot Shot' (EA/v) 🏆H4	CPla GGGa MAsh SLdr SPoG SReu
'Gislinde' (A)	SAko
'Glacier' (EA)	SLdr
glanduliferum	GGGa MHid
- 'Peter the Great'	LMil
glaucophyllum	GGGa LMil MHid
- Borde Hill form	LMil
- 'Deer Dell'	LMil
Glendoick Dove ('Gle025')	GGGa
Glendoick Flamingo ('Gle026')	GGGa
Glendoick Glacier ('Gle009') (EA)	GGGa
Glendoick Goblin ('Gle010') (EA)	GGGa
Glendoick Gold ('Gle011')	GGGa
Glendoick Mystique ('Gle014')	GGGa
Glendoick Petticoats ('Gle015')	GGGa
Glendoick Rosebud ('Gle022') (EA)	GGGa
Glendoick Sherbet ('Gle029')	GGGa
Glendoick Snowflakes ('Gle001') (EA)	GGGa
Glendoick Sorbet ('Gle028')	GGGa
Glendoick Vanilla ('Gle017')	GGGa
Glendoick Velvet ('Gle018')	GGGa
'Gletschernacht'	SAko
glischrum	GGGa
- subsp. ***glischroides***	LMil
§ - subsp. ***rude***	LMil LRHS MHid
'Gloria'	see *R.* 'Bruns Gloria'
'Gloria Mundi' (G)	MPkF
'Glory of Littleworth' (Ad)	LMil
'Glory of Penjerrick'	SLdr
'Glowing Embers' (K)	CDoC CTri GKin LMil LRHS MAsh MGos MMuc NHol NLar SCob SLim SPer SSta
'Goblin'	SLdr
'Gog' (K)	CSBt
'Golden Eagle' (K) 🏆H6	CBcs CBod CDoC CRos GKin LMil LRHS MGos NLar SLdr SPer WFar
Golden Everest ('Hachgold'PBR)	GGGa LMil
'Golden Flare' (A)	CBcs GKin
'Golden Fleece'	LMil

'Golden Gate'	CDoC CSBt MGos MMuc NLar SCob SLdr
(Golden Horn Group) 'Golden Horn'	SLdr
'Golden Lights' (A)	GKin NLar
'Golden Princess'	LMil
'Golden Ruby'	CBcs
'Golden Splendour'	LMil
'Golden Sunset' (K) ♀H6	CBod EPfP LMil LRHS MAsh MPkF WFar
'Golden Torch' ♀H5	CBcs CDoC EPfP LCro LMil LOPS LRHS MAsh MGos MPri NLar SCob SLdr SLim SPer SPoG
'Golden Wedding'	CBcs LMil LRHS LSRN MAsh SLdr SReu
'Golden Wit'	MAsh MMuc
'Golden Wonder'	MAsh
'Goldflimmer' (v)	CDoC EPfP LRHS MAsh MGos MPri NLar SCob SLim SPer SPoG SReu WFar
'Goldika'	LMil
GOLDINETTA ('Hachinetta')	IDee LMil
'Goldkrone' ♀H5	MAsh SCob SPer SPoG SSta
'Goldsworth Orange'	CMac LRHS SLdr
'Goldsworth Yellow'	CSBt
'Goldtopas' (K)	CTri EPfP GGGa GKin LMil LRHS
'Gomer Waterer' ♀H6	CBcs CMac CSBt EPfP GGGa LCro LMaj LMil LOPS LRHS MAsh MGos NLar SCob SLdr SPer SPoG SReu SSta
'Gorbella'	CDoC NLar
Gowenianum Group (Ad)	LMil LRHS MGos SPer
'Grace Seabrook' ♀H5	CBcs CSBt CTri GGGa MMuc SLdr SPer
GRAFFITO ('Hachgraf')	CBcs GGGa LMil
'Graham Thomas'	LMil
'Grand Slam'	MMuc
grande	CBcs GGGa IDee LMil LRHS MHid NLar SReu
- WJC 13804	WCru
gratum	see *R. basilicum*
'Graziella'	GGGa LCro LOPS LRHS MGos MPkF SArc SPoG SSta WFar
'Greensleeves'	LMil
'Greenway' (Kurume) (EA)	CBcs MPkF SLdr
griersonianum	GGGa LMil SReu
- F 30392	LMil
- hybrid **new**	SReu
griersonianum* × *yakushimanum	SReu
griffithianum	MHid SReu
- B&SWJ 2425	WCru
- hybrid **new**	SReu
'Gristede' ♀H5	CDoC CRos LMil LRHS NLar SSta
groenlandicum	LMil NLar SPer WGob
- 'Compactum'	LRHS NLar
- 'Helma'	GBin LMil LRHS NLar
- 'Lenie'	NLar
(Grosclaude Group) 'Grosclaude'	LMil
'Grumpy'	EPfP LMil LRHS MAsh
'Guillemot'	GGGa
'Gwenda' (EA)	CTri SLdr
'Gwendoline' (A)	SSta
habrotrichum	LMil
'Hachmann's Brasilia'	SSta
'Hachmann's Charmant'	GGGa SAko
'Hachmann's Constanze'	LMil
'Hachmann's Eskimo'	IDee LMil SLdr
'Hachmann's Feuerschein'	SAko

	'Hachmann's Juanita' (K)	NLar
	'Hachmann's Junifeuer'	NLar SSta
	HACHMANN'S KABARETT ('Hachkaba')	CDoC CRos LMil NLar
	'Hachmann's Mamamia'	SAko
	'Hachmann's Marlis' ♀H6	LMil LRHS
§	'Hachmann's Metallica'	IDee LMil LRHS
§	'Hachmann's Orakel'	IDee LMil LRHS SSta
	HACHMANN'S PICOBELLO ('Hachpico'PBR)	LMil
	'Hachmann's Pinguin'	SSta
§	'Hachmann's Polaris' ♀H7	CBcs CDoC LMil SReu
	'Hachmann's Porzellan' ♀H6	LMil
§	'Hachmann's Rokoko' (EA)	CEnd LMil SSta
	'Hachmann's Sunny Boy'	LMil LRHS
	haematodes	GGGa LMil
§	- subsp. ***chaetomallum***	LMil
	- subsp. ***haematodes***	LMil
	'Halfdan Lem' ♀H5	CBcs CDoC CRos GKin LMil LRHS MGos MMuc NLar SLim SPer SPoG SSta
	'Halopeanum'	GGGa LMil
	'Hamlet' (M)	LMil
	'Hammondii'	LMil
	'Hampshire Belle'	LMil LRHS SSta
	hanceanum Nanum Group ♀H5	CBcs
	'Hanger's Flame' (A)	LMil
	HANS HACHMANN ('Hachhans')	LMil
	'Hansel'	MAsh MMuc
	'Hardijzer Beauty' (Ad)	SLdr
	'Hardy Gardenia' (EA/d)	SSta
	hardyi	see *R. augustinii* subsp. *hardyi*
	'Harkwood Red' (EA)	SLdr
	Harmony Group	SLdr
	'Harry Tagg'	SLdr
	Harry White's hybrid (A)	SSta
	'Haru-no-sono' (EA)	MPkF SWeb
	'Harvest Moon' (K)	LMil NLar SSta
	'Hatsu-giri' (EA)	CMac LCro LMil LOPS SLdr SReu SSta
	(Hawk Group) 'Crest' ♀H4	CBcs LMil SSta
	'Heather Macleod' (EA)	SLdr
	'Heidi'PBR (EA)	SLdr
	'Helen Close' (Glenn Dale) (EA)	SLdr
	'Helen Curtis' (EA)	SLdr
	'Helena Evelyn' (A)	LMil
	'Helene Schiffner'	SSta
	heliolepis	LMil
	hemsleyanum	LMil MHid SLdr
	heptamerum	see *R. degronianum* subsp. *heptamerum*
	'Herbert' (EA)	CDoC CMac MGos NLar SLdr SLim
§	'Hexe de Saffelaere' (EA)	CDoC NLar
	'High Sheriff'	CBcs
	'High Summer'	LMil LRHS
	'Hilda Margaret'	SSta
	'Hinamayo'	see *R.* (Obtusum Group) 'Hinomayo'
	'Hino-crimson' (Kurume) (EA) ♀H5	CBcs CDoC CMac CRos CSBt CTri GKin LMil MAsh MGos MPkF NHol NLar SCob SLdr SPer SPoG SReu SSta
	'Hinode-giri' (EA)	CBcs CMac CSBt SLdr
	'Hino-scarlet' (EA)	CBcs SReu
	hippophaeoides	CBcs GKev LMil WFar
	- 'Bei-ma-shan'	see *R. hippophaeoides* 'Haba Shan'
§	- 'Haba Shan' ♀H6	LMil WThu

hirsutum	LMil WAbe
hirtipes	GGGa MHid
hodgsonii	LMil MHid SLdr SReu
- B&SWJ 2195A	WCru
- hybrid **new**	SReu
'Holden'	MAsh NLar
'Homebush' (K/d) 🏆H6	CBcs CBod CDoC CMac CRos CTri EPfP GBin LMil LRHS MAsh MGos MMuc NLar SCob SPer SPoG SSta
'Honey Butter'	MGos SLim
'Honeysuckle' (K)	NHol SSta
§ 'Ho-o' (Kurume) (EA)	SLdr
hookeri	LMil
- Tigh-na-Rudha form	GGGa
'Hoppy'	CBcs CDoC LMil MAsh MGos MMuc NLar SCob SLdr SLim
'Horizon Lakeside'	GGGa
'Horizon Monarch' 🏆H4	CBcs CDoC CRos GGGa GKin IDee LMil LRHS MGos NLar SCob SGsty SLdr SLim SPer SSta WFar
'Hortulanus H. Witte' (M)	SSta
'Hot Flush'	IDee LMil
'Hot Shot'	see *R.* 'Girard's Hot Shot'
'Hot Shot Variegated'	see *R.* 'Girard's Variegated Hot Shot' (EA/v)
'Hotei'	CSBt EPfP GKin LMil MAsh NHol SLdr SReu SSta
(Hotspur Group) 'Hotspur' (K)	MMuc
- 'Hotspur Red' (K) 🏆H6	CBod EPfP GKin LMil MAsh MMuc MPkF
huanum	LMil
- EGM 316	LMil
'Hugh Koster'	SLdr
aff. ***huidongense***	LMil
'Huisman's Sun Star' (A/d)	LMil SReu
Humming Bird Group	GEdr IDee LMil SLdr
hunnewellianum	MHid
'Hussar'	LMil
'Hydon Dawn' 🏆H5	CBcs LMil LRHS NLar SLdr SReu SSta
'Hydon Hunter' 🏆H5	SSta
'Hydon Velvet'	CBcs CTsd LMil LRHS MMuc NLar SLdr SReu
hyperythrum	GGGa LMil
'Ice Cube'	MMuc SLdr
'Ice Maiden'	SReu
'Iceberg'	see *R.* (Lodauric Group) 'Lodauric Iceberg'
(Idealist Group) 'Idealist'	LMil
'Ightham Purple'	SReu
'Ightham Yellow'	SLdr SReu
§ 'Ilam Melford Lemon' (A)	LMil
§ 'Ilam Ming' (A)	LMil
'Ilam Violet'	CMac LMil
'Imago' (K/d)	LMil
§ 'Ima-shojo' (Kurume) (EA/d)	CMac CRos LRHS SLdr
impeditum	CBcs CSBt GEdr LCro LOPS MGos SLdr SSta
- 'Blue Steel'	see *R. fastigiatum* 'Blue Steel'
- 'Indigo'	GKin
- 'Pygmaeum'	WAbe WThu
- Reuthe's form	SReu
(Impi Group) 'Impi'	LMil
§ ***indicum*** 'Macranthum' (EA)	SLdr SRms
INKARHO LILAC DUFTHECKE ('Rhodunter 149'PBR)	LMaj LMil NLar
insigne 🏆H6	GGGa LMil MHid
- 'Annie Darling' **new**	LMil
- Reuthe's form	SReu
Intrifast Group	GGGa
'Irene Koster' (O) 🏆H5	CDoC CTho ELan GGGa GKin LMil MGos MPkF NLar SCob SLim SPer
'Irohayama' (Kurume) (EA) 🏆H5	CBcs CEnd CMac EPfP LMil LRHS MAsh MPri NRHS
irroratum	LMil SLdr
- subsp. ***irroratum***	MHid
- 'Polka Dot'	GGGa LMil
- subsp. ***yiliangense***	MHid
- - EGM 339	LMil
'Isabel' (EA)	MAsh
'Isabel' (hybrid)	MPri
iteaphyllum	see *R. formosum* var. *formosum* Iteaphyllum Group
'Ivette' (Kaempferi) (EA)	CMac
'Izumi-no-mai' (EA)	SLdr
'J.C. Williams'	CBcs
'J.M. de Montague'	see *R.* 'The Honourable Jean Marie de Montague'
'Jackwill'	SAko
(Jalisco Group) 'Jalisco Janet'	SLdr
- 'Jubilant'	LMil
'James Burchett' 🏆H6	LMil LRHS SSta
'James Gable' (EA)	MAsh SLdr
Janet Group	LMil
'Janet Rhea' (EA)	SLdr
japonicum (A. Gray) J.V. Suringar	see *R. molle* subsp. *japonicum*
japonicum Schneider var. ***japonicum***	see *R. degronianum* subsp. *heptamerum*
- var. ***pentamerum***	see *R. degronianum* subsp. *degronianum*
jasminiflorum (V)	CTsd
'Jason'	LMil
'Jean Marie Montague'	see *R.* 'The Honourable Jean Marie de Montague'
'Jeff Hill' (EA)	SLdr
'Jenny'	see *R.* (Elizabeth Group) 'Creeping Jenny'
'Jeritsa'	LMil
'Jessica Rose' (A)	LMil
'Joanna'	CBcs
'Jock'	SLdr
Jock Group	CBcs
'Jock Brydon' (O) 🏆H6	GGGa LMil
'Johann Sebastian Bach' (EA)	SLdr
'Johanna' (EA) 🏆H5	CDoC CEnd CTri EPfP LMil LRHS MAsh MGos MPkF MPri NHol NLar NRHS SCob SGsty SLdr SPer SWeb
'John Cairns' (Kaempferi) (EA)	CMac SLdr
johnstoneanum	CBcs GGGa SLdr
- NJM 12.068	WPGP
- 'Double Diamond' (d)	LMil
'Jolie Madame' (Vs) 🏆H6	CDoC CTho ELan EPfP GKin IDee LMil LRHS MAsh MGos MMuc MPkF MPri NLar SReu WFar
'Joseph Hill' (EA)	CEnd NLar
'Jubilee'	SLdr
'July Giant'	SLdr
'June Fire' (A)	SSta
'Juniduft' (A)	GGGa
kaempferi (EA)	LMil SLdr
§ - 'Mikado' (EA)	LMil SLdr
- orange-flowered (EA)	CMac
'Kalinka'	CDoC CRos LMil MAsh MGos SPoG WFar
'Karen Triplett'	LMil
'Karl Naue'	GGGa SSta

	KARMINKISSEN ('Hachkarmin')	IDee LMil
	'Kasane-kagaribi' (EA)	SLdr
	'Kathleen' van Nes (EA)	SLdr
	'Katisha' (EA)	SLdr
	'Katy Watson'	SSta
	'Keija' (EA)	SLdr
	keiskei compact	ITim
	- var. ***ozawae*** 'Yaku Fairy' ♀H5	LMil
	keleticum	see *R. calostrotum* subsp. *keleticum*
	aff. ***kendrickii*** KR 10359	WPGP
	'Kentucky Minstrel' (K)	MPkF
	'Kermesinum' (EA)	CDoC CTri LRHS MAsh MGos NWad SCob SLdr SLim
I	'Kermesinum Rosé' (EA) ♀H5	CDoC CRos CSBt LMil LRHS NLar SLdr SLim
	kesangiae	GGGa LMil SReu
	- var. ***album***	GGGa
	keysii	LMil SReu
	(Kilimanjaro Group) 'Kilimanjaro'	LMil
	- 'Kilimanjaro' × ***yakushimanum***	SReu
	'Kimbeth'	GGGa
	'King George' Loder	see *R.* (Loderi Group) 'Loderi King George'
	kingianum	see *R. arboreum* subsp. *zeylanicum*
	'Kings Ride'	LMil
§	'Kirin' (Kurume) (EA/d)	CBcs LMil SLdr SRms
	'Kirin' (Tsutsuji) (EA)	MPkF
	kiusianum (EA)	LMil WAbe
I	- 'Album' (EA)	LMil WAbe
	- 'Hillier's Pink' (EA)	LMil
	- var. ***kiusianum*** (EA)	SLdr
	'Kleiner Prinz' (EA)	SAko
	'Klondyke' (K) ♀H6	CAby CBcs CBod CDoC CRos CSBt CTri EPfP GGGa GKin LCro LMil LOPS LRHS MAsh MGos MMuc MPkF MPri NLar SCob SLdr SPer
	'Kluis Sensation' ♀H5	CBcs CMac CSBt SLdr SSta
	'Kluis Triumph'	SSta
	'Knap Hill Apricot' (K)	LMil
	'Knap Hill Pink' (K) **new**	SReu
	'Knap Hill Red' (K)	LMil
	'Koichiro Wada'	see *R. yakushimanum* 'Koichiro Wada'
	'Kokardia'	LMil SAko
	'Königstein' (EA)	LMil MGos SSta
§	'Koningin Emma' (M)	LMil SReu
	'Koningin Wilhelmina' (Vuykiana) (EA)	SLdr
	'Koran-yuki' (EA) **new**	SRms
	'Koromo-shikibu' (EA)	MPkF
	'Koster's Brilliant Red' (M)	SSta
	'Kromlauer Parkperle'	SAko
§	'Kure-no-yuki' (Kurume) (EA/d)	CEnd LMil
	'La Ola' (EA)	SAko
	(Lactcombei Group) 'Robert Keir'	SLdr
	lacteum	GGGa LMil SReu
	'Lady Alice Fitzwilliam' ♀H3	CBcs CMac CTsd GKin LMil
	Lady Chamberlain Group	SReu
	- 'Exbury Lady Chamberlain'	SReu
	- 'Salmon Trout'	LMil LSRN
	'Lady Clementine Mitford' ♀H6	CBcs CSBt IDee LMil MMuc SLdr SPer
	'Lady Clermont' × ***yakushimanum*** **new**	SReu

	'Lady Dark' (EA)	SAko
	'Lady Eleanor Cathcart'	SLdr
	'Lady Elphinstone' (Kurume) (EA)	SLdr
	'Lady Louise' (EA)	SLdr
	Lamellen Group	LMil
	lanatoides	GGGa
	lanatum	LMil
	lanatum × ***yakushimanum*** 'Koichiro Wada' **new**	SReu
	'Langworth'	MMuc
	lanigerum	LMil
	lapponicum	GKev
	- Japanese	SReu
	- Parviflorum Group	GGGa
	'Lapwing' (K)	NLar SLdr
	'Laramie'	LMil
	'Lavender Brilliant' (EA)	SLdr
	'Lavender Girl' ♀H6	LMil LRHS SLdr SSta
	'Le Progrès'	LMil LRHS
	'Ledifolium'	see *R.* × *mucronatum*
	'Ledifolium Album'	see *R.* × *mucronatum*
	'Lee's Dark Purple'	LMil SCob
	'Lee's Scarlet'	LMil
	'Lem'	SReu
	'Lemon Dream'	CDoC CRos EPfP LRHS MAsh MGos MPri NLar NRHS SLim
*	'Lemon Drop' (A)	GGGa
	'Lemonora' (M)	CBcs GKin
	'Lem's 45'	SLdr
	'Lem's Cameo' ♀H5	GGGa LMil LRHS SReu SSta
	'Lem's Monarch' ♀H4	CBcs GGGa IDee LMil LRHS MMuc SLdr SReu SSta
	'Lem's Tangerine'	LMil
	'Lemur' (EA)	GGGa LMil NLar
	'Leni'	LRHS MAsh NRHS
	'Leo' (EA)	SLdr
	'Leo' (hybrid)	CMac
	'Leonardslee Giles'	SLdr
	'Leonore'	LMil
	lepidostylum	CMac GGGa LMil MHid WFar
	lepidotum yellow-flowered McB 110	WThu
§	'Leucanthum'	WThu
	leucaspis	CBcs SLdr
	'Lila Pedigo'	MMuc SLdr
	'Lilac Time' (EA)	SLdr
	'Lilactina'	SLdr
	'Lily Marleen' (EA)	CTri
	'Linda' ♀H5	CMac EPfP GGGa LMil LSRN MAsh SLdr
	'Linearifolium'	see *R. stenopetalum* 'Linearifolium'
	'Lingot d'Or' (A)	MPkF
	'Lionel's First'	LMil
	Lionel's Triumph Group	LMil
	'Little Beauty' (EA)	SLdr
	'Loch Awe'	GGGa LMil
	'Loch Earn'	GGGa
	'Loch Faskally'	GGGa
	Lodauric Group	SLdr
§	- 'Lodauric Iceberg'	LMil LRHS
	Loderi Group	SLdr
	- 'Loderi Fairy Queen'	SLdr
	- 'Loderi Game Chick'	LMil SLdr
	- 'Loderi Georgette'	SLdr
	- 'Loderi Helen'	LMil SLdr
§	- 'Loderi King George' ♀H5	CBcs GGGa GKin LMil LRHS SLdr SPer SReu SSta
	- 'Loderi Patience'	SLdr

	Name	Suppliers
	- 'Loderi Pink Coral'	LMil SLdr
	- 'Loderi Pink Diamond' ♀H5	CBcs LMil SLdr SReu
	- 'Loderi Pink Topaz'	SLdr
	- 'Loderi Pretty Polly'	SLdr
	- 'Loderi Princess Marina'	SLdr
	- 'Loderi Sir Edmund'	LMil SLdr
	- 'Loderi Sir Joseph Hooker'	SLdr
	- 'Loderi Titan'	SLdr SReu SSta
	- 'Loderi Venus' ♀H5	LMil SLdr SSta
	- 'Loderi White Diamond'	SLdr
	- pink-flowered **new**	SReu
	aff. Loderi Group	SReu
	'Loder's White' ♀H5	CMac LMil SSta
	longesquamatum	GGGa
	longipes	LMil MHid
	- EGM 336	LMil
	- var. ***chienianum***	LMil MHid
	'Lord Roberts' ♀H6	CBcs CDoC CMac CSBt CTri ELan LCro LMil LOPS MAsh MGos MMuc NHol NLar SCob SLdr SLim SPer SSta
	'Louisa' (EA)	MAsh NLar
	'Louise Dowdle' (Glenn Dale) (EA)	LMil SLdr
	'Lovely William'	CMac IDee LMil SLdr
	'Lucy Lou'	GGGa
	ludlowii	GGGa
	'Lullaby' (EA)	SLdr
	luteiflorum	GGGa MHid
	lutescens	CBcs CMac ITim LMil SLdr SReu
	- 'Bagshot Sands' ♀H3	GGGa LMil SLdr
	- 'Exbury'	CExl
	luteum (A)	Widely available
	- 'Golden Comet' (A)	GGGa SReu
*	'Mac Ovata'	CMac
	macabeanum ♀H4	GGGa GKev GKin IDee LMil LRHS MHid NLar SLdr SReu SSta
	- NAPE 052	GGGa
	- Reuthe's form	SReu
	macabeanum × wardii	GGGa
	macranthum	see *R. indicum* 'Macranthum'
	macrophyllum B&SWJ 9561	WCru
	macrosmithii	see *R. argipeplum*
	'Macrostemon' (EA)	MPkF
	'Madame Ad. van Hecke' (EA)	CTri GKin LMil MAsh MGos SLim
	'Madame Albert van Hecke' (EA)	CDoC LCro NLar SLdr
	'Madame de Bruin'	SLdr
	'Madame Galle'	CDoC SLdr
	'Madame Masson' ♀H6	CDoC CTri ELan EPfP LMil LRHS LSRN MAsh MGos MMuc MPri NLar SCob SGsty SPer SSta WFar
	maddenii	CBcs LMil SAko SReu
§	- subsp. ***crassum***	CBcs CExl GGGa SReu
§	- subsp. ***maddenii*** Polyandrum Group	CBcs
	'Magic Flute' (EA)	LRHS MAsh NRHS
I	'Magic Flute' (V)	LMil SCoo
	magnificum	GKev
	magniflorum	GGGa
	'Mai-ogi' (EA)	SAko
	'Maischnee' (EA)	GGGa
	'Maja' (G)	SSta
§	***makinoi*** ♀H5	LMil MMuc SSta
	- 'Fuju-kaku-no-matsu'	MGos
	mallotum	GGGa LMil SReu
	'Manda Sue'	NLar

	Name	Suppliers
	'Mandarin Lights' (A)	NLar
	'Manderley'	LMil
	'Maraschino' (EA)	MPkF SAko
	'Mardi Gras'	CRos MGos NLar
	'Maria Elena' (EA/d)	CDoC CRos MGos NLar SLdr
	'Marie Fortie'	CDoC CRos MGos NLar
	'Marie Hoffman'	LMil
	'Marilee' (EA)	EPfP LRHS MAsh NLar SLdr
	'Marinja' (EA)	LMil
	'Marinus Koster'	SSta
	'Markeeta's Prize' ♀H4	CDoC EPfP GGGa IDee LMil LRHS MAsh MGos MMuc MPri NLar SLdr SLim SReu
	'Marlies' (A)	NLar
	'Marmot' (EA)	MMuc NLar
	'Marsalla'	SAko
	'Martha Isaacson' (Ad)	LMil SLdr
	'Martha Wright'	CDoC EPfP GGGa LRHS MAsh MPri NLar
	'Maruschka' (EA) ♀H5	CDoC EPfP GGGa LMil LRHS MAsh NLar SAko
	'Mary Desby' (EA)	CEnd
	'Mary Helen' (Glenn Dale) (EA)	CDoC LMil LRHS MAsh MGos NLar NRHS SCoo SLdr SLim
	'Mary Poppins' (A)	CSBt GKin LMil LSRN MGos MPkF NLar SCoo SLdr SLim
	'Marylou'	LMil LRHS
	(Matador Group) 'Matador'	LMil SLdr
	'Mathie' (A)	SSta
	maximum	GKev MHid
	'Maxine Childers'	IDee
§	'Maxwellii' (EA)	CMac SLdr
	May Day Group	CBcs MGos
	- 'May Day' ♀H5	CMac MMuc SLdr
	'Mayor Johnstone'	CTri EPfP MAsh MPri
	meddianum var. ***atrokermesinum*** F 2649	LMil
	Medusa Group	SLdr
	'Megan' (EA)	LSRN MAsh SLdr WGwG
	megaphyllum	see *R. basilicum*
	megeratum KR 9426	LMil
	- 'Bodnant'	ITim NWad WAbe WThu
	mekongense var. ***mekongense*** Rubroluteum Group	see *R. viridescens* Rubroluteum Group
	- - Viridescens Group	see *R. viridescens*
	'Melford Lemon'	see *R.* 'Ilam Melford Lemon'
	'Melina' (EA/d)	LMil
	'Melle'PBR	MPkF
	'Melville'	SSta
	'Merganser' ♀H4	GGGa LMil SLdr
	'Merlin' (Glenn Dale) (EA)	LMil
	METALLICA	see *R.* 'Hachmann's Metallica'
	metternichii	see *R. degronianum* subsp. *heptamerum*
	- var. ***pentamerum***	see *R. degronianum* subsp. *degronianum*
	'Mi Amor'	LMil
	'Michael Hill' (EA)	MAsh
	'Michiko' (EA)	SAko
	micranthum	LMil LRHS
	microgynum	GGGa MHid
	microleucum	see *R. orthocladum* var. *microleucum*
	'Midnight Beauty'	EPfP LMil LRHS SAko
	'Midnight Mystique'	SSta
	'Midsummer'	MMuc SLdr
	'Midsummer Coral' (A)	LMil
	'Midsummer Girl' (A)	LMil

	Name	Suppliers
	'Midsummer Mermaid' (A)	LMil
	'Midsummer Moon' (A)	LMil
	'Midsummer Rose' (A)	LMil
	'Midsummer Star' (A)	LMil
	'Midsummer Wedding' (A)	LMil
	'Mikado' (EA)	see *R. kaempferi* 'Mikado'
	'Millennium' (A)	LRHS
	'Millennium Gold'^{PBR}	LMil
	'Milton' (R)	LMil
	'Mimi' (Kaempferi) (EA)	CMac
	'Ming'	see *R.* 'Ilam Ming'
	'Minnetonka' **new**	CDoC
	minus	CBcs
	- var. ***minus*** (Carolinianum Group) 'Epoch'	LMil
	Mishmiense Group KR 10716	WPGP
	'Moerheim' 🏆H5	CBcs EPfP LRHS MAsh MMuc MPri SLim
§	'Moerheim's Pink'	GGGa LMil SLdr
	(Mohamet Group) 'Mohamet'	LMil
	'Moidart' (Vs)	LMil NLar
	'Moira Salmon' (EA)	SLdr
§	***molle*** subsp. ***japonicum*** (A)	LMil SReu
	Mollis, orange-flowered (M)	GKin SGsty SRms
	- pink-flowered (M)	GKin SGsty SRms
	- red-flowered (M)	GKin SGsty
	- yellow-flowered (M)	GKin SRms
	'Molly Ann'	LSRN
	'Molten Gold' (v)	GGGa LMil LRHS MAsh
	'Monsieur Marcel Ménard' 🏆H6	CBcs CDoC CRos EPfP IDee LMil LRHS MAsh MGos MPri NLar SCob SLdr SReu SSta WFar
	montroseanum	GGGa LMil MHid SReu
	Moonstone Group	CMac
	- 'Moonstone Pink'	SLdr
	- 'Moonstone Yellow'	SLdr
§	'Morgenrot'	CDoC MMuc WFar
	morii	GGGa MHid
	'Morning Cloud'	CDoC EPfP LRHS MAsh MGos NHol SCob SLim SSta
	MORNING RED	see *R.* 'Morgenrot'
	'Moser's Maroon'	CBcs CDoC GGGa LSRN MMuc NLar SGsty SLdr WFar
	'Mother of Pearl'	SLdr
	'Mother's Day' (Kurume) (EA) 🏆H4	CDoC CMac CRos CSBt CTri EPfP GKin LCro LMil LOPS LRHS LSRN MAsh MGos MPri NHol NLar NRHS SCob SLdr SLim SPer SPoG SRms SSta WFar
§	***moulmainense***	CMCN
	'Mount Everest'	LMil LRHS SSta
	'Mount Rainier' (A)	LRHS MPkF
	'Mount Saint Helens' (A)	CDoC LMil NLar SLim SPer
	'Mount Seven Star'	see *R. nakaharae* 'Mount Seven Star'
	moupinense	GGGa SLdr
	'Möwe' (K)	LMil
	'Mrs A.T. de la Mare' 🏆H6	LMil SSta
	'Mrs Betty Robertson'	CMac GBin SLdr
	Mrs C. Whitner Group	SLdr
	'Mrs Charles E. Pearson' 🏆H6	CBcs CSBt LMil SLdr SSta
	'Mrs Davies Evans'	LMil SSta
	'Mrs Emil Hager' (EA)	SLdr
	'Mrs Furnivall' 🏆H6	GGGa
	'Mrs G.W. Leak'	CSBt
	'Mrs J.G. Millais'	LMil
	'Mrs T.H. Lowinsky' 🏆H6	CBcs CDoC CMac GGGa GKin LMil LRHS MAsh MGos MMuc NLar SCob SLdr SLim SPer
§	× ***mucronatum*** (EA)	MPkF SLdr
	mucronulatum	CBcs
	- B&SWJ 786	WCru
	- B&SWJ 8657	WCru
	- var. ***albiflorum***	LMil SLdr
	'Muffet' (EA)	SLdr
	'Mulroy Cream'	LMil
§	***multiflorum*** var. ***purpureum***	GGGa
	'Mum'	LMil
	'Nabucco' (A)	MMuc MPkF NLar SLdr
	nakaharae (EA) 🏆H5	SLdr
	- 'Mariko' (EA)	EPot
§	- 'Mount Seven Star' (EA) 🏆H5	ITim LMil NWad SLdr WThu
§	- orange-flowered (EA)	LMil LRHS MAsh NRHS SLdr
	- pink-flowered (EA)	SLdr
	'Nakahari Orange'	see *R. nakaharae* orange-flowered
	nakotiltum	MHid
	'Nancy Evans' 🏆H5	CDoC CRos CSBt EPfP GGGa GKin IDee LMil LRHS LSRN MAsh MGos MPri NLar SCob SLdr SLim SReu SSta
	'Nanki Poo' (EA)	SLdr
	'Naomi' (EA)	SLdr
	(Naomi Group) 'Exbury Naomi'	LMil
	- 'Naomi Nautilus'	LMil
	- 'Naomi Pink Beauty'	LMil
	- 'Naomi Stella Maris'	LMil
	'Narcissiflorum' (G/d) 🏆H6	CBcs GKin LMil MPkF NLar
	'Naselle'	LMil
	NEGLIGÉ ('Hachneg'^{PBR}) (EA)	LMil MPkF
	neoglandulosum	NLar
	neriiflorum	GGGa GKev LMil
	- CN&W 906	LMil
	- subsp. ***neriiflorum***	MHid
§	- subsp. ***phaedropum***	LMil MHid
	- - KR 9308	LMil
	'Newcomb's Sweetheart'	LMil
	'Niagara' (Glenn Dale) (EA) 🏆H5	CMac LMil SLdr
	'Nicholas de Rothschild' (A/d) **new**	LMil
	'Nico' (EA)	CMac LMil LRHS MAsh
	'Nicola' (EA)	LSRN
	'Night Sky' 🏆H5	CDoC CRos EPfP GGGa LMil LRHS MGos NLar SLdr
	nilagiricum	see *R. arboreum* subsp. *nilagiricum*
	'Nishiki' (EA)	CMac
	nitens	see *R. calostrotum* subsp. *riparium* Nitens Group
	nitidulum	GKev
	- var. ***omeiense***	WThu
	nivale	GKev
	- subsp. ***boreale***	GKev
§	- subsp. ***nivale***	ITim NWad
	niveum 🏆H5	GGGa IDee LMil MHid SReu
	- B&SWJ 2611	WCru
	- B&SWJ 2659	WCru
	- B&SWJ 2675	WCru
	Nobleanum Group	GGGa LMil SLdr SReu SSta
	- 'Nobleanum Coccineum'	CMac LMil SLdr
	- 'Nobleanum Venustum'	LMil SSta
	Nobleanum Album Group	CMac GGGa LMil SLdr SSta

(Norderney Group) 'Oudijk's Sensation'	MAsh MMuc SLdr
'Nordlicht' (EA)	SLdr
'Noriko' (EA)	SLdr
'Northern Hi-Lights' (A)	CDoC CRos GKin LMil LRHS MGos MPkF NLar SCob SLim SPer
'Nova Zembla'	CBcs CDoC CTri EPfP GAbr IDee LCro LMil LOPS LRHS MAsh MGos MMuc MPkF SCob SGsty SLim SPer SReu SSta
'Nuccio's Blue Moon' (EA)	LMil MPkF SLdr SReu
'Nuccio's Wild Cherry' (EA) **new**	SWeb
nudiflorum	see *R. periclymenoides*
nuttallii	LMil SReu
'Oban'	EPot GEdr ITim
Obtusum Group (EA)	SLdr
- 'Amoenum' (EA/d)	CBcs CMac CSBt LMil SLdr SPer
- 'Amoenum Coccineum' (EA/d)	SLdr SSta
§ - 'Hinomayo' (EA) ♀H5	CBcs CMac CTri EPfP GKin LMil SCob SLdr
occidentale (A)	GKev GKin LMil SLdr
- SIN 1830	GGGa
ochraceum ♀H5	GGGa LMil
- C&H 7042	LMil
'Odee Wright'	LRHS MAsh
'Oi-no-mezame' (Kurume) (EA)	SLdr
'Old Port'	LMaj LMil SCob
oldhamii (EA) B&SWJ 3742	WCru
'Olga' ♀H5	LMil SSta
'Olga Niblett' (EA)	SSta
'Opossum' (EA)	GGGa
ORAKEL	see *R.* 'Hachmann's Orakel'
'Orange Beauty' (Kaempferi) (EA)	CBcs ILea MAsh SLdr SRms
'Orange King' (EA) ♀H5	CDoC LMil MGos SLdr SPoG
'Orangeade' (K)	LRHS MPkF
orbiculare ♀H5	GGGa LMil SLdr SReu
- hybrid **new**	SReu
- subsp. ***orbiculare***	MHid
'Orchid Lights'	MAsh
'Oregon' (EA)	SLdr
Oregonia Group	LMil
oreodoxa	LMil SReu
§ - var. ***fargesii*** ♀H5	GGGa LMil MHid
- hybrid **new**	SReu
- var. ***oreodoxa***	LMil MHid
oreotrephes ♀H5	LMil MHid
§ - Exquisitum Group	SLdr
- 'Pentland'	GGGa LMil
'Orion' ambig.	NLar
§ ***orthocladum*** var. ***microleucum***	WThu
'Osaraku Seedling' (EA)	CRos LRHS MPkF
'Osmar' ♀H5	GGGa
'Ostara'	CBcs
'Oudijk's Favorite'	SLdr
'P. den Ouden' × ***williamsianum***	LMaj
pachysanthum ♀H5	GGGa GKin LMil SLdr SReu
- 'Crosswater'	LMil LRHS
- 'Little White Dane' **new**	LMil
pachysanthum × ***yakushimanum***	SReu
pachytrichum	GGGa
- var. ***pachytrichum***	MHid
'Palestrina' (Vuykiana) (EA) ♀H5	CBcs CMac CSBt EPfP GKin MAsh MMuc MPkF SCob SGsty SLdr SPer SSta
paludosum	see *R. nivale* subsp. *nivale*
'Pancake'	CMac
'Panda' (EA) ♀H5	CSBt CTri EPfP GGGa LMil LRHS MAsh SLdr SSta
'Parfait' (EA)	LMil
'Parkfeuer' (A) ♀H6	GGGa
parmulatum	LMil
- KW 5876	LMil
- 'Ocelot'	GGGa
'Patty Bee' ♀H5	CBcs CDoC CSBt CTri EPfP GEdr GGGa LMil LRHS MAsh MGos MPri NLar SCob SLim SSta
'Pavlova' (A) **new**	LMil
'Peach Blossom'	see *R.* 'Saotome'
'Pearce's American Beauty'	LMaj
'Pearl Betteridge'	LMil
'Peep-bo' (EA)	SLdr
'Peeping Tom'	NHol SSta
'Peggy'	LMil
'Pemakofairy'	WThu
pendulum	GGGa MHid
'Penheale Blue' ♀H5	GKin LMil
'Penjerrick'	GGGa
'Penny Tomlin'	SSta
pentaphyllum (A)	GGGa
'Peppermint Candy'	LMil
'Peppina'	LMil
'Percy Wiseman' ♀H5	CBcs CDoC CRos EPfP GGGa GKin LCro LMil LOPS LRHS MAsh MGos NLar SCob SLdr SLim SPer SSta WFar
§ ***periclymenoides*** (A)	GKev LMil
'Persil' (K) ♀H6	CAby CBcs CBod CSBt CTri ELan EPfP GGGa GKin IDee LMil LRHS MAsh MMuc NHol NLar SCob SCoo SLdr SPer SReu SSta WFar
'Peter Bee'	LMil
'Peter Gable' (EA)	SLdr
'Peter John Mezitt'	see *R.* (PJM Group) 'Peter John Mezitt'
'Peter Koster' (M)	MPkF
'Peter Koster' (hybrid)	GKin
petrocharis	GGGa
PETTICOAT ('Hachpett') (EA)	LMil
'Pfauenauge'	GGGa LMil
phaedropum	see *R. neriiflorum* subsp. *phaedropum*
phaeochrysum 'Glossy Dane' **new**	LMil
- var. ***phaeochrysum***	MHid
'Phalarope'	GEdr
'Phyllis Korn'	IDee LMil NLar
§ ***piercei***	GGGa LMil
pingianum	GGGa
'Pink and Sweet' (A)	LRHS MPkF
'Pink Bride'	SLdr
'Pink Cameo'	SReu
'Pink Cherub' ♀H6	LMil MAsh
I 'Pink Delight' (K)	GKin MMuc
'Pink Drift'	CSBt GEdr LMil
'Pink Gin'	LMil
'Pink Mimosa' (Vs)	SLdr
'Pink Pancake' (EA) ♀H4	EPfP LMil LRHS MAsh MPkF MPri SLdr
'Pink Pearl' (EA)	see *R.* 'Azuma-kagami'
'Pink Pearl' (hybrid) ♀H4	CBcs CSBt CTri GGGa LMil MAsh MMuc SLdr SPer SSta
'Pink Pebble' ♀H5	CExl MAsh
'Pink Perfection'	CMac SLdr

'Pink Polar Bear'	LMil
'Pink Spider'^{PBR} (EA) **new**	LMil
'Pintail'	LMil LRHS MAsh
'Pipit'	GGGa
'Pippa' (EA)	CMac
§ (PJM Group) 'Peter John Mezitt'	NLar
platypodum	LMil
- CGG 14005	GGGa
'Pleasant White' (EA)	CDoC LCro LMil LOPS NLar SCob
pocophorum var. ***pocophorum***	MHid
'Polar Bear' (EA)	SLdr SReu
Polar Bear Group	LMil SReu
- 'Polar Bear'	CSBt GKin LMil LRHS
'Polaris'	see *R.* 'Hachmann's Polaris'
'Polarnacht'	CBcs LMil LRHS SLdr
poluninii KR 8231	LMil
polyandrum	see *R. maddenii* subsp. *maddenii* Polyandrum Group
polylepis	MHid
'Polyroy'	GGGa
ponticum	CMac CTri NHol WFar
- 'Filigran'	LMil
§ - 'Variegatum' (v)	CMac CRos EPfP MAsh MGos MPri SLdr SPer SPoG SRms
ponticum* × *yakushimanum	SReu
'Praecox' $\mathbb{Y}^{H6}$	CBcs CDoC CSBt GBin GGGa GKin LCro LMil LOPS LRHS MAsh MGos MPri NLar SLdr SLim SPoG
praestans	GKin LMil
prattii	GGGa MHid
'President Roosevelt' (v)	CMac CSBt EPfP GKin MAsh MPri SCob SLdr SPoG SSta
'Pridenjoy'	LMil LRHS
primuliflorum $\mathbb{Y}^{H5}$	WAbe
- 'Doker-La'	GGGa LMil WAbe
'Prince Camille de Rohan'	LMil
'Princess Alice'	CBcs SLdr
'Princess Anne' $\mathbb{Y}^{H6}$	CBcs CDoC CMac CRos LCro LMil LOPS MGos NHpl NLar SCob SLdr SLim SPer SPoG SReu SSta
'Princess Margaret of Windsor' (K)	LMil
principis	LMil
- 'Lost Horizon'	LMil LRHS
§ - Vellereum Group	MHid
prinophyllum (A)	GGGa LMil
- 'Philip Holmes'	LMil
'Prins Bernhard' (EA)	MAsh SLdr
'Prinses Juliana' (Vuykiana) (EA)	SLdr
'Prinses Máxima'	LMil
'Professor Hugo de Vries'	SLdr
pronum	GGGa
- R.B. Cooke form	GGGa
- Towercourt form	GGGa
proteoides	GGGa
proteoides* × *yakushimanum	SReu
prunifolium (A)	LMil
pseudochrysanthum $\mathbb{Y}^{H6}$	GGGa LMil SReu
- dwarf RWJ 9807	WCru
Psyche Group	see *R.* Wega Group
'Ptarmigan' $\mathbb{Y}^{H6}$	GEdr GGGa LMil WThu
§ 'Pucella' (G)	MPkF
'Pulchrum Maxwellii'	see *R.* 'Maxwellii'
pumilum	WAbe WThu
'Purple Cushion' (EA)	EPfP LMil LRHS MAsh MPri NRHS
'Purple Gem'	CDoC MGos NLar SCob
'Purple Passion'^{PBR}	CDoC CRos LMil LRHS LSRN NLar SLdr SPer
'Purple Queen' (EA/d)	MAsh
'Purple Splendor' (Gable) (EA)	CMac SGsty SLdr
'Purple Splendour'	CBcs CSBt LMil MGos MMuc SCob SSta
'Purple Triumph' (Vuykiana) (EA) $\mathbb{Y}^{H5}$	LMil SLdr
'Purpurkissen' (EA)	LMil
'Purpurtraum' (EA) $\mathbb{Y}^{H5}$	LMil
qiaojiaense NN 0903	LMil
'Quail'	GGGa
'Queen Alice'	CDoC NLar
'Queen Elizabeth II'	LRHS
QUEEN EMMA	see *R.* 'Koningin Emma'
'Queen Mary'	SSta
Queen of Hearts Group	LRHS
quinquefolium (A)	LMil MHid SLdr SReu
RABATZ ('Hachraba')	GGGa LMil SAko
racemosum $\mathbb{Y}^{H6}$	GKev LMil MHid
- BWJ 7811	WCru
- 'Rock Rose' $\mathbb{Y}^{H5}$	EPfP LMil SLdr
'Racoon' (EA)	GGGa LMil
radians (V) **new**	CBcs
radicans	see *R. calostrotum* subsp. *keleticum* Radicans Group
'Ramapo' $\mathbb{Y}^{H6}$	CDoC CPla CRos GGGa LMil LRHS MAsh MGos NLar NRHS SCob SLdr SLim SPer
ramsdenianum	MHid
'Rasputin'	LMil NLar SSta
'Razorbill' $\mathbb{Y}^{H5}$	CDoC GGGa GKin LMil NLar SLim
recurvoides	LMil SLdr
recurvum	see *R. roxieanum* var. *roxieanum*
'Red and Gold'	EPfP GGGa LMil LRHS MPri
'Red Dawn'	LRHS NRHS
'Red Delicious'	LMil SLdr
'Red Diamond'	see *R.* Diamant Group red-flowered
'Red Heart'	LMil
'Red Jack'	MGos MMuc SPoG SSta
'Red Pimpernel' (EA)	SLdr
'Red Wing'	see *R.* 'Hexe de Saffelaere'
'Red Wood'	GGGa
'Redwings' (EA)	SLdr
'Reich's Signifikant'	SAko
Remo Group	CMac
'Rennie' (A)	MMuc
'Renoir' $\mathbb{Y}^{H5}$	CSBt LMil
reticulatum (A)	IDee LMil LRHS
'Reuthe's Purple'	SReu WThu
'Rêve d'Amour' (Vs)	SSta
'Rex' (EA)	MAsh SGsty
rex $\mathbb{Y}^{H5}$	GGGa GKev GKin IDee LMil SLdr SReu
- EGM 295	LMil
§ - subsp. ***fictolacteum*** $\mathbb{Y}^{H5}$	GGGa GKin IDee LMil MHid SLdr
- subsp. ***rex*** $\mathbb{Y}^{H5}$	MHid
'Rhododendronpark Graal-Müritz'	SSta
'Ria Hardijzer' (Ad)	LMil
'Ribbon Candy' (A)	LRHS MPkF
rigidum	GGGa
- 'Album'	LMil
'Ring of Fire'	LMil LRHS
ririei	GGGa
'Robert Croux'	SLdr
'Robert Seleger'	GKin LMil MAsh
'Robert Whelan' (A)	SSta

'Robin Hill Frosty' (EA)	SLdr
'Robin Hill Gillie' (EA)	SLdr
'Robinette'	MAsh
'Rocket'	CDoC LRHS MAsh MGos MMuc SLim SPer SPoG
'Roehr's Peggy Ann' (EA)	LMil MPkF
'Rokoko'	see *R.* 'Hachmann's Rokoko'
'Rosa' (EA)	CDoC
Rosalind Group	CMac
- 'Rosalind'	WFar
'Rosalinda' (EA)	SLdr
'Rosata' (Vs) 🏆H5	SSta
'Rose Bud'	CBcs CSBt CTri WThu
'Rose Elf'	WThu
'Rose Glow' (A)	SSta
'Rose Greely' (Gable) (EA) 🏆H5	NLar SLim SPer
'Rose Haze' (Vs)	SSta
'Rosebud' (EA/d)	CMac SLdr SSta SWeb
'Rosemary Hyde' (EA)	SLdr
roseum	see *R. canescens*
'Roseum Elegans'	CDoC LCro LMaj LOPS LRHS MAsh MMuc SCob SGsty SLim
'Rosevallon'	MHid
ROSINETTA ('Hachrosi') (EA)	LMil
'Rosy Dream'	MAsh MMuc
'Rosy Fire' (A)	LMil
rothschildii	GGGa LMil MHid SLdr
roxieanum	GGGa LMil
§ - var. ***cucullatum***	GKev
- var. ***oreonastes*** 🏆H5	GGGa LMil
§ - var. ***roxieanum***	MHid
'Royal Command' (K)	CBcs CTri EPfP GKin LMil
'Royal Lodge' (K)	MPkF
'Royal Windsor'	LMil
'Roza Stevenson'	SLdr
'Rubicon'	SLdr SReu
rubiginosum 🏆H6	GGGa GKev LMil
- var. ***rubiginosum*** new	MHid
rubroluteum	see *R. viridescens* Rubroluteum Group
'Ruby Hart'	LSRN
RUBY WEDDING	see *R.* 'Firestorm'
rude	see *R. glischrum* subsp. *rude*
§ ***rupicola*** var. ***chryseum***	GKev
russatum 🏆H6	CBcs LMil SLdr
- blue-black-flowered	LMil
- 'Purple Pillow'	SCob
Russautinii Group	SLdr
'Rusty Dane' new	LMil
'Rwain'	NLar
'Ryde Heron' (EA)	SLdr
'Sabina' (EA)	SLdr
'Sacko'	CDoC LMil NLar SLim
'Saffron Queen'	CBcs CTsd LMil LRHS MPkF
'Sahara' (K)	SLdr
'Saint Kew'	SLdr
'Saint Merryn' 🏆H5	CBcs
'Saint Minver'	LMil
'Saint Tudy'	SLdr
'Sakata Red' (EA)	SLdr
'Salmon Sander' (EA)	SLdr
'Salmon's Leap' (EA/v)	CMac ELan LMil LRHS MAsh SSta
saluenense	LMil SLdr WThu
'Samuel Taylor Coleridge' (M)	GKin
sanguineum	LMil
§ - subsp. ***didymum***	GGGa SLdr
- subsp. ***sanguineum*** var. ***haemaleum***	GGGa LMil
- - var. ***sanguineum*** F 25521	LMil
'Santa Maria' (EA) 🏆H5	CDoC LMil LSRN NLar SCob SSta
§ 'Saotome' (EA)	SLdr
'Sappho'	CMac GGGa GKin LMil LRHS SCob SLdr SPer SReu SSta
'Sappho' × ***yakushimanum***	SReu
sargentianum	WAbe WThu
(Sarled Group) 'Sarled' 🏆H5	ITim LMil
'Satan' (K) 🏆H6	IDee LMil LRHS NLar SCob SPer SReu SSta
Satsuki Group (EA)	ITim SLdr SRms SWeb
- 'Gumpo Pink' (EA)	SLdr
- 'Gumpo Pink & White' (EA)	SLdr
- 'Gumpo White' (EA)	LRHS MAsh NRHS SPoG
'Saturnus' (M)	GKin
saxifragoides (V)	LRHS
§ ***scabrifolium*** var. ***spiciferum***	CMac SLdr
'Scarlet Wonder' 🏆H6	CBcs CDoC CSBt EPfP GEdr GKev GKin LMil LRHS MAsh MGos MMuc MPri NHpl SCob SPer WFar
schlippenbachii (A)	CBcs CMCN GGGa LMil SLdr SReu
'Schneebukett' (Inkarho) new	NLar
'Schneekrone' 🏆H6	LMil LRHS
SCHNEEPERLE ('Hachschnee') (EA) 🏆H5	LMil LRHS NRHS
'Scintillation' 🏆H6	CDoC CRos ELan GGGa LMil MAsh MGos MMuc NLar SCob SLdr SPer
scopulorum	SLdr
'Scout' (EA)	LMil MAsh SLdr
scyphocalyx	see *R. dichroanthum* subsp. *scyphocalyx*
'Seaview Sunset'	GGGa MGos
seinghkuense	GGGa LMil
- CCH&H 8106	LMil
§ ***selense*** subsp. ***dasycladum***	MHid
semnoides	LMil
'Sennocke'	IDee LMil
'September Red'	LMil
'September Song' 🏆H4	GGGa LMil MAsh NHol
serotinum	GGGa LMil LRHS MHid
serpyllifolium (A)	CBcs
'Shamrock' 🏆H6	CDoC CTsd EPfP GEdr LRHS MAsh MGos SCob SLim SPoG WFar
'Sheila' (EA)	CSBt MAsh MPri
'Shelley' (EA)	LMil LSRN
'Shiko' (EA)	MAsh
'Shiko Lavender' (A)	LMil SPoG
Shilsonii Group	LMil
'Shin-sekai' (Kurume) (EA/d)	SLdr
sikangense var. ***exquisitum***	MHid
- var. ***sikangense***	MHid
§ 'Silberwolke' 🏆H6	LMil MAsh WFar
SILVER CLOUD	see *R.* 'Silberwolke'
'Silver Edge'	see *R. ponticum* 'Variegatum'
'Silver Glow' (EA)	CMac
'Silver Jubilee' 🏆H4	LMil
'Silver Moon' (Glenn Dale) (EA)	SLdr
'Silver Queen' (EA)	MPkF SPoG
'Silver Sixpence'	EPfP LRHS LSRN MMuc SLdr
'Silver Skies'	LMil

	'Silver Slipper' (K) 🏆H5	CBcs GKin LCro LMil LOPS NHol SSta WFar
	'Silver Sword' (EA/v)	EPfP SPoG
	'Silvester' (Kurume) (EA)	CTri LMil LRHS MAsh SLdr
	simsii (EA)	CMac SLdr
	sinofalconeri	GGGa GKev LMil MHid SReu
	- KR 7342	LMil
	- SEH 229	LMil
	sinogrande 🏆H4	ELon GGGa GKin IDee LMil LRHS NLar SReu
	- KR 4027	LMil
§	'Sir Charles Butler'	LMil
	'Sir Charles Lemon' 🏆H4	CBcs GGGa LMil LRHS MAsh
	'Sir Robert' (EA)	MAsh
	'Sleeping Beauty'	WAbe
	'Sleepy'	CBcs MAsh NHol SReu
	smirnowii	LMil LRHS MHid
	smithii	see *R. argipeplum*
	'Sneezy' 🏆H5	CBcs CRos EPfP LMaj LMil LRHS MAsh MGos MMuc SLdr SLim SReu SSta
	'Snipe'	CDoC CTri CTsd GEdr LMil LRHS MAsh MGos MMuc NLar NRHS SLdr SLim SPer WThu
	'Snow Crown' (*lindleyi* hybrid)	MAsh
	'Snow Hill' (EA) 🏆H5	CEnd LMil
	'Snow Lady'	CBcs CDoC EPfP GEdr GKin MAsh SLdr
	'Snow Pearl'	CRos EPfP MAsh MPri NLar
	Snow Queen Group	LMil
	- 'Snow Queen'	LMil
	'Snowbird' (A)	CBcs CTho ELan
	'Snowflake' (EA/d)	see *R.* 'Kure-no-yuki'
	'Snowwhite' (EA)	CDoC CRos MGos NLar SLdr
	'Soft Lights' (A/d) **new**	LMil
	'Soir de Paris' (Vs) 🏆H6	CEnd CSBt GGGa GKin LMil NHol SSta WFar
	(Solent Group) 'Drury Lane' (K)	LMil
	'Solidarity'	CBcs SLdr SSta
	'Solway' (Vs)	LMil
	'Sonata'	GGGa SReu
	'Sonatine'	LMil LRHS
	'Songbird'	GEdr IDee LMil LRHS SLdr
	sororium (V)	LMil
	- KR 3085	LMil
	souliei	GKev LMil SReu
	'Souvenir de D.A. Koster'	SLdr
	'Souvenir of Anthony Waterer'	SSta
	'Souvenir of W.C. Slocock'	MMuc NLar
	'Spek's Orange' (M)	GKin
	sphaeranthum	see *R. trichostomum*
	sphaeroblastum	MHid
	- 'Super Dane' **new**	LMil
	spiciferum	see *R. scabrifolium* var. *spiciferum*
	spilotum	MHid
	'Spinner's Glory'	MAsh
	'Spitfire'	NHol SSta
	'Spring Pearl'	see *R.* 'Moerheim's Pink'
	'Spring Rose'	SLdr
	'Spring Sunshine'	LMil
	'Squirrel' (EA) 🏆H5	CDoC GGGa GKin LMil LRHS MAsh SLdr SLim
	'Stadt Essen'	LMil LRHS SLdr
§	'Stanway'	LMil
	'Starbright Champagne'	MAsh SSta
	'Statuette'	SAko
	stenaulum	see *R. moulmainense*
§	***stenopetalum*** 'Linearifolium' (EA)	CBcs CMac GBin LMil LRHS SLdr
	stenophyllum	see *R. makinoi*
	stewartianum	MHid SReu
	'Stewartstonian' (EA)	CMac LCro LOPS
	'Stoat' (EA)	NLar
	'Stopham Girl' (A)	LMil
	'Stopham Joy' (A) **new**	LMil
	'Stopham Lad' (A)	LMil
	'Strategist'	SLdr
	'Strawberry Cream'	EPfP LRHS
	'Strawberry Ice' (K) 🏆H6	CBcs CSBt ELan GGGa GKin MMrt SCob
	'Strawberry Sundae'	MMuc SLdr
	strigillosum	GGGa
	- Reuthe's form	SReu
	suberosum	see *R. yunnanense* Suberosum Group
	'Suga-no-ito' (Kurume) (EA)	SLdr
	sulfureum	MHid
	'Summer Blaze' (A)	SLdr
	'Summer Dawn'	LMil
	'Summer Fragrance' (A) 🏆H6	LMil SSta
	'Summer Snow'	SAko
	'Summer Sorbet'	LMil
	'Sun Chariot' (K)	CBcs
	'Sun Fire'	LMil
	'Sun Star' (EA)	GGGa LMil SReu
	Sunkist Group	SLdr
	'Sunte Nectarine' (K) 🏆H6	GKin MPkF
	suoilenhensis	CMCN MHid
	- NVD 18	GGGa
	'Surprise' ambig. (EA)	CTri SLdr
	'Surrey Heath'	CBcs CDoC EPfP LMil LRHS MGos MMuc SCob SLdr SLim SPer
	'Susan' (EA)	IDee NLar SSta
	'Susan' J.C. Williams	LMil
	'Susannah Hill' (EA)	SLdr
	sutchuenense	GGGa LMil
	- var. ***geraldii***	see *R.* × *geraldii*
	'Swamp Beauty'	MMuc
	'Swansong' (EA)	CMac
	'Swift' 🏆H4	EPfP GEdr GGGa LMil LRHS MAsh MMuc NRHS SLdr
	'T.S. Black' (EA)	SLdr
	'Talavera'	LMil
	taliense	LMil
	- SBEC 0350	GGGa
	- 'Honigduft'	LMil
	- 'Woolly Dane' **new**	LMil
	Tally Ho Group	LMil
	'Tamanini' (EA)	MPkF
	'Tama-no-utena' (EA)	SLdr
	'Tangerine'	see *R.* (Fabia Group) 'Fabia Tangerine'
	'Tapestry' PBR	LMil NLar SPer
	tatsienense	GKev
	'Taurus' 🏆H5	CBcs CRos GKin IDee LMaj LMil LRHS MAsh MMuc SAko SLdr SReu
	'Teal'	GEdr
	'Ted Millais'	LMil
	'Teddy Bear'	LMil SReu SSta
	Temple Belle Group	SLdr
	'Tequila Sunrise'	LRHS
I	'Tequila Sunrise' USA	LMil
	'Terracotta'	LMil LRHS NLar
	'Terra-cotta Beauty' (EA)	WThu
	(Tessa Group) 'Tessa'	CMac
	'Thai Gold' (V)	LRHS

§	'The Honourable Jean Marie de Montague' ♀H4	CDoC GGGa GKin LMil MAsh MGos MMuc NLar SPer SSta
	'The Marquis of Lansdowne'	LMil
	'Thomas David' (A)	LMil SReu
	thomsonii	GGGa LMil MHid SReu
	- B&SWJ 2638	WCru
	- WJC 13737	WCru
	'Thor'	GGGa
	'Tibet'	LMil
	'Tidbit' ♀H3	CMac LMil SLdr
	'Tiger' **new**	SReu
	'Tina' (EA) **new**	MPkF
	'Tinkerbird'	CDoC EPfP GGGa LMil MAsh MGos MPri
	'Tinner's Blush'	CBcs
	titapuriense	GGGa
	'Titian Beauty'	CBcs CDoC CSBt ELan EPfP GGGa LMil LRHS MAsh MGos MMuc NRHS SLdr SLim SPer SPoG
	'Titness Park'	LMil
	'Tit-Willow' (EA)	LRHS MAsh NRHS SCoo SLdr
	tomentosum	MGil WThu
	'Too Bee'	GEdr
	'Torchlight' (EA) ♀H5	CDoC CRos LMil MGos NLar
	'Toreador' (EA)	SLdr
	'Torridon' (Vs)	LMil
	(Tortoiseshell Group) 'Champagne' ♀H3	CBcs CDoC CSBt LMil MAsh MPri NLar SPer
	- 'Tortoiseshell Orange' ♀H3	CBcs CDoC CRos CSBt IDee LMil LRHS MGos NLar SCob SGsty SLim SPer SSta
	- 'Tortoiseshell Wonder' ♀H3	EPfP LRHS MAsh
	'Toucan' (K)	CSBt LMil LRHS MPkF
	'Tower Beauty' (A)	LMil
	'Tower Dainty' (A)	LMil
	'Tower Daring' (A)	LMil
	'Tower Dexter' (A)	LMil
	'Tower Dragon' (A)	LMil
	traillianum	GKev LMil
	- var. ***traillianum*** **new**	MHid
	'Treasure' (AE) **new**	SGsty
	'Tree Creeper'	GGGa LMil LRHS
	'Trewithen Orange'	SLdr
	trichanthum 'Honey Wood'	LMil SLdr
	trichocladum	GKev
§	***trichostomum***	GGGa GKev SReu WAbe
	- Ledoides Group	LMil
	triflorum	LMil
§	- var. ***bauhiniiflorum***	CMac
	- var. ***triflorum*** **new**	MHid
	'Tri-Lights' (A)	MPkF
	'Tromba'	IDee LMil LRHS
	'Tropic Glow' (V)	LRHS
	tsariense	LMil
	- var. ***trimoense***	LMil
	- - KW 8288	LMil
	- var. ***tsariense***	MHid
	'Tuffet' (EA)	LMil SLdr
	'Tunis' (K)	EPfP MAsh MPri
	'Turnstone'	GGGa
	'Umpqua Queen' (K)	MPkF
	'Unique' (G)	CBcs EPfP MMuc SPer
	'Unique' (*campylocarpum* hybrid)	MAsh SLdr
	uvariifolium SDR 5149	GKev
	- var. ***griseum***	MHid
	- 'Reginald Childs'	LMil
	'Valentine' (EA)	SReu
	valentinianum	SLdr
	'Van'	CDoC LMil LRHS MGos NLar SLim
	'Van Nes Sensation'	LMil
	Vanessa Group	LMil
	- 'Vanessa Pastel' ♀H4	CMac GGGa LMil SLdr SSta
	vaseyi (A) ♀H5	CBcs GGGa LMil SReu
	- 'White Find'	GGGa
	- white-flowered (A)	LMil
	'Vayo' (EA)	SLdr
§	***veitchianum*** Cubittii Group	CBcs
	vellereum	see *R. principis* Vellereum Group
	venator	GGGa
	'Venetia' (K)	SSta
	vernicosum × ***wardii*** SDR 5026	GKev
	'Veryan Bay'	LMil
	'Vida Brown' (Kurume) (EA/d)	CMac SLdr
	'Vinecourt Dream' (M)	GKin NLar SLdr
	'Vinecourt Duke' (A/d)	GKin MMuc
	'Vineland Dream' (K/d)	GKin
	'Vintage Rosé' ♀H5	LMil MMuc SSta
	'Violetta' (Glenn Dale) (EA)	SLdr
	'Violette Funken'	LMil
	'Virgile' (R) **new**	MPkF
	'Virginia Richards'	MAsh SGsty SLdr
§	***viridescens***	MHid
	- 'Doshong La'	LMil
§	- Rubroluteum Group	SLdr
	viscosum (Vs) ♀H6	CBcs CDoC CMac CRos CTho GGGa LMil LRHS MGos MMrt MMuc NLar SLdr SPer SReu
	- 'Grey Leaf' (Vs)	LMil
	- f. ***rhodanthum*** (Vs)	LMil
	- 'Roseum' (Vs)	LMil
	- 'White Ness' (Vs) **new**	LMil
	'Viscount Powerscourt'	SLdr
	'Viscy' ♀H5	CRos GKin LMil LRHS MMuc SLdr
	'Viscy' (Inkarho) **new**	NLar
§	Volker Group	LMil LRHS NRHS
§	- 'Babette'	SReu
	'Vollblut'	SSta
	'Vulcan' ♀H4	IDee LMil LRHS
	'Vuyk's Rosyred' (Vuykiana) (EA) ♀H6	CBcs CMac CTri GKin LMil MAsh NHol NWad SLdr SPer SPoG SRms SWeb WFar
	'Vuyk's Scarlet' (Vuykiana) (EA) ♀H6	CBcs CMac CSBt CTri GKin LRHS MAsh MPri NHol NRHS NWad SCob SLdr SPer SPlb SReu SSta
	'W.F.H. Group' ♀H3	LMil SLdr
§	WALBERTON'S MAUVE RUFFLES ('Walmauvruf'PBR) (EA/d) **new**	ILea
§	WALBERTON'S SNOW RUFFLES ('Walsnowruf'PBR) (EA/d) **new**	ILea
	WALKÜRE ('Hachwalk')	IDee LMil LRHS
	wallichii	GKev LMil MHid
	'Wallowa Red' (A)	MMuc MPkF
	'Wally Miller'	MAsh
	'Wanna Bee'	LMil
	wardii	LMil LRHS SReu
	- L&S 5679	GGGa
	- hybrid **new**	SReu
	- var. ***wardii***	MHid
	'Ward's Ruby' (EA)	SLdr

wasonii	LMil
– yellow-flowered	GGGa
'Water Baby' (A)	LMil
'Water Girl' (A)	GGGa LMil
'Water Pixie'	LMil
'Waterfall'	SLdr
'Wee Bee' 🏆H5	CBcs CDoC GEdr GKin LMil LRHS MAsh MGos NLar SAko SLim SSta WThu
§ Wega Group	SLdr
'Weinlese'	SAko
'Wendy'	MAsh
'Western Lights' (A)	LRHS MPkF
'Westminster' (O)	LMil
'Weston's Innocence' (A)	MPkF
'Weston's Lollipop' (A)	MPkF
'Weston's Pink Diamond' (d)	LMil
'What a Dane'	GGGa
'Whidbey Island'	LMil
'Whisperingrose'	LMil
'White Brocade'	SSta
§ WHITE DUFTHECKE ('Rhodunter 48'PBR)	LMil
WHITE DUFTHECKE ('Rhodunter 48'PBR) (Inkarho) **new**	NLar
'White Frills' (EA)	LRHS MPkF SLdr
'White Gold'	GGGa
'White Jade' (EA)	SLdr
'White Lady' Indian (EA)	SLdr
'White Lights' (A) 🏆H7	CTri
'White Pearl' (EA)	LSRN
'White Perfume' (A)	SSta
'White Prince' (EA/d)	MPkF
'White Rosebud' (EA)	SSta
'White Swan' (hybrid)	IDee LMil
'White Wings'	SLdr
'Whitestone'	SSta
'Whitethroat' (K/d) 🏆H6	EPfP IDee LMil LRHS MMuc SSta
'Whitney's Dwarf Red'	MMuc
'Whitney's Orange'	SLdr
'Wigeon'	LMil
wightii	MHid
'Wilgen's Ruby'	CDoC CSBt MGos SCob SLdr SLim SPer
'Willbrit'	CBcs GAbr MAsh MMuc SLdr
williamsianum 🏆H5	GGGa LMil SLdr SReu
– Caerhays form	CExl
'Willy' (Kaempferi) (EA)	LMil SLdr
wiltonii 🏆H5	GGGa LMil
'Wine and Roses'PBR	CBcs GGGa LMil MPkF
Winsome Group	CMac MAsh
– 'Winsome' 🏆H5	CBcs CDoC GKin MGos MPri NLar SLdr SSta
'Winston Churchill' (M)	SSta
'Witchery'	GGGa
'Wombat' (EA) 🏆H5	CDoC CTri EPfP GGGa ITim LMil LRHS MAsh MGos MPri NLar SLdr
wongii	CMac
'Woodcock'	SLdr
'Wren' 🏆H5	GEdr GGGa LMil MAsh WThu
xanthocodon	see *R. cinnabarinum* subsp. *xanthocodon*
'XXL'	CRos LRHS SSta
'Yaku Angel'	LMil SAko
'Yaku Incense'	LMil MAsh MMuc SReu
'Yaku Prince'	MAsh MMuc SLdr
yakushimanum 🏆H5	GKin LMil MAsh NHol SCob SLdr SReu SSta
– from Exbury	CMac
I – 'Angel'	SReu
– 'Big Yak' **new**	SReu
– FCC form	see *R. yakushimanum* 'Koichiro Wada'
– hybrid **new**	SReu
§ – 'Koichiro Wada' 🏆H6	CBcs CExl CMac CRos GGGa IDee LMil LRHS SAko SLdr SReu
– 'Rosemoor Beauty' **new**	SReu
– 'Samisen' **new**	SReu
– 'Schneekissen'	SAko SReu
– 'Snow Mountain'	SReu
– 'Wild Wealth' **new**	SReu
'Yellow Hammer' 🏆H5	CBcs CMac GGGa GKin SLdr
Yellow Hammer Group	SPer SSta
'Yellow Petticoats'	SSta
'Yellow Rolls Royce'	LMil
yuefengense	GGGa LMil SReu
yunnanense	GGGa GKev LMil MHid
– 'Openwood' 🏆H3	LMil
– pink-flowered	GGGa
– 'Red Throat'	SLdr
– red-blotched	LMil
– Reuthe's form **new**	SReu
§ – Suberosum Group	SLdr
– white-flowered	GGGa
zaleucum	LMil SLdr
zeylanicum	see *R. arboreum* subsp. *zeylanicum*

Rhodohypoxis ✿ (*Hypoxidaceae*)

'1000 Cranes'	IBal LEdu WPGP
'Alice'	WFar
'Andromeda'	EWes IBal
'Ann Brazier'	NWad
baurii 🏆H3	CAvo CCCN IBal MAsh NSla SEdd SPoG WAbe WAvo WCav WIce
– 'Alba'	CRos EHyd EWes IBal LRHS NRHS SEdd WFar
– 'Albrighton'	CTri EWes GEdr NHol NHpl NWad WAbe
– 'Apple Blossom'	EWes GKev IBal ITim LBee LEdu NHol NWad WFar WPGP
– 'Badger'	ITim NWad WAbe
– var. ***baurii***	CBor EWes LRHS
– 'Bridal Bouquet' (d)	EWes GEdr IBal NHol WFar
– 'Caro'	EWes
– 'Charlotte'	EWes
– 'Coconut Ice'	EWes LEdu WPGP
– var. ***confecta***	CBor CElw CWCL EWes GEdr IBal NHol NWad WFar WTor WTyc
– 'Daphne Mary'	EWes
– 'David Scott'	EWes
– 'Dawn'	CAby CPla CWCL EWes GEdr GKev IBal SDys WAbe
– 'Douglas'	EPfP EWes GEdr GKev IBal LEdu NHol NHpl NWad SEdd WAvo WPGP
– 'Dulcie'	EWes GEdr IBal WAbe
– 'Emily Peel'	EWes GKev IBal ITim
– 'Eva-Kate'	EWes IBal ITim
– 'Fred Broome'	CRos EWes GEdr IBal LEdu NHol NWad WFar
– 'Goliath'	EWes IBal
– 'Harlequin'	CAby EWes GEdr IBal ITim NHol NWad
§ – 'Helen'	CBor EPot EWes GEdr GKev IBal LEdu NHol NHpl NWad WAbe WPGP
– 'Jeanette'	EWes IBal
– 'Kitty'	EWes IBal WFar

- 'Lily Jean' (d)	CAby CPla CRos CTri EPfP EWes GEdr GKev IBal ITim LRHS NHpl NWad SEdd WFar WTyc XEll
- 'Luna'	EWes
- 'Margaret Rose'	EWes IBal NHol
- 'Mars'	CBor CRos EHyd EWes IBal LEdu LRHS NHol NRHS WFar WPGP
- 'Monique'	EWes
- 'Pearl'	LRHS
- 'Perle'	CBor EWes GEdr IBal LRHS NHol NWad
- 'Picta' (v)	EWes GKev IBal LEdu NHol NHpl NWad WAbe
- 'Pink Pearl'	EWes IBal NHol
- pink-flowered	WLov
- var. ***platypetala***	EPfP EWes GEdr GKev IBal NHol NHpl NWad WAvo XEll
- var. ***platypetala* × *milloides***	IBal NHol NWad
- - Burtt 6981	EWes
- 'Rebecca'	EWes
- 'Red King'	EWes IBal
- red-flowered	LRHS SPlb WLov
- 'Ruth'	ELon EWes GEdr GKev IBal NHol SDeJ WFar
- 'Susan Garnett-Botfield'	EWes GEdr IBal LRHS NHpl
- 'Tetra Pink'	CAby EWes GEdr IBal NHol NWad WTyc
- 'Tetra Red'	EWes GEdr GKev IBal NHol NWad SDeJ WFar
- 'The Bride'	EWes GEdr
- white-flowered	LRHS WLov
'Betsy Carmine'	CCCN GEdr IBal NWad WFar
'Beverly' **new**	LCro LOPS
'Bright Eyes' (d)	EWes
'Burgundy'	IBal
'Butterfly Wings'	NWad
'Candy Stripe'	EWes GEdr NWad
'Carina'	EWes
'Caroline'	EWes IBal WFar
'Cathy'	EWes IBal
'Confusion'	EWes LEdu NHol NHpl NWad
'Dainty Dee' (d)	EWes
'Damson' **new**	CBor
deflexa	CBor CRos EWes GKev IBal ITim LEdu LRHS NHol NHpl NRHS NWad SEdd SIvy WAbe WFar WPGP
'Donald Mann'	EWes GEdr GKev IBal ITim NHol
'Dusky'	EWes GEdr IBal NWad
'E.A. Bowles'	EWes IBal NHpl NSla WFar
'Ellicks'	IBal
'Flashing Ruby'	GEdr WFar
'Forge Robies'	EWes
'Garnett'	EWes NWad WFar
'Gemma'	EWes
'Giant Pink' **new**	CBor
'Goya' (d)	CAby NHpl
'Great Scot'	EWes GEdr GKev IBal NHpl NWad WAbe
'Hebron Farm Biscuit'	see *Hypoxis parvula* var. *albiflora* 'Hebron Farm Biscuit'
'Hebron Farm Cerise'	see × *Rhodoxis* 'Hebron Farm Cerise'
'Hebron Farm Pink'	see × *Rhodoxis hybrida* 'Hebron Farm Pink'
'Hinky Pinky'	GEdr NWad
'Holden Rose' (d)	IBal NHol NWad WFar
'Hope' (d)	IBal
'Indy'	IBal
'Jap Double'	CBor
'Jupiter'	CBor GEdr NWad WFar
'Kiwi Joy' (d)	CRos EWes GEdr GKev IBal NHol NHpl NWad SDeJ WTyc
'Knockdolian Red'	GEdr IBal NHol NWad WFar
'Lisette'	EWes
'Louise'	IBal
'Midori'	EWes GEdr IBal NWad SDys WFar
milloides	CAby CBor CPla CRos EWes GEdr IBal ITim LBee LEdu LRHS NHol NHpl NRHS NWad WAbe WFar WPGP XEll
- 'Claret'	CAby CBod CElw CRos CSam ELon EPot EWes GEdr GKev IBal ITim LRHS NHol SDys SEdd SIvy WAbe WFar WTor WTyc
- 'Claudia'	CRos EHyd EMor EPfP GWyn NRHS WFar
- 'Damask'	CRos EWes GKev IBal LRHS SDys
- 'Drakensberg Snow'	EWes
- giant	WFar
- 'Susan'	EWes
'Monty'	EWes GEdr IBal NWad WAbe WFar
'Mystery'	CBor EWes IBal NHol
'Naomi'	EWes
'New Look'	EWes GEdr IBal NHpl NWad SEdd
'Ori Zuru'	GEdr
'Origami'	IBal LEdu
'Pat Lacey'	EWes IBal
'Paula'	IBal
'Pink Ice'	GEdr IBal NWad
'Pink Star'	LRHS
'Pinkeen'	CBor EWes WFar
'Pinkie'	IBal SDys WFar
'Pintado'	CAby CBor CRos EHyd EWes GEdr IBal LEdu LRHS NRHS NWad SDys WFar WPGP WTyc
'Raspberry Ice'	IBal NHol NWad WFar
'Rosalie'	IBal
'Rosie Lee'	CBor EWes
'Ruby Giant'	GEdr LRHS WFar
'Shell Pink'	EWes IBal NHol NWad
'Shirazz' **new**	CBor
Slack Top hybrids	NSla
'Snow'	EWes
'Snow White'	CRos EWes NHol
'Starlett'	EWes NHol
'Starry Eyes' (d)	EWes IBal WFar
'Stella'	CCCN CRos EPot EWes GEdr GKev IBal LRHS NHol NHpl NWad SDys WFar
'Sunburst'	GEdr NWad
'Telios'	IBal
'Tetra Rose'	GEdr
'Tetra White'	see *R. baurii* 'Helen'
thodiana	CBor EWes GEdr IBal NHol NHpl NWad WAbe WFar
TWINKLE STAR MIXED	LRHS
'Two Tone'	EWes
'Venetian'	CBor CMea IBal NHol NWad WFar
'Westacre Picotee'	EWes
'White Prince'	WFar
'Wild Cherry Blossom'	EWes IBal

Rhodoleia (*Hamamelidaceae*)

championii B&SWJ 11603	WCru
- FMWJ 13155	WCru
- WWJ 11858	WCru
aff. ***henryi*** B&SWJ 11782	WCru
- DJHV 0640	WCru
parvipetala FMWJ 13422	WCru

- WWJ 11866 WCru
- WWJ 11943 WCru

Rhodophiala (*Amaryllidaceae*)
rosea GKev

Rhodora see *Rhododendron*

Rhodotypos (*Rosaceae*)
kerrioides see *R. scandens*
§ ***scandens*** CBcs CBod CExl CRos EBee EHyd ELan EPfP GBin GKev IDee LEdu LRHS MGil MMrt MMuc MNrw NHol NLar NQui SBrt SEND SLon SPoG WAvo WCru

× *Rhodoxis* ✿ (*Hypoxidaceae*)
'Abigail' EWes IBal WFar
'Anne Crock' EWes IBal
'Aurora' CRos EWes IBal WFar
'Betsy' EWes GKev
'Bloodstone' EWes IBal NHol NWad
FAIRYTALE ('Hil200802'PBR) MPkF SPad
'Fanny' EWes
'Hebron Farm Biscuit' see *Hypoxis parvula* var. *albiflora* 'Hebron Farm Biscuit'
§ 'Hebron Farm Cerise' CBor CCCN CElw CRos EHyd EWes GEdr GKev IBal LEdu LRHS NRHS SDys WFar
'Hebron Farm Rose' IBal
§ ***hybrida*** EWes
- 'Aya San' EWes GKev IBal LRHS WFar
- FAIRY KISSES ('Im201208'PBR) MPkF SPad
§ - 'Hebron Farm Pink' CAby CBor CElw CPla CRos EWes GEdr GKev IBal LRHS NHol WFar
- 'Hebron Farm Red Eye' CCCN EWes GKev IBal NHpl SEdd WFar
- 'Pink Stars' IBal
- 'Ruby Giant' EWes GEdr IBal
- 'White Stars' EWes
'Jenny' EWes
'Little Pink Pet' EWes IBal WFar
'Otterlo Ruby' CBor EWes GKev WFar
'Pink Glow' IBal
'Pink Tips' IBal
'Red Flyer' EWes IBal
'Ria' EWes
'Sandra' EWes
'Sandy' CBor EWes GKev
'Sonja' CBor GKev
'Sue' EWes WFar
'Summer Pink' IBal
(Summer Stars Series) 'Summer Stars Candy' IBal
- 'Summer Stars Peppermint' IBal WFar
- 'Summer Stars Pink Blush' IBal WFar
- 'Summer Stars Pinky' CDoC IBal WFar
- 'Summer Stars Ruby' IBal

Rhoeo see *Tradescantia*

Rhoicissus (*Vitaceae*)
digitata EShb

Rhombophyllum (*Aizoaceae*)
dolabriforme SSim

Rhopalostylis (*Arecaceae*)
sapida CBrP

rhubarb see *Rheum* × *hybridum*; also AGM Vegetables Section

Rhus (*Anacardiaceae*)
ambigua see *Toxicodendron orientale*
aromatica CAgr MMrt NLar WKor
chinensis CMCN IDee
copallinum EBtc SBrt
coriaria NLar
cotinus see *Cotinus coggygria*
glabra CBcs EPfP SPer
hirta see *R. typhina*
incisa SPlb
potaninii EBee EPfP NLar WPGP
× ***pulvinata*** (Autumn Lace Group) 'Red Autumn Lace' ♀H5 MBlu SPer
radicans see *Toxicodendron radicans*
succedanea see *Toxicodendron succedaneum*
toxicodendron see *Toxicodendron radicans*
trilobata new WKor
typhina CAgr CBcs CBrac CDoC CLnd CMac ELan EPfP GKin LCro LMaj LOPS MAsh MGos MMuc NHol NLar SCob SEND SGol SLim SPer SSta WFar
§ - 'Dissecta' ♀H6 CBar CBcs CDoC CLnd ELan EPfP LMaj MGos MMuc MRav NLar SArc SCob SEND SGol SGsty SLim SPer WFar
- 'Laciniata' hort. see *R. typhina* 'Dissecta'
- RADIANCE ('Sinrus') ♀H6 CRos EHyd LRHS MAsh MBlu NLar SPoG
- TIGER EYES ('Bailtiger'PBR) ♀H6 CBcs ELan EPfP MAsh MGos SCob SGol SWvt
verniciflua see *Toxicodendron vernicifluum*

Rhynchelytrum see *Melinis*

Rhynchospora (*Cyperaceae*)
colorata LLWG LRHS MPkF NPer SBrt
latifolia SDix

Ribes ✿ (*Grossulariaceae*)
alpinum CExl MRav SPer SRms WKor WSpi
americanum 'Variegatum' (v) NWad WLov
aureum misapplied see *R. odoratum*
aureum ambig. CAgr WKor
aureum Pursh. subsp. ***gracillimum*** SBrt
§ × ***beatonii*** CExl CSBt CSde CWld EBee EHyd EPfP EShb GBin IDee IMou LEdu LRHS MMuc NLar SGol SLim SPer SPoG SRms WAvo WCot WFar WMal
'Ben Hope'PBR (B) CAgr CSBt EPom MPri SCoo SWvt
'Black Velvet' (D) CAgr MCoo
bracteosum B&SWJ 14159 new WCru
californicum SBrt
cereum SBrt
× ***culverwellii*** (F) CAgr CCCN CTri EPom LBuc LCro LEdu LOPS NLar SVic SWvt WMat
divaricatum CAgr LEdu WKor
gayanum LEdu NLar WKor
glaciale PAB 3004 LEdu

× ***gordonianum***	see *R.* × *beatonii*
griffithii	CBod WCot
- GWJ 9331	WCru
- PAB 4871	LEdu
jostaberry	see *R.* × *nidigrolaria*
laurifolium	CBcs CEnd CExl CRos CTri EBee EHyd ELan EWes IMou LRHS MMuc MRav NLar SChF SCob SMad SPer WCFE WFar
- (f)	EPfP SRms
- (m)	EPfP
- 'Mrs Amy Doncaster'	CBcs CRos EBee EHyd EPfP LEdu LRHS NRHS SEle SPoG SRms WBor WCot WGob WLov WPGP WSpi
- Rosemoor form	CDoC EBee EPfP LRHS NLar SPoG WCot
longeracemosum	GGGa
menziesii	EWes NQui WCot
nevadense	SBrt
§ × ***nidigrolaria*** (F)	CDoC CMac LBuc SEdi
nigrum (B) PAB 3755	LEdu
- 'Baldwin' (B)	CTri EPfP MAsh NLar SEdi SLim SPer SSFr WMat
- 'Barchatnaja' (B)	CAgr
- 'Ben Alder' (B)	CAgr EPom LRHS SCoo
- 'Ben Connan'[PBR] (B) ♀H6	CAgr CMac CRos CSBt EHyd EPfP EPom LBuc LCro LOPS LRHS LSRN MAsh MGos NLar NRHS SCoo SEND SGbt SKee SLim SPer SPoG SRms SSFr SWvt WMat
- 'Ben Gairn'[PBR] (B)	CAgr MCoo MMuc
- 'Ben Lomond'[PBR] (B)	CAgr CSBt CTri EPfP LBuc LSRN MAsh MGos MNHC MPri MRav NLar SEdi SKee SPer SPoG SRms SSFr SVic WMat
- 'Ben More' (B)	CAgr MPri SPer
- 'Ben Nevis' (B)	CAgr CTri EBee SEdi SKee SPer
- 'Ben Sarek' (B)	CAgr CMac CRos CSBt CTri EBee ECrN EHyd EMil EPfP EPom LBuc LCro LOPS LRHS LSRN MAsh MGos MPri MRav NLar NRHS SEdi SKee SLim SPer SRms SSFr SWvt WMat
- 'Ben Tirran' (B)	CAgr CSBt EHyd EPom LBuc LRHS LSRN MAsh MGos MPri NLar SCoo SRms SWvt WMat
- 'Ben Tron' (B) **new**	CRos
- 'Big Ben'[PBR] (B) ♀H6	CArg CRos EBee EHyd EPfP EPom LBuc LCro LOPS LRHS LSRN MNHC NRHS SGbt SKee SPer SPoG WMat
- 'Black Reward' (B)	CAgr
- 'Boskoop Giant' (B)	CAgr ELan SLim
- 'Byelorussian Sweet' (B)	CAgr
- 'Cassis Blanc' (B)	CAgr
- 'Ebony' (B)	CArg CMac EPom LRHS MPri SVic
- 'Hystawneznaya' (B)	CAgr LEdu
- 'Jet' (B)	CAgr
- 'Kosmicheskaya' (B)	CAgr
- 'Pilot Alexander Mamkin' (B)	CAgr
- 'Polar' (B)	CAgr
- 'Seabrook's' (B)	CAgr
- 'Titania' (B)	LRHS MCoo NLar SEdi WMat
- 'Vertti' (B)	CAgr
- 'Wellington XXX' (B)	CAgr LBuc LEdu SEdi SSFr
§ ***odoratum***	CBcs CMac CRos CSBt CTho CWld EBee ECrN EHyd ELan ELon EPfP LRHS MGos MMuc MNrw MRav NLar SCob SPer SPoG SRms
- 'Black Pearl'	SVic
- 'Crandall'	CAgr LEdu
orientale PAB 7066	LEdu
'Pink Perfection'	CMCN
praecox	CBcs MMuc SEND
rubrum 'Blanka' (W)	CAgr CArg CMac EHyd SVic
- 'Cascade' (R)	CAgr
- 'Cherry' (R)	CAgr
- 'Gloire de Sablons' (P)	EPom SPer SRms
- 'Jonkheer van Tets' (R) ♀H6	CAgr CRos CSBt EBee EHyd EPfP EPom GQue IArd LRHS LSRN MAsh MCoo MPri NLar NRHS SEND SEdi SGbt SKee SLim SPer SRms SSFr WMat
- 'Junifer' (R)	CAgr CRos EHyd EPom LEdu LRHS NRHS SKee
- 'Laxton's Number One' (R)	CAgr CMac CTri EPfP EPom LCro LEdu LOPS LRHS LSRN NLar SGbt SLim SPer SPoG SRms SSFr WMat
- 'Lisette' (R)	LRHS
- 'Red Lake' (R) ♀H6	CAgr CTri ECrN ELan EPfP EPom LBuc LEdu MGos MPri NLar SEdi SGol SKee SPer SPoG SRms SSFr WMat
- 'Redstart' (R)	CAgr CTri LBuc MAsh MMuc SKee WMat
- 'Rolan' (R)	CAgr
- 'Rondom' (R)	CAgr SVic
- ROSA SPORT (P)	LRHS
- 'Rosetta' (R)	CAgr SRms
- 'Rotet' (R)	LEdu
- 'Rovada' (R)	CAgr CArg CMac CRos CSBt EHyd EPfP EPom LBuc LEdu LRHS LSRN MAsh MPri NLar NRHS SEdi SKee SPoG SRms SVic WMat
- 'Roxby Red' (R)	LEdu
- 'Stanza' (R) ♀H6	CAgr SEND
§ - 'Versailles Blanche' (W/C)	CAgr CRos CSBt CTri EHyd EPfP EPom GQue LBuc LCro LOPS LRHS LSRN MGos MMuc MPri NRHS SEdi SKee SLim SPer SRms SSFr WMat
- 'Weisse Langtraubige' (W)	CAgr
- 'White Grape' (W) ♀H6	CTri LEdu
- 'White Pearl' (W)	ELan SEdi SVic
- WHITE VERSAILLES	see *R. rubrum* 'Versailles Blanche'
sachalinense **new**	WKor
sanguineum	SavN
- AMORE ('Annys2003'[PBR]) **new**	NLar
- 'Brianjou'	SRms
- 'Brocklebankii'	CExl CMac EPfP MRav NLar SChF SPer SRms WCFE WSHC
- 'Carneum'	CRos EHyd LRHS NRHS
- 'Elkington's White'	CRos EHyd EPfP EWTr LBuc LCro LOPS LRHS LSRN MAsh MGos NLar NRHS NSti SCoo SLon SRms WBor WCot WSpi
- 'King Edward VII'	Widely available
- 'Koja' ♀H6	CRos EHyd ELon EPfP GBin LEdu LRHS LSRN MAsh MGos MMuc NLar NRHS SCoo SEle SGol SPoG SRms WCot WFar WLov
- 'Lombartsii' ♀H6	CRos EHyd EPfP LRHS MRav NRHS
- 'Pink Rain'	LRHS
- 'Poky's Pink' ♀H6	CRos EHyd LRHS MAsh MRav SPoG SRms
- 'Pulborough Scarlet'	CBcs CBrac CDoC CMac CRos CTri EBee EHyd ELan EPfP GBin LCro LOPS LRHS MAsh MGos MMuc NBir NLar NRHS SCob SEND SGol SLim SPer SPlb SPoG SRms SWvt WFar

- 'Red Bross'	CRos EPfP LRHS MAsh SGsty SWvt
- 'Red Pimpernel'	CRos CSBt EHyd EPfP LRHS MAsh NRHS SRms SWvt WFar
- 'Somerset White'	LRHS MAsh
- 'Tydeman's White'	CExl CSBt EPfP NLar WSpi
- var. ***variegata***	CMac
- WHITE ICICLE ('Ubric') 𝕐^{H6}	CBcs CDoC CRos CTho CTri EBee EHyd ELan EPfP EShb EWTr GBin LRHS MAsh MBlu MHer MRav MSwo NBir NLar NRHS SCob SPer SPoG SRms SWvt WCot WFar WLov
speciosum 𝕐^{H4}	Widely available
uva-crispa 'Annelii' (F)	CAgr
- 'Captivator' (C)	CMac CRos CSBt EPom LBuc LRHS MAsh MCoo MNHC NLar NRHS SGol SKee SPoG SRms WMat
- 'Careless' (C/D) 𝕐^{H6}	CSBt CTri EPom LSRN MAsh MGos SEdi SPer WMat
- 'Early Sulphur' (D)	CTri ELan
- EASYCRISP LADY SUN (D)	LRHS
- 'Greenfinch' (C) 𝕐^{H6}	CAgr
- 'Hinnonmäki' (D)	CAgr LBuc MPri SPer
- 'Hinnonmäki Grön' (D)	CAgr CMac CSBt EBee LRHS LSRN MAsh MPri MRav SEdi SKee SRms
- 'Hinnonmäki Gul' (D)	CAgr CMac EBee EPfP EPom LBuc LEdu LRHS MAsh MGos NRHS SEdi SKee SPer SRms SSFr SVic WMat
- 'Hinnonmäki Röd' (C/D)	CAgr CMac CRos EBee ECrN EHyd EPfP EPom LBuc LCro LEdu LOPS LRHS LSRN MAsh MCoo MNHC MRav NLar NRHS SEdi SKee SPer SPoG SRms SSFr SVic WMat
- 'Invicta' (C/D) 𝕐^{H6}	Widely available
- 'Jubilee' (C/D)	LBuc
- 'Jubilee Careless' (C/D)	EPom
- 'Langley Gage' (D)	MCoo
- 'Larell' (C/D)	CAgr
- 'Leveller' (D) 𝕐^{H6}	MCoo SEdi SPer
- 'London' (C/D)	CTri
- 'Martlet' (D)	MCoo SLim
- 'Mucurines' (D)	CAgr
- 'Pax'^{PBR} (D)	CAgr SLim SSFr SVic
- 'Pixwell' (C)	SGol
- 'Redeva'^{PBR} (D)	CAgr
- 'Rokula'^{PBR} (C/D)	ELan LRHS MCoo WMat
- 'Spinefree' (C)	CAgr
- 'Whinham's Industry' (C/D) 𝕐^{H6}	ELan LBuc LSRN MGos MMuc MPri SEND SEdi SPer SRms
- 'Whitesmith' (C/D)	CTri LSRN MCoo
- 'Xenia' (D)	CArg CRos EHyd EPfP EPom LCro LEdu LOPS LRHS MCoo NRHS SPoG WMat
valdivianum	WCot WFar
viburnifolium	CBcs LRHS NLar SBrt SEND
'Worcesterberry' (C)	CHab IDee

Richea (*Ericaceae*)

dracophylla	CBrP

Ricinus (*Euphorbiaceae*)

communis	CDTJ SPlb WSMil
- 'Carmencita' 𝕐^{H2}	NGBl
- 'Carmencita Pink'	CDTJ
- 'Carmencita Red'	CDTJ
- 'Dominican Republic'	CDTJ
- 'Gibsonii'	CDTJ
- 'Impala'	CDTJ
- 'New Zealand Black'	CDTJ CSpe EShb
- 'Zanzibariensis' 𝕐^{H2}	CDTJ

Ridolfia (*Apiaceae*)

segetum	LCro LOPS LRHS SPhx

Rigidella see *Tigridia*

orthantha	see *Tigridia orthantha*

Riocreuxia (*Apocynaceae*)

torulosa	CCCN SPlb

Robinia (*Papilionaceae*)

§ ***hispida***	CEnd CLnd EPfP MBlu NOrn SPer
- var. ***fertilis***	SBrt
- var. ***kelseyi***	WSpi
- 'Macrophylla'	CEnd
§ - var. ***rosea***	LSRN
- 'Rosea' misapplied	see *R. hispida*, *R. hispida* var. *rosea*
- 'Rosea' ambig.	CBcs EBee
× ***margaretta*** CASQUE ROUGE	see *R.* × *margaretta* 'Pink Cascade'
§ - 'Pink Cascade'	CEnd ELan EPfP MAsh MGos NOra SCob SCoo SEND SGbt SGol SPer WMat
pseudoacacia	CAgr CCVT ELan LBuc MCoo MMuc SEND SGol SPlb
- 'Bessoniana'	ELan EPfP
- 'Frisia'	CBcs CTri EBee ECrN ELan EPfP LRHS LSRN MGos MPri MRav MSwo NLar NOra NOrn SCob SEND SGbt SGol SLim SPer WMat WTSh
- 'Inermis' hort.	see *R. pseudoacacia* 'Umbraculifera'
§ - 'Lace Lady'^{PBR}	CSBt ELan EPfP LBuc LRHS MAsh MGos NLar SCoo SPoG WMat
- 'Myrtifolia'	SMad
- 'Tortuosa'	CEnd EBee SPer
- 'Twisty Baby'	see *R. pseudoacacia* 'Lace Lady'
§ - 'Umbraculifera'	ECrN LMaj LSRN SArc SCob SGsty
× ***slavinii*** 'Hillieri' 𝕐^{H6}	CEnd EBee ELan EPfP LSRN MAsh MBlu NLar NOrn SLon SPer WSpi

Rochea see *Crassula*

Rodgersia ✿ (*Saxifragaceae*)

CLD 1432	CExl
aesculifolia 𝕐^{H6}	Widely available
- SSSE 36	SMHy
- var. ***henrici***	CRos EHyd GLog LRHS MRav NBro NRHS SGbt SPer WBor WHoo
- - KW 21015	WCru
- - 'Cherry Blush'	EPfP GWyn ILea SPad WFar
- - hybrid	NLar XLum
- 'Red Dawn'	IBlr
- 'Red Leaf'	WPnP
'Badenweiler'	ECha EHyd LRHS NRHS
'Blickfang' 𝕐^{H6}	CRos EBee EHyd LRHS MMrt NRHS
'Bloody Mary'	ECtt IMou MHol SCob WFar
'Borodin'	EBee EWTr
'Bronze Peacock'	CPla CRos CTsd EBee ECtt ELan EMor LCro LOPS LSou MHol MPie NDov NEoE NLar SCob SEdd SEle SHeu SMad SPad SPeP SPoG WTor
'Dark Pokers'	CBod EBee ECtt LRHS MCot NLar SRms WFar
'Die Anmutige'	IMou
'Die Schöne'	EBee NLar
'Die Stolze'	GBin IMou LEdu
'Fascination'	IBlr
'Grande Blanche'	EHyd

'Herkules'	EBee ECha ECtt EHyd ELon GMaP GWyn LEdu LRHS MBNS MMuc NLar NQui WCot WPnP WSMil
'Irish Bronze' ♀H6	CAby CBod CRos ECtt EHyd EMor EPfP EShb GPSL GQue LEdu LRHS LSRN MBel MWts NRHS SMad WFar WPnP
'Koriata'	IBlr
'Kupfermond'	EBee NBir SMHy
'La Blanche'	EBee ECtt EHyd ELon LEdu LRHS MHol NLar SEdd WPnP
nepalensis	EBee EHyd LEdu LRHS WPGP
- EMAK 713	IBlr
- HWJK 2140	WCru
- 'High Flier'	WCru
'Parasol'	CBro CMac EHyd IBlr LRHS NBir NHol NWad
pinnata	CRos CTri EBee EPau EPfP EWTr GMaP LEdu LRHS LSRN MBel MGos MRav NHol NRHS SCob SMad SRms WPnP WWtn XLum
- B&SWJ 7741A	CBcs WCru
- L 1670	CExl ELan
- 'Alba'	EHyd EMor LRHS
- 'Buckland Beauty' ♀H6	CRos EHyd EPfP IBlr LRHS NRHS WFar
- 'Cally Coral'	EBee
- 'Cally Salmon'	EWes IBlr IMou
- 'Candy Clouds' (d)	EBee NLar
- 'Chocolate Wing'	Widely available
- 'Crûg Cardinal'	CRos EBee EHyd GBin LRHS NLar NRHS SHeu WCru WPnP
- 'Elegans' ♀H7	CAby CBod CDor CRos EBee EPfP GKev GMaP LEdu LRHS MHol MRav NHol NRHS NWad SCob SPoG SRms SWvt WCAu WCFE
- 'Fireworks'PBR	EBee ECtt EPfP IMou NLar SPer
- 'Hanna'	GBin SHeu
- hybrids	EHyd
- 'Jade Dragon Mountain'	EBee IBlr
- 'Maurice Mason' ♀H6	CExl EBee ECtt GKev IBlr NLar SDix
- 'Panache'	IBlr
- pink-flowered	WCru
- 'Shangri-La'	WCru
- 'Snow Clouds'	CBod EBee
- 'Superba' ♀H6	Widely available
- white-flowered	WCru
pinnata* × *sambucifolia	IBlr
podophylla	Widely available
- B&SWJ 10818	WCru
- B&SWJ 10823	WCru
- 'Braunlaub'	ILea LCro LOPS MCot NBro SMad WPnP
- 'Crûg's Colossus'	WCru
- Donard selection	IBlr
- 'Rotlaub' ♀H6	CAby EBee IMou WBor
- 'Smaragd'	CRos EHyd EShb LRHS MRav NBir NLar NRHS
purdomii hort.	CMac CRos EHyd LRHS NRHS WCot WPGP
'Rosenlicht'	EHyd LRHS
sambucifolia	CBcs CMac CRos EHyd ILea LEdu LRHS MCot MMuc NBir NLar NRHS NSti SCob SEND SPer WCAu WFar WPnP XLum
- B&SWJ 7899	WCru
- large, red-stemmed	NBir
- 'Mountain Select'	EBee
tabularis	see *Astilboides tabularis*

Roemeria (*Papaveraceae*)

hybrida	CSpe

Rohdea (*Asparagaceae*)

delavayi	WCot
japonica	CMac WCot WPGP
- B&SWJ 4853	WCru
- B&SWJ 5091	WCru
- 'Godaishu' (v)	WCot
- 'Gunjaku' (v)	WCot
- 'Lance Leaf'	LEdu WPGP
- long-leaved	WCot
- 'Miyakonojo' (v)	WCot
- 'Talbot Manor' (v)	CBct WCot WPGP
- 'Tama-jishi' (v)	WCot
- 'Tuneshige Rokujo' (v)	WCot
tonkinensis HWJ 562	WCru
watanabei B&SWJ 1911	WCru
wattii new	WCot

Roldana (*Asteraceae*)

§ ***cristobalensis***	CSpe WCot
§ ***petasitis***	CAbb WCot

Romanzoffia (*Boraginaceae*)

californica	EBee
§ ***sitchensis***	CTri
suksdorfii Greene	see *R. sitchensis*
unalaschcensis	SRms

Romneya (*Papaveraceae*)

coulteri ♀H5	Widely available
§ - 'White Cloud' ♀H5	CBct CExl EBee EPfP MGil MRav SChF SMad WPGP WSpi
× ***hybrida***	see *R. coulteri* 'White Cloud'

Romulea (*Iridaceae*)

bulbocodium var. ***crocea***	EPot GKev
- var. ***leichtliniana***	GKev
ligustica var. ***rouyana***	GKev
linaresii subsp. ***graeca***	GKev
ramiflora	CExl
sabulosa	WHil
tempskyana	GKev

Rosa ✿ (*Rosaceae*)

NJM 11.048 from Guizhou, China	WPGP
NJM 11.077 from Guizhou, China	WPGP
NJM 11.079 from Guizhou, China	WPGP
90TH CELEBRATION ('Tan10558') (HT)	MFry
'À Longs Pédoncules' (Ce)	EBls
'A. Mackenzie' (S)	EBls
A ROSE OF DISTINCTION ('Tan98130') (F)	ESty
A SHROPSHIRE LAD ('Ausled'PBR) (S) ♀H6	CArg CRos CTri EBee EPfP LBuc LRHS NLar NRHS SCob SPer SPoG SSea
A WHITER SHADE OF PALE ('Peafanfare'PBR) (HT) ♀H6	CDoC CSBt ECnt ESty LCro LOPS LSRN MFry MRav SApu SLon SPer SSea
ABBIE'S ROSE (F)	LSRN
ABIGAILE ('Tanelaigib') (F)	LSRN
ABRACADABRA ('Korhocsel') (HT)	ESty

ABRAHAM DARBY ('Auscot') (S)	CTri EPfP MAsh MRav NLar SEND SPer
ABSENT FRIENDS ('Dicemblem'^{PBR}) (F)	CBod ESty WBor
ABSOLUTELY FABULOUS ('Wekvossutono'^{PBR}) (F) 🏆^{H6}	CArg CBod CDoC CGro CSBt CWld EBls ECnt ELon EPfP ESty LBuc LRHS LSRN MAsh MFry MPri MRav MWat SApu SCoo SPad SPer SPoG
abyssinica	EBtc LEdu
acicularis var. ***nipponensis***	EBls
'Adam' (ClT)	EBls LSRN
'Adam Messerich' (Bb)	CBod EBls ETWh NLar
ADAM'S ROSE ('Wekromico') (F)	LSRN
'Adélaïde d'Orléans' (Ra) 🏆^{H6}	CArg CBod CRHN EBls ETWh LRHS NLar SEND SPer
'Agatha' (G)	EBls
AGATHA CHRISTIE ('Kormeita') (ClF)	EPfP LBuc LRHS LSRN MAsh
'Agathe Incarnata' (D × G)	EBls
'Aglaia' (Ra)	CPou EBls ETWh
'Agnes' (Ru)	CBcs CBod CDoC CTho EBls EPfP ETWh IArd MRav NLar SPer
'Aimée Vibert' (N)	CBod EBee EBls ELon ETWh NLar SPer
'Alain Blanchard' (G)	CPou EBls ETWh
ALAN TITCHMARSH ('Ausjive'^{PBR}) (S)	LCro LOPS LSRN SPer
ALASKA ('Korjoslio'^{PBR}) (ClHT) **new**	ESty
× ***alba*** (A)	EBls
§ - 'Alba Maxima' (A) 🏆^{H6}	EBls ETWh GBin NLar SEND SPer WFar WHer
§ - 'Alba Semiplena' (A) 🏆^{H6}	EBls ETWh GBin NLar SPer WHer
- CELESTIAL	see *R.* 'Céleste'
- 'Maxima'	see *R.* × *alba* 'Alba Maxima'
'Albéric Barbier' (Ra) 🏆^{H5}	CArg CBod CDoC CRHN CSBt CTri EBee EBls ECnt ELan EPfP ETWh LCro LOPS MCot MFry MRav MSwo MWat NLar SApu SCob SEND SPer WHer
'Albertine' (Ra) 🏆^{H6}	CArg CBcs CDoC CGro CRos CSBt EBls ECnt EHyd ELan ELon EPfP ESty ETWh LCro LOPS LRHS MAsh MFry MGos MPri MRav MSwo MWat NLar SApu SCob SEND SPer SPoG
'Alchymist' (ClS)	CBod CRHN CRos EBls EPfP ESty ETWh LRHS MAsh MRav NLar SPer
ALDEN BIESEN ('Lengrati') (HM)	WKif
ALDERLEY PARK ('Frygladiator') (F)	MFry
ALEC'S RED ('Cored') (HT)	CArg CBcs CTri EBls LSRN MFry MRav MWat SCob SPer SPoG
ALEXANDER ('Harlex') (HT) 🏆^{H6}	CGro EBls LSRN MRav SApu SPer
'Alexander Hill Gray' (T)	EBls
'Alexandre Girault' (Ra) 🏆^{H6}	CRHN EBee EBls ETWh LBuc LRHS NRHS SPer WHer
'Alfred Colomb' (HP)	EBls
'Alfred de Dalmas' misapplied	see *R.* 'Mousseline'
ALFRED SISLEY ('Delstrijor'^{PBR}) (S)	CBod ESty ETWh NLar
'Alfresco'^{PBR} (ClHT)	MSwo
§ 'Alibaba'^{PBR} (ClHT) 🏆^{H6}	CBod CDoC CGro CSBt ECnt EPfP ESty LBuc LRHS LSRN MAsh MFry MPri MRav MWat SApu SPer SPoG SSea
'Alida Lovett' (Ra)	CRHN EBls
ALISON ('Coclibee'^{PBR}) (F)	LSRN
'Alison Wheatcroft' (F)	EBls
ALISSAR, PRINCESS OF PHOENICIA ('Harsidon'^{PBR}) (S)	CPou ETWh NLar
'Alister Clark' (F)	EBls
§ 'Alister Stella Gray' (N) 🏆^{H5}	EBls EPfP ESty ETWh MMuc NLar SPer SSea WBor
ALL AMERICAN MAGIC ('Meiroylear'^{PBR}) (HT)	ESty
ALL MY LOVING ('Fryrisky') (HT)	LRHS MAsh MFry
'Allen Chandler' (ClHT)	EBls
'Allgold' (F)	EBls
ALNWICK CASTLE	see *R.* THE ALNWICK ROSE
'Aloha' (ClHT) 🏆^{H6}	CArg CBcs CGro CTri EBee EBls ELon EPfP ESty ETWh EWTr LRHS MAsh MCot MRav NLar SPer SPoG WSpi
alpina	see *R. pendulina*
'Alpine Sunset' (HT)	CTri EBls ELon MRav MWat SCob SPer SPoG
altaica misapplied	see *R. spinosissima* 'Grandiflora'
altaica Willd.	see *R. spinosissima*
ALTISSIMO ('Delmur') (Cl)	EBls ETWh MAsh SPer SSea
ALWAYS REMEMBER ME ('Macpadspo') (HT)	LSRN
ALWAYS YOU ('Webalways') (HT)	ESty
'Amadis' (Bs)	CBod ETWh
AMANDA ('Beesian') (F)	EBls ESty LSRN
'Amanda Patenotte' (D) **new**	ETWh
AMAZING DAY ('Raw1113') (S) **new**	ESty
'Ambassador Nogami' (S)	EBls
AMBER QUEEN ('Harroony') (F) 🏆^{H6}	CArg CDoC CSBt CTri EBls ELan IArd LCro LOPS MAsh MFry MRav SApu SPer
AMBER SWEET DREAM ('Fryritz') (Patio)	CDoC CSBt MFry MRav
AMBIANCE ('Bensiete') (Patio) **new**	SSea
amblyotis RBS 0262	NLar
'Amélia'	see *R.* 'Celsiana'
AMELIA ('Poulen011'^{PBR}) (Renaissance Series) (S)	ECnt ETWh LSRN
'American Pillar' (Ra)	CArg CBcs CBod CDoC CRHN CRos CSBt CTri EBls ECnt ELan EPfP ETWh LRHS MAsh MMuc MRav MSwo NLar SApu SCob SPer SPoG WBor
AMETHYST QUEEN ('Raw1074') (F)	ESty
AMNESTY INTERNATIONAL ('Delcreja') (Cl)	ESty
'Amy Robsart' (RH)	EBls
ANABELL ('Korbell') (F)	LSRN
'Andersonii' (*canina* hybrid)	EBls
§ 'Anemone' (Cl)	CPou EBls ETWh NLar
anemoniflora	see *R.* × *beanii*
anemonoides	see *R.* 'Anemone'
ANGEL EYES ('Albravo') (HT)	MAsh
ANGELA ('Grifgela') (S)	LSRN
ANGELA RIPPON ('Ocaru') (Min)	CSBt
'Angela's Choice' (F)	LSRN

	Name	Suppliers
	'Angèle Pernet' (HT)	EBls
	ANISLEY DICKSON ('Dickimono') (F)	SPer
	ANN ('Ausfete'[PBR]) (S)	LSRN
	ANN HENDERSON ('Fryhoncho') (F)	LSRN
	ANNA FORD ('Harpiccolo') (Min/Patio) 🏆H5	SCob SPer
	'Anna Olivier' (T)	EBls
	'Anna Pavlova' (HT)	EBls
	ANNA ZINKEISEN ('Harquhling') (S)	EBls
	ANNE BOLEYN ('Ausecret'[PBR]) (S)	CRos EHyd EPfP LRHS MAsh NRHS SCoo
	ANNE HARKNESS ('Harkaramel') (F)	SPer
	ANNE MARIE LAING ('Jospink') (F)	EBls
	'Anne of Geierstein' (RH)	EBls
	'Anne Watkins' (HT)	EBls
	'Anne-Marie de Montravel' (Poly)	EBls
	ANNE'S ROSE ('Frynippy'[PBR]) (F)	LSRN
	ANNIVERSARY WALTZ ('Raw237') (HT)	ESty
	ANNIVERSARY WISHES ('Noa140721') (F)	MAsh
	'Anthony' (S)	EBls
	ANTIQUE ('Antike') (F)	CBod CPou
	ANTIQUE '89 ('Kordalen') (ClF)	EBls ETWh MAsh
	APHRODITE ('Tan00847'[PBR]) (S) 🏆H6	CBod CDoC ELon ESty ETWh LSRN MRav SApu SGsty
	APHRODITE ('Tanetidor') (HT)	CArg
	apothecary's rose	see *R. gallica* var. *officinalis*
	'Apple Blossom' (Ra)	EBls MCot SHar
	'Applejack' (S)	EBls
	'Apricot Silk' (HT)	CTri EBls SPer
	APRICOT SUNBLAZE ('Savamark') (Min)	CSBt
	ARC ANGEL ('Fryorst') (HT)	MFry
	'Archduke Charles' (Ch)	EBls
	'Archiduc Joseph' misapplied	see *R.* 'Général Schablikine'
	'Archiduchesse Elisabeth d'Autriche' (HP)	EBls
	ARCHIE MOSS ('Dickumon') (S)	IDic
	'Arctic Circle' (HT)	ESty
	'Ardoisée de Lyon' (HP)	EBls
	'Ards Rover' (ClHP)	EBls
	'Arethusa' (Ch)	EBls ETWh NLar
§	***arkansana*** var. ***suffulta***	EBls ETWh
	ARMADA ('Haruseful') (S)	EBls
	'Arthur Bell' (F) 🏆H6	CArg CDoC CGro CRos CSBt CTri EBee EBls EPfP ESty IArd LCro LOPS LRHS LSRN MAsh MFry MPri MRav MSwo MWat SApu SCob SMad SPer SPoG SSea WBor
	'Arthur de Sansal' (DPo)	CBod EBls ETWh NLar
	arvensis	CCVT CHab CLnd EBls ETWh LBuc MMuc WTSh
§	'Aschermittwoch' (ClHR)	EBls
	ASCOT ('Tan01757'[PBR]) (HT)	ESty
	ASH WEDNESDAY	see *R.* 'Aschermittwoch'
	'Astra Desmond' (Ra)	EBls MNrw
I	'At Peace Rose' (HT)	LSRN

	Name	Suppliers
	ATLANTIC STAR ('Fryworld'[PBR]) (F)	MFry
	ATTLEBOROUGH ('Beaat') (ClHT)	EBls
	AUDREY WILCOX ('Frywilrey') (HT)	CBod ESty MFry
	'Auguste Gervais' (Ra)	EBls
	'Augustine Guinoisseau' (HT)	EBls
	Austrian copper rose	see *R. foetida* 'Bicolor'
	Austrian yellow	see *R. foetida*
	'Autumn' (HT)	LSRN
	'Autumn Delight' (HM)	EBls ETWh NLar
	AUTUMN FIRE	see *R.* 'Herbstfeuer'
	AUTUMN SONG	see *R.* PURE POETRY ('Jacment')
	'Autumn Sunset' (ClS)	EBls MCot
	'Autumnalis'	see *R.* 'Princesse de Nassau'
	AVEC AMOUR ('Tan04341'[PBR]) (HT)	ESty
	'Aviateur Blériot' (Ra)	CRHN EBls
	'Avon' (HT)	CBod
	AVON ('Poulmulti'[PBR]) (GC)	EBls ETWh MRav SApu SPer
	AWAKENING ('Probuzení') (ClHT)	CRos EBls EPfP ETWh LRHS MAsh MSwo NLar
	'Ayrshire Splendens'	see *R.* 'Splendens'
	BABE ('Raw1090') (F) **new**	ESty
	'Baby Albéric' (Poly)	EBls
	'Baby Faurax' (Poly)	EBls
	BABY MASQUERADE ('Tanba') (Min)	CGro MRav SPer
	BABYFACE ('Rawril'[PBR]) (Min)	ESty
	BADMINTON GIRL ('Dicfiesta') (F) **new**	IDic
	BAILANDO ('Tan02100'[PBR]) (F) **new**	MFry
	'Ballerina' (HM/Poly) 🏆H6	CArg CBod CDoC CGro CRos CSBt CTri EBee EBls ECnt ELan EPfP ESty ETWh LCro LOPS LRHS LSRN MAsh MFry MPri MRav MSwo NLar SApu SCob SMad SPer SPoG SSea
	BALMORAL ('Poulcas027'[PBR]) (Palace Series) (Patio)	MAsh
	'Baltimore Belle' (Ra)	CPou CRHN EBee EBls ETWh NLar
	banksiae (Ra)	CPou SNig SRms SWeb
	- ***alba***	see *R. banksiae* var. *banksiae*
§	- var. ***banksiae*** (Ra/d)	CBcs CBod CPou CRHN CRos CSBt CTri CWld EBls EHyd ELan EPfP ETWh IMou LCro LOPS LRHS NOra SEND SGsty SLon WCot XSen
	- 'Lutea' (Ra/d) 🏆H5	Widely available
	- 'Lutescens' (Ra)	EBls WPGP
	- var. ***normalis*** (Ra)	CSBt EBls EPfP SLon WCot WHer WPGP
I	- 'Rosea' (Ra)	EWTr NLar SGsty
	'Bantry Bay' (ClHT)	CArg CSBt EBls ELan LSRN SLon SPer
	BARAKURA ('Beajap') (GC/S)	EBls
	BARBARA ('Raw1050')	LSRN
	BARBARA ANN	see *R.* SCENT FROM HEAVEN
	BARBRA STREISAND ('Wekquaneze') (HT)	LSRN
	BARKAROLE ('Tanelorak') (HT)	SApu
	'Baron de Wassenaer' (CeMo)	EBls
	'Baron Girod de l'Ain' (HP)	EBee EBls ELon ETWh LSRN NLar SPer

'Baroness Rothschild' ambig.	see *R.* CLIMBING BARONNE EDMOND DE ROTHSCHILD, 'Baronne Adolph de Rothschild'
§ 'Baronne Adolph de Rothschild' (HP)	EBls ETWh
'Baronne Prévost' (HP)	EBls
BAROQUE FLOORSHOW ('Harbaroque'[PBR]) (S)	CDoC MRav
BARRY STEPHENS ('Horcabellero') (HT)	LSRN
BATHSHEBA ('Auschimbley') (Cl)	CRos CSBt ESty
§ × ***beanii*** (Ra)	EBls
BEATRIX POTTER ('Beafolly') (S)	EBls
BEAUTIFUL BRITAIN ('Dicfire') (F)	EBls
'Beauty of Rosemawr' (ClT)	EBls
BEAUTY STAR	see *R.* LIVERPOOL REMEMBERS
'Belinda' (HM)	EBls LSRN
§ BELLA ('Pouljill'[PBR]) (Renaissance Series) (S)	CPou LSRN
BELLA CHRISTINA ('Mandella') (F)	LSRN
BELLA DIANA ('Mandiana') (F)	LSRN
'Bellard' (G) **new**	ETWh
'Belle Amour' (A × D)	CPou EBls ETWh
'Belle de Crécy' (G)	CPou CTri EBls ETWh MAsh MNrw MPri NLar SPer
'Belle des Jardins' misapplied	see *R.* × *centifolia* 'Unique Panachée'
BELLE EPOQUE ('Fryyaboo'[PBR]) (HT)	ESty MFry
'Belle Isis' (G)	EBls ETWh
'Belle Lyonnaise' (ClT)	EBls
'Belle Poitevine' (Ru)	CPou
'Belle Portugaise' (ClT)	EBls
'Belle Vichyssoise' (N)	EBls
§ 'Belvedere' (Ra) ♀H6	CPou ETWh NLar SPer WBor
BENITA ('Dicquarrel') (HT)	IDic
BENJAMIN BRITTEN ('Ausencart'[PBR]) (S)	CDoC CGro EHyd EPfP ESty LBuc LRHS NRHS SPer
§ 'Bennett's Seedling' (Ra)	CBod EBls ETWh
'Bérénice' Vibert (G) **new**	CPou
BERKSHIRE ('Korpinka'[PBR]) (GC) ♀H6	EBls SApu SCob SSea
BERRY DELIGHTFUL ('Chewdelight'[PBR]) (S) **new**	LRHS
BERYL JOYCE ('Tan96145'[PBR]) (HT)	ESty LSRN MRav
BEST IMPRESSION ('Tan04247'[PBR]) (HT)	ECnt ESty
BEST OF FRIENDS ('Pouldunk'[PBR]) (HT)	LSRN
BEST WISHES ('Chessnut'[PBR]) (ClHT/v)	LSRN
'Betty Sherriff' (CRa)	ETWh GBin
'Betty Uprichard' (HT)	EBls
'Betty's Smile' (HT)	LSRN
'Bewitched' (HT)	LSRN
BIANCO ('Cocblanco') (Patio/Min)	CDoC
BIDDULPH GRANGE ('Frydarkeye') (S)	MFry
BIENVENUE ('Delrochipar') (Cl)	ESty
BIG PURPLE ('Stebigpu') (HT)	CPou ECnt SApu
BILLET DOUX ('Delrosar') (S)	ESty
BIRTHDAY BOY ('Tan97607'[PBR]) (HT)	CDoC ESty LSRN MRav SApu SPoG
BIRTHDAY GIRL ('Meilasso') (F)	CBod CDoC CGro CSBt EPfP ESty LSRN MAsh MFry MRav MWat SApu SCob SCoo SPoG
BIRTHDAY SURPRISE ('Guesyoga') (F)	ESty
BIRTHDAY WISHES (Patio)	see *R.* SHRIMP HIT
BIRTHDAY WISHES ('Guesdelay') (HT)	CTri LRHS LSRN SSea
'Bishop Darlington' (HM)	EBls
BLACK GOLD ('Cleblack') (Min) **new**	SSea
'Black Jack' (Ce)	see *R.* 'Tour de Malakoff'
'Black Prince' (HP)	EBls
BLACKBERRY NIP ('Somnip'[PBR]) (HT)	ELon
'Blairii Number One' (Bb)	EBls
'Blairii Number Two' (ClBb)	CArg EBls ETWh NLar SPer
'Blanche de Belgique' (A)	EBls
'Blanche Double de Coubert' (Ru) ♀H7	CArg CBcs CBod CDoC CSBt CTho CTri EBee EBls ECnt ELan EPfP ETWh EWTr LBuc LCro LOPS LSRN MFry MSwo NLar SApu SCob SEND SPer WKif
'Blanche Moreau' (CeMo)	CBod EBls ETWh
'Blanchefleur' (Ce × G)	CPou EBls ETWh
blanda	EBls
BLENHEIM ('Tanmurse'[PBR]) (GC)	SApu
'Blesma Soul' (HT)	CSBt
'Blessings' (HT)	CArg CBcs CSBt CTri EBls LBuc LSRN MAsh MGos MRav MWat SApu SCob SPer
'Bleu Magenta' (Ra) ♀H6	CBod CRHN CWld EBls ELan ETWh GBin IArd NLar SEND
BLOOM OF RUTH ('Harmedley'[PBR]) (HT)	CSBt ECnt ESty LSRN
'Bloomfield Abundance' (Poly)	CPou EBls ETWh MMuc NLar SPer
'Bloomfield Courage' (Ra)	ETWh
'Bloomfield Dainty' (HM)	EBls
'Blossomtime' (ClHT)	SPer
BLUE DIAMOND (HT)	MFry
BLUE FOR YOU ('Pejamblu'[PBR]) (F) ♀H6	CBod CDoC CGro CRos EBls ECnt ELan EPfP ESty LBuc LCro LRHS MAsh MFry MPri NRHS SApu SCoo SMad SPoG SSea
BLUE MOON ('Tannacht') (HT)	CDoC CTri EBls ELan MGos MRav SApu SCob SPer SPoG
BLUE PETER ('Ruiblun') (Min)	ESty
BLUEBERRY HILL ('Wekcryplag') (F)	EBls
BLUESETTE ('Lenmau') (F)	EBls
'Blush Boursault' (Bs)	EBls MMuc
'Blush Damask' (D)	EBls
'Blush Noisette'	see *R.* 'Noisette Carnée'
'Blush Rambler' (Ra)	CSBt EBls ELan EPfP ETWh LBuc MAsh MMuc SPer
'Blushing Lucy' (Ra) ♀H6	CBod CPou CRHN ETWh MNrw NLar SPer
BLYTHE SPIRIT ('Auschool'[PBR]) (S)	MAsh
'Bobbie James' (Ra) ♀H6	CArg CRos CTri EBee EBls EHyd EPfP ETWh EWTr LRHS MAsh MNrw MRav MSwo NLar NRHS SApu SCob SPer SSea WFar

	'Bobby Charlton' (HT)	LSRN
	BOBBY DAZZLER ('Smi 13302'PBR) (F)	CDoC ESty MRav
	BOLLYWOOD ('Poulbt010') (HT)	MFry
	'Bon Silène' (T)	EBls
	BONICA ('Meidomonac') (GC) 🏆H6	Widely available
§	BONITA ('Poulen009'PBR) (Renaissance Series) (S)	ECnt
	BOOGIE-WOOGIE ('Poulyc006'PBR) (Courtyard Series) (ClHT)	ECnt LRHS MAsh
	BORN AGAIN	see *R.* RENAISSANCE
	BOSCOBEL ('Auscousin'PBR) (S)	CRos ECnt EHyd EPfP ESty LBuc LRHS MAsh NRHS
	'Botzaris' (D)	EBls ETWh
	'Boule de Neige' (Bb)	CBcs CBod CTri CWld EBls ECnt ELan EPfP ETWh LCro LOPS LRHS LSRN MRav NLar NRHS SApu SCob SPer
	'Bouquet d'Or' (N)	EBls ETWh NLar
	'Bouquet Tout Fait' misapplied	see *R.* 'Nastarana'
	'Bouquet Tout Fait' (N)	EBee ETWh
	BOWLED OVER ('Tandolgnil'PBR) (F) 🏆H6	ESty
§	***bracteata*** (S)	CRHN EBls ECre ETWh EWes SSea
	BRAVE HEART ('Horbondsmile') (F)	MRav
	BREATH OF LIFE ('Harquanne'PBR) (ClHT)	CDoC EBls ELan MFry MRav SApu SPer
	BREATHTAKING ('Hargalore'PBR) (HT)	ESty
	'Brenda Colvin' (Ra)	EBls
	'Brian's Star' (F)	LSRN
	BRIDE ('Fryyearn'PBR) (HT)	LSRN MFry MRav MWat
	'Bride and Groom'PBR (HT)	CDoC ESty LSRN MRav SApu SCoo
	BRIDGE OF SIGHS ('Harglowing'PBR) (Cl)	ECnt ESty LBuc LRHS MAsh MFry SPoG
	BRIGHT AND BREEZY ('Dicjive') (F)	ECnt
	BRIGHT AS A BUTTON ('Chewsumsigns'PBR) (S) 🏆H5	CSBt EBee ESty ETWh LRHS MAsh MFry NLar SApu SLon SPer
	BRIGHT FIRE ('Peaxi'PBR) (ClHT)	MSwo SPer
	BRIGHT FUTURE ('Kirora'PBR) (Cl)	ELon ESty SApu
	BRIGHT IDEAS ('Horcoffdrop') (ClHT)	CGro EBls EPfP LRHS MAsh MPri
	BRILLIANT SWEET DREAM ('Frysassy') (Patio)	CSBt ECnt MFry
	BRITANNIA ('Frycalm'PBR) (HT) 🏆H6	MFry
	BROADLANDS ('Tanmirsch'PBR) (GC)	NLar SApu
	BROTHER CADFAEL ('Ausglobe'PBR) (S)	CArg CRos CTri EHyd EPfP LRHS MAsh NLar NRHS SCoo SPer
	BROWN VELVET ('Maccultra') (F)	SPer
	BROWNIE	see *R.* CHOCOLATE RIPPLES
§	***brunonii*** (Ra)	CExl CPou EBls EWes GKev WFar
	- CC 7290	EWld
	- KR 10350	WPGP
	- PAB 3083	LEdu
§	- 'La Mortola' (Ra)	EBls ETWh NLar SPer
	BRUSH-STROKES ('Guescolour') (F)	ESty

	'Buff Beauty' (HM) 🏆H6	CArg CGro CRos CSBt CTri CWld EBee EBls ECnt EPfP ETWh EWTr LCro LOPS MAsh MCot MFry MRav MSwo MWat NLar SApu SCob SEND SPer WCFE WFar
	'Bullata'	see *R.* × *centifolia* 'Bullata'
§	'Burgundiaca' (G)	EBls ETWh
	Burgundian rose	see *R.* 'Burgundiaca'
§	BURGUNDY ICE ('Prose'PBR) (F)	CArg CSBt EBee EBls EPfP ESty LBuc LCro LOPS LRHS MAsh MFry MRav MSwo MWat NRHS SApu SCob SCoo SMad SPoG SSea
	'Burgundy Iceberg'	see *R.* BURGUNDY ICE
	'Burgundy Rose'	see *R.* 'Burgundiaca'
	burnet, double pink	see *R.* ***spinosissima*** double, pink-flowered
	- double white	see *R.* ***spinosissima*** double, white-flowered
	BURNING DESIRE ('Frysizzle') (F)	MFry
	BUTTERCUP ('Ausband'PBR) (S)	CRos LRHS
	BUXOM BEAUTY ('Korbilant'PBR) (HT) 🏆H6	CArg EPfP LRHS LSRN SSea
	'C.F. Meyer'	see *R.* 'Conrad Ferdinand Meyer'
§	***caesia*** subsp. ***vosagiaca***	LEdu
	CAFÉ AU LAIT ('Simgrey') (F)	ESty
	californica 'Plena'	see *R.* ***nutkana*** 'Plena'
	'Callisto' (HM)	ETWh
§	CALYPSO ('Poulclimb'PBR) (ClHT)	SApu
	'Camayeux' (G)	CPou EBls ECnt ETWh NLar SPer
	CAMBRIDGESHIRE ('Korhaugen'PBR) (GC)	CBod CTri EBls ETWh NLar SApu SCob SPer SSea
	CAMELOT ('Tan05372'PBR) (ClF)	ESty
	'Cameo' (Poly)	EBls
	CAMILLE PISARRO ('Destricol') (F)	ESty
	'Canary Bird'	see *R.* ***xanthina*** 'Canary Bird'
	CANDY KISSES ('Simwatu') (HT)	ESty
	CANDY LAND ('Wekrosopela'PBR) (ClHT)	ECnt ESty
	canina (S)	CArg CCVT CGro CHab CLnd CTri EBls ECrN EPfP EPom LBuc LCro LOPS MMuc MRav NLar SCob SEWo SGsty SPer WKor WMat WMou WOut WTSh
	'Cantabrigiensis' (S) 🏆H6	EBls ETWh NLar SPer SSea
	CAPEL MANOR HOUSE ('Beajammie') (ClS)	EBls
	'Capitaine John Ingram' (CeMo)	CArg CBod EBls ETWh NLar
	'Captain Christy'	see *R.* 'Climbing Captain Christy'
	'Captain Hayward' (HP)	EBls ETWh
	'Captain Scarlet' (ClMin)	ESty
	'Cardinal de Richelieu' (G)	CArg CBcs CPou CTri EBls EPfP ETWh LCro LOPS LRHS MAsh MCot MRav MSwo NLar SCob SMad SPer SPoG
	CAREFREE DAYS ('Meirivoui'PBR) (Patio) 🏆H6	EPfP LBuc LRHS MAsh MFry MPri NRHS SApu SPoG SSea
	CARIBBEAN DAWN ('Korfeining'PBR) (Patio)	MAsh
	CARING FOR YOU ambig.	LSRN
	'Carmen' (Ru)	EBls

'Carmenetta' (S)	EBls
'Carol' (F)	see *R.* 'Carol Amling'
§ 'Carol Amling' (F)	LSRN
CAROL ANN ('Peapost') (F)	LSRN
'Caroline Testout'	see *R.* 'Madame Caroline Testout'
CAROLINE VICTORIA ('Harprior'^{PBR}) (HT)	LSRN SApu
CAROLYN KNIGHT ('Austurner'^{PBR}) (S)	CRos EHyd EPfP LCro LOPS LRHS LSRN MAsh NRHS
CARRIS ('Harmanna'^{PBR}) (HT)	MAsh MFry NRHS
§ CASINO ('Macca') (ClHT)	CTri EBls ETWh MRav SPer
'Castle Apricot'	see *R.* LAZY DAYS
'Castle Cream'	see *R.* PERFECT DAY
'Castle Peach'	see *R.* IMAGINATION
'Castle Shrimp Pink'	see *R.* FASCINATION
'Castle Yellow'	see *R.* SUMMER GOLD
'Catherine Mermet' (T)	EBls
'Catherine Seyton' (RH)	EBls
§ 'Cécile Brünner' (Poly) 🏆H5	CBod CTri EBee EBls ELan ETWh LSRN MAsh MMuc NLar SPer SSea
CELEBRATION TIME	see *R.* CINCO DE MAYO
§ 'Céleste' (A) 🏆H6	CTri EBls EPfP ETWh NLar SEND SPer
'Célina' (CeMo)	EBls GBin LSRN
'Céline Forestier' (N)	CArg CPou CWld EBee EBls ETWh NLar SEND SPer
§ 'Celsiana' (D) 🏆H7	CBod CPou EBls ETWh LSRN NLar SPer
CENTENAIRE DE LOURDES ('Delge') (F)	EBls
§ × ***centifolia*** (Ce)	EBls ETWh SPer
§ - 'Bullata' (Ce)	EBls
§ - 'Cristata' (Ce) 🏆H6	CArg EBls ETWh LEdu NLar SPer WBor
§ - 'De Meaux' (Ce)	EBls ETWh NLar SPer
§ - 'Muscosa' (CeMo)	EBls ETWh LEdu SCob
- 'Parvifolia'	see *R.* 'Burgundiaca'
§ - 'Shailer's White Moss' (CeMo)	CBod EBls ETWh
- 'Spong' (Ce)	EBls ETWh
§ - 'Unique' (Ce)	EBls ETWh NLar
§ - 'Unique Panachée' (Ce)	CPou EBls ETWh
'Centifolia Variegata'	see *R.* × *centifolia* 'Unique Panachée'
CENTRE STAGE ('Chewcreepy'^{PBR}) (S/GC) 🏆H6	MAsh
'Cerise Bouquet' (S) 🏆H6	EBls ETWh NLar WSpi
CHAMPAGNE CELEBRATION ('Frylimbo') (HT)	MFry
CHAMPAGNE CELEBRATION ('Simluck') (F)	ESty
§ CHAMPAGNE MOMENT ('Korvanaber'^{PBR}) (F) 🏆H6	CArg CBcs CBod CDoC CGro CRos CSBt EBls ECnt ELan EPfP ESty LBuc LRHS LSRN MAsh MFry MGos MPri MRav NRHS SApu SCob SMad SPer SPoG SSea
'Champion of the World' (Bb)	EBls
'Champneys Pink Cluster' (China hybrid)	EBls
CHANDOS BEAUTY ('Harmisty'^{PBR}) (HT) 🏆H6	CBod CDoC CGro CRos ECnt ELon EPfP ESty ETWh LBuc LRHS LSRN MAsh MFry MRav SApu SPoG SSea
'Chanelle' (F)	EBls SDix SPer
Chapeau de Napoléon	see *R.* × *centifolia* 'Cristata'
'Chaplin's Pink Climber' (Cl)	EBls ETWh

CHARDONNAY ('Simtely') (F)	ESty
CHARISMA ('Jelroganor') (F)	CGro MPri
CHARISMA ('Noa16071'^{PBR}) (HT)	EPfP LBuc MFry SPoG
'Charles Albanel' (Ru/GC) **new**	CDoC
CHARLES AUSTIN ('Ausles') (S)	CDoC MRav
CHARLES DARWIN ('Auspeet'^{PBR}) (S)	CRos EHyd EPfP LBuc LRHS MAsh NLar NRHS SCoo SPer
'Charles de Mills' (G) 🏆H6	CBod CDoC CTri CWld EBls ECnt ELan EPfP ETWh EWTr LCro LOPS LRHS LSRN MCot MRav MSwo NLar SPer WHer
CHARLES DICKENS ('Raw1064') (HT)	ESty
'Charles Gater' (HP)	EBls
'Charles Mallerin' (HT)	EBls
CHARLIE'S ROSE ('Tanellepa') (HT) 🏆H6	ESty LSRN SApu
CHARLOTTE ('Auspoly'^{PBR}) (S) 🏆H6	CRos EHyd ELan EPfP ESty LBuc LCro LOPS LRHS LSRN MBNS NLar NRHS SCoo SPer
CHARLOTTE VIELI ('Diclooker') (F)	IDic
CHARMANT ('Korpeligo'^{PBR}) (Min)	MAsh MFry
CHARTERED ('Diclingo') (F)	IDic
CHARTREUSE DE PARME ('Delviola') (S)	CBod CPou ESty ETWh MRav NLar
CHATSWORTH ('Tanotax'^{PBR}) (Patio/F) 🏆H6	SPer
CHECKMATE ('Diclanky') (ClF)	IDic MRav SApu
§ CHEEK TO CHEEK ('Poulslas'^{PBR}) (Courtyard Series) (ClMin)	LRHS MAsh SApu
CHEERFUL CHARLIE ('Cocquimmer'^{PBR}) (F)	LSRN MRav
CHERIE	see *R.* SONGS OF PRAISE
CHERRY BONICA ('Meipeporia'^{PBR}) (S)	CRos ECnt
CHERRY BRANDY '85 ('Tanryrandy'^{PBR}) (HT)	CSBt
CHERRY GIRL ('Korkosieb'^{PBR}) (F)	MAsh
CHERRY HINTON ('Dicprolong') (S)	IDic
'Chevy Chase' (Ra)	EBls LRHS MAsh MCot SApu
'Chewton Rose' (S)	EBls
CHIANTI ('Auswine') (S)	EBls ETWh NLar
CHICAGO PEACE ('Johnago') (HT)	CArg EBls SCob
CHILD OF ACHIEVEMENT	see *R.* BELLA
CHILD OF MY HEART ('Beapeace') (HT)	EBls
CHILTERNS ('Kortemma') (GC)	SCob
'Chinatown' (ClF) 🏆H6	CArg CTri EBls LRHS MAsh MPri MRav SApu SCob SPer
chinensis misapplied	see *R.* × *odorata*
chinensis Jacq. (S)	EBls
- 'Minima' *sensu stricto* hort.	see *R.* 'Rouletii'
- 'Mutabilis'	see *R.* × *odorata* 'Mutabilis'
- 'Old Blush'	see *R.* × *odorata* 'Pallida'
- 'Semperflorens' (S)	EBls
- var. ***spontanea*** (S)	WPGP
- 'White Beauty' (S)	WCot

	Name	Suppliers
	CHLOE ('Poulen003'[PBR]) (Renaissance Series) (S)	CPou ECnt ETWh EWTr LSRN NLar
	'Chloris' (A)	EBee ETWh MMuc
	CHOCA MOCHA ('Simcho') (F)	ESty
§	CHOCOLATE RIPPLES ('Simstripe') (Cl)	ESty
	CHOIR OF ANGELS	see *R.* OUR JANE
	CHRIS ('Kirsan'[PBR]) (ClHT)	CArg ESty LSRN SApu
	CHRISTIAN DIOR ('Meilie') (HT)	EBls
	CHRISTOPHER ('Cocopher') (HT)	LSRN
	CHRISTOPHER COLUMBUS ('Poulbico'[PBR]) (F) **new**	SApu
	CHRISTOPHER MARLOWE ('Ausjump'[PBR]) (S)	MAsh
§	'Chromatella' (N)	EBls
	'Chrysler Imperial' (HT)	EBls
	'Chuckles' (F)	ESty
§	CINCO DE MAYO ('Wekcobeju'[PBR]) (F) 🏆H6	MRav
	'Cinderella' (Min)	CSBt NLar
	'Cinderella' (Ra)	EBee MAsh
	'Cinderella' ambig.	CBod CDoC LRHS
	CINDERELLA ('Korfobalt') (ClS)	CPou ETWh
	cinnamomea misapplied	see *R. majalis*
	CITY LIGHTS ('Poulgan') (Patio)	CSBt
	CITY LIVERY ('Harhero 2000') (F)	LBuc LRHS MAsh
	CITY OF BELFAST ('Macci') (F)	EBls
	CITY OF CARLSBAD	see *R.* HANKY PANKY
	'City of Leeds' (F)	SPer
	CITY OF LONDON ('Harukfore') (F)	CSBt EBls
	CITY OF YORK	see *R.* 'Direktör Benschop'
	CLAIR MATIN ('Meimont') (ClS)	CPou EBls ETWh NLar
	CLAIRE AUSTIN ('Ausprior'[PBR]) (S)	CRos EHyd EPfP ESty LRHS MAsh NLar NRHS SCob SCoo SPoG
	'Claire Jacquier' (N)	CBod EBls ETWh SPer
	CLAIRE MARSHALL ('Harunite'[PBR]) (F)	ECnt ELon ESty MAsh
	CLAIRE ROSE ('Auslight'[PBR]) (S)	LSRN
	'Clarence House' (Cl)	CGro EBls EPfP LRHS MAsh
	CLARET ('Frykristal'[PBR]) (HT) 🏆H6	EPfP ESty MFry MRav SApu
	CLAUDE MONET ('Delstrirocrem') (Cl)	ESty
	CLAUDE MONET ('Jacdesa') (HT)	ESty
	CLEAR COVER ('Poultc013') (Towne & Country Series) (GC/S) **new**	CBod ETWh
	'Clementina Carbonieri' (T)	CBod EBls ETWh NLar
	CLEO ('Beebop') (HT)	LSRN
	CLEOPATRA ('Korverpea'[PBR]) (HT)	LRHS MAsh
	'Cliff Richard' (F)	CBod ESty LSRN
	'Climbing Alec's Red' (ClHT)	SPer
	'Climbing Allgold' (ClF)	EBls
	'Climbing Arthur Bell' (ClF)	CGro CSBt CTri ELon ESty ETWh MAsh MPri MSwo SApu SCob SPer SPoG SSea
	'Climbing Ballerina' (Ra)	CSBt
§	CLIMBING BARONNE EDMOND DE ROTHSCHILD ('Meigrisosar') (ClHT)	CSBt
	CLIMBING BETTINA ('Mepalsar') (ClHT)	EBls
	'Climbing Blessings' (ClHT)	EBls
	'Climbing Blue Moon' (ClHT)	CWld ELan ELon ESty SApu
§	'Climbing Captain Christy' (ClHT)	EBls
	'Climbing Cécile Brünner' (ClPoly) 🏆H5	CArg CSBt CTri EBls ECnt EPfP ETWh LCro LOPS LSRN MCot MRav NLar SApu SCob SEND SPer SSea
	'Climbing Château de Clos-Vougeot' (ClHT)	EBls
§	'Climbing Columbia' (ClHT)	EBls EShb ETWh SPer
	'Climbing Crimson Glory' (ClHT)	CBod CPou EBls EPfP ETWh MAsh SSea
§	'Climbing Devoniensis' (ClT)	CPou EBls ETWh
	'Climbing Ena Harkness' (ClHT)	CRos CTri EBee EBls MRav SEND SPoG
	'Climbing Étoile de Hollande' (ClHT) 🏆H5	CBod CSBt CTri EBee EBls EPfP ETWh LBuc LCro LOPS MPri MRav SApu SMad SPer SPoG SSea WBor
	'Climbing General MacArthur' (ClHT)	EBls
§	'Climbing Golden Dawn' (ClHT)	EBls
	'Climbing Home Sweet Home' (ClHT)	LSRN
	'Climbing Iceberg' (ClF) 🏆H5	CArg CBod CDoC CGro CRos CSBt CTri EBee EBls ELan EPfP ESty ETWh IArd LCro LEdu LOPS LSRN MAsh MFry MPri MRav MSwo NLar SApu SCob SGsty SPer SPoG SSea
	'Climbing Jazz'	see *R.* THAT'S JAZZ
	'Climbing Josephine Bruce' (ClHT)	EBls ETWh
§	'Climbing Lady Hillingdon' (ClT) 🏆H4	CArg CBod CWld EBls ELan EPfP ETWh LBuc LRHS LSRN MCot MRav NLar SPer SSea
	'Climbing Lady Sylvia' (ClHT)	CSBt EBls ETWh LRHS LSRN MAsh NRHS
	'Climbing Little White Pet'	see *R.* 'Félicité Perpétue'
	'Climbing Madame Butterfly' (ClHT) 🏆H6	EBls
	'Climbing Madame Caroline Testout' (ClHT)	CTri EBls ETWh SPer
	'Climbing Masquerade' (ClF)	CBod CGro CPou CTri EBls ELan ETWh MRav SApu SCob SPer SSea
	'Climbing Mrs Aaron Ward' (ClHT)	EBls
	'Climbing Mrs Herbert Stevens' (ClHT)	EBls EPfP ETWh LRHS MAsh MRav SEND SPer
	'Climbing Mrs Sam McGredy' (ClHT)	CArg CSBt EBls ETWh NLar
	'Climbing Niphetos' (ClT)	EBls
	'Climbing Ophelia' (ClHT)	CBod EBls ETWh
	CLIMBING ORANGE SUNBLAZE ('Meiji Katarsar') (ClMin)	SPer
§	'Climbing Paul Lédé' (ClT)	CBod EBls ETWh
	'Climbing Peace' (ClHT)	ETWh
	'Climbing Picture' (ClHT)	EBls
§	'Climbing Pompon de Paris' (ClMinCh)	CTri EBls MNrw MRav SEND SPer

	'Climbing Roundelay' (Cl)	EBls
	'Climbing Ruby Wedding' (ClHT)	LSRN
	'Climbing Shot Silk' (ClHT) ΨH6	EBls ETWh SPer
§	'Climbing Souvenir de la Malmaison' (ClBb)	EBls ETWh SPer
	'Climbing The Queen Elizabeth' (ClF)	CDoC EBls MAsh
	'Climbing White Cloud'	see *R.* WHITE CLOUD
	'Cloth of Gold'	see *R.* 'Chromatella'
	CLOUD NINE ('Fryextra'[PBR]) (HT)	CDoC MFry
	'Clytemnestra' (HM)	EBls
	COCO ('Korferse') (F)	LSRN
	COLCHESTER BEAUTY ('Cansend') (F)	ECnt
§	'Colonel Fabvier' (Ch)	EBls ETWh NLar
	colonial white	see *R.* 'Sombreuil'
	'Columbia' (HT)	CPou
	'Columbian'	see *R.* 'Climbing Columbia'
	'Commandant Beaurepaire' (Bb)	CPou EBls ETWh
	common moss	see *R.* × *centifolia* 'Muscosa'
	'Compassion' (ClHT) ΨH6	Widely available
	'Complicata' (G)	CPou CTri EBls EPfP ETWh LRHS MRav NLar SApu SEND SMad SPer
	'Comte de Chambord' misapplied	see *R.* 'Madame Boll'
	'Comtesse Cécile de Chabrillant' (HP)	CPou EBls ETWh
	'Comtesse de Lacépède' misapplied	see *R.* 'Du Maître d'Ecole'
§	'Comtesse de Murinais' (DMo)	EBls
	'Comtesse d'Oxford' (HP)	EBls
§	'Comtesse du Caÿla' (Ch)	EBls
	'Comtesse O'Gorman' (HP)	EBls
	'Comtesse Vandal' (HT)	EBls
	CONCERT	see *R.* CALYPSO
	'Conditorum' (G)	CPou EBls ETWh LEdu
	CONGRATULATIONS ('Korlift') (HT)	CBcs CBod CSBt EBls ECnt IArd LCro LOPS LSRN MGos MRav SApu SCob SCoo SPer SVic
§	'Conrad Ferdinand Meyer' (Ru)	EBee EBls
	'Constance Spry' (ClS) ΨH6	CArg CBod CDoC CRos CTri CWld EBee EBls EHyd EPfP ETWh LCro LOPS LRHS MMuc MRav MSwo NLar NRHS SCob SEND SPer
§	'Cooperi' (Ra)	CBod CRHN EBls EPfP ETWh EWTr SMad SSea WKif WPGP
	Cooper's Burmese	see *R.* 'Cooperi'
	'Copenhagen' (ClHT)	EBls
	COPPER LIGHTS ('Simhigh') (HT)	ESty
	'Coral Creeper' (ClHT)	CRHN
	'Coral Dawn' (ClHT)	EBls
	CORAL GEM ('Simplan') (HT)	ESty
	CORAL PALACE	see *R.* IMAGINATION ('Pouldron')
	CORAL SWEET DREAM ('Fryrader') (Patio)	MFry
	'Coralie' (D)	EBls
	'Cornelia' (HM) ΨH6	CArg CBcs CTri EBee EBls EPfP ETWh IArd LCro LOPS LRHS LSRN MAsh MRav MWat NLar SCob SMad SPer
	CORONATION STREET ('Wekswetrup') (F)	LSRN
	'Coryana' (S)	EBls ETWh
	corymbifera (S)	EBls
	'Cosimo Ridolfi' (G)	EBls
	COSMOPOLITAN ('Simgrid') (HT)	ESty
	cottage maid	see *R.* × *centifolia* 'Unique Panachée'
	COTTAGE ROSE ('Ausglisten') (S)	LSRN
	COUNTESS CELESTE	see *R.* IMAGINATION
	COUNTESS OF WESSEX ('Beacream') (S)	EBls LRHS MAsh NRHS
	COUNTRY MUSIC ('Harcheer') (S)	LSRN
	COUNTY OF YORKSHIRE ('Korstarnow'[PBR]) (GC) ΨH6	ESty
	'Coupe d'Hébé' (Bb)	EBls
	COURAGE ('Poulduf'[PBR]) (HT)	ECnt
	'Cramoisi Supérieur' (Ch)	EBls ETWh
	CRANFORD ('Frylustre') (HT)	MFry
	CRAZY FOR YOU ('Wekroalt'[PBR]) (F) ΨH6	EBls ESty LBuc LRHS LSRN
	CREAM ABUNDANCE ('Harflax'[PBR]) (Abundance Series) (F)	SApu SSea
	CREAM DREAM ('Koromtar') (HT)	CTri
	CREAMCRACKER ('Dicorigin') (F)	IDic
	CRÈME CARAMEL ('Frynesca') (HT)	MFry
	CRÈME DE LA CRÈME ('Gancre'[PBR]) (ClHT)	CDoC CRos CSBt EBee EBls ECnt ELan ESty ETWh LRHS MAsh MRav SApu SPer SPoG SSea
	'Crépuscule' (N)	EBee EBls ETWh EWTr NLar
	crested moss	see *R.* × *centifolia* 'Cristata'
	CRIMSON CASCADE ('Fryclimbdown') (ClHT) ΨH6	CDoC ESty LBuc MAsh MFry MRav MSwo SApu SPer SPoG SSea
	crimson damask	see *R. gallica* var. *officinalis*
	'Crimson Descant' (ClHT)	ECnt
	'Crimson Glory' (HT)	CArg CTri EBls
	'Crimson Shower' (Ra)	CArg CBod CRos CTri ELan ETWh LRHS MBNS MMuc MRav MSwo NLar SApu SEND SPer WHer
	CRIMSON SWEET DREAM ('Frynogo') (Patio)	CSBt ECnt ESty MFry
	'Cristata'	see *R.* × *centifolia* 'Cristata'
	CROCUS ROSE ('Ausquest'[PBR]) (S) ΨH6	EHyd EPfP LCro LOPS LRHS NLar NRHS SCob SPer
	CROWN PRINCESS MARGARETA ('Auswinter'[PBR]) (S) ΨH6	CRos EHyd ELan EPfP ESty LBuc LCro LOPS LRHS NLar NRHS SCob SCoo SPer SPoG
	cuisse de nymphe	see *R.* 'Great Maiden's Blush'
	CUMBERLAND ('Harnext'[PBR]) (ClF)	CBod ETWh
	'Cupid' (ClHT)	EBls ETWh SPer
I	'Cutie' (Patio)	ESty
	cymosa	EBls
	- 'Rebecca Rushforth' (Cl)	EBee WPGP
	'Cynthia Brooke' (HT)	EBls
	DACAPO ('Poulcy012'[PBR]) (Courtyard Series) (ClPatio)	ECnt
	'D'Aguesseau' (G)	ETWh
	DAILY SKETCH ('Macai') (F)	ESty
	'Dainty Bess' (HT)	EBls ETWh
	'Dainty Maid' (F)	EBls

'Daisy Hill' ('Macrantha' hybrid) ♀H7	EBls
× ***damascena*** var. ***bifera***	see *R.* × *damascena* var. *semperflorens*
- 'Kazanlik' (D)	EBls ETWh
§ - 'Professeur Émile Perrot' (D)	LEdu WFar
§ - var. ***semperflorens*** (D) ♀H6	CPou EBls ETWh NLar SSea
- 'Trigintipetala' misapplied	see *R.* × *damascena* 'Professeur Émile Perrot'
§ - 'Versicolor' (D)	EBls SSea
'Dame Edith Helen' (HT)	EBls
DAME JUDI DENCH ('Ausquaker') (HM) **new**	CRos ESty MAsh MBNS SCoo
'Danaë' (HM)	EBls ETWh
DANCING QUEEN ('Fryfestoon') (ClHT) ♀H6	CArg CDoC CGro ECnt LBuc LRHS LSRN MAsh MFry MRav SApu SSea
DANCING SUNSET ('Guesunusal') (ClHT)	ESty
DANIEL ('Webwhite') (HT)	ESty
DANNY BOY ('Dicxcon'[PBR]) (Patio)	IDic LSRN
DANSE DES SYLPHES ('Malcair') (ClF)	EBls
'Danse du Feu' (ClF)	CArg CBcs CSBt CTri EBls ELan ETWh LRHS MAsh MRav MWat SApu SCob SMad SPer
'Daphne' ambig.	EBls LSRN
DARCEY BUSSELL ('Ausdecorum'[PBR]) (S) ♀H6	CGro CRos CSBt EBee ECnt EHyd ELan EPfP ESty LBuc LCro LOPS LRHS LSRN MAsh MGos NLar NRHS SPer SPoG
'Darling Jenny' (HT)	LSRN
DAVID WHITFIELD ('Gana') (F)	LSRN
davidii (S)	EBls WPav
DAVID'S STAR ('Hordadstar') (HT)	LSRN
DAWN CHORUS ('Dicquasar') (HT) ♀H6	CSBt EPfP ESty LRHS MAsh MRav SApu SCob SPer SPoG SSea
'Daybreak' (HM)	CPou CTri EBls ETWh NLar
'De la Grifferaie'	EBls
'De Meaux'	see *R.* × *centifolia* 'De Meaux'
'De Meaux, White'	see *R.* 'White de Meaux'
§ 'De Resht' (DPo) ♀H7	CArg CBod CDoC CPou CTri EBls ECnt EPfP ETWh EWTr LBuc LRHS MAsh MCot MPri MRav NLar SPer
DEAR BARBARA ('Rawbar') (HT)	LSRN
DEAR DAD ('Smi87-02') (HT)	ESty
'Dear Daughter' (F)	ESty
DEAR JOAN ('Rawjo') (F)	LSRN
§ DEAR MARGARET ('Raw293') (HT)	LSRN
DEAR MICHAEL ('Raw1065') (F)	LSRN
'Dearest' (F)	CArg CTri SCob SPer
'Debbie Thomas' (HT)	LSRN
DEB'S DELIGHT ('Legsweet'[PBR]) (F)	LSRN
'Debutante' (Ra) ♀H7	CRHN EBls ETWh EWTr
DEEP IMPRESSION ('Tan03162') (F) **new**	MFry
'Deep Secret' (HT)	CArg CBcs CSBt CTri EBls ECnt ELan ELon EPfP ESty LBuc LRHS MAsh MCot MFry MPri MRav MWat SApu SPer SSea
'Deidre Hall' (HT)	LSRN
DELIGHTFUL ('Curspoglo') (ClMin)	ECnt ESty
DELLA BALFOUR ('Harblend'[PBR]) (ClHT)	EBls
'Deschamps' (N)	EBls
DESDEMONA ('Auskindling'[PBR]) (HM)	CDoC CGro CRos ECnt EHyd LRHS MAsh MBNS NRHS
'Designer Sunset' (Patio)	CDoC MAsh
§ 'Desprez à Fleur Jaune' (N)	EBls ETWh IArd LRHS
'Deuil de Paul Fontaine' (Mo)	EBls
'Devoniensis' (ClT)	see *R.* 'Climbing Devoniensis'
DIAMOND ('Korgazell'[PBR]) (Patio) ♀H6	LSRN SApu
DIAMOND ANNIVERSARY ('Morsixty') (Min)	CRos LSRN
'Diamond Celebration' (HT)	LSRN
DIAMOND DAYS ('Hartribe'[PBR]) (HT)	ESty LSRN MRav SPoG
DIAMOND DAYS FOREVER ('Fryjess'[PBR]) (F)	ECnt LSRN MFry SApu
DIAMOND EYES ('Wekwibypur') (Min)	CBod ECnt ESty
'Diamond Jubilee' (HT)	CSBt EBls MAsh
DIAMOND JUBILEE ('Tan022260') (HT)	CArg ELan MFry
DIAMOND WEDDING ('Raw1150') (F) **new**	ESty
'Diamond Wishes'	see *R.* MISTY HIT
DIANA ('Tananaid'[PBR]) (HT)	LSRN
DICK'S DELIGHT ('Dicwhistle') (GC)	LSRN
DIENIE STEWART ('Dicpraise') (F)	IDic
DIORESSENCE ('Deldiore') (F)	ESty
§ 'Direktör Benschop' (ClF)	EBls MCot
DIXIELAND LINDA ('Beadix') (ClHT)	EBls LRHS MAsh
DIZZY HEIGHTS ('Fryblissful'[PBR]) (ClHT) ♀H6	CDoC ELon MAsh MFry MRav SApu SPer SSea
'Docteur Grill' (T)	EBls
'Doctor Edward Deacon' (HT)	EBls
'Doctor Huey' (Cl)	CRHN EBls
DOCTOR JO ('Fryatlanta'[PBR]) (F)	MFry
'Doctor W. Van Fleet' (Ra)	EBls
DOLCE VITA ('Delcentoran') (F)	CBod ESty
DOLLY ('Poulvision') (F)	LSRN
'Donald Prior' (F)	EBls
'Doncasteri'	EBls
DONNA ('Pekcoupamaple') (HT)	LSRN
'Doreen' (HT)	LSRN
DORIS MORGAN ('Brimorgan') (Min) **new**	SSea
'Doris Tysterman' (HT)	CTri EBls SCob SPer
DOROTHY ('Cocrocket'[PBR]) (F)	LSRN MRav
DOROTHY HOUSE ('Fryniffi') (F)	MFry
'Dorothy Perkins' (Ra)	CArg CRHN CTri EBls ETWh MAsh MFry MRav NPer SApu SCob SPer WHer
'Dortmund' (S) ♀H7	CBod EBls ETWh NLar SPer

DOUBLE DELIGHT ('Andeli') (HT)	EBls ELan ESty LSRN SCob SPer SSea
DOUBLE GOLD ('Savadouble') (Patio) **new**	SSea
DOUGLAS ('Cocfresco') (F)	LSRN
DREAM LOVER ('Peayetti'[PBR]) (Patio)	ESty
'Dreaming Spires' (ClHT)	MSwo SApu SPer
'Dresden Doll' (MinMo)	EBls
§ 'Du Maître d'Ecole' (G)	EBls WHer
DUBLIN BAY ('Macdub') (ClF) 🏆H6	CArg CBod CDoC CRos CSBt CTri EBls ECnt ELan ELon EPfP ETWh IArd LRHS LSRN MAsh MCot MFry MPri MRav MSwo MWat NLar SApu SCob SPer SPoG SSea WBor
'Duc de Guiche' (G) 🏆H7	EBls EPfP ETWh MMuc NLar SPer WHer
DUCHESS OF CORNWALL ('Tan97157') (HT) 🏆H6	CBod CDoC CSBt EBee EBls ECnt ESty ETWh MFry MRav MWat SApu SMad SPer
DUCHESS OF DEVONSHIRE ('Stortebekerkal 2017') (HT) **new**	MFry
'Duchess of Portland'	see *R.* 'Portlandica'
DUCHESS OF YORK	see *R.* SUNSEEKER
'Duchesse d'Angoulême' (Ce × G) 🏆H7	CBod EBls ETWh
'Duchesse d'Auerstädt' (N)	EBls
'Duchesse de Berry' (G) **new**	CPou
'Duchesse de Brabant' (HT)	EBls
'Duchesse de Buccleugh' (G)	EBls ETWh
§ 'Duchesse de Montebello' (G) 🏆H7	CPou EBls ETWh EWTr NLar SPer
'Duchesse de Rohan' (Ce × HP)	EBls
'Duke of Edinburgh' (HP)	EBls
DUKE OF EDINBURGH (Patio)	see *R.* THE GOLD AWARD ROSE
'Duke of Wellington' (HP)	CPou EBls ETWh
'Duke of Windsor' (HT)	SPer
DUNHAM MASSEY ('Beajelly') (S)	EBee EBls LRHS MAsh
'Dunwich Rose' (SpH)	EBls EPfP ETWh NLar SPer WCot
§ 'Duplex' (S)	EBls ETWh
'Dupontii' (S) 🏆H6	EBls ETWh NLar SPer
'Dupuy Jamain' (HP)	EBls
'Dusky Maiden' (F)	CBod EBls ETWh
'Dutch Gold' (HT)	CArg ELon
DWARF FAIRY ('Korweenu') (Min)	MAsh
DYNAMIC DUO ('Fryvogue') (F)	ECnt ESty
DYNAMITE	see *R.* HIGH FLYER
'E.H. Morse'	see *R.* 'Ernest H. Morse'
'Easlea's Golden Rambler' (Ra) 🏆H5	CArg EBls ETWh MRav NLar
§ EASY DOES IT ('Harpageant'[PBR]) (F) 🏆H6	CBod CDoC ECnt ESty ETWh LRHS MRav NLar
EASY GOING ('Harflow'[PBR]) (F) 🏆H6	IArd MAsh
§ EBB TIDE ('Weksmopur'[PBR]) (F)	CBod CGro CSBt ECnt EPfP ESty LRHS MAsh SApu SPoG
ecae (S)	EBls
'Éclair' (HP)	EBls
'Eddie's Crimson' (*moyesii* hybrid)	LSRN
'Eddie's Jewel' (*moyesii* hybrid)	EBls LSRN
EDEN ROSE '88 ('Meiviolin') (ClHT)	EBls ETWh MAsh SApu SGsty SPer
'Edith Bellenden' (RH)	EBls
EDITH HOLDEN ('Chewlegacy') (F)	EBls
EDWARD'S ROSE ('Smi73/7/97') (F)	ESty LSRN MRav MWat
eglanteria	see *R. rubiginosa*
EGLANTYNE ('Ausmak'[PBR]) (S)	CDoC CRos EHyd ELan EPfP LCro LOPS LRHS NRHS SCob SPer
'Eleanor' (Patio)	LSRN
ELEANOR ('Poulberin'[PBR]) (S)	CBod CPou ECnt ETWh LSRN
§ ***elegantula*** 'Persetosa' (S)	EBls ETWh NLar SPer
§ ELINA ('Dicjana') (HT) 🏆H6	EBls ECnt LSRN MRav SPer
'Elizabeth Harkness' (HT)	EBls SPer
'Elizabeth Harwood' (Cl)	EBls
ELIZABETH OF GLAMIS ('Macel') (F)	CTri EBls SPer
ELIZABETH STUART ('Maselstu') (Generosa Series) (S)	LSRN
ELLE ('Meibderos'[PBR]) (HT)	LSRN
ELLEN ('Auscup') (S)	LSRN
'Ellen Willmott' (HT)	EBls ETWh EWTr SPer
'Elmshorn' (S)	EBls
ELOISE ('Kirsandra'[PBR]) (HT)	LSRN
ELVIS ('Adablarop'[PBR]) (HT)	LSRN
EMILIA MARIA	see *R.* LA ROSE DE MOLINARD
EMILY ('Ausburton') (S)	LSRN
'Emily Gray' (Ra)	CRHN EBee EBls ETWh LBuc LSRN MAsh MPri NLar SCob SPer WHer
EMILY VICTORIA ('Boshipeacon') (F)	LSRN
'Empereur du Maroc' (HP)	EBee EBls ETWh
'Ena Harkness' (HT)	CDoC CTri EBee EBls ELan LBuc LRHS NRHS SCob
ENCHANTRESS ('Tan97281'[PBR]) (HT)	EBee SSea
§ 'Enfant de France' (HP)	EBls LSRN
ENGLAND'S ROSE ('Auslounge'[PBR]) (S)	CRos MAsh
ENGLISH GARDEN ('Ausbuff') (S)	CArg CTri LSRN
'English Miss' (F)	CArg CDoC CPou EBls ECnt LRHS MAsh MFry MRav MWat SApu SCob SPer SPoG
ENGLISH SONNET	see *R.* SAMARITAN
'Erfurt' (HM)	EBee EBls ETWh SPer
§ 'Ernest H. Morse' (HT)	CSBt CTri EBls SPer
ESCAPADE ('Harpade') (F) 🏆H6	EBls
'Esmé' (HT) **new**	ETWh
ESPECIALLY FOR YOU ('Fryworthy'[PBR]) (HT) 🏆H6	CSBt ESty LSRN MFry SApu SSea
ESSEX ('Poulnoz') (GC)	EBls SApu SCob SPer
'Etain' (Ra)	ECnt
§ 'Étendard' (ClHT)	CDoC EBls ETWh MRav NLar SPer SPoG
ETERNALLY YOURS ('Macspeego'[PBR]) (HT)	ESty
ETERNITY ('Ricity') (Min)	LRHS
ETERNITY ('Twoetern') (HT)	MAsh
'Ethel' (Ra)	CBod CPou EBls ETWh LSRN NLar SApu

	Name	Suppliers
	'Étoile de Hollande' (HT)	CArg CBod CDoC CTri EBls EHyd ELan LBuc LRHS LSRN MAsh MCot NLar SCob WSpi
	'Etoile de Lyon' (T)	EBls
	'Eugénie Guinoisseau' (Mo)	CPou EBls ETWh
	EUPHORIA ('Intereup'PBR) (GC/S)	SApu
	EUPHRATES ('Harunique') (*persica* hybrid)	EBls
	EUREKA ('Meizambaizt'PBR) (HT) **new**	MAsh
	'Eva' (HM)	EBls
	'Evangeline' (Ra)	EBls
	EVE RUGGIEN ('Adarylop') (HT)	LSRN
	EVELYN ('Aussaucer') (S)	CArg CSBt EPfP ESty LSRN NLar SApu SLon
§	EVELYN FISON ('Macev') (F)	CSBt CTri EBls LSRN SCob SPer
	'Evelyn May' (HT)	EBls LRHS LSRN MAsh NRHS
	'Everest Double Fragrance' (F)	EBls
	'Excelsa' (Ra)	CBod CSBt CTri EBls EPfP ETWh IArd LBuc MAsh SCob SGsty SPoG WBor
	EYE OF THE TIGER ('Chewbullseye'PBR) (S)	CBod CDoC CRos EBee EHyd ELan EPfP ESty ETWh LRHS MAsh MFry MPri NRHS SLon SMad SPoG SSea
	EYEOPENER ('Interop') (S/GC)	EBls
	EYES FOR YOU ('Pejbigeye') (F) 𝕐H6	CDoC CGro CRos CSBt EBee EPfP ESty ETWh GBin LRHS MAsh MFry MPri NLar NRHS SApu SLon SMad SPer SPoG SSea WKif
	'F.E. Lester'	see *R.* 'Francis E. Lester'
§	'F.J. Grootendorst' (Ru)	CBod EBls ETWh SPer WHer
	FAB AT 50 ('Woraunt') (F)	LSRN
	FABULOUS AT 40 ('Webcountry') (F)	LSRN
	FABULOUS AT 50 ('Rawfabsal') (F)	LSRN
	FABULOUS AT 65 ('Raw1041') (F)	LSRN
	FABULOUS AT 70	LSRN
	FABULOUS AT 80 ('Rawcox') (F)	LSRN
	FAB-U-LOUS! ('Forfab') (HT)	ESty
	'Fabvier'	see *R.* 'Colonel Fabvier'
	FAIR EVA ('Seaeva') (Ra/GC)	ESty
	'Fairy Rose'	see *R.* 'The Fairy'
	FAITHFUL FRIEND ('Beachallenge') (S)	EBls LSRN
	FALSTAFF ('Ausverse'PBR) (S)	CArg CRos CSBt EHyd EPfP LCro LOPS LRHS LSRN MRav MSwo NLar NRHS SCob SPer
	'Fantin-Latour' (Ce) 𝕐H6	CArg CTri EBls ECnt EHyd ELan ETWh LEdu LRHS MCot MMuc NLar SEND SMad SPer
	fargesii hort.	see *R. moyesii* var. *fargesii*
	farreri f. ***persetosa***	see *R. elegantula* 'Persetosa'
§	FASCINATION ('Poulmax'PBR) (F) 𝕐H6	CArg LRHS MAsh MFry SApu SCob SPer
	FATHER'S FAVOURITE ('Gandoug'PBR) (F)	LSRN
	fedtschenkoana misapplied	SPer
	fedtschenkoana Regel	EBls
	aff. ***fedtschenkoana*** **new**	ETWh
	FÉE DES NEIGES	see *R.* ICEBERG
	'Felicia' (HM) 𝕐H6	CArg CSBt CTri EBee EBls ECnt ELan ETWh LRHS MAsh MCot MMuc MRav MSwo NLar SApu SCob SEND SPer SSea WKif
	'Félicité Parmentier' (A × D) 𝕐H6	CArg EBls EPfP ETWh LRHS NLar SPer
§	'Félicité Perpétue' (Ra) 𝕐H6	CArg CBcs CBod CTri EBee EBls EHyd EPfP ETWh LRHS MRav MSwo MWat NLar SApu SCob SEND SPer SSea WFar
	'Fellemberg' (ClCh)	EBls ETWh
	FELLOWSHIP ('Harwelcome') (F) 𝕐H6	EBls LCro LOPS SCob SSea
	'Ferdinand Pichard' (Bb) 𝕐H6	CArg CPou CRos CSBt CTri EBls ECnt EHyd ELon EPfP ESty ETWh EWTr LCro LOPS LRHS MAsh MCot MPri MRav NLar NRHS SApu SMad SPer SSea WFar WKif
	FERDY ('Keitoli'PBR) (GC)	EBls SApu SPer
I	'Fern's Rose' (F)	LSRN
	ferruginea	see *R. glauca* Pourr.
	FESTIVAL ('Kordialo'PBR) (Patio)	CDoC CGro MRav SPer
	FESTIVE JEWEL ('Beacost') (S)	EBls EPfP LRHS
	FIGHTING TEMERAIRE ('Austrava'PBR) (S)	CRos EHyd EPfP LBuc LRHS MAsh NRHS
§	***filipes*** 'Kiftsgate' (Ra) 𝕐H6	CArg CBcs CBod CDoC CGro CSBt CTri EBee EBls ECnt ELan EPfP ETWh GKin LEdu LRHS MAsh MFry MRav MWat NLar NRHS SApu SCob SEND SPer SSea WBor WKif
§	'Fimbriata' (Ru)	CBod CPou EBls ETWh LEdu NLar SPer
	FIONA ('Meibeluxen') (S/GC)	EBls LSRN MSwo
	FIRESTAR	see *R.* EASY DOES IT
	FIRST GREAT WESTERN ('Oracharpam'PBR) (HT)	CSBt ELon ESty
	'Fisher and Holmes' (HP)	EBls ETWh
	FLIRT ('Korkopapp'PBR) (F)	MAsh
	'Flora' (Ra)	EBls
	'Flora McIvor' (RH)	EBls
	'Florence Mary Morse' (S)	SDix
	FLOWER CARPET AMBER ('Noa97400a'PBR) (GC) 𝕐H6	CDoC CGro CRos CSBt EBls EHyd EPfP LBuc LCro LOPS LRHS MAsh MPri NRHS SPoG SSea
	'Flower Carpet Coral'PBR (GC) 𝕐H6	CRos CSBt EBls EHyd EPfP LBuc LRHS LSRN MAsh MPri NRHS SApu SPer SSea
	FLOWER CARPET GOLD ('Noalesa'PBR) (GC)	CDoC CGro CRos EBls ECnt EHyd LBuc LRHS MAsh MPri NRHS SApu SPoG SSea
	FLOWER CARPET PINK	see *R.* PINK FLOWER CARPET
	FLOWER CARPET PINK SUPREME ('Noa168098f') (GC)	EBls MAsh
	FLOWER CARPET RED VELVET ('Noare'PBR) (GC/S) 𝕐H6	CGro CRos EBls EHyd ELan EPfP LBuc LCro LOPS LRHS MAsh MPri NRHS SCoo SPer
	FLOWER CARPET RUBY (GC)	CDoC CRos EBls EHyd LBuc LRHS LSRN MAsh MPri NRHS SApu SPoG
	FLOWER CARPET SCARLET ('Noa83100b'PBR) (GC) 𝕐H6	CDoC CRos EBls LBuc LCro LOPS LRHS MAsh NRHS SSea
	FLOWER CARPET SUNSET ('Deseo') (S)	CDoC CGro CRos LRHS MAsh MPri
§	FLOWER CARPET SUNSHINE ('Noason'PBR) (GC) 𝕐H6	CDoC CRos EBls EHyd LCro LOPS LRHS MAsh MPri NRHS SCoo SPer

FLOWER CARPET WHITE ('Noaschnee') (GC) 🏆H6	CDoC CGro CRos CTri EBls ECnt EHyd EPfP LCro LOPS LRHS LSRN MAsh MPri NRHS SApu SCoo SPer SPoG SSea
FLOWER POWER ('Frycassia'PBR) (Patio) 🏆H6	CDoC CSBt ECnt ESty LCro LOPS LRHS MAsh MFry MPri MRav SApu SPoG
FLOWER POWER GOLD ('Fryneon') (Patio)	CDoC CSBt ECnt ESty LRHS MAsh MFry MPri NRHS SApu SPoG
§ ***foetida*** (S)	EBls ETWh SPer
§ - 'Bicolor' (S)	EBls ETWh NLar SPer
§ - 'Persiana' (S)	EBls
foliolosa	EBls
'Follette' (Cl)	EBls
FOND MEMORIES ('Kirfelix'PBR) (Patio)	ESty LSRN SCoo
FOR YOU WITH LOVE ('Fryjangle') (Patio)	LBuc LSRN MAsh MFry
FOR YOUR EYES ONLY ('Cheweyesup'PBR) (S)	CArg CBod CDoC CGro CRos CSBt EBee ECnt EHyd ELon EPfP ESty ETWh LBuc LRHS LSRN MAsh MFry MNrw MPri MRav NLar NRHS SApu SCoo SMad SPer SPoG SSea
FORGET ME NOT ('Coccharm'PBR) (HT)	ESty
forrestiana (S)	EBls ETWh WPav
× ***fortuneana*** (Ra)	EBls
Fortune's double yellow	see *R.* × *odorata* 'Pseudindica'
'Fountain' (S)	EBls
FOXY LADY ('Simmem') (HT)	ESty
FRAGONARD ('Delparviro'PBR) (HT)	ESty
FRAGRANT BEAUTY ('Smi152-1-4') (HT)	ESty
FRAGRANT CLOUD ('Tanellis') (HT)	CArg CBcs CRos CTri EBls ELan ELon EPfP LBuc LRHS MAsh MGos MRav SCob SPer SPoG
'Fragrant Delight' (F) 🏆H6	CArg CDoC CSBt EBls ELan MRav MWat SCob SPer
FRAGRANT DREAM ('Dicodour') (HT)	ESty SCob SSea
FRAGRANT MEMORIES ('Korpastato'PBR) (HT)	CSBt
FRAGRANT PLUM ('Aroplumi') (HT)	ESty
'Francesca' (HM)	EBls ETWh LSRN NLar SPer
'Francis Copple' (S)	EBls
'Francis Dubreuil' (T)	EBls
§ 'Francis E. Lester' (HM/Ra) 🏆H6	CBod CPou CRHN CRos CSam EBee EBls EHyd ELan EPfP ETWh LCro LOPS LRHS MCot MMuc NLar NRHS SApu SEND SPer SSea
× ***francofurtana*** misapplied	see *R.* 'Impératrice Joséphine'
- 'Empress Josephine'	see *R.* 'Impératrice Joséphine'
'François Juranville' (Ra) 🏆H6	CArg CRHN EBee EBls EPfP ETWh LRHS MMuc MRav NLar SApu SEND SLon SPer WFar WHer
§ 'Frau Karl Druschki' (HP)	EBls ETWh
'Fred Loads' (F) 🏆H7	EBls
FREDDIE MERCURY ('Batmercury') (HT)	ESty LSRN
FREE SPIRIT ('Fryjeru'PBR) (F) 🏆H6	ECnt MFry
FREEDOM ('Dicjem') (HT) 🏆H6	CArg CDoC CTri EBls ECnt MRav SApu SCob SPer
FREEDOM ('Tan97544') (HT)	MWat
'Frensham' (F)	CBcs EBls SSea
FRIEND FOR LIFE ('Cocnanne'PBR) (F) 🏆H6	CDoC LSRN MRav
FRIENDS FOREVER ('Korapriber') (F) 🏆H6	CSBt EPfP LSRN MAsh SLon
FRIENDSHIP OF STRANGERS ('633D9') (Cl)	EBls
FRILLY CUFF ('Beajingle') (S)	EBls LRHS MAsh
'Fritz Nobis' (S) 🏆H7	CArg CPou EBls ETWh NLar SPer
FROTHY ('Macfrothy') (Patio)	ECnt ESty
'Fru Dagmar Hastrup' (Ru) 🏆H7	CArg CBcs CBod CDoC CSBt CTho CTri EBee EBls ECnt ELan EPfP ETWh EWTr LBuc LRHS MAsh MFry MSwo NLar SApu SCob SEND SPer
'Frühlingsanfang' (SpH)	EBls
'Frühlingsduft' (SpH)	CBod EBls ETWh
'Frühlingsgold' (SpH) 🏆H7	CArg CTho EBls ELan ETWh NLar SCob SPer
'Frühlingsmorgen' (SpH) 🏆H7	CBod EBls ETWh SCob SMad SPer
'Frühlingsschnee' (SpH)	EBls
'Frühlingszauber' (SpH)	EBls
'Fulgens'	see *R.* 'Malton'
GAIANA (PatioHit Series) **new**	SPad
§ ***gallica*** (G)	EBls ETWh
§ - var. ***officinalis*** (G) 🏆H7	CBod CRos CTri EBls EPfP ETWh GPoy LEdu LRHS MAsh MHer MNHC MRav NLar SApu SPer SRms WFar WHer
- 'Velutiniflora' (G)	EBls
§ - 'Versicolor' (G) 🏆H7	CArg CBod CDoC CSBt CTri EBee EBls ECnt EHyd EPfP ETWh GPoy LEdu LRHS LSRN MAsh MCot MHer MNHC MRav NLar NRHS NSti SApu SCob SMad SPer SSea WBor WKif
GALWAY BAY ('Macba') (ClHT)	CArg CPou ETWh LRHS MAsh NLar SPer
GARDEN FUN	see *R.* GARTENSPASS
GARDEN OF ROSES	see *R.* JOIE DE VIVRE
'Gardeners' Glory'PBR (ClHT) 🏆H6	CArg CDoC CSBt ECnt ESty LBuc LRHS MAsh MFry MPri MRav SApu SPoG SSea
GARDENERS' JOY ('Beadrum') (S)	EBls
'Gardenia' (Ra)	EBls ETWh MMuc MSwo NLar SPer
'Garnette Carol'	see *R.* 'Carol Amling'
'Garnette Pink'	see *R.* 'Carol Amling'
§ GARTENSPASS ('Korgohowa'PBR) (F) **new**	CBod ETWh
'Gaujard'	see *R.* ROSE GAUJARD
'Gelbe Dagmar Hastrup'	see *R.* YELLOW DAGMAR HASTRUP
GEMINI ('Jacnepal') (HT)	ESty
'Général Jacqueminot' (HP)	EBls
'Général Kléber' (CeMo) 🏆H7	EBls
§ 'Général Schablikine' (T)	EBls ETWh NLar
GENESIS ('Fryjuicy'PBR) (Patio)	CDoC CGro ECnt MFry MRav
gentiliana misapplied	see *R.* 'Polyantha Grandiflora'
gentiliana H. Lév. & Variot	see *R. multiflora* var. *cathayensis*
GENTLE HERMIONE (S) ('Ausrumba'PBR)	CDoC CGro CRos EHyd ELan EPfP LBuc LCro LOPS LRHS MAsh NLar NRHS SCob SPer SPoG
GENTLE TOUCH ('Diclulu') (Min/Patio)	CSBt MRav SPer
GEOFF HAMILTON ('Ausham'PBR) (S)	LSRN MAsh MBNS SCob SPer

'Geoffrey Smith' (Cl)	LSRN NDal
'Georg Arends' (HP)	EBls
GEORGE ('Simetna') (F)	ESty
GEORGE BEST ('Dichimanher'PBR) (Patio) 🏆H6	IDic LSRN
'George Dickson' (HT)	EBls
GEORGE'S PRIDE ('Manpride') (Min)	LSRN
'Georges Vibert' (G)	EBls ETWh
'Geranium' (*moyesii* hybrid) 🏆H6	CArg CBcs CDoC CTri EBls ELan EPfP ETWh EWTr IArd MRav NLar SApu SPer
GERBE D'OR	see *R.* CASINO
'Gerbe Rose' (Ra)	WHer
GERTRUDE JEKYLL ('Ausbord'PBR) (S) 🏆H6	CArg CDoC CGro CRos CSBt CTri EBee ECnt EHyd ELan EPfP ESty GBin LCro LOPS LRHS LSRN MAsh MBNS MGos MRav MSwo NLar NRHS SCob SCoo SPer SPoG SSea WKif
GETTYSBURG ('Poulen001'PBR) (F) **new**	ETWh
'Ghislaine de Féligonde' (HM) 🏆H5	CBod CSam EBee EBls EPfP ESty ETWh LRHS MAsh MCot NLar SApu SEND SMad SPer WBor WMal
GHITA	see *R.* MILLIE
§ GIARDINA ('Tan97289'PBR) (Cl)	ESty
gigantea	WPGP
gigantea* × *longicuspis	WPGP
GIGGLES ('Frynoodle'PBR) (Patio)	MFry SCoo
GINGER SYLLABUB ('Harjolina'PBR) (ClHT)	CGro CPou ECnt ESty MRav SPer SPoG
GIPSY BOY	see *R.* 'Zigeunerknabe'
giraldii (S)	EBls
GISELA'S DELIGHT ('Horpink') (S)	EBls
GLAD TIDINGS ('Tantide') (F)	CTri EBls MRav MWat SPer
GLAMIS CASTLE ('Auslevel'PBR) (S)	CArg CTri SCob SCoo
glauca Vill. ex Lois.	see *R. caesia* subsp. *vosagiaca*
glauca ambig.	MHer MSwo SCob
§ ***glauca*** Pourr. (S) 🏆H7	CBcs CDoC CSBt CSpe CTri EBee EBls ECnt ELan ELon EPfP ETWh EWTr LEdu LRHS MMuc MRav NLar SApu SDix SEND SGol SPer SPoG SSea WCot
'Glenfiddich' (F)	CArg CTri LSRN SPer
'Glenn Dale' (Cl)	ETWh
GLOBAL BEAUTY ('Tan 94448') (HT)	CBod EBee ECnt ELon ETWh MFry MRav SMad SPer SSea
'Gloire de Bruxelles' (HP)	EBls
'Gloire de Dijon' (ClT)	CArg CSBt CTri CWld EBee EBls ECnt ELan ETWh LSRN MCot MRav MWat NLar SCob SPer
'Gloire de Ducher' (HP)	EBls ETWh
'Gloire de France' (G) 🏆H7	CArg EBls ETWh NLar WHer
'Gloire de Guilan' (D)	CPou ETWh
'Gloire des Mousseuses' (CeMo)	CBod CPou EBls ETWh
'Gloire Lyonnaise' (HP)	CPou EBls ETWh MMuc
glomerata (Cl) **new**	WFar
'Gloria Mundi' (Poly)	EBls ETWh
GLORIANA ('Chewpope'PBR) (ClMin)	CArg CBod CDoC ECnt ESty LBuc MAsh MRav SPer SPoG SSea
'Glory of Seale' (S)	SSea
GLOWING AMBER ('Manglow') (Min)	ESty
'Goethe' (Mo)	EBls
GOLD CHARM ('Chewalbygold') (Cl)	MAsh
GOLD SPICE ('Frymega') (F)	MFry
'Goldbusch' (RH)	EBls
'Golden Angel' (Min)	MAsh
'Golden Anniversary' (Patio)	SPer SSea
'Golden Autumn' (HT)	LSRN
GOLDEN BEAUTY ('Clebeau') (Min)	LRHS
GOLDEN BEAUTY ('Korberbeni'PBR) (F) 🏆H6	CArg CPou EBee ETWh MAsh MFry
GOLDEN BERYL ('Manberyl') (Min)	LSRN
GOLDEN CELEBRATION ('Ausgold'PBR) (S) 🏆H6	CArg CBod CDoC CGro CRos CSBt CTri ECnt EHyd EPfP ESty LCro LOPS LRHS LSRN MAsh MMuc MSwo NLar NRHS SLon SPer SPoG SSea
'Golden Dawn' (ClHT)	see *R.* 'Climbing Golden Dawn'
GOLDEN GATE ('Korgolgat'PBR) (ClHT) 🏆H6	CGro ECnt EPfP LBuc LRHS MAsh NRHS SApu SSea
GOLDEN JEWEL ('Tanledolg'PBR) (F/Patio)	ESty
GOLDEN JUBILEE ('Cocagold') (HT)	CArg EBls
GOLDEN MELODY ('Irene Churruca') (HT)	EBls
GOLDEN MEMORIES ('Korholesea'PBR) (F) 🏆H6	CArg CSBt EBls EHyd LBuc LRHS MAsh MGos MPri MRav SCoo
'Golden Moment'PBR (HT)	ESty MRav
GOLDEN OLDIE ('Fryescape'PBR) (HT)	MFry
'Golden Rambler'	see *R.* 'Alister Stella Gray'
'Golden Salmon Supérieur' (Poly)	EBls
'Golden Showers' (Cl)	CArg CBcs CBod CGro CRos CSBt CTri EBee EBls ELan EPfP ETWh LCro LOPS LRHS LSRN MAsh MFry MMuc MRav NLar SCob SPer SPoG SSea WBor
§ GOLDEN SMILES ('Frykeyno'PBR) (F) 🏆H6	CArg CRos ECnt ESty LRHS LSRN MAsh MFry MPri
GOLDEN WEDDING ('Arokris') (F)	CBod CDoC CGro CRos CSBt CTri EBls ECnt ELan EPfP ESty IArd LCro LOPS LRHS LSRN MAsh MFry MGos MRav NRHS SApu SCob SPer SPoG SSea SVic
GOLDEN WEDDING ANNIVERSARY (F)	LSRN
'Golden Wedding Celebration' (F)	LSRN
'Golden Wings' (S)	CArg CPou CTri EBls ELan ETWh GBin MCot MRav MSwo MWat NLar SPer
'Goldfinch' (Ra)	CArg CBod EBls ELan EPfP ETWh EWTr LCro LOPS MAsh NLar SApu SEND SPer WFar
GOLDSTAR ('Candide') (HT)	ECnt
GOOD AS GOLD ('Chewsunbeam'PBR) (ClMin)	CSBt ECnt ESty MFry SPer
GORDON SNELL ('Dicwriter') (F)	IDic

Gordon's College ('Cocjabby'[PBR]) (F) 🏆H6	CSBt
Gorgeous ('Poulpmt009'[PBR]) (HT)	CGro EPfP LRHS MAsh MFry MPri
Gorgeous Girl ('Forshow') (HT)	ESty
Grace ('Auskeppy'[PBR]) (S) 🏆H6	CDoC CRos CSBt EHyd EPfP ESty LBuc LRHS LSRN NLar NRHS SPer
'Grace Abounding' (F)	LSRN
'Grace Darling' (T)	EBls
Grace de Monaco ('Meimit') (HT)	EBls
Grace Sharington ('Mangrace') (Patio) **new**	SSea
'Graciously Pink' (Min)	MAsh
Graham Thomas ('Ausmas') (S) 🏆H6	CArg CDoC CRos CSBt CTri EBee ECnt EHyd EPfP EShb ESty LCro LOPS LRHS LSRN MSwo NLar NRHS SCob SEND SLon SMad SPer SPoG SSea WKif
I 'Granada' Lindquist (HT)	EBls
Grand Award ('Poulcy014'[PBR]) (Courtyard Series) (ClF) **new**	CBod ETWh
Grande Amore	see *R.* My Valentine ('Korcoluma')
'Grandma' (F)	LSRN
Grand-mère Jenny ('Grem') (HT)	EBls
'Grandpa Dickson' (HT)	CArg EBls ELon MAsh SPer
Granny's Favourite (Patio/F)	LSRN
Great Expectations ('Lanican') (HT)	CBcs
Great Expectations ('Mackalves'[PBR]) (F)	EPfP IArd MRav SPer
Great Expectations ambig.	CDoC EBee SSea
§ 'Great Maiden's Blush' (A) 🏆H7	EBls ETWh LEdu NLar
Great North Eastern Rose	see *R.* Sir Galahad
'Great Ormond Street' (F)	EBls
'Great Western' (Bb)	EBls
Greenall's Glory ('Kirmac') (F/Patio)	MRav
Greetings ('Jacdreco'[PBR]) (F)	CArg LBuc MAsh
Greta Hit ('Poulpah076') (Patio)	EPfP
'Grimpant Cramoisi Supérieur' (ClCh)	EBls
'Grootendorst'	see *R.* 'F.J. Grootendorst'
'Gros Chou de Hollande' (Bb)	EBls
Grosvenor House (HT)	LRHS
'Grosvenor House Rose' (S)	MAsh
Grouse ('Korimro') (S/GC)	CBod EBls ETWh NLar SEND SPer
Grouse 2000 ('Korteilhab') (GC) 🏆H6	SApu
'Gruss an Aachen' (Poly) 🏆H6	CBod CPou EBls EPfP ETWh MCot NLar SPer
'Gruss an Teplitz' (China hybrid)	EBls ETWh NLar SPer
'Guinée' (ClHT)	CArg CDoC CRos CSBt CTri EBls EHyd ELan EPfP ESty ETWh LCro LOPS MRav MSwo MWat NLar SApu SPer WCot WKif
Guirlande Rose ('Velwichba') (Ra)	EBls
'Gustav Grünerwald' (HT)	EBls
Guy Savoy ('Delstrimen'[PBR]) (F)	EBls ESty ETWh MRav
Guy's Gold ('Harmatch'[PBR]) (HT)	LRHS MAsh SPoG
Gwent ('Poulurt') (GC)	CSBt EBls SCob SEND SPer SSea
gymnocarpa	EBls
Gypsy Boy	see *R.* 'Zigeunerknabe'
Hallé ('Fryelectric'[PBR]) (HT)	MFry
'Hamburger Phönix' (Ra)	EBls
Hampshire ('Korhamp') (GC)	SCob
Händel ('Macha') (ClHT)	CBcs CBod CDoC CGro CSBt CTri EBls ELan ELon EPfP ETWh LBuc MAsh MFry MPri MRav NLar SApu SCob SPer SPlb SSea
§ Hanky Panky ('Wektorcent'[PBR]) (F)	CDoC CGro EBls ESty MAsh MRav SApu SLon
Hannah Gordon ('Korweiso') (F)	EBls SPer
'Hansa' (Ru)	EBls ETWh LBuc NLar SPer
'Happenstance' (GC)	EBls
Happy 60th Birthday	LSRN
Happy 70th Birthday ('Rawday') (F)	LSRN
Happy 80th Birthday	LSRN
Happy Anniversary ('Bedfranc'[PBR]) (F)	LSRN MPri MWat
Happy Anniversary ('Delpre') (F)	CRos CTri EHyd LRHS MAsh MRav NRHS SPoG
Happy Anniversary ambig.	EPfP
'Happy Birthday' (Min/Patio)	ESty LCro LOPS LSRN SSea
Happy Couple ('Simreg') (F)	ESty
Happy Days ('Harquad'[PBR]) (S)	CDoC MRav
Happy Gardening ('Smi89-2-04') (HT)	ESty
Happy Golden Wedding	see *R.* Golden Smiles
'Happy Memories' (F)	EBls MAsh
Happy Pearl Wedding (HT)	MFry
Happy Retirement ('Tantoras'[PBR]) (F) 🏆H6	CBcs CBod EBls EPfP ESty LBuc LCro LOPS LSRN MAsh MFry MPri MRav SApu SCoo SPoG SSea
Happy Ruby Wedding ('Frynoble'[PBR]) (HT)	CBcs CDoC ECnt MAsh MFry MPri
Happy Silver Wedding ('Frysilva') (F)	CRos LSRN MAsh MFry
× ***harisonii*** (SpH)	EBls
§ – 'Williams' Double Yellow' (SpH)	EBls ETWh
Harlow Carr ambig.	CDoC CRos EHyd LRHS NRHS SCob
Harlow Carr ('Aushouse'[PBR]) (S)	CRos EPfP LBuc LSRN MAsh SCob SCoo SPer
Harper Adams ('Fryflash'[PBR]) (F)	MFry
'Harpippin' (ClHT)	LRHS
'Harry Edland' (F)	LCro LOPS
'Harry Maasz' (GC/Cl)	EBls
'Harry Wheatcroft' (HT)	CArg CBod SPer
Harvest Fayre ('Dicnorth') (F)	SPer
Havana Hit ('Poulpah032'[PBR]) (Patio)	MAsh MFry MPri
'Havering Rambler' (Ra)	ELon

	HAYDOCK PARK ('Fryjak'PBR) (F)	MFry
	'Hazel Le Rougetel' (Ru)	EBls WFar
	HAZEL MCCALLION ('Manhazel') (Patio) **new**	SSea
	'Headleyensis' (S)	EBls ETWh
	HEART OF GOLD ('Coctarlotte'PBR) (HT) 🏆H6	ECnt ESty MRav
	HEART'S DESIRE ('Raw1063') (F)	ESty
	HEATHCLIFF ('Ausnipper'PBR) (S)	CSBt EPfP ESty LBuc MAsh NLar
	HEATHER ('Poulcot007'PBR)	LSRN
	'Heather Muir' (*sericea* hybrid) (S)	EBls
§	'Hebe's Lip' (D × RH)	ETWh
	'Helen Knight' (*ecae* hybrid) (S)	EBls ESty
	'Helen Traubel' (HT)	EBls
	HELENA ('Poulna'PBR) (Renaissance Series) (S)	LSRN
	helenae	CTri EBee EBls ETWh GLog NLar WPGP
	- hybrid	ETWh
	HELEN'S TRUST ('Taytrust') (HT)	LSRN
	hemisphaerica (S)	EBls
§	'Henri Martin' (CeMo) 🏆H7	CBod CTri EBls ETWh LEdu NLar SPer
	HENRI MATISSE ('Delstrobla') (HT)	CBod ESty ETWh MRav SPoG
	'Henry Kelsey' (Cl/S)	EBls
	'Her Majesty' (HP)	EBls
§	'Herbstfeuer' (RH)	EBls ETWh NLar SPer
	'Here's Sam' (HT)	LSRN
	HERITAGE ('Ausblush') (S)	CBod CTri EBee ELan EPfP NLar SCob
	'Hermosa' (Ch)	EBls ETWh NLar
	HERTFORDSHIRE ('Kortenay') (GC) 🏆H6	SCob SEND SPer
	'Hiawatha' (Ra)	EBls
	× ***hibernica***	EBls
§	'Hidcote Yellow' (Cl)	EBls ETWh SPer
	HIDDEN GEM ('Gues11-50') (F) **new**	ESty
	HIGH FLIER ('Fryfandango'PBR) (ClHT)	MFry
§	HIGH FLYER ('Jacsat') (ClHT)	MAsh SSea
	HIGH HOPES ('Haryup'PBR) (ClHT)	EPfP LBuc MAsh SApu SCob SPer SSea
	'Highdownensis' (*moyesii* hybrid) (S)	EBls ELan
	HIGHGROVE ('Hornightshade') (Cl)	CGro EBee EBls EPfP LBuc LRHS MAsh MPri
	'Hillieri' (*moyesii* hybrid)	EBls
	HOLE-IN-ONE ('Horeagle') (F)	LSRN
	holodonta	see *R. moyesii* f. *rosea*
	holy rose	see *R.* × *richardii*
	'Home Sweet Home' (HT)	EBls
	HOME SWEET HOME ('Sim2008/10') (HT)	ESty
	HOMMAGE À BARBARA ('Delchifrou'PBR) (HT)	CBod EBee ESty ETWh MRav WKif
	HONEY BUNCH ('Cocglen') (F)	MRav SPer
	HONEY DIJON ('Weksproulses'PBR) (F)	ESty
	HONEYBUN ('Tan98264'PBR) (Patio)	ESty
	HONEYMOON	see *R.* 'Honigmond'
§	'Honigmond' (F)	CDoC
	'Honorine de Brabant' (Bb) 🏆H6	CPou EBls ETWh LEdu NLar SPer
	HOPE AND GLORY ('Tan01360'PBR) (HT)	MFry
	HOPE FOR JUSTICE ('P48b') (F) **new**	MFry
	HORATIO NELSON ('Beahor') (S)	EBls
	horrida	EBls
	'Horstmanns Rosenresli' (F)	EBls
	HOT CHOCOLATE ('Wekpaltlez') (F) 🏆H6	CArg CDoC CGro CRos CSBt EBls ECnt ELan ELon EPfP ESty LBuc LRHS MAsh MFry MRav SApu SCob SMad SPad SPer SPoG SSea WBor
	HOT PRINCESS ('Tantocnirp') (HT)	ESty
	HOUSE BEAUTIFUL ('Harbingo') (Patio)	MRav MWat
	'Hovyn de Tronchère' (HT)	EBls
	'Hugh Dickson' (HP)	CPou EBls ETWh LSRN NLar
	hugonis	see *R. xanthina* f. *hugonis*
	- 'Plenissima'	see *R. xanthina* f. *hugonis*
	HUMANITY ('Harcross'PBR) (F)	MRav MWat
	Hume's blush	see *R.* × *odorata* 'Odorata'
	HUMMINGBIRD ('Tynpam') (F)	ESty
	'Hunter' (Ru)	EBls
	HYDE HALL ('Ausbosky'PBR) (S)	EHyd LRHS
	ICE CREAM ('Korzuri'PBR) (HT) 🏆H6	CArg CDoC ECnt ESty MRav SApu SCob SPer SPoG
§	ICEBERG ('Korbin') (F) 🏆H6	CArg CBcs CBod CDoC CGro CSBt CTri EBee EBls ECnt ELan EPfP ESty LCro LEdu LOPS LRHS MAsh MFry MGos MPri MRav MWat NRHS SApu SCob SPer SPoG SSea XSen
	'Ilse Krohn Superior' (ClHT)	EBls
§	IMAGINATION ('Pouldron'PBR) (F)	MAsh
	IMOGEN ('Austritch') (S)	CSBt EHyd EPfP ESty LRHS NRHS
	IMPÉRATRICE FARAH ('Delivour') (HT)	ESty
§	'Impératrice Joséphine' (Gn) 🏆H7	EBls ETWh NLar
	IN MEMORY OF	LSRN
	IN MEMORY OF MY CAT ('Webyum') (HT)	LSRN
	IN MEMORY OF MY DOG ('Rawbark') (F)	LSRN
	INDIAN SUMMER ('Harwigwam') (ClMin)	ELon
	INDIAN SUMMER ('Peaperfume') (HT) 🏆H6	CSBt MFry MRav MWat SApu
	INDIANNA MAE ('Beacrunch') (S)	EBls
	'Indigo' (DPo)	CPou EBls ETWh
	INFINITY ('Frytropic') (HT)	CArg EPfP LRHS MAsh
	INGRID ('Maning')	LSRN
	INGRID BERGMAN ('Poulman'PBR) (HT) 🏆H6	CDoC CTri EBls ECnt EPfP ETWh LSRN MFry MGos MRav SApu SPer SSea

'Inspiration' (ClHT)	MAsh
INSPIRE ('Frytempo') (HT)	CSBt ECnt MFry
'Intermezzo' (HT)	EBls
INVINCIBLE ('Runatru') (F)	MFry
'Ipsilanté' (G)	EBls
'Irene Av Danmark' (F)	EBls
'Irène Watts' (Ch)	CArg CPou EBls LSRN NLar
'Irene's Delight' (HT)	ESty LSRN
IRIS ('Coczero') (HT)	LSRN
IRIS ('Ferecha') (HT)	LSRN
IRISH EYES ('Dicwitness'PBR) (F) 𝕐H6	CArg CGro ESty IArd MAsh MRav SApu SCob SCoo SPer
IRISH WONDER	see *R.* EVELYN FISON
'Isabel'	CBod ETWh LSRN
ISABELLA ('Poulisab'PBR) (Renaissance Series) (S)	CPou CTri ECnt NLar
'Isabella Sprunt' (HT)	EBls
ISIS (HT)	see *R.* SILVER ANNIVERSARY ('Poulari')
ISN'T SHE LOVELY ('Diciluvit'PBR) (HT) 𝕐H6	CArg EBls ELan ESty IDic LSRN SApu
'Ispahan' (D) 𝕐H6	CArg CBod EBls EPfP ETWh LRHS NLar SApu SPer WFar
IT'S MAGIC ('Frynote') (F)	MFry
IVOR'S ROSE ('Beadonald') (S)	EBls EPfP LRHS MAsh
IVORY ROMANTICA ('Meisabeyla'PBR) (HT)	LSRN
'Ivory Silk' (Min)	LSRN
'Jack Hume' (ClHT)	ESty
JACK WOOD ('Frydabble'PBR) (F)	MFry
JACK'S WISH ('Kirsil') (HT)	LSRN
§ × ***jacksonii*** 'Max Graf' (GC/Ru)	ETWh NLar SCob
- RED MAX GRAF	see *R.* ROTE MAX GRAF
'Jacky's Favorite' (F)	LSRN
Jacobite rose	see *R.* × *alba* 'Alba Maxima'
JACQUELINE DU PRÉ ('Harwanna') (S) 𝕐H6	CArg EBls ECnt ESty ETWh EWTr LCro LOPS LSRN MCot MRav NLar SApu SEND SLon SPer
JACQUELINE REDMILL ('Dicnuance') (F) **new**	IDic
'Jacques Cartier' misapplied	see *R.* 'Marchesa Boccella'
JAM AND JERUSALEM ('Frymojo'PBR) (F)	CDoC CGro LRHS MAsh MFry MRav MWat
JAMES GALWAY ('Auscrystal'PBR) (S)	CSBt EHyd EPfP ESty LBuc LRHS LSRN MAsh NRHS SCoo SSea
JAMES L. AUSTIN ('Auspike') (S) **new**	CRos ECnt ESty MAsh
'James Mason' (G)	EBls
'James Mitchell' (CeMo)	EBls
JANE'S ROSE ('Webloxley') (F) **new**	CPou
JANET ('Auspishus'PBR) (S)	LSRN
'Janet B. Wood' (Ra)	EBls
'Janet's Pride' (RH)	EBls
§ 'Japonica' (CeMo)	ETWh
§ JARDINS DE BAGATELLE ('Meimafris') (HT)	LSRN MRav SApu
JASMINA ('Korcentex'PBR) (ClHT)	CPou ESty ETWh LRHS
'Jaune Desprez'	see *R.* 'Desprez à Fleur Jaune'
JAZZ (ClF)	see *R.* THAT'S JAZZ
'Jazz' (F)	LSRN
JEAN ('Cocupland'PBR) (Patio)	LSRN
'Jean Rosenkrantz' (HP)	EBls
'Jeanne de Montfort' (CeMo)	ETWh
JEANNE MOREAU ('Meidiaphaz') (HT)	CSBt ESty
'Jenny Duval' misapplied	see *R.* 'Président de Sèze'
'Jenny Wren' (F)	EBls
JENNY'S ROSE ('Cansit') (F)	ECnt LSRN
'Jens Munk' (Ru)	CBod EBls ETWh NLar
JILL'S ROSE ('Ganjil'PBR) (F)	LSRN
JILLY JEWEL ('Benmfig') (Min)	LSRN
JIVE ('Poulyc009'PBR) (Cl)	LSRN
JOAN BEALES ('Beaagile') (S)	EBls
'Joanna Hill' (HT)	EBls
'Jocelyn' (F)	LSRN
JOCKEYS ROSE ('Frynadia') (HT)	MFry
JOHANN WOLFGANG VON GOETHE ROSE	see *R.* PURE POETRY ('Tan04179') (HT)
'John Cabot' (S)	EBls
'John Gwilliam'	MAvo MHCG
'John Hopper' (HP)	EBls ETWh
JOHN INNES ('Beafickle') (S)	EBls
JOHN WILLAN ('Fryeager') (HT)	MFry
§ JOIE DE VIVRE ('Korfloci 01'PBR) (Patio/S) 𝕐H6	CArg CBod CDoC CGro CPou CSBt EBls ELan EPfP ESty ETWh GBin LRHS MAsh MFry MPri MRav NLar SApu SPer SPoG SSea
§ JOSEPHINE ('Weksiamia') (HT)	LSRN
'Josephine Bruce' (HT)	CBcs CBod CTri EBls LSRN SSea
'Joseph's Coat' (ClS)	CBod EBls ETWh IArd
JOY VIELI ('Dickaramel') (F)	IDic
JUBILÉ PAPA MEILLAND ('Meiceazar'PBR) (HT)	CSBt
'Jubilee Celebration' (F)	CDoC EHyd EPfP LRHS NRHS
JUBILEE CELEBRATION ('Aushunter'PBR) (S)	CRos CSBt EHyd LBuc LRHS NLar NRHS SPer SPoG
JUDE THE OBSCURE ('Ausjo'PBR) (S)	CRos EHyd EPfP ESty LBuc LRHS MGos NRHS SPer
'Julia's Rose' (HT)	EBls LSRN SPer
JULIO IGLESIAS ('Meistemon'PBR) (F)	ESty LSRN
JULY RACECOURSE ('Frykeno') (Patio)	MFry
'Juno' (Ce)	EBls ETWh NLar
'Juno' (Ch)	CPou
JUST FOR YOU ('Moryou') (Min)	LSRN
JUST JANE ('Raw1046') (F)	LSRN
'Just Jenny' (Min)	LSRN
'Just Joey' (HT) 𝕐H6	CArg CBcs CSBt CTri EBls ECnt ELan ELon IArd LCro LOPS LSRN MFry MRav SApu SCob SPer SPoG SSea
JUST ROBERT ('Raw1075') (F)	LSRN
JUST STEVE ('Raw890') (F)	LSRN
'Justice of the Peace' (F)	MFry
'Karlsruhe' (ClF)	EBls
'Kassel' (ClF)	EBls
'Kasteel Hex' (S)	EBls
'Katharina Zeimet' (Poly)	CTri EBls ETWh
'Kathleen' (HM)	EBls LSRN

	Name	Suppliers
	'Kathleen Ferrier' (F)	EBls
	'Kathleen Harrop' (Bb)	CBod EBee EBls ETWh MMuc MSwo NLar SEND SPer
	KATHLEEN JANE ('Horcoed') (S)	LSRN
	KATHLEEN'S ROSE ('Kirkitt') (F)	LSRN
	KATHRYN ('Rawkat') (F)	LSRN
	'Katie' (ClF)	LSRN
	KATIE'S ROSE ('Horrapture') (F)	LSRN
	'Kazanlik' misapplied	see *R.* × *damascena* 'Professeur Émile Perrot'
	KEEP SMILING ('Fryflorida') (HT) 🏆H6	CDoC CGro EBls MAsh MFry MRav SPoG
	KEEPSAKE ('Kormalda') (HT)	ESty
	'Keith Maughan' (Cl)	EBls LRHS MAsh
§	KENT ('Poulcov') (Towne & Country Series) (S/GC) 🏆H6	CDoC CSBt EBls ECnt ELan EPfP ESty ETWh LCro LOPS LSRN MFry MMuc MRav MSwo NLar SApu SCob SEND SPer SPoG SSea
	KEW GARDENS ('Ausfence'[PBR]) (S) 🏆H6	CDoC CRos EPfP LBuc LCro LOPS LRHS NLar NRHS SPer
	'Kew Rambler' (Ra)	CBod CRHN EBee EBls ETWh NLar SApu SLon
	'Kiftsgate'	see *R. filipes* 'Kiftsgate'
	'Kiftsgate Superior' (S)	EBls
	'Killarney' (HT)	EBls
	'Kim' (Patio/F)	LSRN
	KIND REGARDS ('Peatiger') (F)	LSRN
	KING'S MACC ('Frydisco'[PBR]) (HT) 🏆H6	MFry
	'King's Ransom' (HT)	CSBt EBls MRav SCob SPer
	KISSES OF FIRE ('Chewmultiseek') (ClMin)	CBod CDoC ECnt ETWh MRav NLar SSea
	KITTY ('Beaarty') (S)	EBls
	× ***kochiana***	CPou EBls ETWh
	kokanica <u>**new**</u>	WPGP
	KOLO ('Poulcy033'[PBR]) (Courtyard Series) (Cl)	ECnt
§	'Königin von Dänemark' (A) 🏆H7	CArg CBod EBls EPfP ETWh GBin LCro LOPS LRHS LSRN MRav NLar SPer
§	'Kordes' Magenta' (S/F)	EBls
	'Kordes' Robusta'	see *R.* ROBUSTA
	'Kordesii' (S)	EBls
	KORONA ('Kornita') (F)	SPer
	'Korresia' (F) 🏆H7	CArg CDoC CSBt CTri EBee EBls ECnt ELon EPfP LRHS MAsh MRav SApu SCob SPer SPoG
	KRONENBOURG ('Macbo') (HT)	EBls
	KRONPRINSESSE MARY ('Poulcas018') (F) <u>**new**</u>	ETWh
	'Kronprinzessin Viktoria von Preussen' (Bb)	CBod EBls ETWh
	L.D. BRAITHWAITE ('Auscrim') (S)	CArg CRos CTri ELan EPfP LRHS MBNS NLar SCob SPer
	'La Belle Distinguée' (RH)	ETWh
	'La Belle Sultane'	see *R.* 'Violacea'
	'La France' (HT)	EBls
	'La Mortola'	see *R. brunonii* 'La Mortola'
	'La Noblesse' (Ce)	EBls
	'La Perle' (Ra)	CRHN
	'La Reine' (HP)	EBls
	'La Reine Victoria'	see *R.* 'Reine Victoria'

	Name	Suppliers
§	LA ROSE DE MOLINARD ('Delgrarose'[PBR]) (S) 🏆H6	CArg CBod CPou ESty ETWh MRav NLar SApu
	LA ROSE DE PETIT PRINCE ('Delgramau') (F)	ESty ETWh
	'La Rubanée'	see *R.* × *centifolia* 'Unique Panachée'
	LA SÉVILLANA ('Meigekanu') (F/GC)	EBls MSwo SApu SPer WCot
	'La Ville de Bruxelles' (D) 🏆H7	EBls ETWh NLar SPer
	LACE ('Frymoody') (HT)	LSRN MFry
	'Lady Alice Stanley' (HT)	EBls
	'Lady Anne' (F)	LSRN
	'Lady Barnby' (HT)	EBls
	'Lady Belper' (HT)	EBls
	'Lady Curzon' (Ru)	EBls
	'Lady Elgin'	see *R.* THAÏS
	LADY EMMA HAMILTON ('Ausbrother'[PBR]) (S) 🏆H6	CGro CRos EHyd EPfP ESty LBuc LCro LOPS LRHS MAsh MBNS NRHS SCoo SPer
	'Lady Gay' (Ra)	ETWh WBor
	'Lady Hillingdon' (T)	EBls MAsh
	'Lady Hillingdon' (ClT)	see *R.* 'Climbing Lady Hillingdon'
	LADY MARMALADE ('Hartiger'[PBR]) (F)	CArg CDoC CGro CSBt ESty LBuc LRHS MAsh MFry MPri MRav SCoo SMad SPer SPoG
	'Lady Mary Fitzwilliam' (HT)	EBls ETWh
	LADY MITCHELL ('Haryearn') (HT)	ECnt
	'Lady Oaksey' (HT)	MFry
	LADY OF MEGGINCH ('Ausvolume'[PBR]) (S)	MAsh
	LADY OF SHALOTT ('Ausnyson'[PBR]) (S) 🏆H6	CRos ECnt EHyd ELan EPfP LBuc LCro LOPS LRHS MAsh NLar NRHS SCob SSea
	LADY PENELOPE ('Chewdor'[PBR]) (ClHT)	CSBt MFry
§	'Lady Penzance' (RH)	CTho EBls
	'Lady Romsey' (F)	EBls
	LADY ROSE ('Korlady') (HT)	MAsh
	LADY SALISBURY ('Auscezed'[PBR]) (S)	CRos EHyd EPfP LBuc LRHS NRHS SCoo
	'Lady Sylvia' (HT)	EBls LSRN SPer
	'Lady Waterlow' (ClHT)	CBod EBls ETWh SPer WSpi
	laevigata (Ra)	EBls MMuc
	- 'Anemonoides'	see *R.* 'Anemone'
	'Lafter' (S)	EBls
	'Lagoon' (F)	EBls
	LAGUNA ('Koradigel'[PBR]) (ClHT)	MAsh
	L'AIMANT ('Harzola'[PBR]) (F) 🏆H5	MRav SApu
	L'ALHAMBRA	see *R.* GIARDINA
	'Lamarque' (N)	CPou EBls ETWh
	LANCASHIRE ('Korstesgli'[PBR]) (GC) 🏆H6	CBod CDoC ECnt ELan ESty ETWh LSRN MRav MSwo SApu SCob SSea
	LANCELOT ('Tan03542'[PBR]) (Cl)	ESty
§	'Lanei' (CeMo)	EBls ETWh
	latibracteata	EBls
	LAURA FORD ('Chewarvel') (ClMin) 🏆H5	CDoC EBls ELan LRHS MAsh MFry MGos MRav SPer SPoG
	'Laura Louisa' (Cl)	EBee EBls ETWh LRHS MAsh
	'Laure Davoust' (Ra)	CPou EBee EBls ETWh MMuc NLar
	LAVENDER ICE ('Tan04249'[PBR]) (F)	EBee ESty LCro LOPS SMad SPoG WSpi
	'Lavender Lassie' (HM)	CPou EBls ETWh NLar SPer

	'Lavender Pinocchio' (F)	EBls WKif
	LAVINIA	see *R.* LAWINIA
§	LAWINIA ('Tanklewi') (ClHT) 🏆H6	CSBt LRHS MAsh SApu SPer
	'Lawrence Johnston'	see *R.* 'Hidcote Yellow'
	laxa	EBls
§	LAZY DAYS ('Poulkalm'[PBR]) (F)	ECnt
	'Le Rêve' (Cl)	ETWh
	LE ROUGE ET LE NOIR ('Delcart') (HT)	ESty
	'Le Vésuve' (Ch)	CPou EBls ETWh
	LEAH TUTU ('Hornavel') (S)	EBee EBls EPfP ESty LRHS MAsh
	LEAPING SALMON ('Peamight'[PBR]) (ClHT) 🏆H6	CArg CBod CGro CSBt ELon ESty ETWh LSRN MRav SApu SCob SPer WSpi
	'Leda' (D)	CArg EBls ETWh SPer
	LEGENDS	see *R.* JOSEPHINE
	'Lemon Pillar'	see *R.* 'Paul's Lemon Pillar'
	LÉONARDO DE VINCI ('Meideauri'[PBR]) (F)	CSBt
	'Léonie Lamesch' (Poly)	EBls
	'Léontine Gervais' (Ra)	CRHN EBls
	'Leo's Eye' (Ra)	CBod CPou EPfP ETWh NLar WFar
	LESLIE'S DREAM ('Dicjoon') (HT)	IDic
	LET FREEDOM RING ('Wekearman') (HT)	ESty
	LET THERE BE LOVE ('Frysoda') (F)	LBuc MAsh MFry
	LET'S CELEBRATE ('Fryraffles'[PBR]) (F)	CDoC CWld EPfP ESty LBuc LRHS MAsh MFry MPri MRav NRHS SPoG
	'Leverkusen' (ClF) 🏆H6	CArg CBod EBls ETWh NLar SCob SEND SPer
	'Leveson-Gower' (Bb)	EBls
	'Ley's Perpetual' (ClT)	CArg EBls ETWh
	× ***lheritieriana*** (Bs)	EBls
	LICHFIELD ANGEL ('Ausrelate'[PBR]) (S) 🏆H6	CRos EHyd EPfP LBuc LRHS MAsh NLar NRHS SCoo
	LICHTKÖNIGIN LUCIA ('Korlillub') (S)	EBls SSea
	LIFE BEGINS AT 40! ('Horhohoho') (F)	LSRN
	LIGHT FANTASTIC ('Dicgottago') (F) 🏆H6	CArg EPfP MAsh MFry
	LIGHTNING STRIKE ('Raw967') (F)	ESty
	LILAC BOUQUET ('Chewlilacdays') (Cl)	ECnt ESty SSea
	LILAC WINE ('Dicmulti') (F) 🏆H5	CBod CDoC CSBt IDic MRav SApu
	LILIANA ('Poulsyng'[PBR]) (S)	CBod CPou EBee ECnt ETWh LSRN SLon
	LILLI MARLENE ('Korlima') (F)	CTri EBls SCob SPer
	LINCOLN CATHEDRAL ('Glanlin'[PBR]) (HT)	SPer
	LINCOLNSHIRE POACHER ('Glareabit') (HT)	ESty
	'Lincolnshire Yellow Belly' (F)	ESty
	LION'S FAIRY TALE	see *R.* CHAMPAGNE MOMENT
	LIONS INTERNATIONAL ('Frycharm'[PBR]) (HT)	MFry
	LISA ('Kirdisco') (F)	LSRN
	LITTLE AMY ('Battamy') (Min)	LSRN
	LITTLE ANGEL ('Poulpal038'[PBR]) (F) **new**	MFry
	'Little Buckaroo' (Min)	SPer
	LITTLE DUET ('Guesbliss') (F)	ESty
	'Little Emily' (Patio)	LSRN SSea
	'Little Fin' (Min)	LSRN
	'Little Flirt' (Min)	ELan
	'Little Gem' (DPMo)	EBls ETWh
	LITTLE JACKIE ('Savor') (Min)	LSRN
	LITTLE RAMBLER ('Chewramb'[PBR]) (MinRa) 🏆H6	CArg CBod CDoC CSBt EBls ECnt ELan ESty LCro LOPS LRHS MFry MGos MMuc MRav NRHS SApu SCoo SPer SSea
	'Little White Pet'	see *R.* 'White Pet'
§	LIVERPOOL REMEMBERS ('Frystar') (HT)	MFry
	LIVING DAYLIGHTS ('Fryradical') (F)	MFry
	LOCHINVAR ('Ausbilda'[PBR]) (S)	MAsh
	'Lolabelle' (S)	CBod CPou ETWh SPer
	'Long John Silver' (Cl)	EBls ELan SApu SSea
	longicuspis misapplied	see *R. mulliganii*
§	***longicuspis*** Bertol. var. ***sinowilsonii*** (Ra)	EBls ETWh
	LOOK GOOD...FEEL BETTER ('Poulcas034'[PBR]) (Castle Series) (Poly)	LRHS
	LORD BYRON ('Meitosier') (ClHT)	ESty
	'Lord Penzance' (RH)	CPou EBls ETWh EWTr NLar SPer
	LORNA ('Cocringer') (F)	LSRN
	LOTS OF LOVE ('Forchriso') (F)	ESty
	'L'Ouche' misapplied	see *R.* 'Louise Odier'
	'Louis Philippe' (Ch)	EBls
	'Louis XIV' (Ch)	CPou EBls ETWh MCot
	LOUISE CLEMENTS ('Clelou') (S)	EBls MCot
	'Louise d'Arzens' (N)	EBls
§	'Louise Odier' (Bb)	CBod CTri EBls ECnt EPfP ETWh IArd LCro LOPS LRHS LSRN MCot MRav NLar SApu SPer
	LOVE & PEACE ('Baipeace'[PBR]) (HT) 🏆H7	ESty SApu
	LOVE KNOT ('Chewglorious'[PBR]) (ClMin) 🏆H6	CArg CDoC CSBt ECnt EHyd EPfP ESty LRHS MAsh MRav
	LOVELY BOY ('Simjas') (HT)	ESty
§	LOVELY BRIDE ('Meiratcan'[PBR]) (Patio)	CRos EHyd EPfP LRHS MAsh NRHS SApu SPoG
	LOVELY LADY ('Dicjubell'[PBR]) (HT) 🏆H6	CSBt EBls ECnt ESty LSRN MRav SApu SPer SSea
	LOVELY MEIDILAND	see *R.* LOVELY BRIDE
	'Lovers' Meeting' (HT)	MRav SPer
	LOVESTRUCK ('Dicommatac') (F)	CDoC CGro CPou CSBt ECnt ESty ETWh IDic LBuc LCro LOPS MAsh MFry SApu
	LOVING MEMORY ('Korgund81') (HT)	CArg CBod CGro CSBt EBls ECnt ESty IArd LCro LOPS LSRN MAsh MFry MGos MPri MRav MWat SApu SCob SPer SPoG SSea SVic
§	LOVING MUM (HT)	CSBt ESty
	LOWTHORPE DELIGHT ('Dicgoofy') (F)	IDic
§	***lucieae***	EBls ETWh
	LUCKY! ('Frylucy') (F) 🏆H6	CArg CBod CDoC CSBt EBls EHyd EPfP ESty LBuc LRHS LSRN MAsh MFry MGos MPri MRav SApu SCoo SPer SPoG

	LUCKY STAR ('Raw1142') (F) **new**	ESty
	LUCY ('Kirlis') (F)	LSRN
	LULLABY ('Kenfrilpin') (ClF)	ESty
	LUSCIOUS LUCY ('Tucklucy') (Patio)	LSRN
	LYDA ROSE ('Letlyda') (S)	EBls
	'Lykkefund' (Ra)	EBls ETWh
	'Ma Perkins' (F)	EBls
	'Mabel Morrison' (HP)	EBls
	Macartney rose	see *R. bracteata*, *R.* THE MCCARTNEY ROSE
	MACMILLAN NURSE ('Beamac') (S)	EBls ELan ESty ETWh EWTr LRHS MAsh MCot NRHS
	MACON ROUGE ('Frynova') (HT)	MFry
	'Macrantha' (Gallica hybrid)	EBls
	macrophylla (S)	WPav
	- B&SWJ 2603	WCru
	- GWJ 9306	WCru
§	- 'Master Hugh' (S)	EBls
	'Madame Abel Chatenay' (HT)	EBls
	'Madame Alfred Carrière' (N) ♀H5	Widely available
	'Madame Alice Garnier' (Ra)	CBod CPou CRHN EBls ETWh SPer
	'Madame Antoine Mari' (T)	ETWh
§	'Madame Boll' (DPo)	CArg CDoC EBls ETWh EWTr MAsh MCot MSwo NLar SApu SMad
	'Madame Butterfly' (HT)	EBls
§	'Madame Caroline Testout' (HT)	CBod CTri EBls
	'Madame de la Roche-Lambert' (DPMo)	EBls ETWh
	'Madame de Sancy de Parabère' (Bs)	EBls ETWh
	'Madame Driout' (ClT)	ETWh
	'Madame Ernest Calvat' (Bb)	CPou EBls ETWh
	'Madame Eugène Résal' misapplied	see *R.* 'Comtesse du Caÿla'
§	'Madame Grégoire Staechelin' (ClHT) ♀H6	CArg CBod CTri EBls ECnt EHyd ELan EPfP ETWh LCro LOPS LRHS LSRN MSwo NLar NRHS SApu SCob SPer SPlb
	'Madame Hardy' (D) ♀H7	CBod CDoC CPou CSBt EBls EHyd EPfP ETWh EWTr LCro LOPS LRHS LSRN MRav MSwo MWat NLar SApu SPer WFar
	'Madame Isaac Péreire' (ClBb)	CArg CDoC CSBt CTri CWld EBls ECnt EPfP ETWh GBin LCro LOPS MCot MRav MSwo NLar SApu SCob SMad SPer WFar
	'Madame Jules Gravereaux' (ClT)	EBls
	'Madame Knorr' (DPo) ♀H7	CPou ECnt EPfP SPer
	'Madame Knorr' misapplied	see *R.* 'Madame Boll'
	'Madame Laurette Messimy' (Ch)	CPou ETWh
	'Madame Lauriol de Barny' (Bb)	EBls ETWh MRav NLar
	'Madame Legras de Saint Germain' (A × N)	CBod CPou EBls ETWh NLar SPer
	'Madame Louis Laperrière' (HT)	EBls
	'Madame Louis Lévêque' (DPMo)	CPou EBls ETWh EWTr NLar
	'Madame Pierre Oger' (Bb)	CArg CTri EBee EBls ECnt ETWh NLar SPer
	'Madame Plantier' (A × N)	CArg CPou EBls NLar SPer WFar
	'Madame Scipion Cochet' (HP)	CPou ETWh
	'Madame Victor Verdier' (HP)	EBls
	'Madame Zöetmans' (D)	ETWh
	'Madeleine Seltzer' (Ra)	EBls ETWh
	'Madge' (HM)	SDix
	'Magenta' (S/F)	see *R.* 'Kordes' Magenta' (S/F)
	MAGIC CARPET ('Jaclover'PBR) (S/GC) ♀H6	CDoC EBls ELan MRav MSwo SApu SPer
	MAGIC MOMENT ('Forrusty') (HT)	ESty
	'Magna Charta' (HP)	EBls
	MAGNETIC EYES ('Dicmimic') (S)	IDic
	'Magnifica' (RH)	EBls
	'Maid Marion' (Ra)	LSRN
	MAID MARION ('Austobias'PBR) (HM)	LSRN MAsh
	'Maid of Kent'PBR (Cl)	LSRN NLar SCob SCoo SPer
	'Maiden's Blush' (A)	CArg CTri ELan EWTr LEdu MAsh SCob SPer WHer
	'Maiden's Blush, Great'	see *R.* 'Great Maiden's Blush'
	'Maigold' (ClPiH) ♀H6	CArg CBcs CGro CRos CTri EBls ELan EPfP ETWh LCro LOPS LRHS MAsh MCot MRav MSwo NLar SCob SMad SPer WBor
§	***majalis***	EBls
	Maltese rose	see *R.* 'Cécile Brünner'
§	'Malton' (China hybrid)	EBls
	MALVERN HILLS ('Auscanary'PBR) (Ra) ♀H5	CRos CSBt EBee EPfP ESty LRHS NLar
	'Maman Cochet' (T)	EBls
	MAMMA MIA! ('Fryjolly'PBR) (HT) ♀H6	CDoC ECnt EPfP ESty LRHS MAsh MFry MRav SApu SPoG
	'Mandarin' (F)	SCob
	MANDARIN ('Korcelin') (Min)	ESty MRav
	'Manettii' (N)	EBls
	MANHATTAN BLUE ('Tanettahn') (F)	MFry
	'Manning's Blush' (RH)	EBls
	'Mannington Cascade' (Ra)	EBls
	'Mannington Mauve Rambler' (Ra)	EBls ESty
	MANY CONGRATULATIONS ('Forshelly') (F)	ESty
	MANY HAPPY RETURNS ('Harwanted') (F) ♀H6	CBcs CBod CDoC CGro CRos CSBt EBls ECnt ELan EPfP LRHS LSRN MAsh MFry MGos MPri MRav MWat NRHS SApu SCob SPer SVic
§	'Marchesa Boccella' (DPo) ♀H7	CArg CPou CTri EBls ETWh LRHS MAsh MPri NLar SApu SPer SSea WHer
	'Marchioness of Salisbury' (HT)	EBls
	'Maréchal Davoust' (CeMo)	LEdu
	'Maréchal Niel' (N)	CPou EBls EShb ETWh NLar SSea
	MARGARET (HT)	see *R.* DEAR MARGARET
	'Margaret' (HT)	LSRN
	MARGARET GREVILLE ('Beajoker') (S)	EBls
	MARGARET MERRIL ('Harkuly') (F)	CArg CBcs CDoC CGro CSBt CTri EBee EBls ELan EPfP ESty IArd LCro LOPS LRHS LSRN MAsh MFry MPri MRav MWat SApu SCob SPer SPoG SSea
	'Marguerite Hilling' (S)	CTri EBls ETWh MCot MSwo NLar SPer

	'Marie Bugnet' (Ru)	EBls
	'Marie Louise' (D)	EBls ETWh
	'Marie Pavič' (Poly)	CPou ETWh NLar
	'Marie van Houtte' (T)	EBls
	'Marie-Jeanne' (Poly)	EBls
	MARIGOLD SWEET DREAM ('Fryprospa') (Patio)	ECnt MFry
	MARJORIE FAIR ('Harhero') (Poly/S) 🏆H6	EBls ELan EPfP SCob
	'Martha' (Bb)	EBls LSRN
	'Martin Frobisher' (Ru)	EBls
I	'Mary' (Poly)	LSRN
	MARY BERRY ('Harupon') (HT)	ESty LRHS
	MARY JEAN ('Haryen') (HT) **new**	ECnt
	'Mary Manners' (Ru)	EBls
	MARY ROSE ('Ausmary') (S)	CRos CSBt CTri EHyd ELan EPfP LRHS LSRN MAsh NLar NRHS SCob SLon SPoG SSea WKif
	'Masquerade' (F)	CDoC CTri EBls ELan NLar SPer
	'Master Hugh'	see *R. macrophylla* 'Master Hugh'
	MATAWHERO MAGIC	see *R.* SIMPLY THE BEST
	MATCHMAKER ('Dicnarrow') (F)	CSBt IDic SApu
	'Maude Elizabeth' (GC)	EBls
	'Maurice Bernardin' (HP)	EBls
	MAURICE UTRILLO ('Delstavo') (HT)	ESty
	'Max Graf'	see *R.* × *jacksonii* 'Max Graf'
	'Maxima'	see *R.* × *alba* 'Alba Maxima'
	MAXIMA ROMANTICA ('Meikerira'PBR) (HT)	ELon MAsh
	'May Queen' (Ra)	CPou CRHN EBls ETWh NLar SEND SPer
	'McCartney Rose'	see *R.* THE MCCARTNEY ROSE
	'McGredy's Sunset' (HT)	EBls
	'McGredy's Yellow' (HT)	EBls
§	MEDLEY RUBY ('Noa140715'PBR) (Min)	MAsh SPoG
	'Meg' (ClHT)	CArg EBls ETWh EWTr LSRN MMuc NLar
	'Meg Merrilies' (RH)	EBls
	MELINA	see *R.* SIR HARRY PILKINGTON
	MEMORY LANE ('Peavoodoo'PBR) (F)	LSRN
	'Merlot' (Min)	LSRN
	'Mermaid' (Cl) 🏆H5	CArg CBcs CSBt CTri EBls EHyd EPfP ETWh LRHS NLar NRHS SApu SCob SEND SMad SNig SPer SSea
§	'Mevrouw Nathalie Nypels' (Poly)	CArg CBod CTri EBls ETWh MMuc MRav NLar SPer
	× ***micrugosa***	EBls
	- 'Alba'	EBls
	MIDDLESBOROUGH FOOTBALL CLUB ('Horflame') (HT)	LSRN
	MIDNIGHT BLUE ('Wekfabpur') (S)	CDoC EBls ESty
	MIDNIGHT ROSE ('Simdamo') (F)	ESty
	MIDSUMMER ('Tan02280'PBR) (F)	MFry
	MIDSUMMER NIGHT'S DREAM ('Rawroyal') (F)	ESty
§	MILLIE ('Poulren013'PBR) (Renaissance Series) (S) 🏆H6	CArg CBcs CBod CDoC CGro EBls ECnt ELan ESty ETWh LBuc LCro LOPS LRHS LSRN MAsh MFry MPri NLar NRHS SApu SLon SPoG
	MILLIE ROSE ('Wekblunez'PBR) (HT)	SApu
	MILLIONAIRE ('Peazara') (F)	LSRN
	MIND GAMES ('Dickylie') (F)	CBod
	MINERVA ('Visancar') (F)	CSBt ESty
	'Minnehaha' (Ra)	CBod EBls SSea
	mirifica stellata	see *R. stellata* var. *mirifica*
	MISCHIEF ('Macmi') (HT)	LSRN SPer
	MISS ALICE ('Ausjake'PBR) (S)	LSRN
	'Miss Edith Cavell' (Poly)	EBls ETWh
	MISS KATE ('Dicpredict') (F) **new**	IDic
	MISS SCARLET ('Forbright') (Cl)	ESty
§	'Mister Lincoln' (HT)	EBls SPer
§	MISTY HIT ('Poulhi011'PBR) (PatioHit Series) (Patio)	CDoC CGro EBls ECnt LSRN MAsh NRHS
	'Misty Moon' (F)	ESty
	MITSOUKO ('Delnat') (HT)	ESty
	MODERN SLAVERY ('Dicpowwow') (F)	IDic
	MOLINEUX ('Ausmol'PBR) (S) 🏆H6	CRos EHyd LRHS LSRN MAsh NRHS SPer
	'Molly Sharman-Crawford' (HT)	EBls
	MOM ('Rawtoks') (F)	LSRN
	MOMENT IN TIME ('Korcastrav'PBR) (F) 🏆H6	CArg CDoC CSBt ECnt MAsh MPri MRav SPer SPoG
	MONICA BELLUCCI ('Meimonkeur'PBR) (HT)	ELon ESty
	'Monique' (HT)	EBls
	MONSIEUR PÉLISSON	see *R.* 'Pélisson'
	MOODY BLUE ('Fryniche') (HT)	CDoC ECnt MAsh MFry MRav MWat
	'Moonlight' (HM)	CArg CTri EBls ETWh MRav MSwo SCob SPer
	MOORCROFT ('Guesyearn') (F)	ESty
	'Morletii' (Bs)	EBls ETWh EWTr MMuc SEND
	'Morning Jewel' (ClF) 🏆H7	SPer
	MORNING MIST ('Ausfire') (S)	CRos EPfP LBuc LRHS MAsh SPer
	MORNING SUN ('Tan08622'PBR) (HT) **new**	MFry
§	'Morsdag' (Poly/F)	LSRN SVic
	MORTIMER SACKLER ('Ausorts'PBR) (S) 🏆H6	CRos EHyd EPfP LBuc LRHS MMuc NRHS SCoo SPer
	moschata (Ra)	CPou EBls ETWh SSea
	- 'Autumnalis'	see *R.* 'Princesse de Nassau'
	- var. ***nepalensis***	see *R. brunonii*
	MOTHER'S DAY	see *R.* 'Morsdag'
I	'Mother's Day'	SPer
	MOTHER'S JOY ('Horsiltrop') (F)	LSRN
	MOULIN ROUGE ('Simmarg') (HT)	ESty
	MOUNT AORANGI ('Sanaran') (HT)	ESty
	MOUNTAIN SNOW ('Aussnow') (Ra)	LRHS
	MOUNTBATTEN ('Harmantelle') (F) 🏆H6	EBls ELan MRav MWat SCob SPer SPoG
§	'Mousseline' (DPoMo)	CArg CPou EBls ETWh
	'Mousseuse du Japon'	see *R.* 'Japonica'
	moyesii (S)	CTri EBee EBls ELan ETWh GKev SPer
§	- var. ***fargesii*** (S)	EBls
	- ***holodonta***	see *R. moyesii* f. *rosea*

§	- f. ***rosea*** (S)	EBls
	'Mr Lincoln'	see *R.* 'Mister Lincoln'
	'Mrs Anthony Waterer' (Ru)	CBod EBls ETWh NLar
	'Mrs Arthur Curtiss James' (ClHT)	ETWh MMuc NLar
	'Mrs F.W. Flight' (ClF)	EBls
	'Mrs Honey Dyson' (Ra)	CPou ETWh EWTr
	'Mrs John Laing' (HP)	EBls ETWh NLar SPer
	'Mrs Oakley Fisher' (HT)	CPou EBls ETWh SMad SPer
	'Mrs Paul' (Bb)	CBod EBls ETWh
	'Mrs Sam McGredy' (HT)	CPou EBls
	'Mrs Yamada' (Bb)	EBls
§	***mulliganii*** (Ra)	EBls EPfP ETWh GKin SPer
	multibracteata (S)	EBls ETWh GLog
	multiflora (Ra)	EBls ETWh LBuc
	- 'Carnea' (Ra)	EBls
§	- var. ***cathayensis*** (Ra)	EBls
§	- 'Grevillei' (Ra)	EBls ETWh MCot MMuc WFar
	- 'Platyphylla'	see *R. multiflora* 'Grevillei'
	- var. ***watsoniana***	see *R. watsoniana*
	MUM IN A MILLION	see *R.* MILLIE
	MUMMY	see *R.* NEWLY WED
	mundi	see *R. gallica* 'Versicolor'
	MUNSTEAD WOOD ('Ausbernard'PBR) (S) ♀H6	CDoC CGro CRos CTri EBee ECnt EHyd ELan EPfP EShb ESty GBin LBuc LCro LOPS LRHS LSRN MBNS NLar NRHS SCob SPer SPoG SSea WSpi
	murielae	EBls
	'Murjami'	EBls
	'Muscosa Alba'	see *R.* × *centifolia* 'Shailer's White Moss'
	'Mutabilis'	see *R.* × *odorata* 'Mutabilis'
	MY BROTHER ('Raw1056') (F)	ESty
	MY DAD ('Boselftay'PBR) (F)	CBcs CBod EBls LSRN SApu
	'My Darling Husband' (F)	LSRN
	'My Darling Wife' (F)	LSRN
	MY GIRL ('Tan00798'PBR) (HT)	CDoC EBee
	'My Joy' (HT)	LSRN
	'My Lovely Mum' (F)	MFry
	MY MUM ('Webmorrow'PBR) (F)	CBcs CBod ESty LSRN SApu SCoo
	MY NAN ('Fornan') (HT)	ESty
	MY SISTER ('Raw1052') (F)	ESty
§	MY VALENTINE ('Korcoluma'PBR) (HT) ♀H6	CSBt LBuc LSRN
	MY VALENTINE ('Mormyval') (Min)	EBls LSRN MAsh
	MYRIAM ('Cocgrand') (HT)	LSRN
	MYSTIC GLOW ('Raw1101') (F) **new**	ESty
	NANCY JEAN ('Ricnancy') (Patio)	LSRN
	NANCY ('Poulninga') (Renaissance Series) (S)	CBod CPou ETWh LSRN
	nanothamnus	SPtp
	'Naomi' (HT)	CPou LSRN MAsh
	'Narrow Water' (Ra) ♀H6	CArg CPou EBls ETWh
§	'Nastarana' (N)	EBls ETWh NLar
	NATALIE ('Poulren014'PBR) (Renaissance Series) (S)	CBod ECnt ETWh LSRN
	NATANIA ('Dicseduce') (F)	IDic
	NATASHA RICHARDSON ('Harpacket'PBR) (F)	ELon MRav
	'Nathalie Nypels'	see *R.* 'Mevrouw Nathalie Nypels'
	'National Trust' (HT)	CArg CTri IArd MFry SCob SPer
	NATURAL BEAUTY ('Rogscriv') (HT)	SSea
	NELSON'S JOURNEY ('Beaflirt') (S)	EBls
	'Nelson's Pride' (F)	EBls
	'Nestor' (G)	EBls ETWh
	'Nevada' (S)	CArg CBod CTri EBls EPfP ETWh IArd LEdu MRav MWat NLar SCob SPer
	NEVER FORGOTTEN ('Gregart') (HT)	LSRN
	NEW ARRIVAL	see *R.* 'Red Patio'
	NEW BEGINNINGS ('Korprofko'PBR) (F) ♀H5	ELan LSRN MAsh
§	'New Dawn' (Cl) ♀H7	Widely available
	'New Home'	LSRN
§	NEWLY WED ('Dicwhynot'PBR) (Patio) ♀H6	LSRN SSea
	NEWSFLASH ('Kendutch'PBR) (F) ♀H5	ESty ETWh
	NICE DAY ('Chewsea'PBR) (ClMin)	CDoC CTri EPfP ESty MAsh MFry MRav SApu SPer SPoG SSea
	'Nicola' (F)	LSRN
	NIGHT LIGHT ('Poullight'PBR) (Courtyard Series) (ClHT)	ECnt SApu
	NIGHT OWL ('Wekpurosot') (Cl)	CBod CDoC CWld ECnt ESty ETWh GBin LRHS MRav NLar NPoe SPer SPoG
	NINA ('Mehnina'PBR) (S)	LSRN
	NINA ('Poulren018'PBR) (Renaissance Series) (S)	CBod ECnt ETWh
	nitida	EBls SCob SPer
	NOBLE ANTONY ('Ausway'PBR) (S)	CRos EPfP
§	'Noisette Carnée' (N) ♀H7	CArg CPou CTri EBee EBls EPfP ETWh GBin LEdu LRHS MAsh MBNS MCot MRav MWat NLar NRHS SApu SCob SPer SSea WBor
	NORFOLK ('Poulfolk') (GC)	CTri EBls MSwo NLar SApu SCob SPer
	NORTHAMPTONSHIRE ('Mattdor') (GC)	SCob
	'Norwell' (Ra)	MNrw
	'Norwich Castle' (F)	EBls
	NORWICH CATHEDRAL ('Beacath') (HT)	EBls
	NORWICH THEATRE ROYAL ('Beacalm') (S)	EBls
	'Norwich Union' (F)	EBls
	NOSTALGIA ('Savarita') (Min)	CGro EPfP LBuc LRHS MAsh
§	NOSTALGIA ('Taneiglat'PBR) (HT) ♀H6	CSBt EBee EBls ECnt ELon ESty MFry MRav SApu SMad SPer SPoG SSea
	NOSTALGIE	see *R.* NOSTALGIA ('Taneiglat')
	'Notre-Dame de Calais' (Cl)	EBee EBls EPfP LRHS MAsh
	'Nova Zembla' (Ru)	EBls
	'Nozomi' (ClMin/GC)	CBod CTri EBls ELan ESty ETWh NLar SApu SPer
	'Nuits de Young' (CeMo) ♀H7	CArg CBod EBls EPfP ETWh NLar SApu
	'Nur Mahal' (HM)	CArg EBls ETWh
	NURSE TRACEY DAVIES ('Frykookie'PBR) (F) ♀H6	MAsh MFry
	nutkana (S)	EBls
§	- var. ***hispida*** (S)	EBls
§	- 'Plena' (S/D) ♀H7	EBls ETWh GKin NLar WHer

	'Nymphenburg' (HM)	ETWh SPer
	'Nyveldt's White' (Ru)	EBls
	OCTAVIA HILL ('Harzeal'PBR) (F)	ETWh EWTr MRav MWat NLar
§	× ***odorata***	CPou EBls
	– 'Fortune's Double Yellow'	see *R.* × *odorata* 'Pseudindica'
	– 'Hume's Blush Tea-scented China' (ClCh)	EBls ETWh
§	– 'Mutabilis' (Ch) 🏆H5	Widely available
§	– 'Ochroleuca' (Ch)	CPou
I	– 'Odorata' (Ch)	EBls
	– old crimson China (Ch)	EBls
§	– 'Pallida' (Ch)	CPou EBls EPfP ETWh LRHS MCot MWat NLar SCob SSea
§	– 'Pseudindica' (ClCh)	EBls IArd
§	– Sanguinea Group (Ch)	EBls ILea SEND XSen
	– – 'Bengal Crimson' (Ch) 🏆H5	CPou CRHN CRos ECre EHyd EPfP ETWh EWTr LRHS NRHS SDix SLon SPoG WAvo WCFE WCot WKif
	– – 'Bob's Beauty' (Ch)	WCot
§	– 'Viridiflora' (Ch)	CPou EBee EBls ETWh LEdu SCob SLon SMad SPer SSea WCot WHer
	ODYSSEY ('Franski'PBR) (F)	ESty
	officinalis	see *R. gallica* var. *officinalis*
	OH WOW! ('Wekspitrib'PBR) (ClHT)	CBod ECnt ESty SSea
	old blush China	see *R.* × *odorata* 'Pallida'
	old cabbage	see *R.* × *centifolia*
	OLD JOHN ('Dicwillynilly') (F)	LSRN
	old pink moss rose	see *R.* × *centifolia* 'Muscosa'
	OLD PORT ('Mackati') (F)	ELon ESty IArd SApu
	old red moss	see *R.* 'Henri Martin', *R.* 'Lanei'
	old velvet moss	see *R.* 'William Lobb'
	'Old Velvet Rose'	see *R.* 'Tuscany'
	old yellow Scotch (SpH)	see *R.* × *harisonii* 'Williams' Double Yellow'
	OLIVIA ('Wekquahofa') (HT)	LSRN
	OLIVIA ROSE ('Wisnut') (Min) **new**	SSea
	OLIVIA ROSE AUSTIN ('Ausmixture'PBR) (S)	CGro CRos CSBt EHyd ELan EPfP ESty GBin LCro LOPS LRHS NRHS SPoG
	'Olympic Flame' (F)	EPfP MAsh
	'Omar Khayyám' (D)	EBls ETWh NLar
	omeiensis	see *R. sericea* subsp. *omeiensis*
	ONE IN A MILLION ('Poulren024'PBR) (S)	ETWh MAsh NLar
	OOH LA LA ('Gues05-64') (F) **new**	ESty
	OPEN ARMS ('Chewpixcel'PBR) (ClMin) 🏆H6	CRos EBls EPfP ESty LCro LOPS MFry MMuc SApu SMad SPer SSea
	'Ophelia' (HT)	EBls NLar
	ORANGE BLOSSOM SPECIAL ('Smi52/02') (ClMin)	ESty
	'Orange Sensation' (F)	CTri
§	ORANGE SUNBLAZE ('Meijikatar'PBR) (Min)	CBod CSBt SCob SPer
	'Orange Triumph' (Poly)	EBls
	ORANGES AND LEMONS ('Macoranlem') (F)	CArg CSBt EBls ESty SApu SCob SSea WBor
	OTHELLO ('Auslo'PBR) (S)	SPer
	OUR BETH ('Beacarol') (S)	EBls EPfP LRHS LSRN MAsh
	'Our Dream' (Patio)	LRHS MAsh
	OUR GEORGE ('Kirrush') (Patio)	LSRN
	OUR HILDA ('Lancoro') (F)	LSRN
§	OUR JANE ('Horengland') (F)	LSRN
	OUR JUBILEE ('Coccages') (HT)	ESty
	'Our Millie' (HT)	LSRN
	OUR MOLLY ('Dicreason') (GC/S)	IDic LSRN SPer
	OUT OF THE BLUE ('Simblue') (F)	ESty
	OVER THE MOON ('Oraclelon') (HT) **new**	ESty
	OXANA ('Dicovadatop') (F)	IDic SApu
	OXFORDSHIRE ('Korfullwind'PBR) (GC) 🏆H6	SCob
	'Pablito' (Min)	MMuc
	PANACHE ('Poultop'PBR) (Patio/Min)	ECnt LRHS MPri
	PAPA MEILLAND ('Meisar') (HT)	CSBt CTri EBls SPer SSea
	PAPER ANNIVERSARY (Patio)	LSRN
	PAPI DELBARD ('Delaby') (ClHT)	CArg CBod EBee ETWh LSRN MRav NLar SSea
	'Papillon' (Ch)	EBls
§	'Para Ti' (Min)	SPer
I	'Parade' (Cl) 🏆H6	CArg EBls ETWh LSRN MFry NLar
	'Parkdirektor Riggers' (Cl)	EBls ETWh LCro LOPS NLar SCob SPer
	Parks's yellow China	see *R.* × *odorata* 'Ochroleuca'
	Parson's pink China	see *R.* × *odorata* 'Pallida'
	PARTRIDGE ('Korweirim') (GC)	EBls SPer
	parvifolia	see *R.* 'Burgundiaca'
	PAS DE DEUX ('Poulhult'PBR) (Courtyard Series) (ClF)	MAsh
	PASCALI ('Lenip') (HT)	CArg CBcs CTri EBls SCob SPer
	PAT AUSTIN ('Ausmum'PBR) (S)	CArg CTri EPfP LSRN MAsh MBNS NLar SCob SEND SPer
	PATRICIA MAY ('Dicscenic') (F)	IDic
	'Paul Crampel' (Poly)	EBls
	'Paul Lédé' (ClT)	see *R.* 'Climbing Paul Lédé'
	PAUL MCCARTNEY (HT)	see *R.* THE MCCARTNEY ROSE
	'Paul Neyron' (HP)	EBls ETWh
	'Paul Noël' (Ra)	CRos LSRN
	'Paul Ricault' (Ce × HP)	EBls ETWh
	PAUL SHIRVILLE ('Harqueterwife'PBR) (HT)	EBls SPer
	'Paul Transon' (Ra) 🏆H6	CPou CRHN CRos EBls EPfP ETWh MMuc NLar SEND WHer
	'Paul Verdier' (Bb)	EBls
	'Paula's Rose' (Patio)	LSRN SSea
§	'Paulii' (Ru/GC)	EBls WSpi
	'Paulii Alba'	see *R.* 'Paulii'
	'Paul's Early Blush' (HP)	EBls
	'Paul's Himalayan Musk' (Ra) 🏆H6	Widely available
§	'Paul's Lemon Pillar' (ClHT)	CArg EBls EPfP ETWh LRHS NLar SPer
	'Paul's Scarlet Climber' (Cl/Ra)	CArg CBod CDoC EBee EBls ETWh LBuc LCro LOPS LRHS MAsh MPri MRav MSwo MWat SCob SPer
	'Paul's Single White Perpetual' (Ra)	CTri EBls ETWh NLar
	PAWS ('Beapaw') (S)	EBls
	'Pax' (HM)	CPou EBls ETWh WKif
	PEACE ('Madame A. Meilland') (HT) 🏆H6	CArg CBcs CRos CSBt CTri EBls ECnt ELan EPfP LCro LOPS LRHS LSRN MAsh MFry MPri MRav MWat NRHS SApu SCob SPer SPoG SSea
	'Peach Grootendorst' (Ru)	CPou ETWh

PEACHY ('Macrelea') (HT)	EPfP MAsh SPoG
PEARL ('Korterschi'PBR) (F) ♀H6	MAsh MRav MWat
PEARL ('Wekpearl') (HT)	CSBt
§ PEARL ABUNDANCE ('Harfrisky'PBR) (F)	SApu
PEARL ANNIVERSARY ('Whitston'PBR) (Min/Patio)	CDoC ESty LCro LOPS LSRN MRav MWat SApu SSea SVic
PEARL DRIFT ('Leggab') (S)	EBls ETWh MCot MSwo SPer
PEAUDOUCE	see *R.* ELINA
§ 'Pélisson' (CeMo)	EBls
§ ***pendulina***	EBls WOut
- 'Nana'	NWad
'Penelope' (HM) ♀H5	CArg CSBt CTri EBee EBls ECnt ELan EPfP ETWh LCro LOPS LRHS LSRN MCot MFry MNrw MRav NLar SCob SPer SSea
'Penelope Hobhouse' (HM)	EBls
PENNY LANE ('Hardwell'PBR) (ClHT) ♀H6	CArg CBod CGro CSBt EBee EBls ECnt EPfP ETWh LBuc LCro LOPS LRHS MAsh MFry MRav NLar SApu SCob SCoo SPer SPoG SSea
PENNY LANE ('Talpen') (Min)	MSwo
PENSIONER'S VOICE ('Fryrelax') (F)	MFry
× ***penzanceana***	see *R.* 'Lady Penzance'
PEPPERMINT SPLASH	see *R.* RACHEL LOUISE MORAN
PERENNIAL BLUE ('Mehv9601') (Ra) ♀H6	CDoC EBls ELon ESty MRav SApu SSea
PERENNIAL BLUSH ('Mehbarbie'PBR) (Ra) ♀H6	CArg CDoC ELan ESty MRav SApu
§ PERFECT DAY ('Poulcrem') (F)	ECnt
PERFECT GENTLEMAN ('Raw1059') (F)	ESty
PERFECT HARMONY ('Tangustedv') (HT)	EBee ESty SSea
PERFECT PET ('Smi 122204'PBR) (F)	ESty
'Pergolèse' (DPo)	EBls ETWh
'Perle des Jardins' (T)	EBls
§ 'Perle d'Or' (Poly) ♀H6	EBls ETWh NLar SDix SPer
PERPETUALLY YOURS ('Harfable'PBR) (Cl)	CDoC CGro MRav
Persian yellow	see *R. foetida* 'Persiana'
PETER BEALES ('Cleexpert') (S)	EBls
PETER PAN ('Chewpan'PBR) (Min) ♀H6	CDoC
PETER PAN ('Sunpete') (Patio)	MAsh
'Petite de Hollande' (Ce)	EBls ETWh NLar SPer
'Petite Lisette' (Ce × D)	NLar
'Petite Orléannaise' (Ce)	EBls
PHAB GOLD ('Frybountiful'PBR) (F)	MFry
PHEASANT ('Kordapt') (GC)	EBls SApu SPer
PHILLIPA ('Poulheart'PBR) (S)	ETWh LSRN SApu
PHOEBE (Ru)	see *R.* 'Fimbriata'
phoenicea	EBls
'Phyllis Bide' (Ra) ♀H6	CArg CRos EBee EBls EHyd ELan EPfP ETWh EWTr IArd LCro LOPS LRHS MBNS MCot MSwo NLar SApu SMad SPer SSea WKif
PICCADILLY ('Macar') (HT)	CSBt CTri SCob SPer
PICCOLO ('Tanolokip') (F/Patio)	SApu
'Picture' (HT)	SPer
PIERRE CARDIN ('Meilolipo'PBR) (HT)	CBod ESty
PIGALLE '84 ('Meicloux') (F)	SCoo
'Pilgrim'	see *R.* THE PILGRIM
pimpinellifolia	see *R. spinosissima*
- 'Altaica'	see *R. spinosissima* 'Grandiflora'
- double yellow-flowered	see *R.* × *harisonii* 'Williams' Double Yellow'
PINK ABUNDANCE ('Harfrothy'PBR) (Abundance Series) (F)	CArg SApu
PINK BELLS ('Poulbells') (GC)	CGro EBls SApu SPer
'Pink Bouquet' (Ra)	CRHN
PINK CHAMPAGNE ('Forchamp') (Cl)	ESty
PINK CHAMPAGNE ('Frysamba') (F)	MAsh MFry
'Pink Cloud' (ClHT)	ELan
'Pink Favorite' (HT)	SCob SPer
PINK FIZZ ('Poulycool') (ClPatio)	ECnt
§ PINK FLOWER CARPET ('Noatraum') (GC) ♀H6	CDoC CGro CRos CSBt CTri EBls ECnt EHyd ELan LCro LOPS LRHS LSRN MAsh MPri NRHS SApu SCoo SEND SPer SPoG SSea
'Pink Garnette'	see *R.* 'Carol Amling'
'Pink Grootendorst' (Ru)	EBls EPfP ETWh LEdu NLar SCob SPer
'Pink Gruss an Aachen' (F)	EBls ETWh
§ PINK HIT ('Poultipe'PBR) (Min/Patio)	EBls ECnt LRHS LSRN MAsh NRHS
'Pink Leda' (D)	ETWh
PINK MARTINI ('Tan04608'PBR) (HT)	CDoC EBee MFry MRav SSea
pink moss	see *R.* × *centifolia* 'Muscosa'
PINK PARADISE ('Delfluoros'PBR) (HT)	ETWh
'Pink Parfait' (F)	EBls SPer
PINK PERFECTION ('Korpauvio'PBR) (HT) ♀H5	CSBt ECnt EPfP LRHS MAsh SSea
'Pink Perpétué' (Cl)	CArg CBod CSBt CTri EBls ECnt EHyd ELan EPfP ETWh MRav MWat NLar SCob SPer SPoG SSea
'Pink Prosperity' (HM)	EBls
'Pink Showers' (ClHT)	MSwo
PINK SKYLINER ('Franwekpink'PBR) (ClS)	EBls
PIPPIN ('Beajaffa') (S)	EBls MAsh
PIROUETTE ('Poulyc003'PBR) (ClS)	ECnt MAsh
PLEINE DE GRÂCE ('Lengra') (S)	EBls LEdu
'Plentiful' (F)	EBls
POETRY IN MOTION ('Harelan'PBR) (HT)	CArg EBls
POLAR STAR ('Tanlarpost') (HT)	CArg CSBt EBls ECnt MFry SCob SPer
'Polly' (HT)	EBls LSRN
§ 'Polyantha Grandiflora' (Ra)	EBls ETWh SVic WBor
pomifera	see *R. villosa* L.
POMPADOUR ('Deldour') (F)	ESty
'Pompon Blanc Parfait' (A)	EBls ETWh
'Pompon de Bourgogne'	see *R.* 'Burgundiaca'
'Pompon de Paris' (ClMinCh)	see *R.* 'Climbing Pompon de Paris'

	Name	Suppliers
	'Pompon de Paris' (MinCh)	WAbe WKif
	POMPONELLA ('Korpompan'PBR) (F) ♀H6	MAsh
	PORT SUNLIGHT ('Auslofty'PBR) (HM) ♀H6	CRos EHyd EPfP ESty LRHS NLar NRHS
	Portland rose	see *R.* 'Portlandica'
§	'Portlandica' (Po)	CTri EBls ETWh SPer
	POUR TOI	see *R.* 'Para Ti'
	POWER POINT ('Bennovecientos') (Patio) **new**	SSea
	prairie rose	see *R. setigera*
	prattii	EBls
	'Precious Amber' (F)	LBuc MAsh
	'Precious Gold' (F)	MAsh MFry
	PRECIOUS GRANDDAUGHTER ('Raw1193') (F) **new**	ESty
	PRECIOUS GRANDSON ('Raw1088') (F) **new**	ESty
	PRECIOUS LOVE ('Kirlowo'PBR) (F)	LBuc MAsh
	'Precious Memories' (Min)	CBod LSRN
	PRECIOUS MEMORIES ('Dichello'PBR) (F)	ESty
	PRECIOUS TIME ('Oramarpa'PBR) (HT)	ESty
§	'Président de Sèze' (G) ♀H6	CArg CPou EBls ETWh NLar SPer
	'President Herbert Hoover' (HT)	EBls
	PRETTY IN PINK ('Dicumpteen'PBR) (GC) ♀H6	ECnt
	PRETTY JESSICA ('Ausjess') (S)	CDoC CGro LSRN MRav SPer
	PRETTY POLLY ('Meitonje') (Min) ♀H6	CDoC EHyd EPfP ESty LCro LOPS LRHS MAsh MFry MRav SCob SPoG SSea
	'Pride of Reigate' (HP)	EBls
	'Prima Ballerina' (HT)	CArg CTri EBls EPfP LRHS MAsh SPer
	primula	EBls ETWh EWTr NLar
	'Prince Camille de Rohan' (HP)	EBls ETWh
	'Prince Charles' (Bb)	EBls ETWh WKif
	PRINCE JARDINIER ('Meitroni'PBR) (HT) ♀H6	CArg CBod ESty LSRN
	PRINCESS ('Korspobux'PBR) (HT)	ECnt
	PRINCESS ALEXANDRA ('Pouldra'PBR) (Renaissance Series) (S) ♀H6	CTri ECnt ETWh NLar
	PRINCESS ALEXANDRA OF KENT ('Ausmerchant'PBR) (S)	CDoC CRos CSBt EHyd EPfP ESty LRHS NRHS SPer
	PRINCESS ALICE ('Hartanna') (F)	LSRN
	PRINCESS ANNE ('Auskitchen'PBR) (S) ♀H6	CRos CSBt ECnt EHyd EPfP LBuc LRHS NRHS
	'Princess Louise' (Ra)	EBls
	'Princess of Wales' (HP)	MWat
	PRINCESS OF WALES ('Hardinkum'PBR) (F) ♀H6	CDoC EBls MRav SApu SPer
§	'Princesse de Nassau' (Ra)	CPou EBls ETWh
	'Princesse Louise' (Ra)	EBls
	'Princesse Marie' misapplied	see *R.* 'Belvedere'
	'Princesse Marie' Jacques (Ra)	EBls
	'Prolifera de Redouté' misapplied	see *R.* 'Duchesse de Montebello'
	PROPER JOB ('Tan02733'PBR) (HT)	CBod CDoC EBee ECnt ESty ETWh MFry SLon SMad SSea
	'Prosperity' (HM) ♀H6	CTri EBls ETWh MCot NLar SPer
	PROSPERO ('Auspero') (S)	ETWh NLar
§	PURE POETRY ('Jacment') (F) **new**	CBod
§	PURE POETRY ('Tan04179') (HT)	EBee ELon ESty ETWh MFry SApu SMad SPer SSea
	'Purezza' (Ra)	EBls NLar SMad
	'Purity' (ClHT)	ETWh
	PURPLE EDEN	see *R.* EBB TIDE
	PURPLE MOON ('Dicmover') (F)	SApu
	PURPLE PRINCE ('Simpurple') (HT)	ESty
	PURPLE SKYLINER ('Franwekpurp'PBR) (ClS)	CBod EBls LRHS MAsh MCot MPri SApu SPer SPoG
	PURPLE TIGER ('Jacpurr'PBR) (F)	CDoC ESty SApu SCob
	'Purpurtraum' (Ru)	SApu
	quatre saisons	see *R.* × *damascena* var. *semperflorens*
	'Quatre Saisons Blanche Mousseuse' (DMo)	CPou EBls ETWh NLar
	QUEEN ANNE ('Austruck'PBR) (S)	ESty LSRN
	QUEEN BEE (F)	MFry
	QUEEN ELIZABETH	see *R.* 'The Queen Elizabeth'
	QUEEN MOTHER ('Korquemu') (Patio) ♀H6	CDoC CSBt EBls ELan EPfP MRav SPer
	'Queen of Bourbons' (Bb)	EBls ETWh LEdu NLar
	QUEEN OF DENMARK	see *R.* 'Königin von Dänemark'
	QUEEN OF SWEDEN ('Austiger'PBR) (S)	CGro CRos ECnt EHyd EPfP LBuc LRHS NRHS SPer
	'Rachel' (HT)	CArg CDoC CPou LBuc LRHS LSRN MAsh MPri NLar SLon
	RACHEL ('Booyol') (S)	EBee
	RACHEL ('Tangust'PBR) (HT) ♀H6	CSBt EBls EPfP ESty ETWh MFry MRav SApu SPoG SSea
§	RACHEL LOUISE MORAN ('Jacdrama'PBR) (HT)	ELon ESty
	RACQUEL ('Poulren023'PBR) (S) **new**	ETWh
	'Rambling Rector' (Ra) ♀H6	Widely available
	RAMBLING ROSIE ('Horjasper'PBR) (Ra) ♀H6	CArg CBod CRos CSBt CWld EBls ECnt EPfP ESty ETWh LSRN MSwo NLar SApu SSea
	'Ramona' (Ra)	EBls ETWh
	RASPBERRY CREAM TWIRL ('Meiteratol'PBR) (ClHT)	MAsh
	'Raspberry Royale' (F/Patio) ♀H6	CDoC EPfP MAsh SPoG
	'Raubritter' ('Macrantha' hybrid)	CPou EBls ETWh SPer
	RAYMOND BLANC ('Delnado') (HT)	CBod ETWh LSRN MRav NLar
	'Raymond Carver' (S)	EBee EBls LRHS MAsh
	REBECCA (Patio)	ESty LSRN
	'Rebecca Claire' (HT)	LSRN
	REBECCA MARY ('Dicjury'PBR) (F)	IDic
	RED ABUNDANCE	see *R.* SONGS OF PRAISE
	RED BELLS ('Poulred') (Min/GC)	EBls SApu

	RED BLANKET ('Intercell') (S/GC)	EBls SPer
	RED DEVIL ('Dicam') (HT)	CArg
	RED EDEN ROSE ('Meidrason'[PBR]) (Cl)	ESty
	RED FINESSE ('Korvillade'[PBR]) (F) 🏆H6	CArg ETWh
	RED FLAME ('Adabaring'[PBR]) (ClHT) **new**	CGro
	'Red Grootendorst'	see *R.* 'F.J. Grootendorst'
	RED LETTER DAY ('Beajackdaw') (S)	EBls LRHS MAsh NRHS
	'Red Max Graf'	see *R.* ROTE MAX GRAF
	red moss	see *R.* 'Henri Martin'
	RED NEW DAWN	see *R.* 'Étendard'
	RED PARFUM DE PROVENCE ('Meiafone'[PBR]) (HT)	ESty
§	'Red Patio' (F/Patio)	LSRN
	RED RASCAL ('Jacbed') (S/Patio)	CSBt MFry SApu
	red rose of Lancaster	see *R. gallica* var. *officinalis*
	'Red Wing' (S)	EBls
	REDOVA ('Poulcy030'[PBR]) (Courtyard Series) (Cl)	ECnt
	REGENSBERG ('Macyoumis'[PBR]) (F/Patio)	CBod EBls LEdu MFry SPer
	'Reine des Violettes' (HP) 🏆H6	CPou CWld EBls ELon EPfP ETWh IArd LCro LOPS LSRN MCot MPri NLar SMad
	'Reine Marie Henriette' (ClHT)	CPou
§	'Reine Victoria' (Bb)	CBod CDoC EBls ETWh LCro LOPS NLar SPer
§	REMEMBER ('Poulht001'[PBR]) (HT) 🏆H6	EBls ECnt EPfP LBuc LRHS MAsh NRHS SPoG
	REMEMBER ME ('Cocdestin') (HT) 🏆H6	CArg CBod CSBt EBls ECnt EPfP ESty IArd LCro LOPS LRHS LSRN MAsh MFry MGos MRav MWat SApu SCob SPer SPoG
	REMEMBRANCE ('Harxampton') (F)	CArg CBod EBls EPfP ESty LBuc LRHS LSRN MAsh MFry MPri MRav MWat SApu SCob SPer SPoG
§	RENAISSANCE ('Harzart'[PBR]) (HT)	CArg CSBt
	'René André' (Ra)	CPou CRHN EBee EBls ETWh NLar
	RÉPUBLIQUE DE MONTMARTRE ('Delparfrou') (F)	CWld
	'Rescht'	see *R.* 'De Resht'
	'Rêve d'Or' (N)	EBls ETWh MCot MMuc
	'Réveil Dijonnais' (ClHT)	EBls
	RHAPSODY IN BLUE ('Frantasia'[PBR]) (S) 🏆H6	Widely available
	RICHARD PORSON ('Beajuniper') (S)	EBls
§	× ***richardii***	EBls ETWh NLar
	RICK STEIN ('Tan96205'[PBR]) (HT)	LSRN
	'Rita' ambig.	WKif
	'River Gardens'	NPer
	'Rivers's George IV' (Ch)	CBod ETWh
	ROALD DAHL ('Ausowlish') (S)	CRos CSBt EHyd ESty LRHS MAsh NRHS SCoo
	ROB ROY ('Cocrob') (F)	EBls SPer
	'Robert le Diable' (Ce × G)	EBls ETWh SPer
	'Robert Léopold' (Mo)	EBls
	'Robin Hood' (HM)	EBls ETWh
	ROBIN REDBREAST ('Interrob') (Min/GC)	EBls
§	ROBUSTA ('Korgosa') (Ru)	EBls
	ROCK & ROLL ('Wekgobnez') (HT)	CSBt ELon ESty LSRN
	'Roger Lambelin' (HP)	EBls ETWh SPer
	ROMANCE ('Tanezamor'[PBR]) (S)	LSRN
	ROMANZE ('Tan03434'[PBR]) (HT)	CArg
	'Rosa Mundi'	see *R. gallica* 'Versicolor'
	ROSARIUM UETERSEN ('Kortersen') (ClHT)	EBls
	'Rose à Parfum de l'Haÿ' (Ru)	CTri EBls
	'Rose Ball' (S)	EBls LRHS MAsh
§	'Rose d'Amour' (S) 🏆H6	EBls
	'Rose de Meaux'	see *R.* × *centifolia* 'De Meaux'
	'Rose de Meaux White'	see *R.* 'White de Meaux'
	'Rose de Rescht'	see *R.* 'De Resht'
	ROSE DES CISTERCIENS ('Delarle') (HT)	CBod ESty ETWh
	'Rose des Maures' misapplied	see *R.* 'Sissinghurst Castle'
	'Rose du Maître d'Ecole'	see *R.* 'Du Maître d'Ecole'
	'Rose du Roi' (HP/DPo)	EBls ETWh
	'Rose du Roi à Fleurs Pourpres' (HP)	EBls
	ROSE FOR ELAINE ('Rawdenqueen') (HT)	LSRN
§	ROSE GAUJARD ('Gaumo') (HT)	CArg EBls LRHS MAsh
	ROSÉE DE MATIN ('Evematch'[PBR]) (S)	EBls
	'Rose-Marie Viaud' (Ra)	CPou EBls ETWh MMuc
	ROSEMARY HARKNESS ('Harrowbond') (HT)	ESty SPer
	'Rosemary Rose' (F)	EBls SPer
	ROSEMOOR ('Austough'[PBR]) (S) 🏆H6	CRos EHyd LBuc LRHS MAsh NRHS SPer
	'Roseraie de l'Haÿ' (Ru) 🏆H7	Widely available
	ROSIE ('Benros') (Min)	LSRN
	'Rosy Cheeks' (HT)	MAsh
	ROSY CUSHION ('Interall') (S/GC)	EBls ETWh EWTr LRHS MCot NLar SApu SPer WKif
	'Rosy Mantle' (ClHT)	CSBt EBls SPer
§	ROTARY SUNRISE ('Fryglitzy') (HT)	CSBt MFry
§	ROTE MAX GRAF ('Kormax') (GC/Ru)	EBls NLar
§	'Rouletii' (Min)	ITim
	'Roundelay' (HT)	CBod EBls ETWh
	roxburghii	CBcs ETWh GKev LEdu
	- PAB 7331	LEdu
	- var. ***hirtula*** (S)	EBls
	- f. ***normalis*** (S)	EBls
	'Royal Air Force' (HT)	ELan
§	ROYAL BROMPTON ROSE ('Meivildo') (HT)	CBod ESty
	ROYAL CELEBRATION ('Wekbiphitsou') (F)	CBod
	ROYAL COPENHAGEN	see *R.* REMEMBER
	'Royal Gold' (ClHT)	EBls
	'Royal Highness' (HT)	EBls
	ROYAL JUBILEE ('Auspaddle'[PBR]) (S)	CRos CSBt EPfP LCro LOPS MAsh SPer
	'Royal Occasion' (F)	SPer
	ROYAL WILLIAM ('Korzaun') (HT) 🏆H6	CArg CDoC CSBt CTri EBls ELan LBuc LCro LOPS LRHS LSRN MAsh MFry MPri MRav SApu SCob SPer

§ ***rubiginosa***	CCVT CTho EBls ETWh GPoy LBuc SCob SPer WKor WMou WTSh
rubra	see *R. gallica*
rubrifolia	see *R. glauca* Pourr.
'Rubrotincta'	see *R.* 'Hebe's Lip'
RUBY ANNIVERSARY ('Harbonny'PBR) (Patio)	CDoC CGro CRos CSBt EBls EHyd ELan ELon ESty LBuc LCro LOPS LRHS LSRN MAsh MFry MRav MSwo MWat SApu SCob SCoo SPer SPoG SSea SVic
RUBY CELEBRATION ('Peawinner'PBR) (F) 𝕐H6	CBod EBls ELon ESty MRav MWat SApu
RUBY ROMANCE	see *R.* MEDLEY RUBY
RUBY RUBY	see *R.* RUBY SLIPPERS
§ RUBY SLIPPERS ('Weksactrumi') (Min)	LRHS MAsh NRHS SPoG
'Ruby Wedding' (HT)	CArg CBcs CDoC CRos CSBt CTri EBee EBls ECnt ELan EPfP IArd LRHS LSRN MAsh MFry MGos MRav MWat NRHS SApu SCob SPer SVic
'Ruby Wedding Anniversary' (F)	LSRN
rugosa (Ru)	CArg CBod CGro CLnd CTri ECrN EPfP EPom GAbr LBuc LRHS MRav SCob SGol SPlb WMat WMou WTSh
- 'Alba' (Ru)	Widely available
- 'Rubra' (Ru)	CBcs CBod CCVT CGro CTho CTri EBee ELan EPfP EPom LBuc LCro LOPS SEWo SEdi SPer SPoG SSea SVic
- var. ***ventenatiana*** (Ru)	EBls
'Rugosa Atropurpurea' (Ru)	EPom
'Ruhm von Steinfurth' (HP)	EBls
'Rumba' (F)	ELan
'Rural England' (Ra)	CGro EBls LRHS MAsh
'Russelliana' (Ra)	EBls ETWh NLar
'Sadler's Wells' (S)	EBls
'Safrano' (T)	EBls
SAINT BONIFACE ('Kormatt') (F/Patio)	CSBt
SAINT EDMUNDS ROSE	see *R.* BONITA
SAINT ETHELBURGA ('Beabimbo') (S)	EBls EPfP LRHS MAsh MCot
Saint John's rose	see *R.* × *richardii*
Saint Mark's rose	see *R.* 'Rose d'Amour'
'Saint Nicholas' (D)	EBls
'Saint Prist de Breuze' (Ch)	EBls
SAINT SWITHUN ('Auswith'PBR) (S)	EHyd EPfP ESty LRHS MAsh NLar NRHS SPer
'Salet' (DPMo)	CPou EBls ETWh NLar
'Sally Holmes' (S) 𝕐H6	CPou EBls ECnt ETWh LSRN MRav NLar SApu SEND SLon SPer
SALLY KANE ('Frygroovy'PBR) (HT)	MFry MRav
SALLY'S ROSE ('Canrem') (HT)	ECnt LSRN
SALSA	see *R.* CHEEK TO CHEEK
SALVATION ('Harlark'PBR) (F)	ESty
§ SAMARITAN ('Harverag') (HT)	CSBt SApu
sancta	see *R.* × *richardii*
'Sander's White Rambler' (Ra) 𝕐H6	CRHN CRos CSam CTri EBee EBls EPfP ETWh LRHS MSwo NRHS SPer WFar
SANDRA ('Koreinek') (HT)	LSRN
SANDRA ('Poulen055'PBR) (Renaissance Series) (S)	ETWh LSRN NLar
SANDRINGHAM ('Beamolly') (S)	EBee EBls
'Sandringham Centenary' (HT)	EBls
'Sanguinea'	see *R.* × *odorata* Sanguinea Group
SARAH (HT)	see *R.* JARDINS DE BAGATELLE
'Sarah van Fleet' (Ru)	CBod CDoC CTho CTri EBls ETWh IArd MMuc MRav MSwo NLar SApu SCob SPer
SARAH, DUCHESS OF YORK	see *R.* SUNSEEKER
SAVOY HOTEL ('Harvintage') (HT)	CArg EBls MFry SApu SCob SPer
'Scabrosa' (Ru) 𝕐H7	CBod EBls ECnt EPfP ETWh LBuc MAsh MCot NLar SPer
SCARBOROUGH FAIR ('Ausoran') (S) 𝕐H6	CRos MMuc
SCARLET FIRE	see *R.* 'Scharlachglut'
SCARLET GLOW	see *R.* 'Scharlachglut'
SCARLET HIT ('Poulmo'PBR) (PatioHit Series) (Min/Patio)	EBls ECnt LRHS LSRN NRHS
SCARLET PATIO ('Kortingle') (Patio)	CRos MAsh SPoG
SCARLET QUEEN ELIZABETH ('Dicel') (F)	EBls
§ SCENT FROM HEAVEN ('Chewbabaluv') (ClHT)	CBod CDoC CGro CRos CSBt ECnt ELon EPfP ESty ETWh LBuc LCro LOPS MAsh MFry MWat SApu SCoo SMad SPer SPoG SSea
SCENTED CARPET ('Chewground'PBR) (GC) 𝕐H6	CBod ECnt ELan ETWh SApu
SCENTED GARDEN ('Chewscentity') (S)	CSBt ESty SSea
SCENTED MEMORY ('Poulht002'PBR) (HT)	ECnt
SCENTIMENTAL ('Wekplapep'PBR) (F)	CBod EBls EPfP ESty LBuc MAsh MRav SApu SSea
SCENT-SATION ('Fryromeo'PBR) (HT)	CDoC MFry MRav MWat SPoG
SCEPTER'D ISLE ('Ausland'PBR) (S)	CDoC CRos CSBt EHyd EPfP LBuc LRHS LSRN MAsh NLar NRHS SCoo SPer
§ 'Scharlachglut' (ClS)	CPou EBls ETWh EWTr SPer
SCHLOSS BAD HOMBURG	see *R.* 'Alibaba'
SCHNEEWITTCHEN	see *R.* ICEBERG
§ 'Schneezwerg' (Ru) 𝕐H7	CTho EBls ETWh NLar SPer
'Schoolgirl' (ClHT)	CArg CBcs CDoC CTri EBls ELan EPfP ETWh LBuc LCro LOPS LRHS MAsh MFry MMrt MPri MRav MSwo SApu SCob SPer
Scotch rose	see *R. spinosissima*
Scotch yellow (SpH)	see *R.* × *harisonii* 'Williams' Double Yellow'
'Seagull' (Ra) 𝕐H6	CArg CTri EBls ECnt EPPr EPfP ETWh LCro LEdu LOPS LRHS LSRN MAsh MRav NLar SApu SCob SLon SMad SPer WHer
'Seale Pink Diamond' (S)	SSea
'Seale White Rambler' (Ra)	SSea
SEALED WITH A KISS ('Simwhat') (HT)	ESty
'Sealing Wax' (*moyesii* hybrid)	CPou EBls ETWh NLar
SELFRIDGES ('Korpriwa') (HT)	ESty
'Semiplena'	see *R.* × *alba* 'Alba Semiplena'
sempervirens (Ra)	EBls
sericea var. ***morrisonensis*** B&SWJ 7139	WCru
§ - subsp. ***omeiensis***	LEdu WPGP

- - BWJ 7550	WCru
- - PAB 2883	LEdu
- - f. ***pteracantha*** (S)	CTri EBee EBls ELan EPfP ETWh GKev IDee LEdu NLar SApu SPer SSea
'Serratipetala' (Ch)	EBls
§ ***setigera***	EBls
setipoda	EBls
seven sisters rose	see *R. multiflora* 'Grevillei'
SEVENTH HEAVEN ('Fryfantasy'PBR) (HT)	MFry
SEXY REXY ('Macrexy') (F)	CArg CBcs EBls LSRN MRav SCob SPer SPoG
'Shailer's White Moss'	see *R.* × *centifolia* 'Shailer's White Moss'
SHANTY ('Tan96191') (F)	ESty
SHARIFA ASMA ('Ausreef') (S)	LSRN MSwo NLar
SHEILA'S PERFUME ('Harsherry') (F) ♀H6	CArg CBod CDoC EBls ECnt EPfP ESty LSRN MAsh MFry MRav SApu SPer SPoG
SHINE ON ('Dictalent'PBR) (Patio) ♀H6	CSBt ECnt MFry
'Shot Silk' (HT)	EBls SCob
SHOWSTAR	see R. 'Loving Mum'
'Showtime' Lindquist (HT)	EBls
SHOWTIME ('Baitime') (ClS)	MAsh SPoG
§ SHRIMP HIT ('Poulshrimp'PBR) (Patio)	EBls ECnt MAsh MFry SPoG
'Shropshire Lass' (S)	SPer
SHROPSHIRE STAR ('Chewsummit') (ClS)	ESty SSea
SIGHTSAVER ('Fryaffair'PBR) (HT)	MFry
SILVER ANNIVERSARY ('Meiborfil') (HT)	ELon
§ SILVER ANNIVERSARY ('Poulari'PBR) (HT) ♀H6	CBod CDoC CRos CSBt EBls ECnt EHyd ELan LRHS LSRN MAsh MFry MGos MPri MRav MWat NRHS SApu SCoo SPer SPoG SSea
SILVER ANNIVERSARY ambig.	CArg CGro LSRN
SILVER CELEBRATION ('Guescloud') (F)	ESty
'Silver Jubilee' (HT)	CArg CBcs CTri EBls IArd LRHS MAsh MRav NRHS SCob SPer
'Silver Moon' (Cl)	EBls
SILVER SHADOW ('Frystereo'PBR) (HT)	ECnt ESty MFry SApu
'Silver Wedding' (HT)	CBcs CDoC CTri EBls ELan IArd MRav MSwo MWat SCob SPer
'Silver Wedding Celebration' (F)	ESty LSRN
SILVER WISHES	see *R.* PINK HIT
SIMBA ('Korbelma') (HT)	LSRN
'Simone' (HT)	CBod CPou EBee ETWh
SIMPLY GORGEOUS ('Formaui') (HT)	ESty
SIMPLY SALLY ('Harpaint'PBR) (Patio)	LSRN
§ SIMPLY THE BEST ('Macamster'PBR) (HT) ♀H6	CArg CDoC CGro CSBt EBls ELan EPfP ESty LRHS LSRN MAsh MFry MGos MPri MRav NRHS SApu SCob SCoo SPer SPoG
sinowilsonii	see *R. longicuspis* var. *sinowilsonii*
'Sir Cedric Morris' (Ra)	EBls ETWh NLar SSea
'Sir Frederick Ashton' (HT)	EBls
§ SIR GALAHAD ('Hareasy') (F)	MRav MWat
'Sir Galahad' white-flowered	see *R.* SIR GALAHAD
§ SIR HARRY PILKINGTON ('Tanema') (HT)	EBls
SIR HENRY CECIL ('Webpegasus') (F)	LSRN
SIR JOHN BETJEMAN ('Ausvivid'PBR) (S)	CRos EHyd EPfP LBuc LRHS NRHS
SIR JOHN MILLS ('Beadaffy') (Cl)	EBls
'Sir Joseph Paxton' (Bb)	ETWh EWTr
SIR PAUL SMITH ('Beapaul') (ClHT)	EBls EPfP LRHS MAsh
SIR WALTER RALEIGH ('Ausspry') (S)	CDoC MRav
§ 'Sissinghurst Castle' (G)	EBls
SISTER ELIZABETH ('Auspalette'PBR) (S)	LSRN
SKYLARK ('Ausimple'PBR) (S) ♀H6	CRos MAsh
'Skyrocket'	see *R.* 'Wilhelm'
SMARTY ('Intersmart') (S/GC)	EBls SPer
SMILING EYES ('Chewrocko'PBR) (S/GC)	EPfP ETWh LRHS MAsh
SMOOTHIE ('Frymemmo') (HT) **new**	MFry
SNAZZEE ('Wekzazette'PBR) (F)	ECnt ESty
SNOW CARPET ('Maccarpe') (Min/GC)	EBls
'Snow Dwarf'	see *R.* 'Schneezwerg'
SNOW GOOSE ('Auspom'PBR) (ClS)	CRos CSBt EBee EPfP NLar
SNOW HIT ('Poulsnows'PBR) (Min/Patio)	ECnt
'Snow Queen'	see *R.* 'Frau Karl Druschki'
SNOW QUEEN ('Simseen') (HT)	ESty
SNOWBALL ('Macangeli') (Min/GC)	LSRN
SNOWCAP ('Harfleet'PBR) (Patio)	ESty SPer
'Snowdon' (Ru)	EBls
SOEUR EMMANUELLE ('Delamo'PBR) (S)	ESty ETWh LSRN MRav
'Soldier Boy' (Cl)	CPou EBls ETWh NLar
'Soleil d'Or' (S)	EBls
SOLEIL VERTICAL ('Delsov') (Cl)	ESty
§ SOLO MIO ('Poulen002'PBR) (Renaissance Series) (S)	ECnt ETWh EWTr NLar
§ 'Sombreuil' (ClT)	CArg EBls EPfP ETWh IArd LRHS MRav NLar SApu SPer
SOME LIKE IT HOT ('Gueschorus') (F)	ESty
SOMETHING SPECIAL ('Macwyo'PBR) (HT)	ESty
SONG AND DANCE ('Frydishy'PBR) (HT)	MFry
SONGBIRD ('Raw1151') (F) **new**	ESty
§ SONGS OF PRAISE ('Harkimono'PBR) (Abundance Series) (F)	CBod EBls SApu
SONIA	see *R.* SWEET PROMISE
'Sophia'	see *R.* SOLO MIO ('Poulen002')
'Sophie's Perpetual' (ClCh)	CPou CTri EBls ETWh SLon
SOPHY'S ROSE ('Auslot'PBR) (S)	CRos LSRN SPer
SORBET FRUITÉ ('Meihestries'PBR) (ClF)	SSea

soulieana (Ra/S)	EBls ETWh
'Soupert et Notting' (DPoMo)	CPou ETWh NLar SPer
'Southampton' (F) $\mathbb{Y}^{H6}$	CArg EBls LSRN SPer SSea
SOUTHERN BEAUTY ('Forauty') (F)	ESty
SOUTHERN BELLE ('Wekspococ') (HT) **new**	ESty
'Souvenir d'Alphonse Lavallée' (ClHP)	EBls
'Souvenir de Claudius Denoyel' (ClHT)	CArg EBls ETWh SPer
'Souvenir de François Gaulain' (T)	EBls
'Souvenir de Jeanne Balandreau' (HP)	CPou EBls ETWh
'Souvenir de la Malmaison' (ClBb)	see *R.* 'Climbing Souvenir de la Malmaison'
'Souvenir de la Malmaison' (Bb)	CArg CWld EBls ETWh MRav NLar SPer
'Souvenir de Madame Auguste Charles' (Bb)	EBls
'Souvenir de Madame Léonie Viennot' (ClT)	EBls ETWh MRav NLar
'Souvenir de Pierre Vibert' (DPMo)	CPou ETWh
'Souvenir de Saint Anne's' (Bb)	EBls ETWh NLar
'Souvenir d'Elise Vardon' (T)	EBls
'Souvenir du Docteur Jamain' (ClHP)	CPou CSBt EBee EBls ELan ELon EPfP ESty ETWh LCro LOPS LSRN MRav NLar SApu SCob SPoG SSea WFar WKif
'Souvenir d'un Ami' (T)	EBls
spaldingii	see *R. nutkana* var. *hispida*
'Spanish Beauty'	see *R.* 'Madame Grégoire Staechelin'
SPARKLE ('Frymerlin'^{PBR}) (HT)	CGro ECnt ESty LBuc MAsh MFry
SPARKLER	see *R.* KENT
SPARKLING BURGUNDY ('Raw1007') (F)	ESty
SPARKLING SCARLET ('Meihati') (ClF)	MAsh
SPECIAL ANNIVERSARY ('Whastiluc'^{PBR}) (HT) $\mathbb{Y}^{H6}$	CBcs CBod CDoC CGro CRos CSBt EBls ECnt ELan ELon EPfP ESty ETWh LCro LOPS LRHS LSRN MAsh MFry MPri MRav MWat NRHS SCoo SPoG SSea
SPECIAL CHILD ('Taniripsa'^{PBR}) (F/Patio) $\mathbb{Y}^{H6}$	CDoC MRav SApu SSea
'Special Dad' (HT)	CGro LCro LOPS
'Special Daughter' (F)	LSRN
SPECIAL EVENT ('Meibrelon') (HT)	ESty
SPECIAL FRIEND ('Kirspec'^{PBR}) (Patio)	ESty LSRN SApu
'Special Grandad' (Patio)	LSRN
SPECIAL GRANDCHILD ('Flimika') (F)	ESty
SPECIAL GRANDMA (F)	ESty LSRN
SPECIAL GRANDPA (F)	ESty
SPECIAL MEMORIES ('Fortop') (F)	ESty
'Special Mum' (F)	LCro LOPS LSRN
SPECIAL OCCASION ('Fryyoung'^{PBR}) (HT)	MFry MRav MWat
SPECIAL SON (F)	ESty
'Spectabilis' (Ra)	CBod CPou EBls ETWh
'Spek's Yellow' (HT)	EBls
'Spencer' misapplied	see *R.* 'Enfant de France'
'Spencer' (HP)	EBls
SPICE OF LIFE ('Diccheeky'^{PBR}) (F/Patio)	EBls
§ ***spinosissima***	CArg CCCN CSde EBls ETWh LBuc MMuc SCob SGol SPer WKor WTSh
- 'Andrewsii' $\mathbb{Y}^{H7}$	EBls MRav
- 'Cedric Morris'	WCot
§ - double, pink-flowered	EBls WBor
§ - - white-flowered $\mathbb{Y}^{H7}$	EBls ECha ETWh LEdu
- 'Falkland'	EBls ECha
§ - 'Grandiflora'	EBls ETWh
- 'Marbled Pink'	ETWh
- 'Mary, Queen of Scots'	CPou EBls ETWh EWTr GBin NLar SRms
- 'Merthyr Mawr'	WCot
- 'Mrs Colville'	EBls
- 'Single Cherry'	EBls
- 'William III'	EBls EWes WCot
SPIRIT OF FREEDOM ('Ausbite'^{PBR}) (S)	CRos EHyd EPfP LRHS MAsh NRHS
§ 'Splendens' (Ra)	EBls ETWh MMuc
SPLISH SPLASH ('Raw1020') (F)	ESty
ST CLARE ('Horbamber') (F)	EBls
ST HELENA ('Canlish') (F)	ECnt
STAMFORD'S SANCTUARY ('Beajealous') (Cl)	EBls
'Stanwell Perpetual' (SpH) $\mathbb{Y}^{H7}$	CArg CTri EBls ELan ETWh EWTr MCot NLar SPer
STAR DUST ('Morstar') (Min)	ELon
'Star of Waltham' (HP)	ETWh
'Star Performer'^{PBR} (ClPatio)	CDoC CSBt ECnt EPfP ESty MAsh SApu SPoG SSea
STARDUST ('Peavandyke'^{PBR}) (Patio/F)	ESty
STARLIGHT EXPRESS ('Trobstar'^{PBR}) (Cl)	CDoC ELon LBuc LRHS MAsh MFry MPri SPer
STARLIGHT SYMPHONY ('Harwisdom') (Cl) **new**	ECnt ESty
STELLA (HT)	LSRN
§ ***stellata*** var. ***mirifica***	ETWh
'Stephen'	LSRN
STORYTELLER ('Diccayman') (F) **new**	IDic
STRAWBERRIES AND CREAM ('Geestraw') (Min/Patio)	ESty
STRAWBERRY FAYRE ('Arowillip') (Min/Patio)	ESty MRav SPoG
STRAWBERRY HILL ('Ausrimini'^{PBR}) (S) $\mathbb{Y}^{H6}$	CRos CSBt EHyd ESty LCro LOPS LRHS MMuc NRHS SCoo
STRIKE IT RICH ('Wekbepmey'^{PBR}) (HT) $\mathbb{Y}^{H6}$	CDoC ESty MRav SApu
§ SUE HIPKIN ('Harzazz'^{PBR}) (HT)	ESty MRav
'Suffolk' (HT)	SCob
SUFFOLK ('Kormixal') (S/GC) $\mathbb{Y}^{H6}$	CSBt EBls MRav SCob
suffulta	see *R. arkansana* var. *suffulta*
SUGAR AND SPICE ('Peaallure'^{PBR}) (Patio)	MWat SPoG
SUGAR 'N' SPICE ('Tinspice') (Min)	CDoC MRav
SUMA ('Harsuma') (GC)	EBls ESty

SUMMER BEAUTY ('Kororbe'^{PBR}) (F) ♀^{H6}	CArg MAsh
SUMMER BREEZE ('Korelasting'^{PBR}) (ClS)	MAsh
SUMMER FRAGRANCE ('Tanfudermos') (Castle Series) (HT)	EBls ELon
§ SUMMER GOLD ('Poulreb'^{PBR}) (F)	MAsh
SUMMER LOVE ('Franluv') (F)	CBcs
SUMMER LOVING ('Raw1152') (Cl) **new**	ESty
SUMMER MEMORIES ('Koruteli'^{PBR}) (Palace Series) (F)	ETWh
SUMMER SONG ('Austango'^{PBR}) (S)	CRos EHyd EPfP ESty LBuc LSRN
'Summer Sunrise' (GC)	EBls
'Summer Sunset' (GC)	EBls
SUMMER WINE ('Korizont'^{PBR}) (ClHT) ♀^{H6}	CSBt EBls ECnt EPfP ETWh EWTr LRHS MAsh SApu SPer SPoG
SUMMERTIME ('Chewlarmoll'^{PBR}) (ClPatio) ♀^{H6}	CArg CDoC CSBt EBls ECnt ELan ELon EPfP LRHS MFry MPri MRav SApu SPer SPoG
SUN HIT ('Poulsun'^{PBR}) (PatioHit Series) (Min/Patio)	CSBt ECnt MRav SPoG
'Sunblaze'	see *R.* ORANGE SUNBLAZE
SUNBLEST ('Landora') (HT)	MAsh MRav SCob
'Sunfire' Barni (F)	ECnt
SUNNY DAY ('Savasun') (S)	CBod ETWh SPer
SUNNY SKY ('Koraruli'^{PBR}) (HT)	CRos CSBt ECnt EHyd EPfP ESty LBuc LRHS MAsh MFry MPri NRHS SCoo SPoG
SUNNY SKY ('Korvestavi') (HT)	CDoC MWat
SUNRISE ('Kormarter'^{PBR}) (S)	EPfP ESty LBuc MAsh SApu SPoG
SUNRISE ROSE FOR WAKEFIELD HOSPICE ('Frynoon') (F)	MFry
§ SUNSEEKER ('Dicracer') (F/Patio) ♀^{H6}	MAsh MFry MRav SPoG
SUNSET BOULEVARD ('Harbabble'^{PBR}) (F)	MAsh SPer
SUNSET CELEBRATION	see *R.* WARM WISHES
SUNSET GLOW	see *R.* 'Alibaba'
SUPER DOROTHY ('Heldoro') (Ra) ♀^{H6}	LSRN
SUPER ELFIN ('Helkleger'^{PBR}) (Ra)	CDoC CRos LRHS MFry MRav NLar SApu
SUPER EXCELSA ('Helexa') (Ra) ♀^{H6}	EBls ELan SApu
SUPER FAIRY ('Helsufair'^{PBR}) (Ra) ♀^{H6}	CDoC EBee EBls ECnt LSRN MFry MRav SApu SMad SPer SSea
§ SUPER STAR ('Tanorstar') (HT)	CArg CDoC EBls MRav MWat
SUPER TROUPER ('Fryleyeca'^{PBR}) (F) ♀^{H6}	CArg CBod CDoC CGro CSBt EBee ECnt ELan ESty LRHS LSRN MAsh MFry MRav MWat SApu SCoo SPer SSea WBor WCot
'Surpasse Tout' (G)	EBls ETWh
§ 'Surpassing Beauty of Woolverstone' (ClHP)	EBls
SURREY ('Korlanum') (GC) ♀^{H6}	CDoC CSBt CTri EBls ELan ESty ETWh LCro LOPS LSRN MRav MSwo NLar SApu SCob SPer SSea
SUSAN ('Poulsue') (S)	ECnt LSRN NLar SLon
SUSAN HAMPSHIRE ('Meinatac') (HT)	EBls
SUSAN WILLIAMS-ELLIS ('Ausquirk'^{PBR}) (S)	CRos EHyd EPfP LRHS NLar NRHS SPoG
SUSIE ('Harwhistle') (ClPatio)	CGro ECnt ESty LSRN
SUSSEX ('Poulave') (GC)	CSBt EBls MSwo SCob SMad SPer
'Sutter's Gold' (HT)	EBls
SWAN LAKE ('Macmed') (Cl)	CArg CPou EBls ECnt EPfP ETWh NLar SCob SPer
SWAN LAKE ('Schwanensee') (Patio)	MFry
SWANY ('Meiburenac') (Min/GC)	EBls ESty MMuc MSwo SApu SPer
SWEET CAROLINE ('Micaroline') (Min)	LSRN
SWEET CHILD OF MINE (HT)	ELon ESty SSea
SWEET DREAM CREAM ('Fryniggle'^{PBR}) (F)	MFry
SWEET DREAM ('Fryminicot') (Patio) ♀^{H6}	CArg CBod CDoC CGro CSBt CTri EBls ELan EPfP LCro LOPS LRHS LSRN MAsh MFry MRav MWat SApu SCob SMad SPer SPoG SSea
'Sweet Fairy' (Min)	CSBt
'Sweet Harmony' (HT)	EBls
SWEET HAZE ('Tan97274'^{PBR}) (F) ♀^{H6}	CSBt MRav SPer
SWEET JESSICA ('Wekneflocjuc') (F) **new**	ESty
SWEET JULIET ('Ausleap') (S)	MSwo
SWEET LEMON DREAM ('Fryrich') (Patio)	CTri MFry
SWEET MAGIC ('Dicmagic'^{PBR}) (Min/Patio) ♀^{H6}	CTri MRav SCob SPoG
SWEET MEMORIES ('Whamemo') (Patio)	CDoC CTri EBls ECnt ELan EPfP ESty LRHS MPri MRav MWat NRHS SCob SCoo SPer SPoG
§ SWEET PARFUM DE PROVENCE ('Meiclusif'^{PBR}) (HT) ♀^{H6}	CArg CBod CRos EBls ELan EPfP ESty LBuc LRHS LSRN MAsh NRHS
§ SWEET PROMISE ('Meihelvet') (GC)	EBls
SWEET REMEMBRANCE ('Kirr') (HT)	SCoo
'Sweet Revelation'	see *R.* SUE HIPKIN
SWEET SYRIE ('Harwilling') (Cl) **new**	ESty
'Sweet Wonder' (Patio)	EPfP MAsh
sweginzowii	GLog
- 'Macrocarpa'	EBls
'Sydonie' (HP)	CPou ETWh
'Sylvia Dot' (F)	LSRN
'Sympathie' (ClHT)	EBls MAsh
'Talisman' (HT)	EBls
TALL STORY ('Dickooky') (F) ♀^{H6}	EBee EBls ETWh NLar SApu
TAM O'SHANTER ('Auscerise'^{PBR}) (S)	EPfP
TANGERINE TANGO ('Cheworangemane') (Cl)	SSea
TANGO SHOWGROUND ('Chewpattens'^{PBR}) (GC)	ESty
TATTON ('Fryentice'^{PBR}) (F)	EBls MFry MRav

§	'Tausendschön' (Ra)	EBls
	TAWNY TIGER ('Frygolly'[PBR]) (F)	MFry
	TEAR DROP ('Dicomo') (Min/Patio)	SApu SCob
	TEASING GEORGIA ('Ausbaker'[PBR]) (S) 𝕐^{H6}	CDoC CRos ECnt EHyd EPfP ESty LBuc LRHS LSRN MMuc NLar NRHS SCob SCoo
	TEMPTRESS ('Korramal') (ClS) 𝕐^{H6}	CPou EPfP
	TENACIOUS ('Macblackpo'[PBR]) (F)	ESty
	TEQUILA SUNRISE ('Dicobey') (HT) 𝕐^{H6}	CArg CBod CGro CTri EBls ELan EPfP ESty LBuc MAsh MFry MRav SApu SPer SSea
	TERRACOTTA ('Meicobuis') (HT)	ESty
	TESS OF THE D'URBERVILLES ('Ausmove'[PBR]) (S)	CRos EHyd ELan EPfP ESty LRHS LSRN NLar NRHS SCoo SPer
	'Tessa' (F)	LSRN
	'Texas Centennial' (HT)	EBls
§	THAÏS ('Memaj') (HT)	EBls
	'Thalia' (Ra)	EBls
	THANK YOU ('Chesdeep'[PBR]) (Patio)	ESty LCro LOPS LSRN
§	THAT'S JAZZ ('Poulnorm'[PBR]) (Courtyard Series) (ClF)	CArg ECnt LSRN MFry
	THE ALBRIGHTON RAMBLER ('Ausmobile'[PBR]) (Ra)	CRos EBee EHyd EPfP LRHS NLar NRHS
	THE ALEXANDRA ROSE ('Ausday') (S)	EPfP MAsh SPer
§	THE ALNWICK ROSE ('Ausgrab'[PBR]) (S)	CRos EHyd EPfP LBuc LRHS MGos NLar NRHS SCob SCoo SPer
	THE ANCIENT MARINER ('Ausoutcry') (S)	EHyd LCro LOPS LRHS NRHS
	THE ANNIVERSARY ROSE	see *R.* SWEET PARFUM DE PROVENCE
	THE BEE'S KNEES ('Guesbehold') (F)	ESty
	THE BOSWORTH ROSE ('Raw1014') (F)	ESty
	THE CHESHIRE REGIMENT ('Fryzebedee') (HT)	MFry
	THE CHURCHILL ROSE ('Horoften') (S)	EBee EBls LRHS MAsh
	THE COMPASSIONATE FRIENDS ('Harzodiac'[PBR]) (F)	CDoC
	THE COVENTRY CATHEDRAL ROSE ('Smi72-02') (F)	ESty
	THE DIAMOND WEDDING ROSE (HT)	EBls LSRN MAsh
	'The Doctor' (HT)	EBls
§	'The Fairy' (Poly) 𝕐^{H6}	CArg CBod CDoC CSBt CTri EBee EBls ECnt ECrN ELan ETWh LEdu LRHS MAsh MCot MFry MRav MWat NLar SApu SCob SDix SMad SPer SSea WBor WCFE WCot WHer XSen
	'The Garland' (Ra) 𝕐^{H6}	CArg EBee EBls EPfP ETWh GBin MMuc NLar SApu SPer
	THE GENEROUS GARDENER ('Ausdrawn'[PBR]) (S) 𝕐^{H6}	CRos CSBt CTri EBee EHyd ELan EPfP ESty LBuc LRHS LSRN NLar MGos NRHS SCob SCoo SPer SSea
§	THE GOLD AWARD ROSE ('Poulac008') (Palace Series) (Patio)	ECnt
	THE HILDA OGDEN ROSE ('Korchakon') (Patio)	MAsh
	THE INGENIOUS MR FAIRCHILD ('Austijus'[PBR]) (S)	EPfP SCoo
	THE JACK DUCKWORTH ROSE ('Korlutmag'[PBR]) (Patio)	MAsh
	THE JUBILEE ROSE ('Poulbrido'[PBR]) (F)	ECnt
	THE LADY ('Fryjingo'[PBR]) (S)	ESty
	THE LADY GARDENER ('Ausbrass'[PBR]) (S)	CDoC CRos EHyd ELan EPfP LRHS MAsh NRHS
	THE LADY OF THE LAKE ('Ausherbert'[PBR]) (Ra)	CRos EHyd EPfP LRHS NLar NRHS SCob SCoo
	THE LADY'S BLUSH ('Ausoscar'[PBR]) (S)	CRos EHyd EPfP LRHS MAsh
	THE LAKELAND ROSE ('Harspiral') (Cl)	SApu
	THE LARK ASCENDING ('Ausursula'[PBR]) (S)	CRos EHyd LBuc LCro LOPS LRHS NRHS SCoo
	'The Margaret Coppola Rose'	see *R.* WHITE GOLD
	THE MAYFLOWER 𝕐^{H6} ('Austilly'[PBR]) (S)	CRos CSBt LBuc LRHS MSwo NRHS
	THE MAYOR ('P48a') (F) **new**	MFry
§	THE MCCARTNEY ROSE ('Meizeli') (HT)	LSRN SApu
	'The New Dawn'	see *R.* 'New Dawn'
	THE ODDFELLOWS ROSE ('Fryriviera') (F)	MFry
	'The One and Only' (HT)	LRHS MAsh
	THE PAINTER ('Mactemaik'[PBR]) (F)	LSRN
	THE PERSE ROSE ('Beajargon') (S)	EBls
§	THE PILGRIM ('Auswalker') (S) 𝕐^{H6}	CRos CSBt CTri EHyd EPfP LBuc LRHS MAsh NLar NRHS SPer SPoG
	THE POET'S WIFE ('Auswhirl'[PBR]) (S)	CDoC CRos CSBt ECnt EHyd EPfP ESty LRHS NRHS SCoo SPoG
	THE PRINCE ('Ausvelvet') (S)	NLar
	THE PRINCE'S TRUST ('Harholding'[PBR]) (Cl)	MAsh
§	'The Queen Elizabeth' (F)	CArg CDoC CSBt CTri EBls ELan LCro LOPS LRHS LSRN MAsh MFry MRav MWat SApu SCob SPer SSea
	THE QUEEN'S JUBILEE ROSE ('Beajubilee') (S)	EBls LRHS MAsh
	THE ROTARIAN	see *R.* ROTARY SUNRISE
	'The Royal Brompton Rose'	see *R.* ROYAL BROMPTON ROSE
I	'The Rugby Rose' (HT)	LSRN
	THE SHEIKH KHALIFA ROSE ('Dickoolkid') (Patio)	IDic
	THE SIMPLE LIFE ('Hartrifle'[PBR]) (Cl)	MRav SSea
	THE SOHAM ROSE	see *R.* PEARL ABUNDANCE
	THE TIMES ROSE ('Korpeahn') (F) 𝕐^{H6}	ECnt SCob SPer
	THE WAINWRIGHT ROSE ('Frylovely') (HT)	MFry
	THE WEDGWOOD ROSE ('Ausjosiah'[PBR]) (ClS)	EHyd EPfP LRHS NRHS
	THE WREN ('Kormamtiza'[PBR]) (F/Patio)	EPfP MAsh
	'Thelma' (Ra)	EBls
	'Thérèse Bugnet' (Ru) 𝕐^{H7}	CTho EBls
	THINKING OF YOU ('Frydandy'[PBR]) (HT) 𝕐^{H6}	EBls ELon EPfP ESty LSRN MAsh MFry SApu SPer SSea

	Name	Suppliers
	'Thisbe' (HM)	CPou EBls ETWh
	THOMAS À BECKET ('Auswinston'[PBR]) (S)	CRos ECnt EHyd EPfP ESty LCro LOPS LRHS MAsh NRHS
	'Thoresbyana'	see *R.* 'Bennett's Seedling'
	THOUSAND BEAUTIES	see *R.* 'Tausendschön'
	threepenny bit rose	see *R. elegantula* 'Persetosa'
	THUMBS UP ('Hornothing') (S)	EBls
	TICKLED PINK ('Fryhunky'[PBR]) (F) ♀H6	CArg CDoC CSBt CTri EBls LCro LOPS LRHS LSRN MAsh MFry MRav SApu SPer SPoG SSea
	TIMES PAST ('Harhilt'[PBR]) (ClHT)	CBod ETWh MRav SApu SPoG
	'Tina Turner' (HT)	LSRN
	TINTINARA ('Dicuptight'[PBR]) (HT) ♀H6	CBod
	'Tipo Ideale'	see *R.* × *odorata* 'Mutabilis'
	'Tipsy Imperial Concubine' (T)	EBls
	TITANIC ('Macdako'[PBR]) (F)	ESty
	'Toby Tristam' (Ra)	EBls
	TOGETHER FOREVER ('Dicecho'[PBR]) (F)	LSRN MAsh MFry
	TOGMEISTER ('Beahappy') (F)	EBee EBls LRHS MAsh NRHS
	'Tom Marshall' (Ra)	CBod ETWh LSRN
	'Tom Wood' (HP) **new**	ETWh
	'Tony Jacklin' (F)	LSRN
	TOP MARKS ('Fryministar') (Min/Patio)	MFry MRav SApu SCob SCoo SPer
	TOPAZ JEWEL	see *R.* YELLOW DAGMAR HASTRUP
	'Topsi' (F/Patio)	SPer
§	'Tour de Malakoff' (Ce)	CPou EBls NLar SPer
	TOYNBEE HALL ('Korwonder') (F)	LRHS MAsh
	'Tradition' (HT) **new**	CBod
	TRADITION (ClHT)	see *R.* TRADITION '95
§	TRADITION '95 ('Korkeltin'[PBR]) (ClHT)	EBee ETWh MAsh NLar
	TRANQUILITY ('Barout') (HT)	EHyd EPfP LRHS NRHS
	TRANQUILLITY ('Ausnoble'[PBR]) (S)	CRos CSBt ECnt ESty LBuc NLar SCoo SPer
	'Treasure Trove' (Ra)	CRHN EBls
	'Tricolore' (G)	EBls
	'Tricolore de Flandre' (G)	EBls ETWh
	'Trier' (Ra)	CPou EBls ETWh NLar WMal
	'Trigintipetala' misapplied	see *R.* × *damascena* 'Professeur Émile Perrot'
	'Triomphe de Laffay' (Ch)	EBls
	triphylla	see *R.* × *beanii*
	'Triple Delight' (S)	LSRN
I	'Trish's Rose' (Ru)	LSRN
	TROIKA ('Poumidor') (HT)	ELon MAsh SPer
	'Tropicana'	see *R.* SUPER STAR
	TRUE FRIEND ('Smi35-2-02') (F)	ESty
	'Truly Loved' (F)	LSRN MAsh
	TRULY SCRUMPTIOUS (HT)	ESty MRav MWat
	TRUMPETER ('Mactru') (F) ♀H6	CArg CGro CTri EBee ECnt IArd LBuc MAsh MFry MRav SPer SPoG
§	'Tuscany' (G)	EBls
	'Tuscany Superb' (G) ♀H7	CArg CDoC CPou CRos CSBt CTri EBee EBls EHyd ELan EPfP ETWh GBin LCro LEdu LOPS LRHS MCot MRav NLar SCob SMad SPer SSea WBor WFar WHer WKif
	TWENTY-FIFTH ('Beatwe') (F)	EBls
	TWENTY-ONE AGAIN! ('Meinimo') (HT)	LSRN
	TWICE IN A BLUE MOON ('Tan96138'[PBR]) (HT) ♀H6	CArg CDoC CSBt EBls ECnt ELon ESty MFry MRav MWat SApu SCob SCoo SPoG SSea
	TWIGGY'S ROSE ('Harteam'[PBR]) (F)	MAsh
	TWIST ('Poulstri'[PBR]) (Courtyard Series) (ClPatio)	CArg ECnt LSRN SApu
	TYNWALD ('Mattwyt') (HT)	SPer
	'Ulrich Brünner'	see *R.* 'Ulrich Brünner Fils'
§	'Ulrich Brünner Fils' (HP)	EBls
	'Uncle Bill' (HT)	EBls
	UNCLE WALTER ('Macon') (HT)	EBls
	'Unique Blanche'	see *R.* × *centifolia* 'Unique'
	VALENTINE HEART ('Dicogle') (F) ♀H6	CArg CSBt ESty IArd LSRN MRav SApu SPoG
	VANESSA BELL ('Auseasel') (S) **new**	CRos ESty MAsh SCoo
	'Vanguard' (Ru)	EBls
	'Vanity' (HM)	EBls
	'Variegata di Bologna' (Bb)	CBod EBls EPfP ETWh
	'Vatertag' (Min)	LSRN
	'Veilchenblau' (Ra) ♀H7	Widely available
	VELVET FRAGRANCE ('Fryperdee') (HT)	CArg CSBt ECnt ESty MFry MRav SApu SCob SPoG SSea
	VERONICA MARGARET ('Dicpursue') (F) **new**	IDic
	'Verschuren' (HT/v)	ESty
	versicolor	see *R. gallica* 'Versicolor'
	'Vick's Caprice' (HP)	EBls ETWh NLar
	'Vicomtesse Pierre du Fou' (ClHT)	EBls
	VICTORIA ('Simlast') (HT)	ESty
	VICTORIA JOY ('Diciwill') (F)	IDic
	VIKING PRINCESS	see *R.* IMAGINATION
	'Village Maid'	see *R.* × *centifolia* 'Unique Panachée'
§	***villosa*** L.	EBls ETWh WKor
§	'Violacea' (G)	CBod EBls ETWh
	VIOLET CLOUD ('Harquick'[PBR]) (Min)	CDoC ESty MRav
	'Violette' (Ra)	CBod CPou CRos EBls ESty ETWh SPer WFar WHer
	'Violinista Costa' (HT)	EBls
	virginea	SPer
	VIRGINIA MCKENNA OBE ('Harsong') (S)	LSRN
	virginiana ♀H7	EBls SCob SDix
	- 'Plena'	see *R.* 'Rose d'Amour'
	'Viridiflora'	see *R.* × *odorata* 'Viridiflora'
	'Vivid' (Bourbon hybrid)	EBls
	vosagiaca	see *R. caesia* subsp. *vosagiaca*
	'Vuosaari' (Ru)	EBls
	WALTZ ('Poulkrid'[PBR]) (Courtyard Series) (ClPatio)	ECnt LSRN
	WARM WELCOME ('Chewizz') (ClMin) ♀H6	CDoC CGro CRos EBls ECnt ELan EPfP ESty LCro LOPS LSRN MAsh MFry MRav NPoe SApu SMad SPer SPoG SSea
§	WARM WISHES ('Fryxotic'[PBR]) (HT) ♀H6	CSBt EBls ECnt EPfP LBuc LRHS LSRN MAsh MFry MRav MWat NRHS SCob SSea
	WARWICKSHIRE ('Korkandel') (GC)	EBls SCob
§	***watsoniana*** (Ra)	EBls EBtc

	Name	Suppliers
	WB YEATS ('Dicoodles') (F)	IDic
	WEDDING BELLS ('Korsteflali'PBR) (HT)	CBod EPfP LRHS LSRN MAsh
	WEDDING CELEBRATION ('Poulht006'PBR) (HT)	EBls ECnt MAsh
	'Wedding Day' (Ra)	Widely available
	'Weetwood' (Ra)	CRHN
	WEISSE WOLCKE	see *R.* WHITE CLOUD
	WELL-BEING ('Harjangle'PBR) (S)	CArg ELon
	'Wendy Cussons' (HT)	CTri EBls MRav SApu SCob SPer
	WESTERLAND ('Korwest') (S) ΥH6	CDoC EBls ETWh LRHS MRav NLar
	WHERE THE HEART IS ('Cocoplan'PBR) (HT)	ESty
	WHISKY MAC ('Tanky') (HT)	CBcs CGro CSBt CTri EBee EBls ELan ELon LSRN MRav MWat SApu SCob SPer
	'White Bath'	see *R.* × *centifolia* 'Shailer's White Moss'
	WHITE BELLS ('Poulwhite') (Min/GC)	EBls
	'White Cécile Brünner' (Poly)	EBls
§	WHITE CLOUD ('Korstacha'PBR) (ClHT)	ELon ESty SApu
	'White Cockade' (ClHT)	CPou EBls ETWh MSwo SPer
	WHITE COVER	see *R.* KENT
§	'White de Meaux' (Ce)	EBls
	WHITE DIAMOND ('Interamon'PBR) (S)	ECnt
	WHITE FOX ROSE ('Harzebek') (F) **new**	ESty
§	WHITE GOLD ('Cocquiriam'PBR) (F) ΥH6	CSBt
	'White Grootendorst' (Ru)	EBls ETWh NLar
	'White Maman Couchet' (HT)	EBls
	WHITE MEIDILAND ('Meicoublan') (S/GC)	LRHS MAsh
	white moss	see *R.* × *centifolia* 'Shailer's White Moss', *R.* 'Comtesse de Murinais'
	'White New Dawn' (Cl)	EBls
	'White Patio' (Min/Patio)	CRos MAsh SPoG
	WHITE PERFUMELLA ('Meicalanq'PBR) (HT)	CBod ELan ESty LSRN
§	'White Pet' (Poly) ΥH6	CArg CTri EBee EBls ECnt ELan EPfP ETWh LCro LOPS LRHS LSRN MCot MRav MWat NLar NPoe SApu SCob SEND SPer WKif
	white Provence	see *R.* × *centifolia* 'Unique'
	white rose of York	see *R.* × *alba* 'Alba Semiplena'
	WHITE SKYLINER ('Franwekwhit'PBR) (ClS)	EBls
	WHITE STAR ('Harquill') (ClHT) ΥH5	ECnt MRav SSea
	'White Wings' (HT)	CArg EBls ETWh EWTr SPer WKif
	wichurana	see *R. lucieae*
	'Wickwar' (Ra) ΥH6	EBls ETWh EWTr NLar
	WILD EDRIC ('Aushedge'PBR) (Ru) ΥH6	ECnt MMuc SCoo
	WILD ROVER ('Dichirap'PBR) (F) ΥH6	EBls ESty MFry SApu
	WILDEVE ('Ausbonny'PBR) (S) ΥH6	CRos EHyd LRHS NRHS
	WILDFIRE ('Fryessex') (Patio)	CArg CGro ECnt ESty LRHS MAsh MFry MRav SApu SPoG
§	'Wilhelm' (HM)	CPou EBls ETWh SPer
	WILLIAM AND CATHERINE ('Ausrapper'PBR) (S)	CRos EPfP LCro LOPS MAsh
	'William Baffin' (S)	EBls
	'William Cobbett' (F)	SSea
§	'William Lobb' (CeMo) ΥH7	CArg CDoC CPou EBls EHyd EPfP ETWh LRHS MCot MNrw MRav NLar NRHS SCob SMad WHer WKif
	WILLIAM MORRIS ('Auswill'PBR) (S)	CRos CSBt
	WILLIAM SHAKESPEARE 2000 ('Ausromeo'PBR) (S)	CArg CRos CSBt ELan ESty MSwo NLar SCob SSea
	WILLIAM SHAKESPEARE ('Ausroyal') (S)	SCob
	'William Tyndale' (Ra)	CBod CPou ETWh
	'Williams' Double Yellow'	see *R.* × *harisonii* 'Williams' Double Yellow'
	willmottiae	EBls ETWh
	WILTSHIRE ('Kormuse') (S/GC) ΥH6	CSBt CTri EBls ECnt ETWh MRav NLar SApu SCob SEND SLon SSea
	WINCHESTER CATHEDRAL ('Auscat') (S)	CArg CGro CRos CTri EHyd ELan EPfP LCro LOPS LRHS LSRN MAsh MSwo NLar NRHS SCob SLon SPer SPoG SSea
	WINDRUSH ('Ausrush') (S)	EBee ETWh
	WINE AND DINE ('Dicuncle') (GC)	EBls
	WISLEY 2008 ('Ausbreeze'PBR) (S)	CRos CSBt EHyd EPfP LBuc LRHS MAsh NRHS SCoo
	WITH THANKS ('Fransmoov'PBR) (HT)	ELon
	'Woburn Abbey' (F)	EBls
	WOLLERTON OLD HALL ('Ausblanket'PBR) (S)	CRos CSBt EBee EHyd EPfP ESty LBuc LRHS MAsh NLar NRHS SCoo SPer
	'Wolley-Dod'	see *R.* 'Duplex'
	WONDERFUL HUSBAND ('Raw982') (F)	ESty
	WONDERFUL NEWS ('Jonone'PBR) (Patio)	ESty
	WONDERFUL WIFE ('Raw1025') (HT)	ESty
	WONDERFUL YOU ('Smi 170-2-4') (HT)	ESty
	woodsii (S)	EBls
	- var. ***fendleri***	EBls ETWh
	- var. ***ultramontana***	EBls
	'Woolverstone Church Rose'	see *R.* 'Surpassing Beauty of Woolverstone'
	WORCESTERSHIRE ('Korlalon'PBR) (GC) ΥH6	CDoC MRav SApu SPer
	'Wretham Rose' (Ce)	EBls
	WYMONDHAM ABBEY ('Beadevil') (ClHT)	EBls LRHS MAsh
§	***xanthina*** 'Canary Bird' (S) ΥH6	CArg CBcs CDoC CSBt CTho CTri EBee EBls ECnt ELan EPfP ESty ETWh LSRN MAsh MFry MNrw MRav NLar SApu SCob SPer SPoG SSea SWvt
§	- f. ***hugonis***	CTho EBls ELan ETWh NLar
	- - 'Flore Pleno'	EBls
	'Xavier Olibo' (HP)	EBls
	YARDLEY BAROQUE ('Beayar') (HT)	EBls
	'Yellow Cécile Brünner'	see *R.* 'Perle d'Or'
§	YELLOW DAGMAR HASTRUP ('Moryelrug') (Ru)	CPou EBls ETWh NLar SApu SPer
	YELLOW FLOWER CARPET	see *R.* FLOWER CARPET SUNSHINE
	'Yellow Mutabilis' (Ch)	EBls

'Yellow Patio' (Min/Patio)	CRos LRHS MAsh SCob SPoG
yellow Scotch	see *R.* × *harisonii* 'Williams' Double Yellow'
YELLOW SUNBLAZE ('Meitrisical') (Min)	CSBt
'Yesterday' (Poly/FCl) ♀H6	EBee EBls ETWh NLar SCob
'Yolande d'Aragon' (HP)	EBls ETWh
York and Lancaster	see *R.* × *damascena* 'Versicolor'
YORK MINSTER ('Harquest') (F)	MRav
YORKSHIRE ('Korbarkeit'[PBR]) (GC)	EBls MRav
YORKSHIRE BANK ('Rutrulo') (HT)	MFry
'Yorkshire Lady' (HT)	LSRN
YORKSHIRE PRINCESS ('Dicmouse') (Patio)	IDic MRav
YOU ARE MY SUNSHINE ('Frykwango'[PBR]) (HT) ♀H6	MFry
'You Only Live Once' (F)	LSRN
YOUNG AT HEART ('Raw922') (F)	ESty
YOUNG LYCIDAS ('Ausvibrant'[PBR]) (S)	CRos CSBt EPfP LBuc LRHS LSRN MAsh NRHS
'Your Wedding Day' (F)	CGro
YOU'RE BEAUTIFUL ('Fryracy'[PBR]) (F) ♀H6	CBod CDoC CSBt EBee ECnt ELan ESty LBuc LCro LOPS LRHS MAsh MFry MRav MWat NRHS SApu SLon SPer SPoG
YVES PIAGET	see *R.* ROYAL BROMPTON ROSE
'Yvonne Rabier' (Poly) ♀H6	EBls ETWh EWTr NLar
'Zéphirine Drouhin' (Bb)	Widely available
§ 'Zigeunerknabe' (S)	EBls ETWh NLar WFar
'Zoe'	LSRN

Roscoea ✿ (*Zingiberaceae*)

sp.	CMac
alpina	CAby CBro CExl CPBP EBee EMor EPot GEdr GKev ILea NBPC NHar WCru WFar XLum
- CC 1820	IBlr
- pink-flowered	IBlr
- purple-flowered	IBlr
- short	WCru
§ ***auriculata*** ♀H5	CAby CAvo CBct CBro CLAP CTsd EPfP EPot GEdr GKev IBlr ILea ITim LEdu MAsh NWad SChF SDeJ SDir SPer WCru WHil
- B&SWJ 2594	WCru
- B&SWJ 2687	WCru
- GWJ 9230	WCru
- 'Anorexia'	IBlr
- brown-stemmed × ***purpurea***	CJun IBlr
- early-flowering	IBlr WCru
- 'Floriade'	CJun LPla SDir WFar WPGP WSHC
- green-stemmed × ***purpurea***	CJun IBlr
- late-flowering	WCru
- 'White Cap'	CJun EBee GKev
auriculata* × *cangshanensis	WCru
auriculata* × *purpurea	WCru
australis	CSam EBee ELon GEdr MAsh MNrw WCru WThu
- purple-flowered KW 22124	IBlr
australis* × *humeana	MAsh
'Ballyrogan Lavender'	IBlr
'Ballyrogan White'	IBlr
× ***beesiana*** ♀H5	CBcs CBod CDTJ EPfP ILea MAsh SMHy
- 'Ballyrogan Purple'	CJun IBlr
- Cream Group	CJun EBee IBlr LEdu NBir SDeJ SDir WCru
- Dark Group	IBlr
- Gestreept Group	CAby CBro CLAP CMea CRos EHyd EMor EPot GEdr GKev LBuc LRHS NBPC NRHS SDir WCru
- - white-flowered	GKev
- 'Lemon and Lavender'	CJun IBlr
- 'Monique'	CDTJ CJun EBee EPfP IBlr WFar
- 'Moonlight'	CJun IBlr
- 'Petite Purple'	IBlr
bhutanica PAB 3826	LEdu
Blackthorn strain	IBlr WCru WHil
cangshanensis	CAby MAsh WFar
- BWJ 7848	WCru
capitata	IBlr
cautleyoides	CAby CAvo CBro CPla CRos CWCL ECha EHyd ELon EMor EPot GKev IBlr ILea LRHS MHid MNrw NBid NGdn NHar NRHS WCot WCru XEll
- blue-leaved	NHar
- var. ***cautleyoides*** f. ***atropurpurea***	IBlr
- - - 'Giraffe'	IBlr
- - white-flowered	CAby
- 'Crûg's Late Lemon'	WCru WFar
- 'Doge Purple'	IBlr
- 'Early Purple'	CJun
- 'Early Yellow'	EBee
- early-flowering	CRos EHyd LRHS NRHS
- 'Himalaya' ♀H5	WHil
- 'Jeffrey Thomas' ♀H5	CJun CRos CSam EHyd ELan LRHS NRHS WHil
- 'Last Emperor'	CLAP
- late, lavender-flowered	IBlr
- 'Lemon Giraffe'	CJun IBlr
- mauve-flowered	WHil
- 'Nguluko Village' new	WFar
- 'Pennine Purple'	IBlr NHar
- plum-flowered	IBlr
- var. ***pubescens***	CJun
- 'Purple Giant'	CJun EBee WHil
- 'Purple Queen' ♀H5	WFar
- purple-flowered	CAby IBlr
- 'Reinier'	CJun
- f. ***sinopurpurea***	GKev IBlr
- 'Stephanie Bloom' ♀H5	EBee LBuc NHar
- 'Vanilla'	CJun LEdu
- 'Washfield Purple'	IBlr
- 'Wine Red'	WHil
- 'Yeti'	CJun
aff. ***cautleyoides***	MAsh MAvo SPlb
cautleyoides* × *humeana	IBlr
debilis var. ***debilis***	IBlr
forrestii f. ***forrestii***	IBlr NHar
- - pubescent	IBlr
- 'Ice Maiden'	IBlr
- f. ***purpurea***	IBlr
'Harvington Evening Star'	CJun CLAP CRos EBee EHyd LRHS MAsh NHar NRHS WFar
Harvington hybrids	NHar
'Harvington Imperial'	NHar
'Harvington Raw Silk' ♀H5	CJun CLAP CRos EBee EHyd LEdu LRHS MAvo NHar NRHS WFar WHil
'Harvington Royale'	CJun CRos EHyd LRHS NHar NRHS WFar

humeana	CAby CBro CRos EHyd EPot GEdr GKev LRHS NHar NRHS WThu
- from Cruickshank Botanic Garden	IBlr NHar
- f. ***alba***	CJun EPot EWld IBlr NHar
- 'Guincho White Stripe'	IBlr
- 'Long Acre Sunrise'	CJun
- f. ***lutea*** ♀H5	CAby CJun GEdr IBlr WFar
- 'Purple Streaker'	CJun
- purple-flowered	EBee
- 'Rosemoor Plum'	CAby CJun
- 'Snowy Owl'	CJun GEdr MHid WFar
- 'Two Tone'	CJun IBlr
- f. ***tyria*** ♀H5	CJun WHil
- - Inkling Group	NHar
'Ice Maiden'	CJun IBlr
'Kew Beauty' ♀H5	CAby CBcs CBod CBro CExl CJun CLAP CMea CRos EHyd EMor EPfP LRHS MPie NGdn NRHS SMHy SPoG WFar WHil
'Lavender Mist'	IBlr
'McBeath's Pink'	CRos EHyd LRHS NRHS WFar
nepalensis	CJun
'Pallid Sun'	IBlr
'Pinky'	CMea
praecox	GEdr IBlr
procera misapplied	see *R. auriculata*
procera Wall.	see *R. purpurea*
'Purple King'	CJun
§ ***purpurea***	Widely available
- CC 1757	IBlr
- CC 3628	CExl IBlr
- HWJK 2020	WCru
- HWJK 2169	WCru
- HWJK 2175	WCru
- HWJK 2400	WCru WFar
- HWJK 2407	WCru
- KW 13755	IBlr
- MECC 2	CJun IBlr
- MECC 10	CJun IBlr
- 'Ant Marian'	GKev
- Blackthorn hybrids	CLAP NHar
- 'Bronzed Albino'	IBlr
- bronze-leaved	CAby
- 'Brown Peacock'	CAvo CJun GKev IBlr MAvo NHar SDir WCot WCru WFar
- 'Butterfly'	GKev
- 'Cinnamon Stick'	CAbb CJun CLAP CWGN ECtt GEdr MAsh NHar WCot
- 'Dalai Lama' ♀H5	GKev WHil
- Emperor Group **new**	NHar
- var. ***gigantea***	WHil
- - CC 1757	IBlr
- 'Himalayan Delight'	IBlr
- 'Julie's Glory'	EBee WFar
- 'Late Lavender'	IBlr
- 'Nico'	CJun ELan IBlr
- pale-flowered	WFar
- 'Peacock'	CJun GKev IBlr WHil
- 'Peacock Eye'	CJun GEdr GKev IBlr WFar
- 'Petticoat Pink'	GKev
- var. ***procera***	see *R. purpurea*
- 'Purple Dwarf'	IBlr
- 'Purple Tower'	IBlr
- 'Red Foot'	EBee WFar
- 'Red Gurkha'	see *R. purpurea* f. *rubra*
- 'Red Riding Hood'	GKev WFar
- Royal Purple hybrids	CJun MAsh NHar WPGP
§ - f. ***rubra*** ♀H5	Widely available
- - 'Gurkha Redstem'	CJun CLAP SPoG WCru
- 'Salt 'n' Pepper'	GKev
- short	IBlr
- 'Slender Wisp'	IBlr
- 'Snow Goose' **new**	WCru
- 'Spice Island'	CAbb CJun CLAP CSpe CWGN ECtt GEdr GPSL IPot MMrt SEdd SPoG WCot WFar
- Sultan Group **new**	NHar
- 'Summer Snow'	EBee GKev
- tall	WCru
- 'Twin Towers'	GKev
- 'Typico'	IBlr
- 'Vannin'	CJun LEdu WCru
- 'Vincent'	CJun EBee EPot GKev MPie WFar
- 'Wisley Amethyst'	CBro CJun CRos EBee EHyd IBlr LRHS MAsh MAvo MNrw NHar NRHS WFar
schneideriana	CJun IBlr WFar WThu
- robust form	IBlr
scillifolia	CBro CRos EHyd GEdr GKev LRHS NBir NRHS SDeJ SPlb
- f. ***atropurpurea***	CAby EPot GKev IBlr MAsh WCru WThu
- black-flowered	NHpl
- f. ***scillifolia***	IBlr MPie NHpl WCru WFar WHil WThu
aff. ***scillifolia*** purple-flowered	GEdr
'Snow Queen' **new**	NHar
'Summer Deep Purple' ♀H5	CJun CRos EHyd LRHS NRHS WFar
tibetica	CPBP GEdr GKev IBlr SPlb WCru WFar WSHC WThu
- ACE 2538	IBlr WCru
- BWJ 7878	WCru
- f. ***atropurpurea*** BWJ 7640	WCru
- f. ***rosea***	WCru
- white-flowered **new**	GRum
'Two Tone'	CJun
wardii ♀H5	CExl IBlr

rosemary see *Rosmarinus officinalis*

Rosenia (*Asteraceae*)

humilis	CPBP

Rosmarinus ✿ (*Lamiaceae*)

'Barwinnock Dwarf Blue'	WHer
corsicus 'Prostratus'	see *R. officinalis* Prostratus Group
× ***lavandulaceus*** misapplied	see *R. officinalis* Prostratus Group
× ***noeanus***	XSen
officinalis	Widely available
- 'Abraxas'	WFar
- f. ***albiflorus***	CBcs CBod CLau CRos EHyd ENfk EPfP EWhm LRHS MHer MNHC NPol SCob SDow SLim SPlb SPoG SRms WCFE WGwG WJek XSen
- - 'Lady in White'	CRos CSBt EHyd ELan EPfP LRHS MAsh NRHS SGol SPer SPoG SRms WGwG WJek
- 'Alderney'	WGwG WJek
- 'Amethyst Beauty'	SDow
§ - var. ***angustissimus*** 'Benenden Blue' ♀H4	CBod CSBt ELan GPoy LRHS MBNS SGol SPer SPlb SPoG SRms WGwG WJek WSpi
- - 'Corsican Blue'	GPoy MHer MHol MNHC SGol SRms WGwG
- 'Arp'	CBod ENfk EWes SEdi WGwG XSen
- 'Aureovariegatus'	see *R. officinalis* 'Aureus'

§ - 'Aureus' (v)	SRms WHer WJek
- 'Barbecue'PBR	CLau ECul ENfk EWhm SRms XSen
- 'Blue Lagoon'	CBod CBrac CDoC CLau ECul ENfk EWhm LRHS MHer MNHC SAko SRms WGwG WHer WJek WRHF
- 'Blue Rain'	CBod MHer MSwo NQui WFar WGwG WHer
- 'Blue Winter' **new**	CBod
- 'Britannia' **new**	CBod
- 'Capercaillie'	SDow WGwG
- 'Collingwood Ingram'	see *R. officinalis* var. *angustissimus* 'Benenden Blue'
- 'Cottage White'	WGwG WHer
- 'Farinole'	MNHC SRms WGwG
- 'Fota Blue'	CLau CTsd EHyd IArd LRHS MHer NPol NRHS SAko SDow SGol SRms SVen SWvt WGwG WJek
- 'Foxtail'	CDoC CLau ENfk LRHS SRms WJek XSen
- 'Frimley Blue'	see *R. officinalis* 'Primley Blue'
- 'Golden Rain'	see *R. officinalis* 'Joyce DeBaggio'
- 'Gorizia'	CBod LRHS SDow SRms
- 'Green Ginger' ♀H4	CBod CLau EBee ELan EPfP GBin LEdu MGos MHer MNHC MRav MSCN NPer SAko SCob SDow SPer SPoG SRms SVen WGwG WJek
- 'Guilded'	see *R. officinalis* 'Aureus'
- 'Haifa'	CCBP CLau CSde ENfk SEdi SRms WGwG
- 'Heavenly Blue'	WGwG WHer
- Israeli	XAbr
- 'Jekka Blue'	WJek
§ - 'Joyce DeBaggio' (v)	MHer SDow WGwG WHer
- 'Knightshayes Blue'	CRos EHyd LRHS NRHS
- ***lavandulaceus***	see *R. officinalis* Prostratus Group
- 'Lilies Blue'	GPoy WGwG
- 'Lockwood Variety'	see *R. officinalis* (Prostratus Group) 'Lockwood de Forest'
- 'Madeline Hill'	CRos LRHS
- 'Majorca Pink'	CBcs CBrac CLau CSBt CSpe ENfk LRHS MHer MNHC SDow SPer SRms WGwG WHer WJek XLum XSen
- 'Marenca'	MNHC SRms WGwG
- 'McConnell's Blue' ♀H4	CRos EHyd EPfP LRHS MGos MNHC NRHS SDow SRms WGwG WHer WJek
* - 'Miss Jessopp's Prostrate'	SEdi
- 'Miss Jessopp's Upright' ♀H4	Widely available
- 'Pointe du Raz'	CDoC EPfP MAsh SRms WGwG WSpi
§ - 'Primley Blue'	CBod CLau CSam EBou ECtt MNHC MRav SGol SRms WGwG WJek
§ - Prostratus Group	Widely available
- - 'Capri'	CBod CRos EPfP LRHS SCob SRms WFar WJek
- - 'Jackman's Prostrate'	GBin SDix
§ - - 'Lockwood de Forest'	WGwG WHer
- - 'Rampant Boule'	CBod CLau EWTr MHer SDow SMad SRms WGwG WJek XLum XSen
- - 'Sea Level'	MHer WGwG
- - 'Sheila Dore'	SPlb SVen
- - white-flowered	GPoy
- - 'Whitewater Silver'	ELan LRHS SPad WJek
- 'Punta di Canelle'	XSen
§ - 'Pyramidalis'	XSen
- f. ***pyramidalis***	see *R. officinalis* 'Pyramidalis'
- ***repens***	see *R. officinalis* Prostratus Group
- 'Rex'	WGwG XSen
- 'Roman Beauty'PBR	CBcs CBod CRos CSBt EBee EHyd EMor EPfP LRHS LSRN MHol MTin NRHS SAko SRms SWvt WFar WHer WSpi
- 'Roseus'	CCBP CRos ECrN ELan ENfk EPfP GPoy LRHS MAsh MHer MNHC NRHS SCob SDow SEND SLim SPoG SRms SVen WAvo WGwG WJek XAbr
- 'Salem'	CBod MHer
- 'Severn Sea' ♀H4	Widely available
- 'Shimmering Stars'	SDow WGwG
- 'Silver Sparkler'	WFar WHer
- 'Sissinghurst Blue' ♀H4	CBod CDoC CRos CSde EBee ECha ECrN ELan EPfP LRHS MAsh MHer MNHC MRav NRHS SDow SGol SPer SPlb SRms SWvt WGwG XAbr
- 'Sorcerer's Apprentice'	SDow
- 'Spanish Snow'	WGwG
- 'Spice Island'	CBod CRos LRHS SPer XSen
- 'Sudbury Blue'	CLau CTsd EWhm SAko SDow SGol SRms SVic WGwG
- 'Sunkissed'PBR	SRms
- 'Tuscan Blue'	CBcs CBod CExl CLau CRos ECha ECtt EHyd EPfP LRHS MBow MHer MSwo NRHS SGol SPer SRms WAvo WGwG XSen
- 'Variegatus'	see *R. officinalis* 'Aureus'
- 'Vatican Blue'	WJek
- WILMA'S GOLD ('Wimtim01'PBR)	CLau
repens	see *R. officinalis* Prostratus Group

Rostrinucula (*Lamiaceae*)

dependens	CBcs CMCN EBee EPfP ESwi EWes IDee LCro LOPS LRHS NLar SBrt SPad WCFE
sinensis	CExl

Rosularia (*Crassulaceae*)

§ ***aizoon***	CRos EDAr EHyd LRHS NRHS SRms WFar
alba	see *R. sedoides* var. *alba*
§ ***chrysantha***	CRos EDAr EHyd LRHS NHpl NRHS SPlb SRms WFar
crassipes	see *Rhodiola wallichiana*
hirsuta	NHpl
libanotica RCB RL 20	WCot
§ ***muratdaghensis***	SPlb
pallida A. Berger	see *R. chrysantha*
pallida Stapf	see *R. aizoon*
pallida ambig.	EPot
platyphylla misapplied	see *R. muratdaghensis*
rechingeri	EDAr SRms
§ ***sedoides*** var. ***alba***	EBou EDAr NHpl SRms XLum
sempervivum	EWes WThu
§ - subsp. ***glaucophylla***	CRos EHyd LRHS NRHS SPlb SRms WFar WHal WThu
serpentinica	WAbe
spatulata hort.	see *R. sempervivum* subsp. *glaucophylla*

Rotheca (*Lamiaceae*)

§ ***myricoides*** 'Ugandense' ♀H1b	CCCN EShb WSFF

Rubia (*Rubiaceae*)

peregrina	EMor GPoy

tinctorum	CHab CHby EMor GJos GPoy MNHC SRms WSFF

Rubus ✿ (*Rosaceae*)

RCB/Eq C-1	WCot
acuminatus	ESwi LEdu SBrt
alceifolius Poir.	SDys
- B&SWJ 1833	WCru
arcticus	EBee EPPr LEdu NHar SHar WKor WPGP XLum
bambusarum	EBee EShb ESwi IMou MRav WCFE WCru
'Benenden' ♀H5	CAby CBcs CExl CRos CTri EBee ECrN EHyd ELan EPfP GKin LRHS LSRN MBNS MMuc MRav NLar SPer SPhx WAvo WBor WCFE WLov WSpi
'Betty Ashburner'	CAgr CBcs CDoC EBee EPPr GLog MCoo MGos MRav SCob SPer SPoG XLum
biflorus ♀H6	LEdu MBlu MMuc SEND WKor WPGP
'Boysenberry' (F)	CArg EHyd LEdu LRHS MPri
boysenberry, thornless (F)	CMac LBuc LSRN MPri SPer
buergeri B&SWJ 5555	WCru
caesius	WCot WKor
calophyllus	CBcs EBee EPfP ESwi WPGP
- PAB 13.171	LEdu WPGP
calycinoides Hayata ex Koidz.	see *R. rolfei*
calycinoides Kuntze	GKev MGil SGol
chamaemorus	GPoy
cockburnianus (F)	CBcs CTri ELan EPfP LBuc LCro LOPS MMuc MRav MSwo NLar NSti SCob SPer SPlb SRms WSpi
- 'Goldenvale' ♀H6	CBcs CDoC CRos EHyd ELon EPfP LRHS MBlu MGos MMuc MRav MSwo NBir NLar NSti SEND SLon SPer SPoG SRms WFar
crataegifolius	MRav
fockeanus misapplied	see *R. rolfei*
formosensis	SBrt
- B&SWJ 1798	EBee ESwi WCru
fruticosus agg.	CArg SCob WSFF
- 'Adrienne' (B)	CAgr CHab CSBt LEdu MAsh SRms SSFr
- 'Apache' (B)	CHab CRos LCro LOPS LRHS MNHC SPoG
- 'Ashton Cross' (B)	SSFr
- 'Asterina' (B)	CMac
- 'Bedford Giant' (B)	CHab CSBt LSRN MAsh MGos SEND SLim SSFr
- 'Black Butte' (B)	CHab EPom SLon SVic
- 'Black Cascade'	see *R. fruticosus* 'Dart's Black Cascade'
- 'Black Satin' (B)	CAgr ECrN MPri NLar SEdi SVic
- 'Chester' (B)	CMac CRos EHyd EPom LEdu LRHS NRHS SKee
§ - 'Dart's Black Cascade' (B) **new**	LCro LOPS
- 'Helen' (B)	CAgr SSFr
- 'Himalayan Giant' (B)	CHab NLar
- 'Karaka Black'PBR (B)	CHab EHyd LBuc LRHS SPoG SSFr SVic
- 'Loch Maree'PBR (B/d)	CHab EPom LEdu MCoo MPri SLon
- 'Loch Ness'PBR (B) ♀H6	CAgr CArg CHab CRos EHyd EPom IArd LCro LOPS LRHS LSRN MPri NRHS SCoo SKee SPer SSFr SVic
- 'Loch Tay'PBR (B) ♀H6	CArg CHab CMac CRos EHyd EPom LRHS NRHS SPoG
- 'Merton Thornless' (B)	CSBt CTri ECrN LBuc LEdu LSRN MAsh MGos MPri SRms
- 'Navaho' (B)	CHab CRos EHyd LRHS NRHS SPoG
- 'Navaho Big and Early' (B)	LRHS
- 'Obsidian' (B)	LEdu
- 'Oregon Thornless' (B)	CAgr CSBt ECrN EPfP LCro LOPS LRHS LSRN MAsh MRav NLar SCoo SEdi SGbt SLim SPer SPoG SRms SSFr SVic WMat
- 'Ouachita'PBR (B)	CMac CRos EPfP LCro LOPS LRHS NRHS SKee SPoG
- 'Purple Opal' (B) **new**	LCro LOPS
- 'Reuben' (B)	CHab CRos EBee EHyd EPfP EPom LBuc LCro LOPS LRHS MCoo MNHC NRHS SKee SPoG SRms WMat
- 'Thornfree' (B)	CAgr CTri EPfP MMuc MPri NLar SGbt SLim WMat
- 'Triple Crown' (B)	CHab CMac MCoo
- 'Variegatus' (v)	CMac MBlu WCot
- 'Waldo' (B)	CAgr LBuc LSRN MAsh MGos MPri SRms SSFr
'Glencoe' (B)	MCoo SVic
henryi	CBcs EBee ESwi GBin NLar SPoG WBor WCot
- var. ***henryi***	WCru
ichangensis	CBcs ESwi
idaeus	GPoy
- 'All Gold' (F) ♀H6	CMac EMil EPom LRHS MPri NLar SCoo SPer SRms SVic WMat
- 'Alpengold'PBR (F)	CRos EBee LOPS LRHS MCoo SPoG
- 'Aureus' (F)	ECha LEdu MRav NBid WCot
- 'Autumn Amber' (F)	LRHS
- 'Autumn Bliss' (F) ♀H6	Widely available
- 'Autumn Treasure'PBR (F)	EMil EPom MPri SLon SVic
- 'Black Jewel' (F)	LOPS
- 'Cascade Delight' (F)	CArg CRos CSBt EHyd EPom LBuc LOPS LRHS MAsh NRHS
- 'Erika'PBR (F)	CRos EBee EHyd EPom LCro LOPS LRHS MCoo NLar NRHS SRms WMat
- 'Fallgold' (F)	LSRN MMuc SKee
- 'Glen Ample'PBR (F) ♀H6	Widely available
- 'Glen Clova' (F)	CAgr CRos CSBt CTri EBee EHyd LRHS LSRN MAsh MGos MPri NLar NRHS SEdi SGbt SKee SLim SPer SPoG SRms WMat
- 'Glen Dee' (F)	SRms
- 'Glen Doll'PBR (F)	CAgr MAsh NLar NRHS SCoo SRms WMat
- 'Glen Fyne'PBR (F)	CAgr
- 'Glen Lyon' (F)	CArg CSBt ECrN EPfP LBuc MAsh MPri SCoo SEdi
- 'Glen Magna'PBR (F) ♀H6	CAgr CArg CSBt MAsh MPri SCoo SEdi SKee SLim SRms
- 'Glen Moy'PBR (F)	CAgr CArg MAsh MGos SCoo SKee SLim SPer
- 'Glen Prosen'PBR (F)	CAgr CSBt LRHS MAsh MGos MPri SCoo SEdi SKee SLim SPlb SPoG SRms SSFr WMat
- 'Heritage' (F)	LSRN MAsh SCoo SGol SRms
- 'Joan J'PBR (F) ♀H6	CArg CMac EPom LBuc LSRN SPer SRms SSFr
- 'Leo'PBR (F) ♀H6	CSBt LCro LOPS MAsh SCoo SKee SRms SSFr
- 'Malling Admiral' (F) ♀H6	CSBt CTri EPom LSRN MAsh SCoo SKee SPer
- 'Malling Delight' (F)	ELan SCoo SEdi SPlb

- 'Malling Jewel' (F) 𝕐H6 — CAgr CArg CSBt CTri EPfP EPom LBuc LSRN MAsh MPri SEdi SKee SPer SRms
- 'Malling Minerva' (F) — CAgr EPom SRms SVic
- 'Malling Promise' (F) — SGol
- 'Octavia' PBR (F) — CAgr CArg CTri EMil EPom LBuc MAsh MCoo NLar NRHS SEdi SLim WMat
- 'Paris' PBR (F) **new** — EPom
- 'Polka' PBR (F) 𝕐H6 — CArg CRos EHyd EPfP EPom LBuc LCro LOPS LRHS LSRN MAsh MCoo MRav NRHS SCoo SKee SLim SPer SRms SSFr WMat
- RUBY BEAUTY ('Nr7' PBR) (F) — CSBt EHyd EPom LBuc LCro LOPS LSRN MGos NRHS SCoo SPoG SRms
- 'Sanibelle' (F) — LRHS
- 'Sugana' PBR (F) — LCro LOPS LRHS MAsh SKee
- 'Tadmor' PBR (F) — CArg CRos EBee EHyd EPom LCro LOPS LRHS NRHS SKee SRms WMat
- 'Tulameen' (F) 𝕐H6 — CAgr CArg CSBt EBee EHyd ELan EMil EPfP EPom LBuc LCro LOPS LRHS LSRN MAsh MMuc MPri NRHS SCoo SEND SEdi SKee SLim SPer SPoG SRms SSFr SVic WMat
- TWOTIMER SUGANA YELLOW (F) — LRHS SRms
- 'Zeva' (F) — SGol SRms
- 'Zeva Herbsternte' (F) — MAsh

illecebrosus (F) — LEdu WKor XLum
irenaeus — LEdu LRHS SEND WHal
Japanese wineberry — see *R. phoenicolasius*
'Kenneth Ashburner' — NLar
laciniatus 'Thornless Evergreen' — MMuc
lambertianus PAB 8931 — LEdu
- var. ***glandulosus*** B&SWJ 14507 **new** — WCru

leucodermis — WKor
lineatus — CBcs CDTJ CRos EHyd EPfP EWes GBin LEdu LRHS MCot NLar WCru WPGP
- B&SWJ 11261 from Sumatra — WCru
- HWJ 892 from Vietnam — ESwi WCru
- HWJK 2045 from Nepal — WCru
- PAB 13.163 — LEdu

× ***loganobaccus*** (F) — CMac
- 'Ly 59' (F) — ECrN EPfP MMuc SEND SKee SRms
- 'Ly 654' (F) 𝕐H5 — CRos CSBt EHyd EPom LBuc LRHS MPri NRHS SPer SSFr SVic
- thornless (F) — CAgr CTri EPfP EPom LEdu SEdi SPoG WMat

malvaceus FMWJ 13324 — WCru
'Margaret Gordon' — MRav
microphyllus 'Variegatus' (v) — MRav
§ ***nepalensis*** — CAgr GKev LEdu WKor WPGP
niveus — WKor
nutans — see *R. nepalensis*
occidentalis **new** — WKor
odoratus — CAgr CExl ELan EPPr EPfP LEdu MBlu NBid NLar SPer WBor WKor
palmatus var. ***coptophyllus*** — MMuc
parkeri PAB 6891 — LEdu
parviflorus — WKor
- 'Bill Baker' — LEdu
- double-flowered (d) — EPPr
- 'Sunshine Spreader' — LEdu

parvus — LEdu
pectinellus var. ***trilobus*** B&SWJ 1669B — NLar WCru
peltatus — NLar
pentalobus — see *R. rolfei*
§ ***phoenicolasius*** — CAgr CBcs CCCN CMac ELan EPPr EPfP LCro LEdu LOPS LRHS MBlu MCoo MRav SPer SPoG SVic WBor WFar WKor WPGP XAbr
reflexus var. ***hui*** — EShb
§ ***rolfei*** — MCoo NWad
- B&SWJ 3546 from Taiwan — WCru
- B&SWJ 3878 from the Philippines — WCru
- 'Emerald Carpet' 𝕐H5 — CAgr NLar

rosifolius NJM 10.142 — WPGP
- 'Coronarius' (d) — CBod EBee ECrN EMor ESwi GBin MHol SMad WCot

rubrisetulosus PAB 9532 — LEdu
'Rushbrook Redleaf' — SBrt
saxatilis — WKor
- PAB 3912 — LEdu

setchuenensis — CMCN EPPr NLar
'Silvan' (F) — EBee MMuc SEND
spectabilis — ELan EPPr LEdu MMuc MRav WKor WOut
- 'Flore Pleno' — see *R. spectabilis* 'Olympic Double'
- § - 'Olympic Double' (d) — Widely available

splendidissimus B&SWJ 2361 — WCru
squarrosus — EBee EShb SMad WFar
'Sunberry' (F) — CCCN LEdu
swinhoei B&SWJ 1735 — WCru
taiwanicola B&SWJ 317 — ESwi
- CWJ 12400 — WCru

Tayberry Group (F) — CRos CSBt CTri EHyd LRHS LSRN MGos MPri NLar NRHS SPer SRms SVic
- 'Buckingham' (F) — CArg EHyd EPom LBuc LCro LOPS LRHS NLar NPer SEdi SVic WMat
- 'Medana Tayberry' (F) — CAgr CMac CTri EBee ECrN EPfP LEdu LRHS MNHC NLar SEdi SKee SPoG WMat

§ ***thibetanus*** 𝕐H6 — CBcs CDoC CMac CRos EBee EHyd ELan EPfP GBin LRHS LSRN MAsh MBriF MGos MMuc MRav MSwo NLar SCob SDix SEND SMad SPer SPoG SWvt WSpi
- 'Silver Fern' — see *R. thibetanus*

treutleri B&SWJ 2139 — WCru
tricolor — CAgr CBcs CBod CDoC CSBt CTri ECrN ELan GKev MBlu MCoo MMuc MRav MSwo NLar SCob SDix SGol SPer
trilobus B&SWJ 9096 — WCru
'Tummelberry' (F) — EHyd LRHS MCoo SVic
ulmifolius 'Bellidiflorus' (d) — EPPr MRav NLar
ursinus — SVic WKor
xanthocarpus — LEdu NLar XLum

Rudbeckia (Asteraceae)

AUTUMN SUN — see *R. laciniata* 'Herbstsonne'
'Berlin' — EBee ECtt GMaP LRHS MHol NLar NRHS SMad
californica — EHyd LRHS
- B&SWJ 14105 — WCru

deamii — see *R. fulgida* var. *deamii*
'Dublin' — ECtt MBNS MHol
fulgida — SWvt WFar

- 'City Garden' ECtt GBin LRHS LSou NLar SRms WFar
§ - var. ***deamii*** ♀^{H6} Widely available
- 'Early Bird Gold' CWGN EBee ECtt EHyd GBin GMaP LCro LRHS MHol NLar NRHS SAko SCob WCAu WFar
- var. ***fulgida*** CCBP CMea EBee EPfP LEdu SPhx SPoG
- 'Little Goldstar'^{PBR} CKno CRos EBee ECtt EHyd ELan EPfP LCro LOPS LRHS MAsh MHol MPri MTin NDov NLar NRHS SCob SLon SPoG SRms WFar WHil
§ - var. ***speciosa*** ♀^{H6} EBee ECha ECtt EHyd ELan EPfP GBin GWyn LRHS MMuc NRHS SEND SEdd SHar SPlb SPtp SRms SWvt WFar WOld XLum
- var. ***sullivantii*** CDoC
- - 'Goldsturm' ♀^{H6} Widely available
- - 'Pot of Gold' CBod NBPC NLar SCob
- VIETTE'S LITTLE SUZY ('Blovi') CBod EHyd LRHS LSou NRHS SRms WFar
grandiflora EHyd LRHS
- 'Sundance' CBod SPhx
hirta AUTUMN COLORS (mixed) EHyd ELan LCro LOPS LRHS NRHS
- 'Cappuccino' EHyd ELan EPfP LRHS NRHS
- CHEROKEE SUNSET (mixed) (d) CSpe EPfP
- 'Cherry Brandy' CSpe EWTr LRHS MNHC NGBl SPhx
- CHIM CHIMINEE (mixed) NGBl
- 'Goldilocks' SVic
- 'Indian Summer' ♀^{H3} CRos EHyd EPfP LRHS MHol MNHC NRHS SPhx
- 'Irish Eyes' SPhx SVic
- 'Marmalade' EHyd EPfP LRHS SPhx SVic
- 'Prairie Sun' CRos EHyd EPfP LRHS MBros NGBl NRHS SPhx
- 'Sonora' NGBl
- TIGER EYE GOLD ('Syntigeygol') SPoG
- Toto Series MBros
- - 'Toto' ♀^{H3} EPfP LCro LOPS SWvt
JULY GOLD see *R. laciniata* 'Juligold'
laciniata CKno CMac CSpe EBee EHyd ELan EMor EPPr GQue LEdu LRHS MNrw NDov NGBl NLar SMHy SPeP SPhx SRms WCot WOld WPGP WWtn XLum
- var. ***digitata*** IMou
- 'Golden Glow' see *R. laciniata* 'Hortensia'
- 'Goldkugel' (d) ♀^{H6} MWat
- 'Goldquelle' (d) CBod CRos CWld EBee ECha ECtt EHyd ELan EPed EPfP GMaP GWyn LRHS MTis NBPC NGBl NGdn NRHS SCob SPer SPoG SRms SWvt WCAu WFar XLum
§ - 'Herbstsonne' ♀^{H6} Widely available
§ - 'Hortensia' (d) EBee LPot MAvo MRav NGBl WBrk WCot WFar WHoo WOld
§ - 'Juligold' CBod CRos EBee ECtt EHyd EPfP LRHS MBNS MPie NGdn NRHS SPoG WBrk WSpi
- 'Starcadia Razzle Dazzle' ♀^{H6} EWld MAvo SAko WCot WFar
maxima CAby CBod CKno CSpe CTsd EBee ECha ELon EMor GBin GQue ILea LEdu LRHS LSun MBel MHol MMuc NDov NGBl NLar NSti SBrt SEdd SMad SPhx SPlb WCot WFar XLum
missouriensis CRos EAJP EHyd EPfP GBin LRHS MMuc MNrw NRHS SPhx
mollis CRos EHyd LRHS NRHS
newmannii see *R. fulgida* var. *speciosa*
nitida WSpi
occidentalis EHyd LRHS NChi NRHS
- 'Black Beauty'^{PBR} NDov WSpi
- 'Green Wizard' CBod CMac CRos EBee ECtt EHyd ELan EPed EPfP GBin GQue GWyn LRHS MCot NGBl NRHS NSti SCob SRms WSpi
* ***paniculata*** CDor EBee NGBl WCot
'Peking'^{PBR} EBee ECtt EPfP MBNS MHol
purpurea see *Echinacea purpurea*
speciosa see *R. fulgida* var. *speciosa*
subtomentosa CRos CSam EHyd EPfP EWes LEdu LRHS MMuc NDov NRHS NSti SDix SMHy WCot WOld WSpi XLum
- 'Henry Eilers' Widely available
- 'Little Henry'^{PBR} CBod CKno CSpe EBee ECtt EHyd ELon EMor EPed EPfP LRHS LSRN MAvo MBNS MBel MCot MHol MTin NRHS NWsh SCob SPoG
- 'Loofahsa Wheaten Gold' GBin MAvo NDov SHar WCot WGoo
- 'Poligny' MNrw
Summerina Series LRHS SCob
- SUMMERINA BROWN ('Et Rdb 03'^{PBR}) CKno CRos EHyd EPfP LRHS MBNS MHol NGBl NRHS NSti SCob SMad SPoG WCot
- SUMMERINA BUTTERSCOTCH BISCUIT ('Et Rdb 410') **new** CRos
- SUMMERINA ELECTRA SHOCK ('Et Rdb 404') **new** CRos
- SUMMERINA ORANGE ('Et Rdb 01'^{PBR}) CRos EHyd EPfP LPla LRHS LSou MBNS MHol NRHS SCob SMad SPad SPoG SRkn
- SUMMERINA PECAN PIE ('Et Rdb 401') **new** SPad
- SUMMERINA PUMPERNICKEL ('Et Rdb 402') **new** CRos
- SUMMERINA YELLOW ('Et Rdb 02'^{PBR}) CRos EHyd LRHS LSou MBNS MHol NGBl NRHS SCob SPoG SRkn WCot
triloba ♀^{H6} CRos CSpe ECha EHyd EMor EPfP LRHS MNrw NGBl NGdn NRHS SCob SDix SPhx WCAu WPGP WSpi
- 'Prairie Glow' CAby CBcs CDor CSpe EAJP EBee ECha EHyd EMor ILea LRHS NGBl SCob SMad SPer SPhx

rue see *Ruta graveolens*

Ruellia (*Acanthaceae*)

amoena see *R. brevifolia*
§ ***brevifolia*** ECre WFib
humilis EBee EWld GEdr MNrw SPhx
macrantha CCCN EShb
strepens EBee
tweediana EShb WFib

Rulingia (*Sterculiaceae*)

hermanniifolia WAbe

Rumex (*Polygonaceae*)

acetosa CAgr CHab CHby CLau CTsd EMor ENfk GPoy MCoo MHer MMuc MNHC NBir SPhx SRms WCot WHer WJek WSFF WWild XAbr

- 'Abundance'	CLau LEdu
- subsp. ***acetosa*** 'Saucy' (v)	EBee LEdu MHol WCot
- broad-leaved **new**	SVic
- 'De Belleville'	CLau
- 'Profusion'	GPoy
- red-veined **new**	LCro LOPS
acetosella	CAgr CHab SRms WSFF
alpinus	LEdu WCot WPGP
flexuosus	CSpe LPot WOut
hydrolapathum	CBod CHab MMuc SEND SPlb WCot WSFF
patientia	CHab CLau
sanguineus	CLau ENfk EShb LEdu NLar NQui SRms XLum
- var. ***sanguineus***	CHby ELan EMor GQue LSun MHer MNHC NBro NGrd WFar WHer
scutatus	CBod CHby CLau EMor ENfk GPoy MNHC NGrd SPlb SRms WJek
- 'Armenian Steel' **new**	LEdu
- subsp. ***induratus***	SEND
- 'Silver Shield'	EPPr LEdu MHer NGrd SRms WFar

Rumohra (*Dryopteridaceae*)

adiantiformis 🏆H3	CCCN CRos EBee EHyd ISha LEdu LRHS MAsh NRHS SEND WFib

Rungia (*Acanthaceae*)

klossii **new**	WJek

Ruschia (*Aizoaceae*)

putterillii	SPlb
spinosa	SPlb
tumidula	SPlb

Ruscus ✿ (*Asparagaceae*)

aculeatus	CBcs CMac ELan EPfP GPoy LEdu MGil MGos NLar SPlb SRms SWvt WMou WRHF
- hermaphrodite	EPfP MMuc MNrw SEND SMad WAvo
- (f)	SCob WSpi
- var. ***angustifolius*** (f)	WCru
- - PAB 254	LEdu
- 'John Redmond'PBR (f/m) 🏆H5	ELan EPfP EShb LRHS NHol NLar NWad SLon SPer SWvt WBor WFar WSpi
* - 'Wheeler's Variety' (f/m)	CJun MRav
colchicus PAB 1753	LEdu
hypoglossum	CMac IArd IMou MMuc SEND WCot WSpi
hypophyllum B&SWJ 15009 **new**	WCru
× ***microglossus*** (f) B&SWJ 14041	WCru
racemosus	see *Danae racemosa*

Ruspolia (*Acanthaceae*)

hypocrateriformis	CCCN

Ruspolia × *Ruttya* see × *Ruttyruspolia*

Russelia (*Plantaginaceae*)

§ ***equisetiformis*** 🏆H1c	WFib
- 'Lemon Falls' 🏆H1c	WFib
- 'Tangerine Falls'	WFib
juncea	see *R. equisetiformis*

Ruta (*Rutaceae*)

chalepensis	SPhx XLum
corsica	XLum
graveolens	CBod CHab ENfk GPoy GQue MNHC SVic WJek XAbr XLum XSen
- 'Alderley Blue'	WJek
- 'Jackman's Blue'	CBcs ELan EMor EPfP GMaP GPoy MGos MHer MNHC MRav MSwo SRms SWvt WFar WSMil WSpi XLum
- 'Variegata' (v)	MNHC NPer SRms

Ruttya (*Acanthaceae*)

fruticosa	CCCN

× *Ruttyruspolia* (*Acanthaceae*)

lutea	CCCN
'Phyllis van Heerden'	CCCN

S

Sabal (*Arecaceae*)

§ ***mexicana***	SPalm
minor	CPHo SPalm SPlb
palmetto	SPalm
texana	see *S. mexicana*

Saccharum (*Poaceae*)

arundinaceum	CKno
brevibarbe var. ***contortum***	WCot
officinarum	SPlb
- purple-stemmed	SPlb WCot
- var. ***violaceum***	LEdu SDix
ravennae	EBee SMad SPlb

sage see *Salvia officinalis*

sage, annual clary see *Salvia viridis*

sage, biennial clary see *Salvia sclarea*

sage, pineapple see *Salvia elegans*

Sageretia (*Rhamnaceae*)

§ ***thea***	CMen
theezans	see *S. thea*

Sagina (*Caryophyllaceae*)

subulata	LRHS SVic XLum
- var. ***glabrata***	MAsh
§ - - 'Aurea'	CMea EBou ECha ECtt EDAr ELan EPfP GMaP MAsh MHer NHpl SPoG SRms

Sagittaria (*Alismataceae*)

graminea	LLWG SBrt
- 'Crushed Ice' (v)	LLWG
japonica	see *S. sagittifolia*
lancifolia	LLWG
latifolia	NPer
§ ***sagittifolia***	CWat EWat LLWG MWts WMAq WPnP XLum
- var. ***leucopetala***	WMAq
- - 'Flore Pleno' (d)	CWat EWat NPer WMAq XLum

Saintpaulia ✿ (*Gesneriaceae*)

'8e-Ajisai'	WDib
'Aca's Red Ember' (v)	WDib
'Ae-Amur Elit'	WDib

'Ajohn's Yellow Submarine' **new**	WDib
'Alamo Quest'	WDib
'Alan's Fallen Angel' (d/v)	WDib
'Alan's White Feather'	WDib
'Alchemy Yellow Star'	WDib
'Allegro Appalachian Trail'	WDib
'Always Pink'	WDib
'Aly's Rosy Baby'	WDib
'Amazing Grace'	WDib
'Amethyst'	WDib
'Anouk'	WDib
'An-Rio Rita' **new**	WDib
'Anthoflores Edith'	WDib
'Apache Maiden' (v)	WDib
'Apache Thunderbolt'	WDib
'Aussie Magic'	WDib
'Baby Brian'	WDib
'Beacon Trail'	WDib
'Beatrice Trail'	WDib
'Berry Splash' (v)	WDib
'Betty Stoehr'	WDib
'Bliznecy'	WDib
'Bloomlover's Cat' (d)	WDib
'Blue Dragon' (d)	WDib
'Blue Tail Fly'	WDib
'Blushing Ivory'	WDib
'Bob Serbin' (d)	WDib
'Bob's Omega'	WDib
'Bol's Evening Holger'	WDib
'Bol's Evening Irja'	WDib
'Bourane' (v)	WDib
brevipilosa	WDib
'Buffalo Hunt' (d)	WDib
'Calico Beauty'	WDib
'Candy Fountain'	WDib
'Candy Swirls'	WDib
'Cathedral'	WDib
'Cedar Creek Stormy'	WDib
'Cedar Creek Trail of Hope'	WDib
'Chantaspring'	WDib
'Cherokee Trail' (v)	WDib
'Cherries 'n' Cream'	WDib
'Chiffon Fiesta'	WDib
'Chiffon Pageant'	WDib
'Chiffon Vesper'	WDib
'Cirelda'	WDib
'Country Romance' (d)	WDib
'Crimson Ice'	WDib
'Crowning Glory' **new**	WDib
'Cupid's Jewel'	WDib
'Cupie Doll'	WDib
'Dawn Michelle' **new**	WDib
'Deep Sky'	WDib
'Definitely Darryl'	WDib
'Delft' (d)	WDib
'Dibley's Beate'	WDib
'Dibleys Kaarina'	WDib
'Dibleys Marion' **new**	WDib
'Dibleys Mercedes'	WDib
'Dibley's Pat'	WDib
'Edee's Rosebud Trail' (d)	WDib
'Ek-Gost'ya iz Budushchego'	WDib
'Ek-Sady Semiramidi'	WDib
'Ek-Shedevr Khudozhnika'	WDib
'Ek-Snezhnyi Bars'	WDib
'Ek-Vrata Raia'	WDib
'Emerald Love'	WDib
'Ethel's Wild Side'	WDib
'Favorite Child'	WDib
'Fire Mountain'	WDib
'Flashy Angel' (v)	WDib
'Flashy Trail'	WDib
'Flower Drum'	WDib
'Frozen in Time' (v)	WDib
'Gecko's Vespa Vino'	WDib
'Gillian' (d)	WDib
'Golden Dawn'	WDib
'Golden Eye'	WDib
'Golden Threads' (d)	WDib
'Goldilocks' (d)	WDib
'Goluboi Tuman'	WDib
'Grandmother's Halo'	WDib
'Green Dragon'	WDib
'Green Lace' (d)	WDib
'Halo's Aglitter'	WDib
'Hand-picked' (v) **new**	WDib
'Happy Cricket'	WDib
'Heaven's A-calling'	WDib
'Hot Summer Day'	WDib
'Ian-Minuet' (d)	WDib
'In the Pink'	WDib
'Indian Trail' **new**	WDib
'Indigo Ruffles'	WDib
ionantha subsp. ***grotei***	WDib
– subsp. ***ionantha***	WDib
– subsp. ***rupicola***	WDib
– subsp. ***velutina***	WDib
'Island Breezes'	WDib
'Jenny Lilac' (d)	WDib
'Jolly Champ' **new**	WDib
'Jolly Gold'	WDib
'Jolly Orchid' (d)	WDib
'Jolly Prize' (d)	WDib
'Jolly Sun Chaser' (d) **new**	WDib
'Jolly Texan' (d)	WDib
'Kosmicheskaia Legenda 2'	WDib
'Kostina Fantaziia'	WDib
'LE-Karusel' (v)	WDib
'LE-Macho'	WDib
'Lemon Whip' (d)	WDib
'Letnaya Noch'	WDib
'Letnie Sumerki'	WDib
'Lil Bit O'Irish'	WDib
'Lilla Blaklockan'	WDib
'Little Axel'	WDib
'Little Bo Peep' **new**	WDib
'Little Seagull'	WDib
'Lollipop'	WDib
'Looking Glass'	WDib
'Louisiana Lagniappe'	WDib
'Louisiana Lullaby' (d)	WDib
'Love Spots'	WDib
'Lubimaia Dochka'	WDib
'Lucky Ladybug' **new**	WDib
'Luminescence'	WDib
'Lyon's Minnie-HaHa'	WDib
'Lyon's Plum Pudding'	WDib
'Mac's Black Jack'	WDib
'Mac's Blowing Bubbles'	WDib
'Mac's Carnival Clown'	WDib
'Mac's Circus Clown'	WDib
'Mac's Glacial Grape'	WDib
'Mac's Just Jeff' (d/v)	WDib
'Mac's Nocturne' (d)	WDib
'Mac's Rouge Rogue'	WDib
'Mac's Southern Springtime' (d)	WDib
'Mac's Strawberry Sundae'	WDib
'Mac's Tiamat' (v)	WDib

'Mac's Walkabout Uluru' (v)	WDib
'Mair'	WDib
'Ma's Ching Dynasty' (d)	WDib
'Ma's Easter Parade'	WDib
'Midget Silver Fox' (v)	WDib
'Midnight Flame' (d)	WDib
'Mikinda Girl' (v)	WDib
'Mindi Brooke'	WDib
'MyJoy' (MyViolet Series)	WDib
'Ness' Antique Red'	WDib
'Ness' Bangle Blue'	WDib
'Ness' Cherry Smoke'	WDib
'Ness' Crinkle Blue' (d)	WDib
'Ness' Midnight Fantasy'	WDib
'Ness' Orange Pekoe'	WDib
'Ness' Satin Rose'	WDib
'Ness' Sheer Peach'	WDib
'Neverfloris'	WDib
'Newtown Ohio'	WDib
nitida	WDib
'Norseman' **new**	WDib
'Number 32'	WDib
'Ode to Beauty'	WDib
'Okie Easter Bunny'	WDib
'Oksana'	WDib
'Optimara Little Moonstone'	WDib
'Otoe' (d)	WDib
'Parnikovyi Effekt'	WDib
'Pat Champagne' (v) **new**	WDib
'Pat Tracey'	WDib
'Pink Mint' (d)	WDib
'Pink Pussycat' (v)	WDib
'Pixie Blue'	WDib
'Pixie Pink'	WDib
'Podvenechnaia' (d)	WDib
'Powder Keg' (d)	WDib
'Powwow' (d/v)	WDib
'Prancing Pony'	WDib
'Purple Passion'	WDib
'Rainbow's Limelight' (d)	WDib
'Rainbow's Quiet Riot'	WDib
'Ramblin' Amethyst'	WDib
'Ramblin' Lassie'	WDib
'Ramblin' Sunshine'	WDib
'Rare Tapestry'	WDib
'Raspberry Crisp'	WDib
'Rebel's Amy'	WDib
'Rebel's Splatter Kake'	WDib
'Rebel's Strawberry Bites' **new**	WDib
'Red Lantern' (d)	WDib
'Reflections of Spring' (d)	WDib
'Rhapsodie Clementine'	WDib
'Rob's Argyle Socks' (d)	WDib
'Rob's Chilly Willy' (d/v)	WDib
'Rob's Dandy Lion' (d/v)	WDib
'Rob's Dust Storm' (d)	WDib
'Rob's Flim Flam' **new**	WDib
'Rob's Hot Tamale'	WDib
'Rob's Ice Ripples' (d)	WDib
'Rob's Jitterbug'	WDib
'Rob's Love Bite' (d)	WDib
'Rob's Mad Cat' (d)	WDib
'Rob's Melon Wedges'	WDib
'Rob's Peedletuck'	WDib
'Rob's Pewter Bells'	WDib
'Rob's Sarsparilla' (d)	WDib
'Rob's Scrumptious'	WDib
'Rob's Shadow Magic' (d/v)	WDib
'Rob's Smarty Pants' (d)	WDib
'Rob's Vanilla Trail' (d)	WDib
'Rob's Wooloomooloo' (d)	WDib
'Rs-Bog Solntsa' (d)	WDib
'Rs-Boyarinya'	WDib
'Rs-Gertsogninea'	WDib
'Rs-Iolanta' (v) **new**	WDib
'Rs-Kabaret'	WDib
'Rs-Korrida'	WDib
'Rs-Romantika'	WDib
'Rs-Strast'	WDib
'Rs-Utonchennyy-vkus'	WDib
'Rs-Vodevil' (v)	WDib
'Ruffled Skies'	WDib
'Santa Anita'	WDib
'Sapphire Halo'	WDib
'Senk's Arctic Fox'	WDib
'Senk's Girl Wasp'	WDib
'Shirl's Hawaiian Lei'	WDib
shumensis	WDib
'Shy Blue'	WDib
'Silverglade Beads'	WDib
'Silverglade Meadows'	WDib
'Sky Bells' (v)	WDib
'Sky Trail'	WDib
'Snow Leopard'	WDib
'Sparkleberry'	WDib
'Special Treat'	WDib
'Sun Sizzle'	WDib
'Sunkissed Rose'	WDib
'Taffeta Blue' (d)	WDib
'The King' **new**	WDib
'The Madam'	WDib
'Tiger' (v)	WDib
'Tina's April Fantasy'	WDib
'Top Dark Blue'	LCro LOPS
'Toy Castle'	WDib
'Tula'	WDib
'Two-w Miss Sophie' (d)	WDib
'Vallartas Campanas Moradas'	WDib
'Warm Sunshine'	WDib
'Whirligig Star'	WDib
'Wild Irish Rose'	WDib
'Wisteria' (d)	WDib
'Wrangler's Jealous Heart'	WDib
'Wrangler's Snowfield's' (v)	WDib
'Yesterday's Child'	WDib
'Zivai' (d) **new**	WDib

Salicornia (*Amaranthaceae*)

europaea	SVic

Salix ✿ (*Salicaceae*)

acutifolia 'Blue Streak' (m) ♀H6	CEnd EPfP EWes MBlu NBir NLar WMou
- 'Pendulifolia' (m)	SGol
'Aegma Brno' (f)	WMou
aegyptiaca	EBtc ECrN MBlu WMou
alba	CCVT CHab CLnd CWiW ECrN LBuc LMaj MAsh SCob SEWo SGol WMou WTSh XAbr
- f. ***argentea***	see *S. alba* var. *sericea*
- 'Aurea'	WMou
- var. ***caerulea***	CLnd SCob WMou
- - 'Wantage Hall' (f)	CWiW
- 'Cardinalis' (f)	CWiW
- 'Chermesina' hort.	see *S. alba* var. *vitellina* 'Britzensis'
- 'Golden Ness' ♀H6	CRos EBee EHyd EPfP LRHS MAsh MBlu NOra NRHS WFar WMat
- 'Hutchinson's Yellow Bark'	EBee NLar

	- 'Liempde' (m)	SCob
	- 'Raesfeld' (m)	CWiW
§	- var. ***sericea*** 🏆^{H6}	CLnd CTho EPfP MBlu MRav NLar SPer WCot WMou
	- 'Splendens'	see *S. alba* var. *sericea*
	- 'Tristis' misapplied	see *S.* × *sepulcralis* var. *chrysocoma*
§	- 'Tristis' ambig.	CBrac CLnd CTri ELan LMaj LRHS MGos MRav MSwo NLar NOra SCob SEWo
	- var. ***vitellina***	CBod EPfP LBuc MBNS MMuc NLar SGol SLon SRms
§	- - 'Britzensis' (m)	Widely available
	- - 'Nova'	ELan
§	- - 'Yelverton' 🏆^{H6}	CRos EBee EHyd EPfP LRHS NOra NRHS SPoG WFar WMat
	- 'Vitellina Tristis'	see *S. alba* 'Tristis' ambig.
	'Americana' (m)	CWiW SWeb
	amplexicaulis 'Pescara' (m)	CWiW
	amygdaloides	CWiW
	'Aokautere'	see *S.* × *sepulcralis* 'Aokautere'
§	***arbuscula***	WAbe XEll
	arenaria	see *S. repens* var. *argentea*
	aurita	MMuc
	babylonica	CEnd WMou
	- 'Annularis'	see *S. babylonica* 'Crispa'
	- 'Bijdorp'	NLar
§	- 'Crispa'	CBod CRos ELan GBin LRHS MMrt NQui NSti SMad SPoG WBor WFar WGrn
	- 'Pan Chih-kang'	CWiW NLar
	- var. ***pekinensis*** 'Pendula'	IArd
§	- - 'Tortuosa' (f)	CBcs CLnd CSBt ECrN ELan EPfP MGos MMuc NBir NGrd NOrn NPer SEND SGol SLon SPer SPlb SRms WFar WSMil
*	- 'Tortuosa Aurea'	LMaj SGol SWvt
	'Blackskin' (f)	CWiW
	bockii	CRos EHyd EPfP ESwi LRHS SDys SPlb
§	'Bowles's Hybrid'	WMou
	'Boydii' (f) 🏆^{H7}	EPfP EPot GAbr GEdr GJos GKev GMaP ITim LEdu LRHS MGos NBir NPoe NRya NSla SAko WAbe WFar WLov WThu
	candida	WFar WOut
	caprea	CArg CBcs CCVT CHab CLnd CTri EPfP LBuc SCob SEWo SPer WMou WSFF WTSh
§	- 'Kilmarnock' (m)	CBcs CCVT CDoC CMac CSBt CTri ECrN ELan EPfP LRHS MAsh MGos MMuc NLar NOrn NRHS SCob SGol SGsty SLim SPer SPoG SWvt WFar WJas WLov
	- var. ***pendula*** (m)	see *S. caprea* 'Kilmarnock' (m)
	- - (f)	see *S. caprea* 'Weeping Sally'
	- 'Pendula'	see *S. caprea* 'Kilmarnock', *S. caprea* 'Weeping Sally'
§	- 'Weeping Sally' (f)	WMat
	capusii	EBee LEdu WPGP
	cashmiriana	GEdr
	'Chrysocoma'	see *S.* × *sepulcralis* var. *chrysocoma*
	cinerea	CBcs CTri SCob SEWo WMou WTSh
	'Coire Kander'	EBee GKev
	daphnoides	CBcs CCVT CLnd ELan EPfP LMaj MGos MMuc MSwo SCob SEND SGol SPer SRms WMou WSFF
	- 'Aglaia' (m) 🏆^{H6}	CTri
	- 'Oxford Violet' (m)	ECrN
§	× ***doniana*** 'Kumeti'	CWiW
	'E.A. Bowles'	see *S.* 'Bowles's Hybrid'
	× ***ehrhartiana***	CNat
§	***elaeagnos***	CCVT CTho ECrN EPfP MBrN MMuc SCob SLon SMHy SPer WMou
§	- subsp. ***angustifolia*** 🏆^{H6}	ELan EPfP MMuc MRav MSwo NLar SEND SRms
	eriocephala 'American Mackay' (m)	CWiW
	- 'Kerksii' (m)	CWiW
	- 'Mawdesley' (m)	CWiW
	- 'Russelliana' (f)	CWiW
	exigua 🏆^{H5}	CBcs CLnd CTho ELan EPfP EWes IDee LBuc LEdu LRHS MBlu MBrN MGos MSwo NLar SChF SCob SMad SPer WMou WPGP
	fargesii 🏆^{H6}	CAby CBcs CBod CBrac CDoC CEnd CExl CMac CRos EBee EHyd ELan EPfP GBin LEdu LRHS MBlu MGos MMuc MRav NBid NOra SBrt SCob WCru WFar WLov
	formosa	see *S. arbuscula*
§	× ***fragilis***	CCVT CHab CLnd WMou WTSh
	- 'Basfordiana' (m)	CLnd CWiW MBNS WMou
	- 'Bouton Aigu'	CWiW
	- var. ***bullata***	LMaj
	- 'Farndon'	CWiW
	- 'Flanders Red' (f)	CWiW XAbr
	- 'Fransgeel Rood' (m)	CWiW
§	- var. ***furcata***	GKev
	- 'Glaucescens' (m)	CWiW
	- 'Golden Willow'	CWiW
	- 'Jaune de Falaise'	CWiW
	- 'Jaune Hâtive'	CWiW
	- 'Laurina'	CWiW
	- 'Natural Red' (f)	CWiW
	- 'Parsons'	CWiW
	- 'Rouge Ardennais'	CWiW
	- 'Rouge Folle'	CWiW
	- 'Russet' (f)	CWiW
	× ***fruticosa*** 'McElroy' (f)	CWiW
	fruticulosa	see *S.* × *fragilis* var. *furcata*
	'Fuiri-koriyanagi'	see *S. integra* 'Hakuro-nishiki'
	furcata	see *S.* × *fragilis* var. *furcata*
	'Golden Curls'	see *S.* × *sepulcralis* 'Erythroflexuosa'
	gracilistyla	WMou
§	- 'Melanostachys' (m) 🏆^{H5}	CAby ECrN ELan EPfP EWTr GBin MAsh MBNS MBlu MBrN MGos MMuc MRav NBir NLar SBrt SGol SPer SRms WBor WFar WLov
	- 'Mount Aso'	CMCN EBee EPfP IDee LCro LEdu LOPS MMrt NLar SBrt SEdd SMad WFar WLov WPGP
	hastata 'Wehrhahnii' (m) 🏆^{H6}	CBcs EBee ELan EPfP GKev MAsh MBlu MMuc MRav MSwo NBir NLar SCob SPer
	helvetica 🏆^{H7}	CBcs CMac EBee ELan EPfP MAsh MBlu MRav NBir NLar SPer WFar
	herbacea	GEdr WAbe
	hibernica	see *S. phylicifolia*
	hookeriana	CExl CTho MBlu MBrN MCoo NLar WCFE WMou
	incana	see *S. elaeagnos*
	integra 'Albomaculata'	see *S. integra* 'Hakuro-nishiki'
	- 'Flamingo'^{PBR}	ELan NLar SPoG WTSh
§	- 'Hakuro-nishiki' (v) 🏆^{H5}	Widely available
	- 'Pendula' (f)	CEnd MAsh NOrn
	irrorata 🏆^{H5}	CLnd EPfP MBlu MSwo NOra WMat
	kinuyanagi (m)	NSti

§	***koriyanagi***	CWiW
	'Kumeti'	see *S.* × *doniana* 'Kumeti'
	'Kuro-me'	see *S. gracilistyla* 'Melanostachys'
	lanata ♀H7	CBcs CMac EBee ELan EPfP GKev MAsh MGos NBir NLar SBrt SPer WCFE
	lapponum	LEdu MMuc NLar SRms
	- compact	GKev
	- 'Corrieshalloch' **new**	GKev
	magnifica	CAby CExl ELan EPfP GBin IArd LEdu LRHS MMuc NLar SMad WCot WFar WHer WMou WPGP WSpi
	'Mark Postill' (f)	CAby CRos EHyd GBin LRHS MBNS MMuc NLar SAko
	matsudana 'Tortuosa'	see *S. babylonica* var. *pekinensis* 'Tortuosa'
	- 'Tortuosa Aureopendula'	see *S.* × *sepulcralis* 'Erythroflexuosa'
	'Melanostachys'	see *S. gracilistyla* 'Melanostachys'
	× ***meyeriana*** 'Lumley' (f)	CWiW
	× ***mollissima***	CWiW
	var. ***hippophaifolia*** 'Jefferies' (m)	
	- - 'Notts Spaniard' (m)	CWiW
	- - 'Trustworthy' (m)	CWiW
	- var. ***undulata***	CWiW
	'Kottenheider Weide' (f)	
	moupinensis	CBcs EPfP
§	***myrsinifolia***	ELan MBlu MMuc NLar WLov
	myrtilloides 'Pink Tassels' (m)	SBrt
	nakamurana	CDoC CRos EBee EHyd ELan EWes
	var. ***yezoalpina***	GEdr GKev LRHS MBlu MMuc MRav NHar NLar SBrt SSta WFar WLov
	nigra	XAbr
	nigricans	see *S. myrsinifolia*
	nivalis	see *S. reticulata* subsp. *nivalis*
	pentandra	CLnd LMaj WMou
	- 'Patent Lumley'	CWiW
§	***phylicifolia***	WMou
	- 'Malham' (m)	CWiW
§	***purpurea***	CCVT SWeb WMou XAbr
	- 'Brittany Green' (f)	CWiW
	- 'Continental Reeks'	CWiW
	- 'Dark Dicks' (f)	CWiW NLar WSFF
	- 'Dicky Meadows' (m)	CWiW
	- 'Goldstones'	CWiW NLar
	- f. ***gracilis***	see *S. purpurea* 'Gracilis'
§	- 'Gracilis'	MMuc SCob WCot
	- 'Green Dicks'	CWiW
	- 'Helix'	see *S. purpurea*
	- 'Howki' (m)	WMou
	- 'Irette' (m)	CWiW
	- 'Jagiellonka' (f)	CWiW
	- var. ***japonica***	see *S. koriyanagi*
	- subsp. ***lambertiana***	CWiW
	- 'Lancashire Dicks' (m)	CWiW
	- 'Leicestershire Dicks' (m)	CWiW
	- 'Light Dicks'	CWiW
	- 'Lincolnshire Dutch' (f)	CWiW
	- 'Nancy Saunders' (f) ♀H6	CTho CWiW EWld GLog LEdu MBNS MBlu MBow MBrN NBir NLar NSti SDix SMHy WCot WGrn
	- 'Pendula' ♀H6	CCVT CEnd CMac ECrN MAsh MSwo NOrn
	- 'Read' (f)	CWiW
	- 'Reeks' (f)	CWiW
	- 'Richartii' (f)	CWiW
	- 'Uralensis' (f)	CWiW
	pyrenaica	EWes
	radinostachya KR 7622	WPGP
	repens	SRms
§	- var. ***argentea***	CRos EHyd ELan EWes LRHS MMuc MRav SCob SPer WFar
	- 'Armando'PBR	WFar
	reticulata ♀H7	EBee NBir NSla WAbe WFar
§	- subsp. ***nivalis***	EPot
	retusa	NBir
	rosmarinifolia misapplied	see *S. elaeagnos* subsp. *angustifolia*
	rosmarinifolia L.	EPfP NLar SCob
	× ***rubens***	see *S.* × *fragilis*
	× ***rubra***	CWiW
	- 'Abbey's Harrison' (f)	CWiW
	- 'Continental Osier' (f)	CWiW
	- 'Eugenei' (m)	ECrN MBlu
	- 'Fidkin' (f)	CWiW
	- 'Harrison's' (f)	CWiW
	- 'Harrison's Seedling A' (f)	CWiW
	- 'Mawdesley'	CWiW
	- 'Mawdesley Seedling A' (f)	CWiW
	- 'Pyramidalis'	CWiW
I	'Salix Red'	WJPR
§	× ***sepulcralis*** 'Aokautere' (m)	CWiW
	- 'Caradoc'	CWiW
§	- var. ***chrysocoma*** ♀H5	Widely available
	- 'Dart's Snake' (m)	ELan EPPr EShb MAsh MRav NLar WCot WFar
§	- 'Erythroflexuosa' (m) ♀H5	CBcs CBod CEnd EBee ELan EPPr EPfP LRHS MAsh MGos MMuc NOra NOrn SCob SEND SGol SGsty SLim SPer SPoG WCFE WMat
	serpyllifolia	GKev
	- 'Chamonix'	NSla
	serpyllum	see *S.* × *fragilis* var. *furcata*
	'Setsuka'	see *S. udensis* 'Sekka'
	subopposita	ELan MGil MMuc SBrt
	× ***tetrapla*** 'Hutchinson's Nigricans'	CNat
	triandra	WMou
	- 'Black German' (m)	CWiW
	- 'Black Hollander' (m)	CWiW NLar
	- 'Black Maul'	CWiW
	- 'Grisette de Falaise'	CWiW
	- 'Grisette Droda' (f)	CWiW
	- 'Long Bud'	CWiW
	- 'Noir de Challans'	CWiW
	- 'Noir de Touraine'	CWiW
	- 'Noir de Villaines' (m)	CWiW WJPR
	- 'Rouge d'Orléans'	EBtc
	- 'Sarda d'Anjou'	CWiW
	- 'Whissander'	CWiW
	udensis 'Golden Sunshine'PBR	CRos EBee EHyd EMil EPfP LRHS MAsh MMrt MPkF NEoE NRHS SEdd SPer SSta
§	- 'Sekka' (m)	CBcs MBlu MMuc NBir WMou
	uva-ursi	WAbe
	viminalis	CCVT CDoC CLnd CMac EPfP LBuc MMuc SCob SEWo SVic WJPR WMou WSFF
	- 'Green Gotz'	CWiW
	vitellina 'Pendula'	see *S. alba* 'Tristis' ambig.
	'Yelverton'	see *S. alba* var. *vitellina* 'Yelverton'

Salpiglossis (*Solanaceae*)

sinuata Royale Series ♀H2	LCro LOPS

Salvia ✿ (*Lamiaceae*)

CD&R 1141	SPin
CD&R 1162	SPhx

	CD&R 1495	SPin
	PC&H 226	SPin
	from Catamarca, Argentina	CFoP SDys SEdd
	absconditiflora	SPin XSen
	acerifolia	SDys SPin
	acetabulosa	see *S. multicaulis*
	adenophora	SPin
	aethiopis	EWes SPhx
I	'African Sky'	CBod CCBP CFoP CSam ECre EHyd EPPr MAvo MCot MHer MPie NRHS SBut SDys SEdd SIvy SMHy SPhx SPin WAvo WGrn WOut
§	***africana***	CFoP EBee SEdd SPin
	africana-caerulea	see *S. africana*
	africana-lutea	see *S. aurea*
	agnes	SDys SPin
	albicaulis	SPin
	'Alegría'	CFoP SDys
	algeriensis	LRHS SPhx
	'Allen Chickering'	SDys
	altimitrata	see *S. lasiantha*
	amarissima	CFoP SPin
	- 175 **new**	SEdd
	'Amber'	IMou LPla SPin
	ambigens	see *S. guaranitica* 'Blue Enigma'
	'Amena' **new**	SPin
	'Amistad'^{PBR} 🏆^{H3}	Widely available
	'Amparito'	XSen
	ampelophylla	SDys
	- B&SWJ 10751	SPin
§	***amplexicaulis***	CFoP EWld LPla MMuc NLar SRms XSen
	amplifrons	SPin
	angustifolia Cav.	see *S. reptans*
	angustifolia Mich.	see *S. azurea*
	'Anna'	SDys
	'Anthony Parker'	CFoP CSam WOut
	apiana	EWld SPhx SPin SPlb SRms SVen XSen
	arborescens **new**	SPin
	(Arctic Blaze Series) ARCTIC BLAZE FUCHSIA ('Novasalfuc')	XSen
	- ARCTIC BLAZE PURPLE ('Novasalpur')	XSen
	- ARCTIC BLAZE RED ('Novasalred')	XSen
	argentea 🏆^{H4}	CBcs CBod CDor CFoP CRos CSpe ECha EHyd ELan EPfP LRHS NRHS SPer SPhx WKif WOut WSMil XSen
	arizonica	CSam EWld MAsh SDys SIvy SPin WSHC
	aspera	SPin
	atrocyanea	CFoP CSam CSpe ECre EWes EWld MAsh MAvo MGil SDys SIvy SMHy SPin WAvo WHal WKif
	atropatana	SMHy SPin WCot
	aucheri	CFoP SPin
§	***aurea***	CBcs CBod CFoP CSpe EBee SPin SPlb XLum
	- 'Kirstenbosch'	CAby CFoP ECtt EWld SDys SEdd WCot WKif WOut
	aurita	CFoP SPin
	- var. ***galpinii***	SPin
§	***azurea***	NBPC SBrt SPhx SPin XSen
	- var. ***grandiflora***	SPin WCot
	bacheriana	see *S. buchananii*
	'Ballerina'	XSen
§	***barrelieri***	CFoP ESwi SPin
	'Bee's Bliss'	XSen
	'Belhaven'	EBee SRms WOut
	benthamiana	SDys SPin
	bicolor	see *S. barrelieri*
	biserrata	CFoP SPin
	BLACK & BLOOM ('Balsaloom') **new**	CDoC CRos
	'Black Knight'	CFoP MAsh
	blancoana	see *S. lavandulifolia* subsp. *blancoana*
	blepharophylla	EWld MHer MSCN WAvo XSen
	- 'Diablo'	ECtt
	- 'Painted Lady'	MAsh SDys SPin
	'Bleu Armor'^{PBR}	SPhx XSen
	'Blue Merced'	SDys
	'Blue Moon'	SDys
	'Blue Note'^{PBR}	CBod CDow CFoP CMea CRos CSpe CWGN CWld EBee ECtt EHyd ELan ELon IPot LCro LLWG LOPS LRHS MHol MPri NDov NRHS SEND SEdd SPoG SRkn WAvo WCot
	'Blue Sky'	EWld
	bogotensis	CFoP SPin
	bowleyana	CFoP SPin
	brandegeei	CFoP SPin
	brevilabra	SPin
	brevipes	SPin
	'Bright Eyes' (Suncrest Series)	CWGN IPot
	broussonetii	CFoP EBee SPin
§	***buchananii*** 🏆^{H2}	CFoP CSam MAsh MHer MRav SDys SPin SRkn WKif
	bulleyana misapplied	see *S. flava* var. *megalantha*
	bulleyana Diels	CBcs CExl EWes GPSL MMuc NQui
	- 'Blue Lips'	CBod EBee ECtt IPot MHol
	bullulata	SPin
	- pale-blue-flowered	CFoP CSam CSpe SDys SPin
	cacaliifolia 🏆^{H2}	CExl CFoP CWCL EBee ECtt EWld MAsh MHer SDys SPin SRkn WAvo
	caerulea misapplied	see *S. guaranitica*
	caerulea L.	see *S. africana*
	caespitosa	SPin XSen
	calolophos	SPin
	campanulata B&SWJ 9232	WCru
	- GWJ 9294	WCru
	- var. ***hirtella*** GWJ 9397	WCru
	canariensis	CFoP SPin WCot
	- f. ***albiflora***	CFoP EBee
	- f. ***candidissima***	CFoP SPin
	candelabrum 🏆^{H3}	CFis CFoP CSpe ECre EWes MHer SPhx SPin WKif XSen
	canescens	XSen
	cardinalis	see *S. fulgens*
	cardiophylla	SPin
	carnea	CFoP MAsh SPin
	- from Valle de Bravo, Mexico	SDys
	- var. ***carnea***	SPin
	caudata	SPin
	'Cavalieri d'Alto'	MAvo SPhx
	'Cavaliero Celeste'	SDys
	caymanensis	CFoP
§	***chamaedryoides***	ELan MAsh SBrt SIvy SPhx SPin XSen
	- var. ***isochroma***	EBee EPfP MAsh SDys WPGP XSen
	- 'Marine Blue'	MAsh MCot
	- silver-leaved	CSpe SEdd SPhx SPin XLum
	chamelaeagnea	CFoP EPPr SDys SEdd SPin XSen
	chapalensis	SPin
	'Cherbourg'	XSen
	'Cherry Queen'	CWGN MAsh WOut
	chiapensis	CFoP MAsh SDys SPin

chionophylla	CFoP SPin
'Christine Yeo'	CElw EBee ECtt ELon EPri MAsh SDys SEND SPin WAvo WGrn WHil WKif XSen
'Christopher Fairweather'	ECtt
chrysophylla	SDys SPin
'Château Cathare' **new**	XSen
cinnabarina	SPin
cleistogama misapplied	see *S. glutinosa*
clevelandii	MHer SPin
- 'Winnifred Gilman'	SDys
clinopodioides	EBee SDys SPin
'Clotted Cream'	CBcs CDoC EPfP WFar WMal
coahuilensis misapplied	see *S. greggii* × *serpyllifolia*
coahuilensis ambig.	MAsh SIvy SLon SRkn WSHC XLum
coccinea 'Coral Nymph' (Nymph Series)	CFoP
- 'Forest Fire'	CFoP
cocuyana B&SWJ 14861	WCru
concolor misapplied	see *S. guaranitica*
concolor Lamb. ex Benth.	SDys SIvy SPin
confertiflora	CBcs CBod CExl CFoP CSam CSpe CWCL EBee ECre ECtt IPot MAsh MHer MHol SDix SDys SEdd SIvy SPhx SPin SPlb SRkn SVen WAvo WFar WHer WKif WOld WPGP
congestiflora **new**	CFoP
corrugata	CBcs CBod CElw CFoP CTsd EBee ECtt LRHS MAsh MCot MHer SDys SIvy SPhx SPin WFar
'Crazy Dolls'	ECtt SDys SIvy
'Crème Caramel'	CFoP EBee ECtt MAsh MAvo MCot SDys
'Cristina Bugatti' **new**	CFoP
cruickshanksii	SPin
cryptantha	SPin
'Crystal Blue' **new**	CWGN LCro LOPS SHar
cuatrecasana	CFoP SPin
curviflora	CElw CFoP CSam CSpe EWld IPot MAsh SDys SEle SGro SIvy SPin WAvo WOut
- 'Tubular Bells'	WFar
cuspidata subsp. ***gilliesii***	SPin
- subsp. ***rosea***	SPin
cyanescens	CFoP EPot SPin XSen
cyanicalyx	CFoP SDys SPin
cyclostegia	CExl
daghestanica	EBee GKev SPhx SPin
'Dancing Dolls'	CWGN IPot XSen
I ***dangitalis***	SPin
- SDR 4332	CExl
darcyi misapplied	see *S. roemeriana*
darcyi J. Compton	CExl CFoP ELan EWes MCot SDys SPin WSHC XLum
davidsonii	SPin
'Day Glow'	ECtt SAdn
densiflora	SPin
deserta	GQue LRHS SBrt SPhx SPin WCot
desoleana	SPin
'Didi'	NDov
digitaloides BWJ 7777	SPin
discolor	CFoP CSpe ECtt EWld MAsh MHer SDys SPin WAvo WOld WTyc
disermas	CFoP SPin SPlb
disjuncta	SBrt SPin
dolichantha	NLar SPin
dolomitica	CFoP SPin
dombeyi	CAby CFoP CSam EBee ECre EWld SDys SPin WAvo WPGP
dominica	SPin
dorisiana	MAsh MHer SDys SPin SVen
'Dorset Wonder'	NDov
durifolia	CFoP
'Dyson's Crimson'	CBod CDoC CFoP CSde ECtt ELan ELon LPot MCot SDys WAul WTre
'Dyson's Gem'	CSpe ECtt MAvo SDys WTre
'Dyson's Joy' 🏆^{H3}	CBcs CDoC CRos ECtt EPPr MAvo MCot MHer SDys SEdd SIvy SRkn WKif
eigii	SPin
eizi-matudae	CFoP SDys SPin
§ ***elegans***	CBor CLau EWes EWhm IDee IPot NPol NWad SEdi SPin WFar WHer WOld WOut WSHC XLum XSen
- 'Golden Delicious'	CAby CBod CFoP EMor ENfk EWes MBriF SRms WFar WSMil
- 'Honey Melon'	CFoP EBou ENfk MAsh SDys
- 'Scarlet Pineapple'	CBod CExl CRos ELan ENfk EWld GPoy MCot MHer MNHC SDys SIvy SRms SVen WHer WJek
- 'Sonoran Red'	SDys
- 'Tangerine'	CBod CLau CTsd ENfk EWhm LCro LOPS MHer MNHC NQui SPin SRms WJek
EMBER'S WISH ('Sal 0101'PBR)	Widely available
'Endless Love'	EBee NDov SIvy SRms
'Eveline'	CFoP CKno CMac CWGN EBee ECtt EHyd EPfP LRHS NLar SHar SRms STPC
excelsa	SPin
exserta	EBee SPin
fallax	see *S. roscida*
farinacea 'Fairy Queen' **new**	SDys
- 'Midnight Candle'	CCht ELan LRHS NRHS
- 'Rhea'	SPoG
- 'Strata'	SPoG
'Fire Dancer' (Suncrest Series) **new**	XSen
'Flamenco Rose' (Suncrest Series)	CRos XSen
§ ***flava*** var. ***megalantha***	CAby CBod CFoP EHyd LRHS LSRN NRHS SPin XSen
florida	SPin
'Flower Child'	CSpe ECtt IPot SDys WFar
forreri	EBee MAsh NDov SDys SEdd SIvy SPin
- 'Karen Dyson'	SDys
§ ***forsskaolii***	CBod CCBP CElw CExl CFoP CSam EMor EPfP GAbr GKev MMuc MNrw MRav NChi NLar NQui NSti SAko SEND SPin SPtp WCAu WCot WFar WTre XLum XSen
- white-flowered	CFoP EBee
§ ***fruticosa***	EHyd LRHS SLon SPhx SPin SRms XAbr XSen
§ ***fulgens*** 🏆^{H3}	CFoP CRos MAsh SDys SPin SRkn WFar WOut
- from Mount Popocatépetl, Mexico	SPin
- green calyx **new**	CFoP
gachantivana	CFoP SEdd SPin
gesneriiflora	ECtt EWld SPin
- mountain form	ECre SDys SEdd
- 'Tequila'	WOut
'Gigi' **new**	WFar
glabrescens	SPin
- B&SWJ 11152	WCru

*	- var. ***robusta*** B&SWJ 11147	WCru
	glechomifolia	SPin
§	***glutinosa***	CBod CFoP CMac CSpe EBee EHyd EWld GWyn IMou LRHS MMuc MNrw NBro NLar NSti SIvy SPin SPtp WCAu WHil XLum XSen
	gracilis	SPin
	grahamii	see *S. microphylla* var. *microphylla* 'Newby Hall'
	'Great Comp'	NDov SDys
	greggii	CRos EHyd EPfP EWes LPot LRHS NRHS SPlb SRms WKif XLum
	- CD&R 1148	SDys
	- 'Alba'	CFoP XLum XSen
	- 'Blush Pink'	see *S. microphylla* 'Blush Pink'
	- 'Caramba' (v)	CDow LRHS
§	- 'Desert Blaze' (v)	CRos CWGN EAJP ECtt EHyd ELan EPfP LRHS MAsh MRav NRHS SDys SEdd SLon SPoG WAvo WGrn XLum
	- 'Devon Cream'	see *S. greggii* 'Sungold'
	- 'Diane'	MAsh
	- 'Emperor'	CWGN EBee EWes IPot MBel SEle SIvy WFar
	- 'Flame'	CWGN
	- 'Icing Sugar'PBR	CBod CDoC CFoP CLau CRos CWGN CWld EBee ECtt EHyd ELan ENfk EPfP LCro LOPS LPot LRHS MAsh MAvo MCot MHol MSpe NDov NRHS SDys SEle SIvy SRkn WCav WKif
	- 'Lara'	LEdu MAvo
	- 'Lipstick'	CExl ECtt EHyd GWyn LCro LOPS MAsh NRHS
	- 'Magenta'	MAvo SPin WHil
	- 'Peach' misapplied	see *S.* × *jamensis* 'Pat Vlasto'
	- 'Peach'	CFoP CWGN EPfP MAsh SDys SPin XLum
	- 'Pink Preference'	CFoP MAsh SDys
	- 'Raspberry Red'	XLum
	- 'Rose Pink' **new**	CRos
	- 'Sierra San Antonio'	see *S.* × *jamensis* 'Sierra San Antonio'
	- 'Sparkler'	see *S. greggii* 'Desert Blaze'
	- 'Stormy Pink'	CSam CSpe ECtt IPot MAsh MBriF MCot MPie WFar WKif WTre
§	- 'Sungold'	CRos CWGN ECtt EHyd EPfP LRHS MAsh SDys SPhx WFar XSen
	- variegated (v)	XSen
	- yellow-flowered	XLum
	greggii × ***lycioides***	see *S. greggii* × *serpyllifolia*
§	***greggii*** × ***serpyllifolia***	CFoP CSam CSpe SDys SPin
	guadalujarensis	SPin
§	***guaranitica***	ECtt MHer SPin WKif WPGP WTre XLum
	- 'Argentina Skies'	CDow CFoP ECtt EPPr SDys SIvy SPin
	- 'Black and Blue'	Widely available
§	- 'Blue Enigma' 🏆H3	CAby CBod CDow CExl CFoP CRos CWGN EBee ECha ECtt EHyd ELan EPfP LRHS MAsh MGos MPie MRav MSpe NRHS SDix SDys SGbt SIvy SPer SPin WGwG WSpi XLum XSen
	- 'Costa Rica Blue'	SDys SIvy WKif
	- 'Indigo Blue'	MAsh
	- 'Midnight'	CFoP CSpe
	- purple-flowered	CFoP SDys
	- small form	CBct
	- 'Super Trouper'	IPot SDys
	- violet-flowered	CFoP SDys
	'Guarini'	SDys
	haematodes	see *S. pratensis* Haematodes Group
	haenkei	CElw SPin
	- 'Prawn Chorus'	MAsh
	'Hannah'	MAvo
	heldreichiana	SPin XSen
	henryi	SPin
	hians	CBod CFoP ESwi ILea LPot SRms
	- CC 1787	CExl
	hierosolymitana	EBee EHyd LRHS NRHS SPhx SPin WHil XSen
	hispanica misapplied	see *S. lavandulifolia*
	holwayi	SDys SPin
	horminum	see *S. viridis* var. *comata*
§	'Hot Lips' 🏆H5	Widely available
	hypargeia	SPin
	'I Cavalieri del Tau'	SDys WFar
	inconspicua	SPin
	'Indiansummer'	SDys
	indica	CFoP LRHS
	'Indigo Spires'	CDow CExl CFoP CMea CSam CSpe CWGN ECre ECtt EPfP IMou MAsh NDov SDix SDys SEle SPhx SPin WAvo WFar WKif WOld XLum
	interrupta	EWld MCot SEdd SPhx SPin WOut XSen
	involucrata 🏆H3	CAby MCot NBro SDys SPin SVen WGrn WSHC
	- 'Bethellii' 🏆H3	CBod CFoP CSde CTsd CWCL EBee ECtt ELan EPfP EWes EWld LRHS MAsh MHer MNrw MPie SDix SDys SEdd SPin SRkn WFar WKif WSHC WSpi XLum
	- 'Boutin' 🏆H3	CFoP LPla MAsh SDys SEle SPin
§	- 'Hadspen'	CFoP CRHN CSam CSpe EPPr EWes SIvy SPin WAvo WOut
	- 'Mrs Pope'	see *S. involucrata* 'Hadspen'
	- 'Pink Icicles'	SDys
	involucrata × ***wagneriana***	SDys
	iodantha	CFoP SPin
	× ***jamensis***	MAsh WHil
	- 'Amarillo'	SDys
	- 'California Sunset'	IPot MAsh SDys
	- 'Dark Dancer'	MAsh SDys SEdd WHil
	- 'Devantville'	XLum
	- 'Dysons' Orangy Pink'	CSpe MAvo NDov SDys
	- 'El Durazno'	XSen
	- 'Flammenn'PBR	CRos EHyd LRHS NRHS XSen
	- 'Golden Girl'	CFoP CSpe CWGN EBee WHil WSHC
	- (Heatwave Series) 'Heatwave Blast'PBR **new**	XSen
	- - HEATWAVE BLAZE ('Eggben005')	EBee XSen
	- - 'Heatwave Glimmer'PBR	CRos CSpe MCot SPin XSen
	- - 'Heatwave Glitter'PBR **new**	XSen
	- - HEATWAVE SCORCHER **new**	CFoP
	- - HEATWAVE SPARKLE ('Eggben004') **new**	XSen
	- 'James Compton'	XSen
	- 'Javier' 🏆H5	CSpe EWld GBin MAsh SDys SPin
§	- 'Jeremy' **new**	CRos ECtt SDys SRms
	- 'Kentish Pink'	SDys SEdd SIvy
	- 'La Luna'	CSam CSpe ECtt EPPr MAsh MPie MRav NDov WSHC XLum XSen
	- 'La Siesta'	MAsh MPie XSen
	- 'La Tarde'	CTri MAsh
	- 'Lemon Light'	XSen

	- 'Los Lirios'	CSpe CTri MCot WAvo WHil
	- 'Maraschino'	ECtt EHyd EPfP LRHS MAsh MBel SDys SIvy SRms WHil XLum
	- 'Melen'[PBR]	EBee SRms XSen
	- 'Moonlight Over Ashwood' (v)	MAsh WSHC
	- 'Moonlight Serenade'	MAsh SDys
§	- 'Pat Vlasto'	CFoP SPin
	- 'Peter Vidgeon' ♀H5	CDow CFoP CRos CWGN EBee ECha EHyd EPPr EPfP GBin LRHS MAsh MBriF MCot MPri NRHS SDys SEdd SIvy SPhx SPin WAvo WMal WPGP WSHC
	- PINK LIPS	see *S.* × *jamensis* 'Jeremy'
	- 'Pleasant Pink'	MAsh
	- 'Pluenn'[PBR]	CRos EHyd LRHS LSRN NRHS XSen
	- 'Raspberry Royale'	CRos ECtt EHyd EPfP IPot LRHS MAsh MHer MPie NRHS SDys SEdd SPin XLum XSen
	- 'Red Velvet'	EBee ECtt MAsh MCot SDys SEdd SPhx WAvo WBrk WHrl WLov WSHC
	- RÊVE ROUGE ('Fauresal02'[PBR])	XSen
	- 'Señorita Leah'	CWGN ENfk MAsh MCot NDov SDys WFar WMal
	- 'Shell Dancer'[PBR]	CRos XSen
§	- 'Sierra San Antonio'	CRos EHyd EPfP LRHS MAsh NRHS SDys XLum XSen
	- 'Stormy Sunrise'	SDys
§	- 'Trebah'	CDow ECre MAsh MCot MPie MSpe SDys WKif
	- 'Trenance'	ECre ELon MHer WMal
	- VIOLETTE DE LOIRE ('Barsal'[PBR])	ECul LRHS LSRN SRms XSen
	'James Curry' **new**	CFoP
	japonica var. ***formosana*** NMWJ 14469	WCru
	'Jean's Jewel'	CFoP SDys SPin
	'Jean's Purple Passion'	MAsh SDys
	'Jezebel' ♀H3	CRos EHyd EPfP GBin LRHS NRHS SDys SPin
	'Joan'	CFoP CSam CWGN MAsh MBriF MCot SDys SPin
	judaica	XSen
	jurisicii	EHyd EPfP LRHS SPin XLum XSen
	karwinskyi	SDys SPin
	karwinskyi* × *univerticillata	SDys
	keerlii	SPin
	koyamae	CFoP EBee SPin
	- B&SWJ 10919	WCru
	'La Mancha'	ECtt SDys WFar
	'Lalarsha'	ELan MAsh MAvo MCot NDov SDys
	lanceolata	CFoP CSpe SPin WOut
	languidula	SPin
§	***lasiantha***	SPin
§	***lavandulifolia***	CRos EBee EHyd ELan EPfP EWes GPoy LRHS MAsh MHer MNHC MRav SBut SGro SPin SRms WHoo WJek WKif XLum XSen
§	- subsp. ***blancoana***	ECha SPhx SPin XSen
	- subsp. ***gallica***	XSen
	- subsp. ***pyrenaeorum***	SPin
	- 'Roquefure'	XSen
	- subsp. ***vellerea***	XSen
	lavanduloides	CFoP SPin
	'Lavender Dilly Dilly'	MAvo WMal
	lemmonii	see *S. microphylla* var. *wislizeni*
	'Lemon Pie'	CFoP SDys SPin WAvo
	leptophylla	see *S. reptans*
	leucantha ♀H2	CCBP CFoP CMCN ECre ELan EWld MAsh MGil MHer MNrw MPie MRav SPin SPlb SRkn SVen WFar WHer WKif WOld WOut
	- 'Eder' (v)	MAsh SDys WOld
	- 'Midnight'	CSam
	- 'Purple Velvet'	CFoP CSpe EBee ECtt MAsh MHer SDix SDys SEdd SIvy WAvo
	- 'Santa Barbara'	CFoP MAsh SDys WFar
	- 'White Mischief'	SEdd
	leucocephala	CFoP SDys SPin
	leucophylla NNS 01-375	SPin
	libanensis	SDys SPin
	littae	SDys SPin
	'Little Azur'	ECtt SDys
	longispicata	SPin
	longistyla	SDys SVen
	LOVE AND WISHES ('Serendip6'[PBR])	Widely available
	lycioides misapplied	see *S. greggii* × *serpyllifolia*
	lycioides A. Gray	CFoP SDys WAvo
	lyrata	EBee
	- 'Burgundy Bliss'	see *S. lyrata* 'Purple Knockout'
§	- 'Purple Knockout'	CRos EHyd EPfP LPot LRHS NRHS SPin XSen
	- 'Purple Vulcano'	see *S. lyrata* 'Purple Knockout'
	macellaria misapplied	see *S. microphylla*
	macrophylla	SDys SPin
	- Cally selection	SPin
	- purple-leaved	CFoP SDys
	macrosiphon	SPin
	'Madeline'[PBR]	CBod CFoP CWGN EHyd EPfP GMaP LCro LOPS LRHS LSou MHol MNrw NDov SPer SPin STPC WHil WTyc
	madrensis	CFoP SDys SPin
	- 'Dunham'	EWld
	'Magenta Magic'	CFoP IPot SDys SPin
	'Magic Potion'	CWGN
	'Mas de Lunès'	XSen
	melaleuca B&SWJ 14863	WCru
	mellifera	CFoP SPin
	mexicana 'Limelight'	CFoP
	- var. ***minor***	EWld SDys SIvy SPin
I	***miahuatlanensis***	SPin
§	***microphylla***	CBod CMac CTri EWes EWhm MBow MHer SVen XLum
	- CD&R 1141	SPin
	- 'Albert' **new**	LCro LOPS
	- 'Belize'	MAsh
	- 'Blind Faith'	MAvo
	- 'Blue Monrovia'	LRHS MRav SEdd
§	- 'Blush Pink'	CFoP MAvo SDys
	- 'Bordeaux'	CFoP CSpe ILea SIvy
	- 'Cerro Potosí' ♀H4	Widely available
	- 'Chalk White'	SMHy SPhx
	- 'Hot Lips'	see *S.* 'Hot Lips'
	- 'Kew Red'	MNrw SPin WAvo
I	- 'Lutea'	CDow ENfk MAsh SDys
	- 'Maroon'	CFoP MAvo MCot SDys SEdd
§	- var. ***microphylla***	CDow CFoP CRHN CTri ECtt ENfk EPPr LCro LOPS LSRN MCot MHer MNHC MRav SEND SPin SRkn SRms SVic XLum
	- - 'La Foux'	SPhx WAvo
§	- - 'Newby Hall'	CBod CSam CSde ECtt EWes LRHS MAvo NWad SPhx WSHC
	- var. ***neurepia***	see *S. microphylla* var. *microphylla*
	- 'Norwell'	MNrw

- 'Orange Door'	SDys
- orange-red-flowered	MRav
- 'Oregon Peach'	CRos EHyd EPfP LRHS NRHS
- 'Pink Blush'	CBod CRos EAJP ECtt EHyd ELan ELon EPfP LRHS MAsh MCot MHer MNHC SEND SEdd SPin SRkn WAvo WHil WHoo WKif WSHC XSen
- 'Pleasant View'	WHil
- 'Robin's Pride'	ECtt SDys
- 'Rodbaston Rosy Cheeks'	MSCN WOut
- 'Ruby Star'	ECtt IPot
- 'San Carlos Festival'	MAsh SDys SPin
- 'Trelawny Rose Pink'	see *S.* 'Trelawney'
- 'Trelissick Creamy Yellow'	see *S.* 'Trelissick'
- 'Trewithen Cerise'	see *S.* 'Trewithen'
- 'Wendy's Surprise'	CWGN ECtt EWld MCot SDys
- 'Wild Watermelon'	CWGN EBee ECtt EWes GPSL IPot MAsh MAvo MHer NQui SDys SIvy WGrn WHil WHrl
§ - var. ***wislizeni***	CElw SPhx
- 'Wollerton White'	MCot MRav SDys
miltiorrhiza	CSpe SPin WHer XLum XSen
miniata	CFoP SIvy SPin
(Mirage Series) MIRAGE BERRY RED ('Balmircher') **new**	CBod WFar
- MIRAGE CREAM ('Balmiream') **new**	WFar WHil
- MIRAGE DEEP PURPLE ('Balmirdepur') **new**	CBod WFar
- MIRAGE NEON ROSE ('Balmirpink') **new**	WHil
- MIRAGE SOFT PINK ('Balmirsopin') **new**	CBod WFar WHil
misella	SPin
mocinoi	SPin
moorcroftiana	SPin
moschata	SPin
muelleri misapplied	see *S. greggii* × *serpyllifolia*
muelleri ambig.	CPla CSpe NDov
muirii	SPin
'Mulberry Jam'	CCBP CDow CSam EAJP ECtt ELan EPfP EWes MAsh MCot SDys SEle SIvy SPin SRkn WFar WKif
§ ***multicaulis*** ♀H3	MAsh SPin XSen
munzii	CFoP SDys SPin
MYSTIC SPIRES BLUE ('Balsalmisp'PBR)	CFoP CSpe CWGN ECtt EPfP MBros MHer NRHS SPoG
'Nachtvlinder' ♀H5	Widely available
namaensis	CFoP SPin WKif
nana	CFoP
- B&SWJ 10272	SPin
- 'Curling Waves'PBR	CBod ECtt LSou MHol
napifolia	EBee EWes LPot LRHS MMuc MNrw NLar
'Nel'	EBee WMal
nemorosa	LSRN LSun SPhx SPin SRms XLum XSen
- 'Amethyst' ♀H7	CRos CWGN EBee ECha EHyd ELon EPed EPfP LCro LOPS LRHS MBel MHol MRav MSpe MTis NDov NRHS SCob SPer SPhx SPin SRms WCAu WCot XSen
- 'Blaureiter'	EBee
- BLUE BOUQUETTA ('Alkif')	CWGN LSou MHol MPri NBPC NLar SDys SPad WNPC
- BLUE MARVEL ('Balsalarv'PBR)	LCro LOPS LRHS LSou MHol SCob SPoG SRms
- BLUE MOUND	see *S.* × *sylvestris* 'Blauhügel'
- 'Bordeau Steel Blue'	CRos EHyd ELon LRHS NRHS SRms
- 'Caradonna' ♀H7	Widely available
- 'Caramia'	CKno
- EAST FRIESLAND	see *S. nemorosa* 'Ostfriesland'
- 'Little Friesland'	CRos EHyd NRHS
- 'Lubecca' ♀H7	CBod CRos CSam ECtt EHyd EPed EPfP LRHS LSou MAsh MBel NDov NGdn NLar SPer SPhx WCAu WFar XSen
- LYRICAL SILVERTONE ('Balyricsil'PBR)	CBod WFar
- LYRICAL WHITE	see *S. nemorosa* SENSATION WHITE
- MARCUS ('Haeumanarc'PBR)	CBod CRos EBee ECtt EHyd ELan ELon EPfP LRHS LSRN MBNS MRav MTin NRHS SAko SDys SPoG WFar
- 'New Dimension Blue'	WCav
- 'New Dimension Rose'	NLar
§ - 'Ostfriesland' ♀H7	Widely available
- 'Pink Beauty'	CRos EHyd LRHS NRHS
- 'Pink Friesland'PBR	CAby ECtt EPfP GMaP LSou NGdn NRHS SAko SCob WSpi
- 'Plumosa'	see *S. nemorosa* 'Pusztaflamme'
§ - 'Pusztaflamme' ♀H7	EBee ECha ECtt EPfP MRav SAko SEdd
- 'Rose Marvel' **new**	MHol
- 'Rose Queen'	CBod ELon EShb EWTr GMaP GWyn NBPC NBir NLar SCob SPhx WCot WFar XLum XSen
- 'Rosenwein'	CDor CRos EHyd EWTr GWyn LRHS NGdn NRHS SGbt SPhx XSen
- 'Schwellenburg'	CRos EAJP ECtt EWes LCro LRHS MHol NLar NRHS SAko
- (Sensation Series) SENSATION BLUE ('Florsalvioblu'PBR)	EHyd LRHS NRHS
- - SENSATION BLUE IMPROVED	EHyd LRHS
- - SENSATION DEEP BLUE ('Florsaldblue')	CRos EBee EHyd ELon LRHS LSou MBros NRHS
- - SENSATION DEEP ROSE ('Flor Sal Roz')	CBod CNor LRHS NRHS
- - SENSATION DEEP ROSE IMPROVED	EHyd LRHS SPoG
- - SENSATION MEDIUM PINK ('Florsalpi') **new**	CBod
- - SENSATION PINK	LRHS NRHS
- - SENSATION ROSE	CBod CRos EHyd LCro LOPS LRHS LSRN LSou MBel MHol MMrt NRHS SCob SHar SRms
§ - - SENSATION WHITE ('Florsalwhite')	CBod CRos CWGN EHyd GKev LRHS MBel MHol NRHS SCob WHil
§ - subsp. ***tesquicola***	NLar SPhx WFar
- 'Theodor'	ECtt
- 'Wesuwe'	ELon NDov
'Neon'	CFoP EBee SEdd SPin WAvo
neurepia	see *S. microphylla* var. *microphylla*
* ***nevadensis***	SPin
nilotica	SPin
nipponica	CFoP EBee SBrt
- B&SWJ 5829	SPin WCru
- var. ***trisecta***	SPin
nubicola	CExl GPoy
'Nuchi'	EHyd LRHS NRHS SDys SPoG
nutans	SPhx SPin XSen
officinalis	Widely available
- 'Albiflora'	CBcs MBriF SPin WJek XSen
- 'Aurea' ambig.	GPoy SCob
- 'Berggarten' ♀H5	CBod CCBP CLau ECha EWhm GBin MHer MRav SPhx SPin WHer WHil XLum XSen

- 'Bicolor'	SPin
- 'Blackcurrant'	CBod CLau WFar
§ - broad-leaved	CLau EMor MHer SEdi WJek
- 'Crispa'	XSen
- 'Grete Stolze'	SEND XSen
- 'Grower's Friend'	CTsd
§ - 'Icterina' (v) ♀H5	CBcs CBod CLau CTri EBee EBou ECha ELan ENfk EWhm GJos MAsh MGos MHer MMuc MNHC MRav MSwo SCob SEND SGol SPer SPoG SRms SVic WFar WJek WKif XLum XSen
- latifolia	see *S. officinalis* broad-leaved
- narrow-leaved	see *S. lavandulifolia*
- 'Nazareth'	XSen
- prostrata	see *S. lavandulifolia*
- 'Purpurascens' ♀H5	Widely available
- 'Robin Hill'	EHyd LRHS NRHS
- 'Rosea'	WOut
- 'Tricolor' (v)	CBcs CBod CRos CTri EBee EHyd ELan EMor ENfk EPfP EWhm GPoy MAsh MHer MNHC SCob SEdi SGol SPer SPoG SRms WFar WJek
- 'Variegata'	see *S. officinalis* 'Icterina'
- 'Würzburg'	XSen
ombrophila	SPin
omeiana	CFoP
- BWJ 8062	WCru
- 'Crûg Thundercloud'	WCru
oppositiflora misapplied	see *S. tubiflora*
oppositiflora ambig.	SDys SPin
orbignaei	SPin
'Orchid Glow' (Suncrest Series)	CRos CWGN IPot XSen
'Othello'	SDys
oxyphora	CAby CFoP MAsh MHer MPie SDys SEdd SIvy SPin WFar
pachyphylla	EHyd LRHS XSen
'Pakhuis Pass'	CFoP SPin
pallida	SEdd SPin
'Pam's Purple'	MAsh
'Pasadena'	SDys
§ ***patens*** ♀H3	CAby CFoP CRos CSpe EBee ECha ECtt EPfP LCro LOPS LRHS MAsh MHer MNHC MRav NGdn SDix SDys SEND SPer SPhx SPin SRms WFar WKif WSHC WSpi WWFP
- 'Alba' misapplied	see *S. patens* 'White Trophy'
- 'Blue Angel'	CCht CWGN EHyd EPfP EWes LEdu
- 'Cambridge Blue' ♀H3	CAby CExl CFoP CRos CSpe CWGN EBee ECtt EHyd ELan EPfP LRHS MAsh MHer MRav NLar NPer NRHS SDix SDys SPer SPhx WFar WSHC
- 'Chilcombe'	CAby SDys WOut
- 'Dot's Delight'	CExl CSpe ECtt IPot LRHS MAsh SDys SHar
- 'Guanajuato'	CExl CSBt CSam ECtt IPot MAsh NLar SDys SEdd SHar WKif WSHC
- 'Holbrook'	CSam
- large	CFoP CSpe
- light blue-flowered	EHyd LRHS NRHS
- OCEANA BLUE ('Salsyll')	EBee EWld
- 'Oxford Blue'	see *S. patens*
- (Patio Series) 'Patio Deep Blue'	CWGN EPfP MBros SPoG WHil
- - 'Patio Sky Blue'	WCav WHil WSpi
- 'Pink Ice'	EBee ECtt EWld SDys WOut
- 'Royal Blue'	see *S. patens*
§ - 'White Trophy'	CExl CFoP ECtt EWes LRHS SDys WOut
pauciserrata	SPin
'Peach Cobbler'	MAvo
'Peach Parfait'	EShb MAvo SDys WAvo
pennellii	SPin
'Penny's Smile'	CElw CMac ELon IPot MAsh MCot MSCN SDys SPhx SPin WFar WGrn WHil WKif WSHC
personata	SPin
'Peru Blue'	CFoP SDys
'Phyllis' Fancy'	CFoP CSam CSde CSpe CWGN EBee EWes EWld LPla MAsh MCot MHer NDov SDys SEdd SIvy SPhx SPin SPlb SRms WAvo WFar WHrl WKif
pinguifolia	SPin
'Pink Icing'	SPin
'Pink Lace'	ECtt SBut SDys
pisidica	SPin XSen
plectranthoides	SPin
polystachya	SEdd SPin
potentillifolia new	SPin
pratensis	CBee CCBP CWld EPfP GJos LCro LOPS MNHC MRav SPin SRms WCot WOut WWild XSen
- W&B BGH-3	WCot
- 'Dear Anja'	see *S.* × *sylvestris* 'Dear Anja'
§ - Haematodes Group ♀H7	MNrw SPin SRms
- 'Indigo' ♀H7	CAby CBod CRos ECtt EHyd ELon GMaP LCro LOPS LRHS MRav NLar NRHS SPhx SPoG WCot WGwG WPGP
- 'Lapis Lazuli'	EBee EWes LPla LRHS
- 'Pink Delight' PBR	CBod EBee ECtt EHyd EPfP EWTr LRHS NBPC NRHS SRms
- 'Rose Rhapsody' (Ballet Series)	CDor EPPr EPfP MMrt NLar SPhx XSen
- 'Rosea'	ECha
- 'Sky Dance' (Ballet Series)	SBut
- 'Swan Lake' (Ballet Series)	CDor EBee GWyn NLar SPhx SPlb WOut XSen
- 'Sweet Esmeralda' (Ballet Series)	CDor EBee NGdn SPhx XSen
- 'Twilight Serenade' (Ballet Series)	CDor EBee EBou ECtt ELan EPPr EPfP MWat SPhx WOut XSen
- 'White Swan'	MWat
aff. ***prattii*** new	EWld
procurrens	CFoP EBee SPin XSen
prunelloides	SPin
przewalskii	CExl CFoP CRos EHyd EWld LRHS NRHS SEdd SPin XSen
- ACE 1157	WCru
- BWJ 7920	WCru XLum
'Purple Majesty'	ECtt SDys WKif WSpi XLum
'Purple Queen'	CBod CElw CRos EAJP EBee EHyd ENfk EPfP EShb LRHS MCot NRHS SDys SEdd SEle WFar WHil
purpurea	LSRN
quitensis	SPin
'Radio Red'	WGrn WHil
radula	EBee SPin
'Raspberry Truffle'	SDys
raymondii subsp. ***raymondii***	CFoP SPin
recognita	EHyd LRHS SPhx XSen
recurva	SPin
'Red Swing' PBR	EBee EHyd LRHS NRHS
reflexa	SPin
regeliana misapplied	see *S. virgata* Jacq.

	regla	MAsh SDys SPin WPGP
	repens	SPin
§	***reptans***	SBrt SIvy SPin
	- from western Texas	SDys SEdd WCot WFar
	- 'Summer Skies' **new**	MSCN
	retinervia	SPin
	'Ribambelle' ♀H3	EAJP IPot MAsh MCot WHrl WMal XLum
	ringens	SPin XSen
	riparia misapplied	see *S. rypara*
	roborowskii	SPin
§	***roemeriana***	CSpe MAvo
	- 'Hot Trumpets'	EHyd LBuc LRHS NRHS
	- 'Red Dwarf'	CFoP
	'Rolando'	CFoP SDys
§	***roscida***	SPin
	'Royal Bumble' ♀H4	Widely available
	'Royal Crimson Distinction'PBR	EBee
	rubescens	SPin
	- B&SWJ 14368	EWld WCru
	- subsp. ***dolichothrix*** **new**	CFoP SPin
	rubiginosa	SPin
	runcinata	SPin
	rutilans	see *S. elegans*
§	***rypara***	SPin
	sagittata	CFoP EBee MHer SDix SPin
	'Saint Jean de Beauregard' **new**	WFar
	'Salmon Dance'	CBod CRos CSpe CWGN ECtt EHyd EMor IPot LCro LOPS LRHS MAvo NRHS WNPC
	scabra	CFoP EBee SPin WOut XSen
	'Scarlet Spires'	SPin
	schlechteri	SPin
	sclarea	CBod CHby EBou ECtt ENfk GPoy MNHC NLar SEdi SRms SVic WOut XAbr XLum XSen
	- var. ***turkestanica*** hort.	see *S. sclarea* var. *turkestaniana* 'Vatican Pink'
§	- var. ***turkestaniana*** 'Vatican Pink'	CDor CFoP CRos CSpe EAJP ECha EHyd EPfP EWTr LRHS LSRN LSun MRav NRHS SDix SEND SPer SPhx SRkn WKif XAbr XSen
§	- - 'Vatican White'	CFoP CPla CRos CSpe EAJP EBee EHyd LRHS NLar NRHS SPhx SWvt WLov XSen
	- white-bracted	see *S. sclarea* var. *turkestaniana* 'Vatican White'
	scutellarioides	SPin
	'Sebastian' **new**	CFoP
	selleana	SPin
	semiatrata misapplied	see *S. chamaedryoides*
	semiatrata ambig.	CFoP EWld SEdd SPhx
	semiatrata Zucc.	EPPr SPin
	serboana	EBee SAko WKif WPGP WSHC
	- B&SWJ 10236	WCru
	'Serenade'	CBod CSam EBee ELon MHol MTis NDov SDys WCot WHoo
	serpyllifolia	SPin
	- white-flowered	SPin
	sessei	SPin
	sessilifolia **new**	SPin
	setulosa	SPin
	'Shame'	MAvo NDov
	'Shy Ruby'	SPin
	sikkimensis	SPin
	'Silas Dyson'	CDow CFoP CRos CSam ECre ECtt EHyd ELan ELon EPfP IPot LRHS MAsh MAvo MCot MHer NDov NRHS SDys SIvy SPin SPoG WAvo WFar WKif WMal WSHC
	'Silke's Dream'	CFoP CRos CSam ECtt EHyd EPfP LRHS MAsh MCot MPie SDys SPin WAvo WMal XSen
	'Silke's Red'	SDys WFar
	sinaloensis	SPin
	'Smoke'	CSpe SDys
	somalensis	CFoP EBee SPin
	'Southern Belle'	SDys SPin
	spathacea 'Avis Keedy'	SPin
	sphacelioides	SPin
	splendens 'Jimi's Good Red'	SDys
	- 'Lighthouse Purple'	CSpe
	- 'Red Indian'	SDys
	- 'São Borja'	SDys WOld
	- 'Vanguard' ♀H3	MPri
§	- 'Van-Houttei' ♀H3	CFoP SDys
	'Spring King'	CKno SDys
	squalens	CFoP SPin
	stachydifolia	SPhx SPin WPGP
	- CDPR 3071	EBee WPGP
	- dark blue calyx	WPGP
	- lavender calyx	WPGP
§	***staminea***	CFoP SPin
	stenophylla	SPin
	'Stephanie'	SDys SPin
	stolonifera	CAby CFoP CSam ECre EWes MAsh MAvo MHer SDys SIvy SMHy SPhx SPin WAvo
	- 723 **new**	SEdd
	striata	SDys SPin
	- pink-flowered **new**	CFoP
	- red-flowered	CFoP SPin
	styphelus	CFoP SDys SEdd SPin
	- 619 **new**	SEdd
	subpalmatinervis	SPin
	subrotunda	CFoP SDys SPin
	- 'Caitymary' **new**	CFoP
	'Sue Templeton'	CFoP
	'Sunset Strip'	CDow SDys
	× ***superba***	CBod CRos EBee ECha ECtt EHyd ELan EPfP LRHS LSRN MWat NRHS SDix SGbt SPer SRms WCAu WHoo
	- 'Adora Blue'	LRHS
	- 'Adrian'	ECtt EHyd ELon EPfP LRHS LSRN SPoG WCot WSHC
	- 'Lyon Rose'	EBee EPfP
§	- 'Merleau'	CRos EHyd EMor LRHS SAko
	- 'Merleau Blue'	see *S.* × *superba* 'Merleau'
	- 'Merleau Pink'	EHyd LRHS
	- 'Merleau Rose'	EBee MRav SRms
*	- 'Rosea'	EBee
	- 'Rubin' ♀H7	ECtt NBre
I	- 'Superba'	CAby ECtt MRav SPhx SRkn
	× ***sylvestris***	LSRN SPin
§	- 'Blauhügel' ♀H7	CBod CDoC CRos CSam EAJP ECha ECtt EHyd ELan EPfP EShb GBin LCro LOPS LRHS MArl MAvo MHol MPri MRav MSpe NDov NRHS SCob SPer SPhx SRms WCAu WHoo XSen
§	- 'Blaukönigin'	CDor CNor CRos CSBt EHyd ELon EPfP GMaP LBuc LRHS NLar NRHS SPer SPlb SPoG SRms SSut SWvt WCot WFar WHil XLum
	- BLUE QUEEN	see *S.* × *sylvestris* 'Blaukönigin'
§	- 'Dear Anja'	CBod EBee ECtt LCro LOPS MHol NDov SPhx WCot

- 'Lye End' MRav WCot
- (Lyrical Series) LYRICAL BLUES ('Balyriclu'PBR) CBod WHil
- - LYRICAL ROSE ('Balyricose'PBR) CBod SPoG WHil

§ - 'Mainacht' ♀H7 Widely available
- MAY NIGHT see *S.* × *sylvestris* 'Mainacht'
- 'Negrito' EBee ECtt MAvo NLar
- 'Rhapsody in Blue'PBR CBod EPfP MBNS MHol MTis NLar WCot
- 'Rose Queen' CMac CRos CSBt ECha EHyd ELan ELon EMor EPfP EShb LCro LOPS LRHS MHol MRav NRHS NSti SCoo SGbt SPer SPhx SPoG SRms SWvt XLum XSen
- 'Rügen' CBod CRos EHyd ELon GQue LRHS NDov NRHS SAko WCAu
- 'Schneehügel' CBod CMac CRos EAJP EBee ECha ECtt EHyd ELan ELon EPPr EPfP GMaP GWyn LCro LOPS LRHS MBNS MBel MRav MSpe MTis NLar NRHS SPer WCAu XSen
- 'Tänzerin' ♀H7 EBee ECtt GBin LRHS MTis NDov NLar SAko SPhx
- 'Viola Klose' ♀H7 CBod CRos EBee ECha ECtt EHyd ELan EPed EPfP EShb IPot LCro LOPS LRHS LSRN LSou MCot NBPC NDov NGdn NLar NRHS SAko SPin SRms WAul

tachiei hort. see *S. forsskaolii*
taraxacifolia SPin XSen
tesquicola see *S. nemorosa* subsp. *tesquicola*
'Theresia' SDys
thymoides SPin WOut
tianschanica SPin
tiliifolia SPin SRms
tingitana CFoP SPin
tomentosa EBee SPin XSen
tortuosa SPin
transcaucasica see *S. staminea*
transsylvanica IMou SPin SRms XSen
- 'Blue Spire' SPhx SRkn
'Trebah Lilac White' see *S.* × *jamensis* 'Trebah'
§ 'Trelawney' ECtt EHyd EWld LRHS MCot MHer MHol MPie NRHS SGbt WGwG
§ 'Trelissick' EHyd LRHS MAsh MCot MHer MSpe NRHS SDys SEND SEle SIvy SPhx SRkn WHrl
§ 'Trewithen' CBod CExl ECre SIvy SPer XLum
trijuga SPin
triloba see *S. fruticosa*
tubifera SPin
§ ***tubiflora*** ♀H2 MAsh SPin
tuerckheimii **new** SPin
'Tutti Frutti' MAvo WHoo
uliginosa ♀H4 Widely available
- 'African Skies' CChe EWTr NRHS SPin WAvo
- 'Ballon Azul' CBod CSpe EBee ECtt ELan EMor EPPr EWes LRHS MAsh SDys SEle SPoG SPtp WLov WPGP WSHC WWFP
- 'Reach for the Skies' **new** SPtp
'Ultra Violet' CWGN
univerticillata SPin
urica CFoP SPin
- short SDys
'Valerie' MPie SDys
'Van-Houttei' see *S. splendens* 'Van-Houttei'
variana SPin
'Vatican City' see *S. sclarea* 'Vatican White'
vazquezii SPin
verbenaca MHer SPin WWild XSen
- pink-flowered WOut
verticillata CCBP EPfP LEdu NLar SBut SPin SRms WFar
§ - 'Alba' CDor CRos EBee EMor EPfP GQue LRHS MRav NGdn NLar NRHS SCob SPer SPin WOut XSen
- 'Hannay's Blue' EPPr GMaP LPla MAvo SMHy SPhx WCAu WFar WHrl
- 'Hannay's Purple' ECtt EPPr
- 'Purple Rain' Widely available
- 'Smouldering Torches' EBee MAvo NDov SCob SPhx
- 'White Rain' see *S. verticillata* 'Alba'
villicaulis see *S. amplexicaulis*
'Violin Music'PBR CBod EBee ECtt EHyd LRHS MSCN NRHS
§ ***virgata*** Jacq. CFoP EBee SPin XSen
- 'Alba' CFoP WHil
viridis CBod CHby MNHC SPin
- blue-flowered **new** LCro LOPS
- 'Blue Denim' LOPS
- Claryssa Series SRms
§ - var. ***comata*** CFoP MCot
- (Marble Arch Series) 'Marble Arch Blue' CSpe
- - 'Marble Arch White' **new** WFar
viscosa ambig. CFoP SBut
viscosa Jacq. SPin WOut
vitifolia CFoP CSpe SDys SEdd WAvo WOut
- B&SWJ 10236 SPin
wagneriana SPin
'Waverly' CFoP EBee EPPr EWTr EWld MAsh MBriF MHer MHol SDys SEdd SEle WOut
'Wendy's Wish'PBR CDoC CRos EBee ECtt EHyd ELan EPfP IPot LCro LRHS LSou MAsh MHol MPri MRav MSpe NDov NRHS SCob SDys SEdd SPoG SRkn SRms WNPC
× ***westerae*** CFoP SPin
- 'Petra' SDys
yunnanensis SPin
aff. ***yunnanensis*** SPin

Salvinia (*Salviniaceae*)

natans CBen LLWG XBlo

Sambucus ✿ (*Adoxaceae*)

'Black Cherry' **new** WCot
BLACK DIAMONDS ('Hyfdia') MPri
caerulea see *S. nigra* subsp. *caerulea*
'Chocolate Marzipan' WCot
coraensis see *S. williamsii* subsp. *coreana*
ebulus EBee EPPr LEdu NSti SMad WCot
formosana WCot
'Gate into Field' WCot
* ***himalayensis*** WCot
mexicana B&SWJ 10349 WCot
'Milk Chocolate' CBod GBin MPie SEdd SPad WCot
miquelii WCot
nigra CArg CBcs CCVT ECrN EPom GPoy LBuc SCob SEWo SPer SReu SVic WKor WMat WMou WSFF WTSh
- 'Albomarginata' see *S. nigra* 'Marginata'
- 'Ardwall' CAgr EPPr GBin WCot
- 'Aurea' CBcs CMac ELan EPom MMuc SCob SPer WCot
- 'Aureomarginata' (v) ECrN ELan EPPr MMuc MRav SEND WCot WFar

	- 'Bont Oosterwoldë'	WCot
	- 'Bradet'	CAgr WCot WFar
	- 'Broadway' (v)	WCot
	- 'Cae Rhos Lligwy'	CAgr WCot WHer
§	- subsp. ***caerulea***	EBee SMad WCot WKor WPGP
	- subsp. ***canadensis***	SPhx WKor
	- - 'Adams' (F)	WCot
	- - 'Aurea'	WCot
	- - 'Johns'	CAgr WCot
	- - 'Maxima'	SDix SMad WCot
	- - 'Rubra'	WCot
	- - 'York' (F)	CAgr WCot
	- 'Castledean'	WCot
	- 'Dart's Greenlace'	WCot
	- 'Dolomite' (v)	WCot
	- 'Donau'	CAgr WCot
	- 'Frances' (v)	EPPr WCot
	- 'Franzi'	CAgr WCot
	- 'Fructuluteo'	WCot
	- 'Godshill' (F)	CAgr WCot
	- GOLDEN TOWER ('Jdeboer001'[PBR])	CDoC MMrt SPoG
	- 'Haidegg 17' (F)	CAgr
	- 'Haschberg'	CAgr SVic WCot
	- 'Heterophylla'	see *S. nigra* 'Linearis'
	- 'Hillier's Dwarf'	WCot
	- 'Ina'	CAgr WCot
	- 'Körsör' (F)	NLar WCot
	- f. ***laciniata*** ♀H6	CBcs CRos EBee EHyd ELan EPfP LRHS MBlu MMuc MRav SCob SDix SLon SPer SPoG WCot WFar
§	- 'Linearis'	MRav NLar WCot
	- 'Long Tooth'	WCot
	- 'Lutea Punctata'	WCot WFar
	- 'Madonna' (v)	CBod LEdu LRHS MBlu MRav NPol NQui SPer SPoG WAvo WCot
§	- 'Marginata' (v)	CMac GBin MHer MRav WCot WFar
	- 'Marion Bull' (v)	WCot
I	- 'Marmorata'	NLar WCot
	- 'Mint Julep'	WCot
I	- 'Monstrosa'	WCot
	- 'Nana'	WCot
	- 'Naomi'	WCot
	- 'Norfolk Speckled' (v)	WCot
	- 'Pingo Trail'	WCot
	- 'Plena' (d)	WCot
	- f. ***porphyrophylla*** 'Black Beauty'	see *S. nigra* f. *porphyrophylla* 'Gerda'
	- - 'Black Lace'	see *S. nigra* f. *porphyrophylla* 'Eva'
	- - BLACK TOWER ('Eiffel 1'[PBR])	Widely available
	- - 'Blue Sheen'	CRos EHyd EPfP LRHS NRHS SCoo WCot
§	- - 'Eva'[PBR] ♀H6	Widely available
§	- - 'Gerda'[PBR] ♀H6	Widely available
§	- - 'Guincho Purple'	CBcs CRos CTri CWld EPPr EPfP LRHS MRav NLar SPlb WCot WFar
	- - 'Purple Pete'	WCot
	- - 'Thundercloud' ♀H6	ELon EWes MAsh MNrw NEoE NLar SPhx WCot WFar
	- 'Pulverulenta' (v)	MRav NQui SPad SRms WCot WFar WRHF
	- 'Purpurea'	see *S. nigra* f. *porphyrophylla* 'Guincho Purple'
	- 'Pyramidalis'	MRav WCot
	- 'Riese aus Vossloch'	WCot
	- 'Robert Piggin' (v)	WCot
	- var. ***rotundifolia***	WCot
	- 'Sambu' (F)	CAgr WCot
	- 'Samdal' (F)	CAgr WCot WFar
	- 'Samidan' (F)	CAgr WCot
	- 'Samnor' (F)	CAgr WCot
	- 'Sampo' (F)	CAgr WCot
	- 'Samyl' (F)	CAgr WCot
	- 'Serenade'	CRos EBee EHyd GBin NEoE NLar NRHS SCob WCot WFar
	- 'Urban Lace'	CAgr WCot
	- 'Variegata'	see *S. nigra* 'Marginata'
	- f. ***viridis***	CAgr WCot
	'Ocean Depths'	GBin NEoE
	palmensis	WCot
	racemosa	EPfP WCot WKor
	- 'Altamont'	WCot
	- 'Aurea'	EPfP WFar
	- var. ***callicarpa***	WCot WFar
	- 'Goldenlocks'	EWes
	- subsp. ***kamtschatica***	WCot
	- LEMONY LACE ('Smnsrd4')	LBuc LRHS
	- var. ***melanocarpa***	WCot
	- 'Plumosa Aurea'	EPfP MGos MRav MSwo NLar SCob SRms WAvo WCot
	- var. ***pubens***	WCot
§	- var. ***sieboldiana***	WCot
	- 'Sutherland Gold' ♀H7	Widely available
	- 'Tenuifolia'	WCot
	sieboldiana	see *S. racemosa* var. *sieboldiana*
	× ***strumpfii*** SERENADE ('Jonade') new	LCro LOPS
	SUNNY DAYS ('Jonsun')	CBod
	tigranii	WCot WFar
	'Vermilion Summers'	WCot
	WELSH GOLD ('Walfinb'[PBR])	CRos EHyd LRHS MAsh SPoG WCot
§	***williamsii*** subsp. ***coreana***	WCot

Samolus (*Primulaceae*)

	valerandi	LLWG

Sandersonia (*Colchicaceae*)

	aurantiaca	CAvo EPot GKev SDeJ SDir

Sanguinaria (*Papaveraceae*)

	canadensis	CAvo EHyd EPPr EPot GEdr GKev GPoy LEdu LRHS MAvo MBel MMuc NHol NHpl NRHS NRya SEND SMHy SPer WFar WPnP
	- 'Jerry Flintoff'	GEdr
	- f. ***multiplex*** (d)	EHyd LRHS NBir NRHS SPhx
	- - 'Plena' (d) ♀H5	CMea CWCL EBee ECha EHyd ELon EMor EPfP GEdr GKev GPoy LRHS NBPC NHar NHol NHpl NPoe NRHS NRya NSla NSti SDeJ SPer WCot WFar WHil WPnP XEll
	- pink-flowered	GEdr
	- 'Star'	GKev

Sanguisorba ✿ (*Rosaceae*)

	from Japan	EBee LPla MAvo
§	***albiflora***	CDoC CKno EBee ELan EPfP EShb EWhm ILea LEdu LRHS MAvo MMuc MNrw MRav MSpe NDov NEoE NGdn SEND SPhx SRkn WCAu
	- 'Cindy's Tall White' new	SPVi
	'All Time High'	GBin LEdu NDov
	alpina	GLog MMuc SEND
	'Ankum's Thums'	MAvo MTis
	applanata	SBrt WCot WFar WPGP
	armena	EBee EWes IMou LEdu MNrw MPie SPhx WFar WWtn XEll

'Autumn Bliss'	EBee GMaP
'Autumn Red'	MAvo
'Beetlewings'	MAvo MTis NDov
'Blacksmith's Burgundy'	LEdu
'Blackthorn'	CKno CMea EBee ECtt GMaP LPla MAvo MBel MTis NDov NLar SMHy SMad SPhx WCAu WCot WHoo
'Burr Blanc'	GMaP MSpe SMHy SPhx
canadensis	Widely available
- hybrid	MAvo
- 'Twisty'	LPla
'Candy Floss'	MAvo
'Cangshan Cranberry'	EBee ECtt GMaP LPla MAvo MBel MHol NDov SMHy SMad SPhx WCot
'Ccc'	MAvo
'Chocolate Tip'	CDor EBee ECtt EPPr GPSL ILea LRHS MAvo NGrd SEdd SPVi SPhx
'Coen's Cranberry'	NDov
dodecandra	EBee MAvo MSpe MTis
'Foxtail'	MAvo SPVi
hakusanensis	CAby CBod CKno EBee EHyd EWhm GKev GMaP LEdu LRHS MAvo MBriF MMuc MNrw NBir NBro NChi NEoE NGBl NLar SBut SPVi SPeP SPhx WCAu WCot WFar WHoo
- B&SWJ 8709	WCru
- 'Lilac Squirrel'	CKno EBee ECtt GBee GBin GMaP ILea IPot LEdu LRHS LSou MAvo MBel MNrw MPie MSCN MSpe MTis NDov NLar SMad SPVi SPhx SRms WCAu WFar WTor
'Ivory Towers'	MAvo SPhx WFar
'John Coke'	EBee NLar
'Joni'	CKno MAvo
'Little Angel'	CAby CBct CKno CSpe CWGN EBee ECtt EMor EWhm GBee LSou MAvo MBNS MBel MHol NBPC NEoE NLar SEdd SMad SPad SPoG WCot WFar WMal WRHF WTor WWtn
magnifica	EWes LEdu
- ***alba***	see *S. albiflora*
menziesii 🏆H7	Widely available
- 'Dali Marble' (v)	EBee ECtt NLar
- 'Misbourne' **new**	LPla
- 'Wake Up'	MBNS NDov
§ ***minor***	CAgr CBod CCBP CHby CLau CTsd EBou EMor GPoy GQue LEdu MBow MHer MNHC NMir NPol SPhx SPlb SRms WHer WWild XAbr XLum
- subsp. ***minor***	CHab
'Misbourne Pink'	LPla
'Miss Elly'	MAvo
'Nettlesworth Wand'	SMHy SPhx
obtusa	Widely available
- 'Chatto'	MAvo NLar WPGP
- silver-leaved	MNrw SMHy WFar
- white-flowered	EBee EWTr MBel MTis WPGP
officinalis	CBod CHab CSpe GKev GQue MBow MHer NEoE NMir NPol SCob SPer SPhx SRms WCAu WFar WOut
- CDC 262	EPPr LEdu SMHy SPhx
- CDC 282	CSpe SPhx
- CDC 292	MAvo WCot
- DJHC 535	LEdu NLar
- from Mongolia	EBee
- 'Arnhem'	CDor CKno EBee ECtt EPPr GPSL ILea LEdu LRHS MSpe MTis NDov NLar SEdd SMHy SPhx WCot
- 'Burgundy Buttons' **new**	CRos
- 'Crimson Queen'	EBee ECtt GQue IPot MTis NLar
- dark-flowered	MAvo
- early-flowering	GMaP GWyn
- 'False Tanna'	WFar
- 'Lemon Splash' (v)	EBee ECtt LEdu WCot WFar WPGP
- 'Lum'	MAvo
- 'Martin's Mulberry'	EBee EWes LEdu MAvo MNrw NDov
- 'Morning Select'	EBee ECtt EPPr GMaP NLar
- 'Red Buttons'	MAvo NDov WMal
- 'Red Thunder'	CSpe EBee ECtt EPPr EWhm GMaP GPSL ILea LCro LEdu LOPS LRHS MAvo MBel MHol MTis NLar SEdd SMad SPVi WCAu WCot WGwG WPGP
- 'Shiro-fukurin' (v)	EBee ECtt EShb EWes EWhm GMaP LEdu MBel MHol MNrw MSpe NLar WCot WFar WHer WSHC
- 'Tsetseguun'	LEdu LRHS MAvo SPhx WPGP
- 'White Tanna'	MBel SCob
parviflora	see *S. tenuifolia* var. *parviflora*
pimpinella	see *S. minor*
'Pink Brushes'	CKno ECtt GMaP GQue ILea IMou IPot LRHS MAvo MBel MBriF MTis NGrd NLar WCAu
'Pink September'	MAvo
'Pink Tanna'	Widely available
'Prim and Proper'	MAvo MHol
'Proud Mary' **new**	NDov
'Purple Tails'	MAvo MTis
'Raspberry Coulis'	MAvo
'Raspberry Mivvi'	MAvo SPhx
'Red Busby'	MAvo
'Rock and Roll'	EBee ECtt EMor EPPr MSpe MTis NLar
'Sangria'	MAvo
'Sanguine Dwarf' **new**	MAvo
'Scapino'	MAvo
sitchensis	see *S. stipulata*
§ ***stipulata***	CMac EBee EHyd LEdu LPla LRHS MHer MNrw NRHS
- var. ***riishirensis***	EMor EPPr MNrw WFar
'Sussex Prairies Cheyenne' **new**	SPVi
'Sussex Prairies Iroquois' **new**	SPVi
'Sussex Prairies Iroquois Alba' **new**	SPVi
'Sussex Prairies Navaho'	SPVi SPhx
'Swarm' **new**	MAvo
'Tanna' 🏆H7	Widely available
tenuifolia	CRos EHyd GKev LRHS NChi NGBl NGrd NLar SPhx WCot
- from Ernst Pagels	MAvo
- var. ***alba***	Widely available
- - CDC	MRav
- - 'Korean Snow'	GMaP LEdu LPla LRHS SMHy SPhx SSut
- 'Big Pink'	MAvo MNrw WFar
- 'Bordeaux'	EBee ECtt MAvo
- 'Henk Gerritsen'	MAvo NLar SEdd SPVi WCAu WFar
§ - var. ***parviflora***	EBee LEdu MAvo NLar SBut WPGP
- 'Pieters'	ILea MAvo
- 'Pink Elephant'	CKno EBee ECtt EMor EPPr EWhm GJos GMaP GQue ILea LEdu LRHS MAvo MSpe MTis NLar

	SCob SEdd SMad SPVi SPhx WCAu WFar
- pink-flowered	SMHy
- var. ***purpurea***	EBee GBin
- 'Purpurea'	CKno EBee EPPr GPSL GQue ILea LEdu LPla MAvo MTis SPhx WCAu WCot WPGP
- 'Stand Up Comedian'	IMou LEdu MAvo NDov NLar SHar WPGP
- 'Strawberry Frost'	MAvo
- 'Strawberry Fruli'	LEdu WPGP
- 'Sturdy Guard'	LEdu
- 'The Invisible'	MAvo WCAu
- 'White Tanna'	EBee EPPr GQue LEdu MAvo MTis SPVi

Sanicula (*Apiaceae*)

europaea	CEls EMor GPoy IMou NGrd

Sansevieria (*Asparagaceae*)

bacularis 'Mikado'	LCro LOPS
cylindrica	EShb
- 'Straight' new	SPad
trifasciata	NGKo
- 'Golden Hahnii' (v) ♀H1b	EShb
- 'Hahnii' ♀H1b	EShb NGKo
- var. ***laurentii*** (v) ♀H1b	CDoC LCro LOPS
- 'Moonshine' ♀H1b	EShb
zeylanica	LCro LOPS

Santolina ✿ (*Asteraceae*)

'Apple Court'	CRos EHyd LRHS
benthamiana	EBtc
§ ***chamaecyparissus***	Widely available
- var. ***corsica*** misapplied	see *S. chamaecyparissus* 'Nana'
- subsp. ***insularis***	XSen
- 'Lambrook Silver'	CBod CFis CRos EBee ECtt EHyd ENfk EPfP LRHS MAsh NRHS SCoo XSen
- 'Lemon Queen'	CBod CCBP CRos ENfk EPfP EWhm LRHS MAsh MSwo NBir NRHS SCob SRms XSen
- subsp. ***magonica***	EBtc XSen
§ - 'Nana' ♀H5	CRos EHyd EPfP LRHS MAsh MHer MNHC MRav MSwo SCob SRms XSen
- 'Pretty Carroll' ♀H5	CBod CDoC CRos EBee EBtc ELan EPfP LRHS LSRN MAsh NLar SPoG WFar
- 'Small-Ness'	ELan EPfP EWes MHer NLar SWvt WHer XSen
etrusca	XSen
incana	see *S. chamaecyparissus*
* ***lindavica***	EBtc XSen
pinnata	CTri EBtc
§ - subsp. ***neapolitana*** ♀H5	ECha ELan ENfk EPfP MRav SCob SDix SEND
- - cream-flowered	see *S. pinnata* subsp. *neapolitana* 'Edward Bowles'
§ - - 'Edward Bowles'	CBod CCBP CRos EBee EPfP EWhm GMaP LRHS LSRN MAvo MHer MNHC MRav MSwo NBir NPer SCob SEdd SPoG SRms SVen SWvt WCFE WGwG WHer WHoo XSen
- - 'Sulphurea'	CDoC CRos EHyd EPfP LRHS MAsh SPer SPhx WKif
rosmarinifolia	CBod CCBP CRos EHyd GPoy LRHS MRav NRHS SCob SEND SLon SPlb SRms WHoo
- 'Green Fizz'	WFar
- 'Lemon Fizz' ♀H5	CBod CDoC CMac CPla CRos EBee EHyd ELan ELon ENfk EPfP GMaP LRHS MAsh MAvo MHer NBir NLar NRHS SCob SCoo SPeP SPer SPoG SRms SWvt WFar WHer WSMil XSen
§ - subsp. ***rosmarinifolia***	ECha ELan ENfk EPfP MHer MRav SCob SDix SPer SRms SWvt WFar WGwG WKif XLum XSen
- - 'Primrose Gem' ♀H5	CBcs CBod CCBP CDoC CRos CTri EAJP ECha EPfP LRHS MAsh MAvo MNHC MSwo NRHS SCob SEND SGbt SPer SRms SWvt XSen
- - white-flowered	WHer
SHADES OF JADE ('Sant101')	EBtc ECrN SCob SRms
tomentosa misapplied	see *S. pinnata* subsp. *neapolitana*
virens	see *S. rosmarinifolia* subsp. *rosmarinifolia*
viridis	see *S. rosmarinifolia* subsp. *rosmarinifolia*

Sanvitalia (*Asteraceae*)

AZTEKENGOLD	see *Melampodium montanum* AZTEC GOLD
procumbens misapplied	see *Melampodium montanum*

Sapindus (*Sapindaceae*)

mukorossi B&SWJ 14689	WCru

Saponaria (*Caryophyllaceae*)

'Bressingham' ♀H5	CMea ECtt EPfP EPot MHol WAbe WIce
Bressingham hybrid	MAsh
caespitosa	EPot EWes
§ ***intermedia***	NDov WCot
× ***lempergii*** 'Fritz Lemperg'	NDov WCot
- 'Max Frei'	CSam EBee ECtt ELon EMor EPPr LCro LOPS LPla MCot MRav NDov SGro SPhx WCot WMal WOld XLum
ocymoides ♀H5	CMea EBee ECha ECtt ELan EPfP MAsh MHol MNHC NHpl SEND SPlb SPoG SRms XLum
- 'Alba'	ECha NSla
- 'Snow Tip'	GRum NGdn WRHF
officinalis	CBod CBre CCBP EMor ENfk GBin GPoy GQue MHer MNHC SPlb SRms WCAu WHer WSFF XAbr
- 'Alba'	CSam
- 'Alba Plena' (d)	CBre MMuc NLar SEND WCAu WFar XLum
- 'Betty Arnold' (d)	EBee ECtt EMor EPPr EWes LPla MHer WCot WGob
- 'Flore Pleno' (d)	CBod GAbr WFar WOut
- 'Red Splash'	WFar
- 'Rosea Plena' (d)	CBre CMac ELan EPfP LEdu MHer MMuc NBPC NBid NBir NGdn SEND SPer WFar WGwG
- 'Rubra Plena' (d)	CCBP ELan EPPr EWes MMuc WGob
× ***olivana*** ♀H5	CPBP ECtt GMaP GRum MAsh NLar XLum
'Rosenteppich'	CPBP
sicula subsp. ***intermedia***	see *S. intermedia*
* × ***sundermannii***	CPBP
zawadskii	see *Silene zawadskii*

Saposhnikovia (*Apiaceae*)

divaricata	SPhx

Saracha (*Solanaceae*)

punctata B&SWJ 14882 **new**	WCru
quitensis B&SWJ 14748	WCru

Sarcococca ✿ (*Buxaceae*)

	confusa 🏆H5	Widely available
	hookeriana	ELon GKin LSRN MBlu MSwo NLar NWad SGbt SWvt SavN WFar WPGP WSpi
	- B&SWJ 2585	WCru
	- HWJK 2393	WCru
	- HWJK 2428	WCru
	- var. ***digyna***	Widely available
	- - SDR 7816	GKev
	- - 'Purple Stem' 🏆H5	CBcs CBod CBrac CDoC CEnd CExl CJun CTri EPfP GKin LCro LOPS LRHS MGos MNrw NLar SCob SCoo SPoG SRkn SWvt WCru WSMil WSpi
§	- - 'Tony Schilling'	CExl CJun WCru
	- var. ***hookeriana***	CJun LSRN
	- - GWJ 9222	WCru
	- - GWJ 9344	WCru
	- - GWJ 9369	WCru
	- - HWJK 2102	WCru
	- - HWJK 2366	WCru
	- - HWJK 2393	WCru
	- - 'Daman'	CExl
	- - 'Ghorepani' 🏆H5	CRos EHyd LCro LOPS LRHS NRHS
	- var. ***humilis***	Widely available
	- WINTER GEM ('Pmoore03'PBR)	CBod CDoC CRos CSBt EHyd EPfP LCro LOPS LRHS LSRN MAsh MGos MSwo NHol NRHS SCob SLon SPoG SRkn WFar WGrn
	orientalis	CBct CExl CJun CMCN CRos EBee EHyd ELon EPfP IDee IMou LEdu LRHS MAsh NLar NRHS NWad SPoG WPGP WSpi
	'Roy Lancaster'	see *S. ruscifolia* var. *chinensis* 'Dragon Gate'
	'Rudolph'	EPfP LRHS
	ruscifolia	Widely available
	- var. ***chinensis***	CJun NLar SLon WCru WPGP
§	- - 'Dragon Gate' 🏆H5	CDoC CExl CJun CRos EBee EHyd ELan ELon EPfP LRHS LSRN MAsh MGos NRHS SLon SPoG SWvt WCru WLov WPGP WSpi
	saligna	CBcs CJun EBee EPfP LRHS MRav SLon WCru WLov
	- HWJK 2428	WCru
	- MF P2056	WCru
	- NJM 12.043	WPGP
I	***taiwaniana*** RWJ 9999	WCru
	trinervia B&SWJ 9500	WCru
	vagans B&SWJ 7285	WCru
	- B&SWJ 9760 from Vietnam	WCru
	- B&SWJ 9766 from Vietnam	WCru
	aff. ***vagans*** from north Thailand B&SWJ 7265	WCru
	wallichii	CBcs CBod CExl ELon LEdu MBlu MGil SPoG WCot WLov WPGP
	- B&SWJ 2291	CJun WCru
	- GWJ 9427	WCru
	- HWJK 2425	WCru
	- HWJK 2428	WCru
	- PAB 13.077	LEdu
	aff. ***wallichii*** NJM 12.043	WPGP

zeylanica B&SWJ 10199	WCru
- var. ***brevifolia*** GWJ 9480	WCru
- - GWJ 9483	WCru

Sarcopoterium (*Rosaceae*)

spinosum	SVen

Sarmienta (*Gesneriaceae*)

repens 🏆H1c	CExl WAbe

Sarothamnus see *Cytisus*

Sarracenia ✿ (*Sarraceniaceae*)

	× ***ahlesii***	CHew
	alata	EECP SHmp WSSs
	- var. ***alata*** **new**	CHew
	- all green	SHmp
	- var. ***atrorubra*** **new**	CHew
	- 'Black Tube' 🏆H3	WSSs
	- heavily veined	SHmp WSSs
	- var. ***nigropurpurea***	CHew WSSs
	- var. ***ornata***	CHew WSSs
	- pubescent	EECP WSSs
	- 'Red Lid'	EECP WSSs
	- 'Red Lid' × ***flava*** red pitcher	EECP
	- var. ***rubrioperculata***	CHew WSSs
	- wavy lid	SHmp WSSs
	- white-flowered	WSSs
	alata × ***flava***	CHew
	alata × ***flava*** var. ***maxima***	WSSs
	× ***areolata***	CHew WSSs
	× ***catesbaei***	CHew SHmp WSSs
	- 'Johnny Marr'	SHmp
	× ***courtii***	SHmp
	'Diane Whittaker' **new**	WSSs
	'Eva' 🏆H3	SHmp WSSs
	× ***excellens***	CHew WSSs
	× ***exornata***	SPlb SRms
	- 'Peaches' **new**	WSSs
	'Fiona'	SHmp
	flava	LCro LOPS WSSs WTyc
	- all green giant	see *S. flava* var. *maxima*
	- var. ***atropurpurea***	EECP SHmp WSSs
	- 'Claret'	WSSs
	- var. ***cuprea***	CHew SHmp WSSs
	- var. ***flava***	CHew EECP WSSs
§	- var. ***maxima***	CHew EECP SHmp WSSs
	- var. ***maxima*** × (× ***moorei*** Brooks's hybrid)	SPlb
	- var. ***ornata***	CHew EECP SHmp WSSs
	- var. ***rubricorpora***	CHew EECP SHmp SPlb WSSs
	- - 'Burgundy'	WSSs
	- var. ***rugelii***	CHew EECP SHmp SPlb WSSs
	- f. ***viridescens*** **new**	CHew
	'Jedi'	WTyc
	'Joyce Cooper' **new**	CHew
	'Judith Hindle' 🏆H3 **new**	WSSs
	leucophylla	CDoC SHmp SPlb SRms WSSs WTyc
	- from Okaloosa Co., Florida	SHmp
	- var. ***alba***	CHew WSSs
	- 'Deer Park Alabama'	SHmp WSSs
	- green	WSSs
	- green and white	WSSs
	- var. ***leucophylla*** **new**	CHew
	- pubescent	WSSs
	- pubescent from Deer Park, Alabama	SHmp

- 'Schnell's Ghost' ♀H3	SHmp WSSs
- 'Tarnok'	WSSs
- f. ***viridescens***	CHew WSSs
leucophylla × ***oreophila***	EECP
leucophylla × (× ***popei***)	EECP
'Lynda Butt' ♀H3	SHmp WSSs
× ***miniata***	EECP SHmp WSSs
minor	EECP SHmp WSSs
- var. ***minor***	CHew
§ - 'Okee Giant'	WSSs
- 'Okefenokee Giant'	see *S. minor* 'Okee Giant'
- var. ***okefenokeensis***	CHew WSSs
× ***mitchelliana***	CHew SHmp WSSs
- 'Bella' ♀H3 **new**	SHmp WSSs
- 'Juthatip Soper' ♀H3	SHmp WSSs
- 'Mr Purplehaze' ♀H3 **new**	WSSs
- 'Rita Soper' ♀H3	SHmp
× ***moorei***	CHew SHmp WSSs
- 'Adrian Slack'	CHew WSSs
- 'Brooks's Hybrid' ♀H4	CHew EECP WSSs
- 'Leah Wilkerson'	CHew WSSs
oreophila	SHmp SPlb WSSs
- var. ***oreophila*** **new**	CHew
- var. ***ornata*** **new**	CHew
× ***popei***	WSSs
psittacina	EECP SHmp SRms WSSs
- var. ***okefenokeensis*** **new**	CHew
- var. ***psittacina*** ♀H3 **new**	CHew
purpurea	SPlb WTyc
- subsp. ***purpurea*** ♀H6	CHew SHmp WSSs
- - f. ***heterophylla*** ♀H6	WSSs
- subsp. ***venosa***	CHew SHmp SPlb WSSs
- - var. ***burkii*** ♀H3	SHmp WSSs
× ***readei***	EECP SHmp WSSs
× ***rehderi***	SHmp WSSs
rubra	EECP WSSs
- subsp. ***alabamensis*** ♀H3	CHew SHmp WSSs
- subsp. ***gulfensis***	CHew SHmp WSSs
- - f. ***luteoviridis*** **new**	WSSs
- subsp. ***jonesii***	CHew EECP SHmp WSSs
- - f. ***viridescens*** **new**	WSSs
- subsp. ***rubra***	CHew SHmp WSSs
- subsp. ***wherryi***	CHew EECP WSSs
- - giant	WSSs
- - yellow-flowered	WSSs
'Scarlet Belle' **new**	SHmp
× ***swaniana***	SHmp SRms
'Tara'	WTyc
'Tygo' **new**	SHmp
'Vogel' ♀H3	SHmp WSSs
× ***wrigleyana***	SRms WTyc

Saruma (*Aristolochiaceae*)

henryi	CAby CPBP CPla EMor ESwi EWld GEdr GKev GLog LEdu MAvo MPie NLar SBrt WCot WCru WFar

Sasa (*Poaceae*)

disticha 'Mirrezuzume'	see *Pleioblastus pygmaeus* 'Mirrezuzume'
glabra f. ***albostriata***	see *Sasaella masamuneana* 'Albostriata'
kurilensis	MWht XCre
§ - 'Shima-shimofuri' (v)	EShb XCre
- 'Shimofuri'	see *S. kurilensis* 'Shima-shimofuri'
- short	XCre
nana	see *S. veitchii* f. *minor*
§ ***palmata***	LCro LOPS MMuc SArc XCre
- f. ***nebulosa***	CBcs MWht NLar SArc XCre
- var. ***niijimae***	MWht
* ***seikoana***	XCre
tessellata	see *Indocalamus tessellatus*
tsuboiana	CBcs MWht NLar SGol XCre
§ ***veitchii***	CBcs GQue MMuc MRav MWht NLar SCob SGol SGsty WFar XCre
§ - f. ***minor***	MMuc

Sasaella (*Poaceae*)

§ ***masamuneana*** 'Albostriata' (v)	CBdn LEdu MMuc MWht XCre
§ ***ramosa***	GBin MWht XCre

Sasamorpha (*Poaceae*)

borealis	XCre

Sassafras (*Lauraceae*)

albidum	CBcs CMCN CRos EHyd ELan EPfP LRHS MAsh MMrt NLar SLon SPoG WPGP

satsuma see *Citrus reticulata*

Satureja ✿ (*Lamiaceae*)

biflora	WJek
coerulea ♀H5	EWes XSen
douglasii	CBod WJek
- 'Indian Mint'PBR	ENfk MHer SRms
hortensis	CBod CLau ENfk LCro LOPS MHer MNHC SRms SVic WJek XAbr
intricata	XSen
montana	CCBP CHby CLau CTsd EBou ELan ENfk EWhm GPoy LCro LOPS MBros MHer MNHC NGrd SDix SEND SPhx SRms SVic WJek XAbr XSen
- 'Aromakugel'	IMou
* - ***citriodora***	GPoy MHer XAbr XSen
§ - subsp. ***illyrica***	SPhx WJek XLum XSen
- 'Purple Mountain'	GPoy MHer
- ***subspicata***	see *S. montana* subsp. *illyrica*
repanda	see *S. spicigera*
§ ***spicigera***	CBod EBou ENfk EPot EWhm IMou LEdu MHer MMuc SPhx SRms WJek XLum XSen
* - 'Prostrata'	CLau
thymbra	SPhx SRms

Sauromatum (*Araceae*)

gaoligongense	WCot
giganteum	GKev
guttatum	see *S. venosum*
§ ***venosum***	CAby CExl CRos EBee EHyd EPfP EShb GKev LEdu LRHS NGKo NRHS SPlb WCot WSMil WTyc XLum

Saururus (*Saururaceae*)

cernuus	CBen CBod CWat ELan LLWG WMAq WWtn XLum
- 'Hertford Streaker' (v)	WCot
chinensis	LLWG SBrt

Saussurea (*Asteraceae*)

costus	GPoy
pseudoalpina	WCot

savory, summer see *Satureja hortensis*

savory, winter see *Satureja montana*

Saxegothaea ✿ (*Podocarpaceae*)

conspicua	CBcs IDee NLar
- weeping	WPGP

Saxifraga ✿ (*Saxifragaceae*)

JJH 9309174	NMen
acerifolia (5)	GEdr
§ 'Afrodite' (*sempervivum*) (7)	EPot NMen WAbe
aizoides (9)	GKev
aizoon	see *S. paniculata* subsp. *paniculata*
'Akibare' (*fortunei*) (5)	GEdr
'Aladdin' (× *borisii*) (7)	NMen
'Alan Hayhurst' (8)	CPBP NSla NWad WAbe
'Alan Martin' (× *boydilacina*) (7)	EPot EWes NMen
'Alba' ambig.	CRos EHyd LRHS NRHS
'Alba' (× *apiculata*) (7) ♀H5	MAsh NMen NRya SPlb SRms
'Alba' (*oppositifolia*) (7)	ELan EWes ITim NWad WAbe WOld
'Albert Einstein' (× *apiculata*) (7) ♀H5	NMen
'Albertii' (*callosa*)	see *S.* 'Albida'
§ 'Albida' (*callosa*) (8)	NWad WAbe
'Albrecht Dürer' (Lasciva Group) (7)	NMen
'Aldo Bacci' (Milford Group) (7)	NMen NSla
'Alfons Mucha' (7)	EPot NMen
'Allendale Accord' (7)	EPot NMen
'Allendale Andante' (× *arco-valleyi*) (7)	NMen
'Allendale Angel' (× *kepleri*) (7)	NMen
'Allendale Argonaut' (7)	CPBP NMen
'Allendale Ballad' (7)	NMen
'Allendale Banshee' (7)	NMen
'Allendale Beau' (× *lismorensis*) (7)	CPBP
'Allendale Beauty' (7)	WAbe WOld
'Allendale Betty' (× *lismorensis*) (7)	EPot NMen
'Allendale Billows' (7)	NMen NSla
'Allendale Bonny' (7)	EPot NSla WAbe
'Allendale Boon' (× *izari*) (7)	NMen
'Allendale Bounty' (7)	NMen
'Allendale Bravo' (× *lismorensis*) (7)	WHoo
'Allendale Cabal' (7)	NMen
'Allendale Carol' (7)	NMen
'Allendale Celt' (× *novacastelensis*) (7)	NMen
'Allendale Charm' (Swing Group) (7)	GKev NMen WAbe WHoo
'Allendale Chick' (7)	EPot
'Allendale Citation' (7)	NMen
'Allendale Delight' (7)	NMen
'Allendale Desire' (7)	WAbe
'Allendale Divine' (7)	NMen
'Allendale Dream' (7)	EPot NMen
'Allendale Duo' (7)	NMen
'Allendale Eden' (7)	CPBP
'Allendale Elegance' (7)	CPBP NMen WAbe
'Allendale Elf' (7)	EPot NMen WHoo
'Allendale Elite' (7)	NMen WAbe
'Allendale Enchantment' (7)	NMen
'Allendale Epic' (7)	CPBP NMen
'Allendale Fairy' (7)	WHoo
'Allendale Fame' (7)	NMen
'Allendale Fancy' (7)	NMen
'Allendale Frost' (7)	NMen WAbe
'Allendale Ghost' (7)	NMen
'Allendale Goblin' (7)	NMen
'Allendale Grace' (7)	NMen WAbe
'Allendale Gremlin' (7)	NMen
'Allendale Hobbit' (7)	NMen
'Allendale Host' (7)	NMen
'Allendale Ice' (7)	NMen
'Allendale Icon' (× *polulacina*) (7)	NMen
'Allendale Imp' (7)	NMen
'Allendale Ina' (7)	NMen
'Allendale Jinn' (7)	CPBP NMen NSla
'Allendale Jo' (7)	NMen WAbe
'Allendale Joy' (× *wendelacina*) (7)	NMen
'Allendale News' (7)	NMen
'Allendale Noon' (7)	NMen
'Allendale Ruby' (7)	NMen
'Allendale Snow' (× *rayei*) (7)	EWes NMen
'Allendale Tommy' (7) **new**	NMen
'Alpenglow' (7)	NMen
alpigena (7)	NSla WAbe
ALPINO EARLY LIME ('Sax20007') (15)	WFar
ALPINO EARLY PICOTEE ('Saxz0010'^{PBR}) (× *arendsii*) (15) **new**	CRos
ALPINO EARLY PINK ('Saxz0009'^{PBR}) (× *arendsii*) (15) **new**	CRos
ALPINO EARLY PINK HEART ('Saxz0008'^{PBR}) (× *arendsii*) (15) **new**	CRos
ALPINO EARLY WHITE ('Saxz0001') (× *arendsii*) (15) **new**	CRos
'Amberglow' (× *anglica*) (7)	NMen NSla
'Amberine' (× *anglica*) (7)	NMen WHoo
'Amedeo Modigliani' (7)	NMen
'Amerigo Vespucci' (Continent Group) (7)	NMen
'Amitie' (× *gloriana*) (7)	NMen
× ***andrewsii*** (8 × 11)	XLum
angustifolia Haw.	see *S. hypnoides*
'Anna' (× *fontanae*) (7)	NMen NSla
'Anne Beddall' (× *goringiana*) (7)	NMen
'Anneka Hope' (8)	GKev
'Antonín Dvořák' (× *arco-valleyi*) (7)	NMen
'Antonio' (× *bertolonii*) (7) **new**	NMen
'Antonio Vivaldi' (7)	EPot NMen
'Aphrodite' (*sempervivum*)	see *S.* 'Afrodite'
× ***apiculata*** *sensu stricto* hort.	see *S.* 'Gregor Mendel'
× ***apiculata*** (7)	EBou GMaP MAsh
'Apple Blossom' (Mossy Group) (15)	ECtt NEoE NRya
'Arabella' (× *edithae*) (7)	NMen
'Aramis' (7)	NMen
§ 'Arco' (× *arco-valleyi*) (7)	EPot
× ***arco-valleyi*** *sensu stricto* hort.	see *S.* 'Arco'
× ***arendsii*** purple-flowered (15)	MMuc SCob SPlb
- white-flowered	SCob
§ 'Aretiastrum' (× *boydii*) (7)	NMen

	'Argia Romani' (7)	NMen
	'Arleta' (Southside Seedling Group) (8)	WIce
	'Arthur' (× *anglica*) (7)	NMen
	'Assimilis' (× *petraschii*) (7)	EPot NMen
	'Athena' (7)	NMen
	'Atropurpurea' (*paniculata* subsp. *cartilaginea*) (8)	GMaP NHol NSla WFar WHoo WIce XLum
	'Audrey Lowe' (*oppositifolia*) (7)	EPot WAbe
	'Auguste Renoir' (Decora Group) (7)	NSla
	'Aurea Maculata' (*cuneifolia*)	see *S.* 'Aureopunctata'
	'Aurea' (*umbrosa*)	see *S.* 'Aureopunctata'
§	'Aureopunctata' (× *urbium*) (11/v)	CMac CRos CTri ECha EHyd ELan EPfP GAbr GKev GMaP LEdu LRHS MHer MPnt MRav NRHS SPer SPlb SPoG SRms WFar XLum
	'Autumn Tribute' (*fortunei*) (5)	GEdr WAbe WFar
	'Ayako' (*fortunei*) (5)	GEdr WFar
	'Ayer's Rock' (7)	NMen WAbe
	'Bacci Cf13' (7) **new**	NMen
	'Balcana' (*paniculata*) (8)	EPot WAbe
	'Baldensis'	see *S. paniculata* var. *minutifolia*
	'Beatles' (Beat Group) (7)	EPot NMen NSla
§	'Beatrix Stanley' (× *anglica*) (7)	CRos EHyd LRHS MAsh NMen NRHS
	'Beautiful Girl' (*fortunei*) (5) **new**	WFar
	'Becky Foster' (× *borisii*) (7)	EPot NMen
	'Bedřich Smetana' (*marginata*) (7)	NMen
	'Beinn Eighe' (× *concinna*) (7)	NMen
	'Beinne Alligin' (× *concinna*) (7)	NMen
	'Ben Loyal' (× *concinna*) (7)	NMen WAbe
	'Beni-karen' (*fortunei*) (5)	GEdr WFar
	'Beni-kirin' (*fortunei*) (5)	GEdr WFar
	'Benimine' (*fortunei*) (5)	GEdr WFar
	'Beni-tsukaji' (*fortunei*) (5)	NBro SHeu
	'Beni-tsukasa' (*fortunei*) (5)	ECtt GEdr GMaP NHar NHpl WFar
	'Beni-zakura' (*fortunei*) (5)	GEdr WFar
	'Berenika' (× *bertolonii*) (7)	NMen
	'Berounka' (Prominent Group) (7)	NMen
	'Bertramka' (Holenka's Miracle Group) (× *megaseiflora*) (7)	NMen NSla
	'Beryl Bland' (Sugestivo Group) (7)	WAbe
	'Bettina' (× *paulinae*) (7)	NMen
	× ***biasolettoi*** *sensu stricto* hort.	see *S.* 'Phoenix'
	× ***biasolettoi*** Sünd. (7)	CRos EHyd LRHS NRHS
	'Bizourtouse' (× *luteopurpurea*) (7)	NSla
	'Black Beauty' (15)	ECtt MHer NWad
	BLACK RUBY (*fortunei*) (5)	Widely available
	'Blackberry and Apple Pie' (*fortunei*) (5) 🏆H4	CExl CMac CRos ECtt EHyd EPfP GEdr LRHS NRHS SGro SWvt WFar
	'Blaník' (7)	NMen
	'Blütenteppich' (Mossy Group) (15)	MAvo
	'Bob Hawkins' (Mossy Group) (15/v)	NHol NWad
	'Bohdalec' (× *megaseiflora*) (7)	CPBP NMen
	'Bohemia' (7)	NMen NSla WAbe
	'Bohemian Karst' (Prominent Group) (7)	NMen
	'Bohemian Paradise' (Region Group) (7)	NMen
	'Bohnice' (× *megaseiflora*) (7)	NMen
	'Bohunka' (7)	NMen
	× ***borisii*** *sensu stricto* hort.	see *S.* 'Sofia'
	'Boston Spa' (× *elisabethae*) (7)	CRos ECtt EHyd LRHS MAsh MHer NBPC NLar NMen NRHS SPlb
	'Boží Dar' (Sessile Group) (7)	EPot
	'Brailes' (× *poluanglica*) (7)	NMen
	'Brian Arundel' (Magnus Group) (7)	NMen
	'Bridget' (× *edithae*) (7)	CRos EHyd LRHS NMen NRHS
	'Brimstone' (7)	NMen
	'Brno' (× *elisabethae*) (7)	NMen
	'Brookside' (*burseriana*) (7)	EPot NMen
	brunoniana	see *S. brunonis*
§	***brunonis*** (1)	GKev
	'Bryn Llwyd' (Vanessa Group) (7)	NMen WAbe
	'Bürgel' (× *poluanglica*) (7)	WOld
	× ***burnatii*** (8)	CRos EHyd LRHS NRHS NSla WFar
	burseriana (7)	NMen WAbe
	'Buster' (× *hardingii*) (7)	NMen
	'Buttercup' (× *kayei*) (7)	NMen
	'Bychan' (*fortunei*) (5)	WAbe
	× ***caesia*** misapplied (× *fritschiana*)	see *S.* 'Krain'
	× ***caesia*** L. (8)	SRms WAbe
§	***callosa*** (8) 🏆H5	CPla CRos EDAr EHyd GKev LRHS MHer MMuc NRHS SEND WAbe
§	- subsp. ***catalaunica*** (8)	WAbe
	- ***lingulata***	see *S. callosa*
	'Candy Floss' (7)	NMen
	× ***canis-dalmatica***	see *S.* 'Canis-dalmatica'
§	'Canis-dalmatica' (× *gaudinii*) (8)	CRos EBou ECtt EHyd GAbr GJos GQue LRHS NRHS NWad SIvy WFar
§	'Carniolica' (*paniculata*) (8)	NBro NHol NWad WOld
	'Carniolica' (× *engleri*) (8)	WAbe
	carolinica	see *S.* 'Carniolica' (*paniculata*)
	cartilaginea	see *S. paniculata* subsp. *cartilaginea*
	catalaunica	see *S. callosa* subsp. *catalaunica*
	'Cathy Read' (× *polulacina*) (7)	NMen
	cebennensis (15)	CPla NMen NRya
	- dwarf (15)	WAbe
	'Celebration'	WAbe
	cespitosa (15)	WAbe
	'Chambers' Pink Pride'	see *S.* 'Miss Chambers'
	'Charles Chaplin' (7)	NMen
	'Charles Darwin' (7)	NMen
	CHEAP CONFECTIONS (*fortunei*) (5)	ECtt GEdr MMrt MPnt NLar SGro SPoG WAul WBor WFar WOld
	CHERRY PIE (*fortunei*) (5)	GEdr NBPC NBir NHpl
	'Cherrytrees' (× *boydii*) (7)	NMen
	'Chodov' (Holenka's Miracle Group) (× *megaseiflora*) (7)	EPot NMen
	'Christine' (× *anglica*) (7)	NMen
	cinerea (7)	WAbe
	'Cio-Cio-San' (Vanessa Group) (7)	NMen
	'Citronella' (7)	NMen
	'Claire Felstead' (7)	WAbe
	'Clare' (× *anglica*) (7)	NHol

§ 'Clarence Elliott' (London Pride Group) (*umbrosa*) (11) ♀H5 — CTri EBou ECtt EWes GJos GKev GMaP LSun MHer NDov NLar NRya NWad WFar WIce
'Claude Monet' (Impression Group) (7) — CPBP NMen
'Claudia' (× *borisii*) (7) — NSla
'Cleo' (× *boydii*) (7) — NMen
§ × ***clibranii*** hort. (15) — WIce
'Cloth of Gold' (*exarata* subsp. *moschata*) (15) — CRos ECha ECtt EHyd ELan EPfP GKev GWyn LRHS MAsh NEoE NHol NHpl NRHS NWad SPlb SPoG SRms WAbe WIce
cochlearis (8) — CRos CTri EHyd LRHS MAsh NBro NRHS NSla WAbe
- hybrid (8) — MAsh
'Cockscomb' (*paniculata*) (8) — ECtt NLar NWad WAbe
columnaris* × *juniperifolia (7) — NMen
× ***concinna*** 'Helvellyn' (7) — WAbe
'Conwy Snow' (*fortunei*) (5) ♀H4 — WAbe WFar
'Conwy Star' (*fortunei*) (5) — GEdr WAbe WFar
'Coolock Gem' (7) — WAbe WHoo
'Coolock Jean' (7) — CPBP WAbe
'Coolock Kate' (7) ♀H5 — NMen NSla WAbe WHoo
'Corennie Claret' — see *S.* 'Glowing Ember'
'Corona' (× *boydii*) (7) — NMen
* × ***correvensis*** — EBou GWyn
'Correvoniana' misapplied — see *S.* 'Lagraveana'
'Correvoniana' Farrer (*paniculata*) (8) — EDAr MHer MMuc SEND WHoo XLum
cortusifolia (5) — NBPC
- var. ***stolonifera*** (5) — CBct XLum
COTTON CROCHET (*fortunei*) (5/d) — ECtt GEdr NBro SHeu WBor WFar WOld
cotyledon (8) — CRos EHyd LEdu LRHS NRHS WAbe WCFE
COVENTRY TEARS — see *S.* 'Slzy Coventry' (× *proximae*)
§ 'Cranbourne' (× *anglica*) (7) ♀H5 — CRos EHyd LRHS MAsh NMen NRHS NSla WAbe
'Crenata' (*burseriana*) (7) ♀H5 — CRos EHyd LRHS NRHS
'Crimscote-love' (*poluanglica*) (7) — NMen
'Crimson Rose' (*paniculata*) — see *S.* 'Rosea' (*paniculata*)
'Crinoline' (7) — NMen NSla WAbe
§ ***crustata*** (8) — CPBP EPot GKev WAbe WThu XLum
- var. ***vochinensis*** — see *S. crustata*
CRYSTAL PINK (*fortunei*) (5/v) — CExl EBee ECtt ELan EMor MBNS MHol NBPC NHpl WCot WFar
'Crystalie' (× *biasolettoi*) (7) — CRos EHyd LRHS NRHS
'Cultrata' (*paniculata*) (8) — NBro
'Cumulus' (7) ♀H5 — EPot NMen SPlb WOld
§ ***cuneifolia*** (11) — IMou MHer NWad XLum
- var. ***capillipes*** — see *S. cuneifolia* subsp. *cuneifolia*
§ - subsp. ***cuneifolia*** (11) — GJos
'Cuscutiformis' (*stolonifera*) (5) — CAby CElw CExl EWld GEdr MAvo MBel MSCN SGro SRms WBor WFar XLum
dahurica — see *S. cuneifolia*
'Dai Uchu' (*fortunei*) (5) **new** — GEdr
'Dainty Dame' (× *arco-valleyi*) (7) — CRos EHyd LRHS NMen NRHS
'Dana' (Prichard's Monument Group) (× *megaseiflora*) (7) — EPot NMen
'Darcies Cross' — EDAr
'David' (7) — NMen
'Dawn Frost' (7) — NMen WIce
'Delia' (× *hornibrookii*) (7) — EPot
§ 'Dentata' (London Pride Group) (× *polita*) (11) — CElw CMiW ECha MPnt SMHy WBor
'Dentata' (× *urbium*) — see *S.* 'Dentata' (London Pride Group) (× *polita*)
I 'Diana' (× *lincolni-fosteri*) (7) — WIce
diapensioides (7) — NSla WAbe
dinnikii (7) — WAbe
× ***dinninaris*** (7) — NSla
'Dobruška' (× *irvingii*) (7) — NMen
'Doctor Clay' (*paniculata*) (8) — CRos ECtt EHyd EPot GKev LRHS NHol NRHS NRya NSla SPlb WAbe
'Doctor Ramsey' (8) — CRos EHyd EWes LRHS NRHS NWad WAbe
'Dominika' (7) **new** — NMen
'Don Giovanni' (7) — NMen
'Donald Mann' (15) — EWes
'Donatello' (7) — NMen
'Donnington Chalice' (7) — NMen
'Donnington Gold' (7) — NMen
'Donnington Rose' (7) — NMen
'Donnington Veil' (7) — NSla
'Dora Ross' (× *baccii*) (7) — NMen
'Drakula' (*ferdinandi-coburgi*) (7) — CPBP CRos EHyd LRHS NMen NRHS NSla WOld
'Earl Grey' (8) — NSla
'Edgar Irmscher' (7) — NMen
'Edith' (× *edithae*) (7) — EHyd LRHS
'Édouard Manet' (Impression Group) (7) — NMen
'Eiga' (*fortunei*) (5) — GEdr WFar
'Elegance' — WFar
× ***elegantissima*** — see *S.* × *clibranii* hort.
'Elf' (7) — see *S.* 'Beatrix Stanley'
'Elf' (*exarata* subsp. *moschata*) (15) — ECtt MAsh SRms
'Elf Rose' (15) — CRos EHyd EPfP LRHS NEoE NRHS
'Eliot Hodgkin' (× *millstreamiana*) (7) — NMen
'Elizabeth Sinclair' (× *elisabethae*) (7) — GKev
'Elliott's Variety' — see *S.* 'Clarence Elliott' (*umbrosa*)
'Emil Holub' (Ethography Group) (7) — NMen
epiphylla (5) BWJ 8177 — WCru
erioblasta (15) **new** — WAbe
§ 'Ernst Heinrich' (× *heinrichii*) (7) — NMen
'Esther' (× *burnatii*) (8) — CMea CRos EBou EHyd GMaP LRHS NRHS NSla SEdd WAbe WHoo
'Eva Hanzliková' (× *izari*) (7) — EPot NSla
'Excellent' (Exclusive Group) (7) — CPBP EPot NSla
'Exee' (7) **new** — NSla
'Exhibit' (Exclusive Group) (7) — NMen
fair maids of France — see *S.* 'Flore Pleno'
'Fairy' (*exarata* subsp. *moschata*) (15) — NBir NEoE
'Faldonside' (× *boydii*) (7) — MAsh WAbe
'Falstaff' (*burseriana*) (7) — NMen WOld
× ***farreri*** hort. — see *S.* 'Reginald Farrer' (Silver Farreri Group)
× ***farreri*** (15) — WFar WIce
'Fasolt' (*sempervivum*) (7) **new** — NMen
§ ***federici-augusti*** (7) — WFar
§ - subsp. ***grisebachii*** (7) ♀H5 — CRos EHyd GKev LRHS NRHS NSla WAbe WFar

ferdinandi-coburgi (7) NSla WAbe
§ - subsp. ***chrysosplenifolia*** var. ***rhodopea*** (7) CRos EHyd LRHS NRHS
- var. ***pravislavii*** see *S. ferdinandi-coburgi* subsp. *chrysosplenifolia* var. *rhodopea*
- var. ***radoslavoffii*** see *S. ferdinandi-coburgi* subsp. *chrysosplenifolia* var. *rhodopea*
'Findling' (Mossy Group) (15) ECtt EPfP NWad SPoG WAbe
'Firebrand' (× *kochii*) (7) WAbe
'Flavescens' misapplied see *S.* 'Lutea' (*paniculata*)
'Fleece' (15) NHpl
§ 'Flore Pleno' (*granulata*) (15/d) CElw CMiW EBee EWes NBir
'Flowers of Sulphur' see *S.* 'Schwefelblüte'
fortunei (5) Y^{H4} CMac NBir SCob SRms WAbe WFar
- f. ***alpina*** (5) NBro
- var. ***koraiensis*** (5) B&SWJ 8688 WCru
- var. ***obtusocuneata*** (5) GEdr GPSL WAbe
- pink-flowered (5) WAbe
'Foster's Gold' (× *elisabethae*) (7) NMen
'Four Winds' (Mossy Group) (15) EWes SPoG
'Francesco Redi' (Renaissance Group) (7) EPot
'Francis Cade' (8) GAbr NSla WAbe
'Frank Sinatra' (× *poluanglica*) (7) NMen
'Franz Liszt' (7) CPBP EPot NMen
'Franzii' (× *paulinae*) (7) NMen
'Freckles' GKev NHpl
frederici-augusti see *S. federici-augusti*
'Frederik Chopin' (7) EPot
'Friar Tuck' (× *boydii*) (7) NMen
'Friesei' (× *salmonica*) (7) EPot
'Fumiko' (*fortunei*) (5) WAbe
'G.W. Gould No. 2' EPot
'Gaiety' (15) CRos EHyd LRHS NEoE NRHS SPoG
'Galaxie' (Holenka's Miracle Group) (× *megaseiflora*) (7) NMen
'Ganymede' (*burseriana*) (7) EPot NMen
× ***gaudinii*** (8) XLum
'Gelber Findling' (7) EPot NMen
'Gelbes Monster' (*fortunei*) (5) EBee ECtt ELan EMor GEdr GPSL NHar NHpl WCot WFar WWtn
'Gem' (× *irvingii*) (7) CRos EHyd LRHS NRHS
'Gemma' (× *megaseiflora*) (7) CRos EHyd LRHS NRHS
'Geoffrey Gould' (7) NMen
'George Gershwin' (Blues Group) (7) NMen
georgei (7) WAbe
§ × ***geum*** (11) GBin MRav SDix WFar
- Dixter form (11) ECha EWes LEdu NDov SMHy SPhx
'Ginkgo 98' (*stolonifera*) (5) WFar
'Gleborg' (Mossy Group) (15) SPoG
'Gloria' (*burseriana*) (7) CRos EHyd EPot LRHS MAsh NMen NRHS NSla WIce
'Gloriana' see *S.* 'Godiva'
× ***gloriana*** *sensu stricto* hort. (7) see *S.* 'Godiva'
'Gloriosa' (× *gloriana*) (7) see *S.* 'Godiva'
§ 'Glowing Ember' (Mossy Group) (15) EWes
§ 'Godiva' (× *gloriana*) (7) NMen
'Gokka' (*fortunei*) (5) NHar NHpl SHeu
'Golden Eye' (× *poluanglica*) (7) NMen
'Golden Falls' (Mossy Group) (15/v) SPlb SPoG
GOLDEN PRAGUE (× *pragensis*) see *S.* 'Zlatá Praha'
'Golem' (7) CPBP NMen
'Goring White' (7) NMen
'Gothenburg' (7) NMen
'Grace Farwell' (× *anglica*) (7) NLar
granulata (15) EWes GJos NAts
'Gratoides' (× *grata*) (7) EPot
'Grébovka' (× *megaseiflora*) (7) NMen
'Gregor' (× *poluanglica*) (7) NMen
§ 'Gregor Mendel' (× *apiculata*) (7) Y^{H5} CMea CRos EHyd EPot LRHS NLar NMen NRHS NSla SRms WAbe WHoo
grisebachii see *S. federici-augusti* subsp. *grisebachii*
- subsp. ***montenegrina*** see *S. federici-augusti*
'Haagii' (× *eudoxiana*) (7) CTri GKev
'Hakubai' (*fortunei*) (5) GEdr WFar
'Halo' (Liberty Ships Group) (7) **new** CPBP NMen
'Hardii' (Mossy Group) (15) EBou
'Hare Knoll Beauty' (8) CRos EHyd EPot GKev LRHS NHol NHpl NRHS NSla NWad WAbe WFar WIce
'Harlow Car' (× *anglica*) (7) EPot NSla
'Harlow Car' (× *anglica*) × ***poluniniana*** (7) NMen
'Harold Bevington' (*paniculata*) (8) NSla
'Harold Lloyd' (7) NMen
'Harvest Moon' (*stolonifera*) (5) WFar WHer
× ***heinreichii*** *sensu stricto* hort. see *S.* 'Ernst Heinrich'
'Helga Hufflepuff' (*cortusifolia*) (5) SGro
'Henri Rousseau' (Conspecta Group) (7) NMen
'Hi-Ace' (Mossy Group) (15/v) NHpl SPlb
'Highlander Red' (Mossy Group) (15) GWyn WIce
'Highlander White' (Mossy Group) (15) GWyn
'Hime' (*stolonifera*) (5) SRms WCru
'Hindhead Seedling' (× *boydii*) (7) CRos EHyd LRHS NMen NRHS WAbe
'Hi-no-mai' (*fortunei*) (5) GEdr WFar
'Hiogi' (*fortunei*) (5) GEdr WFar
hirsuta (11) CMac ESwi EWld LEdu MMuc MNrw WCot WCru
§ 'Hirsuta' (*paniculata*) (8) CPla WFar
hirsuta subsp. ***paucicrenata*** (11) **new** CElw
'Hirsuta' (× *geum*) see *S.* × ***geum***
'Hirtella' misapplied see *S.* 'Hirsuta'
'Hirtella' Ingwersen (*paniculata*) (8) EPot
'His Majesty' (× *irvingii*) (7) NMen
'Hiten' (*fortunei*) (5) EBee
'Hitomebore' (*fortunei*) (5) WFar

	'Hocker Edge' (× *arco-valleyi*) (7)	NMen WAbe
I	'Holden Variety' (*oppositifolia*) (7)	NWad
	'Honeybunch' (Safran Group) (7)	NMen
	'Honington' (× *poluanglica*) (7)	NMen
	hostii (8)	GKev NWad XLum
	- subsp. ***hostii*** (8)	XLum
	- - var. ***altissima*** (8)	XLum
	- subsp. ***rhaetica*** (8)	NBro WThu XLum
	'Hsitou Silver' (*stolonifera*) (5)	WCot
	'Hyoseki' (*fortunei*) (5)	GEdr WFar
§	***hypnoides*** (15)	WAbe
	hypostoma (7)	WAbe
	'Iceland' (*oppositifolia*) (7)	EWes WAbe
	imparilis (5)	WCru
	'Ingeborg' (Mossy Group) (15)	CElw
	iranica (7)	CPBP NMen
	'Irene Bacci' (× *baccii*) (7)	EPot
	× ***irvingii*** *sensu stricto* hort.	see *S.* 'Walter Irving'
	'Iyo Haksui' (*fortunei*) (5) **new**	GEdr
	× ***jacggiana***	NSla
	'James' (7)	NMen NSla
	'Jan Amos Kómenský' (× *anglica*) (7)	NMen
	'Jan Neruda' (× *megaseiflora*) (7)	CPBP EPot NMen
	'Jan Palach' (× *krausii*) (7)	NMen
	'Jan Preisler' (Conspecta Group) (7)	EPot
	'Jaromir' (8)	NMen NSla WAbe
	'Jaroslav Horný' (marginata) (7)	NMen WAbe
	'Jason' (× *elisabethae*) (7)	NMen
	'Jenkinsiae' (× *irvingii*) (7)	CRos EHyd EPot LRHS MAsh MMuc NLar NMen NRHS NSla SEND WAbe WIce
	'Joachim Barrande' (× *siluris*) (7)	EPot
	'Jocelynne Bacci' (7)	NMen
	'Johanka' (7)	NMen
§	'Johann Kellerer' (× *kellereri*) (7)	EPot
	'Johann Wolfgang Goethe' (7)	CPBP
	'John Byam-Grounds' (Honor Group) (7)	WAbe
	'John Tomlinson' (*burseriana*) (7)	NMen NSla
	'Jorg' (× *biasolettoi*) (7)	EPot
	'Josef Čapek' (Holenka's Miracle Group) (× *megaseiflora*) (7)	EPot NMen
	'Joy'	see *S.* 'Kaspar Maria Sternberg'
	'Joy Bishop' (7)	NMen
	'Juliet'	see *S.* 'Riverslea'
§	***juniperifolia*** (7)	SRms XLum
	'Jupiter' (Holenka's Miracle Group) (× *megaseiflora*) (7)	CPBP EPot NMen
	'Kampa' (Holenka's Miracle Group) (7)	NMen
	× ***karacardica*** (7)	NSla
	karadzicensis × ***scardica*** (7)	EPot

	'Karasin' (7)	NMen
	'Karel Čapek' (Prichard's Monument Group) (× *megaseiflora*) (7)	CRos EHyd LRHS NMen NRHS
	'Karlštejn' (× *borisii*) (7)	NMen
§	'Kaspar Maria Sternberg' (× *petraschii*) (7) ♀H5	CRos EHyd LRHS NRHS
	'Kath Dryden' (7)	ITim NMen
	'Kathleen Pinsent' (8)	WAbe
	'Kathleen' (× *polulacina*) (7)	NMen
	'Katrin' (× *borisii*) (7)	NSla
	'Kawazu-beni' (*fortunei*) (5)	GEdr WFar
	'Kbley'	NMen
	× ***kellereri*** *sensu stricto* hort.	see *S.* 'Johann Kellerer'
	'Ken McGregor' (7)	NMen
	'Kestoniensis' (× *salmonica*) (7)	NMen
	'Kineton' (× *poluanglica*) (7)	NMen
	'King Lear' (× *bursiculata*) (7)	CRos EHyd LRHS NRHS
	'Kinki Purple' (*stolonifera*) (5)	CDTJ CDoC CTsd EPPr EPri EShb GBee GBin GWyn MBel WCru WFar WPnP
	'Klondike' (× *boydii*) (7)	EPot NMen WAbe
	'Klonk' (Stratotyp Group) (7) **new**	CPBP NMen
	'Knapton Pink' (Mossy Group) (15)	GBin NEoE SPoG WAbe WIce
	'Koda' (Rezervace Group) (7)	NMen
	'Kokoryu-nishiki' (*fortunei*) (5)	GEdr WFar
	'Komochi-daimonji' (*fortunei*) (5)	GEdr WFar
	'Kon Tiki' (7)	NMen
	'Korin' (*fortunei*) (5) **new**	WFar WOld
	kotschyi (7)	NSla
§	'Krain' (× *fritschiana*) (8)	WOld
	'Krasava' (Prichard's Monument Group) (× *megaseiflora*) (7)	NMen
	'Křivoklát' (7)	NMen
	'Labe' (× *arco-valleyi*) (7)	CMea CRos EHyd EPot LRHS NMen NRHS
	'Ladislav Čelakovský' (7)	NMen
	'Lady Beatrix Stanley'	see *S.* 'Beatrix Stanley'
§	'Lagraveana' (*paniculata*) (8) ♀H5	CRos EHyd GKev LRHS NRHS WFar
	'Laka' (7)	EPot NMen
	× ***landaueri*** *sensu stricto* hort.	see *S.* 'Leonore'
	'Lantoscana' (*callosa* subsp. *callosa* var. *australis*) (8)	GKev
	'Lantoscana Superba' (*callosa* subsp. *callosa* var. *australis*) (8)	NWad WOld
	'Laura Sinclair' (× *fallsvillagensis*) (7)	NMen
	'Lemon Puff'	NSla NWad WFar WIce
	'Lenka' (× *byam-groundsii*) (7)	EPot NMen
	'Leo Gordon Godseff' (× *elisabethae*) (7)	CRos EHyd LRHS NRHS NSla
	'Leonardo da Vinci' (7)	NMen WAbe
§	'Leonore' (× *landaueri*) (7)	CRos EHyd LRHS NRHS
	'Letchworth Gem' (London Pride Group) (× *urbium*) (11)	CRos EHyd GAbr LRHS NRHS WFar
	'Libuse' (7)	NMen

	'Lidice' (7)	NMen WHoo
	lilacina (7)	NMen NSla WAbe
	'Limelight' (*callosa* subsp. *callosa* var. *australis*) (8)	NWad
	'Lincoln Foster' (8)	NWad
	lingulata	see *S. callosa*
	'Lismore Carmine' (× *lismorensis*) (7)	NMen
	'Lismore Mist' (× *lismorensis*) (7)	EPot
	'Lissadell' (*callosa*) (8)	GKev
*	'Little Piggy' (*epiphylla*) (5)	WCru
	'Lizzy' (7)	EPot NMen
	llonakhensis (1)	WAbe
	'Lohmuelleri' (× *biasolettoi*) (7)	WOld
	lolaensis (7)	WAbe
	London Pride Group	LPot
	longifolia (8)	CRos EHyd GEdr GKev LRHS NHpl NRHS NSla XEll
	- var. ***aitanica*** (8)	WAbe
	- hybrids	GKev
	longifolia × ***paniculata*** 'Lutea' (8) **new**	SEdd
	'Louis Armstrong' (Blues Group) (7)	NMen WAbe
	LOVE ME	see *S.* 'Miluj Mne'
	lowndesii (7)	WAbe
	'Loxley' (× *poluanglica*) (7)	NMen
	'Ludmila Šubrová' (× *bertolonii*) (7)	NMen
	'Lutea' (*aizoon*)	see *S.* 'Lutea' (*paniculata*)
§	'Lutea' (*paniculata*) (8)	EBou GMaP MMuc NBro NHol NRya NSla NWad
§	'Luteola' (× *boydii*) (7)	NMen
	'Lydia' (× *hornibrookii*) (7)	WAbe
	macedonica	see *S. juniperifolia*
	'Maigrün' (*fortunei*) (5)	EBee
	'Major Lutea'	see *S.* 'Luteola'
	'Mai-hime' (*fortunei*) (5) **new**	GEdr
	'Mangart' (*burseriana*) (7)	NMen
	'Marcela' (× *megaseiflora*) (7)	NMen
	marginata (7) ♀H5	NMen NSla WAbe
	- var. ***balcanica***	see *S. marginata* subsp. *marginata* var. *rocheliana*
	- var. ***bubakii*** (7)	NMen NSla
	- subsp. ***marginata*** var. ***boryi*** (7)	CRos EHyd LRHS NRHS
§	- - var. ***rocheliana*** (7)	CRos EHyd LRHS NRHS
	'Maria Callas' (× *poluanglica*) (7)	CPBP
	'Maria Luisa' (× *salmonica*) (7)	CPBP
	'Marianna' (× *borisii*) (7)	CMea
	'Marie' (7)	NMen
	'Marilyn Monroe' (Vanessa Group) (7)	NMen
	'Maroon Beauty' (*stolonifera*) (5)	EBee ECtt EPPr LPot MCot NBid NBre WCot WFar
	'Martin Luther' (Wittenberg Group) (7)	EPot
	'Mary Golds' (Swing Group) (7)	GKev NLar NMen NSla
	'Masami' (*fortunei*) (5)	GEdr
	× ***megaseiflora*** *sensu stricto* hort.	see *S.* 'Robin Hood'
	mertensiana (6)	NBir WSHC
	'Meteor' (7)	NHol NSla
	'Michelangelo' (Rutil Group) (7)	NMen
	'Mikawa-beni' (*fortunei*) (5)	GEdr WFar
	'Millstream Cream' (× *elisabethae*) (7)	NMen
§	'Miluj Mne' (× *poluanglica*) (7)	CSma NSla SPlb WAbe WHoo
	'Minor' (*cochlearis*) (8) ♀H5	CRos EHyd LRHS NRHS
	'Mirko Webr' (Harmonia Group) (7)	NMen
§	'Miss Chambers' (London Pride Group) (11)	CBod ECtt EWes LPla SMHy WBrk WCot WFar WSHC
	'Moe' (*fortunei*) (5) ♀H4	GEdr WFar
	'Mollie Broom' (7)	NMen WAbe
	'Momo Tarou' (*fortunei*) (5)	GEdr
	'Monarch' (8) ♀H5	CRos EHyd EWes GAbr GKev ITim LRHS NHpl NRHS NWad WAbe WFar WIce
§	'Mondscheinsonate' (× *boydii*) (7)	NMen
	'Moon Beam' (× *boydilacina*) (7)	NMen
	'Moonlight Sonata' (× *boydii*)	see *S.* 'Mondscheinsonate'
	'Moonlight' (× *boydii*)	see *S.* 'Sulphurea'
	'Morava' (7)	CPBP NMen
	Mossy Group (15)	MHol
	- pink-flowered (15)	GAbr MMuc SPoG
	- red-flowered (15)	SPoG
	- white-flowered (15)	MMuc
	'Mossy Triumph'	see *S.* 'Triumph'
	'Mother of Pearl' (× *irvingii*) (7)	CMea NMen
	'Mount Nachi' (*fortunei*) (5) ♀H4	CRos EHyd EPfP EWes GAbr GEdr GMaP LRHS NBro NHar NHpl NRHS SPlb WAbe WFar WSpi
	'Mrs Helen Terry' (× *salmonica*) (7) ♀H5	CRos EHyd LRHS NMen NRHS
	mutata (9)	GKev
	'Myra' (× *anglica*) (7)	NMen WHoo
	'Myra Cambria' (× *anglica*) (7)	NMen
	'Myriad' (7)	WAbe
	'Myriad Seedling' (7)	NMen
	'Naarden' (7)	NMen
	'Namiyama' (*fortunei*) (5)	GEdr WFar
	'Nancye' (× *goringiana*) (7)	EPot NSla WAbe
	'Neride' (7)	NMen
	'New Europe' (× *krausii*) (7) **new**	NMen
	'Nicholas' (8)	GKev NHpl
	'Nimbus' (*iranica*) (7)	NMen
	'Niobe' (× *pulvilacina*) (7)	EPot
	'Nottingham Gold' (× *boydii*) (7)	EPot NMen
	'Nouhime' (*fortunei*) (5)	GEdr WFar
§	***obtusa*** (7)	NMen
	'Ogon-no-mai' (*fortunei*) (5)	GEdr WFar
	'Oh Yes' (*cochlearis*) (8)	WAbe
	'Olsany' (× *megaseiflora*) (7)	NMen
	'Olympus' (× *boydilacina*) (7)	NMen
	'Omar Khayyám' (7)	EPot NMen
	'Opatov' (× *megaseiflora*) (7)	NMen
	oppositifolia (7)	MAsh NHol NSla SPlb SRms WAbe WSHC
	- subsp. ***oppositifolia*** var. ***latina*** (7)	ELan GKev
	'Orava' (7)	NMen
	'Ottone Rosai' (Toscana Group) (7)	NMen NSla

	'Pablo Picasso' (Conspecta Group) (7)	NMen
	paniculata (8)	EDAr GKev GMaP MHer NSla SPlb SRms WAbe
	- from Austria	CPla
	- from Gorges du Verdon, France	GKev
§	- subsp. ***cartilaginea*** (8)	GKev
	- subsp. ***kolenatiana***	see *S. paniculata* subsp. *cartilaginea*
§	- var. ***minutifolia*** (8)	CPBP CRos EHyd GQue LRHS NBro NHpl NRHS NRya NSla SPlb WAbe
§	- subsp. ***paniculata*** (8)	MAsh
	paradoxa (15)	CRos EHyd EPot LRHS NHol NRHS NWad
	'Parcevalis' (× *finnisiae*) (7 × 9)	WAbe
	'Parsee' (× *margoxiana*) (7)	NMen
	'Paul Gauguin' (Conspecta Group) (7)	EPot NMen
	'Paul Rubens' (7)	WAbe
	'Peach Blossom' (7)	NMen
	'Peach Melba' (7) ♀H5	CPBP CRos CSma EHyd LRHS NHpl NLar NMen NRHS NSla WHoo WIce
	'Peachy Head' (7)	NMen
	'Pearl Rose' (× *anglica*) (7)	EPot NMen
	'Pearly Gates' (× *irvingii*) (7)	NMen
	'Pearly King' (Mossy Group) (15)	ECtt GMaP WAbe
	'Pearly King' variegated (15/v)	GKev
	× ***pectinata*** Schott, Nyman & Kotschy	see *S.* 'Krain'
	'Penelope' (× *boydilacina*) (7)	CRos EHyd EPot LRHS NLar NMen NRHS NSla WHoo
	pensylvanica (4)	IMou
	'Perikles' (7)	NMen
	'Perseus' (7)	NMen
	'Peter Burrow' (× *poluanglica*) (7)	EPot NMen
	'Peter Pan' (Mossy Group) (15)	CRos ECtt EDAr EHyd EPfP GMaP LRHS MAsh MHer NHol NLar NRHS NWad SPoG WCav WFar
	'Petra' (7)	EPot NMen
§	'Phoenix' (× *biasolettoi*) (7)	CRos EHyd LRHS NRHS
	'Pierantonio Micheli' (Renaissance Group) (7)	NMen
	'Pink Candy' (*fortunei*) (5) **new**	WFar
	'Pink Cloud' (*fortunei*) (5)	EPri GEdr NBPC NBro NHar WAbe WFar
	'Pink Haze' (*fortunei*) (5) ♀H4	GEdr WAbe WFar
	'Pink Melba' (7) **new**	CRos
	'Pink Mist' (*fortunei*) (5)	GEdr WAbe WFar
	'Pink Pagoda' (*nipponica*) (5)	EBee WCot WCru WFar
	'Pink Star' (× *boydilacina*) (7)	EPot GMaP NLar NMen
	'Pixie' (15)	ECtt MAsh NHol NRya NWad SPoG SRms WFar WIce
	'Pixie Alba'	see *S.* 'White Pixie'
	'Plena' (*granulata*)	see *S.* 'Flore Pleno'
	'Polar Drift'	CRos EHyd LRHS NRHS NSla NWad WAbe WIce
	poluniniana × 'Winifred' (× *poluanglica*) (7)	EPot
	'Pomona Sprout' (*cortusifolia*) (5)	SGro
	'Pompadour' (15)	NEoE
	'Popelka' (*marginata* subsp. *marginata* var. *rocheliana*) (7)	CRos EHyd LRHS NRHS
	porophylla (7)	EPot GKev
	aff. ***porophylla*** (7)	EPot
	'Portae' (× *fritschiana*) (8)	XLum
	'Precious Piggy' (*epiphylla*) (5)	WCru
	'Primrose Bee' (× *apiculata*) (7)	GKev
	'Primrose Dame' (× *elisabethae*) (7)	EPot WAbe WIce
	'Primulaize Salmon' (9 × 11)	WHoo
	'Primuloides' (*umbrosa*) (11)	EDAr MMuc SRms SWvt
	'Primuloides' variegated (*umbrosa*) (11/v)	SRms
	'Prince Hal' (*burseriana*) (7)	CRos EHyd EPot LRHS NRHS NSla
	'Princess' (*burseriana*) (7)	CRos EHyd LRHS NMen NRHS NSla
	'Probynii' (*cochlearis*) (8)	CPBP EPot WAbe
	'Prometheus' (× *prossenii*) (7)	NMen
	'Prosek' (× *megaseiflora*) (7)	NMen
	× ***prossenii*** *sensu stricto* hort.	see *S.* 'Regina'
	'Pseudo-valdensis' (*cochlearis*) (8)	NMen WAbe
	pubescens (15)	WAbe
	'Punctatissima' (*paniculata*) (8)	NWad
	'Purple Piggy' (*epiphylla*) (5)	WCru
	'Purpurea' (*fortunei*)	see *S.* 'Rubrifolia'
	'Pygmalion' (× *webrii*) (7)	NMen
	'Pyramidalis' (*cotyledon*) (8)	XLum
	quadrifaria (7)	WAbe
	'Quarry Wood' (× *anglica*) (7)	NMen
	'Rachael Young' (× *borisii*) (7)	NMen
	'Rachel' (8)	GKev
	'Radka' (× *megaseiflora*) (7)	NMen
	'Rainsley Seedling' (8)	EPot GKev NBro
	'Ray Woodliffe' (× *dinninaris*) (7)	WAbe
	'Red Poll' (× *poluanglica*) (7)	GAbr NHpl NMen WAbe
*	'Regent'	WAbe
§	'Regina' (× *prossenii*) (7)	NMen
§	'Reginald Farrer' (Silver Farreri Group) (8) ♀H5	WAbe
	'Rembrandt van Rijn' (7)	CPBP EPot NMen WAbe
	retusa (7)	WAbe
	'Rex' (*paniculata*) (8)	NWad
	'River Thame' (× *polulacina*) (7)	NMen WOld
§	'Riverslea' (× *hornibrookii*) (7)	CPBP NMen
§	'Robin Hood' (× *megaseiflora*) (7)	EPot NMen WHoo
	'Rocco Red' (× *arendsii*) (15)	CBod
	'Rockrose'^{PBR} (× *arendsii*) (15)	SPoG
§	'Rockwhite' (× *arendsii*) (15)	WIce
	'Rokujō' (*fortunei*) (5) ♀H4	EBee NBro NEoE NLar SHeu
	'Romulus' (7)	NMen
	'Rosa Tubbs' (8)	EWes
	'Rosea' (× *arendsii*) (15) **new**	SCob
§	'Rosea' (*paniculata*) (8) ♀H5	GMaP GWyn MMuc NBro NRya NSla SEND SRms

	Name	Suppliers
	'Rosemarie' (7)	NMen
	'Rosina Sündermann' (× *rosinae*) (7)	CRos EHyd LRHS NMen NRHS
	rotundifolia (12)	CElw EBee ECha MPnt WBor
	'Roztyly' (× *megaseiflora*) (7)	NMen
	'Rubella' (× *irvingii*) (7)	NMen
	'Rubra' (*aizoon*)	see *S.* 'Rosea' (*paniculata*)
§	'Rubrifolia' (*fortunei*) (5) ♀H4	CMac ECha ECtt GAbr GEdr LEdu NBPC NBro NHpl SMad SWvt WBor WCot WCru WFar WPnP
*	'Ruby Red'	NEoE
*	'Ruby Wedding' (*cortusifolia*) (5)	WFar
	rufescens (5) BWJ 7510	WCru
	- BWJ 7684	WCru
	'Rufina' (7)	NMen
	'Rumba' (7) **new**	NMen
	'Russell V. Prichard' (× *irvingii*) (7)	NMen
	'Ruth Draper' (*oppositifolia*) (7) ♀H5	WAbe
	'Ruth McConnell' (15)	CMea
	'Ruznyě' (× *megaseiflora*) (7)	NMen
	'Saint John's' (8)	GKev WAbe
	'Saint Kilda' (*oppositifolia*) (7)	NWad
	× ***salmonica*** *sensu stricto* hort.	see *S.* 'Salomonii'
	'Salome' (× *lincolni-fosteri*) (7)	EPot NMen
§	'Salomonii' (× *salmonica*) (7)	SRms
	sancta (7)	CRos EHyd LRHS NRHS NSla SRms
	- subsp. ***pseudosancta***	see *S. juniperifolia*
	- - var. ***macedonica***	see *S. juniperifolia*
	'Saotome' (*fortunei*) (5) **new**	GEdr
	'Sara Sinclair' (× *arco-valleyi*) (7)	CMea
	'Šárka' (7)	CPBP NMen
	sarmentosa	see *S. stolonifera*
	'Satchmo' (Blues Group) (7)	NMen NSla
	'Saturn' (× *megaseiflora*) (7)	EPot NMen
	'Sázava' (× *poluluteopurpurea*) (7)	NMen NSla
§	***scardica*** (7)	EPot NBro NMen WAbe
	- var. ***dalmatica***	see *S. obtusa*
§	'Schelleri' (× *petraschii*) (7)	EPfP NMen
§	'Schwefelblüte' (15)	CRos EHyd GMaP LRHS NRHS
	'Seissera' (*burseriana*) (7)	NMen
	sempervivum (7)	NGdn WAbe
	'Seren y Gwanwyn' (*oppositifolia*) (7)	WAbe
	'Shaggy Hair' (*stolonifera*) (5)	WFar
	'Sherlock Holmes' (7)	NMen WAbe
	'Shimanami' (*fortunei*) (5)	EMor MNrw NHar
	'Shimmy'	WAbe
	'Shiomoe' (*fortunei*) (5) **new**	GEdr
	'Shiranami' (*fortunei*) (5) ♀H4	CBcs EBee ECtt ELan EWes GEdr GPSL LSun MBel NHpl SPlb WCot WFar WWtn
	'Sibyll Trelawney JP' (*fortunei*) (5) **new**	GPSL WFar
§	'Silver Cushion' (15/v)	CPla CRos CTri EHyd ELan LRHS NHpl NRHS SPlb SPoG SRms WAbe WIce
	'Silver Edge' (× *arco-valleyi*) (7)	EPot
	'Silver Hill' (*paniculata*) (8)	NSla
	'Silver Maid' (× *engleri*) (8)	NSla
	'Silver Mound'	see *S.* 'Silver Cushion'
	'Silver Velvet' (*fortunei*) (5/v)	CSpe EBee ECtt MBNS MBel MNrw NBPC NHpl SEdd SHeu WCot
	'Sissi' (7)	CPBP EPot NMen WAbe
	'Slack's Ruby Southside' (Southside Seedling Group) (8) ♀H5	ITim NSla NWad WCav WFar WIce
	'Slack's Supreme' (8)	NSla WCot WFar
	'Slavia' (7)	NMen
§	'Slzy Coventry' (× *proximae*) (7)	NMen WAbe
	'Sněhurka' (Fenomen Group) (7)	NMen
	'Snow White' (7) **new**	NMen
	'Snowcap' (*pubescens*) (15)	NMen WAbe
	'Snowflake' (Silver Farreri Group) (8) ♀H5	CRos EHyd LRHS NRHS WAbe
§	'Sofia' (× *borisii*) (7)	EPot
	Southside Seedling Group (8)	CMea CRos EDAr EHyd EPfP EPot EWTr GAbr GKev GMaP LRHS MAsh MBel MMuc NBro NHol NHpl NRHS NWad SAko SEND SMad SPoG SRms WAbe WFar WHoo WIce XLum
	- 'Southside Star' (8) ♀H5	LEdu NHpl WAbe
	spathularis (11)	WCot WHoo
	'Splendens' (*oppositifolia*) (7) ♀H5	EBou EPfP GAbr GKev MMuc SRms WAbe
	'Spotted Dog'	see *S.* 'Canis-dalmatica'
	'Sprite' (15)	SPoG
	spruneri (7)	CRos EHyd LRHS NRHS
	'Stansfieldii' (*rosacea*) (15)	EBou SPlb SPoG
	'Starfire' (8)	GKev
	'Starlight' (8)	GKev
	startorii	see *S. scardica*
	'Štásek' (*dinnikii*) (7)	WAbe WOld
	stellaris (4)	WAbe
§	***stolonifera*** (5) ♀H2	CRos CSpe EShb LRHS NBro SDix SWvt WCot WFar WWtn
	- large-flowered (5)	WCot WGrn
	'Strawberry Melba' (7)	NMen
	stribrnyi (7)	WHoo
*	- var. ***degenii*** (7) **new**	NSla
	'Sturmiana' (*paniculata*) (8)	SRms WOld
	'Sue Tubbs' (8)	GKev
	'Suendermannii Major' (× *kellereri*) (7)	CRos EHyd LRHS NRHS
	'Suendermannii' (× *kellereri*) (7)	CRos EHyd LRHS NMen NRHS
	SUGAR PLUM FAIRY ('Toujya') (*fortunei*) (5) ♀H4	EBee ECtt EShb SHeu WFar
§	'Sulphurea' (× *boydii*) (7)	CMea CRos EHyd LRHS MAsh NRHS NSla WHoo
	'Sun Dance' (× *boydii*) (7)	NMen
	'Superba' (*callosa* subsp. *callosa* var. *australis*) (8)	NSla
	'Symons-Jeunei' (8)	NWad
	'Tamayura' (*fortunei*) (5)	GEdr
	'Tankei' (5)	SAko
	'Tenerife' (Swirly Group) (7)	EPot EWes NMen WAbe
	'Tetín' (Teta Group) (7)	EPot NMen
	'Thalia' (7)	NMen
	'Theoden' (*oppositifolia*) (7)	CMea EWes WAbe
	'Theresa Cooper' (7)	EPot
	'Theseus' (7)	CPBP
	'Thór Heyerdahl' (Ocean Group) (7)	EPot NMen

	'Timmy Foster' (× *irvingii*) (7)	NMen
	tombeanensis (7)	EPot WAbe
	'Torrisholme Rose' (7)	NMen
	TOURAN DEEP RED ('Rockred') (Mossy Group) (15)	CRos EHyd EPfP LBuc LRHS NRHS
	TOURAN LARGE WHITE ('Rocklarwhi'^{PBR}) (Mossy Group) (15)	CRos EHyd EPfP LBuc LRHS NRHS
	TOURAN PINK (× *arendsii*) (15) **new**	CRos
	TOURAN RED ('Saxz0006') (× *arendsii*) (15)	SPoG WIce
	TOURAN WHITE	see *S.* 'Rockwhite' (× *arendsii*) (15)
	TOURAN WHITE IMPROVED ('Saxz0004'^{PBR}) (× *arendsii*) (15)	SPoG WIce
	'Tricolor' (*stolonifera*) (5) 𝕐H2	CDoC EBak
§	'Triumph' (× *arendsii*) (15)	ECtt EPfP GMaP MAsh SPoG WSMil
	'Tully' (× *elisabethae*) (7)	NMen
	'Tumbling Waters' (8) 𝕐H5	CRos EHyd LEdu LRHS NHol NHpl NRHS NSla NWad WAbe
§	'Tvoje Píseň' (× *poluanglica*) (7)	WHoo
§	'Tvůj Polibek' (× *poluanglica*) (7)	EPot NMen
§	'Tvůj Úsměv' (× *poluanglica*) (7) 𝕐H5	NBPC NHpl
§	'Tvůj Úspěch' (× *poluanglica*) (7)	NMen NWad
	'Two Kings' (*fortunei*) (5)	WFar
	'Tycho Brahe' (× *doerfleri*) (7)	GKev WAbe
	'Tysoe' (7)	EPot
	'Tysoe Blush' (Blues Group) (7)	NSla
	'Tysoe Burgundy' (Blues Group) (7)	CPBP NSla
	'Tysoe Everest' (7) **new**	NMen
	'Tysoe Makalu' (7) **new**	NSla
	'Tysoe Pink-Perfection' (Blues Group) (7)	CPBP NMen NSla
	'Tysoe Splendour' (Blues Group) (7)	NSla
	umbrosa (11)	CMac CRos EDAr EHyd EPfP GAbr LEdu LRHS LSun MMuc MRav NRHS SEND SHar SPlb SPoG SRms SWvt WFar XLum
*	- ***subinteger***	MMuc
	unguipetala (7) **new**	NMen
	× ***urbium*** (11) 𝕐H5	CBod CCBP CRos CTri EHyd ELan EPfP GMaP GQue LEdu LRHS MBel MCot NSti SBut SCob SEdd SPer SRms WBor WCAu WHoo WSpi WTor
	'Vaccariana' (*oppositifolia*) (7)	EPot SHar
	'Václav Hollar' (× *gusmusii*) (7)	NMen
	'Valborg'	see *S.* 'Cranbourne'
	'Valentine'	see *S.* 'Cranbourne'
	'Valerie Finnis'	see *S.* 'Aretiastrum'
	'Valerie Keevil' (× *anglica*) (7)	NMen
I	'Variegata' (*cuneifolia*) (11/v)	CBod CRos EBou ECtt EHyd EPfP LRHS NHol NHpl NRHS NRya NWad SPlb SPoG WBrk WHoo
I	'Variegata' (*exarata* subsp. *moschata*) (15/v)	GMaP
	'Variegata' (*umbrosa*)	see *S.* 'Aureopunctata'
I	'Variegata' (× *urbium*) (11/v)	EBee EHyd EPfP GPSL LPot LRHS MBel NLar SCob SPtp SRms WFar WHoo WTor
	vayredana (15)	WAbe
	'Večerní Hvězda' (7)	CPBP NMen WAbe
	veitchiana (5)	NBro WFar XLum
	'Verona' (× *caroli-langii*) (7)	WAbe
	'Vesna' (× *borisii*) (7)	NMen
	'Vikos Gold' (7)	EPot NMen
	'Vincent van Gogh' (× *borisii*) (7)	NMen
	'Vítkov' (× *megaseiflora*) (7)	NMen
	'Vladana' (× *megaseiflora*) (7)	CRos EHyd EPot LRHS NRHS NSla SPlb
	'Vlasta Burian' (7)	NMen
	'Vreny' (8)	GKev
	'Wada' (*fortunei*) (5)	CMac CSpe ECtt EPri GKev GMaP LRHS MBel MNrw MSpe NBir NBro NHar NRHS SPer SRms WAul WBor WCot WFar WOld WSHC
	'Walpole's Variety' (8)	NWad
	'Walter Ingwersen' (*umbrosa*) (11)	SRms
§	'Walter Irving' (× *irvingii*) (7) 𝕐H5	NSla WAbe
	'Welsh Dragon' (15)	WAbe
	'Welsh Red' (15)	WAbe
	'Welsh Rose' (15)	WAbe
	wendelboi (7)	EPot NMen
	'Wendrush' (× *wendelacina*) (7)	NMen
	'Wendy' (× *wendelacina*) (7)	NMen
	'Wheatley Lion' (× *borisii*) (7)	NMen
	'Wheatley Rose' (7)	CRos EHyd LRHS NMen NRHS
	'White Delight' (× *megaseiflora*) (7)	CRos EHyd LRHS NMen NRHS NSla
	'White Imp' (7)	NMen
§	'White Pixie' (15)	CPla EBou ECtt EDAr EPfP MAsh MHer NEoE NHol NRya NWad SPlb SPoG SRms WCAu WFar WIce
	'White Star' (*fortunei*) (5)	CRos EHyd LRHS NRHS
	'White Star' (× *petraschii*)	see *S.* 'Schelleri'
	'Whitehill' (8) 𝕐H5	CMea CRos EBou EHyd ELan EPot GEdr GMaP LRHS NRHS NRya NSla NWad SEdd SGro WHoo
	'William Shakespeare' (Blues Group) (7)	CPBP NMen WAbe
	'Winifred Bevington' (8 × 11)	CRos CSma EBou EDAr EHyd EPot GMaP LRHS MBel NBro NHpl NLar NRHS NRya NWad SGro SIvy SRms WAbe WCav WFar WHoo
	'Winifred' (× *anglica*) (7)	EPot NMen WAbe
	'Winston Churchill' (15)	CRos EHyd EPfP LRHS NEoE NHol NRHS NWad
I	'Winston Churchill Variegata' (15/v)	NHol
	'Winton' (× *paulinae*) (7)	EPot NMen
	'Wisley' (*federici-augusti* subsp. *grisebachii*) (7) 𝕐H5	GKev
	'Yellow Rock' (7)	NMen
	YOUR GOOD FORTUNE	see *S.* 'Tvůj Úspěch'
	YOUR KISS	see *S.* 'Tvůj Polibek'
	YOUR SMILE	see *S.* 'Tvůj Úsměv'
	YOUR SONG	see *S.* 'Tvoje Píseň'
	YOUR SUCCESS	see *S.* 'Tvůj Úspěch'
	'Yunagi' (*fortunei*) (5)	WOld

'Zbraslav' (× *megaseiflora*) (7)	NMen NSla
× ***zimmeteri*** (8 × 11)	NSla
'Ziva' (7)	NMen
§ 'Zlatá Praha' (× *pragensis*) (7)	NMen WAbe
'Zlatý Kůň' (× *laeviformis*) (7)	EPot
'Zlín' (× *leyboldii*) (7)	NMen

Scabiosa (Caprifoliaceae)

africana	CElw
- 'Jocelyn'	EWes SHar
alpina L.	see *Cephalaria alpina*
argentea	EWes WPGP
- PAB 1229	LEdu
atropurpurea	LCro LOPS
- 'Ace of Spades'	ELan EPfP SPhx
- 'Beaujolais Bonnets'	CRos EAJP EBee EHyd EPfP LRHS NGBl NRHS
- 'Black Knight'	CSpe LCro LOPS SPhx
§ - 'Chile Black'	CBcs EAJP EHyd ELan EPfP GWyn LRHS NLar NRHS SCob SPer SPoG SRkn SWvt
§ - 'Chilli Pepper'	LRHS
- Kudos Series **new**	LSou
banatica	see *S. columbaria*
'Barocca'	CRos CWGN EBee EPfP LRHS NLar SCob SRms
'Blackberry Fool' (Dessert Series)	SCob
BLUE DIAMONDS ('Kiescalibu')	GJos MHol WFar
'Blueberry Muffin' (Dessert Series)	SCob
§ 'Butterfly Blue'	Widely available
caucasica	CMac CRos EHyd EPfP GKev LEdu LRHS NRHS XSen
- var. ***alba***	CBcs EPfP ILea NGBl WHoo
- 'Blausiegel'	CBod EShb MRav SGbt
- 'Clive Greaves' ♀H4	CCBP EBee ECha EWTr GMaP LRHS MBNS MHost NLar NRHS SGbt SPad SPer SRms SWvt WCAu WFar
- 'Deep Waters'	LRHS
- 'Fama'	CSpe NBir NGBl NLar SPlb SRms WFar WHoo
- 'Fama Deep Blue'	CBod CNor LRHS MHol NRHS SHar WFar
- 'Fama White'	EHyd LRHS NRHS SHar
- 'Goldingensis'	NGdn WHil
- House's hybrids	MHol NGdn SRms
- 'Isaac House'	CWCL WFar XLum
- 'Kompliment'	WFar
- 'Miss Willmott' ♀H4	CBod CRos CSam EBee ECha ECtt EHyd EShb GBin LRHS MArl MHer MHost MRav MSpe NDov NLar NRHS SGbt SPad SPer SWvt WCAu XSen
- Perfecta Series	CRos EHyd GBin ILea LRHS NGdn NLar NRHS SCob SPoG
- - 'Perfecta Alba'	CBod CDor CRos EHyd ELan EPfP GBin GMaP LRHS MBel MHol NLar NRHS SBut SCob SPer SPoG SPtp WCAu WGwG XLum
- - 'Perfecta Blue'	CBod CDor CMea ELan EPfP EWTr GMaP MBel MHol XLum
- - 'Perfecta Lilac Blue'	EPfP SPer
- 'Stäfa'	CBod EBee ECha EHyd LRHS MHer NLar NRHS NSti SCob SGbt WHoo
'Champanelle'	CBor
'Cherry Pie' (Dessert Series)	SCob
'Chile Black'	see *S. atropurpurea* 'Chile Black'
'Chile Pepper'	see *S. atropurpurea* 'Chilli Pepper'
cinerea	SPhx
§ ***columbaria***	CCBP CFis CHab CRos CWld EBee EHyd EWTr LCro LOPS LRHS MBow NGrd NMir NRHS SBut SPhx WHer WSFF WWild
* - ***alpina***	GKev
- 'Big Blue' **new**	CRos
- 'Blue Note'^{PBR}	MHol MPri
- blue-flowered	NHpl
- FLUTTER DEEP BLUE ('Balfluttdelu'^{PBR})	CBod LSou MHol WHil
- FLUTTER ROSE PINK ('Balfluttropi'^{PBR})	CBod LSou MHol WHil
- 'Mariposa Blue'^{PBR}	LRHS MHol MPri NRHS WHil
- 'Mariposa Blush'	WHil
- 'Misty Butterflies'	CAby ECtt EPfP GJos MHol NCou NGdn NLar SEdd SRms WFar
- 'Nana'	CRos EBee EHyd EPfP GWyn LRHS NBir NGdn NRHS WCFE XLum
§ - subsp. ***ochroleuca***	CCBP CDor CElw CKno CSpe ECha EHyd EWTr LRHS MBel NBir NGBl SBut SEdd SHar SMHy SPhx SPoG SRms SSut WBrk WCAu WOut
- - MESE 344	EBee
- - 'Moon Dance'	CDor CMea CRos CWGN EAJP EHyd EShb LRHS LSun MTis NRHS SAko SCob SGbt SPoG WCot WHoo
- 'Pincushion Blue'	EHyd LRHS LSun NRHS
- 'Pincushion Pink'	CRos EBou EHyd GJos GWyn LRHS NGdn NRHS
- pink-flowered	MMuc
cretica	XLum
drakensbergensis	EWTr EWes GBin GKev ILea LRHS SLon WCot
gigantea	see *Cephalaria gigantea*
graminifolia	CPla CRos EBee EHyd LRHS NBir NRHS SGro SPhx SRms XLum XSen
- 'Green Dome'	GKev
- ***rosea***	EWes
'Helen Dillon'	ECre EWes
incisa	WOut
- 'Kudo'	CBod CKno CRos CWGN EBee ECtt EHyd LCro LOPS LRHS LSou MHol NRHS NSti SHar SPad SPoG SWvt WNPC
- 'Kudo White'	CRos CWGN ECtt LCro LOPS LRHS LSou MHol NSti WNPC
'Irish Perpetual Flowering'	see *S.* 'Butterfly Blue'
japonica var. ***alpina***	EBee EPfP GKev MMuc NGdn SEND SPhx SPtp WFar WHoo XLum XSen
- - 'Blue Star'	EBee NBre SGbt
- - 'Ritz Blue'	CMea EPfP MHer WCav
- - 'Ritz Rose'	CMea
lachnophylla	SPhx WCot
'Little Cracker'	GBin LRHS SLon
'Little Emily'	ELon
lucida	CBod CNor EHyd EPfP LRHS MMuc MRav NRHS SEND SGbt WCAu XLum
MAGIC ('Pmoore02')	NEoE
'Midnight'	CMea
'Miss Havisham'	CElw EWes MNrw
'Misty Pink' **new**	CRos
montana Mill.	see *Knautia arvensis*

ochroleuca	see *S. columbaria* subsp. *ochroleuca*
parnassi	see *Pterocephalus perennis*
'Perpetual Flowering'	see *S.* 'Butterfly Blue'
PINK BUTTONS ('Walminipink')	CBod
'Pink Diamonds'	EBee ELan EPfP MHol MHost WFar
'Pink Mist'	CBod CRos ECtt EHyd ELan EPfP GBin LCro LOPS LRHS MAsh MPie NBir NHpl NLar NRHS SCob SCoo SPer SPoG SRms WTor
pterocephala	see *Pterocephalus perennis*
'Raspberry Sorbet' (Dessert Series)	SCob
rhodopensis	EBee
'Rosie's Pink'	ECtt
rumelica	see *Knautia macedonica*
'Satchmo'	see *S. atropurpurea* 'Chile Black'
stellata	SPhx
succisa	see *Succisa pratensis*
tatarica	see *Cephalaria gigantea*
'Vivid Violet'	CAbb CAby CBod CDor CRos CSpe EBee ECtt EHyd LBuc LRHS LSRN LSou MHol MMuc MNrw NHpl NRHS SAko WBrk

Scadoxus ✿ (*Amaryllidaceae*)

membranaceus	WCot
multiflorus	CCCN EShb GKev SDeJ SDir
§ - subsp. ***katherinae*** ♀H1b	WCot
§ - subsp. ***multiflorus***	WCot
natalensis	see *S. puniceus*
§ ***puniceus***	WCot

Scaevola (*Goodeniaceae*)

aemula 'Blue Fan'	see *S. aemula* 'Blue Wonder'
- BLUE PRINT ('Kingscablin')	LSou MPri
§ - 'Blue Wonder'	NPer SWvt
- 'Fancy' **new**	LSou
- 'Zig Zag'PBR	CCCN MBros
BLAUER FACHER ('Saphira'PBR)	CCCN NLar
'Mini Blue'	CCCN
'Topaz Pink'	LSou

Sceletium (*Aizoaceae*)

tortuosum	SPlb

Schefflera ✿ (*Araliaceae*)

alpina B&SWJ 8247	WCru
- B&SWJ 11827	WCru
- HWJ 936	WCru
- NJM 09.140	WPGP
- NJM 09.157	WPGP
- large-leaved WWJ 11999	WCru
arboricola ♀H1c	SEND XBlo
- 'Gold Capella' ♀H1c	SEND XBlo
- 'Kalahari'	XBlo
brevipedicellata	CDTJ
- HWJ 870	WCru
- KWJ 12224	WCru
aff. ***brevipedicellata*** NJM 10.102	CBct WPGP
§ ***chapana*** B&SWJ 11833	WCru
- B&SWJ 11848	WCru
- HWJ 983	WCru
delavayi	CBct CDTJ WCru WPGP
digitata	CBct CTrC
enneaphylla HWJ 1018	WCru
fantsipanensis B&SWJ 11666	WCru
- B&SWJ 11671	WCru
gracilis	CBcs EBee
- HWJ 622	WCru
- HWJ 878	WCru
gracilis* × *taiwaniana	WCru
hoi B&SWJ 11747	WCru
kornasii B&SWJ 11830	WCru
- HWJ 918	WCru
aff. ***littorea*** BWJ 15158 **new**	WCru
macrophylla B&SWJ 8210	WCru
- B&SWJ 9788	WCru
- B&SWJ 11842	WCru
- WWJ 11681	WCru
microphylla B&SWJ 3872	WCru
multinervia B&SWJ 11727	WCru
aff. ***myriocarpa*** B&SWJ 11828	WCru
nova NJM 13.128	WPGP
pauciflora WWJ 11986 **new**	WCru
rhododendrifolia	CBcs CBct CDTJ CDoC CExl EBee LEdu WPGP
- GWJ 9375	WCru
shweliensis NJM 13.130 **new**	WPGP
- PAB 13.216	LEdu
taiwaniana ♀H4	CBcs CBct EBee WCot WPGP
- B&SWJ 3575	WCru
- B&SWJ 3788	WCru
- B&SWJ 7096	WCru
- RWJ 10000	WCru
- RWJ 10016	WCru
vietnamensis	see *S. chapana*

Schima (*Theaceae*)

argentea	CBcs CCCN CExl CTsd EBee WPGP
aff. ***argentea*** NJM 13.042	WPGP
khasiana	CBcs WPGP
- PAB 3447	EBee LEdu
wallichii	CExl ESwi

Schinus (*Anacardiaceae*)

latifolius	ESwi
lentiscifolius	SPlb SVen
molle	SPlb
patagonicus	MGil
polygama	MGil SPlb

Schisandra (*Schisandraceae*)

arisanensis	MBlu NLar WPGP
- B&SWJ 3050	WCru
chinensis	CAgr CBcs GKev GPoy LEdu MGil MSwo NLar SBrt WPGP
- B&SWJ 4204	WCru
- B&SWJ 4611A	WCru
- B&SWJ 4611B	WCru
- 'Bere'	LEdu WPGP
- 'Sadova No.1'	CAgr
grandiflora ♀H4	CBcs CBod CRos CWCL EBee EHyd ELan EPfP ESwi GBin IMou LRHS MBlu SBrt SNig WPGP
- B&SWJ 2245	WCru WSHC
- PAB 3673	LEdu
- WJC 13666	WCru
- var. ***cathayensis***	see *S. sphaerandra*
- 'Jamu' (m)	WCru
- 'Lahlu' (f/F)	WCru
aff. ***grandiflora*** WJC 13817	WCru
grandiflora* × *rubriflora	MMuc WCru

henryi	WCru
subsp. ***yunnanensis*** B&SWJ 6546	
incarnata BWJ 7898	WCru
incarnata* × *rubriflora	WCru
lancifolia	MBlu
nigra	see *S. repanda*
perulata FMWJ 13100	WCru
aff. ***plena*** HWJ 664	WCru
propinqua	WSHC
- subsp. ***sinensis***	CMac CRHN LEdu NLar WPGP
- - BWJ 8148	WCru
§ ***repanda*** B&SWJ 11455	WCru
- B&SWJ 5897	WCru
rubriflora ♀H5	CBcs CTri EPfP IMou LRHS MBlu MGos NLar NOra SBrt SDix SLon WCFE
- BWJ 7557	WCru
- (f)	IDee WSHC WSpi
- 'Bodnant Redberry' (f)	WCru
§ ***sphaerandra***	CBcs MBlu
- BWJ 7739	WCru
- BWJ 8082	WCru
sphenanthera	EBee MBlu NLar WSHC
- BWJ 8151	WCru

Schizachyrium (*Poaceae*)

§ ***scoparium***	CBod CKno CRos EPfP LRHS NRHS SCob XCre XLum
- 'Blue Heaven'	CKno ELon MAvo NDov SAko SEdd WSpi
- 'Cairo'	EBee
- 'Prairie Blues'	CSpe EBou EHyd ELon EPfP LRHS SEdd SMea WCot XCre
- 'Standing Ovation' **new**	LCro LOPS

Schizanthus (*Solanaceae*)

hookeri	CPla

Schizocarphus (*Asparagaceae*)

nervosus	WCot

Schizocodon see *Shortia*

Schizophragma (*Hydrangeaceae*)

fauriei	NLar
- B&SWJ 1701	WCru
- B&SWJ 6831	WCru
- B&SWJ 7052	WCru
- CWJ 12405	WCru
- CWJ 12433	WCru
- WINDMILLS ('Plooster') **new**	CMil
hydrangeoides	CBcs CBct CCCN CRos EBee EHyd ELan EPfP EWTr LCro LOPS LRHS MBlu MGos NRHS SCob SGol SLim SLon SPer SPoG SWvt WCFE WSpi
- 'Brookside Littleleaf'	see *Hydrangea anomala* subsp. *petiolaris* var. *cordifolia* 'Brookside Littleleaf'
- BURST OF LIGHT (v) **new**	ETho
- var. ***concolor*** B&SWJ 5954	WCru
- - 'Moonlight' ♀H5	CBcs CDoC CMac CRos CWGN EHyd ELan EPfP EWTr LRHS MBlu MGil MGos MMuc NOra NRHS SGol SLon SPoG SWvt WCot WCru WPGP
- var. ***hydrangeoides*** B&SWJ 5489	WCru
- - B&SWJ 5732	WCru
- - 'Iwa Garami'	NLar
- - 'Roseum' ♀H5	CArg CBcs CCCN CMac ELan EPfP EWes IArd LRHS MBlu MGil MGos SCob SGol SLon SPer SWvt WCot WCru WPGP
* - f. ***quelpartensis***	LRHS
- 'Rose Sensation'	CCCN CRos EBee EHyd EPfP LRHS NRHS SGol SLon SPoG
- var. ***taquetii*** B&SWJ 8771	WCru
- - 'Cheju's Early'	WCru
- var. ***ullungdoense*** B&SWJ 8505	WCru
- - B&SWJ 8522	WCru
- var. ***yakushimense*** B&SWJ 6119	WCru
integrifolium ♀H5	CAby CBcs CCCN CRHN CRos EBee EHyd ELan EPfP LRHS MBlu MMuc NLar SPer WKif WPGP
- BWJ 8150	WCru
molle HWJ 1011	WCru
- WWJ 11905	WCru

Schizostylis see *Hesperantha*

Schoenoplectus (*Cyperaceae*)

§ ***lacustris***	CWat LLWG MMuc
§ - subsp. ***tabernaemontani***	CSpe LLWG
- - 'Albescens' (v)	CBen CWat MMuc MNrw WHal WWtn XLum
- - 'Zebrinus' (v)	CBen CWat ELan EWat MNrw SPlb WMAq WWtn XLum

Schoenoxiphium (*Cyperaceae*)

lanceum	XBlo

Schoenus (*Cyperaceae*)

pauciflorus	LLWG

Sciadopitys (*Sciadopityaceae*)

verticillata ♀H6	CBcs CKen CMac CSBt EPfP GKin LRHS MBlu MGil MGos MMuc MPkF NHol SAko SCoo SEND SLim SPoG SWvt WHwl XLot
- 'Dutch Mill'	NLar
- 'Firework'	CKen
- 'Globe'	CKen
- 'Gold Star'	CKen
- 'Golden Rush'	CKen MAsh
- 'Goldmahne'	CKen
- 'Grüne Kugel'	CKen MAsh
- 'Jeddeloh Compact'	CKen
- 'Koja Maki'	NLar
- 'Kupferschirm'	CKen
- 'Lightning Green' **new**	NLar
- 'Marylin Monroe'	NLar
- 'Mecki'	CKen
- 'Megaschirm'	CKen
- 'Mr Happy'	NLar
- 'Ossorio Gold'	CKen
- 'Perlenglanz'	CKen
- 'Picola'	CKen MAsh WHwl
- 'Pygmy'	CKen
- 'Richie's Cream'	CKen
- 'Richie's Cushion'	CKen
- 'Shorty'	CKen
- 'Speerspitze'	CKen
- 'Star Wars'	CKen
- 'Starburst'	CKen
- 'Sternschnuppe'	CKen MAsh NLar
- 'Tsai Cheng'	NLar
- 'Wintergreen'	CKen

Scilla (*Asparagaceae*)

adlamii	see *Ledebouria cooperi*
× allenii	SPhx
- 'Frà Angelico' ♀H6	NDry
amethystina	see *S. litardierei*
amoena	WCot
autumnalis	CAvo CRos EHyd EPot GKev LRHS NRHS WShi WThu
bifolia ♀H6	CAvo EPot GKev IPot SDeJ SPhx WCot WShi
- 'Alba'	SDeJ SPhx
- 'Norman Stevens'	NDry
- 'Rosea'	CRos EHyd ERCP LRHS NRHS SDeJ
bithynica ♀H6	GKev WCot WShi
'Blue Giant'	CAvo ELan EMor EPot ERCP GKev LRHS WCot
campanulata	see *Hyacinthoides hispanica*
chinensis	see *S. scilloides*
cilicica	GKev
§ **forbesii**	CRos EHyd EPot GKev LCro LOPS LRHS NBir NHpl NRHS SDeJ SRms WShi
- 'Violet Beauty'	GKev SDeJ
greilhuberi	CAvo EPPr EPri GKev NDry SGro WCot
hohenackeri	GKev WCot WThu
- BSBE 811	WCot
§ **hughii**	CBro EBee
hyacinthoides	CAby EBee ERCP GKev SDir WCot
- 'Blue Arrow'	CAvo GKev MWat SDir WFar
ingridiae	GKev WCot
italica	see *Hyacinthoides italica*
japonica	see *S. scilloides*
liliohyacinthus	CAvo CBro GKev IBlr NWad WCot WShi
- 'Alba'	CAvo
§ **litardierei** ♀H6	CAby CAvo EPPr EPot EPri ERCP GKev MMuc SDeJ SEND SPhx WShi
luciliae misapplied	see *S. forbesii*
luciliae ambig.	CAvo CRos EHyd GWyn LCro LOPS LRHS NRHS SEND
luciliae Boiss. ♀H6	LCro SDeJ SPer
- 'Alba'	CRos EHyd LRHS MBros NHpl NRHS SDeJ SPer
§ - Gigantea Group	GKev
- - 'Alba'	EPot
- 'Rosy Queen'	GKev
lutea hort.	see *Ledebouria socialis*
madeirensis	WCot
melaina	GKev WCot
mesopotamica	GKev
messeniaca	GKev
- MS 38 from Greece	WCot
mischtschenkoana ♀H6	CAvo CRos EHyd EPot EWld LCro LOPS LRHS NRHS SDeJ WShi
§ - 'Tubergeniana' ♀H6	CMea SPhx WCot
monanthos	GKev
monophyllos	GKev WCot
morrisii	GKev
natalensis	see *Merwilla plumbea*
non-scripta	see *Hyacinthoides non-scripta*
nutans	see *Hyacinthoides non-scripta*
obtusifolia subsp. **intermedia**	WCot
persica ♀H4	GKev WCot
peruviana	Widely available
- SB&L 20/1	WCot
- 'Alba'	CBro CWCL ECha EPot EPri EWes NHpl WCot XLum
- 'Blue Moon' **new**	CDoC CRos
- Carribean Jewels Series	CBod
- 'Hughii'	see *S. hughii*
- 'Sapphire Blue' (Carribean Jewels Series)	WFar
- var. **venusta** S&L 311/2	WCot
- 'White Moon'	ERCP GKev
'Pink Giant'	CAvo CRos EHyd ELan EMor EPot ERCP GKev LCro LOPS LRHS MPie NRHS SDeJ WBor XLum
pratensis	see *S. litardierei*
puschkinioides	GKev
ramburei	GKev
rosenii	CBor CWCL
- 'Cloudy Sky'	WCot
sardensis ♀H6	CAby CRos EHyd EPot ERCP GKev LRHS NRHS SDeJ SPhx SRms WCot WShi
§ **scilloides**	CPBP EPot
* - 'Alba'	SDeJ
siberica ♀H6	CAby CRos EHyd ELan LCro LOPS LRHS MMuc NRHS SPer SPhx WBor WShi
- 'Alba'	EHyd EPot LRHS SDeJ WShi
- subsp. **armena**	GKev
- 'Enem'	GKev
- 'Spring Beauty'	CAvo CMea CRos EHyd EPot ERCP GKev LRHS NRHS SDeJ SRms
siehei 'Rosea'	EMor GKev NHpl
'Tubergeniana'	see *S. mischtschenkoana* 'Tubergeniana'
'Valentine Day'	EPot
verna	GKev WShi WThu
violacea	see *Ledebouria socialis*

Scindapsus (*Araceae*)

aureus	see *Epipremnum aureum*

Scirpus (*Cyperaceae*)

cernuus	see *Isolepis cernua*
'Green Mist'	WCot
lacustris	see *Schoenoplectus lacustris*
- 'Spiralis'	see *Juncus effusus* f. *spiralis*
tabernaemontani	see *Schoenoplectus lacustris* subsp. *tabernaemontani*

Scleranthus (*Caryophyllaceae*)

biflorus	CPla CSma CTrC EDAr EPot EWes GBin GQue LEdu MAsh SPlb WFar XLum
uniflorus	CPla CTrC EPot LEdu NHpl SMad SPlb XLum

Sclerochiton (*Acanthaceae*)

harveyanus	EShb

Scoliopus (*Liliaceae*)

bigelowii	CAby
hallii	EWld GBin LEdu MNrw NHar

Scolopendrium see *Asplenium*

Scopolia (*Solanaceae*)

anomala HWJK 2252	WCru
- PAB 4925	LEdu
carniolica	EPPr EWld GBin GPoy ILea LEdu NChi NLar NSti SPlb WCru WPGP WPav WSHC XLum

- from Poland LEdu
§ - var. ***brevifolia*** CRos EBee EHyd EPPr EPfP EWld LEdu LRHS MPie NRHS SPhx WCot WPGP WPav
- 'Zwanenburg' EPPr EWes LEdu NLar SPhx WFar WSHC XLum
hladnikiana see *S. carniolica* var. *brevifolia*
stramoniifolia WPav

Scorzonera (*Asteraceae*)

hispanica 'Long Black Maxima' new SVic

Scorzoneroides (*Asteraceae*)

autumnalis CHab NMir

Scrophularia (*Scrophulariaceae*)

aquatica misapplied see *S. auriculata*
§ ***auriculata*** CHab NMir NPer WHer
§ - 'Variegata' (v) CBct CRos ECha EHyd EPfP GLog LRHS MHer NRHS NSti SGbt SHar SPer WSMil
buergeriana 'Lemon and Lime' misapplied see *Teucrium viscidum* 'Lemon and Lime'
calliantha SBrt SPtp WMal
macrantha CSpe SPhx
- 'Cardinal Red' ECtt
nodosa GPoy WHer
- variegata see *S. auriculata* 'Variegata'
vernalis CBgR

Scutellaria (*Lamiaceae*)

albida WOut
§ ***alpina*** SPlb SRms
- 'Arcobaleno' GEdr
altissima CFis ECha EMor GPSL MMuc NBro NGrd SBut SPlb WFar WWtn XSen
'Amazing Grace' EWes
baicalensis CSpe GJos GPoy MGil MNHC
canescens see *S. incana*
costaricana CCCN EShb
galericulata CBod CHab ENfk GPoy LEdu LLWG MBow MHer NAts SPhx WHer
hastata see *S. hastifolia*
§ ***hastifolia*** CTri EBou
§ ***incana*** CFis CMea CSpe EHyd LRHS MHol NDov SPhx WCot WGob WSHC
indica GEdr
- var. ***japonica*** see *S. indica* var. *parvifolia*
§ - var. ***parvifolia*** CSpe EBou EWes GEdr GMaP ITim NBir WAbe WFar
- - 'Alba' WAbe
integrifolia SPhx WGob
lateriflora GJos GPoy SRms
- PAB 3921 LEdu
maekawae B&SWJ 557A WCru
orientalis WAbe
pontica EBou SPhx
red-flowered CCCN
scordiifolia CFis CMea CSpe ECha NRya SBut SHar SRms WCav WFar
- 'Seoul Sapphire' GBin LEdu SPtp WPGP
serrata LPla
'Sherbert Lemon' CMea GJos
suffrutescens GJos XSen
- 'Texas Rose' CMea CSpe EBou EDAr EMor EPfP GJos NHpl SEdd WAbe WHil WHoo WIce WTor
supina see *S. alpina*
tournefortii CRos ECtt EHyd LRHS NRHS
* ***zhongdianensis*** EPPr MAvo MSpe

seakale see *Crambe maritima*

Sebaea (*Gentianaceae*)

rehmanii SPlb
thomasii WAbe
- 'Bychan' WAbe

Securigera (*Papilionaceae*)

§ ***varia*** CDor EWld GJos LEdu MMuc SEND SIvy SRms XLum

Sedastrum see *Sedum*

× *Sedeveria* (*Crassulaceae*)

'Harry Butterfield' WCot
'Letizia' SChr
'Starburst' new SAll

Sedum ✿ (*Crassulaceae*)

'Abbey Dore' see *Hylotelephium* 'Abbey Dore'
acre CRos CTri EHyd EPfP GPoy LEdu LRHS MAsh MNHC NMir NRHS SPlb XLum
- 'Aureum' EDAr ELan EPfP MAsh NHpl NLar NRya SPoG SRms SSim WCav WCot WSMil XLum
- 'Elegans' ECtt
- 'Golden Queen' CRos EBou EHyd LRHS NHpl NRHS SPlb SPoG SRms
- 'Minus' CRos EHyd LRHS NRHS SRms
§ - subsp. ***neglectum*** var. ***majus*** NLar
- 'Oktoberfest' GJos
adolphi WOld
aizoon NBre SPlb WFar XLum
- 'Aurantiacum' see *S. aizoon* 'Euphorbioides'
§ - 'Euphorbioides' ECha ECtt ELan LPot MHer MMuc MRav NLar SEND SPlb
§ - subsp. ***maximowiczii*** NWad
alatum WFar
albescens see *S. forsterianum* f. *purpureum*
alboroseum see *Hylotelephium erythrostictum*
§ ***album*** CRos EHyd GJos LRHS MMuc NBro NMir NRHS SEND SRms XLum
- 'Coral Carpet' EBou ECtt EPPr EPfP GFgr GKev GWyn MAsh MRav NHpl NLar NRya SPoG WFar WOld WSMil XLum
- Faro form EPot
- subsp. ***teretifolium*** var. ***micranthum*** 'Chloroticum' XLum
§ - - var. ***murale*** CRos CTri EHyd LRHS NHpl NRHS WFar XLum
alpestre XLum
altissimum see *S. sediforme*
anacampseros see *Hylotelephium anacampseros*
anglicum SSut
athoum see *S. album*
AUTUMN JOY see *Hylotelephium* (Herbstfreude Group) 'Herbstfreude'
batallae ISI 1496 NWad
beauverdii subsp. ***vietnamense*** HWJ 824 WCru
'Bertram Anderson' see *Hylotelephium* 'Bertram Anderson'

	beyrichianum misapplied	see *S. glaucophyllum*
	brevifolium	EWes NHpl
§	- var. ***quinquefarium***	WIce
	burrito	CDoC EShb
	'Carl'	see *Hylotelephium* 'Carl'
	cauticola	see *Hylotelephium cauticola*
	chrysicaulum	EPot
	clavatum ISI 1161	NWad
	compressum	see *S. palmeri* subsp. *palmeri* tetraploid
	confusum Hemsl.	SEND WMal
	crassipes	see *Rhodiola wallichiana*
	crassularia	see *Crassula setulosa* 'Milfordiae'
	cryptomerioides B&SWJ 054	WCru
	dasyphyllum	NBir NHpl NRya SPlb SRms WCot
	- subsp. ***dasyphyllum*** var. ***macrophyllum***	WOld
	- var. ***rifanum*** new	WOld
	dendroideum subsp. ***praealtum***	NWad SChr SEND
	divergens	GKev XLum
	douglasii	see *S. stenopetalum* 'Douglasii'
	drymarioides	NBre
	'Dudley Field'	EPot MHer
	'Eleanor Fisher'	see *Hylotelephium telephium* subsp. *ruprechtii*
	ellacombeanum	see *S. kamtschaticum* var. *ellacombeanum*
	'Elworthy Rose'	CElw
	erythrostictum	see *Hylotelephium erythrostictum*
	ewersii	see *Hylotelephium ewersii*
	fabaria	see *Hylotelephium telephium* subsp. *fabaria*
	fastigiatum	see *Rhodiola fastigiata*
	floriferum	see *S. kamtschaticum* var. *floriferum*
	forsterianum subsp. ***elegans***	SEND SPlb XLum
	- - 'Silver Stone'	GJos MMuc WRHF
§	- f. ***purpureum***	CPla NRya
	furfuraceum	NHpl NWad SPlb WAbe
§	***glaucophyllum***	EDAr GJos XLum
	'Gold Mound'	GWyn NHpl SEdd
	Herbstfreude Group	see *Hylotelephium* Herbstfreude Group
	hernandezii	SSim
	- FO -199	NWad
	heterodontum	see *Rhodiola heterodonta*
	hidakanum	see *Hylotelephium pluricaule*
	himalense misapplied	see *Rhodiola* 'Keston'
	hispanicum	SPlb
	- 'Blue Carpet'	EPPr NHpl SSim WFar WGrn
	- ***glaucum***	see *S. hispanicum* var. *minus*
§	- var. ***minus***	ECtt MMuc NHpl SEND SPlb WCot
	humifusum	EPot NHpl SPlb WAbe WFar
§	***hybridum***	XLum
	- 'Czar's Gold'	GJos NGdn
	'Indian Chief'	see *Hylotelephium* (Herbstfreude Group) 'Herbstfreude'
	indicum var. ***yunnanense***	see *Sinocrassula yunnanensis*
	integrifolium	see *Rhodiola integrifolia*
	'Joyce Henderson'	see *Hylotelephium* 'Joyce Henderson'
	kamtschaticum 🏆H5	EDAr GJos
	- B&SWJ 10870	WCru
§	- var. ***ellacombeanum*** 🏆H5	CRos EHyd LRHS MMuc NRHS SEND WCot XLum
	- - B&SWJ 8853	WCru
§	- var. ***floriferum***	XSen
§	- - 'Weihenstephaner Gold'	CTri EBou ECtt ELan EPfP GJos GKev GMaP LPot MAsh MHer MMuc MRav NBir NSla SPlb SPoG SRms WCav WFar WSMil XLum
	- var. ***kamtschaticum*** 'Variegatum' (v) 🏆H5	CMea CRos EAJP EBou EHyd ELan EPfP LRHS MBel MHer MMuc MSCN NHpl NRHS SPoG SRms SSim SWvt WIce XLum
	'Katharine's Gold'	MNrw
	kimnachii	WOld
	kirilowii	see *Rhodiola kirilowii*
	lanceolatum	NBre
	lineare	CDoC
	- 'Variegatum' (v)	XLum
	'Little Dove'	SGro
	'Little Gem'	see × *Cremnosedum* 'Little Gem'
	'Little Missy' (v)	WFar
	× ***luteoviride***	NWad WOld
§	***lydium***	CTri GFgr NHpl SPlb
	- 'Bronze Queen'	see *S. lydium*
	makinoi	SEdd SSim
	'Manoir de Gaudon'	WCot
	'Matrona'	see *Hylotelephium* 'Matrona'
	maweanum	see *S. acre* subsp. *neglectum* var. *majus*
	maximowiczii	see *S. aizoon* subsp. *maximowiczii*
	middendorffianum	MBrN MHer MMuc SRms WHoo XLum
§	***montanum***	MMuc
	moranense	MMuc WOld XLum
	morganianum 🏆H2	EBak EShb NWad WOld
	morrisonense B&SWJ 7078	WCru
	'Mr Goodbud'	see *Hylotelephium* 'Mr Goodbud'
	'Munstead Red'	see *Hylotelephium* 'Munstead Red'
	murale	see *S. album* subsp. *teretifolium* var. *murale*
	nevii misapplied	see *S. glaucophyllum*
	nevii ambig.	SPlb
	nicaeense	see *S. sediforme*
	nussbaumerianum 🏆H2	NWad
	obtusatum misapplied	see *S. oreganum*
§	***obtusatum*** A. Gray	NBro NSla
	obtusifolium	SGro
	- var. ***listoniae***	EDAr GJos
	ochroleucum	NBre NWad WCot WFar WOld
	- subsp. ***montanum***	see *S. montanum*
	oppositifolium	see *S. spurium* 'Album'
§	***oreganum***	ECha GAbr GKev GMaP LPot MHer NBir SMad SPlb SRms XLum
	- 'Procumbens'	see *S. oreganum* subsp. *tenue*
§	- subsp. ***tenue***	NHol NRya NWad
§	***oregonense***	CRos EHyd LRHS MHer NRHS WFar
	'Oriental Dancer'	see *Hylotelephium* 'Oriental Dancer'
	pachyclados	see *Rhodiola pachyclados*
	pachyphyllum	LPot
	palmeri	MRav NBir SChr WSMil XLum
§	- subsp. ***palmeri*** tetraploid	SEND
	'Parish Plum'	SGro
	pilosum	GKev WAbe
	'Pink Dove'	SGro
	pluricaule	see *Hylotelephium pluricaule*
	polytrichoides 'Chocolate Ball'	CPBP EMor NHpl SEdd SSim WSMil
	populifolium	see *Hylotelephium populifolium*
	porphyranthes new	WOld
	pulchellum	WFar
	quinquefarium	see *S. brevifolium* var. *quinquefarium*
	'Red Cauli'	see *Hylotelephium* 'Red Cauli'
	'Red Star'	MAvo

	reflexum L.	see *S. rupestre* L.
	- 'Cristatum'	NHpl
	- red-leaved	NHpl
	rhodiola	see *Rhodiola rosea*
	rosea	see *Rhodiola rosea*
	rubroglaucum misapplied	see *S. oregonense*
	rubroglaucum Praeger	see *S. obtusatum* A. Gray
	× ***rubrotinctum*** ♀H3	CBod SEND SSim
	- 'Aurora' ♀H2	CDoC SAll
	'Ruby Glow'	see *Hylotelephium* 'Ruby Glow'
§	***rupestre*** L.	ELan GJos GQue MMuc SEND SPhx SPlb WFar XLum
	- 'Angelina'	CBod CKno EBou ECtt EPPr EWes IMou LPot MHer NBir NDov NHol NWad SPoG SSim WCot WFar WGrn WIce WSMil XLum
	- 'Aureum'	WFar
	- 'Blue Spruce' new	IPot
	- 'Monstrosum Cristatum'	NBir WCot WFar XLum
	- 'Viride' new	WOld
	ruprechtii	see *Hylotelephium telephium* subsp. *ruprechtii*
	'Sandra Mottram'	NWad
	sarcocaule hort.	see *Crassula sarcocaulis*
	sarmentosum	XLum
§	***sediforme***	MMuc NBre SEND SRms SSim XSen
	- ***nicaeense***	see *S. sediforme*
	selskianum	GJos NBre NLar SGro XLum
	- 'Goldilocks'	GJos
	sexangulare	EBou ELon GFgr MHer MMuc NRya SPlb SRms WOld XLum
	- f. ***elatum*** new	WFar
	- 'Weisse Tatra' new	WFar
	sibiricum	see *S. hybridum*
	sieboldii	see *Hylotelephium sieboldii*
	spathulifolium	CTri ECha EPot
	- Atropurpureum Group	GQue
	- 'Aureum'	ECtt WAbe
	- 'Cape Blanco' ♀H5	Widely available
	- 'Purpureum' ♀H5	CRos CTri CWCL EBou ECtt EDAr EHyd ELan EPfP EPot GAbr GJos GKev GMaP GWyn LRHS MBel MHer NHol NHpl NRHS NRya NWad SPlb SPoG SSim WAbe XLum
	- 'William Pascoe' new	EPot
	- subsp. ***yosemitense*** 'Red Raver'	CPBP
	spectabile	see *Hylotelephium spectabile*
	spinosum	see *Orostachys spinosa*
	spurium	GJos GKev MMuc SEND SRms WFar XSen
§	- 'Album'	NRya XLum
	- 'Atropurpureum'	ECha XLum
	- 'Coccineum'	GJos GQue MMuc SEND
	- DRAGON'S BLOOD	see *S. spurium* 'Schorbuser Blut'
	- 'Erdblut'	CTri
	- 'Fuldaglut'	CRos CTri EBou ECtt EHyd EPPr LRHS MNrw NRHS NRya SRms
	- 'Green Mantle'	ECha EHyd EPfP LRHS
	- 'John Creech'	ECtt
	- PURPLE CARPET	see *S. spurium* 'Purpurteppich'
	- 'Purpureum'	SRms
§	- 'Purpurteppich'	ECtt GJos MRav NBro NLar NWad SRms SVen
	- 'Roseum'	SRms
	- 'Ruby Mantle'	GKev NBro NEoE SPoG SRms SWvt XLum
§	- 'Schorbuser Blut' ♀H5	CMea CRos ECtt EHyd ELan EPau EPfP LPot LRHS MBow MCot NBir NDov NRHS NRya NSla SEdd SPlb SRms SSim WFar WGwG WHoo WIce XLum
I	- 'Splendens Roseum'	XLum
	- 'Summer Glory'	NLar
§	- 'Tricolor' (v)	CTri EBou ECha EPfP GEdr GKev MHer MRav NHol NRya NWad SPlb SPoG SSim XLum
	- 'Variegatum'	see *S. spurium* 'Tricolor'
	- 'Voodoo'	CBod CPla CWCL EBou ECtt EDAr EPfP EWes LPot MBel MHer NBro NDov NGdn XLum
	stahlii new	WOld
	stefco	XLum
	stenopetalum	SPlb
§	- 'Douglasii'	MHer SRms
	'Stewed Rhubarb Mountain'	see *Hylotelephium* 'Stewed Rhubarb Mountain'
	stribrnyi	see *S. urvillei* Stribrnyi Group
	takesimense	WOld XLum
	- B&SWJ 8493	WCru
	- B&SWJ 8518	WCru
	tatarinowii	see *Hylotelephium tatarinowii*
	telephium	see *Hylotelephium telephium*
	ternatum	MHer
	tetractinum 'Coral Reef'	NBir SRms XLum
	trollii	see *Rhodiola saxifragoides*
	urvillei Sartorianum Group	MHer XLum
§	- Stribrnyi Group	XLum
	ussuriense	see *Hylotelephium ussuriense*
	valens	SPlb
	'Vera Jameson'	see *Hylotelephium* 'Vera Jameson'
	viviparum	see *Hylotelephium viviparum*
	'Washfield Purple'	see *Hylotelephium telephium* (Atropurpureum Group) 'Purple Emperor'
	'Weihenstephaner Gold'	see *S. kamtschaticum* var. *floriferum* 'Weihenstephaner Gold'
	weinbergii	see *Graptopetalum paraguayense*
	yezoense	see *Hylotelephium pluricaule*
	yunnanense	see *Rhodiola yunnanensis*

Seemannia see *Gloxinia*

Selaginella (*Selaginellaceae*)

	apoda	LRHS
	braunii	WCot
	helvetica	EBee IMou WSHC XLum
	kraussiana ♀H2	CTsd ESwi NWad
	- 'Aurea'	CCCN CRos EHyd ISha LRHS MAsh NRHS
	- 'Brownii' ♀H2	CCCN ISha
	- 'Gold Tips'	CCCN CRos EHyd ESwi ISha LRHS MAsh NRHS
	lepidophylla	GKev SVic
	moellendorfii	EHyd ISha LRHS NRHS
	uncinata ♀H1b	EHyd ISha LRHS NRHS
	willdenovii	ISha

Selinum (*Apiaceae*)

	CC 6869	EBee MSpe
	KWJ 12281 from northern Vietnam	WCru
	candollei HWJK 2329	WCru
	carvifolium	CExl CMac CSam ELan EMor LEdu LLWG MNrw NLar SPhx SPtp WCot
	- HWJK 2347	ESwi WCru
	- PAB 2676	LEdu

cryptotaenium FMWJ 13250	WCru
- PAB 8948	LEdu
filicifolium	CAby CBod LLWG MAvo MBel MHol MTis SMad WCot WRHF
tenuifolium	see *S. wallichianum*
§ ***wallichianum*** ♀H6	Widely available
- CC 6869	GKev
- EMAK 886	EBee
- HWJK 2347	WCru
- PAB 3579	LEdu WPGP
- PAB 8969	LEdu WPGP
- WJC 13656 from Sikkim	WCru
- from Bhutan	WPGP
- from Manipur	WPGP
- from Nagaland, India **new**	WPGP

Selliera (*Goodeniaceae*)

radicans	GAbr

Semele (*Asparagaceae*)

androgyna	CRHN WCot

Semiaquilegia (*Ranunculaceae*)

§ ***adoxoides***	GKev SHar
- double-flowered (d)	GKev
§ ***ecalcarata*** ♀H5	CSpe CWCL EBee EWld GKev MNrw NGdn NHpl SBut SRms WHal
'Moody Blues' **new**	CBor WFar
simulatrix	see *S. ecalcarata*
'Sugar Plum Fairy'	CBor CRos CSma EHyd EPfP LBuc LRHS MTis NRHS SPoG WFar
'Tinkerbell' **new**	CBor WFar

Semiarundinaria (*Poaceae*)

§ ***fastuosa*** ♀H6	CBcs CBdn CJun EPfP IMou MMuc MWht SArc SEND SPlb XCre
- var. ***viridis***	MWht WCru
kagamiana	CBdn EPfP IMou MMuc MWht XCre
§ ***lubrica***	MWht XCre
makinoi	MWht XCre
nitida	see *Fargesia nitida*
§ ***okuboi***	CBdn MWht XCre
villosa	see *S. okuboi*
yamadorii	MWht
- 'Brimscombe'	XCre
yashadake	MWht XCre
- f. ***kimmei***	CBod CRos EHyd EPfP LRHS MMuc MWht NLar NRHS SPoG XCre

Semnanthe see *Erepsia*

Sempervivella see *Rosularia*

Sempervivum ✿ (*Crassulaceae*)

'Aaroundina'	NMen
'Abba'	CMea NMen WHal
'Achalm'	GFgr NMen
acuminatum	see *S. tectorum* var. *glaucum*
'Adelaar'	NMen
'Adelmoed'	NMen
'Ageet'	NMen
'Aladdin'	GEdr MSCN NMen SRms
'Alchimist'	NMen XLum
'Aldo Moro'	EDAr GAbr NMen WIce XLum
'Alenco'	NMen
'Alesia'	NMen
'Alfons-Roelands'	NMen
allionii	see *Jovibarba allionii*
'Allison'	GFgr
'Alluring'	NMen
'Alpha'	CMea NMen SRms WHal XLum
altum	CRos EHyd LRHS NRHS SPlb SRms XLum
'Amanda'	MBrN NMen SRms WHoo
'Andinn Tunrida'	NMen
andreanum	see *S. tectorum* var. *alpinum*
'Andrenor'	NMen
'Andrenor' sport	NMen
'Antiquity'	WFar
'Apache' Haberer	NMen
'Apanatschi'	NMen
'Apollo'	XLum
'Apollo's Frog'	NMen
'Apple Blossom'	CMea NMen
'Apricot'	NMen
arachnoideum ♀H7	Widely available
- from the Abruzzi, Italy	NMen
- from Zermatt, Switzerland	XLum
- subsp. ***arachnoideum***	CPla
- 'Ararat'	SDys
- var. ***bryoides***	CRos EHyd LRHS NRHS SRms WFar
- 'Clärchen'	MSCN NMen WAbe XLum
- cristate	XLum
* - ***densum***	EDAr EPPr WAbe
- subsp. ***doellianum***	see *S. arachnoideum* subsp. *tomentosum* var. *glabrescens*
- giant **new**	WFar
- 'Gorges d'Héric'	EPot
- 'Laggeri'	see *S. arachnoideum* subsp. *tomentosum* (C.B. Lehm. & Schnittsp.) Schinz & Thell.
- 'Opitz'	SRms
- 'Peña Prieta'	XLum
- 'Piletina'	WFar
- 'Red Wings'	NMen XLum
- 'Rheinkiesel'	XLum
- 'Rubin'	CBod MCot NHpl SSim WFar
- 'Rubrum'	CDoC CRos EBou GKev GMaP LRHS NRHS SPlb WFar XLum
- 'Spider's Nest'	WFar
- 'Spider's Web'	WFar
- subsp. ***tomentosum*** misapplied	see *S.* × *barbulatum* 'Hookeri'
- subsp. ***tomentosum*** ambig.	EBou EPot XLum
§ - subsp. ***tomentosum*** (C.B. Lehm. & Schnittsp.) Schinz & Thell. ♀H7	CRos EHyd LRHS NPer NRHS NWad SPlb SRms WAbe
§ - - var. ***glabrescens***	SDys XLum
- - 'Minor'	SSim WFar
- - 'Minus'	EHyd EPfP LRHS
§ - - 'Stansfieldii'	CRos EHyd EPPr LRHS NRHS SRms WFar WHal
- 'Web Cluster'	WFar
§ - 'White Christmas'	MHer NMen
arachnoideum × ***montanum***	see *S.* × *barbulatum*
arachnoideum × ***nevadense***	SDys
arachnoideum × ***pittonii***	NMen SRms WAbe
arenarium	see *Jovibarba arenaria*
'Argus Eye'	NMen
'Arondina'	NMen
'Aross'	CMea
'Arrowheads Red'	NMen
'Artist'	NMen
'Ashes of Roses'	MSCN NHol NMen XLum

	'Astrid'	NMen
	'Atlantic'	SRms
	atlanticum	MMuc NMen
	- from Oukaïmeden, Morocco	GAbr NMen SRms
	- 'Edward Balls'	NMen SDys SRms WFar
	'Atlantis' ambig.	NMen SRms
	'Atropurpureum' ambig.	EPot GAbr GEdr MBrN NMen WFar
	'Attraction'	NMen
	'Aureum'	see *Greenovia aurea*
	'Averil'	NMen
	'Babette' **new**	NMen
	'Baby Skrocki'	NMen
	balcanicum	NMen SRms XLum
	ballsii	CRos EHyd LRHS NMen NRHS SRms
	- from Smólikas, Greece	NMen
	- from Tschumba Petzi, Greece	SDys XLum
	'Banderi'	NMen
	'Banjo'	NMen
	'Banyan'	CRos EHyd LRHS NRHS SRms
§	× ***barbulatum***	GAbr NMen SDys
§	- 'Hookeri'	CTri WAbe WHoo XLum
	'Baronesse'	NMen
	'Bascour Zilver'	CMea MSCN SRms WHal
	'Be Mine'	MSCN
I	'Beate' G. Dillmann	NMen
	'Beatles Memory'	NMen
	'Beaute'	NMen
	'Bedazzled'	NMen
	'Bedivere'	NMen SRms
	'Bedivere Crested'	NMen
*	'Bedley Hi'	NMen
	'Bella Meade'	NMen SRms
	'Bellotts Pourpre'	NMen
	'Benala' **new**	NMen
	'Bennerbroek'	NMen
	'Bernstein'	EDAr EPPr GFgr GKev MHer MSCN NMen NWad WHal WIce XLum
	'Beta'	NMen WAbe XLum
	'Bethany'	CMea NMen NWad WHal
	'Bianca'	NMen
	'Bijou'	NMen
	'Birchmaier'	NMen
	'Bitter Chocolate'	GFgr
	'Björn'	NMen
	'Black Beauty'	EBou EPot NMen
	'Black Knight'	CMea CRos EHyd EPot LRHS MHer NRHS SPlb SRms WHal
	'Black Mini'	GAbr GKev NBir NMen SRms
	'Black Mountain'	GKev NMen
	'Black Rose'	NMen
	'Black Velvet'	NMen
	'Black Widow'	NMen
	'Blackcurrant Ice' **new**	GFgr
	'Blade of Steel'	NMen
	'Blauer Ritter'	NMen
	'Blood Tip'	CMea CRos EHyd EPfP GAbr LRHS LSun MHer MMuc NHol NMen NRHS NRya NWad SEND SPlb SPoG SRms WFar WHal WHoo
	'Bloody Goose'	NMen
	'Bloody Mary'	GFgr
	'Blue Bird'	NMen
	'Blue Boy'	CRos EBou EHyd EPPr GAbr GFgr LRHS MSCN NMen NRHS SPlb SRms WFar
	'Blue Knight'	NMen
	'Blue Time'	WFar WHoo XLum
	'Blush'	NMen
	'Boissieri'	see *S. tectorum* subsp. *tectorum* 'Boissieri'
	'Bokkenrijders'	NMen
	'Bold Chick'	NMen
	'Bombardier'	EDAr
	'Booth's Red'	NMen
	borisii	see *S. ciliosum* var. *borisii*
	borissovae	EPot NMen SDys
	'Boromir'	NMen XLum
	'Boule de Neige'	GEdr NMen NRya WFar
	'Bowles's Variety'	NMen
	'Braune Maus'	GFgr
I	'Braunella'	NMen
	'Brilland Red Brun'	NMen
	'Britta'	NMen SDys
	'Brock'	CRos EHyd LRHS NRHS SRms
	'Bronco' ♀H5	CRos EBou EHyd EPfP GAbr GBin LRHS MMuc NHol NMen NRHS NRya NWad SEND SRms SSim WBrk WCot WFar WPGP WRHF XLum
	'Bronze Pastel'	EDAr GFgr MSCN NHpl NMen NSla SRms
	'Brown Owl'	EBou NMen SRms
	'Brownii'	GAbr NMen
	'Brunette'	GAbr
	'Brunhilde'	NMen
	bungeanum hort.	NMen
	'Burgundy'	NMen
	'Burning Bush'	WFar
	'Burnished Bronze'	NMen
	'Burnt Embers'	NMen
	'Butterbur'	NMen
	'Butterfly'	NMen
	'Café'	MSCN NHol NMen SRms
*	***calabricum***	NHol
	calcareum	CMea CRos EBou EHyd EPot GKev GQue LRHS MAsh MCot MMuc NBro NHol NHpl NMen NRHS SArc SEND SPlb SPoG SRms SSim WFar XLum
	- from Cleizé, France	see *S. calcareum* 'Limelight'
	- from Col Bayard, France	GAbr NMen
	- from Colle St Michel, France	SRms
	- from Petite Ceüse, France GDJ 92.16	SRms
	- from Queyras, France	NMen
	- from Triora, Italy	NMen
	- 'Atropurpureum'	CCal
	- 'Benz'	SDys
	- 'Button' **new**	WFar
	- 'Extra' ♀H5	CCal EWes GAbr GEdr MSCN NMen SRms WFar
	- 'Greenii'	CRos EHyd LRHS MSCN NMen NRHS SPlb SRms
§	- 'Grigg's Surprise'	NMen SPlb
	- 'Guillaumes' ♀H5	CRos EHyd GFgr LRHS NMen NRHS SRms WHoo
§	- 'Limelight'	CMea CRos EHyd EPot LRHS NMen NRHS WHal WHoo
	- 'Monstrosum'	see *S. calcareum* 'Grigg's Surprise'
	- 'Mrs Giuseppi'	GAbr GEdr LSun NHpl NMen SRms WAbe WFar WIce XLum
	- 'Nigricans'	NMen
	- 'Pink Pearl'	MSCN NMen SDys SPlb XLum
	- 'Sir William Lawrence' ♀H5	CCal CMea CRos EBou EDAr EHyd GFgr LRHS NMen NRHS SRms WAbe WHal WHoo WThu XLum
	'Cameo'	see *Jovibarba heuffelii* var. *glabra* 'Cameo'

'Campagha'	NMen
'Canada Kate'	NMen
'Cancer'	XLum
'Candy Floss'	NMen
cantabricum	MMuc NMen WFar XLum
- from Navafria, Spain	NMen
- from Riaño, Spain	GAbr
- from San Glorio, Spain	GAbr
- from Ticeros	XLum
- from Valvanera, Spain	NMen
- subsp. ***cantabricum*** from Leitariegos, Spain	GAbr
- subsp. ***guadarramense***	see *S. vicentei* subsp. *paui*
- - from Pico del Lobo, Spain, No 1	SRms
- subsp. ***urbionense***	GEdr SRms
- - from El Gatón, Spain	GFgr
'Caramel'	NMen
'Carlo's II'	NMen
'Carmen'	GAbr NMen
'Carneum'	NMen
'Carnival'	NMen
'Casablanca'	NMen
'Caspara'	NMen
caucasicum	CRos EHyd LRHS NMen NRHS SRms XLum
'Cavo Doro'	NMen
'Celon'	NMen
'Centennial'	NMen
charadzeae	XLum
'Cherry Frost'	NHol NMen XLum
'Cherry Glow'	see *Jovibarba heuffelii* 'Cherry Glow'
'Cherry Tart'	SPlb
'Chilli Pepper'	MSCN
'Chivalry'	NMen
'Chocolate'	NHpl WAbe
'Choctaw'	NMen
'Cholie'	GKev
'Christmas Time'	NMen
chrysanthum	SSim
ciliosum ♀H7	CMea GEdr NMen NRya SPlb SRms
- from Alí Butús, Bulgaria	SDys
§ - var. ***borisii***	EPPr NRya WAbe WFar WHal
- var. ***borisii*** × ***ciliosum*** var. ***ciliosum***	CTri
- var. ***galicicum*** 'Mali Hat'	NMen
'Cindy'	SRms
'Circlet'	NMen
'Claey's Fluweel'	NMen
'Clara Noyes'	NMen
'Clare'	MHer NMen
'Classic Rock'	NMen
'Clemanum'	NMen
'Cleveland Morgan'	XLum
'Climax' ambig.	WFar
'Climax' Ford	NMen
'Cobweb Capers'	NMen
'Cobweb Centres'	EWes NMen
'Colchicum'	SRms
'Collage'	NMen
'Collecteur Anchisi'	GFgr SDys
'Commander Hay'	CTri EBou EWes GKev GMaP MSCN NHpl NMen NPer NRya SRms WHal XLum
'Comte de Congae'	NMen
'Congo'	NMen XLum
'Corio'	NMen
'Corona'	NMen
'Coronet'	NMen

'Corsair'	EPPr GEdr GFgr GKev MBrN MMuc NMen SRms WBrk WFar WOld
'Cream Tea'	GFgr
'Crimson Velvet'	CMea XLum
'Crimson Webb'	WFar
'Cripello'	NMen
§ 'Crispyn' ♀H5	CCal CMea CRos EHyd EPot LRHS MHer MMuc MSCN NMen NRHS SEND SRms WFar
'Crucify'	NMen
'Cupream'	NMen SRms
'Cyclops'	NMen
'Dakota'	EDAr NMen
'Dallas'	NMen SRms
'Damask'	MSCN NMen
'Dancer's Veil'	NMen
'Danji'	NMen
'Darjeeling'	NMen
'Dark Beauty'	CRos EHyd LRHS NHol NRHS SRms WAbe WCot WHal
'Dark Cloud'	GAbr NMen WHoo XLum
'Dark Point'	NMen
'Dark Velvet'	CMea
'De Kardijk'	NMen
'Deep Fire'	NMen SRms
× ***degenianum***	GAbr NMen XLum
'Delta' ♀H5	NMen WHoo
densum	see *S. tectorum*
'Desert Dream'	WFar
'Devil's Teeth'	MSCN
'Devon Glow'	MSCN
'Diavolo'	NMen
'Director Jacobs'	EDAr NHpl NMen
'Direktor General'	NMen
'Ditto'	GFgr
'Dolle Dina's'	NMen
dolomiticum	NMen XLum
dolomiticum × ***montanum***	NBro NMen
'Donarrose'	NMen
'Dornröschen'	NMen
'Downland Queen'	NMen
'Dr Fritz Köhlein'	NMen
'Dragoness'	NMen
'Dream Catcher'	NMen
'Dyke'	CTri NMen WHal
dzhavachischvilii	NMen XLum
'Edge of Night'	SRms
'Edwardine'	NMen
'Eefje'	NMen
'El Greco'	NMen
'El Toro'	NHpl NMen
'Elgar'	NMen
'Elva'	NMen
'Elvis'	NMen
'Emerald Giant'	GFgr SRms
'Emerald Haze'	WFar
'Emerald Lustre'	WFar
'Emerson's Giant'	NMen SRms
'Emmchen'	NMen
'Engle's'	CMea CRos CTri EHyd GFgr GKev LRHS MHer MMuc NMen NRHS SEND SPlb SRms WFar WHal
'Engle's 13-2'	NMen
'Engle's Rubrum'	NMen
'Eos'	NMen
erythraeum	CRos EHyd LRHS NHpl NMen NRHS SPlb SRms WHal
- from Mesta Valley, Bulgaria	NMen
- 'Red Velvet'	NMen
'Essence of Lime'	GFgr

'Euphemia'	NMen
'Evening Glow'	NMen
'Excalibur'	NMen
'Exhibita'	NMen SDys SRms
'Exorna'	EDAr NMen
'Fair Lady'	NMen
'Fairy'	NMen
'Fame'	SPlb
'Faramir'	NMen
'Farida' **new**	NMen
'Fat Jack'	NMen
× ***fauconnetii*** 'Rubellum'	NMen
- 'Thompsonii'	SRms
'Feldmaier'	NMen WFar
'Fernwood'	NMen
'Festival'	NMen
'Fiery Furness'	NMen
'Fiesta' ambig.	NMen WHal
'Fifty One Shades'	WFar
fimbriatum	see *S.* × *barbulatum*
'Finerpointe'	NMen
'Fire and Ice'	NMen
'Fire Flies'	NMen
'Fire Glint'	GEdr NMen SRms WFar
'Firgrove Big Bronze'	NMen
'Firgrove Early Riser'	NMen
'Firgrove Silver'	GFgr
'First Try'	NMen
flagelliforme	XLum
'Flaming Heart'	EDAr MBrN NMen
'Flaming Sword'	NMen
'Flaming Web'	WFar
'Flamingo'	NMen
'Flammenschwert'	NMen
'Flanders Passion'	EWes NMen SRms
'Flasher'	NMen
'Fluweel'	MSCN NMen
'Forden'	GFgr NMen
'Ford's Amiability'	SDys
'Ford's Giant'	XLum
'Ford's Shadows'	SDys
'Ford's Spring'	NMen SRms
'Freckles'	NMen
'Fronika'	NMen
'Frosty'	GFgr NMen SRms
'Fuego' ♀H5	CCal CRos EHyd GFgr LRHS NMen NRHS SRms
'Fuji'	NMen
× ***funckii***	MBrN NMen XLum
'Fuzzy Wuzzy'	NMen
'Fyke'	NMen
'Galahad'	NMen
'Gallivarda' ♀H5	CRos EHyd GFgr LRHS NMen NRHS
'Gambol'	NWad
'Gamma'	NMen SRms
'Garnet'	NMen
'Gay Jester'	CTri NMen WHoo
'Gazelle'	XLum
'Georgette'	NMen XLum
'Georgia Rowan'	NMen
'Gilosum'	EDAr
'Ginger Nut'	NMen
'Ginnie's Delight'	NMen
'Gipsy'	NMen
giuseppii ♀H7	CRos EHyd GKev LRHS MMuc NMen NRHS SRms
- from Peña Espigüete, Spain	SDys SRms
'Gizmo'	NMen
'Glaucum'	see *S. tectorum* var. *glaucum*

	'Glaucum Minor'	NMen
	globiferum	XLum
	subsp. ***globiferum*** 'Minor'	
	'Gloriosum' ambig.	NMen
	'Glowing Embers'	NMen WHal XLum
	'Godaert'	MMuc SEND XLum
	'Gog'	NMen
	'Goldie'	NMen
	'Goldmarie'	NMen
	'Goldschatz'	NMen
	'Goovy'	NMen
	'Granada'	EDAr NMen
	'Granat'	GWyn MHer NMen SRms XLum
	'Granby'	SDys
	'Grand Mère'	NMen
	grandiflorum	NMen WThu XLum
	- 'Fasciatum'	NMen
	'Grannie's Favourite'	NMen
	'Grapetone'	NMen SDys WHal
	'Gratiana'	NMen
	'Graupurpur'	XLum
	'Green Apple'	GAbr NMen SDys
	'Green Caro'	NMen
	'Green Disk'	SRms
	'Green Dragon'	CRos EHyd LRHS MSCN NMen NRHS SRms
	'Green Gables'	EDAr
	'Green Ice'	GFgr NMen
	'Green Wheel'	NMen
	'Greenwich Time'	EDAr NMen
*	***greigii***	EPot MSCN
	'Grey Dawn'	CRos EHyd LRHS NMen NRHS SRms XLum
	'Grey Ghost'	NMen
	'Grey Lady'	NMen
	'Grey Owl'	CRos EHyd GFgr LRHS MSCN NMen NRHS SRms WFar
	'Grey Velvet'	NMen
	'Greyfriars'	CMea CRos EDAr EHyd LRHS MSCN NMen NRHS SRms WOld
	'Greyolla'	NMen
	'Grünschnabel'	XLum
	'Grunspur'	NMen
	'Gulle Dame'	CMea NMen SRms
	'Gwiazda'	GBin WFar
I	'Hall's Hybrid'	GAbr MSCN NBro NMen SRms
	'Happy'	NMen SRms
	'Harriet'	NMen
	'Hart'	GFgr NMen
	'Havana'	NMen
	'Havendijker Splitt'	NMen
	'Havendijks Millenium'	NMen
	'Havendijks Pride'	NMen
	'Hayling'	CRos EHyd EWes LRHS NMen NRHS NWad SRms SSim WFar XLum
	'Heigham Red'	CRos EBou EHyd EPPr GKev LRHS NMen NRHS SRms WFar WIce
	'Heike'	NMen
	'Helen'	EDAr GEdr NMen WFar
	'Heliotroop'	NMen SDys
	helveticum	see *S. montanum*
	'Hermann Näpfel'	NMen
	'Hermine' **new**	NMen
	'Hester'	MBrN NBro
	'Hey-hey'	CRos EHyd EPot LRHS MBrN NMen NRHS SPlb WCot XLum
	'Hidde'	NMen SPlb
	'Highland Mist'	NMen

	'Hirsutum'	see *Jovibarba allionii*
	hirtum	see *Jovibarba hirta*
	'Honymoon'	NMen
	'Hookeri'	see *S.* × *barbulatum* 'Hookeri'
	'Hopi'	NMen
	'Hortulanus Smit'	XLum
	'Hot Boyz'	NMen
	'Hot Peppermint'	NMen
	'Hullabaloo'	EDAr NMen
	'Hurricane'	NMen
	'Icicle'	CMea CRos EHyd LRHS MSCN NBro NHol NMen NRHS SRms
	imbricatum	see *S.* × *barbulatum*
	'Impact'	NMen
	'Imperial'	NMen SPlb
	'Infinity'	GFgr
	ingwersenii	NMen XLum
	ingwersenii* × *pumilum	GFgr NMen SRms
	'Irazu'	CMea CRos EHyd EPot GAbr LRHS MSCN NMen NRHS SDys SRms WHoo
	'Isaac Dyson'	SDys
	'Isabelle'	NMen
	italicum	XLum
	'Itchen'	NMen
	'Ivonne'	NMen
	'Iwo'	GFgr NMen
	'Jack Frost'	NBro NMen XLum
	'Jacquette'	NMen
	'Jadestern'	NMen
	'Janis'	NMen
	'Jelly Bean'	GFgr NMen
	'Jet Stream' 🏆H5	CRos EHyd LRHS MSCN NMen NRHS SDys SPlb SRms WFar
	'Jewel Case'	CRos EHyd LRHS NMen NRHS SRms
	'Jim Knopf'	NMen
I	'John Hobbs seedling No. 2'	NMen
	'John T' × 'Saffron'	NMen
	'Joke'	NMen
	'Jolly Green Giant'	NMen
	'Jo's Spark'	NMen
	'Jubilee'	CMea EDAr ELan GEdr MAsh MHer NMen SRms XLum
	'Jubilee Tricolor'	GEdr NHol NMen SPlb SSim WAbe
	'Jungle Fires'	CCal CMea SDys SRms WHoo
	'Jungle Shadows'	EDAr NMen NWad XLum
	'Jupiter'	GKev XLum
	'Jurrina'	NMen
	'Just Peachy'	EPot
	'Justine's Choice'	NMen SRms
	'Kai'	NMen
	'Kappa'	NBro NMen SDys
	'Karin'	NMen
	'Katmai'	GFgr NMen
	'Keiko'	NMen
	'Kelly Jo'	NBro WBrk
	'Kermit'	NMen
	'Khaleesi'	WFar
	'Kiara'	NMen
	'Kibo'	NMen
	'Kidlington'	NMen
	'Kildare'	NMen
	'Kim'	NMen
	'Kimba'	NMen
	'Kimble'	NMen
	'Kimono'	NMen NWad
	kindingeri	SRms XLum
	'King George'	CTri EBou GKev MMuc NMen SEND SRms WHal WHoo XLum

'Kip'	CMea NMen
'Kismet'	NMen
'Koko Flanel'	CCal GFgr NMen SRms
'Korspel Beauty'	NMen
'Korspel Prince'	NMen
'Korspel Sport'	NMen
'Korspelsegietje'	GAbr NMen SRms
kosaninii	NMen
– from Koprivnik, Slovenia	MSCN WAbe XLum
– 'Hepworth'	SPlb
'Krakeling'	NMen
'Kramer's Spinrad'	CMea EPPr GAbr GEdr GFgr GKev MBel NMen SPlb SRms WFar WHoo WThu
'Krankii'	XLum
'Krater'	NMen
'Lady Di'	NMen
'Lamia'	NMen
'Lancer'	NMen
'Larissa'	GFgr
'Laura Lee'	MMuc SEND
'Lavender and Old Lace'	CRos EHyd EPot LRHS MSCN NMen NRHS SPlb SRms WFar WIce XLum
'Lavenderspross'	NMen
'Le Congai'	NMen
'Legolas'	NMen
'Leneca'	NMen
'Lennik's Glory'	see *S.* 'Crispyn'
'Lennik's Sport'	XLum
'Lentezon'	GFgr
'Leocadia's Nephew'	NMen
leucanthum	XLum
'Lilac Queen'	NMen
'Lilac Time' 🏆H5	CCal CMea CRos EHyd EPPr GFgr LRHS MBrN MHer MSCN NMen NRHS SPlb SRms WFar WHal XLum
'Limbo'	NMen
'Lion King'	CCal GFgr MSCN NMen
'Lioness'	NMen
'Lipari'	SRms WCot XLum
'Lipstick'	GQue NMen
'Little Coffee Cup'	GFgr
'Little Flirt'	MSCN
'Little Rock'	NMen
'Lively Bug'	CRos EHyd EPPr EPot LRHS MSCN NMen NRHS SDys SRms XLum
'Lloyd Praeger'	see *S. montanum* subsp. *stiriacum* 'Lloyd Praeger'
'Long Shanks'	MSCN
'Lonzo'	NMen SRms
'Lord Alan'	GKev NMen
'Lord Morton'	NMen
'Louisse-Marie'	NMen
'Lovely Roset'	NMen
'Lucy Liu'	NMen
'Ludmila'	NMen
'Lumeseen'	NMen
'Lynn's Choice'	GAbr NMen NWad WHal
'Lyra' **new**	NMen
macedonicum	NMen SPlb SRms XLum
'Magic Spell'	NMen
'Magical'	NMen
'Magnificum'	GFgr NMen XLum
'Mahogany'	CTri EDAr GKev MHer MSCN NHol NMen SRms WHal XLum
'Maia'	SSim
'Maigret'	NMen
'Majanka'	NMen
'Majestic'	NMen
'Malby's Hybrid'	see *S.* 'Reginald Malby'

	'Maria Laach'	NMen
	'Marijntje'	NMen
	'Mariska' **new**	NMen
	'Marjory'	NMen
	'Marland Ruby'	NMen
	'Marmalade'	NMen
§	***marmoreum***	CRos EHyd EPot LRHS NMen NRHS SRms WHal
	- from Börzöny, Hungary	XLum
	- from Kanzan Gorge, Bulgaria	XLum
	- from Okol, Albania	NMen
	- 'Brunneifolium'	GAbr NMen XLum
	- subsp. ***marmoreum*** var. ***dinaricum***	MHer NMen
§	- - 'Rubrifolium'	XLum
	'Marshall'	NMen
	'Mary-Beth'	NMen
	'Matthew's Day Dream'	GKev NMen
	'Mauvine'	NMen NWad XLum
	'Mayfair'	EDAr NMen
	'Maytime'	NMen
	'Meadow Blaze'	WFar
	'Medallion'	NMen
	'Meelah'	NMen
	'Melanie'	MBrN NMen
	'Mercury'	CRos EHyd GAbr LRHS NBro NMen NRHS SRms
	'Merlin'	MSCN
	mettenianum	NMen
	'Mickey Mouse'	NMen
	'Midas'	CRos EHyd LRHS NRHS SRms
	'Minaret'	NMen
	'Mini Frost'	NMen
	'Minuet'	NMen
	'Mira'	MHol
	'Mixed Spice'	CMea
	'Moerkerk's Merit'	EHyd LRHS NMen XLum
	'Mona Lisa'	NMen
	'Mondstein'	MSCN SRms
	'Monseigneur Desmet'	GQue
§	***montanum***	XLum
	- from Haute-Loire, France	XLum
	- from Mont Aigoual, France	XLum
	- from the Pyrenees	XLum
	- from Vallée d'Estaing, France	XLum
	- 'Caesar'	MSCN
	- subsp. ***carpaticum*** 'Cmiral's Yellow'	WAbe WFar
	- 'Rubrum'	see *S.* 'Red Mountain'
	- subsp. ***stiriacum***	NMen SRms XLum
§	- - 'Lloyd Praeger'	NMen SDys
	'More Honey'	NMen
	'Morning Glow'	NMen WHal
	'Moss Rose'	NMen
	'Mount Hood'	CRos EHyd LRHS NMen NRHS SRms WHal
	'Mount Usher'	NMen
	'Mulberry Wine'	SRms WHoo
	'Mystic'	MBrN NMen
	'Naemi'	NMen
	'Neon'	NMen
	'Neptune'	GFgr WFar
*	***netaginatum***	XLum
	nevadense	NMen NRya SRms
	- 'Hirtellum'	SRms
	'New Rose'	WFar XLum
	'Nico'	NMen NWad SRms
	'Night Detector' **new**	NMen
	'Nigrum'	see *S. tectorum* 'Nigrum'
	'Niobe'	NMen WHal
	'Nocturno'	NMen XLum
	'Noir'	CRos EHyd EPfP GKev LRHS NBro NMen NRHS WFar XLum
	'Norbert'	NMen SRms XLum
	'Nörtofts Beauty'	NMen
	'Nouveau Pastel'	CMea NMen WHal XLum
	'Nova'	NMen
	'Novalis'	NMen
	'Oberon'	NMen
	'Obsession'	WFar
	'Ockerwurz'	WFar
	'Octet'	NMen
	octopodes	NBir NRya XLum
	- var. ***apetalum***	EPPr GAbr MSCN NMen WHoo
	'Oddity'	MBrN MHer NMen NWad WFar WHal
	'Ohio Burgundy'	CRos EHyd EPot LRHS MSCN NMen NRHS SRms WAbe WFar
	'Olcina'	NMen
	'Old Man Sage'	SPlb
	'Old Rose'	NMen
	'Olivia'	NMen
	'Olivine'	GFgr
	'Omega'	NMen
	'Ornatum'	MHer WAbe WHal
	ossetiense	GAbr NMen XLum
	'Othello' 🏆H5	CTri NBir NMen SRms WCot WPGP XLum
	'Ottelein'	NMen
	'Pachamama'	NMen
	'Pacific Charm'	NMen
	'Pacific Devils Food'	NMen
	'Pacific Hazy Embers'	NMen
	'Pacific Hep'	NMen
	'Pacific Opal'	NMen
	'Pacific Purple Shadows'	NMen WFar
	'Pacific Second Try' **new**	NMen
	'Pacific Sexy'	NMen
	'Pacific Sunset'	NMen
	'Pacific Thunder'	NMen
	'Pacific Velveteen'	GFgr
	'Packardian'	NMen NWad
	'Painted Lady'	NMen
	'Palissander'	EDAr GAbr NMen XLum
	'Pallas'	XLum
	'Papucchini'	NMen
	'Passionata'	NMen
	'Pastel'	CTri GFgr MHer
	patens	see *Jovibarba heuffelii*
	'Patrician'	SRms
	'Pavilion'	NMen
	'Peggy'	CCal NMen
	'Pekinese'	CRos EBou EHyd GEdr LRHS MBrN NBro NMen NRHS SRms WBrk XLum
	'Peridot'	GFgr
	'Peterson's Ornatum'	SDys
	'Petsy'	NMen SRms
	'Phoebe'	NMen
	'Pilatus'	EHyd EPfP LRHS SRms WFar XLum
	'Pine Cone'	GFgr NMen
	'Pineapple Punch'	GFgr
	'Pink Astrid'	NMen
	'Pink Cloud'	NMen
	'Pink Delight'	MSCN
	'Pink Flamingoes'	NMen
	'Pink Grapefruit'	NMen
	'Pink Lemonade'	NMen
	'Pink Mist'	SRms

	'Pippin'	CMea NMen SRms
	pittonii ♀^{H5}	CMea NMen WHal XLum
	'Pixie'	GFgr NMen
	'Plum Frosting'	GFgr MSCN
	'Plum Mist'	NWad
	'Plumb Rose'	NMen
	'Pluto'	NMen XLum
	'Polaris'	NMen
	'Poldark'	NMen
I	'Powellii'	NMen
	'Prairie Sunset'	GFgr NMen
	'President Arsac'	XLum
	'Princess Little' **new**	NMen
	'Probus'	NMen
	'Procton'	NMen
	'Proud Zelda'	EDAr GAbr MSCN NMen
	'Pseudo-ornatum'	SRms
	pulchellum	XLum
	'Pumaros'	SDys
	pumilum	CRos EHyd LRHS NMen NRHS SRms
	- from Techensis, Caucasus Mountains	SRms
	- 'Sopa'	MSCN
	'Purdy'	NHpl NMen WAbe
	'Purdy's 50-6'	GAbr NMen
	'Purdy's 70-40'	NMen
	'Purdy's Big Red'	NMen
	'Purple Beauty'	NMen
	'Purple Dazzler'	NMen
	'Purple Haze'	NMen
	'Purple King'	SDys
	'Purple Passion'	NMen
	'Purple Queen'	CRos EDAr EHyd EPPr GFgr LRHS NMen NRHS NRya SRms WFar
	'Purple Shadows'	NMen
	'Purple Violet'	NMen
	'Pygmalion'	NMen
	'Quax'	NMen
	'Queen Amalia'	see *S. reginae-amaliae*
	'Quintessence'	MSCN NMen SRms
	'Racey'	GFgr
	'Ramses'	SDys
	'Raspberry Ice'	CMea MSCN NBro NHpl NMen
	'Rauer Kulm'	NMen
	'Rauhreif'	XLum
	'Ravenheart'	MSCN
	'Rebecca'	GKev
	'Red Ace'	GEdr NBro NEoE WFar
	'Red Beam'	CRos EHyd LRHS NMen NRHS
	'Red Chief'	CRos EPfP XLum
	'Red Delta'	NBir NMen WCot WPGP WSMil
	'Red Devil'	CRos EHyd EPot LRHS NMen NRHS SPlb SRms WHoo
	'Red Heart' **new**	CCal
	'Red King'	NMen
	'Red Lion'	NMen
§	'Red Mountain'	LSun MMuc NMen SRms
	'Red Pink'	CMea GFgr NMen
	'Red Robin'	NMen
	'Red Spider'	EPot NBro NMen
	'Red West'	NMen
	'Regal'	NMen
	'Regensburger Knirps'	NMen
	reginae	see *S. reginae-amaliae*
§	***reginae-amaliae***	CRos EHyd LRHS NMen NRHS SRms XLum
	- from Kambeecho, Greece, No 2	SDys
	- from Sarpun, Turkey	SDys
§	'Reginald Malby'	CRos EHyd LRHS NMen NRHS SRms
	'Reinhard' ♀^{H5}	CCal CMea CRos EDAr EHyd EPot GEdr GKev GMaP LRHS MAsh MBrN MHer MSCN NHpl NMen NRHS NRya SPlb SRms SSim WBrk WFar WHal WHoo WIce
	'Remus'	ELan NMen SRms
	'Rex'	NMen
	'Rhöne'	NMen
	'Rhubarb Crumble'	GFgr
	'Rita Jane'	GFgr NMen
	'Robin'	NBro NHol NMen SRms XLum
	'Romantik Ritter'	NMen
	'Ronny'	NMen
I	'Ronsdorfer Hybride'	NMen
	'Roosemaryn'	EDAr
	'Rosa Mädchen'	NMen
	× ***roseum***	NMen
	'Rosie'	CCal CMea CRos EHyd EPot GAbr GEdr GMaP LRHS MAsh MMuc MSCN NHol NMen NRHS SRms WBrk WFar WHal WHoo WIce
	'Rotkopf' ♀^{H5}	CCal CRos EHyd GFgr LRHS MSCN NMen NRHS NWad XLum
	'Rotmantel'	NMen
	'Rotund'	GEdr MSCN
	'Royal Opera'	EDAr NMen
	'Rubellum Mahogany'	GFgr
	'Rubikon Improved'	NMen
	'Rubin'	CBod CMea CTri EBou EPfP MAsh MMuc NBir NHpl NMen SPoG SRms SSim WAbe WIce WSMil XLum
I	'Rubra Ash'	NMen
I	'Rubra Ray'	CCal MMuc SEND
	'Rubrifolium'	see *S. marmoreum* subsp. *marmoreum* 'Rubrifolium'
*	'Ruby Glow'	EDAr
	'Ruby Heart'	CBod MCot SSim
	'Ruby Meadows'	WFar
	'Russian River'	CMea WHoo
	'Rusty'	NMen
	ruthenicum	CRos EHyd EPPr LRHS NRHS NRya SRms XLum
	- 'Regis-Fernandii'	XLum
	'Ruth's Choice'	WFar
	'Saffron'	NMen
	'Samwise'	NMen
	'Sanford's Hybrid'	NMen
	'Sanne'	NMen
	'Santis'	NMen
	'Sarah'	EDAr NMen
	'Sarotte'	NMen
	'Sassy Frass'	NMen
	'Saturn'	MSCN NMen SRms WFar
	schlehanii	see *S. marmoreum*
	schnittspahnii	XLum
	'Scooby'	WFar
	'Sea Breeze'	GFgr
	'Sea Urchin'	GFgr
	seguieri	XLum
	'Seren'	GBin
	'Serendipity'	EDAr
	'Sharon's Pencil'	NMen
	'Sha'uri'	NMen
	'Sheila'	GAbr
	'Shepherd's Warning'	WFar
	'Shirley Moore'	NMen
	'Shirley's Joy'	NMen XLum

	'Show Baby'	NMen
	'Sideshow'	NMen
	'Sigma'	NMen
	'Silberkarneol' misapplied	see *S.* 'Silver Jubilee'
	'Silberkarneol' ambig.	GFgr MMuc
	'Silberspitz'	CRos EHyd LRHS MHer NBro NMen NRHS SPlb SRms
	'Silver Andre'	NMen
§	'Silver Jubilee'	CMea CRos EDAr EHyd GQue LRHS NBro NMen NRHS NRya SPlb SRms WFar WHoo XLum
	'Silver Sixpence'	GFgr
	'Silver Thaw'	CRos EHyd LRHS NRHS
	'Silverine'	EDAr
	'Simonkaianum'	see *Jovibarba hirta*
	'Simply Nightfall'	SSim
	'Sioux'	MBrN NMen WHal
	'Sirius'	GBin MHol NMen
	'Skrocki's Beauty'	GAbr NMen SRms
	'Skrocki's Bronze'	CRos EHyd LRHS NMen NRHS
	'Smaragd'	EHyd LRHS NMen XLum
	'Smit's Seedling'	NMen
	'Smokey Jet'	GFgr NMen
	'Snowberger'	CMea EBou NMen SRms WHal
	soboliferum	see *Jovibarba sobolifera*
	'Solamith'	NMen
	'Solar Meadows'	WFar
	'Sombrero'	NMen
	'Soothsayer'	NMen
	sosnowskyi	NMen XLum
	'Soul'	CCal NMen
	'Space Dog'	NMen
	'Spangle'	NMen
	'Spangle' sport	NMen
	'Spartan's Sunrise'	WFar
	'Spherette'	EDAr MBrN NMen WAbe
	'Spice'	NMen
	'Spider's Lair' ♀H5	NMen SRms
	'Spinellii'	NMen WThu
	'Spiver's Velvet'	NMen
	'Sponnier'	XLum
	'Spring Beauty'	NMen
	'Springmist'	CRos EHyd GFgr LRHS NRHS SRms
	'Sprite'	CRos EHyd GEdr LRHS NMen NRHS SDys SRms
	'Squib'	CCal MSCN NMen
	'Standard Green' **new**	CCal
	stansfieldii	see *S. arachnoideum* subsp. *tomentosum* 'Stansfieldii'
	'Starburst'	CRos EHyd LRHS NMen NRHS
	'Starion'	NMen
	'State Fair'	EDAr NMen
	'Steerosentern'	NMen
*	***stoloniferum***	GAbr
	'Storm Chaser'	GFgr
	'Strider'	NMen
	'Stuffed Olive'	NMen SDys SRms
	'Sugary'	NMen
	'Sun Waves'	SDys
	'Sunray Desire'	NMen
	'Super Dome'	GFgr NMen
	'Superama'	NMen
	'Svava'	NMen
	'Sweetheart'	NMen
	'Syston Flame'	NMen
	'Tamberlane'	EDAr
	'Tarita'	NMen
	'T'Boz'	NMen
§	***tectorum*** ♀H7	CHby CTri ELan GPoy MHer MNHC SPlb XAbr XLum
§	- var. ***alpinum***	CRos EHyd LRHS NBro NRHS SRms
	- var. ***andreanum***	XLum
	- 'Atropurpureum'	ELan SRms
	- 'Atroviolaceum'	NMen SPlb XLum
*	- 'Aureum'	GFgr NMen
	- var. ***boutignyanum*** GDJ 94.04 from Route de Tuixén, Spain	SRms
§	- var. ***glaucum***	NMen XLum
	- 'Mettenianum'	XLum
	- monstrose	SPlb SRms
	- 'Murale'	GFgr XLum
§	- 'Nigrum'	MHer NBro SDys XLum
	- 'Red Flush'	MBrN NMen
	- 'Royanum' ♀H7	MSCN NMen SRms
*	- subsp. ***sanguineum***	EDAr SSim
	- 'Sunset'	CMea EDAr EWes GAbr NMen SDys WHal
	- subsp. ***tectorum***	GEdr
§	- - 'Boissieri'	NMen
	- - 'Triste'	NHpl NMen XLum
	- 'Violaceum'	EBou NMen SPlb SRms
	'Teddy Bear'	MSCN NMen
	'Tederheid'	NMen
	'Telfan'	NMen
	'Terlamen'	NMen
	'Terracotta Baby'	CCal CMea GFgr NMen SSim WFar
	'Thayne'	NMen
	'The Platters'	NMen
	'The Rocket'	GFgr
	'Thistle Hill' **new**	NMen
	'Thunder'	NMen
	'Tiger Bay'	NMen
	'Timmy'	NMen
	'Tinner Bell'	NMen
	'Tintenblut'	NMen
	'Tintinabulum'	NMen
	'Tip Top'	EPot GEdr GFgr NMen WFar
	'Tipsy'	NMen
	tissieri	XLum
	'Titania'	NBro NMen WHal
	'Tjabine'	NMen
	'Tommella'	XLum
	'Topaz'	NMen SRms XLum
	'Tordeur's Memory'	MMuc NMen SEND SRms
I	'Tourmalyi'	NMen
	'T'Pol'	NMen
	'Tracy Sue'	XLum
	'Traffic Lights'	GFgr
	'Trail Walker'	NMen SRms
	transcaucasicum	XLum
	'Tree Beard'	NMen
	'Trine'	NMen
	'Tristesse' ♀H5	EDAr GAbr MBrN NMen
	'Trude'	NMen
	'Truva'	GFgr NMen
	'Twilight Blues'	CCal CRos EHyd LRHS NMen NRHS SRms
	'Twist'	NMen
	'Twizzler'	MSCN
	'U4'	NMen
	'Udine'	NMen
	'Uralturmalin'	NMen
	'Uranus'	XLum
	'Urmina'	NMen
	× ***vaccarii***	XLum
	'Van der Steen'	NMen
	'Vanbaelen'	GAbr NMen SDys
	'Vasi Petru'	NMen
	'Vega'	CPla MHol

	'Venus'	NMen XLum
	× ***versicolor***	CPla
	'Veughelen'	NMen
	vicentei	NMen WFar
	- from Gaton, Spain	EHyd LRHS NMen
§	- subsp. ***paui***	NSla
	'Video'	NMen
	'Violet Queen'	CMea GFgr NMen
	'Virgil'	EDAr GAbr MBrN MSCN NMen NWad SDys SPlb WAbe WCot WFar WIce
I	'Virginius'	GAbr
	'Vulcano'	NMen
	'Wasti'	NMen
	'Waterlily'	GFgr NWad
	'Watermelon Rind'	NMen
	webbianum	see *S. arachnoideum* subsp. *tomentosum* (C.B. Lehm. & Schnittsp.) Schinz & Thell.
	'Webbyola'	NMen
	'Wendy'	NMen
	'Westerlin'	NMen
	'Wheel of Fire'	NMen
	'Whirlpool'	GFgr
	'White Christmas'	see *S. arachnoideum* 'White Christmas'
	'White Ladies'	NMen
	'Whitening'	GAbr GEdr WFar
	× ***widderi***	NMen
	'Wilhelm Tell'	NMen
	'Wine Queen'	NMen
	'Winsome'	NWad
	'Wok'	NMen
I	'Woolcott's Variety'	GFgr NBir NMen SRms
	wulfenii	XLum
	- subsp. ***juvanii***	XLum
	'Xaviera'	NMen
	'Yanisha'	NMen
	'Yolanda'	NMen
	'Yvette'	NMen
	'Zaccour'	NMen
	'Zackenkrone'	NMen
	'Zannalee'	NMen
	'Zelca'	NMen
	zeleborii	NMen WHal
	'Zenith'	GAbr NMen SRms
	'Zenocrate'	NHol WHal
	'Zilver Moon'	NMen
	'Zilver Snowflake'	NMen
	'Zilver Suzanna'	NMen
	'Zilverprinsesje'	NMen
	'Zircon'	EDAr NMen
	'Zone'	NMen
	'Zorba'	NMen
	'Zulu'	NMen

Senecio (*Asteraceae*)

	articulatus	see *Curio articulata*
§	***barbertonicus***	EShb
	bidwillii	see *Brachyglottis bidwillii*
	candicans misapplied	see *Jacobaea maritima*, *Senecio candidans*
	candidans ANGEL WINGS ('Senaw')	LCro LOPS MHol WCot
	chrysanthemoides misapplied	see *Euryops chrysanthemoides*
	cineraria	see *Jacobaea maritima*
	cinerascens	SVen
	coccinilifera hort.	see *Kleinia grantii*
	compactus	see *Brachyglottis compacta*
	confusus	see *Pseudogynoxys chenopodioides*
	crassissimus	EShb
	cristobalensis	see *Roldana cristobalensis*
	doria	EShb MMuc SAko SDix WHrl
	elegans	SVen
	ficoides	see *Curio ficoides*
	gerberifolius B&SWJ 10357	WCru
	- B&SWJ 10361	MHol WCru
	'Gregynog Gold'	see *Ligularia* 'Gregynog Gold'
	greyi misapplied	see *Brachyglottis* (Dunedin Group) 'Sunshine'
	greyi Hook. f.	see *Brachyglottis greyi* (Hook. f.) B. Nord.
	haworthii	see *Caputia tomentosa*
	heritieri DC.	see *Pericallis lanata* (L'Hér.) B. Nord.
	hoffmannii	EShb
	kleiniiformis	EShb WSMil
	laxifolius hort.	see *Brachyglottis* (Dunedin Group) 'Sunshine'
	leucostachys misapplied	see *S. viravira*
	macroglossus	EShb
	- 'Variegatus' (v) ♀H1c	EShb
	mandraliscae	see *Curio talinoides* subsp. *mandraliscae*
	maritimus	see *Jacobaea maritima*
	mikanioides	see *Delairea odorata*
	monroi	see *Brachyglottis monroi*
	petasitis	see *Roldana petasitis*
	polyodon	CFis
	- var. ***polyodon***	GBee GBin MMuc SBut SWvt WCAu WCot WWFP
	- var. ***subglaber***	CCCN CSpe EAJP EWes GLog MHol MNrw MPie SPhx WCFE WPGP
	przewalskii	see *Ligularia przewalskii*
	pulcher	CDTJ MHol SGro SHar WWFP
	reinoldii	see *Brachyglottis rotundifolia*
	rowleyanus	see *Curio rowleyanus*
	scandens	see *Delairea odorata*
	scaposus	see *Caputia scaposa*
	seminiveus	EBee
	serpens	see *Curio repens*
§	***smithii***	ELan NBid WWtn
	squalidus subsp. ***aethnensis*** new	WCot
	'Sunshine'	see *Brachyglottis* (Dunedin Group) 'Sunshine'
	talinoides	see *Curio talinoides*
	talinoides 'Himalaya' misapplied (green-leaved)	see *S. barbertonicus*
	tanguticus	see *Sinacalia tangutica*
§	***viravira***	EPri EShb MCot SPhx WSHC

Senna (*Caesalpiniaceae*)

	alexandrina	CCCN EShb
	artemisioides ♀H1b	WCot
§	***candolleana***	CCCN EBee
§	***corymbosa***	CBcs CCCN CRHN CTri ECre
	× ***floribunda***	SBrt
	hebecarpa	SBrt
§	***marilandica***	CSpe EBee MGil
	obtusa Clos	see *S. candolleana*
	septemtrionalis	CCCN EHyd LRHS SEND

Sequoia (*Cupressaceae*)

	sempervirens ♀H6	CBcs CCVT CLnd CMCN CMen CTho CTsd ECrN EPfP LMaj MBlu MMuc NOra SCob SEND SGol WMat WMou WTSh
	- 'Adpressa'	MAsh MGos SCoo
	- 'Cantab'	WMou WPav

- 'Glauca' MAsh
- 'Henderson Blue' SLim
- 'Mount Loma Prieta Spike' NLar
- 'Prostrata' EWhm WPav

Sequoiadendron (*Cupressaceae*)

giganteum ♀H6 CBcs CCVT CLnd CMCN CTho CTri CTsd ELan EPfP LMaj LRHS MAsh MBlu MGil MGos MMuc NOra NOrn SCob SEND SEWo SGol SGsty SLim SPlb WFar WMat WMou WTSh XLot
- 'Barabits Requiem' MBlu NLar
- 'Beautiful Jop' NLar
- 'Bultinck Yellow' MBlu
- 'Chief' NLar
- 'Glaucum' MBlu SGsty SLim WPGP
* - 'Glaucum Compactum' MBlu
- 'Greenpeace' MBlu
- 'Kaatje' **new** SLim
- 'Little Stan' NLar SLim
- 'Pendulum' CCVT ESwi LRHS MBlu SLim
- 'Powdered Blue' LMaj
- 'Von Martin' NLar

Serapias (*Orchidaceae*)

lingua SChF
- peach-flowered WMal

Sericocarpus (*Asteraceae*)

asteroides GKev

Seriphidium see *Artemisia*

Serratula (*Asteraceae*)

bulgarica see *Klasea bulgarica*
coronata see *Klasea coronata*
gmelinii see *Klasea radiata* subsp. *gmelinii*
lycopifolia see *Klasea lycopifolia*
shawii see *S. tinctoria* var. *seoanei*
tinctoria NLar SBut SPhx
- subsp. **monticola** white-flowered EBee
§ - var. **seoanei** CCBP CKno CMea CMiW CSam EBee ELan LEdu MCot MHer MNrw MPie MRav NBid NBir NDov SBut SDix SEdd SHar SPhx SRms SWvt WCot WMal WPGP

Serruria (*Proteaceae*)

florida SPlb
phylicoides SPlb

Sesbania (*Papilionaceae*)

punicea CCCN

Seseli (*Apiaceae*)

elatum PAB 9228 LEdu SPhx
- subsp. **osseum** SPhx
globiferum SPhx
gracile SPhx
gummiferum CSam CSpe EAJP SMad SPhx WHil
hippomarathrum CElw CSpe ECha EPPr MAvo MNrw NGrd SBrt SPhx WCot WFar WHal WHrl WWtn
lehmannii WCot
§ **libanotis** CSam EBee EPPr GBin IPot LEdu LRHS MAvo NAts NLar SPhx WFar
montanum CMiW CSam CSpe EBee IMou LPla NDov SBrt SBut SHar WCot

Sesleria (*Poaceae*)

§ **albicans** EPPr
§ **argentea** CKno LPla
autumnalis CKno EBee ELon EPPr EShb EWes GMaP IMou LCro LOPS SCob SPhx WSpi XLum
caerulea CBod CKno CSam CSde ELan ELon EPfP GMaP GQue IMou LCro LEdu LOPS LRHS SCob SPhx SPoG XCre XLum
- subsp. **calcarea** see *S. albicans*
- 'Malvern Mop' EBee WHrl
cylindrica see *S. argentea*
'Greenlee' CKno LPla
heufleriana CBod EPPr IMou LCro LOPS LPla NRya SMea SPhx SPlb WCot WSpi
insularis EPPr EShb
nitida CBod CKno IMou LEdu LRHS SPhx XCre XLum
sadleriana CBod EBee EPPr EWes

Setaria (*Poaceae*)

italica 'Red Jewel' CSpe
macrostachya SPhx
palmifolia ♀H2 CBod CPla EShb MPie SBrt SDix SPlb WSMil
- BWJ 8132 WCru
viridis WCot

Setcreasea see *Tradescantia*

shaddock see *Citrus maxima*

Sharon fruit see *Diospyros kaki*

Shepherdia (*Elaeagnaceae*)

argentea NLar WKor

Shibataea (*Poaceae*)

chinensis XCre
kumasaca ♀H6 CAbb CBcs LEdu MWht SCob SGol XCre

Shortia (*Diapensiaceae*)

soldanelloides var. **magna** EPot IBlr

Sibbaldia (*Rosaceae*)

procumbens GKev

Sibbaldiopsis (*Rosaceae*)

§ **tridentata** SBrt

Sibthorpia (*Plantaginaceae*)

europaea CExl

Sida (*Malvaceae*)

hermaphrodita SMad

Sidalcea (*Malvaceae*)

'Brilliant' CBcs CBod CNor GBin ILea MNrw NBir SPer WCAu WFar
campestris from Oregon, USA EPPr
candida CBod CRos CSam EBee ECtt EHyd ELan EMor EPfP GMaP GWyn LRHS MBNS MMuc MRav MTis NChi NGBl NGdn NLar NRHS NSti SGbt SPer WCAu WCot
- 'Bianca' EBee EMor EPfP LSun NLar WFar

'Candy Girl'	CBod EBee NLar WCot WFar
'Crimson King'	WFar
'Croftway Red'	CBod CBor CRos EBee ELan LRHS MBel NBPC NBro NGdn NHol NHsp NRHS NWad SPer SWvt WFar
'Elsie Heugh' 🏆H7	Widely available
LILAC CANDICE ('Midawioha')	CBod WFar
'Little Princess'PBR	CBod CBor EBee EHyd EPfP EWes LRHS MHol MNrw NBPC NGdn NHsp NLar NRHS SPoG WCot WFar
'Loveliness'	CBod EBee ECtt EHyd ELan EShb LRHS MBel MRav NBro NDov NHsp NRHS NWad SPoG WFar WGwG
malviflora	SRms
- subsp. ***purpurea***	EHyd LRHS NRHS
'Monarch'	WFar
'Moorland Rose Coronet'	WFar
'Mr Lindbergh'	EBee NHsp NLar SPer WCFE
'Mrs Borrodaile'	CMac MBel MRav NBro NEoE NGdn NLar WFar
'Mrs Galloway'	EHyd LRHS NHsp
'My Love'	NDov NHsp
'Oberon' 🏆H7	CRos EBee EHyd LBuc LRHS MRav NRHS
oregana	NGdn
- subsp. ***spicata***	WFar
'Party Girl'	CMac CRos CSBt EHyd ELan EMor EPfP LRHS MNHC MRav NBPC NBro NGdn NLar NRHS SCob SPlb SPoG WBor WCot WFar XLum
'Purpetta'	CBod ELan EPfP NEoE NGBl NHsp NLar
'Reverend Page Roberts'	MRav WCot
'Rosaly'	CBod CSpe EAJP EHyd EMor LRHS NHsp NLar WFar
'Rosanna'	CRos EBou EHyd EMor EPfP GMaP LRHS NHsp NLar NRHS
'Rose Bud'	EBee NHsp WFar
'Rose Queen'	CBod CRos EBee ECha EHyd GKev LRHS MRav NBro NHol NRHS SGbt SHar SPer SRms WFar
'Rosy Gem'	SCob
Stark's hybrids	CBod EHyd LRHS NRHS SRms
'Sussex Beauty'	CBor CSam EBee EHyd EMor LRHS MBel MHol MRav NDov NGdn SMad SPer SPoG WCot WFar
'Wensleydale'	CRos EHyd LBuc LRHS NRHS WFar
'William Smith' 🏆H7	CRos CSam EBee ECha ECtt EHyd EMor EPfP EWTr EWes GBin LRHS MArl MMuc MRav NBir NGdn NHsp NLar NRHS SEND SGbt SPer WFar WGwG
'Wine Red'	CBod EBee EHyd EMor EShb LRHS MMrt NGdn NRHS SPoG SWvt WGwG

Sideritis (*Lamiaceae*)

syriaca	MHer XSen
- RCB UA 2	WCot

Silaum (*Apiaceae*)

silaus	NMir SPhx

Silene (*Caryophyllaceae*)

RBS	EPPr
acaulis	EDAr EPot GJos SRms WAbe WIce
§ - subsp. ***acaulis***	SPlb SRms WIce
- 'Alba'	WAbe
- 'Blush'	EDAr NSla WAbe WOld
§ - subsp. ***bryoides***	NLar
- 'Correvoniana'	NLar
- subsp. ***elongata***	see *S. acaulis* subsp. *acaulis*
- subsp. ***exscapa***	see *S. acaulis* subsp. *bryoides*
- 'Frances'	CPBP EDAr EPot ITim NLar NRya NSla WAbe
- 'Mount Snowdon'	EBou ELan EWes NHpl NLar SPlb SPoG SRms WHoo
- 'Pedunculata'	see *S. acaulis* subsp. *acaulis*
aegyptiaca	SPhx
alba	see *S. latifolia* subsp. *alba*
§ ***alpestris***	SBut SRms WThu
- 'Flore Pleno' (d) 🏆H7	CPBP EBou EWes NSla WIce
- 'Starry Dreams'	CBod CRos CSpe EHyd LRHS NRHS
argaea	CPla
× ***arkwrightii***	see *Lychnis* × *arkwrightii*
armeria	GJos GQue SDys
- 'Electra'	CSpe MNHC
asterias	EPPr GJos MNrw SBrt WMal
atropurpurea	see *Lychnis viscaria* subsp. *atropurpurea*
caroliniana	CBor
subsp. ***wherryi*** 'Short and Sweet' **new**	
coeli-rosa 'Blue Angel' **new**	SPhx
'Confetti'	CPla CSpe EAJP ECha EDAr EShb
'Country Comet'	NChi
delavayi	EDAr
dinarica	GKev
§ ***dioica***	CBre CHab CWld EBou EMor GJos GQue LCro LOPS MBow MHer MNHC NAts NGrd NLar NMir SBut SPhx SPoG SRms WOut WSFF WShi WWild
- 'Clifford Moor' (v)	ECtt MHer NSti SCoo
- 'Compacta'	see *S. dioica* 'Minikin'
- 'Firefly'PBR (d)	CDor CMac CWCL ECtt NSti SWvt WSHC
§ - 'Flore Pleno' (d)	CBor MHer MHol MRav NBid NBro NGdn WHoo
- 'Inane'	ELon WBor WMal WSHC
- 'Innocence'	NGrd
§ - 'Minikin'	MTis NGdn
- 'Purple Prince'	CBre CWld MMuc SEND
I - 'Ray's Golden Campion'	EMor EPPr NWad
- 'Rollie's Favorite'PBR	CRos EBee ECtt EHyd EMor EPfP LRHS LSou MAsh MHol MNrw MPri MSCN NDov NRHS NSti SPoG WBor WCAu
- 'Rosea Plena' (d)	WSHC
- 'Rubra Plena'	see *S. dioica* 'Flore Pleno'
- 'Stella'	NGrd
- 'Thelma Kay' (d/v)	NGdn
- 'Valley High' (v)	EBee ECtt EWes MHol WCot
elisabethae	NSla
§ ***fimbriata***	CAby CSpe ELan EMor EPPr EShb GWyn ILea MCot MMrt MNrw MRav MWat NLar NSti SBut SDix WCAu WCot WFar WKif WMal WRHF WWtn
frivaldskyana	SPhx
'Frivola Rose' **new**	MHol
gallica	GJos
hookeri	GBin GKev SPlb
- subsp. ***hookeri*** **new**	GKev
- Ingramii Group	WAbe WThu
'Jiggy Pink' **new**	CRos NDov
'Jiggy White' **new**	CRos NDov
keiskei	CPBP

	- var. ***akaisialpina***	NSla
	- - f. ***leucantha***	NSla
	- var. ***minor***	EHyd EWes LRHS NRHS WAbe
	laciniata 'Starburst'	CSpe
	latifolia	CHab GJos MHer MNHC NGrd NMir WOut
§	- subsp. ***alba***	CWld GJos LRHS SEND SPhx
	maritima	see *S. uniflora*
	multifida	see *S. fimbriata*
	multiflora new	EPPr
	noctiflora	CHab WSFF
	nutans	NAts SBut SPhx SRms WSFF
	pusilla	CSpe GJos NHpl NLar
	quadridentata	see *S. alpestris*
	regia	CBod SBrt SPhx
	rubra	see *S. dioica*
	saxifraga	GKev
	schafta 🏆H5	CTri ECha EPfP GJos GKev MMuc MRav NBid SEND SRms WHoo XLum
	- 'Abbotswood'	see *Lychnis* × *walkeri* 'Abbotswood Rose'
	- 'Persian Carpet'	EBou WRHF
	- 'Shell Pink'	CPBP CRos ECha EHyd EPfP EWes GJos LRHS MMuc NBid NRHS NSla SEND WHoo
	sieboldii	see *Lychnis coronata* var. *sieboldii*
	stellata	SPhx
§	***uniflora***	CHab MMuc NAts NBro SBut SPlb SRms SSut WOut
	- 'Alba Plena'	see *S. uniflora* 'Robin Whitebreast'
I	- 'Compacta'	SHar SPhx
§	- 'Druett's Variegated' (v)	CRos CTri EBou ECtt EHyd ELan ELon EPot EWes LRHS MHol NHpl NRHS SPlb SPoG SRms WCav WIce XLum
	- 'Flore Pleno'	see *S. uniflora* 'Robin Whitebreast'
	- pink-flowered	SBut
§	- 'Robin Whitebreast' (d)	ECha EPfP GBin LRHS NBid NBro NWad SPhx SRms WSHC XLum
	- 'Rosea'	ECtt GJos MHol MMuc NHpl SPlb
	- 'Variegata'	see *S. uniflora* 'Druett's Variegated'
	- WEISSKEHLCHEN	see *S. uniflora* 'Robin Whitebreast'
	- 'White Bells'	CTri WKif
	virginica	WCot
	viridiflora	SPhx
§	***vulgaris***	CAgr CHab GJos MMuc MNHC NMir SBut SPhx SRms WHer WOut
	- subsp. ***maritima***	see *S. uniflora*
	wallichiana	see *S. vulgaris*
	'Wisley Pink'	ECtt
	yunnanensis	SPhx WSHC
§	***zawadskii***	GJos GKev LSun MMuc SBrt SEND

Siler (*Umbelliferae*)

	montanum	see *Laserpitium siler*

Silphium (*Asteraceae*)

	integrifolium	IMou LPla SPhx WCot WOld XLum
	laciniatum	CMac CSpe LEdu SBrt SMad SPhx WHal XLum
	mohrii new	SPhx
	perfoliatum 🏆H7	CBod CRos CSpe EBee EHyd EMor GPoy IMou LEdu LPla LRHS MMuc NDov NLar NRHS SDix SEND SPhx WCAu WCot XLum
	- from Great Dixter	IMou
	- var. ***connatum***	SPhx
	terebinthinaceum	CSpe SBrt SPhx WCot XLum
	trifoliatum	EPPr SPhx WCot

Silybum (*Asteraceae*)

	marianum	CCBP CRos EHyd ELan GPoy LRHS MNHC NBir SPhx SRms WOut XAbr
	- white	SPhx

Sinacalia (*Asteraceae*)

§	***tangutica***	CSam GQue MBel NBid NLar NSti SDix WCot WOld WWtn

Sinapis (*Brassicaceae*)

	alba	SVic

Sinarundinaria (*Poaceae*)

	anceps	see *Yushania anceps*
	jaunsarensis	see *Yushania anceps*
	maling	see *Yushania maling*
	murielae	see *Fargesia murielae*
	nitida	see *Fargesia nitida*

Sinningia (*Gesneriaceae*)

*	***caerulea***	WDib
	calcaria	WDib
§	***cardinalis***	EBak WDib
	- 'Innocent'	WDib
	conspicua	WDib
	nivalis	WDib
	speciosa 'Blanche de Méru'	SDeJ
	- 'Hollywood'	SDeJ
	- 'Kaiser Friedrich'	SDeJ
	- 'Kaiser Wilhelm'	SDeJ
	- 'Mont Blanc'	SDeJ
	tuberosa	MCot
	tubiflora	EShb LEdu NSti WCot WFar WKif XLum

Sinobambusa (*Poaceae*)

§	***intermedia***	XCre
	rubroligula	XCre
	tootsik	XCre

× *Sinocalycalycanthus* see *Calycanthus*

Sinocalycanthus see *Calycanthus*

Sinocrassula (*Crassulaceae*)

§	***yunnanensis***	CDoC CPla EShb NHpl SPlb SSim

Sinofranchetia (*Lardizabalaceae*)

	chinensis	CRHN IArd SAko WPGP WSHC
	- DJHS 4117	WCru

Sinojackia (*Styracaceae*)

	rehderiana	IArd
	xylocarpa	CBcs CMCN IMou NLar

Sinopodophyllum (*Berberidaceae*)

§	***hexandrum***	CSpe CWCL EBee ELan EMor EPot GBin GKev GMaP GPoy GQue ILea LPla MNrw MPnt MRav NBid NBir NChi NLar SPlb WAvo WCot WKor WOld WPnP WSHC WTyc
	- from Kangding, Mugecuo Lake, Sichuan, China	SBrt
§	- var. ***chinense***	GEdr GKev LEdu WCru
	- - BWJ 7908	WCru
	- - SDR 4409	CExl
	- 'Chinese White'	CExl

§	- var. ***emodi***	EPfP ITim
	- - 'Majus'	CMiW GBin MCot WHal

Sinowilsonia (*Hamamelidaceae*)

	henryi	CBcs NLar

Siphocranion (*Lamiaceae*)

§	***macranthum***	EBee EWes WPGP WSHC

Sison (*Apiaceae*)

	amomum	CBre

Sisymbrium (*Brassicaceae*)

§	***luteum***	EBee

Sisyrinchium (*Iridaceae*)

	× ***anceps***	see *S. angustifolium*
§	***angustifolium***	CWCL ECha EMor MCot NBir NChi SChF SPlb SRms WBrk WCav
	- f. ***album***	MCot NChi NLar
§	***arenarium***	CWCL
	bellum hort.	see *S. idahoense* var. *bellum*
	bermudiana	see *S. angustifolium*
	'Biscutella'	CBod CKno EMor EPfP GMaP ITim LEdu SPad SPlb WCav WFar WHal WHoo WKif
	'Blue Ice'	GPSL ITim LRHS NLar WAbe
	'Blue Skies'	ITim WCav
	boreale	see *S. californicum*
	brachypus	see *S. californicum* Brachypus Group
	'Californian Skies'	CAby CElw CExl CKno CRos ECha ECtt EHyd GMaP LRHS NBir NDov NRHS NSla SEdd SRms SWvt WAvo WKif
§	***californicum***	CBen CDoC GWyn IMou LLWG LRHS WMAq WSMil XLum
§	- Brachypus Group	CPla CTri EBou EMor EPfP GAbr LPot MAsh NBir NLar SPlb SWvt WKif
	- 'Yellowstone'	CSBt EPfP SRms
*	***capsicum***	CExl
	convolutum B&SWJ 9117	WCru
	cuspidatum	see *S. arenarium*
	'Devon Skies'	CElw CMea CPla CRos CWCL ECtt EDAr EHyd LRHS MEch MNrw NLar NRHS SRms SWvt WAbe WIce
	douglasii	see *Olsynium douglasii*
	'Dragon's Eye'	CElw CKno CMea CPBP EDAr EWes LPot MBrN MHer WFar WHoo WIce
	'E.K. Balls'	CAby CPBP CRos EBou ECtt EDAr EHyd ELan EMor EPfP EPot EWTr GAbr GMaP LLWG LRHS MAsh MCot NHpl NRHS NSla SEdd SPoG SRms SWvt WAbe WIce
	graminoides	GWyn NWad
	grandiflorum	see *Olsynium douglasii*
	'Hemswell Sky'	ECtt GAbr NLar NRya
	'Iceberg'	CElw CKno ECha EWes SEdd
	idahoense	CPla ECha ECtt GAbr NDov NHpl SPlb SRms
§	- var. ***bellum***	CKno EBou EPfP SRms XLum
	- - pale-flowered	CKno SMHy
	- - 'Rocky Point'	CKno CSpe EHyd EPfP EWes LRHS NRHS SPoG WFar
	- var. ***macounii***	GPSL SPlb
§	- - 'Album' ♀^{H4}	CElw CMea ECtt EWes LPot WAbe WFar WIce
	'Janet Denman' (v)	CBor EDAr EShb EWTr EWes SEdd WFar
	junceum	see *Olsynium junceum*
	littorale	CExl
	macrocarpon misapplied	see *S. macrocarpum*
§	***macrocarpum***	EWld
	'Marchants Seedling'	SMHy
	'Marion'	CMea ECtt MBrN WHoo
	'May Snow'	see *S. idahoense* var. *macounii* 'Album'
	montanum	NHpl
	montanum × ***nudicaule***	GAbr
	'Mrs Spivey'	NBir
	'North Star'	see *S.* 'Pole Star'
	nudicaule	NWad
	palmifolium	CSpe LEdu LPla MAvo MHer MNrw NWad SMad WFar WSHC XLum
	patagonicum	CExl CPla GKev
§	'Pole Star'	NLar
	'Quaint and Queer'	CCCN CExl ECha EShb LPot MBrN MNrw NBir SEdd WAvo WSHC
	'Raspberry'	CKno CMea ECha WFar
	'Sapphire'	CAby CCCN CKno ECha ECtt EDAr ELan LPot LRHS MBow MHol NHpl NLar NWad SEdd SPoG WGrn WSMil
§	***striatum***	Widely available
§	- 'Aunt May' (v)	CBcs CBod CCCN CMac ECha EPfP GMaP LRHS LSRN MGos MRav NHpl NRHS NSti SCob SPoG SRms SWvt WCot WPGP WSMil
	- 'Variegatum'	see *S. striatum* 'Aunt May'
	aff. ***unispathaceum*** B&SWJ 10683	WCru

Sium (*Apiaceae*)

	sisarum	CLau GPoy LEdu MBriF NDov SDix WKor WSFF

Skimmia ✿ (*Rutaceae*)

	anquetilia	CMac
	- (f)	WCru
	- (m)	WCru
	arborescens B&SWJ 11799	WCru
	- B&SWJ 13902	WCru
	- PAB 8774	LEdu
	- subsp. ***nitida*** B&SWJ 8239	WCru
	arisanensis B&SWJ 7114	WCru
	- CWJ 12417	WCru
	black-fruited B&SWJ 8259 from northern Vietnam (f/m)	WCru
	× ***confusa*** 'Kew Green' (m) ♀^{H5}	Widely available
	japonica	CDoC CMac CTho MGos SCob SSta SavN WFar
	- (f)	CMac CTri EPfP SRms
	- B&SWJ 5053 (f)	WCru
	- B&SWJ 5053 (m)	WCru
	- 'Alba'	see *S. japonica* 'Wakehurst White'
	- 'Attraction'	MGos
	- 'Bowles's Dwarf Female' (f)	CEnd MRav MWht
	- 'Bowles's Dwarf Male' (m)	NWad
	- 'Bronze Knight' (m)	CBod CMac MAsh MRav NLar NWad SRms
	- 'Carberry' (f)	CMac
	- 'Dad's Red Dragon' (f)	CDoC CMac MAsh NOra SRms
	- DELIGHT ('Delibolwi'^{PBR}) **new**	CDoC
	- 'Emerald King' (m)	NOra

- 'Finchy'PBR (m)	CRos EHyd EPfP LRHS MAsh NLar NRHS
- 'Foremanii'	see *S. japonica* 'Veitchii'
§ - 'Fragrans' (m) 🏆H5	CDoC CMac CRos CSBt CTri EBee EHyd EPfP LCro LOPS LRHS LSRN MAsh MGos MRav NLar NOra NRHS SCob SLim SPer SPoG SRms SWvt WFar
- 'Fragrant Cloud'	see *S. japonica* 'Fragrans'
- 'Fructu Albo'	see *S. japonica* 'Wakehurst White'
- 'Godrie's Dwarf' (m)	CRos EHyd EPfP LRHS MAsh NLar NRHS WFar
- 'Humpty Dumpty' (f)	WFar
- var. ***intermedia*** f. ***repens***	see *S. japonica* subsp. *japonica* var. *intermedia*
§ - subsp. ***japonica*** var. ***intermedia*** B&SWJ 5560	WCru
- - - B&SWJ 11165	WCru
- 'John Turner' (f)	GBin
- 'Kew White' (f)	CAby CBcs CBrac CDoC CRos EHyd ELan EPfP IArd LCro LOPS LRHS MAsh MGos MRav NHol NOra NRHS NWad SLon SPer SSta SWvt WCFE WLov
- LUWIAN ('Wanto') (m)	CRos EHyd LRHS NRHS
- 'Macpenny Dwarf' (m)	CMac SRms
- 'Magic Marlot'PBR (m/v)	CRos EBee EHyd EPfP LRHS MAsh MGos MRav NHpl NLar SPoG SWvt
- 'Marlot' (m)	CDoC CRos EHyd EPfP LRHS NLar NRHS SPoG
- 'Mystic Marlot'PBR	LRHS
- 'Nymans' (f) 🏆H5	CBod CDoC CEnd CRos CTsd EHyd ELan EPfP GBin LCro LOPS LRHS MAsh MGos MRav NOra NRHS SCob SLim SPoG SRms SWvt
- OBSESSION ('Obsbolwi'PBR) (m/f)	LCro LOPS LRHS LSRN MAsh MGos
- 'Olympic Flame' (f)	CDoC CRos EHyd EPfP IArd LRHS MAsh MBlu NLar NRHS SPoG
- 'Pabella'PBR (f)	ELan MAsh SPoG
- 'Pigmy' (f)	CExl
- PINK DWARF ('Moerings 47'PBR) <u>**new**</u>	CDoC
- 'Red Diamonds'	CRos NRHS
- 'Red Princess' (f)	CDoC MAsh NOra
- 'Red Riding Hood' (f)	CBod CRos EHyd ELon LRHS MAsh MMrt NLar NRHS NWad SLon SPer
- 'Redruth' (f)	CBcs CMac CSBt ELon MAsh SEND WAvo WLov
§ - subsp. ***reevesiana***	CBcs CBrac CMac CRos CSBt CTri EHyd ELan EPfP GBin LCro LOPS LRHS MGos MRav MSwo NLar SCob SPoG SRms SWvt
- - B&SWJ 3763	MAsh WCru
- - 'Chilan Choice' (f/m)	WPGP
- - 'Godrie's Little Ruby'PBR	NLar
- - var. ***reevesiana*** B&SWJ 3544	WCru
§ - Rogersii Group	CMac CTri
- - 'George Gardner' (m)	LRHS
- - 'Nana Mascula' (m)	CTri
- - 'Rockyfield Green'	MAsh
- - 'Rogersii' (f)	CMac
- 'Rubella' (m) 🏆H5	Widely available
- RUBESTA ('Moerings3'PBR) <u>**new**</u>	CDoC
- 'Rubinetta' (m)	CBar EPfP IArd MAsh SEND
- 'Ruby Dome' (m)	CDoC LRHS NOra NWad
- 'Ruby King' (m)	IArd LSRN NLar
- 'Scarlet Dwarf' (f)	NHol NOra WAvo
- SEDUCTION ('Redbolwi'PBR)	MGos
- 'Snow White'PBR (m)	WAvo
- 'Tansley Gem' (f)	EHyd LRHS MAsh MWht SPoG
- 'Temptation'PBR (f)	CRos EHyd EPfP LCro LOPS LRHS NRHS
- 'Thereza'PBR (m)	EBee
§ - 'Veitchii' (f)	CBar CBcs CBod CBrac CDoC CMac CSBt CTri EHyd EPfP LRHS LSRN MAsh MGos MMuc MRav NLar NOra NRHS SEND SLim SPer SPoG SRms SWvt WCFE
§ - 'Wakehurst White' (f)	CBcs CMac CSBt CTri EBee EPfP LRHS MAsh MRav NWad SPoG SRms
- 'White Bella' (m)	CRos EHyd LRHS NRHS
- 'Winifred Crook' (f)	EHyd LRHS
- 'Winnie's Dwarf'	MAsh
- 'Wisley Female' (f)	CTri
laureola	CExl MRav SRms WCFE
- GWJ 9364	WCru
- subsp. ***laureola*** HWJK 2095	WCru
- subsp. ***multinervia*** GWJ 9374	WCru
reevesiana	see *S. japonica* subsp. *reevesiana*
rogersii	see *S. japonica* Rogersii Group
'Snowman'	WCFE

Smallanthus (*Asteraceae*)

sonchifolius	LEdu
- 'Morado'	WPGP

Smilacina see *Maianthemum*

Smilax (*Smilacaceae*)

B&SWJ 6628 from Thailand	WCru
aspera	CMac EShb ESwi LEdu WCru WPGP
china B&SWJ 4427	WCru
discotis	SEND
glaucophylla B&SWJ 2971	WCru
nipponica B&SWJ 4331	WCru
rotundifolia	LEdu
sieboldii	LEdu MRav
- B&SWJ 744	WCru

Smyrnium (*Apiaceae*)

olusatrum	CCBP CHab CSpe GJos LEdu SPhx SPtp SRms WHer WOut WSFF
perfoliatum	CBod CSpe EBee ELan ELon EMor EPfP EWes GBin LCro LEdu LOPS NAts NBir SDix SPhx WCot WHal WMal WSHC
rotundifolium	WCot
- PAB 6714	LEdu WPGP

Solandra (*Solanaceae*)

grandiflora misapplied	see *S. maxima*
hartwegii	see *S. maxima*
§ ***maxima***	CCCN

Solanum (*Solanaceae*)

aerial-rooting climbing species B&SWJ 14398	WCru
atropurpureum	CDTJ SPlb WCot
betaceum (F)	CCCN EShb SVic
- yellow-fruited (F)	SPlb
burchellii	SPlb
capsicastrum	SPlb

conchifolium hort. — see *S. linearifolium*
crispum 'Autumnale' — see *S. crispum* 'Glasnevin'
§ - 'Glasnevin' ♀H4 — Widely available
dulcamara — GPoy
- 'Lucia' (v) — CNat
- 'Variegatum' (v) — CMac MAsh
jasminoides — see *S. laxum*
laciniatum — CCCN CDTJ CExl SArc SEND SPlb SVen WSMil
§ ***laxum*** — CMac CRos EBee EHyd LRHS MAsh MRav NRHS SPer SRms SWvt
- 'Album' ♀H4 — Widely available
- 'Album Variegatum' (v) — SCob
* - 'Aureovariegatum' (v) — CMac EBee ELon NOra SPlb
- 'Coldham' — EPPr EWld MNrw SDix SMad
- 'Crèche du Pape' — ECha LRHS SRms
§ ***linearifolium*** — CSpe
lycopersicum — SVic
muricatum (F) — CCCN SPlb
- 'Pepino Gold' (F) — EShb
pinnatum — SPlb
pseudocapsicum 'Thurino' — LSou
- variegated (v) — WCot
pyracanthum — CDTJ ECre SArc SPlb WCot
quitoense (F) — CDTJ SPlb
rantonnetii — see *Lycianthes rantonnetii*
rigescentoides — SPlb
sisymbriifolium — SPlb
aff. ***stenophyllum*** B&SWJ 10744 — WCru
umbelliferum var. ***incanum*** new — SBrt
villosum — SVen
wendlandii — CCCN

Soldanella (*Primulaceae*)

alpina — CTsd GKev NSla SRms WAbe
I - 'Alba' — NSla NWad WAbe
carpatica — GEdr GKev LEdu SPlb WAbe
- 'Alba' — GEdr LEdu WAbe
carpatica × pusilla — MNrw NRya SBut WAbe WSHC
carpatica × villosa — LEdu
cyanaster — GAbr GBin GJos GKev GLog LEdu NHpl NQui WAbe
dimoniei — LEdu NWad WAbe WFar
hungarica — GEdr WAbe
minima — GEdr GJos LEdu NSla WAbe
montana — CFis CPla EMor GBin GJos GKev LEdu NLar WBor WTyc XBar
- hybrid — NSla
pindicola — GEdr LEdu
pusilla — NWad
'Spring Symphony' — CElw CWCL ELan GBin GEdr GMaP GPSL LEdu NHar NWad SAko SPoG WFar WPnP
'Sudden Spring' — CElw GBin LEdu NWad WAbe
villosa ♀H6 — CElw GAbr GBin GEdr GKev GLog GPSL LEdu NRya NWad WSHC

Soleirolia (*Urticaceae*)

soleirolii — CBod CDoC CTri ELan EPot LCro LLWG LOPS MMuc SEND SMad SPer SPtp SVic SWvt WHer XLum
- 'Argentea' — see *S. soleirolii* 'Variegata'
§ - 'Aurea' — EPot NHpl SVic SWvt
- 'Golden Queen' — see *S. soleirolii* 'Aurea'
- 'Silver Queen' — see *S. soleirolii* 'Variegata'
§ - 'Variegata' (v) — LLWG SVic

Solenopsis (*Campanulaceae*)

axillaris — see *Isotoma axillaris*

Solenostemon ✿ (*Lamiaceae*)

scutellarioides 'Angel of the North' — WDib
- 'Autumn Rainbow' — WDib
- 'Beauty of Lyons' — WDib
- 'Brilliant' (v) — WDib
- 'Bronze Pagoda' — WDib
- BURGUNDY WEDDING TRAIN ('Kakegawa Ce10') — WDib
- CAMPFIRE ('Uf12823') — MPri WHil
- 'Chamaeleon' (v) — WDib
- 'City of Sunderland' — WDib
- 'Combat' (v) ♀H1c — WDib
- 'Crimson Ruffles' (v) ♀H1c — WDib
- 'Dazzler' (v) — WDib
- 'Durham Gala' ♀H1c — WDib
- 'Firelight' (v) — WDib
- 'Gay's Delight' ♀H1c — MPri
- HENNA ('Balcenna'PBR) (v) ♀H1c — ECtt MPri
- 'Illumination' — WDib
- 'Inky Fingers' (v) — WDib
- 'Juliet Quartermain' ♀H1c — WDib
- 'Jupiter' — WDib
- 'Kentish Fire' (v) — WDib
- 'Kiwi Fern' (Stained Glassworks Series) (v) — WDib
- 'Lemon Chiffon' — WDib
- 'Lord Falmouth' (v) ♀H1c — WDib
- 'Mrs Pilkington' (v) — WDib
- 'Muriel Pedley' (v) — WDib
- 'Paisley Shawl' (v) — WDib
- 'Peter Wonder' (v) — WDib
- 'Pineapple Beauty' (v) ♀H1c — WDib
- 'Pineapplette' (v) ♀H1c — WDib
- 'Pink Chaos' (v) ♀H1c — WDib
- 'Red Angel' (v) — WDib
- 'Red Velvet' (v) — WDib
- REDHEAD ('Uf0646'PBR) ♀H1c — MPri
- 'Rose Blush' (v) — WDib
- 'Roy Pedley' (v) ♀H1c — WDib
- 'Royal Scot' (v) ♀H1c — WDib
- 'Saturn' (v) — WDib
- 'The Flume' — WDib
- 'Timotei' — WDib
- TRUSTY RUSTY ('Uf06419'PBR) (v) ♀H1c — MPri
- 'Walter Turner' (v) ♀H1c — WDib
- 'Winsome' (v) ♀H1c — WDib
- 'Winter Sun' (v) — WDib
- 'Wisley Tapestry' (v) ♀H1c — WDib

Solidago (*Asteraceae*)

'Autumn Blaze' — WFar
BABYGOLD — see *S.* 'Goldkind'
'Ballardii' — SRms
brachystachys — see *S. cutleri*
caesia — EHyd EWes LRHS NBir SAko SMHy WFar
canadensis — CTri ELan SEND SPlb WBrk WFar WHer WOld XAbr XLum
- var. ***salebrosa*** — EHyd LRHS
- var. ***scabra*** — MMuc
'Citronella' — ECtt

'Cloth of Gold'	CMac ECtt NEoE NHol SGbt SPoG SWvt WGwG
§ 'Crown of Rays'	CRos ECtt ELon EPfP GBin LRHS MRav NRHS SCob WFar
§ ***cutleri***	EBou EDAr NLar SPlb SRms WFar
'Dennis Strange'	MAvo MHol
'Ducky'	SCob
'Early Bird'	NLar WFar
flabelliformis	WCot
§ ***flexicaulis***	GMaP SPhx WCot XLum
- 'Variegata' (v)	CBod EBee EHyd EShb GMaP LRHS NLar NRHS WFar XLum
'Foxbrook Fountain' **new**	MAvo
'Foxbrook Gold'	MAvo WFar
'Gardone' ♀H7	WFar
gigantea	WFar
glomerata	MMuc NLar SEND
GOLDEN BABY	see *S.* 'Goldkind'
§ 'Golden Dwarf'	CWCL SPoG SRms XLum
'Golden Fleece'	see *S. sphacelata* 'Golden Fleece'
'Golden Wings'	CBre
'Goldenmosa' ♀H7	CSBt EWes GMaP SPer WFar
'Goldilocks'	SRms
§ 'Goldkind'	CSBt CTri EBee EBou ECtt EHyd ELan EPfP GAbr LRHS NRHS SCob SRms SWvt WBrk WCav WFar WRHF
GOLDZWERG	see *S.* 'Golden Dwarf'
'Hiddigeigei' (v)	WCot WFar
hybrida	see *S.* × *luteus*
latifolia	see *S. flexicaulis*
'Laurin'	CSam NLar XLum
'Ledsham'	CAby CBod CRos ECtt EHyd GBin LRHS NBre NRHS SPoG
'Lena'	SRms
'Linner Gold'	NBre
'Little Lemon' PBR	CBct EBee ELan MTin NEoE
§ × ***luteus***	EBee SRms WFar XLum
- 'Lemore' ♀H7	CAby CBod CDor CKno CMea CMiW EBee ECha ELan EPPr EPfP EShb GMaP LSou MSpe NSti NWsh SBut SPer SPhx SPoG SRms WCot WFar WHoo XLum
ohioensis	XLum
- 'Four Seasons'	GBin
§ ***ptarmicoides***	EBee MMuc XEll XLum
riddellii	XLum
rigida subsp. ***humilis*** 'Golden Rockets' **new**	SPhx
rugosa	ECha MBNS MBriF MMuc SEND SPhx WCot
- 'Fireworks' ♀H7	Widely available
- 'Loydser Crown'	NDov
sempervirens	EBee EHyd IMou LRHS WFar WOld
'Septembergold'	CSam
shortii 'Solar Cascade'	WHil
'Sonnenschein'	NBre
speciosa	SPhx WCot
spectabilis var. ***confinis*** KM 27-01	EBee
§ ***sphacelata*** 'Golden Fleece'	CBcs EHyd EPfP IMou NBre SRms
STRAHLENKRONE	see *S.* 'Crown of Rays'
'Super'	WCot
SWEETY ('Barseven' PBR)	EHyd LRHS NRHS WHil
'Tom Thumb'	MRav NBir SRms
uliginosa	EShb
virgaurea	CBee GPoy MHer MMuc MNHC NAts NLar SRms WHer
- subsp. ***alpestris*** var. ***minutissima***	IMou
- var. ***cambrica***	see *S. virgaurea* subsp. *minuta*
§ - subsp. ***minuta***	GBin GRum MHol
§ - 'Variegata' (v)	NEoE WOut
vulgaris 'Variegata'	see *S. virgaurea* 'Variegata'
'Yellow Springs'	GJos
'Yellow Stone'	EBee EHyd

× *Solidaster* see *Solidago*

hybridus	see *Solidago* × *luteus*

Sollya (*Pittosporaceae*)

fusiformis	see *S. heterophylla*
§ ***heterophylla*** ♀H3	Widely available
- 'Alba'	CBcs CCCN CRos EHyd ELan EPfP LRHS NRHS SEle SLon SPer SPoG SWvt
- 'Pink Charmer'	CBcs CRos EHyd ELan EPfP LRHS SEle SPer SPoG
- pink-flowered	CCCN CSBt SWvt

Sonchus (*Asteraceae*)

arboreus	CPla
pinnatus	SPlb

Sophora (*Papilionaceae*)

cassioides	MGil
- NJM 08.008	WPGP
§ ***davidii***	CAby CBcs CExl EBee ELon EPfP ESwi LEdu LRHS MBlu SBrt SEND SPoG WCot WGrn
flavescens	SBrt
fulvida	EBee WPGP
howinsula	SNig WCot
japonica	see *Styphnolobium japonicum*
§ 'Little Baby'	CDoC ELan EPfP LSRN MGil MGos SEle SIvy SPoG SWvt WGrn
macrocarpa	SWvt
microphylla	CTri MGil
molloyi 'Dragon's Gold'	CBcs EBee ELan ELon EPfP LRHS MAsh SCoo SEND SEle SPoG SSta SWvt
prostrata misapplied	see *S.* 'Little Baby'
prostrata ambig.	SavN
prostrata Buchanan	CMac
secundiflora	CMCN
SUN KING ('Hilsop' PBR) ♀H4	CBcs CDoC CRos CWGN EHyd ELan EPfP EWes LRHS LSRN MGos NLar NRHS SCoo SLon SPer SPoG SWvt WCot
tetraptera	CBcs CRos CTsd EHyd EPfP LRHS MMuc SEND SWvt
viciifolia	see *S. davidii*

Sorbaria (*Rosaceae*)

aitchisonii	see *S. tomentosa* var. *angustifolia*
arborea	see *S. kirilowii*
§ ***kirilowii***	CExl CMac MRav NLar SMad WOut
lindleyana	see *S. tomentosa*
sorbifolia	CBcs CMCN ELan MGil MMuc SCob SEND SPer SPlb WFar WSpi
- 'Sem' PBR ♀H5	Widely available
§ ***tomentosa***	CPla GBin
§ - var. ***angustifolia*** ♀H5	CRos CTri EBee EHyd ELan EPfP LRHS MMuc MRav NBid SEND SLon
- 'Sticks and Feathers'	SMad

× *Sorbaronia* (*Rosaceae*)

fallax	EPfP NLar
- 'Ivan's Beauty'	ECrN

× *Sorbopyrus* (*Rosaceae*)

§ ***auricularis*** 'Shipova' (F) — CAgr MAsh NOra WMat

Sorbus ✿ (*Rosaceae*)

sp. — CMen
NJM 09.203 — WPGP
section *Discolores* — GKev
- KR 5585 — WCru WPGP
- KR 6308 — WCru
adamii — CMCN
alnifolia — CLnd CMCN EPfP MBlu
- B&SWJ 8461 — WCru
- B&SWJ 10948 — WCru
- 'Red Bird' — EPfP LRHS MBlu
'Amber Light' — EBee NOra SGbt WMat
americana — CLnd
- 'Lafayette' **new** — GKev
amoena — SPtp
'Apricot' — CEnd
'Apricot Queen' — CLnd ECrN SGol WFar
aria — CCVT CHab CLnd CTri ECrN LBuc MGos MMuc SCob SEND SGol WKor WMou WTSh
- 'Aurea' — CLnd SPer
- 'Chrysophylla' — CSBt ECrN
- 'Decaisneana' — see *S. aria* 'Majestica'
- 'Lutescens' ♀H6 — Widely available
- 'Magnifica' — CLnd ECrN ELan ESwi NLar SEWo WJas
§ - 'Majestica' ♀H6 — CCVT CLnd CMac EBee ECrN LMaj MRav SCob WFar WJas
- 'Mitchellii' — see *S. thibetica* 'John Mitchell'
- 'Ottery' **new** — CLnd
aria* × *pseudovilmorinii — EBee WPGP
arnoldiana 'Golden Wonder' — see *S.* 'Lombarts Golden Wonder'
aronioides misapplied — see *S. caloneura*
aronioides Rehder — GKev
§ ***aucuparia*** — Widely available
- 'Aspleniifolia' — CBcs CCVT CMCN CMac CSBt EBee ECrN LRHS MGos MRav NLar NOra NOrn NRHS SCob SLim WFar WJas WMat
§ - 'Beissneri' — CAgr MRav
- CARDINAL ROYAL ('Michred') — CCVT CLnd LMaj MMuc SCob SCoo SEWo SLon
- 'Dirkenii' — WJas WMat
§ - var. ***edulis*** (F) — CArg CLnd LBuc MGos MMuc SPer
- - 'Rossica' misapplied — see *S. aucuparia* var. *edulis* 'Rossica Major'
§ - - 'Rossica Major' — ECrN SEWo
§ - 'Fastigiata' — CEnd CTri ELan EPfP GKin LMaj
- 'Fingerprint'PBR — EBee LRHS
- 'Hilling's Spire' — CTho
- subsp. ***maderensis*** — MBlu WLov
- ***pluripinnata*** — see *S. scalaris* Koehne
- var. ***rossica*** Koehne — see *S. aicuparia* var. *edulis*
- 'Sheerwater Seedling' ♀H6 — CBcs CCVT CMCN CSBt EBee ECrN ELan EPfP GKin LMaj MGos MMuc MRav MSwo NOrn SCob SEND SGol SPer WFar
- 'Wettra' — SGsty
aucuparia* × *scalaris — NOrn
AUTUMN SPIRE ('Flanrock') ♀H6 — CBcs CEnd CLnd ELan EPfP LRHS LSRN MAsh MGos MPri NLar NOra SCoo SGsty SLim SLon SPer SPoG SWvt WMat
bissetii — WLov
- Yu 14299 — WCru
brevipetiolata B&SWJ 11771 — WCru
bulleyana KR 2809 — WCru
- MF 96170 — GKev
§ ***caloneura*** — EBee EPfP LEdu MBlu SPtp WLov WPGP
- Guiz 80 — WCru
carmesina — SPtp
- B&L 12545 — EBee EPfP GKev WCru
- 'Emberglow' — EPfP NOra WMat
cashmiriana misapplied pink-fruited — see *S. rosea*
cashmiriana Hedl. ♀H6 — CBcs CCVT CLnd CMCN CMac CTri ECrN EHyd ELan EPfP GKev LRHS MBlu MGos MMuc MRav MSwo NLar NOrn SCob SGol SPer SPoG WCFE WJas WMat
aff. ***cashmiriana*** ambig. — GKev LCro LOPS MAsh NHol NOra WFar WTSh
- B 751 — WCru
chamaemespilus — GKev WThu
'Chinese Lace' — Widely available
§ ***commixta*** — CEnd CLnd CMCN ECrN LCro LMaj LOPS MBlu MGos MMuc MSwo NLar NOrn SEND SGol SLim SPer WJas
- B&SWJ 10839 — WCru
- B&SWJ 11043 — WCru
- B&SWJ 12640 from Ulleungdo, South Korea — WCru
- 'Carmencita' **new** — MBlu
- 'Embley' ♀H6 — CBcs CCVT CLnd CMCN CSBt CTho CTri ELan EPfP EWTr LCro LOPS MBlu MGos MMuc MRav NOrn SCob SEND SGol SPer
- OLYMPIC FLAME — see *S. ulleungensis* 'Olympic Flame'
- 'Ravensbill' — EBee EPfP NLar NOra SCoo SGbt WHCr WMat
- var. ***rufoferruginea*** B&SWJ 11486 — WCru
- var. ***sachalinensis*** B&SWJ 8515 — WCru
aff. ***commixta*** — WTSh
conradinae Koehne — see *S. esserteauana*
'Copper Kettle' ♀H6 — EBee EPfP LRHS MAsh MBlu NLar NOra SCoo SPer WHCr WMat WMou
'Coral Beauty' — CLnd
corymbifera WWJ 11860 — WCru
'Covert Gold' — CEnd
cuspidata — see *S. vestita*
decipentiformis **new** — GKev
decora 'Gaspé' **new** — GKev
- var. ***nana*** — see *S. aucuparia* 'Fastigiata'
devoniensis — CTho
- 'Devon Beauty' — CAgr
discolor misapplied — see *S. commixta*
discolor (Maxim.) Maxim. — MBlu WJas
- MF 96172 — MAsh
- MF 97103 — WCru
domestica — CLnd MMuc SEND
- 'Maliformis' — see *S. domestica* f. *pomifera*
§ - f. ***pomifera*** — LEdu
§ - f. ***pyrifera*** — LEdu
- 'Pyriformis' — see *S. domestica* f. *pyrifera*
- 'Rosie' — CAgr
dunnii — WPGP
'Eastern Promise' ♀H6 — EPfP LCro MAsh MBlu MSwo NLar NOra NOrn SCob SCoo SGbt SLim WHCr WMat WMou

§	***eburnea***	GKev
	- Harry Smith 12799	WPGP
	eleonorae	SPtp
	ellipsoidalis C 288	GKev
	eminens	CNat
	epidendron	WPGP
§	***esserteauana***	CLnd
	'Ethel's Gold'	MBlu
	eugenii-kelleri **new**	GKev
	fansipanensis NJM 09.176	WPGP
	'Fastigiata'	see *S. aucuparia* 'Fastigiata', *S.* × *thuringiaca* 'Fastigiata'
	aff. ***filipes***	GKev
	folgneri 'Emiel' 𝕐H6	EPfP IArd MBlu NOra WMat
	- 'Lemon Drop'	CEnd CLnd EBee EPfP MAsh MBlu NOra SCoo WMat
	foliolosa	CLnd
	forrestii 𝕐H6	CBcs CMCN EBee EPfP GKev IArd NLar SPtp
§	***frutescens*** 𝕐H6	ELan NWad
	- R 14987	GKev
	fruticosa Crantz	GKev
	- 'Koehneana'	see *S. koehneana* C.K. Schneid.
	'Ghose'	CEnd CTho EBee WMat
	glabrescens	LEdu
	'Glendoick Spire'	EBee LRHS NLar NOra WHCr WMat
	'Glendoick White Baby'	NLar WMat
	'Golden Wonder'	see *S.* 'Lombarts Golden Wonder'
	gonggashanica	EPfP GEdr LRHS SPtp WPGP
	granulosa HWJ 1041	WCru
	'Gresgarth'	GKev
	harrowiana	EBee LEdu LRHS NLar WLov WMat WPGP
	- KW 21009	WPGP
	- from Burma	WPGP
	- from Yunnan	WPGP
	hedlundii	CExl EPfP NLar WMat WPGP
	- GWJ 9363	WCru WPGP
	- KR 1687	WPGP
	- KR 1810	WPGP
	- WJC 13806	WCru
	helenae	LRHS WPGP
	- EN 3088	GKev WPGP
	hemsleyi	CExl CLnd SPtp WPGP
	- 'John Bond' 𝕐H6	NLar NOra WHCr WMat
	× ***hostii***	CLnd
	hugh-mcallisteri CLD 310	GKev
	hupehensis misapplied	see *S. pseudohupehensis*
	- 'November Pink'	see *S. pseudohupehensis* 'Pink Pagoda'
	hupehensis C.K. Schneid. var. ***obtusa*** misapplied	see *S. pseudohupehensis* 'Pink Pagoda'
	- 'Rosea'	see *S. pseudohupehensis* 'Pink Pagoda'
	aff. ***hupehensis***	CSBt ECrN EWTr NOrn WFar WTSh
	hybrida L. 'Gibbsii' 𝕐H6	ELan EPfP MAsh NOra NOrn SPer WMat
	insignis	CLnd WPGP
	intermedia	CBcs CCVT CLnd CSBt CTri ECrN ELan LMaj MMuc SCob SEND SGol WMou
	- 'Brouwers'	CLnd ELan WMou
	japonica	EBee LRHS WMat
	- B&SWJ 10813	WCru
	- B&SWJ 11048	WCru
	'Joseph Rock'	Widely available
	aff. ***karchungii***	EBee
	- AGS/ES 347	EBee WPGP
I	***keenanii*** NJM 13.050	WPGP
I	***keenanii*** × ***wattii*** NJM 13.123	WPGP
	keissleri	EBee WLov
	- NJM 11.004	WPGP
	- NJM 11.056	WPGP
	- NJM 11.060	WPGP
	- PAB 7916	LEdu
	'Keith Rushforth'	WCru
§	× ***kewensis***	CLnd SPlb
	khumbuensis	GKev
	'Kirsten Pink'	CCVT SPer
	koehneana misapplied	see *S. frutescens*
§	***koehneana*** C.K. Schneid.	CLnd CMCN GKev MMrt WCru
	aff. ***koehneana***	see *S. eburnea*, *S. tenuis*
	lanata misapplied	see *S. vestita*
	'Leonard Messel' 𝕐H6	EPfP MAsh NLar NOra SGbt WHCr WMat
	'Likjornaja'	EPfP LRHS
§	'Lombarts Golden Wonder'	MMuc SEND
*	***maculata*** KR 5334	EBee GKev
	matsumurana misapplied	see *S. commixta*
	matsumurana (Makino) Koehne	GKev IArd IDee WPGP
	'Matthew Ridley' **new**	EBee
	megalocarpa	CJun CMCN WPGP
	- var. ***cuneata***	WPGP
	meliosmifolia	SPtp
	- B&SWJ 11709	WCru
	microphylla agg.	CMCN GKev
	- GWJ 9252	WCru
	- SICH 1009	EBee
	monbeigii (Cardot.) N.P. Balakr.	CLnd MGil
	moravica 'Laciniata'	see *S. aucuparia* 'Beissneri'
	muliensis F 22177	EBee GKev
§	***munda***	WCFE
	needhamii NJM 11.005	EBee WPGP
	- PAB 9853	LEdu
	'Nevezhinskaja'	MBlu
	olivacea	GKev SPtp
	aff. ***ovalis*** H 1948	EBee
	pallescens 'White House Farm' **new**	WPGP
	paniculata NJM 13.067	WPGP
	- NJM 13.092	WPGP
	- PAB 9831	LEdu
	parvifructa	EBee GKev WPGP
	'Peaches and Cream'	LCro LOPS
	'Pearly King'	CTho MAsh WJas
§	'Pink Pearl'	EPfP
	'Pink-Ness'	EPfP MBlu NOra SCoo WLov WMat
	pohuashanensis misapplied	see *S.* × *kewensis*
	pohuashanensis ambig.	CMCN
	poteriifolia 𝕐H5	GEdr GKev NHar
	- upright **new**	GKev
	prattii misapplied	see *S. munda*
	pseudobakyonensis	GKev
§	***pseudohupehensis*** 𝕐H6	CLnd CMCN CMac CTho CTri EPfP GLog MMuc SEND SGol SPer WJas
§	- 'Pink Pagoda' 𝕐H6	Widely available
	pseudovilmorinii	CBcs EBee GKev IMou LRHS MGil NLar NOra WCru WMat
	- SBEC 974	WPGP
	randaiensis	EBee SPlb WPGP
	- B&SWJ 156	WPGP
	- B&SWJ 3202	WCru
	reducta 𝕐H5	GBin GKev MMuc NHar NHol NLar NSla WLov

aff. ***reducta***	SRms
reflexipetala misapplied	see *S. commixta*
rehderiana misapplied	see *S. aucuparia*
rehderiana Koehne	GKev NOrn
'Rose Queen'	MBlu
§ ***rosea***	GEdr GKev SPtp
- SEP 492	WCru WPGP
- 'Rosiness' ♀H6	CLnd EBee EPfP LRHS WMat
'Rowancroft Coral Pink'	EBee
rubescens	GKev
rushforthii KR 5789	EBee GKev
rutilans	GKev
'Salmon Queen'	CLnd
sambucifolia	GKev
sargentiana ♀H6	CBcs CCVT CEnd CLnd CMCN CMac CTho CTri EBee ELan EPfP MBlu MGos MRav MSwo NLar NOra NOrn SLim SPer SPoG WMat
- EGM 291	WCru
'Savill Orange'	MMuc
scalaris ambig.	CBcs CMCN ELan MAsh MSwo NOra SPoG
§ ***scalaris*** Koehne	CEnd CTho CTri MBlu WJas WMat
'Schouten'	ECrN MMuc
scopulina misapplied	see *S. aucuparia* 'Fastigiata'
setschwanensis	CMCN
'Showa'	GKev
subulata HWJ 925	WCru
- KWJ 12272	WCru
'Sunshine'	CCVT CLnd LMaj MAsh MGos MMuc SEND WJas
§ ***tenuis***	GKev
§ ***thibetica*** 'John Mitchell' ♀H6	CAgr CBcs CEnd CLnd CMCN CRos EBee ECrN EPfP MBlu MGos NLar NOra NOrn SLim SPoG WMat
aff. ***thibetica*** BWJ 7757a	WCru
thomsonii GWJ 9363	WCru
- WWJ 12004	WCru
§ × ***thuringiaca*** 'Fastigiata'	CLnd EBar SCoo WJas WMat
tianschanica	WCru
'Titan'	EPfP MBlu
torminalis	CAgr CBcs CBrac CCVT CHab CLnd CMCN CMac CTho CTri EBee ELan EPfP MGos MMuc MRav NLar SCob SEND SEWo SPer SPoG WKor WMou WSpi WTSh
ulleungensis B&SWJ 12640	WCru
- 'Dodong'	CSBt LMaj SGsty
§ - 'Olympic Flame' ♀H6	CEnd CTho EBee EPfP GBin LBuc LSRN MAsh MBlu MPri NLar NOra NOrn SCob SCoo SEWo SLim SPer SPoG WHCr WLov WMat WMou
§ ***vestita***	CLnd CTho EPfP WCru
vilmorinii ♀H6	Widely available
- 'Pink Charm'	EPfP MAsh NOra WMat
- 'Robusta'	see *S.* 'Pink Pearl'
aff. ***vilmorinii***	GKin
- KR 5095	GKev
- KR 6453	WCru WPGP
wallichii NJM 13.127 **new**	WPGP
wardii	CBcs CLnd CTho EPfP LRHS MBlu
- KR 21127	EBee WPGP
'White Wax'	CCVT ECrN EWTr MGos SPer
'Wilfrid Fox'	CCVT MGos
wilsoniana	CLnd LRHS WLov
'Wisley Gold' ♀H6	LRHS NOra SCoo SGbt SLim WMat
yuana	EBee WPGP
- clone 1	WPGP
- clone 2	WPGP
zahlbruckneri C.K. Schneid.	WPGP

Sorghastrum (*Poaceae*)

avenaceum	see *S. nutans*
§ ***nutans***	CBod EBou EPPr XCre
- 'Indian Steel'	CBod EBee XCre XLum

sorrel, common see *Rumex acetosa*

sorrel, French see *Rumex scutatus*

Souliea see *Actaea*

soursop see *Annona muricata*

Sparaxis (*Iridaceae*)

'Bright Star'	GKev
bulbifera	WHil
elegans	SPlb WHil
grandiflora ♀H2	WHil
- subsp. ***acutiloba***	CPbh
- subsp. ***grandiflora***	CPbh
'Moonlight'	GKev
'Red Reflex'	GKev
'Skyline'	GKev
'Sunshine'	GKev
tricolor	CAby CGrW CPla GKev SDeJ

Sparganium (*Sparganiaceae*)

§ ***erectum***	CWat NMir NPer WMAq WSFF XLum
ramosum	see *S. erectum*

Sparrmannia (*Malvaceae*)

africana ♀H1c	CCCN ELan EShb SEND SPlb SVen
- 'Flore Pleno' (d)	CBcs

Spartina (*Poaceae*)

pectinata	XLum
- 'Aureomarginata' (v)	CBod CWCL EBee EHyd ELan EPfP GMaP LRHS MMuc NWsh SEND SPer WWtn XCre XLum

Spartium (*Papilionaceae*)

junceum ♀H5	CBcs CBod CCCN CDoC CEnd CMac EBee ELan ELon EPfP LRHS MGos MMuc SEND SPer SRms WAvo XSen
- 'Brockhill Compact'	CDoC CRos EHyd EPfP LRHS

Spartocytisus see *Cytisus*

Spathantheum (*Araceae*)

orbignyanum	GKev WCot

Spathipappus see *Tanacetum*

Spathiphyllum (*Araceae*)

wallisii	SPre
- 'Bellini'	LCro LOPS

Spathodea (*Bignoniaceae*)

campanulata	SPlb

spearmint see *Mentha spicata*

Speirantha (*Asparagaceae*)

convallarioides	see *S. gardenii*
§ ***gardenii***	CBct CDTJ EBee EPPr EPfP IMou LEdu MNrw WCru WHil WOld WPGP

Sphacele see *Lepechinia*

Sphaeralcea (*Malvaceae*)

ambigua	SPlb
'Childerley'	CMea CSpe ECtt MBNS MHol SMad SPad SPoG WCot WMal
coccinea	CPBP SPlb
fendleri	CCCN CSam CSde
'Hopleys Lavender'	CCCN SWvt
incana	CBod CCCN CSpe MGil
- 'Sourup'	EBee ECtt SMHy WCot
malviflora	CDTJ
miniata	CCCN
munroana	CCCN ECtt ELan SMad SRkn
- pale pink-flowered	CSam WABo
'Newleaze Coral'	CCCN EWld MAsh MGil MNrw SIvy SPad SPoG SRkn SWvt WBor WCot WFar
'Newleaze Pink'	SRkn
remota	CExl LPla SPlb
umbellata	see *Phymosia umbellata*

Sphagneticola (*Asteraceae*)

§ ***trilobata***	LLWG

Sphenomeris (*Dennstaedtiaceae*)

chinensis B&SWJ 6108	WCru

Spigelia (*Loganiaceae*)

marilandica	EBee GKev ILea SMad WCot WHil WSHC

Spilanthes (*Asteraceae*)

acmella misapplied	see *Acmella oleracea*
oleracea	see *Acmella oleracea*

spinach see AGM Vegetables Section

Spiraea (*Rosaceae*)

alba var. ***latifolia***	MMuc
albiflora	see *S. japonica* 'Albiflora'
arborea	see *Sorbaria kirilowii*
× ***arguta*** 'Bridal Wreath'	see *S.* 'Arguta'
§ 'Arguta' ♀H6	Widely available
aff. 'Arguta'	WLov
betulifolia	MRav WFar
- var. ***aemiliana***	MMuc
- 'Tor'	EPPr
- 'Tor Gold'PBR	CBcs LRHS MRav SPoG
× ***billardii*** misapplied	see *S.* × *pseudosalicifolia*
blumei CWJ 12829	WCru
× ***bumalda*** 'Wulfenii'	see *S. japonica* 'Walluf'
callosa 'Alba'	see *S. japonica* 'Albiflora'
canescens	CExl GKin
- CC 7281	EWld
- var. ***glaucophylla***	MMuc
chamaedryfolia	GKev
× ***cinerea*** 'Grefsheim' ♀H6	CBcs CBod CSBt EBee ELan LBuc MMuc NLar SCob SGol SLim SPer SPlb
crispifolia misapplied	see *S. japonica* 'Bullata'
densiflora	GKev
- var. ***splendens***	SBrt
DOUBLE PLAY BIG BANG	see *S.* 'Tracy'
douglasii	CMac
formosana B&SWJ 1597	CExl WCru
fritschiana	CMac
hayatana	GKev
- RWJ 10014	WCru
hendersonii	see *Petrophytum hendersonii*
§ ***japonica*** 'Albiflora'	CBrac CMac CRos CSBt CTri EHyd ELan ELon LRHS MRav MSwo NRHS NWad SGbt SGol SLim SPer SRms SWvt WFar
- 'Alpina'	see *S. japonica* 'Nana'
- 'Alpine Gold'	NEoE
- 'Anthony Waterer' (v)	CBcs CBod CBrac CCVT CDoC CMac EBee ECrN ELan EPfP EShb LRHS MAsh MGos MRav MSwo NLar SCob SCoo SGbt SGol SGsty SLim SPer SPoG SRms WFar
§ - 'Bullata'	CMac NLar WAbe
- 'Candlelight' ♀H6	CRos CSBt ELan EPfP GBin GKin LRHS MAsh NLar SCob SCoo SGol SLim SPer SPoG SWvt
- 'Crispa'	EPfP NEoE NWad WFar WGrn
- 'Dart's Red' ♀H6	ELan EPfP GKin
- DOUBLE PLAY ARTISAN ('Galen')	SPoG
- DOUBLE PLAY GOLD ('Yan')	SPoG
- 'Firelight'	CBod CDoC CRos CSBt CTsd EBee ELan ELon EPfP EShb GKin LRHS MAsh MGos MSwo NHol NLar NRHS NWad SCob SCoo SGol SLim SPer SRms SSta SWvt WBor
§ - var. ***fortunei*** 'Macrophylla'	WLov
§ - 'Genpei'	CMac MAsh MMuc SGol SPer SPoG SRms
- 'Gold Mound'	CBar CBrac CExl CMac EBee ELan EPfP MAsh MGos MMuc MRav MSwo NLar SCob SCoo SGol SLim SPer SPlb SRms WFar
- GOLDEN PRINCESS ('Lisp') ♀H6	CDoC CMac CRos CTri EHyd ELan EPfP LBuc LRHS MAsh MGos NLar SCoo SGol SPer SRms SSta WFar
- 'Goldflame'	Widely available
- 'Little Princess'	CBcs CBod CDoC CMac CRos EBee ECrN EHyd ELan EShb LRHS MAsh MRav MSwo NLar NRHS SCob SCoo SGol SGsty SLim SPer SRms SWvt WFar
- MAGIC CARPET ('Walbuma'PBR) (v) ♀H6	CBcs CRos EHyd EPfP LBuc LRHS MAsh MMuc NLar NRHS SCoo SPoG SRms
- 'Magnifica'	see *S. japonica* var. *fortunei* 'Macrophylla'
§ - 'Nana' ♀H6	CSBt MAsh SRms
- 'Nyewoods'	see *S. japonica* 'Nana'
- 'Nyewoods Gold' **new**	CMac
- 'Shiburi'	see *S. japonica* 'Albiflora'
- 'Shirobana' misapplied	see *S. japonica* 'Genpei'
- 'Shirobana'	see *S. japonica* 'Albiflora'
- 'Stanton Gold'	WCFE
§ - 'Walluf'	CMac CTri GBin
- 'White Cloud'	CDoC
- 'White Gold'PBR	CBod CMac CRos CSBt EHyd ELan EPfP LRHS LSou MAsh NEoE NHol NRHS NWad SCoo SPer SPoG SRms SWvt
× ***margaritae***	SWvt
micrantha	CExl
nipponica 'Halward's Silver'	MRav NEoE
§ - 'Snowmound' ♀H6	Widely available
- var. ***tosaensis*** misapplied	see *S. nipponica* 'Snowmound'
palmata 'Elegans'	see *Filipendula purpurea* 'Elegans'

	prunifolia (d)	CBod CMac EPfP MRav SPer WAvo WCFE WFar WLov
	× ***pseudosalicifolia*** 'Triumphans'	MMuc SPer
	rosthornii	GKev
	salicifolia	GKev WFar
	sargentiana	GKev
	schneideriana	GKev
	SPARKLING CHAMPAGNE ('Lonspi'PBR)	CSBt LSRN NEoE NWad SCob SLon
	SUNDROP ('Bailcarol')	LSou
	tarokoensis	CMCN
	thunbergii ♀H6	CBcs CBrac CMac CTri EPfP MMuc MRav SBrt SCob SEND SGol SPer SRms
	- 'Golden Times'	CRos EHyd LRHS SPoG
	- 'Mellow Yellow'	see *S. thunbergii* 'Ōgon'
	- 'Mount Fuji'	CMac MRav WFar
§	- 'Ōgon'	EPfP WFar
*	- 'Variegata' (v)	SRms
§	'Tracy'PBR	NEoE SCob SGsty SReu
	ulmaria	see *Filipendula ulmaria*
	× ***vanhouttei***	CMac CTri ELan EPfP MMuc MRav MSwo SEND SGsty SLim SPer SRms SavN WFar
	- 'Gold Fountain'	CMac ELan EPfP EShb LSRN MMuc NHol NLar SCoo SEND WFar
	- 'Pink Ice' (v)	CBod CMac CRos EHyd EPfP LRHS MAsh MMuc MRav NLar SPer SPlb SPoG SWvt WFar
	veitchii	GLog MRav
	venusta 'Magnifica'	see *Filipendula rubra* 'Venusta'

Spiranthes (*Orchidaceae*)

	cernua	NGdn
	odorata 'Chadd's Ford' ♀H4	CExl LRHS WSHC WTor

Spirodela (*Araceae*)

§	***polyrrhiza***	EWat

Spodiopogon (*Poaceae*)

	sibiricus	CBod CKno EBee EPPr GBin MBNS NDov SMad SPtp XLum
	- 'West Lake'	MAvo

Sporobolus (*Poaceae*)

	airoides	CBod CKno EBee EPPr EShb
	heterolepis	CFis CKno CMea CSpe EBee EPfP GBin GMaP LRHS MBel NDov SMHy SMea SPtp WCot
I	- 'Wisconsin Strain'	EBee IMou
	'J.S. Delicatesse' **new**	WTor
	wrightii	CKno EPPr WAvo

Sprekelia (*Amaryllidaceae*)

	formosissima	EShb GKev LEdu SDeJ SDir WHil

squashes see AGM Vegetables Section

Stachys (*Lamiaceae*)

	abchasica	EMor
	aethiopica 'Danielle'	see *S. thunbergii* 'Danielle'
§	***affinis***	GPoy LEdu SPlb SVic
	balcanica MESE	EBee
	'Bello Grigio'	MHol
	betonica	see *S. officinalis*
§	***byzantina***	Widely available
§	- 'Big Ears'	Widely available
§	- 'Cotton Boll'	CRos ECha LRHS SRms WFar XSen
	- 'Countess Helen von Stein'	see *S. byzantina* 'Big Ears'
	- 'Fuzzy Wuzzy'	WFar
	- gold-leaved	see *S. byzantina* 'Primrose Heron'
	- large-leaved	see *S. byzantina* 'Big Ears'
	- 'Limelight'	WCot XLum
§	- 'Primrose Heron'	ECha GMaP LRHS MBel MRav NLar NRHS SPer SWvt WCAu WMal XLum
	- 'Sheila McQueen'	see *S. byzantina* 'Cotton Boll'
	- 'Silky Fleece'	EBou ECha ELan EPfP GWyn LRHS MMuc NBre SRms XSen
	- 'Silver Carpet'	Widely available
	chamissonis var. ***cooleyae***	GBin
	citrina	CMea XSen
	coccinea	ECtt GEdr SPhx
	cretica	XSen
	densiflora	see *S. monieri* (Gouan) P.W. Ball
§	***discolor***	CFis CMea EWes LRHS NLar SWvt WCAu WCot
	germanica	CNat NAts NBre
	grandiflora	see *S. macrantha*
	'Hidalgo'	CSpe SRms
	lanata Jacq.	see *S. byzantina*
	lavandulifolia	WAbe
	- from Bolkar Dag, Turkey	SBrt
§	***macrantha***	CMac CTri ECha EDAr EHyd GKev GLog LEdu LRHS LSRN NBir NChi NLar NRHS NSti SPhx SRms WCAu WCFE WCot
*	- 'Alba'	ECha
	- 'Ben' (v)	LEdu
	- 'Hummelo'	see *S. officinalis* 'Hummelo'
	- 'Morning Blush'	SPhx WFar
*	- 'Nivea'	CSam NBir
	- 'Robusta' ♀H7	ELan ELon GAbr LEdu MAvo MMuc NBro NGdn WCot
	- 'Rosea'	CElw EHyd ELan GBee GMaP LRHS MArl MAvo NRHS SPlb WCAu
	- 'Superba' ♀H7	CSpe ECtt EPfP GKev GMaP LEdu MAvo MRav NDov NLar SCob SMad SPer SRms SWvt WBor WCAu WCot WFar XLum
	- 'Violacea' ♀H7	EBee NChi WCot
	mexicana misapplied	see *S. thunbergii*
	monieri misapplied	see *S. officinalis*
	monieri ambig.	NLar NSti
§	***monieri*** (Gouan) P.W. Ball	LEdu
*	- 'Rosea'	CBre EBee LEdu NBre NDov NLar SRms
	- white-flowered	GKev
	nivea	see *S. discolor*
	obliqua	NBre
§	***officinalis***	CBee CCBP CHab CWld EMor GPoy GQue ILea LEdu MBow MHer MMuc MNHC NAts NGrd NMir NRya SRms WCot WHer WTre WWild
	- 'Alba'	EMor LEdu MArl MAvo MMuc NBro SMHy WCAu
	- 'Cally Bicolor'	GBin
	- dark-flowered	WHoo
	- dwarf, white-flowered	CBre GRum
§	- 'Hummelo' ♀H7	Widely available
	- 'Marchant's Pink'	SMHy
	- 'Pink Cotton Candy'	EBee SCob SPhx STPC
	- 'Rosea'	NBro WCAu WFar
	- 'Rosea Superba'	ECha GWyn NBre SDix WCot
	- 'Saharan Pink'	EBee EPfP LSRN NLar
	- 'Spitzenberg'	LPla
	- 'Ukkie'	EBee

- 'Wisley White'	CBre CRos ECtt EHyd LBuc LEdu LRHS MHol NGrd NHpl NRHS SCob SRms WCot WFar
olympica	see *S. byzantina*
ossetica	EBee GEdr
palustris	CHab EWat LLWG MCoo MMuc NLar NMir SEND SRms
- from Islay, Hebrides	MMuc SEND
- pale-flowered	WOut
recta	CBee SBut
setifera	NBre XLum
spicata	see *S. macrantha*
sylvatica	CHab NMir WHer WOut WSFF WWild
'The Bride' **new**	NDov
thirkei	WCot
§ ***thunbergii***	MBrN MBriF MNHC WKif
§ - 'Danielle'	ECtt EPfP GJos LRHS NLar SBut SDys SPhx SRkn SRms WMal WWFP
tuberifera	see *S. affinis*

Stachyurus (*Stachyuraceae*)

chinensis	CBcs CJun CMCN CTri EBee MGos NLar
- 'Celina' ♀H5	CJun CRos EHyd ELon EPfP GKin LRHS MGos NLar NRHS SPoG WPGP
- 'Goldbeater'	NLar
- 'Joy Forever' (v) ♀H5	CBcs CDoC CEnd CMac CRos EBee EHyd EPfP LRHS LSRN MGos MPkF NLar NRHS SPer SPoG SSta SWvt WKif
- 'Senna'	NLar
- 'Wonderful Image'	NLar
himalaicus	CBcs NLar
- HWJK 2035	WCru
- pink-flowered	see *S. himalaicus* subsp. *purpureus*
§ - subsp. ***purpureus*** HWJK 2052	WCru
aff. ***macrocarpus*** B&SWJ 14678	WCru
'Magpie' (v)	LRHS
praecox ♀H5	Widely available
- B&SWJ 8898	WCru
- B&SWJ 10899	IDee LCro WCru
- var. ***leucotrichus***	CJun NLar
- var. ***matsuzakii***	CJun NLar
- - B&SWJ 2817	WCru
- - B&SWJ 11229	WCru
- 'Petra'	CJun
retusus	CExl
'Rubriflorus'	CBct CJun EBee EPfP MAsh NLar WPGP
salicifolius	CBcs CExl CJun CTho EBee EPfP IArd IDee IMou SPoG SSta WPGP
sigeyosii	CBcs CExl EBee SSta
- B&SWJ 6915	WCru
- CWJ 12420	WCru
- RWJ 10094	WCru
aff. ***szechuanensis***	CExl
- BWJ 8153	WCru
yunnanensis	CBcs CJun IDee NLar WPGP WSHC

Stapelia (*Apocynaceae*)

grandiflora	SSim
marmoratum	see *Orbea variegata*
variegata	see *Orbea variegata*

Staphylea ✿ (*Staphyleaceae*)

bolanderi	CBcs NLar
bumalda	CJun LEdu NLar
- B&SWJ 11053	WCru
- B&SWJ 12744 from Korea	WCru
colchica	CBcs CMCN CRos EHyd ELan EPfP EWTr EWes LEdu LRHS MGos MMrt MRav NLar SPer WKif
holocarpa	CBcs CJun
- 'Innocence'	CBcs LRHS
- var. ***rosea***	CJun CMCN EPfP MBlu NLar SMad SWvt
pinnata	CAgr CBcs CJun EPfP IDee MCoo MPkF NLar SEND
- PAB 8427	LEdu
trifolia	CAgr CBcs EBee EPfP

Statice see *Limonium*

Stauntonia (*Lardizabalaceae*)

FMWJ 13177 from northern Vietnam	WCru
NJM 10.133 **new**	WPGP
aff. ***chinensis*** DJHV 06175	WCru
hexaphylla	CBcs CCCN CRHN CRos CTri CWGN EBee EHyd EPfP ESwi LEdu LRHS MAsh MGil NLar SAdn SNig SPer SPoG SSta
- B&SWJ 4858	WCru
- B&SWJ 14655	ESwi WCru
libera KWJ 12218	WCru
obovata CWJ 12353	WCru
obovatifoliola B&SWJ 3685	WCru
purpurea	WPGP
- B&SWJ 3690	WCru
yaoshanensis B&SWJ 8223	WCru
- FMWJ 13171 **new**	WCru
- HWJ 1024	WCru WPGP

Stegnogramma (*Thelypteridaceae*)

pozoi	EFer

Stellaria (*Caryophyllaceae*)

graminea	CHab
holostea	CHab MBow MMuc NBir NMir WShi

Stemmacantha see *Rhaponticum*

Stenanthium (*Melanthiaceae*)

gramineum	EBee EWes

Stenomesson (*Amaryllidaceae*)

pearcei	GKev
variegatum	see *Clinanthus variegatus*

Stenotaphrum (*Poaceae*)

secundatum 'Variegatum' (v) ♀H1c	EShb XLum

Stephanandra (*Rosaceae*)

incisa	CExl
§ - 'Crispa'	CBcs CBod CDoC CMac CTri ELan EPfP GKin MBlu MGil MRav NHol SCob SGbt SPer SRms
- 'Prostrata'	see *S. incisa* 'Crispa'
tanakae	CBcs CExl CMac ELan EPfP EWTr MBlu MGil MRav SLon SPer SRms

Stephania (*Menispermaceae*)

aff. ***hernandiifolia*** B&SWJ 14950	WCru

japonica CWJ 12823	WCru
aff. ***tetrandra*** WWJ 11896	WCru

Stephanotis (*Apocynaceae*)

floribunda ♀^{H1a}	CBcs CCCN CDoC LCro LOPS

Sterculia (*Malvaceae*)

rupestris	see *Brachychiton rupestris*

Sternbergia (*Amaryllidaceae*)

candida	CBro
fischeriana	CBro
greuteriana	EPot GKev
lutea ♀^{H4}	CBod CBro CRos CTri ECha EHyd ELan EPot ERCP EWes GKev LCro LOPS LRHS NRHS SDeJ SGro WHoo XLum
- Angustifolia Group	CBro CMea WCot
sicula	CBro EPot
- 'Arcadian Sun'	EPot
- 'Dodona Gold'	GKev
- 'John Marr'	WCot WThu

Stevia (*Asteraceae*)

rebaudiana	CBod CGro ENfk GPoy LCro LOPS SPre SRms WCot WJek

Stewartia ✿ (*Theaceae*)

gemmata	see *S. sinensis*
'Korean Splendor'	see *S. pseudocamellia* Koreana Group
koreana	see *S. pseudocamellia* Koreana Group
laotica new	SReu
monadelpha	CBcs CJun CMen LMaj MBlu MPkF NLar
ovata	CJun
pseudocamellia ♀^{H5}	Widely available
- B&SWJ 11044 from North Japan	WCru
§ - Koreana Group ♀^{H5}	CBct CEnd CJun CMCN EHyd EPfP GKin LRHS MPkF NLar SChF SLim SPer SReu
- 'Ogisu'	NLar
pteropetiolata B&SWJ 11726	WCru
- NJM 10.107	WPGP
- WWJ 11939	WCru
rostrata	CBcs CJun CLnd LRHS MBlu MPkF NLar SPtp WPGP
- 'Hulsdonk Pink'	CJun
serrata	CJun CMCN MPkF WCru
§ ***sinensis*** ♀^{H5}	CBcs CCCN CDoC CJun EPfP IArd IDee IMou LMaj MBlu MPkF NLar SAko WPGP

Stigmaphyllon (*Malpighiaceae*)

ciliatum	CCCN
littorale	CCCN

Stipa (*Poaceae*)

arundinacea	see *Anemanthele lessoniana*
barbata	CSpe ECha EPPr EWes GBin WKif XSen
brachytricha	see *Calamagrostis brachytricha*
§ ***calamagrostis*** ♀^{H4}	CBod CElw CKno CSam CWCL EAJP EBee ECha EHyd ELan EMor EPPr EPed EPfP EShb GMaP LCro LOPS LRHS MRav NBro NRHS SCob SDix SEND SMea SRms WHal XSen
- 'Allgäu' ♀^{H4}	LEdu WCot
- 'Lemperg' ♀^{H4}	EHyd IMou LRHS NDov
capillata	CBod CSpe EBee EHyd EPPr EWhm GBin LRHS MBel MNrw SHar SPhx XCre XSen
* - 'Lace Veil'	WAvo
elegantissima	CDoC CPla
extremiorientalis	EPPr SEND
gigantea ♀^{H4}	Widely available
- 'Gold Fontaene' ♀^{H4}	CKno EPPr EPfP EWes LPla MAvo MNrw NDov SMHy SMad WCot
- 'Goldilocks'	CKno CRos ECha EHyd LEdu NRHS
- 'Pixie'	CRos EBee EHyd EPPr EPfP LRHS NRHS
ichu ♀^{H4}	CKno CRos CSpe EHyd LRHS MAsh MAvo NDov NRHS SDix SMea
joannis	CBod
lasiagrostis	see *S. calamagrostis*
lessingiana ♀^{H5}	CExl CPla EPPr LRHS SEND SPhx
pennata	XCre XSen
pseudoichu ♀^{H5}	CBod CCht CSam ECha ELan EPPr GBin LPla LRHS MAvo MBNS MBel NWsh SPeP SPtp WCot WHoo WPGP WRHF
- RCB/Arg Y-1	EBee ELon
pulcherrima	EPPr
robusta	EPPr
splendens misapplied	see *S. calamagrostis*
splendens Trin.	ECha SAko
stenophylla	see *S. tirsa*
tenacissima	CDoC
tenuifolia misapplied	see *S. tenuissima*
tenuifolia Steud.	CMea LRHS MRav NBir NBro NSti WHal XLum XSen
§ ***tenuissima*** ♀^{H4}	Widely available
- 'Wind Whispers'	CExl LEdu LRHS MBel SPtp
§ ***tirsa***	EWes

Stoebe (*Asteraceae*)

alopecuroides	SPlb

Stokesia ✿ (*Asteraceae*)

cyanea	see *S. laevis*
§ ***laevis***	CRos ECha EHyd EPfP LRHS NLar NRHS SPlb SRms WCAu
- 'Alba'	CRos ECha EHyd ELan EPfP EPri GPSL LEdu LRHS MRav NLar NRHS WCAu
- 'Blue Frills'	CRos ECtt EPfP
- 'Blue Moon' new	MWat
- 'Blue Star'	CAby CBcs CBod CDor CRos CWGN ELan ELon EMor EPfP LEdu LRHS LSou LSun MBel MHer MRav MWat NBPC NRHS SGbt SPad SPer SPhx SPoG SRkn SWvt WCav WHrl WSHC
- 'Color Wheel'	CBod ECtt EHyd LRHS
- 'Divinity'	ECtt SCob
- 'Honeysong Purple'	NLar
- 'Klaus Jelitto'	ECtt EHyd EMor LEdu LRHS SCob SGbt SHar SPoG
- 'Mary Gregory'	CAby CBod CMac CNor CRos EBee ECtt ELan EMor EPfP EWTr LRHS MBel MRav NBPC NLar NRHS SCob SGbt SPhx SWvt
§ - 'Mel's'PBR	CRos ECtt EHyd LRHS MPri NRHS
- MEL'S BLUE	see *S. laevis* 'Mel's'
- 'Omega Skyrocket'	CPou SRms
- 'Peach Melba'	ECtt
- 'Peachie's Pick'	EBee ECtt EMor

- 'Purple Parasols'	CDor CMac CRos CWGN EBee ECtt EPfP LEdu LRHS MBel MPie NRHS SGbt SPoG SWvt WAul
- 'Purple Pixie'PBR	ECtt
- 'Silver Moon'	CBod ECtt EMor EPfP GBin LRHS MBel NBPC NRHS SGbt SPer
§ - 'Träumerei'	CBod CWGN EBee ECtt EMor EPfP LRHS MPie NLar NRHS SGbt XLum
- 'White Star'	see *S. laevis* 'Träumerei'

Stranvaesia see *Photinia*

× *Stranvinia* see *Photinia*

Stratiotes (*Hydrocharitaceae*)

aloides	CBen CWat EWat LCro LLWG LOPS MWts NPer SVic WMAq WPnP

strawberry see *Fragaria*; also AGM Fruit Section

Strelitzia (*Strelitziaceae*)

sp.	CDoC
alba	CCCN WSMil
juncea	XBlo
nicolai	CCCN NPer SPlb XBlo
reginae 🏆H1b	CAbb CBcs CCCN CTsd ELan EShb LCro LOPS NPer SPalm SPlb WSMil XBlo
- 'Kirstenbosch Gold'	XBlo

Streptocarpella see *Streptocarpus*

Streptocarpus ✿ (*Gesneriaceae*)

'Adele'	WDib
'Alana'	WDib
'Albatross'	CTsd WDib
'Alissa'	WDib
'Amanda' Dibley	WDib
'Ambiente' 🏆H1c	WDib
'Amy'	WDib
'Anne' (d)	CTsd WDib
'Anwen'	WDib
'Awena'	WDib
baudertii	WDib
'Bella'	WDib
'Bethan' 🏆H1c	CTsd WDib
'Bianca'	WDib
'Black Gardenia'	CTsd
'Black Panther'	CTsd WDib
'Blue Frills' 🏆H1c	WDib
'Blue Gem'	WDib
'Blue Leyla'	see *S.* 'Leyla'
'Blue Moon'	WDib
'Blue Nymph'	WDib
'Boysenberry Delight'	WDib
'Branwen'	CTsd WDib
'Bristol's Black Bird'	WDib
'Bristol's Very Best'	WDib
caeruleus	WDib
'Caitlin'	CTsd WDib
candidus	WDib
'Cappuccino'	WDib
'Cariad'	WDib
'Carol'	WDib
'Carys' 🏆H1c	CTsd WDib
caulescens	WDib
- var. ***pallescens***	WDib
'Celebration'	WDib
'Charlotte' 🏆H1c	WDib
'Chloe'	WDib
'Chorus Line'	CTsd WDib
'Constant Nymph'	WDib
'Crystal Beauty'	WDib
'Crystal Blush'	WDib
'Crystal Charm'	WDib
'Crystal Dawn'	WDib
'Crystal Ice'PBR 🏆H1c	LCro LOPS WDib
'Crystal Snow'	WDib
'Crystal Wonder'	WDib
cyaneus	WDib
- subsp. ***polackii***	WDib
'Cynthia'	WDib
'Daphne'	WDib
'Dee'	WDib
'Delia'	WDib
'Denim'	WDib
denticulatus	WDib
'Diana'	WDib
'Dinas'	WDib
'Ds-Horus'	WDib
dunnii	WDib
'Dwynwen' **new**	WDib
'Elin'	WDib
'Elsi'	CTsd WDib
'Emily'	WDib
'Eve'	NWad WDib
'Falling Stars' 🏆H1c	CTsd WDib
'Festival Wales'	WDib
'Fiesta'	WDib
'Fiona'	WDib
floribundus	WDib
formosus	WDib
'Franken Alayana'	WDib
'Franken Isabella'	WDib
'Franken Skye'	WDib
'Franken Strawberry Fondant'	WDib
'Freya' WDib	
'Frosty Diamond' 🏆H1c	CTsd WDib
'Full Moon'	WDib
gardenii	WDib
glandulosissimus 🏆H1c	WDib
'Gloria' 🏆H1c	CTsd WDib
'Gold Dust'	WDib
'Gold Rose' **new**	WDib
'Gwen'	WDib
'Hannah' 🏆H1c	WDib
'Harlequin Blue'PBR 🏆H1c	LCro LOPS WDib
'Harlequin Damsel'	WDib
'Harlequin Dawn'	WDib
'Harlequin Delft'	WDib
'Harlequin Lace'PBR 🏆H1c	WDib
'Harlequin Purple'	WDib
'Harlequin Rose'	WDib
'Harriet'	WDib
'Hayley'	WDib
'Heidi'	CTsd WDib
'Helen'	CTsd WDib
'Hope'	WDib
'Iona'	WDib
'Isabella'	WDib
'Jacquie'	WDib
'Jennifer' 🏆H1c	WDib
'Jessica' 🏆H1c	WDib
'Joanna'	CTsd WDib
johannis	WDib
'Joy'	WDib
'Karen'	WDib

	'Katie'PBR 🏆H1c	WDib
	kentaniensis	WDib
	'Kim' 🏆H1c	WDib
	kirkii	WDib
	'Laura' 🏆H1c	WDib
§	'Leyla'PBR	WDib
	'Louise'	WDib
	'Lucy'	WDib
	'Lyndee'	WDib
	'Lynne'	WDib
	'Maassen's White'	WDib
	'Manon' **new**	WDib
	'Margaret' Gavin Brown	WDib
	'Marie'	WDib
	'Marion'	WDib
	'Matilda'	WDib
	'Megan'	WDib
	'Melanie' Dibley	WDib
	'Menai'	WDib
	meyeri	WDib
	'Midnight Flame'	CTsd
	'Minnie' **new**	WDib
	modestus	WDib
	'Myfanwy'	WDib
	'Nadine'	WDib
	'Natalie'	WDib
	'Nerys'	CTsd WDib
	'Nia'	CTsd WDib
	'Nicola'	CTsd WDib
	'Olivia'	WDib
	'Padarn'	WDib
	'Paula'	WDib
	'Pearl' 🏆H1c	WDib
	pentherianus	WDib
	'Pink Leyla' 🏆H1c	WDib
	'Pink Souffle'	WDib
	'Polka-Dot Purple' 🏆H1c	WDib
	'Polka-Dot Red'	WDib
	polyanthus subsp. ***dracomontanus***	WDib
	primulifolius	WDib
	prolixus	WDib
	'Purple Velvet'	WDib
	rexii	WDib
	'Rhiannon'	CTsd WDib
	'Rose Halo'	WDib
	'Rosebud'	WDib
	(Roulette Series) 'Roulette Azur'PBR 🏆H1c	WDib
	- 'Roulette Cherry'	WDib
	'Rubina'PBR	WDib
	'Rubina Pink' 🏆H1c	WDib
	'Ruby'	CTsd WDib
	'Ruth'	WDib
	'Sadie' **new**	WDib
	'Sally'	WDib
	'Sandra'	WDib
	'Sarah'	WDib
	saxorum	CCCN CTsd WDib
	- compact 🏆H1c	CCCN WDib
	'Scarlett'	WDib
	'Seren'	WDib
	'Sian'	WDib
	silvaticus	WDib
	'Sioned' 🏆H1c	WDib
	'Snow White' 🏆H1c	WDib
I	'Stella'PBR Dibleys 🏆H1c	WDib
§	'Stella' Fleischle (Marleen Series) 🏆H1c	WDib
	'Stephanie'	WDib
	stomandrus	WDib
	'Susan' 🏆H1c	CTsd WDib
	'Sweet Melys'	WDib
	'Sweet Rosy'	WDib
	'Tanga'	see *S.* 'Stella' Fleischle
	'Tanya'	WDib
	'Teleri'	WDib
	'Texas Hot Chili'	CTsd WDib
	thompsonii	WDib
	'Tina' 🏆H1c	WDib
	'Titania'	WDib
	'Tracey'	WDib
	'Valor'	WDib
	vandeleurii	WDib
	variabilis	WDib
	'Wawel'	WDib
	wendlandii	WDib
	'Wendy'	WDib
	'White Butterfly' 🏆H1c	WDib
	'Wiesmoor Red'	WDib
	'Winifred'	WDib

Streptopus (*Liliaceae*)

	amplexifolius	EBee GBin MNrw WCru WSHC
	- var. ***papillatus***	GEdr
	roseus	WCru
	streptopoides	EHyd EMor EPPr EPfP LEdu LRHS SLon

Streptosolen (*Solanaceae*)

	jamesonii 🏆H1c	CCCN EBak EShb SWvt

Strobilanthes (*Acanthaceae*)

	CC 4071	CExl
	CC 4573	CExl
	angustifrons	SBrt
	anisophylla	EShb SDys WSpi
	atropurpurea misapplied	see *S. attenuata*
	atropurpurea Nees	see *S. wallichii*
§	***attenuata***	CBod CRos CSam EBee ECtt EHyd EMor ILea ITim LEdu LRHS MBel MHer MPie MRav MSCN NChi NRHS NSti SBut SDix SPoG WCot WCru WOut WSpi
	- 'Blue and White'	EBee
	- 'Blue Carpet'	NDov
	- 'Latham's Form'	WHil
	- subsp. ***nepalensis***	XLum
	- 'Out of the Ocean'	WOut
	dyeriana 🏆H1b	EBak EShb SPlb WCot
	flexicaulis B&SWJ 354	ESwi WCru
	aff. ***inflata*** B&SWJ 7754	WCru
*	***lactea***	EShb
	nutans	CPou CSam EBee EWld NSti SBrt XLum
	pentstemonoides	EPPr
	rankanensis	EBee EPPr GPSL ILea SDys XLum
	- B&SWJ 1771	WCru
	violacea misapplied	EShb
§	***wallichii***	CMac EBee EPfP EWes EWld ILea MHer MMuc NSti SEND WCAu WCru WMal
	- from Picton	WFar

Stromanthe (*Marantaceae*)

	sanguinea 'Triostar'PBR (v)	XBlo

Strophanthus (*Apocynaceae*)

	speciosus	CCCN EShb

Strumaria (*Amaryllidaceae*)
- ***discifera*** subsp. ***bulbifera*** WCot

Struthiopteris (*Blechnaceae*)
- ***niponica*** see *Blechnum niponicum*

Stuartia see *Stewartia*

Stylidium (*Stylidiaceae*)
- ***graminifolium*** CTsd SPlb

Stylophorum (*Papaveraceae*)
- ***diphyllum*** CFis CPou EWld IMou LEdu MAvo MPie WCru WPGP WPnP WWtn
- ***lasiocarpum*** CExl CSpe EMor EPPr EWld GEdr MMrt NBid NSti WCru WPnP

Styphelia (*Ericaceae*)
- ***colensoi*** see *Leucopogon colensoi*

Styphnolobium (*Papilionaceae*)
- § ***japonicum*** CBcs CHab CMCN CMac EPfP EWTr LMaj SPlb WTSh
- - 'China Gold' EBee SPoG
- - 'Flavirameum' SMad
- - 'Pendulum' MPri

Styrax ✿ (*Styracaceae*)
- NJM 11.013 from Guizhou, China WPGP
- NJM 11.085 from Guizhou, China WPGP
- ***americanus*** CBcs EPfP
- - Kankakee form WPGP
- ***confusus*** CExl
- ***dasyanthus*** CExl
- ***faberi*** CExl
- ***formosanus*** CBcs CExl CJun EPfP MBlu SChF
- var. ***formosanus*** WPGP
- - - B&SWJ 3803 WCru
- - - B&SWJ 6786 WCru
- - var. ***hayatiana*** B&SWJ 6823 WCru
- ***grandiflorus*** CExl
- ***hemsleyanus*** 🏆H5 CBcs CExl CTho EPfP IDee IMou LEdu MBlu NLar SPtp
- ***hookeri*** CExl
- ***japonicus*** CBcs CDoC CExl CLnd CMCN CRos CTho CTri EHyd ELan ELon EPfP GKin LMaj LRHS MAsh MBlu MGos MMuc MRav NLar SPer SPoG SReu WHwl WPGP
- - B&SWJ 4405 WCru
- - B&SWJ 8770 WCru
- - B&SWJ 11078 WCru
- - Guiz 216 CExl WPGP
- - PAB 8366 LEdu
- § - Benibana Group SChF WPGP
- - - 'Pink Chimes' CBcs CExl CJun CMCN ELan ESwi EWTr GKin MBlu MPkF NLar NOra SAko WHwl WMat
- - 'Carillon' CJun
- - 'Evening Light'PBR CBcs SMad
- - 'Fargesii' 🏆H5 CBcs CDoC CExl CJun CTho
- - 'Fragrant Fountain' LRHS MBlu MPkF SGsty SReu
- - 'June Snow'PBR **new** NLar WHwl
- - MARLEY'S PINK PARASOL ('JLWeeping') LRHS
- - 'Pendulus' CBcs EPfP NLar WPGP
- I - 'Pink Snowbell' LRHS
- - 'Purple Dress' 🏆H5 CJun MBlu NLar
- - 'Roseus' see *S. japonicus* Benibana Group
- - SNOWCONE ('Jfs-D') **new** SGsty
- - 'Snowfall' CJun NLar
- - 'Sohuksan' 🏆H5 CExl CJun MBlu WPGP
- aff. ***japonicus*** B&SWJ 14182 from Heuksando, South Korea WCru
- ***limprichtii*** CExl
- ***obassia*** CBcs CLnd CMCN CTho EPfP LRHS MBlu NLar WGob WPGP
- - B&SWJ 6023 WCru
- - B&SWJ 10890 WCru
- ***odoratissimus*** CExl WPGP
- ***officinalis*** CBcs CJun
- ***redivivus*** CJun
- ***serrulatus*** CExl
- ***shiraianus*** CExl MBlu NLar WPGP
- ***tonkinensis*** FMWJ 13134 WCru
- ***wilsonii*** CExl
- ***wuyuanensis*** WPGP

Succisa (*Caprifoliaceae*)
- § ***pratensis*** Widely available
- - 'Alba' EWes
- - 'Buttermilk' CDor LEdu
- - 'Derby Purple' CSpe
- - early-flowering LEdu SPhx
- - 'Peddar's Pink' EWes LLWG SPhx

Succisella (*Caprifoliaceae*)
- ***inflexa*** CSpe LEdu LRHS MSpe SPhx WCAu
- - 'Frosted Pearls' CDor CElw CFis LEdu LSun MAvo MMuc NDov NLar SBut SHar

sunberry see *Rubus* 'Sunberry'

Sutera (*Scrophulariaceae*)
- ***cordata*** 'Snowflake' see *Chaenostoma cordatum* 'Snowflake'
- ***microphylla*** see *Jamesbrittenia microphylla*
- ***neglecta*** see *Chaenostoma neglectum*

Sutherlandia ✿ (*Papilionaceae*)
- ***frutescens*** CBod CSpe SPlb
- ***montana*** CSpe SBrt

Swainsona (*Papilionaceae*)
- ***formosa*** SPhx

sweet cicely see *Myrrhis odorata*

sweet corn see AGM Vegetables Section

sweet pepper see *Capsicum*; also AGM Vegetables Section

Swertia (*Gentianaceae*)
- ***bimaculata*** PAB 8845 LEdu
- ***perennis*** GEdr

Syagrus (*Arecaceae*)
- ***botryophora*** XBlo
- § ***romanzoffiana*** SPalm XBlo

× *Sycoparrotia* (*Hamamelidaceae*)

semidecidua	CBcs CBct CCCN CJun EBee EPfP MBlu NLar NOrn
- 'Purple Haze'	CJun IArd IDee NLar
- 'Variegata' (v)	CJun

Sycopsis (*Hamamelidaceae*)

sinensis	CBcs CCCN CExl CJun CRos EBee EHyd EPfP GBin LEdu LMaj LRHS MGil MMuc NLar SSta SWvt WPGP

Symphoricarpos (*Caprifoliaceae*)

albus	CBee CMac MSwo SCob WTSh
- 'Constance Spry'	SRms
§ - var. ***laevigatus***	LBuc
× ***chenaultii***	SRms
- 'Hancock'	CMac EBee ELan EPfP MMuc MRav MSwo SCob SGol SPer
× ***doorenbosii*** 'Magic Berry'	CBrac EBee MRav SCob SGbt SGol
- 'Mother of Pearl'	EPfP LCro LOPS MMuc MRav SCob SPer SRms
- 'White Hedge'	LBuc MMuc SGbt SPer SPlb
guatemalensis B&SWJ 1016	WCru
MAGICAL CANDY ('Kolmcan'PBR)	CRos EHyd ELan LRHS NEoE NRHS SPoG
MAGICAL GALAXY ('Kolmgala'PBR)	CRos EHyd ELan EPfP LRHS NEoE NRHS SPoG
MAGICAL SWEET ('Kolmaswet'PBR)	CRos EHyd LRHS NRHS SPoG
orbiculatus	SLon
- 'Albovariegatus'	see *S. orbiculatus* 'Taff's Silver Edge'
- 'Argenteovariegatus'	see *S. orbiculatus* 'Taff's Silver Edge'
- 'Bowles's Golden Variegated'	see *S. orbiculatus* 'Foliis Variegatis'
§ - 'Foliis Variegatis' (v)	CMac CTri MRav SGol
- 'George Gardiner'	CMac
§ - 'Taff's Silver Edge' (v)	SGol
- 'Variegatus'	see *S. orbiculatus* 'Foliis Variegatis'
rivularis	see *S. albus* var. *laevigatus*

Symphyandra see *Campanula*

asiatica	see *Hanabusaya asiatica*

Symphyotrichum (*Asteraceae*)

§ × ***amethystinum***	MNrw WCot
- 'Freiburg'	ELon EPPr MNrw NDov
'Anja's Choice'	EBee EPPr MTis
'Ann Leys'PBR	EBee SMad WCot XEll
'Aqua Compact' (Autumn Jewels Series)	CBod EHyd NRHS
'Beauté du Nord'	WCot
'Blue Butterfly'	SPhx WOld XLum
'Blütenregen'	WCot WFar XEll
chilense 'Purple Haze'	EPPr
§ ***ciliolatum***	SPhx
'Claudia'	WOld
'Climax' Vicary Gibbs	LEdu MNrw WFar WOld
'Coombe Fishacre' 🏆H7	CAby EBee ECtt ELan ELon GQue ILea LEdu LRHS MNrw NDov NLar SPhx SRms SWvt WCAu WCot WHoo WOld WSpi
§ ***cordifolium***	SPhx XLum
- from Piney Fork	EPPr
- 'Aldebaran'	LEdu WOld
- 'Blue Heaven'	SAko
- 'Chieftain' 🏆H7	LEdu MHCG MNrw SPhx WOld
- 'Elegans'	CSam EBee SDix WOld
- 'Ideal'	ILea NLar SPhx XLum
- 'Silver Spray'	CKno ECtt ELon GMaP ILea MWat WOld XLum
- 'Sweet Lavender' 🏆H7	EBee EHyd LRHS WOld
- 'White Chief'	WOld
'Diamond Jubilee' **new**	WOld
drummondii	SPhx
§ ***dumosum***	CChe CExl
- 'Beryll' **new**	WFar
- 'Biteliness'	NLar
- 'Blue Lapis'	LRHS WFar
- 'Early Blue'	ILea
- SAPPHIRE ('Kiesapphire'PBR) (Autumn Jewels Series)	CAby CBod CChe ELon EWTr LRHS LSRN MHol NCou SRkn SWvt XLum
§ ***ericoides***	WOld
- 'Blue Star' 🏆H7	CDor CRos EHyd LRHS NLar NRHS SPer WOld
- 'Blue Wonder'	CBod XLum
- 'Brimstone' 🏆H7	MRav WOld
- 'Cinderella'	EBee EHyd ELon LRHS NSti WOld
- 'Constance'	MCot WOld
- 'Deep Danziger'	SPhx
- 'Erlkönig'	CBod EBee ELon EPri EShb GQue LEdu NGdn NLar SDix SWvt WCAu WCot WOld XLum
- 'Esther'	ECha ECtt ELan MMrt MNrw WOld
- 'First Snow'	WCot WFar
- 'Golden Spray' 🏆H7	EBee ECtt ELon EPfP EWes GMaP GQue NLar SPer WOld
- 'Herbstmyrte'	EHyd LRHS NRHS
- 'Hon. Edith Gibbs'	WOld
- 'Monte Cassino'	see *S. pilosum* var. *pringlei* 'Monte Cassino'
- 'Pink Cloud' 🏆H7	CBod CRos ECtt EHyd ELon EPfP EPri EShb GQue LEdu LRHS MBel NLar NRHS NWad SAko SDix SHar SPer SPhx WCAu WMal WOld WTre WWtn
- var. ***prostratum***	EPot MRav SAko XEll XSen
- - 'Snow Flurry' 🏆H7	CMea CSpe ECha ECtt ELon GBin GQue IMou LEdu LPla MAvo MHol MNrw NLar SAko SPhx SWvt WCot WHoo WOld XLum
- 'Rosy Veil'	NBir NGdn WOld
- 'Schneegitter'	EHyd LRHS SAko SPhx WCot XSen
- 'Schneetanne'	SAko
- 'Sulphurea'	MWat
- 'Vimmer's Delight'	ECtt LPla WCot WFar
- 'White Heather'	ECtt NLar WOld
- 'Yvette Richardson'	CSam ECtt SMHy WOld
'Ethereal' **new**	WHoo
§ ***falcatum***	WCot
- var. ***commutatum***	WCot WOld
foliaceum from Montana	EPPr
- var. ***parryi***	EBee
'Foxbrook Fairy' (*ericoides* hybrid) **new**	MAvo
§ ***greatae***	EBee
'Herfstweelde'	EBee LEdu SPhx WOld
'Hill Close Blue'	MAvo MHCG
'Hon. Vicary Gibbs' (*ericoides* hybrid)	WOld
'Jessica Jones' **new**	WOld
§ ***laeve***	CDor EBee LEdu NLar SPhx
- 'Anneke Van der Jeugd'	MNrw WFar
§ - 'Arcturus'	CElw LEdu MAvo MBel MNrw MTis NBir SDix WCot WFar WOld XLum
- 'Blauschleier'	EBee
- 'Blue Bird'	WOld

§	- 'Calliope'	Widely available
	- 'Cally Compact'	GQue NLar WFar WOld
	- 'Climax'	CElw EBee ELan MMuc MRav NBid NSti SDix SEND WBrk XLum
	- var. ***geyeri***	MNrw
	- 'Glow in the Dark'	EBee EPPr LEdu MAvo MSpe MWat NLar WBrk WCot WHoo WMal WOld
	- 'Jane Ward' **new**	MNrw
	- 'Les Moutiers'	CMea EPPr LEdu MAvo MNrw SDix WBrk WFar WMal WOld
	- 'Nightshade'	EPPr MAvo MNrw MTis WFar WOld WRHF
	- 'Orpheus'	GBin LEdu MAvo MNrw WBrk WFar WMal
	- 'Vesta'	ECtt MTis WOld
§	- 'White Climax'	CSam MNrw WCot
	- white-flowered	WBrk WOld
	lanceolatum 'Edwin Beckett'	CBre MNrw SWvt WFar WOld
§	***lateriflorum***	SWvt WOld
	- 'Bleke Bet'	WCot WFar WOld
	- 'Buck's Fizz'	WOld
	- 'Chloe'	CDor CSam NLar SPhx WCot WFar WOld
	- 'Datschi'	XLum
	- var. ***horizontale*** ♀H7	CBod CRos CSam EBee ECha ECtt ELan ELon EPfP GQue LRHS MRav MWat NBro NGdn NRHS NWad SCob SDix SGbt SPer SPlb SRms SWvt WCAu WOld WSpi WWtn XEll
	- 'Lady in Black'	Widely available
	- 'Lovely'	CSam WCot
	- 'Prince'	CDor CKno CMac CSBt ECha ECtt ELan ELon EPfP EWes GMaP LRHS MHer MNrw MRav NBir NGdn NRHS NSti NWsh SMad SPoG SRms WCAu WFar WKif WOld WSpi
	'Little Carlow' (*cordifolium* hybrid) ♀H7	Widely available
	'Little Dorrit' (*cordifolium* hybrid)	ECtt NWsh
	(Newstars Series) 'Newstars Fantasy'	MAvo WOld
	- 'Newstars Glory'	WFar
	'Nicholas'	ECtt WCot WFar WOld
	'Nineteen'	MAvo WOld
	'Noreen'	ECha MHCG MTis WOld
§	***novae-angliae***	GKev WOld
	- 'Abendsonne'	SAko
	- 'Alex Deamon'	ELon MAvo WBrk WOld
	- 'Anabelle de Chazal'	ECtt ELon MWat WBrk WFar WOld
	- 'Andenken an Alma Pötschke'	Widely available
	- 'Andenken an Paul Gerber'	ECtt EHyd ELon EPfP LRHS MAvo MNrw MTis NLar NRHS WOld
	- 'Augusta'	ELon MAvo NLar SPhx WBrk WOld
	- AUTUMN SNOW	see *S. novae-angliae* 'Herbstschnee'
	- 'Badsey Pink'	WCot WOld
	- 'Barr's Blue'	CMac EBee ECtt EHyd ELan ELon EPfP IPot LRHS MAvo MMuc MTis MWat NLar NRHS NWsh SCob SEND SPer SRms WBrk WCAu WOld
	- 'Barr's Pink'	CMac EBee ECtt EHyd ELan ELon EPfP LRHS MAvo MCot MMuc MPie MTis MWat NRHS SEND SRms WBrk WFar WOld WSFF
	- 'Barr's Purple'	ECtt WBrk WCFE WOld
	- 'Barr's Violet'	CDow ECtt MAvo NSti SRms WBrk WCot WFar WHal WOld

	- 'Betel Nut'	MAvo WOld
	- 'Bishop Colenso'	EPPr SPhx WBrk
	- 'Blackheart'	ELon
I	- 'Brightness'	WCot
	- 'Brockamin'	EPPr MNrw WBrk WOld
	- 'Brunswick'	MAvo WFar WOld
	- 'Christopher Harbutt'	LEdu
	- 'Colwall Century'	WBrk WOld
	- 'Colwall Constellation'	ELon MAvo WBrk WOld
	- 'Colwall Galaxy'	WBrk WOld
	- 'Colwall Orbit'	ECtt ELon NWsh WBrk WOld
	- 'Connie'	MNrw
	- 'Constanze'	EBee ECtt ELon MAvo MTis
	- 'Crimson Beauty'	ECtt ELon MAvo MHCG MHer MNrw SAko WBrk WFar WOld
	- 'Dapper Tapper'	ECtt ELon MAvo WCot WOld
	- 'Dark Desire'	MNrw
	- 'Denise'	MAvo
	- 'Early Bird'	ELon
	- 'Evensong'	ECtt LEdu MAvo MPie WBrk WOld
	- 'Festival'	WBrk
	- 'Foxy Emily'	ECtt MAvo MHCG WBrk WOld
	- 'Guido en Gezelle'	ELon MNrw
	- 'Harrington's Pink' ♀H7	Widely available
	- 'Helen Picton'	CDor CDow CSam ECtt ELon EPPr LEdu MAvo MBrN MHer MPie MSpe MWat NLar NWsh SRms WBrk WFar WHoo WOld
	- 'Herbstflieder'	EBee
§	- 'Herbstschnee'	Widely available
	- 'Hoo House'	WHoo
	- 'James'	EPPr MAvo
	- 'James Ritchie'	CDow CSam ECtt MCot MTis WHoo WOld
	- 'John Davis'	MNrw WOld
	- 'John Dickinson'	WBrk
	- 'Jon Baker'	WBrk
	- 'Kate Deamon'	ECtt WOld
	- 'Kylie'	ECtt EPPr LRHS LSRN MNrw MPie MTis SPhx WBrk WCot WFar WMal WOld
	- 'Lachsglut'	ELon EPPr LEdu NLar SAko WCot WOld
	- 'Ladies Day'	WOld
	- 'Little Bella'	ECtt MAvo MWat WOld
	- 'Lou Williams'	CDow ECtt ELon MNrw MWat NLar WFar WOld
I	- 'Lucida'	MAvo SPhx SRms WOld
	- 'Lye End Beauty'	CDor CDow ECtt ELon MAvo MHer MNrw MPie MWat WBrk WCot WFar WOld
	- 'Mabelle'	MAvo NDov
	- 'Mandie's Choice'	MAvo WCot
	- 'Marina Wolkonsky'	CAby CDow CMiW ECtt ELon EWes IPot LEdu MAvo MNrw MWat NLar SAko SPhx SRms WBrk WCot WFar WKif WMal WOld
	- 'Millennium Star'	ECtt ELon WBrk WOld
	- 'Miss K.E. Mash'	ECtt NLar WBrk WCAu WFar WOld
	- 'Mrs S.T. Wright'	CTri ECtt EWes LEdu MBrN MNrw NWsh WBrk WFar WOld
	- 'Mrs S.W. Stern'	WBrk WOld
	- 'Nachtauge'	SAko
	- 'Naomi'	MAvo WBrk WOld
	- 'Percy Picton'	LEdu
	- 'Pink Parfait'	CSam ECtt MAvo NGdn SRms WBrk WCot WFar WOld
	- 'Pink Victor'	EPPr SRms WFar
	- 'Pontis Supreme'	MAvo
	- 'Pride of Rougham'	ECtt EWes MAvo WBrk

	- 'Primrose Upward'	ECtt MNrw NDov NWsh SPhx WCot WOld
	- 'Purple Cloud'	CSam ECtt ELon MAvo MHer MWat NGdn WBrk WHal WOld
I	- 'Purple Dome'	Widely available
	- 'Purple Paradise' **new**	WOld
	- 'Quinton Menzies'	ELon MAvo WOld
	- 'Red Cloud'	ECtt ELon LEdu MAvo MHer WBrk WOld
	- 'Rosa Sieger' ♀H7	CSam ECtt ELon EPPr GMaP LEdu MAvo MNrw MTis NGdn SBut SEdd WBor WBrk WFar WHoo WOld XLum
	- 'Rose Williams'	LEdu MAvo MPie WBrk
	- 'Röter Stern'	ECtt MPie WBrk WOld
	- 'Röter Turm'	SAko
	- 'Rougham Pink'	WBrk
	- 'Rougham Purple'	EWes
	- 'Rougham Violet'	WBrk
	- 'Rubinschatz'	EBee ECtt ELon MAvo MTis NWsh SRms WOld XLum
	- 'Rudelsburg'	CDow EBee ECtt ELon IPot MAvo SHar WBrk WOld
	- 'Rudolph'	ECtt EWes MCot
	- 'Saint Michael's'	MAvo MWat WBrk WFar WOld
	- 'Sayer's Croft'	CDow ECtt ELon MAvo MWat SRms WBrk WCot WFar WHoo WOld
	- 'Schneehügel' **new**	CDow
	- SEPTEMBER RUBY	see *S. novae-angliae* 'Septemberrubin'
§	- 'Septemberrubin'	CMea EBee ECtt ELan ELon EMor EPPr EPfP GQue IPot LEdu LPla MAvo MBel MMuc MRav MTis NSti NWsh SEND SRms WCAu WFar WOld WSpi WTyc XLum
	- 'Treasure'	CBre ECtt EHyd ELon EPPr EWes LRHS MAvo SPhx WBrk WOld
	- 'Vibrant Dome'PBR	EHyd LRHS MNrw MTis NLar NRHS SEdd
	- 'Violet Dusk'	ELon WBrk
	- 'Violet Haze'	CMea ELon WBrk WOld
	- 'Violetta'	ECtt EHyd ELon GMaP ILea IPot LEdu LRHS MAvo MNrw MPie MTis NRHS SPhx WBor WBrk WCAu WFar WKif WOld
	- 'W. Bowman'	ECtt MNrw NLar WBrk WOld
	- 'Warm Throng'	WCot
	- 'Wineflower'	MAvo MCot MTis
	- 'Wow'	ELon WOld
§	***novi-belgii***	WHer
	- 'Ada Ballard'	CFis CMac CRos CWld EBee LRHS LSRN NGrd NRHS WFar WOld
	- 'Albanian'	SRms WOld
	- 'Alderman Vokes'	WOld
	- 'Algar's Pride'	ECtt WFar WOld
	- 'Alice Haslam'	CMac CRos EHyd ELan LRHS MHol MSCN NLar NRHS SRms WCAu WFar WOld
	- 'Angela Peel'	EHyd LRHS
	- 'Anita Ballard'	WOld
	- 'Anita Webb'	NBir WOld
	- 'Anneke'	NLar WOld
	- 'Apollo'	CRos EHyd ILea LRHS MSCN MWat NLar NRHS SCob SEdd WFar WOld
	- 'Apple Blossom'	MWat WFar WOld
	- 'Audrey'	CMac CRos GMaP LRHS LSRN MBNS NGdn SRms WFar WOld
	- 'Autumn Beauty'	WOld
	- 'Autumn Days'	WOld
	- 'Autumn Glory'	WOld
	- 'Autumn Rose'	WOld
	- 'Baby Climax'	WOld
	- BAHAMAS ('Dasone') (Island Series)	CRos EHyd EPfP LRHS MPri NRHS NWsh SCob SPoG SRms SWvt WCot
	- BARBADOS ('Dastwo') (Island Series)	CBod CRos EHyd EPfP LRHS MPri NLar NRHS SCob SPoG SWvt WCot WFar
	- 'Beauty of Colwall'	WOld
	- 'Beechwood Beacon'	WFar
	- 'Beechwood Challenger'	MHCG MNrw MPie NWad WOld
	- 'Beechwood Charm'	SDix WFar WOld
	- 'Beechwood Rival'	CDor CTri WOld XEll
	- 'Blandie'	MWat WOld
	- 'Blauglut'	WFar WOld
	- 'Blue Baby'	CMac MPie
	- 'Blue Bouquet'	CTri SRms WFar WOld
	- 'Blue Boy'	WOld
	- 'Blue Danube'	WOld
	- 'Blue Eyes'	WOld
	- 'Blue Gown'	GQue WOld
	- 'Blue Lagoon'	CDor CMea LSRN WBrk WCAu WOld
I	- 'Blue Moon'	MWat WFar WOld
	- 'Blue Patrol'	WOld
	- 'Blue Radiance'	WOld
	- 'Blue Spire'	SPhx WOld
	- 'Blue Whirl'	WOld
	- 'Boningale Blue'	WOld
	- 'Boningale White'	MHCG NHol WFar WOld
	- 'Bonnie' **new**	WOld
	- 'Bright Eyes'	WOld
	- 'Brightest and Best'	WOld
	- 'Brigitte'	CBod CDor EWTr NLar
	- 'Cameo'	WOld
	- 'Cantab'	WOld
	- 'Carlingcott'	WOld
	- 'Carnival'	CMac ECtt EHyd LRHS WOld
	- 'Cecily'	MWat WOld
	- 'Charles Wilson'	CFis WOld
	- 'Chatterbox'	CRos EHyd ELan EPfP LRHS MRav MWat NLar NRHS SRms WFar WOld
	- 'Chelwood'	CAby WFar WOld
	- 'Chequers'	CAby CBod MBNS MHer SGbt SRms WFar WOld
	- 'Christina'	see *S. novi-belgii* 'Kristina'
	- 'Christine Soanes'	WOld
	- 'Cliff Lewis'	WFar WOld
	- 'Climax Albus'	see *S. laeve* 'White Climax'
	- 'Cloudy Blue'	WOld
	- 'Colonel F.R. Durham'	WOld
	- 'Coombe Gladys'	WOld
	- 'Coombe Margaret'	WOld
	- 'Coombe Radiance'	SDix WOld
	- 'Coombe Ronald'	WOld
	- 'Coombe Rosemary'	ECtt NLar WBor WOld
	- 'Coombe Violet'	MWat WOld
	- 'Countess of Dudley'	CFis WFar WOld
	- 'Crimson Brocade'	CDor CRos ECtt EHyd ELan EPfP LRHS NLar NRHS SAko SCob SPoG SRms SWvt WFar
	- 'Dandy'	CMac EHyd ELan EPfP LRHS NBir NGdn NRHS SGbt SRms WFar WOld
	- 'Daniela'	SRms WBrk WFar WOld
	- 'Dauerblau'	WOld
	- 'Davey's True Blue'	CTri WFar WOld XLum
	- 'David Murray'	WOld
	- 'Dazzler'	ECtt WFar WOld
	- 'Destiny'	WOld

- 'Diana' ECtt NWsh
- 'Diana Watts' WOld
- 'Dietgard' MWat WFar WOld
- 'Dolly' NBir SRms WOld
- 'Dora Chiswell' WOld
- 'Dusky Maid' ELon WFar WOld
- 'Elizabeth Hutton' WFar WOld
- 'Elsie Dale' WOld
- 'Elta' WOld
- 'Erica' CElw MWat WOld
- 'Ernest Ballard' WOld
- 'Eva' ELon SRms WOld
- 'Eventide' CTri LSRN WOld
- 'Fair Lady' MWat SDix WOld
- 'Faith' WFar WOld
- 'Farncombe Lilac' MAvo
- 'Feckenham Rival' WMal WOld
- 'Fellowship' 🏆H6 CAby CBod CDor EAJP EBee ECtt EHyd ELon EPfP LEdu LRHS MMuc MNrw MWat NLar NRHS SAko SEND SEdd SHar SRms SWvt WCAu WCot WFar WOld
- 'Flamingo' EHyd LRHS SRms WCAu WOld
- 'Freda Ballard' CRos ECtt EHyd GMaP LRHS MWat NRHS WFar WOld
- 'Freya' CElw LSRN MWat SRms WOld WSHC
- 'Fuldatal' MWat WFar WOld
- 'Gayborder Blue' WFar WOld
- 'Gayborder Royal' WFar WOld
- 'Goliath' MWat WOld
- 'Grey Lady' WFar WOld
- 'Guardsman' WOld
- 'Gulliver' SRms WBrk WFar WOld
- 'Gurney Slade' WFar WOld
- 'Guy Ballard' WOld
- 'Harrison's Blue' MWat WOld
- 'Heinz Richard' CFis ECha MHer NBir NGdn SRms WOld
- 'Helen' ELon WOld
- 'Helen Ballard' NBid SRms WFar WOld
- 'Herbstgruss vom Bresserhof' EHyd LRHS NLar NRHS SAko WFar WOld XSen
- 'Hilda Ballard' WOld
- 'Ibiza' WCot
- 'Ilse Brensell' WOld
- 'Irene' WOld
- 'Janet McMullen' SHar WOld
- 'Janet Watts' WOld
- 'Jean' ELon SRms WFar WOld
- 'Jean Gyte' WOld
- 'Jeanette' SRms WFar WOld
- 'Jenny' CBod CRos CSBt ECtt EHyd ELan EPPr EPfP GMaP IPot LRHS LSRN MRav MWat NBir NGdn NHol NRHS SCob SGbt SGol SMad SPer SRms SWvt WCAu WFar WGwG WOld
- 'Jollity' WOld
- 'Jugendstil' XLum
- 'Julia' WOld
- 'Kassel' SRms WFar WOld
- 'King of the Belgians' WFar WOld
- 'King's College' WOld

§ - 'Kristina' CRos ECha EHyd ITim LRHS MNrw MRav NBir NRHS SDix WFar WOld
- 'Lady Frances' SRms WOld
- 'Lady in Blue' CBod CRos CSBt ECtt EHyd ELan EPfP GWyn LEdu LRHS MBNS MGos MWat NGdn NGrd NRHS NWad SGbt SPer SPoG SReu SRms SSut SWvt WCAu WFar WOld XSen
- 'Lassie' MWat NWsh SRms WFar WOld
- 'Lavender Dream' WOld
- 'Lawrence Chiswell' WFar WOld
- 'Lisa Dawn' WFar WOld
- 'Lisette' LEdu
- 'Little Boy Blue' CDor SRms WOld XLum
- 'Little Man in Blue' WOld
- 'Little Ness' WFar WMal
- 'Little Pink Beauty' CBod CCBP CRos ECtt EHyd ELan EPfP ITim LEdu LRHS MBNS NGdn NGrd NHol NRHS NWad SPer SRms WCAu WFar WOld
- 'Little Pink Lady' SRms WFar WOld
- 'Little Pink Pyramid' SRms WOld
- 'Little Red Boy' WOld
- 'Madge Cato' SRms WOld
- 'Mammoth' WOld
- 'Margery Bennett' WOld
- 'Marie Ann Neil' SRms WOld
- 'Marie Ballard' Widely available
- 'Marie's Pretty Please' WOld
- 'Marie-Theres' SAko
- 'Marjorie' LSRN WOld XLum
- 'Mauve Magic' MWat SRms WFar WOld
- 'Melbourne Magnet' WOld
- 'Midget' WOld
- 'Mistress Quickly' ECtt WFar WOld
- 'Mittelmeer' EHyd LRHS WOld XLum
- 'Mount Everest' CDor WOld
- 'Mrs Leo Hunter' WOld
- 'Nachtlicht' SAko
- 'Neron' IMou MNrw MPie NDov SHar SPhx WFar WMal
- 'Nesthäkchen' WOld
- 'Niobe' WOld
- 'Norman's Jubilee' EBee EHyd EPfP LRHS MHer NBir NRHS WFar WOld
- 'Nursteed Charm' WOld
- 'Oktoberschneekuppel' WOld
- 'Pamela' WOld
- 'Patricia Ballard' (d) CBcs CBod CDor CMac CRos CSBt EBee EBou EHyd ELan EPfP GMaP LCro LOPS LRHS MHer MWat NBir NGrd NLar NPer NRHS NWad SGol SPer WCAu WFar WOld
- 'Peace' MWat WOld
- 'Percy Thrower' WOld
- 'Peter Chiswell' SRms WOld
- 'Peter Harrison' EBee EHyd GMaP LRHS MHol NBir NRHS WOld XLum
- 'Peter Pan' EWTr NLar SCob
- 'Pink Lace' MBNS WOld
- 'Pink Topas' LRHS
- 'Plenty' WOld
- 'Porzellan' CBod CElw CFis CMea ECtt LEdu MAvo MBNS MNrw NGdn NGrd NLar WCot WFar WHal WOld WPGP
- 'Pride of Colwall' SRms WOld
- 'Priory Blush' MWat SRms WOld
- 'Professor Anton Kippenberg' CFis EAJP EHyd ELan EPfP GMaP LRHS MNrw MRav NGrd NLar NRHS SAko SPer SRms SWvt WFar WOld XLum
- 'Prosperity' WOld
- 'Purple Dome' CDor CFis CSBt ECha ELan LEdu LOPS LSRN MHer MWat SBut SDix SHar SRkn WFar WOld
- 'Purple Dream' WFar

	- 'Ralph Picton'	WFar WOld
	- 'Red Robin'	MWat
	- 'Red Star'	SPhx
	- 'Red Sunset'	SRms
	- 'Rembrandt'	MArl NGdn
	- 'Remembrance'	MWat SRms WFar WOld
	- 'Reverend Vincent Dale'	WOld
	- 'Richness'	WOld
	- 'Rose Bonnet'	EHyd LRHS MWat SPlb WFar WOld
	- 'Roseanne'	WOld
	- 'Rosebud'	WOld
	- 'Rosenquartz'	NLar WFar
	- 'Rosenwichtel'	CDor ILea NLar SRms WOld
	- 'Royal Blue'	WOld
	- 'Royal Ruby'	CFis EBee ECtt EHyd IPot LRHS NLar SRms WOld
	- 'Royal Velvet'	WOld
	- 'Rozika'	MNrw WOld
	- 'Rufus'	NWsh WFar WOld
	- 'Saint Egwyn'	WOld
	- 'Sam Banham'	MNrw WFar WOld
	- SAMOA ('Dasthree') (Island Series)	CBod CRos EHyd EPfP LRHS LSou MPri NLar NRHS SPoG SRms WCot
	- 'Sandford White Swan'	MHer WFar WOld
	- 'Sarah Ballard'	NLar WFar WOld
§	- 'Schneekissen'	CRos ECtt EHyd ELan EPfP GMaP LRHS MBNS MHer NRHS SRms SWvt WFar WOld XLum
	- 'Schneezicklein'	GBin GWyn
	- 'Schöne von Dietlikon'	CKno CSpe LEdu MWat WFar WOld XLum
	- 'Schoolgirl'	WOld
	- 'Sheena'	WFar WOld
	- 'Silberblaukissen'	WOld
	- SNOW CUSHION	see *S. novi-belgii* 'Schneekissen'
	- 'Snowsprite'	CBod CSBt EHyd ELan EShb LRHS MWat NLar NRHS SGbt SGol SRms WOld
	- 'Sonata'	GMaP WOld
	- 'Sophia'	MWat WOld
	- 'Starlight'	CDor ECtt ILea NLar WCAu WFar
	- 'Steinebrück'	WOld
	- 'Sterling Silver'	WOld
	- 'Sun Queen'	WOld
	- 'Sunset'	WOld
	- 'Sweet Briar'	WOld
	- 'Tapestry'	WOld
	- 'Terry's Pride'	SRms WFar WOld
	- 'The Archbishop'	ECtt WOld XEll
	- 'The Bishop'	WOld
	- 'The Cardinal'	WOld
	- 'The Dean'	WOld
	- 'The Sexton'	WOld
	- 'Thundercloud'	WOld
	- 'Timsbury'	SRms WOld
	- TONGA ('Dasfour') (Island Series)	CBod CRos EHyd EPfP LRHS MHol NLar NRHS NWsh SCob SPoG SRms SWvt
	- 'Tovarich'	WOld
	- 'Trudi Ann'	NBir WOld
	- 'Twinkle'	WOld
	- 'Victor'	WOld
	- 'Vignem'	NSti
	- 'Violet Lady'	WOld
	- 'Waterperry'	MWat WBrk WOld
	- 'White Ladies'	CBcs CRos EHyd GMaP IMou LCro LOPS LRHS MMuc MNrw MWat NLar NRHS SCob WCAu XLum
	- 'White Swan'	ECtt
	- 'White Wings'	MWat WOld
	- 'Winston S. Churchill'	CAby CDor EHyd ELan EPfP GMaP LEdu LRHS MBel MHer MPie MWat NRHS SPer SPlb SPoG WCAu WOld WTor
	- 'Zwergenhimmel'	SAko
§	***oblongifolium***	NWsh WOld XSen
§	- 'Fanny's'	ECtt MMuc NWad SEND
	- 'October Skies'	EBee EWes MNrw SHar
	'Ochtendgloren' (*pilosum* var. *pringlei* hybrid) $\mathbb{Y}^{H4}$	CMea CSam EBee ECtt ELon EPPr EWes MNrw NLar WHal WHoo WMal WOld
§	'Oktoberlicht'	EHyd EPPr LRHS MNrw WHoo WOld
§	***oolentangiense***	MMuc NLar SPhx WOld
	'Orchidee'	CMea ECtt EPPr EPri EShb EWes MWat WOld
	'Photograph' $\mathbb{Y}^{H7}$	CSam EBee ECtt EHyd EWes LEdu LRHS MPie MRav NRHS WOld WPGP
§	***pilosum***	WCot WFar
§	- var. ***pringlei*** $\mathbb{Y}^{H7}$	ECha EWes MMuc NWad WOld
	- - double-flowered (d) **new**	XEll
§	- - 'Monte Cassino'	CSBt EPfP GQue LPot LRHS MBNS NBro SPer SPhx SRms WCAu WMal WOld WSpi XLum XSen
	- - 'October Glory'	ECtt MMuc WFar
	- - 'Phoebe'	WOld
	'Pink Star'	CRos EBee ECtt EHyd ELon GMaP LEdu LRHS MRav MWat NRHS NSti SPhx WCAu WFar WOld XLum
	'Pinwheel'	SEdd WCot
	'Pixie Dark Eye' (*ericoides* hybrid)	EBee ECtt SDix SMHy SRms WCot
	'Pixie Red Eye' (*ericoides* hybrid)	EBee ELon LEdu WCot WFar
	'Prairie Pink'	WOld
	'Prairie Purple'	CDor ECtt ELon MAvo MTis MWat SMHy SPhx WCot WFar WHoo WMal WOld
	'Prairie Violet'	WOld
	'Primrose Path'	CDor ECtt LEdu MNrw SPhx WBrk WCot WFar WOld
§	***puniceum***	MMuc NLar WOld XLum
	'Purple Diamond' (Autumn Jewels Series)	WFar
	'Ringdove' (*ericoides* hybrid) $\mathbb{Y}^{H7}$	MAvo NSti SWvt WCot WOld
	'Rose Crystal' (Autumn Jewels Series) **new**	CRos
	'Rose Glow'	EPPr
	'Rose Quartz' (Autumn Jewels Series)	NCou
	'Rose Queen'	MMrt MNrw MPie NWsh SRms WOld
§	× ***salignum***	WOld
	- Scottish form	WOld
	'Sea Spray'	WCot
§	***sericeum***	SPhx
	shortii	SPhx
	'Soft Lass'	WCot WOld
	'Speyerer Herbstwoge'	MAvo
	'Star of Chesters'	MWat WOld
	'Sunhelene'	EBee ECtt ELon WCot
	'Superstar'	SPhx WHoo WMal WOld
§	***tradescantii***	MBNS NSti SMad WBrk WCot WOld
	'Treffpunkt'	IMou MAvo SAko
	turbinellum misapplied $\mathbb{Y}^{H6}$	CFis ELon EPfP EWes LRHS MMuc NGdn SMHy SPhx SRkn SWvt
	turbinellum Lindl.	CSam EBee EPfP LEdu MWat NLar NQui SSut WCot WOld WPGP

- 'El Fin'	MNrw
- hybrid	GAbr SDix WOld WSpi
'Vasterival'	IMou LEdu MHer MPie MTis NDov SHar WCAu XLum
× ***versicolor*** 'Altweibersommer'	EBee
'Wood's Blue'	EHyd LRHS NRHS
'Wood's Pink'	CBod EHyd LRHS MTis NRHS WCAu
'Wood's Purple'	EHyd LRHS

Symphytum (*Boraginaceae*)

'Angela Whinfield'	CBre CMea LPla
asperum	CCBP ECha EPPr MRav NLar
* ***azureum***	CWCL LPla MBel NChi WCAu
'Belsay Gold'	NBid NBir SDix WBor
bulbosum PAB 4886	LEdu
caucasicum	ECha GPoy LEdu NLar NSti SPer SRms WOut WWtn XLum
- 'Norwich Sky'	CExl WBor
cordatum	EMor EPPr LEdu MNrw
§ 'Goldsmith' (v)	CMea EBee ECha ELan EMor EPfP MBriF MCot MHol MPie NBPC NBid NBir NLar NPer SCob SGbt SPer SPoG WCAu WFar WWtn
grandiflorum	CMac CTri GKev GPoy LEdu
'Hidcote Blue'	CBre CRos CTri ECha ECtt EHyd EMor EPPr EPfP LRHS MMuc NBro NRHS SEND SPer SPoG SRms WCav WGwG WOut WPnP WWtn
§ 'Hidcote Pink'	CBod CBre CRos ECha ECtt EHyd EPPr LRHS MMuc MNrw NBir NRHS NSti SEND SPer SRms WCAu WCav WFar WGwG WPnP WWtn XLum
'Hidcote Variegated' (v)	CMac SRms
ibericum	CAgr CBod CCBP CSam ECha EHyd EMor GKev GMaP GPoy LRHS MMuc NRHS NSti SEND SRms WGwG WWtn
- 'All Gold'	EBee ECha EHyd LRHS MNrw NRHS WFar
- 'Blaueglocken'	ECha
- 'Gold in Spring'	WFar
- 'Jubilee'	see *S.* 'Goldsmith'
- 'Lilacinum'	CFis WHer
- 'Variegatum'	see *S.* 'Goldsmith'
- 'Wisley Blue'	CBcs CBod SCob WFar
'Lambrook Sunrise'	CMac LEdu NBro SRms WCot
officinale	CAgr CHab ENfk GPoy MHer MNHC MNrw MPri NPer SPer SPoG SRms WCAu WHer WWild XAbr XLum
- var. ***ochroleucum***	WHer
orientale	CCBP EBee EPPr MBel MNrw
peregrinum	see *S.* × *uplandicum*
'Purple Sky' **new**	CBre
'Romanian Red'	SDix
'Roseum'	see *S.* 'Hidcote Pink'
'Rubrum'	CBod CRos EHyd ELan EPfP EWes LEdu LRHS MBel MHer MMuc NBPC NBro NLar NRHS SPer WBor WCAu WWtn XLum
tuberosum	CBre CFis CSam EPPr GPoy LEdu LPla MHer MMuc NGrd NWad WBor WCot WFar WHer WHil XAbr
§ × ***uplandicum***	CLau CTri GPoy MMuc SVic
- 'Axminster Gold' (v)	CMea EWes WCot
- 'Bocking 14'	CAgr CBod CHby EOHP GAbr LCro LEdu LOPS MNHC NGrd SRms WSFF XLum
- 'Droitwich' (v)	WCot
- 'Moorland Heather'	CDor CSpe EAJP ECha LEdu LPla LRHS MBriF MHer MMrt MNrw MPie SPhx WBor WMal WWFP
- purple-flowered	MMuc
- 'Variegatum' (v)	ECtt EHyd ELan EWes LRHS NBir NGdn WAvo WSpi

Synadenium (*Euphorbiaceae*)

grantii 'Rubrum'	EShb

Syncarpha (*Asteraceae*)

vestita	SPlb

Syncolostemon (*Lamiaceae*)

'Candy Kisses'	CBct WCot

Syneilesis (*Asteraceae*)

aconitifolia	GEdr WCot WHal WHil
- B&SWJ 879	LEdu WCru
palmata	GEdr
- B&SWJ 1003	WCru
- B&SWJ 11226	WCru
- B&SWJ 14671	WCru
subglabrata B&SWJ 298	WCru
- NMWJ 14528	WCru
aff. ***tagawae*** B&SWJ 11191	WCot

Syngonium (*Araceae*)

'Pixie' **new**	CDoC
podophyllum 🏆H1a	XBlo

Synnotia see *Sparaxis*

Synsepalum (*Sapotaceae*)

dulcificum	SCit

Synthyris (*Plantaginaceae*)

missurica subsp. ***missurica***	EBee WFar
- subsp. ***stellata***	CAby CBod CMea CRos EBee ECtt EHyd EPfP EPri EWes GAbr GMaP LEdu LRHS MAvo MMrt NBir NHpl NRHS NSti WGwG WHal WSHC

Syringa ✿ (*Oleaceae*)

afghanica misapplied	see *S. protolaciniata*
BLOOMERANG DARK PURPLE ('Smsjbp7'PBR)	LCro LOPS LSRN MAsh SGol SPoG
BLOOMERANG PINK PERFUME	see *S.* 'Pink Perfume'
BLOOMERANG PURPLE ('Penda')	CRos LRHS NRHS
× ***chinensis***	EPfP
- 'Bicolor'	WGob
- 'Saugeana'	MBlu MMuc SPer
× ***diversifolia***	MBlu
emodi 'Aureovariegata'	see *S. emodi* 'Variegata'
- 'Elegantissima' (v)	CBcs CEnd CMac EBee ELan LRHS SPoG
§ - 'Variegata' (v)	CRos EHyd EMil LRHS NLar
× ***hyacinthiflora*** 'Clarke's Giant'	NLar SGol
- 'Dark Night'	WGob
- 'Esther Staley' 🏆H6	EPfP MRav WGob
- 'Maiden's Blush' 🏆H6	SGol WGob
- 'Pocahontas' 🏆H6	LRHS WGob

	- 'Sweetheart' (d)	NOra WMat
	JOSÉE ('Morjos 060f')	CBod ELan ELon EPfP MAsh NLar SGol SWvt WFar WGob WLov
	× ***josiflexa***	CExl
	- 'Agnes Smith'	EBee LRHS NLar SCob
	- 'Anna Amhoff'	NLar
	- 'Bellicent' 🏆H6	CEnd CMac CRos EHyd ELan EPfP LRHS MAsh MMuc MPri MRav NRHS SMad SPer SPoG SRms SWvt WAvo WCFE WFar WLov WSpi
	- 'Lynette'	NEoE
§	- 'Royalty'	SCob
	josikaea	CMCN CSBt EWTr NLar SPer WMat
	- 'Oden' **new**	WMat
	komarowii	ESwi GGGa MGil
§	- subsp. ***reflexa***	EPfP MBlu NLar SLon WPGP
§	× ***laciniata*** Mill.	CJun CRos CTsd CWCL EBee EHyd ELan EPfP LRHS MRav SPer WAvo WCFE WPGP
	'Lark Song'	NLar
	meyeri	SVen
	- (Flowerfesta Series) FLOWERFESTA PINK ('Anny200817'^{PBR}) **new**	LCro LOPS
	- - FLOWERFESTA PURPLE ('Anny200809'^{PBR}) **new**	LCro LOPS
	- - FLOWERFESTA WHITE ('Anny200810'^{PBR}) **new**	LCro LOPS
	- 'Inge'	NLar
§	- 'Palibin' 🏆H5	Widely available
	microphylla	see *S. pubescens* subsp. *microphylla*
	'Minuet'	CBcs LBuc LRHS SGol
	'Miss Canada'	LRHS NLar SCob
	MISS JAPAN	EBee LRHS
	oblata	CMCN
	palibiniana misapplied	see *S. meyeri* 'Palibin'
	patula misapplied	see *S. meyeri* 'Palibin'
	patula (Palib.) Nakai	see *S. pubescens* subsp. *patula*
	pekinensis	see *S. reticulata* subsp. *pekinensis*
	× ***persica*** 🏆H6	CExl CJun CTri EPfP MGos MRav NLar SLon SPer WFar WGob
	- 'Alba' 🏆H6	CJun MRav WAvo WFar WGob
	- var. ***laciniata***	see *S.* × *laciniata* Mill.
§	'Pink Perfume'^{PBR}	CRos EHyd EPfP LCro LOPS LRHS LSRN MAsh NRHS SGol SPoG
	pinnatifolia	CBcs GBin LRHS NLar SAko WCFE WPGP
	× ***prestoniae*** 'Desdemona'	CRos EHyd LRHS MMuc
	- 'Elinor' 🏆H6	ELan EPfP LRHS MRav
	- 'Miss Poland'	LRHS
	- 'Nocturne'	WFar
	- 'Royalty'	see *S.* × *josiflexa* 'Royalty'
§	***protolaciniata***	EShb IDee SGsty
	pubescens	MRav
	subsp. ***julianae*** 'George Eastman'	
§	- subsp. ***microphylla***	CMea
	- - 'Superba' 🏆H6	Widely available
§	- subsp. ***patula***	CMac CRos EHyd EPfP LRHS MMuc MRav NRHS SLim SVen
	- - 'Miss Kim' 🏆H6	CBod CChe CMCN CMac CSBt CTri CWCL EBee ECrN ELan ELon EPfP IArd LRHS LSRN MAsh MGos MRav MSwo NGdn NHol NLar SCoo SLim SPoG SRkn SSta WFar WGob
	'Red Pixie'	CBod CDoC CMac CRos EHyd EPfP LCro LOPS LRHS MAsh MGos MMrt NRHS SCoo SGsty SRkn WGob
	'Red Prince'	MPri
	reflexa	see *S. komarowii* subsp. *reflexa*
	reticulata	CMCN MBlu
	- 'Ivory Silk'	EBtc WMat WPGP
§	- subsp. ***pekinensis***	CMCN
	- - 'Yellow Fragrance'	NLar
	SUGAR PLUM FAIRY ('Bailsugar') (Fairytale Series) **new**	NLar
	× ***swegiflexa***	CExl
	tomentella	EBee SRms WCFE WPGP
	- subsp. ***sweginzowii***	CBcs CWCL EBee EShb EWTr GKin MMuc NLar SPer WBor WSpi
	- - 'Superba'	SGol
	- subsp. ***yunnanensis***	CExl GKev SBrt
	velutina Kom.	see *S. pubescens* subsp. *patula*
	villosa	SPlb
	vulgaris	EPfP
	- 'Amethyst'	CBod
§	- 'Andenken an Ludwig Späth' 🏆H6	Widely available
	- 'Aucubifolia' (d/v)	SEND WGob
	- 'Aurea'	MRav WAvo WFar
	- BEAUTY OF MOSCOW	see *S. vulgaris* 'Krasavitsa Moskvy'
	- 'Belle de Nancy' (d)	CBod CCCN CDoC ELan ELon GAbr MAsh MMuc MRav NLar NOrn SEND SGol SWvt WGob
	- CARPE DIEM	see *S. vulgaris* 'Evert de Gier'
	- 'Charles Joly' (d) 🏆H6	Widely available
	- 'Comtesse d'Harcourt'	EPfP SEND SPer WGob
	- 'Congo'	WGob
	- 'Dappled Dawn' (v)	MMrt
	- 'Dark Koster'	WGob
	- DENTELLE D'ANJOU ('Mindent')	CDoC
	- 'Dwight D. Eisenhower'	WGob
	- 'Edward J. Gardner' (d) 🏆H6	SEND
	- 'Etna'	WGob
§	- 'Evert de Gier'^{PBR}	CBcs CBod GAbr
	- 'Firmament' 🏆H6	MRav SEND SPer WGob WSpi
	- 'G. J. Baardse'	EWTr
	- 'Hope'	see *S. vulgaris* 'Nadezhda'
	- 'Katherine Havemeyer' (d) 🏆H6	Widely available
§	- 'Krasavitsa Moskvy' (d) 🏆H6	CCVT CDoC CTri CWCL EPfP EWTr EWes MAsh MPri MRav NLar NOra SEND SGol WMat
	- 'Lee Jewett Walker'	SSta
	- 'Lila Wonder'^{PBR}	CBod ELan EPfP GAbr SPoG WGob
	- 'Madame Florent Stepman'	CBod CMac CWCL ELon NLar WFar WGob
	- 'Madame Lemoine' (d) 🏆H6	Widely available
	- 'Michel Buchner' (d)	CBcs CDoC CLnd EBee ELan EWTr LMaj MBlu MGos NLar NOra SCob SCoo SLim SPer WMat
	- 'Miss Ellen Willmott' (d)	NLar
	- 'Mrs Edward Harding' (d) 🏆H6	ECrN EPfP MRav NLar WGob
§	- 'Nadezhda' (d)	CBod GAbr WGob
	- 'Pat Pesata'	WGob
	- 'Paul Thirion' (d)	CBod WGob
	- 'Président Grévy' (d)	CBar CWCL EPfP MAsh MPri SGol SLim SPer SPoG
	- 'President Lincoln'	WGob
	- 'Président Poincaré' (d)	WGob
	- 'Primrose' 🏆H6	CBcs CCCN CMac EBee ELan ELon EPfP LRHS MAsh MGos NLar NOra NOrn SCob SCoo SEND SGol SPer SPoG WGob WMat WSpi

- 'Prince Wolkonsky' (d)	EBee ECrN ELan ELon EPfP LRHS LSRN MAsh SEND SPer WFar WGob
- 'Princesse Sturdza'	ELon EPfP NOra
- 'Professor Hoser'	WGob
- ROSE DE MOSCOU ('Minkarl'PBR)	SCob
- 'Saint Margaret'	WGob
- 'Sarah Sands'	WGob
- 'Sensation' ♀H6	Widely available
- 'Souvenir de Louis Spaeth'	see *S. vulgaris* 'Andenken an Ludwig Späth'
- variegated (v)	EWes
- variegated double (d/v)	WCot
- 'Vesper'	IArd
- 'Victor Lemoine' (d)	WGob
- 'Viviand-Morel' (d)	CMac
- 'Wedgewood Blue'	WGob
- 'William Robinson' (d)	WGob
wolfii	EBtc NLar

Syzygium (*Myrtaceae*)

paniculatum	CExl
zeylanicum new	EShb

T

Tabernaemontana (*Apocynaceae*)

coronaria	see *T. divaricata*
§ ***divaricata***	CCCN WFib

Tacca (*Taccaceae*)

chantrieri	CCCN

Taccarum (*Araceae*)

weddellianum	WCot

Tacitus see *Graptopetalum*

Taenidia (*Apiaceae*)

integerrima	SPhx

Tagetes (*Asteraceae*)

'Cinnabar'	CSpe GBin
erecta	SCob
- 'Inca Orange' (Inca Series) ♀H2 new	LCro LOPS
- 'Taishan' new	MBros
- 'Vanilla'	MBros
lemmonii	SDix
- 'Martin's Mutant'	SDix WCot
lucida	CSpe ENfk LEdu MHer SRms WJek WTre
patula	SCob
- 'Alumia Vanilla Cream' new	CSpe
- Bonanza Series (d) ♀H2 new	LCro LOPS MBros
- - 'Bonanza Bee' (d) new	MBros
- - 'Bonanza Bolero' (d) new	MBros
- - 'Bonanza Orange' (d) new	MBros
- - 'Bonanza Yellow' (d) new	MBros
- 'Dainty Marietta' ♀H2	LCro LOPS
- DWARF DOUBLE MIXED (d) new	LCro LOPS
- 'Fireball' (d) ♀H2 new	CSpe
- FRENCH FANCY (mixed) (d) new	LCro LOPS
- 'Strawberry Blonde' (d)	MBros
tenuifolia 'Golden Gem'	LCro LOPS
zypaquirensis B&SWJ 14840	WCru

Taiwania (*Cupressaceae*)

cryptomerioides	IArd IDee SLim WPGP

Talbotia (*Velloziaceae*)

§ ***elegans***	SBrt

Talinum (*Portulacaceae*)

paniculatum	ELan
'Zoe'	CPBP

tamarillo see *Solanum betaceum*

tamarind see *Tamarindus indica*

Tamarindus (*Caesalpiniaceae*)

indica (F)	SPlb

Tamarix (*Tamaricaceae*)

gallica	SArc SEND SWeb WSHC
hampeana	SEND
§ ***parviflora*** ♀H5	CMac CRos EHyd EPfP LRHS NRHS
pentandra	see *T. ramosissima* 'Rosea'
ramosissima	CCCN CTri EBee ELan EPfP MAsh SGsty SLim SLon SRms WAvo WSMil
- 'Hulsdonk White'	CBcs SPer
- 'Pink Cascade' ♀H5	CBcs CCCN CMac EBee EPfP LCro LOPS MBlu MGos MRav SCob SEND SGbt SGol SPer SPoG SWvt
§ - 'Rosea'	CBcs ECrN
§ - 'Rubra'	EPfP SCob SEND SPer
- 'Summer Glow'	see *T. ramosissima* 'Rubra'
tetrandra ♀H5	CBcs CCVT CCoa CDoC CRos CSde CTsd EBee EHyd ELan EPfP LRHS MAsh MBlu MGil MGos MRav MSwo NPer SEND SGol SGsty SPad SPer SPlb SRms SWvt SavN WAvo WSMil
- var. ***purpurea***	see *T. parviflora*

Tanacetum ✿ (*Asteraceae*)

§ ***argenteum***	MRav
- subsp. ***canum***	SLon
§ ***balsamita***	CBod CHby CWld EBee EBou ELan ENfk EPPr GJos GPoy LEdu MHer MMuc MNHC NGrd SEND SRms WHer WJek WSFF XAbr XLum
§ - subsp. ***balsamita***	GPoy GQue WJek
§ - subsp. ***balsamitoides***	CBod MHer SRms
- var. ***tanacetoides***	see *T. balsamita* subsp. *balsamita*
- ***tomentosum***	see *T. balsamita* subsp. *balsamitoides*
§ ***cinerariifolium***	CBod GPoy MNHC
§ ***coccineum***	SVic WFar
- 'Alfred'	MNrw
- 'Duro'	CRos EHyd LRHS NRHS
- 'Eileen May Robinson'	CBod EPfP SGbt WGwG
- 'Garden Treasure'	ECtt
- 'H.M. Pike'	EBee
- 'Laurin'	CBod CRos ECtt EHyd LRHS MHol NBPC NRHS
- pink-flowered new	CFis

- 'Red Dwarf'	ECtt
- Robinson's crimson-flowered	CRos EHyd LRHS NRHS
- - giant-flowered	CRos EHyd LRHS NRHS SRms
- - pink-flowered	CBod EAJP EBee EBou EHyd EPfP GMaP MHol SCob XLum
- - red-flowered	CBod CSBt EAJP EBou EHyd EPfP GMaP GWyn LRHS MHol SCob SPhx SPlb SWvt XLum
- - rose-flowered	CSBt
- 'Snow Cloud'	CBod ECtt EPfP
- 'Vanessa'	MNrw
§ ***corymbosum***	EBee EHyd LRHS NLar WCot
- 'Bukke'	LEdu
- 'Festtafel'	LEdu LPla
densum	WCFE
- subsp. ***amani***	ECha EHyd GKev GMaP LRHS SEND XSen
§ ***haradjanii***	EBou MCot SGro WKif
macrophyllum misapplied	see *Achillea grandifolia* Friv.
§ ***macrophyllum*** (Waldst. & Kit.) Sch.Bip.	EBee ECtt EPPr GWyn SPhx WBor
- 'Cream Klenza'	WCot
niveum	ECha SDix WCot XSen
- 'Jackpot'	EPfP EWes SHar SPhx SWvt
§ ***parthenium***	CBod CCBP CHab CHby EMor ENfk GPoy GQue LCro LOPS MHer MNHC NPer SRms SVic WFar WHer WTre XAbr XLum
- 'Aureum'	CBod EBou ECha ELan EMor ENfk EWes EWhm GPoy MHer MNHC SPer SPlb SRms SWvt WCot WFar WHer WHil XLum
- double white-flowered (d)	NPer SRms
- 'Golden Ball'	WFar
- 'Golden Moss'	XLum
- 'Magic Lime Green' new	MNrw WFar
- 'Malmesbury'	WHer
- 'Plenum' (d)	MNrw
§ - 'Rowallane' (d)	MMuc SEND WCot
- 'Selma Star' (d)	WFar WHer
- 'Sissinghurst White'	see *T. parthenium* 'Rowallane'
- 'White Bonnet' (d)	WHer
poteriifolium	EHyd LRHS NRHS
ptarmiciflorum 'Silver Feather'	SRms SVen
* ***tommansii***	EHyd LRHS
vulgare	CCBP CHab CHby CWld ECha ECtt ENfk GBin GPoy GQue GWyn IRos LCro LOPS MHer MNHC NGrd SRms SVic WFar WSFF WTre XAbr XSen
- 'All Gold'	MBriF SMad SRms
- var. ***crispum***	EBee ENfk MHer MRav SMad SRms WFar
- 'Gold Sticks'	CBod
- 'Golden Fleece'	ECtt EWes LEdu MNHC SDix WCot
- 'Isla Gold' (v)	CDor ECtt EWes LEdu MBriF MHer MMuc NBid SEND WCAu WCot WFar
- 'Silver Lace' (v)	CBre EBee EWes WFar

Tanakaea (*Saxifragaceae*)

radicans	GEdr WSHC

tangelo see *Citrus* × *aurantium* Tangelo Group

tangerine see *Citrus reticulata* Tangerine Group

tangor see *Citrus* × *aurantium* Tangor Group

Taraxacum (*Asteraceae*)

faeroense	NPoe WCot
officinale agg.	CHab
pseudoroseum	MMuc NPoe WFar
rubrifolium	CBre NWad WFar

tarragon see *Artemisia dracunculus*

Tasmannia (*Winteraceae*)

§ ***lanceolata***	Widely available
- (f)	SPer
- (m)	SPer
- 'Red Spice'	EPfP LRHS LSRN MPkF SEle
- 'Suzette' (v)	LRHS MBlu SRms

Taxodium ✿ (*Cupressaceae*)

ascendens 'Nutans'	see *T. distichum* var. *imbricarium* 'Nutans'
distichum	Widely available
- 'Cascade Falls'	MBlu MGos NOra SAko SLim
- 'Falling Waters'	SGol
- var. ***imbricarium***	CMCN
§ - - 'Nutans'	CBcs EPfP IArd MBlu SLim WHwl WMat
- 'Little Leaf'	SLim
- 'Little Twister'	SLim
- 'Minaret'	MBlu
* - 'Pendulum'	IDee LMaj
- 'Pévé Minaret'	CMen MGil MGos NOra SAko SArc SGol SLim
- 'Pévé Yellow'	MBlu SLim
- 'Schloss Herten'	SLim
- 'Secrest'	MBlu
- SHAWNEE BRAVE ('Mickelson')	MBlu SLim
mucronatum	CExl
- NJM 09.037	WPGP

Taxus ✿ (*Taxaceae*)

baccata ♀H7	Widely available
- 'Aldenham Gold'	CKen
- 'Amersfoort'	NLar
- 'Argentea Minor'	see *T. baccata* 'Dwarf White'
- 'Arngost'	NLar
- Aurea Group	ELan SRms
I - 'Aureomarginata' (v)	CBcs MAsh SWvt
- 'Autumn Shades'	NLar
- 'Corleys Coppertip'	CBod CKen LRHS MMuc MRav NLar
- 'Cristata'	CKen MBlu NLar
- 'David'	EPfP IArd LRHS MGos NLar SLim SMad SPoG SWvt
- 'Dorothea'	NLar
- 'Dovastoniana' (m or f)	NLar SMad
- 'Dovastonii Aurea' (m or f/v)	CBcs GKin MBlu NLar SGol SLim SRms
- 'Drinkstone Gold' (v)	SLim
§ - 'Dwarf White' (v)	NLar
- 'Elegantissima' (f/v)	EPfP SCoo SLim SPoG
§ - 'Fastigiata' (f) ♀H7	CBcs CBod CMac CSBt CTho CTri ELan EPfP GEdr GQue LRHS MGos MRav MSwo NOra NOrn SCob SGol SGsty SPer SPoG SRms SWeb SWvt SavN WMat WSpi WTSh
- Fastigiata Aurea Group	CLnd CTho EPfP GQue IArd LMaj LRHS MAsh MGil MGos NLar NOrn SArc SCob SGol SGsty SRms SWeb

	- 'Fastigiata Aureomarginata' (m/v) 🏆H7	CMac CSBt CTri EPfP LBee LRHS MGos MSwo SCoo SLim SLon SPer SPoG SWvt WHwl WTSh
	- 'Fastigiata Robusta' (f)	CSBt ELan EPfP LMaj LRHS MAsh MGos NLar SCoo SGsty SLim SPoG WMat
	- 'Goldener Zwerg'	MBlu
	- 'Gracilis Pendula'	SMad
	- 'Graciosa'	NLar
	- 'Grayswood Hill'	WFar
	- 'Great Column'	MBlu
	- 'Green Column'	CKen NLar
	- 'Green Diamond'	CKen MBlu NLar
	- 'Hibernica'	see *T. baccata* 'Fastigiata'
	- 'Icicle' 🏆H7	LRHS MAsh NHol NLar NWad SLim
	- 'Itsy Bitsy'	CKen
	- 'Ivory Tower'	CKen LRHS NHol NLar NWad SLim
	- 'Jack's Gold'	NLar
	- 'Klitzeklein'	CKen NLar
	- 'Luca'PBR	NLar
	- 'Lutea' (f)	SLim
	- 'Micro'	CKen MAsh NLar
	- 'Nutans'	CKen
	- 'Papageno'	NLar
	- 'Pygmaea'	CKen
	- 'Repandens' (f) 🏆H7	IArd SavN WFar WSpi
I	- 'Repens Aurea' (v) 🏆H7	CMac EPfP NLar SCoo SLim SRms WFar WSpi
	- 'Rushmore'	NLar
	- 'Semperaurea' (m) 🏆H7	CBcs CMac LBuc LRHS MAsh NLar NRya SCoo SGol SLim SPoG WSpi
	- 'Standishii' (f) 🏆H7	CBcs CBrac CKen CMac CSBt ELan EPfP GKin IArd LBee LRHS MAsh MGos MMuc MRav NHol NLar NOra NOrn NWad SLim SPoG SWvt WMat
	- 'Stove Pipe'	CKen
	- 'Summergold' (v)	CBrac ELan LRHS MAsh MRav NBir NLar SCoo WSpi
	cuspidata	CMen
	- 'Aurescens' (v)	CKen NLar
	- 'Minuet'	CKen
	- 'Silver Queen'	SLim
	- 'Straight Hedge'	SLim
	× ***media*** 'Hicksii' (f)	LBuc LMaj SGol
	- 'Hillii'	LBuc
	- 'Nixe'	SLim

tayberry see *Rubus* Tayberry Group

Tecoma (*Bignoniaceae*)

	capensis 🏆H1c	CRHN SVen
	- 'Apricot'	CBcs
	- 'Lutea'	CBcs EPfP EShb
	- yellow-flowered	WLov
	ricasoliana	see *Podranea ricasoliana*

Tecomanthe (*Bignoniaceae*)

	speciosa	CRHN

Tecomaria see *Tecoma*

Tecophilaea (*Tecophilaeaceae*)

	cyanocrocus 🏆H3	CAby EHyd EPot GKev LRHS NDry NRHS
	- 'Leichtlinii' 🏆H3	CAby CAvo EHyd EPot GKev LRHS NDry NRHS SDeJ
	- 'Purpurea'	see *T. cyanocrocus* 'Violacea'
	- Storm Cloud Group	EPot GKev
§	- 'Violacea'	CAvo EHyd EPot GKev LRHS NDry NRHS

Telekia (*Asteraceae*)

§	***speciosa***	CMac CRos CSam CSpe EHyd EPfP GJos GLog LEdu LRHS MMuc NBro NChi NLar NRHS NSti SDix SEND SPlb WBrk WCAu WHoo WSMil

Telesonix see *Boykinia*

Teline see *Genista*

Tellima (*Saxifragaceae*)

	grandiflora	Widely available
	- 'Bob's Choice'	WCot
	- 'Delphine' (v)	EPPr MBriF WCot XLum
	- 'Forest Frost'	CBod CFis CMac EHyd ELan EMor EPPr EPfP EShb LRHS MBNS MBel MBriF MPie MPnt NLar NRHS SWvt WCAu WCot
	- Odorata Group	CBre ECha WCot
	- 'Purpurea'	see *T. grandiflora* Rubra Group
	- 'Purpurteppich'	CRos ECha EHyd EMor EPPr EPfP GPSL LRHS MPnt MRav NRHS SWvt WCot WPnP
§	- Rubra Group	CBre CBro CMac CSam CTri ECha EHyd ELan EPfP GMaP GQue LPot LRHS MBriF MHer NChi NLar NPer NSti SCob SPer SPlb SRms SWvt WCAu WCot WFar WHoo
	- 'Silver Select'	EPPr

Telopea (*Proteaceae*)

§	'Bridal Gown'PBR	CCCN
	'Emperor's Torch'	LRHS
	oreades	SPlb
	SHADY LADY CRIMSON ('T90101'PBR)	CCCN
	SHADY LADY WHITE	see *T.* 'Bridal Gown'
	SHADY LADY YELLOW	CCCN
	speciosissima	CCCN LRHS SPlb
	truncata	CCCN SPlb WCru

Temu see *Blepharocalyx*

Tephroseris (*Asteraceae*)

	integrifolia subsp. ***capitata***	SPlb

Ternstroemia (*Pentaphylacaceae*)

	chapaensis WWJ 11918	WCru
	gymnanthera	WCru
	kwangtungensis FMWJ 13402	WCru
	luteoflora FMWJ 13360	WCru

Tetracentron (*Trochodendraceae*)

§	***sinense***	CBcs CMCN EPfP IArd MBlu WPGP
	- WJC 13818 from the Himalaya	IDee WCru
	- var. ***himalense***	see *T. sinense*

Tetradium (*Rutaceae*)

	austrosinense NJM 09.215	EBee WPGP
§	***daniellii***	CBcs CMCN CTho EBee ELan EPfP ESwi IArd LEdu SAko SEND SPtp WGob WMat WPGP

	- from Korea	WPGP
§	- Hupehense Group	CMCN CTho MCoo NLar
	fraxinifolium PAB 9101	LEdu
	- WJC 13750	WCru
	aff. ***fraxinifolium*** WWJ 11615	WCru
	glabrifolium	IArd
	- B&SWJ 6882	WCru
	- CWJ 12364	WCru
	ruticarpum	LEdu WPGP
	- B&SWJ 3541	WCru

Tetragonolobus see *Lotus*

Tetraneuris (*Asteraceae*)

§	***grandiflora***	GKev SPlb
	scaposa	EPot

Tetrapanax ✿ (*Araliaceae*)

§	***papyrifer*** 🏆^{H3}	CDTJ ELan ESwi SDix SEND SVen WLov XBlo
	- B&SWJ 7135	WCru
	- NMWJ 14580	WCru
	- 'Empress'	SChr WCru
	- 'Meifeng' **new**	WCru
	- 'Rex'	Widely available
	- 'Steroidal Giant'	CDTJ

Tetrapathaea see *Passiflora*

Tetrastigma (*Vitaceae*)

	obtectum	CCCN CTsd EShb EWld SEND WAvo

Teucrium (*Lamiaceae*)

*	***ackermannii*** 🏆^{H5}	CMea EPot MHer WAbe WHoo WIce WPGP XSen
*	***armenum***	EBou
	aroanium	EDAr EPot XSen
	asiaticum	XSen
	botrys	MHer
	capitatum	EDAr
	chamaedrys misapplied	see *T.* × *lucidrys*
	chamaedrys L.	CBar CCBP CRos EHyd ELan ENfk EWTr GJos GMaP GPoy GQue LEdu LRHS LSRN MCot MNHC MRav MSwo NWad SBut SEND SLim SPer SPlb SRms SVen SWvt WBrk WJek XSen
	- f. ***albiflora***	ECha ELan EWes LPla
	- 'Nanum'	GMaP
	- 'Rose'	EBou SRms
	- 'Schneeflocke' **new**	XSen
	- 'Spring Gold'	LRHS
	- 'Summer Sunshine'	WCav
	aff. ***chamaedrys***	MGil
§	***creticum***	SPhx
	flavum	CSde EBee EPPr SBrt XSen
	fruticans	Widely available
	- 'Agadir' **new**	XSen
	- 'Azureum' 🏆^{H3}	CBcs CBod CCoa CDoC CSde EBee EHyd ELan EPfP LRHS LSRN MRav SBrt SCob SEND SIvy SPer SPoG SRkn SRms SWvt WAvo WCFE WKif WPGP WSMil XSen
I	- 'Azureum Compactum'	CBod SCob
	- 'Compactum'	CDoC ELan LRHS LSRN MGil SEdd SLim SLon SPer SPoG SWvt WAvo WCFE WPGP
	- 'Drysdale'	CCoa CDoC CSBt EHyd LRHS SWvt
	hircanicum	CAby CCBP CElw CMea CPla CSam EBou ECha EHyd ELan LRHS LSRN MMuc MNrw NBir NWad SEND SPhx SRkn WCFE WOut XSen
	- PAB 13.341	LEdu
	- 'Paradise Delight'	ECtt GWyn
	- 'Purple Tails'	CBod CSpe CTsd CWCL CWld ELan EMor EPfP MHol MRav NBir NGrd SRms WFar
§	× ***lucidrys***	Widely available
	- 'Chedglow'	CNat
	- 'Lucky Gold'^{PBR}	LRHS SPoG SRms
	lucidum	SLon
	marum	CTri LEdu SBrt SRms WJek XSen
	massiliense misapplied	see *T.* × *lucidrys*
	montanum	XSen
	parviflorum	EDAr
	polium	SPhx XSen
	pyrenaicum 🏆^{H7}	CMea CPBP EPot EWes GEdr SGro
	rosmarinifolium	see *T. creticum*
	scorodonia	CBod CHab MHer MNHC NLar NMir SRms WHer WJek XSen
	- 'Binsted Gold'	NSti
	- 'Crispum'	CCBP CRos EHyd EMor LEdu LRHS MGil MHer MMuc NBro NLar NRHS SPer SRms WAvo WGrn WJek WKif
	- 'Crispum Marginatum' (v)	EBee EBou ECha EPPr EWld LEdu LSou MRav WFar
	- 'Winterdown' (v)	MPie
	subspinosum	EDAr EPot WHoo XSen
§	***viscidum*** 'Lemon and Lime' (v)	NSti

Thalia (*Marantaceae*)

	dealbata	CBen EWat LLWG WMAq XLum

Thalictrum (*Ranunculaceae*)

	CC 4576	CExl
	from Afghanistan	see *T. isopyroides*
	actaeifolium	MBel
	- B&SWJ 4664	WCru
	- B&SWJ 6310	WCru
	- var. ***brevistylum*** B&SWJ 8819	LEdu WCru
	- compact B&SWJ 4946	WCru
	- 'Perfume Star'	CPar EBee ECtt ILea LEdu MMrt NLar SCob SIvy WSpi
	adiantifolium	see *T. minus* 'Adiantifolium'
	alpinum	EPPr NGBl WFar
	angustifolium	see *T. lucidum*
	'Anne'^{PBR}	CDor CKno EBee ECha ECtt EMor EWTr ILea IPot LRHS MAvo MBel MBriF MHol MNrw MTis NDov NGBl NLar SEdd SPeP SPoG WCAu WCot WPnP WSpi
	aquilegiifolium	Widely available
	- 'Album'	CMea CRos EBee ECha EHyd EMor EPed EPfP GBin GMaP LRHS MBel MCot MMuc NBid NRHS SEND SPer SPhx SWvt WCAu WFar WSpi
	- var. ***intermedium*** B&SWJ 10965	WCru
	- 'Purpureum'	NLar NQui
	- var. ***sibiricum***	IMou
	- - B&SWJ 11007	WCru
	- 'Small Thundercloud'	SMHy
	- 'Thundercloud'	Widely available

'Black Stockings' ♀H7	Widely available
calabricum	NLar
chelidonii HWJK 2216	WCru
clavatum	CAby
coreanum	see *T. ichangense*
cultratum	EBee EHyd EPfP LRHS NRHS
dasycarpum	EPPr LPla SMHy SPhx WCot WPnP
§ ***delavayi***	Widely available
- BWJ 7800	WCru
- BWJ 7903	WCru
- var. ***acuminatum***	MBel
- - BWJ 7535	WCru
- - BWJ 7971	WCru
- 'Album'	Widely available
- 'Ankum' ♀H7	CRos EBee EHyd IPot LRHS MNrw NLar NRHS
- var. ***decorum***	CElw CSpe MBel WCot WCru WPGP WSHC
- - BWJ 7770	WCru
- - CD&R 2135 **new**	ESwi
- aff. var. ***decorum***	CExl
- 'Gold Laced'	EBee ECtt NLar
- 'Hewitt's Double' (d)	Widely available
- 'Hinkley'	CMiW ECtt IPot LRHS NLar
- var. ***mucronatum***	MBel WCru
- - DJHC 473	WCru
- purple-stemmed BWJ 7748	WCru
diffusiflorum	EBee IMou LRHS MMrt WAbe WCru WSHC
dipterocarpum misapplied	see *T. delavayi*
dipterocarpum Franch.	CMac CRos EBee EHyd LRHS NRHS XLum
'Elin' ♀H7	Widely available
fendleri	GBin
- var. ***polycarpum***	IMou
filamentosum	EPPr IMou MBel WCot
- B&SWJ 777	WCru
- B&SWJ 4145	WCru
finetii	ECha LRHS
flavum	CBod CHab CMac ELan EWld NBro WFar WShi
- 'Chollerton'	see *T. isopyroides*
§ - subsp. ***glaucum***	Widely available
- - 'Ruth Lynden-Bell' ♀H7	CAby CBod SPoG WCot
- - 'Silver Sparkler' (v)	WCot
- - 'True Blue'	SGbt
- 'Illuminator'	CDor CElw CTri EHyd EPfP EShb LRHS MArl MRav NLar NRHS WCot WFar XEll
flexuosum	see *T. minus* subsp. *minus*
grandiflorum	GEdr
honanense BWJ 7962	WCru
§ ***ichangense***	CBod CSpe EBee ECtt EHyd EPri GAbr GEdr LEdu LRHS MBel MHol MTis NSti NWad SPad WCot
- B&SWJ 8203	WCru
- 'Evening Star' (v)	CAby ECtt MHol SMad WHil
- 'Purple Marble'	CSpe CWGN LEdu MAvo WCot
§ ***isopyroides***	CRos EBee EHyd EMor ESwi GKev GKin LEdu LRHS MBel MHid MHol MRav NRHS NWad SHar WCot WHil
javanicum	LEdu
- B&SWJ 9506	WCru
- PAB 9431	LEdu WPGP
- var. ***puberulum*** B&SWJ 6770	WCru
johnstonii B&SWJ 9127	WCru
kiusianum	CAby CBod CMiW EBee ECha ELan EMor EPfP EWes GEdr LRHS MBel MHol NBPC NBir NGBl NHpl NLar NSla SIvy SMad SWvt WAbe WCot WFar WPnP XEll
- Kew form	WSHC
koreanum	see *T. ichangense*
§ ***lucidum***	CBod CElw CExl CSpe EBee ECtt EHyd EShb GBin IMou LEdu LRHS MHol MMuc MPie MTis NBPC NGBl NLar NQui NSti SEND SEdd SPhx WCot WPnP
minus	EHyd LEdu LRHS SEND XAbr
§ - 'Adiantifolium'	ESwi MBel MRav NGdn SHar SRms WSpi XLum
- 'Chinese Chintz'	WCru
- var. ***hypoleucum*** B&SWJ 8634	WCru
§ - subsp. ***minus***	NBre
- var. ***sipellatum*** B&SWJ 5051	WCru
morisonii	CRos EBee EHyd LRHS NBid NRHS
'Nimbus Pink' (Nimbus Series) **new**	SPad
'Nishiki'	GEdr WFar
omeiense BWJ 8049	WCru
orientale	EBee EHyd LRHS
osmundifolium	WCru
petaloideum	SPhx
platycarpum B&SWJ 2261	WCru
podocarpum B&SWJ 14297	WCru
polygamum	see *T. pubescens* Pursh
przewalskii	WCru
§ ***pubescens*** Pursh	EBee ECha EHyd GJos GMaP LRHS NDov NLar NRHS SHar SPhx
punctatum B&SWJ 1272	WCru
'Purplelicious'	CBor ILea MBel NLar SMad
ramosum	MBel
- BWJ 8126	WCru
reniforme	LEdu
- B&SWJ 13969	WCru
- GWJ 9311	WCru
- HWJK 2403	WCru
- WJC 13761	WCru
rochebruneanum ♀H7	Widely available
- 'Lavender Mist'	LSun SPtp
rubescens B&SWJ 10006	WCru
rugosum	CRos EHyd LRHS NRHS
sachalinense RBS 0279	EBee EPPr NLar
shensiense	CExl
simplex var. ***brevipes*** B&SWJ 4794	WCru
speciosissimum	see *T. flavum* subsp. *glaucum*
* ***sphaerostachyum***	CBod CElw EHyd EMor EPPr EPfP EShb GAbr GPSL LRHS MBel MNrw MPie NDov NRHS SPeP WHal
'Splendide'	Widely available
SPLENDIDE WHITE ('Fr21034'PBR) ♀H7	Widely available
squarrosum	EBee
tenuisubulatum BWJ 7929	WCru
tuberiferum B&SWJ 10999	WCru
- var. ***yakusimense*** B&SWJ 6094	WCru
tuberosum	CBor CElw CMea CMiW CPla CSpe EPot NDov SHar WCot
- 'Rosy Hardy'	WCot

'Tukker Princess' ♀^{H7}	EBee ECtt EWhm ILea MHol NDov NLar SMad WCot
uchiyamae	EBee EWld GKev WCot WPGP
urbainii B&SWJ 7085	WCru
'Yubari Mountains'	WFar
yunnanense	WCru

Thamnocalamus (*Poaceae*)

crassinodus 'Gosainkund'	CDTJ MWht
- 'Kew Beauty' ♀^{H3}	CDTJ EPfP MBrN MWht WCot WPGP
- 'Langtang'	CBdn CDTJ MWht WPGP XCre
- 'Merlyn'	CDTJ EPfP MWht
falconeri	see *Himalayacalamus falconeri*
khasianus	see *Drepanostachyum khasianum*
maling	see *Yushania maling*
spathaceus misapplied	see *Fargesia murielae*
spathiflorus subsp. ***nepalensis***	CBdn MWht
tessellatus	see *Bergbambos tessellata*

Thamnochortus (*Restionaceae*)

cinereus	CPbh
fruticosus	CCtw
insignis ♀^{H3}	CCtw CPbh MPkF SPlb
lucens	SPlb
rigidus	CCCN CCtw CTrC

Thapsia (*Apiaceae*)

decipiens	see *Melanoselinum decipiens*
garganica	SBrt
villosa	SHar
- B&SWJ 14014	WCru

Thaspium (*Apiaceae*)

trifoliatum **new**	SPhx

Thea see *Camellia*

Thelypteris (*Thelypteridaceae*)

kunthii	CLAP EBee ELan EMor ISha LEdu WCot
limbosperma	see *Oreopteris limbosperma*
ovata var. ***lindheimeri***	EHyd ISha LRHS NRHS
palustris	EBee EShb NBir NBro NLar SRms WFib WPnP XLum
phegopteris	see *Phegopteris connectilis*

Themeda (*Poaceae*)

triandra	SMad

Thermopsis (*Papilionaceae*)

caroliniana	see *T. villosa*
chinensis	CRos EBee EHyd ELon EPfP GAbr LPla LRHS MHer MMuc NRHS
fabacea	see *T. lupinoides*
lanceolata	CMea EBee EHyd ELon EPfP LRHS MMuc NQui NRHS SHar SPad WCot WFar
§ ***lupinoides***	CDor ECha SRms
macrophylla	EBee
mollis	CExl NBid
montana	MPie
- var. ***montana***	CBod CWCL EBee EHyd ELan EPfP GBee GMaP LRHS MBel MMuc NBir NGBl NGrd NRHS NSti NWad SEND SGbt SPer
- - NNS 99-480	WCot
§ ***villosa***	EHyd LPla LRHS MRav NGdn NLar SHar

Therorhodion see *Rhododendron*

Thladiantha (*Cucurbitaceae*)

dubia	EBee SBrt SDix WCot

Thlaspi (*Brassicaceae*)

sp.	NGdn
biebersteinii	see *Pachyphragma macrophyllum*

Thryptomene (*Myrtaceae*)

baeckeacea	CCCN

Thuja ✿ (*Cupressaceae*)

'Extra Gold'	see *T. plicata* 'Irish Gold'
§ ***koraiensis***	NLar SLim
occidentalis	GPoy SEND SWeb
- 'Amber Glow'	CKen CSBt LRHS MAsh NHol NLar NWad SCoo SLim SPoG SRms
- 'Anniek'PBR	CKen LRHS SPoG
- Aurea Group	CBrac
- 'Bateman Broom'	CKen
- 'Beaufort' (v)	CKen
- 'Brabant' ♀^{H7}	MGos NLar SCoo SGsty SLim WMou
- 'Brobeck's Tower' ♀^{H7}	CKen NLar SLim
- 'Caespitosa'	CKen
- 'Cuprea'	CKen
- 'Danica' ♀^{H7}	CBrac CMac GKin LCro LOPS MAsh MGos NOrn SCoo SLim SPoG SRms WCFE
- 'Danica Gold'	SLim
- 'Degroot's Spire'	CKen ELan LRHS NLar SLim
- 'Douglasii Aurea' (v)	CKen
- EMERALD	see *T. occidentalis* 'Smaragd'
- 'Ericoides'	SRms
- 'Europa Gold' ♀^{H7}	NLar SGol
- 'Filiformis'	SLim
- 'Filips Magic Moment'PBR	LRHS SPoG
- FIRE CHIEF ('Congabe'PBR)	CKen SLim SPoG
- 'Globosa'	ELan
I - 'Globosa Variegata' (v)	CKen
- 'Gold Drop'	CKen
- 'Golden Anne'PBR	SPoG
- 'Golden Globe'	LSRN SCoo SLim
- GOLDEN SMARAGD ('Janed Gold'PBR)	EPfP LRHS SLim SPoG
- 'Golden Tuffet' ♀^{H7}	CKen CMea ELan GKin LBee NWad SCoo SLim SPoG
- 'Hetz Midget' ♀^{H7}	CKen GKin NWad SCoo SLim SPlb WFar
- 'Holmstrup' ♀^{H7}	CBod CBrac CMac MAsh MGos SGol SLim SRms
- 'Jantar'PBR	LRHS NLar SGsty SLim SPoG
- 'Konfettii' (v)	SLim SPoG
- 'Linesville'	CKen
- 'Little Gem'	SRms
- 'Malonyana Holub'	SAko
- 'Maria Wn'PBR	CKen
- 'Meineke's Zwerg' (v)	CKen
- 'Miky'	LRHS
- 'Milleri'	CKen
- 'Mirjam'PBR (v)	CKen
- 'Mr Bowling Ball'	LRHS NLar SLim
- 'Ohlendorffii'	CKen
- 'Perk Vlaanderen' (v)	LRHS
I - 'Pygmaea'	CKen
- 'Pyramidalis Aurea'	SCob SGsty
- 'Recurva Nana'	NWad

- 'Rheingold' ♀H7	CBcs CBrac CMac CSBt CTri ELan GKin LBee LRHS MAsh MGos MMuc NHol SEND SLim SPlb SPoG SRms WCFE WFar
- 'Rheingold Compacta' new	SPer
§ - 'Smaragd' ♀H7	CBrac CCVT CSBt ELan EPfP LBuc LCro LOPS LRHS MAsh MGos NLar NOrn SCoo SEWo SGol SGsty SLim SPoG SWeb SWvt WCFE WMou
* - 'Smaragd Variegated' (v)	CKen MAsh
- 'Smokey'	CKen
- 'Spiralis'	NLar
- 'Starstruck'	LRHS SLim SPoG
§ - 'Stolwijk' (v)	SLim
- 'Sunkist' ♀H7	CBod CBrac CKen CMac MGos SCoo SRms WFar
- 'Teddy'	EPfP LBee LRHS MAsh NHol NWad SCoo SPoG
- 'Tiny Tim'	CMac SGol SLim SVic
- 'Trompenburg'	CBod
- 'Wansdyke Silver' (v)	CMac SLim
- 'Wareana'	CMac
- 'Waterfield'	NLar NWad
- 'White Smaragd' (v) new	SLim
- 'Yellow Ribbon'	CKen CSBt SGol SLim SRms
orientalis	see *Platycladus orientalis*
plicata	CBcs CBrac CCVT CMac CTho ELan EPfP SCob SPer WMou WTSh
- 'Atrovirens' ♀H6	CBrac ECrN ELan LBee LBuc LCro LOPS LRHS MAsh MGos MHed MMuc NOra SCob SCoo SEND SEWo SGol SGsty SLim SRms SWvt WAvo WMat WMou
- 'Aurea' ♀H6	LMaj MAsh SLim SRms
- 'Can-can' (v)	CBrac
- 'Collyer's Gold'	SRms
- 'Copper Kettle'	CBod CKen GKin LRHS SLim
- 'Cuprea'	CKen
- 'Doone Valley'	CKen NWad
- 'Excelsa'	LMaj WMou
- 'Gelderland' ♀H6	ELan EPfP SCoo SLim SWeb
- GOLDY ('4ever'PBR)	LRHS NLar SGsty SLim SPoG
- 'Holly Turner'	SLim
§ - 'Irish Gold' (v)	CMac LRHS
- 'Martin'	CBrac SRms SWvt
- 'Rogersii' ♀H6	CBrac CKen CMac MAsh NHol SCoo SLim SPoG SRms
- 'Semperaurescens' (v)	CMac
- 'Stolwijk's Gold'	see *T. occidentalis* 'Stolwijk'
- 'Stoneham Gold' ♀H6	CBrac CMac GKin MAsh MGos SRms WCFE
- VERIGOLD ('Courtapli')	MMuc SEND
- 'Whipcord' ♀H6	CBcs CKen ELan EPfP LRHS MMuc MPkF NHol NLar SCoo SLim SPoG
- 'Winter Pink' (v)	CKen
- 'Zebrina' (v) ♀H6	CBcs CBrac CMCN CMac CTri ELan EPfP LRHS MAsh MGos MMuc NLar NOra SCob SCoo SEND SLim SPer SPoG SWvt WAvo

Thujopsis (*Cupressaceae*)

dolabrata ♀H6	CBcs CBrac MMuc SEND SWvt WFar
- 'Aurea' (v)	CKen LRHS NLar
- var. ***hondae***	SLim
- 'Laetevirens'	see *T. dolabrata* 'Nana'
§ - 'Nana'	CKen CMac LRHS NLar SLim SRms
- 'Solar Flare'	LRHS SLim
- 'Variegata' (v)	CMac GKin NLar SRms
koraiensis (Nakai) hort.	see *Thuja koraiensis*

Thunbergia ✿ (*Acanthaceae*)

alata	SPoG
- 'African Sunset'	CCht CSpe EShb
- 'Lemon Queen'	SWvt
- 'Orange Beauty'	CCht SWvt
* ***arborea***	CCCN
battiscombeii	CCCN
coccinea	CCCN
- B&SWJ 7166	WCru
erecta	CCCN
fragrans GWJ 9441	ESwi WCru
grandiflora ♀H1b	CCCN WFib WSFF
- 'Alba'	CCCN
gregorii ♀H1b	CCCN EShb WFib
laurifolia B&SWJ 7166	WCru
'Moonglow'	CCCN
natalensis	CCCN EShb
'Orange Wonder'	CCCN

Thymbra (*Lamiaceae*)

capitata	XSen
spicata	SPhx

thyme, caraway see *Thymus herba-barona*

thyme, garden see *Thymus vulgaris*

thyme, lemon see *Thymus citriodorus*

thyme, wild see *Thymus serpyllum*

Thymus ✿ (*Lamiaceae*)

from Turkey	EWes LEdu SPhx
§ 'Alan Bloom'	CRos EHyd LRHS NRHS
'Albus'	ENfk
'Anderson's Gold'	see *T. pulegioides* 'Bertram Anderson'
azoricus	see *T. caespititius*
'Bressingham'	CBod CMea CRos CTri EBou ECtt EHyd ELon EWhm GMaP GQue LCro LEdu LOPS LRHS MHer MMuc MNHC NRHS SPlb SRms WIce
'Caborn Wine and Roses'	CCBP ENfk SRms WFar WJek
§ ***caespititius***	GPoy MHer NRya SGro SPlb SRms WAbe WJek
caespitosus	see *T. praecox* subsp. *praecox*
camphoratus	ENfk EWes MBros MHer NHpl SEdi SPhx WAbe WFar WJek
- 'Derry'	CSpe
§ ***carnosus*** Boiss.	MHer XSen
'Carol Ann' (v)	ENfk EWes MNHC SRms
cherlerioides new	CPBP
ciliatus	CBod XSen
cilicicus misapplied	see *T. caespititius*
cilicicus ambig.	MNHC SRms
cilicicus Boiss. & Bail.	WAbe
citriodorus misapplied	see *T.* 'Culinary Lemon'
citriodorus ambig.	CTsd GQue MMuc SPhx SRms SVic XLum
citriodorus (Pers.) Schreb.	CLau LEdu
- 'Archer's Gold'	see *T. pulegioides* 'Archer's Gold'
- 'Aureus'	see *T. pulegioides* 'Aureus'
- 'Bertram Anderson'	see *T. pulegioides* 'Bertram Anderson'
- 'Silver Posie'	see *T.* 'Silver Posie'
'Coccineus'	see *T.* Coccineus Group

§	Coccineus Group Υ^{H5}	CBod CTri EBou ECha ECtt ECul ELan EMor ENfk GMaP LCro LOPS MHer MMuc MNHC NHpl NRya NWad SPer SPhx SPoG SRms WAbe WCav WFar WHoo WIce WJek XSen
	- 'Atropurpureus' Schleipfer	see *T.* (Coccineus Group) 'Purple Beauty'
§	- 'Purple Beauty'	CPBP CRos ECtt EHyd EPot LRHS MHer NRHS SRms XSen
§	- 'Red Elf'	GAbr MHer NSla
	'Coccineus Major'	CMea EHyd LRHS MNHC NRHS SRms
	'Creeping Lemon' misapplied	see *T. pulegioides* 'Kurt'
§	'Culinary Lemon'	CBod CHby CLau ENfk GPoy LCro LOPS MBow MBrN MHer MNHC MPri SEdi SSut WJek XLum XSen
	'Dartmoor'	WJek
	'Desboro'	see *T. serpyllum* 'Desborough'
	'Dillington'	ENfk
	doerfleri	XSen
	'Doone Valley' (v)	Widely available
	drucei	see *T. polytrichus* A. Kern. ex Borbás subsp. *britannicus*
	'Duftkissen' PBR	XSen
	'E.B.Anderson'	see *T. pulegioides* 'Bertram Anderson'
	'Elfin Pink Carpet'	MHol
	erectus	see *T. carnosus* Boiss.
	× ***faustinoi*** **new**	CLau
	'Fragrantissimus'	CLau EBou EMor ENfk EWhm GPoy MHer MNHC SPlb WJek
	'Golden King' (v)	ECha ELan EMor ENfk LSRN MAsh MHer SRms
	'Golden Lemon' misapplied	see *T. pulegioides* 'Aureus'
	'Golden Lemon' (v)	WJek
	'Golden Queen' (v)	CBod MHol SRms WFar
§	'Hartington Silver' (v)	CMea CRos CTri EBou ECha ECtt EHyd ENfk EPot EWes GKev LRHS MAsh MHer NBPC NHpl NRHS SPlb SPoG SRms WCav WJek
	herba-barona	CBod CCBP CLau CMea EBou ENfk GPoy GQue LEdu MHer MMuc MNHC SRms WFar WJek
	- ***citrata***	see *T. herba-barona* 'Lemon-scented'
§	- 'Lemon-scented'	ECha GPoy LEdu MHer SRms WJek XSen
	'Highland Cream'	see *T.* 'Hartington Silver'
§	'Iden'	CBod WJek
	'Jekka'	CBod CLau EWhm LCro LOPS MHer SRms WJek
	'Jekka's Autumn Pink'	WJek
	'Jekka's Rosy Carpet'	WJek
	'Kurt'	see *T. pulegioides* 'Kurt'
	'Lammefjord' **new**	XSen
	'Lavender'	SMHy
	'Lavender Sea'	EWes
	'Lemon Caraway'	see *T. herba-barona* 'Lemon-scented'
	'Lemon Curd'	CLau ENfk MNHC NHol SPlb SPoG SRms WJek
*	'Lemon Variegated' (v)	ENfk EPfP EWhm LCro LOPS MNHC SPer SPoG
	'Lilac Time'	ECtt ENfk EWes MHer SPlb SRms WJek
	'Lime'	LEdu WFar
	longicaulis	ECha MHer MMuc SRms
	'Magic Carpet'	WJek
	marschallianus	see *T. pannonicus*
	mastichina	GJos XSen
	- 'Didi'	MHer
	membranaceus	WAbe
	micans	see *T. caespititius*
	minus	see *Calamintha nepeta*
	neiceffii	CMea ECha
	nitens	XSen
	odoratissimus **new**	SPhx
	'Orange'	CBod LEdu SEdi SMHy SRms WFar
§	ORANGE SPICE ('Tm95')	XSen
§	***pannonicus***	MHer
	- PAB 9021	LEdu
	'Peter Davis'	CBod CLau EHyd ENfk LCro LOPS LRHS NBPC NBir SPoG SRms WAbe WFar WIce WJek WTor XSen
§	'Pinewood'	MHer WFar WJek XSen
	'Pink Ripple'	CBod CLau CMea ECtt ENfk EWes EWhm LEdu MHer MNHC SRms WHal WHoo WJek
	polytrichus misapplied	see *T. praecox*
	polytrichus A. Kern. ex Borbás	WWild
§	- subsp. ***britannicus***	CCBP CTri EBou ECha EWhm GBin GMaP GPoy LEdu LOPS MBNS MHer MMuc MNHC NBir SEND SPhx SPlb SRms WJek XLum XSen
§	- - 'Thomas's White' Υ^{H5}	CTri
	'Porlock'	CBod CLau CSam CTri EPfP MHer SRms WHoo WJek
§	***praecox***	CWld EWhm GJos MHer NMir
	- 'Albiflorus'	MRav XSen
	- subsp. ***arcticus***	see *T. polytrichus* A. Kern. ex Borbás subsp. *britannicus*
	- - 'Albus'	see *T. polytrichus* subsp. *britannicus* 'Thomas's White'
§	- subsp. ***praecox***	CTri
	prostrate	CBod EBou
	'Provence'	XSen
	pulegioides	CBod CCBP CHby CTri EBou EMor ENfk GPoy MBow MHer NHpl SRms WFar WJek WSFF XAbr
§	- 'Archer's Gold'	CCBP CRos ECtt EHyd ENfk EPfP EPot LRHS LSRN MAsh MHer MHol MNHC MRav NBPC NBir NHol NHpl NRHS SCob SRms WCav WFar
§	- 'Aureus' Υ^{H5}	ENfk GMaP LCro LOPS MAsh SPer SPlb SRms WHoo
§	- 'Bertram Anderson' Υ^{H5}	CBod CMea CPla EBou ECha EMor ENfk EPfP GMaP MAsh MHer NBPC NBir NRya SPer SPoG SRms WCav WHoo WIce XSen
	- 'Foxley' (v)	CBod CCBP CLau ECul ELon ENfk EPfP EWhm MHer MNHC SPlb SPoG SRms WFar WJek
	- 'Golden Dwarf'	WFar
§	- 'Kurt'	CLau ENfk LEdu MHer SRms WJek
	- 'Sir John Lawes'	MHer
	- 'Tabor'	CBod CLau EBou ENfk EWhm MNHC NBPC SRms WGwG
	'Rainbow Falls' (v)	EPfP NBPC SEdi SRms WFar
	'Rasta' (v)	MHer
	'Redstart'	CBod ECha ECtt ENfk EPot LEdu MHer SRms WJek
	richardii subsp. ***nitidus*** 'Compactus Albus'	see *T. vulgaris* 'Snow White'

	rotundifolius misapplied	see *T. vulgaris* 'Elsbeth'
	'Ruby Glow'	ECtt EWes MHer NBir
	serpyllum ambig.	SVic WFar XLum
	serpyllum L.	EMor GJos LBuc MMuc SPlb SRms WRHF
	- var. ***albus***	CRos ECha EHyd ELon GMaP GPoy LRHS MNHC NRHS SPer SRms WCav WFar WHoo
	- 'Albus Variegatus'	see *T.* 'Hartington Silver'
	- 'Amadé'	XSen
	- 'Annie Hall'	CRos CSma EBou EHyd EPfP EPot LRHS MAsh MHer MNHC NRHS SRms WCFE WJek
	- 'Atropurpureus'	see *T.* (Coccineus Group) 'Purple Beauty'
	- ***coccineus*** 'Minor' misapplied	see *T.* Coccineus Group
	- - 'Minor' Bloom	see *T.* 'Alan Bloom'
	- 'Conwy Rose'	CPBP WAbe
§	- 'Desborough'	MHer
	- 'East Lodge'	MHer MNHC SRms
	- 'Elfin'	CPBP ECtt EWes ITim MRav NSla SPlb SRms WAbe XSen
	- 'Goldstream' (v)	CMea CRos EBou EHyd ENfk LRHS MHer NRHS SPlb SRms
	- 'Iden'	see *T.* 'Iden'
	- 'Minimalist'	see *T. serpyllum* 'Minor'
	- 'Minimus'	see *T. serpyllum* 'Minor'
§	- 'Minor'	CMea CRos CTri EBou ECha ECtt EHyd ENfk LCro LOPS LRHS MHer MMuc MNHC NBPC NRHS NSla SEND SPlb SRms WAbe WFar WHoo
	- 'Minus'	see *T. serpyllum* 'Minor'
	- 'Pink Chintz' ♀H5	CCBP CRos EBou ECha ECtt ECul EHyd EMor ENfk EPfP EPot EWhm GMaP GPoy LCro LEdu LOPS LRHS MHer MNHC NRHS NRya SPer SPhx SPlb SPoG SRms WFar WIce WJek
	- 'Purple Beauty'	see *T.* (Coccineus Group) 'Purple Beauty'
	- 'Red Carpet'	ECtt NWad SRms WFar
	- 'Red Elf'	see *T.* (Coccineus Group) 'Red Elf'
	- 'Russetings'	CBod EBou ECtt ENfk EPfP GKev LCro LOPS MHer MNHC SDix SPoG SRms WCav WFar
	- 'September'	MHer
	- 'Snowdrift'	CCBP CMea ECtt ECul EPfP LCro LEdu LOPS MHer MNHC NWad SPlb SRms WCFE WFar
	- 'Variegatus'	see *T.* 'Hartington Silver'
	- 'Vey'	CRos CSma EHyd EWes LRHS MHer NRHS SRms
	- 'Wirral White'	XSen
	'Silver King' (v)	ENfk
§	'Silver Posie'	Widely available
	'Silver Queen' (v) ♀H5	CBcs EBou ECha ELan EMor ENfk EPfP EWhm GKev GMaP LRHS MNHC NBPC NHol SPer SPhx SPlb SRms SVic WJek
	'Spicy Orange'	see *T.* ORANGE SPICE
	striatus	LEdu
§	***vulgaris***	Widely available
*	- 'Compactus'	CLau ENfk GPoy LEdu MHer MNHC MRav SPhx SRms WFar WJek XSen
	- 'Corbière' **new**	XAbr
	- 'Deutsche Auslese'	see *T. vulgaris*
§	- 'Elsbeth'	MHer
	- English, winter	SRms
	- French	see *T. vulgaris*
	- 'Golden Pins'	MHer
	- 'Lucy'	MHer
	- 'Pinewood'	see *T.* 'Pinewood'
§	- 'Snow White'	EWes
	zygis	XSen

Tiarella ✿ (*Saxifragaceae*)

	'Angel Wings' (Fox Series)	EMor MPnt NSti WNPC
	'Appalachian Trail' (American Trails Series)	CBcs ELan EMor LSou MPnt NWad SHeu
	'Black Snowflake'	EBee MPnt SHeu
	'Black Velvet'	MBel MPnt SHeu
	'Braveheart'	EPfP MPnt SHeu
	'Butter and Sugar'	MPnt
	'Butterfly Wings'	MPnt
	'Candy Striper'	MPnt SHeu
	'Cascade Creeper'PBR	EMor LRHS LSou MPnt NWad SHeu WNPC
	collina	see *T. wherryi*
	cordifolia ♀H5	CBcs CBod CMac CTri ECha ELan EMor EPfP GAbr GMaP LEdu LPot LRHS MCot MGos MPnt MRav NBir NDov NRHS SCob SPer SRms SWvt WCAu WHoo XLum
	- 'Glossy'	MPnt
	- 'Milk Chocolate'	MPnt
	- 'Oakleaf'	MPnt NBro SHeu WCAu
	- 'Rosalie'	see × *Heucherella alba* 'Rosalie'
	- 'Running Tapestry'	MPnt SHeu
	- 'Slick Rock'	EPPr
	'Crow Feather'PBR	LSou MPnt NWad SHeu
	'Cygnet'	CDor MPnt SHeu
	'Dunvegan'	MPnt
	'Elizabeth Oliver'	MPnt
	'Emerald Ellie' (Fox Series)	MPnt WNPC
	'Fairy's Footsteps'	SHeu
	'Happy Trails'PBR (American Trails Series)	EMor MPnt NWad SHeu WNPC
	'Inkblot'	LRHS MPnt NBro SHeu
	'Iron Butterfly'PBR (v)	CBod CDor CMac EBee ECha EPfP GMaP LRHS LSRN MBel MPnt MRav SCob SGbt SHeu SPer SPoG SRms WHoo
	'Iron Cross'	SPlb
	'Jeepers Creepers'PBR	ECha EMor LRHS MPnt NWad SHeu WNPC
	'Martha Oliver'	MPnt
	'Mint Chocolate'	EHyd ELan LRHS MPnt NBir NGdn NLar SHeu SWvt
	'Moorgrün'	EPPr SHeu
	MORNING STAR ('Tntia042')	ELan MPnt SHeu SRkn
	'Mystic Mist'PBR (v)	CDor CWGN ECtt MPnt NWad SEdd SHeu SPoG WNPC
	'Neon Lights'PBR	MPnt NBir NWad SHeu SWvt WNPC
§	'Ninja'	EHyd LRHS MPnt NBir NLar SCob SWvt
	'Oregon Trail' (American Trails Series)	EMor MNrw MPnt NWad SHeu WNPC
	'Pacific Crest'PBR (American Trails Series)	EBee EMor MPnt NWad SHeu WNPC
	'Pink Bouquet'	CBod CMac CSpe ELan EMor MBel MPnt NBro NLar SCob SHeu WFar WPnP
	'Pink Brushes'PBR	MPnt SHeu
	'Pink Skyrocket'PBR	CDor ELan EMor EPau EPfP LSRN LSou MAsh MBel MPnt NBir NGdn NHol NWad SEdd SHeu SMad SPer SPoG SWvt WCav WCot WNPC WPnP

'Pinwheel' MPnt
'Pirate's Patch'PBR MPnt SHeu
polyphylla MPnt SHeu WCru
- 'Baoxing Pink' MPnt WCru
- 'Filigran' EPfP GQue MPnt NHol NWad SHar SHeu
'Raspberry Sundae' (Fox Series) **new** MPnt WNPC
'Running Tiger' MPnt
'Sea Foam' MPnt SHeu
'Simsalabim' MPnt
'Skeleton Key' MPnt
'Skid's Variegated' (v) MNrw MPnt SHeu SPoG SWvt
'Skyrocket' NLar
'Spanish Cross' MPnt SHeu
'Special Star' (Heucheraholics Series) **new** SHeu
'Spring Symphony'PBR CBod CDor CRos EHyd ELan EMor EPfP EShb GKev GMaP GWyn LCro LOPS LRHS MAsh MBel MPnt NPer NRHS NWad SCob SEdd SHar SHeu SPoG WCav WNPC WSHC
STARBURST ('Tntia041'PBR) MPnt NWad SHeu
'Sugar and Spice'PBR CWGN EHyd EPfP GPSL LRHS MPnt NDov NLar NRHS NWad SHeu WCAu WNPC
'Sunset Ridge'PBR EBee EMor MPnt NWad SHeu
(American Trails Series) WNPC
SYLVAN LACE ('Tntiasl') SHeu WNPC
'Tiger Stripe' EBee LRHS MPnt NBro SHeu
'Timbuktu' MPnt SHeu
trifoliata MPnt MRav
- var. ***unifoliata*** MPnt
'Viking Ship' see × *Heucherella* 'Viking Ship'
§ ***wherryi*** ♀H5 CBcs CBod EHyd ELan EMor EPfP EWld LPot LRHS MBel MPnt NBir NBro NRya SCob SPer SPlb SWvt WCAu WPnP XLum
- 'Bronze Beauty' MPnt SHeu
- 'Green Velvet' ECha MPnt SHeu
- 'Heronswood Mist' (v) MNrw MPnt SHeu SWvt
- 'Pink Foam' SHeu

Tibouchina (*Melastomataceae*)

grandifolia CCCN CRHN
'Groovy Baby' CCht EMdy MHol
grossa B&SWJ 10758 WCru
heteromalla CCCN
organensis CBcs CBod CCCN SEdd SEle SHeu SIvy SPoG SWvt
paratropica CBod CCCN CRHN MGil WCot
'Peace Baby' CWGN EMdy
semidecandra misapplied see *T. urvilleana*
§ ***urvilleana*** ♀H2 CBcs CBct CCCN CEnd CSBt CTri CTsd EBak EMdy SDix SPalm SPer SRkn SWvt
- 'Compacta' CCCN
- 'Edwardsii' ♀H2 CRHN SAdn WCot
- variegated (v) CBcs CCCN SPalm SPer SWvt WCot

Tigridia (*Iridaceae*)

chiapensis CPla GKev
immaculata B&SWJ 10393 WCru
§ ***orthantha*** CPla
- 'Red-Hot Tiger' CAby CSpe EBee WCot WCru WSHC
pavonia CAby CExl EShb SDeJ WSHC
- 'Alba' CSpe WSHC
- 'Alba Grandiflora' GKev SDeJ SDir
- 'Aurea' GKev SDir
- 'Canariensis' GKev SDeJ SDir
- 'Lilacea' CPla GKev SDeJ SDir
- 'Speciosa' GKev SDeJ SDir
van-houttei GKev

Tilia ✿ (*Malvaceae*)

americana CLnd CMCN
- 'Redmond' MBlu
amurensis CMCN
- from Korea WPGP
argentea see *T. tomentosa*
begoniifolia see *T. dasystyla* subsp. *caucasica*
callidonta WPGP
§ ***caroliniana*** subsp. ***heterophylla*** CMCN EBee EPfP MBlu WPGP
chinensis CMCN WPGP
- F 30558 WPGP
chingiana CMCN EBee WPGP
concinna WPGP
cordata CAgr CBcs CBee CBrac CCVT CHab CLnd CMCN CMac CSBt CTho CTri ECrN ELan EPfP LBuc LMaj MMuc MSwo NOrn SCob SCoo SEWo SPer SWeb WMat WMou WTSh
- 'Green Globe' **new** LMaj
- 'Greenspire' ♀H6 CArg CCVT CLnd EBar EPfP LMaj MRav NOrn SCob SEWo SWeb WMat WMou
- 'Len Parvin' EBee WPGP
- 'Winter Orange' ♀H6 CBcs CBod CEnd EBee ELan EPfP MBlu MSwo SCoo SEWo WMat
dasystyla CMCN
§ - subsp. ***caucasica*** CMCN EBee WPGP
- - A&L 16 WPGP
- - NJM 13.029 WPGP
endochrysea WPGP
× ***euchlora*** CArg CCVT CLnd CMCN EBee ECrN EPfP LMaj SCob SEWo SPer WMat
§ × ***europaea*** CBcs CLnd ELan MMuc NOrn SEND
- 'Pallida' CLnd LMaj MBlu
- 'Wratislaviensis' ♀H6 EBee EBtc MBlu
§ 'Harold Hillier' CMCN MBlu WPGP
henryana CBcs CEnd CLnd CMCN EBee ELan EPfP IArd IDee MBlu MMuc SCob SEND WLov WMat WMou WPGP
- 'Arnold Select' WPGP
- 'Bluebell' MBlu
- 'Kerdalo' WPGP
- large WPGP
'Hillieri' see *T.* 'Harold Hillier'
insularis misapplied see *T. japonica*
intonsa CMCN
§ ***japonica*** CMCN EBee EPfP WPGP
- 'Ernest Wilson' ♀H6 CMCN MBlu
- large-leaved, from China WPGP
kiusiana CMCN MBlu WLov WPGP
mandshurica CMCN WPGP
maximowicziana CMCN EPfP MBlu WPGP
mexicana EBee WPGP
- CD&R 1318 WPGP
miqueliana CMCN MBlu
× ***moltkei*** CMCN EBee IArd WPGP
mongolica CBcs CMCN EBee EPfP MBlu WMou WPGP
- 'Harvest Gold' CBcs MBlu
monticola see *T. caroliniana* subsp. *heterophylla*

	nobilis KR 226	WPGP
	oliveri	CBcs CMCN EBee MBlu WPGP
	aff. ***oliveri*** HRS 2808	WPGP
	paucicostata	WPGP
	platyphyllos	CAgr CCVT CHab CLnd CMCN CSBt CTho CTri ECrN EPfP EWTr LBuc MMuc SCob SCoo SEND SPer WMat WMou WTSh
	- 'Aurea'	MBlu WMat
	- 'Corallina'	see *T. platyphyllos* 'Rubra'
	- 'Laciniata'	CMCN CTho MBlu
§	- 'Rubra' 🏆H6	CCVT CLnd CTho EBar SCob SEWo
	- 'Tortuosa'	LMaj MBlu WMou
	× ***stellata***	WPGP
§	***tomentosa***	CLnd CMCN MMuc SCoo SEND
	- 'Brabant' 🏆H6	ELan EPfP LMaj SCob
	- 'Petiolaris' 🏆H6	CArg CCVT CEnd CLnd CMCN CTho ECrN ELan EPfP MBlu MSwo SCob SPer WMou
	tuan	WPGP
	- var. ***chenmoui***	CMCN EBtc EPfP MBlu WPGP
I	'Varsaviensis'	WPGP
	× ***vulgaris***	see *T.* × *europaea*

Tilingia (*Apiaceae*)

ajanensis B&SWJ 11202	IMou

Tillaea see *Crassula*

Tillandsia (*Bromeliaceae*)

	sp.	XBlo
	abdita	NCft
	aeranthos	NCft SChr
	- var. ***alba***	NCft
	- 'Bronze'	NCft
	- 'Miniata' **new**	NCft
	- 'Minuette' **new**	NCft
	- purple-flowered **new**	NCft
	- var. ***rosea***	NCft
	aeranthos × ***stricta*** **new**	NCft
	aizoides	NCft
	albertiana	CDoC NCft
	albertiana × ***crocata*** 'Copper Penny' **new**	NCft
	albida	NCft SPlb
	andreana	NCft
	araujei	NCft
	arequitae	NCft
	argentea 🏆H1c	LCro LOPS NCft
	argentina	NCft
	ariza-juliae	NCft
	bagua-grandensis **new**	NCft
	baileyi	NCft
*	- var. ***vivipara***	NCft
	baileyi × ***ionantha***	NCft
	balbisiana	NCft
	balsasensis **new**	NCft
	bandensis	NCft
	bartramii	NCft
	bergeri	NCft SChr SPlb
	brachycaulos	NCft
	- var. ***multiflora***	NCft
	brachycaulos × ***concolor***	NCft
	brachycaulos × ***schiedeana***	NCft
	brachycaulos × ***streptophylla*** **new**	NCft
	brachycaulos × ***xerographica*** **new**	NCft
	bryoides	NCft
	bulbosa	NCft SPlb
	- 'Gigante' **new**	NCft
	butzii	NCft
	- var. ***roseiflora*** **new**	NCft
	cacticola	NCft
	cacticola × ***purpurea*** **new**	NCft
	caerulea	NCft
	caerulea × ***straminea*** **new**	NCft
	'Califano'	NCft
	caliginosa	NCft
	capillaris	NCft
	- f. ***incana*** **new**	NCft
	- f. ***virescens*** **new**	NCft
	capitata	NCft
	- 'Domingensis' **new**	NCft
	- 'Peach'	NCft
	- red-leaved	NCft
	caput-medusae	NCft
	cardenasii	NCft
	caulescens **new**	NCft
	caulescens × ***tenuifolia***	NCft
	cauligera **new**	NCft
	chaetophylla **new**	NCft
	chiapensis	NCft
	chusgonensis	NCft
	circinnatoides	NCft
	cocoensis **new**	NCft
	compressa	NCft
	concolor	NCft
	concolor × ***streptophylla*** **new**	NCft
	'Cotton Candy'	NCft
	crocata	NCft
	- 'Copper Penny'	NCft
	- 'Copper Penny' × ***duratii*** **new**	NCft
	crocata × ***mallemontii*** **new**	NCft
	crocata × ***usneoides*** **new**	NCft
	cyanea	LCro LOPS NCft
	delicata **new**	NCft
	diaguitensis	NCft
	disticha	NCft
	duratii	NCft
	dyeriana 🏆H1c	NCft
	ehlersiana	NCft
	elongata	NCft
	'Eric Knobloch' **new**	NCft
	espinosae	NCft
	exserta	NCft
	exserta × ***juncea*** **new**	NCft
	fasciculata	NCft
	'Feather Duster'	NCft
	festucoides	NCft
	filifolia	NCft
	flabellata 🏆H1c	NCft
	flavobracteata	NCft
	flexuosa	NCft
	floribunda	NCft
	× ***floridana***	NCft
	fresnilloensis	NCft
	fuchsii var. ***fuchsii***	NCft
	- f. ***gracilis***	NCft
	funckiana	NCft SPlb
	- var. ***recurvifolia*** **new**	NCft
	funebris **new**	NCft
	gardneri	NCft

	geminiflora	NCft
	geminiflora* × *recurvifolia new	
	'Gordon C' new	NCft
	grao-mogolensis	NCft
	hammeri new	NCft
	harrisii	NCft
	'Heather's Blush'	NCft
	heteromorpha	NCft
	hondurensis	NCft
	'Houston Enano' new	NCft
	humilis	NCft
	- var. ***simplex*** new	NCft
	incarnata	NCft
	intermedia	NCft
*	***ionantha*** 'Fuego'	CDoC NCft
	- 'Haselnuss'	NCft
	- var. ***ionantha***	NCft
	- - 'Druid'	NCft
	- var. ***maxima*** 'Huamelula'	see *T. ionantha* var. *stricta*
	- 'Peach'	NCft
	- 'Ron'	NCft
I	- 'Rosea'	NCft
	- 'Rubra'	NCft
	- var. ***scaposa***	see *T. kolbii*
	- 'Silver'	NCft
§	- var. ***stricta***	NCft
	- var. ***vanhyningii***	NCft
	- 'Variegata' new	NCft
	ionantha* × *schiedeana new	NCft
	ixioides	NCft
	'Jackie Loinaz'	NCft
	jonesii new	NCft
	jucunda	NCft
	juncea	NCft
	kammii	NCft
	karwinskyana	NCft
	'Kashkin'	NCft
	kautskyi	NCft
	'Kimberly'	NCft
§	***kolbii***	NCft
	latifolia	NCft
	- var. ***divaricata***	NCft
	- 'Enano Latifolia' new	NCft
	- var. ***latifolia*** new	NCft
	lautneri	NCft
	leiboldiana new	NCft
	leonamiana	NCft
	lepidosepela	NCft
	loliacea	NCft
	lorentziana	NCft
	magnusiana	CDoC NCft
	mallemontii	NCft
	marconae	NCft
	'Maria Teresa'	NCft
§	***matudae***	NCft
	mauryana new	NCft
	mereliana new	NCft
	mima var. ***chiletensis*** new	NCft
	mitlaensis	NCft
	montana	NCft
	myosura	NCft
	'Mystic Burgundy' new	NCft
	'Mystic Flame' new	NCft
	'Mystic Haze' new	NCft
	'Mystic Rainbow' new	NCft
	'Mystic Trumpet' new	NCft
	nana new	NCft
	neglecta	NCft
I	- 'Rubra'	NCft
	oaxacana	NCft
	paleacea	NCft
	- var. ***apurimacensis*** new	NCft
	- 'Enano Paleacea' new	NCft
	paleacea* × *tectorum new	NCft
	pardoi new	NCft
	paucifolia	NCft
	pedicellata new	NCft
	plagiotropica	NCft
	pohliana	NCft
	× ***polita*** new	NCft
	polystachia	NCft
	pruinosa	NCft
	- 'Columbia' new	NCft
	pseudobaileyi	NCft
	pseudosetacea new	NCft
	pueblensis	NCft
	punctulata	NCft
	purpurea	NCft
	- 'Shooting Star' new	NCft
	× ***rectifolia***	NCft
	recurvata	NCft
	recurvifolia	NCft
	'Redy' new	NCft
	reichenbachii	NCft
	retorta	NCft
	riohondoensis new	NCft
	schatzlii new	NCft
	schiedeana	NCft
	- 'Major'	NCft
I	- 'Minor'	NCft
	schreiteri	NCft
	seideliana	NCft
	seleriana	NCft SPlb
	setiformis new	NCft
	spiralipetala new	NCft
	sprengeliana new	NCft
	stellifera	NCft
	straminea	NCft
	streptocarpa	NCft
	streptophylla	NCft
	stricta var. ***albifolia***	NCft
I	- 'Amethyst'	NCft
	- 'Grey'	NCft
	- 'Hard Leaf'	NCft
	- var. ***stricta***	NCft
	sucrei	NCft
	tectorum	NCft
	- caulescent	NCft
*	- var. ***filifoliata*** new	NCft
	tenuifolia	NCft
	- blue-flowered new	NCft
	- bronze-leaved new	NCft
I	- 'Minima'	NCft
	- var. ***tenuifolia*** new	NCft
	- var. ***vaginata*** new	NCft
	- white-flowered new	NCft
	tricholepis	NCft
	tricolor var. ***melanocrater***	NCft
	'Twisted Tim' new	NCft
	usneoides	NCft SHmp SPlb WSFF
	utriculata subsp. ***pringlei***	NCft
	variabilis	NCft
	velickiana	see *T. matudae*
	velutina	CDoC NCft
	xerographica	NCft
	xiphioides	NCft
	zecheri	NCft
	- var. ***cafayatensis***	NCft

Tinantia (*Commelinaceae*)

pringlei	LEdu MNrw MPie SBrt SDys WPGP
- AIM 77	EBee MNrw WCot
- variegated (v)	WCot

Titanopsis (*Aizoaceae*)

calcarea 🏆H1c	CCCN SSim
fulleri	SSim

Titanotrichum (*Gesneriaceae*)

oldhamii	GEdr

Tithonia (*Asteraceae*)

rotundifolia 'Torch'	CSpe
'Torchlight'	LRHS

Tofieldia (*Tofieldiaceae*)

coccinea	CSpe GEdr WCot WCru
furusei	GEdr

Tolmiea (*Saxifragaceae*)

menziesii	CBod CMac MCot SPer XLum
- 'Goldsplash'	see *T. menziesii* 'Taff's Gold'
- 'Maculata'	see *T. menziesii* 'Taff's Gold'
§ - 'Taff's Gold' (v)	EMor NBid SPlb XLum
- 'Variegata'	see *T. menziesii* 'Taff's Gold'

tomato see AGM Vegetables Section

Toona (*Meliaceae*)

§ ***sinensis***	CAgr CBcs CLnd CTho ELan EPfP LEdu SEND WPGP
- 'Flamingo' (v)	CRos CTho EHyd ELan EPfP ESwi LCro LEdu LMil LOPS LRHS MAsh MGos MPkF NLar NRHS SChF SPoG SWvt WCot WMat
- 'Lise'	CMCN

Torenia (*Linderniaceae*)

Summer Wave Series	CCCN

Torilis (*Apiaceae*)

japonica	CBre SPhx

Torreya (*Taxaceae*)

nucifera	CBcs IDee

Townsendia (*Asteraceae*)

alpigena	CPla
§ - var. ***alpigena***	GKev
condensata	GKev
formosa	NHpl
hirsuta	GKev
hookeri	CPla
incana	GEdr
montana	see *T. alpigena* var. *alpigena*
parryi	GKev
scapigera	GEdr
spathulata	SPlb

Toxicodendron (*Anacardiaceae*)

§ ***orientale*** B&SWJ 3656	WCru
- large-leaved B&SWJ 10884	WCru
§ ***radicans***	GPoy
§ ***succedaneum***	CDTJ
- NJM 10.154	WPGP
§ ***vernicifluum***	NLar

Trachelium (*Campanulaceae*)

§ ***asperuloides***	SPlb WAbe
caeruleum 'Black Knight'	CPla CSpe WCot

Trachelospermum ✿ (*Apocynaceae*)

from Nanjing, China	EShb
§ ***asiaticum*** 🏆H4	Widely available
- 'Avonbank'	WAvo
- 'Bredon' **new**	WAvo
- 'Copper Tips'	MGil WAvo
- 'Golden Memories'	CBcs CExl CMac CRHN CRos CWCL CWGN EBee EHyd ELan ELon EPfP LRHS LSRN MRav NLar NRHS SIvy SLon SNig SPoG SRms SSta SWvt WCot
- 'Goshiki' (v)	EShb SEle
- 'Kulu Chirimen'	WCot
- 'Ōgon-nishiki' (v)	CCCN CRos EHyd LRHS SEle SMad SPoG WFar
- 'Pink Showers'	CBod CMac CRos CWGN
- 'Summer Sunset'	CBcs CWCL ELan ELon LRHS MGos SGol SRms WCot
- 'Theta'	LRHS WCot WFar WLov WPGP
'Chameleon'	ELan SMad
jasminoides 🏆H4	Widely available
- 'Major'	CMac CWCL EBee ELan EWTr MAsh MGil NOra SRms
§ - var. ***pubescens*** 'Japonicum'	CRHN CRos EHyd LRHS MPri SLon SPoG WBor WSHC
- Star of Toscana ('Selbra'PBR)	CBod CCCN CRos CWGN ECtt EHyd EPfP LCro LOPS LRHS NLar NRHS SPer SPoG
- 'Tricolor' (v)	LRHS SEle SGol SWvt WFar
- 'Variegatum' (v) 🏆H4	Widely available
- 'Waterwheel'	CBcs CMac CSde CWCL ELan ELon EShb LRHS NLar SMad SWvt WLov WSHC
- 'White Wings'	LRHS
- 'Wilsonii'	CBod CExl CMac CRos CWCL ELan ELon EPfP EShb LRHS LSRN MGil MRav NLar NOra SAdn SEND SLim SNig SPer SPoG SWvt WAvo WCot WPGP
majus misapplied	see *T. jasminoides* var. *pubescens* 'Japonicum'
majus Nakai	see *T. asiaticum*

Trachycarpus ✿ (*Arecaceae*)

from Manipur	CPHo
§ ***fortunei*** 🏆H5	Widely available
fortunei × ***wagnerianus***	SWeb
latisectus	CPHo
nanus × ***wagnerianus***	SChr
princeps	CBrP CPHo
takil ambig.	CPHo WSMil
ukhrulensis	LEdu
- NJM 13.085	WPGP
wagnerianus 🏆H5	CBcs CBrP CCCN CDTJ CExl CPHo EPfP SArc SChr SMad SPalm WPGP WSMil

Trachymene (*Apiaceae*)

coerulea	CSpe SPhx

Trachystemon (*Boraginaceae*)

orientalis	CBre CCBP CDor CExl CMac ECha EPfP EWTr ILea LEdu LRHS MAvo MCot MMuc MNrw MRav NBid NLar NWad WBor WBrk

	WCot WCru WHer WOut WPGP WPnP XLum

Tradescantia (*Commelinaceae*)

albiflora	see *T. fluminensis*
× ***andersoniana*** W. Ludwig & Rohw. nom. inval.	see *T.* Andersoniana Group
§ Andersoniana Group	WWtn
- 'Angelic Charm' (Charm Series)	CWGN ECtt
- 'Baby Doll'	XLum
- 'Baerbel'	XLum
- 'Bilberry Ice'	CDor CMac CRos CWCL EAJP ECtt EHyd EPfP GMaP LRHS LSun MBel MTin MWat NBPC NBir NBro NGBl NGdn NLar NRHS SCob SGbt SWvt WGwG WWtn XLum
- 'Blanca'	WWtn
- 'Blue and Gold'	CBcs CRos ECtt EHyd ELon EPfP EWhm LRHS MHol MRav NCou NRHS NSti WCot WGrn WHil
- 'Blue Spider'	MAsh
- 'Blue Stone'	CDor CMea CSBt ECha ECtt EWTr MAvo MRav SRkn SRms WHoo XLum
- 'Bridal Veil'	SChr WDib
- 'Caerulea Plena'	see *T. virginiana* 'Caerulea Plena'
- CARMINE GLOW	see *T.* (Andersoniana Group) 'Karminglut'
- 'Charlotte'	CDor CRos ECha ECtt EHyd ELan LRHS LSRN NBro NGdn NLar NRHS WWtn XLum
- 'Concord Grape' ♀H6	CAby CBod CMac CMea CRos EBee ECtt EHyd ELan EPfP GMaP LRHS LSRN LSun MAvo MBel MGos NBro NChi NGdn NRHS NSti SGbt SPer WCAu WFar WGwG WHoo WKif XLum
- 'Domaine de Courson'	ECtt XLum
- 'Euridice'	EWTr MBel
- 'Good Luck' PBR	MHol
- 'In the Navy'	NLar
- 'Innocence'	CAby CDor CNor CRos CSBt CTri EAJP ECha ECtt EHyd ELan EPfP GMaP GWyn LRHS MBel MMuc NBir NGdn NRHS NSti SCob SGbt SPer SWvt WGwG XLum
- 'Iris Prichard'	EBee GMaP NLar
- 'Isis'	CAby CRos EBee ECtt EHyd ELan EPfP GMaP LRHS MMuc MRav NBir NGdn NRHS SGbt SPer SWvt WGwG WKif WWtn
- 'J.C. Weguelin'	NBir SRms WCAu WWtn XLum
§ - 'Karminglut'	ECtt GLog GMaP NBir NGdn WHoo XLum
- 'Leonora'	EPfP MBel MMuc NLar SCob XLum
- 'Little Doll'	CDor CRos ECtt EPfP LRHS MPie NBro NLar NRHS XLum
- 'Little White Doll'	ECtt NBPC
- 'Lucky Charm' (Charm Series)	NLar
- 'Mac's Double' (d)	EBee NBPC
- 'Melissa'	XLum
- 'Osprey'	CBcs CBod CDor CRos ECha ECtt EHyd ELan LRHS MBel MRav NGdn NRHS NSti SPer SRms WCAu WGwG WHoo WKif XLum
- 'Pauline'	MRav NBir NLar XLum
- 'Perinne's Pink'	CRos EHyd LRHS NRHS NSti WCAu
- 'Pink Chablis'	CBod CRos ECtt EHyd EPfP LRHS MHol NBro NLar NRHS XLum
- 'Pink Spider'	MAsh
- 'Purewell Giant'	CMac CRos CTri EHyd LRHS NBro NLar NRHS SWvt WKif
- 'Purple Dome'	CRos ECtt EHyd EPfP GMaP LRHS MMuc MRav NBir NBro NGBl NGdn NRHS SPoG
- 'Red Grape'	CRos EHyd LRHS NRHS NSti SCob XLum
- 'Rubra'	CRos SRms XLum
- 'Satin Doll' PBR	ECtt
- 'Sunshine Charm' PBR (Charm Series)	CRos EHyd LRHS NCou NLar NRHS WHil
- 'Sweet Kate'	CBod CMac CRos ECtt LRHS LSRN NBro NLar NRHS SGbt SPoG SRms WSMil XLum
- 'Valour'	CRos CSBt EBee EHyd LRHS NRHS
- 'Zwanenburg Blue'	CRos ECha ECtt EHyd ELan LRHS NLar NRHS SPlb SPoG XLum
'Angel Eyes'	EBee
blossfeldiana 'Variegata'	see *T. cerinthoides* 'Variegata'
bracteata	SBrt
canaliculata	see *T. ohiensis*
§ ***cerinthoides*** 'Variegata' (v) ♀H1c	EShb
crassifolia F&M 258	WPGP
§ ***fluminensis***	SChr WDib
§ - 'Aurea' ♀H1c	EShb SChr
- 'Maiden's Blush' (v)	CSpe CWCL EShb SChr SPlb SVen
- 'Quicksilver' (v) ♀H1c	EShb NGBl
- 'Variegata'	see *T. fluminensis* 'Aurea'
'Green Hill'	LCro LOPS
navicularis	see *Callisia navicularis*
§ ***ohiensis***	SBrt
pallida ♀H1c	EShb WSMil
- 'Kartuz Giant'	EShb MPie WCot
- 'Pale Puma'	EShb
§ - 'Purpurea' ♀H3	CBcs EOHP EShb NGBl SPlb
pendula	see *T. zebrina*
'Purple Sabre'	see *T. pallida* 'Purpurea'
purpurea	see *T. pallida* 'Purpurea'
sillamontana ♀H3	EShb MPie SChr
I - 'Variegata' (v)	EShb
spathacea	EShb
- 'Versicolor'	EShb
tricolor	see *T. zebrina*
virginiana	NChi
- 'Alba'	CMac SRms
* - 'Brevicaulis'	ECha NBro
§ - 'Caerulea Plena' (d)	MRav NLar SPer XLum
- 'Rubra'	SPlb
§ ***zebrina*** ♀H1c	EShb
- ***pendula***	see *T. zebrina*
- 'Purpusii' ♀H1c	EShb WDib
- 'Quadricolor' (v) ♀H1c	EShb

Tragopogon (*Asteraceae*)

crocifolius	CSpe LRHS SPhx
porrifolius	CFis LRHS MCot NGBl SDix SPhx SVic WCot WSFF WTre
pratensis	NMir

Trautvetteria (*Ranunculaceae*)

carolinensis	ESwi IMou MAvo MBel WSHC
- var. ***japonica***	GEdr WCru
- - B&SWJ 10861	WCru
- var. ***occidentalis***	EBee LEdu WCru WFar WPGP

Trevesia ✿ (*Araliaceae*)

hardy, KWJ 12217 from northern Vietnam — WCru

Triadica (*Euphorbiaceae*)

sebifera — EBee WPGP
- CWJ 12819 — WCru

Trichodiadema (*Aizoaceae*)

densum ♀H1c — CBod SSim
intonsum — SPlb
mirabile new — SAll

Trichopetalum (*Asparagaceae*)

§ ***plumosum*** — CBro

Trichostema (*Lamiaceae*)

'Blue Bonnets' — MMuc

Tricuspidaria see *Crinodendron*

Tricyrtis (*Liliaceae*)

B&SWJ 3229 from Taiwan — WCru
'Abdane' — GKev
'Adbane' — CLAP ELan EWes WGwG
affinis B&SWJ 2804 — WCru
- B&SWJ 5645 — WCru
- B&SWJ 6182 — WCru
- B&SWJ 11169 — WCru
- B&SWJ 11442 — WCru
- 'Early Bird' — WCru
'Amanagowa' — CLAP
bakeri — see *T. latifolia*
'Blue Wonder' — LBuc LRHS SPer WWtn XLum
dilatata — see *T. macropoda*
'Empress' — CAby CBct CDor CExl CLAP CPla ECha EMor EWes LPot LRHS LSou MAvo MHer NLar NWad SCob SRkn WWtn
flava — EHyd LRHS
formosana — CAvo CTri ECha ELan GKev GLog GMaP ILea LRHS MCot MMuc MNrw SCob SDys SRms WAvo WKif
- B&SWJ 355 — WCru
- B&SWJ 3073 — WCru
- B&SWJ 3616 — CExl WCru
- B&SWJ 3712 — WCru
- B&SWJ 6741 — WCru
- B&SWJ 6970 — WCru
- RWJ 10109 — WCru
- 'Dark Beauty' — CAby CBod CDor CExl CLAP CWCL ECtt ELan EMor ITim LCro MAvo MBel MPnt WCAu WFar WTyc
- 'Emperor' (v) — EBee ESwi
- 'Gilt Edge' (v) — CBct CExl ECtt ELan ELon LPot LSou MBNS MNrw NLar NWad SWvt WFar WSMil
- f. ***glandosa*** B&SWJ 7084 — WCru
- aff. f. ***glandosa*** 'Blu-Shing Toad' — MAvo WCru
- var. ***grandiflora*** 'Long-Jen Violet' new — WFar
- - 'W-Ho-ping Toad' — WCru
- 'Kestrel' (v) — CBct WCot WFar
- 'Samurai' (v) — CWCL EWes MCot
- 'Seiryu' — EBee MBel
- 'Shelley's' — CLAP
- 'Small Wonder' — LEdu WCru
- 'Spotted Toad' — LEdu WCru
§ - Stolonifera Group — CAvo CBcs CBod CDor CMac EHyd ELan EMor EPfP LRHS MCot NRHS NWad SHar
- - B&SWJ 7046 — WCru
- 'Taiwan Toad' — CExl
- 'Taroko Toad' — WCru
- 'Tiny Toad' — WCru
- 'Variegata' (v) — LEdu NBir SRms WCru
- 'Velvet Toad' — WCru
'Hiki-yuri' — NBPC
§ ***hirta*** — CBcs CBod CDor CMac CRos CTri EHyd EMor EWTr GKev ILea LCro LOPS LRHS MCot NBro NChi NHol NRHS SCob SDix SGbt SPlb SWvt WSHC
- B&SWJ 5971 — WCru
- B&SWJ 11182 — WCru
- B&SWJ 11227 — WCru
- 'Alba' — CMac WAvo
- 'Albomarginata' (v) — CBod CMac EHyd EWhm LRHS NRHS NSti SPoG SWvt WFar WWtn
- 'Golden Gleam' — WCot
- var. ***masamunei*** — WCru
- 'Matsukaze' — CExl EWes MAvo
- 'Miyazaki' — CFis CMac ECha ECtt GPSL IPot ITim LRHS MHer MNrw NRHS NSti SPoG WCAu WRHF WSHC WWtn XLum
- 'Taiwan Atrianne' — CDor CLAP ECtt EHyd ELan EMor GPSL LRHS MNrw MPie NRHS NWad SGbt SPoG WCAu WWtn
- 'Variegata' (v) — CTri EBee EHyd EWes GKev LRHS NRHS WCot
Hototogisu — CExl CRos ECha ECtt EHyd ELan LRHS MHer NHol NLar NRHS SPoG WWtn
'Imperial Banner' (v) — CWCL
ishiiana — EBee WCot WCru WSHC
- var. ***surugensis*** — GKev LEdu WCru WFar
japonica — see *T. hirta*
'Kohaku' — EBee
lasiocarpa — ESwi LEdu XLum
- B&SWJ 3635 — CExl WCru
- B&SWJ 6861 — WCru
- B&SWJ 7013 — WCru
- 'Royal Toad' — WCru
§ ***latifolia*** — EHyd GKev GLog LEdu LRHS WCru WFar
- 'Saffron' — WCru
'Lemon Lime' (v) — CAby
'Lightning Strike' (v) — CDor ECha ECtt WCot WFar
macrantha — GAbr GLog WCru WSHC
§ - subsp. ***macranthopsis*** — CAby CBct CExl MNrw WCot WCru
- - 'Juro' (d) — WCru
macranthopsis — see *T. macrantha* subsp. *macranthopsis*
* ***macrocarpa*** — NChi XLum
macropoda — GLog ILea LEdu LRHS
- B&SWJ 1271 from Korea — WCru
- B&SWJ 5013 — WCru
- B&SWJ 5556 — WCru
- B&SWJ 5847 from Japan — WCru
- B&SWJ 6209 — WCru
- B&SWJ 8700 — WCru
- B&SWJ 8829 from Korea — WCru
maculata HWJCM 470 — WCru
- HWJK 2010 — WCru
- HWJK 2411 — WCru
- PAB 3188 — LEdu

'Moonlight Treasure' PBR	CExl EBee NHol WCot
nana B&SWJ 11399	WCru
- 'Karasuba'	WFar
ohsumiensis	CAby ECha
- 'Fukurin-fu' (v) **new**	WFar
perfoliata	LEdu WCru
- 'Spring Shine' (v)	WCru
pilosa	GKev LEdu
PINK FRECKLES ('Innotripf' PBR)	CBct CDoC CDor CLAP ELon EPot ESwi LSou MPnt NCou SWvt
'Raspberry Mousse'	CWCL MAvo MCot
ravenii B&SWJ 3229	WCru
- RWJ 10012	WCru
setouchiensis	WCru
'Shimone'	CExl ECha
'Sinonome'	EBee MNrw
stolonifera	see *T. formosana* Stolonifera Group
suzukii RWJ 10111	WCru
'Taipei Silk' PBR	CLAP LOPS SPad WWtn
'Tojen'	CLAP CRos ECha ECtt ELon EPfP EWes GKev GPSL LRHS MNrw NLar NRHS WCAu WWtn
'White Towers'	CAby CAvo CBro CExl CLAP CRos ECha ECtt EHyd ELan LPot LRHS MBel MRav NRHS NSti SGbt SRms WCAu WFar WSHC WWtn XLum

Trifolium (*Papilionaceae*)

arvense PAB 7952	LEdu
barbigerum	SPhx
var. ***andrewsianum*** **new**	
dubium	SPhx SPre
fragiferum	NAts
fucatum **new**	SPhx
- var. ***virescens*** **new**	SPhx
incarnatum	CSpe MHer
jokerstii **new**	SPhx
macrocephalum	EBee
montanum **new**	SPhx
ochroleucon	CDor EAJP ECha ECtt ELon EWTr GBin GMaP ILea LEdu LPot MBel MCot MPie SBut SEdd SHar SMad SPhx WAul WCAu WFar WPGP
pannonicum	CMea MNrw SPhx WWFP
pratense	CHab MHer NMir SPhx SRms SVic WOut WSFF WWild
- 'Dolly North'	see *T. pratense* 'Susan Smith'
- 'Ice Cool'	see *T. repens* 'Green Ice'
§ - 'Susan Smith' (v)	CCCN ILea
purpureum **new**	SPhx
repens	LCro LOPS SPhx SVic WSFF
- DARK DEBBIE ('Trifpot001' PBR)	LEdu
- 'Debbie'	LEdu
- 'Dragon's Blood'	CMea EPPr GWyn LEdu LPot MMuc MPie SPer WPGP
- 'Estelle' PBR	LEdu
- 'Gold Net'	see *T. pratense* 'Susan Smith'
§ - 'Green Ice'	NSti WFar
- 'Harlequin' (v)	WCot
- 'Isabella' PBR	LEdu WPGP
- 'Pentaphyllum'	see *T. repens* 'Quinquefolium'
- 'Purpurascens'	CBre EHyd EPfP GQue LRHS MAsh MBNS MHer MPie NGrd SPoG WFar
§ - 'Purpurascens Quadrifolium'	CAby CMea ECha EPau EWes GAbr GWyn LEdu MCot NMir NPer SPer SPlb WFar WTor
§ - 'Quinquefolium'	XLum
- 'Tetraphyllum Purpureum'	see *T. repens* 'Purpurascens Quadrifolium'
- 'Wheatfen'	CNat LEdu NDov NPer
- 'William'	CBre LEdu MMuc WCot WFar WHil
rubens	Widely available
- 'Drama'	ELon LEdu MNrw
- 'Frosty Feathers'	CBod CFis CSpe EAJP WOut
- 'Peach Pink'	CSpe ELon EMor EPPr MMrt SHar SPhx WCot
- 'Red Feathers'	CSpe ELon EPPr EWes GQue MBel MHol SHar SMad
'Spring'	LEdu
trichocephalum	EPPr MNrw WOut
variegatum var. ***variegatum***	SPhx
willdenovii **new**	SPhx

Trigonella (*Papilionaceae*)

foenum-graecum	SPhx SVic WSFF XAbr

Trillidium see *Trillium*

Trillium ✿ (*Melanthiaceae*)

albidum ♀H5	CWCL EBee EHyd EPot GEdr LRHS MNrw NRHS
amabile	GEdr
angustipetalum	GEdr
apetalon	GEdr
camschatcense	CExl GEdr
- 'Nemuro' **new**	GEdr
§ ***catesbyi***	CExl EBee EPot GEdr GKev ILea MNrw NChi NWad SDir SEdd
chloropetalum	CBro CElw CWCL EHyd GAbr GEdr LPla LRHS NRHS NWad
§ - var. ***giganteum*** ♀H5	CExl GBin GKev LEdu NHar NHpl NSla SPhx
- - EBG form **new**	GRum
- var. ***rubrum***	see *T. chloropetalum* var. *giganteum*
- white-flowered	GKev
cuneatum	CBcs CBct CExl CMiW CWCL EHyd EPot GEdr GKev GWyn LEdu LRHS MNrw NBir NChi NHol NHpl NRHS NWad SDeJ SDir WFar WPGP WPnP
erectum ♀H5	Widely available
- f. ***albiflorum***	CMea CRos ECha EHyd GKev LRHS MNrw NRHS NWad
- 'Beige'	GKev
- red-flowered	GKev
erectum* × *flexipes	CAby EBee GKev MNrw NBir
flexipes	CAby CBct CWCL EHyd GEdr GKev ILea LRHS MNrw NHol NHpl NWad
- 'Harvington Dusky Pink'	CRos EHyd LRHS NRHS
- 'Harvington Select'	CRos EBee EHyd LRHS NRHS
govanianum	GKev
grandiflorum ♀H5	Widely available
- 'Jenny Rhodes'	LEdu
- pale pink-flowered	EHyd LRHS NRHS
- f. ***polymerum*** 'Flore Pleno' (d)	CRos EHyd GEdr LRHS NHar NHpl NRHS SDir
- - 'Snowbunting' (d)	EHyd EWes GKev LEdu LRHS WThu
- f. ***roseum***	CWCL EHyd GEdr GKev LRHS MNrw NRHS
- white-flowered	MAvo
kurabayashii	CExl CRos EBee EHyd EPot EWld GEdr GKev LRHS MNrw NRHS WPGP
luteum ♀H5	CBcs CExl CMiW CWCL EBee EHyd EPfP EPot GAbr GEdr GKev GMaP ILea LCro LEdu LOPS LRHS MAvo MNrw MSCN NBid NChi NHol NHpl NRHS NWad SDeJ SDir WPnP

nivale	CBct GEdr NDry WThu
ovatum 'Roy Elliott'	CExl NDry
parviflorum	GEdr MNrw
pusillum	CExl GEdr GKev ILea MNrw NHol NHpl
recurvatum	CBcs CWCL EBee GAbr GEdr GKev ILea LEdu NChi NHol NHpl NWad SEdd WPnP
rivale 🏆H4	CExl EPot GEdr GKev NDry WSHC
- Purple Heart Group	GEdr NDry
rugelii	EBee EWes GEdr MNrw WSHC
- Askival hybrids	MNrw
rugelii × ***vaseyi***	EWes MNrw
sessile	CExl CPla CWCL EPot GEdr GKev GPSL GWyn MAvo MNrw NBir NChi NWad SDeJ SDix WKif WPnP WShi XEll
- 'Rubrum'	see *T. chloropetalum* var. *giganteum*
simile	CAby EBee EHyd GEdr LRHS MNrw NHpl NRHS
smallii	GEdr
stylosum	see *T. catesbyi*
sulcatum	CExl EBee EHyd GEdr GKev LEdu LRHS MNrw NHpl NRHS WSHC
- yellow-flowered	GKev
taiwanense B&SWJ 3411	WCru
tschonoskii	GEdr
undulatum	MNrw
vaseyi	CWCL EBee EHyd EWes GEdr GKev LRHS MNrw NRHS SDir
viridescens	GEdr GKev XEll

Trinia (*Apiaceae*)

glauca	SPhx

Triosteum (*Caprifoliaceae*)

erythrocarpum	EMor EWTr SMad
himalayanum	GKev IMou WPnP WSHC
- BWJ 7907	ESwi WCru
pinnatifidum	EBee EWld GKev IMou MMrt

Tripleurospermum (*Asteraceae*)

§ ***maritimum***	WHer

Tripogandra (*Commelinaceae*)

serrulata 'Purple Scimitars'	EShb

Tripolium (*Asteraceae*)

§ ***pannonicum***	CEls WHer

Tripsacum (*Poaceae*)

dactyloides	EPPr

Tripterospermum (*Gentianaceae*)

japonicum	GEdr

Tripterygium (*Celastraceae*)

doianum B&SWJ 11467	WCru
aff. ***doianum*** CWJ 12852	WCru
regelii	CBcs
- B&SWJ 5453	WCru
- B&SWJ 8666 from Korea	WCru
- B&SWJ 10921	WCru
wilfordii	EBee LEdu
- BWJ 7852 from China	WCru
- NJM 11.029 from China	WPGP
- NMWJ 14466 from Taiwan	WCru
- WWJ 12009	WCru

Tristagma (*Alliaceae*)

nivale	EBee

Triteleia (*Asparagaceae*)

'Aquarius'	ERCP GKev MWat
californica	see *Brodiaea californica*
§ 'Corrina'	CAvo EBee EPot ERCP GKev
'Crystal Pink'	SDeJ
'Double Touch' (d)	GKev SDeJ WCot
'Foxy'	EBee EPot GKev IPot MNrw
grandiflora	WCot
hendersonii	GKev
hyacinthina	GKev WCot
- NNS 06-560	WCot
ixioides 'Splendens'	GKev
- 'Starlight'	CTri EPot ERCP SDeJ
§ ***laxa***	ECha
§ - 'Koningin Fabiola'	CCBP EShb GKev MNrw NBir SDeJ SDix WCot
- QUEEN FABIOLA	see *T. laxa* 'Koningin Fabiola'
'Ocean Queen'	EBee ERCP
§ ***peduncularis***	GKev WCot
'Phantasio' (d) **new**	GKev
'Rosy' (d) **new**	GKev
'Rudy'	CAvo CBro CMea CWCL ERCP GKev IPot MMrt MNrw SDeJ WCot
'Silver Queen'	CAvo EPot ERCP GKev SDeJ WCot XEll
'Twilight'	GKev IPot
uniflora	see *Ipheion uniflorum*
'White Cloud'	CAvo GKev

Trithrinax (*Arecaceae*)

brasiliensis	SPalm
campestris	CBrP LRHS SPalm

Tritoma see *Kniphofia*

Tritonia (*Iridaceae*)

crocata 🏆H3	GKev
- 'Baby Doll'	LEdu
- 'Serendipity'	EPri
- 'Tangerine'	CPBP
deusta	CPbh EPri
disticha	SMad SPlb
§ - subsp. ***rubrolucens***	Widely available
gladiolaris	EBee EPri LEdu
- 'Parvifolia'	GKev
laxifolia	EPot GKev
pallida	SPlb
rosea	see *T. disticha* subsp. *rubrolucens*
securigera	LEdu
- subsp. ***watermeyeri***	GKev
squalida	EPri

Trochocarpa (*Ericaceae*)

clarkei	WThu
gunnii	WThu
thymifolia	WThu
- white-flowered	WThu

Trochodendron (*Trochodendraceae*)

aralioides	CBcs CTho CTsd ELan EPfP GBin GKin LRHS MBlu MGos MMuc NLar SAko SDix SLon SPer SSta WPGP
- B&SWJ 1651 from Taiwan	WCru
- B&SWJ 6080 from Japan	WCru

- CWJ 12357 from Taiwan WCru
- RWJ 9845 from Taiwan WCru
- from Taiwan CDTJ WPGP

Trollius (*Ranunculaceae*)

ACE 1187 CExl
acaulis EWes GAbr
altaicus EBee EHyd LRHS NRHS
asiaticus GKev
buddae CBod CWCL EWes MNrw MRav NLar
§ ***chinensis*** ECha GKev GWyn
- 'Golden Queen' 🏆H7 Widely available
- 'Imperial Orange' GWyn
- 'Morning Sun' EPfP SPad WPnP
- orange-flowered GKev
× ***cultorum*** 'Alabaster' Widely available
- 'Baudirektor Linne' MRav NGdn
- 'Byrne's Giant' ECtt GBin
- 'Canary Bird' NGdn SRms WSpi
- 'Cheddar' see *T.* × *cultorum* 'Taleggio'
- 'Earliest of All' CSam CWCL GBin NGdn NLar WSHC WSpi
- 'Etna' CRos NLar
§ - 'Feuertroll' ECha ECtt MRav NGdn WSpi
- FIREGLOBE see *T.* × *cultorum* 'Feuertroll'
- 'Golden Cup' GWyn NBir NGdn
- 'Goldquelle' 🏆H7 EBee GBin GWyn
- 'Goliath' GWyn NBPC NLar
- 'Helios' CSam
- 'Lemon Queen' CMiW CRos CWCL CWat ECtt EHyd EPfP EWTr GKev GMaP GWyn LRHS MRav NLar NQui SCob SGol SPer SRms WWtn
- 'New Moon' CBcs CDor CRos CSpe CWCL EBee EHyd EMor EPfP EShb GBin GWyn LRHS NChi NQui NRHS SPoG WHoo WWtn
- 'Orange Crest' EBee ECtt ELon EPfP WWtn
- 'Orange Globe' GMaP
- 'Orange Princess' 🏆H7 CDor CWat EHyd GWyn LCro LOPS LRHS NBro NLar NRHS SPer SRms
- 'Orange Queen' SWvt
- 'Prichard's Giant' ECtt ELan ELon NBro WCFE WSpi
§ - 'Superbus' 🏆H7 CBod CWCL EHyd ELan ELon EPfP GMaP GWyn LRHS MHol NGdn NLar SPer WFar WPnP WWtn
- 'T. Smith' ECtt NBro
§ - 'Taleggio' CWCL CWld EHyd ELan EMor GMaP ILea LEdu LRHS LSou MPri MRav MTis NBPC NBro NLar NRHS SPoG SRms SWvt WCav WHil WPnP WSpi
'Dancing Flame' CMac EHyd EMor LCro LOPS LRHS NEoE NLar NRHS SHar SPoG SRms
europaeus CWCL ECha EHyd ELan EPfP GBin GWyn LEdu LLWG LRHS MHol MRav NGdn NGrd NRHS NSti SCob SRms
- SDR 6306 GKev
- subsp. ***europaeus*** WFar
- 'Golden Globe' **new** WCav
- 'Lemon Supreme' CRos EBee EHyd EMor EPfP GKev LRHS NRHS WWtn
- 'Superbus' see *T.* × *cultorum* 'Superbus'
farreri GKev
- var. ***farreri*** EBee GKev
- var. ***major*** SDR 2713 GKev
ircuticus EBee EWes GKev
laxus CPla
- 'Albiflorus' CExl EBee GEdr
ledebourii misapplied see *T. chinensis*
macropetalus CWCL EBee GKev
pumilus CRos ECha ELan LRHS NLar NRHS SPer WIce
- ACE 1818 CExl MHer
- 'Double Jeopardy' (d) EBee
ranunculoides GKev
vaginatus EBee GKev
yunnanensis 🏆H6 CRos EBee EHyd EPfP GBin LRHS NRHS
- orange-flowered CExl GKev

Tropaeolum (*Tropaeolaceae*)

azureum CCCN CExl CPla
brachyceras CCCN GKev
ciliatum CCCN CPla EWld GKev NBid WCot WCru WPGP
hookerianum CExl
- subsp. ***austropurpureum*** CExl
incisum CCCN GKev
lepidum CPla
leptophyllum GKev
majus ENfk GPoy SVic
- Alaska Series (v) 🏆H3 ENfk LCro LOPS MNHC
- 'Banana Split' CCCN SCob
- 'Black Velvet' (Tom Thumb Series) LCro LOPS
- 'Blue Pepe' **new** CLau
§ - 'Darjeeling Double' (d) 🏆H3 EPPr
- 'Darjeeling Gold' see *T. majus* 'Darjeeling Double'
- 'Empress of India' CLau LCro LOPS MNHC
- 'Hermine Grashoff' (d) CSpe EPPr
- Jewel Series ENfk
- 'Ladybird' (Ladybird Series) **new** SCob
- 'Margaret Long' (d) CSpe EPPr
- 'Milkmaid' **new** SCob
- 'Red Wonder' CCCN WCot
- 'Strawberry Ice' **new** CLau
- 'Sunset Pink' CLau
- 'Tip Top Alaska Salmon' (Tip Top Alaska Series) (v) **new** LOPS
- Tom Thumb Series MNHC
- Whirlybird Series 🏆H3 **new** LCro LOPS
pentaphyllum CExl CRHN CSpe EBee
polyphyllum 🏆H3 CCCN CWCL EBee EPot NBir SMHy WCot
sessilifolium EBee
smithii WPGP
speciosum 🏆H5 Widely available
sylvestre EWld
tricolor 🏆H2 CAvo CCCN CRHN CWCL GKev SDir WCot XEll
tuberosum CAgr CAvo CEnd GKev GPoy SDeJ SPoG WKor
- var. ***lineomaculatum*** 'Ken Aslet' 🏆H3 CAbb CBcs CBor CCCN CSpe CWCL ECha EHyd ELan EPfP EPot GAbr GKev LEdu LRHS NLar SPer WFar

Tsuga ✿ (*Pinaceae*)

canadensis EPfP LMaj MMuc
- 'Abbott's Dwarf' CKen NHol
§ - 'Abbott's Pygmy' CKen

	- 'Bacon Cristate'	CKen
	- 'Beehive'	NLar
	- 'Betty Rose' (v)	CKen
	- 'Birkett's White'	CKen
	- 'Brandley'	CKen
§	- 'Branklyn'	CKen WCFE
	- 'Cappy's Choice'	CKen
	- 'Cinnamonea'	CKen
	- 'Coffin'	CKen
	- 'Cole's Prostrate' 🏆H7	CKen LRHS MAsh NLar SLim
	- 'Creamey' (v)	CKen
	- 'Curley'	CKen
	- 'Curtis Ideal'	CKen
	- 'Dr Hornbeck'	see *T. canadensis* 'Hornbeck'
	- 'Eisburg'	SLim
	- 'Essex'	CKen
*	- 'Everitt's Dense Leaf'	CKen
	- 'Everitt's Golden'	CKen NLar
	- 'Fantana'	MAsh NHol
	- 'Hedgehog'	NLar
§	- 'Hornbeck'	CKen
	- 'Horsford'	CKen
	- 'Horsford Dwarf' **new**	SLim
	- 'Horstmann' No 1	CKen
	- 'Hussii'	CKen NHol
	- 'Jacqueline Verkade'	CKen MAsh NLar
	- 'Jeddeloh' 🏆H7	GEdr LRHS MAsh NHol NLar SCob SGol SLim
	- 'Jervis'	CKen NHol NWad
	- 'Julianne'	CKen
	- 'Kingsville Spreader'	CKen
	- 'Little Joe'	CKen
	- 'Livingston'	SLim
I	- 'Lutea'	CKen
	- 'Many Cones'	CKen
	- 'Minima'	CKen
	- 'Minuta' 🏆H7	CKen NHol WAbe
	- 'Palomino'	CKen
	- 'Pendula' 🏆H7	CKen LRHS MAsh SLim
	- 'Pincushion'	CKen NLar
	- 'Prostrata'	see *T. canadensis* 'Branklyn'
	- 'Pygmaea'	see *T. canadensis* 'Abbott's Pygmy'
	- 'Rugg's Washington Dwarf'	CKen
	- 'Snowflake'	CKen
	- 'Stewart's Gem'	CKen
	- 'Verkade Petite'	CKen
	- 'Verkade Recurved'	CKen
	- 'Von Helms' Dwarf'	CKen
	- 'Warnham'	CKen MAsh
	caroliniana 'La Bar Weeping'	CKen NLar
	- 'Planting Fields Broom'	CKen
	chinensis	CKen
	diversifolia 'Gotelli'	CKen
	dumosa	CKen
	heterophylla 🏆H6	CBcs CCVT EPfP GJos MMuc SEWo SGol WFar WTSh
	- 'Iron Springs'	CKen NLar
	- 'Laursen's Column'	CKen
	- 'Ray Godfrey'	NLar
	- 'Thorsens Weeping'	CKen NLar SLim
	menziesii	see *Pseudotsuga menziesii*
	mertensiana 'Blue Star'	CKen MAsh NLar
	- 'Elizabeth'	CKen
	- 'Glauca'	CKen
I	- 'Glauca Nana'	CKen
I	- 'Horstmann'	CKen
	- 'Quartz Mountain'	CKen
	sieboldii 'Baldwin'	CKen
	- 'Green Ball'	CKen NLar
	- 'Honeywell Estate'	CKen
	- 'Nana'	CKen

Tulbaghia ✿ (*Alliaceae*)

	acutiloba	CAvo LEdu NHoy
	alliacea	EPri LEdu NHoy WCot
*	***allioides***	CBro
	capensis	LEdu NBir WAvo
	capensis* × *violacea	NHoy
	'Cariad'	LEdu WPGP
	cernua CD&R 199	EBee LEdu
	- hybrid	EPri
§	***coddii***	MHer
	cominsii	CExl CPla EPri LEdu SGro
	cominsii* × *violacea	CAvo CExl EPri WHoo
	'Cosmic'	EBee EMor EPPr EPri LEdu NHoy SMHy WPGP
	'Dark Beauty'	NHoy
	'Elaine Ann'	NHoy
	'Fairy Snow'	LEdu WCot
	'Fairy Star'	CCht CWGN EBee ELan EMor EPri EShb LEdu NHoy SMHy WABo WCot
	'Fairy Star Mk II' **new**	SMHy
	fragrans	see *T. simmleri*
	- 'Alba'	ELan SDeJ
	'Hazel'	CCtw EBee LEdu MHer NHoy SMHy
	'John May's Special'	CCtw EShb LEdu NHoy SMHy WCot WHoo WPGP
	leucantha 🏆H2	EPri LEdu NHoy NWad
	- H&B 11996	LEdu
	ludwigiana	MHer
	maritima	see *T. violacea* var. *maritima*
	Marwood seedling	LEdu MHer
	montana	CBor EBee LEdu MPie NHoy
	'Moshoeshoe'	LEdu NHoy WPGP
	'Moya'	GKev
	natalensis 🏆H2	CBro CPrp GKev
	- B&V 421	EPri
	- clone 2 pink-flowered B&V 421	LEdu
	- pink-flowered	CCtw LPla
	poetica	see *T. coddii*
	'Purple Eye' 🏆H2	CBro CCht CCtw CDoC EBee ELan EMor LEdu LSou MPri NHoy SPoG WABo WCot WPGP WSMil
	'Scented Beauty'	NHoy
§	***simmleri*** 🏆H3	CPrp EBee EPri EWes LEdu SDeJ
	- 'Cheryl Renshaw'	WCot
	- 'Snow Queen'	CPrp
	- white-flowered	CPrp
	'Snow White'	LEdu SMHy WCot
	verdoorniae	LEdu
	violacea 🏆H3	CAvo CBcs CBod CBro CKno CPrp CSpe ECha ELan EPfP EPri ERCP GKev LEdu NHoy SEND SPlb SSut WCFE WHoo WPGP WPnP WTre WTyc XSen
*	- 'Alba'	CMea EBee EPri EShb MHer NHoy SChF WKif WPnP XSen
	- 'Dissect White'	NHoy
I	- 'Fine Form'	CKno
	- 'Harry Hay'	SMHy
	- 'John Rider'	EPri NHoy
*	- var. ***maritima***	CBor EShb LEdu MHer NHoy
	- 'Pallida'	CAvo CBro EBee LEdu NHoy WPGP
	- 'Peppermint Garlic'	LEdu
	- var. ***robustior***	CAby ECha EWes NHoy

	- 'Seren'	LEdu WPGP
§	- 'Silver Lace' (v) ♀^{H3}	Widely available
	- 'Variegata'	see *T. violacea* 'Silver Lace'
	white-flowered	NHoy

Tulipa ✿ (*Liliaceae*)

	(4)	CArg
	'Abba' (2)	CArg SDeJ
	'Absalon' (9)	GKev SDir
	'Abu Hassan' (3)	CAvo ERCP SDeJ WPhe
	acuminata (15)	ERCP SDeJ SPhx WCot WShi
	'Ad Rem' (4) ♀^{H6}	SDeJ WPhe
	'Affaire' (3)	WPhe
	aitchisonii	see *T. clusiana*
	'Akebono' (11)	GKev SDeJ SDir
	'Aladdin' (6)	CArg GKev LCro LOPS SDeJ WPhe
	'Aladdin's Record' (6)	SDeJ SDir
	'Alba Regalis' (1)	GKev SDir
	'Albert Heijn' (13)	SDeJ
	ALBION STAR ('Mieke Telkamp') (13)	CArg SDeJ
	'Aleppo' (7)	SDeJ SDir
	'Alfred Cortot' (12) ♀^{H6}	SDeJ
	'Algarve' (3) **new**	WPhe
	'Ali Baba' (14) ♀^{H6}	WPhe
	'Alibi' (3)	SDeJ
	amabilis	see *T. hoogiana*
	'Amazing Grace' (2) **new**	ERCP WPhe
	'American Dream' (4)	CAby SDir WPhe
	'American Eagle' (7)	SDeJ
	'Ancilla' (12) ♀^{H6}	GKev SDeJ WShi
	'André Rieu' (5)	LCro LOPS
	'Angélique' (11) ♀^{H6}	CAvo ERCP GKev LCro LOPS NBir SDeJ SPer WPhe
	'Angels Wish' (5) ♀^{H6}	CAvo SDeJ SDir WPhe
	'Annie Schilder' (3)	CAvo ERCP
	'Antoinette'^{PBR} (5)	GKev LCro LOPS SDeJ
	'Antraciet' (11)	ERCP LCro LOPS WPhe
	'Apeldoorn' (4)	CArg LCro LOPS SDeJ
	'Apeldoorn's Elite' (4) ♀^{H6}	SDeJ
	'Apricona' (3) **new**	SPhx
	'Apricot Beauty' (1) ♀^{H6}	CAvo ERCP LCro LOPS NBir SDeJ
	'Apricot Delight' (4)	GKev
	'Apricot Emperor' (13)	GKev SDeJ SDir
	'Apricot Foxx' (3)	CArg GKev SDeJ
	'Apricot Impression'^{PBR} (4)	LCro LOPS
	'Apricot Jewel'	see *T. linifolia* (Batalinii Group) 'Apricot Jewel'
	'Apricot Parrot' (10) ♀^{H6}	ERCP SDeJ
	'Aquilla' (11)	SDeJ
	'Arabian Beauty' (3)	LCro LOPS
	'Arabian Mystery' (3)	GKev NHol SDeJ
	'Aria Card' (7)	SDeJ
	'Artist' (8) ♀^{H6}	ERCP SDeJ SDir WPhe
	'Atlantis' (5)	CArg ERCP SDeJ WPhe
	aucheriana (15) ♀^{H5}	CMea EPot GKev
	australis (15)	GKev
	'Auxerre' (7) **new**	WPhe
	'Avenue' (3) **new**	WPhe
	'Aveyron' (11)	GKev
	'Avignon' (5)	GKev SDeJ
	aximensis (15)	EPot GKev
	'Backpacker' (11)	GKev
	bakeri	see *T. saxatilis* Bakeri Group
	'Ballade' (6) ♀^{H6}	ERCP LCro LOPS SDeJ WPhe
	BALLADE DREAM	see *T.* 'Sonnet'
	'Ballerina' (6) ♀^{H6}	CAby CArg CAvo CMea ERCP GKev LCro LOPS SDeJ SPer WPhe
	'Banja Luka' (4)	SDeJ
	'Barbados' (7)	SDeJ WPhe

	'Barcelona' (3) ♀^{H6}	ERCP GKev LCro LOPS
	'Baronesse' (5)	SDeJ
	batalinii	see *T. linifolia* Batalinii Group
	'Beau Monde' (3) ♀^{H6}	SDeJ
	'Beauty of Spring' (4)	GKev
	'Beauty Queen' (1)	SDeJ
	'Belicia' (2)	GKev SDir WPhe
	'Bellona' (3)	SDeJ
	'Berlioz' (12)	SDeJ
	'Bestseller' (1)	GKev SDeJ
§	***biflora*** (15)	EPot ERCP GKev MWat SDeJ SPer
	- var. ***major*** (15)	GKev
I	***bifloriformis*** 'Maxima' (15)	SPhx
	- 'Starlight' (15) ♀^{H6}	GKev
	- wide-leaved (15) **new**	GKev
	'Big Smile' (5)	GKev
	'Black Hero' (11)	CAby CAvo ERCP GKev LCro LOPS SDeJ
	'Black Jewel' (7)	ERCP GKev SDeJ WPhe
	'Black Parrot' (10) ♀^{H6}	CAby CArg CAvo ERCP GKev LCro LOPS SDeJ WPhe
	'Black Swan' (5)	SDeJ
	'Blackjack' (3)	GKev
	'Bleu Aimable' (5)	ERCP GKev SDeJ
	'Blue Beauty' (3)	GKev LCro LOPS
	'Blue Diamond' (11)	CArg CAvo ERCP LCro SDeJ WPhe
	'Blue Heron' (7) ♀^{H6}	ERCP LCro LOPS MCot SDeJ
	'Blue Parrot' (10)	CArg ERCP GKev LCro LOPS SDeJ SPer
	'Blue Ribbon' (3)	LCro LOPS
	'Blue Spectacle' (11)	GKev
	'Blue Wow' (11)	LCro LOPS SPer
	BLUEBERRY RIPPLE	see *T.* 'Zurel'
	'Blumex Favourite'^{PBR} (10)	LCro LOPS
	'Blushing Beauty' (5)	SDeJ
	'Blushing Bride' (5)	SDeJ
	'Blushing Girl' (5)	SDeJ
	'Blushing Lady' (5)	MCot
	'Boa Vista' (11)	ERCP
	'Boutade' (14)	NPer
	'Brest' (7) **new**	WPhe
§	***breyniana*** (15) **new**	EShb
	'Brooklyn' (11)	GKev NPer
	'Brown Sugar' (3)	CAvo ERCP LCro LOPS WPhe
	'Bruine Wimpel' (5)	LCro LOPS
	'Budlight' (6) **new**	WPhe
	'Bulldog' (7)	SDeJ
	'Burgundy' (6)	CAvo ERCP GKev LCro LOPS SDeJ SDir SPer
	'Burgundy Lace' (7)	LCro LOPS SDeJ
	'Burning Heart' (4) ♀^{H6}	CArg SDeJ
	'Buttercup' (14)	SDeJ
	'Café Noir' (5)	ERCP LCro LOPS NHol
	'Cairo' (3)	ERCP
	'Calgary' (3) ♀^{H6}	CAvo LCro LOPS MWat SDeJ WPhe
	'Calgary Flames' (3) ♀^{H6}	CAvo
	'Calypso' (14) ♀^{H6}	CRos EHyd LRHS NRHS
	'Camargue' (5)	SDeJ
	'Canasta' (7) ♀^{H6}	SDeJ WPhe
	'Candela' (13) ♀^{H6}	SDeJ
	'Candy Club' (5)	CAby SDeJ
	'Candy Prince'^{PBR} (1)	CArg CRos EHyd ERCP LRHS NRHS SDeJ WPhe
	'Canova' (7)	SDeJ
	'Cape Cod' (14)	CAvo MPie SDeJ
	'Cape Town' (1) ♀^{H6}	SDeJ WPhe
	'Caractère' (3)	CArg
	'Caravelle' (5)	ERCP GKev MCot SDeJ

	'Cardinal Mindszenty' (2)	EHyd ERCP LRHS SDeJ
	'Caribbean Parrot' (10)	WPhe
	'Carnaval de Nice' (11/v) ♀H6	CAby ERCP LCro LOPS SDeJ WPhe
	'Carnaval de Rio' (3) **new**	MBros
	'Carrousel' (7)	SDeJ
	'Cartouche' (11)	SDeJ WPhe
	'Casa Grande' (14) ♀H6 **new**	LCro
	'Cassini' (3)	SDeJ
	'Catherina' (5)	GKev LCro LOPS
	'Chansonnette' (3)	ERCP
	'Charmeur'PBR (3)	SDeJ
	'Charming Beauty' (11)	GKev
	'Charming Lady' (11)	ERCP
	'Cherry Delight' (4) **new**	GKev
	'China Lady' (14)	SDeJ
	'China Pink' (6) ♀H6	CAvo ERCP GKev LCro LOPS SDeJ WPhe
	'China Town' (8) ♀H6	ERCP GKev LCro LOPS SDeJ SPer
	'Chopin' (12)	NHol
	'Christmas Dream' (1)	SDeJ
	'Christmas Marvel' (1)	SDeJ
	'Christmas Orange' (1) **new**	WPhe
	'Christmas Pearl' (1) **new**	WPhe
	'Christmas Sweet' (1)	CArg
	chrysantha	see *T. montana*
	'Cistula' (6)	SDeJ SPer
	'City of Vancouver' (5)	SDeJ
	'Claudia' (6)	CAby CArg SDeJ WPhe
	'Clearwater'PBR (5)	SDeJ
	'Cleveland' (3) **new**	WPhe
§	***clusiana*** (15)	ERCP GKev
	- var. ***chrysantha*** (15) ♀H6	CExl EHyd GKev LRHS NRHS WShi
	- - 'Tubergen's Gem' (15)	EPot GKev WPhe
	- 'Cynthia' (15) ♀H6	CAby EPot GKev SDeJ SPhx WPhe WShi
	- 'Sheila' (15)	GKev SPhx
§	- var. ***stellata*** (15) ♀H6	GKev
	'Colour Spectacle'PBR (5)	CAby
	'Concerto' (13)	GKev NPer SDeJ
	'Continental' (3)	GKev
	'Cool Crystal' (7)	WPhe
	'Copper Image' (11)	ERCP SPhx WPhe
	'Coquette' (1)	SDeJ
	'Corona' (12)	CAvo SDeJ
	'Corsage' (14) ♀H6	SDeJ
	'Cortina' (9)	SDeJ
	'Couleur Cardinal' (3)	CAvo CRos EHyd ERCP GKev LCro LOPS LRHS NRHS SDeJ
	'Cream Cocktail' (4)	MCot
	'Crème Upstar' (11)	ERCP GKev LCro LOPS SDeJ WPhe
	'Crystal Star' (7)	CArg
	'Cum Laude' (5)	SDeJ
	'Cummins' (7)	CAvo ERCP LCro LOPS WPhe
	'Curly Sue' (7)	ERCP MCot SPer
	'Cutie Honey' (6) **new**	WPhe
	'Czaar Peter' (14) ♀H6	NPer SDeJ WPhe
	'Dance' (13)	SDeJ
	'Danceline' (11)	GKev
	'Darwisnow' (3) **new**	GKev
	dasystemon (15)	GKev
	'Davenport' (7)	ERCP
	'David Teniers' (2)	ERCP SDeJ
	'Daydream' (4) ♀H6	CArg GKev SDeJ
	'Daytona' (7)	CAvo
	'Diana' (1)	CArg
	'Doll's Minuet' (8)	ERCP LCro LOPS SPer

	'Don Quichotte' (3) ♀H6	ERCP LCro LOPS SDeJ
	'Donauperle' (14)	SDeJ
	'Donna Bella' (14)	MMrt SDeJ
	'Dordogne' (5) ♀H6	SDeJ
	'Double Dazzle' (2)	SDir
	'Double Red Riding Hood' (14/v)	SDeJ
	'Dow Jones'PBR (3) **new**	WPhe
	'Dragon King' (3)	GKev SDeJ
	'Dream Touch' (11)	LCro LOPS WPhe
	'Dreamland' (5) ♀H6	SDeJ
	dubia	GKev
	'Duc van Tol Red and Yellow' (1)	SDir
	'Duc van Tol Rose' (1)	SDir
	'Early Glory' (3)	LCro LOPS
	'Early Harvest' (12) ♀H6	GKev SDeJ
	'Easter Surprise' (14) ♀H6	GKev SDeJ
	'Ego Parrot' (10)	LCro LOPS
	eichleri	see *T. undulatifolia*
	'Electra' (5)	NHol
	'Elegant Lady' (6)	CAby CAvo GKev MCot SDeJ
	'Esperanto' (8/v) ♀H6	NPer SDeJ WPhe
	'Esta Bonita'PBR (3) **new**	WPhe
	'Estella Rijnveld' (10)	CAby ERCP GKev LCro LOPS SDeJ
	'Eternal Flame' (2)	GKev LCro LOPS WCot
	'Evergreen' (3)	CAvo ERCP GKev LCro LOPS WPhe
	'Exotic Emperor' (13)	CAvo LCro LOPS MCot SDeJ WPhe
	'Fabio' (7)	CRos EHyd LRHS NRHS
	'Fancy Frills' (7) ♀H6	CAby ERCP GKev SDeJ
	'Fancy Parrot' (10)	SDeJ
	'Fashion' (12)	SDeJ
	ferganica (15)	WCot
	'Fidelio' (3) ♀H6	SDeJ
*	'Finola' (11)	GKev LCro LOPS WPhe
	'Firework' (6) **new**	WPhe
	'Flair' (1)	CRos EHyd LRHS NRHS SDeJ
	'Flamenco' (7)	SDeJ
	'Flaming Evita'PBR (2)	SDeJ
	'Flaming Flag' (3)	GKev LCro LOPS
	'Flaming Parrot' (10)	CAby ERCP GKev LCro LOPS SDeJ
I	'Flaming Purissima' (13)	CAvo GKev SDeJ WPhe
	'Flaming Springgreen' (8)	CAby CAvo ERCP GKev LCro LOPS SDeJ SPer WPhe
	'Flash Point'PBR (2) **new**	WPhe
	'Flashback' (10)	MCot WPhe
	'Florosa' (8)	ERCP LCro LOPS SDeJ
	'Fly Away' (6) **new**	WPhe
	'Fontainebleau' (3)	ERCP SDeJ
	fosteriana (13)	SVic
	'Foxtrot'PBR (2) ♀H6	CAvo ERCP GKev SDeJ
	'Foxy Foxtrot' (2)	SDeJ WPhe
	'Françoise' (3)	SDeJ
	'Franz Léhar' (12)	SDeJ
	'Fringed Elegance' (7) ♀H6	LCro LOPS
	'Fringed Family' (7)	SDeJ
	'Fritz Kreisler' (12)	SDeJ
	'Für Elise' (14)	GKev SDeJ
	'Gaiety' (12)	SDeJ
	'Garden Party' (3)	SDeJ
	'Gavota' (3) ♀H6	CAby CAvo MCot NHol SDeJ WPhe
	'Generaal de Wet' (1)	LCro LOPS SDeJ
	'Gerbrand Kieft' (11) ♀H6	ERCP
	gesneriana (15) **new**	GKev SVic WCot
	'Gipsy Love' (7)	SDeJ
	'Giuseppe Verdi' (12)	CRos EHyd LRHS NRHS

'Golden Apeldoorn' (4)	CArg LCro LOPS SDeJ SPer
'Golden Artist' (8)	GKev LCro LOPS SDeJ
'Golden Emperor' (13)	GKev SDeJ
'Golden Melody' (3)	SDeJ
'Goldwest' (14)	SDeJ
'Gordon Cooper' (4)	SDeJ
'Grand Perfection' PBR (3) 🏆H6	CAvo LCro LOPS SDeJ
'Green Eyes' (8)	SDeJ
'Green River' (8)	SDeJ
'Green Wave' (10)	ERCP LCro LOPS MBros SDeJ WPhe
'Greenstar' (6)	ERCP GKev WPhe
greigii (14)	GKev
grengiolensis (15)	GKev
'Greuze' (5)	LCro LOPS
'Groenland' (8)	CAby CAvo GKev LCro LOPS SDeJ WPhe
hageri (15)	GKev
- 'Splendens' (15)	GKev SDeJ SPhx
'Hakuun' (4)	SDir
'Hamilton' (7)	SDeJ WPhe
'Happy Generation' (3)	LCro LOPS
'Happy Hour' (7)	ERCP
'Havran' (3)	CAby CAvo ERCP GKev LCro LOPS WPhe
'Heart's Delight' (12)	CArg GKev SDeJ
'Heart's Desire' (3) **new**	WPhe
'Helmar' (3) 🏆H6	SDeJ WPhe
'Hemisphere' (3)	CArg CAvo GKev SDeJ
'Hermitage' (3)	ERCP
heweri (15)	EPot GKev
'Hocus Pocus' (5)	SDeJ
'Holland Baby' (2)	SDeJ
'Holland Beauty' PBR (3)	MCot
'Holland Chic' (6)	SDeJ
'Holland Queen' PBR (3)	SDeJ WPhe
'Hollands Glorie' (4)	SDeJ
'Honeymoon' (7)	CAby LCro LOPS WPhe
'Honky Tonk' (15) 🏆H6	CAvo GKev LCro LOPS WPhe
§ ***hoogiana*** (15)	GKev
§ ***humilis*** (15)	CRos EHyd GKev LRHS NRHS SDeJ WShi
- 'China Carol' (15)	GKev SDeJ
- 'Eastern Star' (15)	GKev
§ - 'Lilliput' (15)	CRos EHyd EPot LRHS NRHS
- 'Odalisque' (15)	CRos EHyd EPot GKev LRHS NRHS
- 'Persian Pearl' (15)	CAby CAvo EPot ERCP GKev LCro LOPS SDeJ WPhe WTor
- var. ***pulchella*** Albocaerulea Oculata Group (15)	EPot ERCP LCro LOPS
- 'Rosea' (15)	GKev
§ - Violacea Group (15)	CRos EHyd LRHS NRHS
- - black base (15)	EPot ERCP GKev
- - yellow base (15)	EPot GKev
hungarica	GKev
'Ice Age' (11)	WPhe
'Ice Cream' (11)	ERCP LCro LOPS SDeJ WPhe
'Ice Stick' (12)	GKev SDeJ
'Ice Wing' (6) **new**	GKev
'Île de France' (5)	ERCP LCro LOPS SDeJ
iliensis (15)	EPot
INDELAND **new**	ERCP
'Indian Velvet' (5)	LCro LOPS
'Innuendo' (3)	EHyd LRHS SPer
'Insulinde' (9)	GKev
'Irene Parrot' (10)	SDeJ
'Ivory Floradale' (4) 🏆H6	SDeJ
'Jacqueline' (6)	LCro LOPS
'Jan Reus' (3)	CAvo ERCP LCro LOPS WPhe
'Jazz' (6)	ERCP
'Johann Strauss' (12)	CArg CAvo SPer
'Juan' (13) 🏆H6	CAvo
'Julia Farnese' (9)	GKev
'Jumbo Beauty' (5)	GKev SDeJ
'Keizerskroon' (1)	SDeJ
'Kikomachi' (3)	CRos EHyd LRHS NRHS
'Kingsblood' (5) 🏆H6	ERCP SDeJ
kolpakowskiana (15) 🏆H6	EPot ERCP GKev WShi
'La Belle Époque' (2)	CAvo ERCP GKev LCro LOPS SDeJ WPhe
'Labrador' (7) **new**	WPhe
'Lac van Rijn' (1)	GKev
* 'Lady Diana' (14)	GKev
'Lady Jane' (15) 🏆H6	IPot SPhx WPhe WShi
'Lalibela' (4)	LCro LOPS
'Lambada' (7) 🏆H6	SDeJ WPhe
lanata (15)	GKev WCot
'Lasting Love' (3)	CAby WPhe
'Latvian Gold' (15)	GKev
'Leen van der Mark' (3)	GKev WPhe
'Lemon Flight' (7) **new**	WPhe
'Libretto Parrot' (10)	SDeJ
'Light and Dreamy' (4)	ERCP GKev LCro LOPS SDeJ
'Lilac Crystal' (7)	LCro LOPS
'Lilac Perfection' (11)	ERCP SDeJ
'Lilac Time' (6)	SDir
'Lilac Wonder'	see *T. saxatilis* (Bakeri Group) 'Lilac Wonder'
'Lilliput'	see *T. humilis* 'Lilliput'
'Lilyfire' (6)	SDeJ
'Lingerie' (7)	SDeJ
linifolia (15) 🏆H5	CAvo EPot ERCP GKev SDeJ SPhx WPhe WShi
§ - Batalinii Group (15) 🏆H5	GKev WOut
§ - - 'Apricot Jewel' (15)	EPot
- - 'Bright Gem' (15) 🏆H5	EPot GKev NPer SPhx WHoo WPhe
- - 'Bronze Charm' (15)	CAvo EPot GKev SDeJ WTor
- - 'Red Gem' (15)	GKev WCot
- - 'Red Hunter' (15) 🏆H5	ERCP SDeJ
- - 'Salmon Gem' (15)	CAvo
- - 'Yellow Jewel' (15)	GKev WShi
§ - Maximowiczii Group (15)	GKev
'Lion King' (7)	SDeJ
'Lipgloss' (3)	NHol
'Little Beauty' (15) 🏆H6	CAby CAvo CMea CRos EHyd EPot GKev LCro LOPS LRHS NRHS SDeJ SPhx WCot WHoo WPhe
'Little Princess' (15) 🏆H6	CAvo CRos EHyd EPot GKev LRHS NRHS SDeJ SPhx
'Little Star' (15) 🏆H6	CMea GKev
'Long Lady' (5)	MCot SDeJ
'Love Song' (12)	SDeJ
'Lovely Surprise' (14)	SDeJ
§ 'Lustige Witwe' (3)	SDeJ
'Mabel' (9)	GKev
§ 'Madame Lefeber' (13)	GKev LCro LOPS SDeJ
'Magic Lavender' (3)	GKev
'Maja' (7)	MCot
'Mango Charm' (3)	SDeJ
'Margarita' (2)	GKev LCro LOPS WPhe
'Marie José' (14)	SDeJ
'Mariette' (6)	GKev MCot SDeJ
'Marilyn' (6)	ERCP GKev SDeJ
marjolletii (15)	GKev
'Mascotte' (7)	WPhe
'Mata Hari' (3)	MCot

	'Match' (3)	LCro LOPS
	'Matchmaker' (3) **new**	WPhe
	'Matchpoint' (7/d)	SDeJ
	'Maureen' (5) ♀H6	CAvo ERCP LCro LOPS SDeJ
	mauritiana 'Cindy' (15)	GKev
	'Max Durand' (7)	GKev
	maximowiczii	see *T. linifolia* Maximowiczii Group
	'Maytime' (6)	LCro LOPS SDeJ
	'Melody d'Amour' (5)	GKev
	'Menton' (5) ♀H6	ERCP LCro LOPS SDeJ WPhe
	'Menton Exotic' (11)	ERCP LCro LOPS
	'Merlot' (6)	CAby CAvo ERCP LCro LOPS MBros WPhe
	MERRY WIDOW	see *T.* 'Lustige Witwe'
	'Miskodeed' (14)	SDeJ
	'Miss Elegance' (3)	SDir
	'Mistress' (3)	CAby ERCP LCro LOPS
	'Mistress Mystic' (3) **new**	ERCP
	'Mona Lisa' (6)	SDeJ
	'Mondial'[PBR] (2)	LCro LOPS WPhe
	'Moneymaker' (6) ♀H6	ERCP
	'Monsella' (2)	WPhe
§	***montana*** (15)	EPot WCot
	'Monte Carlo' (2) ♀H6	CArg SDeJ SDir
	'Monte Orange' (2) **new**	WPhe
	'Montreux' (2)	SDir
	'Mount Tacoma' (11)	CAvo ERCP LCro LOPS SDeJ
	'Mr Van der Hoef' (2)	SDeJ
	'Mrs John T. Scheepers' (5)	SDeJ
	'Muriel' (10)	ERCP
	'Mysterious Parrot' (10) **new**	ERCP
	'Mystic van Eijk'[PBR] (4) **new**	ERCP
	'National Velvet' (3)	ERCP GKev LCro LOPS SPhx
	'Negrita' (3)	CArg CAvo ERCP GKev LCro LOPS MCot SDeJ SDir WPhe
	'Negrita Parrot' (10)	CAby
	'New Design' (3/v)	LCro LOPS
	'New Look' (7)	GKev
	'New Santa' (7)	WPhe
	'Nicholas Heyek' (3)	LCro
	'Night Club' (5)	CAby ERCP
	'Nightrider' (8)	CAby LCro LOPS MCot SDeJ WPhe
	'Ollioules' (4) ♀H6	GKev SDeJ
	'Olympic Flame' (4) ♀H6	LCro LOPS SDeJ
	'Orange Angelique' (11)	XEll
	'Orange Bouquet' (3) ♀H6	SDeJ
	'Orange Brilliant' (13)	GKev LCro LOPS
	'Orange Emperor' (13) ♀H6	CAvo ERCP GKev MCot SDeJ
	'Orange Favourite' (10)	ERCP GKev
	'Orange Juice' (3) **new**	WPhe
	'Orange Princess' (11) ♀H6	CAvo EHyd ERCP GKev LCro LOPS LRHS SDeJ SDir WPhe
	'Orange Sun'	see *T.* 'Oranjezon'
	'Oranje Nassau' (2) ♀H6	EHyd LRHS
§	'Oranjezon' (4) ♀H6	ERCP
	'Oratorio' (14) ♀H6	SDeJ
	orphanidea (15)	GKev
	- 'Flava' (15)	ERCP GKev
§	- Whittallii Group (15) ♀H6	CAvo EPot ERCP GKev SDeJ SPhx WCot WShi
	'Oscar' (3)	NHol
	'Page Polka' (3)	SDeJ
	'Pallada' (3) **new**	LCro LOPS
	'Parrot King' (10)	SDeJ
	'Passionale' (3) ♀H6	LCro LOPS SDeJ WPhe
	'Paul Scherer' (3) ♀H6	CAby CAvo ERCP GKev LCro LOPS MMrt SDeJ WPhe
	'Peach Blossom' (2)	CArg CRos EHyd GKev LCro LOPS LRHS NRHS SDeJ
	Peacock Group	SDeJ
	'Peppermintstick' (15) ♀H6	CAvo GKev SDeJ SPhx
	'Perestroyka' (5)	ERCP SDeJ
	'Picture' (5)	ERCP SDeJ
	'Pieter de Leur' (6)	CAvo LCro LOPS
	'Pimpernel' (8/v)	SDeJ
	'Pink Diamond' (5)	CAvo ERCP GKev MBros NHol SDeJ SDir
	'Pink Dwarf' (12)	SDeJ
	'Pink Impression' (4) ♀H6	CArg LCro LOPS SDeJ
	'Pink Sensation' (14)	SDeJ
	'Pink Star' (11)	ERCP
	'Pinocchio' (14)	CArg CRos EHyd GKev LRHS NRHS SDeJ WPhe
	'Pirand' (13) ♀H6	SDeJ
	'Pittsburg' (3)	LCro LOPS
	'Pleasure' (3) **new**	CAby
	'Poco Loco' (13)	GKev SDeJ
	polychroma	see *T. biflora*
	praestans (15)	GKev SPer WShi
	- 'Fusilier' (15) ♀H6	CExl GKev SDeJ
	- 'Shogun' (15)	ERCP GKev SDeJ SPer
	- 'Unicum' (15/v)	ERCP GKev SDeJ SDir
	- 'Van Tubergen's Variety' (15)	GKev NPer
	- 'Zwanenburg Variety' (15)	GKev
	'Pretty Princess' (3)	ERCP SDeJ WPhe
	'Princeps' (13)	SDeJ
	'Princesse Charmante' (14) ♀H6	LCro LOPS
	'Prinses Irene' (3) ♀H6	CArg CAvo CRos EHyd ERCP GKev LCro LOPS LRHS NBir NHol NRHS SDeJ WPhe
	'Prinses Margriet' (3)	ERCP WPhe
	'Professor Röntgen' (10)	ERCP LCro LOPS SDeJ
	'Professor Schotel' (15)	GKev
	pulchella humilis	see *T. humilis*
	'Purified' (3)	GKev
§	'Purissima' (13) ♀H6	CAvo GKev LCro LOPS SDeJ WPhe
	'Purple Bouquet' (3)	SDeJ
	'Purple Doll' (8)	LCro LOPS SPhx
	'Purple Dream' (6)	LCro LOPS MCot SDeJ
	'Purple Flag' (3)	LCro LOPS
	'Purple Peony' (2)	ERCP
	'Purple Prince' (5)	CRos LCro LOPS LRHS NRHS SDeJ
I	'Purple Prince' (1)	CArg EHyd WPhe
	'Purple Tower' (7)	ERCP
	'Quebec' (14)	SDeJ
	'Queen of Marvel' (2)	SDeJ
	'Queen of Night' (5)	CArg CAvo CMea ERCP GKev LCro LOPS MBros MCot NBir SDeJ SDir SPer SPhx WPhe
	'Queensday' (11)	SDeJ
	'Queensland' (7)	WPhe
	'Rai' (10)	SDeJ
	'Real Time' (7)	WPhe
	'Recreado' (5)	CAby CAvo ERCP SDeJ
	'Red Emperor'	see *T.* 'Madame Lefeber'
	'Red Georgette' (5) ♀H6	CAby GKev NBir SDeJ
	'Red Hat' (7) ♀H6	LCro LOPS
	'Red Impression'[PBR] (4) ♀H6	LCro LOPS
	'Red Princess' (11) ♀H6	ERCP WPhe
	'Red Revival' (1)	GKev
	'Red Riding Hood' (14) ♀H6	CArg CAvo CRos EHyd GKev LCro LOPS LRHS NBir NRHS SDeJ SPer

'Red Rover' (3)	LCro LOPS
'Red Shine' (6) ♀H6	ERCP GKev LCro LOPS SDeJ
'Red Springgreen' (8)	GKev LCro LOPS SDeJ
'Red Wing' (7) ♀H6	SDeJ
'Redwood' (14)	SDeJ
'Rems Favourite' (3)	CAby CAvo LCro LOPS SDeJ WPhe
'Renown' (5)	CAby SDeJ
'Request' (3)	ERCP GKev MMrt
'Robinho'[PBR] (11) **new**	GKev
'Rococo' (10)	CAvo ERCP LCro LOPS SDeJ SDir WPhe
'Roi du Midi' (5)	SDeJ
'Ronaldo' (3)	ERCP GKev LCro LOPS
'Rosalie' (3)	ERCP SDeJ
'Rosy Dream' (13)	SDeJ
'Royal Anthos' (14)	SDeJ
'Royal Virgin' (3)	ERCP
'Salmon Impression' (4)	SDeJ
'Sanne' (3) ♀H6	CAvo ERCP SDeJ WPhe
'Santander' (7)	SDeJ
'Sapporo' (6)	ERCP LCro LOPS
saracenica	GKev
saxatilis (15)	GKev LCro LOPS SDeJ
§ - Bakeri Group (15)	SEND
§ - - 'Lilac Wonder' (15) ♀H6	CAby CAvo CExl EPot ERCP LCro LOPS MWat NPer SDeJ SDir SPhx WShi
'Scarlet Baby' (12)	WPhe
schrenkii (15)	EPot ERCP GKev WShi
'Seadov' (3) ♀H6	LCro LOPS SDeJ
'Seattle' (6)	ERCP
'Sensual Touch' (7) ♀H6	SDeJ WPhe
'Shakespeare' (12)	SDeJ
'Shirley' (3)	CAvo ERCP LCro LOPS SDeJ
'Shirley Dream' (3)	SDeJ
'Showtime' (14)	SDeJ
'Showwinner' (12) ♀H6	GKev MBros NHol SDeJ
'Silk Road' (2)	GKev
'Silver Parrot' (10)	WPhe
'Silver Standard' (1)	GKev
'Slawa'[PBR] (3)	CAvo LCro LOPS SPer
'Snow Crystal' (11)	WPhe
'Snow Parrot' (10)	ERCP
'Snow Valley' (7)	ERCP
sogdiana (15)	GKev
§ 'Sonnet' (6)	SDeJ
'Sorbet' (5) ♀H6	SDeJ
sprengeri (15) ♀H6	CAvo CBro CExl CSpe CWCL ECha ERCP EWld GKev SBrt WHal WShi
- Trotter's form (15)	WCot
'Spring Green' (8) ♀H6	CAby CArg CAvo ERCP GKev LCro LOPS MCot SDeJ SPhx WPhe
'Spryng' (3) ♀H6	SDeJ
'Starfighter' (7)	SDeJ
stellata	see *T. clusiana* var. *stellata*
'Stresa' (12) ♀H6	CRos EHyd GKev LRHS NRHS SDeJ
'Strong Gold' (3) ♀H6	SDeJ WPhe
'Stunning Apricot' (5)	LCro LOPS
'Suncatcher' (3)	SDeJ
'Sunny Prince'[PBR] (1)	CAvo SDeJ WPhe
'Super Parrot' (10)	WPhe
'Survivor' (5)	SDeJ
'Swan Wings' (7)	ERCP GKev LCro LOPS SDeJ
'Sweet Desire' (2)	SDeJ
'Sweet Impression' (4)	ERCP
'Sweet Lady' (14)	SDeJ
'Sweetheart' (13)	GKev LCro LOPS MCot SDeJ WPhe
sylvestris (15)	CAby CAvo CSpe EPot ERCP GKev LCro LOPS NBir SDeJ SPhx WCot WOut WShi

'Synaeda Amor' (3) **new**	LCro LOPS
systola (15)	GKev
'Taco' (15)	GKev WPhe
'Tarafa' (14)	SDeJ
tarda (15) ♀H6	CAvo CExl CRos EHyd ERCP GKev LCro LOPS LRHS NRHS SDeJ SPhx WPhe WShi
- 'Kazakhstan' (15)	GKev
'Temple of Beauty' (5) ♀H6	GKev SDeJ
'Texas Flame' (10)	GKev SDeJ
'Texas Gold' (10)	SDeJ
'The First' (12)	MMrt
'The Lizard' (9)	GKev SDir
'Tinka' (15) ♀H6	CMea GKev
'Tiny Timo' (15)	ERCP
'Tom Pouce' (3)	LCro LOPS WPhe
'Toplips' (11)	SDeJ
'Topparrot' (10)	SDeJ
'Toronto' (14) ♀H6	SDeJ
'Toronto Double' (2)	SDeJ
'Toyota' (5)	SDeJ
'Très Chic' (6)	CAvo LCro LOPS SPer
tschimganica (15)	WCot
- yellow-flowered	GKev
turkestanica (15) ♀H5	CAby CAvo CExl EHyd EPot ERCP GKev LRHS MBros NPer NRHS SDeJ WHoo WShi
'Turkish Delight' (14)	NPer
'Uncle Tom' (11)	CAvo ERCP GKev SDeJ WPhe
§ ***undulatifolia*** (15)	WCot
'Unique de France'[PBR] (3)	CAvo
'United States' (14) ♀H6	NPer
urumiensis (15) ♀H5	CAvo EPot GKev SDeJ SPhx WOut
'Valentine' (3)	SDeJ
'Valery Gergiev' (7)	ERCP SDeJ
'Van der Neer' (1)	GKev SDeJ
'Van Eijk'[PBR] (4)	GKev
'Vanilla Cream' (14)	SDeJ
'Verona' (2)	CAby SDeJ WPhe
'Véronique Sanson' (3)	ERCP LCro LOPS SDeJ
'Victoria's Secret' (3)	GKev
'Viking' (2)	WPhe
violacea	see *T. humilis* Violacea Group
'Violet Beauty' (5)	LCro LOPS SDeJ WPhe
'Violet Bird' (8)	GKev LCro LOPS SDeJ SDir
'Virichic' (8)	ERCP GKev LCro LOPS MCot WPhe
'Viridiflora' (8)	SVic
vvedenskyi (15)	EPot
- 'Tangerine Beauty' (15) ♀H6	GKev
'Warbler' (7)	SDeJ
'Washington' (3)	LCro LOPS
'Weber's Parrot' (10)	LCro LOPS MCot
'Wedding Gift' (11)	SDeJ
'Weisse Berliner' (3)	CAby
'West Point' (6)	LCro LOPS SDeJ WPhe
'Whispering Dream' (3)	CAvo WPhe
'White Dream' (3)	CArg GKev LCro LOPS SDeJ SPer
'White Emperor'	see *T.* 'Purissima'
'White Liberstar' (3)	ERCP
'White Marvel' (3)	EHyd LRHS
'White Parrot' (10)	CAvo ERCP GKev LCro LOPS MCot SDeJ
'White Prince' (1) **new**	GKev WPhe
'White Triumphator' (6) ♀H6	CArg CAvo CMea ERCP LCro LOPS MCot NBir SDeJ SPhx WPhe
whittallii	see *T. orphanidea* Whittallii Group

	'Wilja' (5)	GKev
§	'Willem van Oranje' (2)	SDeJ
	'Willemsoord' (2)	EHyd LRHS SDeJ
	WILLIAM OF ORANGE	see *T.* 'Willem van Oranje'
	wilsoniana	see *T. montana*
	'Wisley' (5) ♀H6	LCro LOPS
	'World Expression' (5) ♀H6	SDeJ
	'World Friendship' (3) **new**	GKev
	'World Peace'PBR (4) **new**	LCro LOPS
	'Wow' (11) **new**	ERCP
	'Yellow Flight' (3)	SDeJ
	'Yellow Pompenette'PBR (11) ♀H6	SDeJ
I	'Yellow Purissima' (13) ♀H6	SDir
	'Yellow Spider' (11) **new**	WPhe
	'Yellow Springgreen' (8)	ERCP SDeJ SDir
	'Yellow Sun' (10) **new**	WPhe
	'Yoko Parrot' (10)	SDeJ
	'Yokohama' (3)	SDeJ
	'Yonina' (6)	CArg GKev LCro LOPS SDeJ
§	'Zurel' (3)	CArg ERCP GKev MCot SDir

tummelberry see *Rubus* 'Tummelberry'

Tunica see *Petrorhagia*

Tupistra (*Asparagaceae*)

aurantiaca	GEdr LEdu
- B&SWJ 2267	WCot WCru
- B&SWJ 2401	WCru
chinensis 'Eco China Ruffles'	WCot
grandistigma	WCot
- B&SWJ 11773	WCru
jinshanensis	WCot
urotepala HWJ 562	WCru
wattii B&SWJ 8297	WCru

Turnera (*Passifloraceae*)

diffusa var. ***aphrodisiaca***	GPoy

turnip see AGM Vegetables Section

Turpinia (*Staphyleaceae*)

ternata CWJ 12360	WCru

Tussilago (*Asteraceae*)

farfara	GPoy MHer WHer WSFF

Tweedia (*Apocynaceae*)

§	***coerulea*** ♀H1c	CBcs CCCN CDTJ CSpe SChF SGro SPad SPer SPhx SWvt WSFF

Typha (*Typhaceae*)

	angustifolia	CBen CWat LLWG MMuc NPer SPlb WMAq WPnP
	latifolia	CBen CWat LLWG NBir NPer SVic WMAq XLum
	- 'Variegata' (v)	CWat LLWG MWts WMAq
§	***laxmannii***	CBen LLWG WMAq WPnP XLum
	lugdunensis	MWts
	minima	CBen CWat LLWG MWts NPer WMAq WPnP XLum
	shuttleworthii	CBen LLWG
	stenophylla	see *T. laxmannii*

Typhonium (*Araceae*)

giganteum	WCot
horsfieldii	LEdu MPie
roxburghii	EBee WFar

Typhonodorum (*Araceae*)

lindleyanum	XBlo

U

Uapaca (*Euphorbiaceae*)

kirkiana (F)	XBlo

Uccerodendron see *Disanthus*

ugli see *Citrus* × *aurantium* (Tangelo Group) 'Ugli'

Ugni ✿ (*Myrtaceae*)

	candollei	SVen
§	***molinae***	Widely available
	- PAB 1347	SBrt
	- 'Big Burning Pink' **new**	LEdu
	- 'Butterball'	CBcs CDoC CTrC EBee EPfP LEdu LRHS SPoG SWvt
	- 'Flambeau' (v)	CAgr CBcs CBod CCht CDoC CExl CMac CRos CSde CTrC EBee EHyd ELan EPfP EShb LEdu LRHS MAsh MGil NLar NRHS SEle SLon SPoG SRms SWvt WPav
	- 'Ka-Pow'	CAby CBod CCCN CTrC LCro LRHS MHtn SPad WTyc
	- orange-leaved	WJek
	- 'Variegata' (v)	LEdu WJek
	- 'Villarica Strawberry'	LEdu WPGP

Ulex (*Papilionaceae*)

	europaeus	CBcs CCVT CHab CMac CTri ELan ELon EPfP LBuc MCoo MGil MGos MMuc SCob SEWo SPer WKor
§	- 'Flore Pleno' (d) ♀H6	CBcs CBod CCoa CDoC CMac CPla CSBt CSde ELan ELon EPfP IArd MBlu MMuc NBPC SCob SDix SPer WFar WHer
	- 'Irish Double' (d)	NLar
	- 'Plenus'	see *U. europaeus* 'Flore Pleno'
	gallii 'Mizen Head'	SMad

Ullucus (*Basellaceae*)

tuberosus	LEdu

Ulmus ✿ (*Ulmaceae*)

	americana 'Princeton'	SCob
	× ***androssowii***	WPGP
	bergmanniana	WPGP
	changii	WPGP
	chenmoui	IArd IDee WPGP
	'Columella'	SAko
	davidiana	WPGP
	- var. ***davidiana***	WPGP
	- var. ***japonica***	WPGP
	'Dodoens'	IArd MBlu SCob
	'Frontier'	WPGP
§	***glabra***	EPfP WTSh
	- 'Camperdownii'	CMac ELan WMou
	- 'Lutescens'	CTho EBee NOra WMat
	harbinensis	WPGP
§	× ***hollandica*** 'Dampieri Aurea' ♀H7	CTho EBee ELan ELon EPfP LBuc MAsh MBlu MGos MRav NLar NOrn SPer SPoG WMat

- 'Jacqueline Hillier'	CMac CSpe EBee ELan LRHS MMuc NLar SEND SGol WFar WLov
- 'Wredei'	see *U.* × *hollandica* 'Dampieri Aurea'
'Homestead'	WPGP
laevis	WPGP
'Lobel'	CCVT CLnd LMaj SCob
× ***mesocarpa***	WPGP
minor 'Dampieri Aurea'	see *U.* × *hollandica* 'Dampieri Aurea'
montana	see *U. glabra*
parvifolia	CMCN CMen CTho EShb WPGP
- 'Geisha' (v)	ELan
§ - 'Hokkaido'	EWes NLar SMad WAbe
- 'Pygmaea'	see *U. parvifolia* 'Hokkaido'
- 'Yatsubusa'	EPot MRav WPGP
procera	MCoo MGos WSFF
- 'Argenteovariegata' (v)	NLar
prunifolia	WPGP
pumila 'Beijing Gold'	ELan NLar
'Regal'	WPGP
'Sapporo Autumn Gold'	CCVT MRav SGol WCFE
szechuanica	WPGP
uyematsui	WPGP
VADA ('Wanoux'^{PBR})	SGol
villosa	EBee WPGP

Umbellularia (*Lauraceae*)

californica	NLar WPGP

Umbilicus (*Crassulaceae*)

§ ***oppositifolius*** ♀^{H5}	CAby CBod CCBP CElw CRos CSam CTri ECha EDAr EHyd ELan EPfP GAbr GKev GLog LPot LRHS MMuc MRav NBid NRHS NSla SPlb SRms WFar WKif WSHC XLum
- 'Jane's Reverse' (v)	WCot
§ - 'Jim's Pride' (v)	ECha EWes GKev GPSL MHer MPie MRav NHpl NPer NWad SPlb SRms WFar WSHC
rupestris	SChr SPhx WHer WShi

Uncinia (*Cyperaceae*)

* ***cyparissias*** from Chile	NBir
egmontiana	CBod CPla EBee EHyd EPfP LRHS NWad WGrn
rubra	CBod CChe CEnd CRos CSBt EBee EHyd ELan EPfP EShb GMaP LRHS MGos MRav NRHS NSti NWad SGol SPad SPlb SPoG WFar
§ - 'Belinda's Find'^{PBR}	CBct CBod CKno EBee EHyd ELan LRHS MHol MPri NLar SPoG SRms
- EVERFLAME	see *U. rubra* 'Belinda's Find'
uncinata	CBcs ECha SDix
* - ***rubra***	CDoC CKno MAsh SCob SLim SRms SWvt

Uniola (*Poaceae*)

latifolia	see *Chasmanthium latifolium*

Urginea (*Asparagaceae*)

maritima	see *Charybdis maritima*

Urospermum (*Asteraceae*)

dalechampii	CCCN CSam

Urtica (*Urticaceae*)

dioica 'Bradfield Purpler'	CNat
- 'Chedglow 2' (v)	CNat
- 'Curly-Wurly'	CNat
- 'Good as Gold'	CNat

Utricularia (*Lentibulariaceae*)

sp.	EECP
alpina	SHmp
bisquamata	SHmp
- 'Betty's Bay' ♀^{H2}	CHew
calycifida	SHmp
dichotoma	CHew
exoleta R. Brown	see *U. gibba*
geminiloba new	CHew
§ ***gibba***	EECP
intermedia	EECP
lateriflora	CHew
livida ♀^{H2}	CHew SHmp
longifolia	SHmp
microcalyx	CHew
nephrophylla	CHew
parthenopipes new	CHew
paulineae	CHew
praelonga	CHew SHmp
prehensilis	CHew
reniformis	CHew SHmp
sandersonii ♀^{H2}	CHew EECP SHmp
tricolor	CHew SHmp
uniflora	CHew

Uvularia (*Colchicaceae*)

grandiflora ♀^{H6}	Widely available
- gold-leaved	CAby
- 'Lynda Windsor'	LEdu NHsp
- var. ***pallida***	CAby CAvo CBct CRos EBee EMor EPPr EPfP EPot GBin GEdr IBlr ILea LEdu LRHS MRav NHsp NLar NRHS WCru WFar WPnP
- 'Susie Lewis'	WCru
grandiflora × ***perfoliata***	CMiW NBir
perfoliata	CBct CExl EBee ECha EPPr EPfP EPot GKev GPSL IBlr IMou LEdu MRav NBir NChi NHpl SPlb WCru WFar
- tall	EPPr
sessilifolia	CBct CExl CMiW CRos EHyd EPfP GKev IMou LEdu LRHS MMrt NHsp NLar NRHS WCru
- 'Cobblewood Gold' (v)	EPPr LEdu WCru WFar
- 'Variegata' (v)	EBee

V

Vaccaria (*Caryophyllaceae*)

§ ***hispanica***	SPhx
segetalis	see *V. hispanica*

Vaccinium ✿ (*Ericaceae*)

arctostaphylos	SWvt
'Berkeley' (F)	CAgr CCCN CEnd GKin MBlu SEdi SGsty SPre
BLUE SUEDE ('Th-682') (F)	CBcs LCro LOPS LRHS NLar NRHS
'Bluejay' (F)	CRos EHyd ELan LRHS MAsh NRHS SCoo SEdi SLon SPoG
'Blueray' (F)	GKin
'Brigitta' (F)	CEnd CTrh EBee EPom MAsh NRHS SPoG SPre

chaetothrix	WAbe WThu
'Chandler' (F)	CAgr CArg CEnd CMac CRos CTrh EPom GKin LCro LOPS MAsh NOra SEdi SKee SPer
consanguineum B&SWJ 10486	WCru
corymbosum (F)	CBcs MNHC SCoo SSta
- 'Aurora'PBR (F)	CTrh
- 'Blauweiss-Goldtraube' (F)	CAgr CMac CSBt ELan EPfP GKin MAsh MPri NLar SPoG SVic WTSh
- 'Blue Duke' (F)	LSRN
- 'Blue Sapphire' (F) **new**	LCro LOPS
- 'Bluecrop' (F)	Widely available
- 'Bluegold' (F)	CRos EHyd LCro LOPS LRHS MAsh NRHS SPoG
- 'Bluetta' (F)	CAgr CTri ELan SCoo SPoG
- 'Darrow' (F)	CAgr LRHS NRHS WMat
- 'Dixie' (F)	CSBt LEdu NLar
- 'Draper'PBR (F)	CTrh
- 'Duke' (F) 🏆H6	CArg CTrh ELan EPfP EPom LCro LOPS MAsh MCoo MGos SPre SRkn SSFr
- 'Elliott' (F)	LSRN
- 'Grover' (F)	SEdi
- 'Hardyblue' (F)	CAgr
- 'Hortblue Petite'PBR (F) **new**	SVic
- 'Huron'PBR (F)	CTrh
- 'Jersey' (F)	CAgr CEnd CRos EHyd EPfP LRHS MAsh MGos MMuc NRHS SCoo SEdi SPer SPoG SVic
- 'Legacy' (F)	NRHS
- 'Liberty'PBR (F)	CTrh EPfP LRHS
- 'Nelson' (F)	SCoo
- 'Nui' (F)	CEnd EPom LSRN MRav
- 'Patriot' (F)	CAgr CEnd CMac CRos CSBt CTrh ECrN EHyd ELan EPom GKin LBuc LRHS MGos MPri MRav NLar NRHS SCoo SPer SPre SSFr WMat
- 'Polaris' (F)	CEnd
- 'Reka' (F)	CAgr NPer
- 'Spartan' (F) 🏆H6	CTrh EPom LCro LOPS LSRN MGos SKee
- 'Stanley' (F)	CRos EHyd EPfP LRHS NRHS SPoG
- 'Toro' (F)	SPre
- YELLOBERRY BLUE ('Andval1601') (F) **new**	LCro
crassifolium subsp. ***sempervirens*** 'Well's Delight' (F)	EHyd LRHS MAsh
cylindraceum 🏆H4	CBcs CEnd EBee NLar SSta WPGP
delavayi	LRHS MAsh NLar SSta WThu
dunalianum var. ***caudatifolium*** B&SWJ 1716	WCru
- - NMWJ 14558 **new**	WCru
- var. ***megaphyllum*** HWJ 515	WCru
'Earliblue' (F)	CAgr CSBt CTrh GKin LBuc NRHS SPer SPoG WMat
erythrocarpum	CRos
floribundum	CRos EHyd LRHS MAsh
glaucoalbum 🏆H5	CMac EBee EHyd LRHS MAsh MBlu MRav NRHS SPoG WPGP
'Goldtraube 71'	MAsh SEdi
griffithianum	SSta
'Herbert' (F)	CAgr CTrh EPom LBuc SEdi
macrocarpon (F)	CRos EHyd ELan LRHS MAsh NRHS SPre SRms WKor XAbr
- 'Early Black' (F)	ELan EPom GKin IDee SVic WTSh
- 'Hamilton'	WThu
- 'Langlois' (F)	NLar
- 'Olson's Honkers' (F)	CAgr
- 'Pilgrim' (F)	CAgr CSBt LCro LEdu LOPS LRHS MAsh MCoo MPri SPoG WMat
- 'Red Star' (F)	CTrh
- 'Stevens' (F)	CAgr
moupinense	GEdr LRHS MAsh WThu
myrtillus	CAgr EPom GPoy SVic WKor XAbr
'Northblue' (F)	ELan
'Northcountry' (F)	CTrh
'Northland' (F)	CMac CSBt EPfP EPom MAsh MPri MRav NLar NRHS SCoo SPoG WMat
nummularia	GEdr GRum LRHS NLar WAbe WThu
'Osorno' (F)	CTrh
ovatum (F)	CBcs CMac GKin WLov WThu
- 'Pacific Spear' (F)	SVic
- 'Thundercloud' (F)	CRos EHyd EPfP LRHS MAsh NRHS SSta
§ ***oxycoccos*** (F)	CAgr GPoy MCoo WThu
'Ozarkblue' (F)	EPom LCro LOPS NRHS SEdi
palustre	see *V. oxycoccos*
§ 'Pink Lemonade' (F)	CRos ELan EPom LCro LOPS LRHS MPri NRHS SEdi SPer SPoG SSFr
'Pink Sapphire'	see *V.* 'Pink Lemonade'
retusum	WThu
'Rubel' (F)	NRHS
sikkimense	GRum
'Spring Surprise'	WAbe WThu
'Sunshine Blue' (F)	CAgr CEnd CRos CTrh EHyd ELan EPom LBuc LRHS SPoG SSFr
'Tophat' (F)	CCCN LEdu
vitis-idaea	EPfP EWes GPoy SVic WKor
- 'Aalshorst'	NLar
- 'Autumn Beauty'	NLar
- 'Compactum'	EWes
- 'Erntetraum'	NLar
- 'Ida'	LBuc
- Koralle Group 🏆H5	CAgr EPot GKin NLar NWad
- 'Leucocarpa'	NLar
- subsp. ***minus***	GEdr NLar
- 'Red Candy'PBR	ELan LCro LOPS LRHS NLar
- 'Red Pearl'	CSBt EPom MAsh

Vachellia (*Leguminosae*)

§ ***karroo***	CDTJ SPlb

Vagaria (*Amaryllidaceae*)

parviflora **new**	GKev

Valeriana (*Caprifoliaceae*)

'Alba'	see *Centranthus ruber* 'Albus'
alliariifolia	CSam GQue MSpe NBro SPhx
- PAB 3001	LEdu WPGP
arizonica	EBou
'Coccinea'	see *Centranthus ruber*
dioica	LLWG SBut
hardwickii PAB 8999	LEdu
jatamansi	GPoy SRms
- PAB 6846	LEdu WPGP
montana	EBee LEdu MMuc NBro NRya SPhx SRms
officinalis	Widely available
- subsp. ***sambucifolia***	EMor EPPr MNrw MSpe SHar
phu 'Aurea'	CBod CDor CHby CMac CRos EBee ECha EHyd ELan EPfP GKin GQue LRHS MBriF MPie MRav NBid NBir NBro NLar NSti NWad SPer SPoG SRms WCAu WWtn

pyrenaica EBee ECha EMor EPPr LEdu LRHS MBriF MHol MMuc MNrw MPie SBut SDix SEND SHar SPhx WCot WHrl
wallrothii WCot

Valerianella (*Caprifoliaceae*)

§ ***locusta*** CBod GPoy SVic
olitoria see *V. locusta*

Vallea (*Elaeocarpaceae*)

stipularis CTsd IArd

Vallisneria (*Hydrocharitaceae*)

americana XBlo
asiatica var. ***biwaensis*** XBlo
gigantea XBlo
spiralis LLWG XBlo
- 'Tortifolia' XBlo

Vallota see *Cyrtanthus*

Vancouveria (*Berberidaceae*)

chrysantha CExl EPPr EPfP GEdr GLog NRya WFar WPGP
hexandra CExl CMac EBee ECha EMor EPPr EPfP GEdr GKev GLog ILea LEdu LRHS NBir NSti SPlb WCru WPGP WPnP
planipetala IMou WCru

Vania see *Thlaspi*

Vasconcellea (*Caricaceae*)

§ ***pubescens*** SPlb

Vellozia (*Velloziaceae*)

elegans see *Talbotia elegans*

Veltheimia ✿ (*Asparagaceae*)

§ ***bracteata*** 🏆H2 CAvo CPla EPri GKev SGro SRms
- 'Lemon Flame' GKev
viridifolia Jacq. see *V. bracteata*

× *Venidioarctotis* see *Arctotis*

Venidium see *Arctotis*

Veratrum (*Melanthiaceae*)

album 🏆H7 EBee ECha EMor GEdr GKev GPoy ILea MNrw MRav NBid WCot WCru WPGP WSHC
- PAB 537 LEdu
- 'Auvergne White' EBee LEdu MNrw
- var. ***flavum*** CAby LPla MNrw SPhx WCot WCru
- - 'Primrose Warburg' GEdr
- subsp. ***lobelianum*** LEdu
- 'Lorna's Green' 🏆H7 EBee MNrw WCot
californicum 🏆H3 CAby CBct EBee ECha EMor LEdu LPla MNrw NBid WCru WPGP WSHC WWFP
formosanum CAby EBee GEdr MNrw WCot WSHC
- B&SWJ 1575 WCru
- RWJ 9806 WCru
grandiflorum B&SWJ 4416 WCru
longebracteatum WCru
maackii EBee MAvo MNrw SMad
- B&SWJ 5875 WCru
- green-flowered EBee LEdu MNrw
- var. ***japonicum*** GKev MNrw WCru
- var. ***maackii*** MNrw
- - B&SWJ 5831 WCru
nigrum 🏆H6 CAby CBct CBod EBee ECha EHyd GEdr GKev GMaP ILea LEdu LRHS MNrw MRav NBid NBir SEdd SMad SPhx SPlb WCot WCru WMal
- B&SWJ 4450 from South Korea WCru
schindleri GEdr MNrw
- B&SWJ 4068 WCru
viride EBee EWes LEdu MNrw NBid WCot WCru WPGP

Verbascum (*Scrophulariaceae*)

'Apricot Sunset' SPhx
'Arctic Summer' see *V. bombyciferum* 'Polarsommer'
arcturus SVen
'Argentina' WHer
blattaria NBir SBut WHer
- f. ***albiflorum*** CPla CSpe EAJP NDov NGBl SPhx SPlb WHer
'Blue Lagoon' CWGN SCob
§ ***bombyciferum*** CBre ECha ELan GMaP LRHS NGBl SCob SEND SPhx SRms
* - 'Arctic Snow' SPoG
§ - 'Polarsommer' CSpe EPfP LRHS NBir SPer
- 'Silver Lining' NPer
'Broussa' see *V. bombyciferum*
'Buttercup' EHyd LRHS
'Camelot' EHyd LRHS
'Caribbean Crush' CRos ECtt EHyd ELan GWyn LRHS MBNS SPer SPoG WSpi
chaixii CBod CSam ECha EPPr GJos MArl MMrt NBir SDix WFar
- 'Album' Widely available
- 'Sixteen Candles' CBod GJos IPot NLar WFar
- 'Wedding Candles' CWld ELan EPfP GWyn NGdn SPtp WFar
'Cherry Helen'^PBR EBee LCro LOPS LRHS LSRN MBNS NLar SCob
'Christo's Yellow Lightning' 🏆H6 CBod EBee ECha ECtt GAbr GBin MAvo MHol SDix SEdd SMad SPoG WCot WRHF
'Clementine' CBcs ECtt EPfP ILea LCro LOPS LRHS MHol SCob SPhx
'Coneyhill Yellow' EPPr
(Cotswold Group) 'Cotswold Beauty' CBod CSam CSpe ECtt EHyd EPfP LRHS MRav NDov NGdn NRHS SCob SHar SPer WCAu WCav WHoo
- 'Cotswold Queen' CBod CSam ECtt EHyd EPPr EPfP LCro LOPS LRHS MMrt MRav NDov NRHS SCob SHar SPer SWvt WCAu WSpi
- 'Gainsborough' 🏆H6 CDor ECha ECtt EPfP GMaP LCro LOPS LRHS MArl MRav NLar NRHS NSti SCob SGbt SPer SPoG SWvt WCAu WGwG WHil WSpi
- 'Mont Blanc' LRHS NRHS
- 'Pink Domino' 🏆H6 CBod CSam CWld ECtt EHyd EPPr EPfP EWhm GMaP LCro LOPS LRHS MHer MRav MWat NRHS SCob SPer SWvt WSpi
- 'Royal Highland' CBod CNor CWld EBee ECtt EHyd EPfP LRHS MBNS NRHS SWvt WHoo
- 'White Domino' SPer WSpi

'Cotswold King'	see *V. creticum*
§ ***creticum***	CSpe SCob WCot
'Dark Eyes'PBR	CWGN ECtt LRHS NHpl
delphicum	GKev
dumulosum ♀H4	EPot WAbe
epixanthinum ♀H5	EBee GJos
'Firedance'	CBcs CWld ECtt EHyd EPfP GBin IPot LRHS MHer NGBl NRHS SHar WCAu
'Golden Wings' ♀H4	WAbe
'Guinevere'	EHyd LRHS
'Helen Johnson'	CBod CRos CWCL ECtt EHyd IPot LRHS LSRN MGos MRav NLar NRHS SCob SCoo SGbt SWvt WSpi
'Honey Dijon' **new**	SPad
× ***hybridum*** 'Banana Custard'	EHyd NGBl WSpi
- 'Copper Rose'	EHyd EPfP LRHS
- 'Snow Maiden'	CTri EPfP
- 'Wega'	NLar
'Jackie'	CRos ECtt EHyd LRHS LSRN MAvo
'Jester'	CBcs EBee ECtt MBNS SCob SPoG WSpi
'Jolly Eyes'	ILea
'June Johnson'	CBod ECtt EHyd LRHS NRHS
'Kynaston'	CBcs ECtt EHyd EPfP LRHS NRHS SGbt SHar
'Lavender Lass'	MHol WSpi
'Letitia' ♀H4	EBee EHyd EPot EWes LRHS NRHS SWvt WAbe WIce
longifolium var. ***pannosum***	see *V. olympicum*
lychnitis	GJos NGBl SPhx
'Megan's Mauve'	WSpi
'Merlin'PBR	CBcs EHyd EPfP LRHS MBNS NDov NRHS SGbt
nigrum	CHab GJos NGdn NLar SCob
- var. ***album***	GJos NGdn NLar WSpi
§ ***olympicum***	CBcs CBee CBod CRos EHyd ELan EPfP GJos LRHS MArl NGBl NRHS SCob SDix SRms WCAu WCot
'Petra'	LRHS SPhx
phlomoides	SPhx
phoeniceum	CBcs CSBt ELan EPfP GJos NBro SCob SPlb SPoG WFar WSpi
* - 'Album'	CSpe GJos SCob
- 'Flush of White'	CBod CDor EPfP NGBl NGdn NLar SBut SCob WFar
- 'Rosetta'	CBod EPfP GWyn MCot NGBl WFar WHil WRHF
- 'Temptress White'	CBod
- 'Violetta'	CBod CSpe CTsd CWld EAJP EPPr EPfP GBin GMaP LCro LOPS LRHS MCot MHol MWat NGBl NGdn SBut SGbt SPer SPhx WCAu WCFE WFar WHil
'Pink Kisses'	CRos EHyd LRHS LSRN NRHS
'Pink Petticoats'	MAvo
'Plum Smokey'PBR	ECtt NEoE
'Primrose Path'	EHyd EPfP LRHS MBNS NLar
pyramidatum	EBee SPhx
'Queen of Hearts'	EHyd LRHS
'Raspberry Ripple'	GWyn MRav
roripifolium	SPhx
'Rosie'	ECtt NHpl NLar
'Sierra Sunset'	NLar
'Southern Charm'	CFis EPfP GJos NQui SCob WCav
'Spica'	LRHS
'Sugar Plum'PBR	ECtt LCro LOPS LRHS WCAu
'Temptress Purple'	CBod MHol
thapsus	CHab EBou ENfk GJos GPoy GQue MArl MBow MNHC NBir NMir SEND SRms
'Tropic Sun' ♀H5	SPhx WHoo
'Ventnor Giant'	SVen
'Wessex'	EHyd LRHS

Verbena (*Verbenaceae*)

(G)	see *Glandularia*
Aztec Series	see *Glandularia* Aztec Series
§ ***bonariensis*** ♀H4	Widely available
- 'Little One'	ECha GBin MAsh MAvo
- 'Lollipop'PBR	Widely available
brasiliensis misapplied	see *V. bonariensis*
chamaedrifolia	see *Glandularia peruviana*
hastata	CAby CBod CRos CSpe EBee ECtt EHyd EPfP LEdu LRHS MArl MNHC MNrw NLar NRHS NSti SCob SEle SMad SPer SPhx SPlb SRms SWvt WFar XLum
* - 'Alba'	CAby CSpe EPfP MBel NLar NSti SCob WFar XLum
- 'Blue Spires'	CBod CCBP CNor EPfP IPot
- f. ***rosea***	CAby CBar CBre CElw CSpe EHyd ELan EPfP GKev LCro LEdu LOPS LRHS MNrw MRav NBir NDov NSti SCob SDix SPer SPhx WBor WCAu WFar WSHC XLum
- - 'Pink Spires'	CBod EMor EPfP IPot LRHS
- 'White Spires'	CBod GQue
lasiostachys	EBee
macdougalii 'Lavender Spires'	GBin IPot LRHS NDov SHar SPhx SRms WMal WTre
officinalis	CCBP EBee ENfk GPoy MHer MNHC NAts SRms WHer WSFF XAbr
- var. ***grandiflora*** 'Bampton'	Widely available
Quartz Series	see *Glandularia* Quartz Series
§ ***rigida*** ♀H3	Widely available
- f. ***lilacina*** 'Lilac Haze'	CMac EPfP LRHS
- - 'Polaris'	CCBP CMea CSpe EBee EHyd ELan ELon EPfP EShb GWyn LRHS LSRN NRHS SCob SPer
- 'Santos'	LRHS MHol
scabridoglandulosa	see *Junellia succulentifolia*
serpyllifolia	see *Junellia micrantha*
stricta	CBod EBee NLar SPhx
venosa	see *V. rigida*

Verbesina (*Asteraceae*)

alternifolia	EBee SDix
- 'Goldstrahl'	EMor EPPr WFar
helianthoides	CSam

Vernicia (*Euphorbiaceae*)

fordii S	Plb

Vernonia (*Asteraceae*)

angustifolia	SPhx
angustifolia × ***missurica***	WCot
§ ***arkansana***	CBod CSam EBee ECha ECtt EHyd EWes GLog LEdu LRHS NLar NRHS SDix SPhx WFar
- 'Alba'	EBee ECtt
- 'Betty Blindeman'	EBee LEdu MNrw
- 'Mammuth' ♀H7	CKno CMiW EBee ECtt ELon EMor EWes ILea IPot LEdu LRHS MNrw SDix SEdd SMad SPeP SPhx SPoG WCot WHil WTor

baldwinii	EBee LRHS SPhx
crinita	see *V. arkansana*
fasciculata	EWes LRHS MRav NLar SPhx WCot
gigantea	EWes MMuc MNrw NLar SMad
glauca	SPhx WCot
lettermannii 'Iron Butterfly'	EBee ILea IPot SMad
missurica	LEdu SPhx
noveboracensis	EBee EWhm ILea LEdu NLar SBut SMad WCAu XLum
- 'Albiflora'	EPPr EWes MAvo
- 'White Lightning'	EBee ECha EMor EPPr ILea SDix WHil

Veronica (*Plantaginaceae*)

allionii	GKev
amethystina	see *V. spuria* L.
'Anna'^{PBR}	MTis
armena	EWes MHer MMuc SGro WAbe XSen
(Atomic Ray Series) 'Atomic Hot Pink Ray'	CBod EBee SCob WFar
- 'Atomic Pink Ray'^{PBR}	EBee
- 'Atomic Pink-White Ray'	SCob
- 'Atomic Red Ray'	NGBl SCob
- 'Atomic Silvery Pink Ray'	NLar
- 'Atomic Sky Ray'^{PBR}	NLar SCob
§ ***austriaca***	NBre WCav
- dark blue-flowered	NChi
- var. ***dubia***	see *V. prostrata*
- 'Ionian Skies'	CMea EBou ECha ECtt EPPr EWTr GBin NWad SPer WIce WKif WSHC
§ - subsp. ***teucrium***	CSam EBee SRms WKif
- - 'Blue Fountain'	EHyd LRHS
- - 'Crater Lake Blue' 🏆^{H6}	CDor CTri EBee ECtt EHyd ELan EPfP EWld GWyn LEdu LRHS MArl MAsh MBel MHol MRav NChi SPhx SPlb SRms SWvt WCAu WCot WFar WKif WSHC
- - 'Kapitän'	ECha ECtt EHyd LRHS NGdn NRHS WFar
- - 'Knallblau'	NDov WFar
- - 'Lapis Lazuli'	EBee
- - 'Royal Blue' 🏆^{H6}	CAby CCBP CRos EBee EHyd EPfP GBee GMaP LRHS MAsh MHol NRHS NSti SRms WFar WKif XLum XSen
'Baby Doll'^{PBR}	LSou MBNS SCob SPoG
beccabunga	CHab CWat EWat GPoy LLWG MMuc MWts NPer SEND WMAq WSFF WSpi
'Bergen's Blue'	NLar SHar WSHC
BLUE BOUQUET	see *V. longifolia* 'Blaubündel'
'Blue Indigo'	MNrw NBre NGdn
'Blue Spire'	WSpi
bombycina	WAbe
- subsp. ***bolkardaghensis***	WAbe
bonarota	see *Paederota bonarota*
caespitosa subsp. ***caespitosa***	EPot WAbe
candida	see *V. spicata* subsp. *incana*
× ***cantiana*** 'Kentish Pink'	WAul WCFE WFar XLum
chamaedrys	NMir XLum
CHRISTY ('Henslerone'^{PBR})	ECtt EPfP LBuc MHol
cinerea 🏆^{H5}	SBrt SGro WHoo WSHC XSen
dabneyi	SBut
'Dark Martje'	NLar
'Darwin's Blue'	NLar
'Ellen Mae'	ECtt EWes MNrw WCAu WCot
'Eveline'^{PBR}	ECtt EPfP MHol NDov NHpl NLar SPer
exaltata (d)	NChi WSpi
'Fairytale'^{PBR}	LRHS LSou MBNS NGdn NRHS
'Fantasy'	WGoo
filiformis	XLum
formosa	see *Parahebe formosa*
§ ***fruticans***	GJos ITim
gentianoides	Widely available
- 'Alba'	CMea LEdu NBre
- 'Barbara Sherwood' 🏆^{H7}	CRos EBee EHyd EWTr LRHS NGdn NRHS WFar
- 'Blue Streak'	XLum
- 'Little Blues'	EAJP ECha EDAr LSun
- 'Maihimmel' **new**	WCAu
- 'Mountain Breeze'	EHyd EPfP LBuc NRHS SHar SPoG WFar
- 'Nana'	NBro
- 'Pallida'	GKev LPot MMuc MRav SCob SPlb WBor XLum
- 'Robusta'	CAby CBod EHyd GMaP GWyn LRHS MWat NGdn WFar WHoo
- 'Tissington White'	CAby CBod CRos EAJP EHyd EPfP GMaP LEdu LRHS MCot MHol MPie MPnt MSpe MTis NBPC NBir NBro NGdn NLar NRHS NWad SHar SPoG SRms WCAu WFar
- 'Variegata' (v)	EBee ECha EHyd ELan GMaP GWyn LRHS MRav NBir NWad SPer WGwG WRHF
'Giles van Hees'	MAsh
grandis	EBee MMuc NLar SEND WFar XLum
'Hocus Pocus'	ECtt
incana	see *V. spicata* subsp. *incana*
'Inspiration'	NBre
'Inspire Blue'	CBod CRos LBuc LPot LRHS MMuc MPnt NRHS
'Inspire Pink'	CBod CRos EHyd LRHS MPnt NBir NRHS
kellereri	see *V. spicata*
kiusiana	CMea EBee ECtt NLar NWad
* - var. ***maxima***	CAby
liwanensis	EPot IMou MNrw XSen
longifolia	CBee CMac CSBt ECha ELan MBel NSti XLum
- 'Alba'	CBod ELan MArl MMuc SBut SEND XEll XLum
- 'Antarctica'	EBee
- 'Blaubart'	XLum
§ - 'Blaubündel'	EHyd LRHS NGdn NRHS
- 'Blauer Sommer'	CBod EHyd EPfP LRHS LSou NGdn SPer
§ - 'Blauriesin'	ELan EPfP GMaP GWyn MMrt NLar NSti SAko SPer SRms WSpi XEll
- BLUE GIANTESS	see *V. longifolia* 'Blauriesin'
- 'Blue John'	ECtt EPfP MPie NBre NDov NLar NSti
- blue-flowered	CBod SBut
- 'Charlotte'^{PBR} (v)	CBod CChe CDor CSpe CWGN EBee ECtt EMor GMaP GWyn LCro LOPS LRHS MBel MHol MSCN MTis NDov NGBl NLar SEdd SHar SPer SPoG WCot WTyc
- 'Charming Pink'	CDor LRHS NDov SAko
- 'Christa'^{PBR}	ECtt
- 'Fascination'	ECtt MSCN NEoE NGdn
- FIRST CHOICE ('Allchoice'^{PBR}) **new**	LSou NLar

- First Glory ('Alllord'[PBR])	CBod CMea LRHS LSou MHol NLar NRHS SPad WHil
- First Lady ('Alllady'[PBR])	CBod EPfP LRHS LSou NLar NRHS WHil
- First Love ('Alllove'[PBR])	CMea EBee EHyd EPfP LRHS LSou MMrt MPri MSCN NGdn NLar NRHS SCob SPad SRms WHil
- 'Foerster's Blue'	see *V. longifolia* 'Blauriesin'
- 'Incarnata'	EHyd LRHS
- 'Joseph's Coat' (v)	NBre
- 'Lilac Fantasy'	MRav NSti
- 'Marietta'[PBR]	CBod CDor CRos ECtt EHyd EMor EWTr LCro LOPS LRHS MAvo MBel MHol MTis NCou NDov NLar NRHS SEdd SPer SPoG SRms WCot WHoo WPnP WRHF WTyc
- 'Melanie White'	MAvo SPer WHil WPnP
- 'Oxford Blue'	CBod
- 'Pacific Ocean'[PBR]	NLar
- 'Pink Eveline'[PBR]	CBod EBee ECtt EPfP MHol NDov NGdn NLar STPC
- pink-flowered	CBod CMac SBut
- 'Rose Tone'	GJos
- 'Schneeriesin'	CRos EBee ECha ECtt EHyd EPfP GBin GMaP LRHS MRav MTis NBir NLar NRHS SAko SPer WGwG
lyallii	see *Parahebe lyallii*
'Martje'	XLum
Mauve Moody Blues ('Novavermau') (Moody Blues Series) **new**	CBod CRos
× ***media*** 'Can Can'[PBR] **new**	NDov
- First Kiss ('Allkiss'[PBR])	NLar
- First Match ('Allvglove'[PBR]) **new**	NLar
- First Memory ('Allv1461'[PBR]) **new**	NLar
montana 'Corinne Tremaine' (v)	SRms
officinalis	GJos XLum
oltensis	CPBP EPot ITim WAbe
orchidea	see *V. spicata* subsp. *orchidea*
orientalis subsp. ***orientalis***	EPot
ornata	MAvo SEdd
'Pacific Ocean'	ECtt NLar
pectinata	ECtt
- 'Rosea'	EWes XSen
peduncularis 'Oxford Blue'	see *V. umbrosa* 'Georgia Blue'
perfoliata	see *Parahebe perfoliata*
petraea 'Madame Mercier'	EBou XLum
'Pink Damask'	ECtt ELan ELon EPfP EWTr GMaP MRav MSpe MTis NDov NGdn NLar SCob SDys SRms WHoo
'Pink Harmony'	MHol NGBl
Pink Moody Blues ('Novaverpin') (Moody Blues Series)	CBod MHol WHil
(Plumosa Series) Plumosa Amethyst Plume	ECtt MHol MSCN WFar
- Plumosa Blue Plume	MHol
- Plumosa Hot Pink Plume **new**	CBod
- Plumosa Lavender Plume	CWGN EBee EPfP
porphyriana	MAsh MMuc NLar SAko
prenja	see *V. austriaca*

§	***prostrata*** ♀H5	CMea CSpe CTri ECtt EPfP GJos GKev LRHS MAsh MHol NHol SRms WHoo WIce
	- 'Aztec Gold'[PBR]	CMac
	- 'Blue Sheen'	ECtt EHyd EPfP LRHS MAsh NBir NRHS
	- Goldwell ('Verbrig') (v)	EBee ECtt EPPr WFar
	- 'Lavender Mist'	EHyd LRHS NRHS
	- 'Lilac Time'	CRos EBou ECtt EHyd LRHS MAsh NBir NHol NRHS SRms WFar WIce WRHF WTor
	- 'Little Nell'	ECtt
	- 'Loddon Blue'	CPBP SRms WCot
	- 'Mrs Holt'	CRos EBou ECtt EHyd LRHS MHer NBir NLar NRHS NWad SRms
	- 'Nana'	CPBP EBou ECtt EPot EWes
	- 'Nestor'	CTri SRms XLum
	- 'Rhapsody in Blue'	CRos EHyd NRHS SRms
	- 'Spode Blue' ♀H5	CMac CMea CRos CTri ECtt EHyd GKev GWyn LRHS MHer MMuc NRHS SPoG SRms
	- 'Trehane'	EBou ECtt EHyd EPfP LRHS MAsh MHer MHol NRHS NRya NWad SPlb SPoG SRms WFar WIce
	'Purpleicious Harmony'[PBR]	CBod EBee MBel MTis SCob SPer WHil
	repens	NEoE SPlb
	'Rosalinde'	NGdn
	'Royal Pink'	MRav NLar
	rupestris	see *V. prostrata*
	saturejoides	CPBP SRms
	saxatilis	see *V. fruticans*
	schmidtiana 'Nana'	GAbr GKev
	selleri	see *V. wormskjoldii*
	'Shirley Blue' ♀H6	ELan EPfP EWTr ILea LCro LOPS LPot LSRN MHer MMuc SEND SPer SPhx SRms WCAu WCFE WSpi
	Sky Blue Moody Blues ('Novaversky') (Moody Blues Series) **new**	CBod WHil
§	***spicata***	CSam EHyd ELan EPfP GJos LBuc LRHS MBow MRav NBid NRHS SCob SRms WBrk WFar WShi XLum
	- 'Alba'	CBcs EBee EPfP GAbr GJos LRHS MRav NLar SCob WFar XLum
§	- 'Blaufuchs'	CSam
	- Blue Fox	see *V. spicata* 'Blaufuchs'
§	- 'Erika'	ECtt NBid NBir NGdn
§	- 'Glory'[PBR]	CBcs CBod CDor CWGN EHyd ELan LRHS LSou MMrt MPri MSCN MTis NLar NRHS SCob SEdd SPer SPoG WHoo
	- 'Heidekind'	CBod EBee EBou ECha ELan GKev NBir NGdn SRms WCAu WCav WHoo WIce XLum
	- 'High Five'[PBR]	CBod
	- subsp. ***hybrida***	WHer
I	- - 'Elaine's Form'	WCot
§	- 'Icicle'	EBee SCob WCAu
§	- subsp. ***incana*** ♀H4	EBou ELan EPfP MMuc SPlb SRms XSen
	- - 'Nana'	NBir SRms
	- - 'Silver Carpet'	EHyd LRHS MBel MRav WAul WSpi
	- 'Nana Blauteppich'	CPBP EHyd NLar
§	- subsp. ***orchidea***	SRms
	- 'Pink Goblin'	EAJP EHyd ELan EPfP
	- 'Pink Marshmallow'	CBod NLar SRkn
	- 'Pink Panther'[PBR]	WCot
	- Red Fox	see *V. spicata* 'Rotfuchs'
	- 'Rocket Power Blue' **new**	CRos

- 'Romiley Purple' EBee SPer WSpi
- 'Rosalind' NLar
- ***rosea*** see *V. spicata* 'Erika'
§ - 'Rotfuchs' CBcs CBod CRos ECtt EHyd ELan ELon EMor EPfP GWyn LCro LOPS LRHS MBel MBow MHer MRav NBid NBir NGdn NRHS SCob SPer SPoG SRms WCAu WCFE
- 'Royal Candles' see *V. spicata* 'Glory'
- 'Sightseeing' GJos NBir SRms
- subsp. ***spicata*** 'Nana' XSen
- 'Total Eclipse'PBR EMor
- 'Twilight'PBR ECtt EPfP NLar SCob
- 'Ulster Blue Dwarf' CRos EBee EHyd EPfP GMaP IMou LRHS MAvo NBid NGdn NRHS SCob WCAu XLum
- YOUNIQUE BABY BLUE MBNS
- YOUNIQUE BABY RED ('Versbabyred') MBNS
- YOUNIQUE BABY WHITE ('Versbabywhite') MBNS
§ ***spuria*** L. SEND
stelleri see *V. wormskjoldii*
'Summer Breeze' NBro
'Sunny Border Blue' EBee GWyn MHol NLar
surculosa XSen
teucrium see *V. austriaca* subsp. *teucrium*
§ ***umbrosa*** 'Georgia Blue' ♀H5 Widely available
urticifolia SBrt
virginica see *Veronicastrum virginicum*
'White Icicle' see *V. spicata* 'Icicle'
WHITE MOODY BLUES ('Novaverwhi') (Moody Blues Series) **new** CBod WHil
whitleyi MMuc
§ ***wormskjoldii*** EBou GKev LPot MBrN MMuc SRms XSen

Veronicastrum ✿ (*Plantaginaceae*)

'Adoration' CBod EBee ECtt ELon EPPr IPot LCro LOPS LRHS LSun MBel MHol NDov NLar SMHy SMad SPhx SRkn STPC WCot WFar WSpi
axillare IMou
brunonianum WSHC
japonicum var. ***australe*** B&SWJ 11009 WCru
latifolium WCot
- BWJ 8158 EPPr ESwi NWad WCot WCru WSHC
'Red Arrows' Widely available
sibiricum CKno CRos ECha EHyd EPfP EShb LRHS MMuc NRHS SEND SHar SRms WSpi XLum
- BWJ 6352 NLar WCru WFar
- 'Kobaltkaars' SMHy
- var. ***yezoense*** IMou WFar
- - RBS 0290 EPPr NEoE WFar
villosulum EWes IMou NBro WSHC XLum
§ ***virginicum*** CKno CTri EBee ECtt EMor GPoy NBir NLar SBut SRms WFar WSpi XLum
- 'Album' ♀H7 Widely available
- 'Apollo' Widely available
- 'Challenger'PBR **new** NDov NLar
- 'Cupid' CBod CWCL EBee ECtt ELon EMor EPfP EWTr EWes GBin GMaP ILea LEdu LRHS MNrw NDov NLar SHar STPC WSpi
- 'Diane' EAJP EBee ECtt ELon EMor EPPr EPfP EWhm GMaP ILea IPot LEdu LRHS MAvo MCot MTis NDov NLar SCob SHar SPhx SWvt WCAu WSpi
- 'Du Jardin' LEdu
- 'Erica' Widely available
- 'Fascination' Widely available
- var. ***incarnatum*** see *V. virginicum* f. *roseum*
- 'Klein Erica' CBod
- 'Lavendelturm' ♀H7 Widely available
- 'Pointed Finger' CMea GMaP LEdu LRHS NLar SPhx
§ - f. ***roseum*** CBod ECha EHyd ELan EMor EPPr GMaP GQue LRHS MHol MRav NBro NDov SGbt SPhx SWvt WBor WHrl WKif WSpi XLum
- - 'Pink Glow' Widely available
- 'Spring Dew' CBre EWTr ILea LEdu LRHS MNrw NBid NEoE NGBl NLar SPhx WCAu WSpi
- 'Temptation' CBre EBee EPPr EWTr GMaP ILea IPot LEdu LRHS MAvo MRav MTis NBro NEoE NLar SPhx WPGP

Verschaffeltia (*Arecaceae*)

splendida XBlo

Vesalea (*Caprifoliaceae*)

§ ***floribunda*** ♀H4 CBcs CBod CExl CMac CSde EBee ECre EHyd ELan ELon EPfP LRHS MAsh MGil MRav NLar NOra SBrt SGbt SPer SPoG SRms WCot

Vestia (*Solanaceae*)

§ ***foetida*** CBcs CCCN CExl CMac CRos CTsd EBee EHyd ELan ELon EWld LRHS MGil MNrw SBrt SEND WHil WPav
lycioides see *V. foetida*

Viburnum ✿ (*Adoxaceae*)

NJM 11.008 WPGP
acerifolium NWad
alnifolium see *V. lantanoides*
atrocyaneum CExl CJun EBee NWad SBrt WFar
- B&SWJ 7272 EPfP WCru
- HIRD 113 WPGP
betulifolium CBcs CExl CJun CMCN EBee ELan EPfP EWes GKev GKin SAko WPGP
- f. ***aurantiacum*** CJun
- 'Hohuanshan' SSta WCru
bitchiuense CJun
× ***bodnantense*** CMac CTri EBee WFar
- 'Charles Lamont' ♀H6 Widely available
- 'Dawn' ♀H6 Widely available
- 'Deben' ♀H6 EPfP NLar SCob SPer
brachyandrum B&SWJ 5784 WCru
bracteatum NLar
buddlejifolium CMac EBee EBtc EPfP EWes LRHS MMuc WCru
× ***burkwoodii*** Widely available
- 'Anne Russell' Widely available
- 'Chenaultii' MRav
- 'Compact Beauty' CJun WLov WSpi
- 'Conoy' ELon MAsh WLov
- 'Fulbrook' CRos EHyd EPfP LEdu LRHS MAsh SSta
- 'Mohawk' ♀H6 CDoC CEnd CJun CRos EHyd ELan ELon EPfP LEdu LRHS MAsh MGos MRav NLar NOrn NRHS SCoo SWvt WCFE WLov WSpi

- 'Park Farm Hybrid' ♀H6	CDoC CExl CMac CRos CTri EBee ELan ELon EPfP LEdu LRHS MAsh MGos MRav NHol NLar NOra SPer SPoG SRms SSta SWvt WHwl WKif WSpi
calvum	CExl
aff. ***calvum*** WWJ 12012	EBee WCru
× ***carlcephalum*** ♀H6	Widely available
- 'Cayuga' ♀H5	MAsh WSpi
carlesii	CBcs CBrac CCVT CDoC CMac CTri ELon EPfP GKin LSRN LSou MBlu MGos MRav MSwo SCob SDix SGol SLim SPer SRms SavN WFar
- B&SWJ 8838	WCru
- 'Aurora' ♀H6	Widely available
- 'Charis'	CJun WKif WPGP
- 'Compactum'	CJun MAsh SSta WLov
- 'Diana' ♀H6	CAby CEnd CJun CMac CRos EBee EHyd ELon EMil EPfP LRHS LSRN MAsh MBlu NLar SPer SPoG SSta WLov WPGP WSpi
- 'Marlou'	CJun NLar
cassinoides	CJun EBee WPGP
'Chesapeake'	CJun EWes MMuc SEND
chingii	CJun WCru WPGP
'Chippewa'	CJun
cinnamomifolium ♀H5	CBcs CCoa CExl CRos EHyd ELan EPfP LMaj LRHS NLar SBrt SEND SLon SPer SPoG WCot WSpi
costaricanum B&SWJ 10477	WCru
cotinifolium	CExl
- CC 4541	CExl NLar
cylindricum	CRos EHyd LEdu LRHS SBrt WCru WLov WPGP WPav
- B&SWJ 6479 from Thailand	WCru
- B&SWJ 7239	WCru
- B&SWJ 9719 from Vietnam	WCru
- HWJCM 434 from Nepal	WCru
- 'Chino-Crûg'	WCru
davidii ♀H5	Widely available
- (f)	CAby CBcs CMac CSBt ELan EPfP EWTr MAsh SGbt SPer SPoG SRms WCFE
- (m)	CAby CBcs CMac CSBt ELan EPfP SGbt SPer SPoG SRms
- 'Angustifolium'	CJun EBee NLar WPGP
dentatum	EBtc
- BLUE MUFFIN ('Christom')	CBcs ELan SGol
- 'Moonglow'	NLar
- 'Morton'	SSta
- PATHFINDER ('Patzam')	SSta
- var. ***pubescens*** 'Longifolium'	SSta
- 'White and Blue'	CJun NLar
dilatatum	EBtc
- B&SWJ 5844	WCru
- B&SWJ 8734	WCru
- B&SWJ 10830	WCru
- PAB 6831	LEdu
- 'Asian Beauty'	SSta
- CARDINAL CANDY	see *V. dilatatum* 'Henneke'
§ - 'Henneke'	SSta
- 'Iroquois'	SSta
- 'Michael Dodge'	MBlu
'Emerald Triumph'	CJun
erosum B&SWJ 8735	WCru
- B&SWJ 8893	WCru
- B&SWJ 11083	WCru
erubescens	CJun NLar
- HWJK 2163	WCru
- VdL 4122	WPGP
- var. ***gracilipes***	CJun
- 'Ward van Teylingen'	NLar
'Eskimo' ♀H5	CBcs CCVT CMac CRos CSBt EBee EHyd ELan EPfP LRHS MAsh MBNS MBlu MGos NOra NOrn SAko SCoo SGol SLim SPoG SRms SSta SWvt SavN
fansipanense B&SWJ 8302	WCru
- KWJ 12239	WCru
§ ***farreri*** ♀H6	CBcs CBod CMCN CRos CSBt CTri EBee ELan EPfP EWTr LBuc LEdu LRHS LSRN MGos MRav MSwo NLar SGol SPer SWvt SavN WHwl
- 'Album'	see *V. farreri* 'Candidissimum'
§ - 'Candidissimum'	CExl CMac ELan EPfP LRHS LSRN MRav NLar SCoo SGol SPer SPoG SRms SWvt WAvo WHwl WLov
- 'December Dwarf'	CJun NLar SCoo
- 'Farrer's Pink'	CExl CJun NLar
- 'Nanum'	CJun CMac CRos EHyd EPfP LRHS MAsh MBrN MRav WAvo WCot WHwl WLov
foetens	see *V. grandiflorum* f. *foetens*
foetidum	WCru
var. ***rectangulatum*** B&SWJ 1888	
- - B&SWJ 3451	WCru
formosanum CWJ 12460	WCru
fragrans Bunge	see *V. farreri*
'Fragrant Cloud'	SWvt
furcatum ♀H6	EPfP GKin LRHS NLar SAko WLov
- B&SWJ 5939	WCru
- B&SWJ 10880	WCru
× ***globosum*** 'Jermyns Globe'	CJun CMac MRav NLar SEND SGol SLon SPoG WFar
grandiflorum	NLar
- 'De Oirsprong'	NLar
§ - f. ***foetens***	LRHS
harryanum	CBod CSBt EBtc EPfP EWTr IDee NLar WCru WLov WPGP WSHC
henryi	CJun EPfP WCFE
× ***hillieri*** 'Winton' ♀H6	CBcs CBod CJun CMac CRos EBee EHyd EPfP IArd LRHS LSRN MGos NLar NRHS SChF SGol SLon SPoG WFar WPGP WSpi
hoanglienense	EBee EPfP
- B&SWJ 8281	WCru
- HWJ 934	WCru
- KWJ 12283	WCru
- PAB 7833	LEdu
hupehense MF 93087	SSta
'Huron'	NLar
ichangense	CJun NLar
japonicum	CExl EBee
- B&SWJ 5968	WCru
× ***juddii***	Widely available
kansuense	CExl
- BWJ 7737	WCru
koreanum B&SWJ 4231	WCru
lantana	CBrac CCVT CHab CLnd CMac CTho CTri ECrN ELan EPfP EShb EWTr LBuc MMuc SCob SEWo SPer SVic WMat WMou WTSh
- 'Aureum'	EPfP MAsh MBlu NLar
- var. ***discolor***	NLar
- 'Mohican'	NLar

	Name	Suppliers
	- 'Xanthocarpum'	SWvt WFar
§	***lantanoides***	SSta
	aff. ***lautum*** B&SWJ 10290	WCru
	'Le Bois Marquis'PBR	CDoC CDow CRos EHyd EMil EPfP EShb LCro LOPS LRHS LSRN MAsh MGos SGol SGsty SPoG WCot
	lentago	CMac EPfP LMaj
	luzonicum B&SWJ 3637	WCru
	- var. ***formosanum*** B&SWJ 3585	WCru
	- var. ***oblongum*** B&SWJ 3549	WCru
	- var. ***sinuatum*** B&SWJ 4009	WCru
	macrocephalum	CJun SLon SSta WPGP
	- 'Sterile'	CJun SSta
	mariesii	see *V. plicatum* f. *tomentosum* 'Mariesii'
	mullaha B&SWJ 2251A	WCru
	- GWJ 9227	WCru
	aff. ***mullaha*** GWJ 9388	WCru
	nervosum HWJK 2241	WCru
	- HWJK 2373	WCru
	nudum BRANDYWINE ('Bulk')	EPfP SSta WPGP
	- 'Pink Beauty'	CBod CJun CRos EHyd EPfP LCro LOPS LRHS LSRN MMrt NRHS SChF SGol SGsty SPoG SSta SWvt WFar WGob WPGP WSpi
	- 'Winterthur'	CJun SSta
	odoratissimum misapplied	see *V. odoratissimum* var. *awabuki*
	odoratissimum Ker Gawl.	EBee
	- RWJ 10046	WCru
	- var. ***arboricola*** B&SWJ 3052 **new**	WCru
	- - B&SWJ 3397 **new**	WCru
	- - B&SWJ 6913	WCru
§	- var. ***awabuki***	CExl ECre EPfP LEdu LRHS MBlu MGos NLar SEND SGol SLim SPer WCot
	- - B&SWJ 8404	ESwi WCru
	- - B&SWJ 11374 from Wabuka, Japan	WCru
	- - 'Emerald Lustre'	CBcs LRHS WFar
	aff. ***odoratissimum*** B&SWJ 3913 from the Philippines	WCru
	oliganthum 'Kyo Kanzashi'	WPGP
	'Oneida'	CJun
	opulus	Widely available
§	- var. ***americanum***	NLar WKor
	- - 'Phillips'	CAgr
	- - 'Wentworth'	CAgr
	- 'Amy's Magic Gold'	NLar
	- 'Apricot'	NLar
	- 'Aureum'	CMac CRos ELan EPfP LRHS MAsh MGil MGos MMuc MRav NLar SPer SPoG WCFE
	- var. ***calvescens*** B&SWJ 10544	WCru
	- 'Compactum' ♀H6	Widely available
	- 'Fructuluteo'	CMCN SGol
*	- 'Harvest Gold'	SCoo SGol SLim
	- 'Lady Marmalade'	NLar
	- 'Nanum'	ELan EPfP EPot EShb GBin MRav NLar NWad
	- 'Notcutt's Variety' ♀H6	MAsh WLov
	- 'Park Harvest'	CRos EBee EHyd LRHS MAsh NLar SMad SWvt
§	- 'Roseum' ♀H6	Widely available
	- 'Sterile'	see *V. opulus* 'Roseum'
*	- 'Sterile Compactum'	SWvt
	- 'Sylvie'	NLar
	- 'Xanthocarpum' ♀H6	CBcs CExl CMac CRos CTho EBee EHyd ELan EPfP EShb GBin LRHS MAsh MGos MMuc MRav MSwo NLar SCob SGol SLon SPer SPoG SRms SWvt WFar WSpi
	parvifolium	EPfP NLar
	- B&SWJ 3375	WCru
	- B&SWJ 6768	WCru
	phlebotrichum B&SWJ 11058	WCru
	- B&SWJ 11470	WCru
	pichinchense B&SWJ 10660	WCru
	plicatum	CTri SCob
	- 'Nanum'	see *V. plicatum* f. *tomentosum* 'Nanum Semperflorens'
§	- f. ***plicatum***	SChF
	- - 'Grandiflorum'	CBcs CCCN CMac EPfP LRHS NLar SPer SPoG WCFE
	- - 'Mary Milton'	CJun ELan IArd NLar SSta
	- - 'Pink Sensation'	CJun GBin NLar
	- - 'Popcorn' ♀H6	CDoC CExl CJun CMac CRos EHyd ELan EPfP EShb LRHS LSRN MAsh MMrt NHol NLar SGol SPoG SSta WLov
	- - 'Rosace'	CRos EHyd EPfP LRHS MBlu NLar NRHS SAko
	- - 'Rotundifolium'	IArd MAsh MGos MRav NLar WFar
	- - TRIUMPH ('Trizam')	NLar
	- 'Sterile'	see *V. plicatum* f. *plicatum*
§	- f. ***tomentosum***	IBal SGol SPoG
	- - 'Cascade' ♀H6	CJun ELan EWTr LRHS SAko WSpi
	- - 'Dart's Red Robin'	ECtt MAsh
	- - 'Elizabeth Bullivant'	CRos EHyd EPfP LRHS NRHS
	- - KILIMANJARO ('Jww1'PBR)	CBod CDoC CRos EBee EHyd ELan EPfP GBin LCro LOPS LRHS LSRN MBlu MGos MThu NLar NRHS SCob SGol SPer SPoG WHwl WSpi
	- - KILIMANJARO SUNRISE ('Jww5')	CBcs CRos EHyd LCro LOPS LRHS MGos MPkF NRHS SCoo SGsty WHwl
	- - 'Lanarth'	CBcs CCCN CDoC CExl CMac CRos CSBt CTri EHyd ELan EPfP LRHS LSRN MAsh MBlu MGos NLar NOra SCoo SGbt SGol SGsty SPer SWvt WSpi
§	- - 'Mariesii' ♀H6	Widely available
	- - 'Molly Schroeder'	NLar SSta
§	- - 'Nanum Semperflorens'	CBcs CMCN CMac CMea CRos EHyd EPfP EShb LRHS MGos NLar NRHS SGol SPoG WFar WLov
	- - 'Pink Beauty' ♀H6	CBcs CCCN CDoC CJun CMac CRos CTsd EBee EHyd ELan EPfP EWTr LCro LOPS LRHS LSRN MAsh MBlu MGos MRav NLar NOra SCob SGol SPer SPoG SWvt WFar WKif WSpi
	- - 'Rowallane'	NLar
	- - 'Saint Keverne'	ELan GKin
	- - 'Shasta'	CJun CMCN EPfP EWTr LRHS MMrt NLar SGol WFar WSpi
	- - 'Shoshoni'	NLar SGol WPGP WSpi
	- - 'Summer Snowflake' ♀H6	CBar CCCN CEnd CRos CWGN ECrN EHyd ELan EPfP EShb LRHS MAsh MSwo NLar NRHS SGol SPer SPoG WFar WHwl

	- 'Watanabe'	see *V. plicatum* f. *tomentosum* 'Nanum Semperflorens'
	'Pragense' ♀H6	CBcs CJun CMCN EPfP LRHS MGos NHol NLar SPer
	propinquum	WFar
	- CWJ 12395	WCru
	- CWJ 12426	WCru
	- var. ***propinquum*** Guiz 222	WPGP
	prunifolium	EBtc SGol WCru
	- 'Mrs Henry's Large'	CJun EPfP NLar
	× ***rhytidophylloides*** 'Alleghany'	NLar
	- DART'S DUKE ('Interduke')	WCFE
	- 'Willowwood'	CRos EHyd ELan LRHS MAsh NLar SCob
	rhytidophyllum	CBcs CMac EBee ECrN EPfP LMaj LRHS MGos MMuc MSwo NLar SAdn SArc SCob SEND SGol SPer SRms SWvt WCFE WSFF
	- 'Roseum'	CExl SWvt
	- 'Wisley Pink'	MAsh
	'Royal Guard'	CJun
	sambucinum	EBee
	- HWJ 838	WCru
	- var. ***tomentosum*** HWJ 733	WCru
	sargentii B&SWJ 8695	WCru
	- 'Onondaga' ♀H6	Widely available
	semperflorens	see *V. plicatum* f. *tomentosum* 'Nanum Semperflorens'
§	***setigerum***	EBee EPfP IArd IDee NLar
	- BWJ 8409	WCru
	sieboldii	EBtc
	- B&SWJ 2837	WCru
	- CWJ 12808	WCru
	- 'Seneca'	LRHS
	subalpinum	EPfP NLar
	taitoense CWJ 12406	WCru
	taiwanianum B&SWJ 3009	WCru
	- CWJ 12467	WCru
	ternatum	EPfP
	theiferum	see *V. setigerum*
	tinoides B&SWJ 10612	WCru
	tinus	Widely available
	- 'Bewley's Variegated' (v)	EBee
I	- 'Compactum'	SWvt
	- 'Eve Price' ♀H4	Widely available
	- 'French White' ♀H4	CBod CBrac CCCN CDoC CMac EBee ELan EPfP EWTr LCro LOPS MGos MNHC MRav SCoo SLim SRms SWvt
	- 'Gwenllian' ♀H4	Widely available
	- 'Israel'	EShb LRHS MBNS
	- 'Ladybird'	CDoC
	- 'Lisarose'^{PBR}	CBar CBcs CBod CDoC EBee EPfP LCro LOPS LSRN MAsh MGos NLar SPoG SWvt WSpi
	- 'Lucidum'	CBcs CCoa CSde EPfP LMaj NLar SGol
	- 'Lucidum Variegatum' (v)	CMac SLim
*	- 'Macrophyllum'	EPfP LRHS NLar SWvt
	- 'Peter's Purple'	CRos EHyd EPfP LRHS NRHS SPoG
	- 'Purpureum'	CBcs CBod CSBt ELon EPfP MAsh MGos MSwo NLar SCoo SGol SLim SPer WFar
	- SPIRIT ('Anvi'^{PBR})	CBod CRos CSBt EHyd ELan EPfP LRHS MAsh NEoE NLar NRHS NWad SCoo SPoG SWeb SWvt
	- 'Spring Bouquet'	CJun MAsh
	- subsp. ***subcordatum***	see *V. treleasei*
	- 'Variegatum' (v)	CBod CMac CRos CTri EBee EHyd ELan EPfP LRHS MAsh MGos NLar NPol NRHS SCob SGol SLim SPoG SRms SWvt SavN WFar WLov
	tomentosum	see *V. plicatum* f. *tomentosum*
§	***treleasei*** B&SWJ 12544	WCru
	trilobum	see *V. opulus* var. *americanum*
	triphyllum B&SWJ 10757	WCru
	- B&SWJ 14298	WCru
	utile	NOra WThu
	aff. ***venustum*** B&SWJ 10477	WCru
	wrightii	EPfP IArd IDee MRav
	- B&SWJ 5871	WCru
	- 'Hessei'	WLov
	- var. ***stipellatum*** B&SWJ 5856	WCru
	- - B&SWJ 8780A	WCru

Vicia (*Papilionaceae*)

americana	EBee
benghalensis new	SPhx
cracca	CHab MBow NMir SPhx WSFF
nigricans	SBrt
subsp. ***gigantica*** new	
oroboides	EBee
sativa	CHab

Vigna (*Papilionaceae*)

angularis	SVic
caracalla	see *Cochliasanthus caracalla*
radiata	SVic

Villaresia see *Citronella*

Vinca (*Apocynaceae*)

	difformis	CBod CFis CSpe CTri ECha IDee LPla SDix SPer SRms WAvo WHer XLum
	- 'Alba'	CCBP CDor CSam
	- subsp. ***difformis***	WOut
	- Greystone form	CExl EBee EPPr SEND
	- 'Jenny Pym'	CBod CChe CDor CExl CMac CRos CSam EBee ECha EPPr EPfP EWes EWld LRHS MBNS NLar SEND SGro SIvy SPoG SRms WAvo WOut
	- 'Ruby Baker'	EPPr EPfP EWes NChi SPoG WAvo WFar
	- subsp. ***sardoa***	CRos CSpe ECha EHyd EPPr EPfP EWes LRHS WCot WFar
	- 'Snowmound'	CBod CRos CSBt LRHS MRav NLar SPoG SWvt WAvo
	herbacea RCB UA 21	WCot
	'Hidcote Purple'	see *V. major* var. *oxyloba*
	major	CBcs CBod CBrac CSBt ELan EShb GPoy GWyn LBuc LCro LPot MAsh MGos MSwo NPol SCob SGbt SGol SLim SPer SRms WFar XLum XSen
	- 'Alba'	CMac
	- subsp. ***balcanica***	IMou XLum
	- 'Elegantissima'	see *V. major* 'Variegata'
	- var. ***hirsuta*** misapplied	see *V. major* var. *oxyloba*
§	- subsp. ***hirsuta*** (Boiss.) Stearn	CMac WCot XLum
§	- 'Maculata' (v)	CBcs CSBt ECrN EShb GWyn LRHS MSwo SEND SGol SLim SPer SPoG SWvt WAvo WOut

§	- var. ***oxyloba***	CCBP CExl CFis CRos CTri ECha ELan EPPr EPfP EPri LPla LPot LRHS MRav SRms WAvo WHer
	- var. ***pubescens***	see *V. major* subsp. *hirsuta* (Boiss.) Stearn
	- 'Surrey Marble'	see *V. major* 'Maculata'
§	- 'Variegata' (v) 🏆H6	Widely available
	- 'Wojo's Jem' (v)	CBod CMac CPla CRos EHyd ELan EPfP EWes LRHS MGos NCou NLar NRHS SCob SWvt WAvo WCot
	minor	CBar CBcs CDoC CSBt EHyd ELan GAbr GBin GKin GPoy LCro LOPS LRHS MAsh MGos SCob SLim SVic WFar XLum
	- f. ***alba***	CBcs CDoC CMac CRos ECha EPPr EPfP GJos LCro LOPS LRHS LSRN MAsh NLar NRHS SCob SGol SPer SVic WCot WFar XLum XSen
§	- - 'Alba Variegata' (v)	CBar CBrac CExl LSRN NEoE NWad SRms WCot WFar WHoo WOut
	- - 'Gertrude Jekyll'	Widely available
	- 'Alba Aureovariegata'	see *V. minor* f. *alba* 'Alba Variegata'
	- 'Anna' **new**	NLar
§	- 'Argenteovariegata' (v) 🏆H6	CBcs CBrac CDoC CMac CSBt CSam CTri ECha EHyd ELan ELon EPfP LRHS MGos MMuc MSwo NChi NRHS SCob SGol SLim SPer SRms WFar
§	- 'Atropurpurea' 🏆H6	Widely available
§	- 'Aureovariegata' (v)	CBcs CMac EBee ELan EPPr EPfP GAbr MGos MRav SGol SLim SPer SPlb
§	- 'Azurea Flore Pleno' (d) 🏆H6	CDoC CMac CRos CTri ECha EPPr EPfP GAbr LRHS MRav NChi NLar NRHS SLim SPer SPoG SRms SWvt WFar WHoo WKif XLum
	- 'Blue and Gold' (v)	EPPr
	- 'Blue Drift'	EWes MSwo
	- 'Bowles's Blue'	see *V. minor* 'Bowles's Variety'
	- 'Bowles's Purple'	GMaP NCou SHar SPer
§	- 'Bowles's Variety' 🏆H6	Widely available
	- 'Burgundy'	SRms
	- 'Caerulea Plena'	see *V. minor* 'Azurea Flore Pleno'
	- 'Dartington Star'	see *V. major* var. *oxyloba*
	- 'Double Burgundy'	see *V. minor* 'Multiplex'
	- 'Elisa' **new**	GWyn NLar
	- 'Evelyne'PBR (v)	WFar
	- 'Flower Power'	EPPr NLar
	- GREEN CARPET	see *V. minor* 'Grüner Teppich'
§	- 'Grüner Teppich'	SGol WFar
	- 'Halstenbek'	XLum
	- 'Illumination' (v)	Widely available
	- 'Josefine'	MHol NLar
	- 'La Grave'	see *V. minor* 'Bowles's Variety'
	- 'Marie'	EPPr NLar XSen
	- 'Mrs Betty James' (d)	WCot
§	- 'Multiplex' (d)	EPPr LBuc MSwo SGol SLim SRms WOut
	- 'Purpurea'	see *V. minor* 'Atropurpurea'
	- 'Ralph Shugert' (v) 🏆H6	CDoC CExl CMac CRos EHyd ELan ELon EPPr EPfP EWes GJos LCro LOPS LRHS MAsh MGos MPri NLar NRHS SCob SCoo SGol SPoG SRms WFar
	- 'Rubra'	see *V. minor* 'Atropurpurea'
	- 'Sabinka'	EPPr
	- 'Silver Service' (d/v)	WFar
	- 'Snowdrift'	EPPr
	- 'Temptation' (d) **new**	WTyc
	- 'Variegata'	see *V. minor* 'Argenteovariegata'
	- 'Variegata Aurea'	see *V. minor* 'Aureovariegata'
	- 'White Gold'	NEoE
	- 'White Power'	EPPr EWes

Vincetoxicum (*Apocynaceae*)

cretaceum PAB 3432	LEdu
forrestii	CExl
fuscatum	IMou
hirundinaria	EBee EPPr GPoy LEdu WCot
nigrum	EBee NChi WCot

Viola ✿ (*Violaceae*)

	'Abigail' (Vtta)	WFar
	'Ada Segre' (Vt)	CGro
	'Admiral Avellan'	see *V.* 'Amiral Avellan'
	'Admiration' (Va)	WGoo
	adunca var. ***minor***	see *V. labradorica* ambig.
§	***alba***	EWes
	'Alethia' (Va)	GBee SDys WGoo
	'Alice Kate' (Va)	WGoo
	'Alice Witter' (Vt)	CGro SHar
*	'Alison' (Va)	WGoo
	altaica	SPlb
	'Amelia' (Va)	WGoo
§	'Amiral Avellan' (Vt)	CGro
	'Amy' (Va)	EVic
	'Annaleisia' (Vt)	CGro
	'Annette Ross' (Va)	GBee GWyn WGoo
I	'Annie' (Vt)	CGro
	'Ardross Gem' (Va)	WGoo
	'Arkwright's Ruby' (Va)	MAsh
	arvensis	CHab
	'Ashvale Blue' (dPVt)	CGro
	'Aspasia' (Va) 🏆H5	GAbr GWyn MAsh WGoo
	'Avril Lawson' (Va)	GKev SHar WGoo
	'Barbara' (Va)	ECtt WGoo
	'Baroness de Rothschild' misapplied	see *V.* 'Baronne Alice de Rothschild'
	'Baroness de Rothschild' ambig. (Vt)	CGro WHer
§	'Baronne Alice de Rothschild' (Vt)	CDor SHar
	'Beatrice' (Vtta)	WGoo
	'Becky Groves' (Vt)	CGro
	'Beetroot' (Vt)	CGro
§	'Belmont Blue' (C)	CRos CSam CSpe CTri EBee ELon EWes GBin GKev GMaP LCro LOPS LRHS MAsh MCot MRav NBir SCob SHar SPer SPhx WCAu WFar WGoo WSpi
§	***bertolonii***	WGoo
	'Beshlie' (Va) 🏆H5	WGoo
	biflora	EPPr EWld MNrw
	'Blackout'PBR (C)	CBod ECtt MHol
	'Blue Butterfly' (C)	GWyn MPie
	'Blue Carpet' (Va)	EHyd LRHS
	'Blue Ice' (Va) **new**	WFar
	'Blue Moon' (C)	MAsh WGoo
	BLUE MOON ('Smev1') (Celestial Series) (Va)	GWyn
	'Blue Moonlight' (C)	MPie
	'Blue Sails' (Va)	EVic
	'Blue Tit' (Va)	ECtt
	(Bonnie Lassies Series) BONNIE LASSIES EMMA (Va) **new**	CRos
	- BONNIE LASSIES SARAH (Va) **new**	CRos
	'Bonny' (Va)	EVic
	'Boughton Blue'	see *V.* 'Belmont Blue'

	'Bournemouth Gem' (Vt)	CDor CGro
§	'Bowles's Black' (T)	CSpe EPfP EShb LEdu NBro SRms
	brevistipulata var. ***hidakana***	GEdr WFar
	- var. ***laciniata***	GEdr
	'Bruneau' (dVt)	ECtt LEdu WCot WFar
	bubanii	CPla GKev
	'Burncoose Yellow' (Va)	WGoo
	'Buttercup' (Vtta)	ECtt GWyn MHol SDys SPoG WGoo
	'Butterpat' (C)	MAsh NDov SHar WFar WGoo
	'Candy' (Vt)	CGro EBee WFar
	canina	EMor NBro
	'Carol' (Vt)	CGro WFar
	'Catalina'	CGro
	CELESTIAL TWILIGHT ('Smev3') (C)	MHol
§	***chaerophylloides*** var. ***sieboldiana***	SBrt
	- - pink-flowered	SBrt
	'Charles William Groves' (Vt)	CGro WFar
	'Charles Winston Groves' (Vt)	CGro WFar
	'Charlotte' (Va)	GWyn WGoo
	'Chloe' (Vtta)	CGro
	'Christie's Wedding' (Vt)	CGro WFar
	'Christmas' (Vt)	CGro WFar
	'Clementina' (Va) 🏆H5	MRav WGoo
	'Cleo' (Va)	GWyn
	'Clive Farrell' (Vt)	MNrw
	'Clive Groves' (Vt)	CGro
	'Coeur d'Alsace' (Vt)	CGro CLAP EBee ECtt GMaP IPot NLar SHar SRms WFar WHal XLum
	'Colette' (Va)	WGoo
	'Colombine' (Vt)	CAby CGro MAsh
	'Columbine' (Va)	CRos ECtt EHyd EPfP GWyn LRHS MBow MCot MHer MHol MRav NBir NDov NRHS SPoG WCav WFar WGoo WTor
§	'Conte di Brazza' (dPVt)	GWyn NLar SHar WHer
	'Copperfield' (P)	EHyd
	'Cordelia' (Vt)	CDor
	cornuta 🏆H5	CDor CElw GKev GWyn LRHS MBow MMuc MNrw NBir NBro SCob SHar SRms SSut WFar WGoo WHoo
	- Alba Group (C) 🏆H5	Widely available
	- 'Alba Minor' (C)	EPfP EWes NBro NDov NSla SPhx WFar
	- 'Blaue von Paris' (C)	GWyn
	- blue-flowered	MHer
	- 'Cleopatra' (C)	MNrw MPie SPhx
	- 'Clouded Yellow' (C)	GWyn MNrw WFar
	- 'Cream Gem' (C) **new**	MHol WFar
	- 'Deltini Honey Bee' (Deltini Series) **new**	MBros
	- 'Gypsy Moth' (C)	GWyn SPhx
	- 'Icy But Spicy' (C)	GWyn IPot MAsh MHol MRav NDov WFar WGoo
	- Lilacina Group (C)	ECha
	- 'Maiden's Blush' (C)	WFar
	- 'Minor' (C)	EPfP MAsh NBro NSla WGoo
	- 'Netta Statham' (C)	MHol MPie WGoo
	- 'Pale Apollo' (C)	WFar
	- Purpurea Group (C)	CMea ECha
	- 'Rosea' (C)	ECha
	- 'Spider' (C)	GWyn MAsh MNrw MPie SDys WFar WGoo
	- 'Swallowtail' (C)	GWyn
	- 'Ulla' (C)	WHer
	- 'Victoria's Blush' (C)	CDor CElw CSpe GBin GMaP LRHS MAsh NBir NDov SHar SPhx WGoo
	- 'Violacea' (C)	MAsh MPie
	corsica	CFis CMea CPBP CSpe SPhx WOut
	'Covent Garden' (Vt)	CGro WFar
	'Crepuscle' (Vt)	WFar
§	***cucullata*** 🏆H5	SRms
§	- 'Alba' (Vt)	CBro CGro NBir SRms
*	- 'Striata Alba' (Vt)	NBro
	'Curlylocks'	ECtt
	'Czar'	see *V.* 'The Czar'
§	'Czar Bleu' (Vt)	CGro
	'Daisy Smith' (Va)	WGoo
	'Danielle Molly'	WGoo
	'Dawn' (Vtta)	CAby CMea ECtt EPfP GWyn MCot NLar SPer SPoG WFar WGoo WTor
	'Delicia' (Vtta)	GWyn NDov SPhx WGoo
	'Des Charentes' (Vt)	CGro
	'Desdemona' (Va)	GKev GWyn WGoo
	'Devon Cream' (Va)	WGoo
	'Diana Groves' (Vt)	CGro WFar
	'Dick o' the Hills' (Vt)	CGro WFar
	dissecta var. ***sieboldiana***	see *V. chaerophylloides* var. *sieboldiana*
	'Donau' (Vt)	CGro WCot WFar
	'Doreen' (Vt)	WFar
	'Double White' (dVt)	CGro WHer
	douglasii	SBrt
	'Duchesse de Parme' (dPVt)	CGro GMaP GWyn NLar SRms WHer
	'D'Udine' (dPVt)	CGro ECtt SRms WCot WFar WHer
	'E.A. Bowles'	see *V.* 'Bowles's Black'
	'Eastgrove Blue Scented' (C)	SDys WFar WGoo WMal
	'Eastgrove Ice Blue' (C)	WGoo
	'Elaine Quin'	ECtt GWyn NLar SPoG WGoo WKif
§	***elatior***	CPBP EPPr MNrw SBrt
	'Eliza May Groves' (Vt)	CGro
	'Elizabeth Lee'	WCot
	'Elliot Adam' (Va)	WGoo
	'Elworthy Velvet' **new**	CElw
	'Emperor Magenta Red'	EMor LEdu
	erecta	see *V. elatior*
	'Eris' (Va)	WGoo
	'Etain' (Va)	CAby CRos ECtt EHyd ELan EPfP GMaP GWyn IPot LRHS MAsh MHol NLar NRHS SCob SPer SPoG WFar WGoo WIce
*	'Fantasy'	WGoo
	'Fee Jalucine' (dVt)	CGro
	'Fiona' (Va)	MCot SGro WGoo
	'Fiona Lawrenson' (Va)	WGoo
	'Florence' (Va)	GWyn WGoo
	'Foxbrook Cream' (C)	MAsh WGoo
	'Francesca' (Va)	WGoo
	'Freckles'	see *V. sororia* 'Freckles'
	'Fred Morey' (Vt)	CGro
	glabella	SBrt
	'Gladys Findlay' (Va)	WGoo
	'Glanmore'	WCot WFar
*	'Glenda'	WGoo
	'Glenholme'	GAbr GWyn MAsh WMal
	'Gloire de Verdun' (PVt)	CGro
	'Governor Herrick' (Vt)	CGro ECtt WCot WFar
	gracilis 'Lutea'	CElw
	- 'Major'	WGoo
	'Grovemount Blue' (C)	CMea
	'Gustav Wermig' (C)	MAsh MHol WGoo
	hancockii **new**	SPtp

	'Heartthrob' (v)	ECtt GEdr MNrw NBir NHpl SPeP SPoG WHil WNPC
*	'Heaselands'	SMHy
§	***hederacea***	CExl CTsd GQue GWyn SRms WFar
§	'Helen Mount' (T)	GWyn
	'Helena' (Va)	GWyn WGoo
	'Hespera' (Va)	WGoo
	heterophylla subsp. ***epirota***	see *V. bertolonii*
	'Holdgate'	WGoo
	'Hopleys White' (PVt)	CGro
	'Hudsons Blue'	CElw MNrw
	'Huntercombe Purple' (Va) ♀^{H5}	CRos EHyd LRHS MAsh NBir NRHS WFar WGoo WHal WKif
	'Iden Gem' (Va)	ECtt WGoo
	'Inverurie Beauty' (Va) ♀^{H5}	GBin GMaP GWyn SDys WGoo WKif
	'Irish Elegance'	see *V.* 'Sulfurea'
	'Irish Molly' (Va)	ECtt ELan EPfP EShb GWyn MAsh MCot SPer SPoG WFar WGoo WIce WTor
	'Isabel'	SRms WGoo
	'Isabella' (Vt)	CGro EBee WFar
	'Isobel'	MAsh
	'Ivory Queen' (Va)	GWyn MRav SPhx WFar WGoo
	'Jack Sampson' (Vt)	EBee
	'Jackanapes' (Va) ♀^{H5}	EBee ECtt ELan GWyn LRHS MAsh NLar SPoG WGoo WTor
	'Janet' (Va)	EBee GWyn LSRN SDys SPoG
	'Janette' (Va)	WGoo
	'Jean Jeannie' (Va)	GWyn NDov WFar WGoo
	'Jeannie Bellew' (Va)	ECtt WGoo
	'Jennifer Andrews' (Va)	GWyn SGro WGoo
	'Joanna' (Va)	WGoo
	'John Raddenbury' (Vt)	CGro
	'Johnny Jump Up'	see *V.* 'Helen Mount'
	jooi	CPla CSpe EPfP
	'Josephine' (Vt)	CGro
	'Josie' (Va)	GWyn SGro WGoo
	'Joyce Mary Paul' (Vt)	CGro
	'Judy Goring' (Va)	ECtt GBee WMal
	'Julian' (Va)	ECtt GAbr GWyn WGoo
	'Juno' (Va)	GAbr
	'Jupiter' (Va)	GWyn WCot
	'Kerry Girl' (Vt)	CGro WFar
	'Kim' (Vt)	CGro
	'Kimberley's Alice' (Vt)	EBee
	'Kitten'	MAsh MHol SDys SPhx WFar WGoo
	'Kitty White' (Va)	GWyn SDys SPhx
§	'Königin Charlotte' (Vt)	CBod CGro EHyd EMor EPfP EWTr GMaP LRHS LSou MHer NLar SRms WCAu WCot
	labradorica misapplied	see *V. riviniana* Purpurea Group
	- ***purpurea***	see *V. riviniana* Purpurea Group
§	***labradorica*** ambig.	CTri EWTr GWyn NHpl WCAu WHer
	'Lady Hume Campbell' (dPVt)	CGro WHer
	'Lady Jane' (Vt)	CGro
	'Lavender Lady' (Vt)	CGro
	'Lees Blue' (Vt)	CGro WFar
	'Lees Peachy Pink' (Vt)	CGro MNrw
	'Letitia' (Va)	MAsh MNrw SDys
	'Lianne' (Vt)	CGro SRms WCot
	'Lindsay'	WGoo
	'Lisa Tanner' (Va)	GWyn WGoo
	'Little David' (Vtta) ♀^{H5}	CTri ECtt MCot NDov WGoo
	'Lord Plunket' (Va)	WGoo
§	'Lord Primrose' (Celestial Series) (Va)	MHol

	'Lorna Cawthorne' (C)	MAsh SDys WGoo
	'Louisa' (Va)	GWyn WGoo
	'Lucy' (Va)	MAsh
§	***lutea***	SBut SHar WGoo
	- subsp. ***elegans***	see *V. lutea*
	'Luxonne' (Vt)	CGro
	'Lydia Groves' (Vt)	CDor CGro SRms WCot WFar
	'Lydia's Legacy' (Vt)	CGro
	'Madame Armandine Pagès' (Vt)	CGro
	'Madeleine Mary Groves' (Vt)	CGro
	'Maggie Mott' (Va) ♀^{H5}	ECha ECtt GWyn MAsh MRav WFar WGoo
	'Magic' (C)	NDov WGoo WMal
	mandshurica f. ***albiflora***	SBrt
	- 'Fuji Dawn' (v)	GWyn WCot
	mandshurica × ***patrinii***	SBrt
	'Margaret' (Va)	ECtt WGoo
	'Marie Rose' (Vt)	WFar
	'Marie-Louise' (dPVt)	CGro GWyn
I	'Mars'	LSRN WSpi
	'Martin' (Va) ♀^{H5}	CAby CMea ECha ECtt EPfP GMaP GWyn LRHS LSRN MAsh MCot MHol NDov SBut SPoG WFar WGoo
	'Mary Mouse'	WGoo
	'Marylyn' (Va) **new**	WFar
	'Mauve Haze' (Va)	SBut WGoo
	'Mauve Radiance' (Va)	WGoo
	'May Mott' (Va)	WGoo
	'Mayfly' (Va)	ECtt
	'Melinda' (Vtta)	WGoo
	'Mercury' (Va)	WGoo
	Miracle Series (Vt)	CRos
	- 'Miracle Bride White' (Vt)	MHol WFar
	- 'Miracle Classy Pink' (Vt)	MHol WFar
	- 'Miracle Ice White' (Vt)	NLar
	- 'Miracle Intense Blue' (Vt)	GAbr WFar
	- 'Miracle Vanilla White' (Vt)	SHar
	'Miss Brookes' (Va)	WGoo
	'Misty Guy' (Vtta)	MAsh
	'Molly Sanderson' (Va) ♀^{H5}	CAby CPla CRos EAJP ECha ECtt EHyd ELan EPfP GWyn LRHS MAsh MBow MBros NLar NRHS SCob SPer SPlb SPoG SRms WCav WFar WGoo WIce WMal
	'Moonlight' (Va) ♀^{H5}	CRos EHyd ELan LRHS NRHS WGoo
	'Morwenna' (Va)	ECtt GWyn MAsh MCot NDov WGoo
	'Mrs Lancaster' (Va)	EBee ECtt ELan GMaP GWyn LSRN NBir NLar NWad SDys SPer SPoG SSut WFar WGoo WHil WTor
	'Mrs Pinehurst' (Vt)	CGro EBee GWyn SRms
	'Mrs R. Barton' (Vt)	CDor CGro SRms WHil
	'Myfawnny' (Va)	CRos EHyd LRHS NDov NRHS SDys WFar WGoo WSpi
	'Neapolitan'	see *V.* 'Pallida Plena'
	'Netta Statham'	see *V.* 'Belmont Blue'
	'Nora' (Va)	ECtt NDov WFar WGoo
	'Norah Leigh' (Va)	WGoo
	obliqua	see *V. cucullata*
	odorata (Vt)	CBcs CBod CGro CHab CTsd EBee EBou EWTr GPoy LCro LRHS MBow MRav NGrd NMir SEND SRms SVic WBor WCAu WJek WOut

	– 'Alba' (Vt)	CGro CLAP CTsd EBee ELan EMor EPfP LEdu MHer SEND SRms WCAu WFar
	– 'Amethyst Witch' (Vt)	CGro WFar
	– apricot-flowered	see *V.* 'Sulfurea'
	– 'Bethan Davies' (d/Vt)	WCot
	– 'Carol Lockton' (Vt)	CGro WFar
	– 'Christopher William Groves' (Vt)	CGro
	– 'Copper Pennies' (Vt)	CGro
	– 'Cyclops' (Vt)	CGro
	– 'Dawnie' (Vt)	CGro EBee
	– deep violet-flowered (Vt)	SPtp
	– var. ***dumetorum***	see *V. alba*
	– 'Ellie' (Vt)	WFar
	– 'Elsmeer' (Vt)	ECtt
	– 'Empress Augusta' (Vt)	CGro
	– 'Explorateur Dybowski' (Vt)	CGro
	– 'Hungarian Beauty' (Vt)	EBee LCro LOPS
	– 'Katy' (Vt)	CLAP
	– 'King of Violets' (dVt)	ECtt SHar
	– 'Lees Ivory' (Vt)	CGro
	– 'Little Plum' (Vt)	CGro
	– 'Melanie' (Vt)	CDor CGro CLAP MNrw
	– 'Mrs R.O. Barlow' (Vt)	CLAP WCot WSHC
	– 'Piddle Pink' (Vt)	CGro
	– pink-flowered	see *V. odorata* Rosea Group
	– 'Princess Thirza' (Vt)	CGro
	– ***rosea***	see *V. odorata* Rosea Group
§	– Rosea Group (Vt)	CBod CDor MRav SEND SRms WCot
	– 'Stonehill Shadow' (Vt)	WOut
	– 'Sulphurea'	see *V.* 'Sulfurea'
	– 'Vin d'André Thorp' (Vt)	CGro ECtt LEdu WCot
I	– 'Violett Charm' (Vt)	WCot
	'Olive Edwards' (Va)	WGoo
	'Orchid Pink' (Vt)	CGro EBee GMaP LEdu MNrw
	orientalis	GEdr
§	'Pallida Plena' (dPVt)	CGro WHer
	palustris	EWat NLar WHer WSFF WShi
	'Pamela Zambra' (Vt)	CGro SHar WSHC
	'Panola Beaconsfield' (Panola Series) **new**	SCob
	papilionacea	see *V. sororia*
	'Parchment' (Vt)	CGro EBee GWyn
	'Parme de Toulouse' (dPVt)	CGro EWTr GWyn NLar WHer XLum
	'Pasha' (Va)	GWyn SDys WMal
	'Pat Creasy' (Va)	NDov WGoo
	'Pat Kavanagh' (C)	MAsh WGoo
	'Patience'	WGoo
	'Patricia Lillington' (Va)	GWyn
	pedata	MPie WAbe
	– 'Bicolor' (Vt)	WAbe
	pedatifida white-flowered	GEdr
	pensylvanica	see *V. pubescens* var. *eriocarpa*
	'Perle Rose' (Vt)	CGro SHar
	'Petra' (Vtta)	GWyn SPhx WGoo
	phalacrocarpa	SBrt
	'Phyl Dove' (Vt)	WCot
	'Pickering Blue' (Va)	WGoo
	pinnata	CTri SBrt
	'Primrose Dame' (Va)	ECtt WGoo
	'Primrose Pixie' (Va)	WGoo
	'Prince Henry' (T)	MNHC
	'Princess Diana' (Vt)	EBee
	'Princess of Prussia' (Vt)	CGro WCot
	'Princess of Wales'	see *V.* 'Princesse de Galles'
§	'Princesse de Galles' (Vt)	CGro CTri

	'Prunella' (Va) **new**	WFar
§	***pubescens*** var. ***eriocarpa***	SRms
	QUEEN CHARLOTTE	see *V.* 'Königin Charlotte'
	'Raven' (Va)	LRHS SPhx WGoo
	'Rebecca' (Vtta)	CAby CDor CRos ECtt EHyd ELan EPfP EShb GKev GWyn LRHS LSRN MAsh MBow MBros MCot MHer MHol NBir NDov NLar NRHS SDys SPer SPoG WCav WFar WGoo WHer WIce
	'Rebecca Cawthorne' (C)	MHol
	'Red Charm' (Vt)	CGro WCav
	'Red Giant' (Vt)	CGro MPie
	'Red Lion' (Vt)	CGro
	'Reine des Blanches' (dVt)	EBee ECtt LEdu SRms
	'Reine des Neiges' (Vt)	CBod CDor CGro EMor EWTr LSou
	reniforme	see *V. hederacea*
	riviniana	GJos MBow MMuc WHer WOut WSFF WShi
	– dark pink-flowered	MMuc WOut
§	– Purpurea Group	CBcs CBod CMac EBee ECha EPfP EWes LPot MHer MPie MRav MWat NBir NDov NRya NSti SPer SPhx SPlb SRms WFar WJek
	– 'Rosea'	WJek
	– white-flowered	EWes
	'Roscastle Black' (Va)	CMea CSma CWCL EPfP GBee GWyn MAsh NDov WGoo WSpi
	'Rose Marie' (Va) **new**	WFar
	'Rosy Rayne' (Va) **new**	WFar
	'Royal Elk' (Vt)	CGro
	'Royal Robe' (Vt)	CGro
	'Rubra' (Vt)	EAJP EPfP SVic XLum
*	***rupestris rosea***	CTri WHer
	sagittata	LPot
	'Saint Helena' (Vt)	CGro
	'Sally' (Vtta)	CGro
	selkirkii Pursh ex Goldie	WThu
	– 'Variegata' (v)	XEll
	septentrionalis	see *V. sororia*
	'Sherbet Dip' (Va)	WGoo
	'Showgirl' (Va) **new**	WFar
	'Sidborough Poppet'	EWes
	'Silver Samurai' (Vt)	WCot
	'Skylark' (Va) **new**	WFar
	'Smugglers' Moon' (Va)	GWyn WGoo
	somchetica	WCot
	'Sophie' (Vtta)	WGoo
	Sorbet Series (Va)	LCro LOPS MBros MPri
	– SORBET BLACK DELIGHT IMPROVED ('Pas211779') (Va) **new**	MBros
	– SORBET YELLOW FROST (Va) **new**	LCro LOPS
	– SORBET XP T&M Mix (Va)	MBros
§	***sororia***	CBod ECha GWyn MNrw NBir NBro SCob SPhx WGwG
*	– 'Albiflora' (Vt) ♀H6	EAJP EMor EPPr EPfP GPSL LEdu LRHS LSun MBriF MRav NLar SCob SPhx WJek
	– 'Dark Freckles' (Vt)	CGro EBee EMor NLar NRya SPhx WFar
§	– 'Freckles' (Vt)	Widely available
	– 'Hungarian Beauty' (Vt)	SPer
	– 'Priceana' (Vt)	CBod EMor LEdu MPie MRav NBir SHar SPlb WCot
	– 'Sorority Sisters' (mixed) (Vt)	NChi SVic
	– 'Speckles' (Vt/v)	WCot
	– 'Sweet Emma' (Vt)	SPhx

* 'Spencer's Cottage' (Vt)	WGoo
STARRY NIGHT	see *V.* 'Lord Primrose'
'Steyning' (Va)	WGoo
§ 'Sulfurea' (Vt)	CBod CDor CLAP EBou EMor MBriF MRav WCot
'Sulfurea' lemon-flowered (Vt)	WFar
'Sundowner' (Va)	ECtt
'Sunny Jim' (Va)	EVic
'Sunshine' (Va)	WFar
'Susan Chilcott' (Vt)	CGro
'Susanne Lucas' (Vt)	CGro
'Susie' (Va)	GWyn MHol WFar WGoo
'Swanley White'	see *V.* 'Conte di Brazza'
'Sweetheart' (Va)	EVic
'Sybil' (SP)	WGoo
TEARDROPS MIXED (P)	LCro LOPS
'Thalia' (Vtta)	GWyn
§ 'The Czar' (Vt)	SHar
'Tiger Eyes' (Va)	SPoG
'Titania' (Va)	EBee
'Tom Tit' (Va)	ECtt WGoo
'Tony Venison' (C/v)	ELon EPfP GWyn MHol NLar WFar
tricolor	CBod CHab CWld ENfk EPfP EWhm GJos GPoy LCro LOPS MHer MNHC NGrd SRms WWild XAbr
- 'Sawyer's Black'	ENfk MNHC WJek
vaginata	GEdr
verecunda B&SWJ 604a	WCru
§ - var. ***yakusimana***	WThu
'Victoria'	see *V.* 'Czar Bleu'
'Victoria Cawthorne' (C)	MAsh MHol NDov WFar WGoo WMal
'Violacea' (C)	MAsh
'Virginia' (Va)	GWyn WGoo
'Vita' (Va)	ECtt SRms WFar WGoo WMal
'Wasp' (Va)	ECtt
'White Ladies'	see *V. cucullata* 'Alba'
'White Pearl' (Va)	SPhx WGoo
'White Perfection' (C)	GWyn
'White Swan' (Va)	MAsh WFar
'White Witch' (Vt)	EBee
'Winifred Jones' (Va)	WGoo
'Winnie' (Va) **new**	WFar
'Winona Cawthorne' (C)	MHol
'Wisley White'	CRos EWTr GBin LRHS
× ***wittrockiana***	XAbr
- COASTAL SUNRISE MIXED (P) **new**	LCro LOPS
- Cool Wave Series (P)	LCro LOPS MPri
- 'Joker Light Blue' (Joker Series) (P) **new**	LCro LOPS
- Matrix Series (P)	MBros MPri
- - MATRIX CASSIS (P) **new**	MBros
- - MATRIX CLEAR YELLOW (P) **new**	MBros
- - MATRIX MIDNIGHT GLOW ('Pas12374') (P) **new**	SCob
- - MATRIX MORPHEUS (P) **new**	MBros SCob
- - MATRIX RED BLOTCH (P) **new**	MBros
- - MATRIX SUNRISE (P) **new**	MBros
- - MATRIX YELLOW BLOTCH (P) **new**	MBros
- 'Viking Northern Lights' (Viking Series) (P)	MHol
'Woodlands Cream' (Va)	GWyn WGoo
'Woodlands Lilac' (Va)	WGoo
yakusimana	see *V. verecunda* var. *yakusimana*
'Yesterday, Today, Tomorrow' **new**	LCro LOPS
'Zara' (Va)	WGoo
'Zoe' (Vtta)	ECtt EPfP GWyn LRHS MAsh SPer SPoG WFar WGoo

Viscaria (*Caryophyllaceae*)

vulgaris	see *Lychnis viscaria*

Visnaga (*Apiaceae*)

§ ***daucoides***	CHby CSpe LRHS MNHC SPhx SRms WHal
- 'Green Mist'	LCro LOPS MAvo SBut

Vitaliana (*Primulaceae*)

§ ***primuliflora***	GKev NRya NSla
- subsp. ***cinerea***	EPot GKev
- subsp. ***praetutiana***	CPBP GKev NWad

Vitex (*Lamiaceae*)

agnus-castus	CAgr CBcs CLau CMCN CSde EPri EShb GPoy LEdu LRHS MMrt MRav NLar SLon SPer WCFE WJek XAbr XSen
- f. ***alba***	CRos EHyd LRHS MBlu NRHS SPoG XSen
- - PAB 9281	LEdu
- - 'Silver Spire'	EBee ELan EPfP SRms WPGP
- f. ***latifolia*** 🏆H4	CCBP CRos ECre EHyd ELan EPfP LEdu LRHS LSRN MGos MHer MNHC NLar NRHS SEND SGsty SPoG WPGP
chinensis	see *V. negundo* var. *heterophylla*
incisa	see *V. negundo* var. *heterophylla*
negundo	LEdu
§ - var. ***heterophylla***	EWes XSen
trifolia 'Purpurea'	LRHS

Vitis ✿ (*Vitaceae*)

'Abundante' (F)	WSuV
'Alden' (O/B)	WSuV
'Amandin' (G/W)	WSuV
amurensis	CDoC EPfP WSpi
- B&SWJ 4138	WCru
- B&SWJ 4299	WCru
- B&SWJ 12568	WCru
'Atlantis' (O/W)	WSuV
§ 'Aurore' (W)	CAgr WSuV
'Baco Noir' (O/B)	CAgr WSuV
'Bianca' (O/W)	SSFr WSuV
'Birstaller Muscat' (W)	WSuV
BLACK HAMBURGH	see *V. vinifera* 'Schiava Grossa'
* 'Black Strawberry' (B)	CAgr WSuV
§ 'Boskoop Glory' (O/B) 🏆H5	CMac ELan LBuc MBros SCoo WSuV
'Brant' (O/B) 🏆H5	Widely available
'Brilliant' (B)	WSuV
'Buffalo' (B)	WSuV
'Cabernet Cortis' (B)	WSuV
californica (F)	EPfP NLar
'Canadice' (O/R/S)	WSuV
'Cascade'	see *V.* SEIBEL 13053
'Castel 19637' (B)	WSuV
'Chambourcin' (B)	WSuV
CLARET CLOAK ('Frovit'[PBR]) 🏆H5	CBcs CRos ELan EPfP GBin LRHS LSRN MAsh MBlu NLar NRHS SCoo SPer WPGP WSpi
coignetiae 🏆H5	Widely available
- B&SWJ 4550 from Korea	WCru

	– B&SWJ 4744	WCru
	– B&SWJ 8553 from Korea	WCru
	– B&SWJ 10882 from Japan	WCru
	– B&SWJ 10908 from Japan	WCru
	– var. ***glabrescens*** B&SWJ 8537	WCru
	– Sunningdale form	EBee NLar WGrn
	'Dalkauer' (W)	WSuV
I	'Diamond' (B)	WSuV
	'Dutch Black' (O/B)	WSuV
	'Edwards No 1' (O/W)	WSuV
	'Eger Csillaga' (O/W)	WSuV
	'Einset' (B/S)	WSuV
	ficifolia	see *V. thunbergii*
	flexuosa B&SWJ 5568	WCru
	– B&SWJ 6304	WCru
	– var. ***choii*** B&SWJ 4101	WCru
	– var. ***parvifolia***	NLar
	– – B&SWJ 1946	WCru
	'Fragola' (O/R)	CAgr CMac CTri ECha EHyd ELan EPfP EPom LCro LOPS LRHS MAsh MCoo MRav NLar SLim SPoG SRms WMat WSpi WSuV
	'Gagarin Blue' (O/B)	CAgr EPom SVen WSuV
	'Glenora' (F/B/S)	CAgr WSuV
	'Hecker' (O/W)	WSuV
	henryana	see *Parthenocissus henryana*
	'Himrod' (O/W/S)	CCCN ELan WSuV
	'Horizon' (O/W)	WSuV
	inconstans	see *Parthenocissus tricuspidata*
	'Interlaken' (O/W/S)	CAgr WSuV
	'Johanniter' (W)	SPre WSuV
	'Kempsey Black' (O/B)	CAgr WSuV
	'Kozmapalme Muscatoly' (O/W)	WSuV
	'Kuibishevski' (O/R)	WSuV
	'Kyoho' (B)	WSuV
	Landot 244 (O/B)	WSuV
	Landot 3217 (O/B)	WSuV
	'L'Arcadie Blanche' (W)	WSuV
	'Léon Millot' (O/G/B)	CAgr CSBt LSRN WSuV
	'Lucy Kuhlman' (B)	WSuV
	'Maréchal Foch' (O/B)	WSuV
	'Maréchal Joffre' (O/R)	CAgr WSuV
	'Mars' (O/B/S)	WSuV
	'Merzling' (O/W)	WSuV
	'Munson R.W.' (O/R)	WSuV
	'Muscat Bleu' (O/B)	CCCN EPom LRHS MNHC NLar SKee SLim SPoG SSFr WMat WSuV
	'Nero'PBR (O/O)	CAgr
	'New York Muscat' (O/B) 🏆H5	WSuV
	'New York Seedless' (O/W/S)	WSuV
	'Niagara' (O/W)	WSuV
	'Niederother Monschrebe' (O/R)	WSuV
	Oberlin 595 (O/B)	WSuV
	'Orion' (O/W)	WSuV
	'Paletina' (O/W)	SEdi WSuV
	'Perdin' (O/W)	WSuV
	'Phönix' (O/W)	CAgr CCCN EHyd EPom LBuc LCro LOPS LRHS LSRN MAsh MGos NLar NRHS SKee SLim SPer SPoG SPre SSFr SVic WMat WSuV
	piasezkii var. ***pagnuccii***	WCru
*	'Pink Strawberry' (O)	WSuV
	'Pirovano 14' (O/B)	WSuV
§	'Plantet' (O/B)	WSuV
	'Poloske Muscat' (W)	CCCN EPom NLar WMat WSuV

	pulchra	WCru
	purpurea 'Spetchley Park' (O/B)	CAgr WHwl WSuV
	quinquefolia	see *Parthenocissus quinquefolia*
	'Ramdas' (O/W)	WSuV
	Ravat 51 (O/W)	WSuV
	'Rayon d'Or' (O/W)	WSuV
	'Regent'PBR (O/B)	CAgr CCCN CTri EPom LCro LOPS LRHS MCoo MGos NLar SKee SLim SPer SPoG SPre SVic WMat WSuV
	'Reliance' (O/R/S)	CAgr WSuV
	'Rembrant' (R)	CAgr WSuV
	riparia	NLar
	'Romulus' (O/G/W/S)	WSuV
	'Rondo' (O/B)	CAgr LRHS SPre SVic WMat WSuV
	'Saturn' (O/R/S)	CAgr WSuV
	'Schuyler' (O/B)	CAgr WSuV
	Seibel (F)	CRos EHyd NRHS
	Seibel 5279	see *V.* 'Aurore'
	Seibel 5409 (W)	WSuV
	Seibel 5455	see *V.* 'Plantet'
	Seibel 7053 (R)	WSuV
	Seibel 9549 (R)	WSuV
§	Seibel 13053 (O/B)	CMac CRos EHyd LRHS MAsh NRHS SEND SRms WSuV
	Seibel 138315 (R)	WSuV
	'Seneca' (W)	WSuV
	'Serena' (O/W)	WSuV
§	'Seyval Blanc' (O/W)	CAgr MAsh SEND SVic WSuV
	Seyve Villard ambig.	CRos EHyd LRHS NPer
	Seyve Villard 5276	see *V.* 'Seyval Blanc'
	Seyve Villard 12.375	see *V.* 'Villard Blanc'
	Seyve Villard 20.473 (F)	NPer
	'Sirius' (B)	WSuV
	'Solaris' (O/W)	LRHS MCoo MNHC NLar WMat WSuV
	'Stauffer' (O/W)	WSuV
	'Suffolk Seedless' (B/S)	WSuV
	'Tereshkova' (O/B)	CAgr WSuV
	'Thornton' (O/S)	WSuV
§	***thunbergii*** B&SWJ 4702	WCru
	'Triomphe d'Alsace' (O/B)	CAgr CSBt MCoo NPer WSuV
	'Trollhaugen' (O/B/S)	WSuV
	'Trollinger'	see *V. vinifera* 'Schiava Grossa'
	'Vanessa' (O/R/S)	EPom SPer SVic WSuV
	'Venus' (O/B/S)	LRHS SVic
§	'Villard Blanc' (O/W)	WSuV
	vinifera	LMaj LRHS SGsty SWeb
	– 'Abouriou' (O/B)	WSuV
	– 'Acolon' (O/B)	WSuV
	– 'Adelheidtraube' (O/W)	WSuV
	– 'Albalonga' (W)	WSuV
§	– 'Alicante' (G/B)	CBcs WSuV
	– 'Augusta Louise' (O/W)	WSuV
	– 'Auxerrois' (O/W)	WSuV
	– 'Bacchus' (O/W)	CAgr LBuc LRHS MNHC NLar SLim SVic WMat WSuV
	– 'Baresana' (G/W)	SRms WSuV
	– 'Beauty'	CAgr
	– 'Black Alicante'	see *V. vinifera* 'Alicante'
	– 'Black Frontignan' (G/O/B)	WSuV
	– Black Hamburgh	see *V. vinifera* 'Schiava Grossa'
	– 'Black Monukka' (G/B/S)	WSuV
	– 'Black Prince' (G/B)	CAgr WSuV
	– 'Blue Portuguese'	see *V. vinifera* 'Portugieser'
§	– 'Bouvier' (W)	WSuV
	– 'Bouviertraube'	see *V. vinifera* 'Bouvier'
	– 'Buckland Sweetwater' (G/W)	SLim WSuV

- 'Cabernet Sauvignon' (O/B) CRos EHyd LRHS MAsh MGos NPer NRHS SVic WSuV
- 'Cardinal' (O/R) WSuV
- 'Carla' (O/R) WSuV
- 'Centennial' (O/N/S) WSuV
- 'Chardonnay' (O/W) CAgr CCCN CRos EHyd LRHS LSRN MAsh NPer SPre SVic WSuV
§ - 'Chasselas' (G/O/W) CRos EHyd LRHS WSuV
- 'Chasselas de Fontainebleau' (G/O/W) SVic
- 'Chasselas d'Or' see *V. vinifera* 'Chasselas'
- 'Chasselas Rosé' (G/R) CAgr WSuV
- 'Chasselas Rosé Royal' (O/R) CCCN SVic
- 'Chasselas Vibert' (G/W) WSuV
- 'Chenin Blanc' (O/W) SVic WSuV
- 'Ciotat' (F) EShb MRav WSuV
- 'Cot Précoce de Tours' (O/B) WSuV
- 'Crimson Seedless' (R/S) WSuV
- 'Csabagyöngye' (O/W) WSuV
- 'Dattier de Beyrouth' (G/W) WSuV
- 'Dattier Saint Vallier' (O/W) SVic WSuV
- 'Dolcetto' (O/B) WSuV
- 'Dornfelder' (O/R) CCCN MNHC NLar SLim SPoG SVic WMat WSuV
- 'Dunkelfelder' (O/R) WSuV
- 'Ehrenfelser' (O/W) WSuV
- 'Elbling' (O/W) WSuV
- 'Exalta' (G/W/S) CCCN WSuV
- 'Excelsior' (W) WSuV
- 'Faber' (O/W) WSuV
- 'Fiesta' (W/S) WSuV
- 'Findling' (W) WSuV
- 'Flame' (R/S) CAgr SPer SVic WMat
- 'Flame Red' (O/D) CCCN EPom LRHS
- 'Flame Seedless' (G/O/R/S) CMac EPom WSuV
- 'Forta' (O/W) WSuV
- 'Foster's Seedling' (G/W) WSuV
- 'Freisamer' (O/W) WSuV
- 'Frühburgunder' (O/B) WSuV
- 'Gamay Hâtif des Vosges' (B) WSuV
- 'Gamay Noir' (O/B) SVic WSuV
- Gamay Teinturier Group (O/B) WSuV
§ - 'Garnacha Tinta' SVic
- 'Gewürztraminer' (O/R) CRos EHyd LRHS MAsh NRHS SVic WSuV
- 'Glory of Boskoop' see *V.* 'Boskoop Glory'
- 'Golden Chasselas' see *V. vinifera* 'Chasselas'
- 'Goldriesling' (O/W) WSuV
- 'Grenache' see *V. vinifera* 'Garnacha Tinta'
- 'Gros Colmar' (G/B) WSuV
- 'Grüner Veltliner' (O/W) WSuV
- 'Gutenborner' (O/W) WSuV
- 'Helfensteiner' (O/R) WSuV
- 'Huxelrebe' (O/W) SVic WSuV
- 'Incana' (O/B) ELon LRHS MRav SVen WCFE WCot WPGP WSHC
- 'Irsay Olivér' (O/W) WSuV
- 'Italia' (O/W) SWeb
- 'Juliaumsrebe' (O/W) WSuV
- 'Kanzler' (O/W) WSuV
- 'Kerner' (O/W) WSuV
- 'Kernling' (F) WSuV
- 'King's Ruby' (F/S) WSuV
- 'Lakemont' (O/W/S) CAgr CCCN CMac CRos CTri EHyd ELan EPfP EPom LEdu LRHS MGos MNHC NLar NRHS SEWo SEdi SKee SLim SPoG SPre SSFr SVic WMat WSuV
- 'Lival' (O/B) WSuV
- 'Macabeo' see *V. vinifera* 'Viura'
- 'Madeleine Angevine' (O/W) CAgr CRos EHyd LRHS LSRN MAsh NPer NRHS SPoG SVen SVic WSuV
- 'Madeleine Céline' (B) WSuV
- 'Madeleine Royale' (G/W) WSuV
- 'Madeleine Silvaner' (O/W) CRos CSBt EHyd LRHS MAsh NPer NRHS SPoG WSuV
- 'Madresfield Court' (G/B) WSuV
- 'Merlot' (G/B) CRos EHyd EPfP LRHS NRHS SVic WSuV
§ - 'Meunier' (B) SVic WSuV
- 'Mireille' (F) WSuV
- 'Morio Muscat' (O/W) WSuV
§ - 'Müller-Thurgau' (O/W) CRos LRHS LSRN MAsh SPoG SVic WSuV
- 'Muscat Blanc à Petits Grains' (O/W) SWvt WSuV
- 'Muscat de Lierval' (O/B) WSuV
- 'Muscat de Saumur' (O/W) WSuV
- 'Muscat Hamburg' (G/B) CRos LRHS LSRN MAsh SWvt WSuV
- 'Muscat of Alexandria' (G/W) CBcs CCCN CMac CRHN CRos CTri EHyd LRHS MRav NRHS SLim SRms SVic WMat XBlo
- 'Muscat Ottonel' (O/W) WSuV
- 'Muscat Saint Laurent' (W) WSuV
- 'Nebbiolo' (O/B) WSuV
- 'No 69' (W) WSuV
- 'Noblessa' (W) WSuV
- 'Noir Hâtif de Marseille' (O/B) WSuV
- 'Olive Blanche' (O/W) WSuV
- 'Optima' (O/W) WSuV
- 'Ora' (O/W/S) WSuV
- 'Ortega' (O/W) CCCN WSuV
- 'Parellada' (W) SVic
- 'Perle' (O/W) WSuV
- 'Perlette' (O/W/S) CCCN CRos EPom LRHS WSuV
- 'Petit Rouge' (R) WSuV
- 'Picurka' (O/W/S) SVic
- 'Pinot Blanc' (O/W) CCCN CRos EHyd LCro LOPS LRHS MAsh SVic WSuV
- 'Pinot Gris' (O/B) SVic WSuV
- 'Pinot Noir' (O/B) CCCN SVic WSuV
§ - 'Portugieser' (O/B) WSuV
- 'Précoce de Bousquet' (O/W) WSuV
- 'Précoce de Malingre' (O/W) CAgr
- 'Prima' (O/B) WSuV
- 'Primavis Frontignan' (G/W) WSuV
- 'Purpurea' (O/B) ♀H5 Widely available
- 'Queen of Esther' (B) SLim WSuV
- 'Regner' (O/W) WSuV
- 'Reichensteiner' (O/G/W) CAgr SVic WSuV
- 'Rhea' (G/O/R) SVic
- 'Riesling' (O/W) CCCN CRos EHyd LRHS MAsh SVic WSuV
- RIESLING-SILVANER see *V. vinifera* 'Müller-Thurgau'
- 'Rotberger' (O/G/B) WSuV
- 'Royal Muscadine' (G/O/W) WMat WSuV
- 'Saint Laurent' (G/O/W) SVic WSuV

- 'Sauvignon Blanc' (O/W)	CCCN EHyd LRHS NRHS SVic WSuV
- 'Scheurebe' (O/W)	WSuV
§ - 'Schiava Grossa' (G/B/D)	CMac CRHN CRos CSBt CTri EHyd EPfP EPom LRHS LSRN MAsh MRav NPer NRHS SLim SPer SPoG SPre SVic SWvt WMat WSuV
- 'Schönburger' (O/W)	SVic WSuV
- 'Schwarzriesling'	see *V. vinifera* 'Meunier'
- 'Sémillon' (G/O/W)	CRos EHyd LRHS LSRN MAsh SVic
- 'Senator' (O/W)	WSuV
- 'Septimer' (O/W)	WSuV
- 'Shiraz' (B)	WSuV
- 'Siegerrebe' (O/W/D)	CAgr CRos EHyd LBuc LRHS MAsh NPer SPoG SVic WSuV
- 'Silvaner' (O/W)	WSuV
- 'Spetchley Red' (O/B) ♀H5	CRHN EBee MNrw NLar NOra WAvo WCot WCru WLov WMou WPGP WSpi
- strawberry grape	see *V.* 'Fragola'
- 'Suffolk Red' (G/R/S)	SVic
§ - 'Sultana' (W/S)	CAgr WSuV
- 'Syrah' (G/B)	SVic
- 'Tempranillo'	SVic
- 'Theresa' (O/W)	SLim WSuV
- 'Thompson Seedless'	see *V. vinifera* 'Sultana'
* - 'Triomphe' (O/B)	SVic
- 'Triomphrebe' (W)	WSuV
- 'Verdejo'	SVic
§ - 'Viura'	SVic
- 'Vroege van der Laan' (O/W)	NLar SRms
- 'Wrotham Pinot' (O/B)	WSuV
- 'Würzer' (O/W)	WSuV
- 'Zweigeltrebe' (O/B)	WSuV
* 'White Strawberry' (O/W)	WSuV
'Zalagyöngye' (W)	CAgr WSuV

Volutaria (*Asteraceae*)

muricata new	CSpe

Vriesea (*Bromeliaceae*)

splendens ♀H1a	SPlb XBlo

W

Wachendorfia (*Haemodoraceae*)

multiflora	CPbh
thyrsiflora	CBcs CBod CCht CDoC CExl EBee LEdu SVen WCFE WPGP

Wahlenbergia (*Campanulaceae*)

congesta	NWad
gloriosa	WAbe
pumilio	see *Edraianthus pumilio*
rivularis 'Snow-cap'	CPla
serpyllifolia	see *Edraianthus serpyllifolius*

Waldsteinia (*Rosaceae*)

fragarioides	EBee IMou
geoides	EMor EPPr MGil MMuc NEoE XLum
- 'Goldkäfer'	IMou
ternata	Widely available
§ - 'Mozaick' (v)	EBee EPPr EShb NBir NEoE
- 'Variegata'	see *W. ternata* 'Mozaick'

walnut, black see *Juglans nigra*

walnut, common see *Juglans regia*; also AGM Fruit Section

Wasabia (*Brassicaceae*)

wasabi	see *Eutrema japonicum*

Washingtonia (*Arecaceae*)

× ***filibusta***	CCCN SEND SPlb
robusta	IDee SPalm SPlb SWeb XBlo

Watsonia (*Iridaceae*)

aletroides	CPbh CPrp EBee SDeJ SVen
amatolae	IBlr
angusta	CBor CExl CPrp EBee SPlb
ardernei	see *W. borbonica* subsp. *ardernei* (Sander) Goldblatt 'Arderne's White'
'Ballyrogan Early Pink'	IBlr
beatricis	see *W. pillansii*
§ ***borbonica***	CCtw CPrp EBee
- subsp. ***ardernei*** misapplied	see *W. borbonica* subsp. *ardernei* (Sander) Goldblatt 'Arderne's White'
§ - subsp. ***ardernei*** (Sander) Goldblatt 'Arderne's White'	CCtw CExl IBlr
- subsp. ***borbonica***	IBlr
- 'Peach Glow'	EBee ERCP GKev SDeJ SPeP WCFE
brevifolia	see *W. laccata*
brick red-flowered	EBee LEdu WPGP
coccinea Herb. ex Baker	CPbh
'Curly Blooms'	CPbh
'Dart Sea Trout'	EBee
fourcadei	ECre
fulgens	LEdu
galpinii lavender-flowered	IBlr
- pink-flowered	IBlr
§ ***humilis***	CPrp EBee
knysnana	IBlr
§ ***laccata***	CPbh
- pink-flowered	CCtw EBee
lepida	CPbh SPlb
marginata	CPbh CPrp
meriana	EBee GKev IBlr SDeJ SEdd WABo
- var. ***bulbillifera***	CPrp EBee ESwi GAbr IBlr WSHC
peach hybrid	CSpe
'Peachy Pink Orphan'	EBee
§ ***pillansii***	CAbb CBcs CCCN CExl CPbh CPrp CSpe CTsd EBee ECre EPri EWld GBin ILea LEdu LRHS SVen
- apricot-flowered	CAbb CTsd LRHS
- peach-flowered	CExl
- pink-flowered	CExl CPrp
- red-flowered	CExl
- soft pink-flowered	EPri
pink-flowered	EBee
pyramidata	see *W. borbonica*
roseoalba	see *W. humilis*
'Stanford Scarlet'	CExl CPrp EBee ELon WOut
tabularis	CCtw CPrp IMou
transvaalensis	EBee
'Tresco Dwarf Pink'	CExl CPrp EBee LEdu WPGP
Tresco hybrids	CAbb CCtw CExl CPbh EPri ESwi SRkn
vanderspuyae	CBcs CExl CPrp EPri
wilmaniae	CExl CPrp IBlr WFar

Wattakaka see *Dregea*

Wedelia (*Asteraceae*)

trilobata	see *Sphagneticola trilobata*

Weigela ✿ (*Caprifoliaceae*)

CC 1231	CExl
'Abel Carrière'	CMac CTri ECtt LPot SRms WFar WSpi
ALL SUMMER PEACH ('Slingpink') **new**	LCro LOPS
§ ALL SUMMER RED ('Slingco 1'PBR)	CBod CRos CWGN EHyd EPfP LCro LOPS LRHS MAsh NEoE NRHS SCob SPoG WSpi
'Avalanche' misapplied	see *W.* 'Candida'
'Avant Garde'	IDee MAsh WLov
BLACK AND WHITE ('Courtacad1'PBR)	CBcs CBod CDoC CRos CSpe CWGN EHyd ELan EPfP LRHS LSRN MAsh NEoE NRHS SCob SEle SGol SNig SPoG
'Boskoop Glory'	SPer
§ BRIANT RUBIDOR ('Olympiade') (v)	CAby CBod CMac EHyd LRHS MAsh MGos MMuc MRav NLar NOra NQui SGol SLim SPer SPlb SPoG WAvo WFar WSpi
'Bristol Ruby'	CBar CBcs CBod CBrac CMac CSBt CTri EBee ELan EPfP GKin LCro LMaj LPot LRHS MGos MHer MMuc MSwo SCob SEND SGbt SGol SLon SPer SPlb SRms WAvo WFar WSpi
'Bristol Snowflake'	CBod CMac EPfP MBlu MHer MSwo NLar SCob SLon SRms
§ 'Candida'	CBrac CTri ELan MRav NLar SGol SPer WSpi
CAPPUCCINO ('Verweig 2'PBR)	MBlu NLar SGol
CARNAVAL ('Courtalor') 🏆H6	CBcs MRav SCob
'Chameleon'	NEoE SGol
coraeensis 🏆H6	CBcs CBod EPfP EWld MBlu MGil MMrt MNrw NLar SBrt SPer WLov
CRIMSON KISSES	see *W.* ALL SUMMER RED
decora B&SWJ 10834	WCru
EBONY AND IVORY ('Velda'PBR)	CRos EHyd EPfP LCro LOPS LRHS NLar NRHS SGol SReu
'Eva Rathke'	NLar
'Evita'	MBlu
floribunda B&SWJ 10831	WCru
florida	CMac SavN
- B&SWJ 8439	WCru
* - 'Albovariegata' (v)	CExl
- 'Alexandra'PBR 🏆H6	CBod CDoC CExl CSBt EHyd ELan EMil EShb LSRN MAsh MGos MRav NBro NLar SCob SEle SNig SRkn SWvt WGrn
- 'Bicolor'	CMac ELan
- EYECATCHER ('Walweigeye') (v)	MMrt
- 'Foliis Purpureis'	CBar CBcs CBod CBrac CExl CMac ELan EPfP LRHS MAsh MGos MMuc MRav MSwo NLar SGol SLim SPer SPlb SRms SWvt WAvo WLov
- 'Gustave Malet'	CMCN
- MAGICAL RAINBOW ('Kolmagira'PBR)	CRos EHyd LBuc LCro LOPS LRHS MAsh NEoE NRHS SCob SGol SGsty SPoG
- 'Milk and Honey'	EHyd LRHS SCob
- MINOR BLACK ('Verweig 3'PBR)	EPfP LRHS MGos NBro NEoE NHol SCob SGol SPoG
- MONET ('Verweig'PBR) (v)	CDoC CMac CRos EBee EHyd EPfP EShb LBuc LCro LOPS LRHS LSRN MAsh MGos MMrt NBro NHol NRHS SCob SGol SLim SPer SPoG SRms
- MOULIN ROUGE ('Brigela'PBR)	CRos EHyd ELan EPfP LRHS MAsh MGos
- 'Pink Princess'	CRos EHyd LRHS MSwo
- RUBIGOLD	see *W.* BRIANT RUBIDOR
- SUNNY FANTASY ('Kolsunn')	ECrN NEoE WHil
- 'Versicolor'	CExl SLon SRms
- WINE AND ROSES	see *W. florida* 'Alexandra'
- 'Wings of Fire'PBR	CRos EHyd ILea LBuc LRHS NRHS
'Florida Variegata' (v) 🏆H6	Widely available
'Gold Rush'	NLar
'Golden Candy'	NEoE SCob
hortensis	CExl
- B&SWJ 10808	WCru
'Hulsdonk'	NLar
japonica 'Dart's Colourdream'	CAby EPfP EWes MMuc SEND SGol WGrn
- 'Variegated Dart's Colourdream' (v)	ELon
'Jean's Gold'	MBlu MRav
'Kosteriana Variegata' (v)	CDoC CSBt EBee EHyd EPfP LRHS MAsh MMuc SEle SRms
'Little Red Robin'	CBod NEoE SCob WFar
'Looymansii Aurea'	CBrac CExl CTri ELan EPfP NBPC NLar SGol SPer SRms WFar
LUCIFER ('Courtared')	WSpi
maximowiczii	CExl
§ ***middendorffiana***	CBcs CExl CMCN CMac CRos CTri EBee EHyd ELan EPfP GBin LPot LRHS MAsh MBlu MGil MMuc MRav NLar NSti SChF SCoo SPer SPoG WCru WFar WPGP
- 'Mango'	CRos EHyd LCro LOPS LRHS NRHS
'Minuet'	CRos LRHS MRav MSwo NEoE SGol
'Mont-Blanc'	MAsh MMrt
NAIN ROUGE ('Courtanin')	CTri NLar
'Nana Variegata' (v)	CExl CRos EHyd ELon EPfP LCro LRHS NLar NRHS WFar
NAOMI CAMPBELL ('Bokrashine'PBR)	EBee SGol
'Newport Red'	see *W.* 'Vanicek'
PINK POPPET ('Plangen'PBR)	CBod CRos CSBt EHyd ELan EPfP GBin LRHS LSRN MAsh MGos NLar NRHS SCob SCoo SLim SPoG SRkn SWvt
praecox	ECrN
- B&SWJ 8705	WCru
'Praecox Variegata' (v) 🏆H6	CBod CMac CRos CTri EHyd EPfP LRHS MAsh MRav NBir NRHS SDix SPer SPoG SRms WCFE WKif
'Red Prince' 🏆H6	CDoC CWCL EBee EPfP LRHS MAsh MSwo NLar SCob SGol SNig SReu
'Rosabella'	SReu
RUBIDOR	see *W.* BRIANT RUBIDOR
RUBIGOLD	see *W.* BRIANT RUBIDOR
'Ruby Anniversary'	EHyd LRHS SLon
'Ruby Queen'PBR	CMac EPfP
RUBY WEDDING	LSRN
'Rumba'	CMac
sessilifolia	see *Diervilla sessilifolia*
'Snowflake'	SRms
'Stelzneri'	MMuc
subsessilis B&SWJ 1056	WCru
- B&SWJ 4206	WCru
'Suzanne' (v)	EPPr MAsh NOra

	'Tango'	LRHS MAsh NEoE WAvo WFar
§	'Vanicek'	CBrac SCob
	'Victoria'	CBod CMac EPfP LRHS MGos MSwo NBir NWad SGol SPer
	WHITE LIGHTNING ('Wf-2009') (v)	NEoE

Weinmannia (*Cunoniaceae*)

	trichosperma	IDee

Weldenia (*Commelinaceae*)

	candida	EPot GEdr IBlr NHar SChF WCot

Westringia (*Lamiaceae*)

	brevifolia	CCCN CSde SVen
§	***fruticosa*** 🏆H1c	CBcs CBod CCCN CSde CTsd SRms SVen
	- 'Smokie' (v)	CCCN
	- 'Variegata' (v)	CCCN CPbh CSde SRms SVen
	longifolia	CCCN
	rosmariniformis	see *W. fruticosa*
	'Wynyabbie Gem'	CAbb CBod CCCN CRos EBee EHyd LRHS MNHC SEND SPoG SVen

whitecurrant see *Ribes rubrum* (W); also AGM Fruit Section

Whiteheadia (*Asparagaceae*)

	bifolia **new**	WCot

Wikstroemia (*Thymelaeaceae*)

	gemmata	see *Daphne gemmata*

wineberry see *Rubus phoenicolasius*

Wisteria ✿ (*Papilionaceae*)

	'Betty's Dwarf Blue'	NLar
§	***brachybotrys***	SWeb WSpi
§	- f. ***albiflora*** 'Shiro-kapitan' 🏆H6	Widely available
	- 'Okayama' 🏆H6	CDoC CRos EHyd EMil EPfP LRHS NOra NRHS SGsty SLau SPer SWeb WMat
	- 'Showa-beni' 🏆H6	Widely available
	'Burford'	see *W. × valderi* 'Burford'
	floribunda	CBcs CBrac CRHN SEWo SGol SWeb
	- B&SWJ 12748 from South Korea	WCru
§	- 'Alba' 🏆H6	Widely available
	- BLACK DRAGON	see *W. floribunda* 'Kokuryu'
	- blue-flowered	WLov
§	- 'Domino' 🏆H6	Widely available
	- 'Ed's Blue Dragon' (d)	EBee
	- f. ***floribunda*** **new**	SWeb
	- 'Fragrantissima'	see *W. sinensis* f. *alba* 'Jako'
	- 'Geisha'	CAby CBcs CEnd CRos EHyd ELon EPfP LRHS NOra NRHS SEND SNig SRms WHwl WPGP
	- 'Golden Dragon'	EPfP SWeb
	- 'Harlequin'	CBcs CRos CWCL EHyd ELon LRHS MMuc SEND SNig
	- 'Hon-beni'	see *W. floribunda* 'Rosea'
	- 'Honey Bee Pink'	see *W. floribunda* 'Rosea'
	- 'Issai Perfect'	CRos EHyd LRHS LSRN NLar SCoo SLon
	- 'Issai-naga'	NLar
	- 'Jakohn-fuji'	see *W. sinensis* f. *alba* 'Jako'
	- 'Kimono'	NOra SLau WHwl
§	- 'Kokuryū' 🏆H6	CBcs CDoC CEnd CWCL EMil EPfP GBin IPot NLar NOra NOrn SCob SLau SPoG WLov
§	- 'Kuchi-beni'	CBcs CDoC CEnd CRHN CRos CWCL ELan LCro LOPS LRHS LSRN MGos MRav NHol NLar NOra SCob SEND SLau SMad SPer SPoG SRms
	- 'Lawrence' 🏆H6	CBcs CEnd CMac CRos CWCL CWGN LRHS NLar NOra SLau SPoG
	- 'Lipstick'	see *W. floribunda* 'Kuchi-beni'
	- 'Longissima'	see *W. floribunda* f. *multijuga*
	- 'Longissima Alba'	see *W. floribunda* 'Alba'
	- 'Macrobotrys'	see *W. floribunda* Macrobotrys Group
§	- Macrobotrys Group **new**	CDoC NOrn SGsty SWeb
	- 'Magenta'	CRos EHyd LRHS
	- f. ***microphylla***	WPGP
	- 'Mon-nishiki' (v) **new**	WCot
§	- f. ***multijuga*** 🏆H6	Widely available
	- - 'Cascade'	CBcs
	- MURASAKI-NAGA	see *W. floribunda* 'Purple Patches'
	- 'Nana Richin's Purple'	CEnd CRos EHyd LRHS SLau
	- 'Peaches and Cream'	see *W. floribunda* 'Kuchi-beni'
	- 'Pink Ice'	see *W. floribunda* 'Rosea'
§	- 'Purple Patches'	WSpi
	- REINDEER	see *W. sinensis* f. *alba* 'Jako'
	- 'Rolvenden Bronze' **new**	SLau
§	- 'Rosea' 🏆H6	Widely available
	- 'Royal Purple'	see *W. floribunda* 'Kokuryu'
	- 'Russelliana'	see *W. floribunda* 'Kokuryu'
	- 'Shiro-naga'	see *W. floribunda* 'Alba'
	- 'Shiro-noda'	see *W. floribunda* 'Alba'
	- 'Snow Showers'	see *W. floribunda* 'Alba'
	- 'Variegata' (v)	CWGN
	- 'Violacea Plena'	see *W. floribunda* 'Yae-kokuryu'
	- 'Yae-kokuryū' (d) 🏆H6	Widely available
	× ***formosa***	CEnd LCro LOPS SLau SLim
	- 'Caroline'	Widely available
	- 'Domino'	see *W. floribunda* 'Domino'
	- 'Issai' Wada *pro parte*	see *W. floribunda* 'Domino'
	- 'Ivy Hatch' **new**	WPGP
	- 'Kokuryū'	see *W. floribunda* 'Kokuryū'
	- 'Yae-kokuryū'	see *W. floribunda* 'Yae-kokuryū'
	frutescens	CDoC EBee EPfP
	- 'Alba'	see *W. frutescens* 'Nivea'
	- 'Amethyst Falls'[PBR]	CBcs CEnd CWGN ELan EShb IArd LCro LOPS LRHS LSRN MGos SCoo SLon SPoG
	- 'Longwood Purple'	CRos CWCL EHyd LRHS NOra NRHS SNig
	- var. ***macrostachya*** 'Aunt Dee'	CWGN NLar
	- - 'Blue Moon'	NOra
	- - 'Clara Mack'	CWGN
§	- 'Nivea'	CRos EHyd LRHS NRHS
	Kapitan-fuji	see *W. brachybotrys*
	'Lavender Lace'	CBcs CRos EHyd EPfP LRHS LSRN MAsh NLar SCob SLau
	multijuga 'Alba'	see *W. floribunda* 'Alba'
	sinensis	CArg CBcs CBod CCVT CRos CTri CWCL EHyd EPfP LCro LMaj LOPS LRHS LSRN MGos MPri MRav MSwo NLar SCob SEWo SGol SGsty SLim SRms SSta SWvt WFar WMou
	- f. ***alba***	CAby CBcs CDoC CMen CRos EHyd ELan EPfP LCro LOPS LRHS LSRN MAsh MGil MGos MSwo NRHS SCob SLau SPer SPoG SRms SWeb WFar

§ - - 'Jako' ♀H6 — CEnd NHol
- 'Amethyst' ♀H6 — CArg CBcs CBod CDoC CEnd CRos EHyd EPfP LCro LOPS LRHS LSRN MAsh MGil MGos NOra NRHS SCob SLau SLim SPer SWeb WSpi
- 'Consequa' — see *W. sinensis* 'Prolific'
- 'Cooke's Special' — see *W. sinensis* 'Prolific'
- 'Oosthoek's Variety' — see *W. sinensis* 'Prolific'
I - 'Pink Ice' — EWTr SRms
- 'Prematura' — see *W. floribunda* 'Domino'
- 'Prematura Alba' — see *W. brachybotrys* f. *albiflora* 'Shiro-kapitan'
§ - 'Prolific' ♀H6 — Widely available
- 'Rosea' — EPfP LMaj LSRN SWvt
- 'Shiro-capital' — see *W. brachybotrys* f. *albiflora* 'Shiro-kapitan'
× ***valderi*** 'Burford' ♀H6 — CBod CEnd CMac CRos CWCL CWGN EBee EHyd EMil EPfP LRHS LSRN MAsh MNHC NLar NOra NOrn SCoo SEND SLau SLim SRms WHwl WMat WPGP WSpi
- 'Hocker Edge' — SLau
§ - 'Murasaki-kapitan' — CEnd CMac CRos CTri CWGN EHyd EMil EPfP LRHS SEND
venusta — see *W. brachybotrys* f. *albiflora* 'Shiro-kapitan'
- 'Alba' — see *W. brachybotrys* f. *albiflora* 'Shiro-kapitan'
- var. ***violacea*** misapplied — see *W.* × *valderi* 'Murasaki-kapitan'

Withania (*Solanaceae*)

sinensis BWJ 8093 — WCru
somnifera — GPoy XAbr

Wittsteinia (*Alseuosmiaceae*)

vacciniacea — GEdr WCru

Wodyetia (*Arecaceae*)

bifurcata — XBlo

Wollemia (*Araucariaceae*)

nobilis — CDTJ CTho ELan EPfP ESwi GBin LRHS MGos NPoe SArc

Woodsia ✿ (*Woodsiaceae*)

obtusa — CBdn CDTJ CLAP CWCL EFer EHyd EMor EPfP IBal ISha LRHS MMuc NBro SPoG SRms WCot XLum
polystichoides — SRms

Woodwardia ✿ (*Blechnaceae*)

from Emei Shan, China — CLAP
fimbriata ♀H3 — CBcs CBct CBdn CBod CLAP CRos CWCL EFer EHyd EMor EPfP EWTr IBal LCro LEdu LLWG LRHS MAsh NBro NHol NLar NRHS SEND SIvy SPlb SPoG WBor WCot WFib
orientalis — CLAP EHyd EMor ESwi ISha LEdu LRHS MAsh NRHS WFib WPGP
- var. ***formosana*** — LEdu SPlb
- - B&SWJ 6865 — ESwi WCru
prolifera new — CBdn
radicans ♀H3 — CAby EShb EWes ITim LEdu WFib XBlo
unigemmata ♀H4 — CAby CBdn CLAP EFer EHyd EPfP EShb EWes ISha LEdu LRHS NRHS SPlb WAbe WFib WHal WPGP
virginica — CLAP EHyd ISha LRHS

Worcesterberry see *Ribes* 'Worcesterberry'

Wulfenia (*Plantaginaceae*)

amherstiana — GEdr GKev LEdu
baldaccii — GKev SBrt
carinthiaca — EBee GAbr GEdr GKev LEdu NBir NLar WCot XLum
- 'Alba' — GKev
× ***schwarzii*** — CDor CMiW EBee IMou LEdu WSHC

Wurmbea (*Colchicaceae*)

§ ***stricta*** — WCot

Wyethia (*Asteraceae*)

amplexicaulis — EAJP GEdr
angustifolia — SBrt
mollis B&SWJ 14067 — WCru

X

Xanthisma (*Asteraceae*)

§ ***coloradoense*** — NSla XEll

Xanthoceras (*Sapindaceae*)

sorbifolium ♀H7 — CAgr CBcs CMCN EBee ELan EPfP IMou MBlu MGil NLar SBrt SPoG WSpi

Xanthocyparis (*Cupressaceae*)

§ ***nootkatensis*** — MAsh
- 'Boyko's Sundown' — NLar
- 'Flaming Arrow' — NLar
I - 'Gloria Polonica' (v) — NLar
- 'Golden Waterfall' — NLar
- 'Green Arrow' ♀H7 — CKen NLar NOra SLim WMat
- 'Jubilee' — SLim WCFE WMat
- 'Kanada' — SLim
- 'Moon Shot' new — SLim
- 'Pendula' ♀H7 — CCVT CKen ELan EPfP LRHS MAsh MBlu
- 'Sparkling Arrow' — NLar
- 'Strict Weeper' — CKen NLar SLim
vietnamensis — WPGP

Xanthorhiza (*Ranunculaceae*)

simplicissima — CBcs EPfP EWld LEdu MGil NLar SDys WCot WPGP

Xanthorrhoea (*Xanthorrhoeaceae*)

australis — SPlb
fulva — SPlb
glauca — CCCN
johnsonii — SPlb
preisii — CTsd SPlb

Xerochrysum (*Asteraceae*)

§ ***bracteatum*** — SVen
§ - 'Coco' — CSpe
§ - 'Dargan Hill Monarch' — CSpe SRms

Xeronema (*Xeronemataceae*)

callistemon — CBrP CCCN

Xerophyllum (*Melanthiaceae*)

tenax — LRHS

Xerophyta (*Velloziaceae*)

retinervis new — SPlb

Y

Ypsilandra (*Melanthiaceae*)

cavaleriei	CExl GEdr WCot
thibetica	CBct CExl CMil CSpe EBee EPfP ESwi GEdr GKev LEdu LRHS MHer MNrw WCot WCru WSHC
- narrow-leaved	WCru

Yucca ✿ (*Asparagaceae*)

aloifolia	CCCN CDTJ SArc SPlb
angustifolia	see *Y. glauca*
arizonica	CDTJ
baccata	CAgr CCCN CDoC SPlb XSen
campestris	CDTJ XSen
carnerosana	CDTJ
cernua	WCot
constricta	CDTJ
decipiens	XSen
§ ***elata***	CCCN CTsd XSen
§ ***elephantipes*** 🏆H2	CDTJ LCro LOPS SEND
- 'Jewel' (v)	EPfP SEND
- 'Puck' (v)	SEND
- variegated (v)	SEND
faxoniana	CDTJ SPlb
filamentosa	CBcs CCCN CMac CTri EBee EHyd ELan EPfP LCro LOPS LRHS LSun MGos MMuc MSwo SCob SEND SGol SLim SPer SPlb SRms WSMil XSen
- 'Bright Edge' (v) 🏆H4	CBcs CBrac CMac CPla CTri ELan ELon EPfP LCro LOPS LSRN MRav MSwo SGol SLim SPer SWvt WSMil
- 'Color Guard' (v) 🏆H5	CBod CPla EHyd EPfP SPalm SPoG WSMil
- 'Garland's Gold' (v)	CBcs CCCN
- 'Variegata' (v)	CBcs SRms WSMil
filifera	SPlb
flaccida	XSen
- 'Golden Sword' (v) 🏆H4	CBcs CBrac CMac CTsd EBee ELan EPfP GMaP LRHS LSRN MGos MSwo SCob SGol SLim SPer SRms SWvt WFar
- 'Ivory' 🏆H5	CTsd ELan ELon GBin GMaP LSRN MRav NLar SRms
× ***floribunda***	SArc
§ ***glauca***	SPlb SPtp WCot XSen
gloriosa 🏆H5	CBcs CMac CTri GKev SArc SCob SEND SGsty SPer SPlb SWeb SWvt WFar
- 'Aureovariegata'	see *Y. gloriosa* 'Variegata'
§ - 'Variegata' (v) 🏆H5	CBcs CBod CDoC CMac CRos CSBt CTsd ELan ELon EPfP GMaP LRHS MAsh NRHS SArc SCob SEND SIvy SLim SPer SPlb SPoG SRms SWeb SWvt WCFE
guatemalensis	see *Y. elephantipes*
harrimaniae	WCot
linearis	see *Y. thompsoniana*
mexicana	CDTJ
mixtecana	XSen
queretaroensis	CDTJ
radiosa	see *Y. elata*
recurvifolia 🏆H5	SArc
- BANANA SPLIT ('Monvil') (v)	EBee WCot
- 'Gold Stream' (v)	WCot
rigida	CDTJ XSen
rostrata	CCCN CDTJ SArc SPalm SPlb SWeb WCot WSMil XSen
- 'Sapphire Skies'	CBod CMac
rupicola	WCot XSen
schottii	EShb
§ ***thompsoniana***	CDTJ XSen
torreyi	CDTJ
'Vittorio Emanuele II'	SMad
whipplei	CCCN ELan EPfP LRHS SPtp WPGP XSen
- subsp. ***whipplei*** NJM 11.001	WPGP

Yushania (*Poaceae*)

KR 7698	MWht
addingtonii	XCre
§ ***anceps***	CAgr CBcs CExl MMuc MWht SEND
- 'Pitt White'	CAgr CBdn CExl MWht
chungii	CBdn CExl MWht XCre
maculata	CAgr CBdn CExl MWht
§ ***maling***	CExl
Yunnan 5	CExl MWht

Z

Zabelia (*Caprifoliaceae*)

§ ***biflora***	LRHS
§ ***triflora***	CExl CRos CTho LRHS MMuc NLar SEND WPGP WSHC

Zaluzianskya (*Scrophulariaceae*)

JCA 15665	WAbe
elongata	SPlb
microsiphon	SPlb
ovata	CPBP CPbh CWCL EPfP EPot EWld GBin GKev LCro LOPS MHer NSla SPlb SPoG SPtp WFar WIce XEll
- 'Orange Eye'	CPBP CPbh ELan EWes GKev NHpl NSla WIce
- 'Star Balsam'	CBod CPla LSou NCou
pulvinata	SPlb
'Semonkong'	SWvt

Zamia (*Zamiaceae*)

pumila	SPlb

Zamioculcas (*Araceae*)

zamiifolia	CCCN CDoC LCro LOPS
- RAVEN ('Dowon'PBR) **new**	LCro LOPS

Zantedeschia (*Araceae*)

§ ***aethiopica***	Widely available
- 'Apple Court Babe'	ELon
- 'Childsiana'	CRos EBee EHyd LRHS NRHS
- 'Crowborough' 🏆H4	Widely available
- 'Flamingo'PBR	CDoC
- 'Glencoe'	CAby CBct CBod EBee ECtt GAbr MAvo MHol NWad SMad SPad WBrk WCot WFar WHwl WPGP WRHF WSHC WTyc
- 'Glow'	CExl CMac ECtt WAvo
- 'Green Goddess' 🏆H4	Widely available

- 'Little Gem' SMad
- 'Luzon Lovely' WCru WFar
- 'Marshmallow' CBod ECtt EHyd EPfP LRHS MAsh NBPC NRHS WAvo WFar WGwG WHwl
- 'Mr Martin' CCCN ECtt ELon SWvt WCot WFar
- 'Pershore Fantasia' (v) CDTJ CExl WAvo WCot WFar WHwl
- 'Pink Mist' GKev
- 'Spotted Giant' CDTJ
- 'White Gnome' WCot WFar
- 'White Sail' CBod ECtt EHyd LRHS NBPC NGdn NRHS WGwG

albomaculata GKev SPlb WPGP
'Anneke' CCCN SDeJ
'Apricot Glow' GKev
'Ascari'PBR CCCN
'Auckland'PBR SDeJ
'Black Magic' CCCN CMac GKev SChr
'Black Star' see *Z.* 'Edge of Night'
CALLAFORNIA RED ('Gscccare'PBR) **new** LSou
'Cameo' CCCN SDeJ
'Cantor'PBR CRos EHyd LRHS NRHS
(Captain Series) 'Captain Fuego'PBR **new** GKev
- 'Captain Murano'PBR SPoG
- 'Captain Prado'PBR CRos EHyd LRHS NRHS SPoG
- 'Captain Promise'PBR **new** GKev
- 'Captain Romance'PBR GKev LCro LOPS
- 'Captain Safari'PBR GKev
- 'Captain Tendens'PBR SDeJ
'Chianti' SDeJ
'Coral Passion'PBR **new** LSou
'Crystal Blush' SDeJ
§ 'Edge of Night' CBcs CCCN SDeJ
elliottiana ♀H1c CTri
'Festival'PBR SRms
'Flame' CBcs CCCN GKev MSCN
'Garnet Glow' LCro LOPS MHol
'Golden Nugget' **new** CRos
'Helen O'Connor' CExl
'Hercules' ESwi
'Hot Shot' WMal
'Ice Dancer'PBR **new** LSou
jucunda GKev
'Kiwi Blush' CAby CBod CBro CCCN CDoC CExl CSam CSpe EHyd ELan ELon EPfP LRHS NBPC NRHS WCot WFar WGwG
'Lime Lady' ECha
'Majestic Red' GKev
'Mango' EPri SRms
'Mercedes'PBR CRos EHyd LRHS NRHS
'Mozart' CCCN SDeJ
'Nightlife'PBR SRms
'Odessa'PBR LCro LOPS MSCN
'Philomena' EHyd LRHS
'Picasso'PBR CBcs CCCN GKev MSCN SDeJ
'Pink Melody'PBR **new** LSou
'Pink Mist' SMad
'Pot of Gold' GKev
'Red Alert'PBR EHyd MSCN
'Red Sox'PBR CCCN SDeJ
rehmannii ♀H1c GKev SDeJ SRms
'San Remo'PBR GKev
'Sapporo'PBR EHyd LRHS
'Schwarzwalder'PBR GKev
'Summer Sun'PBR EHyd LRHS
'White Flirt'PBR EHyd LRHS
'White Giant' EPri EWat MAvo WPGP
'Yellow Queen' MSCN

Zanthorhiza see *Xanthorhiza*

Zanthoxylum (*Rutaceae*)

acanthopodium GWJ 9287 WCru
- PAB 8760 LEdu
- WJC 13653 WCru
aff. ***acanthopodium*** WJC 13795 WCru
ailanthoides CDTJ EBee
- B&SWJ 11115 from Japan WCru
- B&SWJ 11394 from Japan WCru
- from Taiwan WPGP
- f. ***inermis*** RWJ 10048 WCru
americanum ELan ESwi LEdu
armatum CAgr
- B&SWJ 12753 WCru
- CWJ 12824 WCru
- FMWJ 13091 WCru
- NJM 11.080 WPGP
- PAB 8902 LEdu
bungeanum GKev NLar
- BWJ 8040 ESwi WCru
coreanum NLar
dissitum FMWJ 13498 WCru
fauriei B&SWJ 11080 WCru
aff. ***fauriei*** B&SWJ 11371 WCru
- B&SWJ 11523 WCru
laetum FMWJ 13175 WCru
myriacanthum B&SWJ 11844 WCru
oxyphyllum CMCN LEdu
- GWJ 9428 WCru
- HWJK 2131 WCru
piperitum CAgr CBcs ELan GPoy LEdu SPtp WJek WPGP
- B&SWJ 11377 WCru
- B&SWJ 14677 WCru
- var. ***inerme*** **new** WPGP
- purple-leaved CBcs CDTJ CExl EBee LEdu WPGP
scandens **new** SPlb
schinifolium CAgr
- B&SWJ 11080 WCru
- B&SWJ 11391 WCru
- B&SWJ 14654 WCru
- B&SWJ 8593 WCru
simulans CAgr CBcs CExl ESwi LCro LEdu LOPS MBlu SBrt SPtp WJek WPGP
stenophyllum CMCN
tomentellum B&SWJ 13903 WCru
aff. ***yuanjiangense*** FMWJ 13498 WCru

Zauschneria (*Onagraceae*)

arizonica see *Z. californica* subsp. *latifolia*
§ ***californica*** CTri MBrN SLon SWvt XLum
§ - 'Dublin' ♀H4 Widely available
- 'Ed Carman' ECha ECtt MGil MMuc WLov
* - subsp. ***garrettii*** SDys XLum
- 'Glasnevin' see *Z. californica* 'Dublin'
§ - subsp. ***latifolia*** XLum
§ - subsp. ***mexicana*** SRms
- 'Olbrich Silver' ECha EWes WAbe WHoo WKif XSen
- 'Solidarity Pink' WAbe

- 'Western Hills' 🏆H4	CFis CTri ECha EPfP EPot EWld MHer MMuc MRav SEND SPhx SRms SWvt WPGP XLum
§ **cana**	ECha XSen
- **villosa**	see *Z. californica* subsp. *mexicana*
I 'Pumilio'	EPot
§ **septentrionalis**	WAbe

Zea (*Poaceae*)

mays 'Variegata' (v)	CSpe

Zebrina see *Tradescantia*

Zelkova ✿ (*Ulmaceae*)

abelicea	CMCN LRHS MBlu
carpinifolia	CMCN WPGP
- PAB 13.047	LEdu
- NJM 13.014 from Azerbaijan	WPGP
- NJM 13.016 from Azerbaijan	WPGP
'Kiwi Sunset'	WMat
serrata 🏆H6	CBcs CCVT CLnd CMCN CMen CTsd EBee ECrN ELan EShb GQue LMaj MGos MMuc SEND SGol WHCr
- B&SWJ 8491 from Korea	WCru
- 'Goblin'	MBlu NLar
- 'Green Vase'	LMaj MBlu
- 'Green Veil'	IDee
- 'Kiwi Sunset' PBR	MGos NOra SPoG
- 'Luminifera'	MBlu
- 'Musashino'	ESwi SGol
- 'Ogon'	SGol
- 'Urban Ruby'	LMaj
- 'Variegata' (v)	CJun CMac MBlu NLar SGol
sicula new	WPGP
× **verschaffeltii**	CMCN IArd MBlu

Zenobia (*Ericaceae*)

pulverulenta	CBcs CDoC CMac EHyd ELan EPfP LRHS MAsh MBlu MGil MGos SLon SSta
- 'Blue Sky'	CBcs CBct CMCN CRos EHyd EPfP IDee LRHS MAsh MBlu MGos MPkF NLar SPer SPoG SSta WPGP
- f. **nitida**	CMac
- 'Raspberry Ripple'	CBcs CRos EHyd LRHS MAsh NLar NRHS SPoG SSta

Zephyranthes (*Amaryllidaceae*)

candida	CBor CBro CRos EBee EHyd EShb EWld GKev LRHS NRHS SChF SDeJ WAvo
citrina	CBor CExl EShb GKev SDeJ
'Krakatau'	WCot
La Bufa Rosa Group	CExl WCot
robusta	see *Habranthus robustus*
rosea	CBor GKev SDeJ

Zigadenus (*Melanthiaceae*)

elegans	CRos EDAr EHyd EPri GAbr IMou LEdu LPla LRHS MAvo MHer NRHS SLon SMad WFar WSHC
nuttallii	CAby GKev

Zingiber ✿ (*Zingiberaceae*)

clarkei	CTsd
mioga	CAgr CLau CSpe CTsd EBee ELan GPoy IMou LEdu LRHS SChr SPlb SPtp SRms WPGP
- 'Crûg's Zing'	LEdu MAvo SBrt WCru WPGP
- 'Dancing Crane' (v)	CMac LEdu SRms WPGP
- 'White Feather'	CTsd LEdu MAvo WPGP
officinale	GPoy SPlb SPre

Zinnia (*Asteraceae*)

DAHLIA-FLOWERED MIXED	LCro LOPS
elegans	SVic
- (Benary's Giant Series) 'Benary's Giant Lime'	CSpe
- - 'Benary's Giant Scarlet' 🏆H1c	CSpe
- 'Queen Lime Red' (Queen Series) (d) 🏆H1c	CSpe
marylandica (Zahara Series) ZAHARA RED ('Pas1118265') new	SCob
- - ZAHARA STARLIGHT ROSE ('Pas719128') new	SCob
- - ZAHARA YELLOW IMPROVED ('Pas951086') new	SCob
Oklahoma Series 🏆H2 new	LCro LOPS
'Red Spider'	CSpe

Zizia (*Apiaceae*)

aptera	SPhx
aurea	LRHS MBriF MNrw SPhx WSHC XLum

Ziziphus (*Rhamnaceae*)

§ **jujuba** (F)	CBcs MBlu
- 'Lang' (F)	CAgr
- 'Li' (F)	CAgr
sativa	see *Z. jujuba*

Zosima (*Apiaceae*)

absinthifolia	WCot

III
RHS AWARD OF GARDEN MERIT
FRUIT

Award of Garden Merit Fruit

This is a directory of fruit offered by nurseries participating in *RHS Plant Finder 2018* that have been awarded an RHS Award of Garden Merit (AGM). It does not represent a complete list of AGM fruit.

Entries are accompanied by a short description and the relevant **hardiness rating** for the UK (see p.39 for an explanation of these). The figures to the left of the rating indicate the year of the award. Cultivars particularly suitable for culinary use are flagged **(C)**, while **(D)** denotes dessert fruit.

Cultivation

All fruits are best grown in sheltered sites, with protection from spring frosts and cold winds. Brief guidance is given below on suitability for different locations, rootstocks, pollination and storage.

Location

Most of the **apple** cultivars listed here succeed all over the country, including the north of England. Those which have been found to be particularly successful in higher-rainfall and colder areas are **marked with an asterisk**; this is also used to highlight other fruits that have been found to be successful in northern regions. **Pears** crop best in sheltered warm situations; in the more exposed areas and northern counties, some pears will benefit from the protection of walls. **Plums** are susceptible to spring frosts and also need warm summers to ripen fully. Only early ripening plums can be relied upon in the shorter season of northern counties.

Currants, **gooseberries**, **raspberries** and **berry fruits** are generally satisfactory in most parts of the country, but cold winds at flowering time can be a problem. **Strawberries** can be grown all over the country, but will need some protection in exposed sites and from spring frosts. **Blueberries** are hardy plants but require light, well-drained, moisture-retentive, acid soil (pH 4.0–5.5).

Figs can crop satisfactorily in sheltered, warm situations in southern England. In northerly areas they will need protection such as a south-facing wall, or to be grown under glass or in polytunnels.

Pollination

Most tree fruits need to be pollinated by another tree of the same kind growing reasonably close by, which flowers at approximately the same time. Flowering groups are given in descriptions; for good pollination, choose cultivars from the same group, though those from adjacent groups will also serve as pollinators. **Apples** and **pears** listed as triploid are poor pollinators and require a normal (i.e. diploid) pollinator to set fruit. Gardeners should be aware that this diploid pollinator will not itself set fruit unless pollinated by another diploid tree. Many *Malus* species and crab apples, such as 'Golden Hornet' and 'Evereste', are also a good source of pollen for dessert and culinary apples. A number of the **plums** listed are self-fertile or partly self-fertile and will produce crops without a pollinator, but a pollinator is needed for all other plums. **Cherries** listed as self-fertile will crop without a pollinator, but otherwise cherries need a pollinator. Soft fruits are self-fertile, except that **blueberries** may need a pollinator.

Rootstocks

All tree fruits are grafted onto rootstocks of varying vigour. Choice of rootstock will determine the ultimate size of the tree and hence needs to be borne in mind when selecting new trees for the garden. For example, **apple trees** on 'M9' rootstock are suitable for small gardens, while those on 'M25' will produce large, standard trees. The size of the tree will also be determined by the vigour of the cultivar. It is often advisable to obtain a very vigorous cultivar, for example 'Bramley's Seedling', on a more dwarfing stock. **Apples** are available on 'M27' (very dwarfing), 'M9' (dwarfing), 'M26' (semi-dwarfing), 'MM 106' (semi-vigorous), and 'M25' (vigorous) rootstocks. **Pears** are available on 'Quince C' (dwarfing), 'Quince A' (semi-vigorous), 'BA 29' (semi-vigorous) and seedling pear (vigorous) rootstocks. Some pear cultivars are incompatible with a quince rootstock and these are sold with a pear interstock (usually 'Beurré Hardy'). **Plums** are available on 'Pixy' (semi-dwarfing) and 'Saint Julien A' (semi-vigorous) rootstocks; cherries on 'Tabel' (very dwarfing), 'Gisela 5' (dwarfing), and 'Colt' (semi-vigorous).

Storage

Early **apples** and **pears** will not store, but many more of the apple and pear cultivars listed will store to Christmas and some to the spring. This calls for good storage conditions, i.e. a cool, dark, frost-free place that is not subject to fluctuating temperatures. Often this can be achieved in sheds and garages, but in general centrally heated houses are not suitable for long-term storage.

Apple (*Malus domestica*)

98 H6 **'Alkmene'** (D)
Pollination group 2. Aromatic, Cox-like flavour. Good, regular crops; some resistance to scab and mildew. Season: late Sept.–late Oct.
CAgr ECrN NOra SKee

'American Mother' *see* 'Mother'

93 H6 **'Arthur Turner'** (C)
Pollination group 3. Flavoursome cooker. Large, golden exhibition fruit. Good, regular crops; prone to mildew; some resistance to scab. Striking deep pink blossom, for which an Award of Merit was given in 1945. Season: Sept.–Nov.
CArg CCVT CHab CLnd CTri ECrN EPom LBuc MWat NOra SKee SSFr WJas WMat

93 H6 **'Ashmead's Kernel'** (D)
Pollination group 4. Intense, fruit-drop flavour. Cropping erratic; prone to bitter pit. Season: Dec.–Feb.
CAgr CArg CHab CLnd CRos CSBt CTho CTri EBee ECrN EPfP EPom LBuc LRHS MRav MWat NOra SEdi SKee SLim SLon SSFT SSFr SVic WJas WMat WWct

93 H6 **'Belle de Boskoop'** (C/D)
Triploid. Pollination group 3. Needs little or no extra sugar when cooked; mellows to brisk eating apple. Good, regular crops; very vigorous tree. Season: Oct.–Apr.; keeps well.*
CAgr CHab ECrN MCoo NOra SKee

93 H6 **'Blenheim Orange'** (C/D)
Triploid. Pollination group 3. Characteristic nutty flavour. Use early for cooking. Some resistance to mildew; very vigorous tree; partial tip-bearer; light crops. Season (C): from late Sept. (D): Oct.–Dec./Jan.*
CAgr CArg CCVT CHab CLnd CSBt CTho CTri ECrN ELan EPfP EPom IArd LBuc LEdu LRHS MAsh MCoo MPri MRav MWat NOra NRHS SCob SEdi SEND SEWo SGbt SKee SPer SSFr SVic WJas WMat WWct

93 H6 **'Bramley's Seedling'** (C)
Triploid. Pollination group 3. Cooks to very sharp, savoury purée; retains acidity to spring. Heavy crops; prone to bitter pit and scab; partial tip bearer; can bear fruit parthenocarpically; tendency to be biennial if over-cropped; blossom susceptible to frost. Very vigorous tree. Season: Nov.–Mar.; stores well.*
CAgr CArg CBcs CCVT CLnd CMac CRos CSBt CTho CTri EBee ECrN ELan EPfP EPom GKin LBuc LEdu LMaj LRHS LSRN MGos MMuc MPri MRav MWat NLar NOra NRHS SCob SEdi SEND SEWo SKee SLim SPer SRms SSFr SSFT SVic SWvt WJas WMat WWct

93 H6 **'Charles Ross'** (C/D)
Pollination group 3. Quite rich flavour; needs no sugar when cooked. Handsome exhibition fruit. Good, regular crops; hardy tree; some resistance to scab. Season: Oct.–Dec.*
CAgr CArg CCVT CHab CLnd CMac CSBt CTho CTri ECrN EPom IArd LBuc LRHS LSRN MAsh MCoo MRav NOra SCob SKee SLim SPer SSFT SSFr WJas WMat WWct

14 H6 **'Christmas Pippin'** (D)
Pollination group 3. Medium vigour; upright spreading habit; good, regular crops. Medium sized apple of attractive appearance, flushed with colour over yellow background with some russet; crisp, juicy, sweet flesh with rich sweet sharp flavour, developing aromatic quality. Well-flavoured, good quality apple.
CArg CRos CTri EBee EPom LBuc LCro LRHS MCoo MPri NLar NOra NRHS SGbt WMat

93 H6 **'Discovery'** (D)
Pollination group 3. Bright red, crisp, juicy; keeps longer than most earlies. Ornamental tree. Good, regular crops; partial tip bearer; good resistance to scab and mildew. Season: mid Aug.–Sept.*
CAgr CArg CBcs CCVT CLnd CMac CSBt CTri EBee ECrN EPfP EPom GBin GKin LBuc LRHS MGos MPri MRav MWat NLar NOra SCob SEdi SGbt SKee SLim SPer SSFr SSFT SVic WJas WMat WWct

93 H6 **'Dummellor's Seedling'** (C)
Pollination group 4. Previously listed as 'Dumelow's Seedling'. Cooks to well-flavoured, juicy purée; retains acidity to spring. Good, regular crops, but fruit can be small for a cooker. Season: Nov.–Apr.*
CHab MCoo NOra SKee

93 H6 **'Edward VII'** (C)
Pollination group 6. Cooks to well-flavoured purée, not as acidic as 'Bramley's Seedling'. Large, regular, exhibition fruit. Deep pink blossom; flowers very late so escapes frosts;

needs late-flowering pollinator. Good, regular crops; resistant to scab; some resistance to mildew. Season: Dec.–Apr.*
CHab NOra SKee WMat WWct

93 H6 **'Egremont Russet'** (D)
Pollination group 2. Characteristic nutty flavour. Good, regular crops; fruit resistant to scab, but prone to leaf scab; very prone to bitter pit and woolly aphids. Season: Oct.–Dec.*
CAgr CArg CCVT CHab CLnd CMac CRos CSBt CTri EBee ECrN ELan EPfP EPom LBuc LEdu LRHS MAsh MGos MMuc MPri MWat NLar NOra SEdi SEND SEWo SKee SLim SPer SRms SSFr SSFT WJas WMat WWct

93 H6 **'Ellison's Orange'** (D)
Pollination group 4. Rich, aniseed flavour. Good, regular crops; some resistance to scab, but susceptible to canker. Season: late Sept.–late Oct.
CAgr CArg CHab CLnd CMac CSBt CTri ECrN EPfP EPom LBuc LRHS MMuc MWat NOra SEND SEdi SGbt SKee SLon SPer SRms SSFr SVic SWeb WJas WMat WWct

93 H6 **'Elstar'** (D)
Pollination group 3. Intense flavour, honeyed, crisp. Heavy regular crops. Season: late Oct.–Dec.
CCVT CLnd ECrN EPom NOra SEdi SKee

93 H6 **'Emneth Early'** (C)
Pollination group 3. Codlin type, cooking to fluffy purée; needs hardly any sugar. Heavy but biennial crops; needs thinning for size. Some resistance to scab and mildew. Season: Aug.–Sept.*
CAgr CArg CHab ECrN NOra SEdi WJas WMat WWct

'Epicure' *see* 'Laxton's Epicure'

93 H6 **'Fiesta'** (D)
Pollination group 3. Aromatic, Cox-like flavour. Heavy, regular crops; frost-resistant blossom; less prone to disease than Cox, but can be susceptible to scab and develop canker in some sites. Season: Oct.–Dec./Jan.*
CAgr CArg CCVT CMac CTri EBee ECrN EPfP EPom LBuc LRHS MAsh MCoo MGos MMuc MPri MRav MWat NLar NOra SCoo SEdi SEND SKee SLim SPer SPoG SRms SSFr WJas WMat WWct

'Fortune' *see* 'Laxton's Fortune'

93 H6 **'Golden Noble'** (C)
Pollination group 4. Cooks to a well-flavoured purée, not as acidic as 'Bramley's Seedling'. Attractive blossom. Good, regular crops; partial tip bearer; some scab and mildew resistance. Season: Oct.–Dec. and longer.
CAgr CTri ECrN IArd MCoo NOra SKee

93 H6 **'Greensleeves'** (D)
Pollination group 3. Crisp, brisk, becoming sweeter. Very precocious and heavy, regular crops; needs thinning for good fruit size. Blossom has some frost resistance. Can be susceptible to scab. Season: late Sept.–Oct.; short season once picked.
CAgr CArg CMac CTri ECrN ELan EPfP EPom MAsh MGos MMuc NLar NOra SEND SEdi SKee SLim SPer SSFT SSFr WJas WMat WWct

93 H6 **'Grenadier'** (C)
Pollination group 3. Cooks to sharp purée. Heavy, regular crops; good disease resistance. Season: Aug.–Sept.*
CAgr CArg CHab CLnd CTri ECrN EPom MGos MMuc NLar NOra SEND SEdi SKee SLon SPer SSFT SSFr WJas WMat

14 H6 **'Howgate Wonder'** (C)
Pollination group 3. Very large, late-season, heavy-cropping apple with a very mild flavour. Vigorous; fruit yellow-green flushed with red. Partially self-fertile.
CAgr CArg CCVT CHab CLnd CSBt CTri ECrN EPfP EPom LBuc LRHS MMuc MWat NOra SEdi SKee SPer SSFr SVic WJas WMat WWct

93 H6 **'James Grieve'** (C/D)
Pollination group 3. Savoury, crisp to melting flesh; when cooked keeps shape, with juicy, delicate flavour. Good, regular crops; fruit bruises easily. Prone to scab, canker; resistant to mildew; requires well-drained soil. Season: Sept.–Oct. and longer.*
CAgr CArg CBcs CCVT CHab CLnd CMac CRos CSBt CTri EBee ECrN EPfP EPom LBuc LMaj LRHS LSRN MAsh MGos MMuc MPri MRav MWat NLar NOra NRHS SCob SCoo SEdi SEND SEWo SGbt SKee SLim SPer SRms SSFr SSFT SVic SWvt WJas WMat WTSh WWct

93 H6 **'Jonagold'** (D)
Triploid. Pollination group 3. Attractive, crisp, honeyed taste; large fruit. Heavy, regular crops; prone to canker. Fruit can be poorly coloured, but many more colourful sports exist. Vigorous. Season: Nov.–Jan./Feb.; stores well.
CArg CLnd CTri ECrN ELan EPom IArd NLar NOra SEdi SGsty SKee SPer SSFr WWct

93 H6 **'Jupiter'** (D)
Triploid. Pollination group 3. Cox-like flavour, but sharper. Heavy crops, but biennial if allowed to over-crop; fruit can be irregular shape and heavily russetted. Vigorous. Season: late Oct.–Jan.*
CAgr CArg CSBt CTri ECrN EPfP LSRN MRav NLar NOra SEdi SKee SLon SSFr WJas WMat

14 H6 **'Kent'** (D)
Pollination group 3. Good flavour; good reliable crops; keeps well. Also sold as 'Malling Kent'.
ECrN

93 H6 **'Kidd's Orange Red'** (D)
Pollination group 3. Very attractive; rich aromatic, perfumed taste. Good, regular crops; fruit prone to coarse russet. Season: Nov.–Jan.
CAgr CArg CLnd CMac CRos CTri ECrN EPfP EPom LBuc LRHS MWat NOra SKee SLon SSFr WMat WWct

93 H6 **'King of the Pippins'** (C/D)
Pollination group 5. Well ripened, good flavour. Cooked, keeps shape, flavoursome; suited to open tarts, etc. Heavy, regular crops; upright habit; good resistance to disease; keeps well. Season: Oct.–Dec.; can store to Feb.*
CArg CHab CLnd CTri ECrN EPom LBuc MCoo NOra SGsty SKee SVic

93 H6 **'Lane's Prince Albert'** (C)
Pollination group 3. Cooks to brisk purée, not as acidic as 'Bramley's Seedling'. Large fruit. Good, regular crops; fruit easily bruised. Hardy; makes neat small tree. Resistant to scab; very prone to mildew; prone to canker on all but very well-drained soils. Season: Nov.–Mar.; stores well.*
CAgr CArg CHab CLnd CSBt CTri ECrN EPfP LRHS MGos MRav MWat NOra SCoo SEdi SSFr SVic SWeb WMat

93 H6 **'Laxton's Epicure'** (D)
Pollination group 3. Delicate, aromatic, Cox-like flavour. Heavy, regular crops; needs thinning for size; prone to bitter pit, canker. Season: late Aug.–Sept. Awarded as 'Epicure'.*
CAgr CHab CTri ECrN SKee

93 H6 **'Laxton's Fortune'** (D)
Pollination group 3. Sweet, lightly aromatic flavour; needs to colour well for good quality. Good crops, but tendency to be biennial. Fruit bruises easily, can be poorly coloured. Prone to canker, good resistance to scab. Season: Sept.–Oct. Awarded as 'Fortune'.
CArg CHab CMac CSBt CTri ECrN IArd LRHS NOra SEdi SKee SSFr WJas WMat WWct

14 H6 **'Limelight'** (D)
Pollination group 3. Crisp and refreshing; heavy-cropping.
CArg EBee MAsh MCoo NLar NOra SCoo SKee SSFT SSFr WMat

93 H6 **'Lord Lambourne'** (D)
Pollination group 2. Sweet, juicy, attractive flavour. Skin can become greasy when stored. Good, regular crops. Partial tip bearer; resistant to mildew. Season: late Sept.–Nov.*
CAgr CArg CHab CLnd CMac CSBt CTri ECrN ELan EPom LSRN MAsh MCoo MGos MWat NLar NOra SEdi SKee SLon SPer SSFr WJas WMat WWct

93 H6 **'Mother'** (D)
Pollination group 5. Sweet, perfumed, distinctive flavour. Crops can be erratic, light; good resistance to scab and mildew. Season: Oct.–Dec.*
CAgr CEnd CLnd CTri ECrN SKee SSFr

93 H6 **'Peasgood's Nonsuch'** (C/D)
Pollination group 3. Cooks to sweet, delicately flavoured purée; needs no or little extra sugar. Exhibition apple with large, handsome regular shape. Good, regular crops; resistance to mildew and red spider; moderate resistance to scab. Season: late Sept.–Dec.
CAgr CArg CHab ECrN EPom IArd LSRN MAsh NOra SKee SLon WMat

93 H6 **'Pixie'** (D)
Pollination group 4. Intensely aromatic, Cox-like flavour, but sharper and firmer-fleshed. Good to heavy crops, but small fruit unless thinned. Season: Dec.–Mar.*
CSBt EPom LRHS MPri MWat NOra SKee SLon WWct

14 H6 **'Red Falstaff'** (D)
Pollination group 3. Late-season, heavy-cropping sport of 'Falstaff' with a fruity flavour and crisp, juicy flesh. Self-fertile and moderately vigorous. Skin flushed with orange-red when ripe. Season: Nov.–Jan.
CAgr CArg CCVT CMac CTri ECrN EPfP GKin LBuc LRHS LSRN MAsh MCoo NLar NOra NRHS SGbt SKee SLim SLon SPoG SSFT WMat WWct

93 H6 **'Ribston Pippin'** (D)
Triploid. Pollination group 2. Intense, rich, aromatic flavour; more acidity and more robust than Cox. Good, regular crops; resistant to scab; prone to mildew and canker. Season: Oct.–Jan.
CArg CTho CTri ECrN MCoo MRav MWat NOra SKee SLon SSFr WJas WMat WWct

93 H6 **'Rosemary Russet'** (D)
Pollination group 3. Sweet-sharp acid drop taste, resembling 'Ashmead's Kernel'. Crops good, regular; vigorous tree with upright habit. Season: Nov./Dec.–Mar.
CAgr CArg CHab CTho ELan MCoo NOra SKee SLon SSFr WMat WWct

93 H6 **'Saint Edmund's Pippin'** (D)
Pollination group 2. Very attractive; richly flavoured when fully ripe. Good, regular crops; fruit bruises easily. Prone to mildew. Season: late Sept.–Oct. AGM reconfirmed 2017.*
CHab CTho ECrN ELan EPfP MCoo NOra SKee SSFr

14 H6 **'Santana'** (D)
Pollination group 4. Medium to quite vigorous tree, with upright spreading habit. Good to

heavy crop, with low susceptibility to scab. Midseason apple; picking early September and keeping well. Bright red flushed; sweet, crisp, juicy flesh; good flavour.
NOra WMat

09 H6 **'Scrumptious'** (D)
Pollination group 3. Regular cropper, good fruit size, attractive ornamental fruit. Good tree habit; easily managed. A good dessert apple: sweet, good flavour, crisp, juicy.
CAgr CArg CCVT CMac CRos CSBt CTri EBee EPfP EPom LBuc LCro LOPS LRHS LSRN MAsh NLar NOra NRHS SCoo SEWo SGbt SKee SLim SLon SPer SPoG SSFr SSFT WJas WMat

93 H6 **'Sunset'** (D)
Pollination group 3. Aromatic, like small early Cox, but sharper. Heavy, regular crops, but small fruit. Resistant to scab; prone to mildew and canker. Season: Oct.–Dec.
CAgr CArg CCVT CHab CLnd CMac CSBt CTri ECrN EPfP EPom GKin LBuc LRHS LSRN MRav NOra SCoo SEdi SKee SLim SLon SPer SSFT SSFr SVic WJas WMat WWct

14 H6 **'Topaz'** (D)
Pollination group 4. Medium vigour, with upright spreading habit. Good crop, with resistance to scab; late season, picking in early/mid October. Medium-sized apple; attractive appearance, red flushed over a yellow background; crisp, juicy flesh, sweet-sharp taste, can be quite sharp, mellows with keeping.
SKee

93 H6 **'Warner's King'** (C)
Triploid. Pollination group 2. Cooks to well-flavoured purée; not as acidic as 'Bramley's Seedling'. Attractive, deep pink blossom. Heavy, regular crops; fruit can be very large. Prone to bitter pit. Vigorous. Season: late Sept.–Dec.
CTri NOra SKee

93 H6 **'Winston'** (D)
Pollination group 4. Aromatic and rich. Good, regular crops; fruit can be rather small; good disease resistance. Season: Dec.–Apr.; keeps very well.*
CAgr CCVT CMac CTri ECrN MCoo SKee SRms SVic SWeb WWct

93 H6 **'Worcester Pearmain'** (D)
Pollination group 3. Intense strawberry flavour when well-ripened and scarlet. Tip bearer; heavy, regular crops. Resistant to mildew; some susceptibility to canker. Season: late Sept.–Oct.
CAgr CArg CBcs CCVT CHab CLnd CMac CSBt CTri EBee ECrN EPfP EPom LBuc LRHS MAsh MMuc MRav MWat NOra SCoo SEdi SEND SEWo SKee SLim SPer SSFr WJas WMat WWct

Blackberry (*Rubus fruticosus* agg.)

Season extends from late July to early September.

93 H6 **'Loch Ness'** (D/C)
Large, well-flavoured berries. Thornless; heavy cropping; moderate vigour; hardy. Good resistance to purple blotch and botrytis, but prone to downy mildew. Reconfirmed after trial 2015.
CAgr CArg CHab CRos EHyd EPom IArd LCro LOPS LRHS LSRN MPri NRHS SCoo SKee SPer SSFr SVic

15 H6 **'Loch Tay'**
No spines; has a good blackberry flavour and shiny fruit. Healthy but not too vigorous, producing good replacement canes. Early.
CArg CHab CMac CRos EHyd EPom LRHS NRHS SPoG

Blackcurrant (*Ribes nigrum*)

Season extends from early July to mid August.

95 H6 **'Ben Connan'** (C)
Large fruit; medium long strigs. Heavy crops; compact habit. Good resistance to mildew, leaf-curling midge. Season: early. Reconfirmed after trial 2012.
CAgr CMac CRos CSBt EHyd EPfP EPom LBuc LCro LOPS LRHS LSRN MAsh MGos NLar NRHS SCoo SEND SGbt SKee SLim SPer SPoG SRms SSFr SWvt WMat

12 H6 **'Big Ben'**
Fairly vigorous medium-sized bush, flowering early to mid season. Fruit large and easy to pick. Good yields, showing resistance to mildew and leaf spot. Fresh fruit flavour pleasant to quite sweet; rich when cooked. Good all-round cultivar.
CArg CRos EBee EHyd EPfP EPom LBuc LCro LOPS LRHS LSRN MNHC NRHS SGbt SKee SPer SPoG WMat

Blueberry (*Vaccinium corymbosum*)

Blueberries begin to ripen mid July and continue to late August.

03 H6 **'Duke'** (D)
Good flavour, medium to large fruit. Crops well; easy to grow. Flowers late; good for frost-prone sites; partly self-fertile. Season: early.
CArg CTrh ELan EPfP EPom LCro LOPS MAsh MCoo MGos SPre SRkn SSFr

03 H6 **'Spartan'** (D)
Excellent flavour; medium-sized fruit. Quite good crops; not self-fertile. Vigorous; upright habit. Good autumn colour. Season: early–mid.
CTrh EPom LCro LOPS LSRN MGos SKee

Cherry (morello) (*Prunus cerasus*)

93 H6 **'Morello'** (C)
Dark red, acid cherry; excellent for preserves, tarts, etc. Regular, good crops; very attractive in blossom; self-fertile. Crops on north-facing site. Season: late July–early Aug.
CAgr CArg CCVT CLnd CMac CSBt CTho CTri ECrN ELan EPfP EPom LBuc LCro LMaj LOPS LRHS LSRN MGos MMuc MPri NLar NOra SEdi SEND SEWo SGbt SKee SLim SPer SSFr SSFT SVic SWvt WJas WMat

Cherry (sweet) (*Prunus avium*)

14 H6 **'Kordia'** (D)
Pollination group 4. Mid to late season; large to very large, true black cherry; bold appearance; excellent rich flavour. Spreading habit; can show some bare wood; medium vigour. Heavy, reliable crops; easy to grow. Not self-fertile; usually pollinated by 'Regina' or 'Sylvia' in commercial orchards; can also be pollinated by 'Summer Sun', 'Stella' (early bloom only). Blossom can be a little frost-sensitive. Good garden cherry.
CArg EPom NOra SKee WMat

14 H6 **'Lapins'**
Pollination group 4. Mid to late season; large, dark red cherry; very good flavour. Upright habit; medium vigour. Heavy, reliable crops. All-round excellent cherry; self-fertile.
CAgr CArg CLnd CTho ECrN EPfP EPom MRav MWat NLar NOra SEdi SKee SSFT SSFr WJas WMat WWct

95 H6 **'Merchant'** (D)
Pollination group 3. Early black cherry; well-flavoured. Regular crops. Pollination: universal donor, but not self-fertile. Season: early July. Reconfirmed 2014.
NOra SEdi SKee SSFT SSFr WMat WWct

14 H6 **'Penny'**
Pollination group 4. Mid to late season; dark red, very large, meaty cherry; excellent flavour. Upright spreading habit; medium vigour; prone to some bare wood. Crops well and regularly on Gisela 5; bred for UK conditions. Not self-fertile; pollinated by late to midseason cultivars, e.g. 'Summer Sun', 'Skeena', 'Regina'; needs sufficient pollination to ensure heavy crops.
CAgr CArg CTri EPom MCoo MWat NOra SKee WMat WWct

93 H6 **'Stella'**
Pollination group 4. Black cherry; large, rich, high quality. Heavy, regular crops; self-fertile. Prone to splitting in wet weather. Season: late July. Reconfirmed 2014.
CAgr CArg CEnd CHab CLnd CMac CRos CSBt CTri ECrN ELan EPfP EPom LBuc LCro LMaj LOPS LRHS MAsh MGos MMuc MRav MWat NLar NOra NRHS SCoo SEdi SEND SEWo SGbt SKee SLim SPer SPoG SSFr SSFT SVic SWvt WJas WMat WTSh WWct

04 H6 **'Summer Sun'** (D)
Pollination group 4. Late (July). Produces firm, well-flavoured, red to black fruit. Very good crops. Some resistance to bacterial canker. Attractive, upright, spreading habit; moderate vigour. Not self-fertile. Reconfirmed 2014.
CAgr CArg CLnd CMac CTho CTri EPom LBuc MAsh MCoo MGos MWat NLar NOra SCoo SKee SLim SPoG SSFT SSFr WMat WWct

14 H6 **'Sweetheart'**
Pollination group 4. Dark red cherry; latest of the season. Good flavour; very firm fruit. Medium vigour, upright spreading habit. Heavy, regular crops; fruits moderate size. Slightly prone to canker and brown rot. Only late-season self-fertile cultivar available. Prolific blossom, making a tree exceptionally pretty in the spring. Sets dense clusters of fruits, which can be prone to botrytis / brown rot.
CAgr CArg CLnd CTri EPom LCro LMaj LOPS LRHS LSRN MAsh MWat NOra NRHS SEWo SKee SLim SPoG SVic WMat

Damson (*Prunus insititia*)

00 H6 **'Farleigh Damson'** (C)
Pollination group 4. Excellent flavour. Regular, heavy crops. Blossom shows some resistance to frost. Season: late Aug.
CAgr CArg CHab EPfP EPom LBuc LEdu NLar NOra SEdi SKee SPer SVic WJas WMat WWct

98 H6 **'Prune Damson'** (C)
Pollination group 4. Larger fruits than 'Farleigh Damson', but typical damson flavour. Regular, good crops. Season: late Aug.
CAgr CArg CHab CLnd CMac CTho CTri EBee EPom LBuc LCro LRHS MAsh MMuc MWat NLar NOra SEND SEWo SGbt SKee SPer SSFr WJas WMat WWct

Fig (*Ficus carica*)

93 H4 **'Brown Turkey'** (D)
Fruits regularly in the open in southern England and in many parts of the Midlands and East Anglia in a warm position. For good crop, root restriction advisable. Season: mid Aug.–mid Sept., depending on site.

CAby CAgr CBcs CBrac CCCN CCVT CJun CMac CRHN CRos CSBt CTho CTri CTsd EBee ECrN EHyd ELan ELon EPfP EPom LBuc LCro LEdu LMaj LOPS LRHS LSRN MAsh MBlu MBros MGos MHer MMuc MNHC MRav NGKo NLar NOra NPer NRHS SEND SEWo SGol SGsty SKee SLim SMad SPer SPlb SPoG SPre SRms SSFT SSta SVen SVic SWeb SWvt WAvo WFar WLov WMat WMou WPGP WTSh XSen

Gooseberry (*Ribes uva-crispa*)

Season extends from early June to mid August. For culinary use, pick from early June. For ripe fruit pick from early July.

93 H6 **'Careless'** (C/D)
Green fruit. Reliable, good crops. Good for tarts, jam, etc. Prone to mildew. Season: mid.
CSBt CTri EPom LSRN MAsh MGos SEdi SPer WMat

94 H6 **'Greenfinch'** (C/D)
Green fruit; compact bush. Some resistance to mildew and leaf spot. Season: mid; similar to 'Careless'.
CAgr

93 H6 **'Invicta'** (C/D)
Green fruit; quite good flavour. Heavy crops; very vigorous; spreading habit; large thorns. Some resistance to mildew. Young shoots can be damaged on exposed site. Season: mid; slightly earlier than 'Careless'. Main use culinary.
CAgr CMac CRos CSBt CTri ECrN EHyd EMil EPfP EPom GBin LBuc LCro LOPS LRHS LSRN MAsh MGos MMuc MNHC MPri NLar NRHS SCoo SEdi SEND SKee SLim SPer SPoG SRms SSFr SVic SWvt WMat

93 H6 **'Leveller'** (C/D)
Large, yellow fruit; good dessert quality. Season: mid to late.
MCoo SEdi SPer

93 H6 **'Whinham's Industry'** (C/D)
Red fruit; quite good dessert quality. Heavy, reliable crops. Very susceptible to mildew. Season: mid.
ELan LBuc LSRN MGos MMuc MPri SEND SEdi SPer SRms

Grape (*Vitis*)

04 H5 **'Boskoop Glory'** (D)
Black grape. Good outdoor vine for the amateur, both dessert and wine; crops reliably; disease-resistant. Moderately good flavour, but better than many shop-bought grapes. Awarded as 'Gloire de Boskoop'.
CMac ELan LBuc MBros SCoo WSuV

04 H5 **'New York Muscat'** (D)
Black grape. A good dessert Muscat with blackcurrant flavour. Disease-resistant. Best when grown on a warm site or wall.
WSuV

Hazelnut (*Corylus maxima*)

14 H6 **'Gunslebert'**
Good-sized nut; kernel fills the shell; very few blanks. Excellent flavour; very tasty. Midseason. Regular, good crops; nuts held as large clusters of four nuts. Medium vigour tree; moderate amount of suckering. Pollinated by 'Kentish Cob', 'Cosford'. Good tree habit, with a natural goblet shape and exceptionally attractive with prolific catkins making it also an ornamental tree. A mainstay of Kent nut production. Reliable, hardy hazel nut, easy to grow in a garden situation; productive and ornamental; requires a pollinator.
CCVT CMac CTri NOra SPoG SRms SSFr WMat

14 H6 **'Kentish Cob'**
Good-sized nut; kernel fills the shell; very few blanks. Excellent flavour; rich and meaty. Early season, cropping before the squirrels become active. Regular, good crops. Medium vigour tree; moderate amount of suckering. Pollinated by 'Gunslebert', 'Cosford', 'Hall's Giant' ('Merveille de Bollwiller'). The main cultivar of commercial nut plantations in Kent. ûReliable hazel nut, easy to grow in a garden situation; needs a pollinator.
CAgr CBcs CMac CSBt CTho CTri EBee ECrN ELan EPfP EPom IArd LBuc LRHS MGos MWat NLar NOrn SEWo SEdi SKee SLim SPer SPoG SRms SSFr SVic SWvt WMat WMou

Loganberry (*Rubus × loganobaccus*)

93 H5 **'Ly 654'** (C)
Large, dark fruit; distinctive flavour; good crops. Thornless. Season: July.
CRos CSBt EHyd EPom LBuc LRHS MPri NRHS SPer SSFr SVic

Medlar (*Mespilus germanica*)

14 H6 **'Nottingham'**
Upright habit with good flavour; fruits small.
CAgr CArg CBcs CCVT CEnd CHab CTho CTri EBee ECrN ELan EPfP EPom LBuc LRHS MAsh MGos MMuc MPri MWat NOra SCoo SEdi SEND SEWo SKee SLim SPer SPoG SSFr SSFT SVic WJas WMat

Pear (*Pyrus communis*)

93 H6 **'Beth'** (D)
Pollination group 4. Attractive; good quality and flavour. Small fruit. Heavy, regular crops. Season: mid/late Aug.–early Sept.; short season once picked.
CAgr CArg CHab CMac CSBt CTri EBee EPfP EPom IArd LBuc LRHS MAsh MGos MPri NLar NOra SEdi SGbt SKee SLim SPer SSFT SSFr WMat

93 H6 **'Beurré Hardy'** (D)
Pollination group 3. Very melting and fragrant with rose-water perfume. Good, regular crops. Very hardy, vigorous tree; slow to bear; resistant to scab. Season: Nov.–Dec.*
CAgr CArg CCVT CMac CSBt CTri ELan EPfP EPom IArd LMaj MCoo MMuc MWat NOra SEND SEdi SKee SPer SSFT SSFr WMat WWct

06 H6 **'Beurré Superfin'** (D)
Pollination group 3. An excellent September-cropping cultivar for the amateur gardener, with a lovely cinnamon-russet colour and an exquisite flavour. Gives a good, consistent yield and is not over-vigorous. Midseason.
SKee SSFr

93 H6 **'Concorde'** (D)
Pollination group 4. Sweet, buttery, fragrant flavour, similar to 'Conference', but superior. Heavy, regular crops; frost-tolerant blossom. Young trees very precocious. Season: late Oct./Nov.–Dec.
CAgr CArg CCVT CMac CRos CSBt CTho CTri EBee ECrN ELan EPfP EPom IArd LBuc LCro LOPS LRHS LSRN MAsh MGos MNHC MPri MRav NLar NOra SEdi SEWo SGbt SKee SLim SPer SPoG SSFr SSFT SVic WJas WMat WWct

93 H6 **'Conference'** (D)
Pollination group 3. Sweet, buttery, quite rich taste. Heavy, regular crops. Can produce fruits without pollinators, but resulting fruits often misshapen. Season: Oct.–Nov./Dec.*
CAgr CArg CBcs CCVT CLnd CMac CRos CSBt CTho CTri EBee ECrN ELan EPfP EPom GBin LBuc LCro LEdu LMaj LOPS LRHS LSRN MAsh MGos MMuc MPri MRav MWat NLar NOra NRHS SEdi SEND SEWo SGbt SGsty SKee SLim SPer SPoG SSFr SVic SWvt WJas WMat WTSh WWct

93 H6 **'Doyenné du Comice'** (D)
Pollination group 4. Very rich flavour; very juicy, buttery, perfumed. Excellent quality, but moderate crops, although older trees more regular. Vigorous tree; prone to scab. Season: Nov.–Dec. Not compatible with 'Onward'.
CAgr CArg CBcs CCVT CHab CLnd CMac CSBt CTri EBee ELan EPfP EPom GBin IArd LBuc LCro LMaj LOPS LRHS MAsh MMuc MPri MRav MWat NLar NOra SEdi SEND SEWo SGsty SKee SLim SPer SSFr SVic WJas WMat WTSh WWct

06 H6 **'Gorham'** (D)
Pollination group 4. A beautiful green pear with a good covering of russet. Has an excellent flavour; a good reliable cropper and is readily available. Late.
CAgr CTho NOra SKee SSFT SSFr WMat

93 H6 **'Joséphine de Malines'** (D)
Pollination group 3. Very rich, buttery and perfumed. Crops good, reliable, but needs warm site. Fruit easily bruised. Tip-bearer; resistant to scab. Season: Nov.–Dec./Jan.
CAgr IArd NOra SKee

Plum (*Prunus domestica*)

00 H5 **'Blue Rock'** (C/D)
Pollination group 1. Quite well-flavoured blue plum. Regular, good crops; not self-fertile. Neat tree. Season: mid Aug.
SKee

95 H5 **'Blue Tit'** (C/D)
Pollination group 5. Pleasant flavour; blue plum. Regular, good crops. Self-fertile. Season: mid Aug.
CAgr EPom MMuc NOra SEND SKee SSFr WMat WWct

98 H5 **'Cambridge Gage'** (D)
Pollination group 4. Honeysweet excellent greengage quality, but more reliable than most greengages. Reasonably regular crops in favourable situations. Partly self-fertile. Season: mid Aug.
CAgr CArg CCVT CEnd CHab CLnd CMac CTri EBee ECrN EPfP EPom LCro LRHS LSRN MAsh MMuc MWat NOra SCoo SEND SEWo SEdi SKee SLim SPer SSFr WJas WMat WWct

93 H6 **'Czar'** (C/D)
Pollination group 3. Well-flavoured; early blue plum; use for jam but also moderate eating quality. Heavy, regular crops. Self-fertile. Season: mid Aug.
CAgr CArg CCVT CEnd CHab CLnd CMac CSBt CTri ECrN ELan EPfP EPom LBuc LCro LMaj LOPS LRHS MAsh MCoo MGos MMuc MPri NLar NOra SEdi SEND SEWo SKee SLim SPer SPoG SSFr SSFT SVic SWvt WMat WWct

14 H5 **'Haganta'** (D)
Pollination group 3. Large dark blue plum, late-ripening, with good consistent crop; juicy,

sweet; sugary; and stone almost free; good flavour; potential for cold storage to extend the eating season to the end of October.
CAgr MCoo NOra WMat

93 H5 **'Imperial Gage'** (C/D)
Pollination group 2. Gage quality but not as rich as 'Cambridge Gage'. Regular crops. Partly self-fertile. Season: mid Aug.
CAgr CArg CLnd CMac CSBt CTho CTri EPom LRHS MMuc NOra SEND SKee SSFT SSFr WMat

94 H5 **'Jefferson'** (D)
Pollination group 1. Yellow flushed with red; rich, gage quality. Moderate, regular crops. Not self-fertile. Season: mid to late Aug.
CAgr CArg CHab CLnd NOra SKee SSFr SVic WMat

00 H6 **'Mallard'** (D)
Pollination group 1. Medium-sized red plum; quite good flavour. Good, regular crops. Moderate vigour; not self-fertile. Season: mid–late Aug.
NOra SKee WMat

93 H5 **'Marjorie's Seedling'** (C)
Pollination group 5. Late blue plum. Good for jam. Reliable good crops; vigorous, upright habit. Self-fertile. Season: late Sept.–early Oct.
CAgr CArg CCVT CEnd CHab CLnd CMac CSBt CTho CTri ECrN EPfP EPom LBuc LCro LOPS LRHS LSRN MAsh MGos MMuc MPri MWat NLar NOra SCoo SEdi SEND SKee SLim SPer SSFr SSFT WJas WMat WWct

95 H6 **'Opal'** (D)
Pollination group 3. Small purple plum; good flavour. Reliable, heavy crops; needs thinning. Partly self-fertile. Blossom buds very prone to bird damage. Season: early–mid Aug.
CAgr CArg CCVT CLnd CMac CRos CTri EBee ECrN ELan EPfP EPom LBuc LCro LMaj LOPS LRHS LSRN MAsh MGos MMuc MWat NLar NOra SCoo SEdi SEND SGbt SKee SLim SPer SSFr SSFT WMat WTSh WWct

93 H5 **'Oullins Gage'** (D)
Pollination group 4. Large, yellow flushed with pink. Not typical gage quality, but quite rich. Heavy, regular crops. Partly self-fertile. Season: mid Aug.
CAgr CArg CCVT CLnd CMac CSBt CTri ELan EPfP EPom LBuc LCro LEdu LOPS LRHS MGos MMuc MPri MRav NOra SEdi SEND SEWo SKee SPer SPoG SSFr SSFT SVic SWvt WJas WMat WWct

14 H5 **'Purple Pershore'** (C)
Pollination group 3. Good flavour; reliable good crops.
CAgr CHab CTri IArd NOra SKee WMat WWct

95 H5 **'Valor'** (C/D)
Pollination group 2. Blue, medium-sized plum. Good quality. Moderately good, regular crops. Not self-fertile. Season: late Aug.
NOra SKee

93 H5 **'Victoria'** (C/D)
Pollination group 3. Red plum; reasonable to good eating quality; excellent for bottling, jam and tarts. Heavy, regular crops. Self-fertile. Season: mid to late Aug.
CAgr CArg CCVT CHab CLnd CMac CRos CSBt CTho CTri EBee ECrN ELan EPfP EPom GKin IArd LBuc LCro LEdu LMaj LOPS LRHS LSRN MAsh MGos MMuc MPri MRav MWat NLar NOra NRHS SCoo SEdi SEND SEWo SKee SLim SPer SPoG SSFr SSFT SVic SWvt WJas WMat WTSh WWct

Quince (*Cydonia oblonga*)

14 H5 **'Meech's Prolific'**
Regular crops of pear-shaped golden-yellow fruits with good flavour.
CAgr CHab CLnd CTri EBee ECrN EPom LCro LOPS LRHS MAsh MGos MRav NLar NOra SEdi SKee SLim SPer SSFT SSFr WMat WWct

14 H5 **'Vranja'**
Large green pear-shaped fragrant fruits, becoming golden-yellow when ripe.
CAgr CArg CEnd CHab CLnd CMac CRos CSBt CTri EBee ECrN ELan EPfP EPom EWTr LBuc LEdu LRHS LSRN MAsh MGos MMuc MRav NLar NOra SEND SGsty SKee SLim SLon SPer SSFr WJas WMat WWct

Raspberry (*Rubus idaeus*)

Raspberries crop from late June to early August. Autumn primocanes from late July to early October.

09 H6 **'All Gold'**
Autumn cropping. Yellow/golden-fruited; needs to be left to ripen well before the flavour is fully tasted. Yield generally peaking at the end of August and early September. An upright habit with easy-to-manage cane.
CMac EMil EPom LRHS MPri NLar SCoo SPer SRms SVic WMat

93 H6 **'Autumn Bliss'** (D)
Autumn cropping. Primocane-fruiting (fruiting on current season's canes). Excellent flavour; large fruit. Good crops. Resistant to aphid vectors of virus disease and phytophthora root rot. Season: crops late July to early Oct. Reconfirmed after trial 2009.
CAgr CMac CRos CSBt CTri EBee ECrN EHyd ELan EPfP EPom LBuc LCro LEdu

LOPS LRHS LSRN MAsh MGos MMuc MNHC MPri NLar NRHS SCoo SEdi SEND SGbt SGol SKee SLim SPer SPoG SRms SSFr SVic WMat

00 H6 **'Glen Ample'** (D)
Summer cropping. Large fruit, excellent flavour. Recommended for freezing. Heavy crops; spine-free canes. Resistant to main aphid vector of virus disease; some tolerance to phytophthora root rot; some susceptibility to leaf and bud mite. Season: mid. Reconfirmed after trial 2009.
CAgr CArg CMac CRos CSBt CTri EBee ECrN EHyd ELan EMil EPfP EPom LBuc LCro LOPS LRHS LSRN MAsh MCoo MNHC NLar NRHS SCoo SEdi SGbt SKee SLim SPer SPoG SRms SSFr SVic WMat

09 H6 **'Glen Magna'** (D)
Summer cropping. A very vigorous cultivar with long, strong fruiting laterals. It has large fruit with a good flavour. Yields high with a long cropping season.
CAgr CArg CSBt MAsh MPri SCoo SEdi SKee SLim SRms

09 H6 **'Joan J'**
Autumn cropping. Easy to grow and pick; upright habit; good berry size.
CArg CMac EPom LBuc LSRN SPer SRms SSFr

93 H6 **'Leo'** (D)
Large firm fruit; excellent flavour. Good crops. Very long laterals. Season: late.
CSBt LCro LOPS MAsh SCoo SKee SRms SSFr

93 H6 **'Malling Admiral'** (D)
Summer cropping. Good quality; medium to large, attractive fruit. Consistent, moderate to good crops; tall canes; withstands wet conditions, but laterals easily damaged in exposed sites. Good disease resistance. Season: mid to late. Reconfirmed after trial 2009.
CSBt CTri EPom LSRN MAsh SCoo SKee SPer

93 H6 **'Malling Jewel'** (D)
Summer cropping. Good flavour and crops. Season: early to mid. Reconfirmed after trial 2009.
CAgr CArg CSBt CTri EPfP EPom LBuc LSRN MAsh MPri SEdi SKee SPer SRms

09 H6 **'Polka'**
Autumn cropping. Early flush of fruit with good berry size and appearance; good upright habit with medium vigorous cane growth.
CArg CRos EHyd EPfP EPom LBuc LCro LOPS LRHS LSRN MAsh MCoo MRav NRHS SCoo SKee SLim SPer SRms SSFr WMat

09 H6 **'Tulameen'**
Summer cropping. Outstanding cultivar, with strong cane growth and upright habit. Spine-free and easily handled, with exceptional fruit quality and high yield. Less prone to pest and disease than other varieties.
CAgr CArg CSBt EBee EHyd ELan EMil EPfP EPom LBuc LCro LOPS LRHS LSRN MAsh MMuc MPri NRHS SCoo SEND SEdi SKee SLim SPer SPoG SRms SSFr SVic WMat

Redcurrant (*Ribes rubrum*)

Redcurrants crop from mid July to early September.

93 H6 **'Jonkheer van Tets'** (C)
Large, handsome fruit; long strigs. Heavy crops. Season: early.
CAgr CRos CSBt EBee EHyd EPfP EPom GQue IArd LRHS LSRN MAsh MCoo MPri NLar NRHS SEND SEdi SGbt SKee SLim SPer SRms SSFr WMat

93 H6 **'Red Lake'** (C)
Good quality medium to large fruit; cropping on long trusses. Prone to wind damage in exposed sites; in summer prune early. Season: mid to late.
CAgr CTri ECrN ELan EPfP EPom LBuc LEdu MGos MPri NLar SEdi SGol SKee SPer SPoG SRms SSFr WMat

93 H6 **'Stanza'** (C)
Medium-sized fruit; good quality. Compact habit; heavy crops. Season: mid to late.
CAgr SEND

Strawberry (*Fragaria* × *ananassa*)

In an early season, strawberries begin to crop mid June; in a late season, mid to late June.

06 H6 **'Alice'**
A good consistent cropper, with a high percentage of mid to large, bright orange-red, sweet, juicy fruit. Scored well in taste tests and performed well at different geographical locations (Stafford, Kent, Dundee) in HDC trials. Has good resistance to verticillium wilt; very useful to home gardener. Mid to late season.
CAgr CMac EPom

93 H6 **'Cambridge Favourite'** (D)
Good flavour; medium size, but rather soft berries. Moderate crops; excellent resistance to disease. Good runner production. Season: mid.
CAgr CArg CMac CRos CSBt CTri EHyd EMil EPfP EPom LBuc LCro LOPS LRHS MGos MMuc MPri NRHS SEdi SPlb

94 H6 **'Hapil'** (D)
Large glossy berries; good flavour. Heavy crops; vigorous. Susceptible to verticillium wilt. Season: early/mid. Reconfirmed after trial 2004.
CTri EMil EPfP EPom LBuc LRHS

93 H6 **'Honeoye'** (D)
Excellent flavour. Heavy crops; susceptible to verticillium wilt. Season: early. Reconfirmed after trial 2004.
CAgr CArg CMac CSBt EMil EPfP EPom LBuc LCro LEdu LOPS LRHS MMuc SPer

94 H6 **'Pegasus'** (D)
Good flavour; quite soft flesh. Good disease resistance; tolerance to verticillium wilt. Season: mid. Reconfirmed after trial 2004 and 2006.
CAgr CRos CSBt EHyd EPfP EPom LRHS NRHS

94 H6 **'Rhapsody'** (D)
Good flavour; medium to large berries. Resistant red core; some resistance to verticillium wilt and mildew. Season: late. Reconfirmed after trial 2006.
CRos EHyd LRHS LSRN NRHS

95 H6 **'Symphony'** (D)
Good flavour; bright, firm berries. Vigorous; good resistance to red core; susceptible to mildew. Good runner production. Season: mid to late. Reconfirmed after trial 2006.
CAgr CRos EHyd EPfP EPom LBuc LRHS LSRN NRHS

WALNUT (*Juglans regia*)

15 H6 **'Franquette'**
Old French variety, known since 19th century; received the designation *appellation d'origine contrôlée* in 1938 as 'Noix de Grenoble' and in 2002 as 'Noix du Perigord'; remains a main market walnut of France; long recommended for planting in UK. Tree upright with rounded crown; moderate vigour; late-leafing; tolerates disease. Good, regular crops; reliable and productive. Nuts easily husked; quite soft shell, and can be cracked with fingers; well-sealed and well-filled nut; medium size, long, oval shape. Flavour excellent. Season: quite late/late. Pollinated by 'Meylanaise', 'Ronde de Montignac', 'Fernette'; reported partially self-fertile.
CAgr NOra WMat

15 H6 **'Lara'**
French cultivar; seedling of American cultivar 'Payne'. One of the main cultivars of modern walnut plantations. Good habit, making broad spreading tree, but not very vigorous; quite early leafing out; lateral bearing; good disease resistance. Good, regular crops; reliable and productive. Nuts easily husked; medium to quite large, globose; well-sealed, well-filled; well-flavoured as fresh nut and as dried nut. Season: early. Pollinated by 'Franquette', 'Meylanaise' and 'Ronde de Montignac'.
NOra WMat

WHITECURRANT (*Ribes rubrum*)

93 H6 **'White Grape'** (D/C)
Attractive, translucent berries; good flavour. Season: mid July.
CTri LEdu

IV

RHS AWARD OF GARDEN MERIT

VEGETABLES

Award of Garden Merit Vegetables

This is a directory of vegetables offered by nurseries participating in *RHS Plant Finder 2018* that have been awarded an RHS Award of Garden Merit (AGM). It does not represent a complete list of AGM vegetables.

Entries are accompanied by a short description and the relevant hardiness rating for the UK. **Hardiness ratings** are explained on p.39. The figures to the left of the rating indicate the year the Award of Garden Merit was made.

Vegetables present some nomenclatural peculiarities that may require explanation. Cultivars that are repeatedly raised by different growers, while retaining their essential characteristics, can become recognisably different. These strains are referred to as maintenances and are often distinguished by the use of **maintenance names** which exist separately from the cultivar name. Here maintenance names appear after the cultivar name separated by a dash following The Vegetable Seed (England) Regulations 2002.

Asparagus (*Asparagus officinalis*)

01 H4 **'Backlim'**
F_1 hybrid; consistently high yield of large spears.
EPom

93 H4 **'Connover's Colossal'**
Early; heavy yield of good quality spears. Reconfirmed after trial 2001 and 2012.
CTsd EKin ELan LCro LOPS LSRN MCtn MNHC NRob SEND SVic

01 H4 **'Gijnlim'**
F_1 hybrid; early. Consistently high yield of mid green spears with purple tips. Reconfirmed after trial 2012.
CRos EKin EPom LCro LOPS LRHS NRob

12 H5 **'Guelph Millennium'**
Bred in Canada. Excellent cold tolerance. Lateness helps to avoid frost damage. Sound yield of slender stems with pleasing flavour.
EPom LCro LOPS NRob

Aubergine (*Solanum melongena*)

95 H1c **'Bonica'**
F_1 hybrid. Early-cropping, good quality, attractive glossy black fruits are a good size. Plants are tall, but also strong and vigorous. Reconfirmed 2008.
MCtn

Basil (*Ocimum basilicum*)

12 H1c **'Aroma 2'**
Standard Genovese type. Lovely aroma, good disease resistance, quite tall.
LCro LOPS

12 H1c **'Lemonade'**
Compact, even plant growing to c.30cm. Aromatic with a sherbet lemon scent and taste. Fine leaves: keeled as young foliage. Flowers are white, and attractive to bees. Plants hold well and show good disease and weather resistance. Previously listed as basil (× *africanum*).
SRms

12 H1c **'Mrs Burns' Lemon'**
Tall, upright, neat habit, growing to c.60cm. Fine, mid green leaves, aromatic and intensely lemon-scented. Flowers white, and attractive to bees.
EKin MCtn SRms WJek

12 H1c **'Pluto'**
Bush type, of small, even, dome-shaped habit, growing to c.20cm. Leaves are fine, mid green and aromatic. Holds form well and slow to flower.
LCro LOPS

Beans

Broad beans (*Vicia faba*)

95 H5 **'Aguadulce'**
Dark green foliage, showing some variability. Long pods; the highest yielding in the trial. May also be sold as 'Aquadulce'. November sown.
CHby

93 H5 **'Aquadulce Claudia'**
Not too tall; a good compact plant. An early crop when spring sown, but can also be sown in November. One of the most reliable cultivars for overwintering. Reconfirmed after trial 1999, 2011.
EKin LCro LOPS MBros MCtn NRob

11 H3 **'De Monica'**
Short pods; well filled. Good ratio of seed to pod; excellent cropping.
EKin MCtn SVic

93 H3 **'Express'**
Quick to mature, with well-filled pods. Spring sown.
EKin MCtn

11 H3 **'Giant Exhibition Longpod'**
Smooth, slender pods of good length; long cropping period.
EKin MCtn NRHS NRob

93 H3 **'Imperial Green Longpod'**
Green-seeded, with long smooth pods; good green colour and flavour; particularly good for freezing. Spring sown. Reconfirmed after trial 1999, 2011.
EKin LCro LOPS MCtn

99 H3 **'Masterpiece Green Longpod'**
Slender, well-filled pods; stands well; good green colour and flavour; suitable for freezing; spring sown. Reconfirmed after trial 2011.
EKin LCro LOPS

11 H3 **'Robin Hood'**
Green-seeded; 3–5 seeds per pod. Good yield. Dwarf cultivar, ideal for containers and small gardens.
MCtn

11 H3 **'Suprifin'**
Pale green pods of mid size; pleasant taste. Early cropping.
LCro LOPS

93 H3 **'The Sutton'**
Dwarf compact plants, with nice flavour; ideal for smaller gardens or containers and windy situations. Spring sown. Reconfirmed after trial 1999, 2011.
EKin LCro LOPS NRob SVic

99 H4 **'Witkiem' - Manita**
Traditional 'Witkiem' type; sets well. Good early yield, with uniform pods; spring sown. Reconfirmed after trial 2011.
CHby EKin LRHS

CLIMBING FRENCH BEANS (*Phaseolus vulgaris*)

00 H2 **'Cobra'**
Very high early yield; round, long, fleshy; very attractive; reconfirmed after trial 2008.
CHby EKin LCro LOPS MCtn NRob

93 H2 **'Eva'**
Very early. Round, long, straight fleshy pods, wider-podded than other round varieties. Reconfirmed after trial 2000 and 2008.
CHby

08 H2 **'Golden Gate'**
Good crop of golden, fleshy, flat pods with a sweet, fresh flavour.
CHby LCro LOPS

93 H2 **'Hunter'**
Attractive long flat stringless pods. Slow to show seed development. Reconfirmed after trial 2000 and 2008.
EKin MCtn NRob

08 H2 **'Limka'**
Consistently high yields of good quality, flat, light green pods with a good flavour.
CHby

DWARF FRENCH BEANS (*Phaseolus vulgaris*)

93 H2 **'Annabel'**
Dark green colour, compact habit, fine foliage, tender fleshy-tasting pods. Reconfirmed after trial 1996 and 2010.
EKin MCtn

01 H2 **'Safari'**
Short, slim, mid green, round, attractive pods. Low yields.
EKin LCro LOPS LRHS MCtn NRHS

93 H2 **'Sprite'**
Heavy yield, with long, dark green pods.
EHyd EKin LCro LOPS LRHS MCtn NRHS

10 H2 **'Stanley'**
Mid to dark green colour; tender and sweet. Taller plant. Uniform and picks over long period.
MCtn

96 H2 **'The Prince'**
Excellent yield; straight pale green pods.
EKin NRob

RUNNER BEANS (*Phaseolus coccineus*)

06 H2 **'Benchmaster'**
Long, fairly straight beans, good yield; reconfirmed after trial 2013.
EKin LCro LOPS MBros

06 H2 **'Celebration'**
High yield of attractive, straight, smooth, good quality, fleshy pods with good colour and flavour. Flowers are a decorative pink. Reconfirmed after trial 2013, 2017.
EKin

13 H2 **'Firestorm'**
Hybrid of runner and French bean parentage. Excellent yield, slender, straight, smooth-skinned, fleshy pods. Self-setting. Reconfirmed after trial 2017.
EKin LCro LOPS MCtn

93 H2 **'Liberty'**
Very long pods; a popular show variety.
NRob

13 H2 **'Moonlight'**
Hybrid of runner and French bean parentage; grown commercially. Very high yielding. Easy to pick; leaves pedicel behind on picking. Smooth, straight, fleshy pods, with good

length and nice colour. Self-setting. Reconfirmed after trial 2017.
EHyd EKin LCro LOPS LRHS MCtn NRHS

99 H2 **'Red Rum'**
Good early and late yield; slim, straight, stringless pods of medium length. Reconfirmed after trial 2006, 2013.
EKin

06 H2 **'St George'**
Bicolour variety; prized for ornamental value. Some French bean parentage. Popular commercial variety; easy to pick, leaving pedicel behind. Slender beans, straight, pale green. Reconfirmed after trial 2013, 2017.
CHby

99 H2 **'White Lady'**
Late; very fleshy pods. Reconfirmed after trial 2006, 2013.
CHby EKin LCro LOPS LRHS MBros MCtn NRHS

Beetroot (*Beta vulgaris*)

05 H3 **'Alto'**
F_1 hybrid; early. Round red roots, cylindrical, uniform, smooth, with very good internal colour and good long shape. Potential to bulk up well. Reconfirmed after trial 2016.
EKin

93 H3 **'Boltardy'**
Open pollinated; good bolting resistance. Round red type, with good size and colour; the most popular beetroot in gardens.
EKin LCro LOPS MBros MCtn SVic

93 H3 **'Forono'**
Open pollinated. Long red roots, cylindrical, with fairly smooth skins and moderate uniformity; good internal colour. Slow to bulk up. Reconfirmed after trial 2005.
EKin

93 H3 **'Pablo'**
Uniform roots with very smooth skins and very good internal colour. Appears to have good bolting resistance. Widely used as a show cultivar. Reconfirmed after trial 2001, 2005 and 2016.
EHyd EKin LRHS MCtn NRHS NRob

01 H3 **'Red Ace'**
F_1 hybrid; uniform round red roots with good flesh colour and no rings. Reconfirmed after trial 2016.
EKin NRob

05 H3 **'Solo'**
F_1 hybrid. Round red roots with slightly flattened shape. Bulks up well; smooth roots of good internal colour. Reconfirmed after trial 2016.
LCro LOPS

93 H3 **'Wodan'**
F_1 hybrid with round red root and slightly flattened shape. Smooth; good internal colour. Bulks up well. Reconfirmed after trial 2005, 2016.
EKin

Borecole or curly kale (*Brassica oleracea* Acephala Group)

15 H5 **'Black Magic'**
Very dark green, strap-leaved type with small blisters. Good yield.
MCtn

99 H5 **'Redbor'**
F_1 hybrid. Tall, uniform plants with open habit; strongly curled purple-green leaves. Good salad leaf, with ornamental value too. Winters well. Reconfirmed after trial 2015.
EKin LCro LOPS MCtn NRob

93 H5 **'Winterbor'**
F_1 hybrid. Tall plants with finely curled blue-green leaves; winters well. Developed from (but superior to) 'Westland Winter'. Reconfirmed after trial 1999, 2015.
EKin MCtn

Broccoli (*Brassica oleracea* Italica Group)

See under Calabrese for Calabrese broccoli

Purple sprouting

13 H5 **'Cardinal'**
Tidy upright plants, some variability in height, as expected for open pollinated cultivars. Dense spears of deep purple. Good for late crop.
EKin

95 H5 **'Claret'**
F_1 hybrid. Very tall; heavy yield of dark purple spears from March through April. Reconfirmed after trial 2013.
LCro LOPS LRHS NRHS

03 H4 **'Red Admiral'**
Early, yielded well with good quality secondaries. Good colour and long stems. Expected to perform better if sown later and grown to produce hardier plants. Reconfirmed after trial 2013.
LCro LOPS

95 H5 **'Red Arrow'**
Early to mid season; long cropping period. Good winter hardiness; bushy, vigorous plants. Good overall quality, cropping over a long period. Reconfirmed after trial 2003, 2013.
MCtn

Brussels sprouts (*Brassica oleracea* Gemmifera Group)

15 H5 **'Brodie'**
Clean buttons, developing unevenly; mild taste when cooked.
LCro LOPS

99 H5 **'Cascade'**
F_1 hybrid; late. Smooth, clean, well-spaced, fairly round sprouts. Uniform plants which stand and yield well.
EKin LCro LOPS

15 H4 **'Crispus'**
Early to mid season. Clubroot-resistant; nice colour, with mild, slightly nutty taste when cooked.
EKin

93 H5 **'Igor'**
F_1 hybrid. Mid to late season; attractive, vigorous, uniform plants producing well-spaced, solid, round, mid green sprouts. Reconfirmed after trial 2006.
NRob

15 H4 **'Marte'**
Tall plants with sprouts well spaced. Buttons quite round; good size; nice and dense. Not bitter, even uncooked.
EKin

06 H4 **'Maximus'**
F_1 hybrid; early to mid season. Leading commercial variety; uniform plants, producing a good crop of mid to dark green, smooth, solid sprouts, slightly sweet and crunchy after cooking. Reconfirmed after trial 2015.
EKin LCro

Cabbage (*Brassica oleracea* Capitata Group)

Early red, non-storing – September to October

96 H3 **'Rookie'**
F_1 hybrid; early. Round to slightly flat heads.
LCro LOPS

Autumn – September to November

09 H3 **'Minicole'**
F_1 hybrid. Good early autumn cultivar with attractive round heads.
EHyd LRHS NRHS NRob

09 H3 **'Red Jewel'**
F_1 hybrid. Attractive, solid, round-headed red cabbage with upright foliage and a short core. Could be grown with a closer spacing.
NRob

Savoy – September to March

01 H5 **'Tundra'**
F_1 hybrid; dark green, slightly blistered leaf; heads solid and attractive. Sweet-tasting; overwinters well. Reconfirmed after trial 2007.
EKin LCro LOPS MCtn

01 H5 **'Wintessa'**
F_1 hybrid; late. Dark green well-blistered leaves, with uniform well-filled heads of good quality and flavour. Plants stand well.
EKin

January King – November to March

08 H5 **'Deadon'**
Uniform, attractive 'January King' type with a flattened round head.
EKin

08 H5 **'January King 3'**
Open pollinated. Attractive heads that develop a good colour. Good yield and long spread of cut.
EKin MCtn

98 H4 **'Noelle'**
F_1 hybrid; flat, round, heads; dark green leaves with good purple colouring. Winters well. Previously listed as 'Holly'. Reconfirmed after trial 2009 for September–November cropping.
LCro LOPS

Winter hybrid – November to March

08 H3 **'Kilaton'**
Late season, large, white cabbage with claimed resistance to clubroot.
EKin

Spring

11 H5 **'Advantage'**
Good heart. Compact, uniform, with little bolting.
MCtn

93 H5 **'Duncan'**
F_1 hybrid. Mid to dark green uniform heads with well-closed bases. A good early yield; compact neat habit; plants heart slowly to produce small, pointed, solid, well-filled heads. Reconfirmed after trial 2001, 2011 as spring greens and hearted cabbage.
LRHS NRHS

11 H5 **'Spring Hero'**
Distinctive round-headed spring cabbage for overwintering. Large, dense ball-shaped heads. Blue-grey, rugose leaves. Showing excellent winter survival.
EKin

Summer – June to August

16 H2 **'Cabbice'**
Hybrid; Japanese flat cabbage. Sweet, heavy and dense, with good flavour.
EKin

04 H2 **'Candisa'**
F_1 hybrid; early. Uniform, medium green, well-filled heads, with short core. Reconfirmed after trial 2016.
EKin

16 H2 **'Caraflex'**
Hybrid; early sweetheart type. Quite big for the garden, but capable of making smaller heads.
EKin LCro LOPS

02 H2 **'Hispi'**
F_1 hybrid; early. Smooth, pointed, dark green outer leaves, with good uniformity and well-filled heart.
CHby LCro LOPS LRHS NRHS NRob

93 H2 **'Stonehead'**
F_1 hybrid; late. Uniform, round, mid green heads. Stands well. Also useful for cropping into the autumn from later planting. Reconfirmed after trial 2016.
EKin LRHS MBros NRHS NRob

CALABRESE BROCCOLI (*Brassica oleracea* Italica Group)

03 H3 **'Belstar'**
F_1 hybrid; May sown. Mid to late season; uniform medium-sized plants, with attractive heads and medium to small buds.
EKin

07 H3 **'Green Magic'**
Autumn-cropping; very good yield of slightly domed, good-sized heads with small beads. Known to make good sideshoots. Reconfirmed after trial 2013.
EKin MCtn

13 H2 **'Ironman'**
Domed, larger heads of blue-green, tight buds, healthy foliage.
EKin

03 H3 **'Kabuki'**
F_1 hybrid; May sown; early. Short, compact plants, producing a good crop of medium green, deep, well-rounded heads with uniform buds. Average yield of medium-sized secondaries, produced 3 to 5 weeks after the primary heads. Could be closely spaced to produce baby heads. Reconfirmed after trial 2007, 2013.
EHyd LRHS MCtn NRHS

13 H2 **'Marathon'**
Dome-shaped heads, uniform, mid size, held high.
EKin LCro LOPS LRHS NRHS

CARROT (*Daucus carota*)

99 H3 **'Adelaide'**
F_1 hybrid; very early. Good weight and colour; sweet-flavoured; quickly forms very smooth, stump-ended roots; almost coreless; fine tops. Ideal for successional sowings and early sowing in frames. Reconfirmed after trial 2006 and 2010 as early, suitable for containers.
EKin LCro LOPS

06 H3 **'Amsterdam Forcing 3'**
Open pollinated. Relatively smooth with good flesh and core colour; bulks up well. Strong foliage that does not grow too tall.
EKin MCtn

05 H5 **'Eskimo'**
F_1 hybrid; medium-length, smooth roots with good colour. Useful size, well-filled. Grows with crowns at or below ground level, so very little crown discoloration. Good overwintering cultivar. Reconfirmed after trial 2014.
EKin LCro LOPS MBros MCtn

99 H3 **'Flyaway'**
F_1 hybrid. Maincrop; medium-length, well-filled, stump-ended roots with good flesh and core colour. Good strong tops. Partial resistance (i.e. lack of attraction) to carrot flies. Reconfirmed after trial 2006.
EKin LCro LOPS MCtn

99 H3 **'Maestro'**
F_1 hybrid. Best lifted before Christmas. Blunt, smooth-skinned, medium to slim, fairly well-filled roots, uniform in size and shape. Mid to pale internal colour with some green shoulders. Widely grown by organic carrot growers. Reconfirmed after trial 2005, 2014.
LCro LOPS

10 H3 **'Marion'**
Early to mature; uniform crop of slightly tapered roots with good weight. Smooth skin, deep orange flesh and good core colour. Suitable for containers.
EKin
EHyd LRHS NRHS

99 H3 **'Nairobi'**
F_1 hybrid; second early / early maincrop. Strong tops, with uniform, broader-shouldered, cylindrical, stump-ended roots. Heavy yields. Reconfirmed after trial 2006, 2014.
EKin

93 H3 **'Napoli'**
F_1 hybrid, very early maturing. Slightly tapering; good weight. Smooth skin, core and flesh deep orange. Strong tops for easy pulling; quick to bulk up. Ideal for successional sowings and early sowing in frames. Reconfirmed after trial 2010 as early, suitable for containers.
EKin

06 H3 **'Primo'**
Hybrid; flavoursome crop of good weight. Smooth skin, deep orange colour, with low

core–flesh ratio. Reconfirmed after trial 2010 as early, suitable for containers.
LCro LOPS

14 H3 **'Resistafly'**
A 'Nantes' type. Bred for intermediate carrot-fly resistance. Smooth skin, good uniformity, well-stumped root, good colour, nice flavour.
SVic

05 H4 **'Sugarsnax 54'**
F_1 hybrid. Very long, smooth, 'Imperator' type with roots of good internal colour. Suited to deep, light soils. Commercially used, cut into short lengths and sold as pre-packed baton carrots.
EKin MCtn

05 H3 **'Sweet Candle'**
F_1 hybrid; short, blunt, quite smooth, well-filled, uniform roots. Good internal colour. Reconfirmed after trial 2014.
EKin LCro LOPS NRob

CAULIFLOWER (*Brassica oleracea* Botrytis Group)

COLOURED AND ROMANESCO

05 H3 **'Graffiti'**
F_1 hybrid. Small to medium, high quality, solid curds of a very attractive amethyst colour. The colour fades a little if boiled, and is retained better if steamed. The raw curds have a good flavour and would be a colourful addition to a salad or dish of crudités. Midseason. Reconfirmed after trial 2006.
EKin LRHS NRHS SVic

05 H3 **'Veronica'**
F_1 hybrid; appetising light green Romanesco type. Uniform good-sized, solid, well-shaped heads.
EKin

AUTUMN HEADING – SEPTEMBER TO NOVEMBER

15 H3 **'Boris'**
Good, deep, round curd.
EKin

15 H3 **'Clapton'**
Neat, well-covered variety, with lovely curds and good upright habit.
EKin

02 H3 **'Moby Dick'**
F_1 hybrid; early with a short cropping period; uniform, very deep, heavy curds. Good width. Reconfirmed after trial 2015.
LCro LOPS

SUMMER HEADING – JUNE TO MID JULY

06 H3 **'Avalanche'**
Hybrid; midseason. Attractive, high quality, medium to large, white, solid curds.
EHyd LRHS NRHS

97 H3 **'Barcelona'**
F_1 hybrid; midseason. Deep, round, solid, well-protected curds.
EKin

97 H3 **'Fargo'**
F_1 hybrid; late. Deep, white, well-protected curds.
EKin

06 H3 **'Flamenco'**
Hybrid; midseason to late. Very high quality, medium to large white, solid curds with good depth.
NRob

97 H3 **'Nautilus'**
F_1 hybrid; late. Vigorous plants with deep, white, well-protected curds of excellent quality.
LRHS NRHS

SUMMER OR AUTUMN HEADING

06 H3 **'Aviron'**
Hybrid; late. High quality, well-protected, large to medium sized solid, white heads. Reconfirmed after trial for autumn heading 2015.
EKin

WINTER FOR SPRING HEADING, MATURING FROM MARCH TO MAY

05 H5 **'Aalsmeer'**
Open pollinated cultivar; early midseason. Produces medium to small, cream-coloured, slightly lumpy, well-protected curds that have a good depth. This cultivar produced several multiple heads and sideshoots, many of usable quality.
EKin NRob

CELERIAC (*Apium graveolens* var. *rapaceum*)

00 H4 **'Prinz'**
Smooth, deep, white-skinned; small to medium, flattened and round; compact plant with healthy foliage. Reconfirmed after trial 2011.
CHby EKin LCro LOPS MCtn SVic

CELERY (*Apium graveolens* var. *dulce*)

93 H2 **'Celebrity'**
Self-blanching, fairly short plants, with ribbed petioles and good flavour. Reconfirmed after trial 2001.
LRHS MCtn NRHS

93 H4 **'Giant Pink' - Mammoth Pink**
Pink-tinged, green variety for blanching or earthing up; solid stems.
NRob

94 H2 **'Victoria'**
F_1 hybrid. Tall, well-filled plants with

medium-green, smooth, fleshy petioles. Widely used for commercial crops. Reconfirmed after trial 2005.
EKin MBros

Chard (*Beta vulgaris* subsp. *cicla* var. *flavescens*)

00 H3 Bright Lights
Good colourful mix, including reds, yellows and whites; very ornamental and decorative.
CHby EHyd LRHS NRHS NRob SVic

00 H3 **'Bright Yellow'**
Bright golden-yellow petioles and mid green puckered leaf; uniform; sweet taste; reconfirmed after trial 2011.
MCtn NRob

11 H3 **'Canary Yellow'**
Green leaves and yellow stem; healthy blister-type attractive glossy leaf. Even stock. Taste is not bitter. No bolting in either sowing during trial.
NRob

00 H3 **'Fordhook Giant'**
Attractive shiny light green, puckered leaf with white stem and long succulent broad white petioles; old blister-leaf chard type.
EKin MCtn NRob

00 H3 **'Rhubarb Chard'**
Dark green leaves and red stem; uniform; blister-type leaf; reconfirmed after trial 2011.
EKin LCro LOPS MBros MCtn NRob SVic

Chicory (*Cichorium intybus*)

Radicchio

02 H5 **'Palla Rossa'**
Medium to large heads; well-filled red hearts; fairly uniform. No bolting.
CHby MCtn SRms

Sugar loaf

02 H5 **'Pan di Zucchero'**
Uniform plants with medium to large frames and dark green outer leaves. Hearts blanch well.
CHby

Chilli pepper (*Capsicum annuum*)

06 H1c **'Apache'**
Decorative, growing to 45cm; does well in both large and small pots. Produces large crop of small, juicy, hot peppers that ripen from bright green to red and are held outwards from the stems. Reconfirmed after trial 2013.
CCCN CRos EHyd EKin LRHS MBros MPri NRHS NRob SPre

13 H1c **'Basket of Fire'**
Multi-branched, open habit, height to c.25cm. Numerous upright fruits, maturing through cream, lemon, yellow and orange to red.
CRos EHyd EKin LRHS NRHS SPre SVic

13 H1c **'Bolivian Rainbow'**
Compact plant, height c.32 cm, with mid green foliage. Stumpy, broad-based fruit held erect. Fruit ripening cream through orange to red.
SVic

06 H1c **'Caribbean Antillais'**
Quite small, blocky, bright red fruits; aromatic and very hot, of a type widely used in South American and Caribbean cooking. Later-cropping, best sown in January and given a higher temperature to germinate.
SVic

06 H1c **'Demon Red'**
A small, ornamental plant, starred with white flowers, producing an abundant crop of tiny upward-pointing fruits that mature to dark, bright red. Fruits are hot and used in Thai cooking. Reconfirmed after trial 2013.
CRos EHyd EKin LRHS MCtn NRHS SPre SVic

06 H1c **'Etna'**
Attractive bunches of erect, shiny peppers that mature from bright mid green to red, carried on compact plants that are suitable for growing in pots. Large crop of very hot peppers.
CRos EHyd LRHS MCtn NRHS

06 H1c **'Filius Blue'**
Attractive, highly ornamental plants. The young leaves are mid green, becoming very dark green with a purple flush; the plants are covered with purple, orange and bright red fruits that are spicy and hot.
NRob

06 H1c **'Fresno'**
Fairly short, upright-growing plants; very productive. The conical fruits ripen from light green to deep scarlet red, with medium thick flesh that is very hot.
LRHS NRHS

06 H1c **'Habanero'**
Very attractive, blocky, orange fruits; very hot. Plants quite compact; good yield; suitable for growing in pots. Best sown in January.
EKin

13 H1c **'Hot Thai'**
Bushy yet compact habit, height to 25cm. Dainty dark green foliage. Small, hot fruits (1.5cm in length, and 1cm wide), held erect. Ideal for a windowsill.
CRos EHyd LRHS NRHS

06 H1c **'Hungarian Hot Wax'**
Conical fruits ripening from pale yellow to bright red; medium hot; very good for frying,

stuffing and using in salads. One of the easiest to grow. Suitable for growing in pots.
CHby EKin LCro LOPS MCtn NRob SVic

13 H1c **'Krakatoa'**
Compact, bushy plant, with dark green foliage; height c.20cm. Erect clusters of glossy fruit, 3cm long, and 1cm across the base.
CRos EHyd LRHS NRHS

13 H1c **'Loco'**
Bushy plant, height c.25 cm, cascading habit which looks especially attractive in a basket or container. Numerous oblong fruit, c.2cm long, held erect above the foliage. Ripening purple to red.
CRos EHyd LRHS NRHS

14 H1c **'Pot Black'**
Upright plant with branching habit; height c.36cm. Stem, foliage, fruit very dark purple. Fruit blocky in shape, held erect above the foliage. Interesting and unusual variety.
SVic

06 H1c **'Prairie Fire'**
Very attractive, short (20cm high), spreading plants covered in a mass of very small, very hot, upright peppers that ripen from white, through yellow and orange, to red. Ideal for pots or a windowsill. Reconfirmed after trial 2013.
CCCN CRos EHyd LCro LOPS LRHS NRHS NRob SVic

06 H1c **'Super Chili'**
Ornamental plants; well suited to growing in pots. Produces a high yield of very hot, thin-walled fruits that are held upright and ripen from light green to orange-red.
SPre SVic

06 H1c **'Tricolor Variegatum'**
Ornamental foliage an attractive mid green, splashed cream and purple. Small fruits mature from purple, through orange to red. Plants 70cm high with a rather spreading habit, but can be pruned to shape.
NRob

CHINESE CABBAGE (*Brassica rapa* Pekinensis Group)

03 H3 **'Yuki'**
Barrel-shaped. Medium green, slightly savoyed outer leaves; very short internal stem; medium-sized heavy head; well-blanched.
EKin MCtn

CORIANDER (*Coriandrum sativum*)

14 H2 **'Calypso'**
Vigorous, bushy strong growth; holds well; good leaf yield. Ideal size for the home gardener.
EKin MCtn

14 H2 **'Confetti'**
Neat and clean, with distinct fern-like look; uniform. Ideal for smaller gardens.
EKin LCro LOPS MCtn

CORNSALAD (*Valerianella locusta*)

94 H3 **'Medaillon'**
Slow-growing, short, thick-leaved under frames.
LCro LOPS

COURGETTE (*Cucurbita pepo*)

93 H2 **'Defender'**
F_1 hybrid. A high yield of medium-sized, slender, very lightly flecked fruits.
EKin LCro LOPS MCtn

93 H2 **'Early Gem'**
F_1 hybrid; a high yield of slender, lightly speckled fruits. Easy to see on the plant.
EKin MCtn

98 H2 **'El Greco'**
F_1 hybrid. Bush type; plant of open habit with mid green fruits.
MCtn

13 H2 **'Orelia'**
Upright plant, producing a good yield of yellow fruits. Vigorous plants, showing good mildew resistance.
EKin

06 H2 **'Parador'**
Hybrid; crops early and gives a high yield. Nicely shaped fruits are cylindrical, straight and an attractive bright yellow. Flowers are held on the fruits until completely faded. Plants are healthy and compact. Also grown as a summer squash.
MBros

07 H2 **'Romanesco'**
Distinctive, heavily ribbed fruits that hold their flowers. Popular in Italy; the flowers are used for stuffing. Semi-trailing plants; good yield.
LCro LOPS

CUCUMBER (*Cucumis sativus*)

02 H1c **'Carmen'**
F_1 hybrid; standard length, dark green, slightly ribbed fruits. Reconfirmed after trial 2009.
EKin NRob

09 H1c **'Cucino'**
Smooth, small, dark green, uniform fruits with good flavour and texture. Highly productive plants.
LRHS NRHS SVic

09 H1c **'Emilie'**
Useful mid length fruits with attractive dark green colour and good flavour. Previously listed as 'Emile'.
LCro LOPS

95 H2 **'Marketmore'**
Ridge cucumber; good yield of short, attractive, dark green fruits. Grown in the open garden. Reconfirmed after trial 2001.
CHby EKin MCtn

09 H1c **'Mini Munch'**
Highly productive plants producing abundant small, crunchy, shiny-skinned fruits with good flavour.
EKin

ENDIVE (*Cichorium endivia*)

96 H3 **'Pancalieri'**
Curled. Very strong cut-leaf type. Does not blanch well.
CHby EKin MCtn

FLORENCE FENNEL (*Foeniculum vulgare*)

96 H2 **'Fino'**
Quick-maturing. Medium large, round, very uniform bulbs of excellent quality.
EKin MCtn NRob

05 H2 **'Orion'**
F_1 hybrid; vigorous foliage; attractive, medium to large bulbs with a good shape, with few sideshoots and clean, with a bright white colour.
EKin

GARLIC (*Allium sativum* var. *ophioscorodon*)

04 H4 **'Early Wight'**
Very early crop (during May); good fat cloves. Hard neck; best used immediately after harvest.
NRob

04 H4 **'Germidour'**
Late-maturing, virus-free selection. Soft necks; well-packed, purple-skinned cloves.
NRob

04 H4 **'Solent White'**
Late. Soft neck; many purple-skinned, very attractive cloves, with appealing bouquet; high yield; keeps beyond Christmas (up to March). Also performed well in trial at Harlow Carr.
EKin LCro LOPS NRob

KOHLRABI (*Brassica oleracea* Gongylodes Group)

97 H3 **'Quickstar'**
F_1 hybrid. Uniform crop of juicy, tender bulbs with a mild flavour. Medium-sized tops. Reconfirmed after trial 2006.
LRHS MCtn NRHS

LEEKS (*Allium porrum*)

09 H5 **'Blauwgroene Winter' - Atlanta**
Good open pollinated cultivar. Dark blue-green, erect flags, with healthy foliage. Medium length of blanch. Late spring.
EKin

09 H5 **'Blauwgroene Winter' - Bandit**
Good open pollinated cultivar. Dark blue-green flags; reasonable length of blanch. Late spring.
EKin

00 H4 **'Jolant' (Swiss Giant Group)**
Maincrop, for December cropping; high yield; medium to dark green flags; long, solid shafts with little bulbing and very few bolters. Low levels of rust infection. Has a long season and peels nicely. Reconfirmed after trial 2002, 2015.
EKin MCtn NRob

15 H5 **'Lancaster'**
Hybrid; lovely leek, dark green and upright; really uniform. Autumn and early winter.
NRob

00 H4 **'Mammoth Blanch'**
A show variety suitable for December sowing. Early-maturing, with high yields of well-shaped leeks with pale green flags, long, heavy shafts and no bolters.
EKin NRob

02 H5 **'Mammoth Pot'**
Maincrop; uniform, with whole stem blanched and light green flag. High December yield. A good short garden plant.
EKin NRob

02 H5 **'Oarsman'**
F_1 hybrid, maincrop; erect plant, with very straight shank, uniform, smooth; flag leaf clean. Good yield. Reconfirmed after trial 2015.
EKin LCro LOPS MCtn

00 H4 **'Pancho'**
Good early yield of medium long, mid green, solid shafts with only slight bulbing. Little rust. Early maturing.
LCro LOPS

LETTUCE (*Lactuca sativa*)

BUTTERHEAD

97 H2 **'Clarion'**
Open heads, with pale to mid green leaves. Reconfirmed after trial 2002. For autumn cropping under protection or summer cropping in the open garden.
LCro LOPS

COS

12 H2 **'Chartwell'**
Neat, mid size green Cos; dense, crisp heart.
EKin

07 H2 **'Chatsworth'**
Medium-sized with rugose leaves; dense hearts make a good weight and have a good blanch. Very good flavour.
LCro LOPS

93 H2 **'Little Gem'**
Small solid heads with mid green, medium-blistered leaves. Reconfirmed after trial 1999, 2007, 2012.
CHby CRos EHyd EKin LCro LOPS LRHS MBros MCtn NRHS NRob

99 H2 **'Little Leprechaun'**
Semi-Cos with dark red leaves.
NRob

93 H2 **'Lobjoit's Green Cos'**
Large, rather open heads, with relatively smooth mid green leaves. Reconfirmed after trial 1999.
EKin NRob SVic

12 H2 **'Maureen'**
Uniform crop, with mid green leaves. One of the most popular commercial 'Gem' varieties.
EKin

99 H2 **'Parris Island'**
Vigorous with pale green uniform heads; reconfirmed after trial 2007.
EKin

00 H2 **'Winter Density'**
Semi-Cos with leafy, erect habit; dark green, very uniform. Reconfirmed after trial 2007, 2012.
EKin LCro LOPS MCtn NRob

Crisphead

01 H2 **'Robinson'**
Medium to large frame, good quality solid hearts; reconfirmed after trial 2014.
NRob

03 H2 **'Sioux'**
Smooth leaves, large frame, with a green heart and outer leaves tipped red. Slow to bolt.
LCro LOPS

Leafy

95 H2 **'Black-seeded Simpson Improved'**
Yellow-green leaves with frilled edges. Cos-like in growth.
MCtn

95 H2 **'Catalogna'**
Strong-growing oak-leaved type. Light green slightly blistered leaves.
MCtn SVic

95 H2 **'Cocarde'**
Large oak-leaved type, with bronze green-tinged leaves.
MCtn

95 H2 **'New Red Fire'**
Large, with puckered light bronze outer leaves.
EKin MCtn

95 H2 **'Salad Bowl'**
Large open hearted plants with light green frilled leaves.
CHby EKin LCro LOPS LRHS MCtn NRHS NRob

Mangetout see under Peas

Marrow (*Cucurbita pepo*)

97 H2 **'Tiger Cross'**
F_1 hybrid. High yield of pale-striped fruits. Claimed CMV tolerance.
EKin LCro LOPS LRHS MCtn NRHS SVic

Melon (*Cucumis melo*)

09 H1c **'Emir'**
Good crop of netted Charentais-type fruits with orange flesh; H2 for outdoor use.
EKin LCro LOPS MCtn

93 H1c **'Sweetheart'**
Early-ripening; globular, medium-sized, cream-coloured fruit with orange flesh.
NRob

Onion (*Allium* species)

From sets

93 H3 **'Centurion'**
F_1 hybrid. Flattened globe-shaped bulbs with straw-coloured skins of good thickness. Reconfirmed after trial 2002, 2013.
NRob

13 H3 **'Rumba'**
Uniform crop; large bulb size, globe-shaped, with brown skin. Stores well.
EKin NRob

02 H3 **'Sturon'**
Very good yield of globe-shaped, slightly high-shouldered bulbs, with good yellow-brown skins. Reconfirmed after trial 2002, 2013.
CHby EKin LCro LOPS NRob

02 H3 **'Stuttgarter'**
High yield, well-shaped, deep bulb, good skin.
EKin LCro LOPS NRob

93 H3 **'Turbo'**
Globe-shaped to slightly conical bulbs with brown skins. Some skin splitting. Reconfirmed after trial 2013.
NRob

Maincrop bulb

93 H3 **'Golden Bear'**
F_1 hybrid; early. Thin-skinned, high-shouldered bulbs; do not store well.
MCtn NRob

Red, globe, from seed and sets

05 H3 **'Red Baron'**
High yield of attractive, dark-skinned, globe-shaped bulbs with good internal colour. Plants in the trial grown from seed produced a higher yield and bolder bulbs than those grown from sets. Reconfirmed after trial 2013.
CHby EKin LCro LOPS LRHS MCtn NRHS NRob

Salad – non-bulbing

04 H4 **'Guardsman'**
F_1 hybrid: cross between *A. fistulosum* and *A. cepa*. Medium to dark green leaves. Very vigorous; well-blanched with some bulbing.
MCtn

96 H3 **'Ishikura'**
Strong-growing; long-stemmed.
MCtn

Salad – traditional

93 H4 **'White Lisbon'**
Medium-green leaves with good length of blanch. Good for early and successional sowing. Reconfirmed after trial 2004.
CHby CRos EHyd EKin LCro LOPS LRHS MBros MCtn NRHS NRob SVic

93 H4 **'Winter White Bunching'**
Strong-growing with dark green leaves. Overwinters well.
EKin

Shallot

01 H3 **'Golden Gourmet'**
Well-shaped, good size; high yield.
EKin LCro LOPS NRob SVic

01 H3 **'Jermor'**
Good skin, uniform shape and size; suitable for exhibition.
NRob

01 H3 **'Longor'**
Good yield and shape; also suitable for exhibition.
LCro LOPS NRob

01 H3 **'Matador'**
F_1 hybrid; thick skins, and good yield.
EKin LRHS MCtn NRHS SVic

93 H3 **'Santé'**
Attractive, reddish brown, uniform bulbs with smooth skins. Plant a month later than others to avoid bolting.
NRob

Pak Choi (*Brassica rapa* Chinensis Group)

10 H3 **'Baraku'**
Good germination rate. Little bolting. Compact and uniform, attractive dark green leaf and petiole. Good size for cooking.
MCtn

10 H3 **'Red Choi'**
Good germination rate. Very little bolting. Stands well. Attractive purple leaves and tender green stem. Good hearting, uniform clean, healthy crop. Ideal size for cooking.
EKin MBros

Parsley (*Petroselinum crispum*)

97 H6 **'Bravour'**
A reliable cropper; good stalks, well curled.
LRHS MHer

97 H4 **'Curlina'**
Compact and uniform; tightly curled.
LCro LOPS

93 H6 **'Moss Curled'**
Aromatic, deeply cut, tightly curled leaves and small umbels of yellow-green flowers in summer.
CHby EHyd EKin LRHS MCtn NRHS NRob SRms

Parsnip (*Pastinaca sativa*)

01 H5 **'Gladiator'**
F_1 hybrid; very smooth skin, good potential yield, uniform shape, shallow lenticels. Reconfirmed after trial 2009.
CRos EHyd EKin LCro LOPS LRHS MCtn NRHS

Peas (*Pisum sativum*)

93 H2 **'Hurst Green Shaft'**
Maincrop; heavy yield of dark green, medium-length, pointed pods. Excellent taste, with good number of peas per pod. Nicely progressive yield. Reconfirmed after trial 1998, 2005, 2017.
EKin LCro LOPS MCtn

05 H2 **'Jaguar'**
Early maincrop; heavy crop of mainly double pods per node. Medium-length pods have an average of seven peas per pod, with good flavour.
MCtn

97 H2 **'Kelvedon Wonder'**
Early maincrop. Long, dark green pods, with an average of 7 to 8 peas per pod. Reconfirmed after trial 2004, 2005.
EKin LCro LOPS MBros MCtn NRob

05 H2 **'Serge'**
Maincrop; semi-leafless plants produce a heavy crop of easy-to-pick pods. Medium-length pods have an average of ten peas per pod, with good flavour.
EKin MBros MCtn

98 H2 **'Show Perfection'**
Maincrop; an exhibition pea, very tall with long dark green pods. A high yield over a long period.
NRob

Mangetout

00 H2 **'Delikata'**
Tall, with similar pods to 'Oregon Sugar Pod'. A shade earlier and carries a heavy crop. Pods soon form strings if not picked regularly. Resistant to mildew and fusarium.
LCro LOPS

09 H2 **'Oregon Giant'**
Clean, healthy, mid height plants. Attractive broad, mid green pods.
EKin

Sugarsnap

00 H2 **'Cascadia'**
Dwarf habit producing very fleshy, crisp, sweet pods, which remain tender and sweet over a longer period than many snaps. Heavy crops over a long picking season. Reconfirmed after trial 2009.
LCro LOPS

00 H2 **'Delikett'**
Dwarf habit. Young, dark green pods stringless but soon form strings; become fleshier and sweeter with age. Very well cropped and a long season of picking. Reconfirmed after trial 2009.
EKin MCtn NRob

00 H2 **'Sugar Ann'**
Medium height. Early to crop and gives a good yield of juicy, sweet pods. Good flavour. Reconfirmed after trial 2009.
CHby EKin

00 H2 SUGAR DWARF SWEET GREEN (**'Norli'**)
Medium height. About the earliest to mature and a heavy cropper, but over a short period and so requires successional sowing. Medium height plants; good for garden use. Reconfirmed after trial 2009.
CHby MCtn

09 H2 **'Sugar Lace'**
Semi-leafless; attractive fleshy pods with good flavour. Pods very uniform and stringless. Good yield.
MCtn

Potatoes (*Solanum tuberosum*)

First early

98 H2 **'Accent'**
A super-tasting new potato, with pale creamy yellow waxy flesh. Eelworm and common scab resistance.
EKin NRob

98 H2 **'Foremost'**
Originally 'Suttons Foremost'. Ever popular new potato with slightly waxy, firm, white, good-flavoured flesh that does not discolour or disintegrate on cooking.
EKin NRob

07 H2 **'Orla'**
Can also be used as a second early and maincrop. Good yield of round to oval creamy white tubers; flesh slightly waxy with good flavour. Popular with organic gardeners.
NRob

98 H2 **'Red Duke of York'**
Oval red sport of 'Duke of York' with moist pale yellow flesh of superb flavour. Excellent roasted, but a good all-rounder as tubers bulk up quickly if left to mature as a late second early.
EKin LCro LOPS NRob

07 H2 **'Vivaldi'**
Can be left to bulk up as summer baker. Good yield of oval, pale yellow, smooth-skinned tubers with creamy flesh.
EKin LCro LOPS NRob

98 H2 **'Winston'**
Bulks up quickly to produce large, even-shaped tubers. Creamy moist flesh of excellent flavour which does not discolour on cooking.
EKin NRob

Second early

98 H2 **'British Queen'**
Heavy and uniform crop of white-skinned and floury-textured tubers of delicious flavour for all cooking purposes.
NRob

98 H2 **'Charlotte'**
Long oval variety producing yellow-skinned and waxy tubers with creamy yellow flesh of first-class flavour either hot or cold. Reconfirmed after trial 2013 as early for container use.
EKin LCro LOPS NRob

98 H2 **'Kondor'**
Large pale red-skinned oval tubers with tasty, almost waxy, yellow flesh. Very high yields. Excellent for baking.
NRob

98 H2 **'Lady Christl'**
Bulks up very quickly and is almost a first early. Long oval, shallow-eyed, pale yellow-skinned and creamy flesh which remains firm on cooking. Eelworm-resistant. Reconfirmed after trial 2007; also in 2013 after trial as early for container use.
EKin NRob

98 H2 **'Nadine'**
Exceptionally smooth skin and shallow eyes. Cream flesh with a moist, waxy texture that does not discolour and remains firm on cooking.

Heavy uniform yields; scab-free. An exhibitor's favourite. Reconfirmed after trial 2017.
EKin NRob

Early in containers

13 H2 **'Casablanca'**
Clean crop, white flesh, uniform size.
EKin LCro LOPS NRob

13 H2 **'Jazzy'**
Attractive, oval, uniform crop. Yellow skin and flesh, waxy tubers with sweet taste.
EKin NRob

13 H2 **'Maris Bard'**
White flesh, thin skin, good flavour and texture; fairly uniform crop.
EKin NRob

13 H2 **'Sharpe's Express'**
Heritage variety; white skin, uniform crop size. Slightly waxy, good flavour.
NRob

Early maincrop

93 H2 **'Maxine'**
Large, smooth, pale red-skinned tubers with white waxy flesh. Uniform tubers so also recommended for exhibitors. Eelworm-resistant. Reconfirmed after trial 1998.
NRob

93 H2 **'Picasso'**
One of the heaviest croppers with creamy skin and striking bright red eyes. Waxy fine-flavoured flesh, particularly when boiled. Eelworm-resistant and good resistance to common scab. Reconfirmed after trial 1998, 2014.
NRob

Maincrop

14 H2 **'Desiree'**
Red skin, light yellow flesh, oval tubers; reliable, and still the world's most popular red.
LCro LOPS

14 H2 **'Maris Piper'**
Cream skin, cream flesh, oval tubers; a massive favourite with gardeners.
LCro LOPS

14 H2 **'Sarpo Mira'**
Red skin, white flesh, oval tubers; still the leading blight benchmark.
LCro LOPS

Salad

98 H2 **'Charlotte'**
Long oval variety producing yellow-skinned and waxy tubers with creamy yellow flesh of first-class flavour either hot or cold. Reconfirmed after trial 2013 as early for container use.
EKin LCro LOPS NRob

03 H2 **'Pink Fir Apple'**
Late main crop (22 weeks from planting). Very vigorous plants; elongated, knobbly tubers; good flavour.
EKin LCro LOPS NRob SVic

03 H2 **'Ratte'**
Early main crop. Oval tubers, waxy, cream flesh; good flavour.
NRob

Radish (*Raphanus sativus*)

13 H2 **'Escala'**
Hybrid. Globe-shaped, bright cherry-red, with thin tap root; not pithy. Very uniform crop.
LCro LOPS

08 H2 **'Lunar'**
Very uniform crop of solid, round, white roots that are crunchy, juicy and have a mild flavour. No pithiness. Tops are short with leaves that are almost entire.
LCro LOPS

08 H2 **'Pink Beauty'**
Attractive, shiny pink roots. Crunchy texture and good, sweet flavour. No pithiness.
LCro LOPS MCtn

96 H2 **'Scarlet Globe'**
Round medium to large red roots.
EKin

96 H2 **'Sparkler'**
Slightly flattened round roots. Unique colour split: red upper with white lower skin. Reconfirmed after trial 2013.
CHby EKin MCtn

Rhubarb (*Rheum* × *hybridum*)

03 H5 **'Grandad's Favorite'**
First early. Vigorous plants, high yield, thick, fairly sweet stem, bright colour, good leaf to stem ratio. Suitable for showing.
CRos EHyd LRHS NRHS

03 H5 **'Hawke's Champagne'**
Second early. Compact plants; high yield potential. Attractive, bright red, medium-length, uniform stems.
WCot

12 H5 **'Raspberry Red'**
First early. High quality rich red stalks. Crops heavily and reliably.
CMac CRos EMil EPfP EPom LCro LOPS LRHS NRHS SPoG

03 H5 **'Timperley Early'**
First early. Thick stems, early, high yield. Bred for forcing; performs very well outside, but even better colour when forced.
CMac CRos CSBt CTri EBee EHyd EKin ELan EMil EMor EPfP EPom LCro LEdu

LOPS LRHS LSRN MAsh MGos MMuc MPri MRav NLar NRHS NRob SCoo SEdi SKee SLim SPer SPoG Wmat

SHALLOT SEE UNDER ONIONS

SPINACH (*Spinacia oleracea*)

08 H2 **'Amazon'**
F_1 hybrid; resistant to mildew races 1–10. Vigorous plants that bulk well; leaves are large, round and a good glossy dark green.
MCtn SVic

00 H2 **'Matador'**
F_1 hybrid. Thick, dark green, upright leaf.
EKin

00 H2 **'Medania'**
Open pollinated; resistant to mildew races 1 and 3. Good yield from slower-growing plants that are slow to bolt. Slightly blistered, large round leaves. Reconfirmed after trial 2008.
EKin MCtn

08 H2 **'Missouri'**
F_1 hybrid; resistant to mildew races 1–10. Heavy yield of bright, medium green leaves with an upright habit.
EKin LCro LOPS

SPINACH BEET (*Beta vulgaris* subsp. *cicla* var. *cicla*)

00 H4 **'Perpetual Spinach'**
Mid to pale green with fairly soft texture, medium vigour; uniform; stable and clean; flat leaf with good green petiole; reconfirmed after trial 2011.
CHby EKin LCro LRHS MBros MCtn NRHS NRob SVic

SQUASHES (*Cucurbita* species)

BUTTERNUT

08 H2 **'Harrier'**
Early crop of small to medium sized, bell-shaped fruits, with a small seed cavity.
LCro LOPS

08 H2 **'Hunter'**
A very high yield of uniformly small to medium, long pear-shaped fruits with a small seed cavity. Early ripening with orange-gold flesh.
EKin MBros MCtn NRob SVic

SUMMER

06 H2 **'Eight Ball'**
Good yield of round, green fruits; easy to see and pick from the compact, upright plants.
SVic

06 H2 **'Geode'**
Early and heavy crop of uniform, round, mid to pale green, marbled fruits with smallish blossom end scar. Clean, healthy plants.
LRHS NRHS

06 H2 **'Parador'**
Hybrid; crops early and gives a high yield. Nicely shaped fruits are cylindrical, straight and an attractive bright yellow. Flowers are held on the fruits until completely faded. Plants are healthy and compact. Reconfirmed after trial 2013 as bush courgette.
MBros

06 H2 **'Peter Pan'**
Uniform crop of light-green, scallop-shaped fruits should be harvested when small.
SVic

06 H2 **'Sunburst'**
Hybrid; attractive yellow, scallop-shaped fruits. Used for baby veg; best harvested when small (5–6cm diameter).
NRob

WINTER

11 H2 **'Crown Prince'**
Large fruits, with blue-grey skin and excellent storage quality. Popular, reliable variety. Fruits have high flesh content, of deep orange colour and excellent flavour.
CHby EKin MCtn NRob SVic

11 H2 **'Harlequin'**
High sugar cultivar. Decorative ridged fruits, striped yellow, gold and green; mid sized with a typical diameter 10–13cm. Good yield per plant and excellent storage quality. Plant has a semi-bush habit. Firm flesh of smooth texture and sweet flavour.
SVic

11 H2 **'Honey Bear'**
High sugar variety. Dark green, mini-acorn-shaped fruits of uniform size, typically 8–10cm in diameter. Sweet flavour; ideal size for baking whole. Compact, bushy habit, giving a reasonable yield of fruits, with excellent storage qualities. Plant demonstrates good resistance to powdery mildew.
MCtn

11 H2 **'Kabocha Large Fruited'**
Dark green flattened fruit, typically 15 to 17cm in diameter. Good storage. Flesh is thick, sweet and smooth. Ideal for desserts.
SVic

11 H2 **'Sweet Dumpling'**
Original sweet dumpling type. Uniform crop of small fruit, approximately 9 to 10cm in diameter; ridged, cream-coloured with green stripes and mottling; sweetly flavoured orange flesh. Trailing habit, producing a

good yield of fruits with excellent storage quality.
CHby EKin MCtn NRob

SUGARSNAP SEE UNDER PEAS

SWEET CORN (*Zea mays*)

03 H2 **'Earlibird'**
F_1 hybrid; 2nd early supersweet. Uniform cobs; good vigour. Reconfirmed after trial 2009, 2016.
EKin MCtn

03 H2 **'Lark'**
F_1 hybrid; 2nd early extra tender sweet. High yield of well-filled cobs with very sweet, clean flavour. Reconfirmed after trial 2009, 2016.
EKin LCro LOPS MCtn SVic

03 H2 **'Mainstay'**
F_1 hybrid; maincrop supersweet. Vigorous plants, reliable crop, well-filled cobs.
MBros

09 H2 MIRAI PICINIC (**'Mirai 003'**)
Early; uniform, small, exceptionally sweet cobs.
LCro LOPS

09 H2 MIRAI WHITE M421 (**'Mirai 421W'**)
Early extra tender sweet. Tall plants, with well-filled cobs and very good flavour. Attractive white cobs are exceptionally tender and sweet. Reconfirmed after trial 2016.
LRHS

03 H2 **'Swift'**
F_1 hybrid; early extra tender sweet. High yield of cobs with excellent eating quality. Good sweet flavour and tender kernels. Very popular variety. Thin pericarp is prone to damage. Reconfirmed after trial 2009, 2016.
EKin LCro LOPS MCtn

SWEET PEPPER (*Capsicum annuum* var. *annuum* Grossum Group)

05 H1c **'Corno di Toro Rosso'**
Open pollinated; later-cropping. Long, horn-shaped, very fleshy fruits that have a good flavour. Maturing from pale green to bright red. Big fruits, huge yield. Reconfirmed after trial 2016.
CHby LCro LOPS

16 H1c **'Demetra'**
Hybrid. Medium cone, uniform fruits, maturing from light green to red. Very high yields. Attractive and vigorous.
EKin

05 H1c **'Mohawk'**
F_1 hybrid. Medium-sized, blocky, bell-shaped fruits that ripen from dark green to bright yellow; good flavour. Dwarf-growing plants are well suited to growing in pots. Reconfirmed after trial 2016.
CRos EHyd EKin LRHS MBros NRHS

05 H1c **'Redskin'**
F_1 hybrid; small to medium, blocky, bell-shaped fruits that ripen from dark green to a glossy, dark red. Compact plants give a high yield and are well suited to growing in pots. Original windowsill pepper. Reconfirmed after trial 2016.
CRos EHyd EKin LCro LOPS LRHS NRHS

TOMATOES (*Solanum lycopersicum*)

97 H1c **'Alicante'**
Good shape; heavy crop of attractive fruits which ripen well. H2 for outdoor use.
CRos EHyd EKin LCro LOPS LRHS NRHS NRob

13 H1c **'Elegance'**
Strong plants producing high yield of large fruits. Trusses of 8–10 flavoursome fruits.
LRHS

97 H1c **'Golden Sunrise'**
Later-maturing; small yellow fruits.
EKin LCro LOPS LRHS MBros MCtn NRHS NRob SVic

93 H1c **'Outdoor Girl'**
Early. Indeterminate, round red fruits with good flavour.
CRos EHyd LCro LOPS LRHS MCtn NRHS NRob SVic

93 H1c **'Shirley'**
F_1 hybrid; fairly early. Uniform trusses; nice round red fruit of medium size and average flavour. Reconfirmed after trial 1997.
CRos EHyd EKin LRHS MBros NRHS NRob SVic

93 H1c **'Tigerella'**
Interesting attractive striped fruit with quite good flavour; reconfirmed after trial 1997. H2 for outdoor use.
CHby EKin MCtn NRob SVic

97 H1c **'Vanessa'**
F_1 hybrid. High yield of greenback-free, succulent fruits with very nice flavour.
NRob

93 H1c **'Yellow Perfection'**
Indeterminate, uniform, round, pale, yellow fruit. H2 for outdoor use.
EKin

BEEFSTEAK

14 H1c **'Beefmaster'**
Multilocular; large fruit; deeply ribbed; light, smooth taste, good yield.
EKin

03 H1c **'Costoluto Fiorentino'**
High yield; medium-sized, attractive bright red, highly ribbed, succulent fruit with good flavour.
LCro LOPS MCtn

14 H1c **'Gigantomo'**
Irregular-shaped heavy fruit; light but pleasant flavour; good yield.
EKin NRob

03 H1c **'Marmande'**
High yield; large, bright red, attractive fruits, with solid flesh and good flavour.
CHby EKin MCtn

14 H1c **'Supersteak'**
Multilocular; smooth skin; good-sized fruit; nice taste, good yield.
CRos EHyd LRHS NRHS

14 H1c **'Tomande'**
Multilocular; smooth skin; good-sized fruit; light taste, good yield.
LCro LOPS

CHERRY

07 H1c **'Apero'**
Good yield of oval fruits on compact trusses; good flavour.
MCtn

07 H1c **'Cherrola'**
high yield, with attractive fruit well spaced on long trusses. Good flavour; not too fleshy inside. Reconfirmed after trial 2017.
LCro LOPS

98 H1c **'Sun Baby'**
Good trusses of uniform, attractive, yellow fruits. H2 for outdoor use.
MCtn

07 H1c **'Sungold'**
Good yield of attractive round golden-orange fruits. Good flavour.
CHby CRos EHyd EKin LCro LOPS LRHS MCtn NRHS NRob SVic

98 H1c **'Sweet Million'**
F_1 hybrid. Long open trusses of sweet, round, bright red fruits; good yield. Reconfirmed after trial 2017.
CRos EHyd LRHS MBros MCtn NRHS NRob

PLUM

04 H1c **'Ildi'**
Vigorous, indeterminate plants; heavy crop of small, attractive, yellow, plum-shaped fruit.
EKin LCro LOPS

04 H1c **'Sweet Olive'**
F_1 hybrid; very early. Very high yield from vigorous, healthy, determinate plants. Small, red, round to plum-shaped fruits, a little difficult to pick, but of good flavour.
MCtn

TURNIP (*Brassica rapa* Rapifera Group)

04 H3 **'Oasis'**
Good early crop of conical white roots.
MCtn

04 H3 **'Primera'**
Uniform crop of flat-shaped roots with purple top and attractive smooth skin. Good internal flesh.
EHyd LRHS NRHS

93 H3 **'Tokyo Cross'**
F_1 hybrid; early. Uniform, medium size, smooth, round, pure white, shiny roots; reconfirmed after trial 1997 and 2004.
LCro LOPS

V
PERFECT FOR POLLINATORS

RHS Perfect for Pollinators

The plants listed below have been selected to help gardeners identify those plants that will provide nectar and pollen for bees and the many other types of pollinating insects.

Key to codes: **T** tree **S** shrub **C** climber **B** bulb / corm **A** annual **Bi** biennial **H** herbaceous perennial † denotes an archaeophyte (a naturalised plant introduced before 1500)

Wildflowers

Short Grass (up to 15cm)

Ajuga reptans bugle H
Bellis perennis daisy H
Campanula rotundifolia common harebell H
Hippocrepis comosa horseshoe vetch H
Lotus corniculatus bird's foot trefoil H
Potentilla anserina silverweed H
Potentilla erecta tormentil H
Potentilla reptans creeping cinquefoil H
Primula veris common cowslip H
Prunella vulgaris selfheal H
Ranunculus repens creeping buttercup H
Sanguisorba minor salad burnet H
Taraxacum officinale dandelion H
Thymus polytrichus wild thyme H
Thymus pulegioides large thyme H
Trifolium pratense red clover H
Trifolium repens white clover H
Veronica chamaedrys germander speedwell H

Hedges, Shrub Borders and Woodland Edges

Acer campestre field maple S or T
Alliaria petiolata garlic mustard Bi
Allium ursinum ramsons B
Aquilegia vulgaris columbine H
Ballota nigra black horehound H
Berberis vulgaris barberry † S
Bryonia dioica white bryony H/C
Buxus sempervirens common box S
Campanula trachelium nettle-leaved bellflower H
Clematis vitalba old man's beard, traveller's joy C
Clinopodium vulgare wild basil H
Cornus sanguinea common dogwood S
Crataegus monogyna common hawthorn S or T
Cytisus scoparius common broom S
Digitalis purpurea common foxglove Bi
Euonymus europaeus spindle S
Ficaria verna subsp. *verna* lesser celandine H
Fragaria vesca wild strawberry H
Frangula alnus alder buckthorn S
Galium mollugo hedge bedstraw H
Galium odoratum sweet woodruff H
Galium verum lady's bedstraw H
Geranium robertianum herb robert A/Bi
Geum urbanum wood avens H
Hedera helix common ivy C
Helleborus foetidus stinking hellebore H
Hyacinthoides non-scripta bluebell B
Hylotelephium telephium orpine H
Ilex aquifolium common holly T
Lamium album white deadnettle H
Lamium galeobdolon yellow archangel H
Ligustrum vulgare wild privet S
Lonicera periclymenum common honeysuckle C
Malus sylvestris crab apple T
Malva sylvestris common mallow H
Myosotis sylvatica wood forget-me-not H
Primula vulgaris primrose H
Prunus avium wild cherry, gean T
Prunus padus bird cherry T
Prunus spinosa blackthorn, sloe S
Rhamnus cathartica purging buckthorn S
Rosa species rose S
Rubus fruticosus blackberry S
Salix caprea goat willow (male forms best) S
Salix cinerea subsp. *oleifolia* grey willow (male forms best) S
Sanicula europaea sanicle H
Silene dioica red campion H
Silene latifolia subsp. *alba* white campion H
Smyrnium olusatrum alexanders † Bi
Sorbus aria common whitebeam T
Sorbus aucuparia rowan, mountain ash T

Sorbus torminalis wild service tree T
Stachys officinalis betony H
Stellaria holostea greater stitchwort H
Symphytum officinale common comfrey H
Teucrium scorodonia wood sage H
Tilia cordata small-leaved lime T
Viburnum lantana common wayfaring tree S
Viburnum opulus guelder rose S
Vicia cracca common tufted vetch H
Vicia sativa common vetch H

Disturbed Ground

Agrostemma githago corncockle † A
Anchusa arvensis bugloss † A
Anthemis arvensis corn chamomile † A
Anthemis cotula stinking chamomile † A
Centaurea cyanus cornflower † A
Cichorium intybus chicory † H
Dipsacus fullonum common teasel Bi
Echium vulgare viper's bugloss Bi
Glebionis segetum corn marigold † A
Iberis amara wild candytuft A
Lamium amplexicaule henbit deadnettle † A
Matricaria recutita scented mayweed † A
Mentha arvensis corn mint H
Myosotis arvensis field forget-me-not † A/H
Onopordum acanthium cotton thistle † Bi
Papaver dubium long-headed poppy † A
Papaver rhoeas common poppy † A
Sinapis arvensis charlock † A
Sonchus arvensis perennial sowthistle H
Tussilago farfara coltsfoot H
Verbascum thapsus great mullein Bi

Flower Beds

Calluna vulgaris heather, ling excl. bud-blooming cultivars S
Erica ciliaris Dorset heath S
Erica cinerea bell heather S
Erica tetralix cross-leaved heath S

Long Grass (above 50cm)

Arctium minus lesser burdock Bi
Carduus crispus welted thistle Bi
Carduus nutans musk thistle Bi
Chamaenerion angustifolium rosebay willowherb H
Cirsium arvense creeping thistle H
Cirsium vulgare spear thistle Bi
Conopodium majus pignut H
Cynoglossum officinale hound's tongue H
Daucus carota wild carrot Bi
Geranium pratense meadow cranesbill H
Heracleum sphondylium hogweed Bi
Hypericum perforatum perforate St John's wort H
Knautia arvensis field scabious H
Lathyrus pratensis meadow vetchling H
Pastinaca sativa wild parsnip Bi
Succisa pratensis devil's bit scabious H
Tanacetum vulgare tansy † H
Thalictrum flavum meadow rue H
Tragopogon pratensis goat's beard Bi
Verbascum nigrum dark mullein Bi/H

Medium Height Grass (up to 50cm)

Achillea millefolium common yarrow H
Achillea ptarmica sneezewort H
Agrimonia eupatoria agrimony H
Anthyllis vulneraria kidney vetch H
Armeria maritima thrift, sea pink H
Blackstonia perfoliata yellowwort A
Campanula glomerata clustered bellflower H
Centaurea nigra common knapweed, hardheads H
Centaurea scabiosa greater knapweed H
Centaurium erythraea common centaury Bi
Echium vulgare viper's bugloss Bi
Erigeron acris blue fleabane A/H
Filipendula vulgaris dropwort H
Helianthemum nummularium common rockrose H
Hypochaeris radicata cat's ear H
Inula conyzae ploughman's spikenard H
Leontodon hispidus rough hawkbit H
Leucanthemum vulgare ox-eye daisy H
Linaria vulgaris common toadflax H
Malva moschata musk mallow H
Ononis repens common restharrow H
Origanum vulgare wild marjoram H
Pilosella officinarum mouse-ear hawkweed H
Ranunculus acris meadow buttercup H
Ranunculus bulbosus bulbous buttercup H
Reseda lutea wild mignonette Bi/H
Rhinanthus minor yellow rattle A
Scabiosa columbaria small scabious H
Scorzoneroides autumnalis autumn hawkbit H
Silene vulgaris bladder campion H
Solidago virgaurea goldenrod H

Ponds, Pond Margins & Wet Soils

Alisma plantago-aquatica water plantain H
Angelica sylvestris wild angelica Bi
Butomus umbellatus flowering rush H
Caltha palustris marsh marigold H
Cardamine pratensis cuckoo flower, lady's smock H
Cirsium dissectum meadow thistle H
Epilobium hirsutum great willowherb H
Eupatorium cannabinum hemp agrimony H
Filipendula ulmaria meadowsweet H
Galium palustre marsh bedstraw H
Geum rivale water avens H
Hypericum tetrapterum square-stalked St John's wort H

Iris pseudacorus yellow iris H
Lotus pedunculatus greater bird's-foot trefoil H
Lychnis flos-cuculi ragged robin H
Lycopus europaeus gypsywort H
Lysimachia nummularia creeping Jenny H
Lysimachia vulgaris yellow loosestrife H
Lythrum salicaria purple loosestrife H
Mentha aquatica water mint H
Menyanthes trifoliata bogbean H
Myosotis scorpioides water forget-me-not H
Nasturtium officinale common watercress H
Nuphar lutea yellow waterlily H
Nymphaea alba white waterlily H
Oenanthe aquatica fine-leaved water dropwort A/Bi
Oenanthe crocata hemlock water dropwort H
Persicaria amphibia amphibious bistort H
Persicaria bistorta common bistort H
Polemonium caeruleum Jacob's ladder H
Pulicaria dysenterica common fleabane H
Ranunculus aquatilis common water crowfoot A/H
Ranunculus flammula lesser spearwort H
Ranunculus fluitans river water crowfoot H
Ranunculus lingua greater spearwort H
Ranunculus sceleratus celery-leaved buttercup A
Sagittaria sagittifolia arrowhead H
Sanguisorba officinalis great burnet H
Scrophularia auriculata water figwort H
Scutellaria galericulata common skullcap H
Stachys palustris marsh woundwort H
Valeriana officinalis common valerian H
Veronica beccabunga brooklime H

Shingle – Gravel Garden

Cakile maritima sea rocket A
Crambe maritima sea kale H
Crithmum maritimum rock samphire H
Eryngium maritimum sea holly H
Glaucium flavum yellow horned poppy Bi/H
Sedum acre biting stonecrop H
Sedum album white stonecrop † H
Silene uniflora sea campion H

Garden Plants

Winter (nov – feb)

Clematis cirrhosa Spanish traveller's joy C
Crocus species crocus (winter-flowering) B
Eranthis hyemalis winter aconite B
× *Fatshedera lizei* tree ivy S
Galanthus nivalis common snowdrop B
Helleborus species and hybrids hellebore (winter-flowering) H
Lonicera × *purpusii* Purpus honeysuckle S
Mahonia species Oregon grape S
Salix aegyptiaca musk willow S
Sarcococca confusa sweet box S
Sarcococca hookeriana sweet box S
Viburnum tinus laurustinus S

Spring (mar – may)

Acer campestre Native plant; field maple S or T
Acer platanoides Norway maple T
Acer pseudoplatanus sycamore T
Acer saccharum sugar maple T
Aesculus hippocastanum horse chestnut T
Ajuga reptans Native plant; bugle H
Arabis alpina subsp. *caucasica* alpine rock cress H
Armeria juniperifolia juniper-leaved thrift H
Aubrieta species aubretia H
Aurinia saxatilis gold dust H
Berberis darwinii Darwin's barberry S
Berberis thunbergii Japanese barberry S
Bergenia species elephant ear H
Buxus sempervirens Native plant; common box S
Caltha palustris Native plant; marsh marigold H
Ceanothus species California lilac S
Cercis siliquastrum Judas tree T
Chaenomeles species Japanese quince S
Cornus mas Cornelian cherry S
Cotoneaster conspicuus Tibetan cotoneaster S
Crataegus monogyna Native plant; common hawthorn S or T
Crocus species crocus (spring-flowering) B
Doronicum × *excelsum* leopard's bane H
Enkianthus campanulatus redvein enkianthus S
Erica carnea alpine heath S
Erica × *darleyensis* Darley Dale heath S
Erysimum species wallflower Bi or H
Euphorbia amygdaloides Native plant; wood spurge H
Euphorbia characias Mediterranean spurge H
Euphorbia cyparissias cypress spurge H
Euphorbia epithymoides cushion spurge H
Euphorbia × *martini* Martin's spurge S
Euphorbia nicaeensis Nice spurge H
Geranium species cranesbill H
Geum rivale Native plant; water avens H
Hebe species hebe S
Helleborus species & hybrids hellebore (spring-flowering) H
Iberis saxatilis alpine candytuft H
Iberis sempervirens perennial candytuft H
Ilex aquifolium Native plant; common holly T
Lamium maculatum spotted dead nettle H
Lunaria annua honesty Bi
Mahonia species Oregon grape (spring-flowering) S
Malus baccata Siberian crab T
Malus domestica edible apple T

Malus floribunda Japanese crab T
Malus hupehensis Hupeh crab T
Malus sargentii Sargent's crab apple T
Mespilus germanica common medlar T
Muscari armeniacum Armenian grape hyacinth B
Nectaroscordum species honey garlic B
Ornithogalum umbellatum common star of Bethlehem B
Pieris formosa lily-of-the-valley bush S
Pieris japonica lily-of-the-valley bush S
Primula veris Native plant; common cowslip H
Primula vulgaris Native plant; primrose H
Prunus avium Native plant; wild & edible cherries T
Prunus domestica wild & edible plums T
Prunus dulcis almond T
Prunus incisa 'Kojo-no-mai' cherry 'Kojo-no-mai' S
Prunus insititia damson T
Prunus laurocerasus cherry laurel S
Prunus mume Japanese apricot T
Prunus padus Native plant; bird cherry T
Prunus pendula f. *ascendens* 'Rosea' flowering cherry T
Prunus persica peach T
Prunus spinosa Native plant; blackthorn S
Prunus tenella dwarf Russian almond S
Prunus × *yedoensis* flowering cherry T
Pulmonaria species lungwort H
Pyrus communis pear T
Ribes nigrum blackcurrant S
Ribes rubrum Native plant; common redcurrant S
Ribes sanguineum flowering currant S
Salix caprea Native plant; goat willow (male form only) S or T
Salix hastata 'Wehrhahnii' halberd willow 'Wehrhahnii' S
Salix lanata Native plant; woolly willow (male form only) S
Skimmia japonica skimmia S
Smyrnium olusatrum Native plant; alexanders † Bi
Stachyurus chinensis stachyurus S
Stachyurus praecox stachyurus S
Vaccinium corymbosum blueberry S

Summer (June – Aug)

Achillea species yarrow H
Actaea japonica baneberry H
Aesculus indica Indian horse chestnut (resistant to leaf-mining moth) T
Aesculus parviflora bottlebrush buckeye S
Agastache species giant hyssop H
Ageratum houstonianum flossflower A
Alcea rosea hollyhock Bi
Allium species ornamental and edibles (when allowed to flower) B
Alstroemeria species Peruvian lily H
Amberboa moschata sweet sultan A
Amsonia tabernaemontana eastern bluestar H
Anchusa azurea large blue alkanet A
Anchusa capensis Cape alkanet A
Angelica archangelica angelica Bi
Angelica gigas purple angelica Bi
Angelica sylvestris Native plant; wild angelica Bi
Anthemis tinctoria dyer's chamomile H
Antirrhinum majus snapdragon A or H
Aquilegia species columbine H
Arabis allionii Siberian wallflower H
Argemone platyceras crested poppy A or H
Armeria maritima Native plant; thrift H
Aruncus dioicus goat's beard (male form only) H
Asparagus officinalis common asparagus H
Astrantia major greater masterwort H
Borago officinalis borage A
Brachyglottis (Dunedin Group) 'Sunshine' brachyglottis 'Sunshine' S
Brachyglottis monroi Monro's ragwort S
Buddleja davidii butterfly bush S
Buddleja globosa orange ball tree S
Buphthalmum salicifolium yellow ox-eye H
Bupleurum fruticosum shrubby hare's ear S
Calamintha nepeta Native plant; lesser calamint H
Calendula officinalis common marigold A
Callicarpa bodinieri var. *giraldii* beautyberry S
Callistephus chinensis China aster A
Calluna vulgaris Native plant; heather S
Campanula carpatica tussock bellflower H
Campanula glomerata Native plant; clustered bellflower H
Campanula lactiflora milky bellflower H
Campanula latifolia Native plant; giant bellflower H
Campanula medium Canterbury bells Bi
Campanula persicifolia peach-leaved bellflower H
Campsis radicans trumpet honeysuckle C
Caryopteris × *clandonensis* caryopteris S
Catalpa bignonioides Indian bean tree T
Catananche caerulea blue cupidone H
Centaurea atropurpurea purple knapweed H
Centaurea cyanus cornflower † A
Centaurea dealbata mealy centaury H
Centaurea macrocephala giant knapweed H
Centaurea montana perennial cornflower H
Centaurea nigra Native plant; common knapweed H
Centaurea scabiosa Native plant; greater knapweed H
Centranthus ruber red valerian H
Centratherum punctatum Manaos beauty A
Cerinthe major 'Purpurascens' honeywort 'Purpurascens' A
Cirsium rivulare 'Atropurpureum' purple plume thistle H
Clarkia unguiculata butterfly flower A
Clematis vitalba Native plant; old man's beard, traveller's joy C
Cleome hassleriana spider flower A
Consolida ajacis giant larkspur A
Convolvulus tricolor dwarf morning glory C/A
Coreopsis species tickseed H or A

Cornus alba red-barked dogwood S
Cosmos bipinnatus cosmea A
Cosmos sulphureus yellow cosmos A
Crambe cordifolia greater sea kale H
Crataegus monogyna Native plant; common hawthorn S or T
Cucurbita pepo marrow, courgette A
Cuphea ignea cigar flower A
Cynara cardunculus including Scolymus Group globe artichoke and cardoon H
Cynoglossum amabile Chinese forget-me-not H
Dahlia species dahlia H
Delosperma floribundum ice plant H
Delphinium elatum candle larkspur H
Dianthus barbatus sweet william Bi
Dictamnus albus dittany H
Digitalis species foxglove Bi
Dipsacus fullonum Native plant; common teasel Bi
Echinacea purpurea purple coneflower H
Echinops species globe thistle H
Echium vulgare Native plant; viper's bugloss A
Elaeagnus angustifolia oleaster S
Erica cinerea Native plant; bell heather S
Erica erigena Irish heath S
Erica vagans Native plant; Cornish heath S
Erigeron species fleabane H
Eriophyllum lanatum golden yarrow H
Eryngium alpinum alpine eryngo H
Eryngium giganteum Miss Willmott's ghost Bi
Eryngium planum blue eryngo H
Eryngium × *tripartitum* eryngo H
Erysimum species wallflower H or S
Escallonia species escallonia S
Eschscholzia californica California poppy A
Eupatorium cannabinum Native plant; hemp agrimony H
Eupatorium maculatum Joe Pye weed H
Euphorbia cornigera horned spurge H
Euphorbia donii euphorbia H
Euphorbia sarawschanica Zeravshan spurge H
Ferula communis giant fennel H
Foeniculum vulgare common fennel † H
Fragaria × *ananassa* garden strawberry H
Fuchsia species fuchsia – hardy types S
Gaillardia × *grandiflora* blanket flower H
Gaura lindheimeri white gaura H
Geranium pratense Native plant; meadow cranesbill H
Geranium species cranesbill (summer-flowering) H
Geum species avens (summer-flowering) H
Gilia capitata blue thimble flower A
Glebionis segetum corn marigold † A
Gypsophila elegans annual baby's breath A
Hebe species hebe S
Helenium species Helen's flower H
Helianthus annuus common sunflower excl. pollen-free cultivars A
Helianthus debilis cucumberleaf sunflower A
Heliopsis helianthoides smooth ox-eye H
Heliotropium arborescens common heliotrope A
Heracleum sphondylium Native plant; hogweed Bi
Hesperis matronalis dame's violet H
Hydrangea anomala subsp. *petiolaris* climbing hydrangea C
Hydrangea paniculata paniculate hydrangea (cultivars with many fertile flowers e.g. 'Kyushu', 'Big Ben', 'Floribunda', 'Brussels Lace') S
Hylotelephium spectabile & hybrids ice plant H
Hylotelephium telephium Native plant; orpine H
Hyssopus officinalis hyssop S
Iberis amara Native plant; wild candytuft A
Ilex aquifolium Native plant; common holly T
Inula species harvest daisy H
Jasminum officinale common jasmine C
Kalmia latifolia mountain laurel S
Knautia arvensis Native plant; field scabious H
Knautia macedonica Macedonian scabious H
Koelreuteria paniculata pride of India T
Lathyrus latifolius broad-leaved everlasting pea H
Laurus nobilis bay tree S
Lavandula angustifolia English lavender S
Lavandula × *intermedia* lavandin S
Lavandula stoechas French lavender S
Lavatera olbia tree lavatera S
Lavatera trimestris annual lavatera A
Leucanthemum × *superbum* Shasta daisy H
Leucanthemum vulgare Native plant; ox-eye daisy H
Liatris spicata button snakewort H
Ligustrum ovalifolium garden privet S
Ligustrum sinense Chinese privet S
Limnanthes douglasii poached egg flower A
Limonium platyphyllum broad-leaved statice H
Linaria maroccana annual toadflax A
Linaria purpurea purple toadflax H
Lobularia maritima sweet alyssum A
Lonicera periclymenum Native plant; common honeysuckle C
Lychnis coronaria rose campion Bi or H
Lychnis flos-cuculi Native plant; ragged robin H
Lysimachia vulgaris Native plant; yellow loosestrife H
Lythrum salicaria Native plant; purple loosestrife H
Lythrum virgatum wand loosestrife H
Malope trifida large-flowered mallow wort A
Malva moschata Native plant; musk mallow H
Matthiola incana hoary stock Bi
Mentha aquatica Native plant; water mint H
Mentha spicata spearmint H
Monarda didyma bergamot H
Myosotis species forget-me-not Bi
Nemophila menziesii baby blue eyes A
Nepeta species catmint H
Nicotiana alata flowering tobacco A
Nicotiana langsdorffii Langsdorff's tobacco A
Nicotiana sylvestris flowering tobacco Bi
Nigella damascena love-in-a-mist A

Nigella hispanica Spanish fennel flower A
Oenothera species evening primrose Bi
Olearia species daisy bush S
Onopordum acanthium cotton thistle Bi
Origanum 'Rosenkuppel' marjoram 'Rosenkuppel' H
Origanum vulgare Native plant; oregano, wild marjoram H
Paeonia species peony H
Papaver orientale oriental poppy H
Papaver rhoeas Native plant; common poppy † A
Parthenocissus tricuspidata Boston ivy C
Penstemon species beard-tongue T
Perovskia atriplicifolia Russian sage S
Persicaria amplexicaulis red bistort H
Persicaria bistorta Native plant; common bistort H
Phacelia campanularia Californian bluebell A
Phacelia tanacetifolia fiddleneck A
Phaseolus coccineus scarlet runner bean A
Phlomis species sage S
Phlox paniculata perennial phlox H
Photinia davidiana stranvaesia S
Phuopsis stylosa Caucasian crosswort H
Pileostegia viburnoides climbing hydrangea C
Polemonium caeruleum Native plant; Jacob's ladder H
Potentilla species cinquefoil H or S
Prostanthera cuneata alpine mint bush S
Ptelea trifoliata hop tree S
Pyracantha species firethorn S
Reseda odorata garden mignonette A
Ridolfia segetum false fennel A
Robinia pseudoacacia false acacia T
Rosa species rose S
Rosmarinus officinalis rosemary S
Rubus fruticosus agg. Native plant; blackberry S
Rubus idaeus Native plant; common raspberry S
Rudbeckia species coneflower H or A
Salvia species sage A or H
Sanvitalia procumbens creeping zinnia A
Scabiosa atropurpurea sweet scabious A
Scabiosa caucasica garden scabious H
Scabiosa columbaria Native plant; small scabious H
Sidalcea malviflora checkerbloom H
Solidago species goldenrod H
Sorbus aria Native plant; common whitebeam T
Sorbus aucuparia Native plant; mountain ash, rowan T
Spiraea japonica Japanese spiraea S
Stachys byzantina lamb's ear H
Stachys macrantha big sage H
Stokesia laevis Stokes' aster H
Symphoricarpos albus snowberry S
Tagetes patula French marigold A
Tamarix ramosissima tamarisk S
Tanacetum coccineum pyrethrum H
Tanacetum vulgare Native plant; tansy † H
Telekia speciosa yellow ox-eye H
Tetradium daniellii bee-bee tree T
Teucrium chamaedrys Native plant; wall germander H
Thymus species thyme S
Tilia × *europaea* common lime T
Tilia maximowicziana lime T
Tilia oliveri lime T
Tilia platyphyllos Native plant; broad-leaved lime T
Tithonia rotundifolia Mexican sunflower A
Trachymene coerulea blue lace flower A
Trollius species globeflower H
Tropaeolum majus garden nasturtium A
Verbascum species mullein Bi
Verbena bonariensis purple top H
Verbena rigida slender vervain A
Veronica longifolia garden speedwell H
Veronica spicata Native plant; spiked speedwell H
Veronicastrum virginicum Culver's root H
Viburnum lantana Native plant; common wayfaring tree S
Viburnum opulus Native plant; guelder rose S
Vicia faba broad bean A
Weigela florida weigelia S
Zauschneria californica Californian fuchsia S
Zinnia elegans youth and old age A

Autumn (sept – oct)

Aconitum carmichaelii Carmichael's monk's hood H
Actaea simplex simple-stemmed bugbane H
Anemone hupehensis Chinese anemone H
Anemone × *hybrida* Japanese anemone H
Arbutus unedo strawberry tree S or T
Campanula poscharskyana trailing bellflower H
Ceratostigma plumbaginoides hardy blue-flowered leadwort H
Chrysanthemum species & hybrids chrysanthemum H
Clematis heracleifolia tube clematis C
Colchicum species autumn crocus B
Crocus species crocus (autumn-flowering types) B
Dahlia species & hybrids dahlia H
Elaeagnus pungens silverthorn S
Elaeagnus × *submacrophylla* Ebbinge's silverberry S
Fatsia japonica Japanese aralia S
Hedera colchica Persian ivy C
Hedera helix Native plant; common ivy C
Helianthus × *laetiflorus* perennial sunflower H
Leucanthemella serotina autumn ox-eye H
Machaeranthera tanacetifolia tansy-leaf aster A
Salvia species sage (autumn-flowering types) H
Symphyotrichum species and hybrids Michaelmas daisy H
Tilia henryana Henry's lime (one of the last to flower) T

VI
NURSERIES

Nursery Codes and Symbols

The first letter of each nursery code represents the area of the country in which the nursery is situated.

Geographical Codes

South West	C
Eastern	E
Scotland	G
Northern Ireland & the Republic of Ireland	I
London Area	L
Midlands	M
Northern	N
Southern	S
Wales & the West	W
Abroad	X

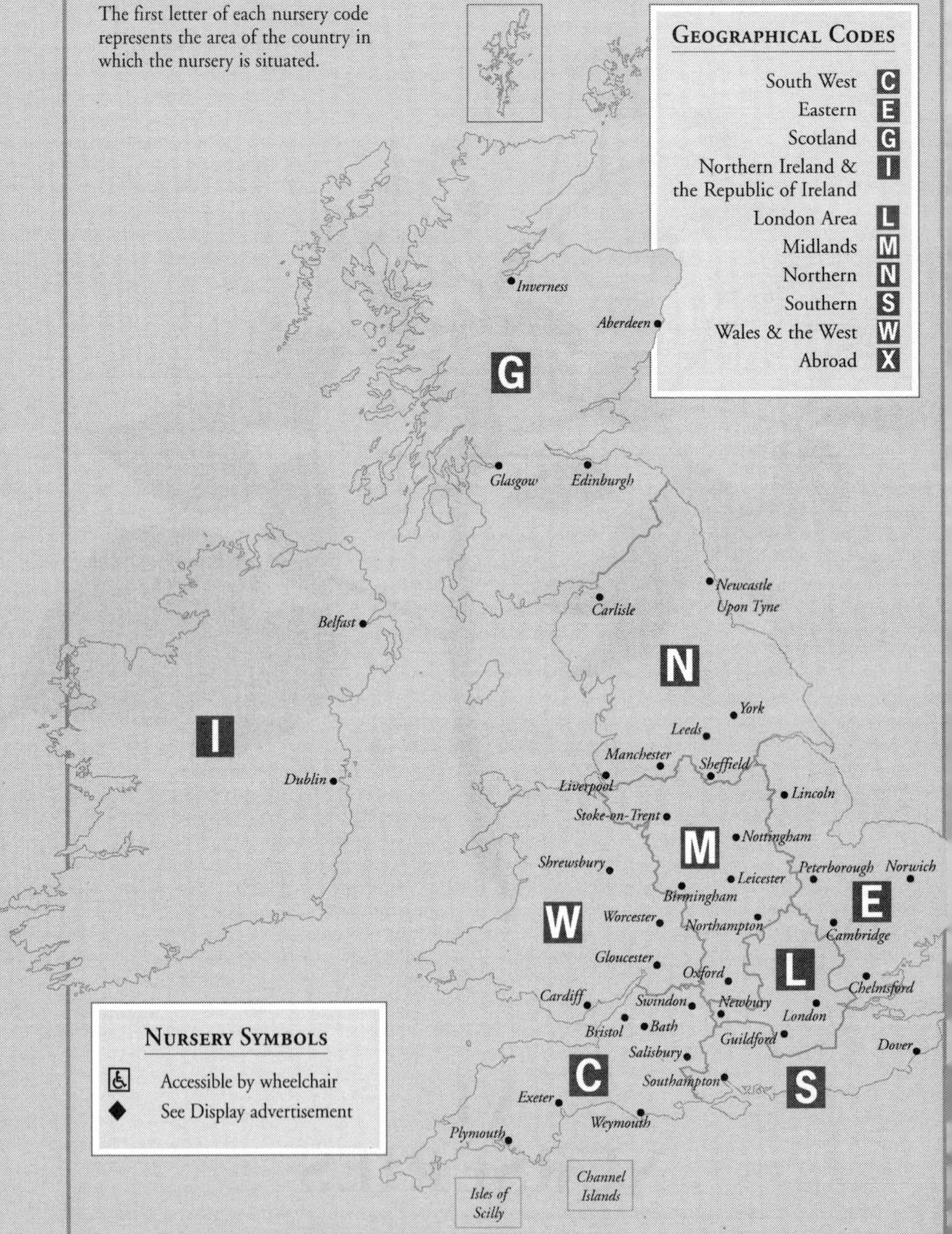

Nursery Symbols

♿ Accessible by wheelchair

◆ See Display advertisement

USING THE NURSERY LISTINGS

Your main reference from the Plant Directory is the Nursery Details by Code listing, which includes all relevant information for each nursery in order of nursery code. The Nursery Index by Name is an alphabetical list for those who know a nursery's name but not its code and wish to check its details in the main list.

1 NURSERY DETAILS BY CODE

Once you have found your plant in the Plant Directory, turn to this list to find out the name, address, opening times and other details of the nurseries whose codes accompany the plant.

KEY
♿ Accessible by wheelchair ◆ See Display advertisement

A geographical code is followed by three or four letters reflecting the nursery's name

ESwi **SWINES MEADOW FARM NURSERY** ♿ ◆
47 Towngate East, Market Deeping,
Peterborough, PE6 8LQ
Ⓣ (01778) 343340
Ⓜ 07432 627766
Ⓔ ceveandsons@btconnect.com
Ⓦ www.swinesmeadowfarmnursery.co.uk
Contact: Colin Ward
Opening Times: 0900-1600 Mon-Sat, 1000-1600 Sun. Closed Jan, except by appt. only.
Min Mail Order UK: £10.00
Min Mail Order EU: £10.00
Credit Cards: All major debit/credit cards except American Express
Specialities: Hardy exotics, tree ferns, bamboos & *Hosta*. Wollemi pine stockist. Many specialities available in small quantities only.
Notes: Delivers to shows. Wheelchair accessible.
OS Grid Ref: TF150113

A brief summary of the plants available

Other information about the nursery

The Ordnance Survey national grid reference for use with OS maps

2 NURSERY INDEX BY NAME

If you are looking for a particular nursery, use this alphabetical index to find it, note its code and then turn to the Nursery Details by Code listing for full information.

Sussex Fruit Trees	SSFT
Dan Sutton	SSut
Swallows Nursery	MSwo
Swines Meadow Farm Nursery	ESwi
Table Bay View Nursery	XBlo
Tan-y-Llyn Nurseries	WTan
Thistlefield Plants and Design	EThi
Thorncroft Clematis Ltd	**ETho**

How to Use the Nursery Listings

The details given for each nursery have been compiled from information supplied to us in answer to a questionnaire. In some case, because of space constraints, the entries have been abbreviated.

Nurseries are not charged for their entries and inclusion in no way implies a value judgement.

Nursery Details by Code (p.868)

Each nursery is allocated a code, for example GPoy. The first letter of each code indicates the region of the British Isles in which the nursery is situated. In this example G = Scotland. The remaining three or four letters reflect the nursery's name, in this case Poyntzfield Herb Nursery.

In this listing, nurseries are given in alphabetical order of code for quick referral from the Plant Directory. All of the nurseries' details, such as addresses, opening times, etc will be found in this index.

Opening Times

These are published as submitted. It is always advisable, especially if travelling a long distance, to double-check with the nursery before setting out.

Mail Order

Many nurseries offer a mail order service. This is often restricted to certain times of the year or to particular genera. Please check the **Notes** section of the nursery entry for restrictions or special conditions.

In some instances the mail order service extends throughout the European Union. Where this is the case, the minimum charge to the EU will be noted. If this is "Nmc" ("no minimum charge") please note that to send even one plant may involve the nursery in substantial postage and packaging costs. Some nurseries may not be prepared to send tender or bulky plants.

Where a nursery offers a mail order only service, this will be noted under **Opening Times** in the nursery entry. Many nurseries offer a mail order online service with some only operating in this way.

Export

This refers to mail order beyond the EU and indicates nurseries that are prepared to consider this. There is usually a substantial minimum charge and, in addition, all the costs of phytosanitary certificates and Customs have to be met by the purchaser.

Catalogue Cost

Only a small number of nurseries now offer a printed catalogue. Some may not charge or may ask for stamps to bear the cost of postage. If plant lists are available in an electronic format, some nurseries have indicated that they will email them to enquirers.

The majority of nurseries now publish their catalogues only on the internet as this is more cost-effective than producing a printed copy and enables them to reflect stock changes throughout the year.

Specialities

This is where nurseries list the plants or genera in which they specialise and any National Collections that they hold. Please note that some nurseries may charge an entry fee to visit a National Collection. Charges may also be levied to visit any garden to which the nursery is attached.

Nurseries also indicate here if they only have small quantities of individual plants available for sale or if they will propagate to order.

Notes

This section contains: information on restrictions to mail order or export; whether payment in euros is accepted; whether nurseries deliver to shows; details of partial wheelchair access; the nursery site address if this differs from the office address; and any other non-horticultural or general information.

Wheelchair Access ♿

Nurseries are asked to indicate if their premises are suitable for wheelchair users.

We use the wheelchair symbol for those nurseries that tell us their site is fully accessible. Where only partial or restricted access is offered, this is stated in the **Notes** section of the nursery's details and the nursery is not marked with the symbol.

Please note that wheelchair access does not necessarily relate to any gardens to which the nursery may be attached.

The assessment of ease of access is entirely the responsibility of the individual nursery.

Delivers to Shows

Many nurseries will deliver pre-ordered plants to flower shows for collection by customers. Contact the nursery for details of shows that they will be attending.

Payment in Euros

A number of UK nurseries will accept payment in euros. You should check with the nursery concerned before making such a payment, as some will only accept cash and some only cheques, whilst others will expect the purchaser to pay bank charges.

OS Grid Ref

Nurseries are also encouraged to provide their Ordnance Survey national grid reference for use with OS Land Ranger Series maps.

Nursery Index by Name

An alphabetical index of nurseries is included (p.950). Nurseries new to the book and those making a re-entry are shown in embolden type.

Deleted Nurseries

Every year some nurseries ask to be removed from the book. This may be a temporary measure because, for example, they are relocating or because their plant stocks are low due to adverse growing conditions, or it may be permanent following closure, sale, retirement or a change in the way they trade.

Some nurseries miss the deadline for submissions and may ask to re-enter the book in the following edition. Other nurseries do not respond at all and, as we have no current information on their trading status, they are not included in the book.

Please, never use an out of date edition

NURSERY DETAILS BY CODE

Please note that all these nurseries are listed in alphabetical order by their code. All nurseries are listed in alphabetical order by their name in the **Nursery Index by Name** on page 950.

SOUTH WEST

CAbb **ABBOTSBURY SUB-TROPICAL GARDENS** ♿
Abbotsbury, Nr Weymouth, Dorset, DT3 4LA
Ⓣ (01305) 871344
Ⓕ (01305) 871344
Ⓔ info@abbotsburygardens.co.uk
Ⓦ www.abbotsbury-tourism.co.uk/gardens/
Contact: David Sutton
Opening Times: 1000-1800 daily, mid Mar-1st Nov. 1000-1500, Nov-mid Mar.
Credit Cards: Access, Visa, MasterCard, Switch
Specialities: Less common & tender shrubs incl. palms, tree ferns, bamboos & plants from Australia, New Zealand & S. Africa.
Notes: Mail order of some plants is possible upon request, please phone/email for details & a quotation. Wheelchair accessible.

CAby **THE ABBEY NURSERY** ♿
Forde Abbey, Chard, Somerset, TA20 4LU
Ⓣ (01460) 220088
Ⓔ theabbeynursery@hotmail.com
Contact: Paul Bygrave
Opening Times: 1000-1700 7 days, 1st Mar-31st Oct.
Cat. Cost: None issued.
Credit Cards: All major credit/debit cards
Specialities: Hardy herbaceous perennials.
Notes: Wheelchair accessible.
OS Grid Ref: ST359052

CAgr **AGROFORESTRY RESEARCH TRUST**
46 Hunters Moon, Dartington, Totnes, Devon, TQ9 6JT
Ⓕ (01803) 840776
Ⓔ mail@agroforestry.co.uk
Ⓦ www.agroforestry.co.uk
Contact: Martin Crawford
Opening Times: Not open. Mail order only.
Min Mail Order UK: Nmc
Min Mail Order EU: Nmc
Cat. Cost: 4 × 1st class.
Credit Cards: All major credit/debit cards
Specialities: Top & soft fruit, nut trees including *Castanea, Corylus, Juglans, Pinus*. Also seeds. Some plants in small quantities only.
Notes: Euro accepted.

CArg **ASHRIDGE NURSERIES**
Grove Cross Barn, Castle Cary, Somerset, BA7 7NJ
Ⓣ (01963) 359444
Ⓕ (01963) 359445
Ⓔ support@ashridgetrees.co.uk
Ⓦ www.ashridgetrees.co.uk
Contact: Rose Hurst
Opening Times: Not open. Mail order only.
Min Mail Order UK: £20.00
Credit Cards: MasterCard, Visa
Specialities: Trees, hedging. Fruit trees & soft fruit. Roses, lavender, climbers & bulbs.

CAvo **AVON BULBS**
Burnt House Farm, Mid-Lambrook, South Petherton, Somerset, TA13 5HE
Ⓣ (01460) 242177 (01460) 249060
Ⓔ info@avonbulbs.co.uk
Ⓦ www.avonbulbs.co.uk
Contact: C. Ireland-Jones
Opening Times: Mail order only.
Min Mail Order UK: Nmc
Min Mail Order EU: Nmc
Cat. Cost: 4 × 2nd class.
Credit Cards: All major credit/debit cards
Specialities: Specialise in named snowdrops, some are only available in small quantities, both 'in the green' in the spring, and as dormant bulbs in the early autumn.
Notes: Can deliver to some shows. Collection of pre-booked orders by arrangement.
OS Grid Ref: ST422187

CBar **Barters Plant Centre & Nursery** ♿
Chapmanslade, Westbury, Wiltshire, BA13 4AL
Ⓣ (01373) 832694
Ⓕ (01373) 832677
Ⓔ plantcentre@barters.co.uk
Ⓦ www.barters.co.uk
Contact: Andrew Stone
Opening Times: 0900-1700 Mon-Sat, Mar-Oct. 0900-1630 Mon-Sat, Nov-Feb. 1000-1600 Sun (closed Sun Jul-Nov & Jan-Feb).
Cat. Cost: Online only.
Credit Cards: All major debit/credit cards except American Express
Specialities: Wide range of shrubs. Ground cover, container trees, ferns, half-hardy perennials, grasses, herbaceous & climbers. Hedging, fruit trees, roses & bare-root stock.
Notes: Also sells wholesale. Wheelchair accessible.
OS Grid Ref: ST830480

CBcs **Burncoose Nurseries** ♿
Gwennap, Redruth, Cornwall, TR16 6BJ
Ⓣ (01209) 860316
Ⓔ info@burncoose.co.uk
Ⓦ www.burncoose.co.uk
Contact: C.H. Williams
Opening Times: 0830-1700 Mon-Sat & 1100-1600 Sun.
Min Mail Order UK: Nmc
Min Mail Order EU: Individual quotations for EU sales.
Cat. Cost: Free.
Credit Cards: Visa, MasterCard, Maestro
Specialities: Extensive range of over 3500 ornamental trees & shrubs and herbaceous. Rare & unusual *Magnolia*, *Rhododendron*. Conservatory plants. 30 acre garden.
Notes: Also sells wholesale. Delivers to shows. Wheelchair accessible.
OS Grid Ref: SW742395

CBct **Barracott Plants** ♿
Old Orchard, Calstock Road, Gunnislake, Cornwall, PL18 9AA
Ⓣ (01822) 832234
Ⓜ 07811 207186
Ⓔ geoffandthelma@barracott.eclipse.co.uk
Ⓦ www.barracottplants.co.uk
Contact: Geoff & Thelma Turner
Opening Times: 0900-1700 Thu & Fri, Mar-end Sep. Other times by appt.
Min Mail Order UK: £20.00
Credit Cards: PayPal
Specialities: Herbaceous plants: shade-loving, foliage & form. *Acanthus*, *Aspidistra*, *Astrantia*, *Begonia*, *Bergenia*, *Convallaria*, *Disporum*, *Liriope*, *Maianthemum*, *Polygonatum*, *Roscoea*, *Schefflera*, *Trillium* & *Uvularia*.
Notes: Also sells wholesale. Delivers to shows. Euro accepted. Wheelchair accessible.
OS Grid Ref: SX436702

CBdn **Bowden Hostas**
Cleave House, Sticklepath, Okehampton, Devon, EX20 2NL
Ⓣ (01837) 840989
Ⓔ tim@bowdenhostas.com
Ⓦ www.bowdenhostas.com
Contact: Tim Penrose
Opening Times: 1000-1700 Mon-Sat, Apr-Sep. Oct-Mar, please ring before travelling.
Min Mail Order UK: Nmc
Min Mail Order EU: Nmc
Cat. Cost: Free.
Credit Cards: Visa, Access, EuroCard, Switch
Specialities: Hostas, ferns, bamboos, *Agapanthus*. National Plant Collection of modern hybrid hostas.
Notes: Also sells wholesale. Exports beyond EU.
OS Grid Ref: SX640940

CBee **Bee Happy Plants & Seeds**
Lakehayes Nursery, South Chard, Somerset, TA20 2NZ
Ⓣ (01460) 221929
Ⓜ 07976 949893
Ⓔ info@beehappyplants.co.uk
Ⓦ www.beehappyplants.co.uk/
Contact: Sarah Holdsworth
Opening Times: By appt. only.
Min Mail Order UK: Nmc
Min Mail Order EU: £10.00
Cat. Cost: Online only.
Credit Cards: All major credit/debit cards
Specialities: *Leptospermum scoparium*.
Notes: Specialist in wild species plants suitable for bees and other pollinators. Also sells wholesale. Delivers to shows.
OS Grid Ref: ST325550

CBen **Bennetts Water Gardens** ♿
Putton Lane, Chickerell, Weymouth, Dorset, DT3 4AF
Ⓣ (01305) 785150
Ⓔ orders@waterlily.co.uk
Ⓦ www.shop.waterlily.co.uk
Contact: James Bennett
Opening Times: 1000-1600 Apr-Sep, Sun-Fri.
Min Mail Order UK: Nmc
Min Mail Order EU: Nmc

Credit Cards: Visa, MasterCard, Maestro
Specialities: National Plant Collection of *Nymphaea* (hardy water lilies).
Notes: Loose plants available by mail order. Potted plants available in store. Wheelchair accessible.
OS Grid Ref: SY650797

CBgR **Beggar's Roost Plants**
Lilstock, Bridgwater, Somerset, TA5 1SU
Ⓣ (01278) 741519
Ⓔ ro@lilstock.eclipse.co.uk
Contact: Lady Rosemary FitzGerald
Opening Times: Not open. Mail order only.
Min Mail Order UK: £10.00
Min Mail Order EU: £15.00
Cat. Cost: 3 × large 2nd class.
Credit Cards: None
Specialities: *Hemerocallis* (incl. heritage) grown in British conditions.
Notes: Mail order for specialty *Hemerocallis*. Ask for list. Euro accepted.
OS Grid Ref: ST168450

CBod **Bodmin Nursery** ♿
Laveddon Mill, Laninval Hill, Bodmin, Cornwall, PL30 5JU
Ⓣ (01208) 72837
Ⓕ (01208) 76491
Ⓔ bodminnursery@aol.com
Ⓦ www.bodminnursery.co.uk
Contact: Mark Lawlor
Opening Times: 0900-1700 Mon-Sat. 1000-1600 Sun.
Credit Cards: All major credit/debit cards
Specialities: Herbs, herbaceous & grasses, hardy geraniums & coastal plants. Interesting shrubs, fruit & ornamental trees.
Notes: Wheelchair accessible.
OS Grid Ref: SX053659

CBor **Border Alpines**
Chasty Court, Chasty, Holsworthy, Devon, EX22 6NA
Ⓣ (01409) 253654
Ⓜ 07841 021557
Ⓔ borderalpines@btinternet.com
Ⓦ www.borderalpines.co.uk
Contact: Janette Lowe
Opening Times: By appt. only.
Min Mail Order UK: Nmc
Min Mail Order EU: Nmc
Cat. Cost: Online only.
Credit Cards: None
Specialities: Alpines, dwarf herbaceous & specimen acers. A family-run nursery, selling a range of British-grown alpines, dwarf herbaceous and other hardy perennial plants. Experienced growers and breeders for over 30 years.
Notes: Delivers to shows.

CBrac **Brackendale Nurseries** ♿
Horton Road, Three Legged Cross, Wimborne, Dorset, BH21 6SD
Ⓣ (01202) 822349
Ⓔ sales@brackendalenurseries.co.uk
Ⓦ www.brackendalenurseries.co.uk
Contact: Nicola Stainer
Opening Times: 0930-1700 Mon-Sat. 1000-1600 Sun. Opening times are subject to seasonal change, please see our website for current opening hours.
Credit Cards: All major credit/debit cards
Specialities: Wide range of plants, especially shrubs, conifers and hedging. Established specimen-sized shrubs. Native, ornamental and fruit trees available. Acid loving azaleas, camellias & rhododendrons together with coastal favourites.
Notes: Wheelchair accessible.

CBre **Bregover Plants**
Middlewood, North Hill, Nr Launceston, Cornwall, PL15 7NN
Ⓣ (01566) 782661
Ⓔ jenbousfield@gmail.com
Contact: Jennifer Bousfield
Opening Times: 1100-1700 Wed, Mar-mid Oct and by appt.
Min Mail Order UK: Nmc
Cat. Cost: 3 × 1st class. Plant list available as pdf download.
Credit Cards: None
Specialities: Unusual hardy perennials grown in small garden nursery. Available in small quantities only.
Notes: Mail order Oct-Mar only. Delivers to shows. Partial wheelchair access.
OS Grid Ref: SX273752

CBro **Broadleigh Gardens** ♿
Bishops Hull, Taunton, Somerset, TA4 1AE
Ⓣ (01823) 286231
Ⓔ info@broadleighbulbs.co.uk
Ⓦ www.broadleighbulbs.co.uk
Contact: Christine Skelmersdale
Opening Times: 0900-1600 Mon-Fri for viewing only (charity donation). Orders may be collected if notice given.
Min Mail Order UK: Nmc
Min Mail Order EU: Nmc
Cat. Cost: 2 × 1st class.
Credit Cards: All major credit/debit cards
Specialities: Jan catalogue: bulbs in growth (*Galanthus*, *Cyclamen* etc.) & herbaceous

woodland plants (*Trillium*, hellebores etc). Extensive list of *Agapanthus* and other South African bulbs. June catalogue: dwarf & unusual bulbs, *Iris* (DB & PC). National Plant Collection of Alec Grey hybrid daffodils.
Notes: Display garden and nursery open. Euro accepted as cash payment only. Wheelchair accessible.
OS Grid Ref: ST195251

CBrP **Brooklands Plants**
25 Treves Road, Dorchester, Dorset, DT1 2HE
Ⓣ (01305) 265846
Ⓔ cycads@btinternet.com
Ⓦ www.botanicalgardenphotography.com
Contact: Ian Watt
Opening Times: By appt. only for collection of plants.
Min Mail Order UK: £50.00 + p&p
Cat. Cost: Online only.
Credit Cards: None
Specialities: Cycad nursery specialising in the more cold-tolerant species of *Cycas*, *Dioon*, *Encephalartos* & *Macrozamia*. Also specialist in cold-tolerant palms as well as plants from New Zealand. Some species available in small quantities only.
Notes: Mail order available on small plants only. Euro accepted.
OS Grid Ref: SY682897

CBur **Burnham Nurseries**
Forches Cross, Newton Abbot, Devon, TQ12 6PZ
Ⓣ (01626) 352233
Ⓔ mail@orchids.uk.com
Ⓦ www.orchids.uk.com
Contact: Any member of staff
Opening Times: 1000-1600 Mon-Sun.
Min Mail Order UK: Nmc
Min Mail Order EU: £100.00 + p&p
Cat. Cost: 1 × 2nd class or online.
Credit Cards: Visa, MasterCard, Maestro
Specialities: Many types of tropical orchid species and hybrids.
Notes: Exports beyond EU, please ask for details. Delivers to shows. Euro accepted. Partial wheelchair access.
OS Grid Ref: SX841732

CCal **Calamazag Nursery**
St Martins, Looe, Cornwall, PL13 1NX
Ⓜ 07958 167096
Ⓔ calamazagnursery@gmail.com
Ⓦ www.calamazagnursery.co.uk
Contact: Stephen & Benedicte Jenkinson
Opening Times: Not open. Mail order only.
Min Mail Order UK: £5.00
Min Mail Order EU: £15.00
Cat. Cost: Online only.
Credit Cards: All major credit/debit cards
Specialities: Wide range of hardy *Dianthus* including Heritage and Species varieties. Also grow a wide selection of hardy *Sempervivum*. Plants are sold in 10.5cm pots ready to be grown on. (Please note these are NOT plug plants and cannot be planted directly outside).

CCBP **CB Plants**
Lower Severalls Nursery, Crewkerne, Somerset, TA18 7NX
Ⓜ 07851 468430
Ⓔ cbplantsinfo@gmail.com
Ⓦ www.cbplants.co.uk
Contact: Catherine Bond
Opening Times: 1000-1700 Wed-Sat. Early Mar-End Sept.
Min Mail Order UK: £5.00 + p&p
Credit Cards: All major debit/credit cards except American Express
Specialities: Nectar-rich hardy perennials and herbs all grown peat-free. Some varieties available in small quantities only.
Notes: Small nursery situated just off the A30, half a mile east of Crewkerne.

CCCN **Cross Common Nursery**
The Lizard, Helston, Cornwall, TR12 7PD
Ⓣ (01326) 290722/290668
Ⓔ info@crosscommonnursery.co.uk
Ⓦ www.crosscommonnursery.co.uk
Contact: Kevin Bosustow
Opening Times: 1000-1700 7 days, Apr, May & Jun. Reduced hours Mar, Jul, Aug & Sep, please phone for opening times.
Min Mail Order UK: Nmc
Cat. Cost: Online only.
Credit Cards: All major debit/credit cards except American Express
Specialities: The most southerly nursery in England, offering a wide range of unusual plants & shrubs. Tropical/sub-tropical, coastal plants & conservatory plants. Wide range of citrus trees. Some plants available in small quantities only.
OS Grid Ref: SW704116

CChe **Cherry Tree Nursery** ♿
(Sheltered Work Opportunities Project), off New Road Roundabout, Northbourne, Bournemouth, Dorset, BH10 7DA
Ⓣ (01202) 593537
Ⓔ contactus@cherrytreenursery.org.uk
Ⓦ www.cherrytreenursery.org.uk
Contact: Stephen Jailler

C

Opening Times: 0830-1530 Mon-Fri, 0900-1500 Sat, Apr-Sep & 0900-1300 Sat, Oct-Mar. 1000-1500 Sun, Mar-Oct.
Credit Cards: All major debit/credit cards except American Express
Specialities: Hardy shrubs, perennials, climbers, grasses & bamboos.
Notes: A registered charity providing work for adults with severe and enduring mental illness. Also sells wholesale. Wheelchair accessible.
OS Grid Ref: SZ083965

CCht **Chestnut Nursery** ♿
(Sheltered Work Opportunities Project), 75 Kingland Road, Poole, Dorset, BH15 1TN
Ⓣ (01202) 685999
Ⓔ info@chestnutnursery.org.uk
Ⓦ www.chestnutnursery.org.uk
Contact: Andrew Verreck
Opening Times: 0800-1600 Mon-Fri. 1000-1600 Sat (Mar-Nov) & 1000-1500 Sat (Nov-Xmas). 1000-1500 Sun (Mar-Sep).
Credit Cards: All major credit/debit cards
Specialities: Wide selection of herbaceous perennials, evergreen shrubs, ornamental grasses, annual bedding and southern hemisphere exotics.
Notes: A registered charity providing work for adults with severe and enduring mental illness. Wheelchair accessible.
OS Grid Ref: SZ018909

CCoa **Coastal Hedging**
Marsh Lane Nursery, West Charleton, Kingsbridge, Devon, TQ7 2AQ
Ⓣ (01548) 531734
Ⓜ 07775 201 595
Ⓔ info@coastalhedging.co.uk
Ⓦ www.coastalhedging.co.uk
Contact: William Hornby
Opening Times: By appt. only.
Min Mail Order UK: £6.95
Cat. Cost: Online only.
Credit Cards: All major credit/debit cards
Specialities: *Elaeagnus, Griselina, Olearia.*
Notes: Euro accepted.
OS Grid Ref: SX752425

CCtw **Kelnan Plants**
Little Kenegie, Gulval, Penzance, Cornwall, TR20 8YN
Ⓣ (01736) 364311
Ⓜ 07773 586603
Ⓔ sales@kelnanplants.com
Ⓦ www.kelnanplants.com
Contact: Chris Osborne
Opening Times: By appt. only.
Min Mail Order UK: Nmc
Credit Cards: All major credit/debit cards
Specialities: *Restio.*
Notes: Sellers at Truro Farmers Market on Wed & Sat. Delivers to shows.

CCVT **Chew Valley Trees** ♿
Winford Road, Chew Magna, Bristol, BS40 8HJ
Ⓣ (01275) 333752
Ⓔ info@chewvalleytrees.co.uk
Ⓦ www.chewvalleytrees.co.uk
Contact: S. Scarth
Opening Times: 0800-1700 Mon-Fri all year. 0800-1630 Sat. Closed Sun. Closed B/hols & Sats Jul & Aug.
Min Mail Order UK: Nmc
Cat. Cost: Free.
Credit Cards: All major credit/debit cards
Specialities: Native British & ornamental trees, shrubs, fruit trees & hedging.
Notes: Also sells wholesale. Wheelchair accessible.
OS Grid Ref: ST558635

CDoC **Duchy of Cornwall**
Cott Road, Lostwithiel, Cornwall, PL22 0HW
Ⓣ (01208) 872668
Ⓕ (01208) 871809
Ⓔ sales@duchyofcornwallnursery.co.uk
Ⓦ www.duchyofcornwallnursery.co.uk
Contact: Nicky Hill
Opening Times: 0900-1700 Mon-Sat, 1000-1700 Sun.
Cat. Cost: None issued.
Credit Cards: All major credit/debit cards
Specialities: Large range of garden plants including trees, shrubs, roses, perennials, fruit and conservatory plants.
Notes: Nursery partially accessible to wheelchair users.
OS Grid Ref: SX112614

CDor **Dorset Perennials** ♿
Berkeley Perennials, Holnest, Sherborne, Dorset, DT9 5PR
Ⓣ (01963) 210643
Ⓕ (01963) 210643
Ⓔ sales@dorsetperennials.co.uk
Ⓦ www.dorsetperennials.co.uk
Contact: Dawn & Martin Preston
Opening Times: Open for collections only. Please check with nursery first.
Min Mail Order UK: Nmc
Cat. Cost: Online only.
Credit Cards: All major credit/debit cards
Specialities: An eclectic mix of hardy

perennials grown. Plants for herbaceous borders & cottage gardens with a good mix of oddities to tempt the discerning.
Notes: All plants available via website. Delivers to shows. Wheelchair accessible.
OS Grid Ref: ST662090

CDow **Downside Nurseries** ♿
143 Upper Westwood, Bradford-on-Avon, Wiltshire, BA15 2DE
Ⓣ (01225) 862392
Ⓕ (01225) 862392
Ⓔ info@downsidenurseries.co.uk
Ⓦ www.downsidenurseries.co.uk
Contact: Lorraine Young
Opening Times: 0900-1700, 7 days.
Cat. Cost: Not available.
Credit Cards: All major credit/debit cards
Specialities: Herbaceous perennials, also shrubs, roses, trees & seasonal bedding.
Notes: Traditional family-run retail working nursery set in over three acres. Supply Private Gardeners, Landscapers and Architects in Bath, Wiltshire and Swindon and surrounding counties with an unrivalled choice of quality plants, trees and bedding stock, much of which is grown on site. Wheelchair accessible.
OS Grid Ref: ST806105

CDTJ **Desert to Jungle** ♿
Henlade Garden Nursery, Lower Henlade, Taunton, Somerset, TA3 5NB
Ⓣ (01823) 443701
Ⓜ 07969 652547
Ⓔ plants@deserttojungle.com
Ⓦ www.deserttojungle.com
Contact: Rob Gudge
Opening Times: 1000-1700 Mon, Tue & Thu-Sun (closed Wed), 1st Mar-31st Oct. Thu, Fri & Sat only Nov-Feb. Opening times may vary during RHS shows, so please phone to check.
Min Mail Order UK: Nmc
Cat. Cost: Online only.
Credit Cards: All major credit/debit cards
Specialities: Exotic-looking plants giving a desert or jungle effect in the garden. Incl. *Agave*, *Canna*, aroids, succulents, ferns, tree ferns & bamboos.
Notes: Nursery shares drive with Mount Somerset Hotel. Also sells wholesale. Delivers to shows. Wheelchair accessible.
OS Grid Ref: ST273232

CEls **Elsworth Herbs**
Farthingwood, Broadway, Sidmouth, Devon, EX10 8HS
Ⓣ (01395) 578689
Ⓔ john.twibell@btinternet.com
Contact: Drs J.D. & J.M. Twibell
Opening Times: By appt. only.
Min Mail Order UK: £10.00
Cat. Cost: By email only.
Credit Cards: None
Specialities: National Plant Collection (Scientific & Reference) of *Artemisia*. Wide range of *Artemisia*. Stock available in small quantities only. Orders may require propagation from collection material, for which we are the primary reference source. Native coastal plants.
Notes: Mail order only on small scale in exceptional circumstances. Partially accessible for wheelchairs.
OS Grid Ref: SY119881

CElw **Elworthy Cottage Plants** ♿
Elworthy Cottage, Elworthy, Nr Lydeard St Lawrence, Taunton, Somerset, TA4 3PX
Ⓣ (01984) 656427
Ⓔ mike@elworthy-cottage.co.uk
Ⓦ www.elworthy-cottage.co.uk
Contact: Mrs J.M. Spiller
Opening Times: By appt. only Apr-Sept & Feb for Galanthus. Open for NGS days.
Cat. Cost: 3 × 2nd class.
Credit Cards: None
Specialities: Unusual herbaceous plants esp. *Galanthus*, hardy *Geranium*, *Geum*, *Crocosmia*, *Epimedium*, *Monarda*, *Pulmonaria* & *Viola*. Some varieties only available in small quantities. *Galanthus* available by mail order in Feb.
Notes: Nursery on B3188, 5 miles north of Wiveliscombe, in centre of Elworthy village. Delivers to shows. Wheelchair accessible. Mail order for *Galanthus* only.
OS Grid Ref: ST084349

CEnd **Endsleigh Gardens Nursery** ♿
Milton Abbot, Tavistock, Devon, PL19 0PG
Ⓣ (01822) 870235
Ⓕ (01822) 870513
Ⓔ info@endsleigh-gardens.com
Ⓦ www.endsleighgardens.co.uk
Contact: Adrian Steele
Opening Times: 0800-1700 Mon-Sat. 1000-1600 Sun.
Min Mail Order UK: Nmc
Credit Cards: Visa, Access, Switch, MasterCard
Specialities: Choice & unusual trees & shrubs incl. *Acer*, alpines, bamboos, climbers, conifers, *Cornus*, heathers, old apple & cherry varieties, *Rosa*, *Wisteria*. Grafting service. Modern fruit trees, soft fruit and good selection of perennials.

Notes: Wheelchair accessible (but no disabled toilets).
OS Grid Ref: SX398780

CExl **Exclusive Plants Nursery**
Tretawn, High Cross, Constantine, Falmouth, Cornwall, TR11 5RE
Ⓣ (01326) 341496
Ⓜ 07775 811385
Ⓕ (01326) 341496
Ⓔ info@exclusiveplants.com
Ⓦ www.exclusiveplants.com
Contact: Paul Bonavia
Opening Times: W/ends or by appt. only.
Min Mail Order UK: Nmc
Min Mail Order EU: £25.00
Cat. Cost: 2 × 1st class.
Credit Cards: All major credit/debit cards
Specialities: A plantsperson's nursery, offering rare & unusual plants from around the world. Also new introductions & the best forms of our better known plants.
Notes: Euro accepted.
OS Grid Ref: SW175131

CFen **Fentongollan Farm** ♿
Merther Lane, St Michael Penkivel, Tresillian, Truro, Cornwall, TR2 4AQ
Ⓣ (01872) 520209
Ⓕ (01872) 520606
Ⓔ admin@flowerfarm.co.uk
Ⓦ www.flowerfarm.co.uk
Contact: James Hosking
Opening Times: 0900-1700 7 days, Aug-end Nov.
Min Mail Order UK: Nmc
Min Mail Order EU: Nmc
Cat. Cost: Free.
Credit Cards: All major debit/credit cards except American Express
Specialities: *Narcissus*. Importers of quality Dutch bulbs.
Notes: Also sells wholesale. Delivers to shows. Euro accepted. Wheelchair accessible.

CFGn **The Forest Garden**
Penjerrick Hill, Budock Water, Falmouth, Cornwall, TR11 5ED
Ⓣ (01326) 250090
Ⓔ simonmiles@theforestgarden.co.uk
Ⓦ www.theforestgarden.co.uk
Contact: Simon Miles
Opening Times: Not open. Mail order only. Will open for pre-arranged plant order collection.
Min Mail Order UK: £10.00
Specialities: Perennial edible forest garden & agroforestry plants.
Notes: Top fruit & nut trees, soft fruit, unusual & less common perennial vegetables, tubers, fruits & herbs. Shelter belts & hedging.
OS Grid Ref: SW178030

CFis **Margery Fish Plant Nursery**
East Lambrook Manor Gardens, Silver Street, East Lambrook, South Petherton, Somerset, TA13 5HH
Ⓣ (01460) 240328
Ⓜ 07710 484745
Ⓔ enquiries@eastlambrook.com
Ⓦ www.eastlambrook.com
Contact: Tom Wild
Opening Times: 1000-1700 Tue-Sat, Feb-Oct, plus B/hols & Suns Feb, May-Jul. Nov-Jan by appt.
Cat. Cost: None issued.
Credit Cards: All major credit/debit cards
Specialities: Hardy geraniums & cottage garden herbaceous plants. Stock available in small quantities only. Major collection of hardy geraniums on site.
Notes: Partial wheelchair access.
OS Grid Ref: ST431188

CFoP **Foxplants** ♿
2 Old Park Cottages, Woodbury Lane, Devon, Axminster, Devon, EX13 5TL
Ⓣ (01297) 35255
Ⓜ 07928 805985
Ⓔ jo_fox2@hotmail.com
Ⓦ www.foxplants.com
Contact: Jo Fox
Opening Times: See website.
Min Mail Order UK: £20.00
Cat. Cost: Online only.
Specialities: Small nursery specialising in salvias and unusual herbaceous perennials.
Notes: All salvias grown by Foxplants are from seed or cuttings collected by reputable plant finders and enthusiasts. Also sells wholesale. Delivers to shows. Wheelchair accessible.

CFst **Forest Edge Nurseries**
Verwood Road, Woodlands, Wimborne, Dorset, BH21 8LJ
Ⓣ (01202) 824387
Ⓕ (01202) 829564
Ⓔ info@theheathergarden.co.uk
Ⓦ www.theheathergarden.co.uk
Contact: David Edge
Opening Times: 0900-1630 Mon. Collection available by arrangement on other days.
Min Mail Order UK: Nmc
Cat. Cost: £2.00

Credit Cards: PayPal
Specialities: Heathers incl. *Calluna*, *Daboecia*, *Erica*.
Notes: Also sells wholesale. Euro accepted.

CGro **C W Groves & Son Ltd** ♿
West Bay Road, Bridport, Dorset, DT6 4BA
Ⓣ (01308) 422654
Ⓔ garden@grovesnurseries.co.uk
Ⓦ www.grovesnurseries.co.uk
Contact: Becky Groves
Opening Times: 0800-1700 Mon-Sat, 10.00-16.00 Sun.
Min Mail Order UK: Nmc
Min Mail Order EU: £15.00 + p&p
Cat. Cost: Free.
Credit Cards: Visa, Switch, MasterCard
Specialities: Established in 1866, a family run garden centre with nursery on site specialising in *Viola odorata*, Parma violets & roses.
Notes: Mainly violets, roses, herbs, soft fruit & grapevines by mail order. Main violet display at nursery in Feb, Mar & Apr. Will export violet seeds only beyond EU. Wheelchair accessible.
OS Grid Ref: SY466918

CGrW **The Great Western Gladiolus Nursery**
9 Ash Lane, Wells, Somerset, BA5 2LT
Ⓜ 07779 273562
Ⓔ info@greatwesterngladiolus.co.uk
Ⓦ www.greatwesterngladiolus.co.uk
Contact: F. Hazell
Opening Times: Mail order only. Open by appt. only.
Min Mail Order UK: Nmc
Min Mail Order EU: Nmc
Cat. Cost: 4 × 1st class (2 catalogues).
Credit Cards: PayPal
Specialities: *Gladiolus* species & hybrids, corms & seeds. Other South African bulbous plants.
Notes: Also sells wholesale. Euro accepted.

CHab **Habitat Aid Ltd.**
Hookgate Cottage, South Brewham, Somerset, BA10 0LQ
Ⓣ (01749) 812355
Ⓔ info@habitataid.co.uk
Ⓦ www.habitataid.co.uk
Contact: Nick Mann
Opening Times: Not open. Mail order only.
Min Mail Order UK: £50.00, incl. p&p.
Cat. Cost: None issued.
Credit Cards: All major credit/debit cards
Specialities: British trees, wildflowers and seeds. Local provenance seed mixes. Native aquatic plants. Cottage garden perennials. Heritage fruit trees.
Notes: Also sells wholesale. Delivers to shows.

CHby **The Herbary**
161 Chapel Street, Horningsham, Warminster, Wiltshire, BA12 7LU
Ⓣ (01985) 844442
Ⓔ info@beansandherbs.co.uk
Ⓦ www.beansandherbs.co.uk
Contact: Pippa Rosen
Opening Times: May-Sep strictly by appt. only.
Min Mail Order UK: Nmc
Min Mail Order EU: Nmc
Cat. Cost: Online only.
Credit Cards: None
Specialities: Culinary, medicinal & aromatic herbs organically grown in small quantities.
Notes: Mail order for seed only. All year for organic vegetable, flower, bean & herb seed. Also sells wholesale. Euro accepted.
OS Grid Ref: ST812414

CHew **Hewitt-Cooper Carnivorous Plants**
The Homestead, Glastonbury Road, West Pennard, Somerset, BA6 8NN
Ⓣ (01458) 832844
Ⓔ sales@hccarnivorousplants.co.uk
Ⓦ www.hccarnivorousplants.co.uk
Contact: Nigel Hewitt-Cooper
Opening Times: Not open.
Min Mail Order UK: Nmc
Min Mail Order EU: Nmc
Cat. Cost: Online only.
Credit Cards: All major credit/debit cards
Specialities: Carnivorous plants.
Notes: Mail order all year. Euro accepted. Delivers to shows.

CHVG **Hidden Valley Gardens** ♿
Treesmill, Nr Par, Cornwall, PL24 2TU
Ⓣ (01208) 873225
Ⓔ hiddenvalleygardens@yahoo.co.uk
Ⓦ www.hiddenvalleygardens.co.uk
Contact: Mrs P. Howard
Opening Times: 1000-1800 Thu-Mon (closed Tue & Wed), 20th Mar-15th Oct.
Cat. Cost: None issued.
Credit Cards: All major debit/credit cards except American Express
Specialities: Cottage garden plants, *Dahlia* & many perennials which can be seen growing in the garden.
Notes: Some stock available in small quantities only. Display garden (opening times same as nursery). Please phone for directions.

Euro accepted. Wheelchair accessible.
OS Grid Ref: SX094567

CJun **JUNKER'S NURSERY**
Higher Cobhay, Milverton, Somerset, TA4 1NJ
Ⓣ (01823) 400075
Ⓔ karan@junker.co.uk
Ⓦ www.junker.co.uk
Contact: Karan Junker
Opening Times: Strictly by appt. only. Contact nursery for directions (do not rely on Sat Nav).
Min Mail Order UK: Nmc
Min Mail Order EU: Nmc
Cat. Cost: Free list available by email.
Credit Cards: None
Specialities: Choice & unusual shrubs & trees incl. grafted *Acer palmatum*, *Betula*, *Cornus*, *Daphne*, *Magnolia* cvs. Also extensive collections of *Euonymus*, *Ilex*, *Liquidambar* & *Viburnum*, all grown on own roots. Many available in larger, more mature sizes. Small quantities only of some hard to propagate plants, esp. daphnes.
Notes: Extensive planted areas showing how the plants look growing in "real world" conditions. Propagate & grow all own plants with an increasing number grown naturally in open ground as well as younger plants in pots, incl. larger sizes. Partial wheelchair access.

CKen **KENWITH CONIFER NURSERY (GORDON HADDOW)** ♿
Blinsham, Off A3124, Beaford, Winkleigh, Devon, EX19 8NT
Ⓣ (01805) 603274
Ⓔ info@kenwithconifernursery.co.uk
Ⓦ www.kenwithconifernursery.co.uk
Contact: Gordon Haddow
Opening Times: 1000-1630 Tue-Sat all year. Closed all B/hols. If travelling a long distance, please phone previous day to ensure nursery will be open.
Min Mail Order UK: £20 + p&p
Cat. Cost: Online only.
Credit Cards: Visa, MasterCard
Specialities: All conifer genera. Grafting a speciality.
Notes: Wheelchair accessible.
OS Grid Ref: SS518160

CKno **KNOLL GARDENS**
Hampreston, Wimborne, Dorset, BH21 7ND
Ⓣ (01202) 873931
Ⓕ (01202) 870842
Ⓔ enquiries@knollgardens.co.uk
Ⓦ www.knollgardens.co.uk
Contact: N.R. Lucas
Opening Times: 1000-1700 Tue-Sat, Feb-Dec. Open B/hols. See website.
Min Mail Order UK: Nmc
Min Mail Order EU: Nmc
Cat. Cost: None.
Credit Cards: Visa, MasterCard
Specialities: Grasses (main specialism). Flowering perennials. National Plant Collection of *Pennisetum*.
Notes: Also sells wholesale.

CLAP **LONG ACRE PLANTS** ♿
South Marsh, Charlton Musgrove, Wincanton, Somerset, BA9 8EX
Ⓣ (01963) 32802
Ⓕ (01963) 32802
Ⓔ info@plantsforshade.co.uk
Ⓦ www.plantsforshade.co.uk
Contact: Nigel Rowland
Opening Times: By appt only.
Min Mail Order UK: £12.00 + p&p
Min Mail Order EU: £30
Cat. Cost: Catalogue available online.
Credit Cards: MasterCard, Visa, Maestro
Specialities: Ferns, woodland bulbs & perennials. Marginal/bog plants. Specialise in plants for shade, carrying a wide range of unusual and tough shade tolerant perennials and ferns.
Notes: Mail order online. Wheelchair accessible. Delivers to shows.

CLau **THE EDIBLE GARDEN NURSERY**
Moorland Barn, Whiddon Down, Okehampton, Devon, EX20 2QL
Ⓣ (01647) 400301
Ⓜ 07905 518666
Ⓔ ediblegardennursery@gmail.com
Ⓦ www.theediblegardennursery.co.uk
Contact: Chris Seagon
Opening Times: 1000-1700 Apr-Oct.
Min Mail Order UK: £9.95
Cat. Cost: Online only.
Credit Cards: All major credit/debit cards, PayPal
Specialities: Edible plants.
Notes: Everything grown is edible in some way. All plants are peat, chemical and pesticide free. Also sells wholesale. Delivers to shows (payment in advance).

CLnd **LANDFORD TREES**
Landford Lodge, Landford, Salisbury, Wiltshire, SP5 2EH
Ⓣ (01794) 390808
Ⓔ trees@landfordtrees.co.uk
Ⓦ www.landfordtrees.co.uk

Contact: C.D. Pilkington
Opening Times: 0800-1700 Mon-Thu, 0800-1530 Fri.
Cat. Cost: Free.
Credit Cards: All major debit/credit cards except American Express
Specialities: Deciduous ornamental trees.
Notes: Also sells wholesale.
OS Grid Ref: SU247201

CLoc **C S Lockyer (Fuchsias)** ◆
Lansbury, 70 Henfield Road, Coalpit Heath, Bristol, BS36 2UZ
Ⓣ (01454) 772219
Ⓕ (01454) 772219
Ⓔ mary@lockyerfuchsias.co.uk
Ⓦ www.lockyerfuchsias.co.uk
Contact: Mary Lockyer
Opening Times: 1000-1300, 1430-1700 most days, please telephone first.
Min Mail Order UK: 6 plants + p&p
Min Mail Order EU: £12.00 + p&p
Cat. Cost: 4 × 1st class or online.
Credit Cards: All major credit/debit cards
Specialities: *Fuchsia.*
Notes: Many open days & coach parties. Also sells wholesale. Exports beyond EU. Euro accepted. Delivers to shows. Partial wheelchair access.

CMac **Mac Pennys Nurseries**
154 Burley Road, Bransgore, Christchurch, Dorset, BH23 8DB
Ⓣ (01425) 672348
Ⓔ office@macpennys.co.uk
Ⓦ www.macpennys.co.uk
Contact: T. & V. Lowndes & S. Lowndes
Opening Times: 0900-1700 Mon-Sat, 1000-1700 Sun & B/hols. Closed Xmas to New Year.
Min Mail Order UK: Nmc
Cat. Cost: A4 sae with 4 × 1st class.
Credit Cards: All major debit/credit cards except American Express
Specialities: Wide range of plants, available in small quantities only.
Notes: Mail order available Oct-Feb incl. UK only. Also sells wholesale. Nursery partially accessible for wheelchairs.

CMCN **Mallet Court Nursery** ♿
Marshway, Curry Mallet, Taunton, Somerset, TA3 6SZ
Ⓣ (01823) 481493
Ⓜ 07713 091521
Ⓕ (01823) 481493
Ⓔ malletcourtnursery@btinternet.com
Ⓦ www.malletcourt.co.uk
Contact: J.G.S. & P.M.E. Harris F.L.S.
Opening Times: 0930-1700 Mon-Fri summer, 0930-1600 winter. Sat & Sun by appt.
Min Mail Order UK: Nmc
Min Mail Order EU: Nmc
Cat. Cost: £1.50
Credit Cards: All major credit/debit cards
Specialities: Maples, oaks, *Magnolia*, hollies & other rare and unusual plants including those from China & South Korea.
Notes: Mail order Oct-Mar only. Also sells wholesale. Exports beyond EU. Euro accepted. Wheelchair accessible.

CMea **The Mead Nursery** ♿
Brokerswood, Nr Westbury, Wiltshire, BA13 4EG
Ⓣ (01373) 859990
Ⓔ info@themeadnursery.co.uk
Ⓦ www.themeadnursery.co.uk
Contact: Steve & Emma Lewis-Dale
Opening Times: 0900-1700 Wed-Sat & B/hols, 1200-1700 Sun, 1st Feb-10th Oct. Closed Easter Sun.
Cat. Cost: 4 × 2nd class.
Credit Cards: All major credit/debit cards
Specialities: Perennials, alpines, pot-grown bulbs and grasses.
Notes: Wheelchair accessible.
OS Grid Ref: ST833517

CMen **Mendip Bonsai Studio**
Byways, Back Lane, Downside, Shepton Mallet, Somerset, BA4 4JR
Ⓣ (01749) 344274
Ⓜ 07711 205806
Ⓔ john@mendipbonsai.co.uk
Ⓦ www.mendipbonsai.co.uk
Contact: John Trott
Opening Times: By appt. only. Mail order Oct-Mar.
Min Mail Order UK: £15.00
Cat. Cost: None issued. Workshop lists available.
Credit Cards: All major credit/debit cards
Specialities: Bonsai, potensai, accent plants & garden stock. *Acer*, conifers, incl. *Aciphylla*, *Davallia*, *Pinus thunbergii* & *Pyrrosia*. Many plants available in small numbers only. Can propagate to order. Young trees for garden or bonsai culture. Many rare & unusual ferns from Japan for 'accent' use and gardens (very limited numbers).
Notes: Education classes, lectures, demonstrations & club talks on bonsai. Stockist of most bonsai pots, related bonsai

sundries & a large range of bronze figurines. Mail orders will normally be despatched late Mar-early Apr, late Sep-Oct. Delivers to shows by arrangement.

CMid **Middlecombe Nursery**
Wrington Road, Congresbury,
North Somerset, BS49 5AN
Ⓣ (01934) 876337
Ⓕ (01934) 876616
Ⓔ middlecombenursery@hotmail.com
Ⓦ www.middlecombenursery.co.uk
Contact: Nigel & Isy North
Opening Times: 1000-1700 Mon-Fri 1000-1600 w/ends & B/hols. Closed w/ends Dec-Feb.
Specialities: Herbaceous shrubs, climbers, grasses and trees including larger specimens. Exotics, palms and bamboos.
Notes: Established in 1982, the nursery has over three acres of stock. Many plants grown onsite alongside quality Dutch and Italian stock. Delivery service available. Also sells wholesale.

CMil **Mill Cottage Plants** ♿
Henley Mill, Henley Lane, Wookey, Somerset, BA5 1AW
Ⓣ (01749) 676966
Ⓜ 07851 698759
Ⓔ millcottageplants@gmail.com
Ⓦ www.millcottageplants.co.uk
Contact: Sally Gregson
Opening Times: By appt. only.
Min Mail Order UK: Nmc
Min Mail Order EU: £25.00 + p&p
Cat. Cost: Online only.
Credit Cards: All major credit/debit cards
Specialities: *Epimedium*, rare *Hydrangea serrata* cvs, *H. aspera* cvs, shade & damp-loving plants.
Notes: Please telephone for directions. Euro accepted. Wheelchair accessible.

CMiW **Millwood Plants**
Millwoods, Colleton Mills, Umberleigh,
Nr Chulmleigh, Devon, EX37 9ET
Ⓜ 07756 515084
Ⓔ millwoodplants@mail.com
Ⓦ www.millwoodplants.com
Contact: Gary Buckingham
Opening Times: 1000-1700 Mon & Thu Mar-Sep or by appt. at other times.
Specialities: Hardy herbaceous perennials for woodland gardens and shade. Old fashioned roses.
Notes: Nursery in the heart of the Taw valley selecting plants that are hardy, unusual or authentic. Traditional propagation methods used to retain colour, size and hardiness. Although only open Mon and Thu or by appt, the nursery welcomes customers at other times if the gates are open. Exhibits at shows around the UK throughout the year. See website for details. Nursery postcode for Sat Nav is EX37 9ES.
OS Grid Ref: SS65882

CNat **Natural Selection**
1 Station Cottages, Hullavington,
Chippenham, Wiltshire, SN14 6ET
Ⓜ 07800 583999
Ⓔ martin@worldmutation.demon.co.uk
Contact: Martin Barber
Opening Times: Please telephone.
Min Mail Order UK: £9.00 + p&p
Min Mail Order EU: Nmc
Cat. Cost: 1 × 2nd class.
Credit Cards: None
Specialities: Unusual British natives & others. Also seed. Only available in small quantities.
Notes: Euro accepted.

CNMi **Newport Mills Nursery**
Wrantage, Taunton, Somerset,
TA3 6DJ
Ⓣ (01823) 490231
Ⓔ john@newportmillsnursery.net
Ⓦ www.newportmillsnursery.net
Contact: John Barrington
Opening Times: Not open. Mail order only.
Min Mail Order UK: Nmc free p&p
Min Mail Order EU: Nmc. EU postal rate per order.
Cat. Cost: Free.
Credit Cards: All major credit/debit cards
Specialities: *Delphinium elatum* hybrids. English scented perpetual flowering carnations. *Dianthus*. Pinks: Exhibition, Modern & Old World.
Notes: Mail order Apr-Sep for young delphiniums in 7cm pots. Euro accepted.
OS Grid Ref: ST318234

CNor **Northbrook Nursery** ♿
47 Northbrook Road, Broadstone, Dorset,
BH18 8HD
Ⓣ (01202) 695256
Ⓔ marg@northbrooknursery.co.uk
Ⓦ www.northbrooknursery.co.uk
Contact: Margaret Bailey
Opening Times: 1000-1600 Thu & Fri end Apr-end Sept.
Min Mail Order UK: Nmc
Cat. Cost: None issued.

Credit Cards: PayPal
Specialities: Perennials. Plants available in small quantities only.
Notes: Delivers to shows. Wheelchair accessible.
OS Grid Ref: SZ001947

CPar **PARKS PERENNIALS**
242 Wallisdown Road, Wallisdown, Bournemouth, Dorset, BH10 4HZ
Ⓣ (01202) 524464
Ⓜ 07977 878546
Ⓔ parks.perennials@ntlworld.com
Contact: S. Parks
Opening Times: Apr-Oct most days, please telephone first.
Cat. Cost: None issued.
Credit Cards: None
Specialities: Hardy herbaceous perennials.
Notes: Delivers to shows.

CPbh **PENBERTH PLANTS**
St Buryan, Penzance, Cornwall, TR19 6HJ
Ⓣ (01736) 810978
Ⓔ info@penberthplants.co.uk
Ⓦ www.penberthplants.co.uk
Contact: Jeff Rowe
Opening Times: Not open. Mail order.
Min Mail Order UK: Nmc
Min Mail Order EU: Nmc
Cat. Cost: Online only.
Credit Cards: All major credit/debit cards
Specialities: *Protea*, *Restio*, succulents and other unusual plants.
Notes: Sells at RHS shows. Open days throughout the year, check website or contact nursery for dates. Card payment accepted at shows. Mail order through website only. Delivers to shows.

CPBP **PARHAM BUNGALOW PLANTS**
Parham Lane, Market Lavington, Devizes, Wiltshire, SN10 4QA
Ⓣ (01380) 812605
Ⓔ parbplants@gmail.com
Contact: Mrs Dot Sample
Opening Times: By appt only. Please telephone first.
Min Mail Order UK: Nmc
Min Mail Order EU: Nmc
Cat. Cost: 2 × 2nd class.
Credit Cards: None
Specialities: Alpines.
Notes: Delivers to shows.

CPhi **ALAN PHIPPS CACTI**
62 Samuel White Road, Hanham, Bristol, BS15 3LX
Ⓣ (0117) 9607591
Ⓦ www.cactus-mall.com/alan-phipps/index.html
Contact: A. Phipps
Opening Times: 1000-1700 but prior phone call essential to ensure a greeting.
Min Mail Order UK: £5.00 + p&p
Min Mail Order EU: £20.00 + p&p
Cat. Cost: Sae or 2 × IRC (EC only).
Credit Cards: None
Specialities: *Ariocarpus*, *Astrophytum* & *Mammillaria*. Species & varieties will change with times. Ample quantities exist in spring. Limited range of *Agave*.
Notes: Specimen-size plants not available by mail order. Euro accepted as cash only.
OS Grid Ref: ST644717

CPHo **THE PALM HOUSE**
8 North Street, Ottery St Mary, Devon, EX11 1DR
Ⓣ (01404) 815450
Ⓜ 07815 673397
Ⓔ george@thepalmhouse.co.uk
Ⓦ www.thepalmhouse.co.uk
Contact: George Gregory
Opening Times: Mail order only. Open by appt. only.
Min Mail Order UK: £5.00
Min Mail Order EU: £10.00
Cat. Cost: 2 × 1st class.
Credit Cards: All major credit/debit cards
Specialities: Palms.
Notes: Also sells wholesale.
OS Grid Ref: SY098955

CPla **PLANT WORLD GARDENS AND NURSERIES**
St Marychurch Road, Newton Abbot, Devon, TQ12 4SE
Ⓣ (01803) 872939
Ⓕ (01803) 875018
Ⓔ raybrown@plant-world-seeds.com
Ⓦ www.plant-world-seeds.com
Contact: Doug De Val
Opening Times: 0930-1700 7 days a week, Apr-Oct.
Min Mail Order UK: Nmc
Min Mail Order EU: Nmc
Cat. Cost: Free.
Credit Cards: Visa, Access, EuroCard, MasterCard
Specialities: Alpines, perennials, small shrubs, succulents, herbaceous & patio plants.
Notes: Four acre garden planted as map of the world (entry charge applies). Mail order for seed only (no mail order for plants). Also sells wholesale. Exports beyond EU. Partial wheelchair access (nursery & café only).
OS Grid Ref: SX893693

C

CPne **Pine Cottage Plants** ♿
Bowdens, Cleave House, Sticklepath, Okehampton, Devon, EX20 2NL
Ⓣ (01837) 840989
Ⓔ sales@bowdenhostas.com
Ⓦ www.bowdenhostas.com
Contact: Tim Penrose
Opening Times: 1000-1600 Apr-Sep. Oct-Mar Please telephone nursery before travelling.
Min Mail Order UK: Nmc
Min Mail Order EU: Nmc
Cat. Cost: Free.
Credit Cards: Maestro, MasterCard, Visa
Specialities: National Plant Collection of *Agapanthus* (Pine Cottage cvs).
Notes: Mail order *Agapanthus*. Wheelchair accessible.
OS Grid Ref: SX642941

CPou **Pounsley Plants** ♿
Pounsley Combe, Spriddlestone, Brixton, Plymouth, Devon, PL9 0DW
Ⓣ (01752) 402873
Ⓜ 07770 758501
Ⓔ pou599@aol.com
Ⓦ www.pounsleyplants.com
Contact: Mrs Jane Hollow
Opening Times: Normally 1000-1600 Mon-Sat but please phone first.
Min Mail Order UK: £10.00 + p&p
Min Mail Order EU: €20.00 + p&p
Cat. Cost: Online only.
Credit Cards: None
Specialities: Unusual herbaceous perennials. Comprehensive range of old roses & large selection of modern roses.
Notes: Mail order solely bare-root roses, Nov-Mar. Also sells wholesale. Delivers to shows. Euro accepted. Wheelchair accessible.
OS Grid Ref: SX521538

CPrp **ProperPlants.com**
Penknight, Edgcumbe Road, Lostwithiel, Cornwall, PL22 0JD
Ⓣ (01208) 872291
Ⓔ sarahwilks52@gmail.com
Ⓦ www.ProperPlants.com
Contact: Sarah Wilks
Opening Times: By appt. only. Please telephone or email first.
Min Mail Order UK: Nmc
Min Mail Order EU: Nmc
Credit Cards: All major credit/debit cards
Specialities: *Agapanthus*, *Crocosmia* & *Hesperantha*.
Notes: Also sells wholesale. Exports beyond EU. Delivers to shows.
OS Grid Ref: SX093596

CQua **R and A Scamp Quality Daffodils**
14 Roscarrack Close, Falmouth, Cornwall, TR11 4PJ
Ⓣ (01326) 317959
Ⓜ 07989 243450
Ⓔ rascamp@daffodils.uk.com
Ⓦ www.qualitydaffodils.com
Contact: R.A. Scamp
Opening Times: Not open. Mail order only. Viewing by appt. only.
Min Mail Order UK: Nmc
Min Mail Order EU: Nmc
Cat. Cost: 4 × 1st class.
Credit Cards: All major credit/debit cards
Specialities: *Narcissus* hybrids & species. Some stocks have less than 100 bulbs.
Notes: Exports beyond EU. Euro accepted.

CRea **Really Wild Flowers**
H V Horticulture Ltd, Heather Cottage, 23 New Close, Bourton, Gillingham, Dorset, SP8 5DL
Ⓣ (01747) 416376
Ⓔ info@reallywildflowers.co.uk
Ⓦ www.reallywildflowers.co.uk
Contact: Grahame Dixie
Opening Times: Mail order & online only.
Min Mail Order UK: £10 + p&p
Cat. Cost: 3 × 1st class.
Credit Cards: All major debit/credit cards except American Express
Specialities: Native wild flowers for grasslands, woodlands & wetlands. Seeds & bulbs. Hedge plants & trees. Soil analysis service.
Notes: Credit card payment accepted for online orders only. Also sells wholesale.

CRHN **Roseland House Nursery**
Chacewater, Truro, Cornwall, TR4 8QB
Ⓣ (01872) 560451
Ⓔ clematis@roselandhouse.co.uk
Ⓦ www.roselandhouse.co.uk
Contact: Charlie Pridham
Opening Times: 1300-1700 Tue & Wed, Apr-Sep. Other times by appt.
Min Mail Order UK: Nmc
Min Mail Order EU: Nmc
Cat. Cost: Online only.
Credit Cards: All major credit/debit cards
Specialities: Climbing & conservatory plants. National Collections of *Clematis viticella* & *Lapageria rosea*. Named *Lapageria* in short supply but occasionally available.
Notes: Garden open to the public. Credit cards accepted from mail order customers only. Delivers to shows.
OS Grid Ref: SW752445

CRos **ROSEMOOR PLANT CENTRE (RHS)** ♿ ◆
RHS Garden Rosemoor, Torrington, Devon, EX38 8PH
Ⓣ (01805) 626842
Ⓔ rosemooradmin@rhs.org.uk
Ⓦ www.rhs.org.uk/rosemoor
Contact: Sam Peard or Emma Marsh
Opening Times: 1000-1800 Mon-Sat, 1130-1730 Sun, Apr-Sep (summer). 1000-1700 Mon-Sat, 1030-1630 Sun, Oct-Mar (winter). Closed Easter Sun & Xmas Day.
Cat. Cost: None issued.
Credit Cards: All major credit/debit cards
Specialities: Wide range of shrubs, herbaceous plants, roses, climbers, alpines & seasonal lines, reflecting where possible the diversity of planting in the garden. Displays of Curator's Choice, garden favourites, AGM plants & Plants for Pollinators.
Notes: Plant centre attached to RHS Garden Rosemoor. Free entry to plant centre, gift shop & restaurant, independent of Garden entry. Accept HTA & RHS vouchers (paper only). Aim to stock and showcase plants growing at RHS Garden Rosemoor. Wheelchair accessible.
OS Grid Ref: SS500176

CSam **SAMPFORD SHRUBS** ♿
Sampford Peverell, Tiverton, Devon, EX16 7EN
Ⓣ (01884) 821164
Ⓔ mainpage@samshrub.co.uk
Ⓦ www.samshrub.co.uk
Contact: M. Hughes-Jones & S. Proud
Opening Times: Calling customers 1000-1700 Wed-Fri 28th Mar-27th Apr 2018. Other times by appt. or mail order.
Min Mail Order UK: £25.00 + carriage
Cat. Cost: Online only.
Credit Cards: All major credit/debit cards
Specialities: Plants particularly suitable for naturalistic gardening, especially herbaceous.
Notes: Mail order through website only, despatched Sep-Mar. Wheelchair accessible.
OS Grid Ref: ST043153

CSBt **ST BRIDGET NURSERIES LTD** ♿
Old Rydon Lane, Exeter, Devon, EX2 7JY
Ⓣ (01392) 873672
Ⓕ (01392) 876710
Ⓔ sales@stbridgetnurseries.co.uk
Ⓦ www.stbridgetnurseries.co.uk
Contact: Sales Dept
Opening Times: 0900-1700 Mon-Sat, 1030-1630 Sun. Closed Xmas Day, Boxing Day, New Year's Day & Easter Sun.
Min Mail Order UK: Nmc
Cat. Cost: Free.
Credit Cards: All major credit/debit cards
Specialities: General nursery propagating a wide range of top quality plants, with two retail garden centres near Exeter. Founded 1925.
Notes: Tours of the Rose field during the summer and tree field during the autumn. See website for details. Mail order available, please contact for prices & carriage charges. Also sells wholesale. Wheelchair accessible.
OS Grid Ref: SX955905

CSde **SEASIDE PLANTS**
Marsh Lane Nursery, West Charleton, Kingsbridge, Devon, TQ7 2AQ
Ⓜ 07775 201595
Ⓔ info@seasideplants.co.uk
Ⓦ www.seasideplants.co.uk
Contact: Michael Hornby
Opening Times: Not open. By appt. only.
Min Mail Order UK: Nmc
Min Mail Order EU: Nmc
Cat. Cost: Online only.
Credit Cards: All major credit/debit cards
Specialities: Wide range, esp. coastal plants, *Elaeagnus*, *Euonymus*, *Fuchsia*, grasses, *Griselinia*, *Hydrangea*, *Olearia* & *Pittosporum*.
Notes: Euro accepted.

CSma **PLANTS FOR SMALL GARDENS**
Goosegate, Bridford, Exeter, Devon, EX6 7LW
Ⓜ 07845 793582
Ⓔ sales@plantsforsmallgardens.co.uk
Ⓦ www.plantsforsmallgardens.co.uk
Contact: Sue Hearnden
Opening Times: Not open. Mail order online only.
Min Mail Order UK: £15.00
Cat. Cost: Online only.
Credit Cards: PayPal
Specialities: Dwarf hardy, rockery and alpine plants, all grown on our nursery in Devon. Range to suit all types of gardeners from *Aubrieta* & *Helianthemum* to more specialist plants such as kabschia saxifrages & *Meconopsis*. Good range of hardy *Geranium*.
Notes: Delivers to shows.

CSpe **SPECIAL PLANTS**
Hill Farm Barn, Greenways Lane, Cold Ashton, Chippenham, Wiltshire, SN14 8LA
Ⓣ (01225) 891686
Ⓔ derry@specialplants.net
Ⓦ www.specialplants.net
Contact: Derry Watkins
Opening Times: 1000-1700 7 days Mar-Oct. Other times please ring first to check.
Min Mail Order UK: £10.00 + p&p

C

Cat. Cost: Free.
Credit Cards: All major credit/debit cards
Specialities: Tender perennials, *Pelargonium*, *Salvia*, hardy geraniums, *Anemone*, *Erysimum*, *Papaver* & grasses. Many varieties propagated in small numbers only.
Notes: Mail order Sep-Mar only. Delivers to shows. Euro accepted.
OS Grid Ref: ST749726

CSta **STADDON FARM NURSERIES** ♿
Staddon Road, Holsworthy, Devon, EX22 6NH
Ⓜ 07547 711189
Ⓔ penny@pennysprimulas.co.uk
Ⓦ www.pennysprimulas.co.uk
Contact: Penny Jones
Opening Times: By appt. only.
Min Mail Order UK: Nmc
Min Mail Order EU: Nmc
Cat. Cost: Online only.
Credit Cards: All major credit/debit cards
Specialities: *Primula*. National Plant Collection of *Primula sieboldii* Japanese cvs. Modest collection of *Epimedium*, ferns and other Asiatic Primulas.
Notes: Exports beyond the UK. Delivers to shows. Euro accepted. Wheelchair accessible.

CTho **THORNHAYES NURSERY**
St Andrews Wood, Dulford, Cullompton, Devon, EX15 2DF
Ⓣ (01884) 266746
Ⓕ (01884) 266739
Ⓔ trees@thornhayes-nursery.co.uk
Ⓦ www.thornhayes-nursery.co.uk
Contact: K.D. Croucher
Opening Times: 0800-1600 Mon-Fri. 0900-1300 Sat.
Min Mail Order UK: £100
Min Mail Order EU: Price on application.
Cat. Cost: Free.
Credit Cards: All major credit/debit cards
Specialities: A broad range of forms of ornamental, amenity & fruit trees incl. West Country apple varieties and choice shrubs. A particular emphasis on disease-resistant forms for the wet and windy west.
Notes: Also sells wholesale. Euro accepted. Partial wheelchair access.

CTrC **TREVENA CROSS NURSERIES** ♿
Breage, Helston, Cornwall, TR13 9PY
Ⓣ (01736) 763880
Ⓕ (01736) 762828
Ⓔ sales@trevenacross.co.uk
Ⓦ www.trevenacross.co.uk
Contact: Graham Jeffery
Opening Times: 0900-1700 Mon-Sat, 1030-1630 Sun.
Min Mail Order UK: Nmc
Credit Cards: All major credit/debit cards
Specialities: Southern Hemisphere plants and plants for windy or exposed sites. *Proteaceae*, *Restionaceae*.
Notes: Family owned business operating as a garden centre and growing most stock on site. Garden kitchen café offering daily coffee and lunches. Wheelchair accessible.
OS Grid Ref: SW61285

CTrh **TREHANE NURSERY** ♿
Stapehill Road, Hampreston, Wimborne, Dorset, BH21 7ND
Ⓣ (01202) 873490
Ⓔ office@trehanenursery.co.uk
Ⓦ www.trehanenursery.co.uk
Contact: Lorraine Keets
Opening Times: 0830-1630 Mon-Fri all year (excl. Xmas & New Year). 1000-1600 Sat in spring & by appt.
Min Mail Order UK: Nmc
Min Mail Order EU: Nmc
Cat. Cost: Free.
Credit Cards: All major credit/debit cards
Specialities: Extensive range of *Camellia* species, cultivars & hybrids. Many new introductions. Blueberries.
Notes: Wheelchair accessible.
OS Grid Ref: SU059000

CTri **TRISCOMBE NURSERIES** ♿ ◆
West Bagborough, Nr Taunton, Somerset, TA4 3HG
Ⓣ (01984) 618267
Ⓔ info@triscombenurseries.co.uk
Ⓦ www.triscombenurseries.co.uk
Contact: S. Parkman
Opening Times: 0900-1730 Mon-Sat.
Min Mail Order UK: Nmc
Cat. Cost: 1 × 1st class.
Credit Cards: None
Specialities: Trees, shrubs, roses, fruit, *Clematis*, herbaceous & rock plants.
Notes: Wheelchair accessible.

CTsd **TRESEDERS NURSERY** ♿
Wallcottage Nursery, Lockengate, St. Austell, Cornwall, PL26 8RU
Ⓣ (01208) 832234
Ⓔ Treseders@btconnect.com
Ⓦ www.treseders.co.uk
Contact: James Treseder
Opening Times: 0900-1700 Mon-Sat, 1000-1600 Sun. Closed Wed.

Min Mail Order UK: Nmc
Min Mail Order EU: Nmc
Cat. Cost: Online or by email only.
Credit Cards: All major credit/debit cards
Specialities: A wide range of choice & unusual plants grown in peat-free compost. Establishing collection of *Prostanthera*.
Notes: Plants sometimes only available in small quantities. Enquiries welcome. Delivers to shows. Wheelchair accessible.
OS Grid Ref: SX034618

CWat **The Water Garden** ♿
Hinton Parva, Swindon, Wiltshire, SN4 0DH
Ⓣ (01793) 790558
Ⓔ ben@thewatergarden.co.uk
Ⓦ www.thewatergarden.co.uk
Contact: Ben Newman
Opening Times: 1000-1700 Wed-Sun.
Min Mail Order UK: £10.00 + p&p
Cat. Cost: 4 × 1st class.
Credit Cards: Visa, Access, Switch
Specialities: Waterlilies, marginal & moisture plants, oxygenators & alpines.
Notes: Also sells wholesale. Wheelchair accessible.

CWCL **Westcountry Nurseries (North Devon) Ltd**
Donkey Meadow, Woolsery, Devon, EX39 5QH
Ⓣ (01237) 431111
Ⓔ info@westcountrylupins.co.uk
Ⓦ www.westcountry-nurseries.co.uk
Contact: Sarah Conibear
Opening Times: Mon-Fri, open for collection of plant orders by appointment ONLY. Please ring beforehand 1000-1530 weekdays only, closed w/ends.
Min Mail Order UK: Nmc
Cat. Cost: 2 × 1st class + A5 sae for full colour cat.
Credit Cards: All major credit/debit cards
Specialities: *Clematis*, *Cyclamen*, *Helleborus*, *Lewisia*, *Lupinus*, select perennials, grasses, ferns & climbers. National Plant Collection of *Lupinus*.
Notes: Delivers to shows.
OS Grid Ref: SS351219

CWGN **Walled Garden Nursery** ♿
Brinkworth House, Brinkworth, Nr Malmesbury, Wiltshire, SN15 5DF
Ⓣ (01666) 826637
Ⓜ 07921 436863
Ⓔ sales@clematis-nursery.co.uk
Ⓦ www.clematis-nursery.co.uk
Contact: Fraser Wescott
Opening Times: 1000-1700, 7 days, Mar-Oct. 1030-dusk, Mon-Fri, Nov & Feb. Closed Dec & Jan.
Min Mail Order UK: £15.00
Credit Cards: All major credit/debit cards
Specialities: *Clematis* & climbers, with a selection of unusual perennials & shrubs.
Notes: Mail order UK mainland only. Wheelchair accessible.
OS Grid Ref: SU002849

CWGr **National Dahlia Collection**
Varfell Farm, Long Rock, Penzance, Cornwall, TR20 8AQ
Ⓣ (01736) 339276
Ⓜ 07753 959856
Ⓔ info@nationaldahliacollection.co.uk
Ⓦ www.nationaldahliacollection.co.uk
Contact: Louise Danks
Opening Times: Garden open in summer. See website or contact nursery for details.
Min Mail Order UK: Nmc
Min Mail Order EU: Nmc
Cat. Cost: Online. Contact nursery for hard copy.
Credit Cards: All major debit/credit cards except American Express
Specialities: National Plant Collection of *Dahlia*. 1600 plus cvs.
Notes: See website for plant availability. Also sells wholesale. Partial wheelchair access.

CWiW **Windrush Willow**
Higher Barn, Sidmouth Road, Aylesbeare, Exeter, Devon, EX5 2JJ
Ⓣ (01395) 233669
Ⓕ (01395) 233669
Ⓔ windrushw@aol.com
Ⓦ www.windrushwillow.com
Contact: Richard Kerwood
Opening Times: Mail order only. Open by appt.
Min Mail Order UK: Nmc
Min Mail Order EU: Nmc
Cat. Cost: 2 × 1st class.
Credit Cards: All major credit/debit cards
Specialities: *Salix*. Unrooted cuttings available Dec-Mar.
Notes: Also sells wholesale. Euro accepted. Carrier charge £5.00.

CWld **Wild Thyme**
(office) The Old Orchard, Friggle Street, Frome, Somerset, BA11 5LH
Ⓣ (01373) 464417
Ⓜ 07956 888477
Ⓔ jess@wildthymeplants.co.uk
Ⓦ www.wildthymeplants.co.uk

E

Contact: Monica Ashman
Opening Times: Not open. Mail order only via online shop.
Min Mail Order UK: £15.00
Credit Cards: Visa, MasterCard, Maestro
Specialities: Wildflowers & fragrant plants.
Notes: Delivers to shows.

CWSG West Somerset Garden Centre ♿
Mart Road, Minehead, Somerset, TA24 5BJ
Ⓣ (01643) 703812
Ⓕ (01643) 706476
Ⓔ wsgc@btconnect.com
Ⓦ www.westsomersetgardencentre.co.uk
Contact: Ms J.K. Webber
Opening Times: 0800-1700 Mon-Sat, 1000-1600 Sun.
Min Mail Order UK: Nmc
Cat. Cost: None issued.
Credit Cards: All major debit/credit cards except American Express
Specialities: Wide general range. *Clematis* & rose varieties change throughout the season.
Notes: Wheelchair accessible.

Eastern

EACa Alpine Campanulas (Bellflower Nursery) ♿
Langham Hall Walled Garden, Langham, Nr Bury St Edmunds, Suffolk, IP31 3EE
Ⓜ 07879 644958
Ⓔ campanulas@btinternet.com
Ⓦ www.bellflowernursery.co.uk
Contact: Sue Wooster
Opening Times: 1000-1600 Thu & Fri, mid-Mar to end Oct. Other times by appt.
Min Mail Order UK: £10.00
Cat. Cost: Online only.
Credit Cards: None
Specialities: *Campanula*. National Plant Collection of Alpine campanulas. Most stock in small numbers only.
Notes: Hardy plant nursery & National Plant Collection within 3.5 acre Georgian walled garden. Groups welcome by appt. Wheelchair accessible but nursery reached by gravel paths through walled garden.
OS Grid Ref: TL978691

EAJP A & J Plants
Chappel Road, Great Tey, Colchester, Essex, CO6 1JR
Ⓣ (01206) 212124
Ⓕ (01206) 212124
Ⓔ mail@aandjplants.com
Ⓦ www.aandjplants.com
Contact: Jackie Rhodes
Opening Times: Not open. Mail order only. Orders can be collected from nursery by prior arrangement.
Min Mail Order UK: Nmc
Specialities: Wide variety of choice perennials and ornamental grasses propagated on the nursery, some in small quantities.
Notes: Plant Centre at Marks Hall Garden (CO6 1TG) stocked with seasonal selection of perennials & grasses. Also sells wholesale. Delivers to shows.

EBak B & H M Baker ♿
Bourne Brook Nurseries, Greenstead Green, Halstead, Essex, CO9 1RB
Ⓣ (01787) 476369
Contact: Clive Baker
Opening Times: 0800-1600 Mon-Fri, 0900-1200 & 1400-1600 Sat & Sun, Mar-Jun.
Cat. Cost: 2 × 1st class + 33p.
Credit Cards: All major credit/debit cards
Specialities: *Fuchsia* & conservatory plants.
Notes: Also sells wholesale. Wheelchair accessible.

EBar Barcham Trees PLC
Eye Hill Drove, Ely, Cambridgeshire, CB7 5XF
Ⓣ (01353) 720950
Ⓔ info@barchamtrees.co.uk
Ⓦ www.barcham.co.uk
Contact: Ellen Carvey
Opening Times: Visits to the nursery by appt. only. 0900-1730 Mon-Fri.
Min Mail Order UK: Nmc
Min Mail Order EU: Nmc
Cat. Cost: £20.00
Credit Cards: All major debit/credit cards except American Express
Specialities: Large grower of containerised trees. 478 varieties available, from 10-12cm to 40cm girth.
Notes: As trees range from 3-8 metres all are despatched on lorries rather than through the mailing service. Also sells wholesale. Exports beyond EU. Delivers to shows. Euro accepted.

EBee Beeches Nursery ♿
Crown Hill, Ashdon, Saffron Walden, Essex, CB10 2HB
Ⓣ (01799) 584362
Ⓕ (01799) 584421
Ⓔ sales@beechesnursery.co.uk
Ⓦ www.beechesnursery.co.uk
Contact: Alan Bidwell
Opening Times: 0830-1700 Mon-Sat, 1000-1700 Sun & B/hols.

Min Mail Order UK: £15.00
Min Mail Order EU: £20.00
Cat. Cost: Online.
Credit Cards: All major credit/debit cards
Specialities: Herbaceous specialists & extensive range of other garden plants. Rarities available in limited numbers only.
Notes: Plants dispatched Oct-Feb only. Orders accepted throughout the year. No trees by mail order. Wheelchair accessible.
OS Grid Ref: TL586420

EBls **Peter Beales Roses** ♿ ◆
London Road, Attleborough, Norfolk, NR17 1AY
Ⓣ (01953) 454707
Ⓔ info@peterbealesroses.com
Ⓦ www.classicroses.co.uk
Contact: Tina Limmer
Opening Times: 0900-1700 Mon-Sat, 1000-1600 Sun & B/hols. Closed 25th Dec-5th Jan.
Min Mail Order UK: Nmc
Min Mail Order EU: Nmc
Cat. Cost: £5.00 outside UK.
Credit Cards: All major debit/credit cards except American Express
Specialities: Large range of perennials, shrubs, *Clematis*, climbers, ornamental trees, fruit, summer & winter bedding. National Plant Collection of Species Roses.
Notes: Display garden, open all year round (free entry). Agent for Classic Garden Element iron work. Also sells wholesale. Exports beyond EU. New wildlife garden. Plant & Food Fair 5th May 2018, Rose Festival 15-16 Jun 2018. Wheelchair accessible.
OS Grid Ref: TM026929

EBou **Boundary Nursery**
Colne Road, Bluntisham, Huntington, Cambridgeshire, PE28 3LU
Ⓣ (01487) 842611
Ⓔ herbsandalpines@gmail.com
Ⓦ https://boundarynursery.co.uk/
Contact: Peter Reason
Opening Times: By appt. only.
Min Mail Order UK: Nmc
Credit Cards: All major credit/debit cards
Specialities: Range of alpine, drought-tolerant plants and herbs.
Notes: Offers a range of shrubs, perennials and herbs for all areas of the garden.
OS Grid Ref: TL369752

EBtc **Botanica**
Chantry Farm, Campsea Ashe, Wickham Market, Suffolk, IP13 0PZ
Ⓣ (01728) 747113
Ⓜ 07887 423964
Ⓔ sales@botanica.org.uk
Ⓦ www.botanicaplantnursery.co.uk
Contact: Daniel Everett
Opening Times: 0900-1700 Mon-Fri (0900-1600 in winter), 1000-1600 w/ends. Closed w/ends Jul-Aug.
Min Mail Order UK: £30 + p&p
Cat. Cost: Online only.
Credit Cards: All major debit/credit cards except American Express
Specialities: Range of rare & unusual hardy plants. All stock is English grown at our nursery and in non-peat based compost.
Notes: Also sells wholesale.
OS Grid Ref: TM328550

ECha **The Beth Chatto Gardens** ♿
Elmstead Market, Colchester, Essex, CO7 7DB
Ⓣ (01206) 822007
Ⓕ (01206) 825933
Ⓔ info@bethchatto.co.uk
Ⓦ www.bethchatto.co.uk
Contact: David Ward
Opening Times: 0900-1700 Mon-Sat, 1000-1700 Sun, 1st Mar-31st Oct. 0900-1600 Mon-Sat, 1000-1600 Sun, Nov-end Feb.
Min Mail Order UK: Nmc
Min Mail Order EU: Ask for details
Cat. Cost: Online only.
Credit Cards: All major debit/credit cards except American Express
Specialities: Predominantly herbaceous perennials, grasses & ferns. Many unusual for special situations.
Notes: Delivers to Shows. Wheelchair accessible.
OS Grid Ref: TM069238

ECnt **Cants of Colchester Ltd**
Nayland Road, Mile End, Colchester, Essex, CO4 5HA
Ⓣ (01206) 844008
Ⓕ (01206) 855371
Ⓔ enquiries@cantsroses.co.uk
Ⓦ www.cantsroses.co.uk
Contact: Angela Pawsey
Opening Times: 0900-1300, 1400-1630 Mon-Fri. Sat varied, please phone first. Sun closed.
Min Mail Order UK: Nmc
Min Mail Order EU: Nmc
Cat. Cost: Free.
Credit Cards: Visa, MasterCard, Delta, Maestro
Specialities: Roses.
Notes: Celebrated 250 years of rose growing

in 2015. Bare-root mail order end Oct-end Mar, containers Apr-Aug. Exports beyond EU. Partial wheelchair access.

ECre **Creake Plant Centre** ♿
Leicester Road, South Creake, Fakenham, Norfolk, NR21 9PW
Ⓣ (01328) 823018
Ⓜ 07760 762499
Ⓕ (01328) 823018
Ⓔ trevor-harrison@btconnect.com
Ⓦ www.creakeplantcentre.co.uk
Contact: Mr T. Harrison
Opening Times: 1000-1300 & 1400-1730 7 days excl. Xmas.
Cat. Cost: None issued.
Credit Cards: All major credit/debit cards
Specialities: Unusual shrubs, herbaceous, conservatory plants, old roses, hellebores. Some plants only available in small quantities.
Notes: Delivers to shows. Wheelchair accessible.
OS Grid Ref: TF864353

ECrN **Crown Nursery** ♿
High Street, Ufford, Suffolk, IP13 6EL
Ⓣ (01394) 460755
Ⓕ (01394) 460142
Ⓔ enquiries@crown-nursery.co.uk
Ⓦ www.crown-nursery.co.uk
Contact: Jill Proctor
Opening Times: 0900-1700 (1600 in winter) Mon-Sat.
Min Mail Order UK: Nmc
Credit Cards: All major credit/debit cards
Specialities: Mature & semi-mature native, ornamental & fruit trees. Heritage fruit varieties.
Notes: Mail order for small/young stock only. Also sells wholesale. Wheelchair accessible.
OS Grid Ref: TM292528

ECtt **Cottage Nurseries** ♿
Thoresthorpe, Alford, Lincolnshire, LN13 0HX
Ⓣ (01507) 466968
Ⓔ bill@cottagenurseries.net
Ⓦ www.cottagenurseries.net
Contact: W.H. Denbigh
Opening Times: 0900-1700, 7 days 1st Mar-31st Oct. 1000-1500, Nov-Feb. Closed 1st Dec-6th Jan.
Min Mail Order UK: £20.00
Cat. Cost: Online only.
Credit Cards: Visa, MasterCard, Maestro
Specialities: Hardy perennials. Wide general range.
Notes: Wheelchair accessible.
OS Grid Ref: TF461776

ECul **John Cullen Gardens Ltd**
Eagle Lodge, Archers Lane, Algarkirk, Lincolnshire, PE20 2AG
Ⓣ (01205) 460567
Ⓜ 07931 634933
Ⓔ design@johncullengardens.com
Ⓦ www.johncullengardens.com
Contact: John Cullen
Opening Times: Not open. Online only.
Specialities: Scented plants, plants for pollinators, herbs, shrubs & bulbs.
Notes: A wide selection of plants from shrubs to perennials, bulbs & herbs. Delivers to shows.

EDAr **D'Arcy & Everest**
Meadowsweet Nursery, Pidley Sheep Lane (B1040), Pidley, Cambridgeshire, PE28 3FL
Ⓣ (01480) 463570
Ⓜ 07715 374440
Ⓕ (01480) 466042
Ⓔ angela@darcyeverest.co.uk
Ⓦ www.darcyeverest.co.uk
Contact: Angela Whiting
Opening Times: Open 1 w/end a month for selected months. See website/contact nursery for dates. Also for nursery tour dates (bookable in advance only). Coach parties welcome by appt. Closed Oct-Feb.
Min Mail Order UK: £15.00 + p&p
Cat. Cost: None available.
Credit Cards: All major credit/debit cards
Specialities: Alpines & sempervivums.
Notes: Delivers to shows. Partial wheelchair access.
OS Grid Ref: TL338762

EECP **Essex Carnivorous Plants**
12 Strangman Avenue, Thundersley, Essex, SS7 1RB
Ⓣ (01702) 551467
Ⓜ 07957 196391
Ⓔ Mark@essexcarnivorousplants.com
Ⓦ www.essexcarnivorousplants.com
Contact: Mark Haslett
Opening Times: By appt. only.
Min Mail Order UK: Nmc
Min Mail Order EU: Nmc
Cat. Cost: 3 × 1st class or online.
Credit Cards: PayPal
Specialities: Good range of carnivorous plants. *Dionaea*, *Sarracenia*. Some stock available in small quantities only.
Notes: Also sells wholesale. Delivers to shows.
OS Grid Ref: TQ797875

EFer **The Fern Nursery** ♿
Grimsby Road, Binbrook, Lincolnshire, LN8 6DH

Ⓣ (01472) 398092
Ⓔ rtimm@fernnursery.co.uk
Ⓦ www.fernnursery.co.uk
Contact: R.N. Timm
Opening Times: 0900-1700 Fri, Sat & Sun Apr-Oct or by appt.
Min Mail Order UK: Nmc
Min Mail Order EU: Nmc
Cat. Cost: Online only.
Credit Cards: All major credit/debit cards
Specialities: Ferns.
Notes: Display garden. Only plants in the mail order part of the catalogue can be sent mail order. Also sells wholesale. Euro accepted. Wheelchair accessible.
OS Grid Ref: TF212942

EFly THE FLY TRAP PLANTS ♿
Cookes Road, Thurton, Norwich, Norfolk, NR14 6AE
Ⓣ (01508) 480348
Ⓜ 07769 256556
Ⓔ sales@tftplants.co.uk
Ⓦ www.tftplants.co.uk
Contact: Pauline Steward
Opening Times: By appt. only.
Min Mail Order UK: Nmc
Cat. Cost: 1 × 1st class sae.
Credit Cards: PayPal
Specialities: All kinds of carnivorous plants, from *Drosera, Pinguicula, Sarracenia*, to *Utricularia* aquatic plants.
Notes: Delivers to shows. Euro accepted. Wheelchair accessible.

EGeo GEORGE'S GORGEOUS GARDENS
Outlaws Cottage, Lugs Lane, Broome, Norfolk, NR35 2HT
Ⓣ (01508) 518559
Ⓜ 07592 491234
Ⓔ georgesgorgeousgardens@gmail.com
Contact: George Gillespie
Min Mail Order UK: £20.00
Min Mail Order EU: £50.00
Cat. Cost: £2.50
Credit Cards: None
Specialities: *Plectranthus*.

EGren GRENVILLE NURSERIES ♿
Cow Watering Lane, Writtle, Chelmsford, Essex, CM1 3SB
Ⓣ (01245) 420400
Ⓕ (01245) 420400
Ⓔ info@grenvillenurseries.co.uk
Ⓦ www.grenvillenurseries.co.uk
Contact: Charlie Lauman
Opening Times: 0830-1730 Mon-Thu. 0830-1900 Fri. 0900-1700 Sat. 1000-1700 Sun.
Cat. Cost: Online only.
Credit Cards: All major credit/debit cards
Specialities: Trees, shrubs, herbaceous ferns, climbers, grasses and bamboo. Seasonal bareroot and rootball hedging and trees. Bulbs available in large quantities.
Notes: Leading plant nursery open to both the public and trade. Growers of seasonal bedding and herbaceous plants. Also stock seasonal bareroot and rootball hedging and trees and bulbs. Also sells wholesale. Wheelchair accessible.

EHDe HARPER & DEBBAGE
33 The Ridgeway, Norwich, Norfolk, NR1 4ND
Ⓣ (01603) 708104
Ⓜ 07889 679444
Ⓔ info@harperanddebbage.co.uk
Ⓦ www.harperanddebbage.co.uk
Contact: Kristopher Harper
Opening Times: Not open except by appt. Plant collection by appt only.
Min Mail Order UK: NMC
Cat. Cost: Online only.
Credit Cards: All major credit/debit cards
Specialities: *Fuchsia*. National Plant Collection of *Fuchsia* introduced by James Lye.
Notes: Sells by mail order. Attends some shows (contact nursery for details).
OS Grid Ref: TG248096

EHyd HYDE HALL PLANT CENTRE (RHS) ♿ ◆
RHS Garden Hyde Hall, Rettenden, Chelmsford, Essex, CM3 8ET
Ⓣ (01245) 402113
Ⓕ (01245) 400013
Ⓔ benmansfield@rhs.org.uk
Ⓦ www.rhs.org.uk
Contact: Ben Mansfield
Opening Times: 0930-1600 Mon-Sat, 1000-1600 Sun, Nov-Feb. 0930-1800 Mon-Sat, 1100-1700 Sun, Mar-Oct. Closed Xmas Day & Easter Sun.
Credit Cards: All major credit/debit cards
Notes: Wheelchair accessible.

EIri IRISESONLINE
Slade Cottage, Petts Lane, Little Walden, Essex, CB10 1XH
Ⓣ (01799) 526294
Ⓔ enquiries@sladecottageirisesonline.co.uk
Ⓦ www.sladecottageirisesonline.co.uk
Contact: Clare Kneen
Opening Times: By appt. only.
Min Mail Order UK: Nmc
Cat. Cost: Online only.
Credit Cards: None
Specialities: *Iris*. Some varieties available in small quantities only.

Notes: Small family-run nursery. Delivers to shows.
OS Grid Ref: TL546416

EKin **E W King & Co. Ltd. (Kings Seeds)**
Monks Farm, Pantling Lane, Coggeshall Road, Kelvedon, Essex, CO5 9PG
Ⓣ (01376) 570000
Ⓕ (01376) 571189
Ⓔ sales@kingsseeds.com
Ⓦ www.kingsseeds.com
Contact: Andrew Tokely
Min Mail Order UK: Nmc
Min Mail Order EU: Nmc
Cat. Cost: Free.
Credit Cards: All major credit/debit cards
Specialities: Vegetable, flower, grass, sweet pea and pea & bean seeds, incl. many hybrid & unusual items.
Notes: Incorporating Suffolk Herbs. Also sells wholesale. Exports beyond the EU.

ELad **Ladybird Nurseries** ♿
Gromford Lane, Snape, Saxmundham, Suffolk, IP17 1RD
Ⓣ (01728) 688289
Ⓦ www.ladybirdnurseries.co.uk
Contact: Mrs M. Booker
Opening Times: 0900-1700, Mon-Sat, 1000-1600 Sun.
Credit Cards: All major credit/debit cards
Notes: Wheelchair accessible.
OS Grid Ref: TM388589

ELan **Langthorns Plantery** ♿
High Cross Lane West, Little Canfield, Dunmow, Essex, CM6 1TD
Ⓣ (01371) 872611
Ⓔ info@langthorns.com
Ⓦ www.langthorns.com
Contact: E. Cannon
Opening Times: 0830-1800 Apr-end June. 0900-1730 or dusk (if earlier) 7 days. Closed Xmas fortnight.
Min Mail Order UK: £ 20.00
Cat. Cost: Online only.
Credit Cards: Visa, Access, Switch, MasterCard, Delta
Specialities: Wide general range with many unusual plants.
Notes: Mail order any plant under 4ft tall. Wheelchair accessible.
OS Grid Ref: TL592204

ELon **Long House Plants** ♿
The Long House, Church Road, Noak Hill, Romford, Essex, RM4 1LD
Ⓣ (01708) 371719
Ⓔ tim@longhouse-plants.co.uk
Ⓦ www.longhouse-plants.co.uk
Contact: Tim Carter
Opening Times: 1000-1700 Fri, Sat & B/hols, 1000-1600 Sun, beginning Mar-end Sep, or by appt.
Credit Cards: All major credit/debit cards
Specialities: Interesting range of choice trees, shrubs, climbers, roses, grasses, herbaceous perennials & ferns. Many unusual varieties. Specialities incl. *Agapanthus*, *Aster*, *Camellia*, *Hemerocallis*, *Iris sibirica*, *Kniphofia*, *Phlox* & *Symphyotrichum*. Some plants available in small quantities.
Notes: Wheelchair accessible. Disabled toilet. See website for garden open days.
OS Grid Ref: TQ554194

EMac **Firecrest Trees & Shrubs Nursery** ♿
Hall Road, Little Bealings, Woodbridge, Suffolk, IP13 6LG
Ⓣ (01473) 625937
Ⓕ (01473) 625937
Ⓔ firecrest98@tiscali.co.uk
Ⓦ www.firecrest.org.uk
Contact: Mac McGregor
Opening Times: 0900-1500 Tue-Fri, 0900-1200 Sat.
Credit Cards: None
Specialities: Trees & shrubs. Japanese maples. Bareroot hedging.
Notes: Also sells wholesale. Bareroot mail order only. Euro accepted. Wheelchair accessible.

EMal **Marshall's Malmaisons** ♿
Hullwood Barn, Shelley, Ipswich, Suffolk, IP7 5RE
Ⓣ (01473) 822400
Ⓜ 07768 454875
Ⓔ jim@malmaisons.plus.com
Contact: J.M. Marshall/Sarah Cook
Opening Times: By appt. only.
Min Mail Order UK: £33.00 incl. p&p
Min Mail Order EU: £36.00 incl. p&p
Cat. Cost: 1st class sae.
Credit Cards: None
Specialities: National Plant Collection of Malmaison Carnations & Cedric Morris *Iris*. Iris stock only available in small quantities.
Notes: Also sells wholesale. Wheelchair accessible.
OS Grid Ref: TM006394

EMdy **Mandy Plants** ♿
(office) 4 Stevens Road, Little Snoring, Norfolk, NR21 0GZ
Ⓣ (01328) 878144
Ⓜ 07432 112245

Ⓔ enquiries@mandyplants.com
Ⓦ www.mandyplants.com
Contact: Liz Spanton
Opening Times: By appt. only.
Min Mail Order UK: Nmc
Min Mail Order EU: £25.00
Credit Cards: All major credit/debit cards, PayPal
Specialities: *Dipladenia*, *Lantana* & *Mandevilla*, other tender perennials.
Notes: Nursery is at Little Snoring, Norfolk. Also sells wholesale. Delivers to shows. Wheelchair accessible.

EMic **MICKFIELD HOSTAS** ♿
The Poplars, Wetheringsett Road, Mickfield, Stowmarket, Suffolk, IP14 5LH
Ⓣ (01449) 711576
Ⓕ (01449) 711576
Ⓔ mickfieldhostas@btconnect.com
Ⓦ www.mickfieldhostas.co.uk
Contact: Mr & Mrs R.L.C. Milton
Opening Times: 1000-1600, Fri to Mon. Closed Tue-Thu during May And June. All other times by appt.
Min Mail Order UK: Nmc
Min Mail Order EU: Nmc
Cat. Cost: Online only.
Credit Cards: All major debit/credit cards except American Express
Specialities: National Plant Collection of *Hosta* containing over 2000 varieties.
Notes: See website for details of cvs held & latest availability. Waiting list for rarities & some limited quantity plants only available at nursery. Will divide parent plants for collectors if feasible. Expect to pay more for root divisions of mature plants. Delivers to shows. Wheelchair accessible.
OS Grid Ref: TM136619

EMil **MILL RACE GARDEN CENTRE** ♿
New Road, Aldham, Colchester, Essex, CO6 3QT
Ⓣ (01206) 242521
Ⓔ plantdesk@millracegardencentre.co.uk
Ⓦ www.millracegardencentre.co.uk
Contact: Annette Bayliss
Opening Times: 0900-1730 Mon-Sat, 1000-1630 Sun.
Min Mail Order UK: £9.00
Credit Cards: All major credit/debit cards
Specialities: Stock available in small quantities only.
Notes: Trees & large shrubs not sent by mail order. Wheelchair accessible.
OS Grid Ref: TL918268

EMor **MOORE AND MOORE PLANTS** ♿
London Road, Billericay, Essex, CM12 9HR
Ⓣ (01277) 563243
Ⓜ 07881 756252
Ⓔ contact@mooreandmooreplants.co.uk
Ⓦ www.mooreandmooreplants.co.uk
Contact: Lynne Moore
Opening Times: By appt. only.
Cat. Cost: Online only.
Credit Cards: All major credit/debit cards
Specialities: Nursery stocking a large range of perennials, bulbs, ferns, grasses and herbs, especially unusual or rare varieties. *Agapanthus*, *Astrantia*, *Athyrium*, *Dryopteris*, *Echinacea*, *Geranium*, *Helenium*, *Hosta* & other plants for shaded areas. Bog garden/ marginal plants. Most plants available in small numbers only.
Notes: See website or contact nursery for details of open days. Delivers to shows. Wheelchair accessible.

NAts **NATURAL SURROUNDINGS**
Bayfield, Nr Glandford, Holt, Norfolk, NR25 7JN
Ⓣ (01263) 711091
Ⓔ wildlife@naturalsurroundings.info
Ⓦ www.naturalsurroundings.info
Contact: Anne Harrap
Opening Times: 1000-1700, 7 days May-Sep. 1000-1600 Tue-Sun Oct-Mar. Open B/hols.
Credit Cards: All major debit/credit cards except American Express
Specialities: British wild flowers, native trees, shrubs and cottage garden plants, plus a selection of unusual hardy perennials. Also seed.
Notes: We propagate and grow in peat-free compost only. Plants available in limited quantities. Follow the brown 'Wildflower Centre' signs. Wildlife-friendly demonstration gardens and semi-natural meadows open to the public (small charge). Group visits by arrangement; talks to garden clubs and societies in Norfolk.
OS Grid Ref: TG048407

ENfk **NORFOLK HERBS** ♿
Blackberry Farm, Dillington, Dereham, Norfolk, NR19 2QD
Ⓣ (01362) 860812
Ⓕ (01362) 860812
Ⓔ info@norfolkherbs.co.uk
Ⓦ www.norfolkherbs.co.uk
Contact: Rosemary or Oliver Clifton-Sprigg
Opening Times: Apr-Aug Mon-Sat 0900-1700. Sun 1000-1300: Mar, Sep & Dec Wed-

Sat 1000-1600: Feb, Oct & Nov Fri-Sat 1000-1600: Closed Xmas to end of Jan. To visit at other times, please contact nursery.
Min Mail Order UK: £8.39
Cat. Cost: 2 × 2nd class.
Credit Cards: All major credit/debit cards
Specialities: Established 1986. Growers & suppliers of naturally raised culinary, medicinal & aromatic herb plants. Bay trees & scented pelargoniums.
Notes: Sells from nursery, online & at local shows. A founding member of Norfolk Nursery Network. Also sells wholesale. Delivers to shows. Wheelchair accessible.
OS Grid Ref: TF967150

ENor **Norfolk Lavender** ♿
Caley Mill, Heacham, King's Lynn, Norfolk, PE31 7JE
Ⓣ (01485) 570384
Ⓜ 07787 550286
Ⓕ (01485) 571176
Ⓔ info@norfolk-lavender.co.uk
Ⓦ www.norfolk-lavender.co.uk
Contact: Shelley Eagle
Opening Times: 0900-1700 7 days, Apr-Oct. 0900-1600 7 days, Nov-Mar.
Min Mail Order UK: Nmc
Cat. Cost: Free.
Credit Cards: All major debit/credit cards except American Express
Specialities: National Collection of *Lavandula*, sect. *L. dentata* & *L. pterostoechas*.
Notes: Wheelchair accessible.
OS Grid Ref: TF685368

EOHP **Old Hall Plants**
1 The Old Hall, Barsham, Beccles, Suffolk, NR34 8HB
Ⓣ (01502) 717475
Ⓔ info@oldhallplants.co.uk
Ⓦ www.oldhallplants.co.uk
Contact: Janet Elliott
Opening Times: By appt. only. Please telephone first.
Min Mail Order UK: Nmc
Min Mail Order EU: Nmc
Cat. Cost: 4 × 1st class.
Specialities: House plants. Some plants available in small quantities.
Notes: Partial wheelchair access.
OS Grid Ref: TM396904

EPau **Paugers Plants Ltd**
Bury Road, Depden, Bury St Edmunds, Suffolk, IP29 4BU
Ⓣ (01284) 850527
Ⓔ enquiries@paugers-plants.co.uk
Ⓦ www.paugers-plants.co.uk
Contact: Geraldine Arnold
Opening Times: 0900-1730 Wed-Sat, 1000-1700 Sun & B/hols, 1st Mar-30th Nov.
Min Mail Order UK: Nmc
Cat. Cost: None issued.
Credit Cards: All major credit/debit cards
Specialities: Hardy shrubs & perennials in large or small quantities.
Notes: Also sells wholesale.
OS Grid Ref: TL783568

EPed **Pernewood Plants**
Popes Hall, Fersfield Road, South Lopham, Diss, Norfolk, IP22 2JY
Ⓜ 07484 332651
Ⓔ info@pernewoodplants.co.uk
Ⓦ www.pernewoodplants.co.uk
Contact: Kevan Milbourne
Opening Times: Not open. Plant collections by appt.
Min Mail Order UK: £30.00
Credit Cards: All major debit/credit cards except American Express
Specialities: Wide range of hardy perennials, ornamental grasses and shade-loving plants and ferns. Plants UK sourced or raised from own nursery stock specimens.
Notes: Small family run online plant nursery. Delivers to shows.
OS Grid Ref: TM055816

EPfP **The Place for Plants** ♿
East Bergholt Place, East Bergholt, Suffolk, CO7 6UP
Ⓣ (01206) 299224
Ⓕ (01206) 299229
Ⓔ sales@placeforplants.co.uk
Ⓦ www.placeforplants.co.uk
Contact: Sara Eley
Opening Times: 1000-1700 (or dusk if earlier) 7 days. Closed Easter Sun. Garden open Mar-Oct.
Min Mail Order UK: Nmc
Cat. Cost: Online only.
Credit Cards: All major credit/debit cards
Specialities: Wide range of specialist & popular plants. National Collection of deciduous *Euonymus*. 20 acre mature garden with free access to RHS members Apr-Sept excl. Suns.
Notes: Mail order. Delivers to shows. Euro accepted. Wheelchair accessible.

EPom **Pomona Fruits Ltd**
Pomona House, 12 Third Avenue, Walton-on-the-Naze, Essex, CO14 8JU
Ⓣ (01255) 440410

Ⓕ (01255) 440420
Ⓔ Info@PomonaFruits.co.uk
Ⓦ www.PomonaFruits.co.uk
Contact: Ming Yang/Claire Higgins
Opening Times: Not open. Mail order only.
Min Mail Order UK: Nmc
Cat. Cost: Free.
Credit Cards: All major credit/debit cards
Specialities: Fruit stock.

EPot **Pottertons Nursery** ♿
Moortown Road, Nettleton, Caistor, Lincolnshire, LN7 6HX
Ⓣ (01472) 851714
Ⓔ sales@pottertons.co.uk
Ⓦ www.pottertons.co.uk
Contact: Robert Potterton
Opening Times: 1000-1600 Tue-Fri, Mar-Oct. By appt. only on Sat & from Nov-Feb.
Min Mail Order UK: Nmc
Min Mail Order EU: Nmc
Cat. Cost: £2.00 in stamps.
Credit Cards: MasterCard, Visa
Specialities: Alpines, dwarf bulbs & woodland plants.
Notes: Talks given nationally & internationally to garden clubs & societies. Group nursery tours by arrangement. Delivers to shows. Euro accepted. Wheelchair accessible.
OS Grid Ref: TA091001

EPPr **The Plantsman's Preference** ♿
Church Road, South Lopham, Diss, Norfolk, IP22 2LW
Ⓣ (01379) 710810
Ⓜ 07799 855559
Ⓔ tim@plantpref.co.uk
Ⓦ www.plantpref.co.uk
Contact: Tim Fuller
Opening Times: 0930-1700 Fri, Sat & Sun Mar-Oct. Other times by appt.
Min Mail Order UK: Nmc
Min Mail Order EU: Nmc
Cat. Cost: Online only.
Credit Cards: All major credit/debit cards
Specialities: Hardy geraniums & ornamental grasses. Unusual & interesting perennials incl. shade/woodland. Some choice shrubs esp. *caprifoliaceae*. National Plant Collection of *Molinia*.
Notes: Mail order all year excl. Xmas-New Year. Delivers to shows. Wheelchair accessible.
OS Grid Ref: TM041819

EPri **Priory Plants** ♿
1 Covey Cottages, Hintlesham, Nr Ipswich, Suffolk, IP8 3NY
Ⓣ (01473) 652656
Ⓜ 07798 627618
Ⓕ (01473) 652656
Ⓔ sue.mann3@btinternet.com
Ⓦ www.prioryplants.co.uk
Contact: Sue Mann
Opening Times: By appt. only. Please ring first to avoid disappointment.
Min Mail Order UK: Nmc
Min Mail Order EU: Nmc
Cat. Cost: Online only.
Credit Cards: None
Specialities: Cottage garden perennials, as well as increasing range of South African plants. *Agapanthus*, *Astrantia*, *Dierama*, *Dietes*, *Eucomis*, *Iris siberica*, *Kniphofia*, *Nerine*, *Tritonia*, *Tulbaghia* & *Watsonia*.
Notes: Sells at plant fairs & agricultural shows. Also sells wholesale. Exports beyond EU. Delivers to shows. Wheelchair accessible.
OS Grid Ref: TM070448

EPts **Potash Nursery Ltd** ♿
Cow Green, Bacton, Stowmarket, Suffolk, IP14 4HJ
Ⓣ (01449) 781671
Ⓔ enquiries@potashnursery.co.uk
Ⓦ www.potashnursery.co.uk
Contact: M.W. Clare
Opening Times: Not open except for collection of pre-ordered plants by appt. only.
Min Mail Order UK: £24.00
Cat. Cost: 1 × 1st class.
Credit Cards: Visa, Delta, MasterCard
Specialities: *Fuchsia*.
Notes: Peat free. Delivers to shows. Wheelchair accessible.
OS Grid Ref: TM055656

ERCP **Rose Cottage Plants**
Bay Tree Farm, Epping Green, Essex, CM16 6PU
Ⓣ (01992) 573775
Ⓔ anne@rosecottageplants.co.uk
Ⓦ www.rosecottageplants.co.uk
Contact: Anne & Jack Barnard
Opening Times: Most Fris Mar-Oct. Also by appt & for special events. See website for details.
Min Mail Order UK: Nmc
Min Mail Order EU: £20.00
Cat. Cost: Online only.
Credit Cards: All major debit/credit cards except American Express
Specialities: Hardy bulbs & *Dahlia*.
Notes: Mail order for Dahlia tubers and hardy bulbs. Delivers to shows.
OS Grid Ref: TL435053

E

EShb **SHRUBLAND PARK NURSERIES**
Maltings Farm, Whatfield Road,
Elmsett, Ipswich, Suffolk,
IP7 6LZ
Ⓣ (01473) 657012
Ⓜ 07890 527744
Ⓔ gill@shrublandparknurseries.co.uk
Ⓦ www.shrublandparknurseries.co.uk
Contact: Gill & Catherine Stitt
Opening Times: See website or contact nursery.
Min Mail Order UK: Nmc
Min Mail Order EU: Nmc
Cat. Cost: Online or free by post.
Credit Cards: All major credit/debit cards, PayPal
Specialities: Conservatory plants, succulents, hardy perennials, climbers, shrubs, ferns & grasses. Some more unusual plants may be in short supply.
Notes: Please check before visiting that nursery is open & that any plants you require are in stock. Delivers to shows.
OS Grid Ref: TM052466

ESMi **STRAIGHT MILE NURSERY GARDENS** ♿
Ongar Road, Pilgrims Hatch, Brentwood, Essex, CM15 9SA
Ⓣ (01277) 374439
Ⓔ gdlsisley@aol.com
Ⓦ www.straightmile.net
Contact: David Sisley
Opening Times: 1000-1700, 7 days (but closed some Weds, phone first.)
Min Mail Order UK: Nmc
Cat. Cost: Epimedium Cat. Only.
Credit Cards: All major debit/credit cards except American Express
Specialities: General nursery stock. Japanese maples, *Epimedium*. Some in small quantities only. Mail order epimediums only.
Notes: Delivers to shows. Wheelchair accessible.
OS Grid Ref: TQ571964

EStr **STRICTLY DAYLILIES**
2 Primes Corner, Histon, Cambridgeshire, CB24 9AG
Ⓣ (01223) 236239
Ⓜ 07765 236880
Ⓔ info@strictlydaylilies.com
Ⓦ www.strictlydaylilies.com
Contact: Paula & Chris Dyason
Opening Times: Mail order only.
Min Mail Order UK: Nmc
Min Mail Order EU: Nmc
Cat. Cost: No charge.
Credit Cards: All major credit/debit cards
Specialities: *Hemerocallis*. Some stock available in small quantities only. National Plant Collection of *Hemerocallis* (post 2014 hybrid registrations).
Notes: Open gardens Fri-Sun in Jul, please phone for confirmation. Also sells wholesale. Exports beyond the EU. Delivers to shows. Euro accepted.

ESty **STYLE ROSES** ♿
(office) Highworth, 56 Spalding Road, Holbeach, Spalding, Lincolnshire, PE12 7HG
Ⓣ (01406) 424089
Ⓜ 07760 626750 or 07780 860415
Ⓕ (01406) 490006
Ⓔ mail@styleroses.co.uk
Ⓦ www.styleroses.co.uk
Contact: Margaret Styles
Opening Times: Vary. Please telephone for appt.
Min Mail Order UK: Nmc
Min Mail Order EU: Nmc
Cat. Cost: Free in UK.
Credit Cards: MasterCard, Visa
Specialities: Standard & bush roses.
Notes: Nursery is at Cackle Hill Farm, Holbeach, Lincs, PE12 8AG. Bush roses available mail order to mainland UK all year round. Standard roses mail order as bare-root plants Nov-Mar, or in pots by collection from nursery/shows all year round. Export to EU Nov-Mar. Exports beyond EU subject to Plant Health Requirements (not USA). Also sells wholesale. Delivers to shows. Wheelchair accessible.

ESwi **SWINES MEADOW FARM NURSERY** ♿ ◆
47 Towngate East, Market Deeping, Peterborough, PE6 8LQ
Ⓣ (01778) 343340
Ⓜ 07432 627766
Ⓔ ceveandsons@btconnect.com
Ⓦ www.swinesmeadowfarmnursery.co.uk
Contact: Colin Ward
Opening Times: 0900-1600 Mon-Sat, 1000-1600 Sun. Closed Jan, except by appt. only.
Min Mail Order UK: £10.00
Min Mail Order EU: £10.00
Credit Cards: All major debit/credit cards except American Express
Specialities: Hardy exotics, tree ferns, bamboos & *Hosta*. Wollemi pine stockist. Many specialities available in small quantities only.
Notes: Delivers to shows. Wheelchair accessible.
OS Grid Ref: TF150113

EThi **Thistlefield Plants and Design**
65 Westgate Street, Shouldham, Kings Lynn, Norfolk, PE33 0BL
Ⓣ (01366) 347365
Ⓜ 07899 994071
Ⓕ (01366) 347365
Ⓔ paul@thistlefieldplants.co.uk
Ⓦ www.thistlefieldplants.co.uk
Contact: Paul Welford
Opening Times: Not open. Sells at plant fairs & shows only.
Min Mail Order UK: Nmc
Cat. Cost: Online only.
Credit Cards: None
Specialities: Perennials. *Tricyrtis* available in small quantities only.
Notes: Delivers to shows.

ETho **Thorncroft Clematis Ltd** ♿
The Lings, Reymerston, Norwich, Norfolk, NR9 4QG
Ⓣ (01953) 850407
Ⓔ sales@thorncroftclematis.co.uk
Ⓦ www.thorncroftclematis.co.uk
Contact: Peter Skeggs-Gooch
Opening Times: Mail order only. Telephones answered 1000-1600 Mon-Fri.
Min Mail Order UK: £7.99
Min Mail Order EU: £20.00
Cat. Cost: £3.50
Credit Cards: All major credit/debit cards
Specialities: *Clematis*.
Notes: Supply, by mail order, mature garden-ready *Clematis* plants of at least 2 years in age. Diverse range from all over the world to include both unusual and popular varieties. Focus on excellent customer service & quality plants. Delivers to shows. Wheelchair accessible.
OS Grid Ref: TG039062

ETWh **Trevor White Old Fashioned Roses**
Bennetts Brier, 59, The Street, Felthorpe, Norwich, Norfolk, NR10 4AB
Ⓣ (01603) 755135
Ⓕ (01603) 755135
Ⓔ sales@oldroses.co.uk
Contact: Trevor White
Opening Times: 0900-430 Mon-Fri (office)
Min Mail Order UK: One plant + P&P
Min Mail Order EU: One plant + P&P
Credit Cards: All major credit/debit cards
Specialities: Old, shrub, climbing and rambling roses.
Notes: Specialist grower of roses for over 30 years. All plants grown by us and available via the website. Unique collection of ancient and modern varieties for all types of garden. Top quality plants lifted to order and not stored.

EUJe **Urban Jungle**
Ringland Lane, Old Costessey, Norwich, Norfolk, NR8 5BG
Ⓣ (01603) 744997
Ⓔ limegarden@sky.com
Ⓦ www.urbanjungle.uk.com
Contact: Niamh Mullally
Opening Times: 1000-1700 7 days incl B/hols, 1st Feb-31st Oct. 1000-1600 Thu-Sun, Nov-Dec. Closed Jan.
Min Mail Order UK: Nmc
Min Mail Order EU: Nmc
Credit Cards: All major credit/debit cards
Specialities: Wide range of choice plants from exotic bedding to hardy evergreens.
Notes: Display gardens & living walls. Delivers to shows. Partial wheelchair access.
OS Grid Ref: TG153127

EVic **Victorian Violas**
85 Fulmar Road, Lincoln, Lincolnshire, LN6 0RX
Ⓣ (01522) 686343
Ⓔ victorianviolas@gmail.com
Ⓦ www.victorianviolas.co.uk
Contact: Robert Chapman
Opening Times: Not open. Mail order only.
Min Mail Order UK: Nmc
Cat. Cost: Online only.
Credit Cards: None
Specialities: Hardy perennial *Viola* (summer flowering). Named cultivars.
Notes: BACS payments accepted. Also sells wholesale.

EWat **Water Garden Plants**
Wayside Aquatics, Blackmore Road, Doddinghurst, Brentwood, Essex, CM15 0HU
Ⓜ 01277 823603
Ⓔ sales@watergardenplants.co.uk
Ⓦ www.watergardenplants.co.uk
Contact: Anna Robinson
Opening Times: Mail order only.
Min Mail Order UK: Nmc
Min Mail Order EU: Nmc
Cat. Cost: Online.
Credit Cards: All major credit/debit cards
Specialities: Range of water garden plants: water lilies, floating plants, oxygenating plants, marginals, marsh plants. Some stock in small quantities.
Notes: Euro accepted.
OS Grid Ref: TQ585995

G

EWes **West Acre Gardens** ♿
Tumbleyhill Road, West Acre, King's Lynn, Norfolk, PE32 1UJ
Ⓣ (01760) 755562
Ⓔ info@westacregardens.co.uk
Ⓦ www.westacregardens.co.uk
Contact: J.J. Tuite
Opening Times: 1000-1700 7 days 1st Feb-30th Nov. Other times by appt.
Cat. Cost: None issued.
Credit Cards: Visa, MasterCard, Delta, Switch
Specialities: Very wide selection of herbaceous & other garden plants incl. *Galanthus*, *Primula auricula* & *Rhodohypoxis*.
Notes: Delivers to shows. Wheelchair accessible.
OS Grid Ref: TF792182

EWhm **Waltham Herbs**
Willow Vale Nursery, North Kelsey Road, Caistor, Lincolnshire, LN7 6SF
Ⓣ (01472) 859481
Ⓜ 07949 883091
Ⓕ (01472) 859481
Ⓔ angelasach2@aol.com
Ⓦ www.waltham-herbs.co.uk
Contact: Steve Penney
Opening Times: By appt. only.
Min Mail Order UK: £3.00
Credit Cards: All major credit/debit cards
Specialities: Herbs, lavenders and perennials, also some shrubs. Peat-free and pesticide-free.
Notes: For open days, see website or contact nursery. Delivers to shows.
OS Grid Ref: TA401509

EWld **Woodlands**
Peppin Lane, Fotherby, Louth, Lincolnshire, LN11 0UW
Ⓣ (01507) 603586
Ⓔ annbobarmstrong@btinternet.com
Ⓦ www.woodlandsplants.co.uk
Contact: Ann Armstrong
Opening Times: 1400-1700 Wed Apr to Aug.
Min Mail Order UK: Nmc
Min Mail Order EU: Nmc
Cat. Cost: None issued.
Credit Cards: None
Specialities: Small but interesting range of unusual plants, esp. woodland, *Codonopsis* and *Salvia*, all grown on the nursery in limited quantity. National Plant Collection of *Codonopsis*.
Notes: Mature garden, art gallery & refreshments. Euro accepted.
OS Grid Ref: TF322918

EWTr **Walnut Tree Garden Nursery**
Flymoor Lane, Rocklands, Attleborough, Norfolk, NR17 1BP
Ⓣ (01953) 488163
Ⓔ info@wtgn.co.uk
Ⓦ www.wtgn.co.uk
Contact: Jim Paine & Clare Billington
Opening Times: 0900-1700 Wed-Sun Feb-Oct or by appt.
Min Mail Order UK: £20.00
Cat. Cost: Online.
Credit Cards: All major credit/debit cards
Specialities: Flowering dogwood: *Cornus florida*, *C. kousa* & *C. nuttalli* cvs. *Malus* cvs.
Notes: Delivers to shows.
OS Grid Ref: TL978973

Scotland

GAbr **Abriachan Nurseries**
Loch Ness Side, Inverness, Inverness-shire, IV3 8LA
Ⓣ (01463) 861232
Ⓔ info@lochnessgarden.com
Ⓦ www.lochnessgarden.com
Contact: Mr & Mrs D. Davidson
Opening Times: 0900-1900 daily (dusk if earlier) Feb-Nov.
Min Mail Order UK: Nmc
Cat. Cost: 4 × 1st class.
Credit Cards: All major credit/debit cards
Specialities: Herbaceous perennials, old-fashioned *Helianthemum*, *Primula*, *Primula auricula*, *Sempervivum* & hardy geraniums.
Notes: Delivers to shows. Partial wheelchair access (to nursery only).
OS Grid Ref: NH571347

GBee **Beeches Cottage Nursery**
Near Hawksland, Lesmahagow, South Lanarkshire, ML11 9PY
Ⓣ (01555) 893369
Ⓜ 07930 343131
Ⓔ thebeeches.nursery@talktalk.net
Ⓦ www.beechescottage.co.uk
Contact: Margaret Harrison, Steven Harrison
Opening Times: 1000-1630 Wed-Sun, 1st Apr-30th Sep.
Cat. Cost: None issued.
Credit Cards: None
Specialities: Traditional & unusual hardy cottage garden perennials which can be seen growing in display gardens at 850ft.
Notes: Group visits by arrangement. Partial wheelchair access.
OS Grid Ref: NS837403

GBin **Binny Plants** ♿
Binny Estate, Ecclesmachan Road, Near Broxburn, West Lothian, EH52 6NL

Ⓣ (01506) 858931
Ⓜ 07753 626117
Ⓔ contact@binnyplants.com
Ⓦ www.binnyplants.com
Contact: Billy Carruthers & David Wong
Opening Times: 1000-1700, 7 days. Closed over Xmas & New Year.
Min Mail Order UK: Nmc
Min Mail Order EU: Nmc
Cat. Cost: 4 × 1st class.
Credit Cards: Visa, MasterCard, EuroCard, Maestro
Specialities: Over 250 varieties of *Paeonia*, plus a good range of herbaceous perennials, grasses & ferns incl. *Astilbe*, *Bergenia*, *Geranium*, *Molinia*, *Persicaria* & *Iris*.
Notes: Also sells wholesale. Exports beyond the EU. Delivers to shows. Wheelchair accessible.
OS Grid Ref: NT050732

GCro **Croft 16 Daffodils**
16 Midtown of Inverasdale, Poolewe, Ross-shire, IV22 2LW
Ⓣ (01445) 781717
Ⓔ sales@croft16daffodils.co.uk
Ⓦ www.croft16daffodils.co.uk
Contact: Duncan & Kate Donald
Opening Times: Not open. Mail order only.
Min Mail Order UK: Nmc
Min Mail Order EU: Nmc
Cat. Cost: Online only.
Credit Cards: PayPal
Specialities: National Plant Collection of *Narcissus* bred pre-1930. Some stocks only available in small quantities. A waiting list for desiderata is in operation.
Notes: Please order by mid-May for delivery in the same year. Orders unfulfilled in one season will take priority the following year. Customers outside the EU should contact nursery.
OS Grid Ref: NG822851

GEdr **Edrom Nurseries**
Coldingham, Eyemouth, Berwickshire, TD14 5TZ
Ⓣ (01890) 771386
Ⓕ (01890) 771387
Ⓔ mail@edrom-nurseries.co.uk
Ⓦ www.edrom-nurseries.co.uk
Contact: Mr Terry Hunt
Opening Times: 0900-1700 Thu, Fri, Sat & Mon (closed Tue & Wed), 1000-1600 Sun.
Min Mail Order UK: Nmc
Min Mail Order EU: Nmc
Cat. Cost: Free.
Credit Cards: All major credit/debit cards
Specialities: *Epimedium*, *Gentiana*, *Primula*, *Meconopsis*, *Rhodohypoxis*, *Trillium*, *Hepatica* & Japanese *Saxifraga*.
Notes: Delivers to shows.
OS Grid Ref: NT873663

GFgr **Firgrove Plants**
21 South Main Street, Wigtown, Newton Stewart, Dumfries and Galloway, DG8 9EH
Ⓣ (01988) 402054
Ⓜ 07749 314394
Ⓔ jenny.mackinnon@virgin.net
Ⓦ http://firgrovehouseleeks.zohosites.eu/
Contact: Jenny MacKinnon
Opening Times: Not open. Mail order only.
Min Mail Order UK: £11.00
Cat. Cost: Sae.
Credit Cards: None
Specialities: Wide range of houseleeks in small quantities.
Notes: Houseleeks by mail order Apr-mid Oct.

GGGa **Glendoick Gardens Ltd**
Glendoick, Perth, Perthshire, PH2 7NS
Ⓣ (01738) 860205
Ⓔ orders@glendoick.com
Ⓦ www.glendoick.com
Contact: Kenneth Cox
Opening Times: Nursery not open to the public. Garden centre open 0900-1730 (summer), 0900-1700 (winter) 7 days. Gardens open Apr & May, details on website or contact nursery for details.
Min Mail Order UK: £500.00
Min Mail Order EU: £500.00
Credit Cards: All major debit/credit cards except American Express
Specialities: Rhododendrons & azaleas, other ericaceous plants & *Meconopsis*. Plants from wild seed. Most but not all plants available at garden centre. Three National Plant Collections.
Notes: Partial wheelchair access to Garden Centre.

GJos **Jo's Garden Enterprise** ♿
Easter Balmungle Farm, Eathie Road, by Rosemarkie, Ross-shire, IV10 8SL
Ⓣ (01381) 621006
Ⓔ jos_garden_enterprise@hotmail.co.uk
Contact: Joanna Chance
Opening Times: 1000 to dusk, 7 days.
Cat. Cost: None.
Credit Cards: None
Specialities: Alpines & herbaceous perennials. Selection of native wild flowers.
Notes: Wheelchair accessible.
OS Grid Ref: NH600742

G

GKev **Kevock Garden Plants**
Kevock Road, Lasswade, Midlothian, EH18 1HX
Ⓣ (0131) 454 0660
Ⓕ (0131) 454 0660
Ⓔ info@kevockgarden.co.uk
Ⓦ www.kevockgarden.co.uk
Contact: Elea Strang
Opening Times: Mail order. Not open.
Min Mail Order UK: £30.00
Min Mail Order EU: £30.00
Cat. Cost: 2 × 2nd class.
Credit Cards: All major credit/debit cards.
Specialities: Chinese and Himalayan plants. *Daphne, Iris, Meconopsis, Paeonia, Primula, Trillium*, woodland plants, alpine plants, rock plants, marginal and bog plants, bulbs, Chinese and Himalayan trees and shrubs, *Sorbus, Rhododendron*.
Notes: Not open to the public. Please purchase plants by mail order or from plant stalls at the shows we attend. Also sells wholesale.

GKin **Kinlochlaich Garden Plant Centre**
c/o Blarchasgaig, Appin, Argyll, PA38 4BB
Ⓜ 07881 525754
Ⓔ fiona@kinlochlaich.plus.com
Ⓦ www.kinlochlaichgardencentre.co.uk
Contact: Fiona Hutchison
Opening Times: 1000-1700 Mar-mid Oct, 1000-1500 or by appt., mid-Oct-Feb.
Cat. Cost: None issued.
Credit Cards: All major credit/debit cards
Specialities: Hardy shrubs, trees, azaleas, perennials. Also Gulf Stream plants such as *Drymis, Embothrium, Eucryphia, Tropaeolum* & more. Good selection of hardy seaside plants.
Notes: Does not offer mail order but will post where possible. Partial wheelchair access (gravel paths), wheelchair accessible toilet.

GLet **Letham Plants**
11a Letham Mains Holdings, Haddington, East Lothian, EH41 4NW
Ⓣ (01620) 822350
Ⓜ 07842 211712
Ⓔ lethamplants@hotmail.co.uk
Ⓦ www.letham-plants.co.uk
Contact: Caroline Samuel
Opening Times: By appt. only.
Min Mail Order UK: Nmc
Min Mail Order EU: Nmc
Cat. Cost: Online only.
Credit Cards: All major credit/debit cards
Specialities: *Astrantia, Dicentra*.
Notes: Also sells wholesale. Delivers to shows. Euro accepted.
OS Grid Ref: NT487730

GLog **Logie Steading Plants** ♿
Logie Steading, Dunphail, Forres, Moray, IV36 2QN
Ⓣ (01309) 611222 or 611278
Ⓕ (01309) 611300
Ⓔ panny@logie.co.uk
Ⓦ www.logie.co.uk
Contact: Mrs Panny Laing
Opening Times: 1000-1700 hours, 7 days, Feb-Xmas.
Credit Cards: All major credit/debit cards
Specialities: Unusual hardy plants, grown in Scotland for Scottish gardens. Large range of hardy geraniums, bold herbaceous plants, grasses & marginal plants, trees and shrubs.
Notes: Logie House Garden open every day. Café, farm shop, art gallery, second-hand books, antiques, whisky & wine, river walk, heritage centre. Wheelchair accessible (except river walk).
OS Grid Ref: NJ006504

GMaP **Macplants** ♿
Berrybank Nursery, 5 Boggs Holdings, Pencaitland, East Lothian, EH34 5BA
Ⓣ (01875) 341179
Ⓕ (01875) 340842
Ⓔ sales@macplants.co.uk
Ⓦ www.macplants.co.uk
Contact: Gavin McNaughton
Opening Times: 1030-1700 7 days, Mar-end Sep. 1030-1600 Mon-Fri, Oct. Closed Nov-end Feb except by appt.
Min Mail Order UK: Nmc
Cat. Cost: 4 × 2nd class.
Credit Cards: MasterCard, Switch, Visa
Specialities: Herbaceous perennials, alpines, hardy ferns & grasses. *Meconopsis*. National Plant Collection of *Sanguisorba*.
Notes: Also sells wholesale. Delivers to shows. Wheelchair accessible.
OS Grid Ref: NT447703

GPer **Perthshire Heathers**
Starr Farm, Cupar, Fife, KY15 4NP
Ⓜ 07734 175937
Ⓔ irene@perthshireheathers.com
Contact: Irene Lang
Min Mail Order UK: Nmc
Specialities: Heathers.
Notes: Mail order for small orders only.

GPoy **Poyntzfield Herb Nursery** ♿
Nr Balblair, Black Isle, Dingwall, Ross-shire, IV7 8LX
Ⓣ (01381) 610352. Phone between 1200-

1300 & 1800-1900 Mon-Sat only.
Ⓔ info@poyntzfieldherbs.co.uk
Ⓦ www.poyntzfieldherbs.co.uk
Contact: Duncan Ross
Opening Times: 1300-1700 Mon-Sat 1st Mar-30th Sep, 1300-1700 Sun May-Aug.
Min Mail Order UK: £10.00 + p&p
Min Mail Order EU: £20.00 + p&p
Cat. Cost: 4 × 1st class.
Credit Cards: All major credit/debit cards
Specialities: Over 400 popular, unusual & rare herbs esp. medicinal. Also seeds.
Notes: Mail order operates in the spring & autumn. Exports beyond the EU. Wheelchair accessible.
OS Grid Ref: NH711642

GPSL **PLANTS, SHOOTS AND LEAVES**
Dovecot Bungalow, Haddington,
East Lothian, EH41 4HA
Ⓣ (01620) 823536
Ⓜ 07885 444241
Ⓔ karen.leys@btinternet.com
Ⓦ www.plantsshootsandleaves.co.uk
Contact: Karen Payne
Opening Times: 1000-1700 1st Apr-1st Oct. Closed Mon. Please phone first. Nursery may be closed when we are attending shows.
Min Mail Order UK: £3.50
Min Mail Order EU: £6.60
Cat. Cost: Online only.
Credit Cards: All major credit/debit cards
Specialities: *Epimedium*. Hardy geraniums. Perennials and some shrubs. Some available in small quantities only.
Notes: Delivers to shows. Euro accepted. Partial wheelchair access.
OS Grid Ref: NT500730

GQue **QUERCUS GARDEN PLANTS LTD**
Whitmuir Farm, Lamancha, West Linton,
Scottish Borders, EH46 7BB
Ⓣ (01968) 660708
Ⓔ rona@quercusgardenplants.co.uk
Ⓦ www.quercusgardenplants.co.uk
Contact: Rona Dodds
Opening Times: 1000-1700 Wed-Sun.
Cat. Cost: Online only.
Credit Cards: All major credit/debit cards
Specialities: Tough plants for Scottish gardens. Wide range of plants, including old favourites and many unusual varieties of herbaceous perennials, grasses, trees, shrubs & plants for shade.
Notes: Plants grown at 850ft above sea level, making them tough and well acclimatised to Scottish growing conditions. Majority of plants propagated on site and grown on for at least one season. Display gardens show customers what can be grown in these challenging conditions.
OS Grid Ref: NT192512

GRid **J & I CRUICKSHANKS** ♿
Ridgeview Nursery, Crossroad by Longridge,
Fauldhouse, West Lothian, EH47 9AB
Ⓣ (01501) 771144
Ⓔ enquiries@ridgeviewnursery.co.uk
Ⓦ www.ridgeviewnursery.co.uk
Contact: Alice Kyle & Andrew Cruickshanks
Opening Times: 0900-1600, 7 days.
Min Mail Order UK: Nmc
Credit Cards: None
Specialities: Rooted *Dahlia* cuttings.
Notes: Wheelchair accessible.

GRum **RUMBLING BRIDGE NURSERY** ♿
Briglands Estate, Rumbling Bridge, Kinross,
Perth and Kinross, KY13 0PS
Ⓣ (01577) 840160
Ⓔ hello@rumblingbridgenursery.co.uk
Ⓦ www.rumblingbridgenursery.co.uk
Contact: Graeme Butler
Opening Times: By appt. only all year round.
Min Mail Order UK: Nmc
Min Mail Order EU: £50.00
Cat. Cost: Online only.
Specialities: *Alpines, Auricula, Cyclamen, Primula*, woodland plants, dwarf shrubs, dwarf ericaceous.
Notes: Most plants grown in peat-free compost except for ericaceous shrubs. Mail order to the public all year round. Also accept pre-booked groups for visits. (Please call to arrange). Delivers to shows. Wheelchair accessible.
OS Grid Ref: NT025994

GWyn **WYNDFORD FARM PLANTS LTD**
Wyndford Farm, Ecclesmachan, West Lothian,
EH52 6NW
Ⓜ 07871 496732
Ⓔ info@wyndfordfarmplants.com
Ⓦ www.wyndfordfarmplants.com
Contact: Adam Fleming
Opening Times: 1000-1700 Apr-Oct 7 days or by appt.
Min Mail Order UK: Nmc
Cat. Cost: Online only.
Credit Cards: All major credit/debit cards
Specialities: Large range of perennials & shrubs, incl. large collection of *Primula sieboldii* and *Viola*.
Notes: Also sells wholesale. Delivers to shows.
OS Grid Ref: NT059731

G

N. Ireland & Republic

IArd **Ardcarne Garden Centre** ♿
Ardcarne, Boyle, Co. Roscommon, F52 RY61 Ireland
Ⓣ +353 (7196) 67091
Ⓕ +353 (7196) 67341
Ⓔ info@ardcarne.ie
Ⓦ www.ardcarne.ie
Contact: James Wickham, Mary Frances Dwyer, Kirsty Ainge
Opening Times: 0900-1800 Mon-Sat, 1300-1800 Sun & B/hols.
Credit Cards: Access, Visa, American Express
Specialities: Native & unusual trees, choice perennials, roses, plants for coastal areas, fruit trees, incl. heritage Irish apple trees, vegetable plants, specimen plants & semi-mature trees. Wide general range.
Notes: Café. Groups & tours welcome. Ample free parking. Garden design & landscape service available. Euro accepted. Wheelchair accessible.

IBal **Bali-Hai Mail Order Nursery**
42 Largy Road, Carnlough, Ballymena, Co. Antrim, N. Ireland, BT44 0EZ
Ⓣ (028) 2888 5289
Ⓜ 07708 257164
Ⓔ balihainursery@btinternet.com
Ⓦ www.mailorderplants4me.com
Contact: Mrs M.E. Scroggy
Opening Times: Mon-Sat by appt. only.
Min Mail Order UK: Nmc
Min Mail Order EU: Nmc
Cat. Cost: Online only.
Credit Cards: All major credit/debit cards
Specialities: National Plant Collection of *Agapanthus* and *Hosta*, part planted in 1.5 acres, open to the public by appt. *Crocosmia*, *Rhodohypoxis*, tree ferns & other perennials. *Hosta* grown to order.
Notes: Also sells wholesale. Export beyond EU restricted to bare-root perennials, no grasses. Euro accepted.
OS Grid Ref: D287184

IBlr **Ballyrogan Nurseries** ♿
The Grange, Ballyrogan, Newtownards, Co. Down, N. Ireland, BT23 4SD
Ⓣ (028) 9181 0451 (evenings)
Ⓔ gary.dunlop@btinternet.com
Contact: Gary Dunlop
Opening Times: Only open by appt.
Min Mail Order UK: £10.00 + p&p
Min Mail Order EU: £20.00 + p&p
Cat. Cost: 1 × 2nd class stamp or by email.
Credit Cards: None
Specialities: Choice herbaceous. *Agapanthus*, *Crocosmia*, *Dierama*, *Erythronium*, *Rodgersia*, *Roscoea* & *Watsonia*.
Notes: Also sells wholesale. Euro accepted. Wheelchair accessible.

IBoy **Boyne Garden Centre**
Ardcalf, Slane, Co. Meath, C15 P92W Ireland
Ⓣ +353 (419) 824350
Ⓜ +353 8724 01156
Ⓔ Aileen@boynegardencentre.ie
Ⓦ www.boynegardencentre.com
Contact: Aileen Muldoon Byrne
Opening Times: 0930-1730 Mon-Sat. 1400-1730 Sun. Mar-Sep. Oct-Feb w/ends only.
Min Mail Order UK: Nmc
Cat. Cost: Online only.
Credit Cards: All major credit/debit cards
Specialities: Plants for pollinators, hardy perennials, ferns, grasses, roses, trees & shrubs.
Notes: Award-winning growers with a unique collection of high quality plants. Delivers to shows. Euro accepted.
OS Grid Ref: N937917

IDee **Deelish Garden Centre**
Deelish, Skibbereen, Co. Cork, P81 FD34 Ireland
Ⓣ +353 (28) 21374
Ⓕ +353 (28) 21374
Ⓔ deel@eircom.net
Ⓦ www.deelish.ie
Contact: Bill & Rain Chase
Opening Times: 1000-1800 Mon-Sat, 1400-1800 Sun.
Min Mail Order UK: Nmc
Min Mail Order EU: Nmc
Credit Cards: Visa, MasterCard, Access, PayPal
Specialities: Unusual plants for the mild coastal climate of Ireland. Conservatory plants. Sole Irish agents for Chase Organic Seeds.
Notes: No mail order outside Ireland & UK. Euro accepted.

IDic **Dickson Nurseries**
Milecross Road, Newtownards, Co. Down, N. Ireland, BT23 4SS
Ⓣ (028) 9181 2206
Ⓔ mail@dickson-roses.co.uk
Ⓦ www.dickson-roses.co.uk
Contact: Colin Dickson
Opening Times: 0800-1230 & 1300-1515 Mon-Thu. 0800-1230 Fri.
Min Mail Order UK: Nmc
Min Mail Order EU: £25.00 + p&p
Cat. Cost: Free.
Credit Cards: None
Specialities: Roses esp. modern Dickson varieties. Limited selection, check website or

contact nursery. Most varieties available in small quantities only.
Notes: Also sells wholesale. Only glasshouses accessible for wheelchairs.

IFro **Frogswell Nursery**
Clooncanlan, Straide, Foxford, Co. Mayo, Ireland
Ⓜ +353 (8621) 06166
Ⓔ frogswell@gmail.com
Ⓦ www.frogswellhardyplants.com
Contact: Celia Graebner
Opening Times: Feb-Oct by appt. Please phone first. Also charity open days & occasional on-site workshops; see website or contact nursery for details.
Credit Cards: None
Specialities: A small garden-based nursery specialising in shade & spring woodland plant incl. hybrid hellebores & hardy geraniums, unusual perennials for the Irish climate and bee and wild pollinator forage plants. All plants raised on site, some in very limited quantities, using organic fertilisers & peat-free media where possible.
Notes: Group visits & talks by arrangement. Euro accepted.
OS Grid Ref: M2497

ILea **Leamore Nursery**
Cronroe, Ashford, Co. Wicklow, A67 Y681 Ireland
Ⓣ +353 (87) 227 8850
Ⓕ +353 (404) 70126
Ⓔ info@leamorenursery.com
Ⓦ www.leamorenursery.com
Contact: Phil Havercroft
Opening Times: Not open.
Min Mail Order UK: €25
Min Mail Order EU: €25
Cat. Cost: Online only.
Credit Cards: All major credit/debit cards
Specialities: *Paeonia* & other perennials. Most items in large quantities. Itoh peonies & some more unusual items only available in small quantities.
Notes: Bare-root peonies supplied in autumn, available to order from Jul (on website). Founding members of the Irish Specialist Nursery Association (ISNA). Also sells wholesale. Delivers to shows. Sterling & Euro accepted.
OS Grid Ref: SG235945

IMou **Mount Venus Nursery** ♿
The Walled Garden, Mutton Lane, Dublin 16, Ireland
Ⓣ +353 (1) 493 3813
Ⓜ +353 08632 18789
Ⓔ mountvenusnursery@gmail.com
Ⓦ www.mountvenusnursery.com
Contact: Oliver & Liat Schurmann
Opening Times: 1000-1800 Wed-Sat, Feb-Nov. 1100-1700 Sun, Apr-Oct.
Min Mail Order UK: €20
Min Mail Order EU: €35
Cat. Cost: Online only.
Credit Cards: All major credit/debit cards
Specialities: Specialist perennials. Grasses & bamboos. Unusual woodland plants, trees & shrubs.
Notes: Also sells wholesale. Delivers to shows. Euro accepted. Wheelchair accessible.

IPot **The Potting Shed** ♿
Bolinaspick, Camolin, Enniscorthy, Co. Wexford, Y21 TD93 Ireland
Ⓣ +353 (5393) 83629
Ⓔ susan@camolinpottingshed.com
Ⓦ www.camolinpottingshed.com
Contact: Susan Carrick
Opening Times: 1100-1700, Wed-Sat. Mid Mar-end Aug.
Min Mail Order UK: Nmc
Min Mail Order EU: Nmc
Cat. Cost: 3 × 1st class.
Credit Cards: MasterCard, Visa, American Express
Specialities: Grow a wide range of unusual, hard to find & new introductions of herbaceous perennials, ornamental grasses *Clematis* and *Wisteria*.
Notes: Member of the Irish Specialist Nursery Assoc. (ISNA). Orders outside Ireland can only be delivered by courier, charges at cost. Delivers to shows. Euro accepted. Wheelchair accessible.

IRos **Ros Ban Wildlife Garden** ♿
Common, Raphoe, Co. Donegal, F93 HH0X Ireland
Ⓣ +353 (74) 91 45336
Ⓜ +353 8608 05214
Ⓔ Rosbangarden@gmail.com
Contact: Ann Kavanagh
Opening Times: Garden open, morning to evening, Easter to Sep.
Credit Cards: None
Notes: Plants available in season from the garden. Please check plant availability with nursery before travelling. Euro accepted. Wheelchair accessible.

ISha **Shady Plants** ♿
Coolbooa, Clashmore, Youghal, Co. Cork, P36 EY19 Ireland

Ⓣ +353 (24) 86998
Ⓜ +353 8605 42171
Ⓔ mike@shadyplants.ie
Ⓦ www.shadyplants.net
Contact: Mike Keep
Opening Times: 1300-1700, Tue-Sat, by appt. only.
Min Mail Order UK: Nmc
Min Mail Order EU: Nmc
Cat. Cost: Online only.
Credit Cards: MasterCard, PayPal, Visa
Specialities: Specialist fern nursery based near the south coast of Ireland.
Notes: Delivers to shows. Euro accepted. Wheelchair accessible.
OS Grid Ref: W613585

ITim **Timpany Nurseries & Gardens** ♿
77 Magheratimpany Road, Ballynahinch, Co. Down, N. Ireland, BT24 8PA
Ⓣ (028) 9756 2812
Ⓜ 07711 428477
Ⓔ s.tindall@btconnect.com
Ⓦ www.timpanynurseries.com
Contact: Susan Tindall
Opening Times: 1000-1730 Tue-Sat, Sun by appt.
Min Mail Order UK: £40.00 + p&p
Min Mail Order EU: £40.00 + p&p
Cat. Cost: £3.50
Credit Cards: All major debit/credit cards except American Express
Specialities: *Androsace, Cassiope, Celmisia, Cyclamen, Dianthus, Galanthus, Meconopsis, Hosta, Primula, Primula auricula, Rhodohypoxis* & *Saxifraga*.
Notes: Delivers to shows. Wheelchair accessible.

London Area

LAyl **Aylett Nurseries Ltd** ♿
North Orbital Road, St Albans, Hertfordshire, AL2 1DH
Ⓣ (01727) 822255
Ⓕ (01727) 823024
Ⓔ info@aylettnurseries.co.uk
Ⓦ www.aylettnurseries.co.uk
Contact: Julie Aylett
Opening Times: 0830-1730 Mon-Fri, 0830-1700 Sat, 1030-1630 Sun.
Cat. Cost: Free.
Credit Cards: All major credit/debit cards
Specialities: *Dahlia*. Two-acre trial ground and garden adjacent to garden centre.
Notes: Wheelchair accessible.
OS Grid Ref: TL169049

LBee **Beechcroft Nursery** ♿
127 Reigate Road, Ewell, Surrey, KT17 3DE
Ⓣ (020) 8393 4265
Ⓕ (020) 8393 4265
Ⓔ enquiries@beechcroft-nursery.co.uk
Ⓦ www.beechcroft-nursery.co.uk
Contact: C. Kimber
Opening Times: 1000-1600 Mon-Sat, 1000-1400 Sun & B/hols. Closed Xmas-New Year.
Cat. Cost: None issued.
Credit Cards: All major credit/debit cards
Specialities: Conifers.
Notes: Wheelchair accessible.

LBuc **Buckingham Nurseries** ♿ ◆
14 Tingewick Road, Buckingham, Buckinghamshire, MK18 4AE
Ⓣ (01280) 822133
Ⓕ (01280) 815491
Ⓔ enquiries@buckingham-nurseries.co.uk
Ⓦ www.buckingham-nurseries.co.uk
Contact: R.J. & P.L. Brown
Opening Times: 0830-1730 (1800 in summer) Mon-Sat, 1000-1600 Sun.
Min Mail Order UK: Nmc
Min Mail Order EU: Nmc
Cat. Cost: Free.
Credit Cards: Visa, MasterCard, Maestro
Specialities: Bare-rooted and container grown hedging. Fruit trees, soft fruit, trees, shrubs, herbaceous perennials, alpines, grasses & ferns.
Notes: Garden centre with restaurant. Wheelchair accessible.
OS Grid Ref: SP676333

LCla **Clay Lane Nursery**
3 Clay Lane, South Nutfield, Nr Redhill, Surrey, RH1 4EG
Ⓣ (01737) 823307
Ⓔ claylane.nursery@btinternet.com
Ⓦ www.claylane-fuchsias.co.uk
Contact: K.W. Belton
Opening Times: Not open. Pre-ordered plants can be collected by arrangement.
Min Mail Order UK: £20.00
Cat. Cost: 3 × 2nd class.
Credit Cards: None
Specialities: *Fuchsia*. Many varieties in small quantities only.
Notes: Mail order by phone prior arrangement.

LCro **Crocus.co.uk**
Nursery Court, London Road, Windlesham, Surrey, GU20 6LQ
Ⓣ (01344) 578000
Ⓕ (01344) 629600
Ⓔ customerservices@crocus.co.uk

Ⓦ www.crocus.co.uk
Contact: Customer Care Team
Opening Times: Mail order only. Order lines open 24hrs, 7 days. Nursery has several open days a year, see website or phone for details.
Min Mail Order UK: Nmc + delivery charges.
Cat. Cost: Free.
Credit Cards: All major debit/credit cards except American Express
Specialities: Large general nursery. Perennials, shrubs, climbers, roses, bulbs, ferns, grasses, herbs & house plants.
Notes: Also sells wholesale.

LEdu **EDULIS** ♿
(office) 1 Flowers Piece, Ashampstead, Reading, Berkshire, RG8 8SG
Ⓣ (01635) 578113
Ⓜ 07802 812781
Ⓔ edulisnursery@gmail.com
Ⓦ www.edulis.co.uk
Contact: Paul Barney
Opening Times: 1000-1600 Tue & Wed, & by appt. Apr-Oct. Nov-Mar by appt. only. See website or contact nursery for open days.
Min Mail Order UK: £20.00 + p&p
Min Mail Order EU: £30.00 + p&p
Cat. Cost: Online only.
Credit Cards: All major debit/credit cards except American Express
Specialities: Unusual edibles, architectural plants, permaculture plants & many of our own collections.
Notes: Nursery is at The Walled Garden, Tidmarsh Lane, Pangbourne, RG8 8HT. Also sells wholesale. Delivers to shows. Euro accepted. Wheelchair accessible.
OS Grid Ref: SU615747

LHom **HOME FARM PLANTS**
Home Farm, Shantock Lane, Bovingdon, Hertfordshire, HP3 0NG
Ⓜ 07773 798068
Ⓔ homefarmplants@gmail.com
Ⓦ www.homefarmplants.co.uk
Contact: Graham Austin
Opening Times: 0900-1730 Fri & Sat, 1000-1600 Sun, viewing by appt. only Mon-Thu, 1st Apr-end Oct (subject to weather conditions).
Cat. Cost: 1st class sae for list.
Credit Cards: All major debit/credit cards except American Express
Specialities: *Delphinium elatum* (over 60 varieties). Hardy perennials & seasonal cut flowers. Show area of 200+ delphiniums (contact nursery for flowering times). Some varieties only available in small quantities.
Notes: If travelling, please contact nursery to confirm plant availability. Delivers to shows. Partial wheelchair access.

LLWG **LILIES WATER GARDENS** ♿
Broad Lane, Newdigate, Surrey, RH5 5AT
Ⓣ (01306) 631064
Ⓜ 07801 166244
Ⓔ mail@davieswatergardens.co.uk
Ⓦ www.lilieswatergardens.co.uk
Contact: Simon Harman
Opening Times: 0900-1700 Thu-Sat, Mar-Aug. By appt. only Sep-Feb.
Min Mail Order UK: Nmc
Min Mail Order EU: Nmc
Cat. Cost: Online only.
Credit Cards: All major credit/debit cards
Specialities: Water lilies, moist perennials, bog-garden plants, primulas, marginal plants, ferns, oxygenating plants. Pond plants, incl. submerged & free-floating, aquatic, water iris, water-garden, floating, stream & deep-water plants. Alpine, rock & creeping plants. Rushes & grasses.
Notes: Flat rate £6.50 UK delivery charge. Wheelchair accessible.

LMaj **MAJESTIC TREES** ♿
Chequers Meadow, Chequers Hill (Junc 9, M1), Flamstead, St Albans, Hertfordshire, AL3 8ET
Ⓣ (01582) 843881
Ⓕ (01582) 843882
Ⓔ info@majestictrees.co.uk
Ⓦ www.majestictrees.co.uk
Contact: Andy Miles
Opening Times: 0830-1700 Mon-Fri. 1000-1600 Sat, Nov-Feb, 1000-1700 Sat, Mar-Oct. Closed Sun, B/hols, Xmas/New Year.
Credit Cards: MasterCard, Visa, Switch, Maestro
Specialities: Semi-mature & mature containerised trees grown in airpots from 50ltr to 5000ltr.
Notes: Also sells wholesale. Delivers to shows. Euro accepted. Disabled access by golf buggy can be arranged by appt. Wheelchair access to building.
OS Grid Ref: TL081408

LMil **MILLAIS NURSERIES** ♿
Crosswater Farm, Crosswater Lane, Churt, Farnham, Surrey, GU10 2JN
Ⓣ (01252) 792698
Ⓔ sales@rhododendrons.co.uk
Ⓦ www.rhododendrons.co.uk
Contact: David Millais

Opening Times: 1000-1700 Mon-Fri all year. Please phone or see website for additional weekend opening in spring.
Min Mail Order UK: Nmc
Min Mail Order EU: Nmc
Cat. Cost: Free list on request. Full catalogue online.
Credit Cards: All major credit/debit cards
Specialities: Rhododendrons, azaleas, magnolias, camellias & acers. Garden open in spring.
Notes: Mail order all year. Also sells wholesale. Wheelchair accessible.
OS Grid Ref: SU856397

L

LOPS **RHS PLANT SHOP: RHSPLANTS.CO.UK** ◆
Nursery Court, London Road, Windlesham, Surrey, GU20 6LQ
Ⓣ (01344) 578822
Ⓕ (01344) 629600
Ⓔ customerservices@rhsplants.co.uk
Ⓦ www.rhsplants.co.uk
Contact: Customer Care Team
Opening Times: Not open. Mail order online only.
Min Mail Order UK: Nmc
Credit Cards: All major debit/credit cards except American Express
Notes: Large range of plants, including a substantial range of RHS AGM plants.

LPai **PAINSHILL PARK TRUST** ♿
Portsmouth Road, Cobham, Surrey, KT11 1JE
Ⓣ (01932) 868113
Ⓔ AndyMills@painshill.co.uk
Ⓦ www.painshill.co.uk
Contact: Andy Mills
Opening Times: 1000-1800 Mar to Oct, 1000-1600 Nov to Feb 7 days. Closed Xmas Day & Boxing Day.
Cat. Cost: None issued.
Credit Cards: All major credit/debit cards
Specialities: Small selection of surplus stock of annuals and perennials grown on site, available in very small quantities only. All funds raised contribute to the continuing restoration & conservation of Charles Hamilton's landscape garden at Painshill.
Notes: Wheelchair accessible.

LPla **THE PLANT SPECIALIST** ♿
7 Whitefield Lane, Great Missenden, Buckinghamshire, HP16 0BH
Ⓣ (01494) 866650
Ⓕ (01494) 866650
Ⓔ enquire@theplantspecialist.co.uk
Ⓦ www.theplantspecialist.co.uk
Contact: Sean Walter
Opening Times: 1000-1700 Wed-Sat, 1000-1600 Sun, Apr-Oct. 1000-1600 B/hols.
Cat. Cost: None issued.
Credit Cards: All major credit/debit cards
Specialities: Herbaceous perennials, grasses, half-hardy perennials, bulbs.
Notes: Wheelchair accessible. Delivers to shows.

LPot **POTASH PLANTS** ♿
Potash Nursery, Drayton Parslow, Milton Keynes, Buckinghamshire, MK17 0JE
Ⓣ (01296) 720578
Ⓜ 07778 398808
Ⓕ (01296) 720578
Ⓔ info@potashplants.co.uk
Ⓦ www.potashplants.co.uk
Contact: Gill Gallon
Opening Times: 0900-1730 Mon-Sat. 1030-1630 Sun.
Cat. Cost: Online.
Credit Cards: All major debit/credit cards except American Express
Specialities: Wide range of traditional and unusual hardy perennials, grasses, trees & shrubs. Some available in small quantities only.
Notes: Nursery on B4032 mid-way between Aylesbury and Milton Keynes. Also sells wholesale. Delivers to shows. Wheelchair accessible.
OS Grid Ref: SP834279

LRHS **WISLEY PLANT CENTRE (RHS)** ♿ ◆
RHS Garden, Wisley, Woking, Surrey, GU23 6QB
Ⓣ (01483) 211113
Ⓕ (01483) 212372
Ⓔ philipwoolf@rhs.org.uk
Ⓦ www.rhs.org.uk/wisleyplantcentre
Contact: Phil Woolf
Opening Times: 0900-1700 Mon-Sat, Oct-Feb. 0900-1800 Mon-Sat, Mar-Sep. 1100-1700 Sun all year, browsing from 1030.
Credit Cards: All major credit/debit cards
Specialities: Over 12,000 plants, many rare or unusual, reflecting the range of the RHS flagship garden at Wisley. Also houseplants, bedding plants, bulbs & seed potatoes, plus a range of garden sundries.
Notes: Plants subject to seasonal availability. For plants not in stock, a reservation service is operated. All plants must be collected from Wisley as no mail order. Wheelchair accessible.

LSou **SOUTHON PLANTS** ♿
Mutton Hill, Dormansland, Lingfield, Surrey, RH7 6NP

Ⓣ (01342) 870150
Ⓔ lyn@southon-plants.co.uk
Ⓦ www.southon-plants.co.uk
Contact: Lyn Southon
Opening Times: See website or telephone for opening hours.
Cat. Cost: Online only.
Credit Cards: All major credit/debit cards
Specialities: New & unusual hardy & tender perennials, specialising in *Agapanthus* (over 30 varieties), & *Heuchera* (over 30 varieties). Many new varieties for tender perennials/patio plants.
Notes: Wheelchair accessible.

LSRN **SPRING REACH NURSERY** ♿
Long Reach, Ockham, Guildford, Surrey, GU23 6PG
Ⓣ (01483) 284769
Ⓜ 07884 432666
Ⓕ (01483) 284769
Ⓔ info@springreachnursery.co.uk
Ⓦ www.springreachnursery.co.uk
Contact: Nick & Lissa Hourhan
Opening Times: 1000-1700 Mon-Sat, 1030-1630 Sun. Open B/hols. Closed 23rd Dec-2nd Jan.
Min Mail Order UK: Nmc
Min Mail Order EU: Nmc
Credit Cards: All major credit/debit cards
Specialities: Shrubs, evergreen climbers, *Clematis*, perennials, roses, grasses, ferns, bamboos, trees, hedging, soft fruit & top fruit. Plants for chalk & clay. Deer & rabbit resistant plants. Specimen & acid-loving plants.
Notes: Please ring for mail order details. Also sells wholesale. Delivers to shows. Wheelchair accessible.

LSun **SUNNYSIDE NURSERY**
Upper Allotments, New Road, Northchurch, Hertfordshire, HP4 1NJ
Ⓜ 07743 552154
Ⓔ philsmith2004@yahoo.co.uk
Contact: Philip Smith
Opening Times: 0900-1700 Mon-Fri Summer. Closed Sat, Sun & B/hols. 1000-1600 Tue-Fri Winter. 10 or more shows during the season. Please contact the nursery for details.
Cat. Cost: Availability list on request.
Credit Cards: All major credit/debit cards
Specialities: Hardy perennials, alpines & ornamental grasses. Some plants available in small quantities only.
Notes: Please phone for stock availability & updates. Trade discounts available with orders of £100+.

LSvl **SAVILL GARDENS VISITOR CENTRE** ♿
Wick Lane, Englefield Green, Egham, Surrey, TW20 0UU
Ⓣ (01784) 485401
Ⓔ veronique.serre@thecrownestate.co.uk
Ⓦ www.windsorgreatpark.co.uk
Contact: Veronique Serre
Opening Times: 0930-1800 (summer), 0930-1630 (winter).
Credit Cards: All major debit/credit cards except American Express
Specialities: Woody plants, incl. Windsor magnolias, herbaceous, *Ligularia* & *Mahonia*. Available in small numbers only.
Notes: Wheelchair accessible.

M

LTop **TOPIARY ARTS**
(Office) 224 Hospital Bridge Road, Twickenham, Middlesex, TW2 6LF
Ⓣ (0208) 8942816
Ⓜ 07775 602704
Ⓔ jcb@topiaryarts.com
Ⓦ www.topiaryarts.com
Contact: James Crebbin-Bailey
Opening Times: By appt. only.
Min Mail Order UK: £30
Cat. Cost: Free.
Credit Cards: PayPal
Specialities: Topiary. Many individual sculptural pieces.
Notes: Nursery is at Walled Garden, Copped Hall, Upshire, Epping, Essex CM16 5HS. Field stock area. English grown plants. Also sells wholesale. Delivers to shows.

LYaf **YAFFLES** ♿
Harvest Hill, Bourne End, Buckinghamshire, SL8 5JJ
Ⓣ (01628) 525455
Contact: I. Butterfield
Opening Times: 0900-1300 & 1400-1700. Please phone beforehand as we may be attending shows.
Min Mail Order UK: Nmc
Min Mail Order EU: £30.00 + p&p
Cat. Cost: 2 × 2nd class.
Credit Cards: None
Specialities: *Pleione*.
Notes: Only Pleione by mail order. Delivers to shows. Wheelchair accessible.

MIDLANDS

MArl **ARLEY HALL NURSERY** ♿
Arley Hall Gardens, Northwich, Cheshire, CW9 6NA
Ⓣ (01565) 777479
Ⓔ arleyhallplantnursery@gmail.com

Ⓦ www.arleyhallandgardens.com
Contact: Rob Groom
Opening Times: 1000-1730 Mon-Sun 1st Mar-31st Oct.
Cat. Cost: 4 × 1st class.
Credit Cards: All major credit/debit cards
Specialities: Wide range of herbaceous incl. many unusual varieties, some in small quantities. Wide range of unusual pelargoniums.
Notes: Nursery is beside car park at Arley Hall Gardens. Wheelchair accessible.
OS Grid Ref: SJ673808

M

MAsh **Ashwood Nurseries Ltd** ♿
Ashwood Lower Lane, Ashwood, Kingswinford, West Midlands, DY6 0AE
Ⓣ (01384) 401996
Ⓕ (01384) 401108
Ⓔ mailorder@ashwoodnurseries.com
Ⓦ www.ashwoodnurseries.com
Contact: Karrina Gilbert & Steve Lampitt
Opening Times: 0900-1700 Mon-Sat & 0930-1700 Sun, excl. Xmas & Boxing Day.
Min Mail Order UK: Nmc
Min Mail Order EU: Nmc
Cat. Cost: 4 × 1st class.
Credit Cards: All major credit/debit cards
Specialities: Large range of hardy plants, shrubs & dwarf conifers. Roses, alpines & herbaceous plants. Also specialises in *Auricula*, *Cyclamen*, *Galanthus*, hellebores, *Hepatica*, *Hydrangea* & *Salvia*. National Plant Collection of *Lewisia*.
Notes: Tea room overlooking display garden. Ample parking. Regular events. Groups by appt. to visit private garden. Wheelchair accessible.
OS Grid Ref: SO865879

MAvo **Avondale Nursery** ♿
(office) 3 Avondale Road, Earlsdon, West Midlands, CV5 6DZ
Ⓣ (024) 766 73662
Ⓜ 07979 093096
Ⓔ enquiries@avondalenursery.co.uk
Ⓦ www.avondalenursery.co.uk
Contact: Brian Ellis
Opening Times: 1000-1230, 1400-1700 Mon-Sat, 1030-1630 Sun, Mar-Sep. Other times by appt.
Cat. Cost: 4 × 1st class.
Credit Cards: All major credit/debit cards
Specialities: Rare & unusual perennials esp. asters, *Crocosmia*, *Eryngium*, *Geranium*, *Geum*, *Sanguisorba* & grasses. National Plant Collections of *Symphyotrichum novae-angliae*, *Anemone nemorosa* & *Sanguisorba*.
Notes: Nursery is at Russell's Nursery, Mill Hill, Baginton, near Coventry CV8 3AG. Display garden open. Groups welcome. Delivers to shows. Wheelchair accessible.
OS Grid Ref: SP339751

MBel **Bluebell Cottage Nursery**
Lodge Lane, Dutton, Cheshire, WA4 4HP
Ⓣ (01928) 713718
Ⓔ info@bluebellcottage.co.uk
Ⓦ www.bluebellcottage.co.uk
Contact: Sue Beesley
Opening Times: 1000-1700 Wed-Sun & B/hols, 1st Apr-end Sep. By appt. only outside these dates.
Min Mail Order UK: £3.95 (based on weight)
Cat. Cost: Online only.
Credit Cards: All major credit/debit cards
Specialities: *Achillea*, *Anthemis*, *Brunnera*, *Centaurea*, *Echinacea*, *Geranium*, *Geum*, *Lychnis*, *Persicaria*, *Potentilla*, *Sanguisorba*, *Thalictrum* & ornamental grasses. Some items stocked in small quantities.
Notes: Mail order available all year round. Mail order plants are fully established, ready to plant out. RHS Partner Garden open Apr-Sep. Refreshments available. Delivers to shows. Wheelchair accessible.
OS Grid Ref: SJ586779

MBlu **Bluebell Arboretum & Nursery** ♿
Annwell Lane, Smisby, Nr Ashby de la Zouch, Derbyshire, LE65 2TA
Ⓣ (01530) 413700
Ⓕ (01530) 417600
Ⓔ sales@bluebellnursery.com
Ⓦ www.bluebellnursery.com
Contact: Robert & Suzette Vernon
Opening Times: 0900-1700 Mon-Sat & 1030-1630 Sun, Mar-Oct. 0900-1600 Mon-Sat (not Sun) Nov-Feb. Closed 24th Dec-1st Jan incl. & Easter Sun.
Min Mail Order UK: £8.95
Min Mail Order EU: Nmc
Cat. Cost: £1.50 + 3 × 1st class.
Credit Cards: Visa, Access, Switch, MasterCard
Specialities: Specialists in rare & unusual plants. Uncommon trees & shrubs. Rare *Acer*, *Betula*, *Cornus*, *Fagus*, *Liquidambar*, *Magnolia*, *Quercus* & *Tilia*. Woody climbers.
Notes: 9-acre woodland garden & arboretum surrounds nursery. RHS Partner Garden. Guide dogs only. Working nursery. Please wear appropriate clothing & sturdy footwear when visiting. Delivers to shows. Wheelchair accessible but please call to check after wet weather.
OS Grid Ref: SK344187

MBNS **Barnsdale Gardens** ♿
Exton Avenue, Exton, Oakham, Rutland, LE15 8AH
Ⓣ (01572) 813200
Ⓔ mailorder@barnsdalegardens.co.uk
Ⓦ www.barnsdalegardens.co.uk
Contact: Nick Hamilton
Opening Times: 0900-1700 Mar-May & Sep-Oct, 0900-1900 Jun-Aug, 1000-1600 Nov-Feb, 7 days. Closed Xmas & Boxing Day.
Min Mail Order UK: Nmc
Min Mail Order EU: Nmc
Cat. Cost: Online only.
Credit Cards: All major credit/debit cards
Specialities: Wide range of choice & unusual garden plants but specialising in perennials.
Notes: Mail order from website or by telephone ordering only. Delivers to shows. Wheelchair accessible.
OS Grid Ref: SK912108

MBow **Fawside Farm Nursery**
Fawside Farm, Longnor, Buxton, Derbyshire, SK17 0RA
Ⓜ 07919 556425
Ⓔ julie.norfolk@acorncapital.co.uk
Ⓦ www.Fawsidefarmnursery.com
Contact: Julie Norfolk
Opening Times: By appt. only.
Min Mail Order UK: £25.00
Cat. Cost: Online.
Credit Cards: PayPal
Specialities: Bee-friendly hardy perennials, British wildflowers and herbs. It is a small nursery so does not have large numbers of all the varieties. Large orders can be grown by arrangement.
Notes: The nursery is situated 1,000ft in the Pennines and we aim to grow hardy species of plants to survive in these conditions as well as being wildlife friendly. We use peat-free compost and use organic growing methods. Also sells wholesale.

MBriF **Bridge Farm Plants**
Bridge Farm, Main Road, Lower Hartshay, Derbyshire, DE5 3RP
Ⓣ (01773) 742848
Ⓜ 07812 350132
Ⓔ alisonfarnsworth@btinternet.com
Contact: Alison Farnsworth
Opening Times: By appt. only.
Specialities: Herbaceous perennials and bulbs.
Notes: Interesting range, including half-hardy and tender. Most in small quantities only.

MBrN **Bridge Nursery** ♿
Tomlow Road, Napton-on-the-Hill, Nr Rugby, Warwickshire, CV47 8HX
Ⓣ (01926) 812737
Ⓔ philipemartino@gmail.com
Ⓦ www.Bridge-Nursery.co.uk
Contact: Christine Dakin & Philip Martino
Opening Times: 1000-1600 Sat, Sun & B/hols Mar-Oct. Other times by appt.
Min Mail Order UK: £10.00
Cat. Cost: Online only.
Credit Cards: All major credit/debit cards
Specialities: Ornamental grasses, sedges & bamboos. Also range of shrubs & perennials. Display garden.
Notes: Limited range available by mail order, please check with nursery. Also sells wholesale. Euro accepted. Wheelchair accessible.
OS Grid Ref: SP463625

MBros **Brookside Nursery** ♿
School Lane, Hints, Tamworth, Staffordshire, B78 3DW
Ⓣ (03333) 356789
Ⓔ sales@brooksidenursery.co.uk
Ⓦ www.brooksidenursery.co.uk
Contact: James Thomas
Opening Times: Mon-Sat 0900-1700, Sun 1100-1600 1st Mar-31st Oct. Closed 1st Nov-28th Feb. Office & Customer Services Mon-Fri 0900-1700 all year.
Cat. Cost: online.
Credit Cards: All major credit/debit cards
Specialities: *Begonia, Geranium, Lobelia, Petunia.*
Notes: Producer of bedding and hanging basket plants. Veg & perennials sold as young plug plants and bare root plants for mail order and as finished plants for collection from the nursery. Wheelchair accessible.

MCms **Chrysanthemums Direct**
Holmes Chapel Road, Over Peover, Knutsford, Cheshire, WA16 9RA
Ⓣ 0800 (046) 7443
Ⓜ 07977 312 593
Ⓔ sales@chrysanthemumsdirect.co.uk
Ⓦ www.chrysanthemumsdirect.co.uk
Contact: Martyn Flint
Opening Times: Not open. Mail order only.
Min Mail Order UK: Nmc
Min Mail Order EU: Nmc
Cat. Cost: 4 × 1st class.
Credit Cards: All major credit/debit cards
Specialities: Chrysanthemums. Young plants grown to order. Delivery within 14 days.

Winner Protected Ornamental Grower of the Year at the UK Grower Awards 2015.
Notes: Delivers to shows.

MCoo **COOL TEMPERATE**
(office) 45 Stamford Street, Awsworth, Nottinghamshire, NG16 2QL
Ⓣ (0115) 916 2673
Ⓜ 07952 019376
Ⓕ (0115) 916 2673
Ⓔ phil.corbett@cooltemperate.co.uk
Ⓦ www.cooltemperate.co.uk
Contact: Phil Corbett
Opening Times: 0900-1700, 7 days. Please ring/write first.
Min Mail Order UK: Nmc
Cat. Cost: Online or via email.
Credit Cards: None
Specialities: Tree fruit, soft fruit, nitrogen-fixers, hedging, own-root fruit trees. Many species available in small quantities only.
Notes: Nursery at Newton's Lane, Cossall, Notts NG16 2YH.
OS Grid Ref: SK473433

MCot **COTON MANOR GARDEN**
Guilsborough, Northampton, Northamptonshire, NN6 8RQ
Ⓣ (01604) 740219
Ⓔ nursery@cotonmanor.co.uk
Ⓦ www.cotonmanor.co.uk
Contact: Caroline Tait
Opening Times: 1200-1730 Tue-Sat, 1st Apr-27th Sep. Also Sun Apr, May & B/hol w/ends. Other times in working hours by appt.
Cat. Cost: Online only.
Credit Cards: All major credit/debit cards
Specialities: Wide-range of herbaceous perennials (1200+ varieties), some available in small quantities only. Also many tender perennials & selected shrubs.
Notes: Garden open. Tea rooms. Garden school. Partial wheelchair access.
OS Grid Ref: SP675715

MCtn **CHILTERN SEEDS LTD**
Crowmarsh Battle Barns, 114 Preston Crowmarsh, Wallingford, Oxfordshire, OX10 6SL
Ⓣ (01491) 824675
Ⓔ info@chilternseeds.co.uk
Ⓦ www.chilternseeds.co.uk
Contact: Any member of staff
Opening Times: Mail order only. Normal office hours, Mon-Fri.
Min Mail Order UK: Nmc
Min Mail Order EU: Nmc
Cat. Cost: Free.
Credit Cards: All major debit/credit cards except American Express
Specialities: Large selection of wild flowers, trees, shrubs, cacti, annuals, houseplants, vegetables & herbs.
Notes: Exports beyond EU. Customer's responsibility to ensure no restrictions & special import requirements apply.

MDon **DONINGTON NURSERIES LTD** ♿
Kings Mills, Park Lane, Castle Donington, Derbyshire, DE74 2RS
Ⓣ (01332) 853004
Ⓕ (01332) 853793
Ⓔ sales@doningtonnurseries.co.uk
Ⓦ www.doningtonnurseries.co.uk
Contact: Rebecca Faulkner
Opening Times: Open daily (hours vary depending on season).
Cat. Cost: None.
Credit Cards: All major credit/debit cards
Specialities: Family-owned nursery stocking wide range of trees, shrubs, perennials & alpines. 50% of stock grown on nursery set within 4-acre former walled garden of Donington Hall. Home grown *Prunus laurocerasus* & *Thuja* hedging available in large quantities.
Notes: Wheelchair accessible.
OS Grid Ref: SK421273

MEch **ECHIUM WORLD**
The Walled Garden, Thoresby Park, Nr Ollerton, Nottinghamshire, NG22 9EP
Ⓜ 07957 602073
Ⓔ echiumworld@gmail.com
Ⓦ www.echiumworld.co.uk
Contact: Linda Heywood
Opening Times: Plant sales or collection from our Echium Garden Open Days: Suns in May. See other opening times at www.echiumworld.co.uk.
Min Mail Order UK: £9.95
Credit Cards: PayPal
Specialities: Specialist growers & suppliers of *Echium* varieties, incl. rare & threatened plants. Also plant varieties used for complementary planting schemes in our showcase Echium Garden. Suppliers of *Echium* plants for wildlife gardens. All plants grown and cultivated at our UK nursery. National Plant Collection of *Echium* species & cvs from the Macaronesian Islands.
Notes: The Echium Garden and plant nursery occupies a corner of the old Victorian walled garden at Thoresby Hall, Nottinghamshire. Currently under renovation, the walls form an idea location and natural space to showcase over 35 varieties of *Echium* including the

giant tree echium, *E. pinanana* that grows to over 5 metres tall.
OS Grid Ref: SK626665

MFry **FRYER'S ROSES AND GARDEN CENTRE** ♿
Manchester Road, Knutsford, Cheshire, WA16 0SX
Ⓣ (01565) 755455
Ⓕ (01565) 653755
Ⓔ webenquiries@bluediamond.gg
Ⓦ www.fryers-roses.co.uk
Contact: Jill Kerr
Opening Times: 0900-1800 Mon-Sat & 1030-1630 Sun.
Min Mail Order UK: £6.50 (bare root)
Min Mail Order EU: Contact nursery.
Cat. Cost: Free.
Credit Cards: All major debit/credit cards except American Express
Specialities: Stocks over 250 varieties of roses. New roses usually launched at RHS Hampton Court Flower Show. Bare root roses available for sale from Nov-Mar, potted roses available all year round.
Notes: Talks held throughout the year, contact nursery for information. Group bookings available. Exports beyond the EU. Wheelchair accessible.
OS Grid Ref: SJ738803

MGil **JOHN GILLIES** ♿
at Russell's Garden Centre, Mill Hill, Baginton, Warwickshire, CV8 3AG
Ⓜ 07546 064961
Ⓔ enquiries@gilliesrareplants.com
Ⓦ www.gilliesrareplants.com
Contact: John Gillies
Opening Times: 1000-1700 Mon, Wed, Thu, Fri & Sat, 1030-1630 Sun Mar-Sept. (Closed Easter Sun). 1000-1600 Wed-Sat Oct-Nov. Other times by appt.
Min Mail Order UK: Nmc
Cat. Cost: Online only.
Credit Cards: All major credit/debit cards
Specialities: Offer a range of choice & rare plants of all types.
Notes: Please contact before visiting to ensure plant you require is currently in stock. Wheelchair accessible.
OS Grid Ref: SP337750

MGos **GOSCOTE NURSERIES LTD** ♿
Syston Road, Cossington, Leicestershire, LE7 4UZ
Ⓣ (01509) 812121
Ⓔ enquiries@goscote.co.uk
Ⓦ www.goscote.co.uk
Contact: James Toone
Opening Times: 7 days, all year round (Not Xmas to New Year).
Cat. Cost: Online only.
Credit Cards: Visa, Access, MasterCard, Delta, Switch
Specialities: Japanese maples, rhododendrons & azaleas, *Camellia, Magnolia, Pieris* & other Ericaceae. Ornamental trees & shrubs, conifers, fruit, heathers, alpines, roses, *Clematis* & unusual climbers.
Notes: Design & landscaping service available. Café & show garden. Also sells wholesale. Wheelchair accessible.
OS Grid Ref: SK602130

MHCG **HILL CLOSE GARDENS** ♿
Bread and Meat Close, Warwick, Warwickshire, CV34 6HF
Ⓣ (01926) 493339
Ⓜ 07533 401934
Ⓔ headgardener@hcgt.org.uk
Ⓦ www.hillclosegardens.com
Contact: Gary Leaver
Opening Times: 1100-1700, 7 days, Apr-Oct. 1100-1600 Mon-Fri only, Nov-Mar.
Min Mail Order UK: NMC
Cat. Cost: 2 × 1st class or online.
Credit Cards: All major credit/debit cards
Specialities: Hold dispersed National Plant Collection of Hardy *Chrysanthemum*. Also specialise in *Symphyotrichum* & *Galanthus*. Only chrysanthemums offered by mail order in the Spring.
Notes: Small retail nursery attached to heritage garden which is open to the public. Wheelchair accessible.
OS Grid Ref: SP277647

MHed **HEDGEXPRESS** ♿
Buckland Road, Bampton, Oxfordshire, OX18 2AA
Ⓣ (01993) 850979
Ⓔ sales@hedgexpress.co.uk
Ⓦ www.hedgexpress.co.uk
Contact: Gavin Stevens
Opening Times: 0900-1600, Mon-Fri.
Min Mail Order UK: £100
Cat. Cost: Online only.
Credit Cards: All major credit/debit cards, PayPal
Specialities: Hedging & lavenders.
Notes: Also sells wholesale. Wheelchair accessible.
OS Grid Ref: SP322024

MHer **THE HERB NURSERY** ♿
Thistleton, Oakham, Rutland, LE15 7RE
Ⓣ (01572) 767658

Ⓔ herbnursery@southwitham.net
Ⓦ www.herbnursery.co.uk
Contact: Peter & Christine Bench
Opening Times: 0900-1700 Mon-Sat, incl. b/hols 1000-1600 Sun. Closed Xmas until 1st Feb.
Cat. Cost: Free with A5 sae.
Credit Cards: All major credit/debit cards
Specialities: Herbs, wild flowers, cottage garden plants, *Lavandula, Mentha, Pelargonium, Thymus.*
Notes: Open garden weekend 16th and 17th Jun (see website for details) Wheelchair accessible.

M

MHid **Hidden Paradise Plants** ♿
7 Lumber Lane, Burtonwood, Newton-le-Willows, Warrington, Cheshire, WA5 4AS
Ⓣ (01925) 229100
Ⓔ timothyatkinson@msn.com
Ⓦ www.sound-garden-designs.co.uk
Contact: Tim Atkinson
Opening Times: By appt. only.
Min Mail Order UK: Nmc
Cat. Cost: 2 × 1st class.
Credit Cards: None
Specialities: Species *Cautleya, Hedychium, Rhododendron.*
Notes: Delivers to shows. Wheelchair accessible.
OS Grid Ref: SJ948901

MHol **Hollies Farm Plant Centre**
Uppertown, Bonsall, Nr Matlock, Derbyshire, DE4 2AW
Ⓣ (01629) 822734
Ⓔ rbrt.wells@gmail.com
Ⓦ www.holliesfarmplantcentre.co.uk
Contact: Robert or Linda Wells
Opening Times: 0900-1700 every day except Wed.
Credit Cards: None
Specialities: Range of rare & unusual herbaceous perennials.
Notes: Garden designers welcome.

MHost **North Staffordshire Hostas**
6 Spinney Close, Endon, Stoke-on-Trent, Staffordshire, ST9 9BP
Ⓣ (01782) 502345 (after 6pm)
Ⓜ 07837 581109
Ⓔ robert.e.barlow@btopenworld.com
Ⓦ www.northstaffordshirehostas.co.uk
Contact: Robert Barlow
Opening Times: By appt. only.
Min Mail Order UK: £20.00
Cat. Cost: Online only.
Specialities: *Astrantia, Carex, Geum, Hosta,* ferns. All plants available in small quantities only.
Notes: Mail order only. 2018 Open days 13 May & 7 Jul 1000-1700. Plants sold at shows and fairs during the year, including RHS Tatton Park. Aim to develop their *Hosta* collection to 450 plus cultivars. Delivers to shows.

MHtn **Hintons Nursery** ♿
Coventry Road, Guy's Cliffe, Warwick, Warwick, CV34 5FJ
Ⓣ (01926) 492273
Ⓔ hintonsnursery@live.co.uk
Ⓦ www.hintonsnursery.co.uk
Contact: Sarah Ridgeway
Opening Times: 0900-1600 Mon-Sat, 1000-1630 Sun Apr-Jun. 0900-1600 Mon-Sat, 1000-1600 Sun Jul-Mar.
Min Mail Order UK: Nmc
Credit Cards: All major debit/credit cards except American Express
Specialities: Specialise in fruit (soft fruit and fruit trees) and vegetables, growing nearly 200 varieties of vegetable plants ready to plant out. Also offer more unusual fruit such as Chilean guava, honeyberries, worcesterberries, *Aronia* and pluots.
Notes: Grow & sell all types of plant from alpines, herbs, herbaceous, shrubs and climbers to trees, aquatics, ferns, bamboos & roses in a range of sizes. Plug plants for summer bedding are available in spring. Also sells wholesale. Wheelchair accessible.
OS Grid Ref: SP289636

MJac **Jackson's Nurseries**
Clifton Campville, Nr Tamworth, Staffordshire, B79 0AP
Ⓣ (01827) 373307
Contact: N. Jackson
Opening Times: 0900-1800 Mon & Wed-Sat, 1000-1700 Sun.
Cat. Cost: 2 × 1st class.
Credit Cards: None
Specialities: *Fuchsia.*
Notes: Also sells wholesale.

MLod **Lodge Farm Plants & Wildflowers** ♿
Case Lane, Fiveways, Hatton, Warwickshire, CV35 7JD
Ⓜ 07977 631368
Ⓔ lodgefarmplants@btinternet.com
Ⓦ www.lodgefarm-plants.com
Contact: Janet Cook & Nick Cook
Opening Times: Open 7 days all year, except Xmas Day & Boxing Day.

Min Mail Order UK: Nmc
Cat. Cost: Availability list online.
Credit Cards: All major credit/debit cards
Specialities: All forms of fruit trees; bush, espalier, fan, stepovers, cordons. Soft fruit. Native trees & hedging. Ornamental trees.
Notes: Courier service to all UK. Offers online & phone sales as well as at nursery. Also sells wholesale. Euro accepted. Wheelchair accessible.
OS Grid Ref: SP223700

MMrt **MORTON NURSERIES LTD** ♿
Morton, Retford, Nottinghamshire, DN22 8HE
Ⓣ (01777) 702530
Ⓜ 07940 434398
Ⓔ enquiries@morton-nurseries.com
Ⓦ www.morton-nurseries.co.uk
Contact: Gill McMaster
Opening Times: 1000-1600 Mon-Fri, 1400-1700 Sat & Sun.
Min Mail Order UK: £5.00 + p&p
Cat. Cost: None issued.
Credit Cards: All major credit/debit cards
Specialities: Shrubs & perennials.
Notes: Delivers to shows. Wheelchair accessible.
OS Grid Ref: SK671187

MMuc **MUCKLESTONE NURSERIES** ♿
Rock Lane, Mucklestone, Nr Market Drayton, Shropshire, TF9 4FA
Ⓣ (07929) 178751
Ⓜ 07714 241667
Ⓔ info@botanyplants.co.uk
Ⓦ www.botanyplants.co.uk
Contact: William & Louise Friend
Opening Times: 0930-1700 (or dusk) Wed-Fri Sept-Apr. 0930-1700 Sat May-Aug.
Min Mail Order UK: Nmc
Cat. Cost: Online.
Credit Cards: All major credit/debit cards
Specialities: Trees, shrubs, grasses, bamboos, rhododendrons, ferns & perennials for acid & damp soils of the north & west UK. Our nursery in Kent grows complementary range for dry, chalk & coast. Extensive grounds where plants can be seen growing. Small numbers only of each variety available. Larger quantities can be propagated to order.
Notes: Please call or text nursery to check opening times or make an appt. Any plants on website incl. those listed under nursery code SEND (in Kent) can be ordered for collection from Mucklestone or sent/delivered direct. Evening garden tours or talks for garden groups in Staffs, Salop or Cheshire by arrangement with William Friend on 07714 241668. For mail order please telephone or email Louise Friend on 07714 241667 or via nursery email address. For enquiries about opening times and collections please telephone 07929 178751. Wheelchair accessible.
OS Grid Ref: SJ728373

MNHC **THE NATIONAL HERB CENTRE** ♿
Banbury Road, Warmington, Nr Banbury, Oxfordshire, OX17 1DF
Ⓣ (01295) 690999
Ⓕ (01295) 690034
Ⓔ info@herbcentre.co.uk
Ⓦ www.herbcentre.co.uk
Contact: Plant Centre Staff
Opening Times: 0900-1730 Mon-Sat, 1030-1700 Sun.
Min Mail Order UK: Nmc
Credit Cards: All major credit/debit cards
Specialities: Herbs, culinary & medicinal. Extensive selection of *Lavandula, Rosmarinus* & *Thymus* in particular.
Notes: Next day delivery UK mainland only, signature required. Carriage charge of £10.00 for orders valued up to £50, more for larger orders. Wheelchair accessible.
OS Grid Ref: SP413471

MNrw **NORWELL NURSERIES & GARDENS** ♿
Woodhouse Road, Norwell, Newark, Nottinghamshire, NG23 6JX
Ⓣ (01636) 636337
Ⓔ wardha@aol.com
Ⓦ www.norwellnurseries.co.uk
Contact: Dr Andrew Ward
Opening Times: 1000-1700 Mon, Wed-Fri & Sun (Wed-Mon May & Jun). By appt. Aug & 23rd Oct-1st Mar.
Min Mail Order UK: £20.00 + p&p
Min Mail Order EU: £40.00
Cat. Cost: 3 × 1st class or online.
Credit Cards: None
Specialities: A large collection of over 2500 unusual & choice herbaceous perennials esp., hardy geraniums, *Geum*, pond & bog plants, cottage garden plants, *Hemerocallis*, grasses, *Trillium* & woodland plants. National Plant Collection of hardy *Chrysanthemum* and *Astrantia*.
Notes: One acre garden & tea room. Talks given and garden tours. Named by the HPS as one of the top 60 perennial gardens. Also sells wholesale. Delivers to shows. Wheelchair accessible.
OS Grid Ref: SK767616

MPhe **PHEDAR NURSERY**
42 Bunkers Hill, Romiley, Stockport, Cheshire, SK6 3DS
Ⓣ (0161) 430 3772
Ⓔ mclewin@phedar.com
Ⓦ www.phedar.com
Contact: Will McLewin
Opening Times: Frequent but irregular. Please phone to arrange appt.
Min Mail Order UK: Nmc
Min Mail Order EU: Nmc
Cat. Cost: Online or write for printed version.
Credit Cards: None
Specialities: Species *Helleborus*, *Paeonia*. Limited stock of some rare items.
Notes: Also sells wholesale. Exports beyond EU subject to destination & on an ad hoc basis only. Please contact nursery for details.
OS Grid Ref: SJ936897

MPie **PIECEMEAL PLANTS** ♿
Whatton House Gardens, Nr Kegworth, Loughborough, Leicestershire, LE12 5BG
Ⓣ (01509) 672056
Ⓜ 07950 757444
Ⓔ nursery@piecemealplants.co.uk
Ⓦ www.piecemealplants.co.uk
Contact: Mary Thomas
Opening Times: 1300-1600 (longer hours in summer) Thu & Fri, early Apr-mid Sep. 1300-1700 Sun May & Jun. See website or telephone for details. Open by appt. all year.
Cat. Cost: Online only.
Credit Cards: All major credit/debit cards
Specialities: Wide range of quality, hardy herbaceous perennials. Unusual varieties & cottage garden favourites. Most in small quantities. Limited selection of shrubs, flowering bulbs, half hardy & tender plants.
Notes: Nursery located at entrance to Whatton Gardens, behind Whatton House. Access via A6 between Kegworth & Hathern. Car parking in front of Whatton House at top of drive. Delivers to shows (mainly Midlands plant fairs). Wheelchair accessible. Gardens also open (see website).
OS Grid Ref: SK494242

MPkF **PACKHORSE FARM NURSERY** ♿
Sandyford House, Lant Lane, Tansley, Matlock, Derbyshire, DE4 5FW
Ⓣ (01629) 57206
Ⓜ 07974 095752
Ⓕ (01629) 57206
Contact: Hilton W. Haynes
Opening Times: 1000-1600 Tue & Wed, 1st Mar-31st Oct. Other times by appt. only.
Cat. Cost: 2 × 1st class for plant list.
Credit Cards: None
Specialities: *Acer*, rare stock is limited in supply. Other more unusual hardy shrubs, trees & conifers.
Notes: Delivers to shows. Wheelchair accessible.
OS Grid Ref: SK322617

MPnt **PLANTAGOGO.COM**
Jubilee Cottage Nursery, Snape Lane, Englesea Brook, Crewe, Cheshire, CW2 5QN
Ⓣ (01270) 820335
Ⓜ 07713 518271
Ⓔ info@plantagogo.com
Ⓦ www.plantagogo.com
Contact: Vicky & Richard Fox
Opening Times: By appt. only. Also open days (no appt. required) 1000-1600 06-08 Apr, 23-24 Jun, 21-23 Sep 2018.
Min Mail Order UK: £9.95
Min Mail Order EU: Price on application
Cat. Cost: Online only.
Credit Cards: All major credit/debit cards
Specialities: *Heuchera*, *Heucherella*, *Tiarella*, also large selection of perennials. Plants listed in the RHS Plant Finder are available in good quantities. Others, not listed here, are available from our collections on request. National Plant Collections of *Heuchera*, *Heucherella* & *Tiarella*.
Notes: Open days throughout the year (see opening times). Also sells wholesale (small amounts). Homemade cake & coffee/tea daily. Delivers to shows. Partial wheelchair access.
OS Grid Ref: SJ750516

MPri **PRIMROSE COTTAGE NURSERY** ♿
Altrincham Road, Styal, Wilmslow, Cheshire, SK9 4JE
Ⓜ 07798 754457
Ⓔ info@primrosecottagenursery.co.uk
Ⓦ www.primrosecottagenursery.co.uk
Contact: Caroline Dumville
Opening Times: 0900-1700 Mon-Sat, 0930-1700 Sun (summer). 0900-1700 Mon-Sat, 0930-1700 Sun (winter).
Credit Cards: All major credit/debit cards
Specialities: Perennials, herbs, patio & hanging basket plants, always lots of new & unusual varieties. Shrubs, roses, ornamental trees, fruit trees, soft fruit bushes, bedding & vegetable plants.
Notes: In Styal Village, close to National Trust Quarry Bank Mill and estate. Wheelchair accessible.

MPtG **PLANTS2GARDENS LTD**
The Nursery, Manor House Farm, Woodford, Kettering, Northamptonshire, NN14 4ES

Ⓣ (01832) 733374
Ⓜ 07397 167539
Ⓔ customerservice@plants2gardens.com
Ⓦ www.plants2gardens.com
Contact: Lindsey Ward
Opening Times: Not open. Mail order only via website.
Min Mail Order UK: Nmc
Credit Cards: All major credit/debit cards
Specialities: Specialist propagator of regal, angel & species *Pelargonium*.

MRav **Ravensthorpe Nursery** ♿
6 East Haddon Road, Ravensthorpe, Northamptonshire, NN6 8ES
Ⓣ (01604) 770548
Ⓔ ravensthorpenursery@hotmail.com
Contact: Jean & Richard Wiseman
Opening Times: 1000-1800 (or dusk if earlier) Wed-Sat. B/hols in May.
Min Mail Order UK: Nmc
Cat. Cost: None issued.
Credit Cards: Visa, MasterCard
Specialities: Huge range of perennials, shrubs & trees with numerous unusual varieties, many of which can be seen growing in the display garden. Some plants only available as lifted from garden during the lifting season.
Notes: Search & delivery service for large orders, winter months only. Wheelchair accessible.
OS Grid Ref: SP665699

MSCN **Stonyford Cottage Nursery** ♿
Stonyford Lane, Cuddington, Northwich, Cheshire, CW8 2TF
Ⓣ (01606) 888970/888128 (answerphone)
Ⓜ 07714 205177
Ⓔ stonyfordcottage@yahoo.co.uk
Ⓦ www.stonyfordcottagenursery.co.uk
Contact: Andrew Overland
Opening Times: 1000-1700 Tue-Sun & B/hols 1st Feb-31st Oct.
Min Mail Order UK: Nmc
Min Mail Order EU: Nmc
Cat. Cost: None.
Credit Cards: All major credit/debit cards
Specialities: Wide range of herbaceous perennials, *Iris*, hardy *Geranium*, moisture-loving & bog plants. *Sempervivum*, *Paeonia*, candelabra *Primula*.
Notes: Also sells wholesale. Wheelchair accessible.
OS Grid Ref: SJ580710

MSpe **SpecialPerennials.com**
Yew Tree House, Hall Lane, Hankelow, Crewe, Cheshire, CW3 0JB
Ⓜ 07716 990695
Ⓔ plants@specialperennials.com
Ⓦ www.specialperennials.com
Contact: Janet & Martin Blow
Opening Times: Not open. Strictly no visitors. Mail order and at Plant Hunters' Fairs only.
Min Mail Order UK: £25.00
Cat. Cost: Online only.
Credit Cards: PayPal
Specialities: *Helenium*, *Phlox*, *Salvia* and other herbaceous plants for summer colour. All plants in fairly small numbers. Plants are propagated here with a few exceptions (e.g. PVR).
Notes: Small nursery growing garden worthy plants. Featured on Gardeners World in 2014. See our website for a list of plant fairs attended where we can bring orders. Orders delivered to plant fairs free of p&p charge.

MSwo **Swallows Nursery** ♿
Mixbury, Brackley, Northamptonshire, NN13 5RR
Ⓣ (01280) 847721
Ⓔ enq@swallowsnursery.co.uk
Ⓦ www.swallowsnursery.co.uk
Contact: Chris Swallow
Opening Times: 0900-1300 & 1400-1700 (earlier in winter) Mon-Fri, 0900-1300 Sat.
Min Mail Order UK: £19.50
Cat. Cost: 3 × 1st class (plus phone number).
Credit Cards: All major credit/debit cards
Specialities: Growing a wide range, particularly shrubs, climbers, trees & roses.
Notes: Trees not for mail order unless part of larger order. Nursery transport used where possible, esp. for trees. Also sells wholesale. Wheelchair accessible.
OS Grid Ref: SP607336

MThu **T. D. Thursfield**
Kerry Hill Nurseries, Eaves Lane, Bucknall, Stoke-on-Trent, Staffordshire, ST2 8NA
Ⓣ (01782) 302498
Ⓜ 07977 464363
Ⓔ tdthursfield@aol.com
Ⓦ www.tdthursfield.co.uk
Contact: Susan Thursfield
Opening Times: 0900-1730 Mon-Fri, 0930-1630 Sat, 1000-1600 Sun.
Cat. Cost: None issued.
Credit Cards: All major debit/credit cards except American Express
Specialities: Broad selection of hardy nursery stock.
Notes: Traditional family nursery founded in the 1930s. Also sells wholesale. Delivers to shows. Wheelchair access to main sales areas.

MTin **The Tiny Plant Company**
25 Owley Wood Road, Weaverham, Cheshire, CW8 3LF
Ⓣ (01606) 851146
Ⓔ thetinyplantco@hotmail.com
Ⓦ www.tinyplantcompany.co.uk
Contact: Matt Wood
Opening Times: Not open. Mail order only.
Min Mail Order UK: £3.00
Cat. Cost: Online only.
Credit Cards: All major credit/debit cards
Specialities: Newly-opened small nursery. All plants available in very small quantities only.
Notes: Delivers to shows.

MTis **Tissington Nursery** ♿
The Old Kitchen Gardens, Tissington, Ashbourne, Derbyshire, DE6 1RA
Ⓣ (01335) 390650
Ⓜ 07929 720284
Ⓔ info@tissington-nursery.co.uk
Ⓦ www.tissington-nursery.co.uk
Contact: Mairi Longdon
Opening Times: 1100-1700 daily, end Mar-end Sep.
Min Mail Order UK: Nmc
Cat. Cost: 4 × 1st class or online.
Credit Cards: All major credit/debit cards
Specialities: Choice & unusual perennials esp. *Achillea*, *Aster*, *Dianthus*, *Geranium*, *Geum*, *Helenium*, *Helianthus*, *Nepeta*, *Phlox*, *Salvia*, *Sanguisorba* & *Sedum*.
Notes: Delivers to shows. Wheelchair accessible.
OS Grid Ref: SK176521

MWat **Waterperry Gardens Ltd** ♿
Waterperry, Nr Wheatley, Oxfordshire, OX33 1JZ
Ⓣ (01844) 339226/254
Ⓜ 07864 678864
Ⓕ (01844) 339883
Ⓔ rjacobs@waterperrygardens.co.uk
Ⓦ www.waterperrygardens.co.uk
Contact: Robert Jacobs
Opening Times: 1000-1730 summer. 1000-1700 winter.
Min Mail Order UK: £30.00
Cat. Cost: Online only.
Credit Cards: All major credit/debit cards
Specialities: General, large range of herbaceous esp. asters, also National Plant Collection of *Saxifraga* (subsect. *Kabschia* & *Engleria*).
Notes: Also sells wholesale. Wheelchair accessible.
OS Grid Ref: SP630064

MWht **Whitelea Nursery** ♿
Whitelea Lane, Tansley, Matlock, Derbyshire, DE4 5FL
Ⓣ (01629) 55010
Ⓕ (01629) 55010
Ⓔ sales@uk-bamboos.co.uk
Ⓦ www.uk-bamboos.co.uk
Contact: David Wilson
Opening Times: By appt.
Min Mail Order UK: Nmc
Cat. Cost: Online only. Price list available 2 × 1st class.
Credit Cards: None
Specialities: Bamboos. Substantial quantities of 45 species/cvs of bamboo, remainder stocked in small numbers only. Limited stocks of grasses, trees & shrubs.
Notes: Mail order limited by carrier restrictions, please contact nursery or see website for details. Also sells wholesale. Wheelchair accessible.
OS Grid Ref: SK325603

MWts **Waterside Nursery**
Sharnford, Leicestershire,
Ⓣ (01455) 273730
Ⓜ 07931 557082
Ⓔ info@watersidenursery.co.uk
Ⓦ www.watersidenursery.co.uk
Contact: Linda Smith
Opening Times: Mail order only.
Min Mail Order UK: Nmc
Cat. Cost: Online only.
Credit Cards: All major credit/debit cards
Specialities: Aquatics, marginal pond plants, miniature waterlilies, water lilies, submerged oxygenating plants, bog garden plants & moisture-loving plants.

Northern

NBid **Bide-A-Wee Cottage Gardens** ♿
Stanton, Netherwitton, Morpeth, Northumberland, NE65 8PR
Ⓣ (01670) 772238
Ⓜ 07976 559416
Ⓕ (01670) 772238
Ⓔ info@bideawee.co.uk
Ⓦ www.bideawee.co.uk
Contact: Mark Robson
Opening Times: 1330-1700 Sat & Wed, 14th Apr-15th Sept 2018. Group visits at other times, except Sun.
Min Mail Order UK: £28.00
Cat. Cost: Online only.
Credit Cards: All major credit/debit cards
Specialities: Unusual herbaceous perennials, *Agapanthus*, *Primula*, ferns, grasses. National

Plant Collection of *Centaurea*.
Notes: Wheelchair accessible.
OS Grid Ref: NZ132900

NBir **Birkheads Secret Gardens & Nursery** ♿
Birkheads Lane, Sunniside, Gateshead, Tyne & Wear, NE16 5EL
Ⓣ (01207) 232262
Ⓜ 07778 447920
Ⓕ (01207) 232262
Ⓔ birkheadsnursery@gmail.com
Ⓦ www.birkheadssecretgardens.co.uk
Contact: Mrs Christine Liddle
Opening Times: 1100-1700 Sat and Sun & 1000-1700 Wed-Fri in summer. Closed Mon & Tue. (Pre-booked coach groups Tue only). Open B/hols. Please check website for spring & winter opening.
Cat. Cost: None issued.
Credit Cards: All major credit/debit cards
Specialities: Hardy herbaceous perennials, grasses, hardy bulbs. Herbs. *Allium*, *Euphorbia*, *Galanthus*, *Geranium*, *Primula*, *Rodgersia* & *Sedum*.
Notes: Nursery & coffee shop wheelchair accessible, please ring for special access directions. Coffee shop closes 30 mins before the gardens. RHS Partner Garden.
OS Grid Ref: NZ220569

NBPC **The Barn Plant Centre & Gift Shop**
The Square, Scorton, Near Garstang, Preston, Lancashire, PR3 1AU
Ⓣ (01524) 793533
Ⓔ sales@plantsandgifts.co.uk
Ⓦ www.sales@plantsandgifts.co.uk
Contact: Neil and Beverley Anderton
Opening Times: 0900-1700 Mon-Fri, 1000-1800 Sat-Sun.
Credit Cards: All major credit/debit cards
Specialities: 800 varieties of perennials.
Notes: Large gift shop & coffee bar.
OS Grid Ref: GR501487

NBre **Breezy Knees Nurseries** ♿
Common Lane, Warthill, York, YO19 5XS
Ⓣ (01904) 488800
Ⓔ admin@breezyknees.co.uk
Ⓦ www.breezyknees.co.uk
Contact: Any member of staff
Opening Times: 1030-1700 7 days 1st May-30th Sept. 1030-1700 Mon-Fri 1st Apr-30th Apr.
Credit Cards: All major credit/debit cards
Specialities: Very wide range of perennials. All can be viewed in 20-acre gardens (open 1st May-30th Sep).
Notes: Wheelchair accessible.
OS Grid Ref: SE675565

NBro **Brownthwaite Hardy Plants** ♿
Fell Yeat, Casterton, Kirkby Lonsdale, Lancashire, LA6 2JW
Ⓣ (01524) 271340 (after 1800 hours).
Ⓦ www.hardyplantsofcumbria.co.uk
Contact: Chris Benson
Opening Times: 1000-1700, 1st Apr-20th Sep.
Min Mail Order UK: Nmc
Cat. Cost: 3 × 1st for fern list.
Credit Cards: None
Specialities: Herbaceous perennials and hardy ferns incl. *Hosta*, *Hydrangea paniculata* & *Hydrangea serrata* varieties *Primula*, *Polystichum*.
Notes: Follow brown signs from A65 between Kirkby Lonsdale & Cowan Bridge. Mail order for Hydrangea & ferns. Delivers to shows. Wheelchair accessible.
OS Grid Ref: SD632794

NCft **Craftyplants**
(office) 21 Woodgreen Drive, Radcliffe, Lancashire, M26 1BF
Ⓣ (0161) 820 8606
Ⓜ 07742 783631
Ⓔ sales@craftyplants.co.uk
Ⓦ www.craftyplants.co.uk
Contact: Graham Sigsworth
Opening Times: Mail order only. Not open except for nursery open days (see website or phone for details).
Min Mail Order UK: Nmc
Min Mail Order EU: Nmc
Cat. Cost: Online. Printed list available on request.
Credit Cards: All major debit/credit cards except American Express
Specialities: *Tillandsia*.
Notes: Nursery at Eezitill, Startley Nook, Preston PR4 4XW. Also sells wholesale. Euro accepted. Delivers to shows.

NChi **Chipchase Castle Nursery** ♿
Chipchase Castle, Wark, Hexham, Northumberland, NE48 3NT
Ⓣ (01434) 230083
Ⓜ 07575 714002
Ⓔ chipchaseplants@aim.com
Ⓦ www.chipchasenursery.com
Contact: Mark Cummings
Opening Times: 1000-1700 Thu-Sun & B/hols, 1st Apr (or Easter if earlier) to end Sep.
Min Mail Order UK: Nmc
Min Mail Order EU: Nmc
Cat. Cost: A5 sae for list.

Credit Cards: All major credit/debit cards
Specialities: Rare & unusual herbaceous esp. *Geranium* (100+), *Geum, Pulmonaria, Potentilla, Primula* & *Vinca*. Some plants only available in small quantities.
Notes: Delivers to shows. Suitable for accompanied wheelchair users.
OS Grid Ref: NY880758

NCou **COURTYARD PLANTERS** ♿
9 Westgate, Otley, West Yorkshire, LS21 3AT
Ⓣ (01943) 462390
Ⓔ katie@courtyardplanters.co.uk
Ⓦ www.courtyardplanters.co.uk
Contact: Katie Burnett
Opening Times: 0930-1700 Tue-Sat. Closed Jan.
Cat. Cost: Online only.
Credit Cards: All major debit/credit cards except American Express
Specialities: Perennials. Plants for heavy clay soils. Peat free.
Notes: Gardening classes & workshops. Also sells wholesale. Wheelchair accessible.
OS Grid Ref: SE201455

N

NDal **DALESIDE NURSERIES LTD** ♿
Ripon Road, Killinghall, Harrogate, North Yorkshire, HG3 2AY
Ⓣ (01423) 506450
Ⓕ (01423) 527872
Ⓔ contact@dalesidenurseries.co.uk
Ⓦ www.dalesidenurseries.co.uk
Contact: Any Member of Staff
Opening Times: 0830-1700 Mon-Sat, 1030-1630 Sun. Winter hours: 0830-1600 Mon-Sat (closed Sun) Jan & 0830-1630 Mon-Sat, 1030-1630 Sun, Feb.
Cat. Cost: Online only.
Credit Cards: All major debit/credit cards except American Express
Specialities: Many plants & trees not generally available. Container-grown fruit trees: apples, pears & soft fruit. Container-grown trees. Conifers, *Clematis* & hardy perennials.
Notes: Wheelchair accessible.
OS Grid Ref: SE287590

NDav **DAVE PARKINSON PLANTS**
4 West Bank, Carlton, Goole, East Yorkshire, DN14 9PZ
Ⓣ (01405) 860693
Ⓜ 07773 564945
Ⓦ www.daveparkinsonplants.co.uk
Contact: Mary Parkinson
Opening Times: Not open. Mail order only.
Min Mail Order UK: £12 + p&p
Min Mail Order EU: Nmc
Cat. Cost: 1st class stamp.
Credit Cards: None
Specialities: Hardy orchids. Terrestrial South African *Disa* orchids, species & hybrids.
Notes: Sells at RHS & Orchid Shows. Delivers to shows.

NDov **DOVE COTTAGE NURSERY & GARDEN** ♿
Shibden Hall Road, Halifax, West Yorkshire, HX3 9XA
Ⓣ (01422) 203553
Ⓔ info@dovecottagenursery.co.uk
Ⓦ www.dovecottagenursery.co.uk
Contact: Stephen & Kim Rogers
Opening Times: 1000-1700 Wed-Sun, 1st Mar-30th Sep & B/hols. Other times by appt. Please check website or phone before travelling.
Cat. Cost: £3.00.
Credit Cards: All major credit/debit cards
Specialities: Herbaceous perennials & selected grasses, many displayed in adjoining naturalistic garden.
Notes: Wheelchair accessible.
OS Grid Ref: SE115256

NDro **DROINTON NURSERIES** ♿
Plaster Pitts, Norton Conyers, Ripon, North Yorkshire, HG4 5EF
Ⓣ (01765) 641849
Ⓜ 07909 971529
Ⓔ info@auricula-plants.co.uk
Ⓦ www.auricula-plants.co.uk
Contact: Robin & Annabel Graham
Opening Times: Open days in spring, otherwise by appt. only.
Min Mail Order UK: Nmc
Min Mail Order EU: Nmc
Cat. Cost: 4 × 1st class.
Credit Cards: All major credit/debit cards
Specialities: *Primula auricula*. More than 1150 cvs of show, alpine, double & border auriculas. Limited stock of any one cultivar. National Plant Collection of *Primula auricula* (borders).
Notes: Also sells wholesale. Exports beyond EU. Delivers to shows. Wheelchair accessible.
OS Grid Ref: SE315753

NDry **DRYAD NURSERY**
130 Prince Rupert Drive, Tockwith, York, North Yorkshire, YO26 7PU
Ⓣ (01423) 358791
Ⓔ dryadnursery@gmail.com
Ⓦ www.dryad-home.co.uk
Contact: Anne Wright

Opening Times: Not open. Mail order only.
Min Mail Order UK: £5.50
Min Mail Order EU: £8.70
Cat. Cost: Online only.
Credit Cards: PayPal
Specialities: Miniature and species *Galanthus, Narcissus* wood anemones, hepaticas and other small bulbs.
Notes: Grower and breeder of miniature daffodils, snowdrops and hepaticas. Holder of large collection of wood anemones. All plants available in limited numbers and from seasonal lists only. Exports beyond the EU.

NEoE **East of Eden Nursery** ♿
Ainstable, Carlisle, Cumbria, CA4 9QN
Ⓣ (01768) 896604
Ⓜ 07788 142969
Ⓔ roger@east-of-eden-nursery.co.uk
Ⓦ www.east-of-eden-nursery.co.uk
Contact: Roger Proud
Opening Times: Mar-Nov. Days & times variable, so please phone or email before calling.
Min Mail Order UK: £10.00
Cat. Cost: None issued.
Credit Cards: All major credit/debit cards
Specialities: Interesting & unusual shrubs, perennials & alpines, esp. astilbes & geums with over 60 new *Geum* cvs, bred & raised on nursery.
Notes: Delivers to shows. Wheelchair accessible.
OS Grid Ref: NY467504

NEqu **Equatorial Plant Co.**
The Dovecote, Newgate, Barnard Castle, Co. Durham, DL12 8NW
Ⓣ (01833) 908127
Ⓕ (01833) 908127
Ⓔ Equatorial9@gmail.com
Ⓦ www.equatorialplants.com
Contact: Dr Richard Warren
Opening Times: Mail order only. Open by appt. only.
Min Mail Order UK: Nmc
Min Mail Order EU: Nmc
Cat. Cost: Free.
Credit Cards: Visa, Access, PayPal
Specialities: Laboratory-raised orchids only.
Notes: Also sells wholesale. Exports beyond EU. Delivers to shows. Euro accepted.

NGBl **Garden Blooms**
Fieldgate, Mill Field Road, Fishlake, Doncaster, Yorkshire, DN7 5GH
Ⓣ (01302) 288145
Ⓔ info@gardenblooms.co.uk
Ⓦ www.gardenblooms.co.uk
Contact: Liz Webster
Opening Times: Open by appt. or on open days. Contact nursery for details.
Min Mail Order UK: Nmc
Cat. Cost: Online only.
Credit Cards: All major credit/debit cards
Specialities: Hardy & tender perennials, especially *Rudbeckia*, & small range of conservatory/house plants. Some plants available in small quantities only.
Notes: Delivers to shows.
OS Grid Ref: SE659148

NGdn **Garden House Nursery** ♿
The Square, Dalston, Carlisle, Cumbria, CA5 7LL
Ⓣ (01228) 710297
Ⓜ 07595 219082
Ⓔ stephickso@hotmail.co.uk
Ⓦ www.gardenhousenursery.co.uk
Contact: Stephen Hickson
Opening Times: 0900-1700 Mon-Sat, 1000-1600 Sun, mid-Mar to Oct. Oct please ring if visiting at w/ends.
Cat. Cost: Plant list online only.
Credit Cards: All major credit/debit cards
Specialities: *Aconitum, Brunnera, Geranium, Hemerocallis, Hosta, Iris,* grasses & *Pulmonaria.*
Notes: Also sells wholesale. Wheelchair accessible.
OS Grid Ref: NY369503

NGKo **Greenkoos**
16 Elm Grove, Droylsdon, Greater Manchester, M43 6LP
Ⓣ (0161) 612 5705
Ⓜ 07806 893816
Ⓔ keeflong@hotmail.com
Ⓦ http://www.greenkooz.uk/home.html
Contact: Keith Long
Opening Times: By appt. only.
Min Mail Order UK: £20.00
Cat. Cost: Online only.
Credit Cards: All major credit/debit cards
Specialities: Exotic and architectural plants including aroids, *Brugmansia, Canna, Eucomis* & *Locromas*. Also grow and sell a wide range of trees, shrubs, perennials, ferns, bonsai and medicinal plants.
Notes: Plant nursery based in Manchester, best known for their Brugmansia. No online shop available yet. Please phone or email nursery for orders or details of plant fairs attended. Delivers to shows.
OS Grid Ref: SJ890119

NGrd **Gardener's Cottage Plants**
Gardener's Cottage, Bingfield, Newcastle-upon-Tyne, Tyne and Wear, NE19 2LE

N

Ⓣ (01434) 672594
Ⓜ 07500 895052
Ⓔ andrew@gcplants.co.uk
Ⓦ www.gcplants.co.uk
Contact: Andrew Davenport
Opening Times: 0800-1700 Thu-Sat, Apr-Nov incl.
Min Mail Order UK: £4.95
Min Mail Order EU: £9.95
Credit Cards: None
Specialities: Perennials, herbs and wildflowers. The nursery runs on sustainable and organic principles whereby all plants sold are propagated on site in peat-free composts and reycled pots.
Notes: Also sells at plant fairs. Contact nursery for details.

N

NHal **Halls of Heddon**
West Heddon Nurseries, Heddon-on-the-Wall, Northumberland, NE15 0JS
Ⓣ (01661) 852445
Ⓕ (01661) 852398
Ⓔ enquiry@hallsofheddon.co.uk
Ⓦ www.hallsofheddon.co.uk
Contact: David Hall
Opening Times: 0900-1700 Mon-Sat 1000-1700 Sun.
Min Mail Order UK: £10.00
Min Mail Order EU: £35.00
Cat. Cost: 3 × 2nd class.
Credit Cards: MasterCard, Visa, Switch, Delta
Specialities: *Chrysanthemum* & *Dahlia*.
Notes: Also sells wholesale.
OS Grid Ref: NZ122679

NHar **Hartside Nursery Garden**
Penrith Road, Alston, Cumbria, CA9 3BL
Ⓣ (01434) 381372
Ⓕ (01434) 381372
Ⓔ enquiries@plantswithaltitude.co.uk
Ⓦ www.plantswithaltitude.co.uk
Contact: Mr Neil Huntley
Opening Times: 1130-1630 Tue-Fri & 1230-1600 Sat, Sun & B/hols, Mar-Jun. 1130-1630 Tue-Fri, Jul-Oct. Other times by appt. only.
Min Mail Order UK: Nmc
Min Mail Order EU: £50.00 + p&p
Cat. Cost: 4 × 1st class.
Credit Cards: All major credit/debit cards
Specialities: *Primula*, including asiatic, petiolaris, European species and forms and *P. allionii* forms. Saxifrages, autumn flowering gentians, *Erythonium*, *Roscoea*, *Trillium*.
Notes: Delivers to shows.
OS Grid Ref: NY708447

NHaw **The Hawthornes Nursery** ♿
Marsh Road, Hesketh Bank, Nr Preston, Lancashire, PR4 6XT
Ⓣ (01772) 812379
Ⓔ richardhaw@talktalk.net
Ⓦ www.hawthornes-nursery.co.uk
Contact: Irene & Richard Hodson
Opening Times: 0900-1800 7 days, Mar-Jun & Thu-Sun, Jul-Oct. Gardens open for NGS.
Min Mail Order UK: £10.00
Min Mail Order EU: Nmc
Cat. Cost: None issued.
Credit Cards: None
Specialities: *Clematis*. National Plant Collection of *Clematis viticella*.
Notes: Check with nursery for National Plant Collection Open Day 2018. Exports beyond the EU. Euro accepted. Wheelchair accessible.

NHip **Hippopottering Nursery**
Orchard House, East Lound, Nr Doncaster, South Yorkshire, DN9 2LR
Ⓜ 07979 764677
Ⓔ hippomaples@hotmail.co.uk
Ⓦ www.hippopottering.com
Contact: Pat Gibbons
Opening Times: By appt. only & open days.
Min Mail Order UK: £15.00 + p&p
Cat. Cost: Online only.
Credit Cards: Visa, MasterCard
Specialities: Japanese maples: *Acer palmatum*, *A. japonicum* & *A. shirasawanum*.
Notes: Mail order to UK throughout year; to EU during winter. Delivers to shows. Wheelchair accessible in dry weather only.

NHol **Holden Clough Nursery** ♿
Holden, Bolton-by-Bowland, Nr Clitheroe, Lancashire, BB7 4PF
Ⓣ (01200) 447447
Ⓔ info@holdencloughnursery.com
Ⓦ www.holdencloughnursery.com
Contact: Kate Lawson
Opening Times: 0900-1700 Mon-Sat, 1030-1630 Sun, incl. B/hols. Closed Xmas Day & Boxing Day.
Min Mail Order UK: Nmc
Min Mail Order EU: Nmc
Cat. Cost: 2 × 1st class.
Credit Cards: All major credit/debit cards
Specialities: Large general list incl. perennials, esp. *Crocosmia*, shrubs, dwarf conifers, alpines, heathers, grasses & ferns.
Notes: Seasonal mail order on some items. Also sells wholesale on some items. Exports beyond EU. Delivers to shows. Wheelchair accessible.
OS Grid Ref: SD773496

NHoy **HOYLAND PLANT CENTRE**
Market Street, Hoyland, Barnsley,
South Yorkshire, S74 0ET
Ⓣ (01226) 744466
Ⓜ 07717 182169
Ⓕ (01226) 744466
Ⓔ hoylandplantcentre@btconnect.com
Ⓦ www.somethingforthegarden.co.uk
Contact: Steven Hickman
Opening Times: Open by appt. only.
Min Mail Order UK: Nmc
Min Mail Order EU: Nmc
Cat. Cost: Free online.
Credit Cards: All major credit/debit cards
Specialities: National Plant Collections of *Agapanthus* & *Tulbaghia*. Also holds a large collection of *Clivia* & *Nerine*.
Notes: Sells mail order or at major flower shows. Also sells wholesale. Exports beyond the EU. Delivers to shows. Euro accepted. Top of the nursery and glasshouse accessible for most wheelchairs.
OS Grid Ref: SE372010

NHpl **HARPERLEY HALL FARM NURSERIES** ♿
Harperley, Stanley, Co. Durham, DH9 9UB
Ⓣ (01207) 233318
Ⓜ 07944 644126
Ⓔ enquiries@harperleyhallfarmnurseries.co.uk
Ⓦ www.harperleyhallfarmnurseries.co.uk
Contact: Gary McDermott
Opening Times: Open on set days only. See website or phone for details.
Min Mail Order UK: Nmc
Min Mail Order EU: Nmc
Cat. Cost: None issued.
Credit Cards: All major credit/debit cards
Specialities: Growers of a wide range of alpine & woodland plants, incl. *Meconopsis* & *Primula*, many of which are rare or unusual. Also growers of a wide range of autumn-flowering gentians.
Notes: Also sells wholesale. Delivers to shows. Euro accepted. Wheelchair accessible.

NHsp **HARE SPRING COTTAGE PLANTS**
Church Orchard, Church Wind, Alne, York, Yorkshire, YO61 1RX
Ⓜ 07792 376805
Ⓔ stella@harespringcottageplants.co.uk
Ⓦ www.harespringcottageplants.co.uk
Contact: Stella Exley
Opening Times: By appt. only.
Min Mail Order UK: Nmc
Min Mail Order EU: Nmc
Cat. Cost: Online only.
Credit Cards: All major debit/credit cards except American Express
Specialities: *Camassia*, *Sidalcea* & *Uvularia*. National Plant Collection of *Camassia*. Some specialist plants available in small quantities only.
Notes: Sells at & delivers to specialist plant fairs. Talks to specialist groups & societies by arrangement. See website for details of 2018 Open days. Also sells wholesale. Delivers to shows. Euro accepted. Please call nursery to discuss accessibility requirements.

NJRG **JRG DAHLIAS**
22 Summerville Road, Milnthorpe, Cumbria, LA7 7DF
Ⓣ (01539) 562691
Ⓔ jack@jrg-dahlias.co.uk
Ⓦ www.jrg-dahlias.co.uk
Contact: Jack Gott
Opening Times: By appt. only.
Min Mail Order UK: £10.00 + p&p
Min Mail Order EU: Price with order.
Cat. Cost: Sae: 110mm × 220mm, 2nd class.
Credit Cards: PayPal
Specialities: *Dahlia*. Some available in small quantities only.
Notes: Delivers to shows.

NLar **LARCH COTTAGE NURSERIES** ♿ ◆
Melkinthorpe, Penrith, Cumbria, CA10 2DR
Ⓣ (01931) 712404
Ⓔ plants@larchcottage.co.uk
Ⓦ www.larchcottage.co.uk
Contact: Peter & Joanne Stott
Opening Times: Daily from 1000-1700 (or dusk in winter), all year. excl Xmas, Boxing Day & New Year's Day.
Min Mail Order UK: £20.00 + p&p
Credit Cards: All major credit/debit cards
Specialities: Comprehensive plant collection in unique garden setting. Rare & unusual plants, particularly shrubs, trees, perennials, dwarf conifers & Japanese maples. *Acer*, *Cornus kousa* cvs, *Hamamelis*, & *Magnolia*. Old-fashioned roses, bamboo & alpines.
Notes: Terraced restaurant, art gallery and shop open everyday. RHS partner gardens open Wed-Sun throughout the summer. Please check website for details. Wheelchair accessible.
OS Grid Ref: NY315602

NMen **MENDLE NURSERY** ♿
Holme, Scunthorpe, North Lincolnshire, DN16 3RF
Ⓣ (01724) 850864
Ⓔ ann.earnshaw@tiscali.co.uk
Ⓦ www.mendlenursery.co.uk
Contact: Mrs A. Earnshaw
Opening Times: 1000-1600 Tue-Sun.

N

Min Mail Order UK: Nmc
Min Mail Order EU: Nmc
Credit Cards: PayPal
Specialities: *Jovibarba*, *Saxifraga* & *Sempervivum*.
Notes: Wheelchair accessible.
OS Grid Ref: SE925070

NMir **Mires Beck Nursery** ♿
Low Mill Lane, North Cave, Brough,
East Riding, Yorkshire, HU15 2NR
Ⓣ (01430) 421543
Ⓕ (01430) 421543
Ⓔ admin@miresbeck.co.uk
Ⓦ www.miresbeck.co.uk
Contact: Sue Hewitt
Opening Times: 1000-1600 7 days, 1st Mar-30th Sep. 1000-1600 Mon-Fri, 1st Oct-30th Apr.
Min Mail Order UK: Nmc
Cat. Cost: 3 × 1st class.
Credit Cards: All major debit/credit cards except American Express
Specialities: Wildflower plants of Yorkshire provenance.
Notes: Mail order for wildflower plants & plugs only. Also sells wholesale. Wheelchair accessible.
OS Grid Ref: SE889316

NNor **Norcroft Nurseries** ♿
Roadends, Intack, Southwaite, Carlisle,
Cumbria, CA4 0LH
Ⓣ (01697) 473933
Ⓜ 07887781555
Ⓔ info@norcroftnurseries.co.uk
Ⓦ www.norcroftnurseries.co.uk
Contact: Stella Bell
Opening Times: Every afternoon excl. Mon (incl. B/hols) Apr-Jul, or ring for appt.
Min Mail Order UK: Nmc
Cat. Cost: 2 × 2nd class.
Credit Cards: None
Specialities: Hardy herbaceous, *Aquilegia*, *Dianthus*, *Hosta*, *Papaver*.
Notes: Also sells wholesale. Euro accepted. Wheelchair accessible.
OS Grid Ref: NY474433

NOra **Orange Pippin Ltd**
(office) 33 Algarth Rise, Pocklington, York,
Yorkshire, YO42 2HX
Ⓣ (01759) 392007
Ⓔ trees@orangepippin.com
Ⓦ www.orangepippintrees.co.uk
Contact: Maureen Borrie
Opening Times: Not open. Mail order online only.
Min Mail Order UK: Nmc
Min Mail Order EU: Nmc
Cat. Cost: Online only.
Credit Cards: MasterCard, Visa
Specialities: Wide range of fruit trees & ornamentals, incl. traditional & modern varieties along with small hardy plants, shrubs. *Clematis* and similar garden plants. Wide choice of rootstocks & tree forms.
Notes: Fruit tree expert available most days. Website incl. extensive tasting notes & variety comparisons. See website for ornamental trees www.pippintrees.co.uk. Order online all year round, deliveries from Aug-Apr. Exports beyond EU (to USA). Website for plants www.pippinplants.co.uk.

NOrn **Ornamental Trees Ltd**
The Nursery Office, Farnley Hall Estate,
Farnley, West Yorkshire, LS21 2QF
Ⓣ (01943) 660870
Ⓔ sales@ornamental-trees.co.uk
Ⓦ www.ornamental-trees.co.uk
Contact: Sally White
Opening Times: Mail order only. 0800-1800, Mon-Fri, 0900-1200, Sat.
Min Mail Order UK: Nmc
Cat. Cost: Online only.
Credit Cards: MasterCard, Visa
Specialities: Specialise in ornamental and fruit trees, including mature trees.
Notes: Delivers to shows.

NPer **Perry's Plants** ♿
The River Garden, Sleights, Whitby,
North Yorkshire, YO21 1RR
Ⓜ 07879 498623
Ⓔ richardperry008@hotmail.co.uk
Ⓦ www.perrysplants.co.uk
Contact: Sharon & Richard Perry
Opening Times: 1000-1700 mid-March to Oct.
Cat. Cost: None published.
Credit Cards: None
Specialities: *Anthemis*, *Erysimum*, *Euphorbia*, *Hebe*, *Lavatera*, *Malva* & *Osteospermum*. Uncommon hardy & container plants & aquatic plants.
Notes: Euro accepted. Wheelchair accessible.
OS Grid Ref: NZ869082

NPnk **Primrose Bank** ♿
Redroofs, Dauby Lane, Kexby, York, Yorkshire,
YO41 5LH
Ⓣ (01759) 380220
Ⓜ 07774 944447
Ⓔ suegoodwill@yahoo.co.uk
Ⓦ www.primrosebank.co.uk
Contact: Sue Goodwill
Opening Times: 1000-1700 Thu-Sat Please telephone for opening times Jul-Oct.

Min Mail Order UK: Nmc
Cat. Cost: None issued.
Credit Cards: All major credit/debit cards
Specialities: *Galanthus*, *Hydrangea* & *Primula*.
Notes: Delivers to shows. Wheelchair accessible.
OS Grid Ref: SE696508

NPoe **Poets Cottage Shrub Nursery** ♿
Lealholm, Whitby, North Yorkshire, YO21 2AQ
Ⓣ (01947) 897424
Ⓜ 07813 252303
Ⓔ enquiries@poetscottage.co.uk
Ⓦ www.poetscottage.co.uk
Contact: Ilona J. McGivern
Opening Times: 1300-1530 Feb, 0900-1700 Mar-Xmas, 7 days. Closed Jan.
Cat. Cost: None issued.
Credit Cards: All major debit/credit cards except American Express
Specialities: Conifers, pines, trees, shrubs, herbaceous, alpines, herbs & *Acer*.
Notes: Wheelchair accessible.

NPol **Polemonium Plantery** ♿
28 Sunnyside, Trimdon Grange, Co. Durham, TS29 6HF
Ⓣ (01429) 881529
Ⓔ dandd@polemonium.co.uk
Ⓦ www.polemonium.co.uk
Contact: David or Dianne Nichol-Brown
Opening Times: By appt. only or see website
Min Mail Order UK: £10.00
Cat. Cost: 3 × 1st class.
Credit Cards: All major credit/debit cards, PayPal
Specialities: National Plant Collections of *Collomia*, *Gilia*, *Fragaria vesca*, *Hakonechloa*, *Leptodactylon (Polemoniaceae)* & *Polemonium*.
Notes: Also sells wholesale. Delivers to shows. Wheelchair accessible.
OS Grid Ref: NZ369353

NQui **Quiet Corner Plants**
(office) 20 Grove Road, Brandon, Co. Durham, DH7 8AW
Ⓜ 07932 159204
Ⓔ hal@uwclub.net
Ⓦ www.quietcornerplants.co.uk
Contact: Howard Leslie
Opening Times: 1200-1700 (or sunset in winter), closed Tue & Thu.
Min Mail Order UK: Nmc
Cat. Cost: Online only.
Credit Cards: All major credit/debit cards
Specialities: Hardy herbaceous & shrubby perennials, incl. small quantities of lesser known and harder to find plants.
Notes: Nursery is at Misty Blue Farm, Rock Road, Kirk Merrington, Co. Durham, DL16 7HJ. Also sells wholesale. Delivers to shows.

NRHS **Harlow Carr Plant Centre (RHS)** ◆
RHS Garden Harlow Carr, Crag Lane, Harlow Carr, Harrogate, North Yorkshire, HG3 1QB
Ⓣ (01423) 724666
Ⓕ (01423) 569521
Ⓔ aliceknowles@rhs.org.uk
Ⓦ www.rhs.org.uk
Contact: Alice Knowles
Opening Times: 0930-1700 Mon-Sun.
Specialities: Wide general range, particularly alpines.
Notes: Programme of free plant events throughout the year. Please ring or check website for details. Customer ordering system for plants which need to be collected from the plant centre (no mail order).

NRib **Ribblesdale Nurseries** ♿
Newsham Hall Lane, Woodplumpton, Preston, Lancashire, PR4 0AS
Ⓣ (01772) 863081
Ⓔ philsd@btinternet.com
Ⓦ www.ribblesdalenurseries.co.uk
Contact: Mr & Mrs Dunnett
Opening Times: 0900-1700 Mon-Sat all year round.
Credit Cards: All major credit/debit cards
Specialities: Trees, shrubs & perennials. Conifers, hedging, alpines, fruit, climbers, herbs, aquatics, ferns & wildflowers. Own grown plants in peat-free compost.
Notes: Wheelchair accessible.
OS Grid Ref: SD515351

NRob **W Robinson & Son (Seeds & Plants) Ltd** ♿
Sunny Bank, Forton, Nr Preston, Lancashire, PR3 0BN
Ⓣ (01524) 791210
Ⓕ (01524) 791933
Ⓔ info@mammothonion.co.uk
Ⓦ www.mammothonion.co.uk
Contact: Miss Robinson
Opening Times: 1000-1600 7 days Mar-Jun, 0800-1700 Mon-Fri Jul-Feb.
Min Mail Order UK: Nmc
Min Mail Order EU: Nmc
Cat. Cost: Free.
Credit Cards: All major credit/debit cards

N

Specialities: Mammoth vegetable seed. Onions, leeks, tomatoes & beans. Range of vegetable plants in the spring.
Notes: Also sells wholesale. Exports beyond EU. Delivers to shows. Euro accepted. Wheelchair accessible.

NRush **RUSHROSE NURSERY**
Berwick Road, Wooler, Northumberland, NE71 6AJ
Ⓣ (01668) 281348
Ⓕ (01668) 932001
Ⓔ info@rushrose.co.uk
Ⓦ www.rushrose.co.uk
Contact: Amy O'Rourke
Opening Times: By appt. only via email.
Min Mail Order UK: £3.00
Min Mail Order EU: £3.00
Cat. Cost: N/A
Credit Cards: All major credit/debit cards
Specialities: *Helianthemum.*
Notes: Please see website for up to date stock availability. Also sells wholesale.

NRya **RYAL NURSERY** ♿
East Farm Cottage, Ryal, Northumberland, NE20 0SA
Ⓣ (01661) 886562
Ⓔ ruthhadden@btinternet.com
Contact: R. Hadden
Opening Times: Mar-Jul by appt. please telephone in advance.
Cat. Cost: Sae.
Credit Cards: None
Specialities: Alpine & woodland plants, mainly available in small quantities only. National Plant Collection of *Primula marginata.*
Notes: Also sells wholesale. Delivers to shows. Wheelchair accessible.
OS Grid Ref: NZ015744

NSla **SLACK TOP ALPINE NURSERY**
Alpine House, 22A Slack Top, Hebden Bridge, West Yorkshire, HX7 7HA
Ⓣ (01422) 845348
Ⓜ 07392 856395
Ⓔ enquiries@slacktopnurseries.co.uk
Ⓦ www.slacktopnurseries.co.uk
Contact: Michael & Allison Mitchell
Opening Times: 1000-1700 Fri-Sun, Mar-Aug & B/hols. Other times by appt.
Min Mail Order UK: £20.00
Min Mail Order EU: £50.00
Cat. Cost: 2 × 1st class A5 sae or online.
Credit Cards: All major credit/debit cards
Specialities: Alpine, rockery & woodland plants.
Notes: Talks given to gardening clubs & other groups by appt. Delivers to shows. Euro accepted. Partial wheelchair access. (Some areas of garden inaccessible).
OS Grid Ref: SD977286

NSti **STILLINGFLEET LODGE NURSERIES** ♿
Stewart Lane, Stillingfleet, York, YO19 6HP
Ⓣ (01904) 728506
Ⓔ info@stillingfleetlodgenurseries.co.uk
Ⓦ www.stillingfleetlodgenurseries.co.uk
Contact: Vanessa Cook
Opening Times: 1300-1700 Wed & Fri, 1st Apr-30th Sep. 1300-1700, 1st & 3rd Sat & Sun in each month.
Cat. Cost: Online only.
Credit Cards: All major credit/debit cards
Specialities: Foliage & unusual perennials. Hardy geraniums, *Pulmonaria*, variegated plants & grasses.
Notes: Wheelchair accessible.

NSue **SUE PROCTOR PLANTS** ♿
69 Ings Mill Avenue, Clayton West, Huddersfield, West Yorkshire, HD8 9QG
Ⓣ (01484) 866189
Ⓜ 07917 006636
Ⓔ hostas@sueproctorplants.co.uk
Ⓦ www.sueproctorplants.co.uk
Contact: Sue Proctor
Opening Times: By appt. only. Please telephone first.
Min Mail Order UK: £3.50
Cat. Cost: 1st class sae.
Credit Cards: All major credit/debit cards
Specialities: *Hosta*, especially miniature hostas.
Notes: Wheelchair accessible.

NTPC **TREE PEONY COMPANY**
Willow Cottage, Rillington, Malton, North Yorkshire, YO17 8JU
Ⓣ (01944) 758280
Ⓔ info@treepeony.co.uk
Ⓦ www.treepeony.co.uk
Contact: Thelma Scruton, Roger Scruton
Min Mail Order UK: £15.00
Min Mail Order EU: Nmc
Cat. Cost: None.
Credit Cards: None
Specialities: Tree peonies. *Paeonia suffruticosa. P.* Gansu Group. *P. rockii.*
Notes: Also sells wholesale. Euro accepted. Delivers to shows.

NWad **WADDOW LODGE GARDEN** ♿
Clitheroe Road, Waddington, Clitheroe, Lancashire, BB7 3HQ
Ⓣ (01200) 429145
Ⓔ peterfoleyhcn@hotmail.co.uk

N

Ⓦ www.gardentalks.co.uk
Contact: Peter Foley
Opening Times: By appt. only all year. Also open under NGS 1300-1700 27th May & 15th Jul 2018 with plant sales for Plant Heritage NW Group.
Min Mail Order UK: Nmc
Min Mail Order EU: Nmc
Cat. Cost: Online only.
Credit Cards: None
Specialities: An ever-developing plantsman's garden with an interesting plant collection. Some plants may only be available in small numbers.
Notes: Open for group visits by appt. (incl. evenings). Wheelchair accessible.
OS Grid Ref: SD732434

NWsh **Westshores Nurseries**
82 West Street, Winterton, Scunthorpe, Lincolnshire, DN15 9QF
Ⓣ (01724) 733940
Ⓜ 07875 732535
Ⓔ westshnur@aol.com
Ⓦ www.westshores.co.uk
Contact: Gail & John Summerfield
Opening Times: By appt. only.
Min Mail Order UK: £15.00
Min Mail Order EU: £15.00
Cat. Cost: Online only.
Credit Cards: All major credit/debit cards
Specialities: Ornamental grasses, autumn flowering perennials & scented pelargoniums.
Notes: Wide selection of talks for gardening clubs and Hardy Plant Society groups located up to 130 miles (or 3 hours) away in one direction.
OS Grid Ref: SE927187

Southern

SAdn **Ashdown Forest Garden Centre & Nursery** ♿
Duddleswell, Ashdown Forest, East Sussex, TN22 3JP
Ⓣ (01825) 712300
Ⓔ info@ashdownforestgardencentre.co.uk
Ⓦ www.ashdownforestgardencentre.co.uk
Contact: Victoria Falletti
Opening Times: 0900-1700 winter, 0900-1700 summer.
Min Mail Order UK: Nmc
Credit Cards: All major credit/debit cards
Specialities: *Fuchsia*, *Lapageria*, conservatory climbers, unusual shrubs. Available in small quantities only.
Notes: Wheelchair accessible.
OS Grid Ref: TQ468283

SAko **Akorn and Oake**
18 Twyford Avenue, Southampton, Hampshire, SO15 5NP
Ⓣ (023) 8034 4040
Ⓜ 07973 149404
Ⓔ stefan.rau@hotmail.co.uk
Contact: Stefan Rau
Opening Times: Open by appt. only.
Specialities: *Saxifraga*.
Notes: Delivers to shows.

SAll **Allwoods (Hassocks) Ltd**
London Road, Hassocks, West Sussex, BN6 9NA
Ⓣ (01273) 844229
Ⓔ info@allwoods.net
Ⓦ www.allwoods.net
Contact: David & Emma James
Opening Times: Office 0900-1630 Mon-Fri. Answer machine all other times. Office is closed B/hols and Xmas-New Year. Visits by prior appt. only.
Min Mail Order UK: Nmc
Min Mail Order EU: Nmc
Cat. Cost: £1.00
Credit Cards: All major debit/credit cards except American Express. PayPal
Specialities: Large collection of *Dianthus*, incl. hardy border carnations, garden pinks, perpetual flowering & spray carnations, Malmaisons & *D. allwoodii*. Unusual & collectors' geraniums & pelargoniums. *Fuchsia*, & other garden plants. Wide range of interesting succulents, British grown direct from our Sussex nursery.
Notes: All listed varieties available as plugs but choice varies depending on time of year. Please phone before travelling to avoid disappointment &/or to ensure order is ready for collection. Also sells wholesale.

SApu **Apuldram Roses**
Crouchers Farm, 163 Birdham Road, Apuldram, Chichester, West Sussex, PO20 7EQ
Ⓣ (01243) 785769
Ⓔ enquiries@apuldramroses.co.uk
Ⓦ www.apuldramroses.co.uk
Contact: Elizabeth Sawday
Opening Times: Winter 1000-1600 Mon to Fri & 1000-1300 Sat. Summer 1000-1700 Mon-Fri & 1000-1600 Sat.
Min Mail Order UK: £10.00
Min Mail Order EU: £10.00
Cat. Cost: N/A
Credit Cards: All major credit/debit cards
Specialities: Roses.
Notes: Specialist Rose grower. Euro accepted.

SArc **ARCHITECTURAL PLANTS LTD** ♿
Stane Street, North Heath, Pulborough, West Sussex, RH20 1DJ
Ⓣ (01798) 879213
Ⓔ enquiries@architecturalplants.com
Ⓦ www.architecturalplants.com
Contact: Sophie Pett-Gallacher
Opening Times: 0900-1700 Mon-Sat & B/hols. Closed Sun.
Cat. Cost: Free.
Credit Cards: All major debit/credit cards except American Express
Specialities: Architectural plants & hardy exotics esp. rare evergreen & seaside exotics, spiky plants, yuccas/agaves, climbers, evergreen trees and shrubs, topiary & bamboos.
Notes: Café & shop. Also sells wholesale. Delivers to shows. Wheelchair accessible (& available on site).
OS Grid Ref: TQ192262

SavN **SAVIN NURSERIES**
Hillside Road, Stondon, Bedfordshire, SG16 6LP
Ⓣ (01462) 850680
Ⓔ savinbase@hotmail.co.uk
Ⓦ www.savinnurseries.co.uk
Contact: Darryl Savin
Opening Times: 0830-1745 Mon-Fri, 0830-1700 Sat, 1000-1600 Sun (Winter)
Credit Cards: All major debit/credit cards except American Express
Specialities: Bonsai, bedding, house plants, acers, perennials, olives.
Notes: Family run nursery growing their own bedding plants, shrubs, perennials and small trees.

SBri **BRICKWALL COTTAGE NURSERY**
1 Brickwall Cottages, Frittenden, Cranbrook, Kent, TN17 2DH
Ⓣ (01580) 852425
Ⓜ 07714 529946
Ⓔ sue.martin@talktalk.net
Ⓦ www.geumcollection.co.uk
Contact: Sue Martin
Opening Times: By appt. only.
Min Mail Order UK: Nmc
Min Mail Order EU: Nmc
Credit Cards: None
Specialities: Hardy perennials. Stock available in small quantities only. National Plant Collection of *Geum*.
Notes: Partial wheelchair access. Open for the NGS during the year. Please contact nursery for details.
OS Grid Ref: TQ815410

SBrt **BRIGHTON PLANTS** ♿
New Hall Lane, Small Dole, Sussex, BN5 9YJ
Ⓜ 07955 744802
Ⓔ brighton.plants@gmail.com
Ⓦ www.brightonplants.blogspot.com
Contact: Steve Law
Opening Times: Open by appt. only. Please email/phone before visiting.
Min Mail Order UK: Nmc
Min Mail Order EU: Nmc
Cat. Cost: 4 × 1st class.
Credit Cards: None
Specialities: Hardy herbaceous and woody plants. Drought-tolerant plants.
Notes: Delivers to shows. Euro accepted. Wheelchair accessible.
OS Grid Ref: TQ208132

SBut **BUTTERFLY COTTAGE GARDEN PLANTS** ♿
Office: 55 Middle Brook Street, Winchester, Hampshire, SO23 8DQ
Ⓣ (01962) 621882
Ⓜ 0796 2869105
Ⓔ andrew.ward203@ntlworld.com
Ⓦ www.butterflycottageplants.co.uk
Contact: Andy & Angela
Opening Times: Open Mar-Sep 1000-1700 Thu, Fri and most Sats. (Please telephone for Sat opening times)
Min Mail Order UK: Nmc
Cat. Cost: Online only.
Credit Cards: All major credit/debit cards
Specialities: Growing perennials to attract a variety of pollinators, including many garden-worthy natives. Limited numbers of each variety as all grown at nursery. Order early to avoid disappointment.
Notes: Nursery is at Cheriton Village, Alresford, Hants SO24 0PW. See website for directions. Please check plant availability before travelling long journeys. Wheelchair accessible.
OS Grid Ref: SU583972

SCac **CACTI & SUCCULENTS**
Hammerfield, Crockham Hill, Edenbridge, Kent, TN8 6RR
Ⓣ (01732) 866295
Contact: Geoff Southon
Opening Times: Flexible. Please phone first.
Min Mail Order UK: Nmc
Cat. Cost: None issued.
Credit Cards: None
Specialities: *Echeveria* & related genera & hybrids. A large range of *Aeonium*, both species & hybrids, possibly the largest collection in the country. Many available in small quantities only.

SCam **CAMELLIA GROVE NURSERY** ♿
Market Garden, Lower Beeding, Horsham, West Sussex, RH13 6PP
Ⓣ (01403) 891412
Ⓔ lp@hortic.com
Ⓦ www.camellia-grove.com
Contact: Chris Loder
Opening Times: 1000-1600 Mon-Sat, please phone first so we can give you our undivided attention.
Min Mail Order UK: Nmc
Min Mail Order EU: Nmc
Cat. Cost: 2 × 1st class.
Credit Cards: All major debit/credit cards except American Express
Specialities: *Camellia japonica*, *C. williamsii*, *C. sasanqua* & *C. reticulata*, from the purest white to richest red flowers.
Notes: Also sells wholesale. Exports beyond EU. Delivers to shows. Euro accepted. Wheelchair accessible.
OS Grid Ref: TQ221255

SChF **CHARLESHURST FARM NURSERY**
Loxwood Road, Plaistow, Billingshurst, West Sussex, RH14 0NY
Ⓣ (01403) 752273
Ⓜ 07736 522788
Ⓔ info@charleshuntplants.co.uk
Ⓦ www.charleshurstplants.co.uk
Contact: Clive Mellor
Opening Times: Normally 0900-1730 Fri, Sat, Sun, Feb-Oct, but please ring before travelling.
Min Mail Order UK: Nmc
Min Mail Order EU: Nmc
Cat. Cost: Online only.
Credit Cards: All major credit/debit cards
Specialities: Shrubs including some more unusual species. Good range of *Daphne* & Japanese maples.
Notes: Delivers to shows. Euro accepted.
OS Grid Ref: TQ015308

SChr **JOHN CHURCHER**
47 Grove Avenue, Portchester, Fareham, Hampshire, PO16 9EZ
Ⓣ (023) 9232 6740
Ⓜ 07717 495861
Ⓔ johnchurcher47@btinternet.com
Contact: John Churcher
Opening Times: By appt. only. Please phone or email.
Min Mail Order UK: Nmc
Min Mail Order EU: Nmc
Cat. Cost: None issued.
Credit Cards: None
Specialities: Hardy exotics for the Mediterranean-style garden, incl. palms, tree ferns, *Agave*, *Aloe*, cycads, echiums, *Musa*, hedychiums & *Opuntia*. Stock available in small quantities only.
OS Grid Ref: SU614047

SCit **THE CITRUS CENTRE** ♿
West Mare Lane, Marehill, Pulborough, West Sussex, RH20 2EA
Ⓣ (01798) 872786
Ⓔ enquiries@citruscentre.co.uk
Ⓦ www.citruscentre.co.uk
Contact: Amanda & Chris Dennis
Opening Times: 0930-1600 Tue-Sat. Phone or check website for Xmas & B/hol opening times.
Min Mail Order UK: Nmc
Min Mail Order EU: Nmc
Cat. Cost: Online.
Credit Cards: Visa, MasterCard
Specialities: Citrus & Citrus relatives.
Notes: Wheelchair accessible.

SCmr **CROMAR NURSERY** ♿
39 Livesey Street, North Pole, Wateringbury, Maidstone, Kent, ME18 5BQ
Ⓣ (01622) 812380
Ⓔ CromarNursery@aol.com
Ⓦ www.cromarnursery.co.uk
Contact: Debra & Martin Cronk
Opening Times: 0930-1630 Sat-Sun. Please check website or phone if travelling far.
Min Mail Order UK: Nmc
Min Mail Order EU: Nmc
Cat. Cost: 2 × 1st class.
Credit Cards: All major credit/debit cards
Specialities: Ornamental & fruit trees.
Notes: Wheelchair accessible.
OS Grid Ref: TQ697547

SCob **COBLANDS ONLINE**
Trench Road, Tonbridge, Kent, TN11 9NG
Ⓣ (01452) 742445
Ⓔ info@coblands.co.uk
Ⓦ www.coblands.co.uk
Contact: Daniel Slinger
Opening Times: 0830-1700 Mon-Fri.
Min Mail Order UK: Nmc
Min Mail Order EU: Nmc
Credit Cards: All major credit/debit cards
Specialities: Wide range of plants esp. herbaceous perennials of garden-worthiness incl. many new varieties. *Brunnera*, *Echinacea*, *Epimedium*, *Hebe*, *Heuchera*, *Hosta*, *Hydrangea*, *Phormium*, *Rudbeckia* & ferns. Wide range of shrubs and established specimen plants.

Notes: Also sells wholesale. Free delivery on online orders over £40.
OS Grid Ref: TQ586487

SCoo **COOLING'S NURSERIES LTD** ♿
Rushmore Hill, Knockholt, Sevenoaks, Kent, TN14 7NN
Ⓣ (01959) 532269
Ⓕ (01959) 534092
Ⓔ Plantfinder@coolings.co.uk
Ⓦ www.coolings.co.uk
Contact: Mark Reeve or Garry Norris
Opening Times: 0900-1700 Mon-Sat & 0900-1630 Sun.
Min Mail Order UK: Nmc
Cat. Cost: None issued.
Credit Cards: All major debit/credit cards except American Express
Specialities: Large range of perennials, conifers & bedding plants. Many unusual shrubs & trees. Third generation family business.
Notes: Display garden. Coffee shop. Wheelchair accessible.
OS Grid Ref: TK477610

SDay **A LA CARTE DAYLILIES**
Little Hermitage, St Catherine's Down, Ventnor, Isle of Wight, PO38 2PD
Ⓣ (01983) 730512
Ⓔ andy.hyjack@googlemail.com
Ⓦ www.alacartedaylilies.co.uk
Contact: Jan & Andy Wyers
Opening Times: Mail order only. Open by appt. only.
Min Mail Order UK: Nmc
Min Mail Order EU: Nmc
Cat. Cost: 3 × 1st class.
Credit Cards: None
Specialities: *Hemerocallis*. National Plant Collection of miniature & small flowered *Hemerocallis* & large flowered *Hemerocallis* (post-1960 award-winning cvs).
Notes: Nursery is difficult to find and on an unmade private road. Please phone/email for directions. Euro accepted.
OS Grid Ref: SZ499787

SDeJ **P. DE JAGER & SONS LTD** ♿ ◆
Church Farm, Ulcombe, Maidstone, Kent, ME17 1DN
Ⓣ (01622) 840229
Ⓕ (01622) 844073
Ⓔ flowerbulbs@dejager.co.uk
Ⓦ www.dejager.co.uk
Contact: George Clowes
Opening Times: Mail order only. Orders taken from 0900-1700 Mon-Fri.
Min Mail Order UK: Nmc
Min Mail Order EU: Nmc
Cat. Cost: Free.
Credit Cards: All major credit/debit cards
Specialities: Wide range of flower bulbs.
Notes: Also sells wholesale. Exports beyond EU. Euro accepted. Wheelchair accessible.

SDir **DIRECT BULBS**
Mault-Ley, 6, Hillside Close, Teg Down, Winchester, Hampshire, SO22 5LW
Ⓣ (01962) 840038
Ⓜ 07766 517703
Ⓔ jo@directbulbs.co.uk
Ⓦ www.directbulbs.co.uk
Contact: Jo Woodland
Opening Times: Mail order only.
Min Mail Order UK: £6.00
Min Mail Order EU: £20.00
Credit Cards: All major credit/debit cards
Specialities: Bulbs.
Notes: Also sells wholesale. Suppliers of spring and summer flowering bulbs.

SDix **GREAT DIXTER NURSERIES** ♿
Dixter Road, Northiam, Rye, East Sussex, TN31 6PH
Ⓣ (01797) 254044
Ⓕ (01797) 252879
Ⓔ nursery@greatdixter.co.uk
Ⓦ www.greatdixter.co.uk
Contact: Michael Morphy
Opening Times: 0900-1700 Mon-Sat, 10.00-1700 Sun Apr-end Oct. 0900-1230 & 1330-1630 Mon-Fri, 0900-1230 Sat. Sun closed Nov-end Mar.
Min Mail Order UK: Nmc
Min Mail Order EU: Nmc
Cat. Cost: £1.00
Credit Cards: All major credit/debit cards
Specialities: *Clematis*, shrubs and plants. Gardens open.
Notes: Usual and unusual shrubs and perennials. Mail order October to end of March. Wheelchair accessible.
OS Grid Ref: TQ821251

SDow **DOWNDERRY NURSERY** ♿
Pillar Box Lane, Hadlow, Nr Tonbridge, Kent, TN11 9SW
Ⓣ (01732) 810081
Ⓔ info@downderry-nursery.co.uk
Ⓦ www.downderry-nursery.co.uk
Contact: Dr Simon Charlesworth
Opening Times: 1000-1700 Thu-Sun, 1st May-30th Sep & B/hols. Other times by appt.
Min Mail Order UK: Nmc

Min Mail Order EU: Nmc
Cat. Cost: Free.
Credit Cards: Delta, MasterCard, Maestro, Visa
Specialities: National Plant Collections of *Lavandula* and *Rosmarinus*.
Notes: Euro accepted. Wheelchair accessible.
OS Grid Ref: TQ625521

SDys **Dysons Nurseries** ♿
Great Comp Garden, Platt, Sevenoaks, Kent, TN15 8QS
Ⓣ (01732) 885094
Ⓜ 07887 997663
Ⓔ dysonsorders@greatcompgarden.co.uk
Ⓦ www.dysonsalvias.com
Contact: William T. Dyson
Opening Times: 1100-1700 7 days 1st Apr-31st Oct. Other times by appt.
Cat. Cost: Online only.
Credit Cards: All major credit/debit cards
Specialities: Salvias & an eclectic range of choice and uncommon plants.
Notes: Delivers to shows. Wheelchair accessible.

SEdd **Eddington House Nursery**
Eddington Road, Nettlestone/Seaview, Isle of Wight, Hampshire, PO34 5EF
Ⓜ 07837 589478
Ⓔ info@eddingtonhousenursery.co.uk
Ⓦ http://ehn-iw.uk
Contact: Ian Chadwick
Opening Times: 1000-1700 Mon-Sat (Closed Sun). Closed end Nov-end Jan except by appt.
Min Mail Order UK: Nmc
Cat. Cost: Online only.
Credit Cards: All major credit/debit cards
Specialities: Salvias, hydrangeas, perennials & dry garden plants planted in display gardens which are being developed.
Notes: Home to the Isle of Wight Rare Plant Fair featuring many specialist nurseries, plant groups and related organisations speakers, café, live band and open gardens. See website for plant availability.
OS Grid Ref: SZ626900

SEdi **Edibleculture** ♿
The Horticultural Unit, The Abbey School, London Road, Faversham, Kent, ME13 8RZ
Ⓣ (01795) 537662
Ⓔ info@edibleculture.co.uk
Ⓦ www.edibleculture.co.uk
Contact: Chris or David
Opening Times: 0900-1700 Mon-Sat 1000-1600 Sun, Mar-Jan. Jan-Feb by appt. only but telephone/email orders taken.
Cat. Cost: online only.
Credit Cards: All major credit/debit cards
Specialities: Herbs, vegetables, fruit trees and soft fruit, herbaceous perennials, hedgerow plants.
Notes: Focus on interesting plants grown sustainably. Specialists in establishing and maintaining orchards. Also sells wholesale. Wheechair accessible.

SEle **Eleplants Nursery**
32 Framfield Road, Uckfield, East Sussex, TN22 5AH
Ⓣ (01825) 760356
Ⓜ 07810 660109
Ⓔ eleplantsnursery@talk21.com
Ⓦ www.eleplantsnursery.co.uk
Contact: Martin Batchelor
Opening Times: Not open. By appt. only.
Min Mail Order UK: Nmc
Min Mail Order EU: Nmc
Credit Cards: All major credit/debit cards, PayPal
Specialities: Shrubs.
Notes: Exports beyond EU. Delivers to shows.

SEND **East Northdown Nurseries** ♿
George Hill Road (B2052), Margate, Kent, CT10 3BN
Ⓣ (01843) 862060
Ⓜ 07714 241667
Ⓔ info@botanyplants.co.uk
Ⓦ www.botanyplants.co.uk
Contact: Louise & William Friend
Opening Times: 0900-1700 7 days, all year except Sun in winter. Closed Xmas week.
Min Mail Order UK: Nmc
Cat. Cost: Online only.
Credit Cards: All major credit/debit cards
Specialities: Chalk & coast-loving plants. Specimen shrubs & bamboos available. Complimentary range of plants for damp/acid conditions available to order from our Mucklestone Nursery (MMuc). Collection of rare Mediterranean plants.
Notes: Tea room & gardens. Close to Botany Bay. Lectures given to gardening groups in Kent. Garden tours by appt. See website or contact nursery for full list & details. Wheelchair accessible.
OS Grid Ref: TR383702

SEWo **English Woodlands** ♿
Burrow Nursery, Herrings Lane, Cross-in-Hand, Heathfield, East Sussex, TN21 0UG
Ⓣ (01435) 862992
Ⓔ sales@englishwoodlands.com
Ⓦ www.englishwoodlands.com

Contact: Joanne Carter
Opening Times: 0800-1700 Mon-Fri. 0800-1600 Sat. Closed Sun & B/hols.
Min Mail Order UK: £25.00
Cat. Cost: Free.
Credit Cards: All major debit/credit cards except American Express
Specialities: Trees, shrubs, hedging. Please telephone to check plant availability before visiting.
Notes: Also sells wholesale. Wheelchair accessible.
OS Grid Ref: TQ567222

SFai **FAIRWEATHER'S GARDEN CENTRE** ♿
High Street, Beaulieu, Hampshire, SO42 7YB
Ⓣ (01590) 612307
Ⓕ (01590) 612519
Ⓔ info@fairweathers.co.uk
Ⓦ www.fairweathers.co.uk
Contact: Sue Greaves
Opening Times: 0900-1700 7 days.
Min Mail Order UK: Nmc
Cat. Cost: None issued.
Credit Cards: Visa, MasterCard
Specialities: *Agapanthus* & *Lavandula*.
Notes: Wheelchair accessible.

SGbt **GILBERT'S NURSERY** ♿
Dandy's Ford Lane, Sherfield English, Romsey, Hampshire, SO51 6DT
Ⓣ (01794) 322566
Ⓔ gilbertsnursery@aol.com
Ⓦ www.gilbertsnursery.co.uk
Contact: Nick Gilbert
Opening Times: 0900-1700 Tue-Sat, 10.00-16.30 Sun, all year round. Dahlia field open from 2nd week Aug to 2nd week Oct.
Min Mail Order UK: Nmc
Min Mail Order EU: Nmc
Cat. Cost: 2 × 1st class.
Credit Cards: All major debit/credit cards except American Express
Specialities: *Dahlia*. Proper plant nursery with many unusual plants & staff happy to share their knowledge & help with plant selection.
Notes: Dahlia field with over 400 cvs on view (grass pathways). See above for opening times or go to www.gilbertsdahlias.co.uk. Tea room. Delivers to shows. Wheelchair accessible.

SGol **GOLDEN HILL NURSERIES** ♿
Lordsfield, Goudhurst Road, Marden, Kent, TN12 9LT
Ⓣ (01622) 833218
Ⓜ 07826 523655
Ⓔ enquiries@goldenhillplants.com
Ⓦ www.goldenhillplants.com
Contact: Roger Butler
Opening Times: 0900-1700 Mon-Sat, 1st Mar-31st Oct. 0900-1600 Mon-Sat, 1st Nov-28th Feb. 1100-1600 Sun from 3rd Sun in Feb-end Nov.
Min Mail Order UK: Nmc
Cat. Cost: Online only.
Credit Cards: All major credit/debit cards
Specialities: *Hydrangea*, specimen trees & shrubs, ground cover and hedging.
Notes: Also sells wholesale. Euro accepted. Wheelchair accessible.

SGro **GROWING DELIGHTS**
Address withheld. Please ring for details.
Ⓜ 07874 678175
Ⓔ growingdelights@gmail.com
Ⓦ www.growingdelights.co.uk
Contact: Lesley Baker
Opening Times: Not open.
Min Mail Order UK: £15 + p&p
Min Mail Order EU: £15+ p&p
Cat. Cost: Online only.
Credit Cards: PayPal
Specialities: Unusual alpines & drought-tolerant plants. Plants to attract bees & butterflies.
Notes: Almost entirely growing peat-free. A small nursery only able to supply plants in small quantities. Mail order mostly for small plants. No mail order sent Dec-Jan. Plants can be collected by arrangement and from sales & shows. Delivers to shows.
OS Grid Ref: SU333190

SGsty **GARDEN STYLE PLANT CENTRE** ♿
Farnham Road, Holt Pound, Farnham, Hampshire, GU10 4LD
Ⓣ (01420) 521092
Ⓔ sales@gardenstyle.co.uk
Ⓦ www.gardenstyle.co.uk
Contact: Elizabeth Nightingale
Opening Times: 0900-1730 Mon-Sat, 1030-1630 Sun.
Credit Cards: All major credit/debit cards
Specialities: Bamboo, climbers, conifers, hedging, evergreen & deciduous shrubs, fruit & ornamental trees, topiary.
Notes: Suppliers of larger plants to enhance gardens since 1991. Also sells wholesale. Delivers to shows. Wheelchair accessible.
OS Grid Ref: SU810354

SHaC **HART CANNA** ♿
Lincluden Nursery, Shaftesbury Road, Bisley, Woking, Surrey, GU24 9EN
Ⓣ (01252) 514421
Ⓜ 07762 950000

Ⓔ sales@hartcanna.com
Ⓦ www.hartcanna.co.uk
Contact: Keith Hayward
Opening Times: By appt. only.
Min Mail Order UK: Nmc
Min Mail Order EU: Nmc
Cat. Cost: Online only.
Credit Cards: All major credit/debit cards
Specialities: *Canna.* National Plant Collection of *Canna.*
Notes: Also sells wholesale. Euro accepted. Delivers to shows. Wheelchair accessible.

SHar **HARDY'S COTTAGE GARDEN PLANTS** ♿
Priory Lane Nursery, Freefolk Priors, Whitchurch, Hampshire, RG28 7FA
Ⓣ (01256) 896533
Ⓔ info@hardysplants.co.uk
Ⓦ www.hardysplants.co.uk
Contact: Rosemary Hardy
Opening Times: 1000-1700 7 days, 1st Mar-30th Sep. 1000-1600 Mon-Fri, Oct. 1000-1500 Mon-Fri, 1st Nov-28th Feb. Closed 23rd Dec-4th Jan.
Min Mail Order UK: Nmc
Cat. Cost: Online only.
Credit Cards: Visa, Access, Electron, Switch, Solo
Specialities: Wide range of herbaceous perennials incl. *Achillea, Gaura, Geum, Geranium, Hemerocallis, Heuchera, Lathryus vernus, Paeonia, Penstemon* & *Salvia.*
Notes: Accepts HTA Gift Tokens. Offers trade discount. Euro accepted. Delivers to shows. Wheelchair accessible.

SHeu **HEUCHERAHOLICS** ♿
Boldre Nurseries, Southampton Road, Lymington, Hampshire, SO41 8ND
Ⓣ (01590) 670581
Ⓜ 07973 291062
Ⓔ jooles.heucheraholics@gmail.com
Ⓦ www.heucheraholics.co.uk
Contact: Julie Burton/Sean Atkinson
Opening Times: By appt. only. Please phone first.
Min Mail Order UK: Nmc
Min Mail Order EU: Please contact nursery to discuss
Cat. Cost: Online only.
Credit Cards: All major credit/debit cards, PayPal
Specialities: *Heuchera, Heucherella, Pulmonaria, Tiarella,* ferns and other foliage plants.
Notes: Working nursery in the New Forest. Toilet facilities. Well-behaved dogs welcome. See website or contact nursery for details of open days. Visits by groups can be arranged, please contact nursery for details. Delivers to shows. Wheelchair accessible.
OS Grid Ref: SZ310934

SHmp **HAMPSHIRE CARNIVOROUS PLANTS**
Stroudwood Nursery, Stroudwood Lane, Lower Upham, Southampton, Hampshire, SO32 1HG
Ⓣ (023) 8047 3314
Ⓜ 07703 258296
Ⓕ (023) 8047 3314
Ⓔ sales@hantsflytrap.com
Ⓦ www.hantsflytrap.com
Contact: Matthew Soper
Opening Times: By appt. only.
Min Mail Order UK: Nmc
Min Mail Order EU: £50.00 + p&p
Credit Cards: All major credit/debit cards
Specialities: Carnivorous plants esp. *Cephalotus, Darlingtonia, Dionaea, Drosera, Heliamphora, Nepenthes, Pinguicula, Sarracenia* & *Utricularia.*
Notes: Also sells wholesale. Exports beyond the EU. Delivers to shows. Euro accepted. Partial wheelchair access.
OS Grid Ref: SU514091

SHyH **HYDRANGEA HAVEN** ♿
Market Garden, Lower Beeding, West Sussex, RH13 6PP
Ⓣ (01403) 891412
Ⓔ lp@hortic.com
Ⓦ www.hydrangea-haven.com
Contact: Chris Loder
Opening Times: 1000-1600 Mon-Sat, please phone first.
Min Mail Order UK: Nmc
Min Mail Order EU: Nmc
Cat. Cost: 2 × 1st class.
Credit Cards: All major debit/credit cards except American Express
Specialities: *Hydrangea*; mophead, lacecap & panicle. *Agapanthus.*
Notes: Also sells wholesale. Exports beyond EU. Delivers to shows. Euro accepted. Wheelchair accessible.
OS Grid Ref: TQ221255

SIri **IRIS OF SISSINGHURST**
Roughlands Farm, Goudhurst Road, Marden, Kent, TN12 9NH
Ⓣ (01622) 831511
Ⓔ orders@irisofsissinghurst.com
Ⓦ www.irisofsissinghurst.com
Contact: Sue Marshall
Opening Times: Contact nursery or see website for opening times.

S

Min Mail Order UK: Nmc
Min Mail Order EU: Nmc
Cat. Cost: Online only.
Credit Cards: None
Specialities: *Iris*, short, intermediate & tall bearded, ensata, sibirica & many species.
Notes: Euro accepted. Delivers to shows (pre-ordered plants).
OS Grid Ref: TQ735437

SIvy **Ivy Hatch Plant Supplies**
Coach Road, Ivy Hatch, Kent, TN15 0PE
Ⓜ 07769 604468
Ⓔ debs@ivyhatchplantsupplies.co.uk
Ⓦ www.ivyhatchplantsupplies.co.uk
Contact: Debs Ednie
Opening Times: By appt. only. Full range avail. by mail order.
Min Mail Order UK: £5.00
Min Mail Order EU: £10.00
Credit Cards: None
Specialities: Hardy salvias and succulents including Echeverias. Good variety of Aeoniums and a range of tropical plants.
Notes: Sole supplier for The World Garden Nursery at Lullingstone Castle. Grower of many unusual and rare varieties not often available in mainstream garden centres. Limited stock but can source or grow to order. Plants available to purchase at select NGS Open Gardens and The World Garden Nursery at Lullingstone Castle. Please contact nursery for details. Also sells wholesale. Exports beyond the EU (restrictions apply).

S

SKee **Keepers Nursery**
Gallants Court, Gallants Lane, East Farleigh, Maidstone, Kent, ME15 0LE
Ⓣ (01622) 326465
Ⓔ sales@keepers-nursery.co.uk
Ⓦ www.keepers-nursery.co.uk
Contact: Hamid Habibi
Opening Times: Limited number of open days & for collection of order by arrangement.
Min Mail Order UK: Nmc
Cat. Cost: Online only.
Credit Cards: Visa, MasterCard, Switch, Maestro
Specialities: A very large range of old & rare as well as modern fruit trees varieties. Soft fruit plants & nut trees.

SKin **Kings Barn Trees**
Kings Barn Farm, Kent Street, Cowfold, West Sussex, RH13 8BB
Ⓣ (01403) 865405
Ⓜ 07908 708915
Ⓔ sales@kingsbarntrees.co.uk
Ⓦ www.kingsbarntrees.co.uk
Contact: Adrian Rumble
Opening Times: Not open. Mail order via website only.
Min Mail Order UK: £3.00
Min Mail Order EU: £9.95
Cat. Cost: Online only.
Credit Cards: All major credit/debit cards
Specialities: Mainly grow containerised trees, specialising in *Eucalyptus*. Also grow willow for sale as whips & setts during the winter/early spring. *Eucalyptus* available in small quantities only.

SLau **The Laurels Nursery**
Benenden, Cranbrook, Kent, TN17 4JU
Ⓣ (01580) 240463
Ⓦ www.thelaurelsnursery.co.uk
Contact: Peter or Sylvia Kellett
Opening Times: 0800-1600 Wed-Fri, 0900-1200 Sat, Sun by appt. only.
Min Mail Order UK: £30
Cat. Cost: Free.
Credit Cards: All major credit/debit cards
Specialities: Open ground & container ornamental trees, shrubs & climbers especially birch, beech & *Wisteria*.
Notes: Mail order of small Wisteria only. Also sells wholesale. Delivers to shows. Partly accessible for wheelchairs.
OS Grid Ref: TQ815313

SLBF **Little Brook Fuchsias** ♿
Ash Green Lane West, Ash Green, Nr Aldershot, Hampshire, GU12 6HL
Ⓣ (01252) 329731
Ⓔ carol.gubler@ntlbusiness.com
Ⓦ www.littlebrookfuchsias.co.uk
Contact: Carol Gubler
Opening Times: 1000-1700 Wed-Sun, 1st Jan-24th Jun.
Cat. Cost: 70p + sae.
Credit Cards: All major credit/debit cards
Specialities: Fuchsias, old & new.
Notes: Nursery located off White Lane in Ash Green. Wheelchair accessible.
OS Grid Ref: SU901496

SLdr **Loder Plants** ♿
Market Garden, Long Hill, Lower Beeding, West Sussex, RH13 6PP
Ⓣ (01403) 891412
Ⓔ sales@rhododendrons.com
Ⓦ www.rhododendrons.com
Contact: Chris Loder
Opening Times: 1000-1600 Mon-Sat, please telephone first.
Min Mail Order UK: Nmc
Min Mail Order EU: Nmc

Cat. Cost: 2 × 1st class.
Credit Cards: All major debit/credit cards except American Express
Specialities: Rhododendrons & azaleas in all sizes. Some in very limited quantities only. *Agapanthus.*
Notes: Also sells wholesale. Exports beyond EU. Delivers to shows. Euro accepted. Wheelchair accessible.
OS Grid Ref: TQ221255

SLim **LIME CROSS NURSERY** ♿
Herstmonceux, Hailsham, East Sussex, BN27 4RS
Ⓣ (01323) 833229
Ⓔ info@limecross.co.uk
Ⓦ www.limecross.co.uk
Contact: Vicky Tate, Anita Green
Opening Times: 0830-1700 Mon-Sat & 1000-1700 Sun.
Min Mail Order UK: Nmc
Min Mail Order EU: £50.00
Cat. Cost: Online only.
Credit Cards: All major credit/debit cards
Specialities: Conifers, trees & shrubs, climbers.
Notes: Wheelchair accessible.
OS Grid Ref: TQ642125

SLon **LONGSTOCK PARK NURSERY** ♿
Longstock, Stockbridge, Hampshire, SO20 6EH
Ⓣ (01264) 810894
Ⓕ (01264) 810924
Ⓔ longstock.park.nursery@waitrose.co.uk
Ⓦ www.leckfordestate.co.uk
Contact: Mark Pitman
Opening Times: 0900-1730 Mon-Sat, 1000-1600 Sun. Closed 25th-27th Dec & 1st Jan.
Min Mail Order UK: £15.00
Credit Cards: All major credit/debit cards
Specialities: A wide range, over 2000 varieties, of hardy trees (ornamental and fruiting), shrubs, perennials, climbers, aquatics & ferns. Extensive collection of *Penstemon.* National Plant Collections of *Buddleja* & *Clematis viticella.*
Notes: Farm shop and café on same site as nursery. Wheelchair accessible.
OS Grid Ref: SU365389

SMad **MADRONA NURSERY** ♿
Pluckley Road, Bethersden, Kent, TN26 3EG
Ⓣ (01233) 820100
Ⓔ madrona@hotmail.co.uk
Ⓦ www.madrona.co.uk
Contact: Liam Mackenzie
Opening Times: 1000-1700 Sat, Mon & Tue, 1300-1700 Sun. 17th Mar-30th Oct. Other times by appt.
Cat. Cost: Free.
Credit Cards: All major credit/debit cards
Specialities: Unusual shrubs, conifers & perennials. *Colletia, Eryngium.*
Notes: Delivers to shows. Euro accepted. Wheelchair accessible.
OS Grid Ref: TQ918419

SMea **MEADOWGATE NURSERY**
Street End Lane, Sidlesham, Chichester, West Sussex, PO20 7RG
Ⓣ (01243) 641997
Ⓜ 07736 523262
Ⓔ meadowgatenursery@tiscali.co.uk
Ⓦ www.meadowgatenursery.co.uk
Contact: David Allen
Opening Times: 1000-1700 Sat-Thu.
Min Mail Order UK: Nmc
Credit Cards: All major credit/debit cards
Specialities: Ornamental grasses.
Notes: Also sells wholesale. Delivers to shows.
OS Grid Ref: SZ854994

SMHy **MARCHANTS HARDY PLANTS** ♿
2 Marchants Cottages, Mill Lane, Laughton, East Sussex, BN8 6AJ
Ⓣ (01323) 811737
Ⓔ graham@marchantsplants.plus.com
Ⓦ www.marchantshardyplants.co.uk
Contact: Graham Gough
Opening Times: 0930-1730 Wed-Sat, Mar to Oct 2018.
Cat. Cost: 3 × 2nd class.
Credit Cards: Visa, MasterCard
Specialities: Uncommon herbaceous perennials. *Agapanthus*, choice grasses, *Galanthus, Miscanthus, Molinia.*
Notes: Euro accepted. Wheelchair accessible.
OS Grid Ref: TQ506119

SMor **MOREHAVENS**
Stocks Lane, Meonstoke, Hampshire, SO32 3NQ
Ⓣ (01489) 878501
Ⓔ morehavens@camomilelawns.co.uk
Ⓦ www.camomilelawns.co.uk
Contact: E. Clements
Opening Times: Mail order only. Open for collection only.
Min Mail Order UK: £21.00
Min Mail Order EU: £21.00 + p&p
Cat. Cost: Free.
Credit Cards: All major credit/debit cards, PayPal
Specialities: *Chamaemelum nobile* 'Treneague' and *C. nobile* dwarf.
Notes: Also sells wholesale.

SNig **Nightingale Nursery** ♿
Gardeners Lane, East Wellow, Romsey, Hampshire, SO51 6AD
Ⓣ (023) 8081 4350
Ⓔ gfnightingale4@gmail.com
Ⓦ www.nightingalenursery.co.uk
Contact: Graham Farmiloe
Opening Times: 0800-1700 Mon-Fri & open 7 days from mid-Mar to mid-Jun. 0800-1630 winter.
Cat. Cost: Free via email.
Credit Cards: All major debit/credit cards except American Express
Specialities: *Clematis*. Also climbers & wall shrubs, herbaceous, seasonal bedding, hanging baskets.
Notes: Also sells wholesale. Wheelchair accessible.

S

SPad **Paddock Plants**
The Paddock, Upper Toothill Road, Rownhams, Southampton, Hampshire, SO16 8AL
Ⓣ (023) 8073 9912
Ⓜ 07763 386717
Ⓔ rob@paddockplants.co.uk
Ⓦ www.paddockplants.co.uk
Contact: Rob & Joanna Courtney
Opening Times: By appt. only. Please telephone in advance.
Min Mail Order UK: £5.00
Cat. Cost: Online only.
Credit Cards: All major credit/debit cards
Specialities: A family-run nursery offering an interesting range of perennials, grasses, ferns & shrubs, incl. some more unusual varieties or plants new to the UK market. All plants are grown in a peat-free medium. Some varieties grown in small quantities.
Notes: Local delivery by our own transport. Courier delivery throughout UK. Delivers to shows.
OS Grid Ref: SU383177

SPalm **Palms-Exotics Ltd**
Abbots Farm, Canada Road, West Wellow, Romsey, Hampshire, SO51 6DE
Ⓣ (01794) 278356
Ⓜ 07979 404077
Ⓔ palmsexotics@icloud.com
Ⓦ Palms-exotics.co.uk
Contact: Michael Carr
Credit Cards: All major credit/debit cards, PayPal
Specialities: Palms, banana, ginger, *Colocasia*, bamboo grasses, perennials, shrubs.
Notes: Family nursery growing a range of exotic plants, many grown from seed or plugs. Larger palms sourced from our own and selected nurseries in Spain.

SPeP **Peake Perennials**
Shaftesbury Road, Child Okeford, Dorset, DT11 8EQ
Ⓣ (01202) 244510
Ⓜ 07088 72918
Ⓔ helen@peakeperennials.co.uk
Ⓦ www.peakeperennials.co.uk
Contact: Helen Day
Opening Times: 0900-1700 Mon-Fri, 1000-1600 Sat, Sun & Bank Holidays. Nov-Dec 1000-1600, Closed January.
Credit Cards: All major credit/debit cards
Specialities: Specialise in tall & unusual herbaceous perennials and grasses but also stock an increasing range of popular perennials often with a twist. Offer a reservation service for out of stock plants and can deliver locally. Also have a range of landscaping perennials.
Notes: For details of special events we attend please telephone or check website for details, register on the website for regular news on events and plants. Delivers to shows.

SPer **Perryhill Nurseries Ltd** ♿
Edenbridge Road, Hartfield, East Sussex, TN7 4JP
Ⓣ (01892) 770377
Ⓕ (01892) 770929
Ⓔ sales@perryhillnurseries.co.uk
Ⓦ www.perryhillnurseries.co.uk
Contact: P.J. Chapman
Opening Times: 0900-1700 7 days, 1st Mar-31st Oct. 0900-1630, 1st Nov-28th Feb.
Min Mail Order UK: Nmc
Cat. Cost: Online only.
Credit Cards: Maestro, Visa, Access, MasterCard
Specialities: Wide range of trees, shrubs, perennials, roses, fruit trees, soft fruit. Unusual & rare plants may be available in small quantities.
Notes: Mail order despatch depends on size & weight of plants. Wheelchair accessible.
OS Grid Ref: TQ480375

SPet **Pettet's Nursery** ♿
Drainless Road, Eastry, Sandwich, Kent, CT13 0EA
Ⓣ (01304) 613869
Ⓜ 07940 337520
Ⓕ (01304) 613869
Ⓔ pettets.nursery@btconnect.com
Ⓦ www.pettetsnursery.co.uk
Contact: Terry Pettet
Opening Times: 1000-1600 Tue-Sun, Mar-Oct. Closed Mon (except B/hol). Closed Nov-Feb.
Min Mail Order UK: £10.00
Cat. Cost: Online only.

Credit Cards: None
Specialities: *Pelargonium*: scented-leaf, decorative regal, unique, angel.
Notes: Delivers to shows. Wheelchair accessible.

SPhx **Phoenix Perennial Plants**
Paice Lane, Medstead, Alton, Hampshire, GU34 5PR
Ⓣ (01420) 560695
Ⓜ 07909 528191
Ⓔ marina@phoenixperennialplants.co.uk
Ⓦ www.phoenixperennialplants.co.uk
Contact: Marina Christopher
Opening Times: By appt. only.
Credit Cards: All major credit/debit cards
Specialities: Perennials, many uncommon & hardy, selected for beneficial insects particularly pollinators. *Agastache*, *Centaurea*, *Salvia*, *Sanguisorba*, *Sedum*, *Thalictrum*, *Verbascum*, bulbs, prairie plants, umbellifers & late-flowering perennials.
Notes: Also sells wholesale. Delivers to shows.
OS Grid Ref: SU657362

SPin **John and Lynsey's Plants** ♿
2 Hillside Cottages, Trampers Lane, North Boarhunt, Fareham, Hampshire, PO17 6DA
Ⓣ (01329) 832786
Ⓔ landjpink@tiscali.co.uk
Contact: Mrs Lynsey Pink
Opening Times: By appt. only.
Cat. Cost: None issued.
Credit Cards: None
Specialities: Mainly *Salvia* with a wide range of other unusual perennials. National Plant Collection of species *Salvia*.
Notes: Stock is only available in small quantities but we are happy to try to propagate anything that we have. Wheelchair accessible.
OS Grid Ref: SU603109

SPlb **Plantbase** ♿
Sleepers Stile Road, Cousley Wood, Wadhurst, East Sussex, TN5 6QX
Ⓣ (01892) 785599
Ⓜ 07967 601064
Ⓔ plantbaseuk@gmail.com
Ⓦ www.plantbase.co.uk
Contact: Graham Blunt
Opening Times: 1000-1700, 7 days all year (appt. advisable).
Min Mail Order UK: Nmc
Min Mail Order EU: Nmc
Cat. Cost: Online only.
Credit Cards: All major credit/debit cards
Specialities: Wide range of alpines, perennials, shrubs, climbers, waterside plants, herbs, Australasian, South African & South American plants in particular. Some available in small quantities only.
Notes: Delivers to shows. Euro accepted. Wheelchair accessible.

SPoG **The Potted Garden Nursery** ♿
Ashford Road, Bearsted, Maidstone, Kent, ME14 4NH
Ⓣ (01622) 737801
Ⓦ www.thepottedgarden.co.uk
Contact: Any staff member
Opening Times: 0900-1730 (dusk in winter), 7 days. Xmas/New Year period opening times on website or answerphone.
Credit Cards: All major credit/debit cards
Notes: Mail order not available. Wheelchair accessible.
OS Grid Ref: TQ810550

SPre **Plants4Presents** ◆
The Glasshouses, Fletching Common, Newick, Lewes, East Sussex, BN8 4JJ
Ⓣ (01825) 721162
Ⓔ plants@4presents.co.uk
Ⓦ www.plants4presents.co.uk
Contact: Emily Rae
Opening Times: Not open. Mail order only.
Min Mail Order UK: Nmc
Cat. Cost: Online only.
Credit Cards: All major credit/debit cards
Specialities: Well-established nursery offering a range of unusual flowering and fruiting plants, incl. citrus trees.
Notes: Delivers to shows.

SPtp **PlantsToplant.com**
Paragon Plants, Fromefield, Ratley Lane, Awbridge, Romsey, Hampshire, SO51 0HN
Ⓣ (01794) 341123
Ⓔ info@plantstoplant.com
Ⓦ www.plantstoplant.com
Contact: David West
Opening Times: Not open. Mail order only.
Min Mail Order UK: Nmc
Cat. Cost: Online only.
Credit Cards: All major credit/debit cards, PayPal
Specialities: Rare & hard to find special garden plants of all types. *Cotoneaster* a speciality.
Notes: Mail order only through website or ebay. Orders can be collected by appt. only.

SPVi **Pineview Plants**
Pineview, 19 Windmill Hill, Sevenoaks, Kent, TN15 7SU
Ⓣ (01732) 882945

Ⓜ 07736 420016
Ⓔ colin@pineviewplants.co.uk
Ⓦ www.pineviewplants.co.uk
Contact: Colin Moat
Opening Times: By appt. only.
Min Mail Order UK: £15.00 + p&p
Min Mail Order EU: £25.00 + p&p
Cat. Cost: Online only.
Credit Cards: All major credit/debit cards
Specialities: Shade loving plants including *Actaea, Epimedium, Sanguisorba, Thalictrum.* Wide range of ferns and herbaceous perennials.
Notes: The majority of plants are propagated on site and many are only available in small quantities. Delivers to shows, see list on website.

S

SReu **REUTHE'S – THE LOST GARDEN OF SEVENOAKS** ♿
Sevenoaks Road, Seal Chart, Sevenoaks, Kent, TN15 0HB
Ⓣ (01732) 810694
Ⓔ info@reuthes.com
Ⓦ www.reuthes.com
Contact: Oliver Schneider
Opening Times: 08.30-16.40 Mon-Sat.
Min Mail Order UK: £10.00
Min Mail Order EU: £30.00
Credit Cards: All major credit/debit cards
Specialities: Rhododendrons & azaleas, *Acer*, trees, woodland plants.
Notes: Rhododendron plantation with one of the finest collections in the country. Founded in1902 from a Victorian plant hunter's collection. Rare and mature specimens available. Stunning 11 acre woodland availabe for events. Café, shop, free parking, small play area. Dogs welcome. Also sells wholesale. Delivers to shows. Wheelchair accessible.
OS Grid Ref: TQ577675

SRiv **RIVER GARDEN NURSERIES**
Troutbeck, Otford, Sevenoaks, Kent, TN14 5PH
Ⓣ 07717 277175
Ⓔ box@river-garden.co.uk
Ⓦ www.river-garden.co.uk
Contact: Jenny Alban Davies
Opening Times: By appt. only.
Min Mail Order UK: £10.00 + p&p
Min Mail Order EU: £50.00 + p&p
Cat. Cost: Online only.
Credit Cards: None
Specialities: *Buxus* species & cultivars. *Buxus* topiary.
Notes: Also sells wholesale. Delivers to shows.
OS Grid Ref: TQ523593

SRkn **RAPKYNS NURSERY** ♿
Street End Lane, Broad Oak, Heathfield, East Sussex, TN21 8UB
Ⓣ (01825) 830065
Ⓜ 07771 916933
Ⓔ rapkynsnursery@hotmail.com
Ⓦ www.rapkynsnursery.co.uk
Contact: Steven Moore
Opening Times: 1000-1700 Tue, Thu & Fri, Mar-Oct incl. or by appt.
Min Mail Order UK: Nmc
Min Mail Order EU: Nmc
Cat. Cost: Online only.
Credit Cards: All major credit/debit cards
Specialities: Unusual shrubs, perennials & climbers. *Aster, Campanula, Ceanothus, Geranium*, lavenders, *Clematis*, penstemons & grasses. New collections of *Anemone, Crocosmia, Coreopsis, Helleborus, Heuchera, Heucherella, Phlox.* Extensive range of salvias.
Notes: Nursery next door to Scotsford Farm, TN21 8UB. Mail order Sep-Apr incl. Also sells wholesale. Delivers to shows. Wheelchair accessible.
OS Grid Ref: TQ604248

SRms **RUMSEY GARDENS** ♿
117 Drift Road, Clanfield, Waterlooville, Hampshire, PO8 0PD
Ⓣ (023) 9259 3367
Ⓔ info@rumsey-gardens.co.uk
Ⓦ www.rumsey-gardens.co.uk
Contact: Mrs M.A. Giles
Opening Times: 0900-1700 Mon-Sat & 1000-1600 Sun & B/hols. Closed Xmas to New Year B/Hol.
Min Mail Order UK: £15.00
Cat. Cost: Online only.
Credit Cards: American Express, Visa, MasterCard
Specialities: Wide general range. Herbaceous, alpines, heathers & ferns. National & International Plant Collection of *Cotoneaster*.
Notes: Wheelchair accessible.

SSea **SEALE ROSE GARDEN**
Seale Nurseries, Seale Lane, Seale, Farnham, Surrey, GU10 1LD
Ⓣ (01252) 782410
Ⓔ catherine@sealenurseries.demon.co.uk
Ⓦ www.sealenurseries.co.uk
Contact: David & Catherine May
Opening Times: 1000-1600 Tue-Sat. Other times by appt. Please phone for winter opening times.
Cat. Cost: None issued.
Credit Cards: Visa, Access, Delta, MasterCard

Specialities: Roses & *Pelargonium*. Some varieties in short supply, please phone first.
OS Grid Ref: SU887477

SSFr **SOUTHERN FRUIT TREES** ♿
The Old Grain Dryer Corner, Blackmoor, Hampshire, GU33 6BP
Ⓣ (01420) 488822
Ⓜ 07811 253530
Ⓔ neil@southernfruittrees.co.uk
Ⓦ www.southernfruittrees.co.uk
Contact: Neil Smith
Opening Times: 0900-1600 7 days, Nov-May. 0900-1600 Fri & Sat only Sept-Oct. Webshop open all year around.
Min Mail Order UK: Nmc
Cat. Cost: Free.
Credit Cards: All major credit/debit cards
Specialities: Over 200 varieties of fruit trees, mostly home-grown, incl. bush, half-standard, cordon espalier and fan-trained fruit.
Notes: Wheelchair accessible.
OS Grid Ref: SU778335

SSFT **SUSSEX FRUIT TREES**
Hook Farm, Nettlesworth Lane, Heathfield, East Sussex, TN21 9EN
Ⓜ 07745 379526
Ⓔ mark@sussexfruittrees.co.uk
Ⓦ www.sussexfruittrees.co.uk
Contact: Mark Piper
Opening Times: 0800-1700, 7 days.
Specialities: Grows & sells a wide range of fruit trees on various rootstocks. Some Sussex apple tree cultivars.
Notes: Also provides delivery, planting, pruning, grafting, orchard maintenance & tree sundries. Delivers to shows (pre-ordered plants).

SSien **SIENNA HOSTAS**
Knap Hill Nursery, Barrs Lane, Knaphill, Surrey, GU21 2JW
Ⓣ (01483) 663160
Ⓔ nursery@siennahosta.co.uk
Ⓦ www.siennahosta.co.uk
Contact: Ollie
Opening Times: Not open. Mail order only.
Min Mail Order UK: £5.00
Credit Cards: All major credit/debit cards
Specialities: *Hosta* growers with over 30 years' experience. Over 800 varieties held within the collection with many available to order via our website. Availability may vary throughout the season.
Notes: Orders sent 1st class Royal Mail all year round. We aim to send out orders placed before 12pm Mon-Thu on the same day. Orders placed Fri-Sun will be sent on Mon.

SSim **SIMPLY SUCCULENTS**
(office) 72 Dover Road, Sandwich, Kent, CT13 0BY
Ⓜ 07548 947357
Ⓔ simplysucculents@gmx.co.uk
Ⓦ www.simplysucculents.co.uk
Contact: John Chandler
Opening Times: Not open. Mail order online only.
Min Mail Order UK: Nmc
Cat. Cost: Online only.
Specialities: Succulents for home, garden & containers.
Notes: Online sales only.

SSta **STARBOROUGH NURSERY** ♿
Starborough Road, Marsh Green, Edenbridge, Kent, TN8 5RB
Ⓣ (01732) 865614
Ⓔ starborough@hotmail.co.uk
Contact: Sales
Opening Times: 0900-1600 Thu, Fri & Sat. Closed Jan, Jul & Aug or open by appt. only. Please phone first if travelling.
Credit Cards: Visa, Access
Specialities: Rare & unusual shrubs esp. *Acer, Daphne*, rhododendrons & azaleas, *Magnolia* & *Nyssa*. Some plants only available in larger sizes.
Notes: Deliveries can be made at cost. Planting & landscaping services available. Wheelchair accessible.

SSut **DAN SUTTON**
(office) 142 Hawks Road, Hailsham, East Sussex, BN27 1NA
Ⓣ (01323) 845270
Ⓜ 07772 869645
Ⓔ suttonnursery@gmail.com
Ⓦ www.suttonnursery.co.uk
Contact: Dan Sutton
Opening Times: By appt. only.
Min Mail Order UK: £5.80.
Cat. Cost: Online only.
Credit Cards: PayPal
Specialities: Herbaceous perennials, bulbs/corms, incl. *Crocosima*, grasses, specimen bamboos, *Fargesia robusta*, *F. scabrida* & *Borinda boliana*. Coastal and drought-tolerant plants.
Notes: Nursery at Park Wood Farmhouse, Upper Dicker, Hailsham, BN27 3QL. Landscape design. Also sells wholesale. Delivers to shows (pre-ordered plants).

STPC **THE PLANT COMPANY** ♿
Coolham Road, West Chiltington, Pulborough, West Sussex, RH20 2LH
Ⓣ (01403) 740100

S

Ⓔ sales@theplantco.co.uk
Ⓦ www.theplantco.co.uk
Contact: Tim Ricketts
Opening Times: 0900-1730 Mon-Fri.
Min Mail Order UK: £8.95
Cat. Cost: Online only.
Credit Cards: All major debit/credit cards except American Express
Specialities: A range of herbaceous, shrubs and grasses.
Notes: Also sells wholesale. Delivers to shows. Wheelchair accessible.
OS Grid Ref: TQ111196

SVen **Ventnor Botanic Garden** ♿
Undercliff Drive, Ventnor, Isle of Wight, PO38 1UL
Ⓣ (01983) 855397
Ⓔ sales@botanic.co.uk
Ⓦ www.botanic.co.uk
Contact: Chris Kidd
Opening Times: 1000-1700 7 days, all year.
Min Mail Order UK: Nmc
Min Mail Order EU: Nmc
Cat. Cost: None issued.
Credit Cards: All major debit/credit cards except American Express
Specialities: Coastal, drought-tolerant, Mediterranean & southern hemisphere plants. Rare & esoteric half-hardy trees, shrubs & perennials. National Plant Collection of hardy & half-hardy *Puya*.
Notes: Also sells wholesale. Wheelchair accessible.
OS Grid Ref: SZ548768

SVic **Victoriana Nursery Gardens** ♿
Challock, Ashford, Kent, TN25 4DG
Ⓣ (01233) 740529
Ⓔ help@victoriananursery.co.uk
Ⓦ www.victoriananursery.co.uk
Contact: Serena Shirley
Opening Times: 0930-1615 (or dusk if sooner) Mon-Fri, 1030-1500 (or dusk if sooner) Sat.
Min Mail Order UK: Nmc
Cat. Cost: Free by post or online.
Credit Cards: All major credit/debit cards
Specialities: Heritage & unusual vegetable plants, seeds, fruit trees & bushes. Specialist grower of chillies & tomatoes, with annual tasting days. Also 600+ varieties of *Fuchsia*.
Notes: Also sells wholesale. Wheelchair accessible.
OS Grid Ref: TR018501

SWeb **Web Garden Centre**
Meadow Farm, Sway Road, Tiptoe, Lymington, Hampshire, SO41 6FR
Ⓣ (01590) 637443
Ⓜ 07786 064018
Ⓔ info@webgardencentre.com
Ⓦ www.webgardencentre.com
Contact: Shaun
Opening Times: By appt. only. Please telephone to arrange.
Min Mail Order UK: Nmc
Min Mail Order EU: Nmc
Cat. Cost: Online only.
Credit Cards: All major credit/debit cards
Specialities: Web Garden Centre specialise in specimen, ornamental and architectural plants, all forms of topiary and evergreen screening plants.
Notes: Web Garden Centre are an online nursery supplying plants daily at great prices throughout the United Kingdom. Next day delivery available. Also sells wholesale.
OS Grid Ref: SZ263971

SWhi **John Hall Plants Ltd** ♿
Whitehall Nursery, Red Lane (Off Churt Road), Headley Down, Hampshire, GU35 8SR
Ⓣ (01428) 715505
Ⓜ 07714 344327
Ⓔ info@johnhallplants.com
Ⓦ www.johnhallplants.com
Contact: John Hall
Opening Times: 0900-1630 Mon-Fri, 0900-1300 Sat, by appt. only.
Min Mail Order UK: Nmc
Min Mail Order EU: Nmc
Cat. Cost: By email only.
Credit Cards: None
Specialities: *Calluna*, *Daboecia* & *Erica*.
Notes: Planting plans supplied. Also sells wholesale. Exports beyond EU. Euro accepted. Wheelchair accessible.
OS Grid Ref: SU837371

SWvt **Wolverton Plants Ltd** ♿
Wolverton Common, Tadley, Hampshire, RG26 5RU
Ⓣ (01635) 298453
Ⓜ 07880 971397
Ⓕ (01635) 299075
Ⓔ plantranch2000@hotmail.com
Contact: Julian Jones
Opening Times: 0900-1700 (or dusk Nov-Feb), 7 days. Closed Xmas/ New Year.
Credit Cards: All major credit/debit cards
Specialities: Wide range of herbaceous perennials & shrubs grown on a commercial scale for the public.

Notes: Horticultural club visits welcome by prior arrangement. Able to source plants for the public and Garden Designers. Also sells wholesale. Euro accepted. Wheelchair accessible.
OS Grid Ref: SU555589

Wales and the West

WAbe **Aberconwy Nursery**
Graig, Glan Conwy, Conwy, LL28 5TL
Ⓣ (01492) 580875
Ⓔ enquiries@aberconwynursery.co.uk
Ⓦ www.aberconwynursery.co.uk
Contact: Tim Lever
Opening Times: 1000-1600 Tue-Fri Mar-Sep incl. Other times by appt.
Cat. Cost: 2 × 2nd class.
Credit Cards: MasterCard
Specialities: Alpines, including specialist varieties, esp. gentians, dionysias, dwarf *Dianthus*, *Primula*, *Saxifraga* & dwarf ericaceous plants. Some choice shrubs & woodland plants incl. smaller ferns.
Notes: Delivers to shows.
OS Grid Ref: SH799744

WABo **Atlantic Botanic** ♿
Whitegates, Moor Lane, Braunton, Devon, EX33 2NU
Ⓣ (01271) 816225
Ⓜ 07989 444461
Ⓔ atlanticbotanic@live.co.uk
Ⓦ www.atlanticbotanic.co.uk
Contact: Kay Tudor
Opening Times: See website.
Min Mail Order UK: At Cost
Credit Cards: All major credit/debit cards
Specialities: *Agapanthus*.
Notes: Wheelchair accessible.
OS Grid Ref: SS467362

WAln **L. A. Allen**
Windy Ridge, Llandrindod Wells, Powys, LD1 5NY
Ⓔ elandem80@gmail.com
Contact: Les Allen
Opening Times: Mail order only. Open by prior appt.
Min Mail Order UK: Nmc
Min Mail Order EU: Nmc
Cat. Cost: 6 × 1st class.
Credit Cards: None
Specialities: All sections of *Primula auricula*, alpine auricula, show-edged, show-self, doubles, show-stripe. Surplus plants from private collection so available in small quantities. Occasionally only 1 or 2 available of some cvs.
Notes: Also sells wholesale.

WAul **Aulden Farm**
Aulden, Leominster, Herefordshire, HR6 0JT
Ⓣ (01568) 720129
Ⓔ pf@auldenfarm.co.uk
Ⓦ www.auldenfarm.co.uk
Contact: Alun Whitehead
Opening Times: Flexible. Individuals & groups welcome. Please contact nursery. Also open for NGS.
Min Mail Order UK: £25.00
Cat. Cost: Online only.
Credit Cards: PayPal
Specialities: National Plant Collection of Siberian *Iris*.
Notes: Informal three acre country garden. Talks given. National Plant Collection of Siberian *Iris* best viewed at the end of May/June.
OS Grid Ref: SO462548

WAvo **Pershore College** ♿
Avonbank, Pershore, Worcestershire, WR10 3JP
Ⓣ (01386) 551177
Ⓔ pershorenurseries@wcg.ac.uk
Ⓦ www.wcg.ac.uk/plantcentre
Contact: Josh Egan-Wyer
Opening Times: 0900-1700 Mon-Sat, 1000-1630 Sun (1600 in winter).
Cat. Cost: £4.50 incl. p&p.
Credit Cards: All major debit/credit cards except American Express
Specialities: Extensive range of shrubs, perennials and good garden plants incl. National Plant Collections of *Penstemon* (pre-1995 cvs) & *Philadelphus* cvs. Several college raised.
Notes: Also sells wholesale. Wheelchair accessible.
OS Grid Ref: SO957447

WBor **Bordervale Plants** ♿
Nantyderi, Sandy Lane, Ystradowen, Cowbridge, Vale of Glamorgan, CF71 7SX
Ⓣ (01446) 774036
Ⓔ bordervaleplants@gmail.com
Ⓦ www.bordervale.co.uk
Contact: Claire E. Jenkins
Opening Times: 1000-1700 Fri-Sun & B/hols Mid Mar-Mid Sep. Very often open Mon-Thu but please make an appt. on these days if travelling some distance.
Min Mail Order UK: £20.00 + p&p
Cat. Cost: 3 × 1st class.
Specialities: Unusual herbaceous perennials, trees, shrubs & roses, as well as cottage garden plants, many displayed in the 2-acre garden.

Notes: Mail order available for smaller items, subject to season. Garden open mid-May to mid-Sep when nursery open. Also open for NGS. See website or contact nursery for details. Delivers to shows. Nursery wheelchair accessible.
OS Grid Ref: ST022776

WBrk **Brockamin Plants** ♿
Brockamin, Old Hills, Callow End, Worcestershire, WR2 4TQ
Ⓣ (01905) 830370
Ⓔ stone.brockamin@btinternet.com
Contact: Margaret Stone
Opening Times: By appt. only.
Credit Cards: None
Specialities: National Plant Collections of *Symphyotrichum novae-angliae*, *Geranium sanguineum*, *G. macrorrhizum* & *G.* × *cantabrigiense*. Plants available in small quantities only.
Notes: Wheelchair accessible.
OS Grid Ref: SO830488

W

WBuc **Bucknell Nurseries** ♿
Bucknell, Shropshire, SY7 0EL
Ⓣ (01547) 530606
Ⓕ (01547) 530699
Ⓔ nickcoull@yahoo.co.uk
Contact: A.N. Coull
Opening Times: 0800-1700 Mon-Fri & 1000-1300 Sat.
Min Mail Order UK: Nmc
Cat. Cost: Free.
Credit Cards: All major credit/debit cards
Specialities: Bare-rooted hedging conifers & forest trees.
Notes: Also sells wholesale. Euro accepted. Wheelchair accessible.
OS Grid Ref: SO356736

WCAu **Claire Austin Hardy Plants**
White Hopton Farm, Wern Lane, Sarn, Newtown, Powys, SY16 4EN
Ⓣ (01686) 670342
Ⓔ enquiries@claireaustin-hardyplants.co.uk
Ⓦ www.claireaustin-hardyplants.co.uk
Contact: Claire Austin
Opening Times: Mail order only. Open day towards start of Jun. See website or contact nursery for details.
Min Mail Order UK: Nmc
Min Mail Order EU: Nmc
Cat. Cost: Free, UK only.
Credit Cards: MasterCard, Visa, Switch
Specialities: *Hemerocallis*, *Iris*, *Paeonia*, & hardy plants. National Plant Collections of Bearded *Iris*.

WCav **Caves Folly Nurseries** ♿
Evendine Lane, Colwall, Malvern, Worcestershire, WR13 6DX
Ⓣ (01684) 540631
Ⓜ 07918 649276
Ⓔ bridget@cavesfolly.com
Ⓦ www.cavesfolly.com
Contact: Bridget Evans
Opening Times: 1000-1700 Thu-Sat Mar-Nov. Other times By appt.
Min Mail Order UK: £6.00
Cat. Cost: Free.
Credit Cards: All major credit/debit cards
Specialities: Organically grown perennials and alpines.
Notes: Caves Folly have been growing plants in peat free organic compost for over 30 years. Certified by the Soil Association (Licence No. G7379) with no chemical sprays used on nursery. Majority of plants grown from their own seed, division or cuttings. Also sells wholesale. Delivers to shows. Wheelchair accessible.
OS Grid Ref: SO751412

WCFE **Charles F Ellis**
Oak Piece Nurseries, Stanway Road, Stanton, Nr Broadway, Worcestershire, WR12 7NQ
Ⓣ (01386) 584077
Ⓔ ellisplants@cooptel.net
Ⓦ www.ellisplants.co.uk
Contact: Charles Ellis
Opening Times: By appt.only.
Min Mail Order UK: £10.00
Cat. Cost: None issued.
Credit Cards: All major debit/credit cards except American Express
Specialities: Wide range of shrubs, conifers, climbers & perennials, some unusual. All available in small quantities only. A few specimen sizes (but not for mail order).
Notes: Euro accepted.

WChG **Chennels Gate Gardens & Nursery** ♿
Eardisley, Herefordshire, HR3 6LT
Ⓣ (01544) 327288
Ⓔ mark.richard.dawson60@gmail.com
Contact: Mark Dawson
Opening Times: 1000-1700 7 days Mar-Oct.
Cat. Cost: None issued.
Credit Cards: None
Specialities: Interesting & unusual cottage garden plants, grasses & shrubs.
Notes: Wheelchair accessible.

WCot **Cotswold Garden Flowers**
Sands Lane, Badsey, Evesham, Worcestershire, WR11 7EZ
Ⓣ nursery: (01386) 833849 or mail order: (01386) 422829
Ⓕ nursery: (01386) 49844
Ⓔ info@cgf.net
Ⓦ www.cgf.net
Contact: Bob Brown
Opening Times: 0900-1730 Mon-Fri &1000-1730 Sat & Sun, Mar-Sep. 0900-1630 Mon-Fri only, Oct-Feb. Closed from Xmas Eve for 10 days.
Min Mail Order UK: Nmc
Min Mail Order EU: Nmc
Cat. Cost: Free.
Credit Cards: All major debit/credit cards except American Express
Specialities: A very wide range of easy to grow & unusual perennials.
Notes: Delivers to shows. Euro accepted. Partial wheelchair access.
OS Grid Ref: SP077426

WCra **Cranesbill Nursery**
1 Waverley Road, Mossley Estate, Bloxwich, Walsall, West Midlands, WS3 2SW
Ⓣ (01684) 770733
Ⓜ 07500 600205
Ⓔ gary@cranesbillnursery.com
Ⓦ www.cranesbillnursery.com
Contact: Gary Carroll
Opening Times: Mail order only. Not open to the public. Collections by appt. only.
Min Mail Order UK: £12.50
Min Mail Order EU: £25.00
Cat. Cost: Free.
Credit Cards: All major credit/debit cards
Specialities: Hardy geraniums, Approx 200 varieties in stock. Can supply large quantities with 6-8 weeks notice. Please contact nursery for further details.
Notes: Cranesbill Nursery is the only nursery in the UK that specialises solely in Hardy Geraniums. Most of our stock is listed on the website when available, however we do also have limited stock of some unusual geraniums, so always ask.
OS Grid Ref: SO940378

WCru **Crûg Farm Plants** ♿
Griffith's Crossing, Caernarfon, Gwynedd, LL55 1TU
Ⓣ (01248) 670232
Ⓜ 07774 980842
Ⓔ mailorder@crug-farm.co.uk
Ⓦ www.mailorder.crug-farm.co.uk
Contact: B. and S. Wynn-Jones
Opening Times: 0930-1630 Thu-Sat, 1st Sat in Apr to 4th Sat in Sep. Or Mon-Fri by appt. all year.
Min Mail Order UK: Nmc
Min Mail Order EU: Nmc
Cat. Cost: Online only.
Credit Cards: All major credit/debit cards
Specialities: Unusual & rare inc. trees, shrubs, herbaceous & bulbous, mostly self-collected new introductions from the Far East & the Americas. Rare woody & climbers esp. *Acer*, *Araliaceae*, *Carpinus*, *Hydrangeaceae* & *Magnolia* with many other extraordinary introductions. Shade plants esp. *Asparagaceae*, *Convallariaceae*, *Liliaceae*, *Ranunculaceae* & *Saxifragaceae*. Many supplied bare-rooted. National Plant Collections of *Coriaria*, *Paris* & *Polygonatum*.
Notes: Delivery by overnight carrier for UK & Ireland. Courier for rest of EU. Delivers to shows. Wheelchair accessible.
OS Grid Ref: SH509652

WDib **Dibleys Nurseries** ♿ ◆
Llanelidan, Ruthin, Denbighshire, LL15 2LG
Ⓣ (01978) 790677
Ⓕ (01978) 790668
Ⓔ sales@dibleys.com
Ⓦ www.dibleys.com
Contact: R. Dibley
Opening Times: 1000-1700 Mon-Sat (closed Sun), Apr-Aug. 1000-1700 Mon-Fri, Mar, Sep & Oct.
Min Mail Order UK: Nmc
Min Mail Order EU: Nmc
Cat. Cost: Free.
Credit Cards: Visa, Access, Switch, Electron, Solo
Specialities: *Columnea*, *Saintpaulia*, *Solenostemon*, *Streptocarpus*, & other gesneriads & *Begonia*. National Plant Collections of *Streptocarpus*, *Saintpaulia* & *Petrocosmea*.
Notes: Also sells wholesale. Euro accepted. Delivers to shows. Wheelchair accessible.

WFar **Farmyard Nurseries**
Dol Llan Road, Llandysul, Carmarthenshire, SA44 4RL
Ⓣ (01559) 363389
Ⓜ 01267 220259
Ⓔ sales@farmyardnurseries.co.uk
Ⓦ www.farmyardnurseries.co.uk
Contact: Richard Bramley
Opening Times: 0900-1700 7 days, excl. Xmas Day, Boxing Day & New Year's Day.
Min Mail Order UK: 3 plants

Min Mail Order EU: 3 plants
Cat. Cost: None issued.
Credit Cards: Visa, Switch, MasterCard
Specialities: Large range of home grown shrubs & herbaceous perennials, incl. *Aster, Convallaria, Crocosmia, Geranium*, hardy chrysanthemums, *Helleborus, Impatiens, Primula* (*auricula* & *sieboldii*), *Rhodohypoxis, Roscoea, Salvia, Saxifraga fortunei, Schizostylis.* Trees, shrubs, climbers, alpines, conifers & bedding plants.
Notes: Additionally sells from shop/yard in Carmarthen. Also sells wholesale. Partial wheelchair access (not garden or some areas of the nursery).
OS Grid Ref: SN421406

WFib **Fibrex Nurseries Ltd** ♿
Honeybourne Road, Pebworth, Stratford-on-Avon, Warwickshire, CV37 8XP
Ⓣ (01789) 720788
Ⓔ aesclepius@sky.com
Ⓦ www.fibrex.co.uk
Contact: Martin Jones
Opening Times: 0900-1700 Mon-Fri, 1st Mar-31st Aug. 0900-1600 Mon-Fri, 3rd Sep-28th Feb. 1030-1600 Sat & Sun, 7th Apr-1st Jul. Closed last week Dec & 1st week Jan. Closed Easter Sun & Aug B/hols.
Min Mail Order UK: £10.00 + p&p
Min Mail Order EU: £20.00 + p&p
Cat. Cost: 3 × 1st class.
Credit Cards: MasterCard, Visa, Maestro
Specialities: *Hedera*, ferns, *Pelargonium*, named tuberous begonias, *Hibiscus rosa-sinensis* cvs, hardy geraniums. National Plant Collections of *Pelargonium* & *Hedera*. Plant collections subject to time of year, please check by phone.
Notes: Also sells wholesale. Delivers to shows. Wheelchair accessible.
OS Grid Ref: SP133458

WGob **The Gobbett Nursery**
Farlow, Kidderminster, Worcestershire, DY14 8TD
Ⓣ (01746) 718647
Ⓔ chrislink59@gmail.com
Ⓦ www.thegobbettnursery.co.uk
Contact: C.H. Link
Opening Times: By appt. only.
Cat. Cost: None issued.
Credit Cards: None
Specialities: *Cornus, Iris ensata, Iris sibirica* & *Syringa.*
Notes: Delivers to shows.
OS Grid Ref: SO648811

WGoo **Wildegoose Nursery, Home of Bouts Violas** ♿
The Walled Garden, Lower Millichope, Munslow, Craven Arms, Shropshire, SY7 9HE
Ⓣ (01584) 841890
Ⓜ 07798 628762
Ⓔ office@wildegoosenursery.co.uk
Ⓦ www.wildegoosenursery.co.uk
Contact: Laura Willgoss
Opening Times: 1100-1600 Fri-Sun, 30th Mar-14th Oct 2018.
Min Mail Order UK: Nmc
Min Mail Order EU: Nmc
Cat. Cost: 1st class sae.
Credit Cards: All major credit/debit cards
Specialities: *Viola*, incl. stock from Bouts Cottage Nursery. Herbaceous perennials & grasses. Some varieties propagated in small quantities.
Notes: Delivers to shows. Wheelchair accessible. Site is on a slope with gravel paths.

WGrn **Green's Leaves** ♿
36 Ford House Road, Newent, Gloucestershire, GL18 1LQ
Ⓣ (01531) 820154
Ⓜ 07890 413036
Ⓔ r.paul.green@hotmail.co.uk
Ⓦ www.greensleavesnursery.co.uk
Contact: Paul Green
Opening Times: By appt. only. Please phone to arrange collection of orders from house (nursery site not open).
Min Mail Order UK: £10.00 + p&p
Cat. Cost: Online only.
Credit Cards: None
Specialities: Range of rare & choice shrubs, also some perennials. Ornamental grasses & sedges. Coloured foliage plants.
Notes: Delivers to shows. Wheelchair accessible.
OS Grid Ref: SO732273

WGwG **Gwynfor Growers**
Gwynfor, Pontgarreg, Llangrannog, Llandysul, Ceredigion, SA44 6AU
Ⓣ (01239) 654151
Ⓔ info@gwynfor.co.uk
Ⓦ www.gwynfor.co.uk
Contact: Steve & Angie Hipkin
Opening Times: Usually 1000-1800 (or sunset if earlier) Wed, Thu & Sun, Mar-end Oct. Other times by appt.
Min Mail Order UK: Nmc
Cat. Cost: Online only.
Credit Cards: All major credit/debit cards, PayPal
Specialities: National Plant Collection of *Rosmarinus* cvs. Specialist supplier of Welsh

fruit trees. Classic & contemporary plants grown organically & peat-free. Some plants available in small quantities only. Rarities propagated to order.
Notes: Plants also available at local farmers' markets, plant fairs & some NGS Open Gardens. Delivers to shows.
OS Grid Ref: SN331536

WHal **Hall Farm Nursery**
Vicarage Lane, Kinnerley, Nr Oswestry, Shropshire, SY10 8DH
Ⓣ (01691) 682135
Ⓔ info@hallfarmnursery.co.uk
Ⓦ www.hallfarmnursery.co.uk
Contact: Christine & Nic Ffoulkes Jones
Opening Times: 1000-1700, Thu-Sat, 1st Mar-29th Sep.
Cat. Cost: Online only.
Credit Cards: Visa, MasterCard, Electron, Maestro
Specialities: Wide range of herbaceous perennials, woodland plants, alpine & scree plants. Herbs and vegetable plants in season.
Notes: Partial wheelchair access.
OS Grid Ref: SJ333209

WHCr **Hergest Croft Gardens**
Hergest Estate Office, Ridgebourne Road, Kington, Herefordshire, HR5 3EG
Ⓣ (01544) 230160
Ⓜ 07968 435627
Ⓔ gardens@hergest.co.uk
Ⓦ www.hergest.co.uk
Contact: Stephen Lloyd
Opening Times: 1200-1730, 7 days, Apr-Oct.
Cat. Cost: None issued.
Credit Cards: All major credit/debit cards
Specialities: *Acer*, *Betula* & unusual woody plants.
Notes: Partial wheelchair access.
OS Grid Ref: SO286567

WHer **The Herb Garden & Historical Plant Nursery**
Frondeg, Gilfachreda, New Quay, Ceredigion, SA45 9SP
Ⓣ (01545) 580893
Ⓔ corinnetremaine@gmail.com
Ⓦ www.HistoricalPlants.co.uk
Contact: Corinne Tremaine
Opening Times: By appt. only.
Min Mail Order UK: Nmc
Min Mail Order EU: Nmc
Cat. Cost: Online only.
Credit Cards: None
Specialities: Rarer herbs, rare natives & wild flowers; rare & unusual & historical perennials, old roses, heritage pinks & Parma violets.

WHil **Hillview Hardy Plants** ♿
(off B4176), Worfield, Nr Bridgnorth, Shropshire, WV15 5NT
Ⓣ (01746) 716454
Ⓜ 07974 391608
Ⓔ hillview@onetel.net
Ⓦ www.hillviewhardyplants.com
Contact: Ingrid, John & Sarah Millington
Opening Times: 0930-1700 Mon-Sat, Mar-mid Oct. At other times, please phone first.
Min Mail Order UK: £10.00 + p&p
Min Mail Order EU: £10.00 + p&p
Cat. Cost: Online only.
Credit Cards: All major credit/debit cards
Specialities: Choice herbaceous perennials incl. *Acanthus*, *Albuca*, *Aquilegia*, *Eucomis*, *Ixia*, *Primula auricula*, South African bulbs. National Plant Collections of *Acanthus* & *Albuca*.
Notes: Also sells wholesale. Exports beyond EU. Delivers to shows. Euro accepted. Wheelchair accessible.
OS Grid Ref: SO772969

WHoo **Hoo House Nursery** ◆
Hoo House, Gloucester Road, Tewkesbury, Gloucestershire, GL20 7DA
Ⓣ (01684) 293389
Ⓕ (01684) 293389
Ⓔ nursery@hoohouse.co.uk
Ⓦ www.hoohouse.co.uk
Contact: Julie & Robin Ritchie
Opening Times: 1000-1700 Mon-Sat, 1100-1700 Sun. Please ring to check Nov-Jan.
Cat. Cost: 3 × 1st class.
Credit Cards: All major credit/debit cards
Specialities: Wide range of herbaceous & alpines grown peat-free. *Aster*, *Cyclamen*, *Geranium*, *Penstemon*, *Saxifraga* & many later-flowering varieties.
Notes: Also sells wholesale. Euro accepted. Partially wheelchair accessible.
OS Grid Ref: SO893293

WHrl **Harrells Hardy Plants**
(office) 15 Coxlea Close, Evesham, Worcestershire, WR11 4JS
Ⓣ (01386) 443077
Ⓜ 07799 577120 or 07733 446606
Ⓔ mail@harrellshardyplants.co.uk
Ⓦ www.harrellshardyplants.co.uk
Contact: Liz Nicklin & Kate Phillips
Opening Times: By appt. only. Please telephone.

Min Mail Order UK: Nmc
Min Mail Order EU: Nmc
Cat. Cost: Online plant list.
Credit Cards: None
Specialities: Display gardens showcase wide range of hardy perennials, esp. *Hemerocallis* & grasses.
Notes: Nursery located off Rudge Rd, Evesham. Please phone for directions or see website. Exports beyond the EU. Partial wheelchair access.
OS Grid Ref: SP033443

WHwl **Howle Hill Nursery** ♿ ◆
Watersedge, Howle Hill, Ross-on-Wye, Herefordshire, HR9 5SP
Ⓣ (01989) 567726
Ⓜ 07961 570409
Ⓔ andy@howlehillnursery.co.uk
Ⓦ www.howlehillnursery.co.uk
Contact: Andy Houghton
Opening Times: 0900-1700 Mon-Fri. 0900-1600 Sat during spring/summer.
Min Mail Order UK: £25
Min Mail Order EU: £25
Cat. Cost: No catalogue at present.
Credit Cards: All major credit/debit cards
Specialities: *Acer palmatum*, *A. japonicum* and *A. shirasawanum* cultivars.
Notes: We grow a wide and varied selection of plants from a 2ltr pot up to 750ltr semi-mature trees. We usually grow between 150-200 varieties of Japanese Maples. Also sells wholesale. Euro accepted. Wheelchair accessible.
OS Grid Ref: SO604892

WIce **Ice Alpines** ♿
Lye Head Road, Bewdley, Worcestershire, DY12 2UW
Ⓣ (01299) 269219
Ⓕ (01562) 510003
Ⓔ icealpines@gmail.com
Ⓦ www.icealpines.co.uk
Contact: Mark Lagomarsino
Opening Times: Mail order. Open by appt. only.
Min Mail Order UK: Nmc
Min Mail Order EU: £18
Credit Cards: All major credit/debit cards
Specialities: British grown alpine & rockery plants.
Notes: Delivers to shows. Wheelchair accessible.

WJas **Paul Jasper Trees**
(office) The Lighthouse, Bridge Street, Leominster, Herefordshire, HR6 8DX
Ⓔ jaspertreescouk@aol.com
Ⓦ www.jaspertrees.co.uk
Contact: Paul Jasper
Opening Times: Not open. Mail order only.
Min Mail Order UK: £25.00 + p&p
Cat. Cost: Online only.
Credit Cards: All major credit/debit cards
Specialities: Many unusual varieties of *Malus domestica* & *Prunus*.
Notes: Full range of fruit & ornamental trees. Over 100 modern and traditional fruit tree varieties plus 100 ornamental tree varieties, all direct from the grower. Less popular varieties available in small quantities only. Regular updates & notes on website. Also sells wholesale.

WJek **Jekka's Herb Farm** ♿
Rose Cottage, Shellards Lane, Alveston, Bristol, South Gloucestershire, BS35 3SY
Ⓣ (01454) 418878
Ⓔ sales@jekkasherbfarm.com
Ⓦ www.jekkasherbfarm.com
Contact: Jekka McVicar
Opening Times: Open on specific days only. Please check website or contact nursery for dates.
Min Mail Order UK: £10.00
Min Mail Order EU: £18.00
Cat. Cost: Online only.
Credit Cards: Visa, MasterCard, Delta, Maestro
Specialities: Specialist herb farm with a herbetum containing over 300 culinary herbs. The collection contains herbs from all around the world.
Notes: Wheelchair accessible.

WJPR **JPR Environmental**
The Malt House, Standish, Stonehouse, Gloucestershire, GL10 3DL
Ⓣ (01453) 822584
Ⓔ enquiries@jprenvironmental.co.uk
Ⓦ www.jprwillow.co.uk
Contact: Elizabeth Hillary
Opening Times: Not open. Mail order only. 0900-1700, Mon-Fri.
Min Mail Order UK: £6.00
Credit Cards: All major debit/credit cards except American Express
Specialities: *Salix*.
Notes: Also sells wholesale.

WKif **Kiftsgate Court Gardens** ♿
Kiftsgate Court, Chipping Camden, Gloucestershire, GL55 6LN
Ⓣ (01386) 438777
Ⓕ (01386) 438777
Ⓔ anne@kiftsgate.co.uk
Ⓦ www.kiftsgate.co.uk
Contact: Mrs J. Chambers

Opening Times: 1200-1800 Sat-Wed, May, Jun & Jul. 1400-1800 Sat-Wed, Aug. 1400-1800 Sun, Mon & Wed, Apr & Sep.
Cat. Cost: None issued.
Credit Cards: All major debit/credit cards except American Express
Specialities: Small range of unusual plants.
Notes: Wheelchair accessible.
OS Grid Ref: SP170430

WKor **Kore Wild Fruit Nursery**
Bridport House, Cilcennin, Lampeter, Ceredigion, SA48 8RL
Ⓣ (01570) 470439
Ⓔ info@korewildfruitnursery.co.uk
Ⓦ www.korewildfruitnursery.co.uk
Contact: Coral Guppy
Opening Times: Not open. Mail order only.
Min Mail Order UK: Nmc
Min Mail Order EU: Nmc
Cat. Cost: Free.
Credit Cards: All major credit/debit cards
Specialities: Range of mainly hardy trees, shrubs and perennials that produce edible fruit and some perennial veg. Unusual plants for indoors. Exotic and native species available.
Notes: Ideal for a range of uses, aspects and soil types. All plants propagated on site in 7cm pots and sold when 1 to 3 years old. Plants available all year round.

WLav **The Lavender Garden**
Ashcroft Nurseries, Nr Ozleworth, Kingscote, Tetbury, Gloucestershire, GL8 8YF
Ⓣ (01453) 860356
Ⓜ 07837 582943
Ⓔ Andrew007Bullock@aol.com
Ⓦ www.TheLavenderG.co.uk
Contact: Andrew Bullock
Opening Times: 1100-1700 Sat & Sun. Weekdays variable, please phone. 1st Nov-1st Mar by appt. only.
Min Mail Order UK: £10.00 + p&p
Min Mail Order EU: £20.00 + p&p
Cat. Cost: Online only.
Credit Cards: All major credit/debit cards
Specialities: *Buddleja*, *Lavandula*, plants to attract butterflies. Herbs, wildflowers. National Plant Collection of *Buddleja*.
Notes: Also sells wholesale. Delivers to shows. Partial wheelchair access.
OS Grid Ref: ST798948

WLov **Lovegroves**
The Old Chapel, Pendock, Gloucestershire, GL19 3PG
Ⓣ (01531) 650918
Ⓜ 07973 331142
Ⓔ clare@plants-paradise.co.uk
Ⓦ www.plants-paradise.co.uk
Contact: Clare Lovegrove
Opening Times: Mail order.
Min Mail Order UK: Nmc.
Cat. Cost: Available by email or download from website only.
Credit Cards: All major credit/debit cards
Specialities: Interesting selection of trees, shrubs, ferns and climbers; many of which are rare or unusual. All grown in peat-free compost.
Notes: Traditional plant nursery, producing an inspiring collection of desirable trees and shrubs grown in the UK. Collection of plants by prior arrangement.
OS Grid Ref: SO786326

WMal **Malcolm Allison Nurseries**
79 Byron Road, St Mark's, Cheltenham, Gloucestershire, GL51 7EY
Ⓣ (01242) 256349
Ⓜ 07817 730509
Ⓔ majallison2000@yahoo.com
Ⓦ http://www.malcolmallisonplants.com
Contact: Malcolm Allison
Opening Times: By appt. only.
Credit Cards: PayPal
Specialities: *Nerine* cultivars.
Notes: Wide range of hardy and half-hardy herbaceous plants, many available only in small quantities.
OS Grid Ref: SO914286

WMAq **Merebrook Water Plants**
Kingfisher Barn, Merebrook Farm, Hanley Swan, Worcestershire, WR8 0DX
Ⓣ (01684) 310950
Ⓜ 07876 777066
Ⓔ enquiries@pondplants.co.uk
Ⓦ www.pondplants.co.uk
Contact: Roger Kings & Biddi Kings
Opening Times: Not open. Mail order only.
Min Mail Order UK: Nmc
Min Mail Order EU: £25.00
Cat. Cost: Online only.
Credit Cards: All major credit/debit cards
Specialities: *Nymphaea*, Louisiana irises & other aquatic plants. International Waterlily & Water Gardening Soc. accredited collection.
OS Grid Ref: SO802425

WMat **The Tree Shop at Frank P. Matthews Ltd.** ♿
Berrington Court, Tenbury Wells, Worcestershire, WR15 8TH
Ⓣ (01584) 812800
Ⓕ (01584) 811830

Ⓔ treeshop@fpmatthews.co.uk
Ⓦ www.frankpmatthews.com
Contact: Steve Grosvenor
Opening Times: 0730-1700 Mon-Fri.
Cat. Cost: 4 × 1st class.
Credit Cards: All major credit/debit cards
Specialities: Fruit & deciduous ornamental trees.
Notes: Also sells wholesale. Wheelchair accessible.
OS Grid Ref: SO571676

WMil **Anne Milner**
Meadow House, Baunton, Cirencester, Gloucestershire, GL7 7BB
Ⓣ (01285) 643731
Ⓔ anne.milner@btinternet.com
Ⓦ www.blissiris.co.uk
Contact: Anne Milner
Opening Times: By appt. only.
Min Mail Order UK: Nmc
Min Mail Order EU: Nmc
Cat. Cost: 50p (UK) £1.00 (EU) to cover postage.
Credit Cards: None
Specialities: National Plant Collection of *Iris* (A.J. Bliss introductions). Available in small quantities only.
Notes: Euro accepted. Delivers to some shows, check with nursery.

W

WMon **National Plant Collection of Monarda** ♿
Glyn Bach, Pont Hywel, Efailwen, Pembrokeshire, SA66 7JP
Ⓣ (01994) 419104
Ⓜ 07828 199303
Ⓔ carole_whittaker@hotmail.com
Ⓦ www.glynbachgardens.co.uk
Contact: Carole Whittaker
Opening Times: Open by appt. & May-Oct for collection of orders only.
Min Mail Order UK: Nmc
Min Mail Order EU: Nmc
Cat. Cost: Online only.
Credit Cards: None
Specialities: National Plant Collection of *Monarda*. Limited stock available.
Notes: Gardens open under Plant Heritage and by appt. Talks given. If travelling some distance please contact nursery to check plant availability. Wheelchair accessible.
OS Grid Ref: SN132275

WMou **Mount Pleasant Trees Ltd** ♿
Rockhampton, Berkeley, Gloucestershire, GL13 9DU
Ⓣ (01454) 260348
Ⓔ info@mountpleasanttrees.com
Ⓦ www.mountpleasanttrees.com
Contact: Tom Locke & Elizabeth Murphy
Opening Times: 0830-1630 Mon-Fri, 0830-1230 Sat, Oct-Apr.
Min Mail Order UK: Nmc
Cat. Cost: Free.
Credit Cards: All major credit/debit cards
Specialities: Wide range of trees for forestry, hedging, woodlands & gardens esp. *Populus*, *Quercus*, *Salix* & *Tilia*.
Notes: Mail order available for plants under 1m in height, quotes on request, p&p quoted on individual basis. Also sells wholesale. Wheelchair accessible.
OS Grid Ref: ST654929

WNHG **New Hope Gardens** ♿
(office) The Old Chapel, Cefn Einion, Nr Bishops Castle, Shropshire, SY9 5LF
Ⓣ Office: (01588) 630750
Ⓔ markwzenick@aol.com
Ⓦ www.newhopegardens.com
Contact: Mark Zenick
Opening Times: Open W/ends: 1200-1700 Sat & Sun, 23rd/24th Jun; 30th Jun/1st Jul, 7th/8th, 14th/15th, 21st/22nd, 28th/29th Jul, 4th/5th Aug. Or by appt.
Min Mail Order UK: Nmc
Min Mail Order EU: Nmc
Cat. Cost: Online only. Plant list on request.
Credit Cards: All major credit/debit cards
Specialities: American bred, British grown, *Hemerocallis*. Ships bare-rooted plants. Daylily plants are growing and for sale at New Hope Gardens, Colebatch Farm, Shropshire on Open w/ends.
Notes: Wheelchair accessible.
OS Grid Ref: SO872317

WNPC **Newent Plant Centre** ♿
Little Verzons Farm, Hereford Road, Ledbury, Herefordshire, HR8 2PZ
Ⓣ (01531) 670121
Ⓔ markmoir999@btinternet.com
Ⓦ www.newentplantcentre.co.uk
Contact: Mark Moir
Opening Times: 0900-1700 Mon-Sat, 1000-1600 Sun.
Credit Cards: All major credit/debit cards
Specialities: Extensive range of *Euphorbia* & *Heuchera*. Herbaceous perennials, climbers, shrubs, trees, alpines, herbs, roses & fruit.
Notes: Coffee shop & deli on site. Delivers to shows. Wheelchair accessible.
OS Grid Ref: SO665395

WOld **Old Court Nurseries**
Colwall, Nr Malvern, Worcestershire, WR13 6QE
Ⓣ (01684) 540416
Ⓜ 07971 522891
Ⓔ oldcourtnurseries@btinternet.com
Ⓦ www.autumnasters.co.uk
Contact: Paul, Meriel or Helen Picton
Opening Times: 1400-1700 Wed-Sat, May-Aug. 1100-1700 Wed-Sun, Aug. 1100-1700 7 days, 1st week Sep-20th Oct. Also by appt. May to Oct.
Min Mail Order UK: Nmc
Min Mail Order EU: Nmc
Cat. Cost: Free.
Credit Cards: All major debit/credit cards except American Express
Specialities: National Plant Collection of Michaelmas Daisies. Herbaceous perennials.
Notes: Mail order sent in spring only. Display garden open Aug-Oct, plus some early season open days. See website or contact nursery for further information.
OS Grid Ref: SO759430

WOut **Out of the Common Way**
Penhyddgan, Boduan, Pwllheli, Gwynedd, LL53 8YH
Ⓣ (01758) 721577
Ⓔ ziggymen22@hotmail.co.uk
Contact: Margaret Mason
Opening Times: By appt only.
Min Mail Order UK: Nmc
Min Mail Order EU: Nmc
Cat. Cost: A5 sae large letter rate postage or online.
Credit Cards: None
Specialities: Labiates, esp. *Salvia*. Also *Crocosmia* & *Geranium*. Native plants. Some plants propagated in small quantities only. Will propagate Salvias to order.
Notes: Delivers to shows. Euro accepted.

WPav **Paviour and Davies Plants** ♿
(office) Dame School, Castle Street, Wigmore, Herefordshire, HR6 9UA
Ⓜ 07966 580812
Ⓔ info@paviouranddaviesplants.co.uk
Ⓦ www.paviouranddaviesplants.co.uk
Contact: Mark Paviour
Opening Times: By appt. only.
Min Mail Order UK: Nmc
Cat. Cost: Online.
Credit Cards: None
Specialities: Plants of Chilean and Argentinian origin together with a selection of unusual plants from Australasia. All plants propagated and grown on site. National Plant Collection of *Azara*. Some plants only available in small numbers.
Notes: Groups welcome by appt. Talks given by arrangement. Delivers to shows. Wheelchair accessible.
OS Grid Ref: SO429556

WPGP **Pan-Global Plants** ♿
The Walled Garden, Frampton Court, Frampton-on-Severn, Gloucestershire, GL2 7EX
Ⓣ (01452) 741641
Ⓜ 07801 275138
Ⓔ info@panglobalplants.com
Ⓦ www.panglobalplants.com
Contact: Nick Macer
Opening Times: 1100-1700 Wed-Sun 1st Feb-31st Oct. Also B/hols. Closed 2nd Sun in Sep. Winter months by appt. please telephone first.
Min Mail Order UK: £25.00
Min Mail Order EU: £35.00
Cat. Cost: 6 × 1st class.
Credit Cards: Maestro, MasterCard, Visa, Solo, Delta
Specialities: A serious plantsman's nursery offering a very wide selection of correctly named, rare & desirable trees, shrubs, herbaceous, bamboos, exotics, climbers, ferns etc. Specialities incl. *Agavaceae*, *Bamboo*, *Betula*, *Hydrangea*, *Magnolia*, *Sorbus* & *Tilia*.
Notes: Wheelchair accessible.
OS Grid Ref: SO750080

WPhe **Pheasant Acre Plants** ◆
3 Pheasant Walk, Pen-y-Fai, Bridgend, Mid Glamorgan, CF31 4DU
Ⓣ (01656) 664086
Ⓜ 07816 236462
Ⓔ sales@pheasantacreplants.co.uk
Ⓦ www.pheasantacreplants.co.uk
Contact: Rob Evans
Opening Times: By appt. only.
Min Mail Order UK: Nmc
Min Mail Order EU: Nmc
Cat. Cost: £1.00
Credit Cards: All major credit/debit cards
Specialities: Bulbous. Ornamental. *Gladiolus*.
Notes: Open days throughout the year. Delivers to shows. Euro accepted.

WPnP **Penlan Perennials** ♿
Wern Rhos, Newchapel, Boncath, Pembrokeshire, SA37 0EN
Ⓣ (01239) 842260
Ⓜ 07857 675312
Ⓔ info@penlanperennials.co.uk
Ⓦ www.penlanperennials.co.uk
Contact: Richard Cain

W

Opening Times: Open for collection of orders & by appt..
Min Mail Order UK: Nmc
Min Mail Order EU: Nmc
Cat. Cost: Online only.
Credit Cards: All major credit/debit cards
Specialities: Aquatic, marginal & bog plants. Shade-loving & woodland perennials, ferns & hardy Geraniums, all grown organically in peat-free compost.
Notes: Mail order all year, next day delivery. Secure online web ordering. Also sells wholesale. Euro accepted. Delivers to shows. Wheelchair accessible.
OS Grid Ref: SN217392

WRHF RED HOUSE FARM ♿
Flying Horse Lane, Bradley Green, Nr Redditch, Worcestershire, B96 6QT
Ⓣ (01527) 821269
Ⓔ redhousenursery@googlemail.com
Ⓦ www.redhousefarmgardenandnursery.co.uk
Contact: Mrs Maureen Weaver
Opening Times: 1000-1700 Mon-Sat all year. 1000-1700 Sun & B/hols.
Cat. Cost: 2 × 1st class.
Credit Cards: None
Specialities: Cottage garden perennials.
Notes: Wheelchair accessible.
OS Grid Ref: SO986623

WSFF SAITH FFYNNON WILDLIFE PLANTS ♿
Whitford, Holywell, Flintshire, CH8 9EQ
Ⓣ (01352) 711198
Ⓕ (01352) 716777
Ⓔ jan@7wells.org
Ⓦ www.7wells.co.uk
Contact: Jan Miller
Opening Times: By appt. only.
Min Mail Order UK: Nmc
Min Mail Order EU: Nmc
Cat. Cost: 2 × 1st class (list only) or full catalogue online.
Credit Cards: All major credit/debit cards
Specialities: Plants and seeds to attract bees, butterflies & other wildlife. Natural dye plants. National Plant Collection of *Eupatorium*. Stock available in small quantities unless ordered well in advance.
Notes: Percentage of profits go to conservation. Credit cards accepted via website only. Also sells wholesale. Euro accepted. Wheelchair accessible.
OS Grid Ref: SJ154775

WSHC STONE HOUSE COTTAGE NURSERIES ♿
Church Lane, Stone, Nr Kidderminster, Worcestershire, DY10 4BG
Ⓜ 07817 921146
Ⓔ louisa@shcn.co.uk
Ⓦ www.shcn.co.uk
Contact: L.N. Arbuthnott
Opening Times: 1000-1700 Wed-Sat, early Apr-early Sep only.
Credit Cards: All major credit/debit cards
Specialities: Small general range esp. wall shrubs, climbers & unusual plants.
Notes: Wheelchair accessible.
OS Grid Ref: SO863750

WShi SHIPTON BULBS
Y Felin, Henllan Amgoed, Whitland, Carmarthenshire, SA34 0SL
Ⓣ (01994) 240637
Ⓕ (01994) 240637
Ⓔ admin@shiptonbulbs.co.uk
Ⓦ www.shiptonbulbs.co.uk
Contact: John Shipton & Astra Shipton
Opening Times: By appt. only.
Min Mail Order UK: Nmc
Min Mail Order EU: Nmc
Cat. Cost: Sae.
Credit Cards: All major credit/debit cards
Specialities: Native British bulbs. Bulbs & plants for naturalising.
Notes: Also sells wholesale. Euro accepted.
OS Grid Ref: SN188207

WSMil SOUTH MILTON PLANT NURSERY ♿
South Milton, Kingsbridge, South Devon, TQ7 3JP
Ⓣ (01548) 561081
Ⓜ 07936 279762
Ⓔ info@southmiltonnursey.co.uk
Ⓦ www.southmiltonnursery.co.uk
Contact: Theo Cooper
Opening Times: 1000-1700 Wed-Sun Feb-Oct. 1000-1500 Wed-Sat Nov-Dec. Closed all of Jan and Mon & Tue all year.
Cat. Cost: Free online catalogue only.
Credit Cards: PayPal
Specialities: *Echium*.
Notes: Also sells wholesale. Wheelchair accessible.
OS Grid Ref: SX691427

WSpi SPINNEYWELL NURSERY
Spinneywell Farm, Waterlane, Oakridge, Stroud, Gloucestershire, GL6 7PH
Ⓣ (01452) 770092
Ⓜ 07879 133046
Ⓔ info@spinneywell.co.uk
Ⓦ www.plantproviders.co.uk
Contact: Julie Asher
Opening Times: 0900-1700 most Sats, Mar-Oct, otherwise by prior appt. only. Please

W

telephone before travelling. Also advertised Open days. Check website or contact nursery for details.
Min Mail Order UK: £10.00 + p&p
Min Mail Order EU: £30.00 + p&p
Cat. Cost: Online only.
Credit Cards: All major credit/debit cards
Specialities: *Buxus*, *Daphne*, *Taxus*, hellebores, euphorbias, hardy geraniums, ferns & *Hemerocallis*.
Notes: Plant sourcing service available. Mail order and organised collections/deliveries only. Also sells wholesale.
OS Grid Ref: SO921044

WSSs **SHROPSHIRE SARRACENIAS** ♿
Beaufort, Coppice Drive, Wrockwardine Wood, Telford, Shropshire, TF2 7BP
Ⓣ (01952) 612452
Ⓔ mike@carnivorousplants.uk.com
Ⓦ www.carnivorousplants.uk.com
Contact: Mike King
Opening Times: By appt. only.
Min Mail Order UK: Nmc
Min Mail Order EU: Nmc
Cat. Cost: 2 × 1st class.
Credit Cards: PayPal
Specialities: *Dionaea muscipula* & forms. *Sarracenia*. Some stock available in small quantities only. National Plant Collections of *Dionaea* & *Sarracenia*.
Notes: Exports beyond EU. Delivers to shows. Euro accepted. Wheelchair accessible.
OS Grid Ref: SJ689085

WSuV **SUNNYBANK VINE NURSERY (NATIONAL VINE COLLECTION)**
Cwm Barn, King Street, Ewyas Harold, Rowlestone, Herefordshire, HR2 OEE
Ⓣ (01981) 240256
Ⓔ Sarah@sunnybankvines.co.uk
Ⓦ www.sunnybankvines.co.uk
Contact: Sarah Bell
Opening Times: Not open. Mail order only.
Min Mail Order UK: £14.00 incl. p&p
Min Mail Order EU: £23.00 incl. p&p
Cat. Cost: Online only.
Credit Cards: None
Specialities: Vines. National Plant Collection of *Vitis vinifera* (hardy, incl. dessert & wine). Small quantities of 60-70 varieties available as rooted plants, the entire collection usually available as bare wood cuttings for own propagation depending upon wood ripening this season.
Notes: Open day once a year advertised on both nursery & Plant Heritage websites. Exports beyond EU by arrangement.

WTan **TAN-Y-LLYN NURSERIES**
Meifod, Powys, SY22 6YB
Ⓣ (01938) 500370
Ⓔ info@tanyllyn-nursery.co.uk
Ⓦ www.tanyllyn-nursery.co.uk
Contact: Callum Johnston
Opening Times: By appt. only. Please phone.
Min Mail Order UK: Nmc
Cat. Cost: None issued.
Credit Cards: PayPal
Specialities: Herbs, alpines, perennials.
OS Grid Ref: SJ167125

WThu **THUYA ALPINE NURSERY**
Glebelands, Hartpury, Gloucestershire, GL19 3BW
Ⓣ (01452) 700548 (ring between 1900-2100 hours)
Ⓜ 07599 957869
Contact: S.W. Bond
Opening Times: 1000-dusk Sat & B/hols. 1100-dusk Sun, Weekdays appt. advised.
Min Mail Order UK: £7.00 + p&p
Min Mail Order EU: £14.00 + p&p
Cat. Cost: 4 × 2nd class.
Credit Cards: None
Specialities: Wide and changing range including rarities, available in small quantities only.
Notes: Will deliver plants to AGS shows only. Partial wheelchair access.

WTor **TORTWORTH PLANTS LTD**
Old Lodge Farm, Tortworth, Wotton-under-Edge, Gloucestershire, GL12 8HF
Ⓣ (01454) 260020
Ⓕ (01454) 260020
Ⓔ info@tortworthplants.co.uk
Ⓦ www.tortworthplants.co.uk
Contact: Rebecca Flint or Tim Hancock
Opening Times: By appt. only.
Min Mail Order UK: Nmc
Cat. Cost: Online or 2 × 1st for plant list.
Credit Cards: All major credit/debit cards
Specialities: Herbaceous perennials & alpines, incl. rare & unusual.
Notes: Also sells wholesale. Partial wheelchair access. Delivers to shows.

WTre **WALLED GARDEN TREBERFYDD**
Llangasty, Brecon, Powys, LD3 7PX
Ⓣ (01874) 730169
Ⓜ 07711 222700
Ⓔ alison@walledgardentreberfydd.com
Ⓦ www.walledgardentreberfydd.com
Contact: Alison Sparshatt
Opening Times: 1000-1700 daily, Apr-Oct. For Nov-Mar opening times see website or contact nursery.

Cat. Cost: Online only.
Credit Cards: All major credit/debit cards
Specialities: Old-fashioned plant nursery in a walled Victorian kitchen garden. Hardy plants grown in Wales which are structural, unusual, herbal or fragrant. Special emphasis on herbs & perennial vegetables. Many varieties propagated in small quantities only.
Notes: Events & workshops throughout the year. Contact nursery for details.
OS Grid Ref: SO128255

WTSh **TREE SHOP LTD**
Unit 16, Harts Barn, Monmouth Road, Longhope, Gloucestershire, GL17 0QD
Ⓣ (01452) 832100
Ⓕ (01452) 831273
Ⓔ office@tree-shop.co.uk
Ⓦ www.tree-shop.co.uk
Contact: Helen Conneely & Lorraine Organ
Opening Times: By appt. only 0830-1600 Mon-Fri. Please phone first.
Min Mail Order UK: Nmc
Cat. Cost: Free.
Credit Cards: All major debit/credit cards except American Express
Specialities: Trees, hedging, shrubs.
OS Grid Ref: SO679185

WTyc **TY CWM NURSERY**
Penfordd, Llanybydder, Ceredigon, SA40 9XE
Ⓣ (01570) 480655
Ⓔ helenwarrington@hotmail.co.uk
Ⓦ www.tycwmnursery.co.uk
Contact: Helen Warrington
Opening Times: 1000-1800, 1st Apr–31st Sep, Tue–Sun. Closed Mon.1st Oct-31st Mar by appt. only.
Min Mail Order UK: Nmc
Min Mail Order EU: Nmc
Cat. Cost: Online only.
Credit Cards: All major credit/debit cards
Specialities: Carnivorous plants & unusual perennials. Also sell shrubs, climbers, bedding, fruit and veg plants. Many items not listed available in small quantities.
Notes: Partial wheelchair access. Delivers to shows.

WViv **VIV MARSH POSTAL PLANTS**
Hunkington Nurseries, Walford Heath, Shrewsbury, Shropshire, SY4 2HT
Ⓣ (01939) 291475
Ⓔ mail@postalplants.co.uk
Ⓦ www.postalplants.co.uk
Contact: Mr Viv Marsh
Opening Times: Open 2 w/ends a year. Please phone or see website for details.
Min Mail Order UK: £30.00
Min Mail Order EU: £30.00
Cat. Cost: Free.
Credit Cards: All major credit/debit cards
Specialities: Specialists in *Alstroemeria*. National Plant Collection of *Alstroemeria*, viewing by appt.
Notes: Partial wheelchair access (to tunnels. No disabled toilet).
OS Grid Ref: SJ445197

WWct **WALCOT ORGANIC NURSERY**
Lower Walcot Farm, Walcot Lane, Drakes Broughton, Pershore, Worcestershire, WR10 2AL
Ⓣ (01905) 841587
Ⓜ 07780 547983
Ⓔ enquiries@walcotnursery.co.uk
Ⓦ www.walcotnursery.co.uk
Contact: Kevin O'Neill
Opening Times: 0800-1700 Mon-Fri. 1000-1300 Sat. Sat only Nov-Mar.
Min Mail Order UK: £15.00
Cat. Cost: Free.
Credit Cards: All major credit/debit cards
Specialities: Organic fruit trees. Apples, plums, pears, cherries, quinces on different rootstocks.
Notes: Also sells wholesale. Nursery buildings accessible for wheelchairs.
OS Grid Ref: SO944461

WWFP **WHITEHALL FARMHOUSE PLANTS**
Sevenhampton, Cheltenham, Gloucestershire, GL54 5TL
Ⓣ (01242) 820772
Ⓜ 07711 021034
Ⓔ victoria@wfplants.co.uk
Ⓦ www.wfplants.co.uk
Contact: Victoria Logue
Opening Times: By appt. only.
Min Mail Order UK: Nmc
Credit Cards: None
Specialities: Hardy perennials.
Notes: A small nursery producing a range of interesting & easy hardy perennials for the garden. Most plants held in small quantities only.
OS Grid Ref: SP018229

WWild **THE WILD FLOWER NURSERY**
Hackett Farm, Reynalton, Kilgetty, Pembrokeshire, SA68 0XN
Ⓜ 07854 845014
Ⓔ info@thewildflowernursery.co.uk
Ⓦ www.thewildflowernursery.co.uk
Contact: Lindsey Jones
Opening Times: Open by appt. only.

Min Mail Order UK: £3.50
Cat. Cost: Online only.
Credit Cards: All major credit/debit cards
Specialities: British wild flower plants.
Notes: Sells online only.

WWtn **Westonbury Mill Water Garden** ♿
Pembridge, Herefordshire, HR6 9HZ
Ⓣ (01544) 388650
Ⓕ (01544) 388650
Ⓔ westonburymillnursery@gmail.com
Ⓦ www.westonburymillwatergardens.com
Contact: Richard Pim
Opening Times: 1100-1700 daily, 1st Apr-30th Sep. By appt. only at other times & to arrange collection. Please contact nursery for orders outside open season.
Specialities: Range of herbaceous plants suitable for a wide range of growing conditions, with special emphasis on plants for the water garden & bog areas. Plants available in small quantities. Seasonal availability varies as stock sells out. Contact nursery to confirm availability before travelling.
Notes: Café. Wheelchair accessible.

Abroad

XAbr **Abriherbs**
La Gigude, Soulatgé, Aude, 11330 France
Ⓣ +33 (685) 651155
Ⓕ +33 (685) 651155
Ⓔ abriherbs@gmail.com
Contact: Cassy
Opening Times: By appt. only.
Min Mail Order UK: Nmc
Min Mail Order EU: Nmc
Cat. Cost: Sae for free plant list.
Specialities: Natural medicinal and rare plants.
Notes: Mostly pure species offered. Natural methods of production with no use of chemicals. Also sells wholesale. Euro accepted.

XBar **Barnhaven Primroses**
Keranguiner, Plestin-les-grèves, Brittany, 22310 France
Ⓣ +33 (2) 9635 6841
Ⓜ +33 (6) 06623687
Ⓔ info@barnhaven.com
Ⓦ www.barnhaven.com
Contact: Lynne Lawson & Rob Mitchell
Opening Times: 1400-1700 Feb-May. For visits outside this period, please phone first.
Min Mail Order UK: Nmc
Min Mail Order EU: Nmc
Credit Cards: Visa, MasterCard, PayPal
Specialities: *Primula*. French National Plant Collection of Barnhaven *Primula* hybrids. Certified collection of *Primula auricula* cvs. Old-fashioned and double primroses. Large collection of Asiatic and Alpine *Primula*. Seeds & plants available worldwide.
Notes: Exports beyond the EU. Euro & sterling accepted. Delivers to shows.

XBlo **Table Bay View Nursery**
c/o 52 Paradise Road, Newlands, Cape Town, 7700 South Africa
Ⓣ +27 (21) 683 5108
Ⓕ +27 (21) 683 5108
Ⓔ info@tablebayviewnursery.co.za
Contact: Terence Bloch
Opening Times: Mail order only. No personal callers.
Min Mail Order UK: £15.00 + p&p
Min Mail Order EU: £15.00
Cat. Cost: £3.40 (postal order)
Credit Cards: None
Specialities: Tropical & sub-tropical ornamental & fruiting plants. Self-harvested seed, predominantly from our own inventory of mother stock plants.
Notes: Due to high local bank charges, cannot accept foreign bank cheques, only undated postal orders. To comply with UK import regulations, prospective buyers must register with DEFRA before placing an order. Exports beyond EU. Euro accepted.

XCre **Crea Paysage**
Lannénec, Allée De La Roselière, Ploemeur 56270, France
Ⓣ +33 (02) 9785 2555
Ⓜ 06249 25588
Ⓔ creapaysage@orange.fr
Ⓦ www.creapaysage.com/fr/
Contact: Audrey Le Borgne
Opening Times: 1000-1730 Tue-Sat (closed for lunch 1230-1330).
Min Mail Order UK: Nmc
Min Mail Order EU: Nmc
Specialities: Bamboo, grasses.

XEll **Ellebore** ♿
La Chamotière, 61360 Saint-Jouin-de-Blavou, France
Ⓣ +33 (2) 3383 3772
Ⓜ +33 6802 28674
Ⓔ pepiniere.ellebore@orange.fr
Ⓦ www.pepiniere-ellebore.com
Contact: Nadine Albouy & Christian Geoffroy
Opening Times: 1000-1800 Wed-Sat, mid-Feb to late Jun & Sep-Dec. 1500-1800 Thu, Fri & Sat, Jul, Aug & Jan to mid-Feb.

Min Mail Order UK: Nmc
Min Mail Order EU: Nmc
Cat. Cost: Free.
Credit Cards: All major credit/debit cards
Specialities: *Cyclamen, Helleborus*. Bulbs.
Notes: Also sells wholesale. Euro accepted. Delivers to shows. Exports beyond EU. Wheelchair accessible.

XFro **FROSCH EXCLUSIVE PERENNIALS**
Ziegelstadelweg 5a, D-83623 Dietramszell, Germany
Ⓣ +49 (172) 842 2050
Ⓕ +49 (8027) 904 9975
Ⓔ info@cypripedium.de
Ⓦ www.cypripedium.de
Contact: Michael Weinert
Opening Times: Not open. Mail order only. Orders taken between 0700-2200 hours.
Min Mail Order UK: £350.00 + p&p
Min Mail Order EU: £350.00 + p&p
Cat. Cost: Online only.
Credit Cards: None
Specialities: *Cypripedium* hybrids. Hardy orchids.
Notes: Also sells wholesale. Exports beyond EU. Euro accepted.

X

XGLG **WWW.GREATLITTLEGARDEN.CO.UK**
Not open to the public
Ⓣ (0333) 003 0516
Ⓔ glg.sales@greatlittlegarden.co.uk
Ⓦ www.greatlittlegarden.co.uk
Contact: Phil McCann
Opening Times: Not open. Mail order only.
Min Mail Order UK: Nmc
Cat. Cost: No catalogue.
Credit Cards: All major credit/debit cards
Specialities: Wide range of plants, trees, climbers and aquatic plants.
Notes: Online retailer delivering plants by mail order only.

XHod **SCEA HODNIK**
1 Place du 19 Mars 1962, 45700 St Maurice sur Fessard, France
Ⓣ +33 (02) 3897 8459
Ⓕ +33 (02) 3897 8939
Ⓔ contact@hodnik.com
Ⓦ www.hodnik.com
Contact: André Hodnik
Opening Times: Not open except by appt. Mail order only.
Min Mail Order UK: Nmc
Min Mail Order EU: Nmc
Cat. Cost: Online only.
Credit Cards: All major credit/debit cards
Specialities: A large number of tropical & Mediterreanean plants which can be grown in a conservatory. French National Plant Collection of *Bougainvillea* & *Brugmansia*.
Notes: Weekly shipments to the UK. Euro accepted.

XLot **LOTTA PLANTS**
Kleine Houtweg 29, Haarlem, Noord Holland, 2012CB Netherlands
Ⓣ +31 (6) 22 20 70 20
Ⓔ sales@lottaplants.eu
Ⓦ www.lottaplants.eu
Contact: Edwin Deen
Opening Times: By appt. only.
Min Mail Order UK: Nmc
Min Mail Order EU: Nmc
Cat. Cost: Online only.
Credit Cards: All major credit/debit cards
Specialities: *Acer, Camellia, Clematis, Cornus, Magnolia*, bulbs & conifers.
Notes: Cooperation of specialised growers, each offering a specific plant type via their web shop which is open 24/7. Most plants available all year round except seasonal Clematis and bulbs.

XLum **ATELIER DU VÉGÉTAL**
Les Coutets, 24100 Creysse-Bergerac, France
Ⓣ +33 (5) 5357 6215
Ⓔ contact@atelierduvegetal.com
Ⓦ www.atelierduvegetal.com
Contact: Jordi & Amélie Tura
Opening Times: 0800-1730 Mon-Sat. Closed Sun.
Min Mail Order UK: Nmc
Min Mail Order EU: Nmc
Cat. Cost: Online only.
Credit Cards: Visa, MasterCard, PayPal
Specialities: Hardy perennials. Grasses. Plants for dry gardens. Large collection of *Acanthus, Aster, Geranium, Miscanthus*.
Notes: Also sells wholesale. Exports beyond EU. Delivers to shows. Euro accepted.
OS Grid Ref: N44 51.789 E0 32.0518

XPou **KOEN VAN POUCKE** ♿
Heistraat 106, Sint-Niklaas, Oost-Vlaanderen, 9100 Belgium
Ⓣ +32 (0377) 77642
Ⓕ +32 (0376) 61698
Ⓔ kvanpoucke@skynet.be
Ⓦ www.koenvanpoucke.be
Contact: Koen Van Poucke
Opening Times: 0900-1230 & 1300-1800, Tue-Sat. Closed Sun & Mon. Closed Jul. Check website before travelling a long distance.
Min Mail Order UK: €100

Min Mail Order EU: €100
Credit Cards: None
Specialities: *Epimedium*. Also rare Asian shade plants. Dahlia.
Notes: Mail order Sep-Apr. Collector's garden open to the public. Delivers to shows. Euro accepted. Wheelchair accessible.

XSen **GAEC Senteurs Du Quercy** ♿
Mas de Fraysse, Escamps, Lot, 46230 France
Ⓣ +33 (5) 652 10167
Ⓔ contact@senteursduquercy.com
Ⓦ www.senteursduquercy.com
Contact: Frédéric Prévot
Opening Times: 1400-1800 spring & summer (excl. Aug). Other times, incl. Aug by appt.
Min Mail Order UK: Nmc
Min Mail Order EU: Nmc
Cat. Cost: €5.00
Specialities: *Iris*, *Lavandula*, *Phlomis*, *Salvia*, *Teucrium* and drought tolerant plants. French National Plant Collection of *Salvia* species.
Notes: Euro accepted. Delivers to shows. Wheelchair accessible.

XWar **W.S. Warmenhoven**
P.O. Box 221, Hillegom, Zuid Holland, 2180 AE Netherlands
Ⓣ 00 (31) 6514 00351
Ⓜ 00 31 6514 00351
Ⓔ riviera@hetnet.nl
Ⓦ www.wswarmenhoven.com
Contact: Peter Warmenhoven
Specialities: *Allium*, *Hippeastrum* & *Ornithogalum*.

X

Nursery Index by Name

Nurseries that are included in the *RHS Plant Finder* for the first time this year (or have been reintroduced after a significant absence) are marked in **bold type**.

Full details of the nurseries will be found in **Nursery Details by Code** on page 868. For a key to the geographical codes, see the start of **Nurseries**.

A & J Plants	EAJP
A La Carte Daylilies	SDay
Abbey Nursery, The	CAby
Abbotsbury Sub-Tropical Gardens	CAbb
Aberconwy Nursery	WAbe
Abriachan Nurseries	GAbr
Abriherbs	**XAbr**
Agroforestry Research Trust	CAgr
Akorn and Oake	SAko
L. A. Allen	WAln
Allwoods (Hassocks) Ltd	SAll
Alpine Campanulas (Bellflower Nursery)	EACa
Apuldram Roses	**SApu**
Architectural Plants Ltd	SArc
Ardcarne Garden Centre	IArd
Arley Hall Nursery	MArl
Ashdown Forest Garden Centre & Nursery	SAdn
Ashridge Nurseries	CArg
Ashwood Nurseries Ltd	MAsh
Atelier du Végétal	XLum
Atlantic Botanic	**WABo**
Aulden Farm	WAul
Claire Austin Hardy Plants	WCAu
Avon Bulbs	CAvo
Avondale Nursery	MAvo
Aylett Nurseries Ltd	LAyl
B & H M Baker	EBak
Bali-Hai Mail Order Nursery	IBal
Ballyrogan Nurseries	IBlr
Barcham Trees PLC	EBar
Barn Plant Centre & Gift Shop, The	**NBPC**
Barnhaven Primroses	XBar
Barnsdale Gardens	MBNS
Barracott Plants	CBct
Barters Plant Centre & Nursery	CBar
Peter Beales Roses	EBls
Bee Happy Plants & Seeds	**CBee**
Beechcroft Nursery	LBee
Beeches Cottage Nursery	GBee
Beeches Nursery	EBee
Beggar's Roost Plants	CBgR
Bennetts Water Gardens	CBen
Bide-A-Wee Cottage Gardens	NBid
Binny Plants	GBin
Birkheads Secret Gardens & Nursery	NBir
Bluebell Arboretum & Nursery	MBlu
Bluebell Cottage Nursery	MBel
Bodmin Nursery	CBod
Border Alpines	CBor
Bordervale Plants	WBor
Botanica	EBtc
Boundary Nursery	EBou
Bowden Hostas	CBdn
Boyne Garden Centre	IBoy
Brackendale Nurseries	**CBrac**
Breezy Knees Nurseries	NBre
Bregover Plants	CBre
Brickwall Cottage Nursery	SBri
Bridge Farm Plants	**MBriF**
Bridge Nursery	MBrN
Brighton Plants	SBrt
Broadleigh Gardens	CBro
Brockamin Plants	WBrk
Brooklands Plants	CBrP
Brookside Nursery	**MBros**
Brownthwaite Hardy Plants	NBro
Buckingham Nurseries	LBuc
Bucknell Nurseries	WBuc
Burncoose Nurseries	CBcs
Burnham Nurseries	CBur
Butterfly Cottage Garden Plants	**SBut**
CB Plants	CCBP
Cacti & Succulents	SCac
Calamazag Nursery	**CCal**
Camellia Grove Nursery	SCam
Cants of Colchester Ltd	ECnt
Caves Folly Nurseries	**WCav**
Charleshurst Farm Nursery	SChF
Beth Chatto Gardens, The	ECha
Chennels Gate Gardens & Nursery	WChG

Cherry Tree Nursery	CChe
Chestnut Nursery (Sheltered Work Opportunities Project)	CCht
Chew Valley Trees	CCVT
Chiltern Seeds Ltd	MCtn
Chipchase Castle Nursery	NChi
Chrysanthemums Direct	MCms
John Churcher	SChr
Citrus Centre, The	SCit
Clay Lane Nursery	LCla
Coastal Hedging	CCoa
Coblands Online	SCob
Cool Temperate	MCoo
Cooling's Nurseries Ltd	SCoo
Coton Manor Garden	MCot
Cotswold Garden Flowers	WCot
Cottage Nurseries	ECtt
Courtyard Planters	NCou
Craftyplants	NCft
Cranesbill Nursery	WCra
Crea Paysage	XCre
Creake Plant Centre	ECre
Crocus.co.uk	LCro
Croft 16 Daffodils	GCro
Cromar Nursery	SCmr
Cross Common Nursery	CCCN
Crown Nursery	ECrN
Crûg Farm Plants	WCru
J & I Cruickshanks	GRid
John Cullen Gardens Ltd	**ECul**
Daleside Nurseries Ltd	NDal
D'Arcy & Everest	EDAr
P. de Jager & Sons Ltd	SDeJ
Deelish Garden Centre	IDee
Desert to Jungle	CDTJ
Dibleys Nurseries	WDib
Dickson Nurseries	IDic
Direct Bulbs	**SDir**
Donington Nurseries Ltd	MDon
Dorset Perennials	CDor
Dove Cottage Nursery & Garden	NDov
Downderry Nursery	SDow
Downside Nurseries	**CDow**
Drointon Nurseries	NDro
Dryad Nursery	**NDry**
Duchy of Cornwall	**CDoC**
Dysons Nurseries	SDys
East Northdown Nurseries	SEND
East of Eden Nursery	NEoE
Echium World	MEch
Eddington House Nursery	**SEdd**
Edibleculture	**SEdi**
Edrom Nurseries	GEdr
Edulis	LEdu
Eleplants Nursery	SEle
Ellebore	XEll
Charles F Ellis	WCFE
Elsworth Herbs	CEls
Elworthy Cottage Plants	CElw
Endsleigh Gardens Nursery	CEnd
English Woodlands	SEWo
Equatorial Plant Co.	NEqu
Essex Carnivorous Plants	EECP
Exclusive Plants Nursery	CExl
Fairweather's Garden Centre	SFai
Farmyard Nurseries	WFar
Fawside Farm Nursery	**MBow**
Fentongollan Farm	CFen
Fern Nursery, The	EFer
Fibrex Nurseries Ltd	WFib
Firecrest Trees & Shrubs Nursery	EMac
Firgrove Plants	GFgr
Fly Trap Plants, The	EFly
Forest Edge Nurseries	CFst
Forest Garden, The	CFGn
Foxplants	**CFoP**
Frogswell Nursery	IFro
Frosch Exclusive Perennials	XFro
Fryer's Roses and Garden Centre	MFry
GAEC Senteurs Du Quercy	XSen
Garden Blooms	NGBl
Garden House Nursery	NGdn
Gardener's Cottage Plants	NGrd
Garden Style Plant Centre	**SGsty**
George's Gorgeous Gardens	**EGeo**
Gilbert's Nursery	SGbt
John Gillies	MGil
Glendoick Gardens Ltd	GGGa
Gobbett Nursery, The	WGob
Golden Hill Nurseries	SGol
Goscote Nurseries Ltd	MGos
www.greatlittlegarden.co.uk	XGLG
Great Dixter Nurseries	**SDix**
Great Western Gladiolus Nursery, The	CGrW
Greenkoos	**NGKo**
Green's Leaves	WGrn
Grenville Nurseries	**EGren**
C W Groves & Son Ltd	CGro
Growing Delights	SGro
Gwynfor Growers	WGwG
Habitat Aid Ltd.	CHab
Hall Farm Nursery	WHal
John Hall Plants Ltd	SWhi
Halls of Heddon	NHal
Hampshire Carnivorous Plants	SHmp
Hardy's Cottage Garden Plants	SHar
Hare Spring Cottage Plants	NHsp
Harlow Carr Plant Centre (RHS)	NRHS
Harper & Debbage	EHDe
Harperley Hall Farm Nurseries	NHpl
Harrells Hardy Plants	WHrl
Hart Canna	SHaC
Hartside Nursery Garden	**NHar**
Hawthornes Nursery, The	NHaw

Out of the Common Way	WOut
Packhorse Farm Nursery	MPkF
Paddock Plants	SPad
Painshill Park Trust	LPai
Palm House, The	CPHo
Palms-Exotics Ltd	**SPalm**
Pan-Global Plants	WPGP
Parham Bungalow Plants	CPBP
Dave Parkinson Plants	NDav
Parks Perennials	CPar
Paugers Plants Ltd	EPau
Paviour and Davies Plants	WPav
Peake Perennials	**SPeP**
Penberth Plants	CPbh
Penlan Perennials	WPnP
Pernewood Plants	**EPed**
Perry's Plants	NPer
Perryhill Nurseries Ltd	SPer
Pershore College	WAvo
Perthshire Heathers	GPer
Pettet's Nursery	SPet
Pheasant Acre Plants	**WPhe**
Phedar Nursery	MPhe
Alan Phipps Cacti	CPhi
Phoenix Perennial Plants	SPhx
Piecemeal Plants	MPie
Pine Cottage Plants	CPne
Pineview Plants	**SPVi**
Place for Plants, The	EPfP
Plant Company, The	STPC
Plant Specialist, The	LPla
Plant World Gardens and Nurseries	CPla
Plantagogo.com	MPnt
Plantbase	SPlb
Plants2Gardens Ltd	MPtG
Plants4Presents	SPre
Plants for Small Gardens	CSma
Plants, Shoots and Leaves	GPSL
Plantsman's Preference, The	EPPr
PlantsToplant.com	SPtp
Poets Cottage Shrub Nursery	**NPoe**
Polemonium Plantery	NPol
Pomona Fruits Ltd	EPom
Potash Nursery Ltd	EPts
Potash Plants	LPot
Potted Garden Nursery, The	SPoG
Pottertons Nursery	EPot
Potting Shed, The	IPot
Koen Van Poucke	XPou
Pounsley Plants	CPou
Poyntzfield Herb Nursery	GPoy
Primrose Bank	**NPnk**
Primrose Cottage Nursery	MPri
Priory Plants	**EPri**
Sue Proctor Plants	NSue
ProperPlants.com	CPrp
R and A Scamp Quality Daffodils	CQua
Quercus Garden Plants Ltd	GQue
Quiet Corner Plants	NQui
Rapkyns Nursery	SRkn
Ravensthorpe Nursery	MRav
Really Wild Flowers	CRea
Red House Farm	WRHF
Reuthe's – The Lost Garden of Sevenoaks	**SReu**
RHS Plant Shop: RHSplants.co.uk	LOPS
Ribblesdale Nurseries	NRib
River Garden Nurseries	SRiv
W Robinson & Son (Seeds & Plants) Ltd	NRob
Ros Ban Wildlife Garden	IRos
Rose Cottage Plants	ERCP
Roseland House Nursery	CRHN
Rosemoor Plant Centre (RHS)	CRos
Rumbling Bridge Nursery	**GRum**
Rumsey Gardens	SRms
Rushrose Nursery	NRush
Ryal Nursery	NRya
St Bridget Nurseries Ltd	CSBt
Saith Ffynnon Wildlife Plants	WSFF
Sampford Shrubs	CSam
Savill Gardens Visitor Centre	LSvl
Savin Nurseries	**SavN**
SCEA Hodnik	XHod
Seale Rose Garden	SSea
Seaside Plants	CSde
Shady Plants	ISha
Shipton Bulbs	WShi
Shropshire Sarracenias	WSSs
Shrubland Park Nurseries	EShb
Sienna Hostas	**SSien**
Simply Succulents	SSim
Slack Top Alpine Nursery	NSla
South Milton Plant Nursery	**WSMil**
Southern Fruit Trees	SSFr
Southon Plants	**LSou**
Special Plants	CSpe
SpecialPerennials.com	**MSpe**
Spinneywell Nursery	WSpi
Spring Reach Nursery	LSRN
Staddon Farm Nurseries	**CSta**
Starborough Nursery	SSta
Stillingfleet Lodge Nurseries	NSti
Stone House Cottage Nurseries	WSHC
Stonyford Cottage Nursery	MSCN
Straight Mile Nursery Gardens	ESMi
Strictly Daylilies	EStr
Style Roses	ESty
Sunnybank Vine Nursery (National Vine Collection)	WSuV
Sunnyside Nursery	LSun
Sussex Fruit Trees	SSFT
Dan Sutton	SSut
Swallows Nursery	MSwo
Swines Meadow Farm Nursery	ESwi
Table Bay View Nursery	XBlo

INDEX OF ADVERTISERS